THE
PHYSIOLOGICAL
BASIS
OF
MEDICAL
PRACTICE

# THE
# PHYSIOLOGICAL
# BASIS
# OF
# MEDICAL
# PRACTICE

CHARLES    HERBERT    BEST

C.B.E., M.A., M.D., D.Sc. (Lond.), F.R.C.S., F.R.C.P. (Canada), *Professor and Head of Department of Physiology, Director of the Banting-Best Department of Medical Research, University of Toronto*

BALTIMORE · 1961

SEVENTH EDITION

*With 31 contributors under the general editorship of* **NORMAN BURKE TAYLOR**

ROBERT W. BERLINER
CHARLES H. BEST
E. RAYMOND BORUN
PAUL C. BUCY
F. W. CAMPBELL
JAMES CAMPBELL
DONALD W. CLARKE
JAY D. COFFMAN
B. T. DONOVAN
J. K. W. FERGUSON
DONALD E. GREGG
REGINALD E. HAIST
G. W. HARRIS
JOSEPH E. HAWKINS, JR.
ANDREW HUVOS
ALBERT A. KATTUS
COLIN C. LUCAS
SIR BRYAN MATTHEWS
FRANK C. MONKHOUSE
WILLIAM C. NORTH
JESSIE H. RIDOUT
JAMES M. SALTER
JOHN W. SCOTT
NATHAN W. SHOCK
DURWOOD J. SMITH
NORMAN B. TAYLOR
J. EARL THOMAS
KLAUS W. C. THURAU
G. RONALD WILLIAMS
E. N. WILLMER
W. B. YOUMANS

# *A Text in*

# *Applied*

# *Physiology*

# NORMAN BURKE TAYLOR

V.D., M.D., F.R.S.(Canada), F.R.C.S.(Edin.), F.R.C.P.(Canada), M.R.C.S. (Eng.), L.R.C.P.(Lond.) *Lately Professor of the History of Medicine and Medical Literature, University of Western Ontario, London, Canada; formerly Professor of Physiology, University of Toronto*

# THE WILLIAMS & WILKINS COMPANY

# THE WILLIAMS & WILKINS COMPANY

First Edition, January, 1937
*Reprinted March, 1937*
*Reprinted August, 1937*
*Reprinted October, 1937*
*Reprinted January, 1939*

Second Edition, September, 1939
*Reprinted May, 1940*
*Reprinted April, 1941*
*Reprinted May, 1942*

Third Edition, March, 1943
*Reprinted June, 1943*
*Reprinted February, 1944*

Fourth Edition, November, 1945
*Reprinted April, 1946*
*Reprinted August, 1946*
*Reprinted March, 1947*
*Reprinted December, 1947*
*Reprinted March, 1948*
*Reprinted July, 1949*

Fifth Edition, January, 1950
*Reprinted May, 1950*
*Reprinted July, 1950*
*Reprinted February, 1951*
*Reprinted January, 1952*
*Reprinted February, 1953*

Sixth Edition, January, 1955
*Reprinted July, 1956*
*Reprinted June, 1957*
*Reprinted October, 1958*
*Reprinted November, 1959*
*Reprinted May, 1960*

Seventh Edition, January, 1961
*Reprinted May, 1961*
*Reprinted July, 1961*
*Reprinted June, 1962*

First Spanish Edition, 1939
Second Spanish Edition, 1941
Third Spanish Edition, 1943
Fourth Spanish Edition, 1947
Fifth Spanish Edition, 1954

First Portuguese Edition, 1940
Second Portuguese Edition, 1945

First Italian Edition, 1955

*Library of Congress Catalog Card Number 60-10082*

COMPOSED AND PRINTED AT THE WAVERLY PRESS, INC., BALTIMORE, MD., U. S. A.

# PREFACE TO THE SEVENTH EDITION

According to a reliable and conservative estimate some half billion words are published annually on medical subjects in the journals of English-speaking countries alone. Much of the mass of scientific writing turned out by the laboratories and clinics comes within the scope of this book, at least for review. With each succeeding revision we became increasingly conscious of the hopelessness of trying to cover so great an expanse of medical literature. Even those whose interests are largely confined to one or another special field are inundated and complain that they often find it hard to keep their heads above the swelling tide. We ourselves now marvel at the intrepid not to say reckless spirit in which this book was conceived and its first edition written. Though we are not abject in our apology we fully realize and regret the insufficiency of the last revision. There was a disconcerting gap between its text and the more recent advances in physiology and related branches of scientific medicine, which made us acutely aware of the necessity of calling upon others for help. This we have done and our colleagues have responded magnificently and most generously to our appeal. We have been extremely fortunate in gathering together for this edition a galaxy of contributors, each of whom is outstanding in the field which his contribution covers. We believe that this, the seventh, is the most comprehensive and authoritative edition since the inception of the book twenty-five years ago. We wish to extend our most cordial thanks to our colleagues for this happy outcome which the excellence of their contributions has brought about.

The names of the contributors are listed alphabetically on page ix.

The section on Circulation, Chapters 14 through 28, has been rewritten, mainly by Dr. Donald E. Gregg and his associates.

Chapters 1 to 13, on the Physiology of the Blood, and those numbered 44 to 49 and 51 to 55, all inclusive, have been revised or rewritten by members of the staff of the Department of Physiology, and of the Banting and Best Department of Medical Research, University of Toronto. Professor C. H. Best has exercised general supervision over these chapters.

More specific reference to the contributions of the several authors will be found in the Table of Contents.

# PREFACE TO FIRST EDITION

Physiology is a science in its own right and the laboratory worker who pursues his researches quite detached from medical problems need offer no apology for his academic outlook. Indeed some of the most valuable contributions to medical science have been the outcome of laboratory studies whose applications could not have been foreseen. Nevertheless, we feel that the teacher of physiology in a medical school owes it to his students, whose ultimate interest it must be conceded is in the diagnosis and treatment of disease, to emphasize those aspects of the subject which will throw light upon disorders of function. The physiologist can in this way play a part in giving the student and practitioner a vantage point from which he may gain a rational view of pathological processes.

We have endeavored to write a book which will serve to link the laboratory and the clinic, and which will therefore promote continuity of physiological teaching throughout the pre-clinical and clinical years of the under-graduate course. It is also hoped that when the principles underlying diseased states are pointed out to the medical student, and he is shown how a knowledge of such principles aids in the interpretation of symptoms or in directing treatment, he will take a keener interest in physiological studies. When such studies are restricted to the classical aspects of the subject, apparently remote from clinical application, the student is likely to regard them only as a task which his teachers in their inscrutable wisdom have condemned him to perform. Too often he gains the idea, from such a course, that physiology is of very limited utility and comes to believe that, having once passed into the clinical years, most of what he has "crammed" for examination purposes may be forgotten without detriment to his more purely medical studies. Unfortunately, he does not always realize at this stage in his education how great has been the part which physiological discoveries have played in the progress of medicine, and that the practice of today has evolved from the "theories" of yesterday.

Many physiological problems can be approached only through animal experimentation. Advances in many fields, most notably in those of carbohydrate metabolism, nutrition, and endocrinology, bear witness to the fertility of this method of research. On the other hand, many problems can be elucidated only by observations upon man, and physiology has gained much from clinical research. The normal human subject as an experimental animal possesses unique advantages for many types of investigation; and in disease, nature produces abnormalities of structure and function which the physiological laboratory can imitate only in the crudest way. Within recent years the clinical physiologist, fully realizing these advantages and the opportunities afforded by the hospital wards, has contributed very largely to physiological knowledge. In many instances, clinical research has not only revealed the true nature of the underlying process in disease, but has cast a light into some dark corner of physiology as well; several examples of clinical investigation which have pointed the way to the physiologist could be cited. In the last century, knowledge of the processes of disease was sought mainly in studies of morbid *anatomy*; biochemistry was in its infancy and many of the procedures now commonly employed for the investigation of the human subject had not been devised. Today, the student of scientific medicine is directing his attention more and more to the study of morbid *physiology* in his efforts to solve clinical problems. This newer outlook has borne fruit in many fields. It has had the beneficent result of drawing the clinic and the physiological and biochemical laboratories onto common ground from which it has often been possible to launch a joint attack upon disease. We feel that this modern trend in the field of research should be reflected in the teaching of medical students, and have therefore given greater prominence to clinical aspects of the subject than is usual in physiological texts.

In order to understand the function of an organ it is usually essential to have a knowledge of its structure. For this reason we have followed the plan of preceding the account of the physiology of a part by a short description of its morphology and, in many instances, of its nerve and blood supply. The architecture and functions of the central nervous system are so intimately related that some space has been devoted to a description of the more important fiber tracts and grey masses of the cerebrum, cerebellum and spinal cord.

We wish to thank our colleagues in physiology, biochemistry and anatomy whom we have drawn upon on so many occasions for information and advice; without their generous help the undertaking would have been an almost impossible one. We are also deeply grateful for the unstinted assistance which we have received from our friends on the clinical staff, several of whom have read parts of the text in manuscript or in proof. We wish especially to acknowledge our indebtedness to Professor A. M. Wynne, who has written the section on the oxidizing systems of living cells, to Dr. J. K. W. Ferguson for his collaboration in the preparation of Chapter 33, and to Professor C. B. Weld and Dr. E. T. Waters whose stimulating criticisms and sound counsel have been invaluable.

Finally, we wish to thank our secretaries, Miss Mabel Cory and Miss Dudley Martin, who have spent so many tedious hours in preparing the manuscript for the press, in checking the references and in compiling the index.

C. H. B.<br>N. B. T.

*October 15, 1936*

# CONTRIBUTORS

ROBERT W. BERLINER, M.D., B.S., Associate Director (In Charge of Research) National Heart Institute, National Institutes of Health, Bethesda, Maryland

CHARLES H. BEST, M.A., M.D., D.Sc. (Lond.), F.R.S., F.R.C.P. (Canada), Professor and Head of Department of Physiology, Director of the Banting-Best Department of Medical Research, University of Toronto

E. RAYMOND BORUN, M.D., Assistant Professor of Medicine, University of California Medical Center, Los Angeles, California

PAUL C. BUCY, M.D., B.S., M.S., Professor of Surgery, Northwestern University Medical School. Director, Section on Neurological Surgery, Chicago Wesley Memorial Hospital

F. W. CAMPBELL, M.A., PH.D., M.D., The Physiological Laboratory, University of Cambridge, England

JAMES CAMPBELL, M.A., PH.D., Department of Physiology, University of Toronto, Canada

DONALD W. CLARKE, B.Sc., M.Sc., PH.D., Department of Physiology, University of Toronto, Canada

JAY D. COFFMAN, B.A., M.D., Capt. M.C., Dept. of Cardiorespiratory Diseases, Walter Reed Army Institute of Research, Washington, D. C.

B. T. DONOVAN, PH.D., Lecturer in Physiology, Department of Neuroendocrinology, Institute of Psychiatry, British Postgraduate Medical Federation, University of London, England

J. K. W. FERGUSON, M.D., B.A., M.A., Connaught Medical Research Labs., University of Toronto, Canada

DONALD E. GREGG, PH.D., M.D., Chief, Department of Cardiorespiratory Diseases, Walter Reed Army Institute of Research, Washington, D. C.

REGINALD E. HAIST, M.A., M.D., PH.D., F.R.S.C., Department of Physiology, University of Toronto, Canada

G. W. HARRIS, M.A., M.D., Sc.D., F.R.S., Fitzmary Professor of Physiology, Department of Neuroendocrinology, Institute of Psychiatry, British Postgraduate Medical Federation, University of London, England

JOSEPH E. HAWKINS, JR., A.B., B.A., PH.D., Associate Professor of Otology, New York University-Bellevue Medical Center, New York

ANDREW HUVOS, M.D., Captain, M.C., Department of Cardiorespiratory Diseases, Walter Reed Army Institute of Research, Washington, D. C.

ALBERT A. KATTUS, M.D., Associate Professor of Medicine, University of California Medical Center, Los Angeles, California

COLIN C. LUCAS, M.A.Sc., PH.D., F.R.S.C., F.C.I.C., Banting-Best Department of Medical Research, University of Toronto, Canada

SIR BRYAN MATTHEWS, C.B.E., Sc.D., F.R.S., Professor of Physiology, University of Cambridge, England

FRANK C. MONKHOUSE, B.A., PH.D., Department of Physiology, University of Toronto, Canada

WILLIAM C. NORTH, M.D., PH.D., Assistant Professor of Anesthesia, Assistant Professor of Pharmacology, Northwestern University School of Medicine, Chicago, Illinois

JESSIE H. RIDOUT, M.A., PH.D., Banting-Best Department of Medical Research, University of Toronto, Canada

JAMES M. SALTER, M.A., PH.D., Banting-Best Department of Medical Research, University of Toronto, Canada

JOHN W. SCOTT, M.A., M.D., Department of Physiology, University of Toronto, Canada

NATHAN W. SHOCK, PH.D., D.Sc. (Honorary), Chief, Gerontology Branch, National Heart Institute and the Baltimore City Hospitals, Baltimore, Maryland

Durwood J. Smith, M.D., Professor and Chairman, Department of Pharmacology, University of Vermont College of Medicine, Burlington, Vermont

Norman B. Taylor, V.D., M.D., F.R.S. (Canada), F.R.C.S. (Edin.), F.R.C.P. (Canada), M.R.C.S. (Eng.), L.R.C.P. (Lond.), lately Professor of the History of Medicine and Medical Literature, University of Western Ontario; formerly Professor of Physiology, University of Toronto

J. Earl Thomas, B.S., M.S., M.D., Professor of Physiology, College of Medical Evangelists, Loma Linda, California

Klaus W. C. Thurau, M.D., Foreign Research Fellow, United States Public Health Service, Department of Cardiorespiratory Diseases, Walter Reed Army Institute of Research, Washington, D. C.

G. Ronald Williams, B.Sc., Ph.D., Banting-Best Department of Medical Research, University of Toronto, Canada

E. N. Willmer, B.A., M.Sc., M.A., Sc.D., Reader in Histology, University of Cambridge, England, Fellow of Clare College

W. B. Youmans, M.D., Ph.D., Professor of Physiology, Chairman of Department of Physiology, University of Wisconsin Medical School, Madison, Wisconsin

# CONTENTS

## SECTION VI.   METABOLISM AND NUTRITION

## SECTION VII.   THE DUCTLESS GLANDS OR ENDOCRINES

## SECTION VIII.  THE NERVOUS SYSTEM

## SECTION IX.  THE SPECIAL SENSES

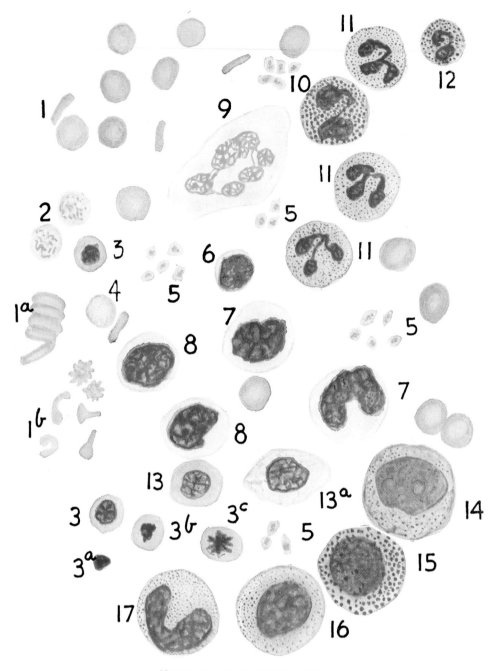

NORMAL BLOOD AND MARROW CELLS

| | | | |
|---|---|---|---|
| 1 | Erythrocytes | 7 | Monocytes |
| 1a | Erythrocytes in rouleau | 8 | Large lymphocytes |
| 1b | Deformed cells (poikilocytes) crenated forms | 9 | Megakaryocyte |
| 2 | Reticulocytes stained with dilute solution of cresyl blue | 10 | Eosinophil leucocyte |
| | | 11 | Neutrophil leucocytes |
| 3 | Early normoblasts | 12 | Basophil leucocyte |
| 3a | Extruded nucleus | 13 | Polychromatophil erythroblast |
| 3b | Late normoblast | 13a | Hemocytoblast |
| 3c | Normoblast in mitosis | 14 | Megaloblast |
| 5 | Platelets | 15 | Eosinophil myelocyte |
| 6 | Small lymphocyte | 16 | Neutrophil myelocyte |
| | | 17 | Neutrophil metamyelocyte |

*1*

# THE PHYSIOLOGICAL PROPERTIES, PHYSICAL
# CHARACTERS AND COMPOSITION

## Outline of the Functions of Blood

In animals whose bodies are composed of many cells (Metazoa) the blood serves those purposes, which for unicellular organisms (Protozoa) are carried out by the fluid medium, the salt or fresh water, which surrounds them and bathes their surfaces. For example, an organism such as the amoeba acquires oxygen by diffusion directly from the environment into the interior of the cell. Similarly the carbon dioxide diffuses outwards. The processes of nutrition and the excretion of the products of the cell's metabolism are accomplished in a manner equally simple. Food is taken in through the cell membrane either in solution or as particulate matter, and waste products pass into the surrounding medium. Other requirements of this organism, such as the maintenance of an optimum temperature and the proper degree of moisture, are dependent on the immediate (internal) environment, the *milieu interne* of Claude Bernard.

The elemental needs of each cell in a multicellular individual from the most primitive type to the highest vertebrate are the same as for the unicellular organism; yet in the evolution of the higher forms the cells composing their bodies have become farther and farther removed from immediate contact with the outside world. Myriads of cells have become packed together, and the deeper ones could not possibly satisfy their needs after the direct and simple fashion of the unicellular forms. The more primitive multicellular types overcame the difficulty by the development of canal systems which opened to the exterior and through which the ocean waters flowed freely in

and out, bringing oxygen and aliment to the more deeply lying cells and bearing carbon dioxide and other excretory products away. This, the first attempt at a circulation, was an open one. As higher forms evolved the circulation became closed and the waters of the environment no longer flowed and ebbed through the body. No longer could the interchange of the respiratory gases and the absorption of nutriment be carried out in this direct and simple way. Yet the vessels of this closed circulatory system were filled with a fluid which took the place of and fulfilled the duties of the watery environment of the more primitive types. The blood and other body fluids may be looked upon as that environment which has become enclosed within the bodies of the higher forms, and has undergone certain modifications in its composition to meet the requirements of the more specialized cells which it bathes.

The similarity between the compositions of sea water and blood which has been stressed by the researches of Macallum lends support to these views on the evolution of the blood.[1] This brief account will also serve as an introduction to a consideration of the functions of the body fluids, since their duties are to satisfy in the same way as did their prototype, the requirements of the individual cells.

[1] Sea water of today differs from blood serum in having a total salt concentration of about 3 per cent, a much higher concentration of magnesium and a lower concentration of potassium. But Macallum points out that the sea water of the geological period when the ancestors of mammalian forms adapted themselves to a terrestrial life was probably closely similar in its inorganic composition to blood serum.

*1. Respiratory.* The transport of oxygen from the air in the lungs to the tissues, and of carbon dioxide from the tissues to the lungs.

*2. Nutritive.* The conveyance of food materials, glucose, amino acids and fats from the alimentary canal to the tissues.

*3. Excretory.* The removal of waste products of metabolism, e.g., urea, uric acid, creatinine, etc.

*4. The maintenance of the water content of the tissues.* Though the blood itself is contained within vascular channels, a constant interchange of fluid through the vessel walls takes place. This fluid which has left the blood vessels and come into direct contact with the tissue cells is known as the tissue or interstitial fluid. It closely resembles the blood plasma in chemical composition, and is identical with lymph. Through the medium of the transuded fluid the final stage in the transportation of oxygen and food materials to the tissues and the first stage in the journey of $CO_2$ and waste products from the tissues are made.

*5. To regulate body temperature.* The body owes its ability to regulate its temperature (ch. 52) largely to the water of the blood and tissue fluids. Water possesses three qualities which fit it pre-eminently to fulfil this purpose.

*a. The specific heat[2]* of water is considerably higher than that of any other liquid or solid. On account of this great heat storage power of water, sudden changes of body temperature are avoided and even a cold-blooded animal such as the frog has, due to this purely physical quality, some ability to maintain a relatively constant body temperature against transient fluctuations in environmental temperature. A man of average weight develops 3000 Calories in 24 hours. This amount of heat is capable of raising the temperature of his tissues (which are largely water) only about 32°C. Heat elimination (radiation, etc.) is able to keep pace with heat production and the body temperature varies but slightly within normal limits. But it has been pointed out by L. J. Henderson that if the tissues had the low heat storage capacity (spec. heat) of most substances, an amount of heat equal to 3000 Calories would raise the temperature of the tissues and fluids of the body by from 100° to 150°C.

*b. High conductivity.* The thermal conductivity of water is greater than that of any other ordinary liquid. The advantage of this in the dissipation of heat from deeply situated regions of the body is obvious.

*c. High latent heat of evaporation.* More heat is required for the vaporization of water than for that of an equivalent amount of any other liquid. One cubic centimeter of water requires about 0.6 Calories for its vaporization. This figure is 50 per cent higher than that of water's closest competi-

tor. Fluid is being constantly lost from the body through evaporation from the lungs and skin. A large amount of heat is lost in the process.

These physical properties of water which make it ideal as a heat regulating medium are enhanced by other purely *physiological factors.* The mobility of the blood and the readiness with which it may be quickly redistributed in the body, combined with the unique physical properties of the fluid itself, render it so highly efficient as a regulator of body temperature. The blood may in a moment be brought from deeper to superficial regions and spread out in fine vessels over a broad area just beneath the skin, and in this way will greatly increase the radiation of heat. At another instant, in order that heat may be conserved, the fluid is drained from the surface areas and collected in the deeper parts of the body—internal organs, muscles, etc.

*6. Protective and regulatory.* The blood and lymph contain certain chemical substances of a complex nature, antitoxins, lysins, and other antibodies, which are the basis of the body's defense against injurious agents of various kinds. The circulating fluids are also the vehicle by which the hormones of the different ductless glands are brought into direct contact with the cells of the tissues.

### The Composition of Blood

The blood is a highly complex fluid in which solid elements are suspended—the *corpuscles or blood cells.* Its specific gravity varies between individuals from 1.050 to 1.060 and its viscosity from 5 to 6 times that of water. If blood is centrifuged before it has had time to clot, or if clotting is prevented by special means (ch. 12), the solid elements are thrown down and separated from the fluid portion. The latter is called the *plasma* and contains *proteins,* as well as many organic and inorganic substances in solution—nutritive and excretory materials, antibodies and hormones, and other substances of an unknown or imperfectly known chemical constitution. The specific gravity of plasma is normally around 1.027 but varies with its concentration in protein. The cells constitute about 46 per cent of the volume of human blood, the plasma 54 per cent. Small variations above or below these values are commonly encountered.

The specific gravity of a small sample of blood or of plasma may be measured by the method of Phillips, Van Slyke and associates. A series of small bottles is set up containing copper sulfate solutions varying by small equal increments (0.004) in specific gravity. A drop of blood or plasma is allowed to fall gently from the tip of a

----

[2] The specific heat of a substance is defined as the number of calories required to raise 1 gram of the substance 1°C.

TABLE 1.1

*Inorganic constituents of plasma, red cells and whole blood, milligrams per 100 cc. average values*

| | Sodium | Potassium | Calcium | Magnesium | Chlorine | Iodine | Iron | Copper | Phosphate | Sulfate | Total Base cc. N/10 NaOH |
|---|---|---|---|---|---|---|---|---|---|---|---|
| Plasma............. | 340 | 20 | 10 | 2.7 | 370 | | 0.2 | | | | 160 |
| Cells................ | 20 | 410 | 0 | 6.0 | 190 | | 100.0 | | | | |
| Whole blood.......... | 190 | 220 | 5.2 | 4.0 | 250 | 0.01 | 50.0 | 0.1 | 3.0 | 2.0 | |

The concentrations of these various inorganic constituents are also commonly expressed as milli-equivalents (m.eq.) per liter. Thus serum contains 100 mg. of calcium per liter. The molecular weight of Ca is 40.07. So being divalent its milliequivalent is 20.03. The concentration of calcium in serum is therefore $\frac{100}{20.03}$ = 4.9 milliequivalents per liter. Sodium is monovalent and has a molecular weight of 23; serum therefore contains $\frac{3400}{23}$ = 147.8 m.eq. per liter.

medicine dropper into each of a number of the bottles whose solutions are within the expected specific gravity range of the blood or plasma sample. The drop of blood or plasma, upon entering the solution, becomes coated with a film of copper proteinate and remains suspended, neither rising nor falling for a few seconds, if it is of the same specific gravity as the solution; thus, since the specific gravity of the solution is known, that of the blood or plasma is indicated.

In the following outline are given the constituents of the blood, grouped upon a physiological basis.

*Whole blood:*

A. *Cells:*
   (1) Red corpuscles or erythrocytes
   (2) White corpuscles or leucocytes
   (3) Platelets or thrombocytes

B. *Plasma:*
   (1) *Water*, 91 to 92 per cent
   (2) *Solids*, 7 to 9 per cent
      (a) *Proteins*, 7 per cent. Serum albumin, serum globulin and fibrinogen.[3]
      (b) *Inorganic constituents*, 0.9 per cent. Sodium, calcium, potassium, magnesium, phosphorus, iodine, iron, copper, etc.
      (c) *Organic constituents* (other than (a) and (d)). Nonprotein nitrogenous substances, (urea, uric acid, xanthine, hypoxanthine, creatine and creatinine, ammonia and amino acids) neutral fats, phospholipids, cholesterol, glucose.
      (d) *Internal secretions, antibodies and various enzymes, (amylases, proteases, lipases, esterases, etc.)*

---

[3] Plasma from which the fibrinogen has been removed through clotting (ch. 12) is spoken of as serum.

INORGANIC CONSTITUENTS

The concentration of the plasma in the various inorganic materials is given in table 1.1.

It will be noted that the plasma is relatively rich in sodium and calcium but poor in potassium and magnesium whereas in the cells conditions are reversed. The cells show a relatively high concentration in potassium and magnesium, but are lacking in calcium and have a low concentration of sodium (human). In the blood of some species sodium is absent or present only in traces. Except for a minute amount of iron in the plasma, this element is confined to the red cells and the greater part of it is attached to the hemoglobin molecule (ch. 6). It has been suggested that the small quantity of nonhemoglobin iron in the erythrocyte is bound loosely with the lecithin of the cell stroma (p. 71); (see also chapter 8).

*Phosphorus*

Phosphorus exists in blood in four main forms. One of these is *inorganic phosphorus* (orthophosphate). The three other phosphorus fractions are in *organic* combination and are as follows:

*1. Ester phosphorus*, e.g., diphosphoglycerate, adenosinetriphosphate, hexose phosphates, glycerophosphate.

*2. Lipid phosphorus*, e.g., the phosphatieds lecithin, cephalin, sphingomyelin.

*3. Nucleic acid phosphorus.*

According to Kay the nucleic acid phosphorus in normal human blood is negligible. It is derived from the nuclei of white cells and the reticulum of the reticulocytes. In abnormal blood containing a large number of leucocytes, reticulocytes or nucleated red cells this fraction may however constitute a considerable proportion of the total phosphorus.

The inorganic phosphorus (3 mg. per 100 cc.) is according to most observers about equally distributed between cells and plasma. The quantity of organic phosphorus in blood is many times greater than the inorganic. In whole blood it amounts to from 35 to 40 mg. per 100 cc. and the greater proportion of this is in the cells.

The inorganic and ester fractions are extracted from blood by the precipitation of the proteins with trichloracetic acid and filtering. The phosphorus contained in the filtrate is spoken of as the acid soluble phosphorus. Upon extraction of blood with alcohol-ether the lipid phosphorus is obtained. The phosphorus of blood is therefore separable into two classes.

(1) *The acid soluble which includes*
    (a) Inorganic phosphorus
    (b) Ester phosphorus
(2) *Alcohol-ether soluble*, i.e., organic phospholipid phosphorus.     rus

The ester, or organic acid-soluble phosphorus is obtained by determing the total acid soluble P and subtracting from it the inorganic phosphorus. Of the ester phosphorus, all of which is intracellular, about one-quarter is hydrolyzable by bone phosphatase (ch. 59). The hydrolyzable portion is mainly adenosinetriphosphate, and the nonhydrolyzable part mainly diphosphoglycerate. Since the nucleic acid phosphorus is negligible in normal blood, the acid soluble + the alcohol-ether soluble phosphorus equals the total phosphorus as determined by wet-ashing.

In the following table is given the distribution of inorganic, ester and lipid phosphorus in normal blood.

### *Phosphorus in whole blood*

Milligrams per 100 cc., average figures

1. Total phosphorus..........................  40
2. Total acid soluble—90 per cent in cells....  27
3. Inorganic—in cells and plasma............  3[4]
4. Ester (2–3)—practically all in cells........  24
5. Lipid (1–2)—in cells and plasma..........  13

The phosphorus compounds of the blood and tissues play an important role in maintaining the electrolyte equilibrium within the red cells and in regulating the acid base balance. Diabetic acidosis, for example, and the acidosis induced by the ingestion of ammonium chloride, are accompanied by increased excretion of phosphorus in the urine and a pronounced reduction of the organic acid-soluble phosphorus in the blood cells. Reverse changes occur in alkalosis; the reduction in the chloride of the blood following pyloric obstruction, and the alkalosis caused by overbreathing are associated with a reduction in the urinary

---

[4] In infants and young children, the inorganic phosphorus is from 1 to 3 mg. per cent higher than it is in adults.

excretion of phosphates and a decrease in the inorganic and ester phosphorus of the blood. In renal insufficiency, the inorganic phosphorus in the plasma and cells and the ester phosphorus (diphosphoglycerate) in the cells are greatly increased. The inorganic and ester phosphorus are reduced in rickets but a rapid increase accompanies the healing process. The inorganic phosphorus is diminished after the injection of insulin and in hyperparathyroidism (ch. 59). In anemias associated with high reticulocyte counts and in leukemia, the concentration of ester phosphorus in the blood is increased. The inorganic phosphorus is increased in some forms of tetany.

### ORGANIC CONSTITUENTS (OTHER THAN ORGANIC PHOSPHORUS)

#### *Plasma Proteins*

The concentration of total protein in the plasma and the proportions of the three fractions —*albumin, globulin* and *fibrinogen*—vary from species to species but under ordinary conditions of health remain relatively constant between individuals of the same species.

Serum globulin can be separated by "salting out" into two fractions—*euglobulin* and *pseudoglobulin*; or into three fractions—$\alpha$-, $\beta$- and $\gamma$-*globulins*—by electrophoresis. The euglobulin is thrown out of solution by saturation with NaCl, half-saturation with $MgSO_4$, or one-third saturation with $(NH_4)_2SO_4$; it is insoluble in water. The pseudoglobulin is not "salted out" by NaCl but is thrown down by saturation of its solution with $MgSO_4$ or half-saturation with $(NH_4)_2SO_4$. It is soluble in water.

The electrophoretic separation of proteins is based on the difference in electric charges of various proteins and consequently their different rates of migration in an electric field. In addition to the "salting out" and electrophoretic procedures two other methods are available: (a) Cohn's chemical fractionation method which utilizes the different solubilities of the proteins and the sensitivity of the solute to variations in ionic strength, in ethanol concentration and in metallic ions. (b) The ultracentrifugalization procedure which separates proteins on the basis of their differences in density.

$\alpha$-, $\beta$- and $\gamma$-globulins have isoelectric points of 5.1, 5.6 and 6.0 pH, respectively. It is questionable whether these fractions are distinct chemical entities. It is more probable that they are merely artificially produced as a result of the methods of treatment employed. In other words, it is likely that serum globulin is a single large molecule which is split into two or three separate parts by laboratory manipulation. Yet however this may be, the γ-globulin is more intimately associated with antibody production, and undergoes an increase in many acute and chronic infections.

Pseudoglobulin contains 85 per cent α-globulin and 15 per cent γ-globulin, whereas, euglobulin contains less α- but more of the β- and γ-globulins.

The several electrophoretic fractions of plasma protein are not pure; all contain lipid and carbohydrate material combined probably as prosthetic groups. The albumin fraction also contains bilirubin (ch. 6). Approximately 75 per cent of the carbohydrate and all of the lipid, bound to protein, is found in the α- and β-globulin fractions. The role played by the lipoprotein complexes in atherosclerosis is discussed elsewhere in the book. Other substances, e.g., calcium, phosphorus, sulfonamide drugs and the dye T-1824 (p. 17) are bound to the albumin fraction (see fig. 1.1).

Fibrinogen has been isolated and prepared in crystalline form. X-ray diffraction studies indicate that its molecule is structurally similar to such fibrous proteins as collagen and myosin (see ch. 53). The molecular weights of the plasma proteins are given on p. 7.

The total plasma protein can be calculated from the specific gravity of the plasma by means of line charts, or by using the formula $P = K (S - A)$, where P is the plasma protein in grams per 100 cc., S the specific gravity and K and A are constants with values of 364 and 1.006, respectively. Thus, if the specific gravity is 1.026, the protein in grams per 100 cc. is $7.28 = 364 (1.026 - 1.006)$).

The values of total protein and of the different fractions in human plasma are given in the following table.

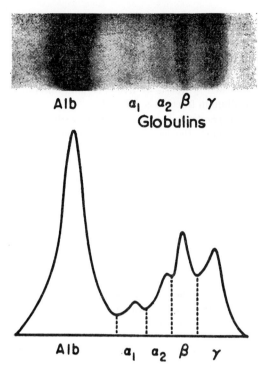

FIG. 1.1. Dyed electrophoretic and corresponding density pattern of human sera.

100 cc. in dog, cow and goat respectively) (see fig. 1.1).

PATHOLOGICAL VARIATIONS IN SERUM PROTEINS. The several protein fractions of plasma may change in value independently of one another, and either with or without alteration in the quantity of total protein; in several pathological states the albumin and globulin fractions may change in opposite directions, i.e., a fall in albumin accompanied by a rise in globulin.

The fibrinogen concentration is increased in *pregnancy* and *menstruation*, in *tissue injury* of various kinds, in *parathyroid overdosage, acute infections, malaria* and several other conditions. This fraction is markedly reduced in animals after hepatectomy or severe liver damage and in several diseases involving the liver. In rare instances it is congenitally considerably below normal or absent.

In *hemorrhage* a loss of all fractions of plasma protein occurs, their concentrations are also diminished as well, since the blood volume is at first made good by the passage of a saline solution or one of low protein concentration from the tissue spaces into the blood stream. In extensive *burns*, on the other hand, especially during the following few days, all fractions are reduced as a result of the leakage of blood fluid from the de-

*Protein fractions in human plasma*

| Fractionation by Electrophoresis grams/100 cc. | Fractionation by Salting out with Sodium Sulfate grams/100 cc. |
|---|---|
| Total protein.6.03–6.72 | Total protein...6.0–8.0 |
| Albumin......3.32–4.04 | Albumin........4.3–5.0 |
| Total globulin 2.23–2.39 | Total globulin..1.1–3.1 |
| α-globulin..0.79–0.84 | Euglobulin...0.1–0.4 |
| β-globulin..0.78–0.81 | Pseudoglob- |
| γ-globulin..0.66–0.70 | ulin........1.0–2.7 |
| Fibrinogen...0.34–0.43 | Fibrinogen.....0.2–0.3 |
| | Albumin/glob- |
| | ulin   (A/G) |
| | ratio........  1.50 |

In some animals the globulin is equal to or exceeds the albumin. Of the three fractions fibrinogen is always in lowest concentration and it is considerably lower in human plasma than in that of some animals (e.g., 0.58, 0.72, 0.60 gram per

nuded surface and into the tissues in the region of the burned area; but since the lost fluid is usually relatively low in its content of protein, the protein concentration of the plasma tends towards an increase. In *cirrhosis of the liver*, *chronic hepatitis* (depressed synthesis by liver), *chronic infections*, the albumin fraction is reduced.

In *nephrotic* and *nephritic conditions* (due to loss of albumin in the urine) and in severe *malnutrition* (owing to the low intake of the necessary amino acids for protein synthesis) the albumin fraction is also reduced. As a result of the diminished concentration of albumin, the oncotic pressure of the plasma tends to fall, less water is held in the vessels and, as a consequence, the plasma volume is reduced. As a consequence of these changes, the globulin, though not raised absolutely, shows increased concentration. In any condition associated with a loss of water from the blood (*dehydration, anhydremia*, p. 25), though no change may occur in the absolute amount, i.e., in the total quantity in the blood, the concentrations of all fractions will show an increase. In order to determine whether an *absolute* reduction or increase in one or other of the plasma proteins exists, it would be necessary to measure the total plasma volume (ch. 3) as well as the concentration of the particular fraction. The γ-globulin shows an absolute increase in *multiple myeloma, cirrhosis of the liver, subacute yellow atrophy of the liver, acute hepatitis* and *acute nephritis, leukemia, tuberculosis, scarlet fever* and in *acute* and *chronic infections*. In liver disease the α-globulin is also increased, and in later pregnancy the concentration of β-globulin, which contains a high percentage of lipid, is raised. Prothrombin appears to be a β-globulin. This fraction serves to bind a considerable proportion of the plasma cholesterol, carotene and phospholipids of the plasma, and is increased in the later months of pregnancy. The isoagglutinins (anti-A and anti-B, and anti-Rh, ch. 5) are associated with the γ- and β-globulin fractions of the plasma.

ORIGIN. In the *embryo*, the mesenchyme cells, through a process of secretion or by the actual solution of their substance, furnish the fluid (embryonic plasma) which floats the primitive blood cells (ch. 11). The albumin fraction is formed earlier than the other proteins which do not appear in the plasma of the chick embryo until after the 14th day of incubation.

In the *adult*, five possible sources of the plasma proteins have been suggested—namely, disintegrating blood cells (red or white), the general tis-

sue cells, reticuloendothelial cells of spleen, bone marrow, etc., and the liver.

It is now well established that the liver is the site of the production of plasma albumin; this fraction undergoes a pronouced reduction in conditions which depress hepatic function. It is thought that the Kupffer cells are especially concerned in the manufacture. The albumin fraction (but not the globulin) in the plasma of dogs can be reduced and maintained at a subnormal level by intravenous injections of a solution of gum acacia (p. 50). In these experiments the hepatic cells become swollen and vacuolated. The fall in serum albumin is therefore considered to be due, in part at least, to the failure of the liver to make good the normal "wear and tear" of serum albumin (which amounts to several grams daily), though, possibly, there is also a withdrawal of albumin from the plasma to the liver as a compensatory response to rectify the increase in oncotic pressure caused by the presence of acacia in the circulation.

The evidence points definitely to the liver as the site of fibrinogen production since, as mentioned above, the concentration of this fraction is reduced by liver damage or hepatectomy. When the liver returns to a healthy state after injury has been induced by an agent such as phosphorus or chloroform, the fibrinogen level also returns to normal. Following slight liver injury or during the repair of a hepatic lesion, which might be expected to stimulate the functional activity of the organ, the fibrinogen may be actually higher than normal.

The origin of serum globulin has not been definitely settled. Elman and Heifetz succeeded in reducing the albumin fraction in the serum of dogs by dietary measures to 50 per cent of the normal. No reduction was observed in the serum globulin. The livers of the animals showed pronounced histological and chemical changes; the water content of the hepatic tissue was increased; the cells became vacuolated. This was accompanied by severe depletion of hepatic protein.

On the contrary, the experiments of Miller and his associates who perfused the intact livers of rats with blood containing lysine labeled with isotopic carbon ($C^{14}$) indicate that the liver furnished about 80 per cent of the serum globulin. The remainder is supplied by extrahepatic tissues, the greater part of which, if not the whole, are derived from the lymphocytes (White and Dougherty, ch. 10). The conflict between the results of the experiments of Elman and Heifetz and those of Miller and associates may be explained perhaps by the great functional reserve of the liver, hepatic lesions in the experiments of the former being insufficient to cripple its globulin producing function.

There is experimental evidence that the adrenocorticoptrophic hormone of the pituitary through its action on the adrenal cortex affects the manufacture of $\beta$- and $\gamma$-globulins. Injections of this hormone or of adrenal cortical hormones into rats causes within 24 hours a rise in $\beta$-globulin of 30 per cent, and in $\gamma$-globulin of from 70 to 80 per cent (White and Dougherty).

FUNCTIONS. 1. Fibrinogen in essential for the *clotting* of the blood (ch. 12).

*2.* All three proteins serve to maintain the *osmotic pressure* (p. 26) of the blood. The large molecules of the proteins do not pass readily through the normal capillary membrane. The osmotic pressure which they exert amounts to, in man, between 25 and 30 mm. Hg. The pressure which each fraction exerts is inversely related to the size of its molecule and directly related to its concentration in the plasma. The molecular weight of fibrinogen is over 200,000 and its concentration is low; it therefore contributes little toward the total osmotic pressure. Albumin is in the highest concentration and its molecule has the least weight (70,000–75,000). The osmotic pressure of the plasma, therefore, depends largely upon this fraction. The molecular weight of serum globulin is between 150,000 and 190,000 and its concentration is considerably less than that of albumin. In equivalent concentrations, serum albumin has an osmotic activity 2.4 times that of serum globulin (Keys); it furnishes about 80 per cent of the oncotic pressure of the plasma.

*3. Viscosity.* The proteins give a certain viscosity to the blood which is a factor in the maintenance of the normal blood pressure.

*4.* They aid in the regulation of the *acid-base balance* of the blood (ch. 13).

*5. Stability of the blood* (see p. 64). The globulin and fibrinogen fractions influence the tendency of the corpuscles to adhere to one another and form rouleaux or clumps.

*6. Trephones.* Carrel has shown that the leucocytes prepare substances from the plasma proteins which are essential for the nourishment of tissue cells grown in cultures. These substances he has termed trephones.

*7. Immune substances* (antibodies) which react with the antigens of several microorganisms, e.g., diphtheria, typhoid and streptococcal infections, and the viruses of mumps, influenza and measles, are associated with the $\gamma$-globulin. $\gamma$-Globulin, separated from the other fractions, is used as a means of artificially immunizing against measles, infectious hepatitis, rubella and poliomyelitis.[5] Certain other antibodies, the isoagglutinins A and B, are present in the $\gamma$- and $\beta$-fractions. As might be expected, the globulin fraction of the serum tends to increase during the process of immunization against the infective diseases mentioned above.

*8.* They serve as a *reserve of protein* upon which for a time the body draws during fasting or when the protein intake is inadequate.

*Plasmapheresis.* The importance of the plasma proteins is demonstrated by this procedure which consists in bleeding an animal and returning the red cells suspended in Locke's solution to the body. A state of shock results, followed by death when the total protein is reduced to between 1 and 2 per cent. No ill effects result however if the cells are suspended in serum before they are reintroduced. When depletion of the proteins is not carried to the point where fatal shock ensues, a marked rise in protein concentration occurs within 15 minutes which indicates that during this time a store of preformed protein is drawn upon for the replacement of the protein which has been removed. The regeneration is slower after this, though fairly rapid for the first 24 hours. It becomes progressively slower during succeeding days. The proteins are restored to the normal level in from 2 to 7 days, provided that the diet contains a sufficiency of high quality protein. Plasma proteins themselves have been found to be best for this purpose; the proteins of liver run a close second.

In more chronic plasmapheresis experiments, edema commences when the total protein concentration reaches a value of 5.5 per cent and albumin a concentration of 2.5 per cent.

*The Nonprotein Nitrogen (N.P.N.) or Noncoagulable Nitrogen of Blood*

By the term nonprotein nitrogen is meant the nitrogen of those substances, e.g., urea, uric acid, creatinine, etc., listed on page 8. They may be extracted from blood or plasma by treating either of these with a reagent, such as trichloracetic acid,

[5] Gamma globulin obtained from any normal person usually contains sufficient immune bodies for protection against measles and infectious hepatitis, but for protection against rubella (German measles), poliomyelitis, whooping cough, chickenpox and mumps, an active immune globulin can be obtained only from subjects convalescent from the particular disease.

TABLE 1.2*

*The nitrogen partition in the blood of normal individuals and the distribution of the various nitrogenous constituents between the cells and serum*

| | Corpuscles | | | Plasma | | | Whole Blood | | |
|---|---|---|---|---|---|---|---|---|---|
| | Maxi-mum | Mini-mum | Aver-age | Maxi-mum | Mini-mum | Aver-age | Maxi-mum | Mini-mum | Aver-age |
| | *mg. per 100 cc.* | | | *mg. per 100 cc.* | | | *mg. per 100 cc.* | | |
| (a) Taken from Wu: | | | | | | | | | |
| Total nonprotein nitrogen .......... | 61 | 39 | 49 | 36 | 20 | 29 | | | |
| Urea N............................. | 22 | 12 | 17 | 23 | 13 | 19 | | | |
| Amino acid N...................... | 11 | 8 | 10 | 8 | 5 | 6 | | | |
| Uric acid.......................... | 4 | 1 | 2 | 5 | 2 | 4 | | | |
| Creatine........................... | 8 | 4 | 6 | 0 | 0 | 0 | | | |
| Creatinine......................... | 3 | 1.6 | 2.5 | 1.5 | 1 | 1.2 | | | |
| Undetermined N................... | | | 19 | | | 2.1 | | | |
| (b) Taken from Berglund: | | | | | | | | | |
| Total nonprotein nitrogen........... | 55 | 38 | 44 | 30 | 18 | 25 | 39 | 28 | 32 |
| Urea N............................. | 13 | 8 | 10 | 17 | 10 | 12 | 15 | 9 | 12 |
| Amino acid ........................ | 11 | 7 | 8 | 6 | 4 | 5 | 8 | 6 | 6 |
| Undetermined N................... | 34 | 18 | 25 | 12 | 2 | 7 | 18 | 10 | 14 |

* Reprinted from Peters and Van Slyke, *Quantitative Clinical Chemistry*, vol. I, p. 267. The Williams & Wilkins Company, Baltimore, 1946.

which precipitates the proteins, filtering and determining the nitrogen in the filtrate. These substances are in part absorbed with, or derived from the food, and in part are the waste products of tissue catabolism. The total N.P.N. of whole blood amounts to from 28 to 40 mg. per 100 cc. It constitutes from 1 to 2 per cent of the total nitrogen of the blood. Its concentration in the cells is nearly double that in the plasma. The proportions of the different constituents are given in table 1.2.

The term undetermined nitrogen embraces the nitrogen of ammonia, purines, and other nonprotein substances of unknown or undefined nature.

PATHOLOGICAL VARIATIONS. The N.P.N. of blood at any given level represents the balance struck between nitrogenous materials formed in the intermediary metabolism of ingested and tissue protein and the excretion of these products in the urine. In renal insufficiency, therefore, the nonprotein nitrogen is elevated, and in certain cases may be ten times the normal. On the other hand, a rise in the N.P.N. occurs in conditions which are associated with excessive tissue catabolism, such as infections, fevers, thyrotoxicosis, starvation or severe malnutrition. It is also increased following hemorrhage into the stomach or upper intestinal tract. In the later months of pregnancy the N.P.N. is reduced. The reduction has been attributed to the diversion of nitrogen to the growing fetus and the reduction of protein catabolism in the maternal tissues.

The chief conditions associated with an elevation of the N.P.N. of the blood are:

Adrenal insufficiency
Dehydration
Hemorrhage into the gastrointestinal tract
Infectious fevers, lobar pneumonia
Intestinal obstruction
Parathyroid intoxication (in animals)
Peritonitis
Renal insufficiency

*Cholesterol*

(See also chapters 39 and 49). This sterol is present in serum in the free form and as cholesteryl esters. The normal value for total serum cholesterol is not known exactly; it varies from 100 to 250 mg. per cent. The esterified cholesterol is about 72 per cent of the total and this ratio varies within a rather narrow range. Its concentration is increased in several diseases, notably in hypothyroidism and lipid nephrosis and in some cases of atheromatosis. Keys and his associates found that within fairly wide limits (2 to 3 grams cholesterol weekly) the content of the sterol in the diet exerted little effect upon the serum cholesterol.

REFERENCES

BLOOR, W. R. J. Biol. Chem., 1918, 36, 49.
CARREL, A. J. A. M. A., 1924, 82, 255; J. Exper. Med., 1922, 36, 385.

ELMAN, R. AND HEIFETZ, C. J. J. Exper. Med., 1941, **73, 417**.

KAY, H. D. Brit. J. Exper. Path., 1930, **11, 148**.

KEYS, A. J. Phys. Chem., 1938, **42, 11**.

KEYS, A. AND ASSOCIATES. J. Nutrition, 1956, **59, 39**.

MILLER, L. L. AND ASSOCIATES. J. Exper. Med., 1951, **94, 431**.

PHILLIPS, R. A., VAN SLYKE, D. D. AND ASSOCIATES. Bull. U. S. Army M. Dept., 1943, **71, 66**.

WHITE, A. AND DOUGHERTY, T. F., Endocrinology, 1945, **36, 207**; Proc. Soc. Exper. Biol. & Med., 1944, **56, 26**.

*Monographs and Reviews*

ALBRITTON, E. C., Ed. Standard values in blood. W. B. Saunders, Philadelphia, 1952.

BIER, M., Ed. Electrophoresis: theory, methods and application. Academic Press, New York, 1959.

FOLIN, O. Physiol. Rev., 1922, **2, 460**.

GUEST, G. M. AND RAPPAPORT, S. Physiol. Rev., 1941, **21, 410**.

HENDERSON, L. J. Fitness of the environment. Macmillan, New York, 1913.

HOWE, P. E. Physiol. Rev., 1925, **5, 439**.

MACALLUM, A. B. Physiol. Rev., 1926, **6, 316**.

MYERS, V. C. Physiol. Rev., 1924, **4, 274**.

PETERS, J. P. AND VAN SLYKE, D. D. Quantitative clinical chemistry. Vol. I. The Williams & Wilkins Co., Baltimore, 1946.

# 2

# THE RED CELLS OR ERYTHROCYTES

## The Size, Shape and Structure of the Red Cell

Human erythrocytes are disk shaped, non-nucleated elements having a mean diameter of 7.2μ (6–9μ: see fig. 2.1) and a thickness of about 2.2μ (2–2.4μ) at the thickest part, i.e., near the circumference, and about 1μ at the center. As a result of osmotic changes[1] and the consequent passage of water into the cell, the diameter increases with a shift in the acid-base balance of the blood toward the acid side. The cell is therefore slightly larger in venous than in arterial blood; its diameter is increased by about 0.5μ in muscular exercise and reduced by forced breathing. The central portion of the cell is much thinner than its edges, which appear heaped up into a circumferential mound around a central depression. This construction gives it a biconcave contour or a roughly dumbbell outline when viewed edgewise (figs. 2.1 and 2.2).[2] The average area of a red cell is 120μ² and the volume 85μ³.

[1] These are the mean dimensions of the cell measured in dry films. In the fresh state the diameter is larger by about 0.5 μ. There is considerable variation between the diameter of the smallest and largest cells found in a sample of normal blood. The range for dried films is shown in figure 2.2.

[2] Hartridge has pointed out the advantage of this design for the transport of oxygen. Of all geometrical figures the sphere is the one in which its center is equidistant from all points upon its surface. The adoption of this form by the red cell would therefore have ensured the diffusion of oxygen to all parts of its interior at equal rates. But a sphere has the disadvantage of possessing the smallest surface in relation to its mass. A thin disk, on the other hand, presents an almost maximal surface area in relation to its bulk, yet in such a shape all parts on the surface are not equally distant from its center; the ends are further removed than the sides. The shape of the red cell—a thin disk with elevated rounded edges—is a compromise between these two forms. It secures the advantages of equal and rapid diffusion of oxygen to its interior and a relatively large surface area for the absorption of the gas.

The biconcave form also gives the red cell a mechanical advantage, in that the changes in volume which the cell undergoes from time to time can be effected with a minimal amount of tension being placed upon the cell membrane. The membrane covering the concavity of the cell moves

There has been in the past a tendency to regard the erythrocyte as almost a dead cell, because of its low oxygen consumption, and its lack of a nucleus. However, it should be noted that the erythrocyte carries out metabolic processes, and it does have a finite, though low, oxygen consumption. It is therefore probably better to consider it as a very specialized type of living cell.

The framework, or stroma of the red cell, comprises somewhat less than 5 per cent of the wet weight of the cell. The major constituents of the stroma are lipids and an insoluble protein. The former is mainly made up of cephalin, lecithin and cholesterol; the latter is albuminlike. Almost half of the lipids are bound to the protein, and a lipoprotein complex called elenin has been isolated from the stroma by Calvin and his coworkers. Elenin seems to contain at least the A, B and Rh antigens. (In general, the antigenic nature of the erythrocyte appears to be a property associated with the stroma.) Hemoglobin makes up about 30 to 34 per cent of the wet weight of the cell. This corresponds to an extremely concentrated solution of the proteins, and means that the hemoglobin molecules are packed very tightly into the interior of the erythrocyte.

The erythrocyte contains the enzymes of the glycolytic system, catalase, carbonic anhydrase, all of the glutathione of the blood, as well as other enzymes and organic and inorganic salts. Potassium is present in high concentration, relative to sodium.

When a drop of freshly drawn normal blood is placed on a glass slide and examined under the microscope, many of the erythrocytes will be seen to group themselves together with their broad surfaces in contact, like a pile of coins. Groups of cells arranged in this way are called rouleaux (sing., *rouleau*). The normal discoid shape of the erythrocytes is a requisite for rou-

freely out or in "like the bottom of an oil-can" as the cell increases or diminishes in volume.

[3] Though very widely accepted, this sex difference has probably been overemphasized. Some workers have found a maximal difference of only 1 per cent in favor of men.

leaux formation, the property being lost if the cells, as in congenital hemolytic jaundice, assume a more globular form. Rouleaux formation does not occur in the circulation under normal physi-

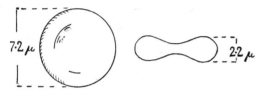

FIG. 2.1. Diagram showing dimensions of the red cell.

ological conditions, the moving cells showing little or no tendency to cohere.

*"Sludged" blood.* In certain abnormal states, e.g., tissue injury and shock, the cells of the circulating blood show a pronounced tendency to stick together and form large clumps or masses which move slowly and cumbersomely through the small vessels—arterioles and capillaries. This "sludged" blood, as it is termed by Knisely who has made an extensive study of the phenomenon, has a deleterious effect upon the general circulation. Normally the blood moves through the minute vessels in stream-lines. The cells remain

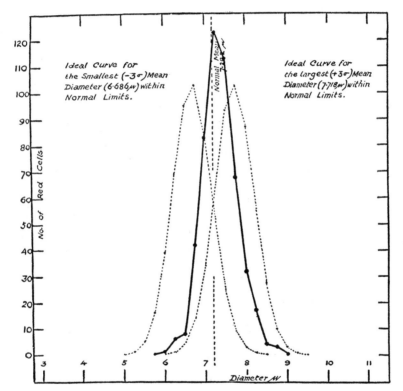

FIG. 2.2. Red cell diameter distribution curve for healthy men (after Price-Jones).

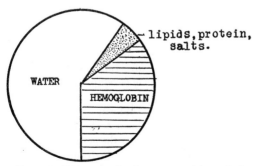

FIG. 2.3. Diagram showing composition of the red cell.

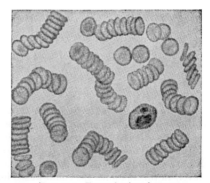

FIG. 2.4. Description in text.

discrete showing little tendency to cohere. The propulsive force of cardiac systole is transmitted throughout the vascular system with the minimum dissipation of energy. Stream-lining is abolished in sludged blood; a large proportion of the energy is wasted in giving a rolling or rotary motion (angular acceleration) to the massed cells. Sludged blood is thought in some instances to be a factor in thrombosis (ch. 12).

### Number

The average number of red cells in man is around 5,000,000 per cu. mm. for males and 4,500,000 for females, but 6,000,000 is not a very unusual figure for a robust young man and 5,500,000 for a healthy young woman.[3] Slight variations in the number of red cells, amounting to about 5 per cent, occur throughout the 24 hours. The count is lowest during sleep, becomes elevated after arising and increases gradually throughout the waking hours. At birth and in infancy the red cells are somewhat more numerous than in later life, but the earlier figures of 7,000,000 and 8,000,000 for the newborn child have not been confirmed by later work. Destruction of a large proportion of the extra cells occurs within the first 10 days, but for a few days the red cell count shows a progressive fall; for some weeks after this the count remains considerably above that of the adult.

The destruction of large numbers of erythrocytes shortly after birth and, as a consequence, the liberation of excessive amounts of hemoglobin into the plasma has been held to be the cause of the physiological jaundice of the newborn, in whom the bilirubin content of the plasma (ch. 39) is from 3 to 5.5 mg. per cent. The infant's red cells are said by some to be more fragile than those of the adult, yet it is questionable, in view of the revised figures for red cell counts in the newborn, that excessive hemolysis plays a very important part in the production of the jaundice. Again, others deny that the red cells at birth are unduly fragile. Immaturity of the excretory function of the liver probably plays the dominant role.

The total number of red cells in the human body estimated upon the basis of 5,000,000 per cu. mm. is about 33,000,000,000,000 which gives a total red cell area exposed to the plasma of between 3500 and 4000 sq. meters. Eamons has made the interesting observation that in the species which he investigated (cat, rabbit, dog and man) the surface area of the individual corpuscles and the corpuscular count varied in opposite directions, so that the cell area per cu. mm. of blood was nearly the same in all—7.24, 7.55, 7.52 and 7.35 sq. cm. for the four species in the order given above. The quantity of hemoglobin per sq. cm. of red cell area is also about equal in all mammalian species.

PHYSIOLOGICAL VARIATIONS IN THE NUMBER OF RED CELLS

*Increase in the number of red cells* occurs under the following conditions:

1. HIGH ALTITUDES. It has been known for many years that the inhabitants of mountainous regions, especially where the elevation above the sea is 10,000 feet or more, have constantly a much higher red cell count than persons living at sea level. The natives of some regions in the Peruvian Andes, where the altitude is 14,000 feet or more, have a red cell count 30 per cent above the normal (over 7,000,000 per cu. mm.). Not only the natives, but travellers sojourning even for a short time at these altitudes undergo an almost immediate increase in the number of their red cells. The corpuscular increase is directly proportional to the altitude, as may be seen from table 2.1.

It is perhaps necessary to point out here that an increase or a decrease in the red cell count does not of itself inform one of an increase or decrease in the red cells of the body as a whole. The red cell count gives only an estimate of the *number of cells per unit quantity of blood* (p. 17). A reduction in the amount of plasma or of the water of the blood, for instance, would cause the *proportion* of red cells in the specimen to be increased. But neither the immediate nor the permanent increase in number of red cells at high altitudes is due simply to a reduction in fluid and a greater concentration of the blood, for estimations of the

TABLE 2.1

| Altitude in Thousands of Feet | Corpuscles in Millions per Cubic Millimeter |
|---|---|
| 0.7 | 4.5 |
| 4.4 | 5.2 |
| 12.0 | 6.8 |
| 15.6 | 7.8 |
| 18.2 | 8.3 |

From Barcroft after Hingston. In this table the altitude (in thousands of feet) multiplied by 0.225 gives a figure which approximates the increase in red cell count (in millions per cu. mm.) above that at sea level. In this instance the count at sea level was 4,250,000.

total volume of blood in the body (see ch. 3) prove that there is an *absolute* increase in the number of circulating cells. How is the *immediate* increase brought about? It is obviously impossible to account for such a rapid rise in the red cell count by a greater production of cells by the bone marrow, and it is at once suggested that large masses of cells are packed away from the general circulation—in a storehouse of some kind —but are quickly mobilized upon demand. When the functions of the spleen are considered (ch. 8) it will be seen that this organ serves as a reservoir for red cells and is responsible for the sudden increase in their number which occurs early in the process of acclimatization to high altitudes.

The *permanent* and great elevation of the red cell count, which is a characteristic feature of the blood of natives and other persons after acclimatization to the rarefied atmosphere, cannot be explained in the same manner, for the number of cells which the spleen can put into circulation is limited. Under these circumstances there is, actually, an increased manufacture of erythrocytes by the blood-forming organ—the bone marrow. The cells which are formed by the overstimulated marrow are discharged into the general circulation at a somewhat immature stage of their development. They are spoken of as *reticulated cells* or *reticulocytes* since their protoplasm shows a delicate filigree or reticulum which stains with basic dyes. The ultimate cause of the corpuscular increase (a physiological polycythemia) is undoubtedly the lowered oxygen tension of the atmosphere, and consequently of the blood, since animals placed in an hermetically sealed cabinet and subjected to lowered oxygen tensions exhibit similar blood changes.

2. MUSCULAR EXERCISE and certain EMOTIONAL STATES cause a temporary increase in the number of red cells as a result of an outpouring of concentrated blood from the spleen.[4] This may be looked upon as an emergency measure and, like that which occurs at high altitudes, is the response of the body to the tissues' call for oxygen.

3. HEIGHTENED ENVIRONMENTAL TEMPERATURE also causes a liberation of red cells from the splenic reservoir.

4. OTHER CONDITIONS which tend to lower the oxygen tension of the arterial blood cause a rise in the number of circulating red cells. As in the response at high altitudes two factors are concerned, e.g., a discharge of blood from the spleen

[4] Though this can be demonstrated in experimental animals, it does not appear to be an important feature in man.

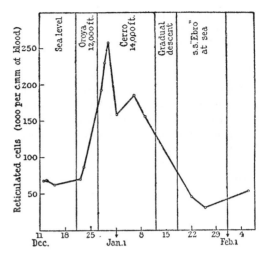

FIG. 2.5. Showing reticulocyte response to altitude (after Barcroft).

and other reservoirs, and a greater production of cells by the bone marrow.

*Reduction in the number of red cells* occurs at high barometric pressures, e.g., when the oxygen tension of the blood is higher than the normal. Animals, for example, living in deep mines have a lower red cell count than those at sea level.

ALTERATIONS IN THE NUMBER OF RED CELLS IN PATHOLOGICAL STATES

*Increase in the Number of Red Cells—Polycythemia*

Increase in the total number of red cells occurs as a compensatory measure in several pathological conditions and then represents apparently the response of the bone marrow to low oxygen tensions in the arterial blood. A red cell concentration of 7,000,000 or more per cu. mm. of blood is not unusual in the following conditions.

1. EMPHYSEMA (p. 518) and other chronic diseases which interfere with the oxygenation of the blood in the lungs (anoxia), e.g., tracheal stenosis, pneumothorax, tumor of the lung, pulmonary tuberculosis and pulmonary arteriovenous aneurysm.

2. CONGENITAL HEART DISEASE (ch. 28).

3. AYERZA'S DISEASE, a condition associated with dilation and marked hypertrophy of the right heart, sclerosis of the pulmonary arteries and their branches with consequent obstruction of the blood flow through the lungs. There is extreme cyanosis; emphysema, dyspnea, and attacks of asthma are common accompaniments. The bone marrow is hyperplastic.

4. CHRONIC CARBON MONOXIDE POISONING.

5. CHEMICALS, e.g., chronic poisoning with

arsenic, phosphorus and manganese, gum shellac, and certain aniline dyes.

6. REPEATED SMALL HEMORRHAGES, the polycythemia then represents an over-response of the bone marrow to the successive blood losses.

POLYCYTHEMIA VERA (synonyms: erythremia, splenomegalic polycythemia, Vasquez-Osler disease). Unlike the preceding types the polycythemia is not secondary to any known pathological condition. The disease appears to be primarily centered in the red bone marrow which is greatly increased in amount and is hyperplastic, extending into the shafts of the bones to displace the fatty marrow, and packed with normoblasts and mature erythrocytes. Megaloblasts are absent or very scarce. The number of red cells in the circulating blood may be as high as 14,000,000 per cu. mm. and a count as high as 20,000,000 has been reported. The total blood volume is greatly increased. The viscosity of the blood is of course greatly elevated. The concentration of hemoglobin in the individual cells and the chemical and physiological properties of the pigment are normal. The size, shape and general features of the red cells as a rule show nothing unusual and the number of reticulocytes is not greatly increased.

The chief features shown by the disease apart from those of the blood itself are cyanosis (ch. 33), dyspnea on exertion, enlargement of the spleen, hemorrhages and a familial tendency. Death may occur from thrombosis of the portal vein or a cerebral vessel. The circulation rate (ch. 28) is slowed and the diffusion rates of oxygen and $CO_2$ (ch. 31) through the pulmonary epithelium are reduced, although during rest the oxygen saturation of the arterial blood is usually normal. The renal blood flow and the filtration fraction (ch. 34) are increased whereas the plasma flow is decreased. The oxygen saturation of the blood is reduced, however, during exercise. Owing to the great increase in hemoglobin concentration the actual *quantity* of oxygen in the blood is greater than normal. If the polycythemia were a compensatory reaction brought about by the lowered rate of diffusion of oxygen through the pulmonary epithelium, one would expect that breathing air with a high pressure of oxygen would be of benefit, but this is not the case. Exposure, in a chamber, to a high oxygen tension for several days does not effect a reduction in the number of red cells. The reduced circulation rate may result in some way from the fact that the blood contains such a large load of oxygen that the tissues can obtain their quota from a smaller quantity of blood than normally. On the other hand, the reduced circulation rate may be due primarily to vasoconstriction in some

part of the circulation. Some believe that narrowing of the caliber of the vessels of the bone marrow and the resulting low oxygen tension produced thereby provide the stimulus for the overproduction of blood cells. Studies of blood lactic acid concentration in polycythemia vera following muscular exercise lend support to the idea that a sluggish blood flow through the tissues is a causative factor. In normal persons and in the secondary types of polycythemia mentioned above, a rise in blood lactate occurs, whereas in polycythemia vera exercise causes a fall. This anomaly could be explained upon the basis of a high resting blood lactate as a result of a slow blood flow and the accumulation of lactic acid in the ischemic tissues. Exercise would then, by causing vasodilation and a freer oxygen supply, in the contracting muscles, tend to reduce the concentration of the metabolite in the blood. That this is the probable explanation is indicated by the observation that vasodilation induced by heat also causes a fall in blood lactate in this disease. The phenomenon appears to be of fundamental significance, and not simply the result of the high erythrocyte concentration, because it is not abolished when the red cell count is brought down to normal by treatment with *phenylhydrazine hydrochloride*, a drug which has been employed in controlling the disease.

Polycythemia can be produced in dogs by the daily administration of cobaltous chloride (8 mg. daily for 2 or 3 weeks). The high red cell count thus induced is reduced to normal by feeding with whole beef or hog liver or by the daily injection of ascorbic acid. The effect of liver suggests the presence of an hepatic hormone possessing a depressant action upon bone marrow activity. Radioactive phosphorus ($P^{32}$) has been used lately with success in the treatment of the disease.

The observations of Schafer have thrown a new light on the pathogenesis of polycythemia vera which may show a way to the rational treatment of the disease. In experiments upon dogs he found that excision of the carotid sinus and the aortic nerves caused the development of polycythemia and hypertension in 40 per cent of the animals. Removal of the paravertebral chain of sympathetic ganglia was followed by a gradual return of the erythrocyte count to normal. A similar result followed paravertebral sympathectomy in a patient suffering from polycythemia. The polycythemic response to removal of the influence of the carotid sinus and aortic nerves is possibly due to constriction of the vessels of the bone marrow, the anoxia caused thereby acting in the usual way to stimulate its hemopoietic function.

*Reduction in the number of red cells* below the normal is known as anemia. The causes and varieties of anemia are manifold and will be considered in chapter 9.

*An apparent decrease or increase* in the number of red cells occurs under certain conditions which upset the water balance of the body. It has already been pointed out that the red cell count gives merely an estimate of the proportion of cells to plasma. There may, for instance, be undue retention of water in the body, and the plasma or its watery constituents may then be increased (hydremia or hemodilution). The blood is diluted, and the number of red cells per unit of blood is reduced, yet there is no absolute decrease in the number of circulating cells. Conversely, a loss of plasma or of merely the water of the blood (anhydremia or hemoconcentration) will increase the red cell count, i.e., the blood becomes more concentrated although the total number of red cells in the body is not altered. Therefore in conditions associated with extreme dehydration (p. 24) of the body the number of red cells per unit of blood is increased.

A practical point to be remembered when counting the red cells or in determining the packed cell volume is that their number may be relatively increased or decreased by purely *local* alterations in blood concentration. Pronounced dilation of the capillaries of the region of skin from which the sample has been taken will cause a local slowing of the blood stream and congestion of the part. The loss of fluid from the vessel into the tissues and the clumping of corpuscles which may result from the greater capillary pressure will give a false estimate of the number of red cells. On the other hand, pressure made upon the part by the examiner in order to hasten the flow of blood from a skin puncture may express fluid from the tissues which will dilute the red cells in the specimen. Moreover, even under ordinary physiological conditions, the concentration of red cells may vary considerably in different parts of the circulation. The proportion of red cells in the capillaries is greater as a rule than in the heart and larger vessels, by around 12 per cent, but in certain states associated with slowing of the peripheral circulation, concentration of red cells in the capillaries may increase the disparity. Trapping of *plasma* in the peripheral vessels may occur in other conditions and will tend to reduce the concentration of cells in the capillary areas below that in the general circulation. These are also important points to bear in mind in estimating the blood volume by the dye method (p. 17).

*Estimation of red cells.* The concentrations of red (or white) cells may be obtained by counting them directly after suitable dilution beneath the microscope, as in the method of Thoma-Zeiss. The instrument used for this purpose is called a *hemocytometer*. The reader is referred to texts on laboratory methods for details. The relative volumes of red cells and plasma are determined by means of a specially devised centrifuge known as an *hematocrit*. The blood, rendered noncoagulable, is drawn into a graduated capillary tube, placed in a centrifuge and revolved at a speed of 3000 r.p.m. 30 to 60 minutes. At the end of this time the original blood will be found to have separated into a clear colorless column of plasma and a red column —the corpuscles. The lengths of the two columns are read off by means of the graduations on the tube. The normal proportions of plasma and corpuscles in human blood are about 54 (53–56) and 46 (44–47) respectively. That is, the volume of cells (*packed cell volume*) is 46 per cent of the total volume of the specimen of blood. The average volume of the individual erythrocytes is obtained by dividing the packed cell volume by the figure for the red cell count. It is important to use an anticoagulant, such as heparin, that does not cause shrinkage or swelling of the cells.

## Variations in Size, Shape and Structure of the Red Cells

Under physiological conditions little change in shape of the red cell occurs, though a few fragmented cells may be found in normal blood. These are, as will be seen later (ch. 8), simply remnants of senile cells which have undergone a natural disintegration in the blood stream. A slight change in volume, about 7.5 per cent occurs, due to osmotic changes incident to the respiratory cycle (ch. 29). The red cells at birth and in early infancy are larger than in adult life. This as well as the higher cell count is responsible for the high packed cell volume (54 per cent) of the infant's blood.

In *disease*, the red cell is subject to many changes in size, shape and structure. The examination of the blood and the identification of the various forms of abnormal cells is an important means employed in diagnosis of the different anemias (ch. 9). Only the more outstanding abnormalities can be touched upon here. The least pronounced departure from the normal blood picture is an increase in the number of *reticulocytes* (see frontispiece). These young red cells resemble the ordinary cells in every way except that after supravital staining (alcoholic solution of brilliant cresyl blue added to blood in the fresh state) a fine reticulum of basophilic material can be seen in the cytoplasm. The reticular material is of cytoplasmic origin, probably γ-globulin, and does not represent nuclear remains. A reticulum of similar nature may sometimes be seen in cells in which the nucleus is still intact. In normal human blood the reticulocytes are from 0 to 2 (av. 0.8) per cent of the total red cell count.[5] They are increased after hemorrhage, at high altitudes (p. 511, by exercise, in acholuric jaundice (p. 77) and in pernicious anemia, especially following specific treatment (p. 82) of the latter condition and during the blood crises. A rise in the reticulocyte count indicates an increased activity of the blood forming tissue—the bone marrow—which as a result of a specific stimulus turns out a larger number of young cells. The maturation of the red cells, that is, the change from reticulocytes to erythrocytes, has been estimated to take from 10 to 24 hours. There is evidence that the thyroid gland liberates a principle which hastens the maturation of reticulocytes.

The next stage in the life of the red cell is represented by the *normoblast*, which appears in the blood in several different types of anemia. This cell, as its name implies, is normal in size and shape, possesses the usual amount of hemoglobin, but contains a nucleus. The bone marrow normally holds large numbers of these immature cells, but in health they do not reach the general circulation. In pernicious anemia and other severe types of anemia large, pale, nucleated cells are seen resembling white cells (lymphocytes, ch. 10). They represent a very primitive stage in the development of the red cells; they are termed *megaloblasts*. The megaloblast contains a small, sometimes a negligible amount of hemoglobin. Its protoplasm also contains a diffuse or punctate arrangement of basophilic material. Hemoglobin is acidophilic, so these cells may stain with acid as well as with basic dyes. This phenomenon of dual staining, which may also be shown by other abnormal cells, is known as *polychromasia*. Other cells of various sizes and shapes may be seen in the anemias. Shrinkage of the contents of the red cell with wrinkling of its limiting membrane, as may result from immersing the cells in a hypertonic solution, is termed *crenation*. In pernicious anemia, in particular, the presence of cells of unequal sizes (*anisocytosis*) and of deformed outline (*poikilocytosis*) is common. The poikilocytes may

[5] These cells are more numerous in rabbit's blood, being from 3 to 3.5 per cent of the total red cell population. The blood of certain other species, also shows a relatively high count.

assume the most bizarre forms; mulberry, flask or hammer shapes may appear. Erythrocytes with a globular form (*spherocytes*), or of an eliptoid or crescentic shape (*eliptocytes* and *sickle cells*) are found in certain types of anemia. Pauling, Itano, Singer and Wells have found that in sickle cell anemia the red cells contain an abnormal type of hemoglobin and they suggest that the formation of certain bonds between the abnormal molecules causes a distortion of the cell. These distorted, more rigid cells, are destroyed more rapidly than the normal cells. *Macrocytes* and *microcytes* are terms denoting cells of usual structure and without nuclei, but larger and smaller respectively than the normal erythrocyte. In certain conditions, e.g., lead poisoning, fine dots of basophilic material, probably a porphyrin (ch. 6) appear throughout the cell, giving it a stippled appearance. This abnormality is known as *punctate basophilia* (see frontispiece). In certain types of anemia rings or twisted strands of basophilic material may be seen near the periphery of the cell. These are derived from the nucleus and are known as *Cabot's rings*. At other times small nuclear fragments—*Howell-Jolly bodies*—are present in the cytoplasm.

## REFERENCES

Calvin, M., Evans, R. S., Behrendt, V. and Calvin, G., Proc. Soc. Exper. Biol. & Med., 1946, **61**, 416.

Hartridge, H. J. Physiol., 1920, **53**, lxxxi.

Knisely, M. H. and associates. Arch. Surg. 1945, **51**, 220; Trans. 4th Conf. on Blood Clotting and Allied Problems. J. E. Flynn, Ed., J. Macy Found. 1951.

Pauling, L., Itano, H. A., Singer, S. J. and Wells, I. C. Science, 1949, **110**, 543.

*Monographs and Reviews*

Barcroft, J. Cambridge University Press, London, 1925.

Eamons, W. F. J. Physiol., 1927, **64**, 215.

Granick, S. Blood, 1949, **4**, 404.

Harrop, G. A., Jr. Medicine, 1928, **7**, 291.

Price-Jones, C. Blood pictures; an introduction to clinical hematology. The Williams & Wilkins Co., Baltimore, 1933.

Schafer, P. W. Ann. Surg., 1945, **122**, 1098.

Wintrobe, M. M. Medicine, 1930, **9**, 195.

# 3

# BLOOD VOLUME: BODY WATER: WATER BALANCE

Blood volume estimations are of value in many clinical conditions associated with a loss or gain of fluid by the body, or for the purpose of checking the results of corpuscular and hemoglobin estimations. It is also sometimes of interest to know, in experimental investigations and in metabolic studies in man, the *total* amounts of certain blood constituents, e.g., protein, calcium, sodium, etc., as well as their concentrations.

## Methods for the Estimation of Blood Volume

### DIRECT METHOD

The first attempts to measure the total quantity of blood in the body were made upon animals by Welcker (1854). His method consisted in taking a small measured quantity of the animal's blood and diluting it to 1 in 100 with normal saline.

The animal was then bled, and after the blood had ceased to flow, its vessels were washed out and the muscles minced and extracted with water. Water was then added to the collected fluid—blood and washings—until its color matched precisely the tint of the original diluted blood specimen. The total collected fluid divided by 100 gave the blood volume.

This method was also employed upon decapitated criminals (Bischoff) in order to obtain a value for the blood volume of man; but since its applicability was obviously very limited, indirect methods were later devised.

### INDIRECT METHODS

Several methods are available for the determination of the blood volume during life. The carbon monoxide method developed by Grehant and Quinquad for animals and modified by Haldane and Smith for man, has been largely supplanted by the dye method.

The dye method was originally devised by Keith, Rowntree and Geraghty. The degree of dilution in the plasma of a known amount of dye injected into the circulation is employed as the basis of calculation. The color of the stained plasma is compared in a colorimeter with that of a standard dye solution of known concentration. There are several qualifications required of a dye before it can be considered suitable for blood volume measurements. In the first place, of course, it must be innocuous. It must not diffuse too rapidly from the blood stream; it must color only the plasma, and not be adsorbed by the cells of the blood nor by the walls of the blood vessels. It must not change color itself after entering the blood, nor cause the liberation of pigment from the red cells (hemolysis), and it must be capable of mixing evenly and thoroughly with the plasma. If it lacked these qualifications, the colorimetric readings obviously would be undependable.

The dye most commonly employed is a blue dye, T-1824 (Evans blue). Evans blue has the advantage that the error due to any discoloration of the plasma by hemoglobin (hemolysis) is minimized. This dye is also eliminated very slowly (4.8 per cent per hour) from the circulation. It remains in the circulation because it combines with protein, although this combination apparently is not strong, for the two can be separated by paper electrophoresis.

In making an estimate of blood volume a sample of plasma is obtained before the dye is injected. Then a known amount of the dye is injected intravenously and blood samples are obtained at 10- or 20-, 30-, 40-, and 50-minute intervals after the injection. The concentration of dye in the plasma is measured. Because the dye leaves the circulation to some extent, it is necessary to determine the fall in concentration of the dye with time. By extrapolating back to zero time from the curve of concentrations, the concentration of the dye at zero time can be computed and this is used to calculate the blood volume. Because T-1824 leaves the circulation slowly, in normal persons it is usually possible to obtain a reasonable estimate of the blood volume from a sample taken 10 minutes after the dye has been injected, but under conditions when mixing is slow, the extrapolated values are preferable. From the con-

17

centration of dye in the sample and the amount of dye injected, the dye dilution and hence the plasma volume can be computed.

If either lipemia or hemolysis is present, the dilution method with T-1824 is not satisfactory unless a lengthy dye extraction procedure is used. Also, as we have seen, in many instances the disappearance rate of the dye from plasma must be known if an accurate plasma volume measurement is to be achieved. Another disadvantage is that repeated injections may cause some discoloration of the conjunctivae and skin.

Plasma volume may also be estimated by the injection of albumin "tagged" with $I^{131}$. This is not affected by hemolysis or lipemia, nor does it stain the tissues, but it also has the disadvantage of requiring information concerning its disappearance rate. Measurements of plasma volumes by the use of T-1824 and by means of $I^{131}$ albumin give similar results. Another procedure has been developed using a dextran fraction which leaves the circulation very slowly. This method has the advantage of requiring only two blood samples, one of which is a control. It is unaffected by lipemia or hemolysis, employs a colorless material and requires no highly specialized equipment for its estimation.

These various procedures give an estimate only of the *plasma* volume. In order to obtain the value for the total blood volume, the proportion of cells to plasma must be determined by means of the hematocrit. If the *packed cell volume* thus obtained is, for example, 45 per cent, the plasma volume is therefore 55 per cent. Thus the total blood volume can be calculated from the plasma volume and the hematocrit reading.

In calculating the blood volume from the plasma volume and the hematocrit reading it is necessarily assumed that the proportion of red cells to plasma is the same throughout all parts of the vascular system, but experimental evidence is strongly against such an assumption. In capillaries the proportion of red cells to plasma may be considerably less or more than in the larger vessels. To eliminate the error of unequal distribution of red cells throughout the circulation, methods have been devised for the estimation of the total circulating red cell volume. These use the dilution of injected red blood cells which have been "tagged" with radioactive iron ($Fe^{55}$), radioactive chromium ($Cr^{51}$) or radioactive phosphorus ($P^{32}$). In the method of Hahn, as modified by Gibson and his colleagues radioactive iron ($Fe^{55}$ or $Fe^{59}$) is incorporated into ferric ammonium citrate, which is injected into a donor belonging

to group O (ch. 5). Newly formed cells take up the iron and appear in the circulation in 24 hours, reaching a maximum in 21 days.

From 70 to 100 ml. of the donor's blood (30 to 40 ml. of red cells), having a radioactivity of from 2500 to 3000 counts per minute per ml. (determined by Geiger counter), are injected intravenously or intraarterially into the subject. The quantity of donor's blood injected will depend upon the volume of red cells which the recipient is expected to have, but injections between 70 and 100 ml. cover a range of red cell volumes of from 1500 to 2500 ml.

Between 10 to 20 minutes are allowed to pass after the injection in order for thorough mixing of donor's and recipient's cells to occur. Samples of 15 ml. of recipient's blood are then taken and are followed at 10- and 20-minute intervals by two more samplings. Two milliliters of donor's blood are diluted to 100 ml.; 10 aliquots are then prepared. The recipient's blood samples are centrifuged at 3000 r.p.m. for 30 minutes. Donor and recipient samples are wet-ashed and the iron deposited electrolytically on copper. The radioactive iron in the two samples is determined by means of a Geiger counter; the calculation of the circulating red cell volume is made from the following equation:

$$Vrr = \frac{CD \times VaD}{VaR}$$

where Vrr is the red cell volume, CD the number of milliliters of donor cells injected, VaD the radioactivity of the donor's cells and VaR the radioactivity of the recipient's cells.

In order to determine the total blood volume, the plasma volume is measured by the dye method and the result added to the value for the circulating red cell volume.

This method is based on two assumptions—(a) that none of the radioactive iron escapes again after being taken up by the erythrocytes, and (b) that all the labelled cells became mixed with the recipient's cells equally throughout the circulation. Only the principle of the method can be given here; for details the reader is referred to the original papers.

Radioactive iron can be used in tests carried out over a long period of time because it persists in the cells and the blood remains radioactive for much longer than when radioactive chromium or phosphorus are used. The methods employing $Cr^{51}$ and $P^{32}$ are simpler to use than the one just described because the labelling of the red blood cells with these materials can be done *in vitro*.

Since it is thus possible to use red blood cells from the individual on whom the test is to be made, the problem of cell compatibility does not arise. All determinations of blood volume, whatever method is used, are made with the patient recumbent and under basal conditions, some 12 to 14 hours after a meal. The loss of the dye or other material into the tissues at the site of injection must be avoided since this of course will vitiate the results which, since the plasma would be less deeply stained, would be too high. Care must also be exercised to prevent evaporation of fluid from the samples after they have been drawn. Otherwise the concentration of the particular test material in the plasma would be raised and the readings (which would indicate a lower degree of dilution) would be too low.

### Normal Values for Plasma and Whole Blood Volumes as Obtained by different Method

In normal subjects, blood makes up roughly 7 per cent of the body weight, with plasma volume a little over 4 per cent and red cell volume about 3 per cent. The plasma volume of adult males is about 40 ml., the red cell volume about 29 ml., and the whole blood volume in the neighborhood of 70 ml. per kg. of body weight. The blood volume of a man of average weight (70 kg.) is therefore around 5 liters. The blood volume in terms of body weight shows considerable variation from person to person. Changes in body density alter this relationship of blood volume to body weight. The relationship between blood volume and body height shows a similar variability. The most constant relationship is found between a combination of body weight and the cube of body height (fig. 3.1).

### Body Water (see also ch. 4)

The blood volume and its variations cannot be considered entirely apart from the fluid content of the body as a whole. Blood volume regulation is largely a question of balance between the fluid within the vessels and in the tissues. When conditions arise which tend to lower or raise the volume of blood, counter forces come into play which restore the normal level. When circulating fluid is lost, the vessels replenish themselves from the extravascular spaces. On the other hand, any tendency for the blood volume to rise is met by a discharge of the excess fluid into the tissues and later from the body in the urine. So, a balance is struck, and in health the blood volume is maintained remarkably constant. For example, after the intravenous injection of a large

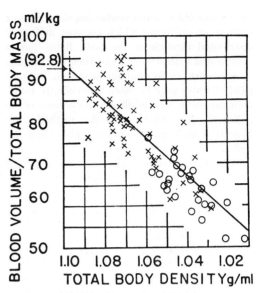

FIG. 3.1. Ratio of measured blood volume to total body mass, plotted against body density (× 55 men; ○ 26 women). Note that the blood content is 92.8 ml. per kg. in hypothetic body of density 1.097. BV was computed from measured PV and hematocrit with correction of the latter to the over-all cell concentration of the circulating blood.

quantity of saline, the volume of circulating fluid (although raised temporarily) is brought back to normal within 30 minutes or less. On the other hand the loss of blood fluid, as by hemorrhage, immediately calls into action processes which may, in a very short time, replenish the blood volume. When an animal is bled to death, at a not too rapid rate, the blood which is withdrawn is found after a few minutes of bleeding to have become diluted—clearly demonstrating the promptness with which fluid (water and salts) has been absorbed into the vessels.

The total volume of the water of the body varies among species but in man has a mean value of approximately 65 per cent (about 10 per cent less for women) of the body weight (it is about 65 per cent in the dog and about 73 per cent for guinea pigs and rabbits). It is difficult to establish proper mean values for body water, because its total volume is related to the mass of the lean tissues of the body rather than to the body weight. In an obese person it is a much lower percentage of the body weight than in one who is lean. The values, therefore, vary widely both between persons and different species of animal in accordance with their fatness or leanness.

The total *volume* of the body water can be determined by injecting into the blood stream a known amount of water containing deuterium or tritium, or antipyrine which becomes uniformly distributed throughout the body fluids (intracellular and extracellular), and then determining its concentration in a sample of serum. Tritium-labelled water may be more conveniently measured than deuterium-labelled water because of the radioactivity of tritium. A further method using N-acetyl-4-aminoantipyrene has also been described.

The water content of various tissues, in average percentages, is given in the following table:

|  | *per cent* |
|---|---|
| Muscle (striated) | 75 |
| Skin | 70 |
| Connective tissues | 60 |
| Adipose tissue | 20 |
| Bone (marrow-free) | 25–30 |
| Blood: | |
|    Plasma | 90 |
|    Cells | 65 |
| Kidney | 80 |
| Liver | 76 |
| Nervous tissue: | |
|    Gray matter | 85 |
|    White matter | 70 |

The *extracellular fluid*, which comprises the blood plasma, the tissue or interstitial fluid, lymph and the fluid in the serous cavities, amounts to about 24 per cent of the body weight; the plasma water constitutes only about 4 per cent of the body weight. The fluid within the cells, the *intracellular fluid* amounts to 41 per cent of the weight of the body, or about two times the extracellular fluid. The skeletal muscles contain about half, the skin about $\frac{1}{5}$ and whole blood only about $\frac{1}{10}$ of the total body water.

In general, the intracellular fluid has a high concentration of potassium and a low concentration of sodium, whereas the extracellular fluids contain relatively large amounts of sodium and small amounts of potassium.[1] In most cells chloride is also in low concentration or is absent; the red blood cells and the cells of the gastric glands are notable exceptions. Substances, such as su-

[1] In the case of muscle at any rate, this distribution of Na and K between intra- and extracellular fluids may be altered in pathological states involving the excessive loss of potassium from the body, e.g., severe and prolonged diarrhea, hyperactivity of the adrenal cortex or the administration of desoxycorticosterone (ch. 58) when muscle potassium is largely replaced by sodium. Increased concentration of K in the serum and other extracellular fluids occurs in adrenal cortical insufficiency, in oliguria or anuria, during tissue breakdown or anoxia, following major surgical operations, and in dehydration.

crose, mannitol, inulin, thiocyanate and to a large extent chloride, when introduced into the body, become uniformly distributed throughout the extracellular fluids, but do not enter the cells in important amounts and, since they are not metabolized and are not excreted too rapidly, can be employed to estimate the volume of the extracellular fluid in the living animal. When, for example, a known amount of thiocyanate, is injected into the blood stream and sufficient time allowed for equal distribution to occur, the volume of the extracellular water can be calculated from the concentration of the solute in a sample of serum. Radioactive sodium or chloride may also be employed for such determinations, but since these solutes are not excluded from all types of cells they are not as dependable as thiocyanate or sucrose, especially if absolute values are sought. The extracellular fluid is visualized as occupying a space of the determined volume, and according to the solute used in the estimation it is customary to speak of the *thiocyanate space, sucrose space,* etc.

The values for the total body water and the extracellular water being known, the intracellular water is found by subtraction (see table below).

*Body water*

| Body Water | Percentage of Body Weight |
|---|---|
| A. Extracellular | |
|   In plasma | 4 |
|   In interstices | 15 |
|   In hollow viscera, eye, etc. | 5 |
| B. Intracellular | 41 |

When calculating intracellular water in this way it is well to appreciate that some of the methods for determining extracellular fluid volume, because they measure only the volume of fluid into which the test substances can freely diffuse, exclude a certain amount of fluid outside cells, such as eye humors, cerebrospinal fluid and secretions of glands, whereas these fluids are usually included in the estimation of total body water.

The characteristic distribution of sodium and potassium between blood plasma and tissue fluid is shown in table 3.1. Determinations of the extracellular fluid volume, total tissue water content and sodium space permit one to obtain information regarding shifts of ions or water across cell boundaries. It is probable that changes in electrolyte concentration are primary and that shifts in intracellular water occur secondarily to such changes. The entrance or exit of water thus depends on the balance of ions inside and outside the cell, water passing freely across the cell boundary. The balance of ions inside and outside the cell, with a high potassium concentration inside and a high sodium concentration outside, is best explained by postulating an active process—a sort of "sodium pump"—which excludes, or even extrudes sodium from the cell. The precise way in which sodium is kept out of the cell is not known, but the process requires energy. The immediate energy source is probably adenosine triphosphate or some related compound, and either glycolysis or oxidation may provide the further energy required. The "sodium pump" may become less efficient under circumstances when energy supply is reduced, as, for example, when the blood supply to a tissue is blocked or when there is some metabolic insufficiency. One can think of changes in intracellular water, therefore, as being related to changes in the molar concentrations of intracellular or extracellular electrolytes, and one way in which an imbalance could be brought about would be through some change in the "sodium pump." Intracellular water under ordinary conditions is a rather fixed quantity, and the fluid of blood is also kept relatively constant. A loss of one-fourth of the body water is usually fatal.

Under physiological conditions the interstitial fluids show the greatest changes. In dehydration the proportion of the total water from extracellular and intracellular compartments varies with the manner in which the negative water balance is produced. When, for example, the dehydration is caused by sucrose diuresis, about 85 per cent of the excreted water is derived from extracellular and 15 per cent from intracellular sources. Whereas, in dehydration resulting from water deprivation, the water loss is from 57 to 67 per cent intracellular (Painter and associates).

*Hyaluronic acid.* Although practically none of the extracellular water is chemically bound, that is to say, substances are dissolved in it readily, and it can be entirely separated from colloidal materials by ultrafiltration, and although free movement and rapid changes of distribution are permitted, its physical state does not appear to be that of a simple solution of electrolytes and protein bathing the cells; it is held in the tissue spaces by a gelating substance. The latter has been identified chemically as a mucopolysaccharide and called *hyaluronic acid.* This substance also enters into the formation of the cement sub-

### TABLE 3.1

*Concentrations of base in the water of blood plasma and in the water of muscle tissue*

(After Gamble, Ross and Tisdall)

|  | Per 100 cc. Plasma | Per 100 cc. Plasma Water | Per 100 cc. Muscle Tissue | Per 100 cc. Muscle Water |
|---|---|---|---|---|
|  | *mg.* | *cc. 0.1 N* | *mg.* | *cc. 0.1 N* |
| $Na^+$....... | 330 | 157.7 | 80 | 45.8 |
| $K^+$........ | 20 | 5.6 | 320 | 108.0 |
| $Ca^{++}$..... | 10 | 5.5 | 8 | 5.3 |
| $Mg^{++}$...... | 3 | 2.7 | 21 | 23.0 |
| Total ... |  | 171.5 |  | 182.1 |

Water of blood plasma is taken as 91 per cent by volume and water of muscle tissue as 76 per cent of weight.

stance binding cells together, and into the production of other gel-like materials, e.g., vitreous body, jelly of the umbilical cord, etc. The physiological significance of this material is dealt with in another place.

### Water Balance

In health, except when new tissue is being formed, the body's intake of water obviously must balance the output. When the output exceeds the intake, the body's water content is reduced and the body is then said to be in negative water balance; dehydration results. When, as during growth, convalescence from an acute illness or in pregnancy, new tissue is being formed, or for a time after a subject has been placed upon a reducing diet, the water balance is positive, the intake exceeding the output, i.e., water is retained.

The antidiuretic principle of the hypophysis constitutes part of the mechanism regulating the volume of body water. In dehydrated states, increased amounts of the pituitary hormone are excreted in the urine (ch. 56).

### THE WATER INTAKE

Body water is replenished in two main ways, (a) by the ingestion of liquids, semisolid and "solid" food (cooked lean meat, for example, is from 65 to 70 per cent water), and (b) by the water formed in metabolism through the oxidation of the hydrogen of the food, or of the body tissues themselves. Water is absorbed mainly from the small intestine, to a smaller extent from the large intestine, and in small amounts only from the stomach. The following table from Rowntree and Brown compiled from the data of Magnus-

Levy gives the quantities of water produced by the metabolism, respectively, of the three main food stuffs and of alcohol.

100 grams of fat        yield 107.1 grams water
100 grams of starch   yield  55.1 grams water
100 grams of protein  yield  41.3 grams water
100 grams of alcohol  yield 117.4 grams water

Water is also formed in the tissues through the polymerization or synthesis of various compounds, i.e., through a metabolic process the reverse of hydrolysis. An ordinary mixed diet yields as a result of oxidative processes from 300 to 350 grams of water daily, or about 14 grams per 100 Calories. When no food or drink is taken, the body materials themselves are utilized for this purpose, the glycogen, protein and fat supplying important quantities of water. The camel's hump, for instance, which is largely composed of fat, is a reservoir for large amounts of water, and the clothes moth kept in a desiccator and fed upon perfectly dry food lays eggs which are 80 per cent water.

For the adult, the amount of water from all sources and under ordinary circumstances which must be ingested daily is around 2500 cc. or about 1 cc. per Calorie of food intake. This usually means that about 1000 cc. of water as such or in beverages must be drunk in order to maintain the water balance.

The water intake under conditions of average temperature, humidity and diet is summarized in the following table:

|  | cc. |
|---|---|
| Solid and semisolid food | 1200 |
| Oxidation of food | 300 |
| Drinks (water, milk, coffee, beer, etc.) | 1000 |

The volume of body water is held constant through a nicely balanced adjustment between intake and output. The intake is regulated mainly by the sensation of thirst.

Even a slight fall in the total volume of body water arouses thirst. This is caused by the inhibition of salivary secretion and the consequent drying of the oral mucosa, as well as by the rise in the osmotic pressure of the blood. Thirst can be aroused experimentally by the intravenous injection of a hypertonic solution. The subject of thirst is dealt with more fully in chapter 43. In experiments on dogs Robinson and Adolph found that when the animals had ready access to water they drank when they had lost water to the extent of 0.5 per cent of their body weight. The amount of water drunk was just sufficient to replace that which had been lost. It is hard to conceive what signaled the cessation of drinking, for it occurred while the water was still in the stomach, that is before it had been absorbed.

## THE WATER OUTPUT

Water is lost from the body in the feces, urine and saliva, and by the evaporation of water from the skin and lungs. The daily loss through these several channels is given in the following table for a man of average size at light occupation in a temperate climate.

|  | cc. |
|---|---|
| Skin (at average temperature and humidity) | 500 |
| Expired air (at average temperature and humidity) | 350 |
| Urine | 1500 |
| Feces | 150 |
| Total | 2500 |

Under usual conditions of air temperature (23–25°C.), humidity and diet, the heat lost from the lungs and the surface of the body by the evaporation of water amounts to about 24 per cent of the total heat production. The measurement of this *insensible water loss* under standard conditions may therefore be employed as a basis for the determination of the basal metabolism (ch. 44).

The loss in the saliva is negligible under ordinary circumstances but may be considerable in mouth breathing (as a result of evaporation) and in those addicted to the spitting habit.

The water lost through the skin and lungs varies greatly with the temperature and relative humidity of the atmosphere and with the extent of the muscular exercise indulged in. At ordinary temperatures slight secretion by the sweat glands is not perceived since the sweat evaporates as quickly as it is formed. This *insensible perspiration*, as it is called, includes the loss of a greater amount of water by evaporation from the moist tissues beneath the skin; this loss is quite apart from the actual secretion of sweat (ch. 52). The diffusion of water through the skin and evaporation from the surface under ordinary comfortable conditions of room temperature and humidity is around 1 mg. per cm.$^2$ of skin surface in a period of 10 minutes. The rate of diffusion is little different for living or dead skin and whether sweat glands are present or absent. The amount of the *insensible perspiration* has the average value given above but may be many times this value; when the air is hot or the body temperature raised, the rate of evaporation of water from the tissues beneath the skin is much more rapid, the secretion of sweat is also likely to be more active, but owing to the higher rate of evaporation a larger quantity of sweat is secreted before it becomes evident. Relative humidity and air movement also influence the rate of evaporation. So, in humid, still atmospheres sweat secretion is more evident though it may be no greater than in a drier atmosphere when evaporation is more rapid. Large quantities of sweat are secreted as a result of muscular exercise or when, as in the tropics, the temperature is high. In hot climates the daily secretion may amount to 3000 cc. daily and in very torrid atmospheres it may be as much as 10 liters. When heavy work is done in a hot environment, sweat may be secreted at the rate of 2 liters per hour. This necessitates the drinking of an equal quantity of fluid in order to maintain the normal water content of the body, since the intake must equal the output.

At ordinary temperatures the inspired air contains negligible quantities of water whereas the expired air is almost saturated with moisture. Any condition which increases the pulmonary ventilation therefore increases the water lost by this route.

*The Relation of the Electrolyte Concentration and Tissue Changes to the Volume of Body Water*

The isotonicity of the body fluid which depends mainly upon its concentration in sodium and chloride is maintained constant largely by the retention or elimination of water, the kidneys playing the primary role in this regulation. A loss of salt is accompanied by a loss of water and the ingestion of salt is followed by water retention. Thus it is possible to increase the volume of body water in normal persons to the point where edema occurs by the administration of large amounts of sodium bicarbonate and to cause the discharge of nephritic or cardiac edema by the reduction or withdrawal of salt from the diet. In the latter instance, only sufficient sodium chloride is available for the production of a more limited amount of isotonic fluid. The fundamental factors controlling the total volume of body water are not clearly understood. The hypothalamus is important in regulating the osmotic pressure of extracellular fluid through its influence on the liberation of antidiuretic hormone by the posterior pituitary gland, and hence its influence on water retention by the kidney (ch. 34). There must be, however, some means of regulating the absolute amount of body water. It is felt that the basic factor in this control is the regulation of sodium excretion by the kidney. Since the transplanted kidney can still regulate body water, this regulation must be finally effected by something carried in the blood. The adrenal cortex undoubtedly is important in this regulation through its influence on the reabsorption of sodium, but other factors must also be involved since even in the absence of the adrenal cortex some regulation of body water can still occur. What starts the chain of events that leads to alterations in renal activity is not clear. Circulatory changes are important. Factors leading to a reduction in circulating blood volume, venous return or cardiac output appear to reduce the excretion of salt and water, whereas factors increasing blood volume or the venous return and cardiac output increase the excretion of salt and water. Whatever the precise initiating factor, it would seem that there must be a mechanism sensitive to changes in the absolute amount of body water as well as one sensitive to changes in the concentration of electrolytes. The details of this mechanism are unknown.

Changes in the diet can bring about changes in the total body water. Protein is laid down in the body with water (about 3 grams of water per gram of solid). During growth or convalescence from wasting diseases, retention of water therefore occurs, i.e., the intake of water, including that derived from solid food, exceeds the output. Fat is laid down with a minimal amount of water (only that in the protein of the connective tissue framework); the deposition of glycogen is accompanied by a small storage of water.[2] Water retention therefore follows a sudden change from a high fat to a high protein diet, and to a less degree from a fat diet to one high in carbohydrate. A change from a diet high in carbohydrate or protein to one high in fat is followed by the loss of water.

Reduction of the caloric value of the diet below the energy requirement is accompanied for a time by the retention of water. During the first week or so on a reducing diet the subject's weight may for this reason show little or no change, the fat catabolized being replaced by water. In a prolonged fast after the fat stores have been depleted, protein is also partly replaced by water, the muscles of animals dying of starvation showing a marked reduction in the proportion of protein.

[2] Zuntz concluded from his experiments that 3 grams of water were laid down with each gram of carbohydrate, but his results have been questioned and are not now generally accepted.

## Dehydration

When the output of water exceeds the intake, the body's water content obviously will be reduced. That is, the body is in negative water balance and the condition known as dehydration results.

### Causes of Dehydration

Dehydration may result from:

*1. Water depletion or primary dehydration.* (a) *Simple deprivation of water* from whatever cause: shipwreck, desert travel, dysphagia, extreme weakness, mental patients refusing to drink, etc. Under such circumstances, though there is an effort to conserve the stores of body water, through a reduction in the amount excreted by the kidney, in the sweat and by other routes, some water is always lost though none be drunk. Dehydration occurs more quickly in fever or if the environmental temperature is high.

*b. Excessive water loss* may result from persistent vomiting (e.g., pyloric or intestinal obstruction) prolonged diarrhea, or the excretion of large quantities of urine or sweat, especially when accompanied by a restricted water and salt intake. In the acute diarrheas of infants, dehydration and loss of weight may occur very rapidly.

In water depletion the osmotic concentration of the extracellular fluid rises, water is drawn from the cells, and both extracellular and intracellular compartments shrink. Extreme thirst is experienced.

*2. Reduction in the total quantity of electrolytes, salt depletion or secondary dehydration.* The electrolytic concentration of the body fluids, both extracellular and intracellular, is maintained constant through the elimination or retention of water. That is, a reduction or increase in the total electrolytes, which comprise chiefly the basic radicles Na (extracellular) and K (intracellular) and the acid radicles $HCO_3$ and Cl, is accompanied by a corresponding decrease or increase in the volume of body water. The sum of the basic elements and acid elements of course must balance. Loss of Cl can be made good by the retention of $H_2CO_3$ and a rise in plasma bicarbonate. Excreted base, however, can be replaced only by basic substances supplied in the food. The total concentration of electrolytes in the body fluids is therefore dependent upon the stores of total base. For example, in pyloric or high intestinal obstruction (p. 712) fluid is secreted in large quantities into the gastrointestinal tract. The fluid may be vomited or may collect and remain in the dilated part of the canal above the obstruction. (The latter occurrence is the rule in the rabbit which cannot vomit.) In either case the secretion of large quantities of gastric juice entails a loss of blood chloride. A similar chloride loss is induced in animals by means of a gastric fistula fashioned by sectioning through the pylorus, stitching the stomach opening to the abdominal wall and allowing the gastric juice to drain to the exterior. In the foregoing instances, the chloride depletion causes at first no ill effects, the normal concentrations in electrolytes of the blood and tissue fluids being maintained for a time by the retention of $CO_2$, and, as a consequence of this, an increase in bicarbonate. The compensation for the Cl loss leads however to alkalosis which is then countered by an increased excretion of base in the urine. This of course is accompanied by diuresis; marked dehydration results.

On the other hand, the continued loss of pancreatic juice (p. 633) to the exterior causes an immediate depletion of base; plasma bicarbonate is reduced. In the adjustment of the acid-base balance the excess of acid radicles is excreted in the urine; this again entails a loss of water. Similarly, the ingestion of acid-producing salts causes a depletion of base, which is used for the neutralization and excretion of the acid radicles. Such salts therefore act as diuretics and dehydrating agents.

In salt depletion the extracellular fluid is hypotonic; water enters the cells, so that the volume of intracellular fluid is maintained, whereas the extracellular fluid (especially the interstitial) is reduced.

Clinically the failure to ingest sufficient salt or the leaching of salt from the body of a seriously ill patient by glucose infusions is a not uncommon cause of salt depletion.

*3. The injection of hypertonic solutions* into the blood stream. When a strong sugar or salt solution is injected, the temporary rise in the osmotic pressure of the blood causes a flow of fluid from the tissues into the vascular system until equilibrium is re-established. The blood volume is increased, but is soon returned to normal by the loss of the excess material into the tissues and its eventual excretion via the kidney and bowels. A net loss of body water results.

### Effects of Dehydration

(*a*) *Loss of weight* due to the reduction in tissue water as well as to the actual breakdown of body substance which occurs in the effort to furnish water for the maintenance of physiological processes. Fat and carbohydrate stores are first drawn upon for this purpose and later, protein. (*b*) *Disturbances in acid-base balance*, usually toward the acid side. The diminished quantity of circulating fluid (loss of plasma water, anhydremia) and the consequent depression of oxidative processes in the tissues is held responsible for the excessive production of acid metabolites, e.g., lactic acid. The slowing of the renal circulation also leads to a reduced excretion of urine and the retention of acids (e.g., phosphoric) which under normal circumstances are eliminated. (*c*) *Rise in the nonprotein nitrogen of the blood*. (*d*) *Rise in plasma protein concentration* and of chloride though there is no absolute increase. There is an absolute increase in blood sugar, especially when the stage of exhaustion approaches. (*e*) *Rise in body temperature* as a result of the reduction in circulating fluid (see ch. 52). (*f*) *Increased pulse rate and reduced cardiac output*. (*g*) *Thirst*. This occurs in water depletion but not in salt depletion; it will be discussed in chapter 43. Any fall in the water content of the tissues is reflected in the glandular activities especially of the salivary glands. Secretion is suppressed; the mouth and throat become dry. In dehydration thirst is extreme and the mouth parched. (*h*) *Dryness, wrinkling and looseness of skin* and a pinched expression to the features result from the loss of subcutaneous fat and of water from the deeper layers of the skin. Other manifestations are, reduced intraocular tension and recession of the eyeball and, in infants, depression of the fontanelle. (*i*) *Exhaustion and collapse*.

### Water Intoxication

When an animal is given large quantities of water by stomach tube, especially if urinary secretion is reduced by the administration of pitressin, the tissues become "water-logged," serious symptoms ensue, e.g., depression of temperature, vomiting, convulsions and coma, which shortly end in death. Similar effects also follow in man if large quantities of water are given to a patient with nephritic edema or, if in a subject of diabetes insipidus, pituitrin be administered while the water intake is maintained at the usual level (see ch. 56). The manifestations of water intoxication are believed to be due to the dilution of electrolytes in the body fluids, and the damage caused thereby to the tissue cells.[3]

[3] Excessive concentration of electrolytes in the tissue fluid with consequent hypertonicity, as occurs in shipwrecked sailors if they drink sea water (which has a concentration in salts about three times that of serum) causes an equally deleterious effect upon the tissue cells. This appears to be the cause of death.

Adrenalectomy reduces the renal response to water drinking, and thus increases the susceptibility to water intoxication. This susceptibility is reduced by the administration of desoxycorticosterone, of 17-hydroxy-11-dehydrocorticosterone, or of thyroid hormone. A similar protective action is exerted by these principles upon normal animals.

In water intoxication, the protein and chloride of the plasma are diminished and the extracellular water *decreased*. The water retained in the body enters the cells of blood and tissues which become swollen. It is not possible to account for the reduction in plasma chloride by increased renal excretion for both adrenalectomized and normal animals actually excrete less salt than usual; apparently the salt is diverted from extracellular to intracellular fluids.

There is no danger from excess fluid being retained in the body through water drinking, for the sense of thirst and its appeasement nicely control the quantity ingested; but the artificial administration of inordinate amounts of water in the form of glucose solution, especially after surgical operations when there is some tendency toward antidiuresis, may cause serious disturbances in water metabolism. The effects of an excess of body water induced in this way can be corrected readily by the administration of hypertonic saline.

When there has been prolonged ischemic injury of tissues, as occurs following tourniquet application and subsequent release, large amounts of sodium are soaked up by the injured tissues. In ischemic shock in mice, as much as $\frac{1}{4}$ of the total extracellular sodium may be lost into the injured region. The uptake of sodium by the injured cells causes its level in the extracellular fluids to fall. Normally, the kidney would respond to this reduction in the electrolyte concentration by excreting more water and electrolyte homeostasis would be maintained. But instead, there is renal retention of water and the sodium level of the interstitial fluid and plasma remains low. Infusions with sodium chloride are effective in promoting survival in this condition, but colloid or glucose solutions *not* containing sodium chloride are ineffective.

### Factors Governing the Interchange of Fluid between the Tissues and the Vessels

According to Starling's view (which is generally accepted) the physical factors which determine the flow of fluid from the tissues into the blood stream as well as in the reverse direction—from the vessels to tissue spaces—are the *osmotic* and *hydrostatic pressures* of the fluids in the two situations.

### OSMOTIC PRESSURE

*Osmosis* is diffusion through a membrane separating water—or an aqueous solution—to which the membrane is permeable, from another aqueous solution to whose dissolved materials the membrane is impermeable. Such a membrane that permits the passage of water or of some substances in solution, but acts as a barrier to the molecules of certain other substances, is called *semipermeable.*

If an aqueous solution of cane sugar be placed in a vessel and a layer of water poured gently upon its surface, the two liquids will remain separate for a time. Gradually, however, sugar molecules will diffuse upward and intermingle with the water molecules, whereas many of the latter will pass downwards into the sugar solution. The diffusion process, which due to the random movement of the molecules and quite independent of gravity or convection currents, will continue slowly until the concentrations of the two types of molecules become equal throughout all parts of the liquid. If now instead of allowing free diffusion between the two solutions to take place, they be separated by a membrane semipermeable with respect to the sugar molecules, equal and free diffusion cannot occur. Since water molecules can cross the membrane into the sugar solution but sugar molecules cannot pass out, the volume of the solution is bound to rise. The water molecules diffuse in both directions, but their concentrations in pure water being higher than in an aqueous solution a greater number will strike the water side of the membrane

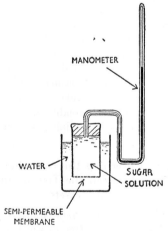

FIG. 3.2. As the pressure rises in the chamber it opposes the inward diffusion of the water molecules.

and more will pass through into the sugar solution than in the opposite direction; water therefore gradually accumulates on the sugar side of the membrane and dilutes the solution. If the compartment containing the solution of sugar is enclosed by rigid walls and connected with a manometer the pressure that develops can be measured. This pressure since it is caused by osmosis is called the *osmotic pressure.* A manometer (fig. 3.2) designed for the measurement of osmotic pressures is called an *osmometer.* Osmosis when related to the transfer of water across cell boundaries is called *endosmosis* or *exosmosis* according to whether water passes into or out of the cell.

Theoretically, the transference of water through a semipermeable membrane, if unopposed by any other force would proceed indefinitely, although at a progressively slower rate, and cause infinite dilution of the osmotically active substance on the other side. The volume of the solution would continue to increase and the osmotic pressure would not cease to rise until the concentrations of water molecules on the two sides of the membrane were equal. However, owing to the presence of the molecules of the dissolved substance such equalization can never be fully attained. But the rise in pressure itself by opposing diffusion of the water molecules into the solution after a time automatically brings osmosis to a standstill.

Great pressures are capable of being developed by osmotically active substances. A 10 per cent solution of cane sugar, for example, can produce an osmotic pressure of over 6 atmospheres, which is a pressure equivalent to that exerted by a column of fluid between 170 and 200 feet high.

Semipermeable membranes vary greatly with respect to the materials that they will or will not allow to pass. Erythrocytes, for example, are permeable to water but not to hemoglobin and the plasma proteins, and are more permeable to chloride and bicarbonate ions than to potassium and sodium ions. Even the red blood corpuscles of different species vary considerably with respect to their relative permeability to these two cations, but generally speaking blood cells as well as other cells are more pervious to $K^+$ than to $Na^+$. The capillary membrane on the other hand permits the passage of all substances of small molecular size dissolved in the plasma and has only a limited permeability to the plasma proteins. The capillary wall of the renal glomerulus lets through very little protein. Artificial membranes such as those made of a precipitate of copper ferrocyanide or of collodion also vary in their permeabilities.

Osmotic pressure measurements give an estimate of the tendency for the diffusion of water to occur across a semipermeable membrane. *The osmotic pressure is a result of the diffusion process, not a cause of it.*

Osmosis is important in many physiological

processes in both animal and plant life, e.g., the excretion of urine, the interchange of materials between the interiors of the blood cells or tissue cells and their surroundings, the flow of sap in plants, as well as the regulation of the blood volume. The fluids of the body contain various electrolytes and organic materials in solution. Semipermeable membranes of various types possessing different selective permeabilities, such as the cell wall, the vascular endothelium, the renal epithelium, and the membranes lining the serous cavities and the alimentary tract, are interposed between fluids with different concentrations of osmotically active substances.

*Isotonic, hypertonic* and *hypotonic* are terms employed to denote the osmotic activity of a solution relatively to that of some other solution. If, for example, two salt solutions of equal strength are separated by a semipermeable membrane neither will develop an osmotic pressure; they are said to be *isotonic*. If the solution on one side of the membrane be stronger, the net amount of water passing to this side will therefore be greater and the solution here is said to be *hypertonic*. The weaker solution from which there is a net transference of water is termed *hypotonic*.

In physiology these terms are used most commonly to indicate the osmotic activity of a solution as compared with that of the body fluids. For example, excised organs or sections of tissue upon which experiments are to be performed are kept moist and viable by a saline solution isotonic with the tissue fluid. Shrinkage of the cells through the loss of water (as would result from the use of a hypertonic solution) or swelling by endosmosis (as would occur if the solution were hypotonic) is thus avoided. Similarly, in order to prevent either shrinkage or swelling of the red blood cells, they must be suspended in a solution, such as plasma, that is isotonic with the fluid in their interiors. See Hemolysis, chapter 7.

### HYDROSTATIC PRESSURE

The other important factor in the interchange of fluid between the blood and the general body fluids according to Starling's hypothesis is the hydrostatic pressure within the capillaries, i.e., the blood pressure, and its relation to that of the extravascular fluids.

### THE RELATION OF OSMOTIC TO HYDROSTATIC PRESSURE IN THE INTERCHANGE OF FLUID ACROSS THE CAPILLARY MEMBRANE

The walls of the capillaries (generally throughout the body, as already mentioned) permit the free passage of water and substances of small molecular size dissolved in the plasma, e.g., glucose, inorganic salts, urea, etc.

Obviously this must be so, otherwise essential nutritive materials could not reach the tissue cells and waste products could not enter the blood stream to be excreted. But the capillary wall is largely impermeable to the large molecules of the plasma colloids. To this partial impermeability the osmotic activity of the plasma is due. Since the albumin has the smallest molecule of the three plasma proteins, it escapes through the vessel in relatively greater amounts than do the globulin and fibrinogen fractions.

By the use of I[131] labelled albumin, it has been found that the amount of plasma protein passing through the capillary wall into the interstitial fluid is considerable, amounting to more than the total protein of plasma each day. The rate of return of protein from interstitial fluid is very important in the maintenance of plasma protein levels. The lymphatic system plays a major role in this return (ch. 4).

The manner in which osmotic and hydrostatic pressures act in regulating the interchange of fluids between the tissues and the muscles may now be seen. The blood at the arterial end of a capillary has a pressure, let us say, of 30 mm. Hg (this is an arbitrary figure and will vary according to the activity of the part). This is a force driving the water and the dissolved crystalloids through the capillary membrane. But the hydrostatic pressure of the tissue fluid on the outer side of the membrane offsets, in part, that within. The pressure of fluid in the tissue spaces is difficult to determine but it is considerably less than that in the capillaries. It probably varies considerably in different regions, being low in those containing much loose areolar tissue. But for illustration let it be assumed to be 10 mm. Hg. The hydrostatic pressure, therefore, which is effective in forcing fluid out of the vessel (filtration pressure) is only the difference between the pressure within and that on the outside of the vessel, namely, 20 mm. Hg. But the osmotic pressures of the plasma and tissue fluids must be taken into account. In the plasma it amounts to about 25 mm. Hg. The tissue fluids have a lower protein content and consequently a lower osmotic pressure. The latter amounts to about 15 mm. Hg. Owing to this disparity of 10 mm. Hg between the osmotic pressures of plasma and tissue fluid, there would be a net tranference of water and diffusible substances inwards across the capillary membrane if such transference were unopposed by any other force. But a net hydrostatic pressure of 20 mm.

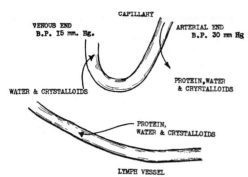

FIG. 3.3. Illustrating the relation of hydrostatic and osmotic pressures in the regulation of the interchange of fluid between the vessels and the tissue spaces.

Hg is set against it at the arterial end of the capillary leaving a balance amounting to 10 mm. Hg which serves to filter water, salts, etc., and a little protein out of the plasma. Now as the blood flows rather slowly through the capillary and loses water in this way by filtration, the protein concentration, and consequently its osmotic activity, rises. Coincidently with the progressive rise is osmotic activity the hydrostatic pressure declines, until at the venous end of the capillary there is a balance of net osmotic pressure over net hydrostatic pressure. Water accompanied by freely diffusible materials is therefore absorbed into the circulation. This picture of filtration at the arterial end of the capillary and absorption at the venous end is going on continually at the periphery of the vascular bed. But it is subject to considerable variation, not only in the same capillary from time to time but in different parts of the peripheral circulation at any moment (see fig. 3.3).

As the blood flows through the capillary, as a result of the passage of water outwards there is a consequent rise in the concentration of protein.

| Blood | | Tissue fluid |
|---|---|---|
| *Hydrostatic pressure*<br>30 mm. Hg | | *Hydrostatic pressure*<br>10 mm. Hg |
| Effective hydrostatic pressure<br>20 mm. Hg | Capillary wall | |
| | | → |
| *Osmotic pressure*<br>25 mm. Hg | | Osmotic pressure<br>15 mm. Hg |
| Effective osmotic pressure<br>10 mm. Hg | | ← |

Driving force → 10 mm. Hg (20 − 10)

Metabolic processes in the tissues bring about changes whereby larger molecules are being broken down into smaller ones; other molecules are removed or built up into larger ones. In this way alterations in molecular concentrations and in the diffusibility of the constituents of the tissue fluids with consequent variations in osmotic relationships are occurring ceaselessly. The actual exchange of water across the capillary wall is rapid. Studies with deuterium and tritium-labelled water indicate that in one minute an amount equal to the total plasma water is exchanged.

Under any circumstance in which the blood volume is increased or diminished, either the hydrostatic pressure or the osmotic pressure or both are altered, and it is through such changes that the blood fluid is restored automatically to its previous level. After hemorrhage, for example, the hydrostatic pressure is lowered in the capillary area but the osmotic pressure is unchanged. Fluid will therefore be absorbed from the tissue spaces. Moreover, constriction of the capillaries tends to reduce, dilation to increase the capillary pressure. Therefore, the capillary constriction which follows a severe hemorrhage will slow the filtration rate at the arterial end of the capillary and increase absorption of interstitial fluid at the venous end. Again, when water is drawn from the blood, in consequence of excessive loss of fluid by the kidney, sweat glands or bowels, concentration of the plasma proteins will result. The increased osmotic pressure of the plasma will then hasten the rate of absorption from the tissues. The intravenous injection of large quantities of isotonic saline, on the other hand, will have the twofold effect of diluting the colloids and temporarily increasing the hydrostatic pressure. The excess fluid in consequence is rapidly eliminated from the blood stream into the tissues and later through the kidney and bowels.

## Alterations in Blood Volume

Many factors are concerned with the regulation of blood volume, the pressure of blood in the capillaries, the concentrations of poorly diffusible substances on the two sides of the capillary wall, the available capillary surface, the permeability of the capillaries and the total capacity of the vascular bed.

### Reduction of the Blood Volume

This may result from:

1. A loss of *whole blood* as in hemorrhage.

2. *Reduction in the total number of red cells*, as a result of increased destruction or diminished production (see anemia ch. 9).

*3.* Loss of *plasma* alone from the vessels as in burns or shock from other causes (ch. 28).

*4. Loss of blood water.* This is called *anhydremia* and is simply a part of a general dehydration and so results from the same causes as the latter.

In the reduction of blood volume resulting from hemorrhage, the concentration of the blood in cells and protein is lowered, since a watery fluid enters the vessels from the surrounding tissues.

When the blood volume is lowered as a result of a loss of plasma, the red cell concentration is increased (hemoconcentration) but the protein of the plasma is little altered.

In anhydremia both the protein concentration of the plasma and the red cell count are raised. The concentration of plasma protein may increase by 50 per cent or more. The viscosity of the blood is therefore raised, and it flows sluggishly from an opened vein. If the anhydremia persists, the red cell count and the protein concentration tend to fall again. Then an estimation of the blood concentration may fail to give a true index of the extent of the blood volume reduction.

*Acute exposure to cold* causes a moderate loss of water from the blood to the tissues (chiefly skin muscle and probably liver), the total water content of the body remaining unaltered. It is not altogether clear by what means this movement of water is brought about. It is, however, an important factor in the regulation of body temperature (ch. 52). The work of Barbour and others furnishes evidence of a nervous element in the mechanism. Animals in which the cord had been divided in the upper thoracic region when placed in a cold bath did not respond in the normal fashion. Concentration of the blood did not result and the temperature of the body fell to that of the environment. The control is exercised evidently through vasomotor nerves. More *prolonged exposure to cold* (6–12 weeks) increases blood volume in experimental animals.

*Posture.* The blood volume of the human subject after 30 minutes or so in the erect posture is some 15 per cent less than that in recumbency. A fluid of low protein concentration leaks from the vessels of the lower limbs into the extracapillary tissues, as a result apparently of the increased hydrostatic pressure in the capillaries of these parts.

### INCREASE IN BLOOD VOLUME

(1) *High temperatures.* In hydrated subjects, exposure to a high temperature leads to an increase in blood volume. This increase reaches a maximum in about 7 days after which it may return toward normal. The extracellular fluid volume increases also, although initially the greater part of this increase is reflected in the elevated plasma volume. In the first few hours after exposure to heat the changes are slight and inconsistent.

(2) *Muscular exercise.* The effect of a bout of vigorous exercise in man is to decrease the plasma volume. The magnitude of this decrease may be exaggerated when measurements are made by the dye method because of a change in the optical properties of the plasma. However the protein concentration of the plasma, and the red cell count increase. The increase does not seem to be progressive. Some elevation in blood volume may occur with muscular training. This can be demonstrated in dogs, but in men accustomed to hard physical work, the red cell volume in relation to height and weight is only slightly increased over that of sedentary individuals.

(3) *Emotional excitement* in animals and in man causes an increase in blood volume.

(4) *Pregnancy.* In pregnant women, the blood volume though somewhat variable increases on the average by 20 to 30 per cent, though in the last few weeks of pregnancy tends to fall again. There is an increase in plasma volume and in interstitial fluid. Associated with this is a retention of sodium. Restriction or the administration of salt reduces or increases, respectively, the volume of extracellular fluid. The increase in plasma volume in pregnancy, combined with a lower protein concentration of the plasma is responsible, in part at least, for the edema of the lower limbs which commonly occurs in the pregnant state.

(5) *Congestive heart failure.* As a result of the retention of sodium, the extracellular fluid undergoes a pronounced increase.

(6) *The administration of desoxycorticosterone* causes a retention of salt and, as a consequence, a rise in the volume of plasma and interstitial fluid. This depends on the salt load. Aldosterone is much more active than desoxycorticosterone in its effect on sodium retention. It helps to keep in equilibrium the fluid volume and sodium retained, fluid retention varying directly with that of sodium.

### SUMMARY OF THE PATHOLOGICAL STATES ASSOCIATED WITH ALTERATIONS IN BLOOD VOLUME

*Reduction*

(*a*) *Hemorrhage* (loss of whole blood), (*b*) *burns* (loss of plasma), (*c*) *dehydration* (loss of water), (*d*) *pernicious anemia* (reduction in red cells, with a moderate increase in plasma), (*e*) *certain chronic anemias other than those of the pernicious type.* In these the total volume of red cells is only slightly or moderately reduced and this is to a large extent compensated for by an increase in plasma above the normal standard. The total blood volume is therefore, as a rule, not greatly below normal as calculated upon the basis of weight or of surface area. (*f*) *Obesity.* The blood volume per kilogram of body weight is much reduced but is normal when considered in relation to the body surface. (*g*) *Myxedema* (reduction of both red cells and plasma but mainly of the former).

*Increase*

(*a*) *Polycythemia vera* (increase mainly of red cells but also of plasma), (*b*) *cirrhosis* of the liver (increase of plasma, (*c*) *leukemia* (increase in white cells and plasma), (*d*) *splenomegaly* with anemia—Banti's disease (increase in plasma), (*e*) *hyperthyroidism* (equal increases both in red cells and plasma), (*f*) congestive heart failure.

It should be pointed out that the proportions of red cells and plasma may vary from the normal though the total blood volume remains unaltered. With regard to the blood volume and the proportion of cells to plasma there are therefore nine possible blood states. Rowntree has introduced the following descriptive terminology. A normal blood volume he terms *normovolemia*. If the ratio of cells to plasma is normal as well, he calls the condition *simple normovolemia*, but a decrease or increase in the number of cells in relation to plasma is termed *oligocythemic* or *polycythemic normovolemia* respectively. *Hypovolemia* and *hypervolemia* are corresponding terms for reduced and increased blood volumes; each of these is divisible into simple, polycythemic and oligocythemic forms (see fig. 3.4).

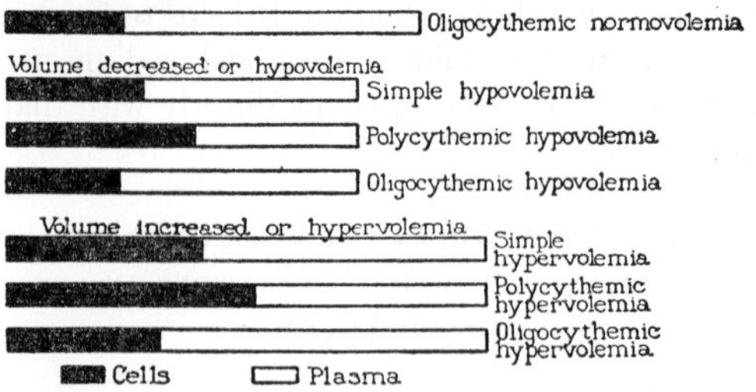

Volume normal or normovolemia
Simple normovolemia
Polycythemic normovolemia
Oligocythemic normovolemia
Volume decreased or hypovolemia
Simple hypovolemia
Polycythemic hypovolemia
Oligocythemic hypovolemia
Volume increased or hypervolemia
Simple hypervolemia
Polycythemic hypervolemia
Oligocythemic hypervolemia
■■ Cells      ☐ Plasma

Fig. 3.4. The nine possible combinations of whole blood, plasma and red cell volumes (after Rowntree).

## THE EFFECTS OF HEMORRHAGE

When more than 30 per cent of the blood volume is lost rapidly, the body is usually unable to repair the loss unaided and, unless transfusion is restored to, death results. In a healthy man the loss of 30 per cent or less of his blood calls readjusting mechanisms into play which may bring the blood volume back to the normal level within a remarkably short time; 500 cc. or so of blood drawn for transfusion purposes are said to be replaced within an hour or so. The restoration of the blood to its previous concentration in erythrocytes, however, takes about 7 weeks on the average. This time may be shortened considerably by the administration of iron and a diet containing a liberal quantity of high quality protein. Fowler and Barer found in a study of 200 blood donors that, after the removal of 550 cc. of blood, the average fall in hemoglobin was 2.3 grams per 100 cc. Regeneration of hemoglobin occurred at the rate of 0.049 gram per cent for men and 0.040 gram per cent for women per day.

The protective mechanisms which automatically come into action after hemorrhage are several and may be divided into two groups—*immediate* or *early* and *delayed.*

### Immediate or Early Effects

If the loss of blood is large, especially if it is of sudden occurrence and from an artery, there is a prompt fall in blood pressure as a result simply of the reduction in circulating fluid. If not too great, the fall in pressure is salutary, since it helps to prevent further bleeding. A moderate loss of blood, 10 per cent of the total amount, produces little or no drop in pressure. This is especially true if the blood is lost gradually and if it comes from a vein, i.e., beyond the peripheral resistance. Under these circumstances compensatory mechanisms easily maintain the pressure of blood at its normal height. Three main compensations relating to the vascular system occur: (a) reduction in the capacity of the vascular bed (b) increased peripheral resistance (c) fluid entry from the tissues. These will be dealt with later.

*Clotting* of the blood (ch. 12) which occurs within a few minutes serves to close the opening in the blood vessel. The blood tends to clot more rapidly than usual after a severe hemorrhage. The initial drop in pressure, when such occurs, aids the formation of the clot. Stanching of the bleeding is also furthered in the case of an artery by the retraction and contraction of the middle fibromuscular coat of the vessel, as well as by the curling up and crenation of its endothelial lining. Platelets are deposited on the injured surfaces and agglutinate to form a plug or a base of attachment for the clot. Some disintegrate also and liberate a vasoconstrictor substance, serotonin, or 5-hydroxytryptamine which is a material aid in hemostasis (ch. 12). These factors, together with the fall in blood pressure, may be sufficient to stanch the flow of blood from an artery as large even as the popliteal. Clot retraction, which also depends on platelets, leads to the formation of a firmer plug.

In small vessels the opposed endothelial surfaces become sticky and coherent.

*Increase in the heart rate.* This is almost invariably an accompaniment of a severe hemorrhage and is one of the mot valuable signs of concealed, i.e., internal, bleeding; this sign is not seen, as a rule, in moderate blood losses or in slow bleeding. It is brought about through carotid sinus and aortic reflexes (ch. 21 and 32) initiated by the fall in blood pressure. Reduction in blood flow through the vessels of the medulla with the consequent anoxemia of the cardiac centers may be an additional factor: Adrenaline liberation (ch. 58) may possibly play a part. Although the nature of the compensation provided by the increase in heart rate is not clear in view of the reduced venous return, it is possible that the increase in heart rate may lower the central venous pressure and hence improve the pressure gradient in the veins. This would improve venous return over what it would otherwise be.

Release of blood from blood reservoirs into the circulation helps to restore the circulating blood volume. These reservoirs are skin, liver, lungs, spleen and the splanchnic venous vessels. The blood from the spleen is richer in cells than the circulating blood. Its reservoir function in some animals is great, but in man it is not of such importance.

*Increased respiration.* The anoxia of the chemoreceptors of the carotid and aortic bodies caused by the reduced blood flow is probably responsible for the increased rate and depth of breathing. When the blood loss is more profound, and consequently the oxygen want more urgent, long deeply drawn inspirations, and expirations of a sighing character ensue (air hunger), or periodic breathing of a Cheyne-Stokes type may develop (p. 500). Gasping respirations precede death.

*Reduction in capacity of the vascular bed and redistribution of the blood.* When the flow of blood has been stopped or considerably lessened by a complete or partial closure of the wound in the vessel, the blood pressure, if this had fallen, rises again. This is the result mainly of a readjustment of the capacity of the vascular system whereby it is made to conform more nearly to the lessened volume of blood. It is this reduction in the vascular capacity which prevents the initial fall in pressure when the loss of blood is gradual. It is effected by the reflex narrowing of innumerable small vessels (vasoconstriction) in regions such as the skin, mucous membranes, intestine and other parts not immediately essential to life. If the hemorrhage has not been too severe the reduction in the capacity of the vascular bed may result in maintenance of an adequate venous return and consequent maintenance of cardiac output and of arterial blood pressure. If the hemorrhage is somewhat greater, then the venous return and cardiac output may fall, but the blood pressure may be maintained by an increase in peripheral resistance along with a reduction in the capacity of the arterial vessels. If the hemorrhage is still greater, then the arterial blood pressure will fall and may be restored by restoration of blood volume through the entrance of fluid into the blood vessels from the tissues. The vascular response is called into play by the underfilled state of the arteries and large veins feeding the heart (see vascular reflexes, chapter 21).

The vasoconstriction is not confined to the small arteries and arterioles but extends to arteries and veins (Heymans), and vasomotion of metarterioles (ch. 15 and 25) and precapillary sphincters is enhanced. These latter vessels also show increased reactivity to mechanical stimulation and to adrenaline (Zweifach and associates). The level of adrenaline and probably also of noradrenaline in blood is increased following hemorrhage. This probably plays a part in the vasoconstriction. These measures whereby the blood remaining in the vascular system is confined to a smaller space are of the utmost importance; they enable the essential centers in the medulla to be supplied with blood under adequate pressure to sustain their vitality. Also a greater quantity of blood than would otherwise be possible is brought to the heart to supply its muscle, fill its cavities and maintain the circulation. The withdrawal of blood from the less important parts of the body is responsible, however, for some of the characteristic manifestations of hemorrhage, notably the pallor of the skin and mucous membranes, and the coldness of the body surface. The cerebral anemia causes sensations of giddiness or faintness, flashes of light or ringing in the ears (tinnitus). The metabolic changes occurring as a result of hemorrhage or fluid loss are anaerobic in type and in the later stages, at all events, may be a consequence of reduced blood supply to tissues, although it is possible that other factors may be involved in the early changes. The rise in blood pressure at this stage is conducive to fresh bleeding. There is danger of the clot becoming dislodged.

In very severe hemorrhage, the hypernormal phase of capillary reactivity gives place to one of reduced capillary responses as the irreversible stage of hemorrhagic shock supervenes. The minute vessels tend toward dilation and become unresponsive, though the larger vessels still remain constricted.

### Delayed Effects

*Replacement of the lost fluid.* This, it has already been mentioned, commences almost upon the instant that the blood is lost, but takes a variable length of time, depending upon the extent of the blood loss, to become complete. It occurs as a result of the low hydrostatic pressure within the capillaries. Fluid from the tissues moves into the vessels and dilutes the blood. The corpuscular concentration is therefore reduced and since fluid is entering the capillaries directly from the tissues and not by way of lymphatics, less protein is returned with the fluid from the tissues and for a short time after hemorrhage the protein content of the plasma is markedly depressed. Very soon, however, the concentration of protein in the plasma shows a rise again as a result of the mobilization of protein stores probably from the tissue stores. Calvin found, that in dogs 50 per cent of the plasma protein removed by bleeding was restored within 4 hours. The extreme thirst which the subject of acute hemorrhage suffers is the call of the tissues for fluid and indicates that their own stores are being drawn into the underfilled vessels. The administration of water will therefore aid the body in recovering its water balance and replenishing the blood volume.

*Replacement of the blood cells* finally occurs through the increased activity of the bloodforming organs. This takes several days or weeks, the rapidity of the process depending to a large extent upon the nutrition and recuperative power of the individual and upon the diet. While the repair process is in progress reticulated cells are found in increased numbers in the blood.

*In summary,* following hemorrhage, if the loss of blood is not great, the circulatory effects of a reduction in blood volume may be compensated by vasoconstriction with decrease in the capacity of the vascular system. Thus the venous return, cardiac output and hence arterial blood pressure, may be maintained. If the loss is greater, the venous return and cardiac output may be reduced somewhat, but the arterial blood pressure may still be maintained by increasing the resistance to outflow from the arteries by vasoconstriction, especially of arterioles. If the loss is greater still, then the venous return and cardiac output will be reduced to such a degree that the increase in peripheral resistance may be insufficient to maintain the arterial blood pressure. The vascular compensations are brought about through reflexes initiated by the stimulation of stretch receptors in the blood vessels, principally in the carotid sinus and aortic arch, but possibly also in the great veins and right atrium. Further compensation comes as a consequence of arteriolar constriction and of increased vasomotion in the terminal vascular bed. As a result of arteriolar vasoconstriction, the blood pressure in the terminal vascular bed as a whole is reduced. As a result of increased vasomotion, the hydrostatic pressure in the true capillaries of the terminal vascular bed is reduced. With the fall in hydrostatic pressure in the capillary vessels, fluid entry into the capillaries from the interstitial spaces is increased and the blood volume tends to be restored. Since relatively less fluid reenters the circulation by way of lymphatics, the protein reentry will be less in relation to the fluid and the blood becomes more dilute. Protein is restored relatively quickly thereafter and a still slower restoration of red blood cells occurs.

### REFERENCES

ALLEN, T. H., PENG, M. T., CHEN, K. P., HUANG, T. F., CHANG, C. AND FANG, H. S. Metabolism, 1956, **5**, 328.

BARBOUR, H. G. AHD HAMILTON, W. F. Am. J. Physiol., 1925, **73**, 315.

BARCROFT, J., KENNEDY, J. A. AND MASON, M. F. J. Physiol., 1939, **95**, 159.

BRODIE, B. B. Methods of Medical Research, Vol. 4. M. B. Visscher, Ed. Year Book Publishers, Chicago, 1952.

BYROM, F. B. Clin. Sc., 1934, **1**, 245 and 273.

CHINARD, F. P. Methods of Medical Research, Vol. 4. M. B. Visscher, Ed. Year Book Publishers, Chicago, 1952.

CRAIG, A. B. AND WATERHOUSE, C. J. Lab. & Clin. Med., 1957, **49**, 165.

CRISPELL, K. R., PORTER, B. AND NIESET, R. T. J. Clin. Invest., 1950, **29**, 513.

CROOKE, A. C. AND MORRIS, C. J. O. J. Physiol., 1942, **101**, 217.

EDER, H. A. Methods of Medical Research, Vol. 4, M. B. Visscher, Ed. Year Book Publishers, Chicago, 1952.

FOWLER, W. M. AND BARER, A. P. J. A. M. A., 1942, 118, 421.

GAMBLE, J. L., ROSS, G. S. AND TISDALL, F. F. J. Biol. Chem., 1923, 57, 633.

GAUNT, R. Endocrinology, 1944, 34, 400.

GIBSON, J. G. AND EVELYN, K. A. J. Clin. Invest., 1938, 17, 153.

GIBSON, J. G. AND COLLEAGUES. J. Clin. Invest., 1946, 25, 605, 617.

GRAY, S. J. AND HEDDY, F. J. Clin. Invest., 1953, 32, 108.

GREGERSEN, M. I., GIBSON, J. J. AND STEAD, E. A. Am. J. Physiol., 1935, 113, 54.

GREGERSEN, M. I. AND STEWART, J. D. Am. J. Physiol., 1939, 125, 142.

HAHN, P. F. AND ASSOCIATES, J. Exper. Med., 1942, 75, 221.

HALDANE, J. S. AND SMITH, J. L. J. Physiol., 1900, 25, 331.

KEITH, N. M., ROWNTREE, L. G. AND GERAGHTY, J. T. Arch. Int. Med., 1915, 16, 547.

KENNEDY, J. A. AND MILLIKAN, G. A. J. Physiol., 1938, 93, 276.

MANERY, J. F. Methods of Medical Research, Vol. 4. M. B. Visscher, Ed. Year Book Publishers, Chicago, 1952.

PAINTER, E. E. AND ASSOCIATES. Am. J. Physiol., 1948, 152, 66.

RAWSON, R. A. Am. J. Physiol., 1942, 138, 708.

READ, R. C. AND GILBERTSEN, S. Arch. Int. Med., 1957, 100, 259.

ROBINSON, E. A. AND ADOLPH, E. F. Am. J. Physiol., 1943, 139, 39.

SCHILLER, R. AND DORFMAN, R. I. Endocrinology, 1943, 33, 402.

SEMPLE, R. E., THOMSEN, A. E. T., BALL, A. J. AND EXCELL, B. J. Am. J. Physiol., 1956, 187, 631.

STEVENSON, J. A. F. Recent progress in hormone research., 1949, 4, 363.

WASSERMAN, K., JOSEPH, J. D. AND MAYERSON, H. S. Am. J. Physiol., 1956, 184, 175.

WASSERMAN, K. AND MAYERSON, H. S. Am. J. Physiol., 1951, 165, 15.

WASSERMAN, K. AND MAYERSON, H. S. Am. J. Physiol., 1952, 170, 1.

ZWEIFACH, B. W. AND ASSOCIATES. Am. J. Anat. 1944, 75, 239. Am. J. Physiol., 1944, 142, 80; 1947, 150, 239. Ann. Surg., 1944, 120, 232. Surg. Gynec. & Obst., 1945, 80, 593. Ann. New York Acad. Sc., 1946, 46, 533, 571. See also CHAMBERS, R. Nature, 1948, 162, 835.

### *Monographs and Reviews*

ADOLPH, E. F. Physiol. Rev., 1933, 13, 336.

ADOLPH, E. F. AND ASSOCIATES. Physiology of man in the desert. Interscience Publishers, N. Y., 1947.

BARBOUR, H. G. Physiol. Rev., 1921, 1, 295.

BERSON, S. A. Bull. New York Acad. Med., 1950, 30, 750.

BROWN, E., HOPPER, J. AND WENNESLAND, R. Ann. Rev. Physiol., 1957, 19, 231.

BULL, G. M. Lectures on the scientific basis of medicine. Brit. Postgrad. Med. Fed., U. of London. Vol. III, p. 219. The Athlone Press, 1953–1954.

LANDIS, E. M. Physiol. Rev., 1934, 14, 404.

LOTSPEICH, W. D. Ann. Rev. Physiol., 1958, 20, 339.

MANERY, J. F. Physiol. Rev., 1954, 34, 334.

MARRIOTT, W. M. Physiol. Rev., 1923, 3, 275.

MILLICAN, R. C. AND ROSENTHAL, S. M. Ann. Rev. Med., 1954, 5, 285.

PETERS, J. P. Body water. Charles C Thomas, Springfield, Ill., 1935.

PINSON, E. A. Physiol. Rev., 1952, 32, 123.

ROSENTHAL, S. M. AND MILLICAN, R. C. Pharm. Rev., 1954, 6, 489.

STARLING, E. H. The fluids of the body. Constable, London, 1909.

# 4

# THE LYMPH AND TISSUE FLUIDS

## Structure of the Lymphatic System

The lymphatic system commences peripherally as a meshwork of delicate vessels (lymph capillaries) which drain the tissue spaces. This is a one-way system, the lymph within it moving toward the great veins. By the confluence of small vessels larger ones are formed which, receiving tributaries along their course, gradually swell in size, and finally form the right lymphatic and thoracic ducts. These pour their lymph into the blood stream by way of the right and left subclavian veins, respectively. The system is a closed one, its vessels possessing complete walls formed of endothelial cells. Small nodes (lymph nodes or glands) are interposed in the course of the larger lymph channels. These vessels, upon reaching the gland, break up into finer channels which, plunging into the node, open into the sinuses of its cortex. After passing through the gland the lymph is collected again on the other side by fine vessels which soon re-form into a few larger trunks. The glands are placed at strategic points along the lymph routes, e.g., the elbow and axilla, knee and groin in the case of the upper and lower limbs, and at points in the abdomen, thorax and neck where several lymph vessels join. Lymph vessels are situated in skin, in subcutaneous tissue, in the fascial planes of muscles, in the linings of the respiratory, gastrointestinal and genitourinary tracts, and in the capsule and septa of the liver. Those in the intestinal villi are known as *lacteals*.

In the walls of the abdominal cavity the lymphatics are most abundant on the under surface of the diaphragm, where the greatest lymphatic absorption of colloidal material and minute particles takes place. The respiratory movements hasten absorption from the abdominal cavity, probably by varying rhythmically the intraabdominal pressure. Absorption also takes place into lymphatics of the omentum. Phagocytes play an important role in absorption through both the diaphragm and omentum. Absorption through the parietal peritoneum is slight and is mainly through the blood capillaries, which absorb only crystalloid solutions. The lymphatic system of the heart consists of intercommunicating plexuses lying beneath the epicardium and endocardium, and within the myocardium. Lymphatics are also present in the areolar tissue underlying the peritoneum and pleurae. They are absent from the central nervous system. In the lung the lymphatics extend no further than the respiratory bronchioles, the alveoli being devoid of lymph capillaries. Because of the poor lymphatic supply to the alveoli, or of its difficulty in penetrating the alveolar wall, protein is not readily absorbed from the interior of alveoli into the lung lymphatics. Water passes readily into the lung capillaries however because of the low pressure within them. The lymphatic system can be considered as taking some part in the regulation of the general circulation although this has not been worked out in detail. For example, if there is an increase in pressure in the pulmonary system there is also a greater pulmonary lymph flow. This fluid can move to a limited extent through lymphatic channels to the systemic circulation. Such a shift would tend to lessen the elevation in pulmonary pressure.

The skin is supplied richly with lymph capillaries. The lymph vessels in the deeper layers of the skin are so abundant, according to McMaster, that the skin cannot be punctured anywhere without tearing them, and since the flow of lymph along these vessels is relatively rapid, foreign material injected into the skin soon reaches the regional lymph nodes. An injection into the skin is, therefore, to a large extent, an injection into the lymphatic system. This is not true for all materials, but protein, so injected, is received by the blood mainly by way of the lymphatics. After destruction of the lymphatics from a region, subcutaneously injected protein does not appear in the blood for a long time and when it is detectable it is only in very small amounts.

The permeability of the lymph capillaries is increased by many agencies, e.g., sunlight, warmth, and by mechanical or chemical stimula-

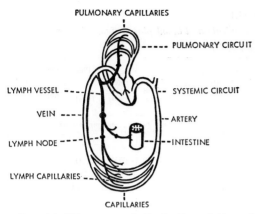

PULMONARY CAPILLARIES

PULMONARY CIRCUIT

LYMPH VESSEL

SYSTEMIC CIRCUIT

VEIN

ARTERY

LYMPH NODE

INTESTINE

LYMPH CAPILLARIES

CAPILLARIES

Fig. 4.1. Diagram to indicate the relation of the lymphatic system to the circulatory system.

tion; histamine is particularly effective. Their walls may become so permeable that they can scarcely be considered as channels walled off from the surrounding tissue spaces.

Lymphatic tissue has a great capacity for regeneration and very active proliferation of lymphatics occurs in an inflamed region.

### The Nodes as Defense Barriers

The lymph nodes must be looked upon as important structures for the defense of the blood against the invasion of bacteria or other injurious agents travelling by the lymph paths. When an infection of a part—a finger for instance—lying distal to a gland occurs, the latter becomes inflamed as a result of the localization therein of some of the bacteria or their toxins carried in the lymph. The gland swarms with motile cells (phagocytes) which attack and destroy the invading organisms. In this way a barrier is raised against the passage of deleterious agents, particularly bacteria, into the blood stream. In the case of the limbs at any rate it appears that no material can pass from the tissues to the blood stream *via* the lymph without filtering through the lymph nodes. The effectiveness of the nodes as filters has been clearly demonstrated by Drinker and his associates. The popliteal and iliac lymph nodes of dogs were perfused with solutions containing virulent streptococci (250,000,000 colonies per cc.). After perfusion lasting for over an hour the fluid collected from the thoracic duct was found to be sterile. After the node itself has been attacked by the microorganisms it may then serve as a source from which the blood stream becomes infected. Though highly efficient as filters for bacteria the nodes appear to offer but slight hindrance to the

passage of viruses. There is evidence that the lymph nodes contribute towards the body's defense in another way, namely, by the production of antibodies.

Barnes and Trueta have shown that bacteria pass from the tissues to the blood solely by the lymph stream, and that even toxins and venoms of large molecular weight (over 20,000) are not carried into the blood if the lymph vessels have been blocked. These observations in part explain the success which has followed the immobilization of infected parts in plaster; this procedure might be expected to reduce to a minimum the lymph flow from the inflamed region and thus to confine the infective process.

### The Composition of Lymph

The lymph of the small peripheral lymph vessels and the fluid of the tissues are closely similar in composition, both resembling the blood plasma. Although this view concerning tissue fluid is based chiefly on evidence from fluid exudates, it is probably true. The protein content of lymph is lower than that of plasma since lymph forms from tissue fluid. Drinker noted that it varied under different conditions from 0.3 to 4.0 per cent in mammals. The higher figure is unusual and, in human leg lymph, concentrations between 0.5 and 0.7 per cent were found.

The total quantity of mobilizable protein in interstitial fluid about equals the entire protein of the plasma. The protein of lymph is derived from this mobilizable mass of tissue fluid protein which varies, of course, with the amount of protein leaking from the capillaries. Differences in the amount of protein and fluid leaving the circulation, and in the amount of fluid reabsorbed by the capillaries as well as differences in the volume flow of lymph, will alter the protein content of the lymph. The amount of protein passing from the plasma into the tissue fluid is related to the surface area of the functioning capillaries and may not necessarily be ascribed to differences in the permeability of the capillaries. Electrophoresis shows the proteins of lymph to be qualitatively identical with the plasma proteins. The protein concentration in thoracic duct lymph, as a rule, is considerably higher than in peripheral lymph, but the lymph flow from the thoracic duct appears to be less than the total flow from several organs or regions. In hepatic lymph, the protein concentration, which is about ⅔ the concentration in plasma, varies inversely with the lymph flow. This suggests

## TABLE 4.1

*Chemical composition of peripheral lymph (cervical) and blood plasma from the dog*

(From Heim, 1933)

| | Protein (Kjeldahl) | Non-protein Nitrogen | Urea | Uric Acid | Creatinine | Sugar | Amino Acids | Chlorides (as NaCl) | Phosphorus | | Calcium |
|---|---|---|---|---|---|---|---|---|---|---|---|
| | | | | | | | | | Total | Inorganic | |
| | per cent | mg. per 100 cc. | mg. per 100 cc. | mg. per 100 cc. | mg. per 100 cc. | mg. per 100 cc. | mg. per 100 cc. | mg. per 100 cc. | mg. per 100 cc. | mg. per 100 cc. | mg. per 100 cc. |
| **Plasma:** | | | | | | | | | | | |
| Average | 6.18 | 32.6 | 21.7 | Tr.* | 1.37 | 123.0 | 4.90 | 678 | 22.0 | 5.6 | 11.70 |
| Range | 5.54– 7.23 | 21.1– 46.0 | 17.9– 28.0 | | 1.22– 1.54 | 112.0– 143.0 | | 649– 721 | 18.3– 26.1 | 4.4– 6.9 | 10.85– 12.95 |
| **Lymph** | | | | | | | | | | | |
| Average | 3.32 | 34.8 | 23.5 | Tr.* | 1.40 | 132.2 | 4.84 | 711 | 11.8 | 5.9 | 9.84 |
| Range | 1.38– 4.57 | 19.8– 45.4 | 19.8– 33.0 | | 1.28– 1.49 | 107.0– 144.0 | | 690– ˙ 730 | 10.2– 13.7 | 4.7– 7.3 | 8.93– 10.84 |
| Number of animals | 16 | 10 | 7 | 3 | 7 | 16 | 1 | 7 | 6 | 3 | 11 |

\* Tr. = trace.

that the rates of exit and reabsorption in liver may be important in producing the relatively high concentration of protein in hepatic lymph. However, labelled albumin exchanges more rapidly between plasma and hepatic lymph than between plasma and intestinal lymph, and still more rapidly than with the lymph of skeletal muscle. Most of the normal components of liver lymph seem to come chiefly if not entirely from blood plasma, with the exception of glucose which is present in higher concentration in liver lymph than in blood plasma. In anaphylactic or peptone shock, heparin, released from the liver, passes into the blood mainly by way of lymph pathways. Lymph contains prothrombin (p. 110) and clots slowly. It contains large numbers of white cells, mostly lymphocytes, but relatively few red cells. The number of leucocytes varies from 1000 to 20,000 per cu. mm. in thoracic duct lymph of the dog and averages 550 per cu. mm. in peripheral lymph. In peripheral lymph there are from 300 to 13,000 erythrocytes per cu. mm. The lymph flowing from the thoracic duct, since it comes largely from the intestine and liver, will vary in composition in accordance with the digestive processes. Its protein content is under ordinary circumstances from 2 to 4.5 per cent. Within 1 or 2 hours after a meal containing much fat the thoracic duct lymph appears milky. The lacteals and the fine lymphatics of the mesentery, being loaded with globules of absorbed fat, are seen as glistening white streaks. The fatty acid of thoracic duct lymph is increased by the ingestion of fat;

on a fat-free diet it is about the same as in the fasted animal.

The composition of plasma and peripheral lymph (i.e., lymph in the subcutaneous vessels of the limbs or neck) are compared in table 4.1.

It will be noted that calcium and total phosphorus, which are in part bound with protein, are in lower concentration than in plasma; the other constituents with the exception of protein and amino acids are in higher concentration.

### The Formation, Pressure and Flow of Lymph

After what has been said with regard to the forces concerned in the regulation of the fluid interchange between the capillaries and the tissues little need be added in explanation of lymph formation. The two processes are interrelated and similar in nature. Any condition which increases the outpouring of fluid from the capillaries into the tissues will tend to increase the flow of lymph. The lymph capillaries are much more permeable than the blood capillaries, and although the tissue spaces, i.e., the clefts between groups of tissue cells, are separated from the lymphatic system in an anatomical sense, the walls of the latter vessels are so permeable that they offer little impediment to the movement of either protein or crystalloids. It has been stated already that of the fluid which transudes from the blood at the arterial end of the capillary much of the water is reabsorbed at the venous end. The protein, however, passes into the lymph. The lymph capillary is therefore the special channel whereby protein is returned (in a round about way) to the blood. It is also concerned with the absorption of other colloids, or of particulate matter which may be introduced into the tissue spaces. Although in mammals the extravascular circulation of the entire plasma albumin takes place in about 20 hours, in the frog, in which the blood capillaries are more permeable to protein than those of mammals, the entire protein of the plasma passes from the blood and back again to blood *via* the lymph system, some 50 times in 24 hours.

Under ordinary conditions the pressure of the thoracic duct lymph is very low but if the duct is obstructed in the dog, a pressure of 15 cm. of water develops. The *rate of flow* along the human thoracic duct (as measured in cases of duct fistulas) is from 1 to 1.5 cc. per minute. Cain and his associates found an average flow of 0.46 cc. per minute in the thoracic duct, of which more than half, about 0.26 cc., was contributed by the lymph vessels of the liver.

The pressures in the peripheral lymph vessels during rest run from 0 to 6 cm. of water according to different observers using various species of animals. In inflammatory states and during activity the pressure in the larger lymph vessels of the part rises considerably above the resting value. Also when a lymph vessel becomes obstructed, the pressure on the distal side (i.e., toward the finer vessels) of the obstruction increases, the vessel becomes distended on this side and collapsed on the proximal side. The lymph pressures decrease from the periphery toward the more central channels, and are higher on the distal side of a lymph node (mesenteric) than on the proximal side. In the lymph capillaries of the mouse's ear pressures up to 2.7 cm. of water were found by McMaster; the latter figure exceeds that usually found by most observers in the larger lymph trunks of other animals.

Obliteration of the lumen of the finer lymph vessels by a high pressure in the tissues is provided against by the fastening of the walls of the vessels by fibrillae to the surrounding tissue cells. When edema fluid collects and the tissue pressure rises, the fine lymphatics do not collapse, but, on the contrary, their lumens become wider (McMaster).

The mechanism governing the passage of tissue fluid into the lymph vessels is obscure, although the action of the pulse in the blood vessels of the part appears to play a part. McMaster and his associates have demonstrated the importance of a pulsatile flow in the vessels of the perfused rabbit's ear, in the spread of vital dyes through the tissues and in the formation and flow of lymph.

Enlarging the capillary surface by vasodilation, or increasing the number of patent capillaries increases the leakage of protein from the circulation. This happens when infusions of saline or dextran are given. The protein of tissue spaces is returned to the blood by the lymph. If the thoracic duct lymph does not reenter the circulation, the plasma proteins may decrease by 15 to 30 per cent in 3 hours. It seems probable that the exit of protein from blood vessels and the efficiency of its return by lymphatics will be important factors in the regulation of fluid interchange, modifying the balance of forces across the capillary wall.

### Functions of the Lymphatic System

1. A primary function of the lymphatic system is to return protein to the blood from the tissue spaces.

2. The lymphatics have a role in the redistribution of fluid in the body, being capable of shifting fluid from one part of the circulatory system to another.

3. The lymphatics remove particulate matter, bacteria etc. from tissues.

4. The lymph flow helps in maintaining tissues. The ligation of lymph vessels in the heart may give rise to myocardial degeneration; in the kidneys it may accelerate the development of hydronephrosis when the ureters are tied; and in the liver it hastens the degenerative changes that follow bile duct ligation.

### Conditions Which Increase the Lymph Flow

1. INCREASE IN CAPILLARY PRESSURE AS A RESULT OF VENOUS OBSTRUCTION. Landis and Gibbon found that in man filtration from the capillaries showed a definite increase when the venous pressure rose above 12 or 15 cm. of water. The rate of filtration from the capillaries was directly proportional to the increase in venous pressure (fig. 4.2). At a given venous pressure the filtration rate increased rapidly at first but gradually slowed and finally ceased. This falling off in the filtration rate is ascribed to the rise in extracapillary pressure, due to the fluid accumulation, which opposes the hydrostatic pressure within the capillary. The accumulation of extracellular fluid is therefore greater in regions which are loose in texture and where the skin is readily stretched. In persons with firm, resistant skin, edema, for the same reasons, is later in making its appearance

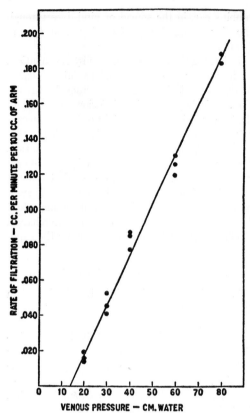

FIG. 4.2. Showing rates of filtration produced during 30 minutes by venous pressures between 20 and 80 cm. water (after Landis and Gibbon).

and is less pronounced than in those with loose, flabby skins, as when weight has been lost rapidly.

Increased pressure in the veins of the portal area, as may be produced by obstructing the portal vein or the hepatic veins, causes increased filtration into the tissues of the abdominal viscera and a great increase in the volume of lymph flowing along the thoracic duct.

Increase in arterial pressure, on the other hand, does not increase filtration in animals until the pressure reaches around 300 mm. Hg.

2. Increase in capillary surface, i.e., increase in the filtering surface. This increases the leakage of protein and fluid. It is due to factors causing distension of the capillary vessels: (a) increase in capillary pressure; (b) increase in the local temperature; (c) infusion of fluid.

3. Increased permeability of the capillaries. (a) a sufficient rise in temperature may increase capillary permeability.

(b) *Capillary poisons. Peptone* increases the flow of lymph from the thoracic duct probably as a result of its injurious effect upon the abdominal

capillaries. The increased flow occurs after removal of the liver so injury to the hepatic vessels is not essential. Other substances which increase lymph flow in this way are extracts of strawberries, crayfish, mussels, leeches, histamine and foreign proteins. To what extent this is due to a change in permeability and to what extent it is a consequence of capillary dilation is not known.

(c) *Reduced oxygen supply* to the tissues (oxygen want), increases lymph flow probably because of dilation of blood vessels but possibly also through damage to the capillary endothelium.

4. Hypertonic solutions. The intravenous injection of a concentrated solution of glucose, sodium sulphate or sodium chloride causes an increased flow of lymph from the thoracic duct. These substances in concentrated solution, though they permeate the capillary wall, exert an osmotic effect until equilibrium between the extravascular and intravascular fluids is reestablished. Water enters from the tissue spaces, particularly of the muscles and subcutaneous tissues of the limbs, which in consequence show a fall in volume; the brain shrinks. The removal of fluid may actually extend to the fluids within the cells which undergo shrinkage; and general desiccation of the tissues may result. The blood volume for the time is greatly augmented, the excess fluid for the most part being accommodated in the capacious capillary and venous areas of the abdomen. The viscera—liver, kidneys, spleen and intestines—increase in volume, due to the distension of their vascular beds, and a great outpouring of fluid as well as of protein occurs, which swells the volume of lymph in the thoracic duct. In this way these substances produce a redistribution of fluid.

The injection of isotonic saline will also increase the passage of protein and fluid from the capillaries and increase lymph flow. This too is probably a consequence of the distension of blood vessels. Protein is returned from the tissue fluid by the lymphatics. The concentration of protein in the returning lymph is higher than would be expected if the saline had caused dilution of the lymph. Sometimes the total plasma albumin actually increases. However if the infusion is large, the protein return is not as great as the protein leakage. So with larger infusions (greater than $\frac{3}{4}$ plasma volume) the protein loss from the blood vessels to the interstitial spaces may be increased.

The effect which hypertonic solutions have upon the movement of tissue fluids had extensive application during the first World War. Sir A. E. Wright introduced the practice of packing wounds with salt crystals or irrigating them with a hypertonic salt solution. This causes an outward flow of lymph and tissue fluid, which results in the mechanical removal of the bacteria and their toxins from the tissues bordering the wound.

5. INCREASED FUNCTIONAL ACTIVITY. When a gland or muscle enters into activity an increase in lymph flow occurs which starts a little after the commencement of the secretory or contractile response, but is nearly synchronous with the increased metabolism resulting from the activity. The increased flow is ascribed to (a) formation of metabolites which increase the osmotic effect of the tissue fluids and cause more fluid to leave the vessels (b) vasodilation, increased capillary pressure and increased fluid and protein leakage.

During rest the flow along the lymph vessels of the muscles and subcutaneous tissues is slight, and the protein content of the lymph is high. During activity the protein concentrations fall since less transuded water undergoes reabsorption into the blood and more is carried away by the lymph channels. This may occur even though the leakage of protein from the vessels is greater. The contracting muscles exert a pumping effect upon the lymph, driving it along the vessels. The rhythmical movements of the intestinal wall are thought to exert a similar effect in promoting the flow in the fine lymphatics of the submucosa. However, during fat absorption, lymph formation and its movement in the thoracic duct does not seem to be influenced by intestinal motility.

6. MASSAGE AND PASSIVE MOVEMENT act to a certain extent like muscular activity. They augment the blood flow, capillary pressure and capillary surface and so increase lymph formation. The manipulations and movements of the muscles serve to propel the lymph along the lymphatic channels.

## Edema (See also p. 575)

Edema is the term applied to an excessive accumulation of fluids in the tissue spaces, and is due to a disturbance in the mechanisms of fluid interchange, which have been considered in the preceding pages.[1] Instead of there being a perfect balance struck between the inward and outward flow of fluid through the capillary membrane absorption is exceeded by transudation. The particular factor or factors of the mechanism that are disordered are not always clear, and a satisfactory explanation of all forms of edema cannot be given.

But from previous discussions it is evident that the following factors will tend to increase the volume of interstitial fluid: (a) reduction in the protein concentration of plasma. Edema commences when the albumin fraction has fallen to between 2.5 and 3 per cent; (b) a general or a local rise in capillary blood pressure; (c) increased permeability of the capillary membrane; (d) increase in the filtering surface as when the capillaries dilate; (e) obstruction of the lymph channels.

There is a tendency for the accumulation of edema fluid to progress so far and then become stationary provided the conditions producing it remain constant, for as we have seen, when the tissue fluid pressure reaches a critical level its opposition to the force driving fluid from the vessels prevents further transudation. It should be appreciated too that plasma, as a source of edema fluid, has definite limitations and unless the total extracellular fluid is increased, a generalized edema cannot be very severe.

Since edema is only a symptom of some primary condition it may have a variety of causes, according to the particular disease with which it is associated.

*1. Cardiac edema.* In congestive heart failure there is both an increase in extracellular fluid and salt retention (ch. 25). It is clear that the volume of extracellular fluid can be reduced by restriction of the salt intake or by the administration of diuretics which remove both water and salt. Or it can be discharged by improving cardiac action, as by administering digitalis, lanatoside, or other suitable drug.

*2. Mechanical obstruction of veins.* When the main veins leading from a part are obstructed by new growth, fibrous tissue, as in cirrhosis of the liver, thrombosis, etc., increased transudation of fluid occurs. This is due in part to the rise in intracapillary pressure and an increase in the filtering surface, but the permeability of the capillary wall may also be increased as a result of the impaired blood supply or, as in the case of new growth, probably by the production of toxic substances as well.

*3. Edema due to renal disease.* In chronic nephritis edema is not usually pronounced unless the heart is failing; however, in the nephrotic syndrome it is an outstanding feature. In nephrosis a reduction in plasma protein as a consequence of the loss of protein in the urine leads to the passage of an abnormally large volume of fluid from the capillaries throughout the body. This in turn is probably responsible in some way for renal retention of salt and as a consequence of this, retention of water.

*4. Inflammatory edema.* In this type several factors combine to produce the fluid infiltration of the tissues. Increased capillary pressure occurs, due to dilation of the vessels and local slowing of the blood stream as well as to thrombosis and obstruction of the returning veins. There is an increase in the filtering surface too and the lymphatics for a variable distance from the inflammatory area are obstructed as well. The capillary walls are also seriously damaged by the bacterial toxin or other injurious agent, so that a fluid with a high protein content escapes from the vessels. The edema is localized to an area of varying extent surrounding the injured site. Certain analgesics, e.g., aspirin, morphine and Demerol, tend to reduce the edema of simple inflammation.

*5. Giant edema.* This is a localized noninflammatory edema which comes on with great rapidity and involves the loose areolar tissue in such regions as the hands, face, external genitalia or larynx. It occasionally runs in families. Little is known definitely regarding the mode of its production. A histaminelike substance liberated at the site of the edema is apparently the immediate cause. The remote exciting cause is frequently a foreign protein consumed in the diet which apparently gains access to the blood stream in a more or less unchanged state, for the attack often follows a particular food to which the subject is susceptible, and is sometimes accompanied by gastrointestinal disturbances. The effects are therefore of an anaphylactoid nature and constitute one type of allergy. This type, also termed *angioneurotic* edema, is allied to the very localized edemas which constitute the condition known as urticaria and which as suggested by Lewis are caused by the liberation of a histaminelike substance in the skin.

*6. Edema caused by malnutrition or to toxic substances.* Edema may occur in the anemias or in conditions in which the general nutrition of the body suffers. When the diet is deficient in vitamins, or there is too little fat or protein in the diet edema may occur, as in beriberi, scurvy, "war edema" or in the faulty nutrition of infants. In animals edematous conditions have actually been induced by general underfeeding, or by a diet deficient in fat and soluble vitamins, or by one deficient in protein alone. The factors responsible for the increased transudation in these cases are not always clear, but in others there is a marked lowering of plasma protein which alone is sufficient to account for the edema. In many instances, on the other hand, hypoproteinemia does not occur.

In such cases the lack of some essential amino acid may be the determining factor. A simple explanation has been offered by Henschel and his colleagues, namely, that owing to the loss of tissue on the famine diet the extracellular fluids (plasma and interstitial fluid) show an apparent increase, that is, though not showing an absolute increase, they are greater than normal in relation to body weight. Henschel and his colleagues in experiments upon a group of normal young men on a semi-starvation diet found that, although the *absolute* volume of extracellular fluid remained fairly constant at the value observed before the subjects were put upon the experimental diet, it increased gradually to aboud 40 per cent above normal when considered in relation to body weight; edema appeared when the relative increase in volume reached from 8 to 10 per cent above normal, which is approximately the same as the increase in volume of interstitial fluid at which other types of edema appear.[1] Increased capillary permeability due to impaired nutrition of the vascular walls was the main cause of the starvation edema in the Netherlands during the last war. In some cases of nutritional edema, excretion of an antidiuretic substance has been reported.

Certain chemical substances such as arsenic, salts of heavy metals, and the toxins of certain infectious diseases, such as diphtheria, acute nephritis, etc., are known to act as capillary poisons and apparently cause edema in this way. An interesting type of a toxic edema is that which may be produced in animals by the injection of hematoporphyrin (ch. 6). This substance appears to sensitize the tissues towards light rays, and the edema occurs only after exposure. Histamine causes local edema at the point of injection by inducing capillary dilation and increased permeability of the membrane.

---

[1] When the subcutaneous tissues are involved these appear swollen, and leave the imprint of the thumb when it is pressed into the skin (pitting). Dropsy (hydrops) is an old-fashioned term which is applied to edema as defined above or to a free collection of fluid within one of the body cavities, e.g., the thorax or the abdomen. *Hydrothorax* is also applied to the former of these conditions and *ascites* to the latter. *Anasarca* is a more or less generalized edema involving the subcutaneous tissues.

It is important to remember that the term edema applies to a gross collection of extravascular fluid. The bulk of tissue fluid fluctuates widely in health, and in pathological states may be very considerably increased before the increase is evident clinically. When, for example, a normal person stands for a time the extravascular fluid of the legs increases; and the immersion of a limb in a hot bath hastens the rate at which fluid transudes from the vessels—the limb volume rises as a result, largely, of fluid accumulation in the tissues. Drury and Jones found that edema appeared when the increase in fluid increased the volume of the leg by 8 per cent.

*7. Edema due to lymphatic obstruction.* Obstruction to the outflow of lymph from the tissue spaces may cause pronounced edema, even though the venous channels and the capillary vessels are unaffected. Edema of this nature is readily produced in frogs by compression of the lymph channels alone. It is more difficult to produce edema in this way in higher animals, but if the obstruction is complete edema occurs in them also. Edema of this nature is seen in infections with the filarial parasite which finds its way into the lymph vessels of the limbs and blocks their lumens with the production of the condition known as elephantiasis. The pleural cavities depend for the absorption of a fluid upon the lymph channels, and accumulations of fluid may occur here as a result of lymphatic obstruction. The edema associated with carcinoma is due chiefly to the filling of the lymphatic channels with cords of cancer cells as well as to venous obstruction caused by the pressure of the growth. The "milk leg" of the puerperium is in part due to lymphatic obstruction. The tissue fluid in these types of edema has a relatively high concentration of protein.

*8. Heat edema.* The effect of heat upon capillary permeability has been mentioned (p. 38). Excessive heat may actually lead to edema in man. It occurs in the tropics and occasionally in so-called temperate zones during an intense heat wave. Increase in blood volume, enlargement of the filtering surface as a result of the opening up of fresh capillaries and the rise in capillary pressure incident to the dilation of capillaries previously patent, are also factors in the production of this type of edema.

## REFERENCES

BARNES, J. M. AND TRUETA, J. Lancet, 1941, 1, 623.

CAIN, J. C. AND ASSOCIATES. Surg. Gynec. & Obst., 1947, 85, 559.

BENSON, J. A., LEE, P. R., SCHOLER, J. F., KIM, K. S. AND BOLLMAN, J. L. Am. J. Physiol., 1956, 184, 441.

DRINKER, C. F., FIELD, M. E. AND WARD, H. K. J. Exper. Med., 1934, 59, 393.

DRURY, A. N. AND JONES, N. W. Heart, 1927, 14, 55.

FRIEDMAN, M., BYERS, S. O. AND OMOTO, C. Am. J. Physiol., 1956, 184, 11.

HENSCHEL, A. AND ASSOCIATES. Am. J. Physiol., 1947, 150, 170.

LANDIS, E. M. AND GIBBON, J. H., JR. J. Clin. Invest., 1933 12, 105. (See also, LANDIS AND ASSOCIATES. J. Clin. Invest., 1932, 11, 63, 717.)

McMASTER, P. D. J. Exper. Med., 1937, 65, 373; 1947, 86, 293. Harvey Lectures, 1941–42, Ser. 37, 227.

MARKOWITZ, C. AND MANN, F. C. Am. J. Physiol., 1931, 96, 709.

MERRILL, A. J. J. Clin. Invest., 1946, 25, 389; Proc. 22nd Sc. Assoc., Am. Heart J. 1949, p. 34.

NEWMAN, E. V. Am. J. Med., 1949, 7, 490.

PARSONS, R. J. AND McMASTER, P. D. J. Exper. Med., 1938, 68, 353, 377.

PETERS, J. P. New England J. Med., 1948, 239, 353.

RICHARDS, D. W. Am. J. Med., 1949, 6, 772.

TAYLOR, G. W., KINMONTH, J. B., ROLLINSON, E., ROTBLAT, J. AND FRANCIS, G. E. Brit. M. J., 1957, i, (Jan. 19), 133.

WARREN, J. V. AND STEAD, E. A. Arch. Int. Med., 1944, 73, 138.

WASSERMAN, K. AND MAYERSON, H. S. Am. J. Physiol., 1951, 165, 15.

### Monographs and Reviews

CUNNINGHAM, R. S. Physiol. Rev., 1926, 6, 242.

DAVIS, J. O. AND SMITH, J. R. Am. J. Med., 1947, 3, 704.

DENZ, F. A. Quart. J. Med., 1947, 16, 1.

DRINKER, C. K. AND FIELD, M. E. Lymphatics, lymph and tissue fluid. The Williams & Wilkins Co., Baltimore, 1933.

DRINKER, C. K. AND YOFFEY, J. M. The lymphatics, lymph and lymphoid tissue. Harvard University Press, Cambridge, 1941.

LANDIS, E. M. Harvey Lectures, 1936–7, Ser. 32, 70.

McMASTER, P. D. Harvey Lectures, 1941–42, Ser. 37, 227.

SIMONSON, E. Ann. Rev. Physiol., 1958, 20, 123.

STARLING, E. H. The fluids of the body. Constable, London, 1909.

# 5

# TRANSFUSION: THE BLOOD GROUPS

The materials employed for restoring the blood volume to normal are: (a) whole blood, (b) plasma or serum, (c) solutions of colloids, e.g., gum acacia, isinglass, dextran, polyvinyl pyrollidone, etc., (d) solutions of crystalloids, e.g., saline or glucose solutions.

## Whole Blood[1]

Theoretically, whole human blood is, of course, the ideal transfusion fluid. The improvements and simplification of technique in recent years and the advance in knowledge of blood incompatibilities have made blood transfusion immeasurably safer and available under circumstances which hitherto would have been insuperable. It is used not only in cases of emergency such as severe hemorrhage or wound shock, but in several other conditions which are included in the following list.

Hemorrhage
Anemias, especially, aplastic anemia and hemolytic disease of the newborn, agranulocytosis and hemorrhagic diseases, e.g., hemophilia and purpura hemorrhagica
Shock (wounds, burns)
Malnutrition in infants, marasmus, acute intoxications
Septic conditions, septicemias

The red cells of the transfused blood survive

[1] Within recent years stored blood (or plasma) is being used to an ever increasing extent. Blood collected from the dead has been employed in Russia, but cadaver blood for obvious reasons has not found general favor. Placental blood or blood removed by venesection from cases of congestive heart failure has also been used, but the blood of healthy donors is preferable. The blood is preserved at a temperature of around 1°C. after dilution with a citrate-dextrose mixture in the proportions of 5 parts of blood, 1 part of 3.2 per cent citrate solution and 6.5 parts of 5.4 per cent dextrose solution. Kept in this way blood remains suitable for transfusion for about twenty days. These so-called *blood banks* have the advantage that a quantity of blood already prepared for transfusion can be obtained at a moment's notice. But there is also the great disadvantage that any blood not used within the time limit must be discarded.

and carry out their functions for several weeks (around 80 days on the average) after their injection. For this reason whole blood is greatly superior to any other transfusion fluid in any condition in which the respiratory capacity of the blood has been greatly reduced, e.g., very severe hemorrhage or hemorrhage in an anemic person, CO poisoning, etc. It is also more effective in traumatic shock than plasma, serum or other blood substitutes. The use of blood as a transfusion fluid, nevertheless, is hedged about by hazards both to the recipient and to some extent to the donor. On this account it is the preferable procedure only when adequate facilities for guarding against these dangers are available, otherwise some blood substitute should be used. The safeguards which must be taken are:

1. The donor must be healthy in every way. Several cases have been reported of disease having been transmitted by transfused blood. Syphilis, malaria and acute diseases have been reported to have followed blood transfusion. In some instances the transmission in the transfused blood of a particular foreign protein of dietary origin, to which the recipient but not the donor is sensitive, has caused an allergic reaction.

A very serious hazard today is the transmission in the donor's blood of a dangerous type of infectious hepatitis. This disease, when contracted through blood transfusion, is called *homologous serum jaundice* or *hepatitis*. It closely resembles the agent, apparently a filtrable virus, which is responsible for the infectious hepatitis, which is seen in both sporadic and epidemic forms.

2. Too rapid transfusion of blood is dangerous, especially in children or undersized persons, for the sudden increase in circulating fluid may cause serious embarrassment to the right side of the heart. In an adult, the usual transfusion rate is from 100 to 200 cc. per hour, which causes little cardiovascular effect, even though the blood volume is considerably increased. At high rates of transfusion the venous pressure may rise unduly, the cardiac output may increase sharply, and an

excessive amount of work may be demanded from the heart. Rapid infusion of fluid into animals causes death from cardiac failure, preceded by an abnormal rise in venous pressure and pulmonary edema. The total quantity injected varies from about 500 to 1500 cc. or more, according to circumstances and the size of the patient.

3. One of the unpleasant and disturbing but rarely dangerous effects of transfusion is the rise in temperature which follows a short time after injection, unless great precaution is exercised in preparing the blood and the necessary apparatus. This pyrogenic action which has been more prominent in infusions and materials other than whole blood is due to substances (*pyrogens*) of unknown but probably protein nature, formed in the distilled water used in the preparation of the blood substitute, in the material itself or contaminating the transfusion apparatus. These fever-producing substances are thought to be in most instances of bacterial or viral origin. Therefore, though every possible care has been taken in their preparation, all artificial transfusion materials must be submitted to a reliable test upon rabbits for pyrogenic action before they can be accepted for clinical use.

4. An ever present potential danger in the use of whole blood is incompatibility. The donor's blood must always be tested for its compatibility with the blood of the recipient. Normal plasma contains substances which have the power to cause the clumping together (agglutination) and subsequent disintegration (hemolysis) of the foreign corpuscles of another species. Agglutination also results when bloods of two persons belonging to certain blood groups are mixed. The bloods are then said to be incompatible and transfusion under such circumstances will lead to very serious if not fatal results.

## The Blood Groups

In the early years of this century, Landsteiner and others found that the blood from different persons could be divided into four groups, which we now call groups A, B, AB and O. The basis for this terminology, and for part of the differentiation, lies in the antigenic nature of the red cells of the donor. In the next few decades, other blood types were found, notably the M and N types. The discovery of the Rh factor late in the 1930's stimulated more interest in blood groups, and within the past few years many more have been found. The clinical importance of these varies greatly.

TABLE 5.1

| Group | Cells Contain Isoagglutinogens | Serum Contains Isoagglutinins |
|---|---|---|
| O | O | $\alpha$ and $\beta$ |
| A | A | $\beta$ (anti-B) |
| B | B | $\alpha$ (anti-A) |
| AB | A and B | Neither |

### The A-B-O Groups

*Reactions.* The presence of agglutinogen[2] A on cells will cause them to react with certain serum agglutinins,[3] anti-A or $\alpha$, in such a fashion that relatively large numbers of these cells stick together, i.e., agglutinate. The nature of this reaction is similar to that between any antigen and its antibody. Similarly, cells with agglutinogen B will react with anti-B or $\beta$-agglutinins. Cells with both A and B agglutinogens will be agglutinated by either agglutinin; cells with neither A nor B (i.e., type O cells) will not be agglutinated by either agglutinin. The $\alpha$- or $\beta$-agglutinins occur naturally in human serum and the mechanism of their production is unknown. In the serum of persons with cell type A, $\beta$-agglutinins occur; in the serum of persons of type B, there are $\alpha$-agglutinins; type AB blood contains no agglutinins, and type O blood contains both agglutinins. The relationships are summarized in table 5.1. Obviously, if the serum from a person of type A is mixed with the cells of a person of type B, agglutination will occur. If such a serum is added to type O cells, no agglutination will occur. Other reactions resulting from mixing cells and sera of other blood types are shown in table 5.2.

### Determinations of Groups

By the use of two antisera, one containing only $\alpha$-isoagglutinin, and the other containing only $\beta$-isoagglutinin, it is possible to determine to which of the four blood types a given sample of

[2] An agglutinogen may be defined as that part of the cell which is responsible for the reaction of the cell (i.e., agglutination with other similar cells) when it is placed in a medium containing specific antibodies directed against this agglutinogen. It is responsible for a specific antigenic action of the cell. Isoagglutinogens refer to those that react with antibodies derived from the same species as the agglutinogen.

[3] An agglutinin is a component of the blood serum which acts as an antibody, in that it can react with a specific part of a cell, (i.e., the agglutinogen) to cause agglutination. Isoagglutinins are antibodies which react with agglutinogens from the same species as mentioned above.

TABLE 5.2

| Corpuscles | Serum | | | |
|---|---|---|---|---|
| | O | A | B | AB |
| O | − | − | − | − |
| A | + | − | + | − |
| B | + | + | − | − |
| AB | + | + | + | − |

+ = Agglutination.
− = No agglutination.

blood belongs. The blood is diluted with physiological saline (0.9 per cent NaCl in water) to give about a 2 per cent suspension of red cells. A drop or two of this suspension is placed on a glass slide and mixed with one or two drops of anti-A serum (containing $\alpha$-agglutinin). Another sample of the cell suspension is mixed with anti-B serum. Agglutination of the cells with the anti-A serum only shows that the cells were of type A. If agglutination occurs with both antisera, the cells must be of type AB, and if agglutination does not occur with either antiserum, the cells must be of type O. These reactions are illustrated in fig. 5.1.

## TEST SERA

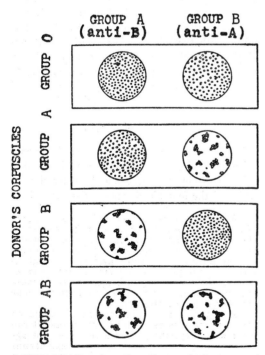

FIG. 5.1. Showing the effects of the sera of groups A and B upon the corpuscles of the several blood groups.

Agglutination usually occurs quite rapidly, especially if the slide has been warmed and is gently rocked to facilitate mixing of the cells and the antiserum. It is shown by the appearance of small clumps of cells, easily distinguished with a low power microscope, and usually readily visible to the unaided eye. If there is no agglutination there are no clumps formed, although there may be a tendency of the cells to move towards the center of the drop, and to show up as a darker colored region of rather variable size and form in the drop. Microscopically, true clumps show up as dense, dark masses. Nonspecific congregation of the cells shows as a diffuse mass of cells, without definite borders.

Suitable controls with cells of known type should always be included in any test. A failure to agglutinate may mean that a certain agglutinogen is not present on the cell, or it may mean that the testing serum has lost its potency, through bacterial contamination, heating, or other careless handling. Conversely, agglutination may be seen in the absence of a specific agglutinogen as a result of the production, by bacterial contamination, of substances which can cause the nonspecific agglutination of red cells.

### Effects of Incompatible Transfusions

The reactions mentioned above, it should be noted, are those observed when *serum* and *cells* from different persons of the types indicated are allowed to react *in vitro*. When blood from one person is transfused into another, the conditions under which the reactions take place are modified, and there is therefore a possibility of a difference in the results.

If blood from a person of type A is transfused into a recipient who belongs to type B, it can be readily seen that there are two possible ways by which there may be agglutination of the red cells. The $\beta$-agglutinins of the donor might agglutinate the B cells of the recipient, and the $\alpha$-agglutinins of the recipient might agglutinate the A cells of the donor. In practice, it seems that usually the isoagglutinins of the donor do not agglutinate the cells of the recipient. This may be because the donor's isoagglutinins are rather well diluted by the time they have mixed with the circulating blood of the recipient. There is some doubt as to whether this "dilution effect" is sufficient to account for the failure to react. On the other hand, there is but little dilution of the isoagglutinins by the (relatively) small amount of blood which is usually given in a single transfusion, and they can readily react with the cells of the donor.

Since it is the donor's cells which are most likely to be agglutinated, it might be thought that such a reaction could be avoided by the use of type O blood. Cells of such a blood could not be agglutinated by any of the isoagglutinins, and the isoagglutinins present in the O blood might not affect the cells of the recipient, as mentioned above. The use of the term "universal donor" for type O blood has therefore come into being. Conversely, persons with type AB blood are sometimes called "universal recipients." The use of such terms is dangerous, however, and they should be discarded. Certain people of type O have a very high concentration of $\alpha$- or of $\beta$-isoagglutinins, and even after the transfused blood is diluted in the recipient's blood stream, there may be a sufficiently high amount of $\alpha$- or of $\beta$-isoagglutinins to react with the recipient's cells. A second very important consideration is that such terminology fails to take into account the other blood types (see below).

If there is a transfusion of the wrong blood type (i.e., incompatible blood) a transfusion reaction may result. Symptoms vary in severity, and are probably a consequence of blockage of blood vessels by the agglutinated red cells. Such cells tend to be hemolyzed more readily than normal cells, and this hemolysis may contribute to such symptoms as severe lumbar pain, a sensation of burning of the face and tightness of the chest. There may be some degree of collapse, followed by a chill and a very rapid pulse. Hemoglobinuria and anuria sometimes occur. The renal insufficiency is thought by some to be due to a blockage of the kidney tubules with hematin, but others believe that it is caused by reduced blood flow through the glomeruli.

As a check against the possibility of transfusion of the wrong type of blood, the procedure known as "cross matching" is carried out. Cells and serum of the donor's blood and of the recipient's blood are separated, and then a suspension of the donor's cells is added to some of the recipient's serum, while another test is run in which the recipient's cells are mixed with some of the donor's serum. Both mixtures are checked to see if there has been any agglutination. Because it is most important to avoid any reaction leading to agglutination of the donor's cells, the test in which they are used is sometimes called the "major cross match." For reasons indicated above, reactions with the recipient's cells are possibly of lesser importance, so the second test is sometimes called the "minor cross match." The absence of agglutination in a simple cross matching test as outlined should not be taken as a sufficient indication that a transfusion may be performed safely. Other blood types, especially the Rh type, should also be considered, and ordinarily the simple cross match will give no indication of the possibility of trouble arising from the subgroups.

*Subgroups.* The existence of subgroups of the A agglutinogens was recognized by von Dungern and Hertzfeld in 1911. They found that there were two distinct, but still related agglutinogens, called $A_1$ and $A_2$. This finding also indicated the existence of two types of AB cells, i.e., $A_1B$ and $A_2B$. About 80 per cent of type A persons have cells of type $A_1$, and these cells are usually agglutinated more strongly with a given anti-A serum than the $A_2$ cells which come from the remaining 20 per cent of persons in the category. Further subgroups $A_3$ and $A_4$ have been reported. The sera of persons of type $A_2$ or $A_2B$ may in rare cases contain an anti-$A_1$ agglutinin, or $\alpha_1$. Certain type O individuals also have anti-$A_1$ agglutinins in their sera. Rare sera from $A_1$ or $A_1B$ individuals contain agglutinins ($\alpha_2$) which react with $A_2$ blood. These $\alpha_2$ agglutinins are not specific for $A_2$ since they also react, even more intensely, with type O cells. Furthermore, they do not react regularly with $A_2B$ cells. It has been suggested that the $\alpha_2$ agglutinin is really an agglutinin directed against O cells, and that it reacts with $A_2$ cells only because they are mostly heterozygous type $A_2O$.

### Inheritance of A-B-O Blood Groups

Early workers in the field felt that there were two genes which determined the inheritance of the A-B-O groups, and that group O was produced by a lack of either of these groups. This theory was shown to be incorrect, and most workers now subscribe to Bernstein's triple allelomorph theory. This states that the inheritance of the main blood groups is by three pairs of allelomorphic genes, A, B and O, for which only one locus is provided on each chromosome of the chromosome pair. These genes cause the production of corresponding specific substances on the cell, but in practice it is sometimes easier to think of group O as representing simply the absence of A and B factors. With these three factors, it is easy to see that an individual's genetic constitution will fall into one of six categories, i.e., AA, AB, AO, BB, BO, OO. Types AA and AO will both be classified as type A, and similarly, BB and BO will be classified as type B. Persons of type O must be homozygous, OO. Since each gene of the diploid pair is derived from one parent, it

TABLE 5.3

| Parental Combinations | No. of Families | No. of Children in Each Blood Group | | | |
|---|---|---|---|---|---|
| | | O | A | B | AB |
| O × O | 1563 | 3772 | (14) | (9) | 0 |
| O × A | 2903 | 2707 | 3749 | (10) | (1) |
| A × A | 1385 | 556 | 2538 | 0 | (2) |
| O × B | 1456 | 1418 | (7) | 1831 | (1) |
| B × B | 554 | 203 | (1) | 1009 | 0 |
| A × B | 1400 | 605 | 957 | 771 | 848 |
| O × AB | 530 | (8) | 633 | 646 | (3) |
| A × AB | 455 | 0 | 533 | 247 | 312 |
| B × AB | 323 | (2) | 183 | 406 | 232 |
| AB × AB | 59 | 0 | 28 | 36 | 65 |

About 45 per cent of individuals from European stock belong to group O, about 42 per cent to group A, 10 per cent to group B and 3 per cent to group AB.

is easy to construct a table to show the possible blood types of children from given parents. Table 5.3 shows the children from various parental combinations. There is an interesting side light to the figures which are in parentheses in this table. If one accepts the explanation that the figures which are in parentheses represent illegitimate children, and further, makes a statistical analysis of the percentage of "illegitimates" among the different blood groups, one finds that there is a higher percentage in B and AB, and a lower percentage in O, than the average. The more interesting conclusion is that B group might be associated with a greater than average degree of promiscuity. It is more likely (but less interesting) that the bracketted figures include not only illegitimates, but also a fair number of errors in blood typing, which just happened to come into the B and AB group.

*Other Sources of Blood Group Substances*

The agglutinogens of the erythrocytes may be looked upon as substances which are incorporated into the structure of the red cell membrane, whether or not they are isolated from the antigenic complex of which they may be a part. Certain other tissues of the body yield materials which show many of the reactions of the A and B agglutinogens. But whether they are identical atom for atom in a particular spatial arrangement cannot be stated, but certainly there must be a close similarity in their molecular architecture.

Witebsky, Landsteiner and others have found in gastric juice, saliva and other body fluids and organ extracts, materials that when added, e.g.,

to anti-A sera will materially reduce the agglutinating power of that serum for A cells. Similarly, many of these materials, when injected, stimulate the production of specific antibodies. Materials from animals, such as hog gastric mucosa, have been found for A, B and some other substances. In recent years the discovery of new blood groups (see below) has been so rapid that it has not been possible to investigate thoroughly other tissues for the presence or absence of substances of a serological nature similar to those relating to the ABO groups.

These substances which have been studied show a low nitrogen content (compared to protein) and a relatively high concentration of reducing sugar and hexosamine. A considerable amount of work has been done in the isolation and purification and with respect to the chemical and physical characterization of some of these materials.

Preparations of these group specific substances are of great value when it is desired to reduce the titer, or effective concentration of a certain antibody in a serum. If the appropriate substance is added (e.g., add A substance to neutralize $\alpha$) to the serum it will combine with its specific antibody, and thus prevent this antibody from causing agglutination of erythrocytes.

*Secretors.* Studies on the amounts of blood group substances which can be recovered from body fluids have shown that although these substances are present in the fluids from most individuals, they are sometimes absent, or present only in very small amounts. Persons whose saliva, gastric juice, etc. contains appreciable amounts of a specific substance are known as *secretors*; the others are *nonsecretors*. It is of interest to note that this characteristic bears a relationship to one of the newer blood factors. Secretors do not have the Lewis factor (Le$^a$), nonsecretors have this factor on their erythrocytes.

*M, N and P factors.* By injecting human red cells into rabbits, and carefully neutralizing or removing known antibodies from the rabbit antiserum thereby produced, Landsteiner and Levine were able to show the existence of a pair of antigens, M and N. With these two factors, cells may be classified as either M, N, or MN. These factors seem to be poor antigens, in that they do not stimulate the production of antibodies in human subjects. The occurrence of anti-M or anti-N in man is rare. A few years after the discovery of the M and N factors, Landsteiner and Levine reported yet another factor. Human red cells may be characterized by the presence or absence of this factor which was designated P, but it is of little clinical importance.

## THE RH FACTOR

Between 1937 and 1940 Landsteiner and Wiener, working with the serum of guinea pigs that had been injected with the red cells of a Rhesus monkey, were able to show that the serum thus produced agglutinated the red cells of a large proportion of blood samples that were tested. Subsequent work showed that a new human blood factor, called the Rh (from Rhesus) factor was responsible for these reactions. About 85 per cent of Caucasians were found to have this factor on their cells, i.e., they are Rh-positive. The remaining 15 per cent are Rh-negative. Later work demonstrated the existence of subgroups, which are discussed below.

In contrast to the $\alpha$- and $\beta$-isoagglutinins, which arise apparently without any antigenic stimulus that is definitely known, antibodies to the Rh factor arise only in consequence of the injection of an Rh antigen. In man, of course, it is only those who are Rh-negative who can develop anti-Rh antibodies. Rh-positive cells given to a person who is already Rh positive would be perfectly compatible, and no antibodies would be developed. There are two ways in which this isoimmunization might take place. Firstly, there may be, in consequence of an error in blood typing, a transfusion of Rh positive cells into an Rh-negative person. Ordinarily this would give no difficulty in the first transfusion, but in subsequent transfusions, after the antibodies had been built up by the recipient, a similar mistake might lead to complications. Secondly, there is a possibility of isoimmunization of the mother occurring during certain pregnancies and this gives rise to erythroblastosis fetalis.

ERYTHROBLASTOSIS FETALIS. In erythroblastosis fetalis the child may be stillborn or may be delivered suffering from many of the symptoms of a transfusion reaction. Frequently symptoms do not appear until a few days after birth and may be mild. It had been thought for many years that erythroblastosis might be a result of an antigen-antibody reaction, and shortly after the discovery of the Rh factor it was shown that reactions involving this antigenic factor and an antibody were indeed the cause of many of these cases and of many hitherto unexplained transfusion reactions.

It is now thought that the sequence of events leading up to erythroblastosis fetalis is much as follows. An Rh+ fetus is carried by an Rh− mother (and the fetus could only be Rh+ under these circumstances if the father were Rh+) and in some unknown manner Rh+ fetal cells or fragments of such cells enter the maternal circulation and thus, acting as a typical antigen, stimulate antibody production. Probably only extremely small quantities of cells are required for this sensitization. The antibodies now move across the placental barrier into the fetal circulation, where they react with the fetal Rh+ cells to cause the observed reactions. Ordinarily, the first Rh+ child does not cause a sufficient rise in maternal antibody level to affect that particular child, but it may so sensitize the mother that in subsequent pregnancies, if there is an Rh+ fetus, the antibody level developed may show an increase sufficient to injure the fetus. Several pregnancies may take place before a reaction develops. It should be noted that a transfusion, even years prior to a pregnancy, of Rh+ cells into an Rh− woman, may severely reduce her chances of having a healthy child.

For poorly understood reasons, the incidence of erythroblastosis fetalis in cases where the mother is Rh− and the child is Rh+ is considerably less than one would expect from the considerations just mentioned. The disease, obviously, is extremely rare where nearly all of the population is Rh+, i.e., in Orientals, Eskimos, American Indians, Negroes.

The treatment of erythroblastosis fetalis consists of slowly bleeding the affected infant, and at the same time replacing its blood with Rh− blood. The cells in this blood cannot be agglutinated by any antibodies which are not removed by the exchange transfusion, so no transfusion reaction can occur. During the next several weeks, the transfused cells will gradually be removed from the circulation, to be replaced by the infant's own Rh+ cells.

Attempts to obtain a "hapten" from Rh cells (i.e., a substance that will neutralize Rh antibodies without stimulating the production of antibodies) which could be transfused into the maternal circulation in order to reduce its titer, have not been successful.

### Antibody Types

It has been found that there are different types of antibodies in anti-Rh sera. Though they may all have the same specificity, they do not all agglutinate red cells under the same experimental circumstances. One type of antibody will cause agglutination of Rh+ cells when physiological saline is used as a diluent for the serum containing the antibodies. This type is sometimes called a complete antibody. Incomplete, or blocking antibodies, will cause agglutination of Rh+ cells if the serum is diluted in some medium containing a high concentration of protein (20 per cent bovine serum albumin is commonly employed). Not only will they fail to agglutinate cells if the diluting medium is saline, but they will inhibit the agglutinating ability of a preparation of a complete antibody. Wiener suggests that the complete antibody is divalent, with two active, specific combining sites, and so can act as a coupling to unite the red cells, whereas the blocking antibody is monovalent, i.e., it has only one combining site. This one active site can combine with the antigenic sites on the red cell and so prevent the action of the complete antibody. In the presence of a high concentration of protein, another reaction allows the monovalent antibodies to be linked together, and hence agglutination may occur.

Still another type of antibody may not give agglutination in either saline medium or in a protein rich medium. The addition of an anti-human globulin (Coomb's serum) will provide antibodies which link, in turn, the antibodies which coat the red cell and thus agglutination may be brought about. It should be noted that the anti-Rh antibodies act as antibodies to the Rh+ cells, but as an antigen in their reaction to the antiglobulin serum. Any or all of these types of antibodies may be the cause of a given case of erythroblastosis.

### Nomenclature

The existence of a multitude of related subgroups of the Rh factor means that the nomenclature is complex. Two different terminologies, whose origins depend on slightly different concepts of the nature of the Rh antigens are in general use, and this adds to the complexity. The reader is referred to the papers of Wiener and his coworkers for detailed discussion on the Rh nomenclature, and to the papers of Fisher and Race for discussion on the CDE nomenclature.

Wiener has classified the different Rh types according to their reactions with three different antisera. Table 5.4 shows these types and their reactions.

In recent years further subgroups have been discovered, and the so-called variants are detected by their reactions with particular antisera. A detailed discussion of them is beyond the scope of this book.

According to Fisher and Race, there are at least three types of antigens (and corresponding antibodies). These antigens are called C, D, E and their antibodies are anti-C, anti-D and anti-E. Factor C corresponds to Wiener's rh', factor D to $Rh_o$, factor E to rh''. The antigenic structure of a particular cell is indicated by writing capital letters for those factors which are present, and using lower case letters for those factors which are absent; thus CDe corresponds to Wiener's $Rh_1$ or $Rh'_o$. A true Rh− type would be shown as cde. It should be noted that the use of lower case letters implies not only the absence of one of the Rh factors, but also the presence of a so-called reciprocal factor, the Hr factor. These will be discussed below.

Variants are indicated by superscripts added to the symbol of the antigen to which they seem to be most closely related, thus $C^w$. There is evidence, too, that there is a fourth subgroup, F.

The subgroups are not of equal clinical importance. The strongest antigen seems to be the $Rh_o$, or D type. Most Rh+ cells are of the type $Rh_1$, or CDe. Typing sera are frequently anti-$Rh_1$, or anti-CD. It is important to note that an individual might have the rh'', or E, factor only, and so with such typing sera would appear to be an Rh− person, though he or she would be, strictly speaking, Rh+. Such people should only be transfused with Rh− blood, as transfusion with blood containing the $Rh_o$ (or D) factor might stimulate the formation of antibodies which could cause a severe transfusion reaction if a similar transfusion were made at a later date. On the other hand, such persons must be considered as Rh+, if they are to be donors. The presence of an antigen could stimulate the production of antibodies if this blood were transfused into a truly Rh− person. Rh− donors must be of the rh (cde) type.

### TABLE 5.4

| Cell Type | Antiserum | | | Cell Type | Antiserum | | |
|---|---|---|---|---|---|---|---|
| | $Rh_o$ | Rh′ | Rh″ | | $Rh_o$ | Rh′ | Rh″ |
| $Rh_0$ | + | − | − | rh | − | − | − |
| $Rh_1$ | + | + | − | rh′ | − | + | − |
| $Rh_2$ | + | − | + | rh″ | − | − | + |
| $Rh_z$ | + | + | + | $rh_y$ | − | − | − |

### Inheritance of the Rh Factors

According to Fisher and Race, the various Rh factors are inherited as 3 (or 4, if F is included) linked genes. Since each germ cell carries its own set of Rh characteristics, the diploid genetic structure of the organism will be described by using one set of characters for the structure derived from one parent, and another set for the structure derived from the other parent. Thus the phenotype CDe would be derived from several genotype combinations, as CDe/CDe, CDe/cde, Cde/cDe, CDe/Cde, CDe/cDe.

According to Wiener, the factors are inherited as multiple allelic genes, and a person of phenotype $Rh'_0$ or $Rh_1$ could have genotypes $Rh_1rh$, $Rh_1Rh_1$, $Rh_0Rh'$. The determination of the genetic structure of an individual requires the use of typing sera which will react with only one of the factors, as well as a study of the Rh types of siblings and immediate ancestors of the particular individual.

*Deletions.* In some very rare cases, the red cells may react neither with an anti-Rh serum of particular specificity nor with the antiserum directed against the reciprocal factor (see below). Race and his coworkers ascribe this to a chromosome deletion, and indicate such a phenotype thus: $-DE$. Types having only the D antigen, and lacking both the c and e factor, have been described, i.e., $-D-$. Wiener suggests that individuals with such cells are homozygous for a new gene $R^x_0$, and that they have the factor $Rh_0$, but lack factors rh' and hr', rh'' and hr'' and hr.

*Other blood types.* With the discovery of the Rh blood groups, a great deal of interest in this whole field was reawakened. Many new blood groups have been recognized and although these are usually of little clinical importance, they may play a part in certain medicolegal questions, in some rare cases of erythroblastosis, and in some rare transfusion accidents.

*Reciprocal groups.* In some cases, there seems to be a reciprocal relationship between two blood groups, i.e., the possession of a certain blood group implies the absence of another (reciprocal) group. An excellent example of two blood groups which bear such a relationship is found in the Rh family. The absence of a particular Rh factor implies the presence of a corresponding factor in the Hr family. If, for example, there is no rh' factor, then the hr' factor must be present or, according to Fisher and Race, the absence of C implies the presence of c. The absence of the rh''

(E) factor implies the presence of hr'' (e). Anti-hr' and anti-hr'' sera have been used to demonstrate the existence of such factors. One might expect that there would be an $Hr_0$ factor, as well as Hr factors corresponding to the Rh variants, but their existence has not yet been demonstrated. Wiener suggests that there is no necessity to postulate their existence.

A determination of the hr factors is of course necessary if it is to be determined whether a person is homozygous or heterozygous.

Other blood factors include the Kell and Cellano factors, which bear a reciprocal relationship, and the Duffy, Diego, Lewis, Lutheran and Kidd factors. Some "private" blood factors have a very high or very low incidence in the general population, and positive or negative reactions occur only in members of a particular family. Among such factors are the Levay, Graydon, Jobbins, Jay and Miltenburger.

*Nonspecific agglutination.* Erythrocytes may also be agglutinated by substances other than the specific antibodies that have been discussed. These irregular agglutinins are of common occurrence in human sera. The so-called autoagglutinins will react with practically all human bloods to cause agglutination. Autoagglutination is characterized by a marked temperature sensitivity, and only occurs in the cold. If the system is warmed, the autoagglutinins will no longer cause clumping of the cells. An apparently related type of antibody also causes agglutination only in the cold, but will not affect all human cells. These are the cold agglutinins. Bacterial action will also give rise to nonspecific agglutination, called panagglutination. This phenomenon is not seen in fresh blood, but if old or contaminated blood is used for testing, there is the possibility of obtaining a false positive test due to this process of panagglutination.

## Human Serum and Plasma

Many of the drawbacks inherent in the use of whole blood for transfusion are obviated by substituting human serum or plasma. These blood derivatives when pooled from a number of donors can be transfused indiscriminately without regard for the blood groups. Furthermore, liquid plasma or serum if collected under strictly sterile conditions can be stored under refrigeration for an indefinite period. Plasma kept in the frozen state is highly recommended by Strumia and McGraw as being safer than storage in liquid form. Plasma or serum dried *in vacuo* from the frozen state (or lyophilized) by the process of Flosdorf, Stokes and Mudd is the preparation *par excellence*, especially for use in the armed services. It can be stored without refrigeration, is easily transported and the dangers of bacterial contamination or of deterioration are at a minimum. But like whole blood it may transmit the virus of homologous serum jaundice. When required for use, distilled water, equal in volume to that which had been removed in the drying process, is added to the desiccated material.

### Solutions of Colloids

The limited availability of whole human blood or of its derivatives, plasma or serum, has inspired a search for a blood substitute which would resemble as closely as possible the physical properties of plasma. The requirements of an artificial transfusion material are several. (a) The molecules (or particles) of the substance must be of such a size that its solution will not leave the circulation too freely. (b) The solution must have an osmotic pressure and a viscosity approaching as closely as possible these properties of whole blood; such qualifications depend upon molecular size and shape. (c) It should be isotonic with the contents of the corpuscles. (d) It must, of course, be nontoxic and innocuous in every respect. (e) It should not hinder normal plasma protein production. In addition, the material should be readily available in large quantities, preferably cheap, capable of being sterilized by simple means, and of being quickly prepared for use. Provided a material is suitable for transfusion in the foregoing respects there appears to be no valid objection to the use of some fluid other than blood or its derivatives to fill the vessels after hemorrhage. The properties which render a fluid suitable for transfusion are physical rather than chemical. Serum or plasma apparently possesses no advantage by virtue of any biochemical characteristics which it possesses. Whole blood is superior to either of these in severe traumatic or hemorrhagic shock.

*Gum acacia* in a 6 per cent solution in saline was introduced by Sir William Bayliss as a transfusion fluid during the first World War and proved highly successful. The osmotic pressure and viscosity of this solution closely resemble those of plasma. The molecules of gum acacia aggregate into particles comparable in size to those of the plasma proteins and do not escape freely through the capillary membrane.

However, experience since the first World War has revealed some undesirable features of gum acacia. Gum acacia is a polysaccharide which the body cannot metabolize. It, like other foreign materials which cannot be disposed of in other ways, is taken up by the reticuloendothelial elements of the liver and elsewhere. In animals, swelling and vacuolization of the hepatic cells have been observed following the transfusion of this material. The liver may become greatly enlarged after repeated transfusions with gum acacia and sometimes shows areas of necrosis. The hepatic function of producing plasma protein is seriously depressed; the concentration of protein in the plasma is lowered following large transfusions of gum acacia and may remain below normal for a considerable time after this blood substitute has been administered.

*Isinglass* (collagen prepared from the swimbladders of certain species of fish, e.g., sturgeon, hake, etc.) has been advocated by Taylor and Waters, in a concentration of 6 per cent in physiological saline, as a blood substitute. Isinglass as now prepared is free from anaphylactic or pyrogenic action. It has been used clinically and found to be effective and quite safe. It has been shown both in patients and in animals to raise the blood pressure to normal after severe hemorrhage and to maintain it at this level for several hours. After its injection the blood shows progressive dilution indicating that not only is it retained within the circulation but exerts an osmotic effect which "draws" interstitial fluid into the vessels. It does not appear to have any depressing effect upon plasma protein production by the liver and has a technical advantage over animal gelatin in being perfectly fluid at room temperature. The molecular weight of isinglass, after autoclaving, is between 18,000 and 30,000.

*Animal gelatin*, which is closely similar to isinglass chemically, or *dextran*, a polysaccharide with a large molecule, have been used clinically with satisfactory results. Polyvinyl pyrollidone has also been used.

The *albumin* fraction of human serum as developed by Cohn, Janeway and their associates is, except for its cost, an ideal transfusion material when only a cell-free fluid is required. It may be given in concentrated solution or in the same concentration as in normal plasma. *Bovine plasma*, if it could be rendered quite safe yet still retain its other qualifications for a transfusion material, would solve the problem of a physiological and relatively cheap blood substitute for those emergencies in which it is not necessary to furnish red cells. The blood proteins of another species are, of course, intensely anaphylactogenic, and several attempts have been made to remove this property (*despeciation*) from bovine plasma or albumin. Masson has described a method involving the use of formaldehyde and heat to despeciate calf plasma. But such procedures which denature the proteins tend at the same time to reduce their osmotic pressure to a degree which greatly lessens their value for transfusion.

## Solutions of Crystalloids

The small molecules of salt or of glucose pass freely through the capillary wall. They exert a negligible osmotic effect; the injected fluid is therefore not retained in the circulation. For this reason such fluids though capable of raising the blood pressure temporarily are quite unable to maintain it for any considerable length of time. Indeed they may do serious harm, for the transfused fluid as it leaks into the tissues carries plasma protein with it. This is particularly likely to occur in the case of saline. Transudation of fluid into the tissue of the lung—pulmonary edema—may result. When, on the other hand, dehydration of the tissues and loss of blood *water*, as shown by the concentration of the plasma proteins, are prominent features, then the subcutaneous or intravenous injection of saline (with the addition of glucose) or water by mouth, would appear, from physiological principles, to be a logical procedure. In the dehydration resulting from chloride depletion (p. 24) sodium chloride is clearly indicated. A solution of this salt serves not only to supply fluid but to replenish the base the loss of which is such an important factor in the development of the dehydrated state. It is also of great value in correcting the hemoconcentration which results from extensive burns.

## REFERENCES

AMBERSON, W. R. AND ASSOCIATES. Science, 1933, **78**, 106; J. Cell. & Comp. Physiol., 1934, **5**, 359; Biol. Rev., 1937, **12**, 46.

BELK, W. P. AND BARNES, B. C. Am. J. M. Sc., 1941, **201**, 838.

COHN, E. J. AND ASSOCIATES. J. Am. Chem. Soc., 1940, **62**, 3396; Chem. Rev., 1941, **28**, 395.

DIAMOND, L. K. AND DENTON, R. L. J. Lab. & Clin. Med., 1945, **30**, 82.

VON DUNGERN, E. AND HERTZFELD, L. Ztschr. Immunitätsforsch., 1911, **8**, 526.

FISHER, R. A., RACE, R. R. AND ASSOCIATES.

Nature, 1944, **153**, 106; 1945, **155**, 543. Ann. Eugenics, 1946, **13**, 15.

FREIDENREIECH. Ztschr. Immunitätsforsch., 1931, **71**, I. (Quoted by Wiener in Blood groups and transfusion, Charles C Thomas, Springfield, 1943).

LANDSTEINER, K. AND LEVINE, P. J. Exper. Med., 1928, **47**, 731.

LANDSTEINER, K. AND WIENER, A. S. J. Exper. Med., 1941, **74**, 309; Proc. Soc. Exper. Biol. & Med., 1940, **43**, 223; J. Exper. Med., 1941, **74**, 309.

LEVINE, P. AND ASSOCIATES. J. A. M. A., 1941, **116**, 825. Ann. Int. Med., 1941, **14**, 1903; J. Pediat., 1943, **23**, 656; Ann. New York Acad. Sc., 1946, **46**, 939.

LEVINE, P. AND STETSON, R. J. A. M. A., 1939, **113**, 126.

PHILLIPS, R. A., VAN SLYKE AND ASSOCIATES. Bull. U. S. Army Med. Dept., 1943, **71**, 66.

RACE, R. R. AND ASSOCIATES. J. Hematol., 1948, **3**, 689; Nature, 1950, **166**, 520.

STRUMIA, M. M. AND McGRAW, J. J. Ann. Int. Med., 1941, **15**, 80.

TAYLOR, N. B. AND WATERS, E. T. Canad. Med. Assoc. J., 1941, **44**, 547.

WIENER, A. S. AND ASSOCIATES. Proc. Soc. Exper. Biol. & Med., 1946, **61**, 382.

WIENER, A. S. AND LANDSTEINER, K. Proc. Soc. Exper. Biol. & Med., 1943, **54**, 167.

WIENER, A. S. AND PETERS, H. R. Ann. Int. Med., 1940, **13**, 2306.

WITEBSKY, E. AND ASSOCIATES. J. A. M. A., 1941, **116**, 2654; article in Blood substitutes and blood transfusions, p. 327, Charles C Thomas, Springfield, 1942; Ann. New York Acad. Sc., 1946, **46**, 887.

YUILE, C. L. AND ASSOCIATES, Blood, 1949, **4**, 1232.

*Monographs and Reviews*

BOYD, W. C. Fundamentals of immunology. Interscience Publishers, Inc., New York.

LANDSTEINER, K. The specificity of serological reactions. Harvard University Press, 1946.

LEVINE, P. Ann. New York Acad. Sc., 1946, **46**, 939.

LEVINE, R. A brief review of the newer blood factors. Trans. New York Acad. Sc. 1951, **13**, 205.

Medical Research Council. War Memorandum No. 9, London, 1943; The Rh Blood Groups, Report No. 27.

MOLLISON, P. L. Blood Transfusion in clinical medicine, Blackwell, Oxford, England, 1951.

POTTER, E. L. Rh—Its relation to congenital hemolytic disease and to intragroup transfusion reactions. Year Book Publishers, Inc., Chicago, 1947.

WIENER, A. S. Blood groups and transfusion, 3rd ed., Charles C Thomas, Sprinfield, 1943; Ann. New York Acad. Sc., 1946, **46**, 969; An Rh glossary, Bull. Dade county Med. A., April, 1949; Rh-Hr blood types, Grune & Stratton, New York, 1954.

# 6

# HEMOGLOBIN

See also Regeneration of Blood, chapter 8.

Hemoglobin, the coloring matter of the erythrocytes, makes up about 95 per cent of the dry weight of the cell. The chief function of the red cell is to store this pigment and carry it around the circulation. About 10 grams of hemoglobin pass through the lungs per second. It takes up a comparatively large load of oxygen which it carries to the tissues. One hundred cubic centimeters of water at the temperature of the body and exposed to an oxygen pressure of 100 mm. Hg absorbs a third of a cubic centimeter of the gas. One hundred cubic centimeters of blood, on the other hand, at the same temperature and pressure will take up about 20.0 cc.—that is, 60 times more. The difference is due to the hemoglobin. The total amount of blood in the human body will hold approximately 1200 cc. of oxygen (200 cc. per liter of blood). This quantity of oxygen is used by the tissues in 5 minutes or so during rest and in a fraction of a minute during muscular exertion. In the absence of hemoglobin, the entire duty for the carriage of oxygen would have to be performed by the plasma, and in order that this should be able to absorb the necessary amount of gas, it would have to be increased at least 60 times in amount. As pointed out by Barcroft, the circulating fluid, instead of being about 6 liters or $\frac{1}{11}$ of the body weight, would then need to be over 350 liters, i.e., more than five times the bulk of the solid tissues.

Besides serving as a carrier of oxygen, hemoglobin plays an important role in regulating the acid-base balance of the blood (ch. 13), and in the carriage of carbon dioxide (ch. 29).

## The Chemical Constituents of Hemoglobin

Hemoglobin is a conjugated protein with a molecular weight of 68,000; it consists of an iron-containing pigment portion combined with a colorless protein of the histone class called *globin*. The pigments belong to a group of compounds called *porphyrins* which possess the property of being able to combine with metals. *Heme* is the name given to the compound of iron and the particular porphyrin which is found in hemoglobin. The iron-porphyrin-globin complex which constitutes hemoglobin can form a loose compound with oxygen, with the iron in the ferrous ($Fe^{++}$) state. Under certain conditions, it may form a more stable compound with oxygen, with the iron in the ferric ($Fe^{+++}$) state. A more detailed consideration of the hemoglobin structure follows.

PORPHYRINS are pigments which, either alone or as the basis of more complex compounds, are found throughout plant and animal life from the highest to the lowest forms. A porphyrin is the pigment basis of chlorophyll—the green coloring matter of plants. One is found as a brown pigment in the shells of many eggs, and also in the dark line running down the back of the earthworm. On the other hand, when conjugated with other substances porphyrins are the basis of the blood and tissue pigments of various animals.

The basic nucleus or framework upon which all *porphyrins* are built consists of four pyrrole rings

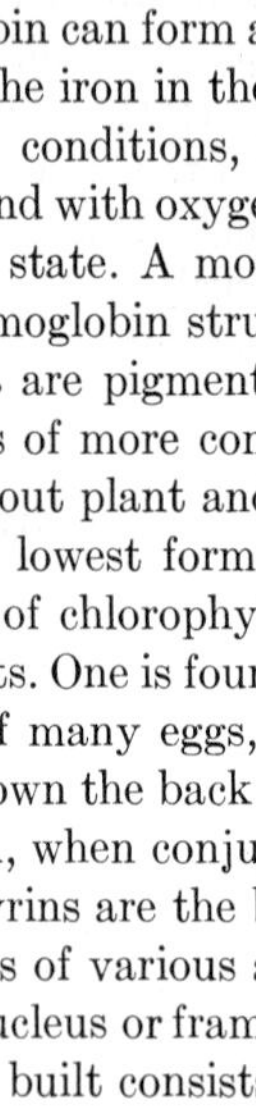

linked together in a larger ringlike structure by four methene couplings. This parent structure is called *porphin* and is shown below:

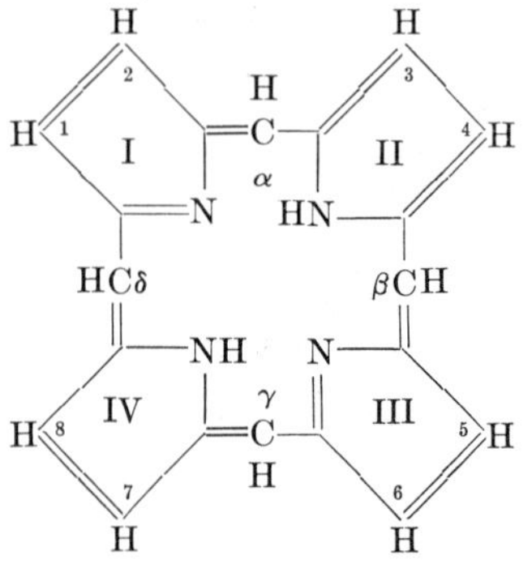

Porphin, $C_{20}H_{14}N_4$

By substitution of its eight hydrogen atoms by various groups—ethyl, methyl, vinyl or propionyl

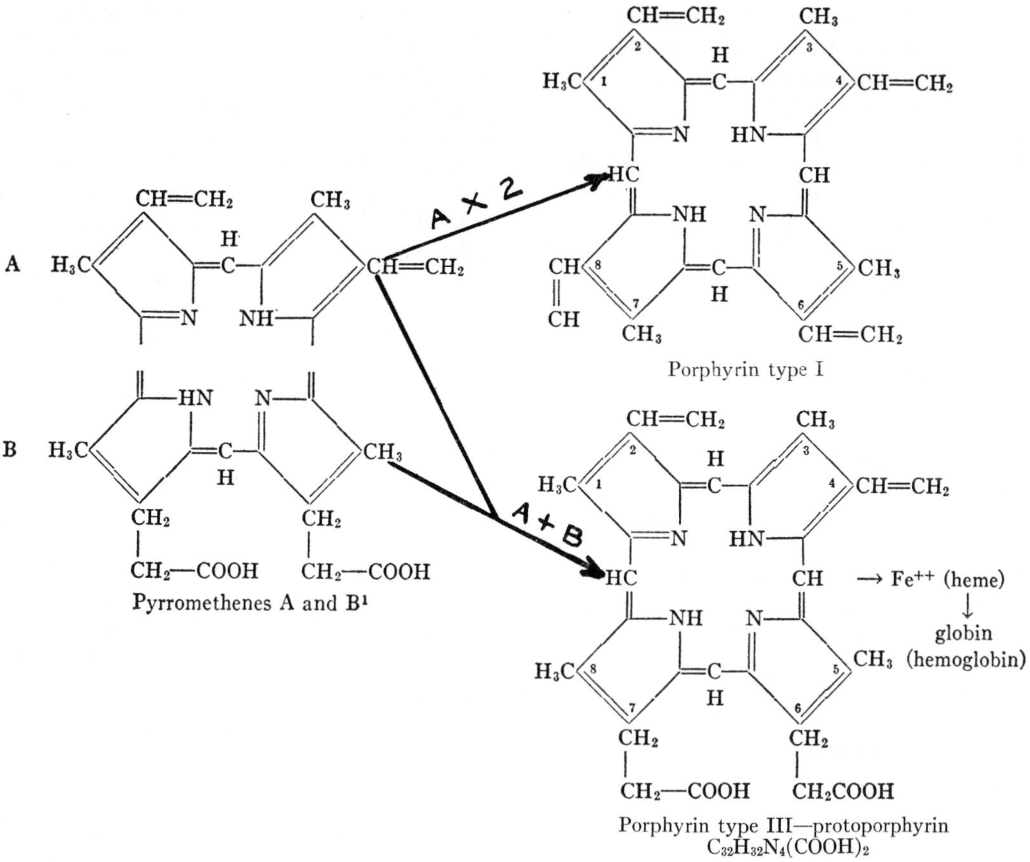

FIG. 6.1

—the several porphyrins in nature are produced. In the animal body it is believed that synthesis occurs in two stages. First, substances composed of two pyrrol groups only are formed and known as *pyrromethenes*. These are of two kinds. In one form, A, in figure 6.1, the four hydrogen atoms are substituted by two methyl ($CH_3$) and two vinyl ($-CH=CH_2$) groups. In the other form, B, the hydrogen atoms are substituted by two methyl and two propionyl ($-CH_2-CH_2-COOH$) groups. When two pyrromethenes of the first type unite, a type I porphyrin is produced. When an A and a B form unite, type III porphyrin is formed.[1] Much smaller quantities of the type I pigment are produced in the body than of type III, but in health a constant ratio exists between the two. Type III porphyrin is the pigment of hemoglobin, myoglobin and certain respiratory enzymes. It is called *protoporphyrin* and is isomeric with *oöporphyrin*, the pale brown pigment in the eggshell of the domestic hen (see fig. 6.1).

Protoporphyrins may be looked upon as pigment complexes in which the eight hydrogen atoms of the porphin nucleus are replaced by three of the groups mentioned above, namely by two vinyl, four methyl, and two propionyl. There are some 15 different isomeric protoporphyrins, the one present in hemoglobin being designated protoporphyrin No. 9. Its vinyl groups are at positions 2 and 4, its methyl groups at 1, 3, 5 and 8, and its propionyl groups at 6 and 7.

Small amounts of free protoporphyrin are present in the erythrocytes and larger amounts in reticulocytes. The presence of this pigment is probably responsible for the red fluorescence exhibited by the latter when viewed under ultraviolet light.

The two animal porphyrins (I and III) remain distinct chemical entities under all circumstances, being synthesized separately and never undergoing interconversion. The conception of a "dualism of the porphyrins" was first advanced by Hans Fischer and has been supported in more modern times by Dobriner, Watson and other workers in this field.

[1] A type II porphyrin might possibly be formed by the union of two B types of pyrromethenes, but such has not been found in nature.

In health, type I porphyrin and sometimes type III are excreted in minute amounts in the urine after being converted to *coproporphyrin* (p. 58). Coproporphyrin I, but not type III, is excreted through the bile. *Uroporphyrin* is not found in normal urine but is excreted in the urine in congenital porphyria.

*Metalloporphyrins.* Porphyrins are capable of forming compounds with various metals. A pigment found in the feathers of a certain South African bird (turaco), for example, and known as *turacin*, is a porphyrin combined with copper. Other metalloporphyrins have been prepared, namely, those of cobalt, nickel, silver, manganese, tin, zinc, etc.[2] Protoporphyrin combined with iron forms the metalloporphyrin of the blood pigment. For instance, if an Fe atom is attached to protoporphyrin we get the iron-porphyrin compound of hemoglobin. This is called *heme* ($C_{34}H_{32}N_4O_4Fe$). The red heme molecules give to hemoglobin its characteristic color. As we shall presently see, however, heme is not peculiar to hemoglobin but is a constituent of other respiratory substances.

The atom of iron, in the ferrous state, is believed to be attached to the porphyrin group in the manner represented below:

Reduced hemoglobin

Oxygenated hemoglobin (oxyhemoglobin)

In the hemoglobin molecule four heme molecules are attached to the globin molecule.

[2] In chlorophyll the porphyrin is combined with magnesium.

Heme is capable of combining with various proteins or nitrogenous substances, e.g., albumin, ammonia, pyridine, nicotine, etc. Such compounds are called *hemochromogens*. When globin is the protein with which heme is combined the resulting hemochromogen is that forming the basis of the blood pigment of vertebrate life. Hemoglobin is, therefore, an iron + porphyrin + globin compound.

HEMIN ($C_{34}H_{32}N_4O_4FeCl$) is the hydrochloride of heme and is prepared by heating oxyhemoglobin with glacial acetic acid and a minimal amount of sodium chloride. Upon cooling, reddish brown prismatic crystals of hemin separate out. The detection of these, which are frequently referred to as Teichmann's crystals (after their discoverer), is used as a test for blood in suspected stains. When hemin is treated with caustic soda oxidized heme is obtained. When the latter is treated with a weak acid the iron is split off and protoporphyrin remains. Hemin or blood itself when treated with concentrated mineral acids in the presence of oxygen yields hematoporphyrin (p. 58).

### The Distribution of Heme in Nature

Heme is almost universally distributed throughout the animal and vegetable kingdoms. Respiratory pigments with this porphyrin-iron compound as their common basis are found in the lowest forms of plant life as well as in the highest species of animals.

CYTOCHROME is a heme compound which is widely distributed in the tissues of plants and animals. It is present in certain aerobic bacteria, in yeast cells, in the onion, in worms, molluscs, crustacea, in the muscles of the bee's wing and in many other insects and their larvae. It is present in the muscles and other tissues of the large number of vertebrate species which have been examined. Cytochrome plays an important part in the oxidation system in the tissues. It undergoes alternate oxidation and reduction but unlike hemoglobin is not autoxidizable or only slightly so (due to component *b*, see below). In order to take up oxygen it requires the aid of tissue oxidase (indophenol oxidase); in order to undergo reduction it requires the presence of dehydrogenases. These activate the hydrogen of organic molecules in the tissue cells which become hydrogen donators. The cytochrome acts as a hydrogen acceptor. In this way cytochrome, it is suggested, serves as an intermediary in the transference of oxygen (liberated from hemoglobin) to the oxidizable materials in the tissue cells. It may also through component *b* serve for the direct transference of oxygen. In the presence of cyanides, carbon monoxide (in the dark) or sulfides which poison the oxidase, the oxidation of cytochrome is inhibited. On the other hand, anesthetics which depress the action of dehydrogenases prevent its reduction. In either case the link in the chain of oxygen usage by the cells is broken.

Cytochrome is a mixture of three hemochromogens; they are referred to by Keilin as a, b and c. Of these only b is autoxidizable. The heme components of the hemochromogens are not all the same, there being two varieties. One of these is identical with that in hemoglobin, the other resembles that in chlorocruorin (see below). The nitrogenous compounds with which the hemes are combined are unknown. Cytochrome is identified in living tissues by its characteristic absorption spectrum. The cytochrome of bees' wing muscle shows four absorption bands at 6046, 5665, 5502 and 5210 Å, respectively. Its oxidation and reduction can be followed in the living cell by means of the microspectroscope, the bands becoming distinct when reduction occurs but almost disappearing when the substance is oxidized.

Heme in the free state, that is, uncombined with a nitrogen compound, has been discovered in many substances such as wheat flour and oatmeal where its presence had never been suspected. The fact that heme is in one way or another of such universal occurrence has prompted Barcroft to remark, "mankind has for countless centuries been eating, all unknowingly, the outstanding constituent of his blood." It has been frequently suggested in the past that chlorophyll which also is constituted of pyrrol rings, was the primitive pigment and that animals probably derived the pyrrol grouping for the manufacture of the pigment of their bloods from this green coloring matter in their diet. It is now seen, however, that heme is a much more ancient pigment since it is found in the most elemental forms of plant life in which chlorophyll does not exist. It is pointed out, however, on page 71, that there is little evidence that either of these pigments in the diet serves as a basis for hemoglobin synthesis.

Hemoglobin itself is by no means so widely distributed as is heme and the heme compound cytochrome, for it is confined to the animal kingdom. It is found in the blood of all vertebrates and of several invertebrates, e.g., worms, a certain snail, in the larvae of some but not in the body fluids of any adult insect. The blood pigments of different vertebrate species vary in their proper-

ties, the hemoglobin of the frog, for example, possesses a spectrum and oxygen dissociation curve different from that of mammals. The variability is due to minor differences in the globins to which the heme is joined and not to different hemes, which are the same throughout the vertebrate phylum.

Though many different porphyrins exist, only one differing from protoporphyrin has been discovered in nature as forming part of a hemoglobinlike substance, i.e., one in which the nitrogenous fraction is probably a globin. A hemoglobinlike pigment, greenish in color, is found in certain worms and is called *chlorocruorin*. It contains this other porphyrin of unknown structure combined with iron. *Helicorubin* is a respiratory pigment found in the gut and liver of the snail. It contains the same heme as hemoglobin as shown by the fact that if its nonpigmented fraction is replaced by pyridine the pyridine-hemochromogen so formed shows a spectrum identical with that of the pyridine-hemochromogen derived from hemoglobin. Chlorocruorin, however, since its heme is different, when treated similarly shows a different spectrum. The nitrogenous part of helicorubin is unknown but presumably it is not globin.

*Hemocyanin* is a respiratory pigment which in certain crustacea and mollusks (king crab, octopus and snail) takes the place of hemoglobin. It is dissolved in the circulating fluid and not confined within cells. This substance contains copper instead of iron but the metal is not combined with a porphyrin as was believed at one time. This pigment is blue when oxidized and colorless when reduced.

## The Molecular Weight of Hemoglobin

The pigment proper (heme) constitutes about 4 per cent, and the globin about 96 per cent of the hemoglobin molecule. If hemoglobin contained only 1 atom of iron which has a molecular weight of 56, then since the percentage of the metal in hemoglobin is 0.334,[3] as determined by direct analyses, the minimum molecular weight of hemoglobin would be $(56/0.334) \times 100 = 16,800$ approximately.

The molecular weight of the hemoglobin molecule has been established by various physical

[3] This is Hüfner's figure, but other investigators have obtained lower, others higher values, namely from 0.305 to 0.338 per cent. The average of values obtained by Bernhart and Skeggs in a number of analyses of hemoglobin crystallized from the pooled blood of 20 human subjects was 0.340. Using this figure in the calculations, a minimal molecular weight of 16,400 and an oxygen capacity of 1.36 ml. per gram of hemoglobin are obtained.

methods to be 66,000 to 68,000. There are 4 sub-units, each containing one heme molecule, and hence there are four iron atoms in each hemoglobin molecule. Evidence suggests that the molecule is a cylinder with a height of 34 Å and a diameter of 57 Å. On the surface of one side of the cylinder there are two hemes, and two hemes are on the opposite side (not the ends) of the cylinder.

Hemoglobin constitutes about 34 per cent of the wet weight of the cell, and at this high concentration there is just sufficient space for the hemoglobin molecules to rotate freely about their three axes.

Human blood contains about 15 grams (14 to 16 grams) of hemoglobin per 100 cc. Since the proportion of iron in hemoglobin is 0.334 per cent, the quantity of the metal in 100 cc. of blood is about 50 mg. and in the total blood of the human body about 4 to 5 grams. The blood contains a small proportion of iron in addition to that combined with hemoglobin.

THE ESTIMATION OF HEMOGLOBIN IN BLOOD. Several methods are available for determining the hemoglobin concentration of blood. But whatever the method used, the fundamental information sought is the oxygen capacity of the blood. This may be found directly by means of the Van Slyke apparatus or the apparatus of Barcroft or Warburg. Or, since the hemoglobin molecule contains 0.334 per cent of iron, the hemoglobin in grams per 100 cc. can be calculated from an analysis of the blood for its iron content.[4] Thus, if the blood contains 50 mg. of iron per 100 cc., its hemoglobin concentration is $(50/0.334) \times 100 = 15$ grams (approx.) per 100 cc. and the oxygen capacity $(15 \times 1.34 =) 20$ cc. (approx.) per 100 cc.

The most convenient method for chemical use is one based upon matching a sample of diluted blood with one of a series of permanent color standards. The best known methods of this type are: the *Haldane-Gowers*, in which the hemoglobin is first converted to carboxyhemoglobin; the *Gowers*, in which the blood sample after dilution and full oxygenation is matched colorimetrically with a picrocarmine standard; and the *Sahli* method, which involves the conversion of the hemoglobin in the diluted sample to acid hematin.

*Myoglobin* or *muscle hemoglobin* (mol. wt. 16,700; 1 atom of iron) the pigment of muscle, resembles blood hemoglobin in its function. The protein component differs from that globin which

is found in hemoglobin. It acts as an oxygen reservoir within the muscle fiber which serves to tide the muscle over from one contraction to the next. It has a higher oxygen affinity than has blood hemoglobin and can combine with oxygen and dissociate from it with great rapidity (less than 1/100 second). Myoglobin starts to give up its oxygen at the instant that the muscle contracts. Its oxygen store is replenished during the resting state.

## The Combination of Hemoglobin with Gases

### OXYGEN (see also chapter 29)

Hemoglobin combines with oxygen by virtue of the iron which it contains. The attachment of the iron to the heme and to the protein molecule is very important in giving to the hemoglobin molecule its peculiar property of ready combination or dissociation with the oxygen molecule.

The iron in hemoglobin is in the ferrous (divalent) state. Heme, by itself, readily reacts with oxygen and the iron changes to the ferric (trivalent) state. The combination of the heme with globin however, brings about a great stabilization of the molecule so this increase in valence does not ordinarily take place, even though there may be a combination with oxygen.

The iron is in a hexacovalent state, with four of the bonds linking it with the planar porphyrin molecule. The resulting heme molecules (4 in number) are attached to the surface of the globin molecule by another of the covalent links of the iron. The nature of the group in the globin molecule to which the heme is attached is not yet settled, though Wyman, and Coryell and Pauling postulate that it is attached to the imidazole group of a histidine residue. The sixth covalent bond, which sticks out from the plane of the heme, is the point of attachment of the molecular oxygen. The details of the changes which take place in the various bonds upon oxygenation of the hemoglobin molecule are beyond the scope of this book, but it is interesting to note that the postulated linkage of iron with the imidazole group can be shown to provide an explanation for the "Bohr" effect, i.e., the greater acidity of hemoglobin with oxygenation.

Since each hemoglobin molecule contains four iron atoms, it can combine with four molecules of oxygen. The oxygenation of one of the four hemes enhances the oxygen-binding capacity of the now partly oxidized molecule, so that this molecule becomes fully oxygenated in preference to other

---

[4] The estimation of hemoglobin by iron analysis is claimed by King and his associates to be the most reliable method, though even this method is not without error, for a certain small proportion of the iron in blood is not in combination with functioning hemoglobin.

hemoglobin molecules. This interaction, i.e., the effect of the oxygenation of one heme upon the ease of oxygenation of the other hemes results in a peculiar sigmoid-shaped curve if the percentage of oxyhemoglobin formed from reduced hemoglobin is plotted against oxygen tension. If there were no interaction, such as in the case of the monomeric myoglobin, a similar plot would yield a curve in the form of a rectangular hyperbola.

The increased acidity of oxyhemoglobin (Bohr effect, above) means that the pH of arterial blood is almost the same as that of venous blood; the greater acidity of this oxyhemoglobin compensates for the increase in carbonic acid found in venous blood.

The capacity of the blood for absorbing oxygen is called the *oxygen capacity* and it is proportional to the hemoglobin concentration. The oxygen capacity of 1 gram of hemoglobin is 1.34 cc.; therefore, the oxygen capacity of 100 cc. of normal blood (15 grams hemoglobin) is 20 cc. (15 × 1.34).

### DERIVATIVES OF HEMOGLOBIN

Some of the variations of the hemoglobin molecule which may be obtained are described below.

The terms *reduced hemoglobin*, or *ferrohemoglobin*, are used for the molecule which has given up its oxygen.

*Oxygenated hemoglobin*, or *oxyhemoglobin*, is applied to the molecule which has oxygen molecules attached.

*Methemoglobin*, or *ferrihemoglobin* results when, by the action of oxidizing agents, the ferrous iron in the heme is changed to ferric iron. Normal blood contains about 0.1 per cent ferrihemoglobin, but in poisoning by drugs such as nitrites, chlorates, sulfanilamides etc., the percentage is increased. The larger quantity of the more darkly-colored ferrihemoglobin gives rise to a type of cyanosis to which the term "toxic" is applied. The discoloration of the skin becomes apparent when the ferrihemoglobin amounts to about 3 grams per 100 cc. of blood. Methylene blue, injected into the blood stream, causes the formation of ferrihemoglobin.

Space and label methemoglobin

A *hemochromogen* of hemoglobin results if the heme with the ferrous iron is combined with a denatured globin.

*Cathemoglobin* is a compound of heme containing ferric iron with denatured globin.

### HYDROGEN SULFIDE

Sulfhemoglobin is formed when ferrohemoglobin is treated with hydrogen sulfide under suitable conditions. It is a green compound, and is formed when blood or hemoglobin undergoes putrefaction.

Except perhaps in extreme cases of intestinal putrefaction hydrogen sulfide is not absorbed in appreciable amounts. But it appears that certain drugs, notably acetanilid and phenacetin (drugs employed for the relief of headache), sensitize hemoglobin so that it combines more readily with hydrogen sulfide. Small quantities of the gas absorbed from the alimentary canal may then cause sulfhemoglobin to reach a relatively high concentration in the circulation and give a bluish or mauve tint to the skin. This so-called *enterogenous cyanosis* occurs when the abnormal compound amounts to from 3 to 5 grams per 100 cc. of blood. The presence in the blood of sulfhemoglobin or of methemoglobin is detected by spectroscopic examination (Table 6.1).

### CARBON DIOXIDE

Carbhemoglobin is formed from the union of carbon dioxide and hemoglobin. Apparently a carbamino compound is formed. Estimates of the amount of carbon dioxide which is carried in this way vary from 10 to 30 per cent of the total.

### TABLE 6.1

*Wave lengths (λ) at the points of maximum intensity of absorption bands of hemoglobin and its derivatives as well as some of the other heme compounds*

| Compound | Number of Bands | Situation of Absorption Bands Wave Lengths in Angstrom Units | | | |
|---|---|---|---|---|---|
| Oxyhemoglobin...... | 2 | 5769 | 5448 | — | — |
| Reduced hemoglobin. | 1 | 5650 | — | — | — |
| Carboxyhemoglobin.. | 2 | 5709 | 5350 | — | — |
| Methemoglobin...... | 4 | 6300 | 5780 | 5400 | 5000 |
| Sulfhemoglobin...... | 3 | 6180 | 5780 | 5400 | — |
| Hemochromogen....{ | 2 | 5585 | 5275 | — | — |
| | 2 | 5580 | 5270 | — | — |
| Reduced heme....... | 2 | 6070 | 5820 | — | — |
| Cytochrome......... | 4 | 6046 | 5665 | 5502 | 5210 |
| Protoporphyrin (in acid).............. | 2 | 6000 | 5540 | — | — |
| Urobilin........... | 1 | 4900 | — | — | — |

### Carbon Monoxide

Carbonmonoxyhemoglobin results from the union of carbon monoxide and hemoglobin. The gas unites with hemoglobin in the same proportion as does oxygen. It competes successfully with the latter for hemoglobin and displaces it volume for volume to form carbonmonoxyhemoglobin. Unlike oxygen, however, it forms with hemoglobin a stable compound which can be disrupted only with the greatest difficulty. The much greater avidity (between 200 and 250 times) which hemoglobin shows for CO renders the gas so highly dangerous when inhaled in any considerable quantity (see p. 523). *Nitric oxide* gas also has a strong affinity for hemoglobin and forms a stable compound with it. The fumes given off by high explosives during their combustion contain large amounts of nitric oxide and the commonest way in which this poisoning occurs is through persons entering a closed space after an explosion, before the gas has cleared away.

### Types of Hemoglobins

There are small but significant variations in the amino acid composition of hemoglobins of different species. Further, there are different types of human hemoglobins. The various hemoglobins show different rates of denaturation, different electrophoretic mobilities, etc., in addition to those differences just mentioned.

The hemoglobins of adult and of fetal humans have been designated hemoglobin A and hemoglobin F, respectively. Several other abnormal varieties have been found in recent years. In all of the cases studied so far, the differences are ascribable to inherited alterations in the globin portion. The heme portion remains unchanged.

### Pigments Derived from Animal Porphyrins

*Hematoporphyrin*, $C_{32}H_{36}O_2N_4(COOH)_2$, is an artificial derivative obtained by the action of strong mineral acids upon hemoglobin or upon hemin. It is closely related to protoporphyrin—the natural porphyrin of hemoglobin—but contains two more molecules of water in its vinyl groups.

*Coproporphyrins* and *uroporphyrins*. Coproporphyrins I and III can be obtained from the corresponding porphyrins (p. 53) by the replacement of two vinyl groups by propionyl groups, or by decarboxylation of *uroporphyrin*. Uroporphyrins I and III are formed by carboxylation of the methyl groups of the corresponding coproporphyrins. Coproporphyrin I is present in small amounts in normal urine and in larger amounts in the feces. Relatively enormous amounts of both types of

coproporphyrin and of uroporphyrin are found in the urine and feces in conditions of disordered porphyrin metabolism (see below). Coproporphyrin (chiefly type III) is present normally in the bone marrow and the erythrocytes: it may be a precursor of protoporphyrin and a step in hemo-

Coproporphyrin I, $C_{34}H_{36}O_4N_4(COOH)$

Uroporphyrin I

globin synthesis (ch. 8). Turacin mentioned on p. 54 is the copper salt of uroporphyrin III. Porphyrins, especially hematoporphyrin, uroporphyrin I and coproporphyrin I have the curious property, when injected into the blood stream or when produced in disease, of sensitizing the skin to sunlight. Of the naturally occurring porphyrins the light-sensitizing action is most pronounced with uroporphyrin I.

By the action of mild reducing agents the vinyl groups of protoporphyrin are replaced by ethyl groups to form *mesoporphyrin*.

*Bilirubin*, $C_{33}H_{36}N_4O_6$, is an iron-free and globin-free derivative of hemoglobin. The ring struc-

*Table of hemoglobin derivatives*

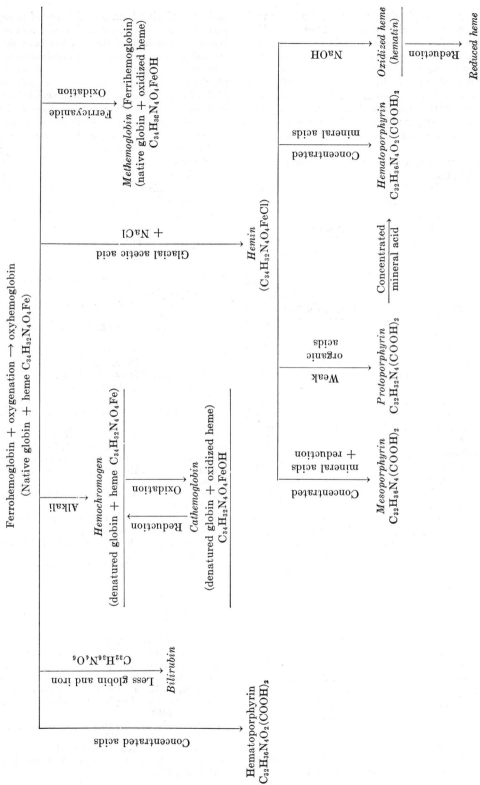

ture of the porphyrin is broken at the alpha position, a straight chain compound resulting. This occurs *before* the iron and globin are split off so that no free protoporphyrin is produced normally in the circulation. Bilirubin is converted by reduction in the intestine to stercobilinogen, also called urobilinogen (p. 642). Urobilin is formed by the oxidation of stercobilinogen, and is present in very small quantities in normal urine, but is not the pigment responsible for the color of urine.

*Absorption spectra.* The various heme pigments and the compounds of hemoglobin when placed in the path of a beam of white light absorb waves of certain lengths but transmit the rest. That is, each possesses a characteristic absorption spectrum and it is by means of spectroscopy that they may be most readily detected. The different hemochromogens, reduced hemoglobin and oxyhemoglobin, CO and NO hemoglobins, hematoporphyrin, coproporphyrin, cytochrome, urobilin, etc. have all their specific absorption bands. See table 6.1.

*Porphyria.* Disorders of porphyrin metabolism in which abnormal porphyrins or large quantities of physiological porphyrins are formed and excreted are called porphyria. There are three type of this disease, which have been termed *congenital*, *acute* and *chronic*. Actually, all three are congenital and familial.

*Congenital porphyria* is characterized by light sensitivity, which may result in blistering and, not uncommonly, necrosis of the skin upon exposure to sunlight, and the excretion of large quantities of coproporphyrin and uroporphyrin, type I, and sometimes small quantities of protoporphyrin. The normal ratio of type I and type III porphyrins is disturbed, the former type being produced in excessive amounts. The urine is stained a port wine color and the pigment is deposited in teeth, bones and skin. Liver extract and ascorbic acid seem to exert a favorable influence upon the disease. In *acute porphyria*, large amounts of porphyrin type III (protoporphyrin) are excreted. Light sensitivity does not occur, but there are abdominal, nervous or mental symptoms, e.g., severe cramps and vomiting, progressive paralysis often of an ascending type, and various forms of psychosis. In the *chronic* form of the disease, coproporphyrin type III and small amounts of coproporphyrin type I are excreted in the urine and feces. There is mild light sensitivity.

*Porphyrinuria.* An increased excretion of porphyrins in the urine in other conditions than the porphyrias is termed porphyrinuria. Increased excretion occurs in various *hepatic diseases*, type I and to a less extent type III being found in the urine and especially in the feces. Type I coproporphyrin is present in excess in the excreta of patients suffering from several types of anemia—*pernicious anemia, hemolytic jaundice* and in *leukemia*. In the first of these it has been demonstrated in the megaloblasts, erythroblasts and reticulocytes. Increased excretion of coproporphyrin type III occurs in *aplastic anemia, Hodgkin's disease, poliomyelitis, chronic alcoholism* and *lead poisoning*. In any condition associated with stimulation of the hemopoietic system prophyrin production is increased, and contrary to what might be expected it is type I rather than type III porphyrins which are produced and excreted in excess. The light sensitivity of *pellagra* may probably be explained by the excessive amounts of coproporphyrin (chiefly type I) which are formed and excreted in this disease, but it is not unlikely that the porphyrinuria is merely secondary to hepatic involvement.

## REFERENCES

Adair, G. S. Proc. Roy. Soc., London, ser. A, 1925, **108**, 627.

Anson, M. L. and Mirsky, A. E. J. Physiol., 1925, **60**, 50.

Bernhart, F. W. and Skeggs, L. J. Biol. Chem., 1943, **147**, 19.

Dobriner, K. and associates. J. Biol. Chem., 1936, **114**, xxvi. Proc. Soc. Exper. Biol. & Med., 1937, **36**, 752, 755; Physiol. Rev., 1940, **20**, 416.

Fischer, Hans, Ztschr. Physiol. Chem., 1915, **95**, 34; **96**, 148; 1916, **97**, 109.

Gowers, W. R. Tr. Clin. Soc., London, 1879, xxi, 64.

Granick, S. Blood, **1**, 1949, 4, 404.

Haldane, J. J. Physiol., 1900–01, **25**, 497.

Hüfner, G. Arch. Anat. Physiol., 1894, p. 130.

Keilin, D. Proc. Roy. Soc., London, ser. B, 1926, **100**, 129.

King, E. J. and associates. Lancet, 1947, **2**, 789; 1948, 1, 282, 478; **2**, 563.

Meulengracht, E. and associates. Acta med. scandinav., 1938, **96**, 462.

Northrop, J. H. and Anson, M. L. J. Gen. Physiol., 1929, **12**, 543.

Sahli, H. Klinische Untersuchungsmethoden, Leipzig and Vienna, 5th ed., 1909, 845.

*Monographs and Reviews*

Anson, M. L. and Mirsky, A. E. Physiol. Rev., 1930, **10**, 506.

Barcroft, J. Physiol. Rev., 1924, 4, 329; 1925, **5**, 596. The respiratory function of the blood. Part II, Haemoglobin. Cambridge University Press, London, 1928.

Drabkin, D. L. Physiol. Rev. 1951, **31**, 345.

Gray, C. L., The bile pigments. Methuen and Co., London, 1953.

Mason, V. R., Courville, C. and Ziskind, E. Medicine, 1933, **12**, 355.

Watson, C. J., Lancet, **1**, 539, 1951.

Watson, C. J. and Larson, E. A. Physiol. Rev., 1947, **27**, 478.

# 7

# HEMOLYSIS AND SUSPENSION STABILITY OF THE BLOOD

## Hemolysis or the Laking of Blood

Under normal circumstances the plasma contains no appreciable quantity of hemoglobin. If normal blood is centrifuged the corpuscles are driven to the bottom of the tube whereas the supernatant plasma is clear but faintly straw-colored. Under certain conditions, however, changes may occur in the red cell which will allow the hemoglobin to escape into the surrounding fluid, which then becomes discolored. This is called *hemolysis* or *laking*, and may be carried out in a test tube by means of various agencies both physical and chemical. Certain biological substances such as the toxins of bacteria and snake venoms are intensely hemolytic. On the other hand, substances belonging to the class of immune substances or antibodies, and known specifically as *hemolysins*, are formed in the blood. These have the power to hemolyze foreign red cells. After the action of certain hemolytic agents the dim colorless outline of the red cells—shadow cells or "ghosts"—may be seen; they represent the incompletely destroyed framework or stroma[1] (see frontispiece). Some of the means by which hemolysis may be induced will now be considered in greater detail.

### Hypotonic solutions

The membranes of plant and animal cells are semipermeable (p. 26). They allow the passage into the cell of water and various substances in solution, but offer a barrier to the entrance or egress of others. The red cell is no exception; it contains substances which cannot pass out, and is surrounded by a fluid (plasma) containing materials which cannot pass in. We have here then a minute and almost perfect osmometer

[1] When hemolysis is induced by certain reagents, e.g., linoleic acid, but the cell structure remains intact, the addition of electrolytes causes the reappearance of hemoglobin in the cells ("reversed hemolysis"). This phenomenon is due probably to shrinkage of the cells and the concentration of a residue of unliberated pigment and not to the return of hemoglobin to the cell.

(p. 26), and indeed much of our knowledge of osmotic phenomena has been gained from the study of the behavior of plant and animal cells when placed in solutions of different concentrations. In normal blood the plasma and the corpuscles are in osmotic equilibrium, i.e., the fluids separated by the corpuscular membrane are isotonic. If, however, the dissolved substances in the plasma are diluted by the addition of distilled water, a flow of water into the corpuscles occurs. An osmotic pressure is developed within it which the cell membrane is unable to withstand. The cell swells and becomes globular, the membrane stretches and the hemoglobin is liberated.

The process is in reality rather more complicated than this. It is probable that the hemoglobin is not contained within the red cell merely as in a bladder, or even in a number of smaller compartments, but is closely bound in some way to the cell structure. One reason for this belief is that purely mechanical agencies will not liberate the pigment. The cell may be torn into the finest shreds, yet each minute particle still retains its hold upon the hemoglobin. The pigment, however, is soon released when the surrounding fluid is made hypotonic. This suggests that the cell structure consists of semipermeable partitions of almost infinite fineness.

The normal red cell offers a certain resistance to the disintegrating effect of hypotonic solutions. A slight lowering of the osmotic pressure of the surrounding fluid will not produce hemolysis. The normal percentage of salts in human plasma is approximately 0.94. Normal cells may be placed in a 0.6 per cent saline solution without being hemolyzed. The cell increases in volume, but the hemoglobin does not escape. The first trace of hemolysis appears when the saline concentration is about 0.42 per cent and the cell volume increased to about 145 per cent. At 0.35 per cent the cells are fully "laked," i.e., hemolysis is complete; the cell volume is around 165 per cent of normal just before this occurs. The resistance which erythrocytes offer to the hemolytic action of hypotonic solutions is used in this way as an index of the fragility of the red cells.

In performing a fragility test a series of tubes is set up containing solutions of NaCl graded in strength from 0.9 to 0.20 per cent at intervals of 0.05 per cent above and below the range at which hemolysis is expected, and at intervals of 0.025 within that range. A sample of blood is introduced into the saline in each tube, and the one in which hemolysis commences and the one in which the process is complete are noted. A *mechanical fragility test* is sometimes employed, a sample of blood being placed in a flask with glass beads and rapidly rotated. The liberated hemoglobin is then measured. The mechanical fragility is increased in acholuric jaundice, certain other hemolytic anemias and in sickle cell anemia. The degree of hemolysis may be determined by centrifuging the diluted blood sample and estimating colorimetrically the quantity of hemoglobin in the supernatant fluid.

In pernicious anemia the red cells have been found to be actually less fragile than normal whereas in other conditions, e.g., some forms of purpura (p. 118) and acholuric jaundice (ch. 9), their fragility is increased.

Cells that show reduced resistance to hypotonic saline may show a normal resistance to other hemolytic agents, e.g., lysolecithin (p. 63) and *vice versa*. Erythrocytes of spherical form, such as those characteristic of acholuric jaundice, show a lowered osmotic resistance mainly because the cells cannot increase their volume by as great an increment as can normal cells without injury to the cell structure (see p. 10). The resistance to hemolysis by lysolecithin on the other hand is not influenced by the shape of the cells, the hemolytic process being chemical in nature.

The permeability of the membrane of the red cell is quite different from that of the capillary membrane which, as we have seen (ch. 3), allows the passage of all crystalloid substances and to some extent of plasma protein, and is also freely permeable to hemoglobin. The membrane of human erythrocytes, on the other hand, is impermeable under physiological conditions to hemoglobin, the plasma proteins, and to $Ca^{++}$, $K^+$, $Mg^{++}$ and organic phosphate ions, but permits the passage of water, $H^+$, $NH_4^+$, and of $Cl^-$, $HCO_3^-$ and $PO^{\equiv}$. Potassium escapes freely from the cells under conditions which injure the cell membrane, the potassium loss is closely related to the escape of hemoglobin, i.e., to hemolysis. The human red cell membrane is not absolutely impermeable to the sodium ion for even under physiological condi-

tions and therefore in the absence of hemolysis minute amounts may pass from the plasma into the erythrocytes.[2] Since the red cell is impermeable to potassium whereas sodium can cross the membrane, the selective permeability of the latter cannot be explained simply upon the theory that the cell membrane is a sievelike structure whose "pores" are of such a size as to allow the smaller ions, but not the larger ones, to pass. The lipid soluble theory is also unsatisfactory, for the inorganic anions are lipid insoluble. The cell membrane is freely permeable to amino acids, urea and uric acid, so these substances under ordinary circumstances do not enter into the osmotic relationships between cells and plasma. Osmotic changes occur, however, when $CO_2$ enters the blood and diffuses into the cell (see p. 462).

The exchange of inorganic phosphate across the cell membrane is associated with the enzymatic synthesis and breakdown of organic phosphate esters within the erythrocyte. In the former process inorganic phosphate passes from the serum into the cell and in the reverse direction when organic phosphate compounds are broken down.

### Chemical Substances

*Ether, chloroform, benzene and alcohol* act by dissolving the lipid constituents of the envelope and stroma of the cell. Other substances, e.g., *bile salts, acids and alkalis* and *saponin* cause hemolysis, but the manner in which they act is not altogether clear. Bile salts probably act by combining with the protein constituents, and saponin with the cholesterol. As a result of the chemical changes induced by either of these substances, destruction of the cell stroma—*stromatolysis*—occurs. Acids probably act by penetrating the cell and increasing the osmotic concentration within. Swelling and liberation of the hemoglobin occurs in a manner analogous to that of hypotonic solutions. The stroma is not as a rule destroyed. Alkalis, particularly ammonia, are powerfully hemolytic, as is also ammonium chloride. The $NH_3$ enters the cell and through the increase in osmotic pressure causes swelling and liberation of the hemoglobin. Stromatolysis accompanies hemolysis by alkali.

*Certain chemical poisons* such as carbolic acid, nitrobenzene, pyrogallol, ricin, arsenical preparations used in the treatment of syphilis, and many other substances are capable of causing red cell destruction.

[2] The results of various investigators in the past have differed rather widely with respect to the permeability of the red cell to the sodium and potassium ions, but the experiments of Kurnick who employed radioactive isotopes of Na and K give strong support to the statement made here.

## Substances of Bacterial Origin or Formed in the Animal Body

1. SPECIFIC HEMOLYSINS. If blood is injected into the veins of an animal of another species, or as already mentioned (ch. 5) into an individual of the same species but whose blood group is incompatible with the blood group to which the injected blood belongs, agglutination of the red cells of the donor occurs, and hemolysis follows as a secondary effect. But if a series of injections of erythrocytes is made over a period of days into the blood of another species the serum of the latter develops a substance which promptly destroys the foreign cells through a *primary* hemolytic effect quite independent of agglutination. This hemolytic reaction, which was first demonstrated by Bordet, is specific, that is to say, it is only the particular species of erythrocyte to which the animal has been sensitized by previous injections that is destroyed by the hemolytic substance. The latter on this account is known as a *specific hemolysin*. It belongs to the class of immune substances or antibodies. Bodies of similar nature cause the destruction of other foreign cells and are known as cytolysins and bacteriolysins. All are part of a general protective mechanism which the body is able to build up against the invasion of foreign cells. When referring to these and other immune reactions the substance which upon entering the body causes their development is referred to as the *antigen* (i.e., the foreign red cells in the case of hemolysins). The antibody itself (e.g., the hemolysin) is heat stable and is spoken of as the *amboceptor*. The latter (which is specific) requires for its action another body which is nonspecific, is present in all sera and is destroyed by heat. It is known as the *complement*. Three factors (antigen, amboceptor and complement) are therefore necessary for the hemolytic or bacteriolytic reaction. After the action of the hemolytic or bacteriolytic amboceptor has been annulled through destruction of the complement by heat, the reaction may be restored by the addition of any serum (i.e., by supplying fresh complement).

When serum which has developed a bacterial antibody is incubated with an emulsion of the particular bacteria which has served as antigen, a reaction occurs which "fixes" or binds the complement. The phenomenon is spoken of as *complement fixation*. These facts were applied by Wassermann to the diagnosis of syphilis, and by subsequent workers as a test for other diseases, e.g., tuberculosis. For example, the previously heated serum of a subject suspected to be suffering from syphilis is incubated with (a) an emulsion of syphilitic liver[3] tubercle or typhoid bacilli respectively (the antigen) together with (b) complement furnished by normal guinea pig's serum. If the suspected serum contains a specific antibody (amboceptor) for the antigen employed, the former will bind the complement to the latter, i.e., fixation of complement will occur. The foregoing is an account of a bacteriolytic system. An hemolytic system is employed to render the reaction visible. Washed sheep's corpuscles are added to the former system, together with the previously heated serum of a rabbit which has been sensitized to the latter cells by repeated injections. This serum supplies the hemolytic amboceptor but its complement has been destroyed. If the test is positive no hemolysis of the corpuscles occurs, since the complement (nonspecific) of the patient's serum has been already fixed by the bacteriolytic amboceptor and the hemolysin of the rabbit serum is therefore unable to exert its usual effect.

2. TOXIC SUBSTANCES OF BACTERIAL OR PARASITIC ORIGIN. The toxins of bacteria responsible for many diseases, e.g. streptococcus, staphylococcus, tetanus bacillus and the organism of scarlet fever may cause a destruction of red cells; it may also occur in extensive burns. The more virulent types of other infectious fevers, e.g., smallpox, diphtheria, are also sometimes accompanied by intense hemolysis. When the hemolysis is of moderate degree but occurs over longer periods the hemoglobin is converted into bile pigment. This, if formed in amounts greater than can be disposed of by the liver, undergoes partial retention in the plasma, which together with the solid tissues, especially of the skin and mucous membranes, becomes stained a yellowish tint—hemolytic jaundice (ch. 5). In hemolytic states of long standing an iron-containing derivative of hemoglobin termed *hemosiderin* is frequently deposited in large amounts in the tissues, particularly of the liver and spleen (p. 79).

3. THE VENOMS OF CERTAIN POISONOUS SNAKES, e.g., the cobra, and the poisons of various stinging insects and spiders cause a destruction of the red cells to a greater or less degree. Snake venom (cobra) has been shown to act indirectly. It contains a principle which has power to remove unsaturated fatty acids from the lecithin molecule. The resulting product which is called *lysolecithin*, is intensely hemolytic. Since lecithin is present both in erythrocytes and plasma and indeed in all cells, the entrance of snake venom into the body causes the production of this intensely hemolytic substance. Kephalin is acted upon by snake venom in a like manner with the production of a lysokephalin which has a similar hemolytic action.

4. HEMOLYSINS FROM NORMAL TISSUES. A nonspecific hemolysin has been extracted by simple means from healthy tissues and identified as cisvaccinic acid; it probably exists in the free state in the tissues. Other nonspecific hemolysins have

---

[3] As a matter of fact syphilitic liver has been found to be unnecessary, since lecithin and other materials for some unexplained reason will serve as antigens.

been isolated from various tissues after incubation at 37° and extraction with alcohol. These are thought to be present but bound to an inhibitory substance, and may be liberated in active form by disease or injury.

### Hemoglobinuria

When the hemolysis reaches such a degree that the hemoglobin cannot be converted into bilirubin as rapidly as it is liberated, as in severe malaria (blackwater fever) *hemoglobinuria* occurs, that is, the pigment is passed in the urine, which is usually turned port wine color or a dark brown or even black, due to the action of the urinary acid in converting the pigment into acid hematin and methemoglobin. The concentration of hemoglobin must, as a rule, reach a level of about 0.13 gram per 100 cc. of blood before it appears in the urine. It should be remembered that hemoglobin once it has escaped from the erythrocytes is functionless. Not only is it unable to be retained within the capillaries on account of the relatively small size of its molecule but the environment of the plasma is unsuitable for its action.

The hemolysis in *blackwater fever* is not due to the destruction of erythrocytes by the malarial parasite, nor does the parasite affect the hemopoietic tissue in such a way that it produces cells which are unduly fragile. The cells are apparently not defective, but the work of Macgraith and his associates may provide an explanation of the high degree of hemolysis in this disease. They found that normal human tissues contain a hemolysin which is inhibited in its action by normal serum but not by the serum of a patient suffering from blackwater fever. It is suggested, therefore, that there is no special hemolytic agent in the blood in blackwater fever but rather an absence of a normal inhibitory substance.

*Paroxysmal (cold) hemoglobinuria.* This form of hemoglobinuria occurs most usually upon exposure to cold. There may be fever, headache, abdominal pain, vomiting and transient jaundice. It is sometimes associated with Raynaud's phenomenon, in which condition spasmodic constrictions of the small vessels of the peripheral parts of the body occur, particularly after exposure to cold. The occasional association of the two conditions has suggested to some that they have a common cause, but direct evidence for this is lacking. It is an interesting observation that the blood of a subject of paroxysmal hemoglobinuria if cooled (to 5°C.) outside the body and subsequently warmed undergoes hemolysis (Donath phenomenon). There is apparently no defect, however, of the subject's corpuscles; they seem to be no less resistant than normal to hypotonic saline; the serum, on the other hand, has the power to hemolyze the cells of a normal person. The great majority of subjects are syphilitic. The hemoglobin, it seems, is liberated from the erythrocytes by the action of an endogenous hemolysin which in the presence of complement becomes fixed to the red cells when the blood is chilled (cold phase). The presence of some thermolabile component of complement is required when the blood is again brought to ordinary body temperature (warm phase) to bring about hemolysis (see Siebens and associates). The phenomenon is quite distinct from cold auto-agglutination (p. 49).

*March hemoglobinuria.* Hemolysis may occur and hemoglobin appear in the urine even in healthy persons after strenuous muscular effort. In certain persons this tendency is exaggerated and hemoglobinuria may follow relatively mild muscular exercise. It is seen not infrequently in soldiers after long marches. The free pigment in the blood and urine of such cases is oxyhemoglobin, not myoglobin as might be expected. The fragility of the red cells is not increased and neither hemolysins nor autoagglutinins which might account for the hemolysis have been discovered.

In the third type of paroxysmal hemoglobinuria —the *nocturnal hemoglobinuria of Marchiafava*— hemoglobin or hemosiderin (p. 79) is passed almost continuously in the urine, but in greatest amounts at night. It is accompanied by a severe hemolytic anemia. The cause of the hemolysis is believed to be a peculiar susceptibility of the red cells to acid metabolites, their greater destruction at night being attributed to the accumulation of carbon dioxide during sleep. The abnormal cells are hemolysed when incubated in serum made slightly acid (Ham), or in any normal serum, but normal cells are not destroyed by the patient's serum. The fault in the patient's cells is thought to be some abnormality of the stroma protein.

### The Suspension Stability of the Blood Erythrocyte Sedimentation Rate (E.S.R.)

The blood is a suspension of cells in a viscous fluid, the plasma. It is only the constant movement of the fluid that keeps the cells evenly distributed throughout. When the circulation comes to rest the cells at once commence to sink. Under ordinary circumstances the sedimentation of the cells in a sample of blood can progress to only a negligible extent, for it is soon circumvented by the clotting process which fixes them in a jellylike matrix. If for any reason, the blood is delayed from clotting, sedimentation may continue until an upper layer of clear plasma becomes separated from the cells which have descended through the fluid. When clotting then ensues the blood consists of two strata, a thin yellowish or buff-colored layer of clotted plasma laid upon a much deeper red stratum of cells. When blood had clotted in this way the upper layer was known to the older physiologists as the "buffy coat" (see also p. 109).

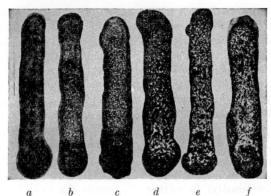

$$a \qquad b \qquad c \qquad d \qquad e \qquad f$$

Fig. 7.1. Showing the naked-eye appearances of specimens of blood spread upon glass slides. The specimens, left to right, are from (a) healthy man, (b) healthy woman, (c) healthy pregnant woman, (d) man, appendicitis, (e) man, pneumonia, (f) sepsis. Note the especially granular appearance of specimens e and f (after Fahraeus).

Ancient and medieval physicians carried out crude observations of the quantity of clear fluid which separated from blood upon standing as a means of diagnosis. In conformity with their humoral theories of disease, they believed it to be the "phlegm" which had separated from the other humors.

Biernaki (1891) was the first in modern times to draw attention to the increase in the rate of sedimentation of the blood in various pathological states. The subject has been studied in more recent times by Fahraeus and the *erythrocyte sedimentation rate* (E.S.R.) has come to be recognized as a useful diagnostic procedure. The sedimentation rate is measured by the depth in millimeters of clear plasma which is formed at the top of a vertical column of blood at the end of one hour. For the determination of the E.S.R. either Westegren's or Wintrobe's method is usually employed. In Westegren's method, the blood for examination (about 1.5 ml.) is diluted 4 parts to 1 of a 3.8 per cent solution of sodium citrate.[4] It is then drawn into a graduated glass tube about 300 mm. long, and having a bore of 2.45 mm.[5] The upper end of the tube which is fixed in a strictly perpendicular position is left open, whereas the lower end is closed, usually by a removable rubber cap held in position by a spring.

---

[4] This is isotonic with plasma and has the same specific gravity.

[5] Since the concentration of the blood in red cells influences the sinking rate, Walton recommends that their number be standardized to 5,000,000 per cu. mm. by the addition or removal of plasma if the subject's blood is below or above this level. In Wintrobe's method his hematocrit tube is employed, the packed cell volume (p. 18) being determined if desired after measuring the E.S.R. In the final calculation of the latter, a factor is used to correct for any existing anemia.

The determinations should be made at a temperature of 20°C.

The sedimentation rates expressed as the height of supernatant plasma, in mm. per hour for normal blood of men, women and infants, are given in the following table.

|  | *mm. per hour* |
|---|---|
| Men | 1–3 |
| Women | 4–7 |
| Newborn children | 0.5 |

In normal pregnancy and in certain pathological states, the sinking rate of the red cells is found to be very markedly increased; in other words, the suspension stability of the blood is reduced. The average figure during pregnancy is about 35 mm. per hour. The rate is also increased during menstruation. The pathological states which show the most noteworthy increase in the rate are septicemia, 100 mm. per hour, and pulmonary tuberculosis, 65 mm. Anemia (sickle cell anemia and acholuric jaundice excepted), malignant tumors, inflammatory conditions of the female pelvic organs and many other conditions increase the rate moderately above the normal. *Reduction* in the sedimentation rate is rare; it occurs in allergic states, in peptone shock and in sickle cell anemia and acholuric jaundice.

TABLE 7.1

*Showing the sedimentation rates of corpuscles from the same sample of blood suspended in different protein fractions of plasma (from Zozaya)*

| Protein Fraction | E.S.R. |
|---|---|
| Fibrinogen | 41–61 mm. |
| Euglobulin | 42–64 mm. |
| Pseudoglobulin | 5–12 mm. |
| Albumin | 3– 6 mm. |

The physical changes in the blood which might cause this unusually rapid rate of red cell settling are of considerable interest and were investigated thoroughly by Fahraeus. In considering the sedimentation rate of particles suspended in a fluid when they are of a size comparable with that of the red cells, four factors must be taken into account. These as applied to blood are:

*1. Specific gravity* of the plasma as compared with that of the corpuscles. Corpuscles of high specific gravity would sink more quickly in normal plasma, and normal corpuscles more quickly in a plasma with a low specific gravity. In neither corpuscles nor plasma was any significant change of this nature found to explain an increase in the E.S.R.

*2. Lowered viscosity* of the plasma is another factor which could cause an increase in rate of sinking, but no such change could be detected.

*3. Increased size of the corpuscles* would increase their mass disproportionately to their surface and in consequence enhance their rate of sinking, but no significant alteration in size was found.

*4. Clumping* together of cells of normal size would have the same effect as an increase in size of the individual cells for just as lumps of clay sink rapidly in water, whereas clay in the form of fine particles remains suspended almost indefinitely, so aggregation of the corpuscles would cause their more rapid sedimentation.

This last factor is the chief cause of the lowered stability of the blood suspension in the pathological conditions cited above. The roughness and granular appearance of the blood, due to the corpuscular aggregation is evident to the naked eye when the blood is spread in a film upon a slide (fig. 7.1). Normal blood, in marked contrast, forms a smooth homogeneous film. Under the microscope the crowding together of the cells in large masses is quite obvious. An increase in the fibrinogen and euglobulin fractions of the plasma is held responsible for the effect. Dextran increases the sedimentation rate and is used to produce more rapid separation of plasma and formed elements. These substances act upon the corpuscles in some unknown way to make them adhere to one another and form clumps of agglutinated cells.[6] It is probable that it is the relative proportions of the fibrinogen, globulin and albumin fractions of the plasma rather than their absolute concentrations which are of importance in determining the E.S.R. Thus a fall in the albumin concentration alone may have as great an accelerat-

ing effect as a rise in the other fractions. That the character of the plasma and not that of the cells is the principal determining factor is shown by the fact that if erythrocytes from blood with a high sedimentation rate (e.g., of pregnancy) are suspended in the plasma of blood having a low rate of sedimentation (e.g., of newborn) they settle at the slower rate, and conversely, erythrocytes with a normal sedimentation rate in their own plasma settle rapidly in plasma from blood with a high E.S.R. See table 7.1.

Though the protein constitution of the plasma is usually the most important single factor affecting the sedimentation rate, several other factors exert an influence, e.g., (a) the *shape* of the erythrocytes, any tendency toward a spherical form by reducing the proclivity of the cells to cling together (rouleaux formation) will retard sedimentation; (b) *temperature*, a rise in temperature above 20°C., as a rule, accelerates the E.S.R., a fall retards it; (c) the *lecithin-cholesterol ratio* of the plasma, the rate is retarded by an increase in the lecithin concentration and accelerated by cholesterol; (d) *red cell concentration*, a high erythrocyte count retards the E.S.R., a low count accelerates it.

The nonspecificity of the test is evident; nevertheless determinations of the sedimentation rate are of considerable value, especially, (a) in gauging the degree of activity of tuberculous processes; (b) as an aid in the differential diagnosis of certain gynecological lesions. Benign tumors of the pelvic organs cause no change in rate whereas, as already mentioned, malignant growths, inflammatory states and pregnancy cause a pronounced rise; (c) as an index of the extent and intensity in pyogenic infections, and (d) in estimating the activity of the inflammatory process in rheumatic fever.

## REFERENCES

Biernaki, E. Ztschr. Physiol. Chem., 1894, **19,** 179.

Kurnick, N. B. J. Biol. Chem., 1941, **140,** 581.

Macgraith, B. H. and associates. Lancet, 1941, **2,** 530.

Siebens, A. A. and associates. Blood, 1948, **3,** 1367.

Walton, A. C. R. Quart. J. Med., 1935, **2,** 79.

*Monographs and Reviews*

Fahraeus, R. Acta med. scandinav., 1921, **55,** 3. Physiol. Rev., 1929, **9,** 241.

Gillygan, D. R. and Blumgart, H. L. Medicine, 1941, **20,** 341.

Ponder, E. The erythrocyte and the action of simple haemolysins. Oliver, Edinburgh, 1924.

Yuile, C. L. Physiol. Rev., 1942, **22,** 19.

[6] The red cells of normal blood show an incipient tendency to cling together in chains—the so-called *rouleaux formation* (pseudoagglutination).

# 8

## THE SPLEEN; THE LIFE OF THE RED CELL; THE REGENERATION OF BLOOD; IRON METABOLISM

### The Structure of the Spleen

The spleen is an important part of the reticulo-endothelial system. Its structure is such that blood is brought into intimate contact with phagocytic cells. Dotted throughout the spleen, like islands, and surrounded by the pulp are lighter areas of lymphoid tissue. These are the Malpighian corpuscles. The Malpighian corpuscle (fig. 8.1) is pierced by a small artery. It is analogous to similar areas in lymph nodes, and serves the same function, namely the manufacture of lymphocytes. Blood enters the substance of the spleen by fine arterial vessels which pass through the Malpighian corpuscles and out into the splenic pulp. Here two different descriptions of its circulation have been given. Briefly, one of these indicates that the vessels open into and flood the splenic pulp, from which it passes back into the venous sinuses through numerous perforations in their walls. According to this view, the circulation through the splenic pulp is an open one. Others contend that the blood vessels are continuous throughout the splenic pulp and lead into the splenic sinuses. According to this view, the circulation through the splenic pulp is closed, the blood cells passing into the pulp or out from the pulp through openings in the vessel walls.[1]

### The Functions of the Spleen

The spleen has several important functions. The first three of these below are common to all parts of the reticuloendothelial system: (a) It has a part in the final disposal of red blood cells; (b) it phagocytoses bacteria and other particulate matter; (c) it produces antibodies; (d) it manufactures lymphocytes; (e) it has actions, possibly hormonal in nature, which influence the length of life of the erythrocytes and exert some influence

on hematopoiesis; (f) it influences the number of platelets and leucocytes; (g) it has an important reservoir function in many animals, though little in man.

*1. The role played by the spleen in the destruction of the blood cells.* In the pulp of the spleen are to be found relatively enormous mononuclear ameboid cells which have the power to engulf foreign particles of various sorts. They are known as *macrophages* and at times may be seen with fragments of erythrocytes or even whole corpuscles within their cytoplasm. These cells belong to the reticuloendothelial system (ch. 11). In certain conditions in which a great destruction of red cells is a feature, immense numbers of these phagocytic cells may be seen loaded with erythrocyte fragments of various sizes. Sometimes merely a dust-like residue (*hemoconia*) containing hemoglobin is all that remains of the blood cell. The disposal of abnormal or overmature erythrocytes by the spleen may not be a phagocytic process entirely.

Attempts to demonstrate the red cell disposal function of the spleen by comparative estimates of the corpuscular contents of the arterial (ingoing) and venous (outgoing) bloods have not, on the whole, been very successful. But Mann and his associates have been able, by spectroscopic examination of the arterial and venous bloods, to show a definite excess of bilirubin (iron-free pigment) in the blood of the splenic vein over that of the splenic artery. The bilirubin in the venous blood of other organs was no greater in amount than that in the arterial blood. In diseases with marked red cell destruction, the spleen becomes impregnated with iron and with an iron-containing pigment, *hemosiderin*, derived from the hemoglobin of the disintegrated cells. Similar deposits occur in the liver and to a less extent in other tissues.

Although evidence derived from microscopical studies and from bilirubin estimations shows undoubtedly that red cell disintegration occurs in the spleen, it is believed that only fragmented,

---

[1] Weiss contends that the walls of the splenic sinusoids are made up of reticuloendothelial cells in flattened form. Some of these cells may become round and form "core" tissue, whereas others remain flat in the walls of the sinusoids.

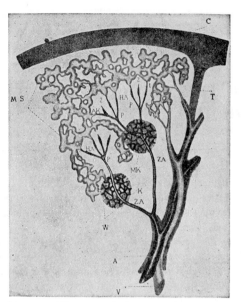

FIG. 8.1. Diagram of the human spleen. (A) artery and vein (V) in a trabecula (T) of the capsule (C); ZA, central artery of the corpuscle of Malpighi (MK); P, small arteries; HA, arteries with a sheath; AK, arterial capillaries which terminate in the sinuses (*1*) or in the meshes of the reticulum (*2*); MS, venous sinuses; W, white pulp (from Cajal after Szymonowicz).

dead, or effete and senile erythrocytes or those which are abnormal are disposed of in this way. The organ is believed not to attack healthy circulating cells. The reticuloendothelial cells of the spleen, in common with those elsewhere, conserve the iron from hemoglobin.

*2. Other phagocytic activity.* The phagocytic activity of the reticuloendothelial cells of the spleen, which has been considered in relation to the removal of red blood cells, is also important in the defense against infection, bacteria or other particulate matter being taken up by these cells. After splenectomy, animals become more susceptible to certain parasitic and bacterial infections. Although the spleen may hold only a small percentage of any particulate matter injected intravenously, nevertheless it also can be stimulated to form more reticuloendothelial cells and discharge them into the circulation. The phagocytic activity of the spleen, in common with other parts of the reticuloendothelial system, is influenced by various hormones. It can be strongly stimulated by estrogenic materials such as diethyl stilbestrol and estradial benzoate, and its phagocytic activity is greatly depressed by cortisone.

*3. Antibody production.* This function of the spleen is important, especially when the antigen is in particulate form, and its production of antibodies is relatively rapid. Somehow, the primitive reticular cells of the spleen are stimulated to divide and produce antibody-forming elements which subsequently mature into lymphocytes and plasma cells.

*4. Lymphocyte production.* The spleen contains much lymphoid tissue and manufactures lymphocytes and other mononuclear cells.

*5. The hemopoietic function of the spleen in the embryo.* In the embryo, the spleen in common with the bone marrow and liver is active in the production of erythrocytes and granulocytes as well as of lymphocytes. But erythropoiesis and granulopoiesis in the spleen normally cease at birth. Yet, many observations point to the spleen as exerting an influence upon the erythrocytes.

*6. Suggested influences of the spleen on the structure and number of the blood cells.* Although, as mentioned before, the spleen destroys abnormal cells (e.g., the spherocytes of chronic congenital hemolytic anemia, the erythrocytes in sickle cell anemia) it does not normally destroy erythrocytes until after they have served their purpose. The levels of circulating erythrocytes, leukocytes and platelets increase after splenectomy. The number of circulating reticulocytes is elevated also; they are thinner than normal and show nuclear changes. Because of the reticulocytosis after splenectomy, the suggestion has been made that a normal inhibition of the release of erythroid cells from the bone marrow diminishes after splenectomy, permitting an earlier release of these cells into the circulation. The increase in circulating leukocytes following splenectomy is thought also to be due to the removal of an inhibitory effect of the spleen on the production or release of leukocytes.

The spleen is concerned in some way with the life history of the platelets. In normal animals and in patients suffering from thrombocytopenic purpura, splenectomy increases the number of circulating platelets. This suggests some splenic influence on the production of platelets from megakaryocytes, since evidence for platelet destruction by the spleen is lacking.

*7. Reservoir function of spleen.* Animal experiments in dogs, cats, and a number of other mammals have shown that the spleen has a large reservoir capacity. The splenic blood was found to be richer in red cells so that with splenic contraction, in the cat, there might be expelled into the circulation an amount of blood equal to one-sixth of the blood volume and red cells equal to one-fourth of the body's total supply. In these animals, splenic contraction occurs with exercise, anoxia, hemorrhage, when the pressure in the carotid sinus is reduced, and when splanchnic nerves are stimulated or adrenaline injected. Although the reservoir function in animals may be of great importance, in man, under normal conditions, it is slight. The total volume of the spleen in man is not great and, at best, only a relatively small volume of blood could be released into the general circulation from it.

*8. Other effects.* A curious and unexplained action of the spleen has been discovered by Cullumbine and Simpson, who found that toxic doses of the antithyroid compound, thio-thymine (2-thio-5-methyl-uracil) causes the death of normal rabbits from pulmonary edema, but not of splenectomized animals. Moreover, if a splenectomized animal is injected with an aqueous-acid extract of hog or beef spleen, its susceptibility to the action of the drug in causing pulmonary edema is restored. Splenic extracts alone produce no such effect.

HYPERSPLENISM. Hypersplenism is a condition in which there is an excess of one of the normal functions of the spleen affecting the blood cells. It is a complication of splenomegaly. One or more of such blood states as thrombocytopenia, leucopenia, and anemia may be present. Various causal factors have been suggested: (a) antibody production (b) excessive phagocytosis (c) excessive production of an agent suppressing marrow activity.

IRRADIATION AND THE SPLEEN. Animals can be protected from usually lethal, although not massive, doses of irradiation of the general body surface by shielding the spleen with lead, or by the intravenous injection of ground up spleen or bone marrow. In the latter instance the protective effect is obtained with that part of the material containing the cell nuclei. It has been suggested that relatively undifferentiated cells in the material injected or discharged by the shielded structures protect, in some way, the hematopoietic tissue exposed to the irradiation, or restore it if it has been injured, as it is thought that the cells, although injured, still retain their potentiality to divide and mature.

### Enlargement of the Spleen

Enlargement of the spleen is associated with a large number of pathological states; only a few will be mentioned.

In *thrombocytopenic purpura* the spleen is enlarged and its removal is followed by a rise in the platelet count and amelioration of the symptoms. Also, substances such as antiplatelet serum or diphtheria toxin, which when injected cause platelet destruction, are rendered much less effective if the spleen has been removed. Splenectomy frequently brings about a cure in *hemolytic jaundice* (acholuric jaundice). The spleen may be considerably enlarged in *pernicious anemia* but splenectomy exerts no effect upon the course of the disease. In *splenic anemia* (congestive splenomegaly, Banti's disease), the spleen is tremendously enlarged and the liver becomes cirrhotic. There are portal hypertension and repeated hemorrhages. Splenectomy has been practiced in this disease with variable success. Relief of the portal hypertension and splenic congestion by anastomosis of the portal vein to the inferior vena cava is advocated by Whipple. Splenic enlargement is a feature of many other abnormal conditions, such as malaria, Hodgkin's disease, leukemia, etc., but in these, benefit does not follow its removal. The organ is also enlarged sometimes enormously in *polycythemia*, but splenectomy fails to cure the condition, and indeed is attended by grave risks to life (Moynihan).

*Gaucher's disease* is an interesting although rare condition which, commencing usually in childhood, is associated with a colossal enlargement of the spleen. The enlargement is due to hypertrophy and hyperplasia of reticuloendothelial elements. Masses of very large vesicular cells (Gaucher's cells) filled with a cerebroside called *kerasin* are seen in the lymphoid tissue and venous sinuses of the spleen. Hyperplasia of reticuloendothelial elements also occurs in other locations, e.g., bone marrow and liver. The disease is due apparently to some disorder of lipid metabolism. Splenectomy is the only effective treatment. *Niemann-Pick's disease* is a somewhat similar condition affecting the reticuloendothelial system and lipid metabolism. Characteristic cells, known from their appearance as "foam cells," are present in large numbers; they are loaded with sphingomyelin. Accumulations of this phospholipid are found also in the liver and brain. Subjects of this and the preceding disease are usually children of the Jewish race. *Von Jaksch's disease* occurs in infants and is characterized by splenomegaly, anemia and an increase in the number of white blood cells. Great enlargement of the spleen also occurs in *glycogen storage (von Gierke's) disease*. The chief characteristics are hypoglycemia, with ketosis, a slight rise only in the blood sugar after an injection of adrenaline (ch. 58), and extensive deposits of glycogen, particularly in the liver, associated usually with a deficiency in glucose-6-phosphatase.

From its position in the portal circulation the spleen is also very susceptible to enlargement, either as a result of mechanical obstruction to the veins or to high venous pressure resulting from cardiac or hepatic disease.

### The Life of the Red Cell

From the amount of bile pigment which is excreted daily by the liver the conclusion must be drawn that a very large amount of hemoglobin (since this is the sole or at least the main source of bile pigment) is liberated from disintegrated red cells in 24 hours.

There are three possible ways in which erythrocytes normally might be destroyed in the body: (a) by the macrophages of the spleen, (b) by the action of a hemolytic substance in the blood, (c) through simple wear and tear and disintegration in the blood stream. There is no evidence that hemolysis occurs to any significant extent in normal blood and the phagocytic cells of the normal spleen seem quite inadequate to account for the wholesale destruction of cells which evidently must be going on continually in the body. The work of Rous indicates that the erythrocytes to a very large extent undergo disintegration in the blood stream as a result of the stresses and strains to which they are incessantly subjected during their passage through the vessels. When it is considered how delicate is the structure of the red cell and to what violent treatment it is exposed during its lifetime, this wastage is not surprising. The cells are flung from the heart into the arteries at high velocity. In their voyage around the circulation they are exposed to jostlings and innumerable collisions with one another and with the arterial walls. At times they are forced through channels which are too narrow to permit their passage without marked distortions of their shape; or they may be caught in a fork at the branching of a vessel and become "saddlebagged" over it. Their membranes are almost continually undergoing alterations in tension as a result of osmotic changes. At last, becoming older, they are unable to withstand these abuses and undergo fragmentation. Fragments of different shapes and varying in size from that of a half or a quarter of the whole cell, to mere dustlike remnants containing hemoglobin (hemoconia) may be found in the circulating blood, in the spleen and to a limited extent occasionally in other tissues.

From determinations of bile pigment excretion it has been estimated that in health between 7,000,000 and 10,000,000 cells are destroyed in this way every second—and of course the same number must be formed afresh by the blood-form-

ing tissue. The loss of hemoglobin is between 16 and 24 grams daily. The number of red cells and hemoglobin concentration in the circulation at any moment represents the balance struck between blood wastage and blood formation by the bone marrow.

Many attempts have been made to determine the life span of the erythrocyte. Several methods have been employed, e.g., stimulation of the discharge of reticulocytes from the marrow and determining the time of their maturation, measuring the bile pigment excretion. The simplest and most commonly employed method is some form of the *selective or differential agglutination technique*, introduced in 1918 by Ashby. This method consists in transfusing compatible red cells and later examining the recipient's blood from time to time for the presence of the foreign corpuscles, which are counted in a hemocytometer. The foreign cells are distinguished from the transfused person's own cells by means of the serum of another belonging to a group with which the recipient's cells, but not the foreign cells, are incompatible[2] (p. 5). That is, the recipient's cells are agglutinated but not the foreign (donor's) cells. A plot of the number of surviving cells against time gives a straight line which meets the time axis at a point indicating the life span. To obtain accurate results it is necessary to agglutinate the recipient's cells completely; potent agglutinating sera must therefore be used.

Using this method, it has been found that the life of the average red cell is about 120 days.

Landsteiner, Levine and James have employed the M and N groups in a similar way, injecting M cells into an N recipient, or vice versa, and using anti-M or anti-N serum to agglutinate the *transfused* cells, leaving the recipient's cells unagglutinated. A more recent method is that which employs the isotope of nitrogen ($N^{15}$) to tag the red cell in the bone marrow. This is done by feeding glycine into which the isotope has been incorporated; this amino acid is utilized in the synthesis of protoporphyrin. It is necessary to the method that the isotope should not leave the cell and be utilized again for the manufacture of hemoglobin, but should persist throughout the life of the cell. Since the uptake time is long, the tagged cells are not all of the same age and hence with this pro-

[2] Thus if corpuscles of Group O are transfused into a person belonging to Group AB then, when the recipient's blood is mixed outside the body with Group B (anti-A) or Group A (anti-B) serum, the recipient's corpuscles but not the foreign cells will be agglutinated.

cedure it is difficult to obtain a precise determination of the survival time. The life span of the red cell as determined in man by this method is 127 days. Whipple and Hawkins, by determinations of the bile pigment excretion, obtained a figure in dogs, of 120 days.

Survival of cells tagged with radioactive iron or radioactive chromium may also be followed. The values obtained for the life span are rather similar to those obtained by the differential agglutination procedure. Using differential agglutination, Mollison reported that normal erythrocytes infused into patients with hereditary spherocytosis survived normally, but erythrocytes from such patients had a short survival time in normal recipients. Ashby has found that in pernicious anemia the average life of transfused cells was 110 days; in aplastic anemia, 41 days; in malignant cases, 52 days, whereas in transfusions given postoperatively to ordinary surgical cases, uncomplicated by severe anemia or malignancy, the survival time of the transfused cells averaged 124 days.

### The Regeneration of Blood

The red blood cells are formed in the red bone marrow (ch. 11). Anoxia, no matter how produced, is a fundamental factor in stimulating erythrocyte production. This stimulating effect seems to be a consequence of an increase in the blood level of a hematopoietic factor of extramedullary origin which results from the anoxia. Anoxia is important also in bringing about the release of iron from its stores.

THE MATERIALS NECESSARY FOR ERYTHROCYTE FORMATION

*1. The red cell stroma.* It is doubtful whether the materials required for the construction of the framework of the cell, e.g., nucleoprotein, globulin, lecithin and cholesterol are ever lacking. The body possesses large supplies of these materials and an ordinary diet contains them in adequate amounts. In certain anemias, however, e.g., pernicious anemia and Cooley's anemia, the failure of the body to assemble these materials for the manufacture of cell stroma may possibly be a fundamental causative factor.

*2. Hemoglobin* is added to the red cell only after the cell's development has progressed to a certain stage (ch. 11). Synthesis is believed to take place in the nucleus of the cells in the bone marrow. The complete history of hemoglobin in the body has yet to be written, but it is now established that

the body can synthesize pyrrol groups from simpler and readily available compounds, possibly, as suggested by Hans Fischer, from acetoacetic acid; glycine,[3] proline, oxyproline and tryptophane have been proposed by others as possible building stones. Given the pyrrol group, synthesis of protoporphyrin is readily effected (ch. 6). An interesting experiment in this connection is described by Whipple and his associates. When hemoglobin was given intravenously to anemic dogs, the animals' hemoglobin was increased by an amount equal to that injected. At the same time the excretion of bile pigment was increased by a corresponding amount. This paradoxical result is interpreted in the following way. The pyrrol of the injected hemoglobin is excreted as bilirubin, whereas the globin part of the molecule is utilized for the production of new hemoglobin, the pyrrol groups of which must therefore be derived from some other source—food or body tissue—and synthesized to protoporphyrin. It has already been pointed out that heme (porphyrin + iron) is a universal material and is present in the great majority of foodstuffs. So here, it might be supposed, was a source of an almost unlimited supply of the necessary pigment element. Yet heme cannot be split by the digestive secretions and it is generally agreed that iron so combined cannot be utilized for hemoglobin synthesis. Globin, of course, is required to complete the hemoglobin molecule. Whipple and his associates have found that this protein is well utilized for hemoglobin synthesis, yielding from 30 to 40 grams of blood pigment for each 100 grams fed to anemic dogs. Hemoglobin or globin, or a digest of the latter when given intravenously to anemic animals forms hemoglobin almost gram for gram. They found that, as compared with the porphyrin part of the molecule, globin was of much greater importance for hemoglobin regeneration; this protein apparently is a limiting factor in hemoglobin synthesis. Upon a diet low in protein but adequate in iron, hemoglobin regeneration was minimal. The amino acids necessary for the construction of hemoglobin are present in milk, meat, and other sources of first class protein. Globin can also be synthesized to a limited extent apparently from endogenous sources. This function is probably situated in the liver. Certain amino acids, espe-

---

[3] The most convincing evidence that this amino acid is a precursor of pyrrol has been obtained by Shemin and Rittenberg who fed glycine to rats and to men, after incorporating isotopic nitrogen into its molecule, and found it in the newly formed protoporphyrin.

TABLE 8.1

*Hemoglobin production influenced by diet*

| Diet, Grams Daily | Hemoglobulin Production (Two-Week Feeding Period) |
|---|---|
| | *grams* |
| Bread 400 | 3 |
| Milk 450, bread 400 | 3 |
| Cream 100, bread 400 | 10 |
| Butter 100, bread 350 | 15 |
| Asparagus 200, bread 300 | 9 |
| Spinach 200, bread 300 | 15 |
| Raspberries 200, bread 300 | 5 |
| Raisins 200, bread 300 | 25 |
| Apricots 200, bread 300 | 48 |
| Eggs 150, bread 300 | 45 |
| Whole fish 250, bread 300 | 13 |
| Beef muscle 250, bread 300 | 17 |
| Pig muscle 250, bread 300 | 30 |
| Chicken gizzard 250, bread 200 | 80 |
| Kidney 250, bread 300 | 70 |
| Chicken liver 250, bread 300 | 80 |
| Beef liver 300, bread 300 | 80 |
| Beef liver 450 | 95 |

cially proline and threonine, were found to increase hemoglobin regeneration after hemorrhage, which suggests that they are used for the synthesis of globin. Histidine which constitutes 8 per cent of the globin molecule is, contrary to expectation, less effective. It seems likely, that coproporphyrin is a precursor of protoporphyrin and thus constitutes a step in hemoglobin synthesis. The evidence for this is that: (a) in pernicious anemia the protoporphyrin of the erythrocytes is closely correlated with the reticulocyte percentage, and (b) when the disease is in relapse the protoporphyrin is very low and coproporphyrin cannot be demonstrated, but after treatment with vitamin $B_{12}$ the coproporphyrin increases rapidly and in advance of the protoporphyrin.

Whipple, Hooper and Robscheit carried out a series of experiments upon animals made anemic through repeated bleedings, and tested their power to regenerate hemoglobin when fed upon various diets. Meats were found to be the most potent for this purpose. Carbohydrates in the form of bread and sugar were found to be ineffective. In fact they had actually a definitely depressing effect upon the hemoglobin repair process, for animals regenerated their blood more rapidly when starved than when fed upon a bread and sugar diet. In explanation of this fact Whipple suggested that the starved animal drew upon

its tissues to supply the basic elements for hemoglobin synthesis, whereas carbohydrate food on account of its well known protein-sparing effect prevented the tissues from being utilized in this way. Infection or very severe liver damage markedly depresses hemoglobin regeneration in anemic dogs. The depressing effect upon regeneration of hemoglobin which is seen in the Eck fistula animals is apparently due to interference with liver function (defective protein synthesis) and to the reduction in iron absorption.

These workers found that, of all protein foods, liver was by far the most effective for blood regeneration. Next in order came kidney and chicken gizzard. Milk had little regenerating effect. Table 8.1 shows the comparative values of the various articles of diet. A bread mixture consisting of potato and wheat flour, bran, sugar and the necessary salts and vitamins was used as the basal diet. This was practically inert so far as the regeneration of hemoglobin was concerned. The article to be tested was added to this basal diet.

The animals (dogs) were rendered anemic by three or four successive bleedings until the hemoglobin had been reduced to 30 per cent of the normal. The item of food to be tested was then added to the basal diet and the animal bled from time to time in order to maintain the hemoglobin at the original level of 30 per cent. The amount of blood removed expressed in grams of hemoglobin gave a direct measure of the amount of pigment regenerated in a given time.

### Iron Metabolism

Being an essential constituent of the hemoglobin molecule, this mineral must be available in adequate amounts in order that normal blood regeneration shall occur. Iron provides the keystone for hemoglobin construction; unless it is supplied in appropriate amounts the maturation of the red cells is retarded, and the numbers discharged from the bone marrow into the general circulation reduced.

#### ABSORPTION, STORAGE AND EXCRETION OF IRON

Iron is absorbed to some extent throughout the entire intestinal tract, but in by far the greatest amount from the upper part of the small intestine. The absorption is by way of the blood. There is no evidence for a significant uptake by lymphatics. After absorption the element is stored in the intestinal mucosa, the liver and to a less extent in the spleen and kidney. Liver iron is readily increased by iron feeding or injection. Under ordinary circumstances only minute quantities of iron are detectable in the plasma, the normal amount being about 0.1 mg./100 ml., although the iron-binding capacity of plasma is about three times this value. The great proportion of the iron of the blood is present in the red cells. A smaller quantity is present in the muscle (myoglobin, cytochrome, etc.); the remainer is stored in liver, kidney, and various other tissues as *ferritin* and *hemosiderin*. Whole blood contains from 45 to 50 mg. per cent and the total quantity in the adult human body is between 4 and 5 grams. See table 8.2. Iron is present in the blood mainly as (a) plasma iron, and (b) iron combined with hemoglobin, which accounts for from 92 to 98 per cent of the total. There is very little excretion of iron by the bowel or kidney under ordinary conditions. The daily loss in adults is about 1 mg. The view of McCance and Widdowson that normally the iron stores of the body are regulated not by excretion but through the *control of absorption* is now generally accepted. Iron is, therefore, very largely a "one way" element. That which is absorbed is held by the body with great avidity and the iron liberated from hemoglobin is used again for the manufacture of new hemoglobin, the pigment part of the molecule alone being excreted in the bile.

Several factors influence iron absorption. It will be affected by the acidity of the intestine and motility of the gut and by the presence of reducing agents such as ascorbic acid. The level of phosphate also has an important effect, its presence decreasing absorption and its absence increasing it. Indeed a low level of phosphate in the diet accompanied by a high intake of iron may lead to a very high absorption of iron. Interference with the external pancreatic secretion by duct ligation or ethionine damage also enhances iron absorption. Inorganic iron seems to be more readily absorbed than the iron found in various foods. The iron in milk, cereal and meat is absorbed relatively well. When given with phytic acid the absorption or iron is poor. It is now known that the truly organic iron of foods, namely that combined in heme, is not available since it is not released by peptic or tryptic digestion, whereas the inorganic iron which may represent 50 per cent or more of the total iron of the food is available. About 5 to 10% of the food iron is absorbed. Severe infection reduces iron absorption very markedly, sometimes to only one-tenth of the normal.

In iron deficiency anemia the absorption of iron is enhanced. This seems to be related to a reduction in the hemoglobin levels and an increase in

hematopoietic activity rather than to the state of the iron stores, though this point is still somewhat controversial.

A conception of the mechanism whereby the iron absorption occurs has been offered by Granick and his associates. Their results with radioactive iron indicate that ferrous iron passes from the intestinal lumen into the mucosal cells, and is here oxidized to the ferric form (FeOH). The ferric iron, as ferric hydroxide phosphate, combines with a protein known as *apoferritin* (mol. wt. around 460,000) the iron-phosphorus-protein complex *ferritin* being formed. Ferritin is thus a conjugated protein containing about 23 per cent of iron. The iron-phosphorus portion has the approximate formula $[(FeOOH)\cdot(FeOPO_3H_2)]$.

At the vascular surface of the mucosal cell the iron of ferritin is reduced to the ferrous form; the conversion is facilitated by vitamin C. Immediately upon entering the blood stream it is oxidized and combined with the $B_1$-iron-binding globulin, named *transferrin* or siderophilin, of the plasma; in this complex form iron is carried. At the periphery of the circulation ferric ions diffuse across the capillary wall into the tissue fluids but iron enters the cells in the ferrous form. Probably under some circumstances, especially when the oxygen supply to the tissues is low, ferrous iron passes directly into the plasma without going through the ferritin stage. When saturated with ferritin the mucosal cells act as a sort of block. If, on the other hand, there should be a scarcity of iron in the intestinal lumen the iron thus stored in the epithelial cells is released into the circulation. Thus the ferritin mechanism tends to stabilize the level of plasma iron. However, the so-called mucosal block is by no means perfect, for iron,

TABLE 8.2

*The distribution of iron in the body of a dog weighing 20 kilograms (Hahn)*

|  | mg. | per cent total body iron |
|---|---|---|
| Blood hemoglobin iron......... | 900 | 57 |
| Muscle hemoglobin iron........ | 110 | 7 |
| Total hemoglobin iron..... | 1010 | 64 |
| Parenchyma iron (muscle and other tissues)................ | 240 | 16 |
| Available visceral storage (liver, spleen and marrow).......... | 225 | 15 |
| Available iron of other tissues (estimated).................. | 75± | 5± |
| Total iron................. | 1550 | 100 |

if in high concentration in the intestinal contents continues to be absorbed into the plasma. But the homeostasis of plasma iron is not dependent altogether upon the ferritin mechanism, for even while iron is passing in considerable amounts into the blood, its concentration in the plasma shows little or no rise. This is because it is taken up for the manufacture of hemoglobin by the red bone marrow, and when this has been satisfied, by the reticuloendothelial and parenchymal cells of other tissues where it is stored, especially in the liver and spleen, or utilized in the formation of muscle hemoglobin, respiratory enzymes and other complexes. These compounds, and to a much greater extent, the hemoglobin of effete erythrocytes is continually yielding iron to the plasma. The endogenous iron amounts to about 24 mg. daily, and, except for the very small amount that is excreted in the urine, feces and bile, is available for re-use. The level of plasma iron represents the balance struck at any moment between the iron from such sources, together with that absorbed from the intestine, and the iron taken up by the bone marrow and other tissues. Excretion plays a negligible part in the stabilization of the plasma level of iron. Ordinarily, the greater part of the iron in the parenchymal cells is in the form of ferritin; but in the reticuloendothelial cells it is deposited mainly as hemosiderin. Generally speaking, when iron storage increases, the proportion deposited in the tissues as hemosiderin also increases.

An adequate supply of pyridoxin is essential for the normal absorption of iron from the intestine.

The main features of iron metabolism are summarized in the following scheme.

Besides its well known function as an essential element in the hemoglobin molecule, and as a constituent of other respiratory pigments, iron appears to play a role in the nutrition of epithelial surfaces. Abnormal nail growth, glossitis, fissures around the corners of the mouth and localized thickening of the mucous lining of the esophagus leading to dysphagia occur in anemias due to iron deficiency, and are cured by iron administration.

It has been calculated by Moore that the adult male loses 0.5 to 1.5 mg. of iron per day. This loss is increased by about 0.5 to 1 mg. per day in the adult female before the menopause, and during pregnancy the iron requirements of the female are further increased by 1 to 2 mg. per day. Children require 0.35 to 0.6 mg. per day to build up their iron stores during growth. Since, normally, about 10 per cent of the dietary iron is absorbed, it will be evident that the daily requirement for the adult male, i.e., the amount required to replace the small amounts lost in the excreta and in discarded cells from the skin and gastrointestinal tract, is approximately 12 to 15 mg. It will also be clear that for growing children and for women before the menopause or during pregnancy, the requirement for iron will be very considerably increased.

Iron is sometimes given parenterally but it should be remembered that plasma has a limited iron-binding capacity and that the free metal exerts a toxic effect. If this iron-binding capacity is not exceeded, injected ionized iron will combine with the metal-combining protein as does the iron absorbed from the gut. Injected colloidal iron will be taken up by reticuloendothelial cells and will be dealt with much like the iron from hemoglobin breakdown.

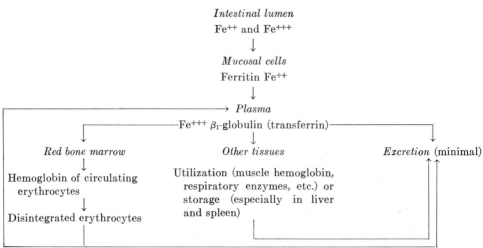

## The Significance of Copper, Manganese and Cobalt

*Copper* is believed to act as a catalyst in some stage of hemoglobin synthesis. It does not itself enter into the structure of the hemoglobin molecule. Waddell, Elvehjem, Steenbock and Hart found that in young rats rendered anemic by being placed upon a diet of whole cow's milk, iron alone failed to promote hemoglobin regeneration.[4] When the iron was supplemented by a very small quantity of copper, blood regeneration was induced. *Manganese* exerts a similar though less pronounced supplementary effect. The liver is the main storehouse for copper and minute amounts (0.1 to 0.5 mg.) are present normally in blood.

Though anemia due to copper deficiency is unknown in man, a severe and even fatal anemia due to the lack of this metal may occur in farm animals, e.g., the "falling sickness" of South African cattle.

*Cobalt* has a powerfully stimulating effect upon red cell production and in repeated doses may induce polycythemia. When rats were injected with cobaltous chloride their plasma rather quickly showed a high titer of a factor stimulating erythropoiesis. Cobalt is also an essential dietary constituent for the synthesis of hemoglobin. Experimental animals kept upon a diet adequate in all respects for normal erythropoiesis, except for the absence of cobalt, develop a severe anemia. Cattle and sheep grazing upon land lacking in this mineral become anemic and fail to respond to iron therapy, but are cured dramatically by the administration of traces of cobalt. Cobalt is a constituent of vitamin $B_{12}$.

### Hemochromatosis

This is a disturbance in iron metabolism in which extensive deposits of a colloid iron-containing pigment called *hemosiderin* are found in the cells of the liver, spleen and other tissues. Hemosiderin contains up to 55 per cent of iron, but its exact chemical composition is unknown. The total iron content of the body is greatly increased; it may be 10 times the normal amount. A second yellow pigment known as *hemofuscin* is also sometimes present in the connective and muscular tissues. Other features of the condition are *bronzing of the skin, cirrhosis of the liver, sclerosis of the pancreas* with diabetes (bronzed diabetes), and sometimes testicular atrophy. The disease may appear after repeated transfusions.

Hemochromatosis has been attributed to a high iron content of the diet combined with a deficiency of some essential constituent. A condition resembling hemochromatosis has been reported in Negroes of certain South African tribes who subsist mainly upon a diet of maize and ingest excessive amounts of iron derived from the pots in which the food is cooked. In rats and dogs on a somewhat similar diet, a high absorption of iron was obtained. The low phosphate level of the diet was thought to be a major factor. It is probable that other factors are involved however in hemochromatosis. A patient suffering from hemochromatosis absorbs 20 per cent of a dose of ferrous iron given orally, or more than 10 times the amount absorbed by a normal person. Yet the quantity found in the blood is less that than present in the blood of a normal person receiving such a dose.

*Hemosiderosis* is the term applied to the deposit of hemosiderin in the tissues which occurs as a result of the excessive breakdown of red cells in malaria and hemolytic types of anemia. It may be looked upon simply as an exaggeration of the normal process of iron deposition.

### REFERENCES

Ashby, W. J. Exper. Med. 1919, **29**, 267. Blood, 1948, **3**, 486.

Balfour, W. M. and associates. J. Exper. Med., 1942, **76**, 15.

Cullumbine, H. and Simpson, M. Nature, 1947, **159**, 782.

Elvehjem, C. A., Hart, E. B. and Sherman, W. C. J. Biol. Chem., 1933, **103**, 61.

Erslev, A. J. Blood, 1955, **10**, 954.

Granick, S. Science, 1946, **103**, 107; Chem. Rev., 1946, **38**, 379.

Granick, S. and Michaelis, L. J. Biol. Chem., 1943, **147**, 91; Bull. New York Acad. Med., 1949, **25**, 403; Physiol. Rev. 1951, **31**, 489.

Gray, C. H. and Neuberger, A. Biochem. J., 1949, **44**, xlvii.

Grindlay, J. H. and associates. Am. J. Physiol., 1939, **127**, 119.

Hahn, P. F. Fed. Proc., 1948, **7**, 493.

Ham, T. H. Arch. Int. Med., 1939, **69**, 1271.

Hawkins, W. B. and Whipple, G. H. Am. J. Physiol., 1938, **122**, 418.

Hill, R. Proc. Roy. Soc., London, ser. B, 1930, **107**, 205.

Hughes, J. H. and Latner, A. L. J. Physiol., 1936, **86**, 388.

Landsteiner, K., Levine, P. and James, M. L. Proc. Soc. Exper. Biol. & Med., 1928, **25**, 672. (See also Wiener, A. S. J. A. M. A., 1934, **102**, 1779.)

McCance, R. A. and Widdowson, E. M. Lancet, 1937, **2**, 680.

Nicol, T., Bilbey, D. L. J. and Ware, C. C. Nature, 1958, **182**, 534.

---

[4] Some experimenters have obtained a certain degree of hemoglobin regeneration with iron alone, although the rate of regeneration was much increased by the addition of copper.

SHEMIN, D. AND RITTENBERG, D. J. Biol. Chem., 1946, **166**, 621.

WADDELL, J., STEENBOCK, H., ELVEHJEM, C. A. AND HART, E. B. J. Biol. Chem., 1929, **83,** 243, 251.

WHIPPLE, A. O. Ann. Surg., 1945, **122,** 449.

WHIPPLE, G. H., HOOPER, C. W. AND ROBSCHEIT, F. S. Am. J. Physiol., 1920, **53,** 151, 167.

WHIPPLE, G. H. AND ASSOCIATES. Am. J. Physiol., 1936, **115,** 651. J. Exper. Med., 1937, **66,** 565; 1938, **67,** 89; 1939, **69,** 315. Proc. Soc. Exper. Biol. & Med., 1937, **36,** 629.

### *Monographs and Reviews*

BARCROFT, J. Lancet, 1925, **1,** 319.

BARCROFT, J. Features in the architecture of physiological function. Cambridge University Press, London, 1934.

BERLIN, N. I., WALDMANN, T. A. AND WEISSMAN, S. M. Physiol. Rev., 1959, **39,** 577.

BOND, V. P. AND CRONKITE, E. P. Ann. Rev. Physiol., 1957, **19,** 299.

HAHN, P. F. Medicine, 1937, **16,** 249.

JOSEPHS, H. W. Blood, 1958, **13,** 1.

LE ROY, G. V. M. Clin. North America, 1953, **37,** 181.

MOLLISON, P. L. The life-span of red blood cells. Lectures on the scientific basis of Medicine, University of London. The Athlone Press, 1954.

MOORE, C. V. Am. J. Clin. Nutrition, 1955, **3,** 3.

PERLA, D. AND MARMORSTON, J. The spleen and resistance. The Williams & Wilkins Co., Baltimore, 1935.

ROBSCHEIT-ROBBINS, F. S. Physiol. Rev., 1929, **9,** 666.

ROUS, P. Physiol. Rev., 1923, **3,** 75.

SHELDON, J. H. Haemochromatosis. Oxford University Press, London, 1935.

# 9

# THE ANEMIAS

## Classification

We have seen that in health the population of red cells and the concentration of hemoglobin in the blood are kept at normal levels by a nice balance between the new formation and the wastage of erythrocytes. Anemia results when the balance is tipped one way or the other, i.e., by a defect of blood formation or an increase in blood wastage. Basically, it is a condition in which the hemoglobin level of the blood is reduced below the normal limits. The anemias may be classified broadly into (A) *those associated with blood loss or increased blood destruction* and (B) *those caused by defective blood formation.*

A. *Anemias caused by blood loss or increased blood destruction.*

I. *Posthemorrhagic anemias*

*Hemorrhage*

a. *Acute*

b. *Chronic,* as a result, for example of peptic ulcer, uterine bleeding, ankylostomiasis (hookworm disease), purpura, etc.

II. *Hemolytic anemias*

*Red cell destruction,* as a result of:

a. *Chemical hemolytic poisons,* lead, arseniureted hydrogen and certain coal tar derivatives.

b. *Certain specific infections,* e.g., malaria, septicemia.

c. *Abnormal structure of the red cells* which render them more susceptible to phagocytosis or to disintegration in the blood stream, e.g., chronic congenital hemolytic (Lederer's) anemia, and thalassemia (Cooley's anemia, Mediterranean anemia or erythroblastic anemia).

d. *An endogenous hemolysin of unknown nature,* e.g., chronic congenital hemolytic jaundice and the anemia associated with paroxysmal hemoglobinuria.

e. *Anti-Rh, and occasionally anti-A and anti-B agglutinins,* causing hemolytic disease of the newborn.

In the hemolytic group the increased blood destruction is manifested by a rise in the concentration of bile pigment in the plasma which gives an indirect van den Bergh reaction, a greater excretion of bile pigment and porphyrin in the urine and feces, and the deposit of an iron-containing pigment in the liver and other tissues. There is frequently jaundice of a slight or moderate grade.

*Sickle cell anemia* is believed to be caused by blood destruction as a result of a congenital anomaly of the red cells. In this type, which occurs almost exclusively in Negroes, elongated crescent or sickle shaped birefringent erythrocytes some 15 $\mu$ or so in length are a characteristic feature. Such cells are found in the blood of a high percentage of Negroes (8 to 9 per cent) though only relatively few, 1 in 40, of these develop anemia. There is also a proportion of Negroes and also a few whites whose red cells become sickle shaped under certain adverse conditions, especially as a result of reduction in the oxygen tension of the blood. This is spoken of as the *sickle cell trait* and is due to a single sickle cell allelomorphic gene (sickle cell anemia being caused by the presence of two genes). It has been shown by electrophoretic studies that the hemoglobin (probably the globin rather than the heme) of the erythrocytes in sickle cell anemia, in those showing sickle cells but no anemia, or those in which sickling can be induced, differs somewhat from normal hemoglobin. The abnormal hemoglobin constitutes 100 per cent of the blood pigment in sickle cell anemia, 60 per cent when sickle cells are present but there is no anemia, and 40 per cent in those in whom sickling can be induced by a low oxygen tension.

*Chronic congenital hemolytic jaundice.* Synonyms, *acholuric jaundice, spherocytic anemia, hereditary spherocytosis, chronic familial jaundice, hemolytic splenomegaly.* The chief features of this form of anemia are *jaundice* and a high incidence of pigment gall stones, *spheroid erythrocytes* (i.e., the diameter of the cells is reduced but their thickness is increased, their volume being approximately normal), *reticulocytosis* up to 60 per cent or more of the total red cell population, increased *fragility* of the cells and *enlargement of the spleen.* Splenectomy is usually followed by the disappearance of jaundice, a return of the red cell count to normal and a marked reduction in the reticulocytosis. The spherocytosis gradually disappears and with it usually though not invariably the increased fragility of the erythrocytes. These facts indicate that disordered function of the spleen is not the primary cause of the condition. The cause of the hemolysis is unknown though it may be due simply, as in certain other anemias, to the reaction of the macrophages of the spleen to the defective cells produced by an abnormally functioning bone marrow. Others believe that an endogenous hemolytic agent is responsible, a view which receives support from the experiments of Dameshek and Schwartz in which a hemolytic serum produced by the injection of guinea pig's cells into rabbits was employed to produce anemia. The injection of this anti-guinea pig hemolytic serum into guinea pigs caused a profound drop in the red cell count and the appearance of cells with spheroid shape, increased fragility and a reticulocytosis. These observers suggest that the greater fragility of the red cells is simply a function of their globular shape and that spherocytosis is a reaction of the bone marrow to excessive destruction of red cells caused by a circulating hemolysin. Others have shown that there are changes in the metabolism of the erthrocyte, there being a defect in glycolysis which may be a result of deficient phosphorylation. The administration of glucose diminishes the hemolysis in this condition.

Some divide the disease into two distinct forms: congenital and acquired. Justification for the division is provided by the fact that in the *acquired* form the patient's cells, after transfusion into a normal person, have a normal life span, but normal cells transfused into the patient survive only for about one-fourth of the normal time. This points to a hemolysin. In the *congenital* type the behavior of the cells is reversed; the patient's cells injected into a normal subject are removed rapidly but normal cells persist in the patient's circulation for the usual time. This suggests that in the congenital type the abnormality of the cells is due primarily to some defect of bone marrow function. These experiments were performed by Loutit and Mollison, who consider that in the congenital form the spherocytes are unduly susceptible to normal hemolytic processes, that a hemolysin acting under normal conditions may be lysolecithin, and that the slow movement of blood through the spleen favors the hemolytic action. This would explain the benefit which follows removal of the spleen, as well as why this operation does not always reduce the fragility of the cells.

*Lederer's anemia* is an acute hemolytic anemia. The leucocytes are increased in number and phagocytosis of red cells may be a pronounced feature. In Thalassemia major, or Cooley's anemia, there is microcytosis and some of the red cells show concentric rings like a target ("*target cells*"). The disease is congenital, being inherited as a Mendelian dominant. With some forms of the disease there may be also splenomegaly and bony changes. It is thought that the fundamental abnormality is a defect in the formation of hemoglobin.

*B. Anemias due to defective blood formation.*

*I. Nutritional anemias*

    *a. Iron deficiency*—hypochromic, microcytic anemias. The deficiency may be due either to the excessive loss of iron from the body as in chronic hemorrhage or to an inadequate quantity of this element in the diet. The former is the usual cause in adult males, but in infants and adolescents, and in pregnancy or other conditions where the iron requirement is increased, the latter may be a factor. Under some circumstances too, a failure in the absorption of iron may be a cause of the intractability of anemia to iron administration by mouth.

    *b. Protein deficiency*, although in itself a less common cause of anemia, is not infrequently a contributory factor.

    *c. Lack of folic acid.* In man, lack of vitamin C is a possible factor also and in animals, deficiency of certain other vitamins, pyridoxin riboflavin, nicotinic and pantothenic acids.

    *d.* The macrocytic anemias of sprue and pregnancy are usually classed with the nutritional anemias.

*II. Lack of or failure in the absorption or in the utilization of the specific antianemic factor (cyanocobalamin, vitamin $B_{12}$)*—Addisonian pernicious anemia and certain related hyperchromic macrocytic anemias with a megaloblastic type of bone marrow. Bone marrow for microscopical examination is obtained by puncturing the sternum, iliac crest or a spinous process with a specially designed styletted needle and aspirating a small sample.

*III. Macrocytic anemias (hypo- or hyperchromic) with normoblastic or macroblastic bone marrow.*

*IV. Toxic agents which induce aplasia of the bone marrow or depress its function*—*aplastic anemias*. Among such agents are quinacrine, gold salts, benzol, arsphenamine, radium, X-rays, and sometimes bacterial and syphilitic toxins. The red marrow is greatly reduced in amount, being replaced by fatty tissue. Blood formation is profoundly depressed. Anemia of the aplastic type may also result from exhaustion of the bone marrow following a long period of overactivity induced by some other type of anemia, or may appear without a known cause (*idiopathic aplastic anemia*).

V.  *Infections*—the anemia accompanying infection is usually a mild, normocytic, normochromic type. As a rule, hemolysis is not a factor. The exact defect is not clear but there is a decreased production of hemoglobin associated with decreased absorption of iron, decreased $\beta$, metal-combining globulin of plasma and a decreased plasma iron level.

The cause of *splenic anemia* (Banti's) is unknown; it is therefore difficult to fit this type into any of the preceding categories. According to some there is increased blood destruction, but important factors appear to be depressed marrow function and the loss of blood resulting from repeated gastrointestinal hemorrhages. An anemia very closely resembling Addisonian or true pernicious anemia results from infestation with the fish tapeworm, *Diphyllobothrium latum*. Some believe that an important factor in its causation is the competition of the parasite for vitamin $B_{12}$.

*Blood indices.* The following indices calculated from the hemoglobin concentration, red cell count and packed cell volume of a specimen of blood are employed to express the characters of the individual cells in the different types of anemia.

The *color index.* This is a numerical expression of the hemoglobin content of the individual red cells. It is obtained by dividing the hemoglobin value in grams per 100 cc. by the red cell count, both values being expressed as percentages of the normal. (The normal weight of hemoglobin per 100 cc. is taken as 14.5 grams and the red cell count as 5,000,000.) Thus, if the hemoglobin is 60 per cent of normal and the red cell count 50 per cent, then $60/50 = 1.2$ color index. But if the hemoglobin percentage is reduced to a greater degree than the red cell percentage the index will be less than unity. That is, each red cell contains less than its normal quota of hemoglobin. On the other hand, the hemoglobin concentration of the blood may be greatly reduced but if the reduction runs parallel with the reduction in red cell percentage the index will have the normal value of 1.0.

*Mean corpuscular volume* (M.C.V.). This expresses the volume of the individual red cell in $\mu^3$ (1 ml. = $10^{12}$ $\mu^3$). The mean corpuscular volume in $\mu^3$ is obtained by dividing the volume of packed cells expressed in ml. per liter by the red cell count in millions per cu. mm. (e.g., $\frac{450}{5} = 90$)

Anemias may be classified according to the M.C.V. as macrocytic (over 96), normocytic (86 to 96), and microcytic (under 86).

*Mean corpuscular hemoglobin concentration* is the hemoglobin in grams per 100 ml. of blood divided by the packed cell volume per 100 ml., expressed as a percentage (e.g., $\frac{15}{45} \times 100 = 33$ per cent). This value is never greater than normal but may be normal (above 30 per cent, normochromic) or less than normal (below 30 per cent, hypochromic).

*Mean corpuscular hemoglobin* (M.C.H.) is the hemoglobin per red cell expressed in $\mu\mu$g ($10^{-12}$ g.). This may be obtained by dividing the hemoglobin in grams per liter by the red blood cell count in millions per mm.$^3$ (e.g., $\frac{150}{5} = 30$ $\mu\mu$g.). The mean corpuscular hemoglobin may vary with the concentration of hemoglobin within the cell and with the volume of the cell.

Attempts have been made to estimate the *total erythropoietic activity* of bone marrow from the erythroid-myeloid ratio, plasma iron turnover and fecal urobilinogen, and the effective *erythropoiesis* (i.e., the proportion of cells produced by the bone marrow that are delivered into the circulation), by means of erythrocyte count, and by the uptake of radioactive iron by the red cells. It has been found that the effective erythropoiesis can be increased three times in acute anemia, and six times in chronic anemia.

## Hypochromic Microcytic Anemias—Iron Deficiency

In this group the essential defect is one of hemoglobin formation. The hemoglobin percentage of the blood is reduced to a greater extent than the number of red cells. These, indeed, may show only a slight reduction. The color index and M.C.H. are considerably below the normal, which means that each red cell has received less than its normal quota of pigment. The erythrocytes are also smaller than normal, so the M.C.V. is also low. The low M.C.H. is in part the result of the smaller size of the red cell but also of a reduced concentration of pigment throughout the red cell's substance. Some of the corpuscles are so pale that they resemble "ghosts" or only the peripheral zone of the cell is colored (anisochromasia) (see figs 9.1 and 9.2, and frontispiece.)

Iron deficiency is considered to be the essential cause of the anemias belonging to this class. The deficiency may result from increased iron requirements coupled with an inadequate amount of iron in the diet or from defective absorption of the metal from the food but the usual cause, in adult males, is blood loss.

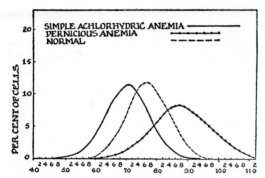

FIG. 9.1. Red cell diameter distribution curves in simple achlorhydric anemia and in pernicious anemia compared with the normal (after Haden; see also fig. 9.2).

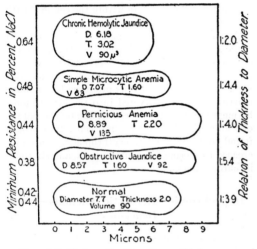

FIG. 9.2. Red cell diameter, thickness and volume in various clinical conditions compared with the normal (after Haden). *D*, diameter; *T*, thickness; *V*, volume.

Hypochromic anemia occurs most frequently in women of childbearing age when there is a dietary deficiency, especially of iron. The anemia is aggravated by the losses of iron incident to menstruation or repeated pregnancies. Davidson has recently emphasized the need for larger amounts of iron during this period in women. In the previous chapter, iron loss and iron requirements have been discussed.

### ANEMIA OF INFANTS

The fetus accumulates a store of iron in the liver in the later months of gestation. This serves as a reserve that is drawn upon for the manufacture of hemoglobin in infancy. The high red cell concentration (p. 12) with which the infant comes into the world also contributes to the iron reserves. In the normal infant the iron stores are sufficient for the manufacture of hemoglobin for the first six months or so. Growth, however, makes heavy demands upon the iron supplies and after the first half year it is necessary to provide a diet which will contain adequate amounts of iron in order to guard against the development of anemia of the hypochromic type. Milk, it will be recalled, is very poor in both iron and copper. The iron content of milk is doubled by the pasteurization process and tripled in the drying or evaporation processes. The development of anemia in milk-fed rats has been mentioned and the anemia of sucklings is a problem in the breeding of farm animals. If the iron stores are deficient at birth as in premature infants or as a result of maternal anemia, anemia may occur in the very young infant.

The hypochromic anemias respond in a spectacular fashion to the administration of inorganic iron (e.g., ferrous chloride, ferrous carbonate, etc.) The administration of copper is rarely necessary since this occurs in sufficient quantity in the diet and as an impurity in iron preparations.

A macrocytic anemia with a megaloblastic type of bone marrow also occurs in infants. It responds to vitamin $B_{12}$ and to folic acid. It is frequently accompanied by leukopenia and splenomegaly.

### Pernicious Anemia (Addison's Anemia) and Related Macrocytic Anemias

*Pernicious anemia* is due essentially to a defect in the formation of the red blood cells.

CHIEF FEATURES of the blood picture are:

*1. Great reduction* in the number of red cells and consequently in the hemoglobin percentage. The blood count in a very severe case may be less than 10 per cent of the normal.

*2.* The red cells are reduced in number below the normal to a greater extent than is the hemoglobin percentage. The M.C.V. and M.C.H. are therefore *raised* above normal. The high M.C.H. is due to the greater size of the cells.

*3.* Large cells—the average diameter of the cells is increased to between 8 and 9 $\mu$ and exceptionally large cells called *macrocytes* are plentiful. The average volume of the individual red cells (figs. 9.1 and 9.2) is about 135 $\mu^3$ (normal about 90 $\mu^3$). *Normoblasts* and earlier forms are present in the circulation, and a characteristic large nucleated cell containing basophilic material in its cytoplasm and little or no hemoglobin is a feature of the blood picture. This cell, known as the *megaloblast*, differs chemically and morphologically from any normal cell of the erythrocyte series found either in bone marrow or blood. The reticulocytes are around 3 per cent.

PLATE I

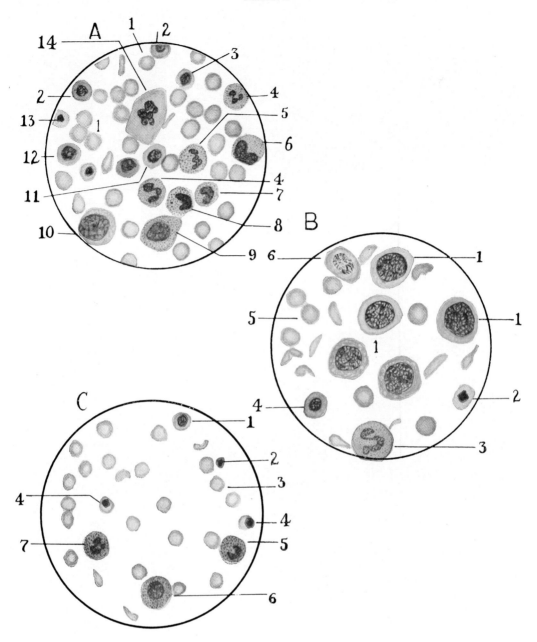

Samples of bone marrow obtained by sternal puncture

A. Normal

1. Erythrocytes
2. Erythroblasts
3. Early normoblast
4. Neutrophil leucocyte
5. Eosinophil leucocyte
6. Neutrophil metamyelocyte
7. Basophil metamyelocyte
8. Eosinophil metamyelocyte
9. Neutrophil myelocyte
10. Myeloblast
11. Hemocytoblast
12. Lymphocyte
13. Late normoblast
14. Megakaryocyte

B. In pernicious anemia

1. Megaloblasts
2. Late normoblast
3. Giant neutrophil leucocyte
4. Erythroblast
5. Erythrocytes (macrocytes)
6. Megaloblast in mitosis

C. In microcytic anemia due to iron deficiency

1. Early normoblast
2. Erythrocytes (microcytes)
3. Extruded nucleus from normoblast
4. Late normoblasts
5. Eosinophil leucocyte
6. Myelocyte
7. Neutrophil leucocyte

*4.* The total *number of leukocytes is reduced* but the lymphocytes are relatively increased.

*5.* Great variation in the size of the cells—*anisocytosis*, the cells varying from those smaller than normal to the large cells mentioned above. *Poikilocytes* are moderate in number.

*6. Increase in iron and bilirubin* of the plasma; increased excretion of pigment (urobilin)—indirect van den Bergh.

*7. Blood volume reduced* mainly as a result of the red cell diminution, the plasma volume being around the normal level.

*8. Fragility of the red cells* usually slightly reduced.

OTHER FEATURES:

*1. The red bone marrow* is hyperplastic. It extends into the shafts of the bones displacing the yellow marrow and even the bony walls may be eroded. Upon microscopical examination the marrow shows megaloblasts and other immature forms in large numbers (see ch. 11 and Plate I).

*2.* Achlorhydria almost always exists.

*3.* Sore, shiny tongue, *glossitis*, atrophy of lingual papillae.

*4.* Chronic *combined degeneration of the cord.*

*5.* There is an atrophy of the mucosa of the fundus and body of the stomach.

*6.* Urobilin appears in the urine in severe cases; and in all those in which plasma bilirubin is increased urobilinogen is in excess in the feces. In health from 1/140 to 1/340 of the total amount of hemoglobin in the blood is excreted daily as urobilinogen. In pernicious anemia 1/10 of the total hemoglobin may be excreted as urobilinogen. Hemosiderin deposits (p. 75) occur.

*7.* The disease shows remissions and relapses. During the remissions, the blood picture approaches the normal and the percentage of reticulocytes increases—*reticulocyte crises.* During the relapses, the characteristic hematological features of the condition are exaggerated.

The essential factor in the production of pernicious anemia is not believed to be increased blood destruction, but rather a defect in blood formation. Increased blood destruction undoubtedly occurs as evidenced by the rise in plasma bilirubin, but it is a secondary effect. The abnormal erythrocytes probably stimulate the phagocytic activities of the reticuloendothelial cells in the spleen, liver and elsewhere. Since the fragility of the red cells is reduced rather than increased it would not appear that they disintegrate more readily in the blood stream. The discovery of an antianemic principle in liver and subsequent researches arising from the employment of this principle in the treatment of pernicious anemia

have shed a flood of light upon the nature of the disease.

LIVER, LIVER EXTRACT, GASTRIC TISSUE AND THE ANTIANEMIC FACTOR

In 1926 Minot and Murphy, inspired by the laboratory finding of Whipple and his associates, namely, that liver was the most effective article of diet for the treatment of anemia in dogs, tried the effect of adding liver to the diet of pernicious anemia patients. The spectacular success which followed this treatment is well known and today lightly cooked liver (from $\frac{1}{2}$ to 1 pound per day) but preferably an extract of liver, or the essential principle, vitamin $B_{12}$, is recognized as a specific for the disease. Kidney tissue was shown to have a similar though less pronounced curative effect. The hematopoietic substance present in the liver and in nonprotein extracts of liver tissue and which is effective in the treatment of pernicious anemia is known as vitamin $B_{12}$, or cyanocobalamin and formerly as the antianemic or hematinic principle. The action of vitamin $B_{12}$ is several times more potent given parenterally than when given orally. It may be mentioned here that Wilkinson found that the antianemic principle was present in normal human liver and in the livers of pernicious anemia patients who had received specific treatment, but was absent from the livers of untreated subjects of the disease.

*The Chemical Identification of the Antianemic Factor, $B_{12}$*

In 1948 Rickes and his associates and Smith reported the isolation of red, needle-shaped crystals of a substance which was many times more potent than the most purified extracts of liver in the treatment of pernicious anemia, causing a reticulocyte response in pernicious anemia patients in a parenteral dose of 1 $\mu$g., or even less. The red crystalline material, now generally referred to as vitamin $B_{12}$, has since been shown to be a cobalt complex, and is apparently the antianemic factor in pure or nearly pure form. It also contains phosphorus and nitrogen, but no sulfur; its molecular weight is around 1350 and its formula is $C_{63}H_{90}O_{14}N_{14}PCo$. Its chemical designation is cyanocobalamin.

Several analogues of this compound have been obtained from bacterial cultures, from the gastrointestinal contents of animals and from feces, sewage, etc.

It may be mentioned that the cobalt ion by itself elicits no hemopoietic response in pernicious anemia.

Besides its importance in hemopoiesis and its action in promoting the growth of certain bacteria, vitamin $B_{12}$ is a growth factor for higher animals, including man. It also has an influence upon the metabolism of certain sulfur containing amino acids (e.g., conversion of homocystine to methionine). According to Niewig, vitamin $B_{12}$ is essential for the synthesis of ribonucleic acid, a constituent of the nuclei of all cells; this would account for the neurological defects in pernicious anemia, and for the abnormalities of certain epithelial surfaces, such as that of the tongue (in the production of glossitis), as well as for the failure in erythrocyte maturation.

Vitamin $B_{12}$ is by far the most potent hemopoietic principle known, being several thousand times more potent weight for weight than folic acid. $B_{12}$ is also effective in arresting the course of the neurological lesions of pernicious anemia.

### The Production of the Antianemic Principle, Intrinsic and Extrinsic Factors

As already mentioned, irreversible gastric atrophy occurs and achlorhydria is virtually an invariable accompaniment of pernicious anemia. The significance of this fact was demonstrated in 1929 by Castle who found that the gastric contents of a normal person during the digestion of meat were curative when fed to a subject of pernicious anemia. Later Castle and his associates showed that pure gastric juice obtained from a normal person by the administration of histamine when incubated with beef steak produced the curative material. The active principle was not produced when beef was incubated with gastric juice of a patient with pernicious anemia. The production of the anti-anemic principle is not due to the action of hydrochloric acid, pepsin, rennin or lipase but to the presence of an enzymelike but unidentified substance which acts at a pH of 7 (the optimal pH for the action of pepsin is 1.6). Before this, Sturgis and Isaacs found that gastric tissue contained the material necessary for the formation of the antianemic factor, it being, like liver itself, effective in the treatment of pernicious anemia. Desiccated defatted hog stomach is, therefore, also employed as an alternative to liver or liver extract for oral administration. The gastric factor is less stable than the liver principle, being destroyed by temperatures above 45°C. or by digestion with pepsin or trypsin. In the hog, the gastric factor is produced by the mucosa of the pyloric and cardiac regions of the stomach and the commencement of the duodenum, i.e., regions which secrete an alkaline juice (pyloric, cardiac and Brunner's glands). In the human subject the factor, according to Fox and Castle, is formed in the fundus and body of the stomach; none is found in the pyloric region nor in the duodenal secretions.

Two factors, therefore, were recognized as being essential for normal erythropoiesis: one in the food, especially in such items of diet as are rich in the vitamin B complex; it was called the *extrinsic* factor and for years eluded the keenest research, but was finally identified as vitamin $B_{12}$ ; the other factor is secreted in the gastric juice and is known as the *intrinsic* factor.

A characteristic lesion is found in pernicious anemia which readily explains the achlorhydria, and the lack of the intrinsic factor. The fundus and body of the stomach show atrophy of the mucosa and extreme thinning of all coats. The gastric glands are almost completely destroyed; the muscular coat is atrophic. The pyloric region, which does not produce the intrinsic factor, is normal. One would be led to expect that total gastrectomy in man would be followed by pernicious anemia. If the survival time following total gastrectomy is sufficient to permit exhaustion of the vitamin $B_{12}$ stores an anemia of the pernicious type develops.

### The Extrinsic Factor; the Action of the Intrinsic Factor

The extrinsic factor (vitamin $B_{12}$) is present in liver, beef, rice polishings, yeast, and other substances rich in the vitamin B complex. It is also found in the intestinal contents of normal persons, as well as in the feces of patients with pernicious anemia. There is, therefore, no reason to believe that a dietary deficiency of this factor is the cause of the disease. The basic defect in pernicious anemia is the failure of the gastric mucosa to produce, at least in effective amounts, the intrinsic factor. It is now believed that this factor is essential for the adequate *absorption* of vitamin $B_{12}$ . This may involve some combination with the vitamin or it may influence some specific process in the gut wall involved in the absorption of the vitamin. When the intrinsic factor is given, the fecal excretion of vitamin $B_{12}$ labelled with radioactive cobalt is reduced. There is also the possibility that the intrinsic factor by binding vitamin $B_{12}$ keeps it from being taken up by the intestinal bacteria, thus ensuring that it will be available for absorption. In the absence of the intrinsic factor there is "starvation in the midst of plenty" in so far as the extrinsic factor is concerned. For this reason $B_{12}$ is effective given parenterally in pernicious anemia in a fraction of the dose that is required by mouth. However, if $B_{12}$ is administered with normal gastric juice the size of the effective oral dose is much reduced. In concluding this section the following remarks of Castle may be quoted:

"The disease would not develop if the patient could effect daily the transfer of a millionth of a gram of vitamin $B_{12}$ the distance of a small portion of a millimeter across the intestinal mucosa and into the blood stream. This he cannot do, principally as a result of failure of his stomach to secrete into its lumen some essential but still unknown substance. Yet the patient may each day absorb without much difficulty the products of the digestion of many grams of carbohydrate, fat and protein from foods that in addition may contain consequential amounts of vitamin $B_{12}$ in terms of his trivial need."

### Other Megaloblastic Anemias

Though pernicious anemia is the most common type of anemia showing a megaloblastic bone marrow, there are other forms with closely similar marrow and blood pictures but whose pathogeneses are not altogether clear. Such megaloblastic anemias occur in *tropical sprue, pregnancy, carcinoma of the stomach, gastrocolic fistula* which short circuits the region of the small intestine from which $B_{12}$ is absorbed, and *infestation with the tapeworm, Diphyllobothrium latum*. The anemia of sprue, in which the absorption of fat is defective, is due possibily to the interference with the absorption of vitamin $B_{12}$ other than through a lack of the intrinsic factor, though in certain cases the latter is absent even though there is not achlorhydria. In the megaloblastic anemia of pregnancy the marrow and blood pictures are similar to those of pernicious anemia, but there is as a rule not true achlorhydria, nor degenerative changes in the spinal cord; recovery follows childbirth. Also, many cases of this disease, like that described by Wills as occurring in the tropics, and called *tropical nutritional (or macrocytic) anemia*, are unresponsive to the administration of vitamin $B_{12}$, but respond readily to crude liver extracts or to folic acid.[1] In carcinoma of the stomach there is achlorhydria and the anemia may be indistin-

---

[1] Tropical nutritional anemia occurs most frequently and severely in pregnant women. An anemia with similar characters, which is resistant to treatment with purified preparations of liver, but is amenable to crude liver extracts or folic acid can be produced in monkeys.

guishable in every way from pernicious anemia, even to the neurological symptoms; it is probably produced in the same manner—lack of the intrinsic factor. In the anemia caused by *Diphyllobothrium latum*, there is no lack of the intrinsic factor, but the worm interferes in some way with the utilization of the vitamin. Possibly this is caused by the parasite producing a principle that inhibits the specific action of the intrinsic factor, or by its absorbing or utilizing the vitamin in its own metabolism. The investigations of von Bonsdorff indicate that the parasite must be situated high up in the small intestine in order to cause anemia. Finally, a rare type of megaloblastic anemia which fails to respond to the hematinic principle was described originally by Wilkinson and Israels. It is not due to the lack of the erythrocyte maturation factor ($B_{12}$), but to failure of the latter to be utilized by the bone marrow. It was, therefore, named *achrestic anemia*.

### The Response to Liver or Gastric Tissue

The antianemic principle acts upon the bone marrow, restoring the blood-forming processes to normal. It is believed that megaloblastosis is not the result of a simple arrest of the maturation of red blood cells, but that the megaloblasts result from a long resting phase between stages of mitoses. Hence factors retarding cell division can lead to the production of this type of cell. The slow cell production results from the deficient for-

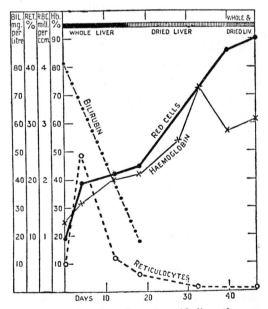

FIG. 9.3. Showing effect of specific liver therapy upon the reticulocytes, erythrocytes, hemoglobin and plasma bilirubin (after Dyke).

mation of DNA (desoxyribonucleic acid) and RNA (ribonucleic acid) which is a consequence of a lack of vitamin $B_{12}$. The direct effect of $B_{12}$ upon erythropoiesis has been demonstrated in man; when the vitamin is injected into megaloblastic bone marrow, the abnormal erythropoiesis is corrected locally before a general effect occurs (i.e., on the marrow in other situations).

The first detectable effect of specific treatment in pernicious anemia is a rise in the reticulocytes. In untreated cases of pernicious anemia these constitute 2 per cent or less of the red cells. Within 2 to 5 days after vitamin $B_{12}$, a potent liver extract, or a preparation of gastric tissue has been administered, large numbers of reticulocytes appear. The increase reaches its maximum about the fifth day, when the percentage is from 10 to 40 per cent. From then on the reticulocyte population declines, and there is an increased number of mature erythrocytes. The lower the red cell count before treatment, the greater is the reticulocyte response to specific therapy.

The rise in the hemoglobin concentration of the blood lags behind the multiplication of the red cells. If the stimulus to erythropoiesis is intense, the hemoglobin cannot be manufactured in suffi-

**Pteroylglutamic Acid. Synonyms: Folic Acid, Vitamin $B_c$[4], Liver *Lactobacillus casei* Factor, Norite-eluate Factor, Vitamin M, Wills Factor, Factor U**

In 1941 Mitchell and his associates obtained a substance with acidic properties from the green leaves of various plants, e.g., spinach, peas, clover, etc., and gave it the appropriate name of *folic acid*. What has since proved to be the same principle had previously, from microbiological studies, been found in concentrates of liver and yeast (*norite-eluate factor*). It stimulates the growth of certain microorganisms, e.g., *Lactobacillus casei*, *Streptococcus faecalis* R (or *S. lactis* R), and is essential for the existence of certain protozoa and insects. It is, therefore, also known as the *liver L. casei factor*, but is now more commonly referred to by its chemical name *pteroylglutamic acid* (PGA). It is made up of a pteridyl ring joined through para-aminobenzoic acid to a molecule of glutamic acid. Para-aminobenzoic (PAB) acid appears to be a precursor from which pteroylglutamic acid is synthesized in nature. The chemical structure of pteroylglutamic acid is shown below.

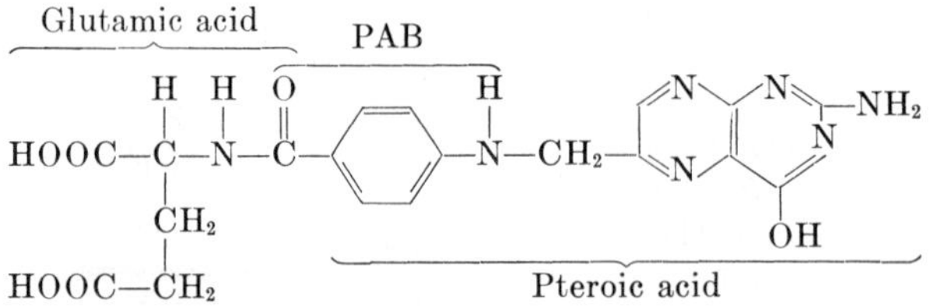

Pteroylglutamic acid: N-[4-{[(2-amino-4-hydroxy-6-pteridyl) methyl] amino}-benzoyl] glutamic acid.

cient quantities to furnish each cell with its quota of pigment and the color index and M.C.H. fall well below the normal value.

With the improvement in the blood picture the general symptoms of the disease abate, but the secretion of acid gastric juice is rarely if ever restored. Specific treatment therefore does not remove the primary cause of the disease, but must be persisted in for the rest of the patient's life. The maintenance dose is, of course, much less than that required originally for the restoration of the normal blood picture. The neurological symptoms may improve if vitamin $B_{12}$ is given early, and in a dosage considerably greater than that required for maintaining the normal blood picture. The degenerative changes in the cord are due to the lack of the hematinic principle, and are not simply secondary to and caused by the anemia.

Of fundamental importance in the physiology of pteroylglutamic acid is its indispensability for the synthesis of desoxyribonucleic acid, a constituent of the nuclei of all cells (ch. 47). Certain analogues of folic acid, such as, *aminopterin* (4-aminopteroylglutamic acid, or 4-aminofolic acid), *amethopterin* (4-amino-10-methyl pteroylglutamic acid) *aminoan-fol*) (4-aminopteroylaspartic acid) antagonize this action of the vitamin. Pteroylglutamic acid is synthesized in the intestine of some mammals, especially of the rat, and the analogues are useful in producing folic acid deficiency for experimental purposes. They have also been used in the treatment of acute leukemia, especially in children; the number of leukemic cells is reduced, and temporary remissions of the disease induced. A permanent cure does not, however, result, and the administration of the compounds is attended by certain toxic symptoms, e.g., stomatitis, diarrhea, alopecia and deafness.

### THE HEMOPOIETIC ACTION OF PTEROYLGLUTAMIC ACID

Several observations had pointed to the existence in liver, or in crude liver preparations, of a principle effective in certain macrocytic anemias which failed to respond to highly purified liver extracts. There also appeared reports of a beneficial action of preparations of brewer's yeast, which does not contain vitamin $B_{12}$, in macrocytic anemias and in the nutritional anemia of monkeys. Suspecting that the unknown hemopoietic substance in crude preparations of liver was "folic acid," Spies and his associates administered it to pernicious anemia patients with remarkable success. Pteroylglutamic acid is also effective in other anemias characterized by a megaloblastic bone marrow, e.g., the anemias of sprue and pregnancy, but fails in the treatment of macrocytic and other types of anemia with a normoblastic or macroblastic bone marrow. It relieves the nutritional leukopenia of monkeys and stimulates the production of granulocytes, and is therefore of value in the treatment of agranulocytosis (p. 96). *It has no effect whatever in arresting the progress of the neurological lesions (chronic combined degeneration of the cord) in pernicious anemia.* Indeed, the neurological signs appear to be aggravated by its administration. Its action in restoring the bone marrow to normal is identical with that of the vitamin $B_{12}$.

Pteroylglutamic acid was synthesized by Angier and associates in 1945. The synthetic compound is as therapeutically effective as the natural principle.

The chief sources of "folic acid" are liver, kidney and green vegetables; its concentration in plant foods appears to run parallel with their chlorophyll content.

### THE POSSIBLE RELATIONSHIP OF THE ANTIANEMIC FACTOR OF LIVER AND PTEROYLGLUTAMIC ACID

The chemistry and actions of "folic acid" and of the antianemic factor of liver show that they are separate and distinct principles. Moreover, it soon became evident that the concentration of "folic acid" in highly purified and potent liver extracts is equivalent to only a small fraction of the amount required to elicit a reticulocyte response in pernicious anemia. Again, as mentioned above, pteroylglutamic acid is wholly ineffective in arresting the cord changes of pernicious anemia. The nonidentity of the two principles was finally settled by the isolation of crystalline $B_{12}$.

Both vitamin $B_{12}$ and folic acid seem to be essential in the synthesis of nucleoproteins. It is thought that folic acid is necessary for DNA formation, but that vitamin $B_{12}$ is essential for both DNA and RNA synthesis. Since both DNA and RNA are necessary for the maintenance of the structure and function of neurons, this may explain why $B_{12}$ is effective in improving the neurological condition in pernicious anemia, and folic acid is not.

*"Citrovorum factor"; "folinic acid"; leucovorum.* A derivative of pteroylglutamic acid which promoted the growth of the microorganism, *Leuconostoc citrovorum*, was isolated in 1948 by Sauberlich and Baumann from liver extracts and yeast. This substance which is now known as the *"citrovorum factor"* has an action similar to that of pteroylglutamic acid in pernicious anemia and other megaloblastic anemias; it also annuls the toxic effects of such folic acid antagonists as aminopterin and amethopterin. Substances with the same action, and apparently identical with the "citrovorum factor" have been prepared artificially, and named *"folinic acid"* (Shive and associates), and *leucovorum* (Jukes and associates).

*Other antianemic agents.* The pyrimidine base *thymine* (5-methyluracil) and *xanthopterin* (uropterin) give a hematopoietic response, but one which is much inferior to that of pteroylglutamic acid. An amount of thymine several thousand times the weight of an effective dose of pteroylglutamic acid is required to produce a reticulocyte response in pernicious anemia (Spies and associates).

## Macrocytic (Hypochromic or Hyperchromic) Anemias with Normoblastic Bone Marrow

Macrocytic anemias showing a resemblance to Addisonian anemia, in so far as the blood picture is concerned, occur in various diseases, e.g., carcinoma (other than gastric), syphilis, etc. But the bone marrow is of the normoblastic type. Since they are not due to deficiency of the antianemic principle, they do not respond to the administration of liver extract or of gastric tissue. Nor do they respond to the administration of "folic acid."

## Idiopathic Aplastic Anemia

This is a comparatively rare type of anemia in which there is a rapidly progressive reduction in all the blood cells—erythrocytes, leukocytes and platelets. There is little or no evidence of blood regeneration, reticulocytes are very scarce and nucleated forms are usually absent. The red cell count may reach an extraordinarily low figure— 213,000 per cu. mm. in a case reported by Ehrlich.

Granulocytes and platelets may entirely disappear. The marrow is hypoplastic or aplastic; there is a great reduction in its cellular elements and almost complete absence of hemopoietic activity. The lymphocytopenia which also occurs, but is less marked than the reduction in granulocytes, suggests that the entire hemopoietic system is affected. The causes of the bone marrow hypoplasia have been mentioned.

A number of cases have been reported (Thompson, Richter and Edsall; Anderson) in which the typical blood picture of aplastic anemia was associated with a normal or even a hyperplastic marrow. In these, to which the term "pseudoaplastic anemia" might be applied, there would appear to be some interference with the maturation and delivery of the cells into the blood stream rather than to absolute suppression of marrow function.

## Conclusions

It is only upon pernicious anemia or macrocytic anemias of the pernicious anemia type with a megaloblastic bone marrow that vitamin $B_{12}$ or "folic acid" therapy has any specific effect. Other macrocytic types (with a normoblastic type of marrow), the microcytic anemias and aplastic anemia fail to respond to the administration of liver extract, gastric tissue or pteroylglutamic acid. It has been mentioned that certain megaloblastic anemias (e.g., that of pregnancy) are resistant to the action of vitamin $B_{12}$ but respond to folic acid. In posthemorrhagic anemia and certain other secondary anemias *whole liver* is of value, not from any specific action but simply because it furnishes iron and protein of high quality.

## REFERENCES

ANGIER, R. B. AND ASSOCIATES. Science, 1946, 103, 667.

VON BONSDORFF, B. Blood, 1948, 3, 91.

CASTLE, W. B. AND ASSOCIATES. Am. J. M. Sc., 1929, 178, 764. New England J. Med., 1948, 239, 911; 1953, 249, 603.

DAMESHEK, W. AND SCHWARTZ, S. O. Am. J. M. Sc., 1938, 196, 769.

ERSLEV, A. J. Blood, 1955, 10, 954.

FOX, H. J. AND CASTLE, W. B. Am. J. M. Sc., 1942, 203, 18.

GIBLETT, E. R., COLEMAN, D. H., PIRZIO-BIROLI, G., DONOHUE, D. M., MOTULSKY, A. G. AND FINCH, C. A., Blood, 1956, 11, 29.

JACOBSON, B. M. AND SUBBAROW, Y., J. Clin. Invest., 1937, 16, 573.

JUKES, T. H. Fed. Proc., 1953, 12, 633; B-vitamins for blood formation, Am. Lecture Series, Charles C Thomas, Springfield, Ill., 1952.

KARRER, P. Schweiz. med. Wchnschr., 1941, 71, 343.

LOUTIT, J. F. AND MOLLISON, P. L. J. Path. Bact., 1946, 58, 711.

MINOT, G. R. AND MURPHY, W. P. J. A. M. A., 1926, 87, 470; 1927, 89, 759.

MITCHELL, H. K., SNELL, E. E. AND WILLIAMS, R. J. J. Am. Chem. Soc., 1944, 66, 267.

MULLER, G. L. Am. J. Physiol., 1927, 82, 269.

NIEWEG, H. O., CITED BY CASTLE, W. B., New England J. Med., 1953, 249, 603.

PFIFFNER, J. J. AND ASSOCIATES. Science, 1945, 102, 228. J. Biol. Chem., 1945, 157, 413.

REISSNER, E. H. Blood, 1958, 13, 313.

RICKES, E. L. AND COLLEAGUES. Science, 1948, 107, 396, 398; 108, 134.

SAUBERLICH, H. E. AND BAUMANN, G. A. J. Biol. Chem., 1948, 176, 165.

SHIVE, W. AND ASSOCIATES. J. Am. Chem. Soc., 1950, 72, 2818.

SMITH, E. L. Nature, 1948, 161, 638.

SPIES, T. D. AND ASSOCIATES. South. M. J. 1945, 38, 590; Blood, 1946, 1, 271; Lancet, 1948, 2, 519.

STURGIS, C. C. AND ISAACS, R. J. A. M. A., 1929, 93, 747.

SUÁREZ, R. AND ASSOCIATES. J. Lab. & Clin. Med., 1946, 31, 2384.

THOMPSON, W. P., RICHTER, M. N. AND EDSALL, K. S. Am. J. M. Sc., 1934, 187, 77.

WILKINSON, J. F. AND ISRAELS, M. C. G. Brit. M. J., 1935, 1, 139.

*Monographs and Reviews*

CASTLE, W. B. Harvey Lectures, 1934–1935, 30, 37.

CASTLE, W. B. New England J. Med., 1953, 249, 603.

DAVIDSON, L. S. P. AND LEITCH, I. Nutrition Abstr. & Rev., 1934, 3, 1.

HEATH, C. W. AND PATEK, A. J. Medicine, 1937, 16, 267.

JACOBS, M. H. Ann. Rev. Physiol., 1958, 20, 405.

JOSEPHS, H. W. Medicine, 1936, 15, 307.

JUKES, T. H. AND STOKSTAD, E. L. R. Physiol. Rev., 1948, 28, 51.

MOORE, C. V. Am. J. Clin. Nutrition, 1955, 3, 3.

PINEY, A. AND WYARD, S. Clinical atlas of blood diseases. J. and A. Churchill, Ltd., London, 1932.

SPIES, T. D. Experiences with folic acid. Year Book Publishers, Inc., Chicago, 1947.

VAUGHN, J. M. The anaemias. Oxford University Press, London, 1934.

WELCH, A. Fed. Proc., 1947, 6, 471.

WINTROBE, M. M. Medicine, 1930, 9, 195.

WINTROBE, M. M. Clinical hematology. Lea and Febiger, Philadelphia, 1956.

WINTROBE, M. M. AND BEEBE, R. T. Medicine, 1933, 12, 187.

# 10

# THE WHITE BLOOD CORPUSCLES OR LEUKOCYTES— THE PLATELETS

## Classification and Morphology

The white blood cells differs from the erythrocyte in that it contains no hemoglobin and has a nucleus. The majority of the white cells are also considerably larger than the erythrocytes, measuring from 8 to 15 $\mu$ in diameter, the size depending upon the particular variety. They are much less numerous than the red cells; in the adult they number from 5000 to 9000 per cu. mm. of blood. In infancy they are twice as numerous and throughout childhood the count is higher than in the adult. When a film of adult blood is examined under the microscope the white cells appear very sparsely scattered here and there among the crowds of colored corpuscles which outnumber them more than 600 to 1.

On a basis of morphological differences the colorless corpuscles are divided first into two main groups: (I) *Cells with a single nucleus and a clear nongranular cytoplasm*—the lymphocytes and the monocytes; (II) *cells having a lobed or incompletely partitioned nucleus, and a cytoplasm containing fine chromophil granules*—the granulocytes. Each of these two main classes is divided further into subgroups on a basis of differences in structure or staining properties[1] (see frontispiece).

### I. THE NONGRANULAR LEUKOCYTES— AGRANULOCYTES

These are of three varieties: (1) *Small lymphocyte*, (2) *large lymphocyte*, (3) *monocyte*. Although these forms show no granules in the protoplasm under the ordinary methods of staining, granulation may be demonstrated after staining with azure blue. The lymphocytes contain a few coarse azurophil granules; those of the monocytes are fine and very numerous.

[1] The term leukocyte is employed by most authors to denote all the white cells, and this from the simple meaning of the word seems logical. Some, however, confine the term to the granulocytes. The first of these usages will be followed in this text.

1. SMALL LYMPHOCYTES. These are slightly larger than the red cells—about 8 $\mu$ in diameter. The nucleus is relatively large, slightly indented and stains more deeply with basic dyes than the surrounding narrow rim of cytoplasm which separates it from the boundary of the cell. The small lymphocytes originate in lymphoid tissue and are found in large numbers in the lymph nodes and spleen. They constitute in the adult from 20 to 25 per cent of the total number of white cells in blood and are the commonest cells found in lymph. In childhood lymphoid tissue is much more abundant than in adult life and the lymphocytes are more numerous. They amount to from 50 per cent or more of the leukocytes in early childhood and to about 35 per cent at the age of 10 years.

2. LARGE LYMPHOCYTES. These resemble the preceding in general appearance but are considerably larger, being 12 $\mu$ or more in diameter. The cytoplasm forms a wider zone about the nucleus, which is oval or kidney shaped. These cells are found in insignificant numbers in adult blood but are more plentiful in the blood of young children. They are largely confined under physiological conditions to the lymphoid tissue, but even here they are greatly outnumbered by the small lymphocytes. They are considered by many as a younger form of the small lymphocyte.

3. MONOCYTES are from 10 to 15 $\mu$ in diameter. They possess a relatively larger amount of cytoplasm. The nucleus has a deep indentation on one side, which gives it a kidney or saddlebag shape. On the supposition that this cell represented a stage in the development of the polymorphonuclear leukocyte, it was called the "transitional leukocyte" by Ehrlich. This view has since been shown to be wrong, for the monocyte bears a relationship to the lymphocytes rather than to the polymorphonuclears. It has been mentioned that the monocyte contains, like the lymphocytes, azurophil granules in the cytoplasm. The monocytes are actively motile and phagocytic, and are considered by most observers to be derived from fixed histiocytes (p. 102). Such an origin would

class them as circulating elements of the reticulo-endothelial system. According to Maximow, however, they arise from lymphocytes. They constitute from 5 to 7 per cent of the white cells.

Small numbers (0.2 per cent) of a slightly different type of monocyte are also found in blood. Its nucleus instead of being kidney-shaped is round or oval. It was previously known as the large mononuclear leukocyte, but it is probably simply a younger form of the preceding variety.

## II. The Granulocytes

These are divided into three groups according to the staining reactions of their granules. One type—the *eosinophilic*—stains with acid dyes, e.g., eosin; another—the *basophilic*—stains with basic dyes, e.g., methylene blue; and the third type—the *neutrophilic*—with neutral dyes, i.e., mixtures of acid and basic dyes. These staining reactions apply to human leukocytes, but such distinctions cannot always be made in other animal species. The nucleus of a granulocyte is composed of two or more lobes connected together by strands of chromatin.

1. Eosinophils are not numerous; they amount to no more than 2 to 4 per cent of the total white cell count. The granules which are oval and much coarser than those in the other two varieties are stained a bright red with eosin. The cell is also slightly larger and the nucleus usually bilobed. In certain pathological conditions which will be mentioned later they may form a much larger percentage of the leukocyte population.

2. Basophils are present to the extent of only

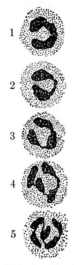

1
2
3
4
5

Fig. 10.1. Arneth stages.

0.15 per cent or less. Their granules stain deeply with methylene blue. Their significance is not known. They have been considered by some observers to be degenerated neutrophils, but there appears to be little doubt that they are a distinct type and like the other granulocytes are a product of the bone marrow. Support is lent to the latter view by the fact that they are increased in conditions associated with excessive marrow activity, e.g., chronic myelocytic leukemia and polycythemia vera. They are also increased in chronic inflammation of the accessory nasal sinuses.

3. Neutrophils are by far the most numerous, constituting from 65 to 70 per cent or more of the total number of white cells. Their granules are quite small and are stained a violet tint with neutral dyes. As will be seen presently the neutrophils are actively ameboid in character, i.e., they are capable of locomotion and ingest foreign particulate matter. They are about 10 or 12 $\mu$ in diameter. Their nuclei show a variable number of lobes depending upon the age of the cell.

### The Arneth Count or Index

It was pointed out by Arneth that the number of lobes in any neutrophil depends upon the cell's age, the older cells having the larger number.[2] A five-lobed nucleus for instance indicates a stage in the life of a cell just preceding its final dissolution; an unlobed but deeply indented nucleus, a very young cell. Five stages in the life history of the polymorphonuclear leukocyte are therefore distinguished corresponding to the number of lobed developed in the nucleus. A count of the nuclear lobes in the cells of a blood film will give the proportion of cells of different relative ages. In figure 10.1, stage I shows a nucleus with a single lobe. Constriction of the nucleus can be seen but the nuclear substance is continuous from one part to the other. In stage II the nucleus is partitioned into two parts which are connected only by chromatin threads. In the next stage 3 lobes are seen and so on to the last or senile stage in which the nucleus has five or more lobes. The cells of this stage are large, edematous and nonmotile; their granules strain poorly or not at all. In some conditions, e.g., acute septic infections and pernicious anemia, enormous neutrophils (up to 20 $\mu$) with a great number of nuclei are seen. These are known as *macropolycytes*.

The Arneth index is determined by counting the number of nuclear lobes in each of 100 neutrophils. The cells in the different stages are expressed as

[2] The extent of the previous activity of the cell, rather than its age, may be the important factor determining the number of nuclear lobes.

percentages of the total. The count under the ordinary conditions of health is as follows:

|  | *Percentages of leukocytes* |
|---|---|
| Stage I | 5 |
| Stage II | 30 |
| Stage III | 45 |
| Stage IV | 18 |
| Stage V | 2 |

In certain diseases the youngest cells (stage I) are much more numerous and may constitute 50 per cent of the total. There may be an entire absence of cells in the later stages (IV and V). An increase in the percentage of cells of the earlier stages is spoken of as a "shift to the left." It is seen in conditions which stimulate the bone marrow to a greater production of white cells, e.g., pyogenic infections. It is also seen in tuberculosis and after exposure to the X-rays and after the injection of thyroid extract. In children a shift to the left occurs much more readily than in adults. In pernicious anemia the percentages of the older cells increase—"shift to the right"—and in some cases, as mentioned above, macropolycytes appear. Except in the case of the senile nonmotile cells a relationship between the phagocytic activity of a particular cell and its age has not been demonstrated.

*The Schilling index* employs a simpler classification of the neutrophils but includes marrow elements. Four stages are recognized (see table 10.1) (a) the myelocyte which shows a single spherical nucleus; (b) young metamyelocyte with a slight indentation of the nucleus; (c) older metamyelocytes with the process of lobulation definitely indicated; this is known as the band cell of Schilling or "Staff" cell and corresponds to the first stage of Arneth; (d) older neutrophils, i.e., the other stages of Arneth. Stages (a) and (b) are not found normally in the blood. They appear when a pronounced "shift to the left" occurs (see frontispiece and ch. 11).

The nonmotile cells of the last or fifth stage of Arneth appear, periodically in increased numbers—in "showers"—in the blood stream. They are replaced by young cells from the marrow. Like the red cell the dying neutrophils disintegrate in the circulation or are disposed of by the macrophages of the spleen or the tissues. The life span of the neutrophils has been variously estimated. By some it is believed to be no more than about 3 days and by others no more than a few hours. Ponder, however, puts it at 21 days. He induced a leukocytosis and shift to the left in the Arneth stages by the injection of thyroid extract and followed the blood picture until the poly-

## TABLE 10.1

*Showing Schilling index and differential count of mature cells; figures indicate percentages*

| Neutrophils | | | | Eosinophils | Basophils | Lymphocytes | Monocytes |
|---|---|---|---|---|---|---|---|
| Myelocytes | Juvenile metamyelocytes | Older metamyelocytes | Nucleus lobular | | | | |
| 0 | 0–1 | 3–5 | 55–70 | 2–4 | 0–1 | 20–25 | 5–7 |

nuclear count returned to normal. Since the rise in the count is due to discharge of young cells (Stage I) from the marrow, when the count again showed the normal percentage of cells of Stage V it was assumed that the discharged cells had reached the end of their life span. At any rate the average life of the neutrophils is apparently much shorter than that of the red cell (p. 70).

### The Functions of the Leukocytes

The neutrophilic polymorphonuclear leuko- as well as the monocytes and other reticuloendothelial elements constitute probably the most important elements which the body possesses for its defense against invading microorganisms. Their power to attack bacteria depends upon their motility and a proclivity for the ingestion of solid particles. The latter action, which was first demonstrated by Metchnikoff, is termed *phagocytosis* (phago—I eat). These two varieties of white blood cell are free lances among the body cells; they wander from place to place through the tissues and practically no part of the body is barred to them. They insinuate a process (*pseudopodium*), improvised at the moment from their cell protoplasm, through one of the joints in the endothelium of the capillary wall. Then by causing the semifluid substance of the cell body to stream into the protoplasmic projection, they pass out of the blood vessels "at will." By this action of *diapedesis*,[3] as it is called, myriads of white corpuscles may pass out of the vessels in a remarkably short time. Reaching a point where the bacteria have entered the body they surround the threatened area and proceed to destroy the invaders. If, for instance, an actively inflamed region should be examined under the microscope, masses of neutrophils would be seen, and many of these would be

[3] The term diapedesis, literally a "leaping through," is sometimes applied to the passage of red cells through an unbroken capillary wall, but the term is scarcely appropriate for a passive process of this nature.

observed to hold bacteria imprisoned within their bodies. As many as 15 or 20 microorganisms may be seen at times within a single cell. It has been shown that the bacteria are ingested alive and remain so for a time within the leukocyte (fig. 10.2).

When a tissue such as the mesentery or web of a frog, in which the capillaries are clearly visible, is examined in the living state a short time after a culture of bacteria has been injected into it, the small vessels leading to the site of inoculation are found swarming with neutrophils. In the surrounding tissues the ameboid cells are seen moving somewhat ponderously hither and thither to engulf the offending bacteria. When the latter are intensely virulent in nature this normal leukocyte reaction may be seriously depressed. The monocytes, though much less numerous, also join in the general attack and show their phagocytic propensities to a marked degree. After the first flooding of the tissues with neutrophils and monocytes, numbers of the latter come to rest and together with other reticuloendothelial elements of the tissues undergo transformation and aid in isolating the infected area from the neighboring healthy tissues. Until this is accomplished the danger of the infection becoming more widespread always exists. In their struggle against bacteria, equipped as these are with powerful toxins, many of the white cells are killed. These collect within the center of the inflamed area together with exuded plasma, liquefied tissue cells and a few red cells that have escaped through the injured walls of the capillaries. This material constitutes pus, and the so-called pus cells are dead leukocytes. The circumscribing wall and its semifluid contents constitute an abscess. By the action of the phagocytes, aided by a protein-digesting ferment (protease) which they elaborate, the overlying structures whether connective tissue, mucosa or skin are in part removed piece-

meal. In this way a communication with the exterior is effected and the contents of the cavity are discharged.

Not only bacteria but practically any foreign material, whether a rose thorn or a catgut suture, is attacked and removed if possible, or loosened by the neutrophils aided by the monocytes and other phagocytic cells of the tissues. The removal of dead tissue or of blood clot or the separation of necrotic from living structures is accomplished in the same way. Devitalized bone, although not removed in its entirety, unless it is of very small size is nevertheless eroded and separated from the living tissue by the leukocytes. The disappearance of effete organs such as the tail and gills of the metamorphosing tadpole or the creeping muscles of insect larvae, as these develop to the mature form, is effected by similar phagocytic cells. The application of heat to a part also attracts leukocytes in large numbers to the capillaries from which they immediately commence to migrate.

The activity of the leukocytes is best studied by the method of Sandison and Clarke, in which a transparent chamber is inserted into the tissues, e.g., the rabbit's ear. After a time fine vessels grow into the chamber through openings in its sides which may be examined under the microscope. Another very simple method is that of *supravital staining*. A thin film of a non-toxic (supravital) dye, e.g., neutral red, azure, or brilliant cresyl blue, is laid upon a glass slide and allowed to dry; a film of blood is laid over this and covered with an ordinary cover glass which is then sealed with vaseline around the edges. The preparation is kept warm and examined under the microscope, the cells remaining alive and active. The neutrophils seen in such preparations are not uniformly spherical as in fixed smears, but are continually changing their shape. Pseudopodia are in constant movement and the granules can be seen streaming through the cytoplasm with each movement of the cell. The rate of progression of the neutrophil is from 30 to 35 $\mu$ per minute at body temperature (fig. 10.2).

Of the functions of the other varieties of granulocytes—the *eosinophils* and *basophils*—little is known. The eosinophils are not markedly motile and only slightly phagocytic.

The *lymphocytes*—although, generally speaking, they are not phagocytic—appear to exert such an action upon certain pathogenic microorganisms, notably, pneumococci types III and IV. A great migration of lymphocytes characterizes certain chronic types of inflammation.

An important function of the lymphocytes is the manufacture of serum globulin, both $\beta$- and $\gamma$-fractions having been found in extracts of lymphocytes. Immune substances (antibodies) are rec-

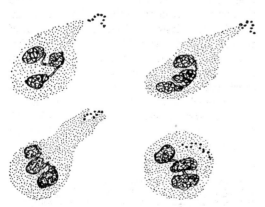

Fig. 10.2 Drawing of a neutrophil at half-minute intervals to show motility and phagocytosis of bacteria.

ognized as being associated with the γ-globulin fraction, so it was presumed that the lymphocytes occupied a key position in defense reactions of an immunological nature. The investigations of White and Dougherty have gone a long way to substantiate this idea. The lymphocytes and serum of mice which had been immunized to sheep erythrocytes contained an antibody which lysed these cells, but none was found in the lymphocytes or serum of nonimmunized mice. Furthermore, extracts of the lymphocytes of the immunized animals contained antibody in a concentration from six to eight times higher than that found in the serum. Antihemolysins to staphylococcus toxin have also been demonstrated in the lymphocytes of mice immunized to this toxin. The production of antibodies in the lymph nodes was first demonstrated by McMaster and Hudach in 1935, and Ehrich found that a threefold increase in output of lymphocytes from the nodes accompanied the antibody production.

The manner in which the lymphocytes add globulin to the plasma appears to be by a process of cytoplasmic budding and ultimate dissolution in the lymphoid tissues and blood stream. Budding can be observed within a Sandison-Clarke chamber inserted into the tissues.

The supply of globulin to the blood is apparently under the control of the pituitary gland through the action of its adrenocorticotrophic hormone upon the adrenal cortex. The pituitary-adrenal influence was demonstrated by White and Dougherty in the following way. Rabbits were immunized to sheep corpuscles and, after the specific antibody had appeared in the circulation, were left untreated for a period of three months, when all antibody had disappeared. They were then divided into four groups. One group was injected with the original antigen; no significant rise in antibody concentration of the blood of these animals occurred. Of the remaining three groups, one was injected with steroid fractions of the adrenal cortex, another with the adrenocorticotrophic hormone of the pituitary (ACTH) and the third with an aqueous extract of adrenal cortex. The steroid hormones caused an increase in antibody concentration, nearly as great as that caused originally by immunization—a maximal dissolution of lymphocytes in the lymphoid tissues and a scarcity of lymphocytes in the circulation. The response to the pituitary principle was also pronounced, although not as great as that given by the steroids, whereas the aqueous extract caused a relatively small reaction. The adrenal cortical fractions which exert this effect are those with an

oxygen atom in the 11 position (see chapter 58). Corticosterone and 11-dehydro-17-hydroxycorticosterone are therefore effective in this respect but not desoxycorticosterone.

It has also been found that injections of adrenal cortical hormone, or of the pituitary principle, increase the bulk of lymphoid tissue as a result of edema, the edema fluid containing larger numbers of lymphocytes undergoing dissolution. Later, after the edema has subsided, the tissue shrinks until its weight is less than before the injections. Adrenalectomy is followed by an increase in the mass of lymphoid tissue.

The reduction in lymphocytes in response to adrenal cortical hormones and ACTH is of moderate degree. The eosinophils show a much more pronounced reduction in number following the administration of these principles. The eosinopenia occurs so consistently and is so delicate that it is employed as a means of assaying the potency of cortisone and ACTH. Adrenaline also causes eosinopenia, perhaps by stimulating ACTH production. Adrenalectomized animals show a lymphocytosis, and overgrowth of lymphoid tissue is not an uncommon feature of adrenal insufficiency (Addison's disease) in man.

### The Fate of the Lymphocytes

This has been a puzzling question for a number of years, for it has long been known that immense numbers of these cells disappear from the circulation daily. According to one estimate, the entire population of lymphocytes in the circulation of the dog are replaced twice each day (Drinker and Yoffey); replacement five times daily is given for the cat (Sanders and associates). Some have thought that lymphocytes were transformed into other types of cell, others that they returned to the lymph nodes and were destroyed in the germinal centers. But the most widely accepted explanation of the wastage of lymphocytes has been that they are shed from the mucosa of the gastrointestinal tract, and no doubt large numbers are discharged from the body in this way. Nevertheless, little effect is exerted upon the disappearance of lymphocytes in rabbits by the removal of the entire gastrointestinal tract and the injection of some 300,000,000 leukocytes into such a preparation does not cause a rise in the leukocyte count. It appears now from the work of the authors mentioned above that the large daily turnover of these cells is to a great extent at least the result of their dissolution in the lymphoid tissues and blood; thus globulin is supplied to the plasma.

### Variations in the Number of Leukocytes in the Blood Stream

#### LEUKOCYTOSIS

In the event of some damage to the tissues which calls forth a leukocytic response, not only is there a migration of leukocytes from the blood to the site of injury, but also a discharge of these cells from the marrow and an increase of their number in the general circulation. Instead of the normal count of 7000 or 8000 per cubic millimeter the colorless cells may number from 20,000 to 30,000 within a short time. *Leukocytosis* is the term used to designate an increase in the total number of white cells. All varieties of the white cells do not necessarily share in the increase. In one instance it may be the neutrophils, in another the lymphocytes or the eosinophils that are increased, and it is the presence in abnormal numbers of one or other of these which then gives the high total leukocyte count. It is often of great diagnostic value to know which type of cell is responsible for the leukocytosis, and in order to determine this a so-called *differential count* of the cells is made. That is, the numbers of the different types in a stained smear of blood are counted and their percentages of the total count determined. Also, changes in the proportions of the different white cell types may occur although their total number is normal. Such alterations can be revealed only by a differential count. The following example is given in illustration; the lymphocytes and monocytes are relatively increased; the neutrophils and eosinophils reduced.

| | |
|---|---|
| Total white cells per cu. mm...... | 7500 |
| Lymphocytes, per cent........ | 35 |
| Monocytes, per cent.......... | 8 |
| Neutrophils, per cent.......... | 56 |
| Eosinophils, per cent.......... | 0.7 |

Very commonly an increase in the neutrophils is entirely responsible for the leukocytosis. On this account the latter term is used frequently but somewhat loosely to imply an increase in the count caused by the neutrophilic elements alone. *Neutrophilia* is a more precise term that has come into use for the latter condition. *Lymphocytosis, monocytosis* and *eosinophilia* are the respective terms employed to designate increase in the other elements.

Acute infections by the pus-forming organisms —staphylococcus, streptococcus, etc., are the most potent causes of a neutrophilic increase. On this account the examination of the white cells furnishes a valuable diagnostic sign for the detection of hidden inflammatory conditions, e.g., appendicitis, empyema, etc. A neutrophilic leukocytosis occurs also in pneumonia, whooping cough, scarlet fever and some other infectious fevers. The nuclear count shows an increase in the young stages at the expense of the older (ch. 11).

Pteroylglutamic ("folic") acid is a dietary constituent required by many species for the production of granulocytes by the bone marrow, and for the maintenance of the normal population in the circulation. Absence of this vitamin from the diet of monkeys and chicks is followed by a profound leukopenia.

#### *Chemotaxis; Chemical Factors in Inflammation*

*Chemotaxis* is the term applied to the unknown "force" which draws the white cells from the blood stream, to the point of injury in the tissues. This property of responding by a locomotory movement to chemical substances is not peculiar to leukocytes, but is possessed by many types of free-living, unicellular organisms. Chemotaxis may be positive (i.e., attractive) or negative (repellant) and, although the former is most commonly observed in leukocytic behavior, certain chemicals produce the opposite effect.

It was formerly thought that the chemical properties of the bacterial toxin were responsible for this effect, but it has since been shown that nucleic acid and its derivatives guanine, adenine, adenosine, etc. or some other principle supplied by the tissues (see below) are the specific stimulants. Injections of these substances cause a rapid rise in the leukocyte count. Toxins or other injurious agents act probably indirectly by liberating nucleic acid from the tissue cells as well as from injured leukocytes themselves. It has been suggested that the actual force which attracts the cells from the vessels to the tissue focus may have changes in surface tension of the blood cell membrane as its basis, for during the early stages of the inflammatory reaction the leukocytes in the small vessels near the injured site appear "sticky." They collect and cling to the walls of the vessels and are thus separated from the red cells which occupy the axis of the stream. An artificial cell model may be used to illustrate the surface tension theory. When a small globule of mercury is placed in a weak solution of nitric acid, the globule moves rapidly toward a crystal of potassium dichromate dropped near it upon the surface of the solution, as a result of a chemical reaction leading to surface tension effects; or if the mercury is placed in a dilute dichromate solution, it will move away from a drop of nitric acid in its vicinity (negative chemotaxis). Experiments, however, upon unicelular organisms such as the amoeba, to which the white cell bears a strong resemblance, have failed to show that the spontaneous movements are surface tension phenomena. It must be admitted that the problem of chemotaxis remains unsolved. Phagocytosis does not necessarily depend upon chemotaxis but may occur quite apart from it, as when chemically inert material, e.g., particles of carbon or silica are engulfed by leukocytes coming into contact with them at random. On the other hand, a positive chemotactic effect may not be followed by phagocytosis; for neutrophils may be attracted by some dead or foreign material and more toward it with the apparent "intention" of devouring it, but not do so.

Menkin has obtained a nitrogenous, crystalline principle from inflammatory exudates which increases capillary permeability, allowing the free escape of plasma protein, and induces the migration of leukocytes through the cpillary wall. This substance, named *leukotaxine*, appears to be a simple polypeptide and is related neither to histamine nor to nucleic acid. It has also been found by others in the succus entericus of the rabbit. It seems to be the factor responsible for the swarm of leukocytes which in infective and inflammatory states are attracted from the circulation into the tissues of the affected part. Four other substances have been recovered by Menken from inflammatory exudates; these are called *the leukocytosis-promoting factor* (L.P.F.), *necrosin*, *pyrexin* and the *leukopenic factor*.

The *leukocytosis-promoting factor* causes the discharge of immature leukocytes from the bone marrow and hyperplasia of granulocytes and megakaryocytes within the latter. It is a pseudoglobulin, or closely associated with this fraction of the exudate, and is presumably responsible for for the leukocytosis which is so often a feature of the blood in infective states. Although increased manufacture of granulocytes is induced by L.P.F., the rapid increase in leukocytes suggests that preformed cells are discharged into the circulation, and there is evidence that in the early stages of leukocytosis capillary sinuses of the marrow, harboring masses of leukocytes, are suddenly opened up and their cellular contents discharged. This suggests a vasomotor reaction, which is substantiated by the fact that even saline (1 cc.) injected intravenously into a rabbit causes about 300,000,000 mature neutrophils to enter the general blood stream within 1 hour.

*Necrosin*, which is associated with the euglobulin fraction of inflammatory exudates, is the substance which causes tissue injury, lymphatic obstruction and necrosis in inflammation. The lymphatic blockage, according to Menken, is salutory since it tends to limit the spread of the infection. Injection of this substance intravenously into animals causes widespread injury, e.g., hemorrhages into the gastrointestinal tract, focal necrosis of the liver and leukocytic infiltration of the kidneys. Necrosin is thermolabile and nonpyrogenic.

*Pyrexin* is a thermostable fraction associated also with the euglobulin. It appears to be a glycoprotein. It induces fever.

The *leukopenic factor* causes leukopenia as a result of the trapping of leukocytes in the lungs, spleen and liver. This factor causes nausea and vomiting when injected intravenously. It is closely associated with pyrexin and, although it can be separated by incomplete hydrolysis from the pyrogenic factor, it has not been shown with certainty that the two factors are separate and distinct.

Inasmuch as the leukocytes, especially the neutrophils, are essential elements in the defensive mechanisms of the body against infective microorganisms, their attraction to an infected part must be looked upon as a physiological and salutary response. It should, therefore, not be discouraged in any way by agents, e.g., many antiseptics, which, although themselves inimical to bacterial growth, defeat their own purpose by destroying the leucocytes, or reducing their activity. Such agents may even act to repel the neutrophils from the injured region. Sulfanilamide, on the contrary, is claimed to actually stimulate leukocyte activity either directly or by rendering the invading microorganisms less resistant, or more "appetizing," to the phagocytes. Some interesting observations have been made by Mallery and McCutcheon on the movements of leukocytes in attack, which give a meaning to the well worn phrase "lowered resistance." The neutrophils in samples of blood from patients acutely ill and from those convalescent from various diseases were observed, and their rates of approach to a minute clump of bacteria measured and compared with the rates of approach of the observer's cells under identical conditions. In the acutely ill patients the rate of approach was 9.7 $\mu$ per minute, as compared with the normal of 16.1 $\mu$ per minute. No significant difference was observed between the phagocytes of the convalescent patients and those of the observer.

*Physiological leukocytoses.* It had formerly been taught that an increase in the neutrophils occurred during digestion—*digestive leukocytosis*—but it seems that this was a misconception. These cells show spontaneous rhythmical variations in their numbers, the total white cell count reaching its maximum of about 7000 to 8000 in the afternoon, and its minimum, 5000 to 6000, in the early morning. These variations occur quite independently of meals. Leukocytosis also occurs during pregnancy, parturition and menstruation, in muscular exercise and after adrenalin administration, or in states such as fear, pain, anoxia, etc., which cause the liberation of adrenaline from the adrenal gland. In infants and young children the leukocyte count is considerably higher than in adults; the count is also less constant in infancy, varying without apparent cause by 2000 or more per cu. mm.

*Eosinophilia,* or increase in the number of circulating eosinophils, occurs in several conditions, notably allergic states, e.g., asthma and anaphylactic shock, and in infections by various animal parasites, e.g., *hookworm (ankylostoma duodenal) disease,* in which the eosinophils may be 30 per cent of the total white cell count, and *trichinosis.* In the latter infection there is a general leukocytosis, with the eosinophils running as high as 50 per cent of the total. Infections with hydatids, ascaris and other worms also cause eosinophilia to a greater or lesser degree. The significance of this association of eosinophilia with parasitic infection is unknown. These white cells are also increased in Leoffler's disease and in a number of skin diseases; the tissues in the neighborhood of the cutaneous lesions may be infiltrated with eosinophils. During the acute stage of pyogenic infections the eosinophils are usually reduced in number (eosinopenia); in the convalescent stage they are, as a rule, increased. The eosinopenia caused by ACTH and by adrenaline has been mentioned.

*Lymphocytosis.* The neutrophils are not stimulated by tuberculous, malarial, or syphilitic infection. In the active stage of such conditions either an absolute or relative increase in the number or circulating lymphocytes is the rule. In other chronic inflammatory states and in infections with the colon or diphtheria bacillus also, it is the lymphocytes rather than the neutrophils that are increased in number. They indicate in general an inflammatory condition that is undergoing repair, is being held in check, or at the most is making slow progress. Lymphocytosis, therefore occurs as an aftermath of acute infections. The neutrophils on the other hand represent the "shock troops" and their presence indicates that a more active campaign is being waged. In young children a relative lymphocytosis is the rule.

*Monocytosis.* An increase in the monocytes is seen much less frequently than that of the other leukocytic types. Apart from monocytic leukemia and glandular fever (see below), the chief conditions in which they appear in greater numbers than normal are tuberculosis, malaria, syphilis, brucellosis and bacterial endocarditis. According to Cunningham, a decline in the lymphocyte count with an increase in the monocytes in pulmonary tuberculosis is an indication that the tuberculosis process is being arrested.

## Pathological Increases in the Leukocyte Population; Leukemia, Glandular Fever

The leukocytic increases discussed in the foregoing sections, even those associated with abnormal states, are moderate in degree, and are due to reactions which in themselves are of a "purposeful" character and on the whole physiological. But in the *leukemias* we find an altogether uncontrolled and often relatively enormous increase (up to 1,000,000 per cu. mm.) in the number of leukocytes, and a distorted mode of white cell production with the appearance of immature forms in the circulation.

The disease occurs spontaneously in the fowl (*chicken leukosis*) and in many mammalian species, and can be transmitted by the transfusion of viable leukemic cells of one animal into the circulation of a normal animal. The transfused cells multiply in the blood of the host. That leukemia can be transferred in a similar way from man to animals has not been proved. The disease in fowl can also be transmitted by cell-free blood passed through a Birkefeld filter, and is therefore believed to be due to a virus, probably a proteinlike substance. This substance does not pass from an affected to a normal bird—under natural conditions. The disease in man or in other mammals has not, as yet, been related to a virus. Whatever may instigate the abnormal blood state, its influence is impressed upon the earliest progenitors of the white cells in the bone marrow or lymphoid tissue, which results in the production of abnormally formed and malignant blood cells. This same morbid state may produce tumor masses (lymphosarcoma or myelosarcoma), clearly indicating its malignant nature.

In experimental leukemia in mice, which is closely similar or identical with the human disease, genetic factors are prominent. The influence of heredity is often evident also in human leukemia. By inbreeding mice which are susceptible to the spontaneous development of leukemia, strains have been produced in which from 80 to 90 per cent of the animals show the disease at the age of from 6 to 9 months. Little is known of the other factors which may be concerned, whether hormonal, humoral, metabolic or nutritional (e.g., vitamin or mineral deficiency). Miller and Turner and Wearn and his colleagues have found that the urine of patients with leukemia contains principles which stimulate leukopoiesis in guinea pigs and produce a blood picture in these animals resembling that of human leukemia. The actions of these substances suggest that they are specific stimulators of leukocyte production. It is postulated that they are normal principles (one of which induces hyperplasia of lymphocytes, the other of granulocytes), but produced in excess in leukemia. The lymphocyte-stimulating principle appears to be a hydroxy-acid, whereas that which causes granulocyte hyperplasia is believed to be a noncarbonol acid. A second myeloid-stimulating substance, obtained from the urine of patients with myeloid leukemia, has the character of a protein or of a glycoprotein.

It has been suggested by Miller and Turner that these two principles normally act reciprocally to control leukopoiesis and maintain a nice balance between the production of myeloid and lymphoid elements. The myeloid stimulating substance induces proliferation of myeloid elements, inhibition of lymphocytic hyperplasia and maturation of lymphocytes, whereas the lymphoid material acts to stimulate the proliferation of lymphocytes, to inhibit myeloid proliferation and to induce myeloid maturation.

The incidence of the disease in mice is greater in females than in males, which has suggested an influence of the sex hormones, and the administration of estrogen or androgen has been found to increase or reduce, respectively, the susceptibility of these animals to the experimental transmission of the disease. 11-Dehydro-17-hydroxycorticosterone for a time reduces the number of leukocytes in the leukemia of mice and causes the shrinkage of lymphosarcomatous tissue; little lasting effect upon the course of the disease has been observed. Adrenalectomy has a pronounced effect in increasing the susceptibility of mice to the experimental disease.

The thymus appears also to have a definite effect upon the incidence of spontaneous leukemia in mice, removal of this structure causing a very marked reduction. The nature of the relationship is unknown.

The leukemias are usually classified on the basis of the cell type—lymphoid or myeloid (e.g., granulocytic)—involved in the malignant hyperplasia. Thus, *lymphatic* (*lymphoblastic* or *lymphocytic*) *leukemia* and *myeloid* (*myelocytic* or *myeloblastic*) *leukemia*, respectively, are usual designations. Either of these may be classed as *acute* or *chronic*. This latter division is based not so much upon the clinical course of the disease as upon the degree of immaturity of the cells in the blood and bone marrow, the acute form, as compared with the chronic, being characterized by cells in the earliest stage of development. In *acute myeloid* (*myeloblastic*) leukemia the type-cell is the *myeloblast*. The myeloblast is an entirely abnormal cell and not simply an immature leukocyte, as seen normally in the bone marrow. It is a large cell about 20 $\mu$ in diameter with a single round or oval nucleus which nearly fills the cell. The chromatin is distributed evenly throughout the nucleus with little condensation into masses. The nucleus contains from four to five nucleoli. The cytoplasm is strongly basophilic, shows no granulation and is thin and irregular at the cell boundary. In suitable preparations a slow snail-like movement of these cells can be demonstrated by slow cinematography. Undifferentiated myelocytes are also found in the blood. In the chronic form of *myeloid leukemia* (*myelocytic leukemia*) myeloblasts are infrequent and the myelocytes more plentiful.

In *acute lymphatic* (*lymphoblastic*) leukemia, the characteristic cell is the *lymphoblast*. This cell closely resembles, but can be distinguished from the myeloblast by the coarser chromatin structure in its nucleus, by possessing only one or two nucleoli, and by showing a characteristic movement described by Wintrobe as "stately" and apparently purposeful. In the chronic form of *lymphatic* (*lymphocytic*) *leukemia*, the leukocytosis is due to small lymphocytes, which make up over 90 per cent of the total number of white cells, and may be 250,000 per cu. mm. Few immature cells are seen.

Leukemias in which the type cell is the monocyte, basophil, or even the megakaryocyte also occur rarely.

The somewhat redundant or contradictory terms *leukemic leukemia*, *subleukemic leukemia* and *aleukemic leukemia* are used, respectively, to designate the abundance, scarcity or absence of leukocytes in the blood. The first mentioned term is applied to those leukemias in which the blood picture is dominated by leukocytes. In subacute leukemia, the white cell count is normal or near the normal and only an odd immature form can be found, and in the aleukemic type few or no abnormal cells are present; the total count is not increased and may be subnormal. But this is only a phase of the disease, a rise in the leukocyte count eventually occurs, the leukemia being usually of the lymphatic type.

In the treatment of the leukemias, the destructive action of the X-rays upon lymphoid tissue and bone marrow is widely employed. The life of sufferers from the chronic form is thereby prolonged, but neither X-ray nor any other agent is of any avail in the acute forms. Internal radiation with radioactive phosphorus ($P^{32}$) is also used in the chronic form and acts like X-rays, but has a more selective action. Within recent years several chemical agents have been advocated for the treatment of chronic leukemias, e.g., *urethane* (ethyl carbamate), especially in the chronic myeloid type, *nitrogen mustards*, 4-amino-methyl-pteroylglutamic acid (aminopterin) or other folic acid antagonist.

In *Hodgkin's disease*, which is allied to the leukemias, there is general enlargement of the lymphoid tissue and usually a moderate leukocytosis (15,000 to 25,000 per cu. mm.), in which neutrophils predominate and lymphocytes are reduced.

The monocytes and lymphocytes are increased, in the condition originally named *glandular fever* by Pfeiffer (1889) and *infectious mononucleosis* by Sprunt and Evans (1920). There is enlargement of the cervical lymph glands, spleen, and liver, and a leukocytosis, usually not exceeding 20,000, of which the mononuclear leukocytes (monocytes and leukocytes) constitute from 60 to 90 per cent or more. A characteristic serological feature of this disease is the usual, although not invariable, finding of a high titer of agglutinins against sheep corpuscles (heterophil antibodies), as first shown by Paul and Brunnell.

## LEUKOPENIA

Leukopenia means a reduction in the number of circulating leukocytes. It is seen in certain diseases, notably typhoid fever, and may be induced experimentally by injections of the toxin of the typhoid bacillus—or emulsions of the dead organisms, and also by the injection of Menken's leukopenic factor (p. 93); the action of the adrenal cortical hormones and ACTH in producing a reduction in lymphocytes (*lymphopenia*) has been mentioned (p. 91). Leukopenia is also a feature of "folic acid" deficiency in some species, e.g., monkey and chick. In some cases in which the white cells are reduced in number in the blood, the reduction is due to their attraction to some solid organ such as the lung or spleen. This has been shown by taking blood counts from various regions. In other words leukopenia may be due to a redistribution of leukocytes in the body, rather than to an actual reduction in their number. A temporary fall in the leukocyte count may precede a leukocytosis. Certain poisons, e.g., benzol, cause leukopenia by depressing the activity of the bone marrow.

*Granulocytopenia, agranulocytosis, etc. Granulocytopenia* is the term applied to an abnormally low leukocyte count due to the reduction in granulocytes. The lymphocytes and monocytes are but slightly reduced or not at all, so that their proportion of the total count is increased. One or both of these types of agranular cells sometimes show an *absolute* increase. There may be complete absence of granulocytes when the term *agranulocytosis* is applicable. In most instances the absence of granulocytes is associated with a severe septic or necrotic condition of the throat. This condition, called *agranulocytic angina*, is fatal in the great majority of cases. The cause of these states is unknown but the fault is evidently one of the bone marrow, and is probably induced by some toxic agent. The marrow shows, frequently, an almost complete suppression of granulocyte formation but is normal so far as erythropoiesis is concerned. In animals reduction in the granulocytes is readily induced by the administration of benzol, which acts specifically to depress marrow activity, and there is a belief that in some cases agranulocytosis is induced by certain benzol derivatives employed for their antipyretic or analgesic properties. The arsenobenzenes, dinitrophenol and, rarely, sulfanilamide and sulfathiazole have been incriminated. Amidopyrine was the first drug shown to exert this effect but other drugs, e.g., sulfonamides, arsenicals, certain derivatives of quinine, and chloramphenicol sometimes cause the disease. In the treatment of these conditions, pentose nucleotide has been employed with the object of stimulating the granulopoietic functions of the marrow; but pteroylglutamic acid ("folic acid") appears to be the most promising agent yet discovered for the treatment of granulocytopenia (see fig. 10.3).

In some cases of agranulocytosis the bone marrow shows an increase in the number of primitive cells of the granulocyte series (myelocytes and myeloblasts), and cells of these stages appear in the circulation. The maturation of granulocytes is apparently arrested at an early stage (ch. 11). From the analogy between this fault in granulopoiesis and the erythropoietic abnormality seen in pernicious anemia, the condition has been termed *pernicious leukopenia*, or the *maturation type* of the disease.

### The Blood Platelets (Thrombocytes)

These are commonly stated to be simply fragments of protoplasm (i.e., non-nucleated) derived from the cytoplasm of the megakaryocytes (p. 106). Their colorless cytoplasm contains two types of granules. Those of one type are arranged centrally in clumps or chains and stain supravitally with neutral red or azure blue. Those of the other type are discrete, stain supravitally with Janus green and are scattered throughout the body of the cell. The platelets have an average diameter about a third that of a red cell, namely, 2.5 $\mu$, and number from 200,000 to 400,000 per cu. mm. The most usual figure found in health is around 250,000 per cu. mm. These blood elements vary considerably in shape. Their best known function is concerned with the mechanism of blood clotting (ch. 12). The disintegration of the platelets is said to occur more readily in blood drawn during the digestion of a meal of meat.

Variations in the number of platelets occur in the following conditions. They are *increased* after a meal of meat, after hemorrhage, and in certain allergic conditions, in myeloid leukemia and in convalescence from infections.

They are *diminished* in purpura hemorrhagica, aplastic anemia, pernicious anemia, in anaphylaxis and in the acute stage of septic infections and as a result of irradiation.

The number of platelets per cubic millimeter may be determined by diluting a sample of blood with a fluid composed of sodium citrate 3.8 per cent, formalin 0.2 per cent and brilliant cresyl blue 0.1 per cent, and counting immediately. The proportion of platelets to red cells (normally about 1 to 20) is determined. If the number of red cells per cubic millimeter is known then the corresponding number of platelets is readily calculated. More commonly now a count of the platelets is made after diluting the blood with a solution which destroys the red cells. Probably the most accurate method is that described by Brecher and Cronkite who used ammonium oxalate as a diluting fluid and phase contrast microscopy for counting.

Besides their well known role in the coagulation of blood (ch. 12) the platelets probably serve other functions. They have a pronounced tendency to agglutinate into masses and to form deposits upon any roughened surface or foreign material. Particles of India ink or microorganisms injected into the body become surrounded by a mass of agglutinated platelets. They may therefore aid in the body's defense against infective

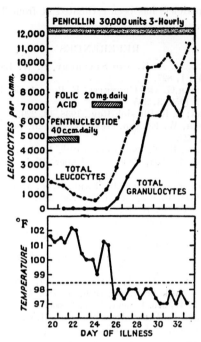

Fig. 10.3. Showing the effect of folic acid upon the granulocytes, in agranulocytosis. (After Black and Stanbury, slightly modified.)

agents. It is probable also that they serve to seal leaks in the capillaries by adhering to small defects which may occur from time to time in the delicate endothelial wall. They constitute the first defense against the loss of blood from larger vessels. Collecting around the margins of the vascular wound they help to close it, or at any rate, serve to fasten the clot, which subsequently forms, to the vascular wall; through their action in inducing retraction and consolidation of the clot, they narrow the opening in the vessel and form a firm plug within its lumen. They liberate a vasoconstrictor principle which is identical with a substance extractable from serum (serotonin or 5-OH-tryptamine). Platelets possess substances which exert complex antigenic effects. They contain some materials which appear to be identical with the ABO blood antigens and others which are distinct and seemingly specific. According to Harrington antibodies for platelet antigens may be naturally-occurring or immune, complete or incomplete, agglutinins or lysins. Platelets prepared by differential centrifugation are relatively free from the other formed elements of the blood. These preparations may be effective in improving vascular tone and preventing loss of blood in severe thrombocytopenia. The length of life of the platelets has been estimated at from 3 to 5 days.

## REFERENCES

BLACK, O. A. K. AND STANBURY, S. W. Lancet, 1947, 1, 827.

BRECHER,G. AND CRONKITE, E. P. J. Appl. Physiol.; 1950, 3, 365.

CLARK, E. R. Physiol. Rev., 1938, 18, 229.

EHRICH, W. E. Ann. New York Acad. Sc., 1946, 46, 823.

HEINLE, R. W. AND COLLEAGUES. Ann. Int. Med., 1942, 17, 902; Proc. Soc. Exper. Biol. & Med., 1945, 58, 5.

KLEIN, E., ARNOLD, P., EARL, R. T. AND WAKE, E. New England J. Med., 1956, 254, 1132.

LEEKMAN, C. H. W. AND COHEN, J. A. Nature, 1955, 175, 552.

MALLERY, O. T. AND McCUTCHEON, M. Am. J. M. Sc., 1940, 200, 394.

McMASTER, P. D. AND HUDACH, S. S. J. Exper. Med., 1935, 61, 783.

MENKIN, V. Am. J. Path., 1943, 19, 1021. Ann. New York Acad. Sc., 1946, 46, 789. Arch. Path., 1946, 41, 376. Lancet, 1947, 1, 660.

MILLER, F. R. AND TURNER, D. L. M. Clin. North America, 1944, 28, 1376.

PONDER, E. AND FLINN, Z. M. Quart. J. Exper. Physiol., 1926, 16, 207, 277, 241.

SANDERS, A. G. AND ASSOCIATES, Brit. J. Exper. Path., 1940, 21, 254.

SPRUNT, T. P. AND EVANS, F. A. Bull. Johns Hopkins Hosp., 1920, 31, 410.

TULLIS, J. L. Blood, 1952, 7, 891.

WHITE, A. AND DOUGHERTY, T. F. Proc. Soc. Exper. Biol. & Med., 1944, 56, 26; Ann. New York Acad. Sc., 1946, 46, 859.

### *Monographs and Reviews*

BERNSTEIN, A. Medicine, 1940, 19, 85.

DRINKER, C. K. AND YOFFEY, J. M. Lymphatics, lymph and lymphoid tissue. Harvard University Press, Cambridge, 1941.

KIRSCHBAUM, A. Yale J. Biol. Med., 1944–45, 17, 163.

McCUTCHEON, M. Physiol. Rev., 1946, 26, 319.

MENKIN, V. The Physiol. Rev., 1938, 18, 366.

TOCANTINS, L. M. Medicine, 1938, 17, 155.

WINTROBE, M. M. Clinical hematology, Ed. 3. Lea and Febiger, Philadelphia, 1951.

WHITE, A. Influence of endocrine secretions on structure and function of lymphoid tissue. Harvey Lecture, 1947–1948, 43, 43.

# *11*

# THE ORIGIN OF THE BLOOD CELLS—HEMATOPOIESIS

## Introduction

There are two main schools of thought concerning the development of the blood cells in postnatal life. (a) The *unitarian* or *monophyletic* school holds the view that all types of blood cells are derived from a common primitive free cell which they term the *"stem cell"* or *hemocytoblast*. (b) The *dualistic* school believes in the existence of two distinct types of stem cell, one in the bone marrow which gives rise to the myeloid elements— erythrocytes, granulocytes and megakaryocytes —and the other in lymphoid tissue which is responsible solely for the genesis of the lymphocyte. It is not possible to speak unreservedly for either theory, though the unitarian view seems to have the balance of evidence in its favor and will be followed in this text. Both schools are agreed, however, that in the early embryo the mesenchyme gives rise to a primitive free cell from which all the blood cells are derived. It is also generally conceded that certain cells (reticular cells) of the bone marrow and lymphoid tissues of the adult are the representatives of the mesenchyme cells of the embryo and to such cells all the blood cells trace their lineage.

The point at issue is, "Do the bone marrow and lymphoid tissues give rise to two cell types, with their potentialities restricted, the one to the development of erythrocytes and granulocytes, the other to the development of lymphocytes?" Or, "Do both types of tissue, myeloid and lymphoid, give rise to a primitive free cell—the stem cell or hemocytoblast—with potentialities for the production of all types of blood cells, but whose development along one or other line is determined simply by its immediate environment?" The latter is the monophyletic view (Pappenheim, Maximow).

It is not maintained, however, that the individual blood cells arise, under ordinary circumstances, in direct line of development from the stem cells, that is, each blood cell from a hemocytoblast. In health, the blood cells are produced through the multiplication of cells belonging to later stages of hemopoiesis (erythroblasts and

myelocytes, p. 106 and fig. 11.1). In other words a single stem cell is the ancestor of many millions of mature blood cells. This type of development, involving the proliferation of cells of later stages and the production of daughter cells of the same type which then undergo maturation, is called *homoplastic hemopoiesis*.

Under pathological conditions, on the other hand, the stem cells may undergo active proliferation, and produce, directly, immature blood cells (erythroblasts of various ages, myeloblasts and myelocytes). This is termed *heteroplastic hemopoiesis*.

Scheme I, and figures 11.1 and 11.2 will enable the reader to follow the description of the blood cell origins which will now be given.

## Hematopoiesis (Blood Formation) at Different Embryonic Ages

### IN THE EARLY EMBRYO

THE YOLK SAC. The first signs of blood and blood vessels appear in the mesenchyme of the wall of the yolk sac, i.e., outside the embryonic area proper. At a very early stage groups of mesenchyme cells in this situation—*the blood islands of Pander*—are first observed to arrange themselves into cords or columns which soon separate into a central and two outer layers.

The outer two enclosing layers form the walls of the primitive blood vessel—*primitive endothelium*. Of the central group some go to form the first blood cells, whereas the secretion or actual solution of others forms the plasma in which the cells are suspended. These free elements are known as the *primitive blood cells*. After this the mesenchyme loses its power to produce blood cells directly. A few primitive blood cells may arise from the primitive endothelium from time to time, but they are few in number and the process is believed to be relatively unimportant in most mammals, and does not persist for long. The further development of the primitive blood cells follows one or another of two courses. (a) Some of the cells—*primary erythroblasts* and *erythrocytes*— acquire hemoglobin and serve as oxygen carriers. These are short lived and soon disappear forever. (b) The rest remain colorless and apparently un-

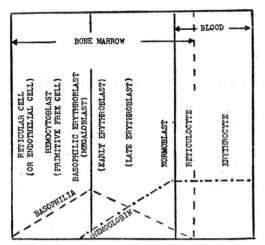

FIG. 11.1. Diagram showing maturation of the red cells. The view of Sabin, Doan and associates is indicated by the parenthesized terms (see footnote, p. 105). As mentioned in the text the early and late erythroblasts of these observers are termed polychromatophil erythroblasts by Maximow. This term has been omitted from the diagram for the sake of simplicity (modified from Sabin).

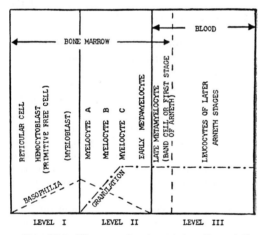

FIG. 11.2. Diagram showing maturation of the granulocytes. Parenthesized terms are those of Sabin, Doan and associates (modified from Sabin).

changed from their primitive state; *they are very similar to, if not identical in appearance with, the large lymphocyte.* These cells are found in adult bone marrow and lymphoid tissue, and in small numbers in circulating blood. They are termed by Maximow *"hemocytoblasts"* and upon them the monophyletic conception of blood formation in postembryonic life is based. They are the "stem cells" and are, according to the unitarians, potentially capable of producing any of the blood cells in the adult. Though these cells are identical, morphologically, with the primitive blood cells of which they are an older stage, apparently they are

functionally different, for they form *secondary* erythroblasts and erythrocytes (which the primitive cells do not) but never *primary erythrocytes* (Scheme I). They also give rise to megakaryocytes. The latter are enormous cells (40 μ) with multilobed nuclei. The primitive endothelium as well as the primitive blood cells gives rise to hemocytoblasts and also to a few histiocytes (p. 102) which show phagocytic proclivities, devouring degenerated red cells. In mammals few granulocytes are formed within the yolk vessels. They arise extravascularly from hemocytoblasts derived from the mesenchyme cells.

IN THE BODY OF THE EMBRYO. Although these stages of blood development are proceeding in the mesenchyme of the yolk sac, the heart and vessels are developing in the embryonic area. Soon the embryonic and extraembryonic systems of vessels form communications with one another and the primitive blood plasma, primary erythrocytes and hemocytoblasts flow into the body of the embryo. The mesenchyme cells of the general connective tissues of the embryo's body also form hemocytoblasts at this time. From these stem cells secondary erythrocytes and later, granulocytes and lymphocytes are produced. Blood formation throughout the general mesenchyme is, however, of short duration. Hemopoiesis soon becomes localized in the liver, spleen, bone marrow and lymph glands. Normally it is only in these situations that the mesenchyme cells exhibit their powers of producing hemocytoblasts; therefore, it is exclusively in these tissues that the hemopoietic function for a time is carried on.

### IN LATE EMBRYONIC AND POSTNATAL LIFE

In the later part of prenatal life of most animals, the liver and spleen (except the lymphoid tissue of the latter) lose the power to produce stem cells and so no longer serve as blood forming organs. The hemopoietic function from now on resides solely in the bone marrow and lymphoid tissues (p. 104). The marrow is concerned with the production of red cells, granulocytes and platelets; the lymphoid tissue of lymph glands, of the Peyer's patches of the intestine, and of the spleen and thymus form lymphocytes. In certain animals, such as the opossum and frog, the formation of red cells (erythropoiesis) and of granulocytes (granulopoiesis) is continued throughout adult life by the spleen. In the bird, although the marrow is the chief organ for blood formation, the liver still retains in part its embryonic hemopoietic function.

In late embryonic and postnatal life the mesenchyme gives rise to three main types of cells:

1. Those which retain their embryonic potencies throughout adult life, being capable of producing

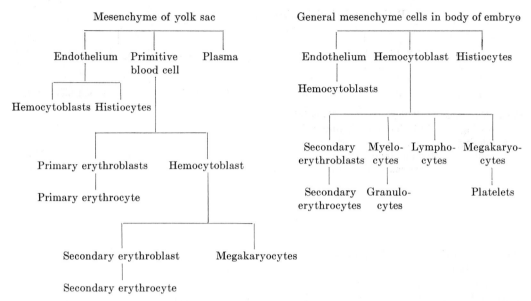

hemocytoblasts (stem cells) and so of generating any or all of the blood cells. Some of these, called the *embryonic reticular cells*, are situated in the reticulum of the bone-marrow and of the lymphoid tissue. Ordinarily these cells, as stated on page 107, are restricted in their hemopoietic activities, the great majority of the blood cells in conditions of health being formed by the divisions and re-divisions of cells of their own kind (homoplastic hemopoiesis). Cells having similar potencies are also present in the general connective tissues, and in these situations are spoken of as *undifferentiated mesenchyme cells*. Under ordinary circumstances these latter cells do not give rise to stem cells. As the result of some abnormal stimulus, however, their dormant powers inherited from their mesenchyme ancestry may become aroused and they may then give rise to the various types of blood cells. For example, areas resembling marrow tissue may be produced by the experimental stimulation of these undifferentiated cells; the several types of blood cells are formed within such areas. Maximow rendered the kidney of the rabbit necrotic by tying the renal vessels, and thereby induced in this situation hemopoietic activity resembling that which occurs in adult red marrow. Marrow-like tissue producing erythrocytes and granulo-cytes may also arise as a result of an abnormal stimulus in the spleen, liver, adrenals, aorta, lymph nodes and other sites. In certain forms of anemia, especially of infants, the extramedullary formation of red cells sometimes occurs (in kidney, spleen, liver, etc.) and in leukemia, granulo-cytes, which normally arise only in the bone marrow, are produced by the spleen.

2. The second type of cell has retained a certain measure of its embryonic characteristics. These cells are endowed with the remarkable power of altering their form and functions under appropriate stimulation. They are found in the general connective tissues lying among the fibroblasts. They are allied to the connective tissues on the one hand and on the other to certain white cells (monocytes) of the blood and so form a connecting link between the tissues and the circulating cells.

The cells of this group constitute what has been termed as Aschoff the *reticuloendothelial system* (Scheme II).

3. In the general connective tissues the great majority of the original mesenchyme cells become transformed into the ordinary and completely differentiated connective tissue elements—the fibroblasts. These, once formed, remain practically unchanged in structure and in function.

## The Reticuloendothelial System

To the cells of this system the general term *histiocyte* has been applied. The term simply means a tissue cell, and on this account is without descriptive value. But it would be difficult to coin a word that would embrace all the various cell types of this system, and yet would be sufficiently explicit to distinguish them from some of the blood cells. *Pyrrol* cells is a term that has been used in the past for a reason that will appear presently. The different types of histiocytes possess one characteristic in common. They are phago-cytic for foreign particles of all sorts; for this reason they were called *macrophages* by Metchnikoff to distinguish them from the much smaller

Reticuloendothelial cells or histiocytes—macrophages

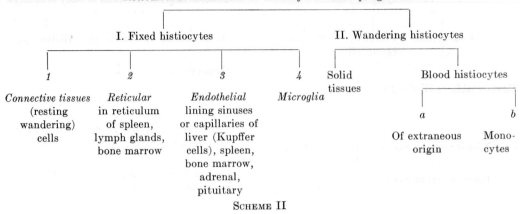

|  | I. Fixed histiocytes |  |  | II. Wandering histiocytes |  |
|---|---|---|---|---|---|

| *1* | *2* | *3* | *4* | Solid tissues | Blood histiocytes |
|---|---|---|---|---|---|
| *Connective tissues* (resting wandering) cells | *Reticular* in reticulum of spleen, lymph glands, bone marrow | *Endothelial* lining sinuses or capillaries of liver (Kupffer cells), spleen, bone marrow, adrenal, pituitary | *Microglia* |  |  |

|  |  |
|---|---|
|  | *a*       *b* |
|  | Of extraneous origin    Mono- cytes |

SCHEME II

phagocytes of the blood—the neutrophils or *microphages*. In one particular, however, the histiocytes differ from all other cells of the body—neutrophils included. They are stained in the living state by weak solutions of certain colloidal dyes—pyrrol-blue, trypan blue, lithium carmine, etc. The vital or supravital staining reaction is simply a process of ultramicroscopic phagocytosis. That is, the fine ultramicroscopic particles of the dye are taken up from the solution (which is too dilute to stain ordinary cells) and as a result of their accumulation into larger masses in the cytoplasm become visible under the microscope. It is by means of this reaction that the macrophages can be detected among the ordinary tissue cells from which it is sometimes difficult otherwise to distinguish them.

### VARIETIES OF RETICULOENDOTHELIAL (R.E.) CELLS

The reticuloendothelial cells or histiocytes may be divided for the convenience of description into two groups—*fixed* and *wandering* (cf. scheme II).

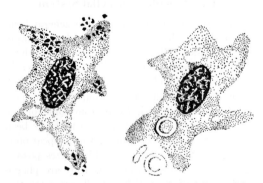

FIG. 11.3. *A*, macrophage loaded with particles of India ink; *B*, macrophage showing processes. *C*, red cell (semidiagrammatic).

### *Fixed R.E. Cells*

1. OF THE COMMON CONNECTIVE TISSUES ("TISSUE" HISTIOCYTES) and of the loose tissue of the serous membranes, e.g., omentum, pleura, etc. These are also sometimes referred to as "resting wandering cells." Their morphological characteristics are various. Some are round or spindle-shaped, others are squamous, whereas many have long mobile processes. They lie among the fibroblastic elements and often can be distinguished from the latter only with difficulty except by their special staining reactions. They may at any time as a result of some stimulus, particularly one of an inflammatory nature, become free and wander through the tissues. After the stimulus has been removed they may again come to rest.

2. OF THE RETICULUM of the spleen, lymph glands, and bone marrow. These are large cells joined to one another by means of long branching processes. They lie among, and are attached to, the fibers of the reticular stroma. They too, given the necessary stimulus, may become detached and actively motile.

3. FLAT ENDOTHELIAL-LIKE CELLS lining the blood sinuses of the spleen, bone marrow, adrenal cortex and pituitary. This group also includes those most interesting structures—the large flattened stellate cells in the blood sinuses of the liver (Kupffer cells). The latter possess many branching processes and project into the capillary lumen. In many instances they are almost free, being moored to the capillary wall by a delicate strand of protoplasm. At other times they may become detached and are carried away in the blood stream (fig. 11.3).

4. MICROGLIA of the central nervous system.

### *Wandering R.E. Cells or Free Histiocytes*

1. OF THE SOLID TISSUES. From the foregoing it is seen that many of the fixed histiocytes may upon occasion become actively motile. Large cells

of this type are found in the general connective tissues, in the omentum, in the splenic pulp and in the lymph glands, bone marrow, etc. (fig. 11.1). The wandering cells may on the other hand come to rest and become fixed for the time. On account of the many different forms which these wandering macrophages may assume as a result of an inflammatory stimulus Maximow has named them *polyblasts*.

2. OF THE BLOOD. (a) *Of extraneous origin.* Under certain circumstances as a result of some intense pathological stimulus (e.g., leukemia, bacterial endocarditis), the ordinary tissue macrophages already mentioned may be found in large numbers in the blood stream. They arise chiefly from the spleen and bone marrow and swarm into the venous system, but rarely reach the arterial side for, on account of their huge size (30 $\mu$), they are strained out by the capillaries of the lung. Large numbers may be obtained from the right heart but few if any from the left.

(b) *Monocytes* (see p. 87). The origin of these normal elements of the blood has been the subject of considerable controversy. According to some, they arise solely from histiocytes, especially of the spleen and bone marrow, and are therefore classed with the reticuloendothelial system. Lewis has shown that in hanging drop cultures macrophages may be transformed into monocytes, or *vice versa*. Maximow, on the contrary, believes that the monocytes arise from lymphocytes, stating that in certain situations, e.g., in the spleen, all transitional stages from lymphocyte to monocyte may be seen.

### FUNCTIONS OF THE RETICULOENDOTHELIAL SYSTEM

The word "endothelial" is not quite appropriate. The cells lining the blood sinuses are not true endothelial cells. The ordinary endothelial cell of the blood vessels is a highly differentiated cell like the fibroblast and has no characters in common with the so-called endothelial cells of the sinuses of the bone marrow, spleen, etc. These are called *littoral* (shore) *cells* by Maximow. They are relics of the primitive endothelium.

From the account of the histiocytes which has been given it is quite evident that phagocytosis is one of their chief functions. In this they constitute one of the most important and powerful means by which the defense of the body is sustained. Their action, though similar to that of the neutrophilic leukocytes, is less mobile and more localized in character. They, with the aid of the lymphocytes, contribute toward the repair process which follows the acute phase of a tissue injury. The various types are for the most part

readily transformable, one into another, the different forms which they assume being determined by local environmental conditions and the nature of the stimulus. Any of the stationary cells may change into wandering histiocytes (macrophages) or mobile cells may become fixed and either retain in the sessile state their special phagocytic properties or lose these entirely and become converted into the ordinary connective tissue elements— fibroblasts—or into epithelioid cells. The fibroblasts, however, never undergo the reverse change and assume ameboid characters; once formed they remain fixed. According to Maximow, lymphocytes may give rise to macrophages. The latter, however, never give rise to lymphocytes.

In chronic inflammation or in the repair stage of an acute process, the histiocytes play an important rôle. Some (the so-called *dust cells* of the lung) are responsible for the removal of foreign particles which have been carried into the pulmonary alveoli by the inspired air. The ability of the Kupffer cells to take up ingested thorium dioxide (Thorotrast) which is opaque to the X-rays is made use of to delineate the liver in the living subject. The spleen, placenta, ureter and kidney pelvis, the vessels of the extremities or of the brain and the cerebral ventricles, can also be outlined radiographically by means of this agent. The administration of Thorotrast is not, however, free from danger. It is radioactive, the alpha ray activity of 25 cc. of Thorotrast being equivalent to that ot 1 $\mu$g of radium which is sufficient to produce pathological changes in susceptible persons. Thorium dioxide is eliminated from the body in insignificant amounts, almost all being permanently stored in the reticuloendothelial cells of the bone marrow, spleen and lungs, as well as in the Kupffer cells, and even though no deleterious effects result from its radioactive properties it sets up a proliferation of connective tissue by acting as foreign material.

The epithelioid and giant cells of certain specific inflammatory processes, e.g., tubercle, which are derived from the histiocytes is but another instance of the latter's protean nature, and it is owing to these activities that the tissues are rendered so remarkably adaptable and plastic in their reactions to altered conditions. The omentum for example has long enjoyed a reputation as a protective structure, owing to its ability to form adhesions which serve to seal perforations of the gastrointestinal tract or to isolate infected regions within the abdominal cavity. The omental tissue is particularly richly supplied with both stationary and wandering histiocytes. It contains also, even in health, immense numbers of lymphocytes, which, in part, are derived from division of their own kind locally, and, in part, have come from the blood stream. Normally the presence of these various cells in such numbers gives an appearance closely resembling a defense reaction— the "physiological inflammation" of Rossle. Histiocytes and lymphocytes are continually being cast in showers into the peritoneal cavity at all times but to a much greater extent in irritative conditions. Monocytes have been studied in transparent chambers inserted into the tissue of the rabbit's ear. They have been observed to leave the circulation and to become motile and phagocytic, and otherwise indistinguishable from tissue histiocytes.

The formation of bile pigment (ch. 39) and the final destruction of the blood cells (ch. 8) in the spleen are other well established functions of the histiocytes. The reticuloendothelial system is also believed to be concerned with antibody formation.

In certain pathological conditions, the lipemia of diabetes, Gaucher's disease and Niemann-Pick's disease (ch. 8) the reticuloendothelial elements, especially of the spleen, are markedly increased in number and become loaded with lipid material.

### The Blood-Forming Organs of Postnatal Life

Red cells, granulocytes and possibly platelets are formed in the bone marrow, and lymphocytes in the lymphoid tissue. The stroma or reticulum of these structures is the essential blood-forming tissue. The latter consists of (a) a fine network of cylindrical or ribbonlike fibers which can be stained by silver preparations and (b) large cells— *reticular cells*—which are fused together by branching processes to form a loose network; the latter is intimately associated with the network of fibers which appear as reinforcing strands. The reticular cell (embryonic reticular cell, p. 101) is the nearest approach in the adult body to the primitive mesenchyme cell. The blood-forming capacity of the myeloid and lymphoid tissue depends upon the ability of these cells to form hemocytoblasts which in turn, according to the environment in which they are situated, are capable of developing into red cells, granulocytes or megakaryocytes on the one hand or lymphocytes on the other.

### The Bone Marrow

The red bone marrow is the hematopoietic tissue for erythrocytes and granulocytes in postnatal life. In the adult, this tissue is almost entirely confined to the flat bones, such as, the sternum, ribs, diploë of the skull and the bodies of the vertebrae. There is little or none, usually, in the long bones, such as, the tibia and the bones of the

forearm, although small amounts may be found in the ends of the femur and humerus in young robust adults. The total volume of red bone marrow in the adult human body amounts to about 1400 cc. In infancy red marrow is present, not only in the ends of the long bones, but it fills the cavity of the shaft which in adult life contains only a yellow fatty material; this is not hematopoietic. However, even in the adult the fatty marrow retains the essential reticular structure of hematopoietic tissue and is, therefore, capable under appropriate stimulation of blossoming into red marrow. So, under certain conditions, for example in pernicious anemia, and to a much less extent during residence at high altitudes, or in any state associated with long-continued oxygen lack, the red marrow is increased in amount. It encroaches upon the medullary cavity of the shaft, replacing to a greater or less degree the fatty tissue.[1] In aplastic anemia on the other hand the fatty marrow increases at the expense of the red marrow.

In old age the volume of the red marrow is much reduced and most of the flat bones contain minimal amounts.

Drinker has shown that the circulation of the marrow is closed, i.e., the blood and the reticular tissue are separated by a complete membrane. This is contrary to the older view that the blood came into direct contact with the marrow cells through gaps in the capillary walls. The vascular bed of the marrow is a meshwork of small blood sinuses (sinusoids) lined by flat endothelial-like cells similar in character to those lining the sinuses of the spleen. Not all the sinusoids, however, are open at one time. It has been estimated by Doan that the marrow contains a great many more of these vessels than could possibly be accommodated within the resistant bony encasement, were they all in the dilated state. Some of the sinusoids are completely collapsed and impervious to the blood. Others are dilated but, owing to the vessels that lead to and from them being constricted, they are isolated from the general circulation. Regions of low oxygen tension are in this way provided. It has already been pointed out (p. 13) that a low oxygen tension serves as a stimulus to red cell formation.

[1] In some cases of rapidly developing anemia fat droplets may appear in the peripheral blood, and after some cases of hemorrhage the fatty acids of the blood increase. These facts suggest a dispersal of the medullary fat in order to make room for an extension of the blood forming tissue—the red marrow.

The blood cells, if the observations of Maximow are accepted, are formed extravascularly and subsequently enter the blood stream.[2] Their pressure upon the endothelial wall causes its erosion or rupture and the cells invade *en masse* the lumen of the sinusoid where further growth and maturation of the cells follows. Finally, through the opening up at certain periods of the vessels leading from the hemopoietic region, the mature cells escape into the general circulation. The sudden showers of young cells that occur in pernicious anemia (blood crises) may be explained by a process of this nature. That the delivery of red cells into the circulation is normally intermittent is also suggested by the fact that the red cell count is not constant but shows a diurnal rhythm, the highest counts occurring in the morning hours. There may be a difference of 300,000 cells or so between the maximal and minimal daily levels of the red cell count. Normally no cells enter the general blood stream until maturation is nearly complete. Drinker, for instance, was unable to cause the passage of immature forms into the blood by prolonged perfusion of the marrow or by muscular exercise. The perfusion fluid evidently was unable to open a way into these isolated pools and wash out the immature forms. From what we know of the capillary circulation in other situations this is not unexpected (ch. 15, 25 and 26).

Since the introduction of the technique of bone marrow puncture and of culture methods our knowledge of the cellular structure of human marrow under normal and pathological conditions has been greatly advanced. The total number of nucleated cells per cubic millimeter in the bone marrow is around 75,000. Cells of the granulocyte series make up about 25 per cent and those of the erythrocyte series from 50 to 60 per cent. The remainder are megakaryocytes and unidentified cells (see Plate I).

### The Maturation of the Blood Cells
*Erythrocytes—Erythropoiesis*

The red cells pass through several stages before they attain full maturity. In the examination of a simplified (hypoplastic) marrow, such as may be induced in the pigeon by underfeeding or in mammals after poisoning with benzol, most of the stages can be followed (cf. fig. 11.2 and frontispiece). The *reticular* cell, as we have seen, gives

---

[2] Sabin, Doan and others contend that only the granulocytes have an extravascular origin, the erythrocytes being derived, not from reticular cells but from the endothelial elements (littoral cells of Maximow) of the marrow capillaries.

rise to the *hemocytoblast*. The latter divides into two daughter cells which stain deeply with basic dyes. These are called *basophilic erythroblasts* by Maximow; they contain no hemoglobin. The next stage which may be distinguished is, following Maximow's terminology, the *polychromatophil erythroblast*. The earliest cells of this stage are large, with a large, round and often vesicular nucleus; their cytoplasm is rich in basophilic material but also contains traces of hemoglobin. The hemoglobin concentration increases in amount as development advances, the more mature cells being well supplied with pigment. Hemoglobin is acidophilic, so the cells of the erythroblast stage, since they have retained a relatively large amount of basophilic substance, stain with both acid and basic dyes. This property of dual staining, known as *polychromasia*, diminishes again as the cells mature beyond the erythroblastic stage and gradually lose their basophilic material.

Several authors (Sabin, Doan and associates) distinguish three types of cells during this stage of development—the *megaloblast* and the *early* and *late erythroblasts*. The megaloblast of these authors corresponds to the youngest of the polychromatophil erythroblasts mentioned above, i.e., a large nucleated cell which, owing to its relatively large proportion of basophilic material, shows only a very slight tendency to polychromasia. Maximow avoids the term megaloblast, advising that it be reserved for the large cell of pernicious anemia to which it was originally applied. He and other hematologists claim that the latter cell, although resembling the primitive cell of normal marrow, is not identical with it (see p. 104).

The older erythroblasts give rise to *normoblasts*. The normoblast, as the name itself implies, resembles the mature erythrocyte in size and hemoglobin content but still retains its nucleus which, however, shows condensation of its chromatin material (*pyknosis*) and stains more deeply. In the final stage of the maturation process, the nucleus is extruded from the cell and the now nearly mature erythrocyte is discharged from the marrow into the general circulation. It betrays its youth only by a fine basophilic reticulation of its cytoplasm and is therefore called the *reticulocyte* (p. 13). It is probably not until the reticulocytes have reached a certain concentration in the marrow that they become discharged into the general blood stream.

In healthy marrow the multiplication of the red cells which occurs to replace those lost from the circulation through wear and tear is effected almost entirely by the division and redivision of later forms, i.e., of normoblasts and older erythroblasts (homoplastic development) and to a negligible extent through the multiplication and subsequent maturation of the more primitive forms. The youngest erythroblasts (basophilic and polychromatophilic erythroblasts), for example, in normal marrow are absent or amount to no more than 0.01 to 0.04 per cent of the total nucleated cells of the erythrocyte series, according to Sabin; the older erythroblasts make up about 30 per cent and the normoblasts 70 per cent or so. In pernicious anemia, on the other hand, large numbers of very primitive cells including the characteristic megaloblast are present. In this disease erythropoiesis is abnormal in that the cells produced are not only of a more primitive type but are different from ones ever seen at any stage of normal erythropoiesis. It is not then merely a matter of reversion to a primitive but otherwise normal mode of red cell development. The benefits of liver therapy apparently depend upon the power of the hepatic principle to restore the normal mode of red cell development.

### Granulocytes—Granulopoiesis

The earliest stage in the differentiation of the granulocytes from the primitive reticular cell of the marrow is that of the so-called *myeloblast*. It is generally agreed that the origin of the granulocytes is extravascular and that they pass into the marrow vessels only after they acquire motility. Maximow considers the myeloblast to be nothing more or less than the polyvalent hemocytoblast or stem cell, identical with the large lymphocyte, the minute differences in structure between it and the latter being due, it is thought, to the environment in which it is placed, i.e., the bone marrow. Here it gives rise to the three types of granulocyte. The myeloblast is given added interest since

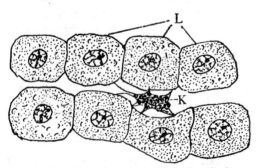

Fig. 11.4. Liver from an animal after the intravenous injection of India ink. *K*, Kupffer cells loaded with ink particles; *L*, liver cells.

a cell similar to, but not identical with it, is predominant in the blood and marrow of certain forms of *leukemia* (p. 94) when it may constitute 90 per cent of the white cells. It forms only a very small percentage of the cells of normal marrow.

After the stage of the myeloblast a few specific granules begin to appear in the cytoplasm which at the same time becomes less basophilic in character. Also present are a few azurophyl granules. In the subsequent history of the cell up to its discharge into the circulation four stages, based upon the development of specific granulation and the reduction in basophilic material, are recognized. The cells of the first three of these stages are termed *myelocytes A, B* and *C*, respectively. The cells of the fourth stage are called *metamyelocytes*. In the youngest stage (A) the granules, as mentioned above, are very few[3] and are in greater numbers in myelocyte B and in maximum quantity in myelocyte C. The nucleus in these stages is oval or spherical and shows no attempt at lobulation. The metamyelocyte is characterized by slight indentation of the nucleus and the first evidence of typical ameboid movement. Finally the nucleus becomes deeply indented or constricted at one or more points and is discharged into the circulation as a young leukocyte (neutrophil, eosinophil or basophil). This is the first stage of Arneth mentioned on page 88. It is also referred to by Schilling as the older metamyelocyte or the band cell. As shown in figure 11.4 three levels of development are distinguished. Level I extends from the reticular cell to, and includes, the myeloblast. Level II embraces the myelocyte and the metamyelocyte; cells at this level multiply actively and have the power of growth. Level III includes those forms present in normal blood (Arneth stages); the cells have lost the power to divide and grow.

As in the case of erythropoiesis the earliest stages of white cell development—myeloblastic and early myelocytic—are little in evidence in normal bone marrow. The leukocytes are supplied to the blood through the division and redivision of the later forms of white cell elements—i.e., the myelocytes. A census taken of the colorless elements of the marrow in normal rabbits gives an average of about 1 per cent myeloblasts, 90 per cent myelocytes C and metamyelocytes,

[3] This cell, myelocyte A, resembles closely its progenitor the myeloblast and represents a transition stage between the latter cell and the older myelocyte. It is often referred to as the promyelocyte. Some use this latter term to include also myelocyte B.

of which the great majority are neutrophilic, and about 4 per cent young leukocytes. Younger myelocytes make up the balance. The number of leukocytic elements is three times greater than the number of red cell elements—erythroblasts and normoblasts. The ratio of granulocytes to red cells in blood, on the other hand, is 1 to 600. The difference in the cell ratios in marrow and in blood is ascribed to the greater mortality of the leukocytes and the consequent necessity for a greater hemopoietic activity in order to replace them.

In myeloid leukemia the process of granulopoiesis is pushed back to a more embryonic type and immature forms appear in the blood. The marrow picture indicates a great activity of the early myelocytic and myeloblastic stages. The marrow of the fetus and to a less degree that of the newborn show also a relatively large proportion of immature cells.

## Lymphoid Tissue and the Formation of Lymphocytes

The central areas of the follicles in lymphoid tissue (lymph glands, spleen, etc.) stain more lightly with the ordinary stains than the peripheral zones. These lighter areas, about 1 mm. in diameter and pierced near the center by a small arteriole, are generally known as the "germ centers." In the embryo and in newborn animals the earliest stage in the development of the lymphocytes is represented in lymphoid tissue as well as in the bone marrow by a large lymphocyte or hemocytoblast. It is analogous and practically identical in structure with the myeloblast. It is called the *lymphoblast.* In postnatal life, lymphocytes arise only from lymphoid tissue. The ancestral cell or hemocytoblast stems from the undifferentiated primitive reticular cell of the lymphoid stroma similar to that in the marrow from which the myeloblast and, according to Maximow, the erythroblast arise but, as in the case of the myeloid cells, the lymphocytes normally arise from the division of cells of later stages.

The total mass of lymphoid tissue amounts to between 1 and 3 per cent of the body weight, and its output of cells is relatively enormous. Yoffey estimated the daily production at 35,000,000,000; the tremendous wastage has already been mentioned (p. 70).

An interesting experiment of Maximow's supports the view that the large lymphocyte or hemocytoblast is the common precursor of the granulocyte and lymphocyte and that the course of development which the stem cell shall follow is determined by its immediate environment. Lymphoid tissue was cultured in an environment prepared to simulate that of the bone marrow by the use of a preparation of blood plasma and marrow extract. Proliferation of the large lymphocytes and their differentiation into myelocytes were clearly observed.

## Distinguishing Features of the Different Stages of the Leukocyte Series

### Oxidase Granules

The mature granulocytes, the myelocytes and myeloblasts (except the very youngest) and the primitive monocytes, contain fine, reddish-brown granules (*oxidase granules*) which become evident when the cells are stained in the following way (Washburn technique). The cells are first treated with a solution consisting of benzidine, 0.3 gram in 99 cc. of alcohol and 1 cc. of a saturated solution of sodium nitroprusside. Ten drops of this solution are applied to a dried blood film and allowed to stand for $4\frac{1}{2}$ minutes. Five drops of a solution of hydrogen peroxide in 25 cc. of water are then added. After standing for another $4\frac{1}{2}$ minutes the film is washed and dried and stained with Lieshman's stain. Cells of the lymphoid series do not contain oxidase granules.

### Motility and Phagocytosis

When stained supravitally the primitive monocyte is phagocytic and actively motile, whereas myeloblasts and lymphoblasts are usually stated to be nonmotile. In hanging drop preparations, however, Rich states that both of the last mentioned cells also show definite motility and that the mode of locomotion of each type is characteristic. The myeloblasts and the younger myelocytes exhibit a wormlike motion, whereas the lymphoblast protrudes a long tongue of cytoplasm in a direction opposite to that in which it is moving; it thus assumes a shape resembling that of a hand mirror or a frying pan.

### Nuclear Structure

The nucleus of the myeloblast shows a delicate reticular structure and no definite nuclear membrane; the nucleoli are indefinitely marked off from the rest of the nuclear material. The nucleus of the lymphocyte on the contrary is well defined, as are also the nucleoli, and the reticulum is coarser.

These distinguishing features of the various cell types are employed in diagnosing the different forms of leukemia.

### The Platelets

These are generally stated to arise from giant cells of the marrow (40 $\mu$ or more in diameter) known as megakaryocytes. The latter have an irregular, ring-shaped nucleus, and are capable of ameboid movements. It was first suggested by Wright that fragments of their protoplasm became detached to form the blood platelets. Normally, the marrow contains only a few of these cells, but it has been stated that an increase or decrease in their number is followed by corresponding changes in the number of circulating platelets.[4]

### The Origin of Monocytes (see p. 103)

[4] Wright's view of the origin of the platelets from megakaryocytes, though very widely held, has not gone unquestioned. Various alternate theories have been advanced with respect to the origin of the platelets. Some believe that they are formed from the cytoplasm of leukocytes, and others that they are simply precipitates from the plasma. Howell and Donahue concluded from their experiments that the platelets are derived from megakaryocytes in the lungs. They based their view on the finding that both in cats and in man the platelet count was somewhat higher in arterial than in venous blood. The ratio of platelets to erythrocytes in arterial blood was 1:21.4, as compared with 1:23.8 in the blood of the corresponding vein, which implies that platelets are destroyed or removed from circulation in the capillaries and replenished in the lungs. Further evidence was derived from the observation that a smear of lung tissue showed large numbers of giant cells, whereas only a few were found in a similar specimen of bone marrow. It is probable, however, that the lung megakaryocytes do not originate in the lungs but have their source in the bone marrow and, owing to their large size, are merely trapped in the pulmonary capillaries. Several observers have expressed the belief that they are fragments of degenerated red cells. In support of this view Watson reports the observation that phenylhydrazine which damages the erythrocytes causes a sharp rise in the platelet count and a reduction in the number of red cells. This observer also found

### REFERENCES

BEDSON, S. P. Brit. J. Exper. Path., 1926, 7, 317.
BOGOMOLETZ, A. A. Ann. Rev. Soviet Med., 1943, 1, 101; Brit. M. J., 1943, ii, 203.
HOWELL, W. H. AND DONAHUE, D. D. J. Exper. Med., 1937, 65, 177.
RICH, A. R. Bull. Johns Hopkins Hosp., 1939, 65, 291.
STRAUS, R. AND ASSOCIATES. J. Immunology, 1946, 54, 155.
WATSON, C. H. Edinburgh Med. J., 1932, 39, 229.
WRIGHT, J. H. J. Morphol., 1910, 21, 263.
YOFFEY, J. M. J. Anat. 1936, 70, 507.

### Monographs and Reviews

ASCHOFF, L. Lectures on pathology. I. Reticuloendothelial system. Paul B. Hoeber, Inc., New York, 1924.
DOAN, C. A. Medicine, 1931, 10, 323.
ERSLEV, A. J. Blood, 1955, 10, 954.
GORDON, A. S. Physiol. Rev., 1959, 39, 1.
ISAACS, R. Physiol. Rev., 1937, 17, 291.
JACOBS, M. H. Ann. Rev. Physiol., 1958, 20, 405.
JAFFÉ, R. H. Physiol. Rev., 1931, 11, 277.
MAXIMOW, A. A. AND BLOOM, W. Text-book of histology. W. B. Saunders Company, Philadelphia, 1934.
SABIN, F. R. Physiol. Rev., 1922, 2, 38; 1928, 8, 191.
SACKS, B. Physiol. Rev., 1926, 6, 504.
Symposium: Hematopoietic mechanisms. Ann. New York Acad. Sc., 1959, 77, 407–820.
WHITNEY, C. Medicine, 1928, 7, 1.

that, when erythrocytes were suspended in a counting chamber, degeneration of the red cells occurred whereas bodies indistinguishable from platelets appeared. Furthermore, the platelet count, as shown by Bedson, is increased by splenectomy, or by "blocking" the reticuloendothelial macrophages (which, as we have seen, engulf red cell fragments) by injections of India ink. The term "blocking" refers to the overloading of the reticuloendothelial cells with the ink particles and the consequent suppression of their phagocytic properties.

# 12

# THE COAGULATION (CLOTTING) OF BLOOD

## General Description of Clot Formation

If blood is collected into a test tube it will be found at the end of 5 or 6 minutes that it has lost its fluidity and has set into a jelly. The tube may be inverted, but the blood, which is now said to have *clotted* or *coagulated*, does not escape. If it were possible to magnify this clot many times and to look within it, one would see a mesh of very delicate fibrils, among which were entangled, as in a net, the red and white cells and many fragmented platelets. The fibrils can be readily revealed when a thin section of the clot is examined under the high power of the microscope. They are composed of *fibrin* formed by the conversion of the fibrinogen of the plasma from a soluble (hydrosol) into an insoluble form (hydrogel). The fibrin forms ultramicroscopic crystal-like needles which, as they are deposited, create tenuous, interlacing filaments within the structure of the protein. The process by which this change of fibrinogen from a liquid to a more or less rigid structure (fibrin) is effected has been compared by Mommaertz to the manner in which a matted feltlike mass is formed from elongated objects—as reeds floating in water become tangled and coherent. It will be recalled that fibrinogen itself is composed of long fiberlike molecules. The immobilization of the molecules in this manner is called *coacervation*[1] by de Jong.

If the clot is permitted to stand for an hour or so, it will be found to have shrunk, and in shrinking to have expressed from its interstices a clear, faintly straw-colored fluid. This is the *serum*. The latter remains perfectly fluid and is quite incapable of clotting. The shrinking and condensation of the clot is due to the gradual shortening of the fibrin threads which enmesh the corpuscles. In this retraction of the clot or *syneresis*, as it is

[1] De Jong defines this as the process occurring in a condensed colloidal system, in which particles with positive and negative electric charges are mutually attracted. According to the view of Mommaertz, a profibrin is first produced and then, through electrostatic attraction of its particles, a meshlike interlacement occurs to produce fibrin.

termed, the platelets play an essential role. Though numbers of platelets undergo distintegration when the blood is shed (see below), others become attached here and there in groups of knotlike clumps to the fibrin threads, and in some unexplained way cause bending and shortening of the latter. Clots formed in blood deficient in platelets are soft and friable, and do not retract in the normal way. It used to be thought that the intact platelets which were seen in sections of blood clots served as nuclei from which the fibrinogen to fibrin conversion started, but it has been demonstrated by Tocantins that the platelets take up their positions *after* the fibrin has formed. The full retraction of the clot and the separation of the serum ordinarily takes a considerable time, but separation can be brought about within a few minutes by rapid centrifuging.[2]

If the blood is centrifuged as soon as it is shed and the cells in this way are separated from the plasma, a clot forms in the latter, due, as before, to the formation of fibrin threads. After a time the colorless clot shrinks and, as in the case of whole blood, expresses the transparent serum. The clotting process is therefore essentially a phenomenon of the plasma. The straw-colored layer—the so-called "buffy coat"—which forms on the surface of blood which clots slowly, and so allows a certain degree of sedimentation of the cellular elements to occur, is clotted plasma.

## The Clotting Mechanism

The clotting mechanism in the simplest possible terms is shown in the following scheme.

[2] There is a direct relationship between the platelet count and the rapidity and degree of clot retraction and the resulting firmness of the clot. The effect of the platelets upon clot retraction is exerted only when they disintegrate. The concentration of thrombin, which induces lysis of these elements, therefore influences the retraction of the clot. The concentration in the blood of the other formed elements affects clot retraction in the opposite way. In anemia, for example, clot retraction is more pronounced than normally, whereas, in polycythemia the clot is soft and friable. Increase in the fibrinogen concentration acts in a manner similar to that caused by a high platelet count, hastening the retraction of the clot.

Prothrombin + thromboplastin + calcium →
thrombin

thrombin + fibrinogen → fibrin (clot)

The four primary factors, *prothrombin, thromboplastin, calcium* and *fibrinogen*, have long been recognized as being fundamentally involved in the coagulation of the blood.

Plasma also contains considerable amounts of antithromboplastin which is capable of preventing the formation of thromboplastin or inactivating it after it has been formed.

Normally, the blood remains fluid in the vessels, not only because it is in motion, but also because thromboplastin is present in the circulation in only minute amounts, or in an inactive form, and because the platelets remain intact. Therefore, thrombin, the coagulating enzyme, is not formed. Moreover, an antithrombin is present in normal blood, which serves to guard against any thrombin which might arise in sufficient amount to cause intravascular clotting.

No field in physiology is more complex or has been so confused by contradictory results, differences of interpretation and diversity of opinion as that of blood coagulation. Each fact discovered, instead of simplifying the subject, usually brings new problems in its train. The relatively simple mechanism expressed above must now be elaborated in the light of modern findings. This can best be done by considering that the reactions resulting in coagulation take place in three stages: (a) the formation of thromboplastin, (b) the conversion of prothrombin to thrombin and (c) the conversion of fibrinogen to fibrin (see fig. 12.1).

It is now known that platelets contain little or no thromboplastin; yet the platelets are necessary for the development of the thromboplastic activity of plasma. The formation of plasma thromboplastin can be considered as the first stage in blood coagulation. Although there is no unanimity of opinion regarding the order in which various plasma factors react to form thromboplastin, there is general agreement as to the importance of these factors. At least three hemorrhagic conditions have been observed in which the common defect is in the formation of plasma thromboplastin. Each appears to be due to the lack of (or inactivation of) specific proteins present only in minute amounts. Since any hypothesis of blood coagulation must take these facts into account, a suggested scheme for the events in the first stage of coagulation is shown in figure 12.1. Antihemophilic factor (AHF), plasma thromboplastin component (PTC) and possibly other proteins (Stuart factor, Hageman factor) react with a lipid material (phosphatidyl ethanolamine or cephalin) from platelets to establish thromboplastic activity. The reaction is apparently initiated by contact with a 'wettable surface' or injured area. This suggests that lysis of platelets may be the initiating factor. (MacFarlane believes that PTC and AHF join with calcium ions to form an intermediate product which then combines with platelets.)

AHF is present in normal fresh plasma but is lacking, or inactive, in serum or aged plasma. It is not readily adsorbed on the usual prothrombin adsorbing reagents. Lack of this factor results in a condition now known as *Hemophilia A*. PTC or Christmas factor is present in both normal plasma and serum and is readily adsorbed on prothrombin adsorbing reagents. Lack of this factor results in a condition known as *Hemophilia B*. Rosenthal and his colleagues have described a third type of hemophilia attributed to lack of a plasma factor which, although not adsorbed by the prothrombin adsorbing reagents, is found in normal serum. They have called this factor PTA. According to the work of Tocantins a thromboplastin inhibitor exists in plasma. He has isolated this material from both normal and hemophilic plasma. It probably inhibits the development of thromboplastin as well as inactivating thromboplastin after the latter has been formed. The thromboplastin which can be obtained from tissues appears to be incomplete and needs a factor from plasma to make it fully active.

The conversion of prothrombin to thrombin normally depends on the presence of thromboplastin and thus can be considered the second stage in blood clotting (fig. 12.1). The work of several laboratories has indicated the existence of certain plasma and serum factors which accelerate the conversion of prothrombin to thrombin. The plasma factor was discovered independently in widely separated laboratories and has been referred to by a variety of names (see table 12.1). It appears to be associated with the globulin fraction of plasma and is normally present only in trace amounts. It is labile and is not easily adsorbed on $Al(OH)_3$, $Ca_3(PO_4)_2$ or other prothrombin-adsorbing agents. One of the first patients found to be deficient in this factor was studied by Owren. He called the condition parahemophilia. Seegers and his colleagues found that the activity of plasma AC-globulin was greatly increased during coagulation, and that plasma AC-globulin fraction was made more potent by small amounts

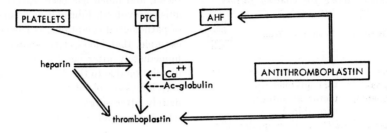

Stage I: Formation of Plasma Thromboplastin

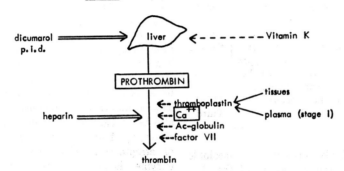

Stage II : Formation of Thrombin

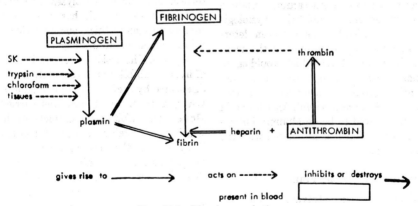

Stage III : Change of Fibrinogen to Fibrin

FIG. 12.1. Blood coagulation.

of thrombin. This suggested an autocatalytic type of reaction and led to a great deal of investigation regarding clotting accelerators in serum. It is now generally accepted that serum contains an activating material that is not always present in plasma. The active material is readily adsorbed on prothrombin adsorbing reagents and is more stable than the plasma fraction. The term "factor VII" is most commonly used to designate the serum active factor but many other terms are used (see table 13.1). Clinical cases with factor VII deficiency have been reported by Alexander and Owren. Seegers and his colleagues have shown that a derivative of purified prothrombin acts as an accelerator and have suggested that the serum factor is derived from prothrombin during the coagulation process. In support of this hypothesis it may be pointed out that during Dicumarol or Tromexan administration both prothrombin and factor VII levels in the blood are decreased, with factor VII being the first to be affected.

Once thrombin is formed it acts enzymatically

## TABLE 12.1

*Synonymous terms for clotting factors*

| Name Used Here | Synonymous Terms | Stage of Blood Coagulation |
|---|---|---|
| PTC (plasma thromboplastin component) | CF (Christmas factor); platelet cofactor 2; autoprothrombin 2 | First |
| AHF (antihemophilic factor) | AHG (antihemophilic globulin); thromboplastinogen | First |
| Ac globulin | Labile factor; factor V; proaccelerin | First and second |
| Factor VII | Stable factor; autoprothrombin 1; proconvertin; SPCA; cothromboplastin | Second |
| Plasminogen | Profibrinolysin | Third |
| Plasmin | Fibrinolysin | Third |

to convert the soluble fibrinogen into insoluble fibrin which forms the framework of the clot. This reaction can be considered the *third* stage in coagulation and is illustrated in figure 12.1. Plasma, and to a lesser extent serum, contain a substance known as antithrombin, the physiological importance of which has not yet been determined. Its function may be to prevent the accumulation of thrombin to levels which would cause intravascular clotting. Attempts to correlate decrease in antithrombin with a tendency towards thrombosis have been unsuccessful. Antithrombin was originally believed to be an albumin but recent work indicates that it is associated with the α-globulin fraction.

### DEFIBRINATED BLOOD: FIBRINOLYSIS

Blood which has been extravasated into the pleural, peritoneal or other body cavity is usually found to be fluid, if any considerable time has elapsed since the hemorrhage occurred. Such blood is found to be incoagulable, for it has already clotted and then undergone a natural process of defibrination, the clots having been dissolved as a result of the digestion of the fibrin (fibrinolysis) by proteolytic enzymes. The fluidity of menstrual blood is caused in the same way. A fibrinolysin, although not present in normal blood under ordinary circumstances, appears in plasma after shaking with chloroform.

A great deal of work has been carried out in recent years on the fibrinolytic activity of the blood, and much has been learned of the mechanisms involved. Fibrinolysis occurs in a number of pathological conditions. It has been found, for example, that blood clots removed from a body immediately after sudden death undergo rapid dissolution due to the development of fibrinolytic activity. Also, blood taken from patients immediately after surgical operations, or from those who have suffered severe burns or hemorrhage, contains fibrinolysin, sometimes in high concentration. Through the action of fibrinolysins the fibrinous exudate filling the alveoli of the consolidated lung in lobar pneumona is dissolved preparatory to its absorption. The blood normally contains a proferment, which has been called profibrinolysin or plasminogen (i.e., fibrinolysin in an inactive form), which under certain circumstances may be converted to the active enzyme by a second principle derived from the tissues. This is known as fibrinokinase. Activation can also be brought about artificially, as mentioned above, by chloroform and also by certain strains of streptococci, which possess an activating enzyme, known as streptokinase. The latter substance together with streptodornase (desoxyribonuclease), an enzyme also produced by streptococci, and which hydrolyzes desoxyribonucleoprotein of cell nuclei, has been employed in surgery to liquefy thick pus, and thus to render it more amenable to drainage.

*Heparin.* The action of certain impure extracts of liver in inhibiting the coagulation of blood was discovered by McLean, a pupil of Howell, in 1916. Later, a series of studies was carried out by Howell and Holt upon extracts of liver from which they obtained a powerful anticoagulant. They gave it the appropriate name of *heparin.* Howell and Holt obtained their material from dog's liver, but it was later (in 1933 at the University of Toronto) prepared in larger quantities by Charles and Scott from beef liver. Lung, muscle and intestinal wall also contain heparin in relatively large amounts. Smaller quantities are contained in spleen, heart and thymus. It is present in negligible quantities, if at all, in normal blood. Heparin is active both *in vivo* and *in vitro*; when it is injected into the living animal the blood remains incoagulable for several hours. A unit of heparin is defined as the quantity of material which will prevent for 24 hours the clotting of 1 cc. of cats' blood when kept in the cold. A very potent crystalline preparation has been obtained from beef liver by

Charles and Scott. This contains nearly 100 units per milligram.

The anticoagulant action of heparin is complex and depends upon at least three effects which it exerts upon the clotting mechanism. (a) In association with a plasma fraction, heparin cofactor, it inhibits the action of thrombin in converting fibrinogen to fibrin. (b) Heparin is also an antiprothrombin, i.e., it prevents the activation of prothrombin to thrombin. This property has been questioned until recently, but the experiments of Ferguson and of Quick have firmly established this action of heparin. (c) Through its effects (a) and (b) in inhibiting the formation and action of thrombin, heparin reduces or prevents the agglutination and lysis of platelets.

Jorpes found that, like certain other anticoagulants, such as azo dyes and germanin, the heparin molecule contains sulfuric acid groups, in virtue of which it acts as a relatively strong acid. It belongs to the same chemical group as that to which mucoitin and chondroitin sulfuric acids belong. It is a complex carbohydrate containing esters of mucoitin-sulfuric acid and yields glucuronic acid, glucosamine and sulfuric acid groups upon hydrolysis. Anticoagulants have been prepared by Chargaff and Olson by the introduction of sulfuric acid groups into such polysaccharides as cellulose, glycogen and starch and into the cerebrosides, cerebron and kerasin.

Since heparin is absent from the circulation, or present only in minute amounts, it cannot be responsible for maintaining the fluidity of the blood in the living body. The most probable reasons that the blood does not clot intravascularly have been stated on page 110.

From the evidence procured by Wilander, heparin appears to be a product of the "mast cells" of Ehrlich (i.e., mobile cells in the tissues containing fine basophil granules) which may be seen in clusters around the minute vessels of those tissues which give a high yield of haparin. Mellanby suggests that the significance of heparin in tissues is that it serves as a *local* anticoagulant, preventing the clotting of blood circulating in the small vessels. The fine granules to be seen in these cells show the metachromatic staining reaction, turning violet when treated with toluidine blue or azure A. Heparin itself gives this reaction and the granules are therefore believed to be the anticoagulant in the form of minute droplets.

Chargaff and Olson found that protamine (salmine) annuls the action of heparin both *in vitro* and *in vivo*. Protamine, a simple protein with basic properties (see also p. 771) combines with heparin, the resulting compound being quite free from anticoagulant action. Thus it is possible to determine the quantity of heparin in a sample of blood by ascertaining the quantity of protamine required to give the shortest coagulation time. By this means the great lengthening of the coagulation time in anaphylaxis (up to 2 days or more) and peptone shock has been shown by Waters, Markowitz and Jaques to be due to the high concentration of heparin in the circulation (*heparinemia*, p. 112 and p. 118). Heparin is most effective when administered intravenously, much larger doses being required when it is given by subcutaneous injections. Besides its action in prolonging the coagulation time, heparin, as shown by Murray, Jaques and Best, hinders the agglutination and deposition of platelets and thus discourages thrombus formation. Heparin has been recognized for a number of years as a valuable anticoagulant for use in physiological experiments, but it is only comparatively recently that purified preparations suitable for clinical use have become available. Its most important field of usefulness is in blood transfusions, in operations upon the blood vessels and to check the extension of coronary, and certain other types of thrombosis. Its employment as a preventive against postoperative and other thrombotic states which carry the threat of fatal pulmonary embolism (p. 120) has been advocated by several investigators (Howell, Mason, Hedenius, and Murray and associates). Widström and Wilander have suggested its use to prevent the formation of fibrinous adhesions in pleurisy; in heparinized rabbits the inflammatory exudate caused by the injection of iodine into the pleural cavity is incoagulable. The systematic use of heparin and, later, of other anticoagulants for the prevention of the spread of coronary thrombi was initiated by Irving Wright and his colleagues.

### THE PROPERTIES OF PROTHROMBIN AND THROMBIN AND OF THROMBOPLASTIN

Prothrombin and thrombin, according to Seegers, are carbohydrate-containing proteins. This investigator has prepared from beef plasma highly potent preparations of these agents. At a pH of 7.0 prothrombin and thrombin are highly soluble in water or physiological saline, it being possible to prepare a 60 per cent solution of either material. Prothrombin is insoluble at a pH of 4.9 and thrombin at about 4.3. Both substances are completely and permanently inactivated by acid (pH 3.5) and by alkali (pH 11.0). They are destroyed by heating to 60°C. for 30 minutes. The estimated concentration of prothrombin in blood is around 25 mg. per 100 cc. Prothrombin is formed in the liver and its production depends on an adequate amount of vitamin K.

A linear relationship (inverse law) can be shown to exist between the relative concentration of thrombin in the plasma and the reciprocal of the coagulation time, i.e., the higher the thrombin concentration, the shorter the time required for a clot to appear.

Thromboplastin is present in all tissues—lung, placenta, and brain being especially rich sources. Although it is the general custom to speak of thromboplastin as a single principle, the term refers to an "activity" rather than a precise factor. Thromboplastin concerned with normal coagulation is formed by an interaction between the products of lysis of platelets and plasma proteins as has already been described.

Evidence now available indicates that tissue thromboplastin is not "complete," since incubation with plasma or serum will augment its activity.

### The Means Used to Prevent or Retard Coagulation—Anticoagulants

COLD. Since the clotting mechanism consists of a series of chemical and enzymatic reactions, it is to be expected that coagulation will be retarded by lowering the temperature. Keeping blood at a temperature of from 5 to 10°C. postpones coagulation but does not absolutely prevent its occurrence. Cold, e.g., ice, etc., applied to the surface of the body as a means of arresting hemorrhage has, however, no effect in retarding the coagulation process. Actually a hemostatic action is exerted in such instances as a result of the vasoconstriction reflexly induced.

AVOIDANCE OF CONTACT OF THE BLOOD WITH FOREIGN MATERIALS OR INJURED TISSUES. Drawing the blood directly from an artery or vein (in order to prevent contact with the tissues—a source of thromboplastin), and collecting it into a receptical whose walls have been made smooth and *unwettable* by a coating of paraffin, or preferably of *silicone*, will slow greatly the coagulation process. Silicone is the most effective substance known for this purpose; it acts like the vascular endothelium in inhibiting the break down of platelets (Jaques and associates) and the formation of thromboplastin activity. Plasma, after collection in silicone-lined apparatus and centrifuged at high speed in order to remove the platelets as completely as possible, will remain fluid for 3 or 4 days even at room temperature. Avian

blood collected in this way will remain unclotted almost indefinitely. The importance of a smooth surface in maintaining the fluidity of blood is also shown clearly in the classical experiment of the "living test tube." If a section of the jugular vein of an animal, e.g., the horse, be isolated between ligatures and carefully removed with its contained blood, this will not clot for a long period, not until changes occur in the lining of the vessel wall and the necessary thromboplastin is thereby provided.

On the other hand, if the blood flows over a rough surface, coagulation is hastened. The blood coming from a ragged wound which involves a greater destruction of tissue, is also likely to clot more quickly than if it issues from a blood vessel that has been cleanly incised, as by a scalpel or a razor. The contact of a sponge or a powdered substance to the wound by increasing the extent of surface exposed also hastens the formation of the clot.

DECALCIFICATION. The addition of oxalate (sodium, potassium or ammonium) or a fluoride to blood to the extent of 0.1 per cent or more, completely destroys its power to clot spontaneously. In the former instance the calcium is precipitated as calcium oxalate. Oxalated blood recovers its ability to clot if shaken with chloroform, but the fibrin which forms redissolves after the blood has stood for a time. Fluoride does not precipitate the calcium but forms a weakly dissociated calcium compound. Sodium citrate also prevents coagulation. In this instance a double salt—calcium sodium citrate—is formed which again is only slightly dissociated. If calcium in the ionic form, e.g., the chloride, be added to the oxalated, fluoride or citrated plasma (recalcification), the power of the blood to clot is regained. Also the addition of thrombin or of thromboplastin to the decalcified blood causes it to clot.

NEUTRAL SALTS. Magnesium sulfate solution in a strength of 27 per cent mixed in the proportion of 1 to 4 of blood postpones coagulation for some time, but does not prevent it indefinitely. Sodium sulphate in half saturated solution added to an equal quantity of blood has a similar effect, as has also a 10 per cent solution of sodium chloride in the same proportion. The manner in which these substances act is not clear. They do not decalcify the blood. That the activity of some or other elements necessary for the clotting process is merely suspended and that none is destroyed, is shown by the fact that mere dilution of the "salted" blood is followed by clotting. Some think that these substances may act by preserving the platelets and corpuscles from disintegration and so hindering the liberation of thromboplastin. Zinc. suplhate in 0.5 per cent solution prevents coagulation by precipitation of the fibrinogen. Sodium thiosulfate and germanin are anticoagulant, this action depending apparently upon their sulfur content.

AZO DYES, such as Chicago blue 6 B, Trypan red, Trypan blue, Chlorazol fast pink, B.K.S. etc., are powerfully anticoagulant. Chicago blue, the anticoagulant property of which was discovered by Rous and his associates in 1930, is more potent either *in vivo* or *in vitro* than the earlier preparations of heparin. One milligram of purified Chicago blue will prevent for 60 hours the coagulation of 1 cc. of rabbit's blood kept on ice.

CERTAIN SUBSTANCES OF A BIOLOGICAL NATURE. (a) *Hirudin*, a substance secreted by the buccal glands of the leech and extracted commercially, has a very powerful anticoagulant effect. It is a typical antithrombin, i.e., it inactivates thrombin. Hirudin has been used extensively in the past to prevent coagulation during physiological experiments. (b) *Snake venoms*. The poisons of some snakes, particularly of the cobra, are powerfully anticoagulant. One hundredth part of a milligram per kilogram of body weight will, according to Howell, entirely prevent coagulation. Its anticoagulant effect is thought to be due to some chemical change which is produced in the thromboplastin. The anticoagulant effect of cobra venom is probably intimately associated with its hemolytic action (p. 63). Some other snake venoms however, have just the reverse effect and cause intravascular clotting. (c) *Heparin*. (d) *Peptone solution* when injected prevents coagulation. According to Howell it acts by stimulating the liberation of heparin from the liver. Confirmatory evidence for this explanation has been furnished by others (Quick, and Waters and associates). Peptones also have an anticoagulant action when added to shed blood. The anticoagulant effect under these circumstances is ascribed by Mills and by Pickering to the increased resistance of the platelets to disintegration induced by the peptone solution. (e) In *anaphylactic shock* the blood remains incoagulable indefinitely (up to 2 days at least). Waters, Markowitz and Jaques have shown that this is due to the liberation of heparin from the liver. Anaphylaxis produced in hepatectomized dogs is not accompanied by a prolonged coagulation time, (f) *Cysteine*. (g) *Dicumarol* 3,3'-methylene bis (4-hydroxycoumarin), present in spoiled sweet clover hay, see p. 117. Schofield in Canada and Roderick in N. Dakota showed that hemorrhagic disease of farm animals could be cured by replacing spoiled sweet clover in the diet with fresh fodder. The latter observer also showed that the reduced coagulability of the blood was due to diminution in prothrombin. Link demonstrated that the toxic principle was the substance now generally known as Dicumarol, a derivative of coumarin, $(C_9H_6O_2)$ the odorous principle in new-mown clover hay. Dicumarol does not act *in vitro* as an anticoagulant nor in the body except after it has been partially metabolized. When Dicumarol is administered intravenously, only traces can be detected in the circulation after from 20 to 24 hours, yet it is not excreted in the urine or feces. Most of the drug has disappeared before any appreciable reduction in the concentration of prothrombin in the blood has occurred.

It has long been known that the administration of salicylates, e.g., acetylsalicylic acid (aspirin) and sodium salicylate, is often followed by spontaneous bleeding, which has been shown to be associated with hyperprothrombinemia. Salicylates also cause a diminution in the number of platelets. The anticoagulant action of salicylates is antagonized by vitamin K.

## SUBSTANCES WHICH HASTEN THE CLOTTING PROCESS (HEMOSTATICS)

It has been widely accepted that adrenaline hastens coagulation, but such an effect has not been proved. The effects of thrombin and thromboplastin have been discussed. Tissue extracts especially those of lung and thymus which are rich in thromboplastin are powerfully coagulant, as are also the venoms of some species of snakes. The coagulant property of such venoms depends upon their containing a proteolytic enzyme which converts prothrombin to thrombin; the conversion occurs in the absence of ionized calcium.

Thrombin sprayed upon the bleeding surface in conjunction with fibrinogen to form a covering film or foam of fibrin, is an effective means of arresting bleeding, especially from numerous small vessels. Among other hemostatic agents used to hasten the clotting process are sodium alginate, derived from seaweed, and a gauze made of oxidized cellulose, which swells when soaked with blood. When sodium alginate comes into contact with the blood and serum of the wound, it is converted to calcium alginate, which "clots" to form a tenacious layer.

### Tests Employed in the Investigation of Defects in the Clotting Mechanism

*Coagulation time.* This is the time which the blood takes to clot after it has been shed. Obviously, any condition which decreases the coagulability of the blood lengthens the coagulation time and *vice versa*.

A number of methods have been devised to determine the precise moment when clotting occurs. The clotting time as determined by different methods varies considerably since the index or criterion of coagulation is not the same in all, and the conditions to which the blood is subjected are also different. On this account the values are not absolute and the results obtained by different methods cannot be compared strictly with one another.

A simple but rough method when a considerable quantity can be secured is to collect the blood into a small test tube and take as the coagulation time, the period elapsing from the moment the blood was shed to when it congeals, as indicated by tilting the tube from time to time. This procedure is employed in the Howell and the Lee-White methods. In the latter, 1 cc. of blood is collected in a thoroughly cleaned Wasserman tube about 8 mm. in diameter. The coagulation time of normal human blood as determined by this method is from 6 to 15 minutes.

An alternative method and one which requires only a drop of blood is the following. The blood is drawn into a capillary glass tube about 4 or 5 inches long. A section of the tube is broken off from time to time. The time elapsing from the moment when the wound was made to that when fine threads of fibrin appear between the ends of the broken sections of the tube is taken as the coagulation time. The normal coagulation time by this method is about 5 minutes. There are many other methods for determining the coagulation time, e.g., Brodie's Gibbs', Cannon and Mendenhall's, etc., but all have their defects and the foregoing is probably just as accurate as more elaborate procedures.

*Prothrombin time, determination of the prothrombin concentration.* Quick's method is as follows. Nine volumes (about 2 cc.) of blood obtained from a vein in a silicone-coated syringe are decalcified by the addition of 1 volume of 0.1 mol. solution of sodium oxalate. After centrifuging, 0.1 cc. of the oxalated plasma is mixed with 0.1 cc. of thromboplastic material (prepared from fresh rabbit's brain) and recalcified with 0.1 cc. of 0.025 mol. solution of calcium chloride. The time from the addition of the calcium until the first fine mesh of fibrin filaments appears is recorded by a stop watch. The test is carried out in a water bath at 37.5°C. The prothrombin concentration in per cent of the normal is calculated as follows:

$$\text{Prothrombin concentration} = \frac{K}{\text{c.t.} - a}$$

(per cent of normal)

c.t. = clotting time; K, a constant = 303; a, a second constant = 8.7. Thus if the clotting time is 21 seconds the prothrothrombin concentration is $303/(21 - 8.7) = 25$ per cent of normal (approx.).

*Clot retraction time.* This is measured by collecting a few cubic centimeters of blood in a test tube. After clotting has occurred the clot is separated from the walls of the tube by means of a fine wire and the tube placed in an incubator set at a temperature of 37°C. The clot of blood, normally,

retracts to a firm mass, the serum separating out without a couple of hours. In certain types of purpura (thrombocytopenic) the clot remains bulky, soft and friable. In hemophilia, on the contrary, when clotting does occur, the clot usually retracts normally.

*The bleeding time.* The determination of the bleeding time simply consists in pricking the skin and noting the time the drop of blood takes to clot sufficiently in order to close the puncture in the skin and stop the bleeding. The precise moment when bleeding ceases is determined by touching the blood from the tiny wound every few seconds with a piece of filter paper. The moment when the latter ceases to be stained is taken as the end point. The normal bleeding time is about 2½ minutes.[3] One might suppose that the bleeding time would be a better gauge of the body's ability to protect itself against hemorrhage than the coagulation time, but the fact that it is normal, as a rule, in hemophilia (see below) shows that this is not so. The ability to seal a wound in a minute vessel is dependent more upon vascular factors, contraction of the vessel wall and "glueing" together of endothelial surfaces, than upon the clotting of the blood. Actually, there is little relationship between the bleeding time and the coagulation time. The former is prolonged in conditions associated with low platelet counts. It is shortened by the local application or intravenous injection of platelet extracts, by the application of solutions with a low pH (around 5), or by the injection of posterior pituitary extracts.

### THROMBOPLASTIN GENERATION TEST

Immediately before the test is started 0.1 ml. of platelet-poor, citrated plasma is pipetted into each of several small tubes of uniform diameter which are placed in a water bath at 37°C. In a further tube in the water bath at 37°C. is placed 0.3 ml. of alumina plasma diluted 1 to 5, 0.3 ml. of platelet suspension, or phosphatidyl ethanolamine, and 0.3 ml. of serum diluted 1 to 10. To this is added 0.3 ml. of M-40 $CaCl_2$. At intervals of 1 minute 0.1 ml. of the mixture is withdrawn into a graduated Pasteur pipette and discharged simultaneously with 0.1 ml. of M-40 $CaCl_2$ into one of the tubes containing 0.1 ml. of substrate.

---

[3] Ivy and his associates recommend first raising the venous pressure in the arm by constricting it above the point where the skin puncture is to be made. A constricting pressure of about 40 mm. Hg is applied. Tocantins has devised an instrument which makes an incision of approximately uniform length and depth.

The clotting times of the substrate samples are recorded. These clotting times give a measure of the rate of generation of thromboplastin in the incubation mixture.

## Hemorrhagic Diseases

It is well to emphasize here that a low serum calcium is never a cause of hemorrhagic disease. In hypoparathyroidism, in which the serum calcium may be depressed to less than half the normal value, the coagulation time is not lengthened.

### HYPOPROTHROMBINEMIA

Depression of the prothrombin level in the blood—*hypoprothrombinemia*—occurs under several conditions, such as vitamin K deficiency and severe liver damage. A bleeding tendency is not shown, however, according to Quick, until the prothrombin concentration falls to about 20 per cent of the normal. Other observers, however, place the critical level somewhat higher.

*Hemorrhagic disease of the newborn* has been shown quite definitely to be the result of a low prothrombin concentration. At birth and up to 6 hours thereafter, the prothrombin level is not far below normal, but apparently the baby comes into the world with a small reserve. This tends to become quickly exhausted, so that the prothrombin concentration may reach a low level at the end of 24 hours. This physiological hypoprothrombinemia is due, mainly, to lack of vitamin K. When the infant commences to take food, bacteria are introduced into the intestinal tract which, acting upon the contents of the intestine, synthesize the antihemorrhagic vitamin (ch. 43) and the hypoprothrombinemia is corrected automatically. Should the hemorrhagic state actually develop it is quickly arrested by the administration of vitamin K. Large doses may be given to the mother in the later months of pregnancy as a preventive. Hypoprothrombinemia and a hemorrhagic tendency also occur in certain diseases, e.g., acute yellow atrophy, associated with severe liver damage, in certain intestinal diseases, e.g., sprue and ulcerative colitis, and in the hemorrhagic disease of farm animals caused by eating spoiled sweet clover. In the animal disease the low prothrombin level is due to a toxic substance (*dicoumarol*, p. 115). The mode of action of this compound is not explained by any damaging effect which it might have upon the liver for in therapeutic doses it appears to have no such action, although in large doses it may have. In the latter instance its anticoagulant action is then enhanced as a result of the interference with prothrombin manufacture by the liver. It appears to antagonize the action of vitamin K, being more effective when the concentration of this vitamin is low. It may, therefore, be classed with the antivitamins.

The bleeding tendency which for years has been recognized to be a feature of obstructive jaundice, or when bile is lost to the exterior through a biliary fistula, has been shown to be the result of vitamin K lack. The deficiency is not due, however, to any dearth of the vitamin in the intestinal tract, but simply to the absence of bile salts without which the vitamin cannot be absorbed into the blood stream (p. 914).

Hypoprothrombinemia may be caused by bacteriostatic agents, e.g., sulfonamides active against the intestinal flora responsible for the synthesis of vitamin K.

### HEMOPHILIA

The coagulation time but not the bleeding time as defined above is greatly prolonged in this condition.[4] In some cases the blood after removal from the body may show no signs of clotting after an hour or so. On this account a fatal hemorrhage may follow a wound that would be trivial in a normal person. The extraction of a tooth, a slight accident or a minor operation have resulted in death on many occasions. The subjects are known popularly as "bleeders." Hemophilia is transmitted as a sex-linked recessive character. The males are affected but do not transmit the disease; the females, though they transmit the disease do not suffer themselves (law of Nasse (1820)). A father, then, who is a *"bleeder"* does not transmit the disease to his children in a manifest form. His sons are entirely free from any taint but his daughters inherit the disease in a masked or latent form and transmit it to their offspring. Of these the males show the disease, and the daughters again are not "bleeders" but are "carriers" for the next generation. In other words the manifest disease skips a generation. Some of these bleeder families have been traced back for a hundred years or so and cover in some cases five generations and hundreds of individuals. The incidence of the disease in these in-

---

[4] Not every person with a tendency to bleed can be classed as a hemophiliac. True hemophilia answers to the following criteria: (a) history showing characteristic type of inheritance; (b) coagulation time of drawn blood, but not the bleeding time, is greatly delayed; (c) no reduction in platelets.

stances followed in general the plan outlined above. It is theoretically possible, should a "bleeder" and a "transmitter" marry, for the female as well as the male children to be "bleeders." Such a coincidence is so very rare, and the cases of true hemophilia in the female, therefore, so few, that it is usually stated that hemophilia is confined to the male sex.

The defect in the clotting mechanism of hemophiliacs is not definitely known, but a factor seems to be a lack of a sufficient amount of active plasma thromboplastin. The plasma thromboplastin may be actually deficient in amount, fail to undergo conversion from an inactive to an active (Quick) form, or is inactivated or antagonized in some way by inhibitory substances (Tocantins). Tissue thromboplastin or normal platelet-free plasma added to hemophiliac blood restores the normal clotting time. Thus, there is no lack of prothrombin, nor is heparin responsible for the prolongation of the clotting time. The platelets in hemophilia are not reduced in number, but they are less fragile than normal. Yet, platelet stability is not the cause of the bleeding in hemophilia. The platelets, contrary to a previous belief, do not contain significant amounts of thromboplastin so that they do not, through their failure to disintegrate readily, withhold this principle from the plasma. Moreover, complete disintegration of the platelets in hemophiliac blood by saponin (Pickering) does not correct the defect in the clotting mechanism, and Quick found that platelets from the blood of a hemophiliac restored to normal the clotting time of blood which, due to a deficiency of platelets, clotted slowly.

It may seem surprising that the bleeding time is not prolonged in hemophilia, but it must be remembered that the wound which is made in determining the bleeding time is very small, and even though the clotting mechanism itself is defective, it is capable of being sealed by the contraction of the walls of the minute vessels, and the sticking together of the apposed endothelial surfaces. It is when larger vessels are opened that persistent hemorrhage occurs in hemophilia.

Logically, the measure to be used to arrest bleeding in hemophilia, and the one that has proved most effective, is to furnish the missing thromboplastic material either by transfusion of fresh blood, or plasma that has been stored at $-20°C$. Some success has been achieved recently by the use of fraction I prepared from fresh human plasma.

Two other rare hemorrhagic conditions are *haparinemia* and *afibrinogemia*. Heparinemia, as its name indicates, is the presence of heparin in the blood. The blood may be rendered quite incoagulable. The bleeding is unaffected by vitamin K administration, but may be checked by protamine or toluidine blue given intravenously. As already mentioned (p. 115), the experimental production of peptone or anaphylactic shock is associated with the discharge of heparin into the circulation. Oddly enough, tumors of mast cells which contain relatively enormous quantities of heparin do not affect the coagulability of the blood. A congenital absence or very low concentration of fibrinogen—*afibrinogemia*—is a very rare anomaly of the blood-clotting mechanism.

*Purpura.* This term is applied to a variety of hemorrhagic states in which spontaneous bleeding occurs beneath the skin, from the mucous membranes or into joints. The subcutaneous hemorrhages appear as small or large purplish spots (*Petechiae* and *ecchymoses* respectively) which gradually pass through the color changes characteristic of a bruise. Since purpura is so varied in its characters and occurs in diseased states that are so widely different, it should be considered as a symptom of a disorder of the blood-vascular system rather than as a disease in itself. It occurs in the malignant forms of many acute diseases— smallpox, scarlet fever, diphtheria, streptococcal infections, etc. Subcutaneous and submucous hemorrhages are also features of scurvy, leukemia, certain anemias and of the action of various toxic agents, e.g., snake venoms, drugs and chemicals. In some types of purpura (e.g., infectious and toxic forms) *deterioration of the capillary wall* probably plays the chief role—the red cells escaping into the subcutaneous tissues or from the mucous membranes through capillary defects. On the other hand a great *reduction in platelets* (thrombocytopenia) appears to be an important if not the essential defect in other types and a condition resembling purpura hemorrhagica (see below) has been induced in animals by the injection of an antibody developed for the destruction of platelets. Nevertheless, the experiments of Bedson suggest that reduction of platelets or even their entire absence is not capable alone of inducing purpura. Some injury to the capillary wall must exist as well. This observer also found that splenectomized guinea pigs were highly resistant to the action of the antiplatelet serum. A theory has been advanced which causally relates the capillary defects to the thrombocytopenia. It is probable that the platelets serve, normally, to protect the capillary wall and, by their deposition upon the endothelium, act as a seal against the escape of red cells through weakened points which are constantly occurring from general wear and tear. The reduction in platelets may result from several causes. There may be increased destruction of these elements or the normal mechanism of their production may be interfered with, as in aplastic anemia and leukemia.

The coagulation time in purpura is usually within normal limits but the bleeding time is as a rule prolonged. The clot which forms in the blood after it has been shed is said to be softer than the normal and does not contract and express the serum in the usual way.

### The Capillary Resistance Test

When cutaneous purpuric spots do not occur spontaneously they may be induced in susceptible persons (latent purpura) by means of a tourniquet or blood pressure cuff applied to the upper arm so as to obstruct the venous return but not the blood flow in the artery. The obstruction is maintained for 5 minutes. In scurvy and other conditions associated with weakness of the capillary membrane the increased intracapillary pressure so induced results in the formation of small hemorrhagic points (petechiae) beneath the skin of the forearm. A more precise method consists of the application to the skin (usually of the forearm just below the antecubital fossa) of a small suction cup and determining the minimum negative pressure which, when applied for one minute, is required to produce petechiae. In health this lies between −200 and −300 mm. Hg. A minimum effective pressure less than −200 mm. Hg is abnormal.

*Purpura hemorrhagica* or Werlhof's disease (thrombocytopenic purpura) is associated with a great reduction in the platelet count. They may be almost absent from the circulation. Splenectomy is followed by an increase in platelets and frequently effects a cure. Recently snake venom has been successfully employed in the treatment of this disease. The observations of Troland and Lee point to the spleen in this disease as the source of a toxic material having a destructive action upon platelets. An acetone extract of the spleens of patients suffering from thrombocytopenic purpura when injected into rabbits caused a progressive fall (from 640,000 to 20,000 in 24 hours) in the platelet count. They have given the name *thrombocytopen* to the unidentified active principle in the extracts. Extracts prepared in the same way from normal spleens were without effect upon the platelet count. An abnormal number of megakarocytes in the bone marrow especially of younger forms has been reported in purpura hemorrhagica and it is suggested that the failure of these to produce platelets is the fundamental fault.

In one form of purpura—*purpura fulminans*—the hemorrhages are exceptionally severe and the subcutaneous extravasations often extensive. Death may occur within a few days from loss of blood. In this state there is undoubtedly an affection of the capillary endothelium as well as reduction in the number of thrombocytes. Purpuric manifestations may occur with more or less severe symptoms of gastrointestinal irritation—*Henoch's purpura*—or in others bleeding into the joints (*Schonlein's disease*) is a prominent feature. In either of these forms the purpuric spots may occur in association with urticarial wheals or more generalized edematous swellings of the subcutaneous tissues. Capillary damage is probably either the essential or a contributory factor in these states.

Calcium is commonly employed in the treatment of the various types of purpura and appears to reduce the hemorrhagic tendency but the manner in which the effect is brought about is obscure; it is not through increasing the coagulability of the blood.

### Intravascular Clotting—Thrombosis

Coagulation within the vessels may be brought about experimentally: (a) By the injection of thrombin into the blood stream. Repeated injections of small amounts of thrombin cause the blood, after the first immediate increase of coagulability, to become for a few hours less coagulable than normal (negative phase). This is due apparently to some decrease in the fibrinogen level of the blood. No *permanent* reduction in coagulability can however be produced by repeated injections of thrombin over a period of several weeks. (b) By the rapid injection of a tissue extract (thromboplastin) particularly of the lung, thymus or lymph glands. The repeated injection of *small* amounts of tissue extract may have the reverse effect—decreased coagulability. This was shown by Mellanby and later by Mills and his associates to be the result of the gradual deposition of fibrin upon the vascular walls. The blood failed to clot simply because it had been depleted of fibrinogen. (c) By injury to the vessel wall either by chemical, mechanical or infective agencies, a roughened surface being thereby exposed to the blood stream. Thromboplastin is also liberated from the injured vascular wall.

The formation of a compact and solid mass of platelets, red cells, or blood clot or mixture of these materials in a vessel (vein or artery) which partially or completely occludes its lumen is spoken of as *thrombosis*. The plug itself is termed a *thrombus*. A thrombus may be formed simply by the clotting of the blood in the usual way, as occurs in a grossly damaged vessel. On the other hand the cellular elements of the blood may form a solid mass within a vessel and block its lumen independently of the clotting process. This occurs sometimes in the smaller vessels when the red cells become agglutinated into large clumps (agglutinative thrombus) as after the transfusion of incompatible blood; or when the blood forms a sludge (p. 11). Once the vessel has become plugged in this way a true clot forms eventually in the stagnant column of blood behind the block.

When a thrombus, or a portion of it, becomes detached and carried away in the blood stream to become impacted in a vessel at some remote point in the circulation, it is spoken of as an *embolus*. When arising from a venous thrombus the embolus is likely to lodge in a vessel of the lung. If formed in the left heart it may plug a cerebral artery. The main vessel leading to a circumscribed area may become obstructed and the anastomosing channels may be insufficient to maintain the nourishment of the tissue. The isolation of an area in this way by the obliteration of its artery is spoken of as *infarction*, and the necrotic area as an *infarct*.

### Causes of Thrombosis in Man

The causes of thrombosis in the human subject may be grouped under the following heads.

Injury to the vessel. Complete mechanical obstruction of the circulation as by a ligature or pressure upon a vessel from without does not alone cause thrombosis. The latter is usually associated with some injury to the inner coat of the vessel; unless this occurs the blood may remain fluid for a considerable time. A thrombus, often very small in size, may form later merely as the result of the slowing of the stream, the formation of eddies in the blind pocket and the deposition and lysis of platelets. Septic infection is one of the commonest causes of endothelial damage leading to thrombosis. Some degree of thrombosis is always associated with acute inflammatory processes of septic origin. The thrombosis may be strictly localized to the smaller vessels at the site of the infection, or may extend into larger venous trunks, and is then due to the spread of the infection along the vein walls (phlebitis). The thrombosis of the femoral vein during the puerperium or of a cerebral sinus following mastoid disease are typical examples of infective thrombosis.

Agglutination of corpuscles (agglutinative thrombus).

Toxic thrombosis. Certain chemical poisons, e.g., arsenical compounds, mercury, potassium chlorate, etc., may cause intravascular clotting. Poisonous mushrooms, certain snake venoms, as well as toxins formed within the body, as in eclampsia; or extensive burns, may induce thrombosis. The manner in which these various agencies act, whether by injury to the vessel wall, disintegration of blood elements, or through their effects upon some phase of the clotting process is obscure.

Spontaneous or postoperative thrombosis; pulmonary embolism. Spontaneous thrombosis may occur under a variety of conditions, and in practically any vein in the body. Thrombosis, particularly of the veins of the lower limbs, not infrequently follows operations upon the abdominal or pelvic organs. When it occurs under these circumstances it is always a cause of anxiety to the surgeon because of the danger of the clot becoming detached and carried to the lung where it may block a branch of the pulmonary artery (pulmonary embolus). Infection is frequently blamed for the thrombosis, but in most cases no evidence for this can be found. Also, the point where the thrombus forms—usually in the deep veins of the lower limb, such as the plantar or calf veins, or the femoral vein—lies at a distance from the field of operation and is separated from it by a considerable extent of healthy tissue. This precludes direct spread either of infection or of thrombus formation from the site of the wounded tissues.

The principal factors concerned in spontaneous thrombosis, especially following operation, will now be discussed.

*1. Endothelial damage.* Some injury or a slight alteration in the vascular lining which makes it "wettable" probably initiates the process.

*2. Slowing of the blood stream* as a result of enfeebled heart action, prolonged confinement to bed, debilitating diseases associated with a low metabolic rate and hypotension, or immobility of the limbs, seems to be an important factor in causation. It encourages the deposition of platelets on the vascular wall, and may be accompanied by "sludging" of the blood (p. 11).

*3. Deposition of platelets.* Aschoff, some years ago, made an experimental study of postoperative thrombosis and gave an interesting and logical explanation of the processes involved. He states that when the vein is completely obstructed, as is usual, the thrombus has a white portion or head which is directed proximally (toward the heart) and a dark red portion or tail. If the flow of blood is not completely blocked the thrombus consists of the white portion alone. A minute examination reveals a framework of ribs or beams extending from the wall of the vein and traversing the entire substance of the white thrombus. The ribs are made up chiefly of massed platelets covered with a layer of leukocytes. *There is little or no sign of fibrin* or of red cells; this white plug is not a clot in the ordinary sense. The longer red portion or tail of the thrombus extends distally for a variable distance along the vessel and is made up of all the elements of the blood in their normal proportions. Fibrin threads are plentiful. This portion is evidently formed by the coagulation of the blood *en masse*. The mode of deposition of the platelets is compared to the manner in which sand, although kept in suspension in a rapid stream, is deposited in a ribbed pattern upon the sea shore or at a river's mouth where the current is slowed. Although the flow of blood in the veins is continuous it is not absolutely even; eddies occur in the venous current and even slight muscular movement causes a certain irregular wavelike motion of the blood column which accounts for the deposition of the platelets, not in a continuous even layer but in ripples. Also, owing to their specific gravity the platelets leave the axis or core of the stream and, separating from the other blood elements, come to occupy the more slowly moving zone next to the vessel wall. Finally, it is the reduction of the velocity in this outer zone of the current to a certain critical level that causes the platelets to settle upon the vascular walls. The ribs or ridges increase in height by the aggregation of fresh platelet masses, and secondary ridges are later formed upon the primary ones until at last the fabric extends like a coral growth into the axis of the stream.

In view of later investigators, some change in the endothelial lining must occur to render it "wettable," (1) above, before platelets will adhere and undergo lysis.

In the auricles during auricular fibrillation, in the slowing of the stream caused by a local dilation of the blood channels, e.g., in an aneurysm or varicose vein, and wherever eddies are produced, a white thrombus either with or without a covering of clotted blood, is likely to form as a result of platelet deposition.

The observations of Sandison are pertinent to the question of thrombus formation. Examining the blood flow through the capillaries of the rabbit's ear by the transparent chamber method, he observed thrombi in the process of formation. When the blood flow was retarded platelets were seen to cling to the wall of the capillary or venule. By the deposition of successive layers, a white thrombus was formed which as it grew extended a considerable way along the blood channels. A small proportion of leukocytes were included in the mass, but no erythrocytes.

*4. Blood changes.* The platelets are increased after operations, and these elements show a greater tendency than is normal to clump together. The greater stickiness is due, according to Wright, to newly formed cells discharged from the bone marrow. The fibrinogen also is increased and, as a result of this, the rate of sedimentation of the corpuscles is hastened (ch. 7); clot retraction is usually more pronounced than normally.

*The coagulation time* is shortened for the first few days after operation but it is doubtful whether an altered relationship between the different factors concerned in the clotting mechanism itself is of prime importance in the production of postoperative thrombosis. At first sight the liberation of thromboplastin from the damaged tissues would seem to be a probable cause of the thrombosis. Yet if this were responsible one would expect that the thromboses would occur immediately following operation and not as is actually the case a week or ten days later. Moreover, thrombi composed of masses of platelets have been induced in animals whose blood had been rendered incoagulable, and postoperative thrombosis may occur in subjects whose blood shows a clotting time within the normal range.

Although some alteration in the vascular endothelium and slowing of the venous blood flow are probably the most important factors in the production of postoperative thrombosis, alterations in the blood itself which follow tissue injury, namely, the increase in the number of platelets and the rise in fibrinogen concentration, no doubt encourage the formation of the white thrombus. Anhydremia by increasing the viscosity of the blood may also favor its occurrence.

## The Relation of Blood Fat to Clotting and its Possible Role in Atherosclerosis

During the past few years much evidence has been obtained which suggests that consumption of excessive amounts of fat may be an etiological factor in *atherosclerosis* and *thrombosis*. Results of studies of the effect of fat meals on clotting times in man have been contradictory. This is probably due to the variety of tests used by different investigators. In general there does appear to be a tendency towards a shortening of clotting time after the ingestion of fat. The change however is not a large one and is by no means universally accepted. In any event the part played by fats in blood coagulation may not be related to their rôle in the development of thrombosis or atherosclerosis.

### Summary

The most probable sequence of events in the formation of a thrombus postoperatively is as follows: first, some abnormality occurs in the endothelial lining of a vessel and its unwettable property is lost. Platelets adhere and agglutinate at this point and a white thrombus forms. Platelet accumulation and the growth of such a white thrombus are favored by a sluggish blood flow. As the platelets disintegrate, the series of reactions leading to thrombin production and the formation of a fibrin net (with or without entrapped red cells) is initiated. The platelet thrombus with the clot subsequently formed may adhere firmly to the vascular lining, in which event the thrombus remains fixed and, though it may occlude the vessel, there will be relatively little danger of its being swept away in the blood stream to block a distant vessel. Quick attaches much importance to clot retraction as a factor to the further growth of the clot and the production of an embolus. If clot retraction is pronounced, as in anemia or when the platelet count is high, thrombin is expressed from the interstices of the fibrin net and causes extension of the clot. The latter, attached by its base to the endothelium, but with its other end floating in the circulation and pointing in the direction of the blood flow, is continually adding to its length by fresh accretions of clotted blood. This elongated mass has a rather precarious hold and after a time, loosened by the force of the blood stream or perhaps by some sudden movement of the patient, is detached and carried away. According to this conception, clot retraction which draws the thrombus from the vascular wall (except at its base to which for a time it is moored) favors its enlargement in the blood stream, and is an essential factor in its ultimate detachment as an embolus. The abnormality in the vascular lining which starts the train of events leading to thrombosis cannot always, nor perhaps often, be demonstrated, even histologically, but from indirect evidence some such alteration is believed to be present almost invariably.

The following are the chief measures which have been employed in attempts to prevent postoperative thrombosis.

1. Early movement of the limbs, to favor the venous flow.

2. Avoidance of any restriction to respiration—which is an important factor in aiding the venous return from the limbs.

3. Thyroid extract administration, to raise the metabolism and increase the circulation rate.

4. Plenty of fluids, to prevent dehydration, and a diet composed largely of carbohydrate since the platelet count and the fibrinogen are raised by a high protein diet.

5. The treatment of any anemia which may exist.

6. The use of anticoagulants such as heparin by continuous intravenous administration or of Dicumarol by mouth, which tend to prevent platelet agglutination.

## REFERENCES

BARNETT, B. AND MACFARLANE, R. G. Lancet, 1934, 2, 985.

BEST, C. H., COWAN, C. AND MACLEAN, D. L. J. Physiol., 1938, 92, 20.

BRINKHOUS, K. M. Fed. Proc., 1947, 6, 389.

BRODIE, T. G. AND RUSSELL, A. E. J. Physiol., 1897, 21, 403.

CANNON, W. B. AND MENDENHALL, W. L. Am. J. Physiol., 1914, 34, 225.

CHARGAFF, E. AND OLSON, K. B. J. Biol. Chem., 1937, 122, 153.

CHARLES, A. F. AND SCOTT, D. A. J. Biol. Chem. 1933, 102, 425, 437; Biochem. J., 1936, 30, 1927.

DRINKER, C. K. AND DRINKER, K. R. Am. J. Physiol., 1910, 41, 5.

FANTL, P. AND NANCE, M. Nature, 1946, 158, 708.

FERGUSON, J. H. Am. J. Physiol., 1937, 119, 755; Proc. Soc. Exper. Biol. & Med., 1939, 42, 33.

HEDENIUS, P. Lancet, 1937, 2, 1186.

HOWELL, W. H. AND HOLT, E. Am. J. Physiol., 1918, 47, 328.

IVY, A. C., SHAPIRO, P. F. AND MELNICK, P., Surg. Gynec. & Obst., 1935, 60, 781.

JAQUES, L. AND ASSOCIATES, Canad. M. A. J., 1946, 25, 26.

JORPES, E. Naturwissenschaften, 1935, 23, 196.

DE JONG, B. La Coacervation. Herman, Paris, 1936.

LINK, K. P. AND ASSOCIATES. J. Biol. Chem., 1941, 138, 21; 1943, 147, 463. Harvey Lectures 1943–44, 39, 162. Fed Proc., 1944, 4, 176.

MASON, E. C. Surg. Gynec. & Obst., 1924, 39, 421.

MCLEAN, J. Am. J. Physiol., 1916, 41, 250.

MOMMAERTZ, W. F. H. M. J. Gen. Physiol., 1946, 29, 103, 113.

MONKHOUSE, F. C. AND CLARKE, D. W. Canad. J. Biochem. Physiol., 1957, 35, 373.

MOOLTON, S. E. AND ASSOCIATES, Arch. Int. Med., 1949, 84, 667.

MURRAY, D. W. G., JAQUES, L. B., PERRETT, T. S. AND BEST, C. H. Surgery, 1937, 2, 163.

OCHSNER, A., Surgery, 1945, 17, 240.

OWREN, P. A. Thesis, Oslo, 1947. Lancet, 1947, 1, 446.

PICKERING, J. W. Proc. Roy. Soc., London, ser. B., 1929, 104, 512.

PINNINGER, J. L. AND PRUNTY, F. T. G. Brit J. Exper. Path., 1946, 27, 200.

POOLE, J. C. F. Brit. M. Bull., 1958, 14, 253.

QUICK, A. J. Am. J. Clin. Path., 1945, 15, 560; Proc. Soc. Exper. Biol. & Med., 1946, 62, 249; Lancet, 1947, ii, 379, 772; Am. J. Physiol., 1947, 151, 63.

RODERICK, L. M. J. Vet. M. A., 1929, 74, 314.

ROUS, P. AND ASSOCIATES. J. Exper. Med., 1930, 51, 807.

SANDISON, J. C. Anat. Rec., 1931, 50, 355.

SCHOFIELD, F. W. Canad. Vet. Rec., 1922, 3, 74; Am. Vet. M. A., 1924, 64, 553.

SEEGERS, W. H. AND ASSOCIATES. Blood, 1946, 1, 156; Nature, 1958, 182, 1031.

TOCANTINS, L. M. Am. J. Physiol., 1936, 114, 709; 1943, 139, 265. Am. J. Clin. Path., 1936, 6, 160. Blood, 1946, 1, 156.

TROLAND, C. E. AND LEE, F. C. Bull. Johns Hopkins Hosp., 1937, 62, 85.

WARNER, E. D. AND ASSOCIATES. Arch. Path., 1934, 18, 587. Am. J. Physiol., 1936, 114, 667. J. Exper. Med., 1937, 66, 801.

WATERS, E. T., MARKOWITZ, J. AND JAQUES, L. B. Science, 1938, 87, 582.

WIDSTRÖM, G. AND WILANDER, O. Acta med. scandinav., 1936, 88, 434.

WILANDER, O. Skandinav. Arch. Physiol., 1938, 81, (Supp. 15) 89.

WRIGHT, H. P. J. Path. & Bact., 1942, 54, 461.

*Monographs and Reviews*

ASCHOFF, L. Lectures on pathology. XI. Thrombosis. Paul B. Hoeber, Inc., New York, 1924.

BIGGS, R. AND MacFARLANE, R. G. Human blood coagulation and its disorders. 2nd ed., Blackwell Scientific Publications, Oxford, 1957.

HOWELL, W. H. Harvey Lectures, 1916–17, 12, 272.

JORPES, J. E. Heparin, Ed. 2, Oxford University Press, London, 1949.

MacFARLANE, R. G. Physiol. Rev., 1956, 36, 502.

MANN, F. D. Ann. Rev. Physiol., 1957, 19, 205.

QUICK, A. J. Hemorrhagic diseases. Lea and Febiger, Philadelphia, 1957.

SEEGERS, W. H. Advances Enzymol, 1955, 16, 23.

SILBERBERG, M. Physiol. Rev., 1938, 18, 197.

WELCH, W. H. Allbutt and Rolleston's System of medicine, 1901, 6, 691.

# 13

## THE MECHANISMS REGULATING THE REACTION
## OF THE BODY FLUIDS

### Physicochemical Principles

#### THE ELECTROLYTIC DISSOCIATION THEORY

When certain chemical substances, such as acetic acid, hydrochloric acid and many others, are dissolved in water a proportion of their molecules—the proportion varies with the particular substance—undergo dissociation into their constituent *ions*. The latter move through the solution in all directions, some collide with one another and recombine, whereas a corresponding number are produced by the dissociation of other molecules. By the junction of some ions and the separation of others, the balance between undissociated (un-ionized) and dissociated (ionized) molecules is kept constant. That is, equilibrium is established. Substances whose molecules are dissociated in this way are known as *electrolytes*. An ion is an electrically charged atom or group of atoms and is referred to as a *cation* or an *anion* respectively according to the nature of the charge—positive or negative—which it holds. Cations are denoted by a plus sign or simply by a dot placed above the atomic symbol. The negative ion (anion) is indicated by a minus sign or an oblique dash. Thus HCl dissociates into the ions $H^+$ and $Cl^-$; $H_2O$ itself into $H^+$ and $OH^-$ and $H_2CO_3$ into $H^+$ and $HCO_3^-$. When an electric current is passed through the solution each ion carries a charge of electricity to one electrode or another, the anions (negative ions) migrating to the positive electride or anode and the cations (positive ions) to the cathode. The conduction of an electric current through the solution will therefore be influenced by the concentrations of ions in the solution (i.e., upon the degree of dissociation of the particular electrolyte). Solutions of such substances as sodium chloride are good conductors, whereas solutions of other substances such as cane sugar which undergo little or no dissociation are not much better conductors than pure water.

When (a) the degree of dissociation of an acid or other electrolyte and (b) the total concentration of the acid in the solution are known, then the concentrations of dissociated and undissociated molecules can be calculated. It is found that after

equilibrium has been established the product of the concentrations of ions divided by the concentration of the undissociated molecules gives, at a given temperature and for a given electrolyte, a constant value which is known as the *ionization* or *dissociation constant*. This represents the operation of the mass law[1] as applied to the dissociation of electrolytes. So if HA represents an acid which is dissociated into cations $H^+$ and anions $A^-$ then $K_a$ represents the dissociation constant of the acid. The brackets enclosing the letters represent molar concentrations. Thus

Dissociated

$$\frac{[H^+] \times [A^-]}{[HA]} = K_a \text{ (ionization constant)}$$

Undissociated

After equilibrium has been reached the velocity at which the molecules HA dissociate into $H^+$ and $A^-$ is equal to that at which the latter combine to form HA. In this way an equilibrium between dissociated and undissociated molecules is maintained; thus, $HA \rightleftarrows H^+ + A^-$. For weak electrolytes the degree of dissociation increases with dilution, so that at infinite dilution the dissociation is complete. The greater the degree of dissociation the higher will be the numerator of the equation, and the higher consequently will be the value of the dissociation constant.

#### HYDROGEN ION AND HYDROXYL ION CONCENTRATIONS

##### The Ionization of Acids

If a measured amount of a normal solution of acetic acid be titrated against a normal solution of sodium hydroxide a definite amount of the base will be required for neutralization. If the same quantity of a normal solution of HCl be taken and

---

[1] The mass law states that the velocity of a chemical reaction is proportional to the concentrations of the reacting substances. Although this law holds for dilute solutions of such weak electrolytes as are present in blood it is inaccurate in the case of strong electrolytes in concentrated solutions.

titrated as before, it will be found that precisely the same amount of base will be required for complete neutralization. From this it might be assumed that the two acids are equally strong. But it is known that at similar concentrations the acid properties of hydrochloric are incomparably greater than those of acetic acid. The former inverts cane sugar more powerfully, it tastes more acid, it has a greater destructive effect upon animal tissues, and it will displace acetic acid from its salts.

Hydrochloric acid is dissociated into hydrogen ions and chlorine ions. To the H-ion it owes its acid properties; it is the hydrogen *ion* concentration and not the total number of hydrogen atoms in its molecule that is responsible for the acid characters of any acid. The greater the degree of dissociation of the acid, the greater is the number of H-ions which it will yield in solution, i.e., the greater will be the H-ion concentration, and the greater consequently will be its acid nature. Thus HCl, although it contains only one atom of hydrogen in its molecule, undergoes almost complete dissociation and consequently is a much stronger acid than carbonic ($H_2CO_3$), whose molecule contains two hydrogen atoms but dissociates to a very small extent into $H^+$ and $HCO_3^-$; carbonic acid dissociates in two stages. Phosphoric is another weak acid which contains three atoms of hydrogen. It dissociates, however, to a greater extent than carbonic acid and in three stages:

$$H_3PO_4 \rightleftarrows H^+ + H_2PO_4^- \rightleftarrows 2H^+ + HPO_4^= \rightleftarrows$$
$$3H^+ + PO_4^\equiv$$

The greater the degree of dissociation of an acid the higher will be the value of its dissociation constant. The latter therefore is a true measure of "acid properties." The dissociation constant of a very weak acid such as carbonic is only 0.0000003 (first stage); the first dissociation constant of phosphoric acid is 0.011.

### The Ionization of Bases

The OH ion on the other hand gives to bases in aqueous solution their characteristic properties, and when a base and acid neutralize one another it is the union of the hydrogen ion of the acid with the hydroxyl ion of the base with the formation of a molecule of water that brings about neutralizations, thus:

$$H^+ + Cl^- + Na^+ + OH^- \rightleftarrows Na^+ + Cl^- + H_2O$$

The ionization of a base may therefore be represented by an equation analogous to that given for an acid. Thus:

Dissociated

$$\frac{[B^+] \times [OH^-]}{[BOH]} = K_b$$

Undissociated

If the hydrogen ions are in excess the solution is acid; if the hydroxyl ions are in greater concentration the solution is alkaline.

### *The Ionization of Water—the Reaction of a Solution Expressed in Terms of Hydrogen Ion Concentration*

The dissociation of water may be represented by the equation

$$\frac{[H^+] \times [OH^-]}{[H_2O]} = K_w$$

Pure water has a definite although very slight conductivity value. The concentration of the molecules that are dissociated into $H^+$ and $OH^-$ as compared with those undissociated is almost infinitesimal; the concentration of the $H^+$ and $OH^-$ is so small that their presence produces no measurable decrease in the concentration of the total water molecules. The equation then may be written simply—

$$[H^+] \times [OH^-] = K_w$$

$K_w$, the dissociation constant for water therefore represents the product of these ionic concentrations and amounts to no more than 0.00000000000001.

Expressed more briefly, though perhaps more cryptically, the value is $1 \times 10^{-14}$. The symbol $-14$ to the right of the figure 10 is termed the negative exponent or index, and means that in order to express the value in the form of a decimal fraction, as in the preceding paragraph, the figure 1 must be placed 14 places to the right of the decimal point. Expressed as a vulgar fraction $10^{-14}$ would be $\frac{1}{100000000000000}$.

Other examples of this system of notation are

$10^{-1}$ means 0.1 or $\frac{1}{10}$
$10^{-2}$ means 0.01 or $\frac{1}{100}$
$10^{-3}$ means 0.001 or $\frac{1}{1000}$ and so on.

We already know that the $H^+$ and $OH^-$ must be present in equal concentration and that the dissociation constant $1 \times 10^{-14}$ is the product of these concentrations, i.e., the square of either. Therefore the square root of $10 \times 1^{-14}$, i.e., $1 \times$

$10^{-7}$ indicates the concentration either of the $H^+$ or of the $OH^-$.

The *actual weight* of ionized water in 1000 cc. (1 liter) of water is therefore

$1 \times 10^{-7}$ grams H ions (atomic weight of hydrogen = 1)

$17 \times 10^{-7}$ grams OH ions (atomic weight of oxygen = 16)

Total $18 \times 10^{-7}$ grams ionized $H_2O$

A solution containing 1 gram of hydrogen ion per liter is known as one having a normal concentration of hydrogen ions. Seventeen grams of OH ions in the same quantity of fluid is known as a normal solution of hydroxyl ions. Water is therefore $10^{-7}$ normal in both $H^+$ and $OH^-$ ions. Since both are in equal numbers per unit of fluid, water is neutral in reaction.

If hydrochloric acid is added to water it is dissociated to the extent of over 90 per cent into $H^+$ and $Cl^-$. The concentration of $H^+$ in the water will therefore be greatly increased by the addition of acid. But it has already been seen that the product of the concentration of $H^+$ and $OH^-$ in water is constant ($K_w$). This statement applies not only to pure water but to all aqueous solutions. *This is a fundamental fact* and upon it the determinations of the hydrogen ion concentration and the notations used for its expression are based. When therefore the $H^+$ are increased the $OH^-$ must undergo a reciprocal reduction. If, for instance, the $H^+$ concentration is increased above its value in pure water, that is from $1 \times 10^{-7}$ to say $1 \times 10^{-6}$ (0.0000001 N to 0.00000001 N), then the concentration of $OH^-$ must undergo a reduction to $1 \times 10^{-8}$ in order that the product of these two shall remain the same ($1 \times 10^{-6} \times 1 \times 10^{-8} = 1 \times 10^{-14}$). On the other hand if a base be added to water and the $OH^-$ concentration increased from its value in pure water, i.e., from $1 \times 10^{-7}$ to, let us say, $1 \times 10^{-6}$, the $H^+$ concentration must undergo a corresponding diminution from $1 \times 10^{-7}$ to $1 \times 10^{-8}$ (0.0000001 N to 0.00000001 N). Therefore all that is required in order to indicate the concentrations of both $H^+$ and $OH^-$ ions is an expression which denotes the concentration of either one. The concentration of the $H^+$ has therefore been chosen to express the reaction of a solution. The term "hydrogen ion concentration" is abbreviated to the symbol cH. If the hydrogen ion concentration (cH) is greater than that of pure water the reaction is acid, if less than this value, the reaction is alkaline, and if precisely the same, the reaction is neutral. Thus:

If cH equals that of pure water, i.e., $1 \times 10^{-7}$ the reaction is neutral.

If cH exceeds that of pure water, e.g., from $1 \times 10^{-7}$ to $1 \times 10^{-1}$ the reaction is acid.

If cH is less than that of pure water, e.g., from $1 \times 10^{-7}$ to $1 \times 10^{-14}$ the reaction is alkaline.

The values represent the $H^+$ concentrations in terms of a normal solution (i.e., one containing 1 gram of ionized hydrogen per liter). No matter how concentrated in a solution the $H^+$ may be, some $OH^+$ are always present, and *vice versa*, with maximum alkalinity a small number of $H^+$ are always present.

### The Symbol pH

The value of the hydrogen ion concentration as indicated above was found inconvenient. When the cH was $1 \times 10^{-6}$, $1 \times 10^{-5}$ etc., the first factor could, for the sake of simplicity, be omitted. The expression then became cH $10^{-6}$, etc. But when the first factor was other than unity, e.g., as in $5 \times 10^{-6}$ or $1.3 \times 10^{-7}$ or $4 \times 10^{-8}$, this obviously could not be done. The writing of such expressions became cumbersome and the hydrogen ion concentrations which they represented were difficult to keep in mind.

Sorensen in 1909 introduced a system of notation by which the negative exponent of the common logarithm (i.e., to the base 10) of the decimal fraction expressing the H-ion concentration is employed as a positive number. For example the H-ion concentration of serum is 0.00000004 normal. The cH might be expressed either as $4 \times 10^{-8}$ N, or as $1 \times 10^{-7.40}$ N. The latter expression is simplified by omitting the 10 and replacing the minus sign of the negative exponent by the symbol pH (hydrogen ion exponent). The value 7.40 is derived as follows. The log of the figure in the cH expression above, i.e., 4, is 0.6021 (cf. log tables). This log subtracted from the negative exponent, i.e., 8, gives the required figure 7.40. Similarly a solution 0.000005 normal in H-ions may be expressed either as cH $5 \times 10^{-6}$ or as cH $1 \times 10^{-5.3}$. The log of 5 is 0.6990; the pH is, therefore, $6 - 0.6990 = 5.3$.

It must be remembered that a rise or fall in the pH indicates a change in hydrogen ion concentration (cH or $[H^+]$) in the opposite direction. Thus a pH of 5.00 indicates a higher acidity than a pH of 6.00, and a pH of 9.00, a lower hydrogen ion concentration than a pH of 8. pH 7.00 of course indicates neutrality. Attention should be drawn to another point that is not quite so obvious, namely that a solution of a pH 5.00 is more acid not simply by a sixth than a solution of pH 6.00,

TABLE 13.1

| HCl Added | $\dfrac{H_2CO_3}{NaHCO_3}$ | $[\overset{+}{H}]$ | $[\overset{-}{OH}]$ | Relative Acidity | Relative Alkalinity |
|---|---|---|---|---|---|
| *grams* | | | | | |
| 0 | 2.27:11.9 | 0.000000057 N | 0.000000176 N | 0.57 | 1.76 |
| 10 | 2.27:11.5 | 0.000000059 | 0.000000170 | 0.59 | 1.70 |
| 50 | 2.27:10.0 | 0.000000068 | 0.000000142 | 0.68 | 1.47 |
| 100 | 2:27: 8.2 | 0.000000083 | 0.000000120 | 0.83 | 1.20 |
| 150 | 2.27: 6.3 | 0.000000108 | 0.000000093 | 1.08 | 0.93 |
| 200 | 2.27: 4.4 | 0.000000154 | 0.000000065 | 1.54 | 0.65 |
| 250 | 2.27: 2.6 | 0.00000026 | 0.000000039 | 2.6 | 0.39 |
| 300 | 2.27: 0.68 | 0.0000010 | 0.000000010 | 10 | 0.10 |
| 310 | 2.27: 0.31 | 0.0000022 | 0.0000000045 | 22 | 0.045 |
| 318 | ∞ | 0.00026 | 0.00000000039 | 260 | 0.0039 |
| 320 | — | 0.00045 | 0.00000000022 | 450 | 0.0022 |
| 330 | — | 0.0027 | 0.000000000037 | 2700 | 0.00037 |

but is in fact ten times more acid. A pH of 3.00 represents an acidity 1000 times greater than a pH of 6.00. Similarly a solution of pH 11.00 is 1000 times more alkaline than one of pH 8.00. Recalling the decimal fraction that these figures represent will make this clear. Thus pH 5.00 = 0.00001 normal and pH 6.00 = 0.000001 normal.

### BUFFERS

These are substances which when present in a solution maintain that solution at a relatively constant pH when an acid or alkali is added to it. That is, a buffer has the power to "soak up" or "tampon" the acid or base; it takes up the shock, so to speak, of the strong acid or base; hence the term buffer. A buffer or buffer system consists of two parts—a weak acid and one of the salts of that acid. Acetic acid and sodium acetate; carbonic acid and sodium bicarbonate; phosphoric acid and sodium phosphate, are a few examples of such buffer pairs. Solutions of buffers are used in physiological experiments when for any reason it is desired to maintain the fluid medium at a constant hydrogen ion concentration, as for example in the study of the action of ferments.

*The hydrogen ion concentration of a buffer solution is proportional to the ratio of the concentration of the free acid to the concentration of acid bound to base.* The ratio of the buffer pair may be expressed as follows:

Concentration of free acid

$$\dfrac{[HA]}{[BA]}$$

Concentration of bound acid

The hydrogen ion concentration of the solution is *equal* to the product of the dissociation constant of the acid (K) and the ratio of the buffer pair. Thus:

$$\text{Hydrogen ion concentration } [H] = K\,\dfrac{[HA]}{[BA]}$$

In order to express the H ion concentration in terms of pH, the value for K is converted by means of logarithms to the corresponding pK figure. The equation then becomes:

$$pH = pK_1 + \log\dfrac{[BA]}{[HA]}$$

This is known as the Henderson-Hasselbalch equation (see also pp. 135 and 466).

The effect of a buffer in preventing changes in reaction of a solution when acid is added may be illustrated by an example given by L. J. Henderson (table 13.1).

One hundred liters of a 1 per cent solution of sodium bicarbonate is made up and kept in contact with an unlimited atmosphere containing 0.1 per cent of carbon dioxide. Time is allowed for the solution to absorb $CO_2$ and for equilibrium to be established between the pressure of gas in the atmosphere and that in the fluid. The temperature is kept constant at 17°C. The solution to start with is slightly alkaline. Hydrochloric acid is added in successive amounts up to 330 grams. It may be seen from the accompanying table that the reaction of the solution is little altered after as much as 150 grams of HCl have been added. Even after the addition of 250 grams the H-ion concentration is no more than 2.6 times that of a neutral solution. It is not until the bicarbonate has been completely used up that the acid exerts any great effect. The ratio $\dfrac{H_2CO_3}{NaHCO_3}$ remains almost unchanged until some 50 grams of HCl have been added.

The reaction may be expressed as follows:

$$HCl + NaHCO_3 = NaCl + H_2CO_3$$

In this reaction three things have occurred:

1. The very strong acid, hydrochloric, has disappeared, the very weak acid, carbonic, having taken its place.

2. The weak carbonic acid is volatile and is quickly diffused into the atmosphere. This continues until equilibrium between the pressure of gas in the atmosphere and that in the solution has been re-established.

3. The bicarbonate has served as a reserve of base which has soaked up or buffered the added acid. The bicarbonate has of course been reduced and (finally) completely used up in the process.

### THE DONNAN THEORY OF MEMBRANE EQUILIBRIUM

The Donnan effect is a state of ionic equilibrium set up between two sides of a membrane by the presence in a solution of electrolytes of an ion (such as protein) to which the membrane is impermeable. It is explained best by an illustrative example. Let two electrolytes, $Na^+Cl^-$ and $Na^+P^-$, be separated by a membrane which is permeable to the ions $Na^+$ and $Cl^-$ but impermeable to $P^-$. Thus,

$$
\begin{array}{c|c}
Na^+ & Na^+ \\
P^- & Cl^-
\end{array}
$$

When equilibrium has become established the product of the concentrations of the *diffusible* ions ($Na^+$ and $Cl^-$) on one side of the membrane equals the product of the concentration of these ions on the other side.

$$[Na^+] \times [Cl^-] = [Na^+] \times [Cl^-]$$
$$[P^-] \Big|$$

Also on either side of the membrane the total concentration of anions (whether diffusible or nondiffusible) is equal to the concentration of cations, each solution being electrically neutral.

$$[Na^+] = [Cl^-]$$

Since the anion $P^-$ is nondiffusible it follows that the diffusible ions $Na^+$ and $Cl^-$ must be unequally distributed on the two sides of the membrane. In other words, the nondiffusible ion hinders (through electrostatic attraction) the free diffusion of the oppositely charged $Na^+$ ions. Therefore the concentration of the $Cl^-$ ion is less and

that of the $Na^+$ ion is greater on the side occupied by the nondiffusible ion, thus:

$$[Cl^-] < [Cl^-]$$
$$[Na^+] > [Na^+]$$
$$[P^-] \Big|$$

The ratio of the $Na^+$ concentrations on the two sides of the membrane (which may conveniently be styled *right* and *left*) is the same as, but reciprocal to, the ratio of the $Cl^-$ concentrations. Thus:

$$\frac{[Na^+\ left]}{[Na^+\ right]} = \frac{[Cl^-\ right]}{[Cl^-\ left]}$$

A difference in electric potential—*membrane potential*—is created between the solutions on the two sides of the membrane which is proportional to the logarithm of this ratio. When the ratio is 1:10 the potential difference at 19°C. amounts to 58 mv. The ionic distribution may be represented thus:

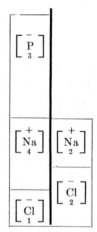

*Numbers indicate concentrations in arbitrary units*

The Donnan equilibrium is responsible for many physicochemical effects of the utmost physiological importance, e.g., a difference of pH on two sides of a cell membrane across which H ions can diffuse, differences of electrical potential between two sides of a membrane and differences in osmotic pressure between the interior of a cell and the extracellular fluids (see also ch. 3).

### The Regulation of the Acid-Base Equilibrium of the Blood

Acids such as phosphoric, sulfuric and hydrochloric, carbonic and lactic as well as certain organic acids are continually being formed in the processes of metabolism. In disease, e.g., diabetes, acids such as $\beta$-hydroxybutyric and acetoacetic acids are produced in excess. Yet in health the reaction of the blood remains remarkably constant at about pH 7.4, and even in disease may show little or no variation from the normal, for the adjusting mechanisms called into play to neutralize and remove excess acid perform their duties with extraordinary efficiency.

The reaction of the blood is protected by three lines of defense: (a) the buffer systems of the blood; (b) excretion of carbon dioxide by the lung; and (c) excretion of fixed acid by the kidney. The intestinal mucosa also assists to some extent in the removal of acid, particularly of a part of the phosphoric. The role played by the kidneys in the regulation of the acid-base balance is considered in chapter 34.

THE BUFFER SYSTEMS OF THE BLOOD may now be enumerated.

I. *In the plasma (primary buffers):*
1. Carbonic acid (free acid) and acid bound as sodium bicarbonate. Ratio 1 to 20.

$$\frac{H_2CO_3}{NaHCO_3} = \frac{1}{20}$$

2. The acid and alkaline phosphates of sodium. Ratio 1 to 5.

$$\frac{\text{Acid sodium phosphate}}{\text{Alkaline sodium phosphate}} \; \frac{NaH_2PO_4}{Na_2HPO_4} = \frac{1}{5}$$

$NaH_2PO_4$ may be regarded as a weak acid and $Na_2HPO_4$ as the salt of the buffer pair.
3. Plasma proteins which at the reaction of the blood behave as acids and so combine with base.

$$\frac{\text{H protein}}{\text{Na proteinate}}$$

II. *In the corpuscles (secondary buffers).* It is to be remembered that whole blood consists of two liquid phases separated from one another by the membrane of the corpuscles. Different materials in different concentrations exist within the red cell and in the plasma. The corpuscles as well as the plasma contain important buffers and an interchange of water, anions and $H^+$ occurs between the two across the membrane. The corpuscular membrane, on the other hand, is impermeable to $K^+$ and almost impermeable to $Na^+$ as well as to the colloidal anions, hemoglobin and plasma protein. The buffers of the red cells are:

1. Oxyhemoglobin and reduced hemoglobin act each as a weak acid of a buffer pair of which the potassium salt of the pigment acts as the other half. Thus:

$$\frac{\text{H oxyhemoglobinate}}{\text{Potassium oxyhemoglobinate}} \; \frac{HHbO_2}{KHbO_2}$$

and

$$\frac{\text{H hemoglobinate}}{\text{Potassium hemoglobinate}} \; \frac{HHb}{KHb}$$

2. The potassium salts of phosphoric acid:

$$\frac{\text{Acid potassium phosphate}}{\text{Alkaline potassium phosphate}} \; \frac{(KH_2PO_4)}{(K_2HPO_4)}$$

The reactions by which acids are buffered in the blood may now be considered in more detail. They may be grouped under the following heads:
1. *Fixed acids* formed during metabolism, e.g., lactic, sulfuric, phosphoric, etc., are buffered by the bicarbonate in a way analogous to that already described on pages 127–8. Taking lactic acid (HL) as a type the reaction may be expressed by the following equation:

| HL | + | NaHCO$_3$ | = | NaL | + | H$_2$CO$_3$ |
|----|---|-----------|---|-----|---|-------------|
| Lactic acid | | Sodium bicarbonate | | Sodium lactate | | Carbonic acid |

The comparatively strong fixed acid is thus replaced by a neutral salt. Phosphates, sulfates, lactates, etc., are excreted in the urine; lactic acid is also removed to a large extent through its conversion to glycogen in the liver and muscles. Carbonic acid is removed through the diffusion of $CO_2$ into the alveolar air. The great value of bicarbonate in maintaining neutrality of the body fluids is not due so much to its true buffering action, i.e., to the replacement of a strong by a weak acid, but to the fact that the latter is volatile and can be eliminated by the lungs.

Some of the fixed acid also reacts with the alkaline phosphate with the production of a salt of the acid and a greater proportion of acid phosphate.

| HL | + | Na$_2$HPO$_4$ | = | NaL | + | NaH$_2$PO$_4$ |
|----|---|---------------|---|-----|---|---------------|
| Lactic acid | | Alkaline phosphate | | Sodium lactate | | Acid phosphate |

The ratio $NaH_2PO_4/Na_2HPO_4$ is readjusted by the excretion of the excess acid phosphate in the urine. The phosphate mechanism for removal of acid from the body is much less efficient, however, than in the bicarbonate system, for the reasons that (a) the excretion by the kidney is relatively slow, and (b) base is lost from the body in combination with the acid. Plasma protein also yields base to neutralize fixed acids.

HL + Na protein = NaL + H protein

2. *Carbonic acid* which as a product of tissue activity is produced in much greater quantities (800 to 900 grams daily) than any other acid; it is buffered mainly by base released from hemoglobin. When carbon dioxide enters the blood the sodium bicarbonate of the plasma increases. The increase occurs to a much less extent if plasma separated from the red cells is exposed in the same way to a high tension of $CO_2$. The rise in the sodium bicarbonate of whole blood is the result of interchanges between corpuscles and plasma.

It was thought at one time (Zunz) that the rise in plasma bicarbonate was due to the passage of base from the corpuscles into the plasma. It was shown by Gürber and by Hamberger, however, that the rise of bicarbonate was accompanied by a reduction in chloride. It was concluded that chloride derived from the NaCl of the plasma diffused into the red cell and the base (Na) thereby released combined with carbonic acid to form bicarbonate. This mechanism is referred to as the *"chloride shift."* The interchanges between the corpuscles and plasma are believed to occur as follows. As the blood passes from the arterial to the venous side $CO_2$ is absorbed and diffuses into the red cell. Herein, through the action of an enzyme—*carbonic anhydrase*—(ch. 29), it is converted to carbonic acid ($H_2CO_3$). The oxyhemoglobin becomes at the same time reduced. Reduced hemoglobin is a much weaker acid than oxyhemoglobin and so gives up its alkali to the carbonic acid. Bicarbonate ($KHCO_3$) and HHb are formed. The base which previously had been bound to the nondiffusable hemoglobin is now bound as bicarbonate. The concentration of bicarbonate ions ($HCO_3^-$) in the cells is thereby raised above that in the plasma and, as a result, this anion diffuses across the corpuscular membrane. Since the cations cannot diffuse, the ionic equilibrium between the plasma and the interior of the cell will tend to become disturbed. The equilibrium (p. 468) is sustained by the diffusion of Cl ions from the plasma into the corpuscle where they combine with base. The $HCO_3$ ions which leave the cells combine with the sodium released from chloride to form plasma bicarbonate (see fig. 29.11).

The exchanges just described increase the concentration of osmotically active substances within the cells; water therefore passes from plasma to corpuscle, which as a result increases in volume. Although described in steps, the reactions actually occur simultaneously. In the lungs reverse ionic interchanges occur between the cells and plasma. $H_2CO_3$ within the corpuscles is acted upon reversibly by carbonic anhydrase; $CO_2$ enters the plasma and diffuses into the alveolar air; oxygen is absorbed and diffuses into the cell. The oxyhemoglobin so formed, being a stronger acid, recaptures the base which it had lost. Cl ions leave the cells and recombine with plasma base, whereas $HCO_3$ ions enter the cells and recombine with base released from chloride. Thus the plasma bicarbonate is reduced and the plasma chloride increased. Water leaves the cells for the plasma.

Carbonic acid is also buffered to a minor extent in the plasma through the protein and phosphate buffer systems. The plasma protein yields base and more free (acid) protein is produced. The alkaline phosphate is converted to the acid phosphate with a consequent fall in the $Na_2HPO_4/NaH_2PO_4$ ratio.

It is evident from the foregoing description of the interchanges between the corpuscles and the plasma that whole blood as compared with plsama possesses a much greater power to buffer $CO_2$. For this reason plasma separated from the red cells without precautions to prevent the escape of $CO_2$ is called "separated plasma" to distinguish it from plasma of whole blood, i.e., plasma in contact with the red cells. Only when precautions have been taken to prevent the escape of $CO_2$ during the separation of plasma from the cells will the separated plasma have the same reaction and amount of bicarbonate as existed when it was in the body. Only then will the equilibrium between cells and plasma be maintained unchanged. Such plasma is therefore referred to as "true plasma" (see also ch. 29).

## Alkali Reserve—Acidosis and Alkalosis
### THE ALKALI RESERVE

This term was brought into use by Van Slyke and Cullen to denote the amount of base in the blood which is available for the neutralization of fixed acids, e.g., lactic, hydrochloric, etc. When $CO_2$ enters the blood, base is liberated in the manner already described and bicarbonate, $NaHCO_3$, is formed in the plasma. The plasma bicarbonate then is a measure of the base left over after all acids stronger than $H_2CO_3$ have been neutralized and indicates the reserve of alkali readily available for the neutralization of such acids. The quantity of plasma bicarbonate therefore gives indirectly a measure of the extent of the production of fixed acids in the body. If acid production is increased the bicarbonate becomes reduced, its base being given up for the neutralization of the stronger acids. The term alkali reserve, it should be emphasized, refers only to base bound as bicarbonate and not to the total base of the blood. A large quantity of base, Na, K, Mg and Ca is already bound as salts of fixed acids, chiefly sodium chloride, which the weak acid $H_2CO_3$ is unable to displace (fig. 13.1). Though changes in the alkali reserve may result from alterations in the body's store of total base, they also occur quite independently of any such change, i.e., simply from variations in the distribution of base between carbonic acid and fixed acids.

It is also important to remember that the term alkali reserve refers to the *absolute* quantity of bound $CO_2$ in the plasma and has no reference to the ratio between this value and the quantity of the free $CO_2$. Upon this ratio—$H_2CO_3/NaHCO_3$ —the pH of the plasma depends. The plasma bicarbonate may therefore be greatly depleted, yet if the free carbonic acid is reduced to a corresponding extent and the normal ratio of 1:20 thereby maintained, the hydrogen ion concentration will show no appreciable change. Large quantities of acid may be formed in the body yet such is the store of bicarbonate that these, as in the case of the example given on page 128, are taken care of and not until extreme depletion of the bicarbonate buffer occurs does any great change in blood reaction result.

Rapid adjustments of the ratio $H_2CO_3/NaHCO_3$ are brought about through the exquisite sensitivity of the respiratory mechanism to changes in pH, and to the chloride shift between plasma and red cells. The slightest reduction in plasma bicarbonate through its decomposition by acid is met by increased pulmonary ventilation and an equivalent reduction in the numerator of the above expression, i.e., by the elimination of $CO_2$ by the lungs. Low arterial and alveolar $CO_2$ tensions are therefore associated with a low alkali reserve.

On the other hand, when excess $CO_2$ is contained in the blood a compensatory increase in bicarbonate results (chloride shift). So high arterial and alveolar $CO_2$ tensions are associated with a high alkali reserve.

When excessive amounts of $CO_2$ are removed from the body (e.g., by forced breathing) a movement of chloride and bicarbonate ions occurs in

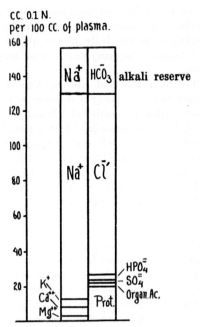

FIG. 13.1. Diagram illustrating normal acid-base balance (modified from Gamble, Ross and Tisdall).

the reverse direction; the plasma bicarbonate is reduced.

## THE NORMAL ACID-BASE BALANCE AND ITS VARIATIONS

The pH of the arterial blood in health varies between 7.39 and 7.44. The normal value for the plasma bicarbonate of venous blood ranges between 53 and 75 volumes $CO_2$ per cent. The free $CO_2$, being one-twentieth of this, amounts therefore to from about 2.5 to 3.5 volumes per cent.

In disease the pH of the blood, unless in the terminal stage, e.g., diabetic coma, never becomes actually acid, i.e., reaches a pH below 7.0, and as just stated, a reduction in the alkali reserve may occur with little or no change in blood reaction. The limits of pH compatible with life are probably not higher or lower respectively than 7.8 and 6.8. A pH of the latter value has been observed in a patient who was in a diabetic coma but who ultimately recovered under insulin treatment. The pH of venous blood during rest is lower by 0.02 than that of arterial blood. The red cells are more acid than the plasma by 0.08 to 0.14 pH.

## ACIDOSIS AND ALKALOSIS—DEFINITIONS

Few terms in physiology have caused more confusion than these. "Acidosis" has been used with at least two different meanings. The term was originally introduced by Naunyn to denote the production in the body of the abnormal acid metabolites, $\beta$-hydroxybutyric and acetoacetic acids.

The term was used later by Van Slyke and Cullen to mean simply a decrease in the alkali reserve (plasma bicarbonate) below the normal level. This is the sense in which the term has been usually employed. Since the bicarbonate represents the base in the blood which is left over after the nonvolatile acids have been neutralized, a reduction in alkali reserve indicates frequently— although not necessarily—that an excess of fixed acids are being produced or retained in the body. We have seen how very efficient the compensatory mechanisms are in keeping the pH constant, and that an acidosis either in the sense of a reduction in alkali reserve or of an increased acid production may or may not be associated with a depression of the pH (reduced alkalinity). We also know that the term acidosis cannot mean any *real* acidity of the blood—a pH below 7.00—for this is incompatible with life, and only occurs when the alkali reserve is very greatly reduced and the bicarbonate buffer ratio cannot be maintained anywhere near the normal value. *Alkalosis* carries the corresponding meaning of an increased alkali reserve. This may or may not be associated with a rise in blood pH (i.e., increased alkalinity).

Van Slyke in a later paper recognizes nine possible acid-base states, one normal, and eight abnormal (fig. 13.2). He avoids the terms acidosis and alkalosis, using the more precise designations, alkali deficit or $CO_2$ excess, and alkali excess or $CO_2$ deficit, respectively. In any one of these, the ratio $H_2CO_3/NaHCO_3$ may be either increased or diminished, with a consequent elevation or depression of pH; the acid-base condition is then said to be *uncompensated*. On the other hand, when adjustments occur to maintain the ratio at the normal value the condition is said to be *compensated*.

The nine acid-base states are described as follows:

*1. Uncompensated alkali excess.* In this condition the $[NaHCO_3]$ is increased without a proportionate rise in $[H_2CO_3]$. The pH is raised (i.e., the alkalinity of the blood is increased). This may result from the ingestion of large quantities of alkali (sodium bicarbonate) or from the loss of HCl by vomiting as in pyloric obstruction (area 1, in figure 13.2).

*2. Uncompensated $CO_2$ deficit.* In this the $[H_2CO_3]$ is reduced below normal; the $[NaHCO_3]$ is also lowered, but not sufficiently to maintain $H_2CO_3/NaHCO_3$ ratio at its normal value. The pH

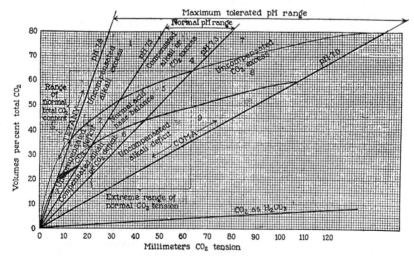

Fig. 13.2. Normal and abnormal variation of the $[BHCO_3]$, $[H_2CO_3]$, $CO_2$ tensions and pH in oxygenated human whole blood drawn from resting subjects at sea level.

The curved lines are the $CO_2$ dissociation curves (ch. 29) of reduced (upper curve) and oxygenated blood (lower curve). The straight slanting lines indicate different $NaHCO_3/H_2CO_3$ ratios, the pH at each ratio having been calculated from the Henderson-Hasselbalch equation. The $CO_2$ present as bicarbonate at any point is obtained by subtracting from the total $CO_2$ the relatively small amount present as $H_2CO_3$, indicated by the line near the bottom of the chart. The ratio, and so the pH, is the same at all points along a given line. Thus, the intersection of the $CO_2$ dissociation curves by these so-called isohydrionic lines marks off nine areas corresponding to the acid-base states described above (after Van Slyke.)

therefore is raised. A disturbance of this nature may result from forced breathing, or the hyperventilation induced by hot baths, high altitudes or shallow breathing (p. 522). It is sometimes also referred to as "gaseous alkalosis." Partial compensation occurs as evidenced by the reduced excretion of acid and ammonia in the urine and the increase in the urinary bicarbonate (areas 2 and 3).

*3. Compensated alkali excess.* The [NaHCO₃] is rasied but a parallel rise occurs in [H₂CO₃]. The pH is therefore normal. A disturbance of this nature will result from conditions which cause (1) but of less severe degree (area 4).

*4. Compensated CO₂ excess.* [H₂CO₃] increased but accompanied by a proportional rise in [NaHCO₃]; pH is normal. This state occurs in conditions in which there is retention of CO₂, e.g., emphysema (area 4).

*5. Normal acid-base balance.* [H₂CO₃], [NaHCO₃] and pH are normal (area 5).

*6. Compensated alkali deficit.* [NaHCO₃] is reduced and [H₂CO₃] diminished proportionately; pH normal. The condition results from the abnormal production of fixed acid as in diabetes; acid retention as in nephritis; or from the ingestion of mineral acids or acid producing salts (CaCl₂, NH₄Cl). This and (9) are the acid-base states to which the term "acidosis" has been usually applied. The compensatory adjustments are evident in the increased acid and ammonia excretion in the urine and the lowered CO₂ tension in the alveolar air. Alkali deficit may also result from the increased excretion of base as occurs in dehydrated states (ch. 3) and in animals following the production of a pancreatic fistula (area 6).

*7. Compensated CO₂ deficit.* This is a reduction in [H₂CO₃] and a parallel reduction in [NaHCO₃]. The pH is therefore normal. This state results from less severe grades of the conditions which cause (2) above. The excretion of NaHCO₃ by the kidney is much slower than the excretion of CO₂ by the lungs, so a condition of CO₂ deficit, which is uncompensated to start with, later tends to become compensated (area 6).

*8. Uncompensated CO₂ excess.* [H₂CO₃] is increased but is not balanced by a proportional rise in [NaHCO₃]. The pH is lowered (i.e., blood is less alkaline). This is sometimes referred to as "gaseous acidosis." Such a state results from a hindrance to the excretion of CO₂ as may occur in pneumonia, obstruction to breathing or depression of the respiratory center by morphine. There is partial compensation, i.e., the bicarbonate is raised above the normal and there is an increased excretion of acid and ammonia by the kidneys (areas 7 and 8).

*9. Uncompensated alkali deficit.* [NaHCO₃] is reduced without there being a parallel reduction in [H₂CO₃]. The pH is lowered (i.e., the blood becomes less alkaline). Such an acid-base state occurs when large quantities of fixed acids—β-hydroxybutyric and acetoacetic—are produced as in diabetic coma and in the terminal stages of nephritis when acid excretion is greatly impaired. The plasma bicarbonate is severely depleted; the CO₂ combining power of the plasma may be less than 20 volumes per cent (area 9).

It will be evident after a consideration of some of the foregoing acid-base states that the terms "acidosis" and "alkalosis" if used to denote respectively a fall or a rise in plasma bicarbonate are misleading, since the blood may be no more acid or alkaline than normally. For example, in (2) above, the blowing off of CO₂ will result in a certain degree of compensatory reduction of NaHCO₃. The reduction in the alkali reserve would therefore entitle it to be called acidosis though the blood was actually more alkaline than normally. In (8) on the other hand the blood is less alkaline than normally yet a certain degree of compensatory increase in the alkali reserve would have occurred. The term alkalosis would therefore apply, though its use would give an erroneous idea of the true state of the acid-base balance. It is now more common practice to use the terms *respiratory alkalosis* when the pCO₂ is reduced by voluntary hyperventilation and *respiratory acidosis* when the pCO₂ is rasied by an increase in the CO₂ tension of alveolar air. The term *metabolic alkalosis* is used to indicate an increase in CO₂ combining power as a result of metabolic reactions, and the term *metabolic acidosis* a decrease in CO₂ combining power. *Metabolic alkalosis* can be produced by the administration of sodium bicarbonate and *metabolic acidosis* by giving ammonium chloride.

## MEASUREMENT OF THE HYDROGEN ION CONCENTRATION OF THE BLOOD

### *Electrometric Method*

*1. By means of hydrogen electrodes.* Two hydrogen electrodes are employed. The method is derived from the fact that in a suitable concentration cell a difference of potential between a metal electrode (e.g., mercury) and a solution of its ions (e.g., mercurous chloride) is set up which is proportional to the ion concentration. A hydrogen electrode, composed of spongy platinum saturated with hydrogen gas, is therefore used to determine the hydrogen ion concentration of a solution. The platinum is contained in a small tube and partially immersed in a normal solution of KCl. The tube above the solution is filled with hydrogen gas, which is adsorbed by the platinum. The hydrogen electrode is balanced against a calomel electrode (metallic mercury in contact with a normal KCl solution saturated with HgCl), or against another hydrogen electrode dipping into a solution of known hydrogen ion concentration. When, as in the latter instance, the two hydrogen electrodes are connected, an electromotive force is developed, which varies with the difference in hydrogen ion concentration of the two solutions. This can be measured by a suitable instrument. Another electrometric method involves the use of quinhydrone—*quinhydrone electrode*. One platinum or gold electrode is placed in a solution of known hydrogen ion concentration; and the other dips into the unknown solution. A small quantity of quinhydrone is added to each solution. The quinhydrone undergoes oxidation to quinone or reduction to hydroquinone according to the hydrogen ion concentration of the solution. A potential difference is set up between the two electrodes and from its magnitude the H ion concentration is calculated.

*2. By means of the glass electrode.* Like the hydrogen electrode the potential of the glass electrode, in an electrical system similar to that just described for the latter, varies with changes in pH. It must be calibrated with solutions of known hydrogen ion concentration.

The glass electrode, as shown in figure 13.3, consists of a tube G of thin (0.001 mm.), soft glass of special composition, closed at its lower end and sealed into tube A of ordinary glass. Filling the larger tube and surrounding the surface of special glass is a 0.1 N solution of HCl, into which dips a

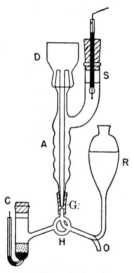

Fig. 13.3. Description in text

silver-silver chloride electrode S. The solution, whose hydrogen ion concentration is to be determined, is introduced into the cup D, which fits the tube G. C is a calomel electrode and R a reservoir of saturated solution of KCl. Through the stopcock H contact is made with the glass tube containing the solution to be tested. The theory of the electrode is complicated and not fully understood. Electrolytic dissociation must occur within the special glass itself, since a minute electrical current can pass through it.

The glass electrode has largely superseded other types of electrode which have been used for the hydrogen ion determinations. It has the advantages of being less cumbersome, more durable, being unaffected by oxidizing agents and of requiring only a small amount of fluid for testing, for the tube D need contain only a drop or so.

### Colorimetric Method

In the method of Levy, Rowentree and Marriott as modified by Dale and Evans, the blood is placed without loss of $CO_2$ in a collodion sac and dialyzed for 15 minutes against a solution of normal saline. A few drops of 0.02 per cent of the indicator neutral red are added to the dialysate. The latter is then placed in a comparator and its color matched with that of a phosphate mixture of known pH and containing neutral red in the same concentration as the blood dialysate. The reader is referred to Dale and Evans' article for the details of the method.

It might be thought that the H ion concentration would be reduced through the dilution of the dialyzed substance by the saline in the apparatus. But, since the pH of a buffered solution depends upon the ratio of free to bound acid and this of course will not be altered, so, moderate dilution does not effect the result. In the colorimetric method of Cullen, the pH is determined directly (i.e., without dialysis) upon plasma which is diluted 20 times; phenol red is used as indicator. In this method a correction must be made for dilution and also for protein content.

### From the $H_2CO_3/NaHCO_3$ Ratio

The total $CO_2$ in a sample of plasma is obtained as described on page 465. The free $CO_2$, i.e., the $CO_2$ in simple solution, is obtained by calculation from the partial pressure of $CO_2$ with which the sample was equilibrated. The calculation is made as follows. The figure for the partial pressure of $CO_2$ is multiplied by the absorption coefficient of $CO_2$ in plasma, which at 38°C. is 0.510 (p. 465). If, then, the partial pressure of $CO_2$ is 40 mm. Hg (as in normal arterial blood), the quantity of gas dissolved in 100 cc. of plasma is

$$40 \times \frac{100 \times 0.510^*}{760} = 2.68$$

The total $CO_2$ is, say, 56 volumes per cent. Then the combined $CO_2$ is $56 - 2.68 = 53.32$ volumes per cent.

The pH may now be calculated from the Henderson-Hasselbalch equation (pp. 127 and 466).

$$pH = pK_1 + \log \frac{[BHCO_3]}{H_2CO_3}$$

The value of $pK_1$† for plasma is 6.10, therefore

$$pH = 6.10 + \log \frac{53.32}{2.68}$$

---

* $100 \times (0.510/760) = 0.0672$ is a constant factor by which the $CO_2$ partial pressure (in mm. Hg) is multiplied to give the volumes of dissolved $CO_2$ .

† $K_1$ includes the first dissociation constant of $H_2CO_3$ and a figure representing the dissociation of $NaHCO_3$ under the conditions existing in plasma.

## REFERENCES

CULLEN, G. E. J. Biol. Chem., 1922, **50**, xvii.

DALE, H. H. AND EVANS, C. L. J. Physiol., 1920, **54, 157**.

DAVENPORT, H. W. The ABC of acid-base chemistry, 4th ed., University of Chicago Press, Chicago, 1957.

LEVY, R. L., ROWNTREE, L. G. AND MARRIOTT, W. M. Arch. Int. Med., 1915, **16,** 309.

VAN SLYKE, D. D. J. Biol. Chem., 1917, **30,** 347; 1921, **48,** 153.

VAN SLYKE, D. D. AND CULLEN, G. E. J. Biol. Chem., 1917, **30,** 289.

*Monographs and Reviews*

HENDERSON, L. J. Blood; a study in general physiology. Yale University Press, New Haven, Connecticut, 1928.

OGSTON, A. G. Physiol. Rev., 1947, **27,** 228.

ROUGHTON, F. J. W. Physiol. Rev., 1935, **15,** 241.

# SECTION TWO
## *Circulation*

# *14*

# BASIC PROPERTIES OF THE HEART

The important characteristics of the heart include excitability, rhythmicity, conductivity, contractility, and distensibility.

## Excitation of Cardiac Muscle

The ability of a tissue to respond to a stimulus is spoken of as excitability or irritability. In the case of muscle, the response is the development of a potential difference and shortening of its fibers. The motion of the heart is controlled by these changes of the potential difference between the inside and the outside of individual myocardial fibers. For many years the monophasic action potential of the heart recorded with one electrode on injured or depolarized and supposedly inactive tissue, and the other electrode on active or normal tissue has been employed to show or to reveal the time course of depolarization and repolarization of the myocardial muscle membrane. Measurement of this action potential has been employed to correlate changes in the state of the membrane with observed variations in excitability and with the simultaneous cardiac electrogram or myogram. Use of the monophasic action potential, however, has numerous drawbacks and, at best, can serve only as a record of the average time course of the membrane potential change in many cells.

The studies of Weidmann, 1949, and Woodbury, 1951, showed that the potential difference across a limited area of muscle membrane of a single heart fiber could be faithfully recorded in the beating heart by use of an intracellular micro electrode of the type developed by Ling and Gerard, 1949. Glass tubes of about 1 mm. external diameter are drawn out to an extremely small tip of about $0.2\,\mu$. When these are filled with concentrated potassium solution and inserted through the fiber membrane into the sarcoplasm, they can be used to measure the potential difference between the outside and inside of a single fiber in the beating heart. By cutting off the tip of the glass capillary electrode and suspending it on a wire, the electrode is free to move up and down. Thus artefacts from heart movements are minimized and recordings from human hearts during cardiac surgery have been made. Where studied simultaneously, the transmembrane potentials from fibers in the intact heart are qualitatively and quantitatively similar to those recorded from single fibers of isolated preparations of either atria or ventricles. Information thus obtained concerning the state of polarization of the muscle membrane serves as a much better basis for correlation with studies of excitability and refractoriness than the less direct and more variable measurements obtained with surface electrode techniques (fig. 14.1).

TRANSMEMBRANE POTENTIALS OF VENTRICLE AND ATRIUM. Figure 14.2a shows the potential changes that are observed when a capillary microelectrode is inserted into a single fiber of a rhythmically beating ventricle. When both the microelectrode and the indifferent electrode are outside the cell, there is no potential difference. When, however, the tip of the microelectrode penetrates the membrane of a single myocardial fiber, a sudden potential of 80 to 90 mv. is recorded with the inside of the fiber negative to the indifferent electrode. This resting potential difference across the muscle membrane remains at the same value as long as the tissue is quiescent. Following stimulation, however, there is an extremely rapid phase of depolarization (1 to 2 msec.) and change in the

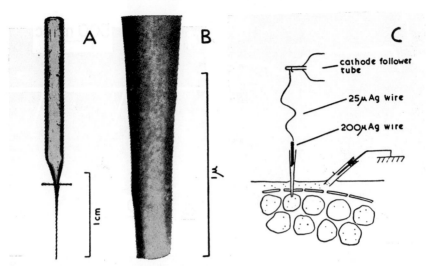

FIG. 14.1. Microelectrodes used for determining transmembrane potential in single myocardial fiber as modified by Alexander and Nastuk from Ling and Gerard.

membrane potential so that the intracellular microelectrode momentarily becomes positive with respect to the indifferent electrode. Therefore, at the peak of the action potential, the membrane is not only depolarized but actually exhibits a reversal of polarity or exhibits overshooting amounting to 15 to 30 mv., and lasting 6 to 15 msec. Immediately after this reversal there is a plateau of about 100 msec. and then a moderately rapid repolarization of the membrane for 100 to 150 msec., as the resting potential is restored. On pulling back the electrode, the potential jumps back to the zero level. It is believed that use of an intracellular microelectrode gives a true picture of the time course of depolarization and repolarization in a single cardiac muscle fiber and provides an accurate measurement of the size of transmembrane potentials.

Transmembrane potentials recorded from the atria and auricles in the open chest dog (or from single fibers of isolated preparations) are not significantly different from those of the ventricles except that following depolarization, the atrial records show an immediate slow phase of repolarization without an intervening plateau such as occurs in ventricular muscle (fig. 14.2b).

The temporal relationship between the action potential of a single fiber and the local ventricular electrogram of the intact and *in situ* heart is shown in figure 14.2a. The upstroke of the action potential coincides with the R wave of the electrogram, the plateau with the R-T segment, and the phase of repolarization with the T wave. Although the mechanism is unexplained, the temporal relation between the electrical and mechanical activity is very close (fig. 14.2e). Contraction starts a few milliseconds after depolarization, and tension reaches a peak when the membrane undergoes repolarization. The state of contraction is maintained as long as the fiber is depolarized, and relaxation sets in as soon as the resting potential is re-established. Under some conditions it has been possible to obtain dissociation between mechanical and electrical events, i.e., electrical activity is obtainable when there is no longer a recorded mechanical response.

The transmembrane potential and mechanical response of cardiac muscle are very sensitive to certain inorganic ions. Changes in concentration of potassium, calcium, and to a lesser extent sodium, have a profound effect on the excitability and contractile response of the mammalian myocardium. Magnesium has little action in the presence of normal calcium concentration, but when the latter concentration is decreased both magnesium and strontium have a marked effect on membrane potential. It is possible that changes in myocardial function which are encountered in man in disease states can be explained on the basis of the known effects of these ions on the membranes of cardiac muscle fibers.

TRANSMEMBRANE POTENTIALS OF SPECIALIZED TISSUES. Of the 3 specialized tissues in the mammalian heart, i.e., the sinal atrial node, the atrial ventricular (A-V) node, and the ventricular conducting system (Purkinje fibers), only the latter has been studied extensively by microelectrode techniques. Figure 14.2c illustrates the electrical

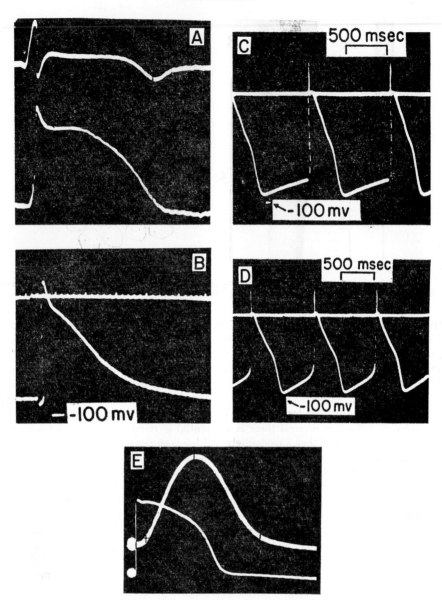

FIG. 14.2A. Transmembrane action potential of a single ventricular fiber (*lower curve*) and simultaneous ventriculogram of the intact heart *in situ*. The upstroke of the action potential coincides with the R wave of the electrogram, the plateau with the R-T segment, and the phase or repolarization with the T wave. (After Brooks and associates.) *B*, Normal transmembrane potential recorded from a single fiber of the intact auricle. (After Brooks and associates.) *C*, Transmembrane action potential of a single Purkinje fiber in a nonpacemaker activity. Note slow loss of resting potential during diastole. (After Brooks and associates.) *D*, Spontaneous activity recorded from Purkinje fiber in a pacemaker area. Note slow depolarization during diastole and then abrupt onset of spontaneous depolarization. (After Brooks and associates.) *E*, Temporal relation between action potential and mechanical contraction recorded from a papillary muscle. (After Dudel and Trautwein.)

peculiarities of Purkinje fibers in the dog heart. In contrast to the constant diastolic membrane potential in auricular and ventricular muscle, there is in the ventricular conducting system a slow depolarization throughout diastole when local electrical activity is induced by a distant pacemaker. When pacemaker activity originates in the local area there is, in addition, a slow upward curvature in late diastole which continues until a level of instability is reached and a more rapid depolarization, the action potential, spontaneously begins (fig. 14.2*d*). This peculiarity was first described by Bozler. The assumption is made that normal pacemaker activity in the sino-atrial, A-V nodal tissue, and in undifferentiated ventricular muscle of the mammalian heart is similar to the above when they act as pacemakers, but as yet this has been shown to be true for these areas only in the frog and turtle heart.

As to be expected, the electrical properties of the pacemaker region change with factors that alter heart rate. Vagus stimulation, acetylcholine and hypothermia lower heart rate by decreasing the rate of diastolic repolarization and thus lengthening the time taken to reach a critical level at which an action potential is initiated, whereas sympathetic stimulation and epinephrine injection, by inducing a faster rate of depolarization with an earlier firing, accelerate heart rate.

MECHANISM OF TRANSMEMBRANE POTENTIAL. What causes the resting potential and what causes this potential difference to change during myocardial contraction and relaxation is not known. There is no doubt that the state of membrane permeability is the basis for excitability. About all that is known is that at rest potassium is not diffusible and that sodium is freely diffusible through the muscle membrane, and that this is caused by metabolic activity. Largely through the work of Hodgkins and associates, ion movements that may be responsible for change in membrane potential have been partially identified. It is assumed that the resting potential across the myocardial membrane depends upon the concentration gradient of potassium to which the membrane is not permeable. It is believed that depolarization arises from an increased permeability which permits sodium ions to move from the extracellular phase (rich in sodium) into the cardiac fibers, while repolarization arises as the result of increased permeability to potassium ions which now move from the cell (rich in potassium) to the outside. Thus, following each action potential the inside of the fiber has gained a small quantity of sodium ions and lost a comparable quantity of potassium ions. In order to maintain ionic equilibrium, the shifts have to be reversed during the period of diastole. The ions must be "pumped" against electrochemical gradients and this necessitates metabolic energy.

Experimental verification of the preceding is difficult but for the turtle heart at least, it has been demonstrated that potassium is released from the myocardium during its activity (fig. 14.3). To study this, potassium[42] was injected into the peritoneum of a living turtle. A few hours later, the heart was cut out and the coronary

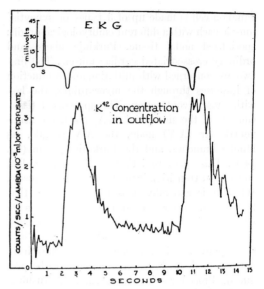

FIG. 14. 3. K[42] effluogram of a turtle ventricle. (From Wilde and associates.)

circulation perfused with radio inactive Ringer's solution. Samples of the coronary outflow were collected at short intervals and counted for the isotope. The results show a large increase in potassium[42] outflow associated with each period of activity, that is, with each systole, and when corrections are made for the travel time between the release of the potassium in the muscle fibers and the arrival at the venous outflow, then the extra potassium[42] release occurs some time during the Q-T interval of the ECG.

From what has been said, our knowledge of the electrophysiology of the heart is obviously of a descriptive nature. Answers are not available to such fundamental queries as to (1) the nature of change in selective permeability and in transmembrane passage of ions in the presence of altered permeability, (2) the linkage between depolarization and mechanical shortening of muscle, and between metabolism and active ion transport.

## Rhythmicity and Conductivity

To produce efficient pumping of blood, the complex mass of myocardial fibers must contract more or less simultaneously. The conducting system is responsible for periodic initiation of excitation and the rapid spread of excitation to all parts of the ventricular walls so that the conduction is sufficiently simultaneous to produce effective pumping. This is a stereotyped and repetitive sequence of events during each cardiac cycle.

Cardiac tissue in addition to nerve fiber and

ganglion cell is made up of 3 types of syncytial muscle each with a different embryological origin: specialized nodal tissue, Purkinje fibers, and ordinary cross-striated cardiac muscle. The first two are concerned with initiation and conduction of impulses through the myocardium, the last with muscle contraction. The specialized tissue consists of the sino-atrial (S-A) node, the atrio-ventricular (A-V) node, the A-V bundle, its bundle branches, and the Purkinje system (fig. 14.4). This specialized tissue ends by a gradual end-to-end transition into ordinary heart muscle. While it is generally considered probable that these peculiar specialized cells are the agents which conduct the stimulus to the ventricles, absolute proof that the sympathetic fibers which accompany the bundle and its branches have nothing to do with conduction is yet to be produced. Procedures involving cutting, crushing, ligation or injection must, of necessity, damage both these characteristic cells and the nerve cells also because of their intimate admixture.

The time of arrival of excitation in various regions of the mammalian heart has been determined in different ways: for the epicardial surface from the deflection obtained by placing one electrode directly on different areas of the epicardium and a second electrode on a distant part of the body, or from paired contiguous electrodes; for the nodal and specialized conducting tissue from the deflection obtained with intracellular elec-trodes; for the ventricle proper from deflections obtained with multiple intramural electrodes.

IMPULSE INITIATION. Keith and Flack, 1907, suggested that the S-A node embedded in the right atrial wall near the entrance of the superior vena cava is the focus in the mammalian heart from which each heart beat normally starts. Evidence of such origin is that (1) its excision or inactivation causes cessation or slowing of the atrial or ventricular contractions, (2) temperature change of the node but not of the surrounding tissue changes heart rate, (3) the node becomes electrically active before any other region of the heart. This cannot be regarded as positive proof of origin from the S-A node but rather from this general region which includes other types of cells including ganglion cells.

Although spontaneous and repetitive depolarization arises normally only in this region, there are other areas in which electrical activity can arise under some circumstances and initiate cardiac contraction. When the S-A node is destroyed or inactivated, the A-V node becomes the sight of impulse formation and develops spontaneous depolarization. In turn, in the presence of inactivation of the A-V node, the ventricles develop a slow rhythm. Since both ventricles receive the excitation through natural pathways and contract in a coordinated way, the rhythmical center is the A-V bundle. If both bundle branches are cut, impulse initiation arises in the ventricular

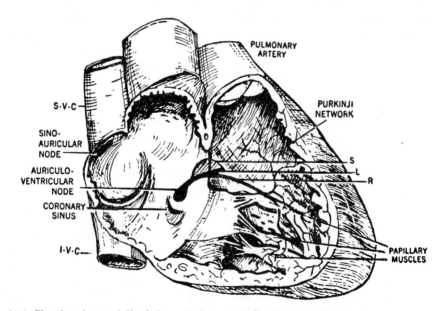

FIG. 14.4. Showing the specialized tissue of the mammalian heart. *S.V.C.*, superior vena cava; *I.V.C.*, inferior vena cava; *S*, membranous part of interventricular septum; *L*, left branch of bundle; *R*, right branch of bundle.

muscle. The natural rate of automaticity of these areas is of a descending order of magnitude, the S-A node being 70 to 80 per min., atria 60 per min., A-V node 40 to 60 per min., and ventricles 20 to 40 per minute. It is obvious that normally, the atria, A-V node, and ventricular tissue cannot set the heart rate because the S-A node repolarizes and automatically discharges more rapidly than any of these tissues. Hence, an impulse from the S-A node will always depolarize these tissues before either could initiate a rhythm. On occasion, however, an ectopic focus in the atrium or ventricular muscle can assume a rhythm faster than that of the S-A node, and hence, it becomes the pacemaker.

PATHWAYS OF CONDUCTION. Following each spontaneous depolarization in the region of the S-A node, near the mouth of the superior vena cava, the activation process is transmitted radially throughout the muscle of both atria at about 1 meter per sec., and reaches the outermost por-

tions of the atria in about 50 msec. (fig. 14.5a). No specialized tissue appears to be present although the transmission is thought to follow at least partially, certain direct muscular fasciculi; thus, the impulse reaches the A-V node in advance of its arrival at the wall of the left atrium. The plan of activation of human atria has not been directly studied.

As the depolarization approaches the interatrial septum, it reaches a mass of specialized tissue, the A-V node, which is located near the posterior margin of the interatrial septum near the entrance of the coronary sinus into the right atrium. Complete dissociation of the auricles and ventricles follows cutting, tying, or crushing of an A-V node or bundle, thus creating what is called complete heart block. Delay of the impulse for from 80 to 120 msec., normally occurs at the A-V node, for the activation process travels slowly (0.2 meters per sec.) through this tissue. Although the cause is unknown, this delay is helpful for it

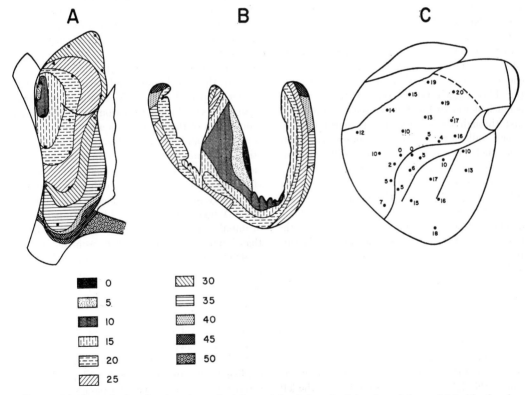

A            B            C

| | |
|---|---|
| ■ 0 | ▨ 30 |
| ▦ 5 | ▤ 35 |
| ▦ 10 | ▦ 40 |
| ▦ 15 | ■ 45 |
| ▦ 20 | ▦ 50 |
| ▨ 25 | |

FIG. 14.5A. Spread of activation through right auricle of dog. Auricle viewed from right side showing superior and inferior venae cavae, coronary sinus and atrial appendage. Time of activation in milliseconds following activation of the S-A node. (From Puech.) *B,* Frontal plane section showing spread of activation through the ventricular septum and ventricular walls of the canine heart. Lower left part of septum is activated first at time zero. Time of activation of other portions in milliseconds. (From Sodi-Pallares.) *C,* Spread of excitation on the ventral surface of the dog heart. Region near the interventricular sulcus on the right ventricle excited first. Time of activation of other portions of epicardial surface in milliseconds. (After Harris.)

permits completion of atrial contraction and emptying during diastole of the ventricles. The aggregate potential by these few fibers is too small to be recorded except locally. After leaving the A-V node, the wave of excitation passes rapidly (4 to 5 meters per sec.) by the common A-V bundle, its branches, and by the Purkinje network of subendocardial fibers to spread throughout the endocardial surfaces of both ventricles. The exact course by which the wave of excitation is distributed throughout the ventricular musculature from the endocardial surface is not definitely established except that it penetrates the ventricular wall from endocardial to epicardial surface. Present evidence indicates that such spread of excitation is not by anatomical muscle bundles but by the specialized tissue. By some this is believed to be not merely a subendocardial layer but a profuse myocardial network ramifying in many muscle planes and extending deeply into the myocardium. This would cause almost simultaneous activation of much of the ventricular muscle mass. At all events, the intraventricular septal surface is excited first, the papillary muscles next, but conduction is so fast that the inner surfaces of both ventricles are excited almost simultaneously, the whole of the endocardium being activated in about 50 msec. (fig. 14.5*b*). Excitation of the ventricular muscle is much slower (0.4 meters per sec.) and proceeds first through the septum and then through the lateral walls of the ventricles from endocardial to epicardial surfaces. This is entirely different from the spread of excitation in the atrial muscle which is radial. Muscle activation occurs first in the subendocardial layers of the midportion of the left ventricular septum to spread inward; this is quickly followed by inward activation from the right endocardial surface of the septum. Within 10 to 20 msec. after first activation of the septum, deflections are recorded on the anterior surface of the left ventricle along the interventricular groove near the apex. Within 25 to 30 msec., all the right ventricular surface is activated. Regions of the lateral wall of the left ventricle are excited slightly later (at 25 to 35 msec.) since the wall is much thicker. Finally, at 40 to 45 msec., the epicardial surface over the pulmonary conus region of the right ventricle and the base of the left ventricle and septum respond. In general, excitation of the epicardial surface occurs 1 to 20 msec. later than its endocardial counterpart. Many investigations with more refined techniques have confirmed the original findings of Lewis that the maximum difference in time of excitation of different regions of the ventricular surfaces is also quite small, being of the order of 10 to 20 msec., and that surface excitation of the ventricles proceeds from point to point as it does in the atria (fig. 14.5*c*). In the human, the patterns of activation have not been detailed but are believed to be similar to those in the dog heart. However, the time for activation might be twice as long because of the much thicker myocardium.

EFFECT OF CARDIAC NERVES ON RHYTHMICITY AND CONDUCTIVITY. The inherent automaticity and conduction properties of the heart can be altered antagonistically through the action of the sympathetic and vagus nerves to the myocardium. The parasympathetic fibers from the right vagus terminate mainly near the S-A node but some fibers spread throughout the atria. Most left vagal fiber endings supply the A-V node and the A-V bundle. Many endings are spread throughout the atrial muscle but they have not been demonstrated in the ventricles.

Stimulation of vagal fibers to the heart presumably results in the secretion of acetylcholine at the vagal endings in the heart causing slowing of the heart through S-A nodal depression (chronotropic effect), decrease in the rate of the depolarization wave through the atria and through the A-V bundle, and an increase in the refractory period of the A-V bundle. Very often, as to be expected from its anatomical distribution, stimulation of the right vagus affects mainly the heart rate and atrial contractility: left vagal stimulation may result mainly in a partial functional heart block at the A-V node. Very strong stimulation of either one or both vagi generally completely stops the rhythmical contraction of the S-A node or completely blocks transmission of impulses through the A-V node and bundle so that impulses are no longer transmitted to the ventricles. Ventricular beats in the open chest dog can be stopped in this manner for at least a minute although the usual effect is for a few seconds only. The ventricles then establish their own slow rhythm. Vagal stimulation in the turtle or frog heart can arrest the ventricles for 2 to 4 hours.

The sympathetic fibers to the heart are derived from the cervical and upper thoracic ganglia. The cardiac fibers supply the S-A node, A-V node, atrial muscle, and unlike the parasympathetics, the ventricular muscle as well. Sympathin, an epinephrinelike substance, secreted at the sympathetic nerve endings causes effects almost exactly opposite to those of acetylcholine. Stimulation of cardiac nerve fibers isolated from the stellate ganglia releases sympathin, increases the rate of rhythm of the S-A node, increases the rate of conduction through all parts of the heart, and increases the refractory period of the A-V bundle, Purkinje system, and muscle fibers. Maximal sympathetic stimulation can, at times, almost triple heart rate. Epinephrine has essentially the same effects. Thus, sympathin release or stellate stimulation increases the over-all heart rate.

### Contractility and Distensibility

CONTRACTILE PROCESS. The chambers of the heart are surrounded by walls made up of bundles and sheets of myocardial fibers. The fibers form a syncytium which gives protoplasmic continuity between adjoining fibers and throughout an entire mass of cardiac muscle (fig. 14.6).

The major organized parts of the fibers are the myofibrils, the sarcosomes or cytochondria, and the sarcoplasm. The fibrils are the fundamental contractile units of the heart. The nature of the contraction and relaxation of muscle is on a theoretical basis and beyond the present scope. It is, however, generally believed that the contractile elements in cardiac, also skeletal and smooth muscle fibers, are formed from myosin, a protein of rather short molecular rods, and actin, a long continuous protein thread, both of which are dissociated in resting muscle and neither of which will contract independently. Excitation passing along the muscle results in the formation of actomyosin which is unstable in its extended or resting state and which now dissipates energy either by shortening or increased tension. Actomyosin is thus changed to its energy poor state and may accomplish work if it shortens.

In terms of metabolism, the fibrils are the structures which, with the purpose of generating mechanical work utilize the metabolic agent which supplies chemical energy to be transformed into work. In the past, the assumption has been made, based on indirect evidence, that the immediate source of energy or the metabolic agent in contracting muscle is the enzymatic hydrolysis of adenosine triphosphate or creatine phosphate. Direct measurements, however, show no such breakdown in a single muscle twitch and even a tetanic contraction can take place without significant decomposition of these compounds. Inorganic phosphorus is, however, liberated during the contraction from an unidentified precursor in just sufficient amounts to supply the required energy but whether this source is the phosphate bond energy of an unidentified compound such as another nucleotide has not been determined. At all events, regeneration of such a substance is the task of metabolism. Glycolysis as a source of such energy is carried out in the sarcoplasm but in a heart which cannot accumulate a large oxygen debt, this is scarce. Respiration is a function of the sarcosomes and, presumably, such regenerative processes are carried in the sarcosomes which are abundant in the heart. However, very little is known regarding the mechanism of reloading and muscle relaxation.

While there are some differences among the actomyosin complexes in skeletal, smooth and cardiac muscle, the contractile mechanisms appear to be closely related. In functional characteristics, however, the myocardium resembles visceral smooth muscle more than skeletal muscle from the standpoint of autogenic excitation and inherent rhythmicity, and intercellular transmission of excitation and nervous control. Both have rapid depolarization and tend to remain depolarized for a period about equal to the duration of contraction; both are not directly innervated by motor nerves, but waves of excitation originate in the muscle fibers and are conducted through the contiguous cells (although smooth muscle is not strictly speaking a syncytium); both are controlled by the autonomic nervous system by way of release of hormonal substances.

PREPARATIONS AND METHODS. In the earlier investigations of the physical properties of the myocardium, the hearts of the frog and tortoise were used. Later, with the development of better technics in methodology, the isolated hearts or heart-lungs of warm-blooded animals such as the cat and dog were used. Subsequently, studies were made on the heart *in situ* in the open and closed-chest anesthetized dog, in the unanesthetized dog, and more recently studies of the heart of the dog and of man *in situ* in which, by means of a heart-lung oxygenator system, the systemic

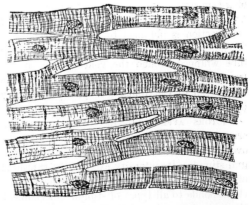

FIG. 14. 6. Cardiac muscle fibers.

circulation is maintained while only the coronary flow to the heart muscle is maintained, i.e., the left ventricle is empty and the right ventricle is a conduit for coronary venous return. These studies have been very fruitful and have revealed some of the fundamental characteristics of the myocardial process.

In estimating the myocardial or contractile response in these preparations, measurements of interest are the contractile force (contractility) and the distensibility (extensibility) of the myocardium. The term "contractility" although very useful is rather difficult to define. For purposes of consideration, increase in contractility signifies that the mechanical response during contraction is faster (steeper gradient), higher (greater amplitude), generally shorter in time, and that the muscle has a more abrupt and rapid relaxation. Similarly, a decrease in distensibility (extensibility) occurs if the resistance to stretch (muscle tension) increases in a muscle strip or the pressure within a ventricular cavity at rest rises. Such comparisons should be made at the same resting muscle fiber length or size of ventricular cavity.

Such measurements are comparatively easy in isolated strips of myocardium but they are difficult in the whole heart especially within the body. Both are measured in the beating, exposed, empty, or full heart by stretching all or a small portion of the ventricular mass and then determining by use of a strain gauge arch or by direct measurement the isometric tension developed at different muscle lengths during rest and during stimulation. Distensibility as well as contractility is also estimated in the beating heart by measuring the intraventricular pressure, stroke volume, and stroke work responses to changes of ventricular volume (used as a guage of myocardial fiber length). The ventricular volume in systole and diastole is determined directly by a mechanical plethysmograph or by a dye dilution technique. An index of directional change in ventricular cross-section is obtained by a sonar technique, by change in resistance of a mercury filled rubber tube wrapped around the ventricle, by an intraventricular diameter gauge, and by surface calipers, or by electromagnetic plethysmography (see ch. 18).

FACTORS AFFECTING THE CONTRACTILE RESPONSE. The impulse from the sinoatrial node over the cardiac syncytium constitutes the natural stimulus. Its intensity exceeds the threshold of response by 4 to 5 times. Quiescent heart muscle responds to all types of stimuli—mechanical, thermal, electrical, and chemical.

*A. Intensity of stimulation.* The existence but usually not the magnitude of the contractile response depends upon the intensity of the stimulus. When a quiescent ventricle is excited directly by properly widely spaced electric shocks of increasing intensity, all stimuli above threshold result in contractions of the same amplitude. This was called the "all or nothing response" by Bowditch (1871). It is due to the spread of the excitatory process to all parts of the cardiac syncytium. A single skeletal muscle fiber responds in the same way but an entire skeletal muscle gives an increasing response with increasing effective stimuli because more and more of the fibers which are insulated from each other now respond.

Although this reaction in cardiac muscle means that the response is not related to stimulus strength, it does not follow that contractile force cannot change with repetitive stimulation. As in a single skeletal muscle fiber with altered condition of the muscle, a minimal effective stimulus at one time may at another be subliminal should the excitability of the muscle be reduced. On the other hand, should the excitability increase, a subminimal stimulus may become effective and the size of the response may vary with the same stimulus if the conditions of the muscle are altered. This is illustrated by the fact that enhancement of contraction with the same intensity of stimulation can be observed to follow increased cardiac work without change in frequency of the heart beat, and increased frequency of stimulation from slow to fast rates (fig. 14.7a). This is called Treppe or staircase. If the stimulus is too close to the previous contraction, the mechanical response becomes small or may disappear. Thus, by some unknown mechanism each preceding contraction alters the internal condition of the muscle to change its responsiveness.

*B. Spacing of stimuli.* The existence and actual magnitude of the contractile response is dependent upon the time of the stimulus relative to the previous contraction (fig. 14.8). In the beating heart, stimuli are generally not effective during the period of contraction since the muscle remains depolarized throughout the period of contraction, and since the muscle must be repolarized in order to induce a new state of contraction. This period is called the absolute refractory period.

During early relaxation, excitability increases progressively but only stimuli still stronger than normal are effective. This is called the relative refractory period. On occasion this refractory period is followed by a subsequent phase in which

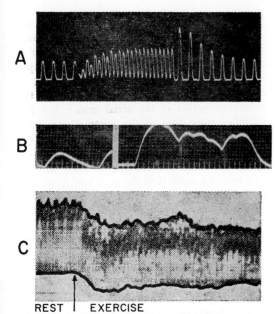

REST | EXERCISE

Fig. 14.7A. Staircase phenomena due to change in frequency of stimulation. Pressure change in right ventricle during isometric contraction. Perfused heart. S-A node crushed. Frequency of stimulation of left auricle: 1.5, 4, and 1.5 per sec. pressure scale: mm.Hg. (After Rosenblueth 1959a.) B, Summation of contraction in isolated papillary muscle of cat heart. Temperature 24° C. *Left*, single contraction from single stimulus; *right*, incomplete tetanus from repetitive stimulation. Frequency of stimulation 200 per sec. (After DiPalma.) C, Response of left ventricular "diameter" of a dog running on a treadmill at 5 per cent grade. Recorded with very slow camera. A ventricular "diameter" was determined continuously by a sonar technic. Top of record represents diastolic diameter; bottom of record, systolic diameter; difference is stroke volume change in diameter. *Left*, dog is at standing rest. *Arrow*, onset of exercise. Note that during exercise diastolic diameter decreases and stroke volume diameter does not increase. (After Rushmer 1959.)

a subnormal stimulus gives a contraction (super normal period).

This prolonged period of refractoriness normally present in heart muscle prevents the passage of a second impulse over the heart until the preceding contraction is over, and thus allows the ventricles to relax and fill with blood before another contraction can occur and also permits the maximum development of tension by the myocardium. By contrast, the refractory period of skeletal muscle is very brief since in skeletal muscle the duration of depolarization lasts only 1/300 of a second. Therefore, a rapid series of stimuli timed to fall just after this short refractory period will produce a rapid series of shortenings of skeletal muscle which fuse into an apparently

maximal contraction (tetanus) which is maintained as long as stimulation continues or until fatigue occurs.

It is obvious that an effective stimulus not coming from the sinoatrial node can affect the cardiac rhythm. A long pause follows the contraction caused by the artificial stimulus (fig. 14.9). The artificially induced contraction is called an extrasystole or premature contraction. The long interval following the extrasystole is termed the compensatory pause since its duration is such that when the next normal beat is resumed, it occurs at precisely the same time as it would have appeared had no premature contraction been provoked. The occurrence of the long pause is explained as follows. The normal impulses pass from the auricle to the ventricle in a perpetual stream and in orderly sequence. When the ventricular muscle is stimulated artificially during diastole, and an extra contraction induced, the normal impulse when it arrives from the auricle at the usual time finds the ventricle already in the contracted state and, in consequence, refrac-

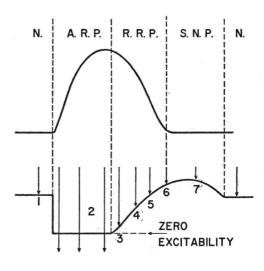

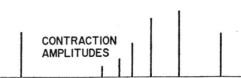

Fig. 14.8. Diagram illustrating excitability cycle of heart muscle during contraction and relaxation. *Upper curve*, isometric; *middle curve*, excitability changes: *1*, control excitability at rest; *2*, zero excitability during contraction; *3 to 6*, recovery of excitability during relaxation; *6 to 7*, supernormal excitability. Length of arrows indicates relative intensity of shocks required to obtain mechanical response. *Bottom curve*, resulting effects on amplitude of contraction. (After Wiggers.)

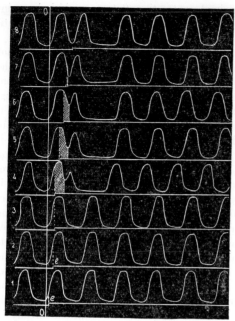

Fig. 14.9 Myograms of frog's ventricle showing effect of excitation by break induction shocks at various moments of the cardiac cycle. The line 0 indicates in all tracings the commencement of the beats during which the shocks were sent in. It will be noted that in 1, 2 and 3, the heart is refractory to the stimulus. The signal (the break in the horizontal line) indicates the moment at which the stimulus was applied. The latent period (hatched area) does not alter as this figure shows. See text. The extrasystoles increase in height from 4 to 8, each being followed by a compensatory pause. (After Marey.)

tory. The impulse is therefore ineffective. Not until the arrival of the next normal impulse is the muscle in a condition to respond. This accounts for the fact that the time elapsing between the normal beats preceding and following, respectively, the premature contraction, is equal to the length of two normal cardiac cycles. In other words, the heart after the interruption in its rhythm again "gets into step."

The long refractory periods of the cardiac muscle serve to preserve the cardiac rhythm. The absolute refractory phase makes the summation of contractions and the production of tetanus impossible. The relative refractory period tends to discourage the occurrence of a second contraction before sufficient time has elapsed to allow the complete relaxation of the muscle from a preceding contraction. When a premature contraction does occur, its refractory period serves to restore the normal rhythm.

The problem of identification of the boundaries of the refractory period is an old one, and the boundaries are not always in accord with the previous considerations. The absolute refractory period may be altered by various agencies. It is shortened by a rise in temperature and by rapid heart action. It is prolonged by the action of certain drugs. Vagal stimulation shortens the refractory period of the atrial muscle but has no effect upon that of the ventricular muscle. This refractory period does not necessarily last throughout the contraction period but the muscle may respond by a contraction in early diastole to a stimulus applied at the very end of systole. Presumably this arises from the fact that in any muscle mass composed of so many fibers, a considerable number have repolarized and are responding by contraction to the stimulus while a great majority of the fibers are still in the depolarized state. In addition, when very strong ventricular stimuli up to 30 ma., and of 10 to 15 msec. duration are used in the open chest dog, there is in some hearts practically no absolute refractory period. It is also possible to show summation and tetanic response in isolated cardiac muscle of the rat under normal condition and of the frog and cat under unusual conditions of temperature and drugs. For example, papillary muscle maintained at a temperature of 26° C., or less, exhibits summation and tetanus similar to that seen in skeletal muscle (fig. 7b).

*C. The effect of stretch.* When an isolated ventricular strip is moderately stretched, its tension rises progressively, and upon electrical stimulation the amplitude and duration of its contraction increase (fig. 14.11). This relationship between length and contractile response which is firmly established for the amphibian and mammalian heart has been demonstrated in various ways. Muscle tension rises progressively as the whole mass of an isolated heart with perfused coronary arteries and contracting isometrically is stretched. Intraventricular pressure rises as the intraventricular volume (index of fiber length) is increased (1) by vagal stimulation owing to the resultant slower heart rate and increased diastolic stretch and filling, (2) as the return of blood to the heart is augmented by infusion in the isolated heart, heart-lung, open and closed chest anesthetized dog, or (3) as the exit of blood from a ventricle is temporarily blocked in the isometrically contracting heart in the open chest dog (fig. 14.10).

Despite the preceding, in any one ventricle the relation of the contractile response to muscle length at any one length is not constant but can

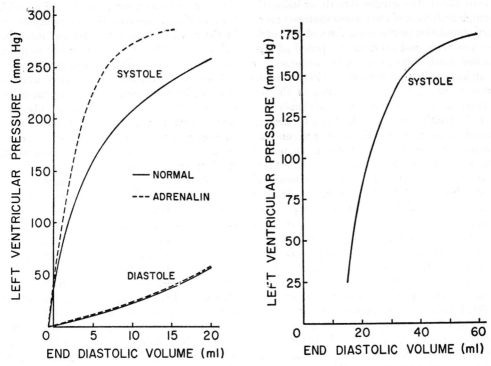

Fig. 14.10 (*Right*). Effect of plethora and hemorrhage on the relationship between left ventricular end diastolic volume and left ventricular systolic pressure in the anesthetized dog. Estimate of trend based on data from experiments. (After Holt.) (*Left*) Pressure volume curves of the left ventricle in the open chest dog under isometric conditions. Broken line curves, relation of ventricular end diastolic and systolic pressure, respectively, to ventricular end diastolic volume under normal conditions. Solid line curves, relationship of ventricular end diastolic pressure and systolic pressure, respectively, to ventricular end diastolic volume following administration of epinephrine (35γ) intravenously. To obtain the curves, the pulmonary venous return to the left ventricle was occluded and the ventricle emptied of blood by manual compression. The aorta was then occluded and successively known volumes of blood were injected into the ventricular cavity and the ventricular pressures recorded. Note that ventricular distensibility with epinephrine is increased during systole but is unchanged during diastole. (After Ulrich and Kramer.)

be made to vary, or varies spontaneously under many conditions including the normal state, i.e., ventricular volume at rest can vary without corresponding changes in diastolic pressure (change in distensibility), while the pressure or output of the ventricle during systole can vary without change in diastolic volume (change in contractility). As illustrated in figure 14.10 left, epinephrine causes no change in resting distensibility whereas it increases distensibility during systole. These active changes in distensibility and contractility can be brought about under many conditions and are generally caused by nervous and humeral influences. Thus, the heart is not a passive servant of the peripheral circulation; it does not merely pass on what it receives but is capable of changing its performance at the same diastolic size, thereby initiating circulatory modifications irrespective of primary changes in filling

of the heart by venous return and in the arterial resistance to flow.

Some of the cardiac nerve fibers are quite potent in this respect. Vagal stimulation leads to depression of vigor of atrial contraction (inotropic effect). Histologically, however, vagal fibers have not been demonstrated to reach the ventricles and if cholinergic substances are released in the atria, they are presumably destroyed before they reach the ventricles. Despite this, attention is called to experiments in which continuous stimulation of vagus nerves in the neck of the open chest dog resulted in a decreased stroke volume and stroke work of the left ventricle, for the same left atrial pressure and in the presence of a constant (but high) heart rate. This suggests a depressor action of the vagi on the ventricles.

The effect of sympathetic fibers on the myocardium has been observed by stimulating electrically the stellate ganglia directly or indirectly through activation of the carotid sinus receptors. Such stimulation increases the force of both atria and ventricles, and shortens the period of contraction much more than can be accounted for by an increase in heart rate. With selective stimulation, when all known connections to the peripheral vascular bed have been previously cut, only the positive inotropic effect can be demonstrated in which the arterial blood pressure and cardiac output rise greatly through augmented force of contraction. Stimulation of stellate fibers to the heart, epinephrine injection or treadmill exercise in unanesthetized dogs reduce ventricular volume while maintaining or increasing stroke volume; they also give more rapid myocardial relaxation or increased distensibility during diastole thus facilitating diastolic filling, while during ventricular systole the myocardium contracts more rapidly, ventricular pressure rises more rapidly and blood ejection is more complete (fig. 14.7c). Finally, if in the open chest dog the perfusion pressure in the carotid sinus is decreased, the circulatory response to such baroreceptor stimulation is dominantly an increased heart action; the effector portion of this reflex appears to be sympathetic fibers from the stellates to the heart, since, following their section these effects disappear and cannot again be induced.

*D. Other determinants.* In addition, myocardial hypoxia (within limits), an increase in muscle temperature, an increase in the calcium content of the blood, all increase the contractile force. Conversely, deletion of functional cardiac muscle blocks, by crushing, burning or coronary occlusion,

decrease in temperature, addition of acetylcholine, increased concentration of inorganic ions in the blood such as potassium and magnesium will decrease the excitability or the contractile force of the myocardium. Temporary functional deletion of contractions also occurs when two opposing impulses from different directions block each other out. Smaller responses also occur when different fractions of heart muscle are excited more slowly than others. This happens with beats from ectopic foci or with abnormal impulse distribution as in bundle branch block.

*E. Isometric versus isotonic contraction.* The tension or contractile force developed by a contracting ventricle is different in the isometric and isotonic states (fig. 14.11). When a muscle first contracts isometrically and then is allowed to shorten abruptly, the tension produced falls abruptly because a portion of the energy of contraction is used to overcome the high resistance from viscosity of the myocardium. This situation is comparable to that during systolic ejection since blood cannot be ejected from a ventricle without shortening of its fibers. In general, the contractile energy lost in overcoming myocardial viscosity and in creating tension between muscle layers is less at large diastolic volumes. Similarly, a relaxed myocardium responds to a rapid stretch by an immediate increase in tension which progressively diminishes as the muscle remains stretched. This has its counterpart in the intact heart in which, if inflow is rapid, the ventricular myocardium exerts tension to resist rapid elongation, thus stopping filling in early diastole while a slow inflow would prolong the period of diastolic filling.

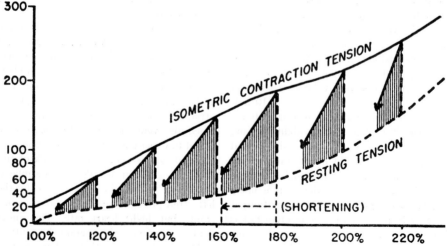

Fig. 14.11. Tension developed by stretched isolated muscle strip during rest and isometric contraction. (After Rushmer 1955.)

During late diastole the tension developed between ventricular muscle layers is minimal. The myocardial layers of the two ventricles which are oriented in different directions contract in different directions and shorten by different amounts during systole. Since these layers are firmly fixed to each other, some of the tension from the shortening myocardial fibers will be used to stretch the connections. This is wasted energy which opposes ventricular ejection. During ventricular relaxation, however, this stored energy is released and is helpful in early diastolic filling. Here also, the greater the systolic and diastolic volumes, the less the contractile energy lost in creating tension between muscle layers.

According to the law of LaPlace ($T = P.R.$), the tension (T) developed in the ventricular wall is related to the pressure developed within the cavity and to the radius of the cavity. For the active ventricle, this indicates that the greater the ventricular size, the greater the wall tension needed to maintain a given intraventricular pressure.

## REFERENCES

Alexander, J. T. and Nastuk, W. L. An instrument for the production of microelectrodes used in electrophysiological studies. Rev. Sci. Instr., 1953, 24, 528.

Anzola, J. and Rushmer, R. F. Cardiac responses to sympathetic stimulation. Circulation Res., 1956, 4, 302.

Bowditch, H. P. Ueber die Eigentöumlichkeiten der Reizbarkeir, welche die Muskelfasern des Herzens zeigen. Berichte d. Konigl. Sachs d. Ges. d. Wissen, Bd. 1871. 23, 652.

Bozler, E. The initiation of impulses in cardiac muscle. Am. J. Physiol., 1943, 138, 273.

Coraboeuf, E. and Weidmann, S. Potentials d'action du muscle cardiaque obtenus a l'aide de microelectrodes intracellulaires. Presense d'une inversion de potentiel. Compt. rend. Soc. Biol., 1949, 143, 1360.

DiPalma, J. R. and Mascatello, A. V. Excitability and refractory period of isolated heart muscle of the cat. Am. J. Physiol., 1951, 164, 589.

Draper, M. H. and Weidmann, S. Cardiac resting and action potentials recorded with an intracellular electrode. J. Physiol., 1951, 115, 74.

Dudel, J. and Trautwein, W. Das Aktionspotential under Mechanogramm des Herzmuskels Unter den Einfluss der Dehnung. Cardiologia, 1954, 25, 344.

Fleckenstein, A., Janke, J., Davies, R. E., and Krebs, H. A. Contraction of muscle without fission of adenosine triphosphate or creatine phosphate. Nature, 1954, 174, 1081.

Hajdu, S. Mechanism of staircase and contracture in ventricular muscle. Am. J. Physiol., 1953, 174, 371.

Harris, A. S. The spread of excitation in turtle, dog, cat and monkey ventricles. Am. J. Physiol., 1941, 134, 319.

Hill, A. V., Weber, H. H., Astbury, W. T., Dubuisson, M., Bailey, K., Pryor, M. G. M., Lundsgaard, E., Needham, D., Elliott, A., Barber, R., MacArthur, I., and Edsall, J. T. A discussion on muscular contraction and relaxation; their physical and chemical basis. Proc. Roy. Soc., London. Ser. B, 1950, 137, 40.

Hoffman, B. F. and Suckling, E. E. Cardiac cellular potentials: effect of vagal stimulation and acetylcholine. Am. J. Physiol., 1953, 173, 312.

Hoffman, B. F., deCarvalho, A. P., Mello, W. C., and Cranefield, P. F. Electrical activity of single fibers of the atrioventricular node. Circulation Res., 1959, 7, 11.

Holt, J. P. Effect of plethora and hemorrhage on left ventricular volume and pressure. Circulation Res., 1957, 5, 273.

Hutter, O. F. and Trautwein, W. Vagal and sympathetic effects on the pacemaker fibers in the sinus venosus of the heart. J. Gen. Physiol., 1956, 39, 715.

Keith, A. and Flack, M. The form and nature of muscular connection between primary divisions of the vertebrate heart. J. Anat. & Phys., 1907, 41, 172.

Lewis, T., Meakins, J., and White, P. D. The excitatory process in the dog's heart. I. The auricles. Phil. Trans. Roy. Soc., London, Ser. B, 1914, 205, 375.

Lewis, T. and Rothschild, M. A. The excitatory process in the dog's heart. II. The ventricles. Phil. Trans. Roy. Soc., London, Ser. B, 1915, 206, 181.

Ling, G. and Gerard, R. W. The normal membrane potential of frog sartorius fibers. J. Cell. & Comp. Physiol., 1949, 34, 383.

Mommaerts, W. F. H. M. The proteins of muscle and their participation in the process of contraction. Am. J. Phys. Med., 1955, 34, 11.

Mommaerts, W. F. H. M. Investigation of the presumed breakdown of ATP and phosphocreatine during a single muscle twitch. Am. J. Physiol. 1955, 182, 585.

Puech, P., Esclavissat, M., Sodi-Pallares, D., and Cisneros, F. Normal auricular activation in the dog's heart. Am. Heart J., 1954, 47, 174.

Robb, J. S. and Robb, R. C. The normal heart. Am. Heart J., 1942, 23, 455.

Robb, J. S. and Kaylor, C. T. A study of specialized heart tissue at various stages of development of the human fetal heart. Am. J. Med., 1948, 5, 324.

Rosenblueth, A., Alanis, J., Rubio, R., and Lopez, E. The two staircase phenomena. Arch. Intern. physiol. et biochem., 1959a, 67, 374.

Rosenblueth, A., Alanis, J., Lopez, E., and Rubio, R. The adaptation of ventricular muscle to different circulatory conditions. Arch. Intern. physiol. et biochem., 1959, 67, 358.

Rosenblueth, A., Alanis, J., and Rubio, R. Some properties of the mammalian ventricular muscle. Arch Intern. physiol. et biochem., 1959, 67, 276.

RUSHMER, R. Constancy of stroke volume in ventricular responses to exertion. Am. J. Physiol., 1959, **196, 745.**

SCHER, A. M. Direct recording from the A-V conducting system of dog and monkey. Science, 1955, **121,** 398.

SCHER, A. M., RODRIGUEZ, M. I., LUKANE, J., AND YOUNG, A. C. The mechanism of atrioventricular conduction. Circulation Res., 1959, **7,** 54.

SCHER, A. M., YOUNG, A. C., MALMGREN, A. L., AND PATON, R. R. Spread of electrical activity through the wall of the ventricle. Circulation Res., 1953, **1,** 539.

SCHER, A. M., YOUNG, A. C., MALMGREN, A. L., AND ERICKSON, R. V. Activation of the interventricular septum. Circulation, 1955, **3,** 56.

SHIPLEY, R. E. AND GREGG, D. E. The cardiac response to stimulation of stellate ganglia and cardiac nerves. Am. J. Physiol., 1945, **143,** 396.

ULLRICH, K. J., RIECKER, G., AND KRAMER, K. Das Druckvolumdiagramm des Warmbluterherzens, Isometrische Gleichgewichtskurven. Pflugers Arch. Bd., 1954, **259,** 481.

WHITEHORN, W. V. Summation and tetanus in cardiac muscle. Efforts of temperature, epinephrine and digitoxin. Proc. Soc. Exper. Biol. & Med., 1954, **85,** 268.

WIGGERS, C. J. AND WEGRIA, R. Ventricular fibrillation due to single localized induction and condenser shocks applied during the vulnerable phase of ventricular systole. Am. J. Physiol., 1940, **128,** 500.

WOODBURY, J. W. AND BRADY, A. J. Intracellular recording from moving tissues with a flexibly mounted ultramicroelectrode. Science, 1956, **123,** 100.

WOODBURY, L. A., HECHT, H. H., AND CHRISTOPHERSON, A. R. Membrane resting and action potentials of single cardiac muscle fibers of the frog ventricle. Am. J. Physiol., 1951, **164,** 307.

WOODS, R. H. Applications of a physical theorem to membranes in the human body in a state of tension. J. Anat. & Physiol., 1892, **26,** 362.

*Monographs and Reviews*

BROOKS, C. McC., HOFFMAN, B. F., SUCKLING, E. E., AND ORIAS, O. Excitability of the heart. Grune & Stratton, Inc., New York, 1955.

CRANEFIELD, P. F. AND HOFFMAN, B. F. Electrophysiology of single cardiac cells. Physiol. Rev., 1958, **38,** 41.

HODGKIN, A. L. AND HUXLEY, A. F. Movement of sodium and potassium ions during nervous activity. Vol. 13, p. 176. Cold Spring Harbor Symposia on Quantitative Biology, Long Island Biological Association, 1952.

HUTTER, O. F. Mode of action of autonomic transmitters on the heart. Brit. M. Bull., 1957, **13,** 176.

KRAMER, K. Druckvolumdiagramm der Ventrikel und dynamische Faktoren der Herztätigkeit im intaken Kreislauf. Herzinsuffizienz und Digitaliswirkungen. Bad Oeynhausener Gespraeche III, 1958.

LaPLACE, P. S. Mechanique celeste, Vol. 10, 1841.

LEWIS, T. The mechanism and graphic registration of the heart beat. Ed. 3. Shaw and Sons, London, 1925.

LUNDIN, G. Mechanical properties of cardiac muscle. Acta physiol. scandinav., 1944, **7,** Suppl., 20.

MITCHELL, F. A. G. Cardiovascular innervation. E. & S. Livingstone, Ltd., Edinburgh and London, 1956.

MOMMAERTS, W. F. H. M. The actomysin system and its participation in organized enzyme reactions. Henry Ford Hospital International Symposium on Enzymes. Academic Press, Inc., 1956.

RUSHMER, R. F. Cardiac diagnosis. A physiological approach. W. B. Saunders Company, Philadelphia and London, 1955.

SODI-PALLARES, D. AND CALDER, R. M. New bases of electrocardiography. C. V. Mosby Company, 1956.

STARLING, E. H. The linacre lecture on the law of the heart. Cambridge University Press, London, and Longmans, Green & Company, Inc., New York, 1918.

SZENT-GYORGI, A. Chemical physiology of contraction in body and heart muscle. Academic Press, Inc., New York, 1953.

WEIDMANN, S. Elektrophysiologie der Herzmuskelfaser. Sammlung Innere Medizin und ihre Grenzgebiete, Hubr, Bern, Switzerland, 1956.

WEIDMANN, S. Electrical events underlying the cardiac contraction. Proc. of Harvey Tercen. Congress, May 1958, Circulation, 1958, 100.

WEIDMANN, S. Transport of ions across cardiac membranes. Metabolic aspects of transport across cell membranes, edited by Q. R. MURPHY. University of Wisconsin Press, 1957.

WHITELOCK, O. V. The electrophysiology of the heart. Ann. New York Acad. Sc., 1957, **65,** 653.

WIGGERS, C. J. Physiology in health and disease, Ed. 5. 1949.

WILDE, W. S. The pulsatile nature of the release of potassium from heart muscle during the systole. Ann. New York Acad. Sc., 1957, **65,** 693.

# 15

# FUNCTIONAL CHARACTERISTICS OF THE SYSTEMIC
# AND PULMONARY CIRCULATION

The hemodynamic characteristics of the systemic and pulmonary circulations have profound effects on the function of the heart. The principal function of the heart is to convert or change chemical energy into mechanical energy or work so that blood is moved through the cardiovascular system. The external work performed by the heart is measured by the quantity of blood ejected and the pressure developed during each ventricular contraction. The magnitude of both factors is determined by conditions in the circulatory bed which is served by the right and left ventricles. In turn, the amount of external work or useful work performed by the ventricle balances precisely the frictional loss of energy as the blood flows through the vascular circuit.

Figure 15.1 illustrates diagrammatically some of the primary characteristics of (1) the systemic circulatory system of man beginning at the aorta, extending to the venae cavae and emptying into the right atrium, and (2) the lesser circulatory system or the pulmonary circulation consisting of the right ventricle, the pulmonary venules, the veins and the left atrium. The ventricles pump the blood from the terminal reservoirs of the collecting systems, i.e., the atria into the distributing systems under an initial pressure sufficient to insure a continuous capillary flow as well as a return of the blood to the heart.

## The Systemic Circulation

### VOLUME FLOW

The anatomical complexity of the circulation may obscure some basic facts which should be stressed. The volume flow of blood through any part of the circulation must equal that flowing through any other part, i.e., the flow through all the arteries equals that through all the capillaries, all the arterioles, all the veins, the right ventricle, etc. There may be regional shifts of flow so that some arteries or capillaries carry more or less flow than in other arteries or capillaries, or there may be a small difference in the blood volumes put out by the two ventricles, but the former does not affect the relative total flow through the capillaries and arteries while the latter can only exist momentarily for a few heart beats, else the organism dies.

DIAMETER AND CROSS-SECTIONAL AREA. If the left ventricle is regarded as a cylinder, then its diameter might be 6 cm. The diameter and cross-sectional area of the ascending aorta approximate 2.5 cm. and 4.5 cm.², respectively. The large branches of the aorta have a total cross-sectional area which is approximately the same as that of the parent vessel, but the total cross-sectional area of all arteries is much greater. In the periphery, as the vessels become very narrow and short their total cross-section becomes very large because of the large number of vessels involved. The total cross-section of the arterioles with an individual diameter of .016 mm. and length of the order of .015 mm., might be 400 cm.², whereas the cross-section of the capillaries might be 4500 cm.² (based on an estimated capillary diameter of .008 mm., length 0.05 cm., and about 3,000 million capillaries). This is about 700 times that of the aorta. The figure for the number of capillaries is probably quite low since the capillary bed does not inject very well and there is every reason to believe that not all capillaries are open or shut at the same time, i.e., their state of patency varies with different physiological conditions. The cross-sectional area of the venules is also high, approximating that of the capillaries but with their confluence into veins and then into the venae cavae, their total diameter and cross-section progressively diminish so that the diameter and cross-section of the latter are about two and four times, respectively, those for the corresponding aorta and arteries.

BLOOD CONTENT. An important function of various parts of the circulation is the dynamic storage of blood. Its importance lies in the fact that it is this blood which is mobilized in time of stress to fulfill the needs of the body. The blood content of the various portions of the systemic

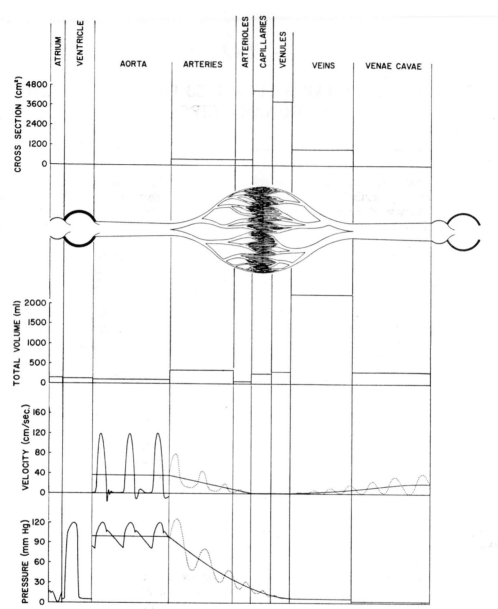

Fɪɢ. 15.1*A*. Schematic representation of the cross-sectional area, blood distribution, velocity and pressure in different regions of the systemic and pulmonary circulations. ?—values not available; dotted waves of pressure and velocity indicate estimated trends only.

circulatory tree bears no relation to its cross-sectional area (fig. 15.1). Quantitation of the blood volume existing during life in different parts of the vascular system is fraught with great difficulty, and the values obtained are only approximate. They are, however, helpful in orienting our thinking. The aorta contains about 100 cc., or 2 per cent of the blood volume of 5500 cc. The arteries contain about 8 per cent of the blood volume; the arterioles about 1 per cent.

The capillaries probably contain from 75 to 250 cc., or about 5 per cent of the blood volume. Since the capillaries are about one-half a millimeter long, the blood remains in the capillaries not more than 1 to 2 seconds. This figure for blood content of the capillaries is obviously quite variable since not all capillaries are patent at one time.

Thus, the blood content of the arterial or high pressure system is quite small being about 800

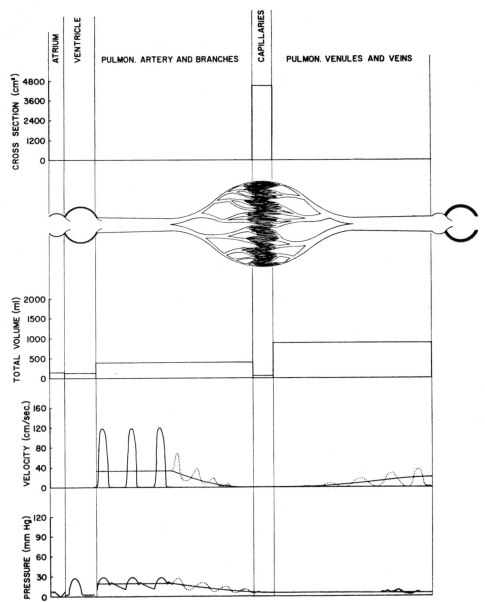

FIG. 15.1*B*. See figure 15.1*A*.

cc., or 15 per cent of the total volume. The systemic venous system accommodates the major portion (at least 50 per cent or about 3200 cc.) of the blood volume; the four heart cavities (600 cc. or 12 per cent); the pulmonary circuit 1000 cc. or 18 per cent. Thus, the low pressure system or, as it is sometimes called, the extra-arterial system which is made up of the systemic venous and pulmonary circuit up to the left ventricle, contains about 80 to 85 per cent of the blood volume.

The blood content of different areas is not constant but is continuously changing and is avail-able for redistribution to other vascular areas where it may be needed. The volume in any one compartment depends not only upon the basic anatomical size of the bed but upon dynamic changes induced by passive and active changes in capacity and content, i.e., distensibility. Although obviously very important, it is very difficult to make comparisons of distensibilities of different anatomical compartments of the vascular system. Such comparisons would be based upon plots (preferably *in vivo*) showing the relations of percentage increase in volume (dv)/(dV) of the vas-

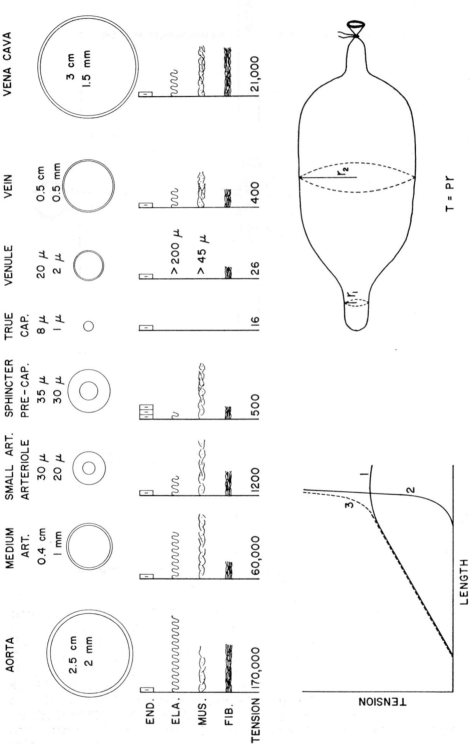

Fig. 15.2. Illustrated are the lumen diameters, wall thickenss, relative amounts of different tissues and wall tensions in the various blood vessels. *Lower left*; tension-length diagrams of elastic (1) and collagen fibers (2) presented alone and in combination (3). *Lower right*; balloon demonstrating pressure-tension relation. The pressure (P) within the balloon is equally transmitted to all parts of the contained air (Pascal's law), and the tension (T) in the balloon varies with the radius (r) in that portion. La Place's Law. (Modified after Burton, Physiol. Rev., 1954, 34, 619; and Wolf, Science, 1952, 115, 243.)

cular compartment to the increase in intravessel pressure (dp). Experimental data pertaining to distensibility of vessels containing much smooth muscle or which have an active response such as arterioles (resistance vessels), veins, or cardiac chambers, present a rather confusing picture since passive changes in their lumina is normally counteracted by "active" changes of the wall. This balance is very easily changed. Despite this, from available information the different distensibilities are suggested in figure 15.1 by the thickness of the lines. The distensibility of the capillaries has not been documented.

*A. Basic control.* Such storage can be on a long term basis (blood reservoir) and/or it can change rapidly during a cardiac cycle (compression chamber). Both are dependent on the blood content of the cardiac cavities and of the vessels at zero internal pressure and on their distensibility, i.e., change of diameter and length with change of internal pressure; in turn, the basic distensibility of the cavities is governed by the myocardial resistance to stretch. For example, the distensibility of a heart cavity actively changes if, for the same resting size or volume, the pressure within the cavity is altered. As pointed out in chapter 14, the distensibility of the ventricles can be grossly altered by nervous, humoral, and other influences. The distensibility of the vessels is governed by their content of elastic and collagen tissue and smooth muscle (fig. 15.2). All varieties of blood vessels except the arterioles, capillaries and venules have a prominent component of elastic tissue, and in some vessels such as the aorta, as much as 40 per cent by weight is elastic tissue. The elastic fibers with their great range of extensibility before their elastic limit is reached, produce maintenance tension without energy expenditure against the normal blood pressure. In the wall of every type of blood vessel except the capillary, there are white collagenous fibers in a matrix penetrating between the other elements. The collagenous fibers act in a similar way to the elastic fibers but, because of the architecture of the wall, are stretched only at higher than normal blood pressure and have a protective supporting role (fig. 15.2). If, however, the vessels reacted in a purely passive way based on their content of collagen and elastic fibers, their internal pressure would be determined only by the volume of contained blood and, at any constant mean pressure the mean volume of blood within them would also not change. However, many types of vessel contain much smooth muscle which does not contribute significantly to the elastic tension of

the wall. Its function is to produce active tension under vasomotor stimulation or local action of various chemicals (vasodilator and vasoconstrictor substances and oxygen lack) and so change the size of the lumen. Such vascular tone adjustment is seen in most vascular areas. It counteracts distensibility by inducing smooth muscle reaction which, at times, is strong enough to induce a net decrease in vascular lumina in the presence of an elevated pressure. Such activation will, of course, change completely the pressure-volume relationship in a vascular bed or area.

*B. Aorta and its arterial branches.* The pressure-volume relationship or distensibility of the isolated aorta has been exhaustively studied *in vitro*. The distensibility varies widely in different aortae in the same age group (fig. 15.3). There is no statistically significant correlation between age and absolute distensibility. However, aortic size or capacity increases considerably with age so that the average diameter of the aorta may exceed that of the sum of its branches and the contained volume at a diastolic pressure of 80

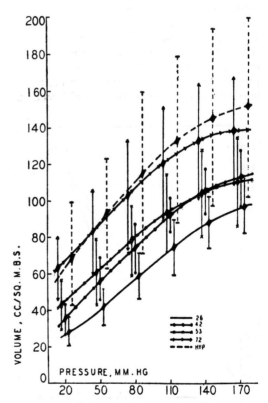

Fig. 15.3. Influence of age on the volume-pressure relations of human aortas. Each curve represents the average values for a given age group. Vertical lines represent standard deviations. (Remington and associates, Am. J. Physiol., 1948, **153**, 298.)

mm. Hg may almost double. This shift toward larger volumes with increasing age indicates that the enlarged aorta does not now need to expand as much to accomodate the same systolic ejection. The distensibility of an isolated aortic segment studied *in vivo* and *in vitro* differs mildly during its inflation and deflation, the resulting curves forming a loop (fig. 15.4). This is presumably because of hysteresis of the elastic fibers.

Although such studies aid in orientation, there is no guarantee that the characteristics of the aorta or, indeed, any vessel postmortem apply to conditions in the intact normal animal or man. Since the systemic arterial system contains only about 10 per cent of the total blood in the systemic circulation, even if smooth muscle contraction reduced its volume by 25 per cent (or 125 cc.), its function as a reservoir would be small. Actually, during systole and cardiac ejection, much of the pressure and flow are transferred immediately to the periphery. However, the aorta and some of its immediate branches belong to the elastic type of arteries, i.e., elastic tissue is abundant and muscle fibers are relatively scarce. Because of their large distensibility, the walls of these large central arteries act as compression chambers which serve to buffer the more peripheral branches from too sudden an increase in pressure and flow. The volume of blood suddenly injected into the aorta by the powerful ventricu-

lar action is only partly moved forward; a considerable portion is stored locally by the successive expansion of the large vessels. Although earlier work indicated that there is no radial expansion of the aorta beyond the arch, later work using cinematographic films at 1500 frames per second showed dilation of the thoracic aorta during systole of 15 to 20 per cent of its diastolic diameter which corresponds to a 30 to 40 per cent increase in volume per unit length of the artery; radial enlargement of the more distal aorta was somewhat less. Thus, it is estimated that up to one-half of the pressure and flow discharged during systole is stored here and that this moves forward during diastole through the elastic recoil of the arterial walls. This enables a portion of the blood to run off into the capillaries during diastole and not during systole.

Whether active changes in aortic distensibility normally occur is only incompletely investigated. Simultaneous measurements have been made of phasic aortic blood pressure by an appropriate pressure manometer and of changing aortic circumference during a cardiac cycle. In the open-chest dog the latter is obtained by noting the movement of a pair of recording mechanical calipers placed around the aorta; in the unanesthetized dog, aortic circumference is detected by measuring the changing resistance in a mercury filled rubber tube wrapped around it. In the open-chest dog, when the arterial blood pressure is elevated to a high level by mechanical constriction of the aorta, the size of the aorta during diastole initially increases but then decreases in the presence of an elevated internal pressure, and at the same time, its distensibility increases, i.e., the pulse pressure becomes larger. A large intra-arterial injection of adrenaline constricts an aortic segment being perfused *in vivo* so that it may contain less than half the volume of the normal aorta in the low pressure range, while in the high pressure range the volumes are almost equal, i.e., the constricted aorta now has a much greater distensibility than the normal aorta. These changes are presumably related to active changes in the smooth muscle which is abundant in these vessel walls. However, these experiments must be interpreted cautiously, for preliminary measurements in intact unanesthetized dogs have shown an intimate relation between the aortic pressure and aortic circumference Thus, the actual amount of and the significance of active alteration of aortic size under changing physiological states is not known.

The more peripheral arteries such as the ca-

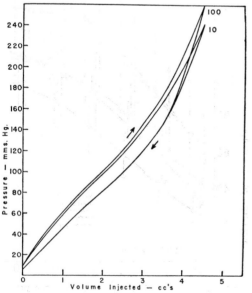

Fig. 15.4. Pressure volume diagrams obtained from an isolated segment of thoracic aorta by injections and withdrawals (arrows) at rate of 10 and 100 cc. of blood per minute. Alexander, Circulation Res., 1954, **2,** 140.

rotid, brachial, and femoral and their branches, are predominantly muscular types of arteries containing circularly arranged smooth muscle fibers in large numbers which, by their shortening, can reduce the lumen of these vessels considerably. Such a set-up obviously permits adaptation or adjustment of this distributing system to accommodate changing volumes of circulating blood. This is initiated by heat, cold, trauma, and many other physiological events. In the latter instance, pressure-volume curves done *in situ* on small (1.2 mm. or less internal diameter) and very muscular arterial segments of the intestine showed that with elevation of the aortic distending pressure, directly or through an increased portal venous pressure, the segment diameter may actually decrease. Since intra-arterial procaine did not block the response and since the vessel constriction was abolished after ischemia, papaverine or cyanide, an active response of the arterial smooth muscle wall (and probably of myogenic origin) is suggested which is caused by the elevated wall tension.

It can also be demonstrated that the femoral artery dilates in response to contraction of the peripheral muscles. This persists with local nerve section, occurs only on the stimulated (active muscle) side, and is abolished by local procaine or cutting of the artery distal to the point of measurement of femoral artery volume. Therefore, the response is by way of a conducting system in the arterial wall. The velocity of such peripheral conduction is 10 cm. per sec., and therefore, the conducting elements are probably the smooth muscle of the media of the vessel wall.

*C. Arterioles.* The arterioles contain the smallest blood volume of the cardiovascular system, but the pressure and flow in the circulatory system are more sensitive to minute changes in blood content of the arterioles than to that of any other part of the circulatory system. The arterioles are the final or end branches of the distributing system and operate as stopcocks which control the run-off of blood from the arterial system into the capillaries. The caliber of these vessels is controlled by the state of contraction of their circularly disposed and strongly developed smooth muscle fibers. The latter are regulated by local metabolic processes and by blood borne substances. They are also supplied with vasomotor fibers which are controlled by centers in the spinal cord and medulla. Their distensibility other than through myogenic change has not been determined.

*D. Capillaries.* The blood content of the cap-

illaries (75 to 300 cc.) is also very small. It is probably the most important blood volume since not only is all gas and nutrient exchange effected through its walls, but the number of patent capillaries and the size of their lumina is exceedingly variable. The arteries even as far as the commencement of the true capillaries are impervious. It has been calculated by Krogh that the total filtering surface by the capillary endothelium in the adult human body amounts to about 6300 m.² (68,000 ft.²). The summed areas of the capillary walls in all regions could be imagined, therefore, as constituting an endothelial membrane over 12 miles long and a foot wide, yet so thin that when tightly rolled, it would form a cylinder of about the thickness of a lead pencil.

The capillary wall proper is composed of a single layer of endothelial cells and is about the most tenuous structure conceivable (fig. 15.5). It does not exceed half a micron in thickness. The endothelial cells which are flat are joined at their fringes by a so-called "intercellular cement" which fills in between adjacent cells. The cellular area makes up more than 99 per cent of the total area across which exchange takes place, the small nonliving zone (cement) less than 1 per cent. The cement substance which binds the endothelial cells at their edges is being continuously washed away and renewed again by the endothelial cells. Its basic structure is a porous network of a complex cement substance, presumably a calcium proteinate. At one time it was thought to be hyaluronic acid, but this idea is no longer held. Superimposed on this network, either by electrical, chemical or surface tension forces, is a large adsorbed molecular component of protein which lines the inner surface and plugs most of the large pores in the cement, considerably reducing the perviousness of the structure. The capillary endothelial tube is enclosed and supported by a delicate sheath or membrane of fine fibrils derived from or closely related to the surrounding connective tissue. The intervening space between capillary and this membrane contains a freely

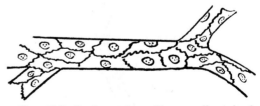

Fig. 15.5. Section of capillary wall stained with silver nitrate to demonstrate the intercellular cement. Nuclei of the cells stained with hematoxylin.

moving fluid. Surrounding this in the interstitial spaces is the so-called tissue fluid which is of a gel-like consistency.

It is still debatable whether the bulk of exchange occurs across the entire surface area or is restricted for most molecules to the pervious intercellular cement. Ions and small molecules diffuse across the capillary wall at such an incredibly fast rate (at least 100 per cent exchange within 1 minute) that it has been suggested that the whole capillary wall is permeable to these substances. The penetration, however, of capillary walls by water and dissolved substances appears to take place solely by processes which require no energy transformation by the capillary endothelial cells. From this has arisen a general belief that the capillary walls, or specifically the intercellular cement, is pierced with numerous ultramicroscopic openings or pores with an average diameter of about 30 Å which are generally too small to allow the passage of plasma protein molecules, but are of sufficient size and number to account for the observed rates of passage of water and nonprotein constituents of the plasma. Considerable evidence has been adduced that lipid soluble molecules, such as oxygen and carbon dioxide, can penetrate rapidly the plasma membranes of the capillary endothelial cells and are not restricted to the aqueous intercellular spaces. Finally, the evidence is fairly clear that penetration of large molecular aggregates and formed elements, such as the red and white cells, occurs through the intercellular portion of the wall.

Although the preceding generalization is probably true, one must not lose sight of the fact that capillary permeability is by no means uniform throughout the body. For example, skeletal muscle capillaries are about one hundredfold less permeable to water than the glomerular capillaries. Using as a gauge of permeability the protein concentration of the lymph draining different regions, it is found that liver lymph may contain 7 per cent protein (plasma has 6 per cent); lymph from lungs, heart, kidney and intestines, 3 to 4 per cent protein; skin, 1 per cent protein.

The functional anatomy of the capillaries has been worked out for some cold-blooded animals, for the rat and dog mesentery through microscopic observations of the *in vivo* vessels, and for the myocardium by both anatomical and microscopic observations (fig. 15.6). Briefly, blood flows generally from the arterioles directly into a metarteriole, and then into capillaries. The metarterioles lead directly into channels which are main thoroughfares from the capillary bed to the venules. The true capillaries concerned with interchange between blood and tissues are inter-anastomosing side branches of the main channels through the bed. At the ostia of each capillary is a small pre capillary sphincter of smooth muscle which is controlled by nerves presumably from the sympathetic nervous system, in the same manner that these nerves control the arterioles and metarterioles. In the body, the metarterioles and their precapillary sphincters undergo periodic contractions at intervals of 15 seconds to 3 minutes. When the tissue is in a resting state, the constrictor phase of this rhythm predominates and the precapillary sphincters may be completely closed. When the tissue becomes active, the dilator phase of the metarterioles predominates and the precapillary sphincters are open. Thus, in skeletal muscle, it is believed that the increase in blood flow with exercise comes in large measure from this opening up of large numbers of additional capillaries. It is believed that the factors that affect the degree of constriction and relaxation of the metarterioles and the precapillary sphincters during vasomotion are the same factors that affect arteriolar diameters

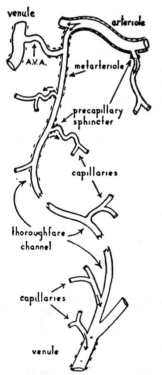

Fɪɢ. 15.6. Diagram of a functional unit of the capillary bed; A.V.A., metarteriolar-venular anastomosis. (Chambers and Zweifach.)

These are the nervous and hormonal stimuli and local conditions in the tissues. Thus, sympathetic stimuli and epinephrine in the blood intensify the constrictor phase of vasomotion in most areas of the body in the same manner that these two constrict the arterioles. On the other hand, vaso-dilator substances decrease the vasoconstrictor phase. The significance and value of this arrangement generally to capillary beds and to over-all circulatory dynamics remains to be established.

Although controversy has raged for many years, at present it is believed that change in capillary diameter is on a purely passive basis, i.e., by change in intracapillary pressure or in extravascular tissue pressure; supposedly, the active changes in capacity previously described by many workers is probably due to the activation of smooth muscle whose presence was unsuspected at that time in the metarterioles and A-V capillaries.

*E. Veins.* Since the systemic veins contain such a large proportion of total blood volume, they must function as blood reservoirs. The responses by which they may counteract distending forces and thus prevent excessive pooling of blood have been of great interest and have been documented in animals and human experiments. As the venules merge to form larger veins, they acquire a layer of connective tissue and then distinct muscle fibers. These vessels have a larger blood content than the corresponding arteries. Their walls are also much thinner and contain less elastic tissue but have a rather well-developed muscular coat. When the volume of blood in a normally partially collapsed vein is augmented, the intra-vascular pressure barely increases until the vein becomes round and has a certain degree of fullness. The volume increase up to this point is similar to the filling of a collapsible tube without distending the walls. True distension now occurs when further volume increments lead to an elevation of intravascular pressure (fig. 15.7). Veins excised or within the organism have a very low distensibility when the increase in volume is rather rapid. With prolonged elevation of intra-venous pressure, there is a delayed compliance or passive yielding of the venous walls which is attributed to the visco-elastic properties of the smooth musculature. Thus, although initially the low distensibility of veins may prevent blood pooling, the delayed compliance favors it. It is estimated that the ability of the venous system to take up blood is at least 100 times that of the whole circulatory system. Thus, if 1000 cc. of blood is transfused in a human, about 990 cc. will reside in the extra-arterial or low pressure system, and 10 cc. in the arterial system. The pressure in the whole circulation might rise by 5 mm. Hg.

The diameter of these venous capacitance vessels may be changed either passively by external forces (gravity, respiration or pressure breathing) or actively by contraction or relaxation of their walls. There is considerable evidence to indicate that the venous system (including the pulmonary system) behaves somewhat like an elastic bag. For example, change in posture has no particular effect on their state of contraction; when human subjects are bled or transfused with about 500 cc. of blood, the pressures in the central veins, the pulmonary artery, and left atrium rise and fall in parallel as the blood volume is changed by bleeding or transfusion (fig. 15.8).

While this leads to the conclusion that the venous system operates in a passive manner, it must also be emphasized that this may be true only if the induced changes in central blood volume are moderate or gradual and not in the nature of emergency reactions. It is easy to demonstrate that a fixed pressure-volume relationship need not apply to the veins and venules for they are the most sensitive of all vessels to all types of mechanical, chemical and temperature impacts. For example, the trauma attendant to dissection or to needle insertion may completely close a medium sized vein. In addition, they are supplied with vasomotor nerves through the action of which the distensibility and capacity of the venous system can be actively and greatly changed. This provides a means by which the volume of the venous system can change within wide limits without significant corresponding changes in venous pressure. Such innervation has been demonstrated for the vena cava and veins of the hind

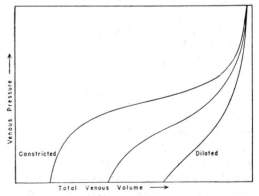

FIG. 15.7. Venous distensibility patterns with different degrees of vasomotor tone. (Alexander, Circulation Res., 1954, **2**, 405.)

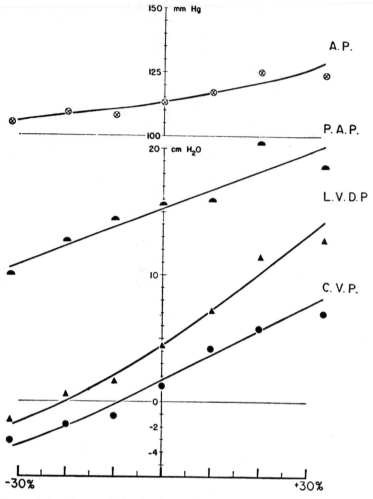

Fig. 15.8. Effects of changing total blood volume (by transfusion (+) or bleeding (−)) upon aortic (A.P.), pulmonary artery (P.A.P.), left ventricular diastolic (L.V.D.P.) and central venous pressures (C.V.P.). (Gauer and associates, Circulation Res., 1956, 4, 79.)

limb and mesentery in animals. Active contraction or relaxation of the venous smooth muscle (venoconstriction or dilation) can be elicited by activation of local stretch receptors in the venous walls, and reflexly by activation of the baroreceptors (stretch receptors) in other veins and in the aorta and carotid arteries, and by direct local action of adrenergic or cholinergic substances (fig. 15.7). Reflex venomotor activity has also been measured in normal subjects by means of pressures developed within isolated segments of superficial veins. An arm superficial vein segment without tributaries is temporarily isolated by applying pressure at the segment ends so that the volume is held constant and vein contraction can be reflected by an increase in pressure which is recorded continuously by an indwelling needle

connected to a pressure manometer. Strong contractions are caused by the Valsalva maneuver, cold, exercise and hyperventilation. Persons with postural hypotension show little or no segment or central venous response to these stimuli, indicating impaired reflex venomotor activity. Although the entire venous bed may be regarded as a large variable blood depot, the central systemic veins constitute the most important part of this depot for supplying the right heart. It is estimated from observations in dogs that the pressure-volume curve of the venae cavae in the intact living dog can be varied by 15 to 20 times and with only a small effect on venous pressure. This means that translocation of large volumes of blood to the pulmonary and systemic arterial circuit is easily effected.

### VELOCITY CHANGES

*A. In different vessels (fig. 15.1).* Just as the cross-sectional area varies greatly in different parts of the cardiovascular system, so does the velocity of blood flow. Since the velocity of flow is inversely proportional to the cross-sectional area of the vessel through which it flows, velocity will be maximal in regions of the circulation with the smallest total cross-sectional area. Hence, the blood velocity in the aorta is the most rapid of that in any part of the body, but even here the average velocity of about 40 cm. per. sec., is low. In the capillaries, it is least, at about 0.07 cm. per sec. This slow rate of passage in the peripheral capillaries, of course, provides time for the exchange of materials across the capillary membranes or walls. After passing into the veins, the blood again accelerates as the cross-sectional area progressively decreases. However, since the caliber of the veins is larger than that of the corresponding arteries, the velocity of venous blood flow never becomes equal to that of the arterial blood and generally equals about ¼ of that in the arteries. For example, the flow of blood along the two venae cavae which together have a cross-sectional area some 4 times as great as that of the aorta, is only about 8 to 10 cm. per sec. under resting conditions.

Although the average blood velocity is low, the peak velocity of blood flow may be high since this changes greatly from moment to moment during each heart beat in the systemic arterial system. In the ascending aorta near the aortic valves, the peak velocity during systole may be 120 cm. per sec.; during most of diastole, the velocity may approximate zero. Further down the thoracic aorta and in the abdominal aorta, the small back flow present in the ascending aorta at time of closure of aortic valves is greatly accentuated and extended, while forward flow during diastole is increased. In the major aortic branches these violent fluctuations of velocity, although somewhat damped, are largely retained. However, except for the coronary, femoral, and axillary arteries, backflow disappears, and the flow curve is often patterned after its corresponding pressure pulse. At the capillary level, these fluctuations in velocity are pretty well removed so that a smooth rate of flow is attained. In the venules and as the veins become larger, fluctuations or variations in the velocity of flow again reappear. In the venae cavae near the right atrium, blood velocity may become much greater during ventricular systole than during its diastole, indicating that contraction of the myocardium itself draws blood towards the heart. During inspiration, the whole flow curve in the venae cavae is greatly elevated.

*B. Across a blood vessel.* Finally, the velocity of flow will vary in different portions of the cross-sectional area of a blood vessel, especially in the larger vessels (fig. 15.9). In the larger vessels there is a cylindrical layer of blood which adheres to the vessel wall and wets it. Inside this motionless layer is another cylindrical fluid layer which flows and rubs against it, and inside this there is another flowing faster, and so on, until the central axial core of blood is reached which has the maximum velocity. In arterioles and vessels of quite narrow caliber, red cells are concentrated pretty much in the axial part of the blood stream so that plasma flows along the walls. As a result, the red cells move faster than plasma by a significant amount, and hence, the hematocrit in capillaries is somewhat less than that of the larger vessels. The effect of this is, of course, to change the distribution of the velocity in the various parts of a cross-section of such a vessel.

The flow of blood is laminar or streamlined in most portions of the circulatory tree. When the velocity of flow is increased above some critical level, turbulence develops. The formula $RVD/v = $ a critical constant for turbulence (Reynolds number) expresses the conditions producing turbulence in fluid flowing through tubes of constant diameter in which, v is viscosity, D is density, V is mean velocity, R is tube radius. This indicates that turbulence occurs when low viscosity fluid flows through tubes of large diameter at quite high velocity. If this formula ap-

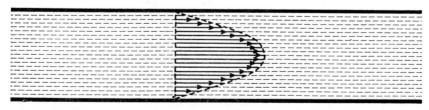

FIG. 15.9. Schematic representation of the variable velocity of blood flow in vessels. Flow is fastest in the central axial stream and progressively decreases to zero at the vessel wall.

plies to the cardiovascular system, the big variable is the blood velocity since the blood viscosity and vessel diameter do not change greatly. Blood flows rapidly through the biggest arterial channels and with the highest velocities at the roots of the aorta and of the pulmonary artery. It is debatable whether the critical level for turbulence is normally exceeded at these points during the rapid ejection phase of ventricular systole.

### PRESSURE CHANGES

*A. Kinetic and potential energy, lateral and end pressure.* Of the energy developed by the left ventricle, more than 98 per cent is normally in the form of potential energy, 1 per cent or less as kinetic energy. When the left ventricle pumps out blood, it increases the radius and length of the aorta and its large branches to store potential energy as tension in the arterial walls. Because of the motion (velocity) of the blood during ejection, a certain amount of kinetic energy is also transferred to the blood. During exercise with a very large cardiac output or in the presence of aortic stenosis, as much as 10 to 50 per cent of the energy expended by the heart is used for increasing blood velocity. Ultimately, however, most of the potential energy is changed to kinetic energy to produce flow through vascular elements, and then is finally dissipated as heat through friction. The kinetic energy of flow can have a real effect on intravascular pressure. This can be demonstrated by inserting into the flowing bloodstream small catheters or cannulas connected to pressure manometers (fig. 15.10). With the catheter opening pointing upstream, end pressure or potential energy is measured; with the opening at right angles to direction of flow, *lateral* pressure or the pressure actually pressing on the vessel is measured. In the vessels of humans, end pressure and lateral pressure are almost equal except in the aorta and its immediate branches in which the kinetic energy is sufficiently high from prevailing blood velocity to cause the lateral pressure to be significantly lower, i.e., lateral pressure is inversely proportional to the blood velocity (Bernouilli effect). At rest, the average aortic lateral pressure is about 1 mm. less than the end pressure; with exercise, the difference might be 15 mm. Hg. If one is recording phasic aortic pressure throughout the cardiac cycle, then with exercise the lateral pressure might be 40 mm. Hg less than the end pressure during the period of rapid blood ejection (first third of systole). Ultimately, most of the potential energy is converted into kinetic energy in producing flow. In this exchange no energy is lost. However, as blood progresses from the aorta to the atrium, the intravascular pressure decreases to very low values. This permanent loss of energy or pressure arises from fluid friction developed within the vessels with gradual change of energy into heat.

*B. In different vessels.* (*fig. 15.1*). Pressure in the aortic arch reaches a maximum during midsystole, and a minimum at the end of diastole. The numerical difference between these pressures is called the "pulse pressure." Similarly, pressures in the thoracic and abdominal aorta and their major branches, i.e., the carotid, the radial, and especially the femoral, show that the values for the systolic pressure increase and those for diastolic pressure decrease, i.e., pulse pressure increases. In still smaller arteries, the pulse pressure progressively diminishes, systolic pressure falling more than diastolic. However, this does not represent a frictional loss of energy but merely a replacement or shift in the temporal relations of pressure during a cardiac cycle, since the mean pressure, for example, in the femoral arteries is the same as that in the aorta.

As the arteries divide and subdivide, the caliber of the individual vessels diminishes and the pressure gradients become correspondingly steeper,

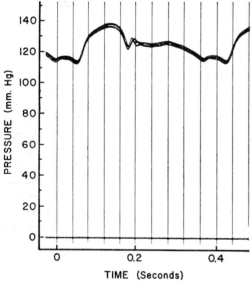

FIG. 15.10. Reproduction from original record of lateral, upstream and downstream phasic pressure patterns taken at the subclavian level in the aorta of a large open chest dog by means of 3 strain gauges adjusted to identical zeros and sensitivities. The patterns and pressure values of the 3 curves are almost identical at systolic pressure 139 mm.Hg; diastolic pressure 115 mm.Hg; heart rate 150 minute.

particularly in the arterioles and capillaries. Not only is the pressure gradient steeper, but the oscillations of pressure during a cardiac cycle are reduced to a minimum at the time the arterioles are reached. At the arterioles there is a pronounced decrease in pressure gradient, a second abrupt decrease in the capillaries with almost no residual pressure fluctuations. A more gradual pressure decline occurs in the venules and veins until a negative pressure is actually reached in the central veins owing to the effect of the subatmospheric pressure within the thorax.

FUNCTIONAL CHARACTERISTICS OF THE PULMONARY CIRCULATION. In many respects the pulmonary vascular bed (pulmonary artery through pulmonary veins) is similar to the systemic circuit but certain differences deserve emphasis. The pulmonary circulation is a low resistance circuit, arterioles being essentially absent; the pulmonary vessels supply only one type of tissue (alveoli) so vasomotor requirements are low; pulmonary blood volume is less than that in the systemic circuit; extravascular conditions (within the thoracic cage) are fairly uniform (fig. 15.1).

The main pulmonary artery and its branches are structurally similar and of about the same or slightly larger diameter than the aorta, but their walls are one-third the thickness and their branches are much shorter and of very small capacity. Small arteries in both systems have thick muscular walls. Arteries less than 0.1 mm. in diameter are endothelial tubes without muscle. There are no vessels corresponding to arterioles, i.e., no small bore high resistance vessels. The capillaries are somewhat larger, appear to take off very densely from the above endothelial tubes, and have multiple anastomoses. There are numerous A-V shunts. The pulmonary veins are short and contain less blood than the systemic veins.

The pulmonary artery and pulmonary bed in general are many times more distensible than the systemic portion of the arterial circuit and probably represent the most distensible part of the low pressure system. *In vivo* pressure-volume curves of the entire pulmonary vascular bed and of the pulmonary veins (and left atrium) have pretty much the shape of venous pressure volume curves in the relaxed state (fig. 15.11). The blood volume of the pulmonary system is only 800 to 1200 cc., of which 75 to 100 cc. is in the capillaries, and the rest is in the major arteries and veins. Since the pulmonary vessels are a low pressure distensible system, a minute increase in outflow pressure at the left ventricle, or an in-

crease in pressure at the right ventricle results in a sizeable accumulation of blood in the lungs. With change in posture in man, it is estimated that as much as 400 cc. goes into and out of the lungs. Thus, the blood volume of the pulmonary vascular bed (about 25 to 30 per cent of circulatory blood volume) has an important reservoir function and is about the most important depot for supplying the left heart.

There is some evidence that the distensibility of the pulmonary vessels can be altered. This is based on the findings that the pulmonary vessels contain considerable smooth muscle; plastic casts of two sides of a lung are very different if one side is perfused with adrenaline up to the moment of plastic injection (this especially affects vessels less than 25 $\mu$ in diameter); stimulation of the carotid body chemoreceptors decreases pulmonary vascular resistance; extreme hypoxia (4 per cent oxygen) in one lung causes vessel constriction in that lung; intrapulmonary artery injection of acetylcholine decreases the pulmonary hypertension caused by breathing a low oxygen mixture. It is obvious, however, that the functions of dilation and constriction have been demonstrated under rather extreme conditions. There is thus no strong evidence that the distensibility characteristics (pressure-volume) of the pulmonary circulation can be significantly altered under normal

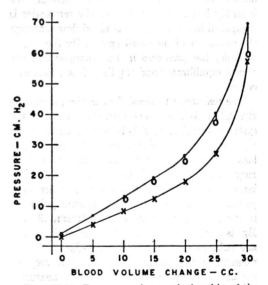

FIG. 15.11. Pressure volume relationship of the pulmonary vascular bed. Injections and withdrawals made at 10-second intervals. Dots: pressures immediately after end of each injection. Circles: pressures 5 seconds after end of each injection. Crosses: pressures immediately after each withdrawal. (Sarnoff and associates, Am. J. Physiol., 1952, **171**, 238.)

conditions and, hence, it is believed to be mainly a passive vehicle for blood flow. Present experimental evidence (fig. 15.8) supports the view that the pulmonary circulation together with the systemic veins or capacitance vessels form a functional unit or reservoir in which passive and/or active changes in the capacitance system regulate the store of blood in the pulmonary reservoir where it is handled passively.

Since the stroke volume and mean velocity of flow are almost identical in the aorta and pulmonary artery, the kinetic energies of the two bloods are the same, but because the potential energy imparted to the blood by the right ventricle is much less, the kinetic factor is a greater proportion of the energy output of the right ventricle. Phasic variations in blood flow velocity are possibly even more marked in the pulmonary artery than in the aorta. In contrast to the systemic circulation, a markedly pulsatile flow is retained in the pulmonary capillary bed during rest and after exercise. During systole, blood is accelerated in the right ventricle and pulmonary artery by contraction of the right ventricle. The blood gains kinetic energy or energy of motion. As blood distends the arterial tree, the latter acquires potential energy (elastic and hydrostatic). At the same time, energy is partially dissipated by resistance to systolic flow in the small vessels. During diastole the potential energy in the arterial tree is partly lost in hysteresis, and the remainder is dissipated in elastic recoil as blood flows through the resistance of the small vessels. By the end of diastole, the pressures in the vascular bed are almost equilibrated and capillary flow practically ceases.

The resistance to blood flow in the pulmonary circulation is about one-thirteenth that of the systemic circulation. This is because there are no high resistance arterioles, the pulmonary capillaries are large and very numerous; the pulmonary vessels are so easily distended passively, and large portions of the pulmonary bed are only partially used normally. The pressure pulsation in the pulmonary artery of 22/8 (mean 13 mm. Hg) is fairly well maintained in the capillary bed and pulmonary veins since the capillary flow is so pulsatile during a cardiac cycle. However, the capillary pressure has not been directly measured. Phasic pressures taken indirectly through a catheter passed through the pulmonary artery until it is "wedged" in its small branches have been assumed to represent "capillary" or left atrial pressures since the blood obtained through the catheter is well-oxygenated. However, what such

recorded phasic pressure curves represent has never been clearly defined. The pressure gradient through the pulmonary bed is quite small. Its highest pressure (pulmonary artery 13 mm. Hg mean) drops to about 7 mm. Hg in the left ventricle at the end of diastole and at the site of outflow from the pulmonary circuit. This pressure gradient of about 6 to 7 mm. Hg causes to flow through the pulmonary circuit the same volume of blood as flows through the systemic system with a pressure gradient of about 90 mm. Hg.

T INTERRELATION BETWEEN CALIBER OF VESSELS, INTRAVESSEL PRESSURE AND WALL TENSION. The law of LaPlace is that the tension (T) in the wall of a cylinder is directly proportional to the product of the intracylinder pressure (P) and the radius of the tube (R), i.e., (T = P × R). This has been graphically portrayed using a rubber balloon (fig. 15.2). With partial inflation, the upper part of the balloon expands largely, the distal portion only slightly. Internal pressure is the same throughout, but the greatly expanded portion of the balloon with the large radius has a high tension as evidenced by its resistance to indentation, while in the slightly distended area the walls are soft and easily deformed. Burton has pointed out the application of this law to the ventricular cavities and the vascular system and has calculated the wall tension in the various vessels. In the aorta with a radius of 1.2 cm., it takes the highest wall tension of 170,000 dynes per cm. length to support the transmural pressure of 100 mm. Hg, while in the capillaries with a radius of 4 $\mu$, it takes the lowest tension, only 16 dynes, to support a blood pressure of 30 mm. Hg. In the same capillaries in the legs while standing, the pressure can be 100 mm. Hg. Thus, it takes only about $\frac{1}{10,000}$ as much wall strength in the capillaries as in the aorta to support the same range of internal blood pressure.

As has already been pointed out, the tension in a vessel wall that resists the prevailing internal pressure is supplied by the elastic tissue at normal pressures and by the collagenous fibers at higher pressures. A second important function of the elastic tissue is to make possible a graded constriction or dilation under vasomotor change induced by active wall tension change via smooth muscle. When, however, elastic tissue is absent or in very small amounts, vessels can only be completely closed or open when under vasomotor tone. Intermediate diameters would not be possible. This may explain why tissues deficient in elastic tissue but with smooth muscle, such as A-V shunts and precapillary sphincters, are always either widely open or closed. Thus, with the combination of elastic tension and active tension, grading of degree of vessel constriction is possible but only over a limited range. If the pressure in a vessel is reduced far enough, its wall will eventually reach its unstretched length and the elastic tissue is not functioning. At pressure lower than this, in spite of elastic tissue there will be no elastic tension to provide the automatic adjustment needed for stability, the vessel will become unstable and close. Such "critical closing" pressures have been experimentally demonstrated in many vascular beds and may under certain circumstances approximate a prevailing blood pressure of 100 mm. Hg.

INTERRELATION BETWEEN PRESSURE, FLOW AND RESISTANCE. Hemodynamics is the study of the forces which cause, alter, and regulate the flow of blood through the body. The central problem in hemodynamics is, "What is the relation between the rate of flow of blood in the vascular bed and the pressure which drives it?" Knowledge and understanding of the factors that determine the shape of the curves of flow and pressure is essential to proper interpretation of the changes in blood flow and blood pressure in normal or pathological physiology.

A simple association of pressure and flow can obviously serve as an index of total peripheral resistance (TPR) to flow in the cardiovascular system

$$\frac{\text{(aortic pressure}}{\text{(aortic flow}} \text{ or } \frac{\text{pulmonary artery pressure)}}{\text{pulmonary artery flow)}}$$

or to local resistance in single bed or organ, for example:

$$\frac{\text{(renal artery pressure)}}{\text{(renal artery flow)}}.$$

Such measurements and calculations have been used extensively in recent years in clinical and experimental investigation and, especially in the aorta, to separate the resistance changes due to central or cardiac factors from those due to peripheral factors. The architecture of the whole circulatory distributing system is such that the organs are supplied through many parallel shunts. In this the total peripheral resistance (TPR) is

$$\frac{1}{\text{TPR}} = \frac{1}{\text{r1}} \text{ plus } \frac{1}{\text{r2}} \text{ plus } \frac{1}{\text{r3}} \cdots \frac{1}{\text{r}^n},$$

but since the aorta supplies all the regions with pressure and flow, TPR can be calculated as mean aortic pressure divided by cardiac output. A

little reflection will indicate, however, that the resistance to flow can arise from active changes in the smooth muscle of the particular vascular bed in question, or it could be related to passive changes in the geometry of the same vascular bed due to internal and external variations of the pressure. The above approach does not permit separation and quantitation of active and passive changes in vessel size which is essential to the proper understanding of pressure and flow relations. In a modified form, some physical laws derived from hydrodynamics have application to the flow of blood, and they will be considered next.

A. *Poiseuille's Law.* Generally stated, the volume (F) of blood flowing through a circulating system increases with the perfusing pressure (P) and decreases with the resistance (R) to flow as indicated by the equation $F = P/R$. This is Poiseuille's experimental law which is expressed in more detail as:

$$F = (P_1 - P_2) \cdot \frac{(\pi r^4) \ (1)}{(8L) \ (v)}$$

in which F is flow per unit of time; $P_1$ is pressure at an upstream point in the tube; $P_2$ is the pressure at a downstream point in the tube; $\pi$ is 3.1416; r is the tube radius; L is tube length; v is fluid viscosity. Poiseuille's experiments were based upon measurements of stream-lined flow (nonturbulent) in nondistensible tubes with Newtonian fluids at constant temperature. This means that flow is augmented by an increase in any factor in the numerator and decreased by any factor in the denominator. Thus, flow would decrease by one-half if tube length is doubled or if blood became twice as viscous. Blood is caused to flow from one point to another in a tube by the difference of pressure between such points. This means that doubling the pressure gradient ($P_1 - P_2$) along the tube will double the flow. Change of radius is much more effective in changing flow for doubling the radius will increase flow 16 times.

The resistance to flow, defined as the ratio of the driving force to the flow, is obtained by a rearrangement of the above formula in which:

$$R = \frac{P}{F} = \frac{(8L) \ (v)}{\pi r^4 \ (1)}.$$

Resistance to flow is made up of two distinct factors. These are the viscosity (v) or inner friction of the fluid and the geometry of the tube

$$\frac{(8L)}{(\pi r^4)}$$

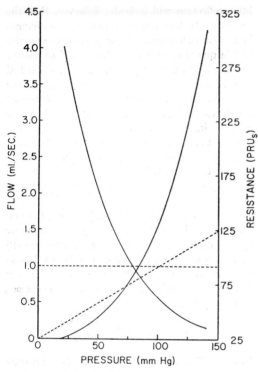

FIG. 15.12. The relationships of flow, pressure and resistance in nondistensible tubes using Newtonian fluids (*dotted lines*) at constant temperature (Poiseulle's law) and blood in vessels (*solid lines*). See text for details.

which is made up of the radius and length. In his system, the resistance was constant since both the viscosity and the geometry of the tube were unchanged and did not change with rate of flow or pressure. A plot of flow versus pressure gave a straight line through the origin, and one of resistance versus pressure a horizontal straight line (fig. 15.12).

*B. Application of Poiseuille's law to the circulation.* The applicability of this law *in toto* to the circulation depends upon whether resistance is independent of pressure and flow. In the circulatory system peripheral resistance is a measure of the totality of all factors affecting blood flow. These include change (decrease) in apparent blood viscosity (which is known to occur with increase in perfusion pressure, occasioned by the movement of the red cells to form a central axial rod) the existence of stream-lined versus turbulent flow, the length of vessels and the cross-sectional areas of the blood vessels. The latter is determined by the extravascular pressure provided by surrounding tissue; by mechanical dilation with rising perfusion pressure; by opening of new capillaries and vessels with change in metab-

olism and with rising perfusion pressure, and by active changes in the state of contraction of the muscular walls through vasomotor nerves, humoral substances and metabolic products.

The flow-pressure curves obtained with blood in vascular beds are quite different from those obtained in the artificial system used in Poiseuille's experiments. The chief differences are: the curves do not pass through the origin, and flow is insignificant until a critical level of pressure is attained (called by Burton the critical closing pressure). The curves for dilated vessels are almost linear but with increasing tone the curves become sigmoid and then convex to the flow axis. At sufficiently high pressures, the curves tend to become straight lines pointing toward the origin. The resistance is almost constant at high pressure but rises as the pressure is reduced to reach very high values near the critical closing pressure. Such deviations could arise if (1) the geometric factor of Poiseuille's law is not constant but varies with the distensibility of the blood vessels and (2) blood has anomalous viscosity so that the viscosity factor of Poiseuille's equation varies with the rate of flow and, hence, the driving pressure. While experimental evaluation is difficult, it does appear that vessel distensibility is the major factor responsible for the deviation of *in vivo* pressure-flow curves from Poiseuille's law. This in turn is related to the active tension or contraction of smooth muscle in the vessel walls and to the combined effects of elastic and collagenous fibers in the architecture of the vessels. Apparently anomalous viscosity is a minor factor. While the viscosity of moving blood does change, i.e., with increased flow rates there is an axial accumulation of red cells, any change of viscosity from such accumulation of red cells is complete at very low flow levels and, throughout most of the physiological range of flow, viscosity does not change appreciably with flow. This is borne out by the experimental observations that flow-pressure curves using fluid of normal viscosity, such as plasma, are essentially similar to those obtained when blood is used but, when blood is used in rigid, nondistensible tubes, the flow-pressure curves are almost linear within the physiological range.

*C. Use of peripheral vascular resistance as an index of vasomotor activity.* In view of the multiplicity of factors which affect peripheral resistance in the cardiovascular system, it remains to be seen to what extent changes of peripheral resistance may be used to interpret vasomotor activity. Still, in studies of peripheral circulation reactions, it is desirable to measure the peripheral resistance. This represents the ratio of transmural pressure to the rate of flow through the organ or region being studied. Vascular tone or vasomotor action represents the active contraction of the muscular walls of the blood vessels and is influenced physiologically by vasomotor nerve impulses, humoral substances and metabolic products. The fact that changes in intravascular lumen occur with altered intraluminal pressure on a purely physical basis, points up the difficulty in establishing to what extent alteration of peripheral resistance may be used to interpret vasomotor activity.

The interpretation of changes in peripheral resistance in the presence of an alteration of vasomotor activity associated with a rise or fall of blood pressure or blood flow is difficult. In this instance, changes in vasomotor activity cannot be deduced unless it is possible to know in some way what portion of the change in peripheral resistance would have resulted from the observed alterations of pressure or flow alone. It is obvious that as long as either arterial pressure or the blood flow remain constant while the other is changing, or if pressure and flow change in opposite directions, the fluctuations of peripheral resistance correctly indicate the direction and, roughly, the magnitude of alteration of vasomotor activity. A fairly satisfactory and practical way of estimating change in vascular tonus due to vasomotor activity when pressure and flow change in the same direction, is to determine during a control period, the pressure-flow relationship over the range of flows anticipated during the experimental period and thereafter to compare these with the pressure-flow ratios during the experimental period. Their difference would be caused by a vasomotive change. Possibly the most useful approach is to calculate resistance values from directly measured levels of pressure and flow while either the pressure or flow is controlled by a pump. This type of measurement has been made in the conscious dog and man.

## REFERENCES

ALEXANDER, R. S. The influence of constrictor drugs on the distensibility of the splanchnic venous system, analyzed on the basis of an aortic model. Circulation Res., 1954, 2, 141.

ALEXANDER, R. S. The participation of the venomotor system in pressor reflexes. Circulation Res., 1954, 2, 405.

ALEXANDER, R. S., EDWARDS, W. S., AND ANKENEY, J. L. The distensibility characteristics of the portal vascular bed. Circulation Res., 1953, 1, 271.

BAYLISS, W. M. On the local reactions of the arterial wall to changes of internal pressure. J. Physiol., 1902, 28, 220.

BRAUNWALD, E., FISHMAN, A. P., AND COURNAND, A. Estimation of volume of a circulatory model by the Hamilton and Bradley methods at varying flow volume ratios. J. Appl. Physiol., 1958, 12, 445.

BURCH, G. E. AND ROMNEY, R. B. Functional anatomy and "throttle valve" action of pulmonary veins. Am. Heart J. 1954, 47, 58.

BURTON, A. C. Improvement in construction of apparatus for demonstrating turbulence. J. Appl. Physiol., 1954, 6, 719.

BURTON, A. C. On the physical equilibrium of small blood vessels. Am. J. Physiol., 1951, 164, 319.

BURTON, A. C. AND ROACH, M. R. The reason for the shape of the distensibility curves of arteries. Canad. J. Biochem. &. Physiol., 1957, 35, 681.

COULTER, N. A., JR. AND PAPPENHEIMER, J. R. Development of turbulence in flowing blood. Am. J. Physiol., 1949, 159, 401.

DALY, I. deB. AND DALY, M. deB. The effects of stimulation of the carotid body chemoreceptors on pulmonary vascular resistance in the dog. J. Physiol., 1957, 137, 436.

DuBois, A. B., AND MARSHALL, R. Measurements of pulmonary capillary blood flow and gas exchange throughout the respiratory cycle in man. J. Clin. Invest., 1957, 36, 1566.

FOLKOW, B. AND LOFVING, B. The distensibility of the systemic resistance vessels. Acta physiol. scandinav., 1956, 38, 37.

FOLKOW, B. Intravascular pressure as a factor regulating the tone of the small vessels. Acta physiol. scandinav., 1949a, 17, 289.

GAUER, O. H., HENRY, J. P., AND SIEKER, H. O. Changes in central venous pressure after moderate hemorrhage and transfusion in man. Circulation Res., 1956, 4, 79.

GREEN, H. D., LEWIS, R. N., NICKERSON, N. D. AND HELLER, A. L. Blood flow, peripheral resistance and vascular tonus, with observations on relationship between blood flow and cutaneous temperature. Am. J. Physiol., 1944, 140, 518.

HALLOCK, P. AND BENSON, I. C. Studies on the elastic properties of human isolated aorta. J. Clin. Invest., 1937, 16, 595.

HAYNES, R. H., AND BURTON, A. C. Role of non-Newtonian behaviour of blood in hemodynamics. Am. J. Physiol., 1959, 197, 943.

HENRY, J. P., GAUER, O. H., AND SIEKER, H. O. The effect of moderate changes in blood volume on left and right atrial pressures. Circulation Res., 1956, 4, 91.

HILTON, S. M. A peripheral arterial conducting mechanism underlying dilatation of the femoral artery and concerned in functional vasodilatation in skeletal muscle. J. Physiol., 1959, 149, 93.

JOHNSON, P. C. Myogenic nature of increase in the intestinal vascular resistance with venous pressure elevation. Circulation Res., 1959, 7, 992.

LOFVING, B. AND MELLANDER, S. Some aspects of the basal tone of the blood vessels. Acta physiol. scandinav., 1956, 37, 134.

McDONALD, D. A. The occurrence of turbulent

flow in the rabbit aorta. J. Physiol., 1952, **118**, 340.

McDonald, D. A. Lateral pulsatile expansion of arteries. J. Physiol., 1953, **119**, 28P.

Page, E. B., Hickham, J. B., Sieker, H. O., McIntosh, H. D., and Pryor, W. W. Reflex venomotor activity in normal persons and in patients with postural hypotension. Circulation, 1955, **11**, 262.

Pappenheimer, J. R., Renkin, E. M., and Barrero, L. M. Filtration, diffusion and molecular sieving through peripheral capillary membranes. A contribution to the pore theory of capillary permeability. Am. J. Physiol., 1951, **167**, 13.

Patel, D. J. and Burton, H. C. Active constriction of small pulmonary arteries in rabbit. Circulation Res., 1957, **5**, 620.

Petersen, L. H. Participation of the veins in active regulation of circulation. Fed. Proc., 1951, **10**, 104.

Poiseuille, J. L. M. Recherches sur les causes du movement du sang dans les veines. J. Physiol. et pathol., 1830, **10**, 277.

Provenza, D. V., and Scherlis, S. Demonstration of muscle sphincters as a capillary component in the human heart. Circulation, 1959, **20**, 35.

Remington, J. W., Noback, C. R., Hamilton, W. F., and Gold, J. J. Volume elasticity characteristics of the human aorta and prediction of the stroke volume from the pressure pulse. Am. J. Physiol., 1948, **153**, 298.

Renkin, E. M. Capillary permeability to lipid-soluble molecules. Am. J. Physiol., 1952, **168**, 538.

Reynolds, S. R. M. Nondilation of arteries with pulsating blood flow. Science, 1952, **115**, 485.

Reynolds, O. An experimental investigation of the circumstances which determine whether the motion of water shall be direct or sinuous, and the laws of resistance in parallel channels. Phil. Trans. 1883, **174**, 935.

Rushmer, R. F. Pressure-circumference relations in the aorta. Am. J. Physiol., 1955, **183**, 545.

Salzman, E. W. Reflex peripheral venoconstriction induced by carotid occlusion. Circulation Res., 1957, **5**, 149.

Sarnoff, S. J. and Berglund, E. Pressure-volume characteristics and stress. Relaxation in the pulmonary vascular bed of the dog. Am. J. Physiol., 1952, **171**, 238.

Shipley, R. E., Gregg, D. E., and Schroeder, E. F. An experimental study of flow patterns in various peripheral arteries. Am. J. Physiol., 1943, **138**, 718.

Spencer, M. F., Johnston, F. R., and Dennison, A. B. Dynamics of the normal aorta: "Inertiance" and "compliance" of the arterial system which transforms the cardiac ejection pulse. Circulation Res., 1958, **6**, 491.

Whittaker, S. R. F. and Winton, F. R. The apparent viscosity of blood flowing in the isolated hind limb of the dog, and its variation with corpuscular concentration. J. Physiol., 1933, **78**, 339.

Wiggers, C. J. Active changes in size and distensibility of the aorta during acute hypertension. Am. J. Physiol., 1938, **124**, 603.

Wilens, S. L. The postmortem elasticity of the adult human aorta. Its relation to age and to the distribution of intimal atheromas. Am. J. Physiol., 1937, **13**, 811.

Woods, R. H. A few applications of a physical theorem to membranes in the human body in a state of tension. J. Anat. & Physiol. 1892, **26**, 362.

Wolf, A. V. Demonstration concerning pressure-tension relations in various organs. Science, 1952, **115**, 243.

### Monographs and Reviews

Best, C. H. and Taylor, N. B. The physiological basis of medical practice. Ed. 6. The Williams & Wilkins Company, Baltimore, Maryland, 1955.

Burton, A. C. Relation of structure to function of the tissues of the wall of blood vessels. Phys. Rev., 1954, **34**, 619.

Chambers, R. and Zweifach, B. W. Intercellular cement and capillary permeability. Physiol. Rev., 1947, **27**, 436.

Danielli, J. F., and Stock, A. The structure and permeability of blood capillaries. Biol. Rev., 1944, **19**, 81.

Franklin, K. J. A monograph on veins. Charles C Thomas, Publishers, Springfield, Illinois, 1937.

Gauer, O. H. and Henry, J. P. Beitrag zur Homeostase des extraarteriellen Kreislaufs. Klin. Wchnschr., 1956, **34**, 356.

Haddy, F. J. Vasomotion in systemic arteries, small vessels and veins detected by direct resistance measurements. Minnesota Med., 1958, **41**, 162.

Krogh, A. Anatomy and physiology of the capillaries. Yale University Press, New Haven, 1929.

Landis, E. M. Capillary pressure and capillary permeability. Physiol. Rev., 1934, **14**, 404.

Pappenheimer, J. R. Passage of molecules through capillary walls. Physiol. Rev., 1953, **33**, 387.

Rappaport, E. and Dexter, L. Pulmonary "Capillary" Pressure. Methods in Med. Research, 1958, **7**, 85.

Sjostrand, T. Volume and distribution of blood and their significance in regulating circulation. Physiol. Rev., 1953, **33**, 202.

Sjostrand, T. Distribution of blood and regulation of the blood volume. Klin. Wchnschr., 1959, **34**, 561.

Wearn, J. Myocardial Capillaries. Harvey Lectures, 1939–40, **35**, 243.

Wezler, K. and Sinn, W. Das stromungsgesetz des Blutkreislaufes. Editio Cantor K G./Aulendorf, Wurtt, 1953.

Zweifach, B. W. Structural make-up of the capillary wall. Ann. New York Acad. Sc., 1955, **61**, 670.

# 16

## ELECTROCARDIOGRAPHY

Electrocardiography may be defined as that branch of physiology which is concerned with the recording and analysis of the electrical activity of the heart. The electrocardiograph is an instrument which receives the electrical impulses as they vary during the heart cycle and transforms them into a graphic record. The electrocardiogram is the graphic record which has been inscribed by the electrocardiograph.

### Instrumentation

The first electrocardiogram was obtained in 1887 by Waller who employed a capillary electrometer as his electrocardiograph. It was Einthoven who became the real father of electrocardiography when he described the string galvanometer in 1903. This instrument became the standard apparatus for the recording of electrocardiograms until it was largely supplanted by the vacuum tube, amplifier-driven oscillograph in the 1930's. This type of instrument was later modified by stepping up the amplification to a strength adequate to drive a mechanical lever arm so that directly written records might be obtained either with an ink writer or a hot stylus applied to specially waxed paper. Recently transistorized modifications of the vacuum tube type of oscillographic instrument have come on the market. Common to all these instruments is the property of faithfully inscribing the variations of the cardiac voltages on an accurate time scale abscissa.

The cathode ray oscilloscope has been employed for specialized research in electrocardiography and recently it has been adapted by means of the sweep circuit to give a constant visual display of the electrocardiographic pattern which can be monitored during surgery or other critical clinical conditions.

### Depolarization and Repolarization of Cell Aggregates

The electrocardiogram which is recorded from body surface electrodes is the result of a vast number of systematically propagated electrical events taking place in the individual muscle cell fibers of the heart. We have seen that the individual myocardial fiber is depolarized and repolarized with large voltage fluctuations across the cell membrane, but with only small potential differences being recorded outside the cell. How then does the transmembrane action potential relate to the electrocardiogram recorded first from the surface of the heart and ultimately from the surface of the body?

It must be remembered first that the depolarization of a portion of a fiber initiates a flow of current from the polarized zone to the depolarized zone. This flow of current propagates the wave of depolarization until the entire tissue is depolarized. Since the heart is really a syncytium of muscle fibers, it follows that if one portion of the muscle becomes depolarized it will initiate a wave of activation that will eventually depolarize the entire heart. That such is indeed the case is shown by the fact that extra systoles may be produced by touching the epicardium of the exposed heart at surgery or by touching the endocardial surface with a cardiac catheter during diagnostic studies. The localized point of depolarization initiated by the mechanical stimulus is propagated to the entire heart muscle.

### The Isolated Muscle Strip

The relationship between the surface electrocardiogram and the spread of depolarization through the muscle is illuminated by experiments on isolated strips of heart muscle. Figure 16.1 illustrates the sequence of events when a wave of activation sweeps over a strip of myocardium with electrodes applied directly to its surface. On the resting polarized muscle there is no difference of potential since all parts of the surface are equally positive in charge. Hence the galvanometer records only a straight line at zero potential. When the strip is stimulated at the region of the negative electrode to the left of the drawing, this zone becomes depolarized and is electrically neutral. The other end of strip is now positive with respect to the depolarized zone, and the galvanometer records a positive deflection. As the wave of activation approaches the

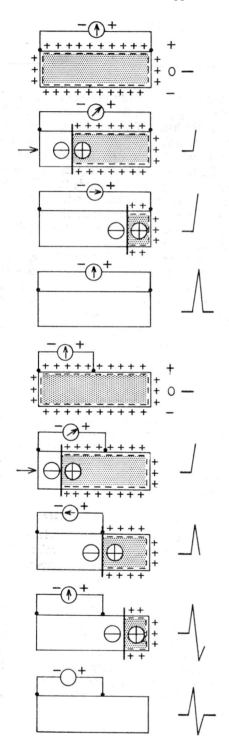

positive electrode more and more positivity is recorded until the cell is completely depolarized whereupon there is no longer a potential difference, and the recording galvanometer drops the tracing abruptly to the zero line.

When the positive electrode is placed in the middle of the strip, positivity is recorded until the wave of activation passes beneath the positive electrode whereupon the recording drops abruptly to a negative potential which returns to the zero line when the strip becomes completely depolarized. In a series of simple but beautifully conceived experiments, Craib was able to show that this phenomena could best be accounted for in terms of the migration of a dipole across the length of the muscle strip.

A dipole may be conceived of as two points of opposite electrical charge separated by a small but infinite distance. If these points are connected by a wire it is understood by convention that current will flow along the wire from the positive pole to the negative pole. (In point of fact the electrons actually flow from the negative to the positive pole.) If the dipole is immersed in a volume conductor such as a pool of weak saline solution, then a three dimensional field will be set up with the lines of current flow distributed in a pattern as illustrated in figure 16.2. Isopotential lines are arranged at right angles to the lines of current flow. Thus, all points which lie on the plane perpendicular to the center of the axis connecting the two points of the dipole are at zero potential. The human electrocardiogram may be analyzed in terms of the body surface potentials generated by a series of dipoles within the heart and distributed throughout the body which behaves as a volume conductor.

This concept may be clarified by reference to an isolated heart muscle strip immersed in a volume conductor as shown in figure 16.3. In the resting state the strip is polarized with in-

---

Fig. 16.1. Depolarization of a strip of myocardium with electrodes in direct contact with tissue. During the resting stage no difference of potential is recorded. When stimulated at *arrow*, depolarization begins, and stimulated end becomes negative to opposite end. Positivity is recorded from positive electrode until activation is completed whereupon no more difference in potential exists and recording drops to zero. With positive electrode in middle of strip positivity is recorded until the activation wave arrives under the electrode. Since the plane that divides a dipole is at zero potential, the recording drops immediately to zero. As soon as the dipole passes the electrode, maximum negativity is recorded and it gradually lessens until the return to zero when activation is completed.

numerable dipoles distributed about the surface of the strip, positive charges on the outside and negative charges on the inside. Since the positive charges facing the electrode are exactly balanced by the positive charges facing away from the electrode, there is no difference of potential, and no deflection is registered on the galvanometer or on the electrographic tracing.

When a stimulus is applied to the end of the strip facing away from the electrode, depolarization begins at that point. The dipoles at the point of stimulus are obliterated by a flow of current across the stimulated membrane, the electrical resistance of which has dropped precipitously. The stimulated area then loses all surface charges, but this entire area now is electrically negative with reference to the remainder of the strip which is still positively charged. Thus, the plane that divides the depolarized from the polarized portion may be considered as an innerface separating the positive and negative poles of a dipole, and the propagation of the wave of depolarization down the muscle strip may be thought of as the sweep of a dipole across the length of the muscle strip. As the dipole approaches the electrode higher and higher voltages are recorded as the electrode intersects isopotential lines of higher and higher voltage. Maximum potential is reached when the dipole arrives at the end of the strip nearest the electrode. When the entire strip becomes depolarized, it suddenly becomes electrically inert and the galvanometer and electrogram immediately fall to zero.

In figure 16.4 are illustrated the electrograms which are inscribed with electrodes placed at the stimulated end of the strip and at the midpoint of the strip.

## REPOLARIZATION

The process of repolarization we have seen from the monophasic action potential recorded by the micropuncture technique from the single fiber is of long duration in contrast to the rapid spike of depolarization. Since the resting transmembrane potential is fully restored after each beat, the total electrical charge of repolarization must be equal and opposite to the discharge of depolarization. If it were presumed that repolarization followed the same pathway across the muscle strip as the wave of depolarization, then one would expect that the repolarization wave should be inscribed by the recording oscillograph as a slow deflection opposite in direction to the depolarization spike but encompassing the same area. While this is indeed the case in the isolated muscle strip electrogram, it is not the case in the normal human electrocardiogram in which the depolarization and repolarization deflections usually have the same direction, and the areas of the two are rarely if ever the same. The reasons for the paradoxical orientation of repolarization in the human electrocardiogram will be discussed in a subsequent section.

Since repolarization is of long duration, different phases of it are proceeding simultaneously in various portions of the muscle strip and indeed throughout the heart (fig. 16.3). Repolarization,

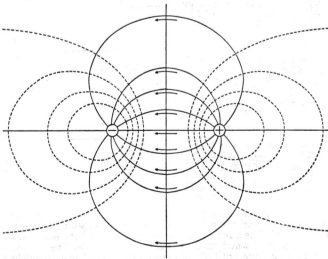

FIG. 16.2. Electrical field of a dipole in a volume conductor. Solid lines are current flow. Dotted lines are isopotential lines. (From Fulton.)

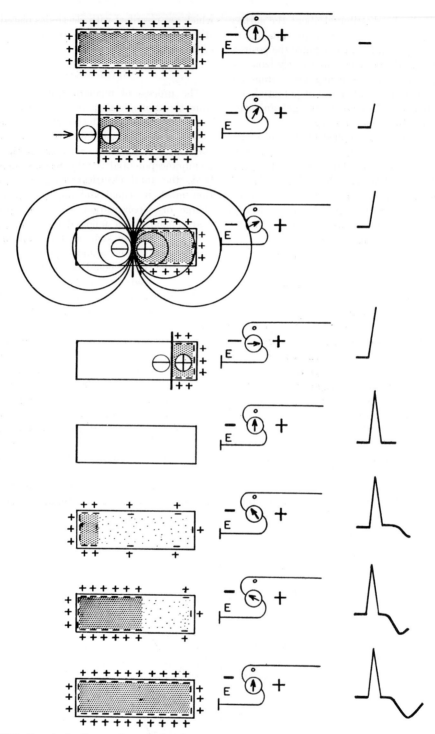

FIG. 16.3. Depolarization and repolarization of a strip of myocardium immersed in a volume conductor. Electrode E connected to positive pole of recording galvanometer which is paired with a distant electrode at near zero potential. The advancing dipole at the border between activated and inactivated muscle produces an electrical field which moves toward the electrode. The electrode is intersected by isopotential lines of increasing force until all difference of potential is extinguished by completion of depolarization. Recovery occurs in all parts of the muscle simultaneously but is completed at the stimulated end first thus producing relative negativity at the side facing the electrode and giving rise to a negative repolarization wave.

therefore, cannot be analyzed as a sequence of propagated electrical events and cannot be viewed as a wave front sweeping across the muscle. Changes in temperature, chemical environment and pharmacological agents may produce marked alterations of the repolarization wave without noticeably affecting the depolarization spike.

### CURRENT OF INJURY

When a portion of myocardium becomes injured, whether it be mechanically, chemically or thermally, the cell membranes in the injured area become more permeable to sodium ions which leads to a lessening of the ionic concentration gradients of sodium and potassium across the cell membranes and thus to a reduction of the charge density in the resting polarized state. This reduction of positivity in the injured area produces a gradient of charge from the uninjured to the injured zone. A current flows from the area of high positivity to the area of low positivity; this current is called the current of injury. It flows during the resting polarized state.

Figure 16.5 shows how the injury current affects the depolarization and repolarization waves of the electrogram of the isolated muscle strip. Prior to injury the polarized muscle strip gives rise to no potential difference and the electrogram tracing is at zero. Upon injury of a portion of the strip near the electrode, the tracing shows the onset of a negative deflection since the charge density at the injured area is less than that over the remainder of the strip. The injured area is thus electrically negative to the noninjured area. When the strip is stimulated from the noninjured side the dipole of the depolarization wave sweeps toward the electrode producing a positive deflection. The tracing shows an increasing positive spike until the entire strip has become depolarized whereupon the electrogram deflection falls to the zero potential line which is well above the origin of the depolarization spike. Repolarization then begins at the zero potential line giving the appearance of elevation of the repolarization wave.

If the electrode is placed on the opposite side of the strip, then the injury potential displaces the baseline upward from the zero line. The depolarization spike is negative, and its termination at zero falls below the point of origin. The repolarization wave commencing at this point gives the appearance of depression of the repolarization wave. Thus, the injury potential produces elevation of the origin of the repolarization wave when the electrode faces the injured zone and depres-

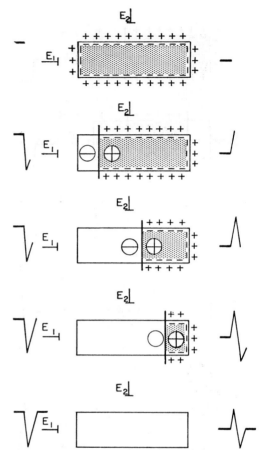

FIG. 16.4. Form of complexes inscribed from electrodes placed at positions $E_1$ and $E_2$ during depolarization of a strip of myocardium suspended in a volume conductor. Each electrode paired with a distant indifferent electrode. Tracings on the left side are related to $E_1$ while tracings on the right relate to $E_2$ electrode.

sion of the origin of the depolarization wave when the electrode faces the noninjured zone.

Another form of the injury potential may become apparent when the injured zone fails to depolarize. In this situation the resting injury potential produces depression of the isoelectric line so that the activation potential begins from a negative position. As the dipole of the depolarization advances toward the electrode, increasing positivity is inscribed until the activation wave arrives at the border of the injured zone where it is blocked. At this point, the injured zone maintains its weakly polarized state, but the noninjured zone has become depolarized making it electrically negative to the injured zone. The persistence of the dipole at the completion of activation maintains positivity at the electrode until the repolarization process in the uninjured

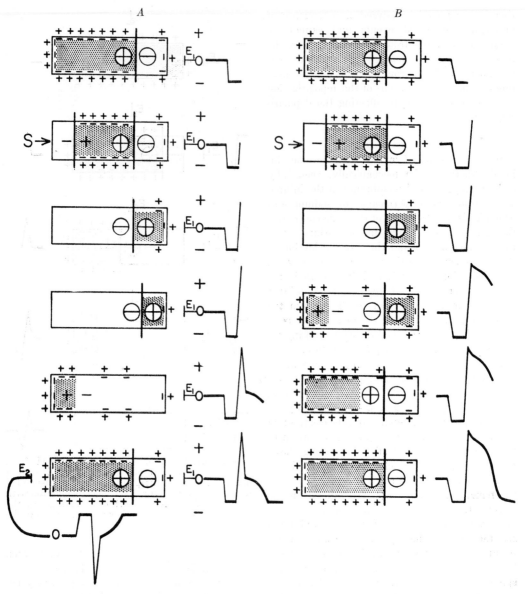

Fig. 16.5. Sequence of electrical changes in myocardial strip which has been injured at end near electrode $E_1$. When portion of strip becomes injured, there is leakage of ions and reduction of surface charge density making injured zone less positive than noninjured zone. A dipole is thus produced at border of injured zone with negative pole facing the electrode during the resting phase. Isoelectric line is, therefore, displaced downward to negative position. Following stimululation, the dipole of depolarization sweeps toward electrode, producing positive force which neutralizes effect of injury dipole. In 5A, the injured zone becomes depolarized and injury dipole is abolished. Upon completion of depolarization, recording falls to original zero position. As repolarization is completed from left to right, the injury dipole is re-established and tracing returns to negatively displaced isoelectric line, giving appearance of elevation of onset of repolarization deflection. If electrode is on opposite side of strip, isoelectric line is displaced upward, and onset of repolarization appears to be displaced downward. 5B shows the sequence when injured zone fails to depolarize. The impulse is blocked at the boundary of the injured zone which remains polarized and, therefore, during systole presents a dipole with its positive pole facing the electrode holding the recording in a positive position until repolarization returns the tracing to the negative isoelectric line. This phenomenon is called the monophasic injury wave.

zone slowly returns the tracing to the isoelectric line. The resulting complex representing a fusion of depolarization and repolarization waves has been called the monophasic injury wave (fig. 16.5).

## The Mammalian Electrocardiogram

### NOMENCLATURE

The mammalian electrocardiogram contains three major components during each cardiac cycle (fig. 16.6). According to the nomenclature devised by Einthoven, the component produced by atrial activation is called the P wave, the one produced by ventricular activation is the QRS complex, and the component produced by ventricular recovery is the T wave. The P wave is separated from the QRS complex by an isoelectric interval called the PR segment. Individual deflections in the QRS complex are labelled as follows: if the initial deflection is negative (downward from the baseline) it is a Q wave, the first positive (upward) deflection is an R wave, and a negative deflection following the R is an S wave. Subsequent positive and negative deflections in this complex are labelled R′ and S′, respectively. The interval between QRS and T is the ST segment. The junction between the end of the QRS complex and the ST segment is called the ST junction or J point. A small after-potential called the U wave is sometimes seen following the T. The duration of the components and the intervals between them vary with species and age. The intervals also vary inversely with heart rate. In the normal adult human the P wave is 0.07 to 0.12 seconds in duration, the PR interval measured from the beginning of the P wave to the beginning of the QRS complex is 0.12 to 0.20 seconds, the QRS complex is 0.05 to 0.10 seconds, and the QT interval measured from the beginning of the QRS complex to the end of the T wave is 0.26 to 0.45 seconds at normal heart rates.

### THE DISTRIBUTION OF ELECTRICAL FORCES IN THE BODY

In accordance with dipole theory, the wave front of activation is considered to be a polarized surface with positive charges on its leading side and negative charges on the trailing side. The axis between each pair of positive and negative charges is perpendicular to the polarized surface, and the density of charges is considered to be a constant. Atrial and ventricular activation are schematically described by the development of polarized surfaces which spread across the myocardium and are extinguished when they reach a margin of the myocardial syncytium or an area of activated muscle. Laws governing the distribution of electricity in a volume conductor define the electrical field produced in the body by such polarized surfaces.

When viewed from a sufficiently distant point P, a polarized surface can be represented by a single central resultant dipole with its axis perpendicular to a plane intercepting the boundary of the surface and its charge proportional to the area of this plane (fig. 16.7$a$). The electrical potential ($V_p$) at a distant point in a large volume conductor containing a dipole with charges close together is proportional to M cos $\theta/R^2$, where M is the electrical force on the dipole (determined by the quantity and distance between charges), R is the line from P to the center of the dipole axis, and $\theta$ is the angle between R and the dipole axis. Polarity of $V_p$ is determined by the charge on the polarized surface facing P. The direct relationship between $V_p$ and cos $\theta$ indicates that potential at P is maximal when the dipole axis is parallel to R and zero when it is perpendicular to R. $V_p$ is also proportional to the solid angle at P which is subtended by the boundary of the polarized surface (fig. 16.7$B$). This solid angle is equal to the area cut on a unit sphere by lines drawn from its center at P to all points on the boundary of the polarized surface. When two or more polarized surfaces subtend solid angles at P, the resultant $V_p$ is proportional to the sum of the solid angles with due regard

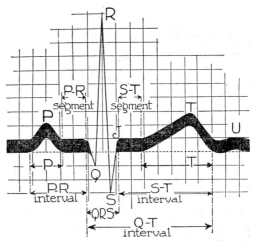

FIG. 16.6. A single electrocardiographic complex giving nomenclature of the deflections and the intervals. (Burch and Winsor)

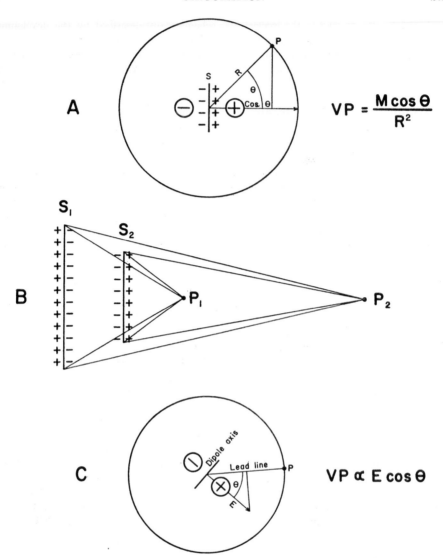

FIG. 16.7*A*. Calculation of positive potential (V) at point P when polarized surface S is considered as a single dipole. *Arrow* indicates axis of dipole. If P is located on a unit sphere, then R = 1. As point P moves away from the dipole axia, its potential diminishes as cos $\ominus$ diminishes from 1 toward zero. The numerical value of cos $\ominus$ is given by the distance on the axis from the center of the circle to the perpendicular dropped from P. M = dipole moment. *B.* Illustration of solid angle principle. Two charged surfaces $S_1$ and $S_2$ have similar charge density but different areas, and opposite orientation of charge. At point $P_1$ the net potential is positive because $S_2$ subtends a larger solid angle than $S_1$. At point $P_2$ the net potential is negative because $S_1$ subtends the larger solid angle. *C.* Determination of voltage at point P when strength of dipole is represented by vector E. Voltage is proportional to E cos $\ominus$ and is found by drawing perpendicular from the lead line terminus of vector. Distance from center of dipole to perpendicular on lead line determines voltage at P.

for their sign. The electrical potential at any point in the body or on its surface can theoretically be predicted in terms of the solid angles subtended by polarized surfaces developed in the heart during activation, and this has been done in a qualitative fashion. However, it is impossible to derive information about the size and orientation of the polarized surfaces from the resultant solid angles. It has been more practical to analyze

tracings recorded at a distance from the heart in terms of resultant vectors which indicate the magnitude and mean direction of electrical forces developed during the cardiac cycle without any implications about the polarized surfaces responsible for them. When viewed from a distance, the total electrical forces of the heart at any instant can be considered as a single dipole that is described by a vector oriented in the direction of the dipole axis with magnitude proportional to the dipole moment. This vector represents the sum of many individual vectors each of which describes a dipole at a polarized surface.

## Vector Analysis and Electrocardiographic Leads

A vector quantity is represented geometrically by an arrow with its direction and length related to the direction and magnitude of the quantity it describes. It can be shown that electrical potential ($V_p$) at a point P in a volume conductor is proportional to the geometric projection of an arrow representing a dipole vector onto a line (the lead line) drawn from P to a point of zero potential at the center of the dipole axis. $V_p$ is proportional to $E \cdot \cos \theta$ when E is the magnitude of the dipole vector and $\theta$ is the angle between the vector and the lead line (fig. 16.7$C$). An electrocardiograph will record this potential if one electrode is placed at P and the second electrode is placed at a point of zero potential. However, when two electrodes are placed on the body surface, the tracing recorded represents only the difference between potentials of the same order of magnitude at each electrode and does not give any specific information about the potentials at either point. Einthoven described a method for vector analysis of such tracings recorded from electrodes on the body surface at a distance from the heart. He assumed as a first approximation that electrical forces of the heart originate in a relatively small area at the center of a homogeneous volume conductor, and that the regions where each arm and the legs join the trunk are points equidistant from each other. The extremities behave as linear conductors connected to the trunk so that an electrode placed anywhere on an extremity is equivalent to one at its junction with the trunk. Electrodes placed on each arm and a leg are then considered to be located at the apices of an equilateral triangle with the heart at its center, and differences in potential recorded between these points represent the projection of vector forces originating from a dipole at the center of the triangle onto lead lines drawn between its apices. Potential differences between the extremities are customarily recorded in three standard limb leads obtained by connecting two of the limb electrodes at a time to the electrocardiographic instrument in the manner illustrated in figure 16.8. The polarity of the electrode connections is such that a positive charge facing the left shoulder will produce a positive deflection (upward from the base line) in

lead I, and a positive charge facing the foot will produce positive deflections in both leads II and III. Einthoven deliberately arranged the polarity of lead II in a manner inconsistent with the other two leads so that ventricular activation would produce positive deflections in all three leads of most normal records. The differences in potential are recorded in the three leads according to the following relationship: I = VL − VR, II = VF − VR, III = VF − VL, where VR, VL, VF represent potentials at the right arm, left arm and left leg respectively. Since the three leads form a closed circuit the algebraic sum of their potential differences at any instant is zero. Because of the reversed polarity of lead II, this relationship (Einthoven's law) is actually: I − II + III = O or I + III = II. The validity of this equation does not depend on any assumptions relating to the electrical homogeneity and geometry of the volume conductor or location of the heart.

It is possible to derive the potentials at each extremity from these bipolar leads if Einthoven's hypotheses are correct. That is, if the extremity electrodes are equivalent to the apices of an equilateral triangle on the surface of a homogeneous volume conductor with a point source of electrical potential in the center, then VR + VL + VF = O and it can be demonstrated algebraically that VR = −(I + II)/3, VL = (I − III)/3, and VF = (II + III)/3. However, if

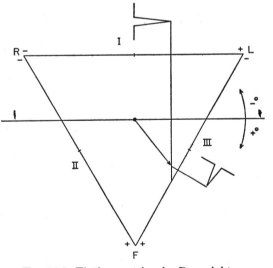

Fig. 16.8. Einthoven triangle, R = right arm, L = left arm, F = foot. Mean electrical axis is derived from lead I and lead III QRS complexes by drawing perpendiculars from the lead lines at points determined by amplitude of QRS. Intersection of perpendiculars determines the mean electrical axis.

Einthoven's hypotheses are correct it is also possible to obtain an indifferent electrode of zero potential from a network connecting the three extremities, and then one may record potentials at any point in the body with an exploring electrode. Wilson demonstrated that the potential (VT) at a central terminal connecting the three extremities through equal resistances is equal to the mean of the potentials at the extremities, and so VT = (VR + VL + VF)/3 = 0 in this special situation. Differences between resistances at the three skin-electrode interfaces which would affect VT are minimized by a high input resistance in the circuits of modern electrocardiographic instruments. Although Einthoven's hypotheses are only a first approximation of actual conditions, several studies suggest that changes in VT are so small during the cardiac cycle that they can usually be disregarded for most clinical purposes, and the central terminal is considered to have a constant or "zero" potential. Tracings which record differences in potential between an exploring electrode and the central terminal are called "V" leads and are often described as "unipolar leads" to indicate that they essentially represent changes in potential at the site of the exploring electrode. The exploring electrode in V leads is always attached to the positive pole

of the electrocardiograph so that when a positive charge faces the exploring electrode a positive (upward) deflection is recorded. Since the central terminal is considered to have a zero potential, the lead lines of the V leads extend from the exploring electrode to the center of the cardiac dipole axis, and projections of vector forces on these lines can be analyzed as described previously. Clinical electrocardiograms usually include six V chest leads recorded with the exploring electrode at the positions indicated in figure 16.9. The normal precordial lead $V_1$ displays a small R wave due to the initial activation of the septum from left to right. The small R is followed by a deep S wave due to activation of the free wall of the left ventricle which produces electrical forces directed to the left and away from this electrode. Leads $V_5$ and $V_6$ are more or less the inverse of $V_1$. They usually show a small Q wave followed by a large R wave. In the intermediate leads progressing from $V_2$ to $V_5$ there is increasing R wave amplitude and decreasing S amplitude. Usually at $V_3$ there is approximately equal R and S amplitude. This is referred to as the transition point. Occasionally the transition point will be as far to the right as the $V_2$ position or as far to the left as $V_4$.

Goldberger suggested that the potential at an

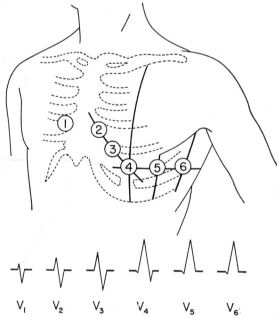

FIG. 16.9. Positions of the chest electrodes for 6 standard precordial leads. $V_1$, 4th intercostal space to right of sternum. $V_2$, 4th intercostal space at left of sternum. $V_4$, 5th interspace at midclavicular line. $V_3$, midway between $V_2$ and $V_4$. $V_5$, anterior axillary line, same level as $V_4$. $V_6$, mid axillary line, same level as $V_4$ and $V_5$. Below are shown general form of QRS in normal precordial leads. $V_3$ represents transition zone from predominant negativity on the right to predominant positivity on left. (Lipman and Massie.)

extremity could be obtained simply by disconnecting one extremity electrode from the central terminal and recording the difference in potential between it and the remaining two electrodes. Such tracings have the same configuration and 1½ times the amplitude of a V lead recorded with exploring electrode on the same extremity. The Goldberger arrangement for recording "augmented" extremity leads (named aVR, and aVL and aVF) is incorporated into the lead selector switch of modern electrocardiographic instruments.

Knowledge about the pathway of activation of the mammalian heart and the geometry of lead lines as developed from the Einthoven hypotheses can be utilized to schematically describe the effects of cardiac activation on the extremity leads. Ventricular activation can be described by a series of instantaneous vectors, each of which is the resultant of dipoles representing the polarized surfaces present at that instant. It is usual to consider only three or four such instantaneous resultant vectors (fig. 16.10): 1) Initial activation of the septum is represented by a small vector directed to the right and forward. 2) Simultaneous activation of the lower septum, free wall of the right ventricle and anterior left ventricle is represented by a resultant vector directed to the left, forward, and downward. 3) Continuation of the activation process in the postero-lateral left ventricular wall after its completion in most regions of the right ventricle is next represented by a large vector directed to the left and backward. 4) Terminal activation of the postero-basal left ventricle and upper septum is represented by a small vector directed backward and upward.

The interval between these instantaneous vectors is 0.01 to 0.015 seconds in the dog heart and approximately twice as long in the human heart. One can roughly predict the configuration of tracings in various leads by projecting these hypothetical vectors onto the appropriate lead line, or one may derive the instantaneous vectors from the recorded tracings. For example, potentials recorded at the same instant in two standard limb leads are measured and plotted in arbitrary units along the appropriate lead line axes of an equilateral triangle, starting from the center of the line and extending toward the end with the proper polarity. Perpendiculars drawn from either end of the linear plots on two lines will meet at points which define the origin and terminus of the instantaneous mean vector responsible for that particular deflection. Derivation of a series of

instantaneous vectors in this manner is a laborious process and requires special equipment to record two leads simultaneously. A single vector depicting the mean direction of the total electrical forces developed during ventricular activation can be derived by plotting the algebraic sum of positive and negative deflections in QRS complexes from each of two leads on the appropriate lead lines and dropping perpendiculars as described above. The similarity between this derived vector, called the "mean electrical axis", and the true mean cardiac vector depends on the validity of the Einthoven hypotheses. The electrical axis is described according to a system of polar coordinates with 0° at the right hand end of a horizontal line, positive values are below and negative values above this line (fig. 16.8). In normal humans, the electrical axis commonly falls between 0° and +90°; displacement in a

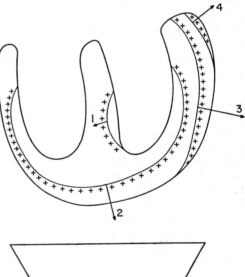

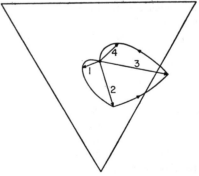

Fig. 16.10. The four major dipole vectors generated during ventricular activation giving rise to the deflections of the QRS complex. By Einthoven's hypothesis these vectors may all be considered as originating from a single point at the center of an equilateral triangle. When the termini of all resultant instantaneous vectors are connected, a loop is described. The loop is the vectorcardiogram.

clockwise direction beyond +90° is called right axis deviation, and displacement in a counterclockwise direction beyond 0° is called left axis deviation. The electrical axis is influenced by the position of the heart, changes in the functioning myocardial mass or the pathway of activation and changes in the conducting medium surrounding the heart. A change in the direction of the long axis of the heart produces a shift in electrical axis in the same direction. The electrical axis will shift toward an area of hypertrophied myocardium and away from an area of infarcted myocardium. Since the electrical axis is determined from body surface potentials, it will also be influenced by changes in the conducting medium, such as the introduction of air or fluid into the pleural space. The electrical axis determined from the limb leads represents the projection of spatial vectorial forces onto a frontal plane defined by the Einthoven triangle; an additional lead having a lead line in an anteroposterior direction is required to estimate the spatial orientation of these forces.

The problem of whether the direction of electrical forces originating from a dipole in the heart can be accurately determined from limb lead tracings has been investigated by placing an artificial dipole generator in or near the human heart. The frontal plane projection of the dipole axis was determined with fair accuracy from the limb lead potentials. However, recent studies with a dipole generator in torso models indicate that the eccentric position of the heart in the body significantly distorts its electrical field. For example, when the dipole generator in the torso model is placed in the region of the heart, a relatively smaller electrical potential is recorded at the right shoulder than at the left shoulder or pubic region, so the right shoulder must be more "distant" from the heart in an electrical sense than the other apices of the Einthoven triangle. The irregular contour of the body surface and differences in tissue conductivity cause less distortion in the electrical field than does the eccentric location of the heart.

The validity of the assumption that the electrical forces of the heart at any instant can be considered to originate from a single resultant dipole depends on the distance from the heart at which the potentials are recorded. The solid angles subtended at a distant electrode by polarized surfaces in various regions of the heart will not be significantly influenced by the relatively small differences in their distance from the electrode,

and dipoles representing each surface may be considered to originate at a single common point. On the other hand, when the electrode is close to the heart, the solid angle subtended by an adjacent region of myocardium will be much larger than that subtended by any other region of similar area, and dipoles from various regions cannot be considered to originate at a single point. Instantaneous forces of ventricular activation may be described by a resultant dipole vector when they are recorded from an electrode more distant than 2 heart diameters from its surface.

Recent studies suggest that potentials recorded from exploring electrodes on the chest wall also represent to a major degree electrical forces from single instantaneous dipole vectors. When Wilson introduced the use of V chest leads, he pointed out the similarity of the tracings to those recorded with direct epicardial leads. He re-emphasized the concept of Lewis that the large rapid deflection in a direct epicardial lead (the intrinsic deflection) represented the activation of myocardium directly under the electrode, and suggested by analogy that the major deflection in chest surface leads (the "intrinsicoid" deflection) also represented local activation of myocardium closest to the electrode and could be used to time the arrival of the activation process in that area. However, it appears likely from recent studies that the major deflection in chest leads represents a change in direction of the instantaneous resultant cardiac vector rather than local activation of adjacent myocardium.

Although the process of ventricular activation has been schematically represented by four instantaneous resultant vectors, it is described more adequately by a great number of such instantaneous vectors distributed at short intervals throughout the cardiac cycle. A line joining the termini of all the instantaneous resultant vectors will form a loop representing the sequential change in amplitude and direction of the resultant electrical forces throughout the cardiac cycle. Such a loop can be derived by graphic or electronic integration of potentials from two simultaneously recorded leads. When a loop is obtained by electronic integration on an oscilloscope, it is called a vectorcardiogram. The spatial orientation of the loop can be derived by using three leads with mutually perpendicular lead lines to obtain projections of the loop onto three planes. The hope that most information about the electrical forces of the heart could thus be derived from three mutually perpendicular leads stimulated several investigators to devise leads that are approximately orthogonal in an electrical sense. The recently proposed orthogonal lead systems employ networks of electrodes and resistances to minimize the distorting influences of cardiac eccentricity and body geometry. It is not feasible to evaluate the relative merits of these newer lead systems at the present time.

## The Recovery Process and the Ventricular Gradient

The recovery process, which is simply a reversal of changes that occur during activation, is characterized by deflections of much longer duration and lower amplitude than the activation process. Atrial recovery produces a prolonged deflection ($T_p$ or $T_a$ wave) which continues through the PR interval and into or beyond the QRS complex, but it is generally of such low amplitude that it is clearly defined only in tracings where P waves are widely separated from the QRS complexes, as in heart block. The $T_p$ is opposite in direction to the P wave in tracings obtained from strips of atrial muscle and also from the intact heart which indicate that the recovery process follows the same sequence as activation, since the two processes have opposite electrical signs. Ventricular recovery occurs during inscription of the ST segment and T wave. The ST segment corresponds to the plateau and the T wave corresponds to the rapid final phase of repolarization recorded from single myocardial fibers. The electrocardiogram generally shows little or no deflection from the base line during inscription of the ST segment when large areas of myocardium are undergoing recovery simultaneously. The T wave occurs when recovery is complete in some areas but is continuing in other regions. The T wave recorded from muscle strips is opposite in direction to the QRS, as expected when recovery occurs in the same sequence as activation, but this is not true in direct leads on the surface of the intact ventricle where the T wave is in the same direction as the major deflection of the QRS. This indicates that the sequence for completion of recovery is opposite in direction to the activation process, and therefore occurs later at endocardium than at epicardium.

It has not been possible to map the sequence for completion of the recovery process in different regions of the heart by methods used to study the activation process because there are no rapid "intrinsic" deflections that can be correlated with change in potential in local areas. However, vector analysis has been used to study both the instantaneous and mean resultant forces of the recovery process. The instantaneous forces during ventricular recovery produce a loop in the vectorcardiogram which is oriented in the same general direction as the loop inscribed during activation. The relationship between the orientation of the electrical forces during activation and recovery has been expressed in vector terms by Wilson, Ashman and Beyer, and others. These investigators determined the net area enclosed by QRS deflections and that enclosed by ST and T deflections in the limb leads, and used these areas (which represent the product of time and voltage) to plot mean vectors called $\hat{A}$ QRS and $\hat{A}$ T respectively. The resultant of these two vectors is called the ventricular gradient $\hat{G}$. If $\hat{A}$ T was equal in amplitude and opposite in direction to $\hat{A}$ QRS, as expected on a theoretical basis from electrograms of muscle strips, their resultant or ventricular gradient would be zero. The degree to which the actual $\hat{A}$ T deviates from the theoretical one is expressed by the vector $\hat{G}$. The gradient is thus a reflection of the difference between the sequence of activation and recovery. The normal ventricular gradient is explained on the basis of a delay in recovery of the subendocardial region due to local differences in some metabolic or mechanical factors which influence the recovery process. QRS amplitude and duration may change due to a difference in the activation pathway, as occurs with a premature ventricular beat or bundle branch block, without effecting the metabolic or mechanical factors which determine the normal ventricular gradient. Changes in amplitude or duration of the QRS are then accompanied by equivalent changes of the T wave in the opposite direction and $\hat{G}$ may remain unchanged. Such T wave changes are called secondary, in contrast to primary T wave changes due to factors which specifically influence the recovery process and are therefore accompanied by changes in the gradient. Primary T wave changes may occur after excerise or eating, with decreases in coronary perfusion due to atherosclerosis or in a variety of other physiological and pathological situations. Calculation of changes in ventricular gradients should theoretically allow one to differentiate between primary and secondary T wave changes, but this has not proven very useful in clinical electrocardiography because of the wide range of normal gradients and the fact that both physiological and pathological factors can cause either primary or secondary T wave changes.

## Abnormalities of the Electrocardiogram

### LEFT VENTRICULAR HYPERTROPHY

Enlargement of the left ventricle commonly gives rise to four deviations from the normal electrocardiogram not all of which need be present to establish the diagnosis (fig. 16.11). These deviations are: (1) increased voltage in the leads exploring the left ventricle, (2) increased duration of the QRS complexes, (3) rotation of the mean electrical axis toward the left and posteriorly, and (4) secondary ST and T wave abnormalities over the left ventricular leads.

The increased voltage is seen primarily as increased negativity over the right precordial leads $V_1$ and $V_2$, and increased positivity over the left precordial leads, $V_5$ and $V_6$. The reasons for this increased voltage are not entirely clear. It may be that the hypertrophied myocardial cells have a greater charge density or that closer proximity to the chest wall of the enlarged ventricle imparts a higher voltage to the exploring electrode which subtends a larger solid angle. It has been postulated that the increased thickness of the hypertrophied left ventricle permits the activation wave of this area to continue unopposed after completion of activation of the right ventricle. Increased positivity is inscribed in a leftward and posterior direction as the left ventricular free wall completes its prolonged activation.

Sokolow has shown that if the absolute sum of the positivity in $V_5$ and the negativity in $V_1$ is 3.5 mv. or more there is a strong statistical likelihood of left ventricular hypertrophy. These values, however, may be seen in normal young adults particularly if there is a thin chest wall.

The increased duration of the QRS appears to be due to the longer time necessary for the wave of activation to spread from endocardium to epicardium through the thickened ventricular wall. In many cases of left ventricular hypertrophy, the onset of the intrinsicoid deflection is delayed over the left precordial leads beyond 0.05 seconds, and the total duration of QRS may be 0.10 or 0.11 seconds.

Since the thickest portion of the free wall of the left ventricle lying just beneath the atrioventricular groove faces the region of the left shoulder and is the last part of the left ventricle to be depolarized, it is not surprising that hypertrophy of the ventricular wall directs more and more voltage toward the left posterior shoulder region.

In the limb leads, the mean electrical axis lies in the 0 to $-90°$ quadrant (left axis deviation). The posterior displacement is seen in the horizontal plane vectorcardiogram, and it may be apparent in the precordial leads by a shift of the transition zone to the left.

When left ventricular hypertrophy becomes severe, the QRS changes are usually accompanied by ST and T wave abnormalities which may vary from flattening of the T waves in the left precordial leads to depression of the ST segment with downward slanting of ST and deep T wave inversion in these leads.

The exact mechanism by which these ST-T changes are produced is not understood. Some believe that they are secondary to the increased area of the QRS. Others believe that they may be primary changes perhaps due to relative ischemia of the subendocardial layers of the hypertrophied ventricular wall.

### RIGHT VENTRICULAR HYPERTROPHY

The right ventricle is thin-walled and lies in an almost direct anterior anatomical position. Normally the voltages generated by this ventricle are greatly overbalanced by the voltages coming from the much greater mass of the left ventricle. The right ventricle may undergo a great deal of hypertrophy before its muscle mass begins to approach the mass of the left ventricle. In the lesser stages of hypertrophy of the right ventricle, the electrocardiographic changes are the result of rotation of the heart on its long axis in a clockwise direction when viewed from the apex. The enlarging right ventricle restricted anteriorly by the sternum pushes the left ventricle around toward the left and downward toward the diaphragm. The electrical forces are still dominated by left ventricular voltages which may be somewhat smaller than normal since they are opposed by larger right ventricular voltages. The net effect is to direct the major left ventricular voltages posteriorly and inferiorly toward the foot producing a vertical electrical axis in the frontal plane as visualized in the limb leads. In the precordial leads there is a delay in transition with an S wave persisting through $V_5$ and perhaps $V_6$. These changes are due primarily to rotation of the heart by the enlarging right ventricle. They are likely to be seen in chronic cor pulmonale due to pulmonary disease and in mitral valvular disease.

In severe pulmonic valvular stenosis, in severe pulmonary hypertension, and in advanced stages of mitral valve disease there may be sufficient

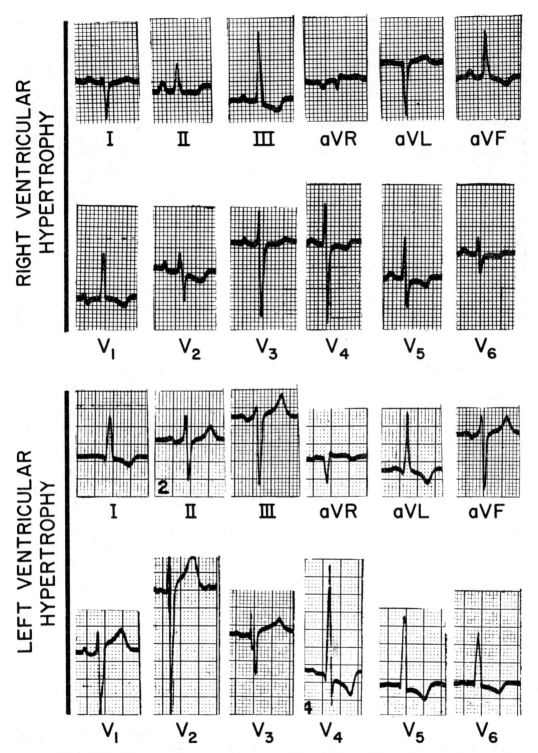

FIG. 16.11. Electrocardiogram patterns of right and left ventricular hypertrophy.

right ventricular hypertrophy to exceed the muscle mass of the left ventricle. In this situation the major voltages are generated in the right ventricle, and the major electrical forces are directed anteriorly and to the right.

In the frontal plane, the limb leads show right axis deviation with a mean electrical axis usually greater than +105°. The precordial leads show predominant positivity in $V_1$ with R usually far exceeding S in amplitude. The transition toward the left discloses a progressively diminishing R wave and an increasing S wave. This is opposite to the normal QRS precordial transition.

ST and T wave changes similar to those seen in left ventricular hypertrophy may be seen in right ventricular hypertrophy. These changes will be seen in those leads showing maximal positivity, that is, in $V_1$ and $V_2$ and in II, III, and in AVF. Their pathogenesis is just as uncertain in right ventricular hypertrophy as it is in left ventricular hypertrophy.

### Right Bundle Branch Block

Although Lewis and his associates carried out experiments in which one or the other of the major conducting bundles was interrupted and changes in the electrocardiogram were observed, it was the work of Wilson and his associates that firmly established the nature of bundle branch block. The concepts described here stem from their beautiful and precise experiments.

Recalling the normal sequence of activation of the heart it will be remembered that the right side of the septum becomes depolarized very soon after the left side and that the free wall of the right ventricle is depolarized simultaneously with the free wall of the left ventricle and that the greater thickness of the left ventricle produces voltages far in excess of those produced by the right ventricle. Thus, the only rightward directed voltages seen on the normal electrocardiogram are those generated initially in the septum and in some instances a small late voltage from a late activation of the pulmonary conus.

When the right conducting bundle is blocked either by cutting it experimentally or by some pathological process, the activation of the right ventricular free wall is greatly delayed (fig. 16.12). The first portion of the QRS complex up to about 0.04 seconds proceeds normally as it records the activation of the left ventricle. When the left ventricle has become completely depolarized, there still remains a considerable portion of the right ventricular free wall which has not been depolarized. Since the impulse cannot be trans-

mitted almost simultaneously to all parts of the right ventricular endocardium through the blocked Purkinje fibers, the wave of activation must be slowly transmitted directly through the muscle in a tangential direction rather than in the normal direction of endocardium to epicardium. This slow late right ventricular activation wave, now unopposed by left ventricular forces and not having the high proportion of internal cancellation voltages characteristic of normal transmission, produces a large voltage directed anteriorly and to the right which appears late and prolongs the QRS to a duration of 0.12 seconds or more.

This late right ventricular voltage is inscribed in the electrocardiogram as a late slurred R wave in $V_1$ and aVR and a late slurred S wave in $V_5$, $V_6$ and aVL.

### Left Bundle Branch Block

Interruption of the left conducting bundle causes delay in activation of the left ventricle. The first portion of the heart to be activated is now the right side of the septum by way of the right bundle branch. The septum is thus activated from right to left producing a large voltage directed leftward. This large leftward voltage is opposed to a small degree by a rightward voltage from the almost simultaneous activation of the free wall of the right ventricle, but because of the greater muscle mass of the septum the net initial voltage is directed toward the left. The effect on the electrocardiogram is to produce initial positivity in leads I, $V_5$ and $V_6$. The normal septal Q wave is thus abolished in these leads.

The wave of activation is transmitted through the septum to the free wall of the left ventricle through which it passes slowly in a tangential direction from apex to base. It is probable that there is also some transmission from the anterior and posterior septum circumferentially so as to envelope the free wall in the activation wave. The slow activation of the left ventricle continues to produce leftward directed voltages which are inscribed in the electrocardiogram as broad notched or slurred R waves in the left precordial leads $V_5$ and $V_6$. Duration of these complexes is 0.12 seconds or greater. In general the ST and T waves are opposite in direction to the QRS complexes. If the concept of the ventricular gradient is a valid one this divergence of the direction of QRS and T would be considered to be secondary to the increased area of the QRS. The large increase in the magnitude of the QRS vector would necessitate a reversal of the direction

**RIGHT BUNDLE BRANCH BLOCK**

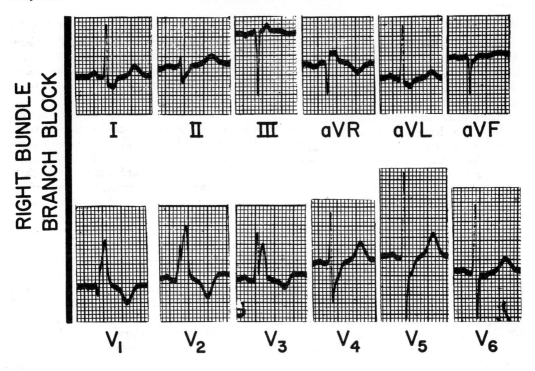

**LEFT BUNDLE BRANCH BLOCK**

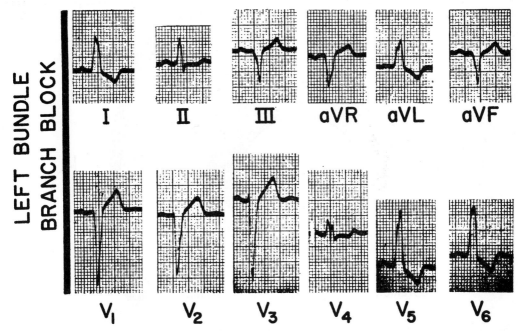

FIG. 16.12. Patterns of right and left bundle branch block.

of the T vector in order to preserve the magnitude and direction of the ventricular gradient. Whether or not the ventricular gradient is adequate to explain the ST and T abnormalities of left bundle branch block, one would expect to see abnormalities in the repolarization waves simply because the pathway of depolarization is so drastically altered from normal in this condition.

## Myocardial Ischemia, Injury and Necrosis

In animal experiments epicardial leads applied directly to the surface of the heart have been used to study the electrocardiographic changes associated with impairment of the coronary blood flow (fig. 16.13). When a coronary artery is gradually compressed, the first change seen in tracings from the area of myocardium supplied by that vessel is a deep and symmetrical inversion of the T wave. This symmetrical form of T wave inversion is referred to as T wave inversion of the ischemic type. It is believed to be due to delay in recovery at the epicardial region so that there is reversal of the normal order of repolarization.

The ischemic T wave inversion is rapidly reversible if adequate circulation is restored to the myocardium. When the blood supply to the myocardium is more drastically impaired by sudden ligation of a coronary artery, the direct epicardial tracing shows the rapid onset of elevation of the ST segment. This elevation may be almost as high as the QRS complex and may yield a wave form closely resembling the transmembrane action potential obtained with micropuncture of a single myocardial fiber. The ST elevation is believe to be due to a strong current of injury directed away from the electrode and causing marked depression below the zero line of the point of origin of the QRS complex. This ST displacement may be accompanied by ischemic changes in the T waves. This injury pattern is also rapidly reversible upon restoration of adequate blood flow.

When a coronary artery is permanently ligated, a portion of the myocardium becomes infarcted. The presence of electrically inert necrotic myocardium results in alterations of the QRS complexes of the direct epicardial lead. If the infarction is completely transmural from epicardium to endocardium this mass of tissue contributes no potential of its own, but simply conducts to the surface the potentials which are to be found in the underlying cavity. The depolarization wave in this case is a purely negative QS complex identical to that found in the left ventricular cavity. The repolarization phases contain elements of injury and ischemia patterns derived from adjacent viable portions of the myocardium.

Exploration of the adjacent areas of myocardium about a zone of necrosis discloses a zone of injury surrounding the necrotic areas (fig. 16.13). Complexes recorded from the injury zone are characterized by marked elevation of the ST segment without significant change in the morphology of the early portion of the QRS. The

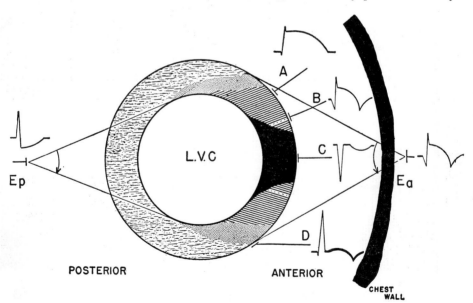

Fig. 16.13. Schematic diagram of direct epicardial leads taken over an area of myocardial infarction and over adjacent zones of injury and ischemia. Also shown is a chest lead facing the infarct, and a lead from the opposite side of the heart. At *C* cavity negativity is reflected in the epicardial lead over the necrotic zone. At *A* is recorded a monophasic injury wave over the injured zone. At *B* the complex reflects a combination of necrosis and injury. At *D* there is only T wave inversion of the ischemic type over the ischemic zone. At $E_A$ over the chest the complex combines features of all three zones, and on the opposite side of the heart there are reciprocal changes of increased positivity of the R wave and depression of ST (From Barker).

injury zone is surrounded by a zone in which the T waves show inversion of the ischemic type. This is called the ischemic zone. Beyond it lies normal muscle disclosing normal QRS-T complexes.

Electrocardiograms made from the surface of the body include potentials from the entire heart and, therefore, the precise localization of zones of necrosis, injury and ischemia cannot be derived from the clinical electrocardiogram. When infarction is present, all of the phenomena observed in the three zones will be reflected in the appropriate electrocardiographic lead. Even a precordial lead which may be taken very closely adjacent to a large area of infarction is influenced by electrical events in other parts of the heart and is likely to disclose elements derived from all three of the zones of necrosis, injury and ischemia.

Thus the classical pattern of myocardial infarction consists of a deep wide Q wave, ST segment elevation and, T wave inversion. Muscle necrosis cannot be identified with certainty from the electrocardiogram without the appearance of a pathological Q wave which indicates a removal of electrically active myocardium. ST and T wave changes of injury and ischemia may occur when myocardium becomes temporarily or even chronically hypoxic but not sufficiently so to produce muscle death. On the other hand, there may be myocardial necrosis in areas completely surrounded by viable tissue or in subendocardial zones such that the general pathway of activation might not be markedly altered. In such intramural or subendocardial infarctions abnormal Q waves may not appear even though injury and ischemic ST and T changes may be present. In such cases, the presence of muscle necrosis cannot be proven by the electrocardiogram. Evidence of its presence might, however, be obtained by other clinical means.

## LOCALIZATION OF INFARCTION OR INJURY

The general anatomical localization of areas of cardiac infarction may readily be made by the standard nine or twelve lead electrocardiogram. Each lead constitutes, so to speak, an electrical view of the heart from a different point in space (fig. 16.14). In accord with both solid angle and dipole analyses, positive electrodes record maximum positivity when the wave front of ventricular activation is advancing directly toward the electrode. Thus, the early positivity in $V_1$ derives from the left to right activation wave across the septum. $V_2$ and $V_3$ derive their positive deflections mainly from the anterior left

ventricle near the septum. $V_4$ positivity derives mainly from the anterior free wall of the left ventricle, and $V_5$ and $V_6$ positivity originates mainly from the activation of the lateral left ventricular free wall. Lead aVF and lead III receive their positive potentials from the posterodiaphragmatic wall of the left ventricle and aVL its positivity from the high lateral left ventricular wall. In general then, a positive electrode receives its maximal positive forces from the area of myocardium toward which it faces.

Infarction of myocardium abolishes positive forces, and this loss of positivity is reflected maximally in those leads which face the infarcted area. Loss of positive forces advancing toward the electrode leaves unopposed forces moving away from the electrode. The result is the appearance of Q waves in leads facing the infarcted areas of myocardium. ST and T wave changes of injury and ischemia derived from adjacent viable tissue are also reflected in these leads but may be considerably more widespread into leads which do not demonstrate alterations in the QRS.

The appearance then of the infarction pattern in leads $V_1$, $V_2$ and $V_3$ indicates anteroseptal infarction, in $V_3$ and $V_4$, anterior infarction, in $V_5$ and $V_6$ lateral infarction, in aVF and III posterior or diaphragmatic infarction, in aVL high lateral infarction. Depending upon the size and extent of the infarct there may be various combinations of these such as posterolateral when the changes are in aVF and $V_6$, or anterolateral when the changes are in $V_4$, $V_5$ and $V_6$. Sometimes the appearance of right bundle branch block associated with the anteroseptal infarction pattern gives evidence of extensive involvement of the septum.

Left bundle branch block in most instances completely obscures the pattern of myocardial infarction because of the gross alteration of the pathway of activation, particularly because the reversal of the direction of depolarization of the septum produces initial positivity in the left ventricular cavity and thus prevents the appearance of Q waves over an area of infarction of the left ventricular free wall. Only when there is extensive destruction of the lower septum and apical portions of the left ventricle does a Q wave appear in the left precordial leads in the presence of left bundle branch block.

## LOCATION OF MYOCARDIAL INJURY

Well known clinical conditions illustrate the electrocardiographic effects of temporary injury to subepicardial and subendocardial heart muscle.

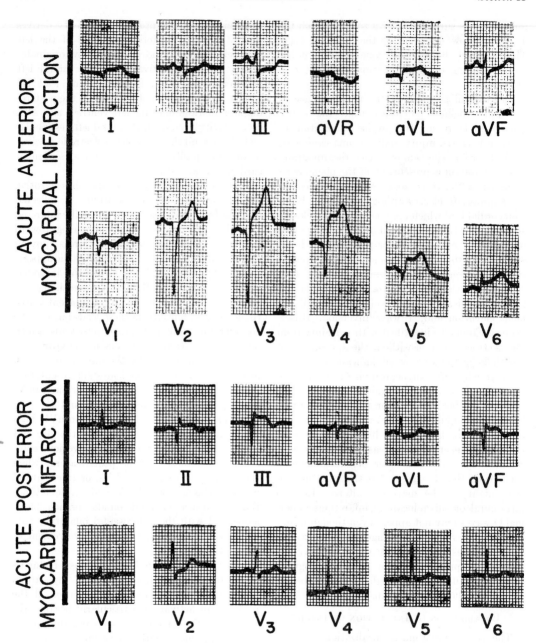

ACUTE ANTERIOR MYOCARDIAL INFARCTION

I  II  III  aVR  aVL  aVF

$V_1$  $V_2$  $V_3$  $V_4$  $V_5$  $V_6$

ACUTE POSTERIOR MYOCARDIAL INFARCTION

I  II  III  aVR  aVL  aVF

$V_1$  $V_2$  $V_3$  $V_4$  $V_5$  $V_6$

FIG. 16.14. Patterns of acute anterior and posterior myocardial infarcts.

When subepicardial myocardium is injured, whether by disease such as pericarditis or by the intentional instillation of irritating substances into the pericardial sac, elevation of ST segments appears in all leads except those which explore primarily the heart cavities (aVR and $V_1$). In other words, leads taken from electrodes facing the injured surface display positive ST segment displacement. On the other hand, when there is subendocardial injury such as may occur in coro-nary insufficiency during an attack of angina pectoris, there is ST segment depression in many of the leads exploring the free wall of the left ventricle. In this case, injury to the side of the myocardial wall facing away from the electrode produces negative ST segment displacement. The principle is borne out by the observation that a localized infarction on one side of the heart leading to elevation of SR segments in leads taken from that side will produce ST depression in leads recorded from the opposite side of the heart. In acute posterior infarction with Q waves and ST elevation in leads III and aVF there will often be found ST depression in leads $V_2$ and $V_3$. The ST depressions in the anterior leads are said to be reciprocal to the elevations in the posterior leads.

### DRUGS AND ELECTROLYTES

Digitalis produces a characteristic alteration of the ST and T complex which might sometimes be mistaken for an injury effect (fig. 16.15). The change consists of a shortening of the QT interval and a sagging of the ST segment. The sagging ST has a "scooped-out" or "cuplike" concavity that is easily recognized. This electrocardiographic sign of digitalis effect is not related to the adequacy of the dose of the medication nor to drug intoxication.

Quinidine and procaine amide have similar effects on the electrocardiogram. The earliest sign is prolongation of the QT interval with apparent stretching out of the entire ST-T complex. Later on as the dose is increased slowing of conduction through the ventricle is produced with resulting widening of the QRS complexes. Normal complexes of 0.06 to 0.08-second duration may be prolonged to 0.12 to 0.14 second by increasing quinidine or procaine amide doses. Upon finding such prolongation most clinicians would elect to stop the drug or reduce its dose for fear of stopping all conduction and precipitating ventricular standstill.

Among electrolyte ions calcium and potassium appear to be the most significant in their effects on the ECG. Hypocalcemia leads to prolongation of the QT interval which is rather strikingly different from that found in quinidine effect. With low serum calcium the ST segment itself becomes long but it remains flat and is followed by a normal appearing T wave of normal duration. Micropuncture studies of transmembrane action potentials have shown that the long ST segment is due to prolongation of the plateau phase of the recovery process. The later phases continue at their usual rates.

Elevation of the serum calcium has the opposite effect of shortening the ST segment by shortening the plateau phase of the monophasic action potential. The T wave itself appears undisturbed.

Reduction of serum potassium appears to have two effects; one on the ST-T complex and one on the U wave. When the potassium level in the serum falls to about 3 m.eq. per liter, the ST begins to sag and the T wave becomes lower as the U wave becomes more prominent. The T and U seem to merge into a single wave separated only by a slight indentation or dimple on the crest. This gives the impression of markedly prolonged QT which is really not the case. With very low levels of potassium the ST segment becomes depressed below the base line and the U wave exceeds the T in height. This gives the appearance of a stepwise ascent of the ST-T complex. This pattern is usually seen with serum potassium of 2.5 m.eq. per liter or less.

Elevation of serum potassium leads first to an increasing amplitude of the T wave in leads where the T is normally upright. The increasingly tall T waves have a tentlike appearance with similar slopes on the upward and downward limbs. With higher levels of serum K (8 m.eq. per liter approximately) the PR interval becomes prolonged and the QRS begins to widen out as conduction becomes impaired. At about 9 m. eq. per liter, the P wave disappears entirely and the QRS takes on a bizarre shape merging with the tall T wave to produce a distorted sine wavelike

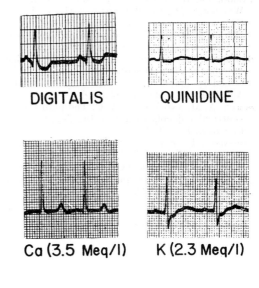

DIGITALIS      QUINIDINE

Ca (3.5 Meq/l)      K (2.3 Meq/l)

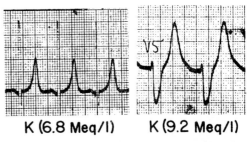

K (6.8 Meq/l)      K (9.2 Meq/l)

FIG. 16.15. Patterns of digitalis and quinidine effect, low serum calcium, low serum potassium and high serum potassium.

pattern which usually heralds terminal ventricular fibrillation or standstill.

## REFERENCES

ABILDSKOV, J. A. The atrial complex of the electrocardiogram. Am. Heart J., 1959, 57, 930.

BARBATO, E., PILEGGI, F., DEBES, A. C., FUJIOKA, T., MAGALHARE, M. S., TRANCHESI, J., SAN JUAN, E., AND DECOURT, L. V. Study of the sequence of ventricular activation and the QRS complex of the normal human heart using direct epicardial leads. Am. Heart J., 1958, 55, 867.

CRAIB, W. H. A study of the electrical field surrounding active heart muscle. Heart, 1927, 14, 71.

EINTHOVEN, W., FARH, G., AND deWAART, A. On the direction and manifest size of the variations of potential in the human heart and on the influence of the position of the heart on the form of the electrocardiogram. Am. Heart J., 1950, 40, 163.

MACLEOD, A. G. The electrogram of cardiac muscle: an analysis which explains the regression of T deflection. Am. Heart J., 1938, 15, 165.

MACLEOD, A. G. The electrogram of cardiac muscle. II. The lengths of the stages of activity. Am. Heart J., 1938, 15, 402.

PIPBERGER, H., SCHWARTZ, L., MASSUMI, R. A., WEINER, S. M., AND PRINZMETAL, M. Studies on the mechanism of ventricular activity. XXI. The origin of the depolarization complex with clinical applications. Am. Heart J., 1957, 54, 511.

SOKOLOW, M. AND LYON, T. P. The ventricular complex in left ventricular hypertrophy as obtained by unipolar precordial and limb leads. Am. Heart J., 1949, 37, 161.

SCHER, A. M. AND YOUNG, A. C. The pathway of ventricular depolarization in the dog. Circulation Res., 1956, 4, 461.

SIMONSON, E., SCHMITT, O. H., DAHL, J., FRY, D. L., AND BALKEN, E. E. The theoretical and experimental bases of the frontal plane ventricular gradient and its spatial counterpart. Am. Heart J., 1954, 47, 122.

WALLER, A. D. Demonstration on man of the electromotive changes accompanying the heart's beat. J. Physiol., 1887, 8, 229.

WILSON, F. N., MACLEOD, A. G., AND BARKER, P. S. The distribution of the action currents produced by heart muscle and other excitable tissues immersed in extensive conducting media. J. Gen. Physiol., 1933, 16, 425.

WILSON, F. N., ROSENBAUM, F. F., AND JOHNSTON, F. D. Interpretation of the ventricular complex of the electrocardiogram. Advances in internal medicine. Vol. II, Interscience Publishers, Inc., New York, 1947.

*Monographs and Reviews*

BARKER, J. M. The unipolar electrocardiogram, A clinical interpretation. Appleton - Century-Crofts, Inc., New York, 1952.

BURCH, G. E. AND WINSOR, T. A primer of electrocardiography. Ed. 3. Lea & Febiger, Philadelphia, 1955.

FULTON, J. F. A textbook of physiology. Ed. 16. W. B. Saunders Company, Philadelphia, 1951.

KOSSMANN, C. E (Editor). Advances in electrocardiography. Grune & Stratton, Inc., New York and London, 1958.

LEPESCHKIN, E. Modern electrocardiography. The Williams & Wilkins Company, Baltimore, 1951.

LEWIS, T. The mechanism and graphic registration of the heart beat. Ed. 3. Shaw and Sons, London, 1925.

LIPMAN, B. S. AND MASSIE, E.: Clinical unipolar electrocardiography. Ed. 3. The Year Book Publishers, Inc., Chicago, 1956.

SODI-PALLARES, D. AND CALDER, R. M. New bases of electrocardiography. The C. V. Mosby Company, St. Louis, 1956.

WHITELOCK, O. V. (Editor) The electrophysiology of the heart. Ann. New York Acad. Sc., 1957, 65, 653.

WILSON, F. N. Selected papers of, edited by F. D. Johnston and E. Lepeschkin. Heart Station, University Hospital, Ann Arbor, Michigan, 1954.

# 17

## DISORDERS OF THE HEART BEAT AND THEIR INVESTIGATION BY GRAPHIC METHODS

The following is a convenient classification of cardiac irregularities:

A. *Affections of rhythm due to impaired conduction through the A-V bundle.*
  I. Stem of bundle
   (1) Delayed conduction
   (2) Missed beats, partial heart block
   (3) Complete heart block
B. *Wolff-Parkinson-White syndrome*
C. *Affections due to abnormal impulse formation*
  I. Extrasystoles
   (1) Ventricular
   (2) Nodal
   (3) Auricular
  II. Paroxysmal tachycardia
      Auricular, nodal and ventricular
  III. Auricular flutter
  IV. Auricular fibrillation
  V. Ventricular fibrillation
D. *Alternation of the heart*
E. *Affections due to vagal influences*
  I. Sinus arrhythmia
  II. Phasic irregularity
  III. Sinus bradycardia
  IV. Sino-auricular block
  V. Auriculoventricular block

### A. Affections of Rhythm Resulting from Impaired Conduction

#### I. In the A-V Node or Stem of the Bundle Auriculoventricular Block

In animals, conduction from auricle to ventricle can be depressed or blocked by crushing, cutting, or the application of cold to the A-V bundle. This strategic point in the pathway of the excitation wave is also attacked by disease, and conduction through it may be depressed or completely abolished. Depression of conduction through the node or bundle varies in degree. Three stages are recognized.

#### (1) Delayed Conduction

In this stage conduction is merely slowed; every impulse reaches the ventricle. The intervals between the auricular and ventricular systoles ($A_s$-$V_s$ intervals) are lengthened and may have a duration of 0.5 second, though, as a rule, they are considerably shorter than this. The condition can be recognized only be means of the electrocardiograph or a venous pulse tracing. Lengthening of the P-R interval in the former tracing, or of the *a-c* interval in the latter, beyond the normal maximum of 0.2 second is taken to indicate delayed conduction (fig. 17.1).

#### (2) Missed Beats—Partial Heart Block

When impaired conduction reaches a certain degree, impulses from time to time fail to reach the ventricle, and a beat is missed. The auricular beats are perfectly regular, and in this way the condition differs from sino-auricular block (p. 204). A ventricular beat may be missed only occasionally and at irregular intervals. The P-R interval of the electrocardiogram, or the *a-c* interval of the venous pulse, may generally, though not invariably, be seen to lengthen progressively for several heart cycles preceding the dropped beat. The periods of delayed conduction preceding the missed beat are called, after their discoverer, the Wenckebach periods. The interval of the cycle succeeding the missed beat is shortened again to near the normal length. In a further stage of the condition the beats are dropped more frequently and may be spaced at either regular or irregular intervals in the tracing. When the grade of block is still more advanced, impulses fail to penetrate the bundle after every second auricular beat; or three, or even four auricular contractions may occur before an impulse reaches the ventricle, i.e., the ventricle responds only to every third or fourth auricular beat. So, an auriculoventricular rhythm becomes established in

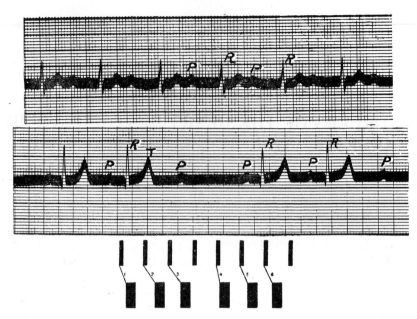

FIG. 17.1. Upper tracing, delayed conduction, lead I. Lower tracing, incomplete heart block, lead I (missed beats). (Kindness of Dr. John Hepburn.) The diagram below (after Lewis) represents incomplete heartblock. The thin rectangles, A, represent contractions of the auricle, the thicker ones, V, contractions of the ventricle. The obliquely directed lines represent conduction over the A-V bundle; the slower the conduction rate the more oblique the line. The gaps in the lower rectangles indicate missed beats of the ventricle. It will be noted that delay in conduction increases progressively in successive cycles until a beat is missed. Heavy vertical lines = $\frac{1}{5}$ sec.

which the two chambers beat in the ratio of 2:1, 3:1, or 4:1. The first of these is seen most frequently, the second is the least common (fig. 17.1).

### (3) Complete Heart Block

When the A-V node or bundle offers an absolute barrier to the passage of the impulse, the dissociation of the rhythms of the two ventricles is complete (fig. 17.2). The auricles beat at their own rate of about 70 per minute and the ventricle at its inherent rate of about 35. The latter is then spoken of as the idioventricular rhythm. Both ventricles beat simultaneously. This fact suggests that when the ventricle assumes this rate it is under the control of some single region possessing the power of rhythmical activity. From experimental investigation it appears that the controlling center is the A-V bundle below the site of the lesion. The speed with which a particular region of the heart can develop and discharge impulses apparently determines its ability to dominate other regions. It has been mentioned that when a region of higher rhythmicity is destroyed or isolated the region next in order of rhythmical power assumes the role of pacemaker (ch. 14). When, for instance, the S-A node is destroyed or isolated the A-V node assumes control, and when this or the upper part of the bundle is separated from the tract of tissue below, the lower lying portion takes over the government of the ventricular rate.

Partial and complete heart block are accompanied by changes in the rhythm of the arterial

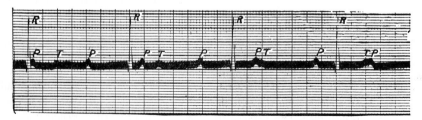

FIG. 17.2. Complete heart block, lead I (kindness of Dr. John Hepburn).

pulse. When beats are missed occasionally the pulse intermits either at regular or irregular intervals. In the more fully developed conditions marked slowing (bradycardia) of the pulse occurs. Visible pulsations in the veins at the root of the neck may occur, for the auricle, in contracting upon a larger volume of blood accumulated as a result of the infrequency of the ventricular contractions, causes a pronounced wave to be transmitted along the jugular. A certain proportion of the venous pulsations may be seen to be unassociated with an arterial pulse. Sometimes a sound may be heard over the heart at the time of the isolated venous pulsation since the auricular contraction is unusually forceful and the sound vibrations thus set up are not smothered by the first heart sound which, in the normally beating heart, follows so closely upon auricular systole.

The venous pulse tracing and electrocardiogram show characteristic features. The *a* and P waves of the respective records occur at the usual times, but the ventricular complex (*c* and *v* in the venous curve and QRS and T in the electrocardiogram) is absent, a gap appearing in the tracing each time a beat of the ventricle is missed. In incomplete heart block, as one would expect, a relationship between a ventricular complex and a preceding auricular wave can always be made out, whereas in complete block there is no relationship. In the venous pulse, for example, the *a* and *c* waves may occur simultaneously, and produce a large *a* + *c* wave. Or the *a* and *v* waves may coincide. Corresponding effects are produced upon the electrocardiogram.

*Temporary heart block* may result from various toxic agents, e.g., digitalis, strophanthus, quinidine, etc., which exert a specific effect in depressing auriculoventricular conduction. Heart block may be a sequel or an accompaniment of several acute infectious maladies, e.g., diphtheria, rheumatic fever, etc. It is produced in animals by asphyxia. Increased vagal tone is sometimes responsible for delayed conduction over the A-V bundle. Partial heart block is not uncommonly seen in the course of rheumatic fever and is then, in many instances, of vagal origin, being temporarily abolished by atropine. *Persistent* heart block due to increased vagal tone and abolished by atropine occasionally occurs. Some cases are congenital.

*Stokes-Adams syndrome.* This condition was first described by Adams (1827) and later by Stokes (1842). Its features are a slow pulse and syncopal attacks or convulsive seizures, usually epileptiform in character. The term includes any condition of vascular origin in which these features are associated, and it is probable that the underlying morbid state upon which the syndrome depends is not identical in all instances (see also carotid sinus, ch. 21). In the majority, however, the slowed

cardiac action is the result of the heart block, and the cerebral symptoms result from temporary periods of cardiac standstill or ventricular fibrillation. Occasionally seizures may result from sudden slowing of the pulse such as that which occurs when the heart rhythm shifts back and forth between normal rhythm and complete heart block. Such episodes have been documented repeatedly in human electrocardiograms. In recent years Zoll has been able to treat a number of such patients successfully by use of an external electric artificial pacemaker. Recently tiny transistorized pacemakers have been developed for long term treatment of Stokes-Adams syndrome. These require that a small wire electrode be sutured directly to the myocardium. Isoproterenol has proven to be the most potent pharmacological agent for treatment of this condition.

## B. Wolff-Parkinson-White (WPW) Syndrome

In this rare congenital anomaly the P-R interval of the electrocardiogram is shortened and the QRS complex prolonged. The P-R interval is 0.12 second or less and the QRS complex extended to over 0.10 sec. The shortened P-R interval may be due, in some cases, to an accessory conducting strand between auricle and ventricle. Butterworth and Poindexter fashioned an extra electrical conduction pathway in the dog's heart, which, when stimulated, produced an electrocardiogram similar to that characteristic of the syndrome. Wood and Wolferth, in the histological examination of the heart of a patient which had shown this syndrome, also found three accessory pathways from the right auricle to the ventricle.

On the other hand, cases of the WPW syndrome occur in which no anatomical anomaly in the conducting system can be demonstrated, and even when such exists there is no conclusive evidence that it is the cause of the accelerated auriculoventricular conduction. Prinzmetal and his colleagues have produced typical WPW complexes in dogs by applying a noninterrupted direct current of subthreshold strength to the A-V node; but such complexes could not be induced after severance of the A-V bundle—an indication that the impulses traverse the normal A-V connections. These investigators carried out a large number of similar experiments in which the movements of the heart were recorded by high speed cinematography, and the records analyzed after slowing down to half speed. They conclude from their observations that the accelerated conduction of the WPW syndrome is due to shortening of the delay of the impulse at the A-V node to a fraction of the normal which amounts to about 0.12 seconds.

These experiments have thrown considerable doubt upon the anatomical explanation of the WPW syndrome. Prinzmetal and his colleagues consider it to have a physiological rather than an anatomical basis.

The prolongation of the QRS complex is attributed to early activation of a portion of myocardium followed by normal activation of the remaining muscle.

## C. Disturbances of Rhythm Due to Abnormal Impulse Formation

I. EXTRASYSTOLES OR PREMATURE CONTRACTIONS

An extrasystole can be induced experimentally by stimulating the cardiac muscle at any time except during its phase of absolute refractoriness

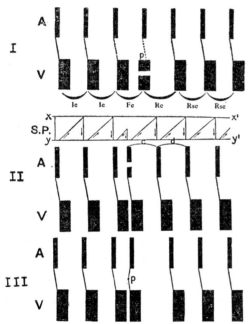

FIG. 17.3. (After Lewis). I. A diagram illustrating disturbance of the heart's mechanism when a systole is caused by exciting the ventricle during diastole. Ic, initial cycle, Fc, forced or extrasystolic cycle; Rc, returning cycle; and Rsc, restored cycles. p is the premature or forced beat. Note that the auricular rhythm remains undisturbed. The forced and returning cycles are together equal in length to two initial cycles. II. A diagram illustrating the events when a premature contraction is excited from the pacemater. Stimulus production in the tissue which originates the heart rhythm is indicated by the line S.P.; the impulse is supposed to discharge when it reaches the line xx' and to fall at each contraction of the heart to the level yy'. c and d are equal in length. III. A diagram illustrating a premature beat arising in the A-V node.

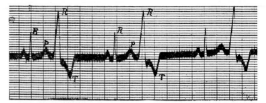

FIG. 17.4. Ventricular extrasystoles (bigeminal pulse, p. 196) arising in right ventricle—left axis deviation (ch. 16). (Kindness of Dr. John Hepburn.)

Extrasystoles occur in the human heart as a result of some abnormal process of impulse formation. Though extrasystoles may be associated with organic heart disease they more frequently occur in its absence; they may then be of reflex origin initiated from the abdominal viscera or be due to some form of intoxication, e.g., digitalis, chloroform anesthesia, hyperthyroidism, excessive smoking, etc. Beattie, Brow, and Long produced extrasystoles in cats by stimulation of the hypothalamus (ch. 66), and their occurrence in man following brain lesions has been reported by Lucke and by Korth, which indicates that in some instances they are of central origin. The auricle or the ventricle may be the site of origin of the premature contraction, or the extra impulse may arise in the A-V node (see diagrams, fig. 17.3).

### (1) Ventricular Extrasystoles

The premature contraction occurs after the normal ventricular beat has ceased and the muscle has recovered from its absolute refractory state. It is not preceded by an auricular contraction, and is not dependent upon an impulse received from the upper chamber (fig. 17.4). The premature contraction is followed by a long pause. This is usually of just sufficient duration to cause the succeeding normal ventricular beat to occur at the instant that it would have occurred had there been no premature contraction. The cause of this *compensatory pause* has been explained elsewhere (p. 145). Briefly, it is due to the normal impulse reaching the ventricle when the muscle is still refractory as a result of the premature beat. The interval between the normal beat and the one following the premature contraction is therefore equal in length to two normal cardiac cycles (fig. 17.3, I). Sometimes, however, when the extrasystole occurs early in diastole and the heart rate is slow, there may be no compensatory pause. The auricular impulse then reaches the ventricular muscle after it has recovered from the refractory state resulting from the premature beat; the auricular impulse therefore brings about a response at, or (as a result of some lengthening of the As-Vs interval following the premature beat) slightly after the usual time. The normal ventricular systoles are then all equally or nearly equally spaced and the extra contractions are interposed here and there between them. That is, the time interval from the normal beat preceding the extra contraction to that following it is of normal length or but slightly lengthened. Premature beats of this nature are called *interpolated extrasystoles*.[1]

### (2) Auricular Extrasystoles

The premature contraction arises in the auricle at some point outside the S-A node. The abnormal impulse reaches the ventricle along the usual paths and evokes a ventricular contraction, unless the auricular beat is so premature that sufficient time has not elapsed to permit the recovery of the ventricular muscle from its refractory state. The latter, except for its time relations, is approximately normal. An auricular extrasystole, therefore, causes a premature contraction of the whole heart. The premature auricular beat prevents the occurrence of the next normal auricular impulse and the pause of the auricle which follows the abnormal auricular contraction is usually precisely equal to a normal interval. This fact has been explained upon the assumption that, normally, impulse formation in the S-A node is the result of the liberation of energy which has been built up during the previous quiescent period. Upon the occurrence of the abnormal impulse this store of energy, accumulated for the normal impulse, is discharged and a definite time interval must elapse before it is again built up to the required level (see fig. 17.3, II). Sometimes, however, the interval following the premature contraction is slightly lengthened, suggesting that the rate at which the S-A node builds up its store of energy is lowered. In any event, there is rarely a long (compensatory) pause following the beat of the *ventricle*, the interval between the two normal beats, i.e., from the beat preceding to the one succeeding the premature contraction, being nearly always shorter than two normal cycles. In other words, the normal auricular impulse following the premature auricular contraction

---

[1] It should be noted that except in the case of interpolated beats there is not an extra or additional beat, as the term extrasystole seems to imply. The premature beat, in effect, displaces the normal beat.

upon reaching the ventricle does not "miss-fire", as in the case of ventricular extrasystole, but calls forth a response from the ventricle.

### (3) Nodal Extrasystoles

Extrasystoles occur sometimes as a result of impulse formation in the A-V node or supraventricular part (stem) of the bundle. On account of its central position between the two chambers, impulses arising in the A-V node pass upward and downward to cause simultaneous or nearly simultaneous responses from auricle and ventricle. Sometimes the ventricular contraction may actually occur first, in which case it is suggested that the impulse has arisen in the stem of the bundle and so has its course to the ventricular muscle considerably shortened. The extra cycle is usually, though not invariably, followed by a compensatory pause (fig. 17.3, III).

In rare instances extrasystoles arise as a result of abnormal impulses initiated in the sino-auricular node—*sinus extrasystoles*. Except for the interposition of the extra beat the rhythm of auricles and ventricles is but little disturbed. The interval following the extra beat is normal in length or slightly shortened.

### The Effects of Extrasystoles upon the Characters of the Electrocardiogram and of the Arterial Pulse

THE ELECTROCARDIOGRAM. In *ventricular extrasystoles* the electrocardiogram shows irregularity in the spacing of the ventricular complexes. The following characteristics are found:

(1) The intervals between the R wave caused by the premature beat and the corresponding waves of the normal beats preceding and following it, respectively, are altered in length. The interval between the last normal R wave and the premature R wave is short, while the interval following this to the next normal R wave is prolonged—compensatory pause. The time elapsing between the two normal R waves is usually equal to the length of two normal cycles.

(2) The premature R wave is not preceded by a P wave. Since the premature ventricular contraction occurs unrelated to auricular systole it frequently happens that a normal contraction of the auricle occurs about the same time as the ventricular extrasystole. P and R waves then become fused. At other times the P wave follows closely upon the premature R wave.

(3) The P waves are equally spaced and some appear which are not succeeded by a ventricular

complex (refractory period of the ventricular muscle). In the case of the *interpolated* type of extrasystole, however, each P wave is followed by an R wave, and no long pause is seen.

(4) Ventricular extrasystoles also show abnormalities of the QRS complex which distinguish them from premature contractions of auricular or nodal origin. An impulse arising in the heart below the point where the bundle forks will activate one ventricle slightly in advance of the other. It is to be expected then that the QRS deflections of the electrocardiogram will be a record of unbalanced electrical effects. This is actually the case (fig. 17.4). In other words, if the extrasystole arises in the left ventricle its record will be deformed much in the same manner as that already described (p. 184) for right bundle branch block. If the premature beat arises in the right ventricle the electrocardiogram will show the features of a left branch defect.

In *auricular extrasystoles* the electrocardiogram shows disturbances in the timing of both the auricular and the ventricular complexes, but, as already mentioned (p. 195), a normal or only a slightly lengthened pause follows the extra beat. The P waves are unequally spaced but each is followed by a ventricular complex. The abnormal auricular wave may coincide with and be buried in the QRS complex of the preceding normal cycle.

The records of *extrasystoles arising in the A-V node* or supraventricular part of the bundle are variable according to the timing of the auricular and ventricular contractions. When the auricles and ventricles are excited simultaneously, the P and R waves become fused. When the two chambers are not activated simultaneously, the P precedes the R wave by a short interval, or the order of the waves may be reversed (R-P interval).

THE ARTERIAL PULSE. It has been demonstrated that several long-recognized irregularities of the pulse are the result of extrasystoles. For example, in the irregularity known as *intermittent*

*pulse* there appear from time to time relatively long intervals during which no beat is felt in the radial (fig. 17.5a). The intervals are most pronounced when a premature contraction of the ventricle which is too weak to open the semilunar valves occurs. This most commonly happens when the heart muscle receives the abnormal impulse during the earlier part of its relative refractory phase. The premature beat may be detected by hearing a faint first heart sound which is not succeeded by a second sound (p. 248). No pulse is produced in the radial at the time, nevertheless the extrasystole may be followed by a compensatory pause, and graphic records show as a rule that the gap in the radial tracing is just equal to two normal cycles. That is, a beat is dropped completely from the arterial record. The detection of an extra contraction of the ventricle, however, enables the irregularity to be distinguished from the missed beats of partial heart block (p. 191) which may give an arterial tracing with similar characters.

If ventricular extrasystoles which fail to open the semilunar valves are repeated after each normal beat, the long intervals separating the latter will cause pronounced slowing of the pulse rate. The pauses between the arterial pulses are doubled in length and the pulse frequency as a consequence is reduced to half the normal. Bradycardia produced in this way and sometimes termed *false heart block* is distinguished from true heart block by a study of the venous pulse or the electrocardiogram which reveals the extra ventricular complexes; or the faint sounds of the extra contractions may be heard upon auscultation.

When the extrasystoles are forceful enough to open the semilunar valves, and occur regularly one after each normal systole, paired pulse beats, each couple being followed by a long pause, are felt in the radial (fig. 17.5b). This type of pulse irregularity, which is sometimes seen following overdosage with digitalis, is called the *bigeminal pulse (pulus bigeminus)*.

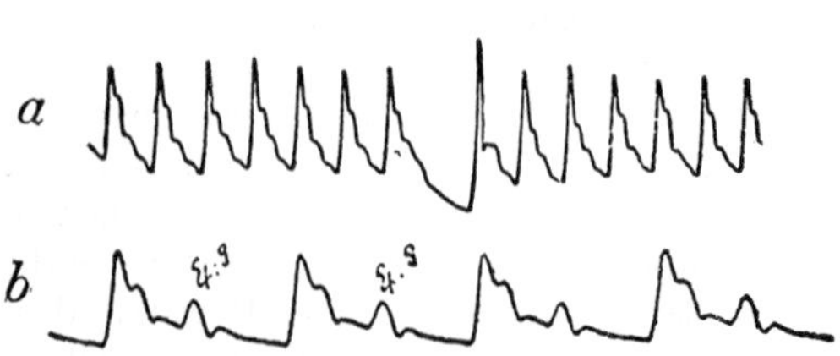

## II. PAROXYSMAL TACHYCARDIA

This may be defined as a condition in which the rate of the heart is greatly accelerated for a longer or shorter period without obvious cause. The rate varies in different cases from 140 to 250 per minute. The onset of the paroxysm is sudden and the increased rate is maintained for a variable length of time with perfect regularity, successive cycles usually not varying in length by more than a hundredth of a second. The paroxysm lasts for only a few beats in some instances, in others it

FIG. 17.5. (After Price.) *a*, intermission of the pulse; *b*, pulsus bigeminus, due to a single extrasystole with its succeeding compensatory pause occurring regularly after each normal beat. *Ex.S.*, extrasystole.

persists for a few minutes, hours or even days, though attacks of more than ten days' duration are very rare (Lewis). The attack ceases as abruptly as it commenced, the heart resuming its normal rate almost instantly.

The paroxysm, it is believed, consists of a series of rapidly recurring extrasystoles which completely submerge the physiological rhythm. The site of origin of the extrasystoles, as in the case of single premature beats, may be in the *auricle*, the *A-V node or stem of the bundle*, or in the *ventricle* (fig. 17.6). The auricular type is the most common; each auricular impulse spreads to the ventricle and causes a contraction whose features as indicated by the electrocardiogram are normal. The P wave is frequently inverted.

When the impulses arise in the A-V node or supraventricular part of the bundle, the P-R intervals of the electrocardiogram are shortened. Inversion of the P waves is common. Or, the contractions of the two chambers may be simultaneous, the P waves being then buried in the ventricular (QRS) complexes. Again, the contraction of the ventricle may occur before that of the auricle; it then sometimes happens that a progressive lengthening of the intervals between the R and P waves (R-P interval) of the electrocardiogram is seen; ultimately an auricular beat is missed. This is termed *reversed heart block*. In other instances, as the R-P intervals reach a certain length, a contraction of the ventricle occurs prematurely, and is not followed by a contraction of the auricle. It is thought that the ventricular contraction is caused by the same impulse that caused the preceding auricular beat. That is, the impulse arising in the node first excites the auricle, then re-enters the junctional tissue, which has now recovered from its refractory phase, and passes downwards to the ventricle. This is spoken of as *reciprocal rhythm*.

When the impulses arise in the ventricle the QRS complexes have the characteristics of those caused by ventricular extrasystoles (p. 194). The auricular rhythm is usually undisturbed, but occasionally it is abnormal, for when a series of rapidly recurring contractions arises in the ventricle, the impulses may pass along the bundle in a retrograde fashion and activate the auricle to the exclusion of the normal impulse. In other words, the ventricle then sets the pace, and the auricle follows. In such instances the P waves are inverted and succeed the QRS deflections, or are buried in the ventricular complexes as in the nodal type mentioned above.

### III. Auricular Flutter

There are two forms of this disorder, *pure* and *impure flutter*. In both types the auricle beats

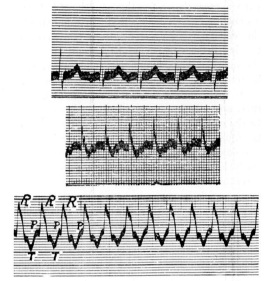

FIG. 17.6. Top tracing, auricular tachycardia; middle tracing, nodal tachycardia; bottom tracing, ventricular tachycardia. (Kindness of Dr. John Hepburn.)

at the phenomenally rapid rate of from 250 to 400 beats per minute, but in pure flutter the rhythm is regular, in impure flutter it is irregular. Flutter differs from paroxysmal tachycardia in the following particulars.

(a) The auricular rate of beating is usually much greater than that seen in paroxysmal tachycardia.

(b) The disorder is of much longer duration, persisting unchanged for months or years, though it is sometimes transient.

(c) The ventricle fails as a rule to follow the rate of the auricle; a state of relative heart block becomes established as a result of the comparatively long refractory phase of the functional tissue.

(d) It is produced by the passage of the impulse over one or more circular pathways—*circus movement* (p. 198).

Auricular flutter may become converted to paroxysmal tachycardia.

In pure flutter the rhythm is remarkably regular (fig. 17.7). The lengths of the auricular cycles

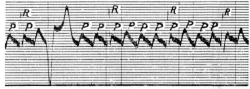

FIG. 17.7. Pure flutter with a ventricular extrasystole. (Kindness of Dr. John Hepburn.)

vary no more than a few thousandths of a second over comparatively long periods. In impure flutter this constancy of cycle length is not seen and varying degrees of irregularity occur. In flutter the auricular walls do not completely relax. That is, though the proportion of active to inactive fibers varies during the rapid beating, at no one time are all the fibers in the relaxed state. In the electrocardiogram, therefore, the level of the tracing between the P waves lies for the most part above the isopotential line, only touching the latter for an instant. The level of the tracing is continually changing and the electrical changes of the auricle are carried over to alter the form of the ventricular complex. On the other hand, the fibers are never all contracted at the same time, so that auricular systole as well as diastole is incomplete.

The ventricle rarely keeps pace with the racing auricle, the refractory phase of the conducting tissue being longer as compared with that of the auricular muscle. As a consequence, a state of relative heart blocks develops and an auriculo-ventricular rhythm of 2 to 1, or less frequently, of 3 to 1 or 4 to 1, becomes established. Sometimes there is variable block with 2 to 1, 3 to 1, 4 to 1, and occasionally even greater intervals occurring in the same strip of record. Should the ventricle respond to each beat of the auricle, as occasionally happens, serious circulatory disturbances follow; ventricular diastole is so shortened that the ventricle receives a greatly reduced load of blood. The output of the heart may be so reduced as a result that loss of consciousness resulting in death may follow.

### IV. AURICULAR FIBRILLATION

This condition so far as fundamental causes are concerned may be looked upon as an advanced stage of flutter. The auricular muscle is the seat of incomplete contractions which recur at a frequency of from 400 to 600 per minute. So incomplete are the contractions and so rapidly are they produced that the individual beats are scarcely distinguishable from one another. The auricular cavity is never emptied of blood and its wall is a quivering sheet of muscle. Auricular fibrillation is the most common of all the serious cardiac irregularities, being associated, according to

FIG. 17.8. Auricular fibrillation, lead 2 (after Lewis).

Lewis, in 60 to 70 per cent of all cases of cardiac failure in hospital practice. It is most frequently seen in mitral stenosis and in thyrotoxicosis (ch. 57), but sometimes occurs in the absence of myocardial disease.

Only a proportion of the auricular impulses pass through the A-V bundle and activate the ventricle. The relatively long refractory period of the conducting tissue shields the ventricle from the high rate of the auricular beating. The arterial pulse, nevertheless, is usually considerably faster than the normal (100 to 150) though it may be normal or even slowed. Those impulses which reach the ventricle do so in a somewhat haphazard manner, and indeed one of the most characteristic features of fibrillation of the auricles is absolute irregularity in the rate and force of the ventricular beats. These features are expressed in the terms *"delirium cordis"*, *"complete irregularity of the pulse"* or *"perpetual arrhythmia"*, which were applied to the condition before its true nature was recognized. A proportion of the heart beats are frequently so weak that they fail to cause pulse in the radial. The apex beat is therefore much more rapid than the pulse. The former, for example, may be 150 and the latter only 60 or 70. The difference is called the *pulse deficit*. With treatment and improvement in the condition of the cardiac muscle, the pulse rate therefore may increase.

The venous pulse in auricular fibrillation is of the ventricular form; *a* waves are absent, being represented by a series of rapid vibratory waves (*f* waves). Similarly in the electrocardiogram, small rapid undulations replace the *P* waves (fig. 17.8).

THE UNDERLYING PROCESSES CONCERNED IN THE PRODUCTION OF FLUTTER AND FIBRILLATION OF THE AURICLES.[1] *The circus movement theory versus the theory of numerous separate points of excitation.* The observation that fibrillation could be induced in animals by electrical stimulation has led to a much clearer understanding of auricular fibrillation and flutter in man. Lewis, employing faradization as the method of inducing fibrillation, studied the subject intensively and, applying the results of the fundamental work of Mayer, of Mines and of Garrey conceived that the excitation wave followed a circular pathway through the auricular muscle—the so-called *circus movement.* That is to say, the wave starting at one place took a devious course through the cardiac musculature, returned to the point from which it started and re-entered the path which it had previously traversed. Mayer induced a circus movement in the umbrella of the jellyfish (Medusa) by creating a local block and applying a stimulus to one side of the blocked region (fig. 17.9, I,A). The contraction wave which resulted was forced as a result of the block to take a unidirectional course, and after completing the circuit of the disk of tissue returned to the region of the block, which by this time had disappeared. If the tissue from which the wave had been initiated was again excitable, i.e., had passed from the refractory state, the wave circled the ring a second time, then a third time, and so on repeatedly. When, on the other hand, the disk was stimulated in the absence of a block, a contraction wave set out in both directions and the two waves meeting, after having completed half the circumference of the strip, were suppressed at B (fig. 17.9, II). That is, further progress of the waves was arrested, for each came to a region of tissue which, being occupied by the other wave, was refractory.

Mines and Garrey linked up Mayer's observations upon Medusa with the fibrillation of cardiac muscle. Mines showed that a similar circular motion of the contraction wave could be induced in the cold-blooded heart. Muscular rings cut from the auricles of large rays were employed. Garrey thought that he had refuted the prevailing belief at that time, namely, that fibrillation of the auricle was due to the initiation of impulses from multiple foci throughout the auricular muscle—as proposed originally by McWilliam. Garrey found that if he cut a small piece from the fibrillating auricle, the severed tissue at once ceased to fibrillate, an event which he contended could not occur if numerous points of excitation existed; but such would naturally result if the impulses travelled over a circular pathway from which other parts of the auricle were excited. He induced a circulating contraction wave in large annular strips cut from turtles' ventricles.

Evidence was obtained by Lewis which seemed to show that the impulses in the fibrillating auricle travelled in the natural rings of muscle encircling the openings of the vena cavae.

The theory of circus movement has been very widely though not universally accepted. Brams and Katz contended that if a circus movement is responsible for flutter and fibrillation more than one circulating wave must exist. They base this conclusion upon the observation that if after experimental flutter or fibrillation has been established, the auricles (or in the case of ventricular fibrillation, the ventricles) are separated from one another by crushing between them the rapid beating persists with little change in each of the separated parts. Scherf, as a result of his failure to abolish auricular fibrillation by clamping or ligaturing the auricular muscle in the path of the supposedly circulating waves, was one of the first (1928) to throw doubt upon the existence of a circus movement. A little later Andrus and Carter

concluded, from their experimental results in which fibrillation was induced by a single induction shock applied to the auricular appendix, that the waves did not originate and travel in a ring of muscle.

The most recent and convincing evidence against the circus movement theory has been secured by Prinzmetal and his associates. They induced auricular fibrillation by the application of aconitine to the auricles of dogs and observed the auricle by means of high speed cinematography. They saw no indication of a circus movement. Two types of activity were observed; (a) contractions and relaxations of microscopic or minute segments of muscle, which they term the *"M" activity*; and (b) stronger contractions and relaxations of macroscopic or larger muscle segments which appear upon the background of the innumerable "M" contractions. This type of movement they have designated the *"L" activity*. Both types of activity are heterorhythmic and utterly chaotic, and apparently arise from numerous discrete ectopic foci.

*The Actions of the Cardiac Glycosides, such as Digitalis, and of Quinidine upon Fibrillation and Flutter, and in Heart Failure*

DIGITALIS belongs to a class of drugs known as the *cardiac glycosides*, which also includes strophanthin, ouabain (G-strophanthin from *S. gratus*), and squill. Digitalis in therapeutic dosage exerts a threefold effect upon the action of the heart. (a) It increases the force of the ventricular contraction both of the failing (hypodynamic) heart, and of the normal myocardium as shown for the isolated papillary muscle of the cat by Cattell and Gold. This is the drug's most valuable property. Ouabain and strophanthin have a similar action. (b) It depresses A-V conduction, and (c) it stimulates the vagus, a reflex effect through the carotid sinus and the vagus center (Heymans and associates).

These last two effects cause slowing of the ventricle in fibrillation and flutter, but exert no significant effect upon the rapid auricular rate of sinus tachycardia. The depression of A-V conduction shields the ventricle from the fibrillating

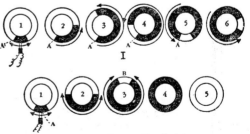

FIG. 17.9. (Modified from Lewis.) Black = contraction wave. Description in text.

auricle; the weaker impulses fail to reach the ventricle, the pulse therefore becoming slower and more regular. In therapeutic dosage the drug has little or no effect upon the rate of the heart if the auricular rate is normal. In overdosage the drug may cause complete blockage of impulse conduction in the A-V bundle. It used to be thought that digitalis was of value only in fibrillation or flutter, but it has been shown conclusively within the last two decades that it strengthens the ventricular beat, and is of the utmost value in cardiac failure whether or not either of these arrhythmias are present. The digitalis glycosides have been shown to be useful in converting superventricular tachycardias back to normal sinus rhythm. This is probably mediated largely through the vagus effect but it is not at all clear why vagus tone should affect ectopic auricular foci.

Certain effects of the cardiac glycosides upon the metabolism of the myocardium have been demonstrated which help to explain their beneficial action upon the cardiac contraction. (a) They increase the oxygen consumption of the heart. (b) They increase the utilization of glucose and of lactic acid. (c) They cause a partial restoration of the adenosinetriphosphate and phosphocreatine contents of the failing myocardium in which these energy-rich phosphate-bond metabolites are depleted. In overdosage these drugs themselves cause depletion to the extent of 50 per cent or more of these materials.

The action of digitalis and other cardiac glycosides appears to be mainly in improving the utilization of chemical energy by the myocardium, rather than by increasing the total amount of energy liberated, though the latter probably also occurs.

The cardiac glycosides exert no beneficial effects upon myocardial insufficiency due to anoxia, in thyrotoxicosis, or in vitamin $B_1$ deficiency. The reason for this is unknown.

QUINIDINE (an isomer of quinine) also exerts a threefold action in fibrillation. (1) It depresses or abolishes vagal tone and so lengthens the refractory period of the auricular muscle and decreases the transmission rate. This action upon the vagus is therefore opposite to that of digitalis. (2) It acts directly upon the auricular and ventricular muscle, lengthening the refractory period (by from 50 to 100 per cent) and slowing the transmission rate. (3) It depresses conduction in the junctional tissues—a direct action. The abolition of the fibrillation of the auricle and the restoration of the normal rhythm was believed, on the basis of the circus movement theory, to be due to the lengthening of the refractory period of the auricular muscle, and as a consequence, to closure of the gap of excitable tissue between the crest and tail of the wave (see fig. 17.9). In other words "the head catches up to the tail" (Osler). But however

fibrillation is produced, we know at any rate that quinidine restores the normal auricular rate and thus acts upon this arrhythmia in a manner different from that of digitalis. In the restoration of the normal auricular rhythm by quinidine fibrillation is frequently converted first to flutter.

The different effects of quinidine upon the heart interact in a complicated manner. For example, its action upon the ventricular rate will be the resultant of the following three effects.

(1) Rapid auricular beating tends automatically to depress conduction through the A-V connections. Therefore when the rate of the auricle is reduced by the drug, A-V conduction is increased.

(2) The reduction in vagal tone also increases A-V conduction.

(3) The direct effect of the drug upon A-V conduction, as stated above, is one of depression.

As a matter of fact (1) and (2) frequently overbalance the last effect (3) and some increase in the ventricular rate results.

Quinidine in overdosage produces severe toxic effects among which are auriculoventricular block, extrasystoles, paroxysmal tachycardia, and even death as a result of ventricular fibrillation. The return of the normal auricular contractions under quinidine treatment is sometimes, though rarely, followed by the dislocation of an intra-auricular thrombus and death from embolism. Complete standstill of the heart has also been reported as a result of the paralysis by the drug of the sino-auricular and auriculoventricular nodes and other tissues capable of impulse initiation. Procaine amide has an action closely akin to quinidine. It appears to be less effective on the auricular arrhythmias than quinidine but being less toxic than quinidine it may be given intravenously. It is most useful in converting ventricular tachycardia back to normal rhythm by intravenous administration. It is also used orally in suppressing frequent ventricular premature beats.

## V. VENTRICULAR FIBRILLATION

The ventricular muscle may pass into a state of rapid, tremulous and ineffectual contractions closely similar in nature to the condition just described as occurring in the auricle. In animals, ventricular fibrillation may be initiated by direct electrical stimulation of the ventricular muscle, as was first shown by Ludwig in 1850. Mechanical stimulation of the ventricle, especially by pricking the tissue in the A-V groove, ligation of a coronary artery (Porter) or certain chemicals and drugs in excess, e.g., digitalis or calcium chloride, may induce fibrillation. Levy found that chloroform anesthesia renders the hearts of experimental animals (cats) highly susceptible to fibrillation. A mere touch of a finger or instrument, the stimulation of a sensory nerve, section of the vagi or their paralysis by atropine, may set the ventricle fibrillating. The heart behaves as though sensitized by the anesthetic and ready at the least provocation to fibrillate. Adrenaline was found to greatly enhance the effect of chloroform—a fact which indicates the danger of adrenaline administration while a subject is under the effect of this anesthetic. Fibrillation may also ensue spontaneously under chloroform, and Levy found that the condition is more likely to supervene when the animal is passing from deep to light anesthesia. Cyclopropane, like chloroform, has the effect of sensitizing the heart to the action of adrenaline in inducing ventricular tachycardia and fibrillation, but these cardiac irregularities are rarely seen under ether anesthesia. Quinidine reduces the susceptibility to fibrillation during cyclopropane anesthesia.

The effects of ventricular fibrillation upon the circulation are incomparably more serious than those of the corresponding auricular condition. This is evident when the importance of the two musculatures in the dynamics of the circulation are compared (p. 244). In fibrillation of the lower chamber the propulsive force of its contraction is practically abolished and the circulation comes to an end; death follows within a few minutes.

From experiments upon animals it is believed that many instances of cardiac failure in patients under chloroform are due to fibrillation of the ventricles. This is generally considered to be of sudden onset, but it has been shown that when the condition is induced in animals by chloroform it is frequently ushered in gradually. A solitary extrasystole first occurs, which is followed after a time by coupling, tripling, and later by short runs of extrasystoles. Longer paroxysms of rapid beating follow. Finally as the tachycardia becomes more rapid it merges into fibrillation.

When fibrillation is induced suddenly as by electric shock its development may be somewhat different. According to Wiggers and his associates, only the first contraction is a true premature beat; those which follow are caused by re-entry of the excitation wave. These investigators, who induced ventricular fibrillation in dogs by the application of single strong induction shock to the ventricle late in systole, recognize four stages in the development of fibrillation. In the *first* or *undulatory stage*, which lasts for only a second or two, the contractions are rapidly repeated but do not follow the same course over the surface of the ventricle; the electrocardiographic deflections show considerable variability in form. In the *second* stage of *convulsive incoordination*, which lasts for from 15 to 40 seconds, the contractions are more frequent and involve smaller areas of the ventricular muscle. The contractions of different areas of the muscle are out of phase so that the ventricle appears to be pulled about convulsively. The *third* stage of *tremulous incoordination* lasts for 2 or 3 minutes, the surface of the muscle is broken up into independently contracting areas of ever-decreasing size which are out of phase with one another. Thus, a tremulous appearance is given to the ventricles. The *final* stage of *atonic fibrillation* develops when the developing anoxia of the cardiac muscle causes weakening of its contractile force. This stage appears usually within from 2 to 5 minutes following the first stage and is marked by weak contractions or wavelets which travel only a short distance over the ventricular surface. It ends in complete cessation of all activity.

Ventricular fibrillation in man may result from:

a) Electric shocks—electrocution, lightning stroke.
b) Chloroform or cyclopropane anesthesia.
c) Coronary occlusion and other causes of severe anoxia.
d) Trauma to heart or chest wall.
e) Ventricular paroxysmal tachycardia, in which fibrillation may be a terminal event.
f) Toxic doses of digitalis or quinidine.
g) Various diseases during the death agony.

The fundamental factor or factors leading to fibrillation of the ventricles have been the subject of research by several investigators. Kebar and Hooker have found microscopical tissue changes in the dog's heart, in which fibrillation was induced by electric shock. There also occurred an increase in potassium in the outflowing fluid perfused through the heart. They attribute the fibrillation to a leakage of potassium from the cells and an unbalance of the potassium ion. The addition of potassium to the perfusion fluid brings the fibrillation immediately to an end and restores the normal beat. According to Nahum and Hoff, the essential condition for the onset of fibrillation is the establishment of a block or blocks of the conducting system in a heart whose automaticity is simultaneously stimulated; either factor alone is ineffective. They found that the rapid injection of a concentrated solution of KCl throws the ventricles immediately into fibrillation. This does not occur if the injection is made slowly, for then automaticity instead of being stimulated is depressed; block of the conducting system occurs, but fibrillation does not ensue. Thus, they believe that the two essential elements in the production of ventricular fibrillation are intraventricular block and automaticity of the ventricles. Ventricular fibrillation, though usually fatal is not invariably so, for rare instances have been reported in which the ventricles after fibrillating for a brief period resumed their normal rate and recovery occurred. Two methods, chemical and electrical, have been used in attempts to restore the normal rhythm to the fibrillating ventricles. Hooker has shown the efficacy of an excess of potassium in stopping fibrillation and of calcium in restoring the normal beat in the hearts of dogs subjected to electric shock. A 0.5 per cent solution of KCl is injected under pressure into the carotid toward the heart, so that it reaches the coronary system. This stops the heart. When a 0.023 solution of $CaCl_2$ is then introduced by the same route, the normal cardiac rhythm, in a successful experiment, is restored. Hooker and his associates showed that defibrillation of the dog's heart can be accomplished and the normal beat restored if a countershock, consisting of an alternating current of about one ampere, is passed through the heart. In fibrillation due to anoxia (e.g. caused by coronary occlusion) the heart may be defibrillated by either of these two means but the heart muscle is usually unable to develop a forceful contraction owing to the oxygen lack. Wiggers has modified Hooker's procedure by sending into the heart a series of shocks (3–7) of about one second duration and one or two seconds apart. He recommends that when fibrillation follows coronary occlusion cardiac massage should be practiced while the countershocks are being given, in order to increase the blood flow to the ventricular muscle. In fibrillation due to electrocution or other cause, the countershocks may be applied through the chest wall although much stronger currents (20 to 30 amperes) will be required.

A number of reports have appeared in the literature of human lives saved when patients suddenly developed ventricular fibrillation. In these cases the chest was rapidly opened and circulation restored by manual compression of the heart until defibrillating counter-shock equipment could be obtained. The increasing number of such reports points up the necessity that all physicians learn the technic of thoracotomy and cardiac massage. It has been well established that unless circulation can be restored in less than 4 minutes, irreparable cerebral damage will have occurred, and even though heart action might be restored, a decerebrate patient will be the result.

## D. Alternation of the Heart. Pulsus Alternans

This is a condition in which every second wave in a pulse tracing is of relatively small amplitude. This peculiarity of the arterial pulse is due to alternate variations in the strength of the ventricular systoles, and to a smaller quantity of blood being ejected into the aorta during the weaker beat. Figure 17.10 shows a typical sphygmogram of this condition. There is as a rule little or no difference in the lengths of the intervals between pulse beats. When a slight difference does exist, the interval succeeding the strong beat is then longer than that following the weak beat. It will be remembered that in the bigeminal pulse, which might in some instances be confused with alternation, there is inequality in cycle lengths (p. 196), but the longer interval follows the *weak* (premature) beat. Furthermore, in alternation the ventricular rhythm does not share, or does so very rarely, in any irregularity of the pulse intervals which may occur in the arterial tracing. The electrocardiogram, for instance, shows no discrepancies in the length of the intervals between the R waves. The slight variations in the pulse intervals are attributed by Lewis to a slower rate of transmission of the weaker pulses to the periphery. When records are taken simultaneously of the apex and the arterial pulse, it is sometimes found that the weak beats of the former coincide with the strong beats of the latter. This discordance between apex and arterial beats is explained upon the assumption that those muscle fibers which contract during the weak apical impulses though less numerous are actually more effective in ejecting the blood than those causing the stronger thrusts at the apex (see, Theory of Alternation, below). The appearance of alternation in the electrocardiogram (e.g., alternate variations in the height of the R wave) is rare. When this so-called *electrical alternation* does occur the larger deflections sometimes correspond to the weaker pulse beats. But, it will be recalled in this connection that the deflections of the electrocardiogram are determined by the balance of the electrical forces developed during the cardiac contraction rather than upon their total value. Electrical alternation may occur without alternation of the pulse.

Sometimes it is not possible to detect pulsus alternans by palpation of the pulse, the variations in strength of the pulse beat being too slight to be perceptible, but it is clearly revealed in the sphygmogram (fig. 24.10). It may also be de-

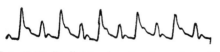

FIG. 17.10. Radial tracing showing pulsus alternans. (After Mackenzie.)

tected by means of a blood pressure armlet. The pressure in the armlet is raised gradually, when it is found that at a certain level the weaker beats are suppressed, but the stronger beats get through. The pulse at the wrist is then precisely half the ordinary rate. The pressure during the weaker beats may be as much as 25 mm. Hg below that during the stronger, but usually the pressure difference is not more than 5 or 10 mm. Persistent alternation of the heart when the pulse is slow or of normal frequency is usually indicative of grave disease of the myocardium. Alternation sometimes also occurs at rapid rates of beating, e.g., auricular fibrillation, paroxysmal tachycardia etc., but it is then of less serious significance.

THEORY OF ALTERNATION. The "all or none" law states that the cardiac muscle responds maximally to any stimulus that is capable at all of evoking a response. It is apparently difficult to reconcile this principle with the varying force of the ventricular contractions in alternation, unless it be assumed that during the weak beat a smaller proportion of the heart fibers respond than during the strong beat. This is the prevailing view.

The heart, it is thought, must be in what has been called a *hypodynamic* state in order for alternation to occur. That is, the heart muscle is so depressed that only half of its fibers have recovered from the previous contraction before the impulse arrives. These fibers alone contract, and when the next impulse arrives they are still refractory, but those which had not previously contracted have recovered their irritability and now respond. In this condition all beats are weak but equal. Should a ventricular extrasystole occur in such a heart, the long pause which follows shifts the balance between the refractory and the non-refractory fibers and precipitates the alternating rhythm. After the long pause of the premature beat a larger proportion of fibers have had time to recover and are therefore able to respond to the impulse. The next impulse, however, finds the muscle in a partial refractory state, i.e., only a small proportion of the fibers have by this time recovered. They only can respond—a weak beat results. This small proportion of fibers when the next impulse arrives will in turn be refractory, but the larger proportion which had not previously contracted will now respond—a strong beat results. So the alternating rhythm is perpetuated, the fibers which responded during one contraction fail to contract at the next beat and conversely those which had failed to respond to one impulse respond to the next.

### E. Irregularities Due to Variations in Vagal Tone

#### I. SINUS ARRHYTHMIA (fig. 17.11, I)

This is a condition in which rhythmical variations in the rate of the whole heart occur synchronously with respiration. It is due to alterations in the strength of the vagal influence upon the pacemaker (S-A node) as a result of the respiratory excursions, the heart rate increasing toward the end of inspiration and slowing toward the end of expiration. It is a youthful irregularity,

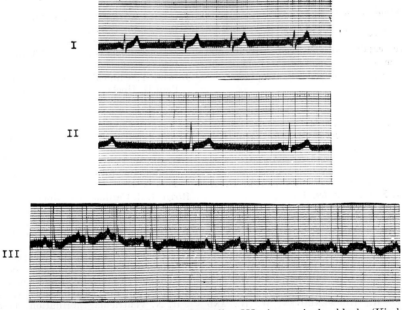

FIG. 17.11. *I*, sinus arrhythmia; *II*, sinus bradycardia; *III*, sino-auricular block. (Kindness of Dr. John Hepburn.)

being very common in children, and may be considered a physiological phenomenon. That it is entirely of vagal origin is shown by the fact that it is abolished by atropine. It also disappears when the heart rate increases as a result of exercise, fever, etc., but is enhanced by deep breathing.

## II. Phasic Irregularity

In this disorder periodic slowing of the heart occurs for a few seconds quite independently of the respirations. It also is a vagal effect since it is abolished by atropine. The manner of its production is unknown. It occurs in convalescence from acute fevers, and sometimes during the administration of digitalis.

## III. Sinus Bradycardia (fig. 17.11, II)

This is a persistent slowing of the whole heart due to increased vagal tone influencing the sino-auricular node. The rate may be as slow as 40 per minute. Bradycardia of this nature occurs in apparently healthy persons, many of whom are athletes.

## IV. Sino-auricular Block (fig. 17.11, III)

The entire heart (auricles and ventricles) misses a beat at regular or irregular intervals. The condition thus differs from A-V block in which only the ventricle misses (p. 192). A complete set of waves is therefore dropped from the venous or electrocardiographic tracing, and the arterial pulse intermits. Since the condition is temporarily abolished by atropine and may be induced by stimulation of the vagus, it is probable that the missed beats are due to the action of the nerve upon the S-A node. Sino-auricular block sometimes results from digitalis administration.

## V. Auriculoventricular Block

Defective conduction between auricle and ventricle due to heightened vagal tone is occasionally seen; it is abolished by atropine.

## REFERENCES

Barker, P. S., Macleod, A. G., and Alexander, J. Am. Heart J., 1930, **5**, 720.

Beck, C. L., Pritchard, W. H., and Feil, H. S. J. A. M. A., 1947, **135**, 985.

Brams, W. A. and Katz, L. N. Am. Heart J., 1931, **7**, 249.

Butterworth, J. S. and Poindexter, C. A. Arch. Int. Med., 1942, **69**, 437.

Cattell, McK. and Gold, H. Arch. Int. Med., 1940, **65**, 263. J. Pharmacol. & Exper. Therap., 1938, **62**, 116.

Garrey, E. W. Am. J. Physiol., 1914, **33**, 397.

Heymans, C., Bouckaert, J. J., and Regniers, P. Compt. rend. Soc. Biol., 1932, **110**, 572.

Hooker, D. R. Am. J. Physiol., 1929, **91**, 305; Ibid., 1930, **92**, 639; Ibid., 1932, **99**, 279. Ibid.,

Hooker, D. R., Kouwenhoven, W. B., and Langworthy, O. R. Am. J. Physiol., 1933, **103**, 444.

Katz, L. N., Mendlowitz, M., and Kaplan, H. A. Am. Heart J., 1938, **16**, 149.

Kehar, N. D. and Hooker, D. R. Am. J. Physiol., 1935, **112**, 301.

Levy, A. G. Heart, 1913, 4, 319; Ibid., 1914, **5**, 299; Ibid., 1919, **7**, 105, Brit. Med. J., 1914, **2**, 502.

McWilliam, J. A. J. Physiol., 1887, **8**, 296; Proc. Roy. Soc., 1918, **B90**, 302.

Mayer, A. G. Papers from Tortugas Laboratory, Carnegie Inst., Washington, 1908, **1**, 115.

Mines, G. R. J. Physiol., 1913, **46**, 349; Trans. Roy. Soc. Can., Sec. IV, 1914, **8**, 43.

Nahum, L. H. and Hoff, E. H. J. Pharmacol. & Exper. Therap., 1939, **65**, 322.

Prinzmetal, M., Corday, E., Brill, I. C., Oblath, R. W., and Kruger, H. E. The auricular arrhythmias. Charles C Thomas, Springfield, Illinois, 1952.

Prinzmetal, M., Corday, E., Brill, I. C., Sellers, A. L., Oblath, R. W., Flieg, W. A., and Kruger, H. E. Circulation, 1950, **1**, 241.

Prinzmetal, M., Oblath, R. W., Corday, E., Brill, I. C., Kruger, H. E., Smith, L. A., Fields, J., and Kennamer, R. J. A. M. A., 1951, **146**, 1275.

Roberts, G. H., Crawford, J. H., and Abramson, D. I.: Am. Heart J., 1932, **7**, 505; J. Clin. Invest., 1935, **14**, 867.

Weirich, W. L., Paneth, M., Gott, V. L., and Lillehei, C. W.: Circulation Res., 1958, **6**, 410.

Wiggers, C. J., Bell, J. R., Paine, M., Shaw, H. D. B., Theisen, H., and Maltby, A.: Am. J. Physiol., 1930, **92**, 223; Am. Heart J., **20**, 399, 413 (1940).

Wilson, F. N., Macleod, A. G., and Barker, P. S. Am. Heart J., 1931, **6**, 637.

Wood, F. C. and Wolferth, C. C. Am. Heart J., 1943, **25**, 454.

### *Monographs and Reviews*

Garrey, W. E. Auricular fibrillation. Physiol. Rev., 1924, 4, 215.

Hecht, H. and Sandberg, A. A. The mechanism of auricular fibrillation and flutter. Circulation, 1953, 7, 594.

Lewis, T. Clinical disorders of the heart beat. Paul B. Hoeber, Inc., New York, 1916.

Lewis, T. The mechanism and graphic registration of the heart beat. Shaw, London, 1920.

Lewis, T. Clinical science. Shaw, London, 1934.

Mackenzie, J. Diseases of the heart. Frowde, London, 1913.

Pardee, H. E. B. Clinical aspects of the electrocardiogram. Ed. 4. Paul B. Hoeber, Inc., New York, 1941.

Roth, I. R. Cardiac arrhythmias, clinical features and mechanism of the irregular heart. Paul B. Hoeber, Inc., New York, 1928.

Wollenberger, A. Cardiac energy metabolism. Pharmacol. Rev., 1949, 1, 311.

Wilius, F. A. Clinical electrocardiograms. Their interpretation and significance. W. B. Saunders Company, Philadelphia and London, 1929.

Zoll, P. M., Linenthal, A. J., and Zarksy, L. R. N. Ventricular fibrillation. Treatment and prevention by external electric currents. New England J. Med., 1960, **262**, 105.

# 18

# ESTIMATION OF VOLUME OF BLOOD FLOW, VELOCITY OF BLOOD FLOW, VOLUME OF ORGANS, CAVITIES AND REGIONS: CIRCULATION TIME

Our knowledge of the modus operandi of the circulation has progressed no faster than advancement of methodology that has given answers to certain problems.

## Volume Flow of Blood

The most important measurement in the circulation is that of the volume flow of blood through the aorta or through any vital region or organ. This is so because the blood flow is most sensitive to a change in dilation in a vascular bed. If the blood pressure is doubled, the blood flow might also double but doubling the mean bore of a vascular bed might increase the blood flow by 16 times. In the past, advancement of flow methodology has been slow and limited in large measure to devices applicable under highly abnormal conditions. In use, the animals have been exposed to so much insult by anesthesia, surgery and trauma that the measurements do not necessarily have resemblance to normal values, i.e., the relative importance of factors regulating flow can be quite different. More recently, progress has been much more rapid because of methods applicable to the normal circulation in the resting and unanesthetized active states.

VISUALIZATION (HUMAN OR ANIMAL). Direct *in vivo* visualization with the aid of a microscope of the components of the microcirculation (terminal arteries, arterioles, capillaries, venules, and very small veins) offers a means for studying qualitatively the peripheral circulation and control of blood flow in various regions. When capillaries, arterioles or any of the above vessels are observed to decrease in diameter, they are assumed to have constricted and thus to decrease flow. However, interpretation is always difficult for the apparent change in flow could arise from decrease in perfusion pressure, enlargement of other already patent vessels, opening of other drainage vessels, or increase in pressure in the surrounding tissue. Despite this, such observations have contributed greatly to our knowledge of the circulation. Direct microscopic and high

speed photography have been used in the frog skin, bat wing, rat mesoappendix, dog omentum, lungs of the open-chest dog, transparent viewing chamber of the rabbit's ear, bulbar conjunctiva and skin of humans, and pial vessels of the brain through a transparent viewing chamber. Change in small terminal arteries (and arterioles?) has been visualized in the coronary circulation of the heart of the closed-chest dog and in humans with cinéphotography following injection of contrast medium directly into the coronary arteries. Progress using the latter approach has been very rapid in the last few years so that gross encroachment by an atheromatous process on the coronary arterial lumen can be detected. Future comparable advancement might permit detection of early small lesions and study of factors which affect their growth.

VENOUS DRAINAGE. One of the oldest, simplest and most satisfactory means of determining blood flow is to collect and measure the outflow from a cannulated vein draining a particular organ. The rate of flow can be read from a graduate; or from the change in weight of a collecting container on a scale directly read or indicated by a strain gauge mounted under the collecting container. It can be indicated by causing the venous blood to enter the bottom of a closed chamber and with a bellows in the chamber recording the increase in pressure or volume of displaced air as the fluid level rises, or by recording in an open chamber the changing height of a float riding on top of the fluid. For very low rates of flow, drop recorders are used in which each drop shorts a pair of contacts in an electrical system or interrupts a photocell light beam. In all cases, the blood is generally returned to the circulation by some form of atraumatic pump that does not cause significant hemolysis of the red cells. Such collection of venous drainage has its modern counterpart considered in more detail in the next section in which total venous drainage in perfusion systems applied to humans and animals is collected and metered before its return to the body. In

205

general, this approach has the advantage that it does not interfere with the nervous control of the blood vessels which is the case when metering is done on the arterial side. It has the disadvantage that it generally measures only a portion of the arterial inflow since most organs have multiple venous drainage channels.

PERFUSION SYSTEMS FOR USE WITH ISOLATED ORGANS (WITHIN OR WITHOUT THE BODY), WITH REGIONS OF THE BODY, AND WITH THE WHOLE BODY. For many investigations and to permit certain surgical procedures, it is desirable to have controlled perfusion of an organ, body region, or the whole body at constant controlled flow rates and/or at constant perfusion pressures which are the same or different from the prevailing aortic pressure. Over the years a very large number of such systems have been devised. Because of their practical use to the surgeon, the development of pumps or pump-oxygenator systems for maintaining blood flow at a constant rate or constant pressure has been rapid. Such pump systems have been used to perfuse many isolated organs and to perfuse in the unanesthetized as well as the anesthetized animal, the vessels of an extremity, the brain, liver, kidney, and the coronary vessels of the heart. Such mechanical pumps serve also as temporary replacement for the left ventricle, right ventricle, and the whole heart, i.e., the whole body including the coronary arteries is perfused with a pump. The minimal criteria that must be satisfied in such artificial systems are: the blood must be maintained at a constant temperature, preferably near body temperature; it must be suitably oxygenated; the pH of blood should be maintained at approximately a normal level; the blood flow rate should be adjusted to that which normally exists without a pump; excessive trauma to the red cells must be avoided. To minimize hemolysis, valves to direct the flow are generally avoided, and blood is moved through rubber or plastic tubing by multiple fingers or by a continuous roller over the tubing.

The use of such systems for bypass of the right heart, left heart and whole heart is shown in principle in figure 18.1*A, B,* and *C.*

For the right heart bypass, the systemic venous return is prevented from entering the right atrium and right ventricle by special fenestrated catheters passed through the right appendage and tied in the superior and inferior venae cavae. The collected blood flows by gravity into a reservoir from which it is pumped through the pulmonary artery. The coronary venous drainage which under this arrangement continues to enter

the right atrium and fill the right ventricle, can by an appropriate catheter be made to drain into the same venous reservoir, thus insuring collection of total systemic venous flow. This type of bypass (1) permits measurement of coronary venous flow and coronary A-V oxygen and, therefore, presumably gives an index of total coronary flow and myocardial oxygen usage; (2) permits hemodynamic studies on the left or right heart separately; (3) permits operative procedures on the right heart in the presence of a dry field.

For the left heart bypass, the pulmonary venous return is prevented from entering the left ventricle by a clamp between it and the left atrium. It is drained by gravity into a reservoir from which it is pumped into the aorta. Since the left ventricle is now mechanical with a constant output, this arrangement (1) permits study of those factors which regulate the vascular volume and the systemic venous return, especially the state of the venous system and activity of the right ventricle (this can be determined from observation of the height of blood in the reservoir); (2) permits operative procedures on the left heart with a dry field.

For total heart bypass, the systemic venous return is prevented from emptying into the right ventricle and is drained by gravity into a reservoir from which it is pumped through some form of oxygenator to a second reservoir from which it is pumped by a second pump (set at the same flow rate) into the aorta. To obviate filling up of the left ventricle from bronchial flow drainage into the pulmonary veins and left atrium, a condition which is not prevented by this procedure, a catheter is inserted into the left atrium. Initially, the blood was oxygenated by passing it through a donor human or animal in which the lungs oxygenated the blood; later, the blood was passed through autogenous lungs. With present technical development of artificial blood oxygenators, this is not necessary and, after priming with blood, an artificial pump-oxygenator system can support the circulatory system for some time. After about 30 minutes of whole body perfusion, physiological problems arise and postoperative recoveries may be poor. This will be considered in a later chapter.

Various expedients have been used to perfuse an organ or region (fig. 18.1*D*). (1) The simplest arrangement is to connect the peripheral end of the artery (which feeds an organ or region) to a reservoir at an appropriate elevation so that it drains by gravity. The flow rate is read from graduations on the reservoir or from one of the flow meters (described in this chapter) which is interposed. (2) Air expansion chambers are used which permit constant pressure perfusion. In these, the peripheral end of the artery of an organ is connected to an air chamber, the lower portion of which contains blood exposed to the desired pressure in the chamber. Flow into the organ is indicated by one of the appropriate blood flow meters interposed between the organ and chamber. The supply of chamber blood for infusion is replenished by letting it flow into the chamber from a convenient artery under the animal's own blood pressure. (3) An end of a pump is connected to a local arterial source and the other end of the same pump to the artery of the organ or region being supplied. Either the perfusion pressure or flow rate can be varied separately. (4) The output side of a pump can be connected to a blood-air reservoir in which the air pressure is maintained constant at any desired perfusion pressure level and whose outlet is connected to the organ being perfused.

These approaches obviously have the important advantage that they enable the investigator to study separately the peripheral factors in the organ or region that regulate flow.

MEAN FLOW RECORDERS (FIG. 18.2). Because of the imposed resistance to flow, most mean flow recorders are not suitable for use in the path of venous flow but are acceptable in the arterial system where a small drop in pressure across the meter is not so important. The types that have given much information regarding the operation of the cardiovascular system include the mechanical stromuhr, bubble flow meter, rotameter, and turbinometer. Their present operation is extensive. In use, they have the disadvantages that they require anesthesia, injection of anticoagulant, insertion between the cut ends of the vessel in which flow is being measured, and their response time is slow, the fastest (the rotameter) being of the order of 90 per cent complete in 1 second. Despite this, and although arterial flow is highly phasic, these devices have been most helpful.

*A. Mechanical stromuhr.* The stromuhr of Ludwig is one of the oldest and best-known. It consists of an ingoing and an outgoing cannula which are inserted, respectively, into the proximal and distal sections of a divided artery. The blood flowing from the artery into the instrument enters a small pear-shaped flask of known capacity filled with oil. Upon the entrance of the blood, the oil is forced over into another flask of identical size but which has previously been filled with blood. The entrance of the oil forces the blood in turn into the peripheral section of the artery. The position of the flasks can be reversed by rotating through a semicircle and the process of filling and emptying repeated, or by appropriate means the flow can be automatically reversed in direction through the flasks. From the number of fillings of the flasks during the period of observation, the volume of blood flowing in a unit of time is readily calculated.

*B. Rotameter.* This device originally developed for commercial use was first adapted in 1942 to quantitation of blood flow. Basically the device consists of a vertical transparent tube with tapered bore within which the height of a float is determined by the rate of flow. With upward flow through the tube, the float is lifted until it reaches a height determined by a balance of the downward force (weight of float minus weight of displaced fluid), and the upward force (pressure drop across the float times maximal cross-sectional area of float). As flow increases, the balance is altered, and the float rises to a new position at which the increase in the annular orifice is large enough to reduce the pressure drop across the float to that existing at the previous flow level. The position of the float may be read visually, or for continuous recording, the vertical position of the float is detected by an induction mechanism. It is possibly the best method for continuous and accurate quantitation of mean blood flow in the aorta and arteries. Flow quantitation is with an error of ±5 per cent.

*C. Turbinometer.* The turbinometer consists of a turbine of known capacity per revolution which is driven by the flowing blood stream. In the turbine is a rotating magnet which induces a recordable signal in an adjacent coil and which indicates the number of turbine rotations. Because of starting frictional resistance to turbine rotation, the turbinometer does not turn with less than 400 to 500 cc. blood flow per minute, and the pressure drop across it in operation is quite high. Consequently, it is used for measuring rather large flows and is used exclusively in the aorta.

*D. Bubble flow meter.* Mean rate of blood flow in arteries has been measured by timing visually or photoelectrically the passage of an injected air bubble through a glass tube of known length and volume which is placed between the cut ends of the vessel through which flow is being measured. Because of the resistance to flow from the long (1 meter) tube used, the device cannot be

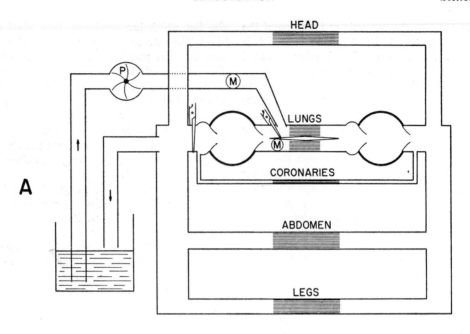

RIGHT HEART BYPASS

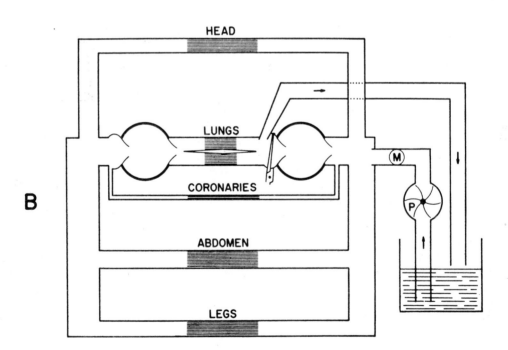

LEFT HEART BYPASS

FIG. 18.1. Schematic representation of techniques; *A*, for right heart bypass; *B*, for left heart bypass; *C*, for total cardiac bypass; *D*, for studying regional blood flow while either perfusion pressure or blood is maintained constant.

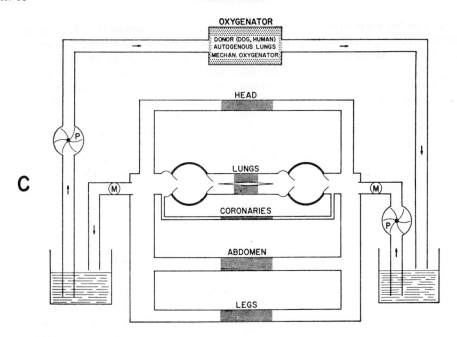

TOTAL HEART-LUNG BYPASS

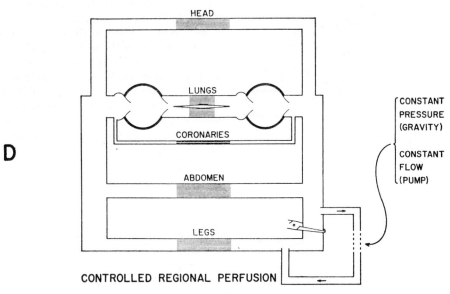

CONTROLLED REGIONAL PERFUSION

Fig. 18.1.

used in veins. However, for quantitating flow in the smaller arteries, it is inexpensive and easy to use and has a linear calibration curve.

*E. Thermostromuhr.* Mean flow through ar-

teries or veins has been determined by several types of thermostromuhrs which operate on the principle that when a circuit is formed of two wires of different metals and one of their junctions is at a higher temperature than the other, an electromotive force is produced in the circuit. The two thermal junctions are mounted in a plastic sleeve, and the proper temperature difference is created by a high frequency or direct current heater. This is either snugly fitted around an intact vessel or is inserted between the cut ends of a vessel so that the flowing blood is in close contact with the thermocouples and heater. A part of the heat is carried away by the flowing blood, hence the rate of cooling of the thermal element depends upon the rate of blood flow. Since the cross-section of the vessel is held constant, volume of flow is related to the differential temperature of the two junctions provided environmental factors do not alter this relationship. However, several external and internal factors other than rate of blood flow influence significantly and unpredictably the flow readings by altering the relative rates of heat loss to the environment at the two junctions or the heat distribution between the junctions so that its reliability is questionable.

PHASIC FLOW METERS (FIG. 18.3). These de-

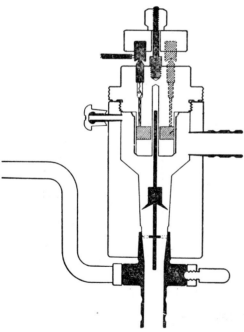

FIG. 18.2A. Full scale sectional view of 0-400 cc. per minute rotameter constructed of lucite or plexiglass, showing tapered flow chamber, metal float with soft iron upper rod extension, float rest at zero ow, and coil for detecting float position. Float is shown in position it would occupy in middle of flow range. (After Shipley and Wilson, Proc. Soc. Exper. Biol. & Med., 1951, **78,** 724.)

vices faithfully record the phasic or moment to moment changes in arterial and or venous flow during a cardiac cycle. The differential pressure and pendulum types must be used with heparin and inserted between the cut ends of a vessel; the electromagnetic and sonar flow meters are used to measure blood flow in intact vessels in unanesthetized active animals, and the former has been used in anesthetized humans.

*A. Differential pressure flow meters.* By introducing a device between two points in a flowing stream, a pressure difference is created which varies with the velocity of blood flow. The ways of creating the pressure difference are illustrated (fig. 18.3a). Of these, only the orifice meter and Pitot tube will be considered.

The orifice meter makes use of the velocity with which blood is flowing. The lateral pressure difference is determined between two regions above and below a region of constriction (the orifice) in a flowing bloodstream, the cross-sectional area of which is constant. Because of the higher stream velocity just below the constriction, the downstream lateral pressure is lower. The pressure difference is proportional to the flow.

With the Pitot tube method, the difference in pressure is determined in two tubes inserted into a vessel, one directed upstream, the other downstream. In the tube pointed upstream, the energy of movement is added to the existing potential energy (pressure on the wall) and a higher pressure is thus recorded in the tube. In the tube pointed downstream, the kinetic energy of movement is deducted from the potential energy (pressure). The pressure difference is entirely a function of the velocity of flow at the two points.

In the past, for these two types of flow meter the pressure difference which is proportional to flow has been optically recorded by a differential manometer. The manometer is a rubber membrane optical pressure manometer except that the rubber is very thin and a chamber filled with saline surrounds the front surface of the membrane for application of the downstream pressure. Membrane excursions are recorded by light passing through a glass window in the outer chamber to a small mirror mounted on the membrane. Recent replacement of the optical differential manometer by an electrical system and amplification has improved the fidelity of differential flow meters.

Until recently most of our information regarding phasic blood flow in the aorta, venae cavae,

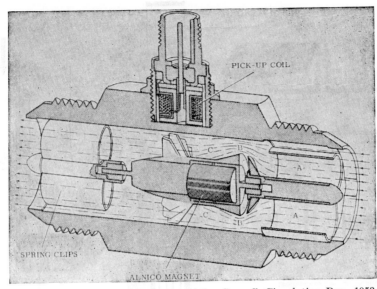

FIG. 18.2*B*. The Potter electroturbinometer. (After Sarnoff, Circulation Res., 1953, **1**, 724.)

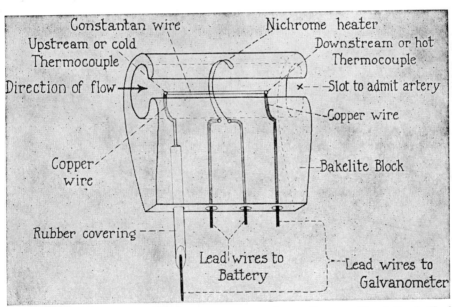

FIG. 18.2*C*. Diagram of direct current thermostromuhr. (Gregg, Coronary Circulation in Health and Disease, Lea & Febiger, Philadelphia, 1950.)

and various arteries has come from the use of these two flow meters. Both are quite satisfactory. The orifice meter causes a considerable pressure drop, the Pitot meter does not; hence, the former is adequate for arterial flow, the latter for venous flow. The question has been raised whether the orifice meter, by imposing resistance to flow gives a correct phasic flow curve in an artery such as a coronary, in which blood temporarily reverses its direction of flow during a portion of the cardiac cycle. However, recent experiments in the author's laboratory have shown that flow curves are similar with the orifice meter and with an electromagnetic flow meter in which no resistance to flow is imposed by the meter.

*B. Pendulum flow meters.* In principle first de-

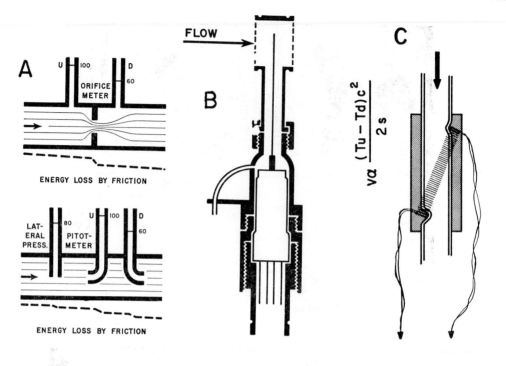

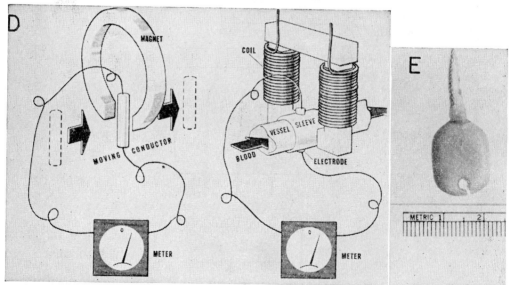

FIG. 18.3. Phasic blood flow meters. *A*. Schematic drawing illustrating the principle of the orifice meter and the Pitot tube (after Brecher, Venous return, Grune & Stratton, Inc., New York, 1955). *B*. Schematic diagram of the bristle flow meter cannula utilizing a subminiature vacuum tube and flow-sensing element (after Brecher, Venous return, Grune & Stratton, Inc., New York, 1955). *C*. Sonar flow meter principle (Franklin *et al.*, Am. J. Physiol., 1959, 14, 809). *D*. Electromagnetic flow meter principle. *E*. Electromagnetic flow meter probe.

scribed in the 15th century, a small pendulum, paddle, reed, wire, or bristle which is introduced into a blood vessel is deviated from its resting position by the flowing blood, the amount of deviation being proportional to the velocity of flow.

At least two successful types are in use. In one type, the electromagnetic pendulum flow meter, the pendulum is made of ferro magnetic material which moves in an induction field. The induction changes are then amplified. In a second type, the bristle flow meter, the bloodstream deviates a small bristle, one end of which is inserted into the blood vessel and the other end is attached to the plate pin of a subminiature vacuum tube (fig. 18.3*B*). When the bristle is deviated by the flowing blood, the electron current from cathode to anode varies in proportion to the distance between them which is determined by the degree of deviation. The electrical signal is amplified. These two types of devices have the advantages of smallness and compactness, good frequency and sensitivity, minimal resistance to flow, low drift and equal response to forward and backward flow. A big drawback is that the pendulum or bristle are very sensitive to position changes (gravity effect) as well as to flow.

*C. Sonar and electromagnetic flow meters.* The optimal flow meter for physiological investigation would be made up of a miniature sensing agent which is mounted chronically on the external surface of intact blood vessels. It would record instantaneous flow for extended periods, weeks to months without change in calibration, and would have sufficient sensitivity and frequency response to monitor flow in arteries and venous trunks. Two different types of flowmeter, the sonar and electromagnetic, have been developed in the attempt to satisfy these demands (figs. 18.3*C* and *D*).

An electrosonic meter has been used to measure flow in the arteries, aorta and vena cava, and to measure left ventricular diameter of unanesthetized dogs. Earlier models were developed by Kalmus with some miniaturization by Herrick. In principle, the transit time of sound moving downstream is determined by the velocity of sound in the motionless medium plus the velocity of the medium. The transit time of the sound upstream is determined by the velocity of sound in the motionless medium minus the velocity of the medium. Thus the difference in transit time of the ultrasonic waves upstream and downstream is proportional to the velocity of the medium. In practice, barium titrate crystals are mounted at diagonally opposed positions near the end of a lucite cylinder divided longitudinally and this is clamped about an artery. Bursts of ultrasonic waves (3 megacycles per sec.) emitted by one crystal pass through the vessel wall and diagonally through the stream of flowing blood to reach the opposite crystal. Bursts are emitted at about 12,000 per sec. with direction reversal at 800 per sec. The difference in transit time of the ultrasonic waves is converted into a direct current

voltage, amplified and recorded. By turning off the ultrasonic pulse generator, the flow beam reaches a position which is the same as that following temporary mechanical occlusion of the vessel. This device appears to be usable on both artery and vein.

The electromagnetic flow meter has been used for pulsatile flow recording in the aorta and arteries of the dog and man. A number of different types have been produced, some commercially. In the author's laboratory, the Kolin type somewhat modified has been used. This was first crudely designed 24 years ago. In principle, an electromotive force or voltage is induced in a conductor moving through a magnetic field at right angles to the lines of force. In biological use, blood moving within an intact blood vessel serves as the conductor and the induced voltage which is proportional to the blood velocity is picked up by a pair of electrodes positioned against the vessel wall, perpendicular to the magnetic field and to the direction of blood flow. The flow meter which is encased in plastic, consists of a miniature electromagnet made up of coils of wire mounted on steel laminations, a slotted plastic tube into which the vessel is inserted, two electrodes, and wires for energizing the electromagnet and for leading off the induced voltage (one-millionth volt) which is amplified and recorded. In use, the probe is implanted around an intact blood vessel by temporarily decompressing and forcing the vessel through the longitudinal slit in the probe. Its main advantages are its ability to measure mean and phasic flow in unopened large and small vessels of chronic animals, its linearity of calibration and its high frequency of response. The flow beam can be made to approximate the zero flow position by "electronic zeroing" or repeated mechanical flow zeros can be easily obtained even in the exercising dog by temporary (3 to 4 sec.) inflation of a rubber pneumatic cuff just distal to the flow meter.

Fick principle. Much of our information concerning blood flow, especially the output of the heart is derived from the use of methods based on the Fick principle. To employ the Fick principle to determine blood flow through the whole body or an organ, it is necessary to have a substance that is either removed from or added to the blood during its period of flow through the vessels under study. The amount which is added or removed from the organ by the blood is equal to the difference between the amount brought into the organ and the amount carried away from the organ. The amount of the substance in the blood is expressed as the volume multiplied by the concentration. Thus $Q = F_1 \times C_1 - F_0 \times C_0$ in which $Q$ = amount of reference substance picked up or released by the organ, $F_1$ = blood flow into organ, $F_0$ = blood flow out of organ, $C_1$ = concentration of reference substance in the inflowing blood, and $C_0$ = concentration of reference substance in outflow blood. Since the inflowing and outflowing volumes are assumed to be the same, the equation becomes

$$F = \frac{Q}{C_0 - C_1} = \frac{Q}{\Delta C}.$$

*A. For cardiac output with oxygen and carbon dioxide.* Measurement of the output of blood by the animal or human heart has been calculated from the difference between the oxygen content of the mixed venous blood and that of the arterial blood and the total oxygen consumption. It must be evident that if the quantity of oxygen which a unit of blood delivers to the tissues (or takes up from the lungs) is known, together with the total quantity of oxygen consumed over a given period, then the volume of blood which had been engaged in the carriage of this quantity of gas can be calculated. To take an example. The arterial blood contains about 19 volumes of oxygen per 100 cc. It gives up, let us say, 6 volumes to the tissues, i.e., the mixed venous blood coming to the lungs contains 13 volumes per cent. The arteriovenous (A-V) oxygen difference is, therefore, 6 volumes per cent. If the total quantity of oxygen consumed per minute is found to be 250 cc., then the cardiac output is:

(Total $O_2$ consumption per minute)

$$\frac{250}{19 - 13} \times 100 = \begin{array}{l} \text{(Output per minute)} \\ \text{4.16 liters} \end{array}$$

(Arteriovenous $O_2$ difference).

The oxygen consumption must be measured very accurately for several minutes. The arteriovenous oxygen difference should be obtained simultaneously and must be based on blood from any artery and mixed venous blood since the quantity of oxygen contained in venous blood from different regions is grossly different depending upon the vascular bed from which it drains. Even the oxygen content of blood in the superior vena cava differs from that in the inferior vena cava by 1 to 2 volumes per cent. Mixing of the blood occurs in the right ventricle and is generally complete by the time the blood reaches the pulmonary artery where sampling is made.

The cardiac output can be calculated in a similar way from the total carbon dioxide elimination and the arteriovenous carbon dioxide difference ($CO_2$ in mixed venous blood less $CO_2$ in arterial blood). However, the vagaries of cardiac output calculation on this basis are such that the measurement is generally ignored. The unreliability of the Fick method when carbon dioxide is used is related to the fact that small changes in ventilation strongly influence carbon dioxide storage by the body and a steady state is hard to reach.

The direct Fick method was first employed in man in Germany in 1929 by Forssmann, who experimented upon himself, and a little later by Klein. Cournand and his associates established the safety of the procedure and stimulated widespread utilization of the method. The technique of cardiac catheterization has been described in detail by Cournand, Sosman, and Dexter. A sample of mixed venous blood is drawn from the pulmonary artery by means of a urethral catheter (No. 7 or 8), passed up an appropriate arm vein. The introduction of the catheter is guided by X-ray visualization (fluoroscope). A sample of arterial blood is obtained by arterial puncture. The blood samples can be analyzed for their oxygen contents, and after the total oxygen consumption has been determined in the usual way, calculation of the cardiac output is made from the formula already given. The oxygen contents can be measured with the Van Slyke apparatus or for more rapid determination, a photoelectric method has been developed which is only slightly less accurate than the Van Slyke (fig. 18.5*A*). Blood for analysis is drawn through a cuvette which is transilluminated by a constant intensity light source. The light passing through a 628 filter falls upon a photomultiplier tube. This method has a high degree of accuracy and has proved only slightly less accurate than the Van Slyke procedure.

The method presupposes that the oxygen consumption and the A-V oxygen difference are obtained simultaneously and are constant during the time of measurement. Both cardiac and respiratory cyclic changes in the concentration difference of oxygen and the flow rate are capable of introducing large errors in cardiac output calculations. These changes do not appear to occur to any significant degree in man under normal circumstances.

A potentially serious error of the Fick application arises from storage in, or liberation of, gas from the body including the lungs. This would occur when the relation of aerobic to anaerobic metabolism of the body is altered and, thus, the level of blood oxygen would be altered without relation to blood flow. Thus, the Fick calculation is dubiously related to cardiac output as the organism goes into or comes out of an anoxic state or in the presence of congenital heart disease with cyanotic episodes. In the latter instance, the shunts between the pulmonary and systemic circuits induce rather large errors in calculation of systemic flow. Special formulas have been developed to calculate the volume of blood flow through such shunts.

Cardiac output determined by the Fick method probably has an error of $\pm 10$ per cent when very carefully done. However, it is to be remembered that cardiac catheterization gives rise to considerable apprehension and may in itself abnormally increase the cardiac output values.

*B. For cardiac output with foreign gases.* Most of the early figures for cardiac output were based on the Fick principle using a foreign gas. For this, the lungs are used as a gas aerotonometer to measure the gas tensions of mixed venous blood and, hence, its gas content. A subject breathes an inert foreign gas (i.e., one which becomes dissolved in plasma but does not combine with hemoglobin, lipoid or other constituents of the blood). If the rate of gas absorption by the blood, its alveolar tension and its stability in blood are known, then the quantity of blood which has passed through the lungs can be calculated.

Flow

$$= \frac{\text{rate of gas absorption}}{\text{alveolar concentration of gas} \times \text{blood solubility}}$$

This is the principle upon which a foreign gas method is based. Nitrous oxide ($N_2O$), ethyl iodide ($C_2H_5I$), and especially acetylene ($C_2H_2$) have been used in the past. The main difficulty of the method is that equilibrium between alveolar air and the venous blood must be effected before recirculation. Originally, it was felt that the circulation time was 25 to 30 seconds, and hence, that a respiratory mixture could be left in the lungs for that length of time without exposure to recirculated blood. However, the correct figure for circulation time is much shorter, 10 to 18 sec., which is often an insufficient time for equilibrium to be established; hence, the figure for resting cardiac output of 2.2 liters $M^2$ per

minute established by this method is often lower than the normal figure and, at times, grossly in error. Recently nitrous oxide has been used to estimate not only cardiac output but the instantaneous capillary blood flow since it is so soluble that it is immediately picked up by blood entering the capillary bed of the lungs (fig. 18.4*A*). If a subject is in an airtight chamber and takes and holds a single breath of $N_2O$ for 8 to 10 sec., the chamber pressure falls at a rate which indicates the rate of absorption of the gas by the blood and, consequently, the rate of pulmonary capillary blood flow or cardiac output. Recirculation is not a problem during this short time. The instantaneous rate of blood flow can be calculated since the rate of $N_2O$ absorption, the alveolar gas tension and its blood solubility are known.

*C. For regional blood flow.* Of the methods considered, except for the electromagnetic flow meter and sonar techniques, measurements of volume of blood flow passing through the splanchnic bed or kidney cannot be made directly even in experimental animals without destructive surgical procedures or unphysiological interference with function. The Fick principle has been used to determine mean blood flow in man and animal through the liver, and kidneys, as well as the coronary and cerebral circulation. The introduction of venous catheterization has made it possible to obtain blood issuing from the hepatic vein in intact animals and man, thus permitting the development of methods of measuring flow on the basis of the Fick principle. Bromsulphalein (BSP) has proved especially useful here because it is taken up by the liver with remarkable efficiency. Of the total removed from the blood each minute, when the plasma BSP concentration is maintained by constant intravenous infusion below 2 or 3 mg. per cent, no more than 5 per cent can be attributed to escape through extrasplanchnic portals. For practical purposes, therefore, the hepatic removal of BSP equals the rate of infusion as long as the plasma level is constant. The splanchnic blood flow may be calculated by dividing the removal rate by the difference between BSP concentrations in peripheral arterial and hepatic venous blood. The flow value is generally referred to as the estimated hepatic blood flow since sampling is made in only one of several hepatic veins. A number of other substances such as Rose Bengal and $I^{131}$, have been used in the same way to measure splanchnic blood volume.

Similarly, the blood flow through the human kidney can be determined. Diodrast, when in low

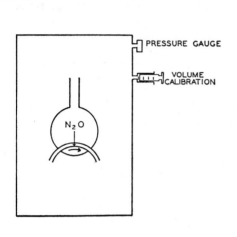

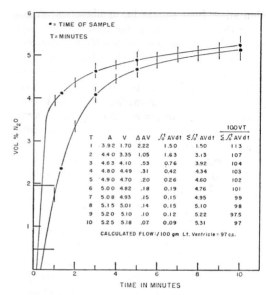

| T | A | V | ΔAV | $\int_0^t AVdt$ | $\Sigma\int_0^t AVdt$ | $\dfrac{100VT}{\Sigma\int_0^t AVdt}$ |
|---|---|---|---|---|---|---|
| 1 | 3.92 | 1.70 | 2.22 | 1.50 | 1.50 | 113 |
| 2 | 4.40 | 3.35 | 1.05 | 1.63 | 3.13 | 107 |
| 3 | 4.63 | 4.10 | .53 | 0.76 | 3.92 | 104 |
| 4 | 4.80 | 4.49 | .31 | 0.42 | 4.34 | 103 |
| 5 | 4.90 | 4.70 | .20 | 0.26 | 4.60 | 102 |
| 6 | 5.00 | 4.82 | .18 | 0.19 | 4.76 | 101 |
| 7 | 5.08 | 4.93 | .15 | 0.15 | 4.95 | 99 |
| 8 | 5.15 | 5.01 | .14 | 0.15 | 5.10 | 98 |
| 9 | 5.20 | 5.10 | .10 | 0.12 | 5.22 | 97.5 |
| 10 | 5.25 | 5.18 | .07 | 0.09 | 5.31 | 97 |

CALCULATED FLOW:/100 gm Lt. Ventricle = 97 c.c.

FIG. 18.4. *Left.* Diagram illustrating the principle of measurement of pulmonary capillary blood flow (DuBois, J. Clin. Invest., 1957, **36,** 1566). *Right.* Graph indicating typical nitrous oxide saturation curves obtained in determining coronary flow per 100 grms per left ventricle per minute in dog. *Upper curve* from carotid artery; *lower curve* from coronary sinus by catheter. (Gregg, Coronary circulation in health and Disease, Lea & Febiger, Philadelphia, 1950.)

concentration in the plasma, undergoes virtually complete clearance, i.e., it is removed from the plasma in a single passage of blood through the kidney. This substance is excreted largely by the tubules, only a small fraction (about 16 per cent) being filtered through the glomerulus. Knowing the amount excreted in the urine within a time, and the plasma concentration, the quantity of blood that has passed through active renal tissue can be calculated. For example, if 600 mg. of diodrast are excreted in the urine per minute, and each milliliter of plasma contains 1 mg., then to deliver 600 mg. of Diodrast, 600 cc. of plasma went through the kidney, or with an hematocrit of 40, about 1,000 ml. of blood flow. Diodrast can be used in a similar way to estimate renal blood flow.

Mean blood flow has been successfully determined through the coronary circulation with nitrous oxide inhalation and through the cerebral circulation with nitrous oxide or krypton inhalation. It is the only method available for such studies in man (fig. 18.4B). In use in the heart or brain, several simultaneous arterial (any artery) and venous (coronary sinus for the heart and the internal jugular vein for the brain) samples are drawn from the beginning of $N_2O$ inhalation (mixture of nitrogen, 64 per cent; $N_2O$, 15 per cent; $O_2$, 21 per cent) to the time of its equilibrium in the bloodstream or during denitrogenation after previous inhalation of the nitrogen

mixture. Continuous simultaneous samples can also be drawn from the artery and vein for analysis. The flow per unit of time through these organs is equal to the amount of the substance taken up by that organ in a given time divided by the difference in concentration of the substance in the arterial blood and venous drainage of the organ in the same time period. The flow is determined by dividing the nitrous oxide uptake by its arteriovenous difference in the brain or left ventricle. The denominator in the Fick equation is found by computing the integrated difference between the concentrations of $N_2O$ in arterial and venous blood during the period of equilibration with a low concentration of $N_2O$. The concentration of gas in the tissue at the time of equilibration (the numerator in the Fick equation) is unobtainable directly and is assumed to be equal to the product of the venous blood concentration of the gas (after equilibrium is established) and a partition coefficient (1.0 in case of the heart and 1.3 for the brain). When the equation is multiplied by 100, units for blood flow are obtained which are expressed as cubic centimeters of flow per 100 grams of heart or myocardium.

As compared to direct measurement of cerebral and coronary flow with a rotameter, the method shows a reasonable accuracy and, in humans, has furnished almost all of our information regarding the cerebral and coronary blood flows.

INDICATOR DILUTION PRINCIPLE. The principle

is based on observation of the rate at which a known quantity of material introduced into a vessel or heart cavity is diluted by blood flow through the vessel or cavity. In the principle as originally applied by Stewart and modified by Hamilton, it has been shown that the average rate of blood flow can be stated:

$$F = E \left/ \int_0^\infty C \, dt \right.$$

where F = average rate of flow, E = total quantity injected, C = instantaneous concentration of the injected material. From this relationship, it is possible to determine the average flow rate in almost any cavity or vessel of reasonable size if the amount of injected material is known and if the concentration-time function can be accurately determined.

For good quantitation, however, various precautions are necessary. The procedures and indicator substances used must cause little discomfort or injury; minimal volumes of added solution or volume of blood should be removed for analysis. In addition, the indicator should stay inside the blood vessels between the points of injection and sampling (such loss would be calculated as an increment of flow); the indicator should not diffuse into or out of red cells during its passage. Dilution of the indicator in the cavity or vessel can be determined in the same cavity or a small distance downstream in the vessel, or far removed from the injection site. In all cases, and especially the first, the injection must be made almost instantaneously, and in most sites, the injection should be made with special apertures in the catheter tip so that turbulence is induced and mixing is immediately complete and sampling is on an accurate dilution basis. This in itself leads to certain difficulties when the injection is made into the systemic circulation. It has long been known that rapid intra-arterial injection is followed by some hemolysis which liberates vasoactive substances. This gives rise to a vasodilation sometimes of considerable magnitude in the organs deriving their blood from the ventricle, aorta, or artery in question, so that the quantity to be measured is altered at the very moment it is measured. Thus, although the methodology may give correct flows, they are too high. This obstacle is difficult to circumvent.

*A. Indicator substances.* A variety of indicator substances have been used to modify in a quantitative way, the optical, electrical, thermal, and radioactive characteristics of the passing blood. (1) The optical density of the blood has been altered by the injection of plasma and dyes such as brilliant vital red, Evans blue (T 1824), Cardiogreen and Rie 1743. The latter two dyes are especially useful since they have a high extinction value around the isobestic point of reduced oxyhemoglobin at 805 m$\mu$ and, therefore, they do not require constancy of oxygen saturation of the blood as do the other dyes. Thus, with their use the blood flow in cyanotic patients or in the veins of normal subjects can be determined. Of course, constancy of hemoglobin quantity in the light path is required during the registration of each dilution curve. (2) The electrical conductivity of the blood has been changed by injection into it of hypertonic salt solution (fig. 18.5$B$). It is critically important that calibration of this method be done with exactly the same blood and injection solution whose mixing is actually recorded. Following salt injection, the increase in electrical conductivity is due partly to the increase in sodium chloride concentration and partly to red cell dilution. (3) A thermal dilution technique has been employed in which cool (18 to 22° C.) sodium chloride or 5 per cent glucose has been injected. One must be very careful of the obvious possibility of heat exchange between the cold injectate and the warm tissues of the central circulation. (4) Changes in radioactivity of the blood have been induced by the injection of radioactive inorganic $P^{32}$, radioactive iodinated serum albumin, organic radioactive iodine, $D_2O$, potassium$^{42}$ chloride, $Rb^{86}$ chloride, and 4-iodoantipyrine ($I^{131}$).

*B. Indicator detectors.* For recording continuously the different properties of arterial blood which are changed by such injections, four types of detector are used. One type is inserted directly into the bloodstream through the vessel or cavity wall in a needle or catheter; this is used to indicate changes in conductivity (conductivity cell), in temperature (thermistor), and in the optical density of the bloodstream to the right ventricle. A second type of detector encloses a segment of unopened vessel monitoring changes in conductivity or optical density of the bloodstream using a photocell. In a third type, the blood is pushed or pulled through an indwelling tube, after which it is discarded or mixed or analyzed or returned to the body by vein or artery (fig. 18.5$A$). This is the most widely used and follows optical changes and radioactive emanations of the blood. The changes in optical density and radioactivity concentration are detected by having the blood flow continuously, in the first case, by a photocell or photomultiplier tube and, in the second case, by a continuous scanner. Analysis can also be

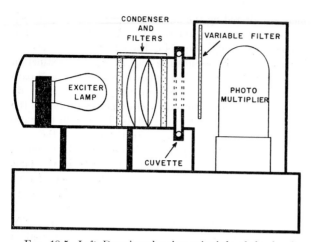 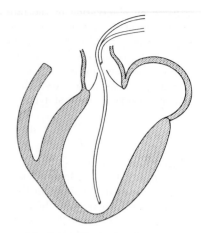

FIG. 18.5. *Left*. Drawing showing principle of the densitometer used to determine instantaneous cardiac output and continuous blood $O_2$ saturation. *Right*. Principle by which change in blood conductivity in a ventricular cavity is used to determine diastolic ventricular volume and stroke volume.

made with the Beckman spectrophotometer and counters on multiple individual samples taken every second. The fourth type, easiest but empirical, is applied to the external intact skin to obtain a curve of radioactivity or transillumination of the pinna of the ear for opacity changes. This type is obviously subject to many uncontrollable difficulties for much unrelated tissue is interposed between the detector and area in which flow is to be measured.

*C. Uses*. The various approaches have been used in a variety of situations. In general, the conductivity method has been used for determining cardiac output and diastolic volume of the heart; the thermal, dye, and radioactivity methods for cardiac output and flow in arteries and veins. In addition, the radioactivity method has been applied to the fractional distribution of cardiac output to various organs of very small animals (as well as large animals). For this, simultaneous measurement of the flow fractions to the organs is based on the principle that for a short time (6 to 60 sec.) after a single intravenous injection of any foreign substance, the organ reservoir for its dilution is so large in relation to the inflow rate of the substance that it does not appear in the venous circulation and, consequently, its extraction ratio is 1. The substance is, therefore, distributed in the same manner as the cardiac output. Although sound in principle, the accuracy of the method has not yet been established. It would be expected to furnish only very rough values because of the anesthesia and trauma associated with the determination of the isotope content of the individual organs.

Figure 18.6 illustrates the principle applied to

determination of cardiac output in the unanesthetized human. In this approach, a tracer material (Evans Blue dye, T1824) that affixes itself to the albumin of the blood plasma is introduced into the large veins near the superior vena cava and the diluted material that issues from the heart is continuously sampled at a peripheral artery (radial). This blood is drawn at a constant rate through the cuvette of a densitometer which gives a continuous record of the changing optical density of the blood induced by the injected dye. The dye dilution curve is plotted at one second intervals as the logarithm of deflection against time and the straight line downslope is extrapolated to 1.0 mm. deflection. The average height of this plot, calculated by area per unit of time, is then converted to an average concentration of dye in milligrams per cc. by means of the calibration curve and this value is used in the formula for calculating the cardiac output.

Most work with indicators deals with what happens when a "slug" of indicator is introduced as rapidly as possible. A variation of this procedure is to give a constant rate of infusion of the indicator, and to observe its resultant plateau. Experiment and theory demonstrate, however, that such an equilibrium concentration or plateau is a very dubious possibility (fig. 18.6). This is because recirculation of the indicator prevents attainment of a plateau, and the curve must begin to rise, because of this, before it has stopped rising toward the equilibrium level. On the other hand, recirculation is easily detected with the "slug" injection technique.

The indicator dilution technique especially dye dilution, is a standard procedure for measuring

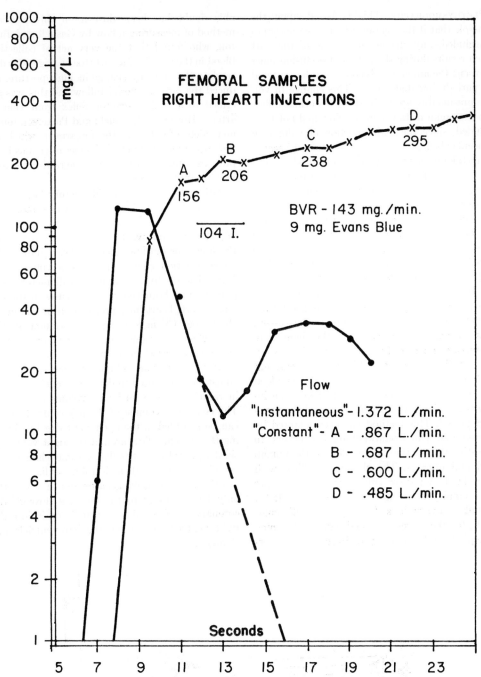

Fig. 18.6. Concentration curves resulting from continuous infusions of brilliant vital red (BVR) and rapid injection of T1824 (Evans Blue), both started at zero seconds. Short horizontal lines and figures denote the expected concentration plateau levels of the continuous infusion on the basis of "instantaneous" injection (I) or the measured flow (M) plotted on three logarithmic decades. (Hamilton *et al.*, Am. J. Physiol., 1953, **175**, 173.)

cardiac output. Its accuracy is about the same as that of the Fick procedure. It has the added advantages that cardiac output can be determined from only a few heart beats, and it is not neces- sary to immobilize the subject because of the presence of an intracardiac catheter; cardiac output measurements can be made during violent exercise on a treadmill.

PLETHYSMOGRAPHY. This is based upon the principle that if the venous return from an organ is occluded, any change in volume of the part which results during the period of occlusion must represent the amount of blood which has entered the part during that period. This change in volume presumably approximates the normal inflow into the organ if its venous outflow had not been occluded, since the major portion of volume in a vascular bed is on the venous side and because it can take up large volumes of blood with minimal change in pressure. Still, the time during which the vein is compressed and, consequently, the duration of the observation must obviously be brief, for interference with the venous flow will quickly slow the bloodstream and give a fallacious result. In use, an organ with its blood vessels intact is placed in an air-tight chamber. At the point where the vessels enter and leave the chamber, a soft material, e.g., sponge or tow packing smeared with vaseline, is used to form a hermetic seal but does not compress the vessels. A tube leads from the interior of the chamber to a tambour and recording apparatus. The excursions of the latter are calibrated to represent cubic centimeters of blood. To estimate the blood flow, the vein is suddenly clamped and the increase in volume of the organ recorded over a short period. This method has been adapted by Hewlett and Van Zwaluwenburg and others, to the estimation of the volume flow in the human hand and forearm. The chamber is filled with air or fluid. A narrow cuff encircling the upper arm is employed to compress the veins (fig. 18.7). A number of variations of this type of plethysmograph, for the finger, toe, and leg, on the same principle have been designed. Recently consider-

able doubt has been thrown on this classical method of measuring inflow by Gaskell and Burton, who found that the very act of collecting blood in the vessels of a part (toe or finger) by distending the veins by change in limb posture, reduced the rate of arterial inflow and this was ascribed to a veni-vasomotor reflex from vein to artery. However, Greenfield and Patterson found no evidence for this in the forearm in which inflow was unaltered in the presence of venous back pressure sufficient to increase the resting forearm volume by 2 per cent.

Although no entirely satisfactory method is yet available, ventricular volume in systole and diastole has long been determined by some form of plethysmography. It is not necessary to occlude the inflow or outflow since the heart induces by its contraction change in its own volume (fig. 18.8). The plethysmograph or cardiometer is applied around both ventricular cavities in the isolated heart, heart-lung preparation or the open-chest dog. Changes in external volume of the ventricles create small pressure changes within the cardiometer which are recorded and calibrated against ventricular volume. Under special circumstances it is used to determine cyclic changes in right and left ventricular volume separately. The change in volume of the left ventricle alone can be recorded in the open-chest dog by shunting the systemic flow around the right ventricle; similarly, right ventricular volume change can be followed where there is total cardiac bypass using a heart-lung oxygenator and in which the only blood supply to the heart is through the coronary arteries which eventually drain into the right ventricle and leave the left ventricle unchanged.

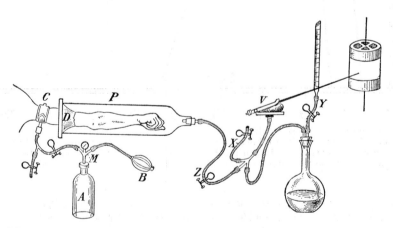

FIG. 18.7. Diagram showing Hewlett and Van Zwaluwenburg's method for estimating the rate of blood flow in the arm. (After Hewlett and Van Zwaluwenburg.)

QUALITATIVE OR EMPIRIC METHODS. There are a number of methods using sound principles but which, because they must be applied in a biological environment rather poor for their operation, give qualitative or directional trends or which achieve their degree of validity from constants derived by comparison with a primary method.

*A. The ballistocardiographic method.* This method for determining cardiac output was originated by Henderson many years ago and has been elaborated and modified in recent years by Starr and his colleagues. The cardiac output is calculated from the record made by the recoil of the body caused by oppositely directed movements of the heart and by the impact of the blood during systole. It involves the basic principle that "every reaction has an opposite and equal reaction." The apparatus or ballistocardiograph consists of a table suspended in different ways and braced to prevent any but a horizontal movement in the long axis of the body (fig. 18.9*A*). The patient lies supine on the table with his feet braced against a footboard. The movements of the table are opposed by a strong spring and magnified greatly. The normal ballistocardiogram shows three principal waves, H, I, and J, inscribed during systole. The stroke volume is calculated from the areas of the waves I and J, and by applying the following formula:

$$\text{Stroke volume} = 7\sqrt{[I + J] \, AC \, 2/3}$$

where I and J are the areas of the waves so designated, A is the diameter of the aorta (calculated from age and surface area according to Bazett's data) and C the duration of the cardiac cycle; the minute volume is obtained by multiplying the value of the stroke volume by the pulse rate. Different correction values are needed to apply to such calculations to make them match the accepted cardiac output values obtained simultaneously in normal and disease states.

This method should not be used for cardiac output. Such calculations of cardiac output from ballistic waves must be on an empirical procedure which cannot give valid values since, although the usual ballistocardiogram represents movements along the longitudinal axis of the body, the blood ejected from the two ventricles moves simultaneously in several directions (3 dimensions) after leaving the heart. Since the amplitude of the deflections is influenced by the rate of blood acceleration, variation in pattern should reveal changes in force of ventricular contraction.

It should, therefore, be possible to recognize empirical relationships between different types of cardiac dysfunction and characteristic ballistocardiographic patterns.

*B. X-ray kymography.* An indication of possible directional changes in ventricular blood volume has been obtained in various ways. The area of shadow on x-ray film during diastole has been used as a cross-section of the whole heart, and a fairly accurate nomographic chart of the relation of this heart shadow to cardiac volume has been worked out for the anesthetized dog. Planimetric measurements of a cross-section of either the right or left ventricular cavity during systole and diastole have been made from successive motion picture frames following injection of contrast medium into the right ventricle through a cardiac catheter or into the left ventricle by retrograde catheterization by way of the carotid arteries and the aortic valves. Except in the first instance, these methods have never been validated against a direct measurement. Hence, interpretation of results with their use should be made with great caution unless the change in size of the cardiac silhouette is very large.

*C. Pulse pressure.* From the time of Erlanger and Hooker, a large amount of experimental work has been applied to the development of the possibility that the product of heart rate and the systemic pulse pressure to an organ (and especially in the case of the central aorta to the body as a

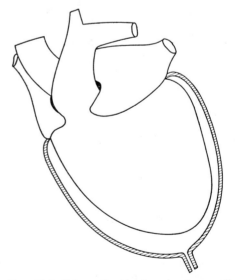

FIG. 18.8. Schematic drawing showing cardiac plethysmograph. A rubber cuff secures the chamber to the base of the heart at the A-V ring. Pressure-volume changes are tapped from the small outlet and recorded as in figure 18.7.

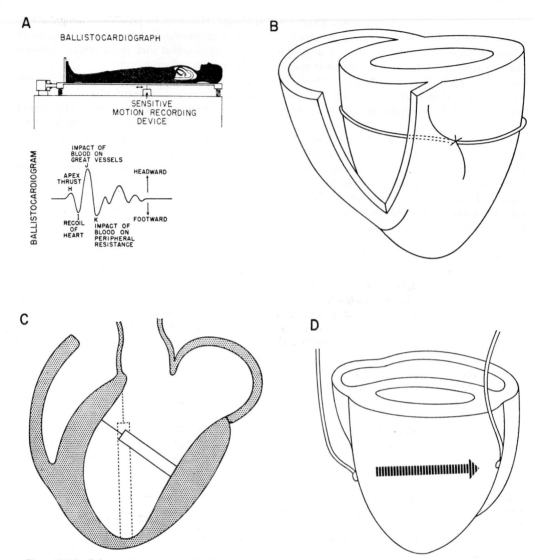

Fig. 18.9*A*. Schematic showing the ballistocardiograph and typical ballistocardiogram (Modified after Rushmer, Cardiac Diagnosis, W. B. Saunders Company, Philadelphia, 1955). *B*. Principle of Whitney gauge as applied to a ventricle. As the mercury-filled rubber tube changes in length its electrical resistance is altered (Whitney, J. Physiol., 1953, **121,** 1). *C*. Variable inductance gauge used to measure a ventricular dimension (Rushmer, Circulation Res., 1954, **2,** 14). *D*. Sonar principle used to measure a ventricular dimension (Rushmer, Circulation Res., 1956, **4,** 684).

whole) might quantitatively represent the blood flow through that organ. To do this effectively, one must know the volume of blood required to expand the arterial tree, as the pulse wave passes out over the arteries, and the volume of blood which drains out of the arterioles during systole. Such pressure-volume curves should be linear, if possible, but at least must be constant among animals or individuals. The distensibility of the four main divisions of the arterial tree (aortic arch, head, viscera and legs) and the effective pressure change in each area brought about by

the pulse wave have been laboriously determined in animals and the arteriolar outflow during systole calculated from Poiseuille's law (see ch. 15), on the basis that it is the product of the prevailing pressure and flow, with the assumption that the arterioles do not change in diameter. In dogs the pulse contour method gives results which compare reasonably well with those obtained simultaneously with the Fick, dye injection, or rotameter method. However, there are many circumstances in which the values are poor, such as in the presence of high aortic diastolic pressure, and following prolonged venous stasis. Why the distensibility of the arterial system varies spontaneously under circumstances such as these and others, is not known. In humans the attempt has been made to "calibrate" the distensibility of the subject's arteries before an experimental investigation by first making an actual cardiac output measurement with the Fick or dye dilution technique. This is not helpful for it assumes that thereafter arterial distensibility will not change, a highly unlikely assumption.

*A. Plethysmography.* Two types of plethysmographs, the electrical impedance and the mercury-rubber strain gauge (Whitney gauge, fig. 18.9*B*) have been used successfully for indicating the blood flow through the extremities of man or animal. In principle, the electrical impedance plethysmograph measures the change in electrical conductivity of an extremity induced by the changing number of ions brought to the segment by the heart action, i.e., the electrical impedance is a function of the volume of the part. Without venous occlusion, this represents volume pulsation of the extremity, with occlusion, the inflow of blood. For the Whitney gauge, a delicate rubber tubing is filled with mercury and sealed at each end with insulated wires. It is wrapped around a finger or arm of man, or the aorta, left or right ventricle of the unanesthetized dog. Lengthening of the gauge reduces the cross-sectional area and increases the length of the mercury column producing a corresponding increase in electrical resistance. The gauge forms one arm of a Wheatstone bridge. An index of ventricular cross-sectional area has also been obtained in active unanesthetized dogs by measuring the change in inductance of a variable inductance gauge implanted in a ventricle (fig. 18.9C), by the change in transit time of sound waves across the cavity (fig. 18.9D), and by the use of an electromagnetic principle.

A third type of plethysmograph utilizes a photocell to detect vascular changes by the absorption of light from transilluminated skin. Light from an illumination source enters the skin and scatters; the resulting variations in the photoelectric current caused by changes in blood flow can be recorded. Blood flow in skin areas, not accessible by other means, can be estimated by this method. The amplitudes of the photoelectrically recorded cutaneous pulses may be calibrated by use of a "filter" and correlated with finger blood flow measured by other methods. However, the volume pulse depends on the relationship between arterial inflow and venous

outflow and, at best, is only a qualitative measure of actual blood flow.

*B. Isotope clearance.* A small amount of radioactive ion ($Na^{24}$ or $I^{131}$) is injected into a tissue such as muscle and the rate of clearance from the area is then followed by a counting device. There is doubt that this measures blood flow since, in some instances, the rate of clearance does not parallel the blood flow simultaneously measured.

*C. Thermal methods.* Devices using the principle of heat clearance have been widely used to indicate directional changes in blood flow in a localized area of skin, muscle or internal organ, or through part or the whole of an extremity. One type of device consists of a thermocouple or thermistor (connected in series with a reference thermocouple or thermistor) mounted in the end of a hypodermic needle. The needle is inserted a variable distance into the tissue and a constant source of heat is used to raise the temperature of the test thermocouple 2 to 3° C above tissue temperature. The temperature difference between the test and reference junctions is essentially determined by the heat output of the heater and by the carrying away of the heat by the blood flow. The more rapid the blood flow, the smaller will be the junction temperature difference. A variation of this arrangement is to supply a variable amount of heat to the test junction at a rate just sufficient to maintain a small difference in temperature between the heat source and the reference junction. As blood flow through the tissue increases, progressively higher rates of delivery of heat will be required to maintain this constant temperature difference between heat source and "heat sink." The "rate of flow" will follow the magnitude of the electric current supplied to the heat source.

A second type of device has been much used in recent years to measure blood flow through part or all of an extremity. It is based on the thesis that when the limb is in a water bath, the blood flow is equal to the amount of heat given out to the water, divided by the temperature difference of arterial and venous blood, times the specific heat of blood. However, the arteriovenous temperature difference is not measurable, and there is no guarantee that the ingoing and outgoing temperature reach water bath temperature. A variation is to circulate the water and to measure the heat exchange from the volume of water flow and temperature difference. As with the thermal needle, an index of blood flow can also be obtained by setting the calorimeter water temperature below mouth temperature and then measuring the amount of current necessary to keep the bath temperature constant.

This approach has been found very useful and has given much valuable information despite the facts that there is no good way of calibrating the deflections against known blood flows; zero flow is difficult if not impossible to obtain; in the case of the needle, the surrounding tissue is not normal and in addition to capillary flow, the device may be affected by flow in nearby veins.

*D. Oxygen electrode.* When a very small negative voltage is applied to a metallic electrode in a solution containing dissolved oxygen, there is a reduction of the oxygen at the electrode surface resulting in a small flow of current through the electrode. At such a voltage, the oxygen is reduced as quickly as it reaches the electrode surface and a straight line relationship exists between the oxygen concentration and the current that flows. In use, a platinum wire protrudes through a fine glass tip inserted into the skin; mercury makes contact between the platinum and the circuit. It is assumed that the electrode is in contact with a number of capillaries and that as blood flow increases, it will indicate the rising oxygen tension in the tissue. This has been used to indicate blood flow in the skin, skeletal muscle, and myocardium. It is at best a qualitative indication of tissue blood flow and has most of the disadvantages of the thermal methods.

### Blood Velocity

Of the two measurements, volume flow of blood in milliliters per minute and the velocity of flow in centimeters per second, the former is probably more important. The major function of the circulation is to supply the metabolic needs of the tissues and volume flow is closely related to this, whereas measurement of velocity of flow alone does not necessarily tell us anything about the blood supply to the tissues. Despite this, knowledge of the flow velocity is highly important to an understanding of hemodynamics of the circulation. Flow velocity measurements have been made under direct vision, by use of the various flow meters that have been described, by observation of movement of injected substances, and finally, by determination of the differential pressure within an unopened and unrestrained vessel.

VISUALIZATION. There is a natural tendency to assume that when one actually sees the movement of blood within a vessel, this must supply the most certain evidence. However, when this is done, one tends to be impressed by the movement of the red cells and not by that of the blood as a whole. Even if this were not so, there is not necessarily any relation between the observed velocity and volume flow. For example, in the presence of local constriction in a vessel without constriction in other areas, flow velocity will increase, but flow will decrease. In the presence of general as well as local constriction, velocity and volume flow will both decrease.

FLOW METERS. By insertion into or application on to a blood vessel of almost any of the flow meters described, one automatically measures the velocity of flow since the meter insures a fixed diameter through which the flow occurs. This is because $V = v/\pi r^2$, where $V$ = velocity in millimeters per second, "$v$" volume flow of blood in milliliters through the meter per unit of time, and "$r$" the radius of the vessel. For example, if a large rotameter is used to quantitate aortic flow and the flow is 3,000 ml. per min., vessel diameter is 2.4 cm., then the velocity approximates 12 cm. per sec.

MOVEMENT OF INJECTED MATERIALS. Various noteworthy attempts have been made to follow cyclic changes in velocity in the unopened vessel by recording the movements of various injected foreign materials such as air bubbles, dyes, and x-ray opaque fluid. This is a difficult technique since the moving front of the injected material, i.e., the difference of optical density between blood and the contrasting medium, is often difficult to detect. This is because the velocity is not the same at different points along the radius of the blood column, the flow being much greater in the axial part of the stream than toward the periphery, and also because the flow is not always unidirectional. This gives the mean or average velocity which is derived from the flow indicated by mean flow meters. It, of course, ignores very large fluctuations in velocity which occur during a cardiac cycle. The moment-to-moment or phasic velocity is recorded by those pulsatile flow meters whose frequency of response is sufficiently rapid to follow it.

DIFFERENTIAL PRESSURE VELOCITY. The instantaneous blood velocity has been determined in the aorta and arteries from the instantaneous pressure difference between two points located along the axis of flow or along the vessel (ch. 15, fig. 15.9). Such pressure gradients have been measured by simultaneous recording of arterial pressure at the two points either with individual pressure manometers or by use of a double lumen catheter attached to a differential pressure strain gauge. In the double lumen catheter which has been used in the aorta of humans, the lateral opening of one catheter tip opens at a point about 5 cm. from the other. From the pressure gradients, velocity curves and flow curves have been calculated which agree well with those directly measured. A consideration of this highly technical approach is beyond the scope of this section.

A rough approximation to mean linear aortic velocity in man can be made from the use of the cardiac output and the cross-section of the aorta of a man of this size in a cadaver. The velocity in centimeters per second =

$$\frac{\text{cardiac output}}{\text{cross-sectional area}}.$$

### Circulation Time (C.T.)

By this is meant the shortest time which a particle of blood takes to go from one point in the circulation to another. It is obvious that there are as many circulation times as there are vessels or regions in which to make the measurement. Circulation time is, however, most often determined for a portion of the circulation, such as, from the right to left side of the heart.

The circulation time of a particle of a substance can be accurately determined if it is injected instantaneously into a blood vessel, if it moves at the same rate as the blood stream and if its arrival further down the vessel is accurately detected. Practically, the situation is much more complicated. When a reasonable amount of a substance is injected, its arrival time is so spread out at the downstream detection point that detection is difficult. If the circulation time is made across an organ or a major portion of the circulatory system, the spreadout is even greater. In addition, if all the blood channels between the two points are not approximately uniform in length and diameter, only a part of the blood will pass from point to point at the rate indicated by the measurement. Despite these considerations, measurements of circulation time can be semiquantitative.

The clinical methods for estimating circulation time use injected substances, such as, decholin and ether that signal their arrival by effects on special receptors, such as, the tongue. With decholin, the normal range of arm to tongue (bitter taste) time is 8 to 17 seconds; with ether, the normal arm to lung (patient first smells ether) is from 4 to 8 seconds. For greater precision in

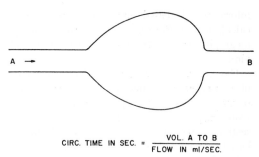

$$\text{CIRC. TIME IN SEC.} = \frac{\text{VOL. A TO B}}{\text{FLOW IN ml/SEC.}}$$

FIG. 18.10. Schematic diagram illustrating the relation between circulation time, volume flow, and the volume of the vascular bed.

experimental investigations, these classical methods have been superseded by the injection of dyes and radioactive tracers whose arrival is easily and objectively detected by densitometers, conductivity cells and isotope counters. The main technical difficulty is the proper calculation of the average transit time. In a symmetrical curve, the mean (average of all transit times), the mode (time coordinate of the peak), and the median (time coordinate which halves the area) all coincide. But as the curve becomes asymmetrical, and particularly as the terminal portion stretches out more in time than the initial part, the three measures depart more and more from each other. The mean circulation time (MCT) it takes all dye to pass is computed as the center of gravity of the curve (fig. 18.6).

The significance of a change in circulation time is debatable. The circulation time between two points in the vascular system is equal to the volume of the vessels between the two points divided by the flow (fig. 18.10). The validity of this relationship has been checked in glass models and mathematically. From this, it is obvious that a change in circulation time could be due to a change in volume of the vascular bed between the point of injection and sampling, as well as to change in flow. Since change in flow follows any vasomotor change, and since the resultant redistribution of pressures causes local volume change, both numerator and denominator of the ratio for circulation time (volume over flow) change simultaneously. They generally change in the same direction, and so the circulation time could be a very poor indicator of blood flow, volume of blood or vasomotor change.

### Volume of Organ, Vessel, Cavity and Region

Information is not abundant concerning regional blood volume, and the alterations that occur in normal humans and animals. Available information is based largely on some form of calculation, on the use of some form of plethysmography, and on the use of the dilution technique.

CALCULATION. For example, the blood volume of a single capillary may be derived from measurement of its length and diameter by microscopic inspection. Calculation of the total cross-sectional area of the capillary bed in man is based on the fact that the same volume of blood going through one part of the vascular bed, such as the aorta, goes through the total capillary bed, i.e., cross-sectional area of aorta times average velocity in the aorta = cross-sectional area of the capillary bed times the average velocity in the capillaries. Since the aortic velocity and cross-section, and capillary velocity (by inspection) can be determined experimentally, then cross-section of capillaries =

$$\frac{\text{cross-section of aorta} \times \text{aortic velocity}}{\text{average capillary velocity}} .$$

PLETHYSMOGRAPHY. The plethysmographs used are those already described to determine volume flow, but they are used without local venous occlusion. These have been used successfully on the heart, liver, spleen and vessels of animals. Dimensional, cross-sectional or possibly directional change in volume have been obtained in unanesthetized active dogs with the use of some of the various gauges previously described; for the heart cavities, large arteries and veins, the impedance plethysmograph, sonar cardiometer, strain gauge arch, Whitney gauge and mutual inductance coils have been used; for organs, there are used the sonar cardiometer, impedance plethysmograph and Whitney gauge. Most of these techniques are not applicable to man except under unusual conditions. However, determination of variations in blood distribution in man can be made to some extent using plethysmography. For example, changes in quantity of blood in the lower extremities are determined by measuring the volume of the legs after occlusion of the circulation by applying pressure cuffs to the thighs and inflating them to a pressure greater than arterial. Changes in the quantity of blood in the trunk are determined by recording simultaneously the trunk volume with a plethysmograph and determining any change in pulmonary air volume by a spirometer. Variations in average blood volume in the heart are established by estimating the heart volume by x-ray. Values obtained by these techniques are admittedly rough but are helpful in establishing large directional or qualitative shifts in blood distribution resulting from change of position, fainting, injection of drugs, etc.

The plethysmograph is also used to measure the pressure-volume characteristics of the distensible venous system in a limb segment. The pressure in a congesting cuff on the limb proximal to the plethysmograph is increased 30 mm. Hg by increments of 5 mm. Hg, and the corresponding increases in limb volume with each pressure rise are recorded. The effective venous pressure can then be plotted against the volume in a graphic representation of the volume of blood that the venous system will accept with a given change of effective venous pressure. Venoconstriction or venodilation would result in lesser or greater distensibility, respectively, of the venous bed. Thus, an alteration in venous volume, determined by this method, implies a change in venous tone assuming that the volume of a blood vessel varies directly with the effective intravascular pressure, if other factors are controlled.

DILUTION TECHNIQUE. Provided certain conditions are fulfilled, the volume of a vascular compartment (cavity or vessel) can be measured in man and animal by analysis of a dilution curve obtained at the outlet of the compartment after rapid injection of an indicator at the inlet to the compartment. The blood content can be calculated from the following equation: $C = Q(60/T)$ where $C$ = the cardiac output per minute, $Q$, the quantity of blood, and $T$, the circulation time. Thus, the volume is represented by the product of cardiac output and mean transit time of the indicator particles, both values being automatically available when cardiac output is quantitated with the dilution technique as described earlier in this chapter.

Calculation of a central blood volume from the cardiac output and mean transit time obtained following the injection of the indicator has been used experimentally and clinically for many years. Its accuracy has been established mathematically by perfusion experiments, by model systems, and *in vivo*. In the latter, the above measurement in the anesthetized dog was compared to the determination of the actual amount of blood in the heart and lungs by injecting cells tagged with $Cr^{51}$ and then calculating the local blood volume from the total radioactivity in the blended homogenate of these organs.

This is the only method presently available which can be used to quantitate regional blood

## TABLE 18.1
*Regional distribution of blood volume*

| Vascular Compartment | Site of Injection | Site of Sample |
|---|---|---|
| 1. Systemic venous blood volume and right side of the heart | Femoral vein | Pulmonary valves |
| 2. Right side of the heart | Superior vena cava | Pulmonary valves |
| 3. Systemic venous volume (1 − 2) | | |
| 4. Lungs and left side of the heart | Pulmonary artery | Aortic valves |
| 5. Pulmonary artery to brachial artery | Pulmonary artery | Brachial artery |
| 6. Left atrium to brachial artery | Left atrium | Brachial artery |
| 7. Pulmonary blood volume (5 − 6) | | |

distribution in man. In addition to central blood volume, it has been used for cardiac volume, systemic venous volume, and other areas. For example, the systemic venous blood volume can be derived from a dilution curve recorded at the right atrium after injection into the femoral vein; the cardiopulmonary blood volume by injection into the right atrium and sampling at carotid artery or aorta. Since, however, in practice a major precaution is adequate mixing at the sites of sampling and injection, in most instances somewhat more accurate results are obtained by combinations of volumes in which adequate mixing is reasonably assured. The following table indicates how this may be accomplished.

## REFERENCES

BRADLEY, S. E., INGELFINGER, F. J., BRADLEY, G. P., AND CURRY, J. J. The estimation of hepatic blood flow in man. J. Clin. Invest., 1945, **24**, 890.

BRAUNWALD, E., FISHMAN, A. P., AND COURNAND, A. Estimation of volume of a circulatory model by the Hamilton and the Bradley methods at varying flow volume ratios. J. Appl. Physiol., 1958, **12**, 445.

BRUNER, H. D. Bubble flow Meter. Methods in Med. Research, 1948, **1**, 80.

COURNAND, A. AND RANGES, H. A. Catheterization of the right auricle in man. Proc. Soc. Exper. Biol. & Med., 1941, **46**, 462.

DENNISON, A. B., SPENCER, M. P., AND GREEN, H. D. A square wave electromagnetic flow meter for application to intact blood vessels. Circulation Res., 1955, **3**, 39.

DuBois, A. B. AND MARSHALL, R. Measurements of pulmonary capillary blood flow and gas exchange throughout the respiratory cycle in man. J. Clin. Invest., 1957, **36**, 1566.

ECKENHOFF, J. E., HAFKENSCHIEL, J. H., HARMEL, M. M., GOODALE, W. T., LUBIN, M., BING, R. J., AND KETY, S. S. Measurement of coronary blood flow by the nitrous oxide method. Am. J. Physiol., 1948, **152**, 356.

ECKSTEIN, R. W., STROUD, M., III, DOWLING, C. V., AND PRITCHARD, W. H. Factors influencing changes in coronary flow following sympathetic nerve stimulation. Am. J. Phys., 1950, **162**, 266.

FICK, A. Ueber die Messung des Blutquantums in den Herzventrikeln. Sitzungsb. der phys. med, Gesellsch. zu Würzburg, 1870, p. 16.

FISHMAN, A. P., McCLEMENT, J., HIMMELSTEIN, A., AND COURNAND, A. Effects of acute anoxia on circulation and respiration in patients with chronic pulmonary disease studied during the steady state. J. Clin. Invest., 1952, **31**, 770.

FORSSMANN, W. I. Die Sondierung des rechten Hertzen. Klin. Wchnschr., 1929, **8**, 2085.

FOX, I. J., BROOKER, L. G. S., HASELTINE, D. W., ESSEX, H. E., AND WORD, E. H. A tricarbocyanine dye for continuous recording of dilution curves in whole blood independent of variations in blood oxygen saturation. Proc. Staff Meet., Mayo Clinic, 1957, **32**, 478.

FRANKLIN, D. L., ELLIS, R. M., AND RUSHMER, R. F. Aortic blood flow in dogs during treadmill exercise. J. Appl. Physiol., 1959, **14**, 809.

FRONEK, A. AND GANZ, V. Measurement of flow in single blood vessels including cardiac output by local thermodilution. Circulation Res., 1960, **8**, 175.

FRY, D. L., MALLOS, A. J., AND CASPER, A. G. T. A catheter tip method for measurement of instantaneous aortic blood velocity. Circulation Res., 1956, **4**, 627.

GASKELL, P. AND BURTON, A. C. Local postural vasomotor reflexes arising from the limb veins. Circulation Res., 1953, **1**, 27.

GIBBS, F. A. A thermoelectric blood flow recorded in the form of a needle. Proc. Soc. Exper. Biol. & Med., 1933, **31**, 141.

GILFORD, S. R., GREGG, D. E., SHADLE, D. W., FERGUSON, T. B., AND MARZETTA, L. A. An improved cuvette densitometer for cardiac determination by the dye-dilution method. Rev. of Sci. Instr., 1953, **24**, 696.

GOODYER, A. V. N., HUVOS, A., ECKHARDT, W. F., AND OSTERBERG, R. O. Thermal dilution curves in intact animals. Circulation Res., 1959, 7, 432.

GREENFIELD, A. D. M. AND PATTERSON, G. C. The effect of small degrees of venous distension on the apparent rate of blood inflow to the forearm. J. Physiol., 1954, **125**, 525.

GREEN, E. W., ZIEGLER, R. F. & KAVANAGH-GRAY, D. Clinical use of retrograde left ventricular catheterization in congenital heart disease (Abstract) Circulation, 1959, **20**, 704.

GREGG, D. E., SHIPLEY, R. E., ECKSTEIN, R. W., ROTTA, A., AND WEARN, J. T. Measurement of mean blood flow in arteries and veins by means of the rotameter. Proc. Soc. Exper. Biol. & Med., 1942, **49**, 267.

GREGG, D. E. AND GREEN, H. D. Registration and Interpretation of normal phasic inflow into a left coronary artery by an improved differential manometric method. Am. J. Physiol., 1940, **130**, 114.

GREGG, D. E., LONGINO, F. H., GREEN, P. A., AND CZERWONKA, L. J. A comparison of coronary flow determined by the nitrous oxide method and by a direct method using the rotameter. Circulation, 1951, **3**, 89.

HAMILTON, W. F., HOWARD, A. R., AND DOW, P. Limitations of the continuous infusion method for measuring cardiac output by dye dilution. Am. J. Physiol., 1953, **175**, 173.

HAMILTON, W. F. AND REMINGTON, J. W. The measurement of the stroke volume frcm the pressure pulse. Am. J. Physiol., 1947, **148**, 14.

HAMILTON, W. F., MOORE, J. W., KINSMAN, J. M., AND SPURLING, R. G. Studies on the circulation. IV. Further analysis of the injection method and of changes in hemodynamics under physiological and pathological conditions. Am. J. Physiol., 1932, **99**, 534.

HENSEL, H., RUEF, J., AND GOLENHOFEN, K. Human muscle and skin flow. Angiology, 1955, **6**, 190.

HERTZMAN, A. B. The blood supply of various skin areas as estimated by the photoelectric plethysmograph. Am. J. Physiol., 1938, **124**, 328.

HERTZMAN, A. B., RANDALL, W. C., and JOCHIM, K. E. The estimation of the cutaneous blood flow with the photoelectric plethysmograph. Am. J. Physiol., 1946, **145**, 716.

HEWLETT, A. W. AND VAN ZWALUWENBURG, J. G. The rate of blood flow in the arm. Heart, 1909, **1**, 87.

HOLT, J. P. Estimation of the residual volume of the right ventricle of the dog's heart. Circulation Res., 1957, **5**, 323.

HUFF, R. L., FELLER, D. D., JUDD, D. V., AND BOGARDUS, G. M. Cardiac output of men and dogs measured by *in vivo* analysis of iodinated ($I^{131}$) human serum albumin. Circulation Res., 1955, **3**, 564.

IRISAWA, H., WILSON, M. F., AND RUSHMER, R. F. Left ventricle as a mixing chamber. Circulation Res., 1960, **8**, 183.

KALMUS, H. P. Electronic flow meter. Natl. Bur. Standards (U. S.), Tech. News Bull. 1953, No. 2, 37.

KETY, S. S. AND SCHMIDT, C. F. The determination of cerebral blood flow in man by use of nitrous oxide in low concentrations. Am. J. Physiol., 1945, **143**, 53.

KETY, S. S. Measurement of regional circulation by local clearance of radioactive sodium. Am. Heart J., 1949, **38**, 321.

KOLIN, A. AND KADO, R. T. Miniaturization of the electromagnetic blood flow meter and its use for the recording of circulatory responses of conscious animals to sensory stimuli. Proc. Natl. Acad. Sc. 1959, **45**, 1312.

KRAMER, K. AND ZIEGENRÜCKER, U. G. Die Bestimmung des Herzminutenvolumens unabhängig von der Sauerstoffsättigung des Blutes, an uneröffneten Arterien mit Hilfe eines neuen im nahen Infrarot absorbierenden Farbstoffes. Klin. Wchnschr., 1957, **35**, 468.

LACY, W. W., UGAZ, C., AND NEWMAN, E. V. The use of indigo carmine for dye dilution curves. Circulation Res., 1955, **3**, 570.

LITTER, J. AND WOOD, J. E., JR. The venous pressure-volume curve of the human leg measured in vivo. J. Clin. Invest., 1954, **33**, 953.

LONGINO, F. H. AND GREGG, D. E. Comparison of cardiac stroke volume as determined by pressure pulse contour method and by a direct method using a rotameter. Am. J. Physiol., 1951, **167**, 721.

MARSHALL, R. J., WANG, Y., AND SHEPHERD, J. T. Components of the "central" blood volume in the dog. Circulation Res., 1960, **8**, 93.

McCLURE, J. A., LACY, W. W., LATIMER, P., AND NEWMAN, E. V. Indicator dilution in an atrioventricular system with competent or incompetent valves. A complete analysis of the behavior of indicator injected simultaneously or continuously into either chamber. Circulation Res., 1959, **7**, 794.

McDONALD, D. A. The relation of pulsatile pressure to flow in arteries. J. Physiol., 1955, **127**, 533.

MENDLOWITZ, M. AND FEITELBERG, S. A bloodless thermal recording digital flowmeter. J. Appl. Physiol., 1956, **8**, 671.

MILNOR, W. R. AND BERTRAND, C. A. Estimation of venous blood volume in the dog by the indicator-dilution method. Circulation Res., 1958, **6**, 55.

MIXTER, G. Respiratory augmentation of inferior caval flow demonstrated by a low-resistance flow meter. Am. J. Physiol., 1953, **172**, 446.

MONTGOMERY, H. AND HORWITZ, O. Oxygen tension of tissues by the polarographic method: introduction: oxygen tension and blood flow of the skin of human extremities. J. Clin. Invest., 1950, **29**, 1120.

PETERSEN, L. H., HELRICH, M., GREEN, L., TAYLOR, C., AND CHOQUETTE, G., Measurement of left ventricular output. J. Appl. Physiol., 1954, **7**, 258.

PIEPER, H. AND WETTERER, E. Strompendel fur Elektrische Registrierung der Blutstromungsgeschwindigkeit. Ztschr. Biol., 1953, **105**, 214.

REINDELL, H., WEYLAND, R., KLEPZIG, H., SCHILDGE, E., AND MUSSHOFF, K. Über Anpassungsvorgänge und Schädigungsmöglichkeiten beim Sportherzen. Schweiz. Ztschr. f. Sportmed. 1953, **1**, 97.

RODBARD, S., GRAHAM, G. R., AND WILLIAMS, F. Continuous and simultaneous measurement of total coronary flow, venous return and cardiac output in the dog. J. Appl. Physiol., 1953, **6**, 311.

ROSE, J. C., BROIDA, H. P., HUFNAGEL, C. A.,

GILLESPIE, J. F., RABIL, P. J., AND FREIS, E. D. A method for the study of the circulation in the dog using a mechanical left ventricle. J. Appl. Physiol., 1955, **7**, 580.

ROSE, J. C., COSIMANO, S. V., HUFNAGEL, C. A., AND MASSULLO, E. A. The effects of exclusion of right ventricle from the circulation in dogs. J. Clin. Invest., 1955, **34**, 1625.

RUSHMER, R. F., FRANKLIN, D. L., AND ELLIS, R. M. Left ventricular dimensions recorded by sonocardiometry. Circulation Res., 1956, **4**, 684.

RUSHMER, R. F. Continuous measurement of left ventricular dimensions in intact unanesthetized dogs. Circulation Res., 1954, **2**, 15.

SABISTON, D. C., KHOURI, E. M., AND GREGG, D. E. Use and application of the cuvette densitometer as an oximeter. Circulation Res., 1957, **5**, 125.

SAPIRSTEIN, L. A. Regional blood flow by fractional distribution of indicators. Am. J. Physiol., 1958, **193**, 161.

SARNOFF, S. J. AND BERGLUND, E. The Potter electroturbinometer. Circulation Res., 1953, **1**, 331.

SCHLAUT, R. C., NOVACK, P., KRAUS, W. L., MOORE, C. B., HAYNES, F. W., AND DEXTER, L. Determination of central blood volume. Comparison of Stewart-Hamilton method with direct measurements in dogs. Am. J. Physiol., 1959, **196**, 499.

SCHREINER, B. F., JR., LOVEJOY, F. W., JR., AND YU, P. N. Estimation of cardiac output from precordial dilution curves in patients with cardiopulmonary disease. Circulation Res., 1959, **7**, 595.

SHIPLEY, R. E. AND WILSON, C. An improved recording rotameter. Proc. Soc. Exper. Biol. & Med., 1951, **78**, 724.

SMITH, H. W., RANGES, H. A., CHASIS, H., AND GOLDRING, W. The dispersion of glomerular activity in the normal and hypertensive kidney. Am. J. Physiol., 1941, **133**, 450.

STARR, I., RAWSON, A. J., SCHROEDER, H. A., AND JOSEPH, N. R. Studies on estimation of cardiac output in man and of abnormalities in cardiac function from heart's recoil and blood's impact. Am. J. Physiol., 1939, **127**, 1.

STEWART, G. N. Research on the circulation time and on the influences which affect it. IV. The output of the heart. J. Physiol., 1897, **22**, 159.

VISSCHER, M. B. AND JOHNSON, J. A. The Fick principle: analysis of potential errors in its conventional application. J. Appl. Physiol., 1953, **5**, 635.

WALDER, D. N. The local clearance of radioactive sodium from muscle in normal subjects and those with peripheral vascular disease. Clin. Sc., 1953, **12**, 153.

WARNER, H. R., SWANN, J. H. C., AND WOOD, E. H. Quantitation of rapid stroke volume changes in man from aortic pulse pressure changes. Am. J. Physiol., 1952, **171**, 777.

WEST, J. W. AND GUZMAN, S. V. Coronary dilatation and constriction visualized by selective arteriography. Circulation Res., 1959, **7**, 527.

WEVER, R. AND ASCHOFF, J. Durchflussmessung mit der diathermiethermostromuhr bei pulsierender stromung. Arch. ges. Physiol., 1956, **262**, 152.

WHITNEY, R. J. The measurement of volume change in limbs. J. Physiol., 1953, **121**, 1.

WOOD, E. H., BOWERS, D., SHEPHERD, G. T., AND FOX, I. J. Oxygen content of "mixed" venous blood in man during various phases of respiration and cardiac cycles in relation to possible errors in measurement of cardiac output by conventional application of the Fick method. J. Appl. Physiol., 1955, **7**, 621.

WOOD, E. H. AND SWAN, H. J. C. Definition of terms and symbols for description of circulatory indicator-dilution curves. J. Appl. Physiol., 1954, **6**, 797.

WOOD, J. E. AND ECKSTEIN, J. W. A tandem forearm plethysmograph for study of acute responses of the peripheral veins of man: The effect of environmental and local temperature change and the effect of pooling blood in the extremities. J. Clin. Invest., 1958, **37**, 41.

*Monographs and Reviews*

ALGIRE, G. H. The transparent chamber technic for observation of the peripheral circulationn. In Peripheral Circulation in Man. A Ciba Foundation Symposium, Little, Brown & Company, Boston, 1954.

ALLEN, G. Extracorporeal circulation. Charles C Thomas, Springfield, Illinois, 1958.

ARNULF, G. Systematic coronary arteriography with acetylcholine cardiac arrest. Progress in Cardiovascular Disease 1959, **2**, 197.

ASMUSSEN, E. AND NIELSEN, M. Cardiac Output during Muscular Work and Its Regulation. Phys. Rev., 1955, **35**, 778.

BRECHER, G. A. Critical review of bristle flowmeter techniques. IRE Trans. on Med. Electronics, 1959, ME-6, 294.

BRECHER, G. A. Venous return. Grune & Stratton, New York, 1955.

DOW, P. Estimation of cardiac output and central blood volume by dye dilution. Physiol. Rev., 1956, **36**, 77.

FULTON, G. P. AND ZWEIFACH, B. Factors regulating blood flow. Proceeding of the Third Conference on Microcirculatory Physiology & Pathology, American Physiological Society, Washington D. C., 1958.

GREGG, D. E. Thermostromuhr. Methods in Med. Research, 1948, **1**, 89.

GREGG, D. E. Coronary circulation in health and disease. Lea & Febiger, Philadelphia, 1950.

HADDY, F. J. Vasomotion in systemic arteries, small vessels and veins determined by direct resistance measurements. Minnesota Med., 1958, **41**, 162.

HAMILTON, W. F. The Physiology of the Cardiac Output. Circulation, 1953, **8**, 527.

LEHMAN, J. S. Coronary arteriography: practical considerations. Progress in Cardiovascular Disease 1959, **2**, 36.

MEIER, P. AND ZIERLER, K. L. On the theory of

the indicator-dilution method for measurement of blood flow and volume. J. Appl. Physiol., 1954, **6,** 731.

MORRIS, L. E. AND BLUMGART, H. L. Velocity of blood flow in health and disease. Circulation, 1957, **15,** 448.

NILSON, N. J. Oximetry. Physiol. Rev., 1960, **40,** 1.

NYBOER, J. Electrical impedance plethysmography. The electrical resistive measure of the blood pulse volume, peripheral and central blood flow. American Lectures on Medical Physics, Charles C Thomas, Springfield, Illinois, 1960.

SCARBOROUGH, W. R. Current status of ballistocardiography. Progress in Cardiovascular Diseases 1959, **2,** 263.

STEWART, G. N. Studies on the circulation in man. Harvey Lectures 1912, **8,** 86.

# *19*

# BLOOD PRESSURE MEASUREMENTS

The development of adequate methods and the overcoming of instrumental obstacles are the essential preliminaries to the solution and consideration of problems dealing with the circulation. One must discuss the various devices and procedures that have been used to study the circulation and to point out their respective merits and shortcomings. Indication will be made of the degree of adequacy and the principles upon which a limited number of these devices operate. Such consideration should reveal the proper basis for the interpretation of the present and subsequent studies of the circulation.

Of the three principal attributes of the circulation, blood pressure, flow and blood volume, the pressure is most easily determined and recorded. Measurements in both man and animal are direct and indirect.

## Direct Blood Pressure Measurements

In the direct approach, a catheter or needle is inserted into a vessel or heart cavity and connected to a hydrostatic column of fluid or to a special device. The pressures thus obtained have been quantitated and studied in almost all parts of the cardiovascular system of animal and man. Direct pressure measurements have value in determining certain aspects of function of the circulation. They should not, however, as is pointed out elsewhere, be used as an index of change in flow through or volume of a blood vessel or heart cavity. Whenever a change in volume is empirically deduced from a change in pressure, potentially active changes in caliber are ignored which are known to occur in every vessel except the capillaries.

MEANS OF PRESSURE PICK-UP. Most of these approaches have been worked out in acute experiments in anesthetized animals, but techniques are now widely used in chronic animal preparations and in humans without anesthesia, and both at rest and during physical activity.

In techniques used only on animals, various regions of the circulatory system are made accessible by a previous operation so that pressures can be determined atraumatically and repeatedly over many months. These include the carotid loop (exteriorization of a carotid artery in a tube of skin) in the dog and rabbit, cardiopexy in the dog (attachment of the apex of the heart to the chest wall just under the skin to permit easy access to the left ventricle), an indwelling silver tube with one end sutured to the exterior surface of a vessel or cardiac cavity and the other end sutured just under the skin, an indwelling polyvinyl tube filled with heparin with one end penetrating a vessel or cardiac cavity and the other plugged end protruding from the skin. In the last instance, the tube is connected directly to the appropriate pressure transducer; in the others, a needle and/or catheter connected to a pressure transducer penetrates the vessel or cavity.

A number of techniques are also applicable to both normal man and animal without previous preparation. Needles and catheters can be passed into many accessible veins and arteries. For the right side of the circulation, one procedure is to "float" a polyvinyl catheter with a balloon tip down the jugular vein into the right ventricle or pulmonary artery without benefit of fluoroscopy. The standard procedure, however, is to pass a catheter under fluoroscopy *via* the jugular vein (dog), or an arm or leg vein (human), into the venae cavae and their venous tributaries from the liver and kidney, or into the right arium, right ventricle or pulmonary artery.

Various techniques have been used in man as well as in animals for direct measurement of pressures in the left heart which is not normally accessible. A catheter passed by the right heart and impacted in a branch of the pulmonary artery, is presumed by some, to give an approximation to the pressure in the venous end of the pulmonary capillaries. Other approaches include transbronchoscopic and transesophageal entrance for pressure recording from the left atrium, left ventricle, and aorta, a percutaneous needle approach through the anterior chest wall for left ventricular pressure, retrograde femoral artery catheterization of the left ventricle through the aortic valves, transeptal left atrial puncture. In the latter technique, the left atrium is punctured by a retractable needle introduced through a cardiac catheter passed up a leg vein, the tip of which is positioned against the interatrial septum.

MEASUREMENT OF NONOSCILLATORY OR NEARLY NONOSCILLATORY PRESSURES. A vertical column of fluid with attached millimeter scale, and with some form of anticoagulant between it and the vessel whose pressure is being tapped, is the only device needed to determine the pressure in most intravascular pressure regions. To measure the pressure, the column is filled from a side tube, and the column is then allowed to seek its own level by drainage into the vessel (fig. 19.1). For the low pressure regions such as the venous system, atrium and pulmonary artery, the column is saline solution; for higher pressure as in the arteries, the column is filled with mercury to keep it short. This is generally in the form of a "U" tube. To minimize the pressure fluctuations, the tubing between the mercury manometer and the vessel is constricted to dampen the oscillations. By placing a float with a writing point on top of the saline or mercury, the venous or arterial blood pressure can be continuously recorded. Such a

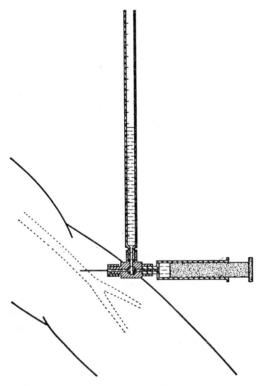

FIG. 19.1. Method for measuring pressure in a superficial vein using a vertical column of saline.

fluid manometer is the basic instrument for pressure recording and most complicated pressure devices are calibrated against such pressure indicators. Very often, complicated pressure devices are used when this simple arrangement would suffice. For measuring intravascular pressure in arterioles, capillaries and venules, cerebrospinal fluid and extravascular pressure in the tissue space in skin, muscle, kidney, subcutaneous tissue, etc., water or saline manometers are used in which little or no fluid enters or leaves the tissue space. This is very important for the addition or removal of even small volumes of fluid may grossly affect the absolute pressure level obtained. This consists of a small hypodermic needle attached to a horizontal glass capillary tube partially filled with sterile saline to a reference line. Except for the water monometer, the rest of the system is filled with air. Upon insertion into the tissue, the pneumatic bulb is compressed, and the meniscus is returned to the reference line when the pressure in the manometer equals the tissue pressure. A correction must be made for the capillarity of the system. This system may also, of course, be used to determine venous pressure.

Since the pressures in veins and extravascular spaces change slowly, they can be accurately indicated visually with these two simple fluid manometer systems. When the mercury filled manometer is applied to an artery, a pressure is recorded which is a rough mean of the existing intra-arterial pressure but which does not normally exist as such. To accurately measure the widely fluctuating pressures during systole and diastole, in the arteries and in the ventricular cavities, or to continuously record electrically or photographically these, as well as nonoscillating pressures, more complicated and sophisticated instrumentation is necessary.

MEASUREMENT OF PRESSURE PULSES. The pattern of variation of pressure occurring with each heart beat (but not the pressure values) can be recorded from the surface of the accessible large arteries and veins without interference with them. In arteries, a crude representation of the pulse can be made by applying the principle that the relatively minute natural excursions of an artery are increased by applying a button with such a tension that the extra-arterial approximates the intra-arterial pressure. This amplified excursion of the vessel wall is further magnified by mechanical levers. In arteries, a more precise indication of the pressure pulse pattern is obtained by following the volumetric change in diameter of the artery by means of a cup system placed over it. An open cup or receiver is firmly pressed to the skin over an artery such as the carotid and connected by tubing to a highly sensitive pressure recorder. For registration of the venous pulse, the patient is placed in the recumbent position to neutralize the effects of gravity, and a cup receiver is applied snugly over the right supraclavicular fossa or over the internal jugular bulb at the margin of the sternocleidomastoid muscle, or over the suprasternal notch. In turn, this is connected by an air system to a sensitive pressure manometer.

Apparatus and requisite techniques for registering pressure curves in a proper manner have improved rapidly in the last few years because of increasing interest in cardiac catheterizations; chief improvements lie in the use of expedients for giving greater amplification, flexibility and ease of operation. The simple principles involved, however, are unchanged, and the classical curves of Wiggers and others, using older optical manometers, have not been improved upon.

Basically, all types of pressure apparatus involve measurement of the displacement of some type of elastic membrane which is moved by generation of pressure in a vessel or cavity. In one group of manometers, an essentially nondis-

tensible conduit (needle, lead tube, cannula or catheter) is filled with fluid and connected to the membrane outside the body; this, in turn, is connected to a form of amplification and recording; in the other, a micromanometer membrane or its equivalent is mounted in a catheter tip at the pressure source, and the catheter serves only as a conduit for wires to the amplifying and recording assembly (fig. 19.2). The detection and transmission of the movements of the membrane can take place by mechanical, optical or electrical means, or by a combination of these principles. Owing to their technical imperfection, purely mechanical systems are now only of historical interest. Pretty much in the same category are manometers which combine optical and electrical systems.

*Manometers with fluid-filled conduit. A. Optical manometers (fig. 19.2).* In the case of the optical type of manometer (which was largely used until recently), the entire system consists of a stiff rubber or metal membrane of minimum diameter connected to a fluid filled conduit of high elasticity and of minimal volume, and which is inserted into the source of pressure variation. Movements of the membrane induced by pressure change are recorded by reflecting from an

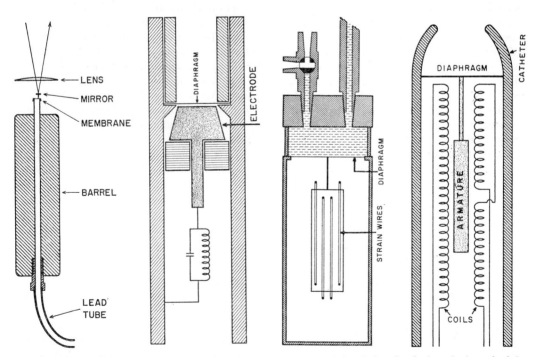

Fig. 19.2. Externally recording pressure gauges. *Left,* principle of the classical optical method for determining biological pressures. A flexible, short, nondistensible, lead tube, offering little damping effect, connects to the pressure source. *Center left,* capacitance transducer; *center right,* strain gauge transducer; and *right,* catheter mounted inductance transducer.

attached mirror a weightless beam of light as a lever to give rapid response with adequate sensitivity. A number of different forms of such manometers have been developed and widely used.

B. *Electrical transducers.* The common feature of the methods dependent on electrical principles is that the movement of the manometer membrane is transformed into electrical energy which is then transferred to a recorder. In practice, the transformation of the pressure impulse is effected by a piezo-electric effect, or by a change in capacitance, resistance and inductance. The piezo-electric principle which depends on the difference in potential occurring in certain crystals exposed to mechanical pressure, is little used since stationary difference of crystal potential cannot be maintained and constant pressures cannot be accurately measured.

For most present day determinations of biological pressures, the pressure fluctuations in a cavity or vessel are transmitted as in the optical manometer through a long nondistensible catheter filled with fluid. This activates an electronic pressure transducer in which movements of a stiff membrane with minimal fluid displacement and high frequency produces a change in capacitance, resistance or inductance.

One of the first of the electronic pressure transducers was devised by Lilly (1942), in which a stiff metal membrane separated from an electrode by a very small air gap, formed a condenser. Movements of the membrane relative to the electrode vary the capacitance which is measured by a radio frequency circuit. This device is rather temperature sensitive and has considerable zero pressure drift (fig. 19.2).

The electronic transducer in most common use today is the resistance wire strain gauge. Strain sensitive wire responds to a change in pressure with a change in the resistance to flow of an electric current. A membrane is displaced by increased pressure in a chamber attached to the pressure source (fig. 19.2).

MANOMETERS MOUNTED IN AN EMPTY CATHETER TIP. In this type of gauge, the pressure sensitive element is mounted in the catheter tip, the catheter contains no fluid, serving only as a conduit for wires leading to an amplifier. Inductance pressure gauges of this type are coming into use in which the variable mutual inductance between a pair of coils can be altered by changing the position of an iron core within its magnetic field. If the iron core connected to the center of an elastic membrane is mounted between two coils, move-

ment of the membrane moves the core within the coils, changing their inductance. Change in inductance, monitored by an appropriate bridge circuit indicates the extent of membrane displacement (fig. 19.2). This instrument was first devised by Wetterer and has been considerably modified and improved by others. The strain gauge principle has also been applied to a micromanometer mounted in the end of a catheter. In this, a strain wire wrapped around a metal reed with multiple longitudinal slits is stretched by the pressure source.

Both the inductance and strain gauge type of micromanometer faithfully record the pressure pattern but are difficult and expensive to build. Inductance gauges have been used in animals and, at times, in humans, but their use has been limited because it has not been possible to determine accurately the zero pressure with the Wetterer type. Although the strain gauge type does not have this disadvantage and has been used with some patients, its initial expense is more, and it has the added drawback that no way has been found to disconnect it from its catheter which wears out first.

AMPLIFICATION AND RECORDING. The signal from the various pressure transducers (except the optical manometer) is amplified electronically to drive a high frequency galvanometer or oscilloscope. The devices used to record the pressure pulses are the optical manometer with camera, the direct pen writing galvanometer, the optical galvanometer, and the cathode ray oscilloscopic camera. Many types of pressure transducer-amplifier combinations are available commercially. In terms of ascending order of frequency of response, the systems may be graded as follows: the direct writing galvanometer, the optical manometer, the optical galvanometer, and the oscilloscope. However, no ideal system exists at present. For any specific application, the combination of transducer, recorder, and amplifier, is a compromise of sensitivity, stability, convenience of use, and frequency of response.

FREQUENCY OF MANOMETER SYSTEMS. The accuracy with which a manometer system records change of pressure without lag and with correct phasic relations depends on its natural frequency. Reasonably good reproduction of a wave form can be recorded by such a system which has uniform response to the tenth harmonic of its fundamental frequency. With a heart rate of 240 beats per minute, the pulse frequency is 4 per second, and its tenth harmonic is 40 cycles per second.

With such a frequency, rapid changes in pressure are fairly well recorded.

The frequency response characteristics of the entire system of transducer, amplifier, and galvanometer must be determined rather than that of a component part, since the net frequency is limited by the lowest component of the system. The frequency of a manometer with a fluid filled conduit is governed by its effective mass and the elasticity of its membrane, i.e., frequency is increased by a decrease in the mass to be moved by the pressure and by a decrease in the size and distensibility of the membrane. In the case of the optical manometer, this is the sole determinant of frequency response since the rest of the system is a weightless light beam which does not affect the frequency. The normal frequency of such manometers is 120 to 160 double vibrations per second. In the case of the other types of manometer with a fluid filled conduit, the frequency is often limited as well by the type of recorder used and may vary from 5 to 100 cycles per sec. In the manometer in which the catheter is used only as a conduit for wires, the basic frequency is generally higher than in the other types and is determined solely by the characteristics of the membrane at the catheter tip since there is no fluid space central to the membrane.

The fact that a recording manometer system has an adequate frequency and sensitivity does not insure that the recorded pressures are free of artefacts. Impact of a cardiac cavity or vessel on the side or tip of the catheter very often leads to very large artefacts in the recorded pressure curve, which invalidates a goodly portion of records taken in catheterization laboratories for diagnostic purposes. In the manometer with a fluid filled catheter, this type of artefact is maximal and, despite all precautions, it is very often impossible to obtain technically perfect records. The response characteristics of such curves can be somewhat improved by "critical damping" through mechanically constricting the conduit system. However, this is not to be recommended since it is almost impossible to maintain a fixed degree of damping, and slight increases in it completely deform the pressure curve. In the pressure manometers in which the membrane is mounted in the catheter tip, the phasic pressure patterns invariably are excellent and artefacts are almost nonexistent. This is the pressure manometer of the future.

STANDARD ZERO REFERENCE PLANE FOR PRESSURE MEASUREMENTS. The numerical value obtained from pressure measurements in the cardiovascular system depends, of course, upon the horizontal plane to which zero pressure is referred. Most commonly, this has reference to the assumed level of the center of the atrium. The exact level is easy to establish in the open-chest animal or human, by adjusting the needle or catheter end attached to the recording manometer to the level of the midpoint of the atrium. This is zero pressure. When the chest is closed, it is difficult to determine precisely the proper zero point of reference and to obtain comparable figures in different subjects or in a series of measurements. It is not surprising, therefore, that many different reference planes or levels have been used. Possibly, the one closest to the truth is that described by Winsor and Burch. The reference level or heart level used is an axis running transversely through the thorax at the point of junction of a plane passing cross-sectionally through the fourth intercostal space adjacent to the sternum, with a frontal plane passing midway between the posterior surface of the body and the xiphoid process of the sternum. Horizontal planes passing through this axis are the zero pressure reference levels to be used for that particular position of the patient.

This, however, measures the intravascular pressure against the atmospheric pressure as a reference. Most vessels are imbedded in tissues which have a significant tissue pressure that is either lower (in the thorax) or higher (in the abdomen and skeletal muscle) than the atmospheric pressure. For precise quantitation, the intravascular pressure should be measured against the extravascular or tissue pressure which is around the vessel. The terms, effective, transmural or net pressure, have been introduced to indicate the pressure difference between the intravascular and extravascular pressure. Precise determination of extravascular pressure is unreliable and the artefacts are especially large in measuring tissue pressure in solid organs, especially the heart, and least in recording pressure surrounding the great vessels and the heart. Intrathoracic pressure is taken as an approximation for the latter, but even here, calculation of transmural pressure must be made on the basis of the immediately contiguous intrathoracic pressure since regional intrathoracic pressure is quite variable.

## Indirect Blood Pressure Measurements

### *Human*

Although the blood pressure can be determined in man by the insertion of a hollow, wide-bore needle into an artery and connecting it with a suitable manometer, such a method is usually reserved for human cardiopulmonary diagnostic work. Convenience and safety demand that any method for general clinical use must be indirect. The principle employed consists in balancing air pressure against the pressure of the blood in the brachial artery and then estimating the former by means of a mercury or an aneroid manometer.

The instrument used for this purpose includes a flat rubber bag covered by an undistensible envelope of cotton fabric. The cavity of the bag is connected by a length of rubber tubing with the manometer and by another tube with a hand bulb or small pump. By this means the bag can be inflated to any desired pressure. A small valve between the bulb or pump and the bag permits the escape of air, and the reduction of the pressure as required. The uninflated rubber bag (usually referred to as the cuff or armlet) which should be at least 12 cm. wide is wrapped snugly around the upper arm just above the elbow. The bag is then inflated until the air pressure within it overcomes the arterial pressure and obliterates the arterial lumen. The pressure is increased a little beyond this point and is then cautiously reduced again,[1] by the release of the valve, until the arterial pressure just overcomes the air pressure and blood escapes beyond the cuff into the peripheral section of the artery. At this instant the pressure in the bag is read from the manometer. Since the air pressure practically balances the systolic arterial pressure the manometer reading must indicate the value of the latter. It is essential to the method that the manometer reading be taken at the instant when the blood escapes beneath the cuff.

One of the three methods, the *palpatory, oscillatory* or *auscultatory*, may be employed to determine the latter. In all three procedures the value for the lateral pressure in the brachial artery is obtained, whereas direct methods, which entail the introduction of a straight, unbranched cannula, or a large-bore needle, into an artery, measure the end pressure. The latter is greater because it includes not only the lateral pressure on the elastic arterial wall, but also that derived from the conversion of the kinetic energy of the moving blood column as it meets the obstruction, as well as an increment of pressure caused by the reflected wave from the obstruction.

*A. The palpatory method.* In this method the examiner takes the moment that the pulse is felt

at the wrist as the index of the systolic pressure. This method is now rarely used since it lacks accuracy. It assumes that the first escape of blood beneath the cuff will cause pulsation in the peripheral artery, but there is no evidence that the amount of blood which escapes beneath the cuff when the artery first opens is sufficient to produce a pulse wave detectable by the finger. Definite pulsation may not occur until the cuff pressure has been lowered 5 to 10 mm. below the point when the artery first becomes pervious. This method therefore gives readings that are too low. Another disadvantage of the palpatory method is that the diastolic pressure cannot be measured satisfactorily.

*B. The oscillatory method.* In this method a tambour or capsule covered with a very delicate membrane, or a second bag connected with the cuff, is used to pick up and magnify the pulsations transmitted from the artery to the upper edge of the latter. The pulsations are made to appear as oscillations of the indicator needle on the clock-face dial of an aneroid manometer. Pressures are marked by figures on the dial; as the cuff is inflated or deflated, the needle moves to indicate the applied pressure at the moment. At pressures exceeding systolic the oscillations are minimal, but as the pressure is gradually lowered and the pulsations pass beneath the cuff, a sudden increase in their amplitude and duration occurs. This is the criterion of systolic pressure. The oscillations show little change in magnitude as the cuff is deflated further, until the pressure has fallen to the diastolic level at which they suddenly become smaller. At this instant the figure on the dial to which the needle points is noted.

*C. The auscultatory method.* This procedure is the one generally employed clinically. It was introduced in 1905 by the Russian physician Korotkow. Certain sounds heard during auscultation of the brachial artery below the cuff are taken as the criteria for the systolic and diastolic pressures. Under ordinary circumstances if a stethoscope is placed upon the brachial or any other artery, no sound can be heard, the flow of blood along the aterial channels being inaudible. If however the artery is compressed by the manometer cuff so as to completely arrest the flow of blood for a moment, a sharp light tapping sound in rhythm with the heart beat will be heard when the pressure in the cuff is again released and falls just sufficiently to permit the arterial lumen to open and allow a jet of blood to pass beyond. As the pressure in the cuff is progressively lowered the sound undergoes a series of changes in quality and intensity.

Four phases of the sound, each having its distinctive character, may be heard in succession in the normal individual, as the pressure is gradually reduced from about 120 to 80 mm. of mercury or less. These are given below with the average pressures at which they are normally heard:

---

[1] Should deflation be carried out too rapidly the mercurial type of clinical manometer shows a considerable lag, due to the time required for the air above the mercury column to reach atmospheric pressure. The rate of deflation should not exceed from 2 to 3 mm. Hg per second.

*Sounds of Korotkow*

Phase   I. Sudden appearance of a clear, but
          often faint, tapping sound growing
          louder during the succeeding 10 mm.
          Hg fall in pressure.

Phase  II. The sound takes on a murmurish
          quality during the next 15 mm. fall
          in pressure.

Phase III. Sound changes little in quality but
          becomes clearer and louder during
          the next 15 mm. fall in pressure.

Phase IV. Muffled quality lasting throughout
          the next 5 to 6 mm. Hg fall. After
          this all sound disappears.

The beginning of the first sound is taken as the *index of systolic pressure*. As it is quite faint at its commencement it may not be caught at this time by the ear of the inexperienced, or if the observer's hearing is distracted by other sounds. The sound then will not be picked up until the pressure has dropped below the level at which it could be heard in quiet surroundings, and the reading of the systolic pressure will be too low.

The pressure at the time of complete disappearance of the fourth sound is taken as the index of the diastolic pressure. This sound coincides with the moment that the blood escapes beneath the armlet in a continuous stream rather than intermittently.

It should be clearly understood that arterial blood pressure cannot be measured with precision by means of sphygomanometers. It is attended by inaccuracies dependent upon the presence of normal arrhythmia and respiration, and the resistance of the tissues of the part. To compensate for the latter, a rule of thumb is that the inflatable arm bag should be approximately 20 per cent wider than the arm diameter, or approximately 12 cm. for adults, 8 cm. for children less than 8 years, 5 cm. for children less than 4 years, 2½ cm. for children less than 1 year. Despite use of such cuffs, a mean error of ±8 mm. Hg may be expected in individual readings of systolic and diastolic pressures. In the arms of people with much fat tissue, the error is further exaggerated: in subjects with well-defined arrhythmias, deep breathing, or with an abnormal arterial wall, the errors are still larger. Variations in the resistance of the arterial wall in different individuals, as a result of sclerotic changes or simple hypertonus of the muscular coat, give readings that are too high. Repeated compression and decompression just before the actual determination is made may soften the artery or remove any spasm of its walls sufficiently to reduce this source of inaccuracy. Though lower readings as a rule are not obtained in a normal individual by repeated readings, in others with apparently normal arteries, the reading obtained after the third or fourth trial may, as a result of

the reduction in tone of the vessel wall, be lower than the initial observation by several millimeters.

*Animals*

These involve placing a cuff around a carotid loop in the dog (Van Leersum), or around the tail or foot of the rat, and detecting the onset of blood flow under the cuff as its pressure is lowered. In the dog this is done with the auscultatory method; in the rat, the volume of blood passing into the tail or foot when the cuff pressure drops below systolic, is insufficient to cause an audible sound. The first blood flow under the cuff and, hence the volume change, is detected in the tail by noting the onset of volume change in a small water-filled plethysmograph just beyond the cuff, or by having the expanding tail press on a carbon button causing a change in tone pitch in ear phones. In the foot, the increase in volume with the lowering of cuff pressure is indicated by the sudden decrease in current flow from a photocell which receives light through the foot.

## Use of Simultaneous Measurements of Pressure, Flow, and Volume

In addition to the direct information supplied by blood pressure measurements, knowledge of its association with other phenomena in the circulation, such as blood volume and blood flow, has contributed greatly to advancement in this field. Some reference has already been made to this relationship in chapters 15 and 18. As has been pointed out here, differential pressure measurements in the aorta have enabled calculation of the patterns of flow velocity even in the aorta of man, and the use of such a principle when the pressure pick-up is mounted in a rigid sleeve or vessel, has permitted, in animals, not only patterns of flow velocity but also absolute values for phasic and mean flow. Pressure determination has been particularly useful in estimating the contractility of the heart muscle and the distensibility of the ventricles, arteries and veins. Because of its extreme importance, consideration of this subject will also be found in chapters 14 and 20.

## REFERENCES

ALLISON, P. R. AND LINDEN, R. J. Bronchoscopic measurement of left auricular pressure. Circulation 1953, 7, 669.

BURTON, A. C. AND YAMADA, S. Relation between blood pressure and flow in the human forearm. J. Appl. Physiol., 1951, 4, 329.

BURTON, A. C. Peripheral Circulation. Ann. Rev. Physiol., 1953, **15**, 220.

COLERIDGE, J. C. G. AND LINDEN, R. J. The measurement of effective atrial pressure. J. Physiol., 1954, **126**, 304.

COURNAND, A., LANSON, H. D., BLOOMFIELD, R. A., BREED, S. S., AND BALDWIN, E. DEF. Recording of right heart pressures in man. Proc. Soc. Exper. Biol. & Med., 1944, **55**, 34.

FRANK, O. Ein neues optisches Federmanometer. Ztschr. Biol., 1925, **82**, 49.

FRY, D. L., NOBLE, F. W., AND MALLOS, A. J. An evaluation of modern pressure recording systems. Circulation Res., 1957, **5**, 40.

GAUER, O. H. AND GIENAPP, E. A miniature pressure recording device. Science, 1950, **112**, 404.

GREEN, E. W. Clinical use of retrograde left ventricular catheterization in congenital heart disease (Abstract). Circulation 1959, **20**, 704.

GREGG, D. E., ECKSTEIN, R. W., AND FINEBERG, M. H. Pressure pulses and blood pressure values in unanesthetized dogs. Am. J. Physiol., 1937, **118**, 399.

GREGG, D. E. AND DEWALD, D. The immediate effects of the occlusion of the coronary veins on the collateral blood flow in the coronary arteries. Am. J. Physiol., 1938, **124**, 435.

GREGG, D. E. AND ECKSTEIN, R. W. Measurements of intra myocardial pressure. Am. J. Physiol., 1941, **132**, 781.

HAMILTON, W. F., BREWER, G., AND BROTMAN, I. Pressure pulse contours in the intact animal; analytical description of the new high frequency hypodermic manometer with illustrative curves of simultaneous arterial and intracardiac pressures. Am. J. Physiol., 1934, **107**, 427.

LAMBERT, E. H. Strain gauges: resistance wire. Medical Physics, Vol. 2, p. 1090. The Year Book Publishers, Chicago, 1950.

LANDIS, E. M. The capillary pressure in frog mesentery as determined by micro-injection methods. Am. J. Physiol., 1925, **75**, 548.

LATEGOLA, M. AND RAHN, H. A self-guiding catheter for cardiac and pulmonary arterial catheterization and occlusion. Proc. Soc. Exper. Biol. & Med., 1953, **84**, 667.

LILLY, J. C., LEGALLAIS, V., AND CHERRY, R. A variable capacitor for measurements of pressure and mechanical displacements; a theoretical analysis and its experimental evaluations. J. Appl. Physics, 1947, **18**, 613.

MUNNEL, E. R. AND GREGG, D. E. The production of chronic systemic hypertension in the rat with a small adjustable renal artery clamp. J. Lab. & Clin. Med., 1950, **36**, 660.

ROBERTS, L. N., SMILEY, J. R., AND MANNING, G. W. A comparison of direct and indirect blood-pressure determinations. Circulation, 1953, **8**, 232.

ROSS, J., BRAUNWALD, E., AND MORROW, A. G. Transseptal left atrial puncture. New technique for measurement of left atrial pressure in man. Am. J. Cardiology 1959, **3**, 653.

RUDOLPH, A. M. AND PAUL, M. H. Chronic catheterization of pulmonary and systemic circulations: a technique for repeated measurement of cardiac output and pulmonary and systemic pressures in the unanesthetized dog. J. Appl. Physiol., 1957, **10**, 327.

SODEMAN, W. A. Direct venous pressure determinations by use of a new instrument. Am. Heart J., 1952, **43**, 687.

SOULIE, P., LAURENS, P., BOUCHARD, F., CORNU, C., AND BRIAL, E. Enrigistrement des pressions et des bruits intracardiaques a l'aide micromanometre. Bull. et mém. Soc. méd. hôp. Paris, 1957, **22, 23, 24**, 713.

WARNICK, A. AND DRAKE, E. H. A new intracardiac pressure measuring system for infants and adults. Institute of Radio Engineers National Convention Record, Part 9, New York, 1958.

WETTERER, E. AND PEIPER, H. Eine neue manometrische sonde mit elektrischer transmission. Ztschr. Biol., 1952, **105**, 49.

WIGGERS, C. J. AND BAKER, W. R. A new universal optical manometer. J. Lab. & Clin. Med., 1924, **10**, 54.

WINSOR, T. AND BURCH, G. E. Phlebostatic axis and phlebostatic level. Reference levels for venous pressure measurement in man. Proc. Soc. Exper. Biol. & Med., 1945, **58**, 165.

WOOD, E. H. Physical response characteristics of pressure transducers for the reproduction of physiological phenomena. Communications and Electronics, 1956, **23**, 56.

### Monographs and Reviews

American Medical Association, Recommendations for human blood pressure determination by sphygmomanometers. J. A. M. A., 1951, **147**, 632.

GREEN, H. D. Circulatory system: Methods. In Medical Physics, 1950, p. 208. Year Book Publishers.

HANSEN, A. T. Pressure measurement in the human organism. Acta physiol. scandinav., 1949, **19**, suppl., 68.

HARKEN, D. E. Technic of left heart catheterization. Methods in Medical Research, 1958, **7**, 94. Year Book Publishers.

NOBLE, F. W. Electrical methods of blood pressure recording. Charles C Thomas, Publisher, Springfield, Illinois, 1953.

RAPPAPORT, E. AND DEXTER, L. Pulmonary "capillary" pressure. Methods in Medical Research, 1958, **7**, 85.

# 20

## THE HEART AS A PUMP

### Functional Anatomy

Knowledge of the functional anatomy of cardiac contraction is essential for an understanding of cardiac action. Actually, the two ventricles have different anatomical and functional characteristics. The energy released during systole of the heart represents the combined effects of various bundles of myocardial fibers. The contribution of each bundle depends not only on its contractile power but also on its anatomical orientation within the cardiac walls.

STRUCTURE. Four valve rings of dense connective tissue join to form a fibrous skeleton of the heart. The atria and arterial trunks are attached to the superior surface of this fibrous skeleton; to its inferior aspect are fastened the arteriovenous (A-V) valves and ventricular chambers. The atrial musculature is thin and arranged as bands radiating from the sulcus terminalis. The atria have two muscular systems, one common to both atria and encircling them, the other arranged at right angles and independent for each atrium. From a functional point of view, the ventricular musculature has two groups of myocardial bundles, the spiral muscles and the deep constrictor muscles (fig. 20.1). The superficial spiral muscles which arise from the mitral and tricuspid rings cover very thinly almost the entire surface of both ventricles to a depth of about 1 mm. They course diagonally around the surface of both ventricles to converge at the apex where they are strongly twisted and where they make up the full wall thickness. They penetrate to the interior of both ventricles to form there its inner thin layer of spiral muscle and the lower third of the interventricular septum. They spiral upward in reverse directions to form the papillary muscles from which fibrous tendons (chordae tendinae) attach to the valve leaflets (A-V valves). The inner and outer spiral muscles follow oblique directions about 90° apart since they spiral in opposite directions. As they contract, the oblique traction by the outer layer is opposed by tension in the opposite direction by the inner layer. The

net result of their action is a shortening of the ventricular cavities longitudinally rather than a rotation of the ventricles. Interposed between the thin exterior and interior spiral muscles are the heavy constrictor muscles which make up the basilar two-thirds of the septum and lateral wall of the left ventricle. In the right ventricle these deep circular fibers from a thin middle layer but its contribution to thickness is small compared to that of the inner and outer spiral layers. Because the left ventricular wall contains a large mass of circularly arranged constrictor fibers, its contraction would be expected to result predominantly in a reduced ventricular diameter with minimal shortening from apex to base whereas in the right ventricle with its dominance of spiral muscle, the ventricle should shorten with little movements of its lateral wall.

ROLE OF THE PERICARDIUM. The pericardium is a double-walled sac containing a few cubic centimeters of serous fluid which gives a smooth lubricated surface for the heart's movements. Although its potential volume is larger than that occupied by the normal heart in diastole, still, after moderate enlargement of the contained heart, the interpericardial sac pressure rises greatly with small volume influence. Thus, in case of left ventricular stress and enlargement such as occur in hypertension, the pericardium restrains disatolic expansion especially of the right ventricle, and therefore, limits right ventricular work. This protects the left ventricle from overload and the pulmonary circulation from congestion. The pericardium also protects against tricuspid or mitral valve regurgitation at high ventricular filling pressures. However, congenital lack of a pericardium is not uncommon in animals and humans who live to a ripe old age without evidence of cardiac distress.

ATRIAL AND VENTRICULAR BLOOD VOLUME. In man the atrial capacities are slightly greater than those of the corresponding ventricles, thus assuring the presence of sufficient blood to fill the ventricular cavities completely. In the dead hu-

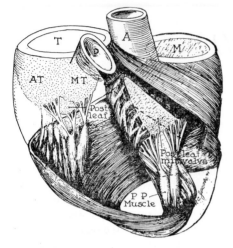

SUPERFICIAL BULBO SPIRAL          SUPERFICIAL SINO SPIRAL

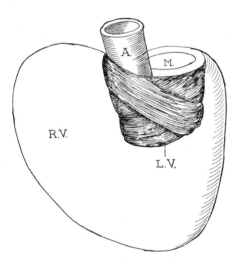

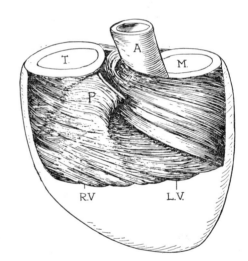

DEEP BULBO SPIRAL               DEEP SINO SPIRAL

Fig. 20.1. Demonstration of the superficial and deep ventricular myocardial bundles (Robb and Robb, Am. Heart J., 1942, 23, 455).

man heart, the right atrium has 163 cc., the right ventricle 137 cc., the left atrium 140 cc., the left ventricle 120 cc.

Such *in vitro* measurements are of limited interest and do not give information as to the diastolic volume of the ventricles during life, or the portion of the diastolic volume which is expelled nor the portion which remains in the ventricle at the end of each heart beat. It is now well-established that the heart is not completely emptied of blood during ventricular contraction, i.e., a residual ventricular volume of blood remains at the

end of ejection. Nylin was the first to demonstrate that the diastolic volume of the human heart under working conditions is about 540 cc., of which about 140 cc. is ejected by the two ventricles. The difference, 400 cc., is an estimate of the volume of blood which is normally available at the end of systole for refilling the two ventricles. However, what fraction of this is in the atria and what fraction is in the ventricles is not known. Observations in dogs indicate that the right ventricle and left ventricle both empty in a fractionate manner, ejecting 40 to 45 per cent of their end diastolic volume with each stroke and retaining a residual volume of 55 to 60 per cent. The stroke volume in the resting untrained human approximates 60 cc. On the basis of the dog, this would give a diastolic volume of 130 cc. in the human ventricle. As yet, precise observations have not been made in humans although attempts have been made to do so for the right ventricle, and it does appear that this volume is increased in congestive heart failure.

PATTERNS OF VENTRICULAR EMPTYING. Traditional concept has it that the ventricles eject blood primarily by shortening of the longitudinal axis accompanied by a rotational action comparable to a wringing out of a wet rag. Direct measurements, however, of changing ventricle dimensions in unanesthetized dogs by cinefluorographic techniques with contrast media, by intraventricular gauges and by external resistance gauges, indicate that the left ventricle resembles a cylinder with a conoid apical segment. The cylindrical portion is made of a strong cuff of deep fibers between thin layers of spiral muscle. The conoid section is made primarily of closely woven spiral muscle entering and leaving "the vortex." Left ventricular contraction involves primarily a reduction in transverse diameter. This action accounts for most of the power and volume of the ejection since the contained volume decreases with the square of the radius in a cylinder. There is relatively little rotation or shortening of the longitudinal axis. All this would be expected since the bulk of the fibers is circularly arranged.

By contrast, right ventricular ejection of blood can be effected by three means. (1) Longitudinal shortening of the chamber, i.e., base moving toward apex is the most obvious movement. This might be expected since the inner and outer layers of spiral muscle making up most of the right ventricle are oriented at about 90° from each other. Hence, simultaneous contraction of the two layers of spiral muscle produces shortening along the longitudinal axis of the right ventricle chamber. (2) The right ventricular chamber is roughly triangular in shape, being bounded by a convex septal well and a concave free or lateral wall which enclose a crescent shaped area between them. The free wall of the right ventricle moves toward the convex surface of the septum. This movement although slight could be extremely effective in moving blood, and it would operate like a bellows used to kindle a fire, i.e., since the sides of the ventricle or bellows are large compared to their enclosed space, slight movement toward each

other should cause displacement of a large volume of blood. (3) Contraction of the left ventricle must produce a greater curvature of the septum, and thus, since this is attached to the right ventricular lateral wall, traction on it will add to the bellows action. The action of this or the other factors has not been quantitated. That it can be a potent mechanism, however, is borne out by the observation that right ventricular ejection can be maintained when the free wall of the right ventricle has been almost completely destroyed by cautery in the dog or by coronary occlusion in man.

The reduction in diameter and circumference necessary to eject the stroke volume is different in the two ventricles because of their shape and manner of contraction but they are small in both cases. With present methodology, it is not possible to quantitate the extent of myocardial fiber shortening associated with ventricular ejection of blood. However, some rough estimates are instructive. Under normal circumstances the ventricles function at relatively large diastolic and systolic dimensions since possibly half their contained volume is not ejected with each contraction. If the left ventricle is regarded roughly as a cylinder which ejects approximately half its contained volume of 130 cc., then the diameter can decrease from 5.2 cm. to 3.9 cm., and the circumference from 16.5 cm. to 12.1 cm.

The right ventricle has some semblance to a segment of a sphere, and a small shortening of its fibers will eject a large blood volume. If its volume is also 130 cc., and half is ejected, the diameter will decrease from 6.3 cm. to 5.1 cm., and the circumference from 19.8 cm. to 16.0 cm. The average shortening of the right and left ventricle walls might be estimated as 20 per cent and 25 per cent of the diastolic size. The extent of myocardial shortening also varies greatly for the same volume of ejection depending on the size of the cavity or the fiber length before ejection takes place. It takes a much smaller reduction in fiber length of a larger sphere or cylinder to eject the same volume. For example, if in a heart enlarged by congestive failure of the circulation the right ventricle contains 500 cc. blood, then ejection of 60 cc. will decrease the diameter from 9.8 cm. to 9.4 cm., or by 0.4 cm., and the circumference from 30.8 cm. to 29.5 cm.

It would be expected that the shortening of muscle fibers of the lateral wall of the right ventricle at different depths would be similar since the wall is so thin. In the left ventricle, however, the circumferentially arranged deep constrictor fibers form a cuff of muscle making up most of the muscle wall which is so thick that the inner layers near the endocardium have a much smaller radius and circumference than the outer layers near the epicardium. With the onset of contraction, the inner layers must shorten more than the outer layers in ejecting a particular volume. Thus, presumably, no two layers of the myocardial fibers shorten to the same extent during ejection.

## Pressure and Volume Events of a Cardiac Cycle

It is important to consider the means by which the heart cavities are able to pump the necessary volume of blood from the systemic veins to the arteries and to impart to it a pressure sufficient to cause a continuous flow of blood through the capillaries. The sequence of events can be considered in terms of atrial, ventricular, and arterial pressures, and of variations in the volume of and means of emptying the cardiac cavities. The events of the cardiac cycle for both left and right hearts are depicted in figure 20.2. Terminology and symbols given to the various phases of the cardiac cycle by Wiggers are used. The curves are synthesized in part from records obtained in dogs. In the main, however, pressure values and temporal relations are based upon pressure pulses obtained from all four cardiac chambers, pulmonary artery and aorta, by direct needle puncture at the time of thoracotomy in human subjects clinically free of cardiovascular disease. The schematized volume curve is based on recordings of volume of both ventricles in which a cardiometer has been placed around the ventricles up to their A-V junction in the open-chest dog. No adequate recordings of moment-to-moment changes in volume of a ventricular cavity during a cardiac cycle are yet available.

Sequence of events. Ventricular contraction begins at "1", and almost instantly closure of the mitral valve occurs as the ventricular pressure curve exceeds the left atrial pressure curve. The "c" wave in the atrial curve begins at this time and is due to the rising pressure in the ventricle which is transmitted through the closed A-V valves which bulge into the atrium. It marks the onset of the left ventricular isometric contraction period which consists of a slow and then a rapid phase of pressure rise. The isometric contraction period in which the ventricle is a closed cavity, ends at "2" the moment at which the ventricular pressure exceeds the aortic pressure. The aortic valves are forced open as indicated by the onset of the pressure rise in the aorta, and blood is discharged from the ventricular cavity.

From the moment that the aortic valves open at "2", until they close at "4", ventricle and aorta are common cavities and, consequently, their pressure pulses have a similar contour. Ventricular volume starts now to decrease. The period of maximum ejection lasts until the peak of the aortic pressure pulse and is followed by a period of reduced ejection which is completed at the beginning of the incisura (3), a point which is often difficult to identify on the records. This is the end of ejection of blood and of ventricular systole. The ventricular cavity still retains more than half its original diastolic volume. During protodiastole (3 to 4), the pressure within the ventricle continues to decline and this phase ends at the moment of aortic valve closure (4), i.e., at the bottom of the incisura of the aortic pressure curve. Isometric relaxation (4 to 5) then follows. At this time, the atrium and ventricle are relaxed and the left ventricular cavity is completely closed off from the atrium and aorta and only partially filled.

During the preceding ventricular contraction, the left atrial pressure undergoes a temporary abrupt decline as a result of an artefact imposed by cardiac movement. As blood, however, pours into the cavity of the left atrium from the pulmonary veins, the atrial pressure rises continuously to the end of the isometric relaxation period forming the "V" wave. This atrial blood which has accumulated during the previous ventricular contraction is now transferred to the ventricle. Ventricular filling begins at the time the intraventricular pressure drops below the intra-atrial pressure and the A-V valves reopen (5).

The period of rapid ventricular filling, i.e., the early diastolic inflow period is marked by a continuous decline in ventricular pressure and in the "V" wave of the atrial pressure curve. Inflow into a ventricular cavity is regulated by mechanisms operating in both its systole and diastole. Since no blood enters the ventricles until it has passed through the atria, it is important to know their means of filling. It is not possible to measure flow into the atria, but since they are continuous with the venae cavae without intervening valves, vena caval flow should indicate atrial flow. Caval flow into the atria shows three phases. It is reduced nearly to zero during atrial contraction. During ventricular diastole inflow is considerable, but the volume of atrial inflow is greater during ventricular systole when the A-V valves are closed and no blood can enter the ventricle, than during ventricular diastole when A-V valves are open and atria and ventricles form a common cavity.

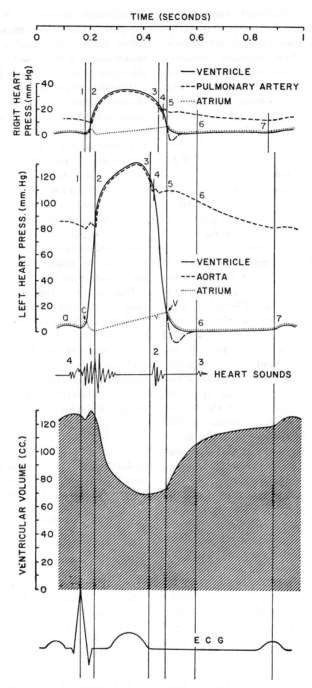

FIG. 20.2. Schematization of the sequential cardiac events relating pressure-volume changes to the phono- and electrocardiograms: *upper tracings*, right and left heart pressures; *middle tracings*, phono-cardiogram and ventricular volume; and *bottom tracings*, electrocardiogram. Vertical lines correspond temporally to the following: 1, onset of isometric ventricular contraction and closure of A-V valves; 2, end of isometric contraction and opening of semilunar valves; 3, incisura or end of ventricular ejection and ventricular systole; 4, closure of semilunar valves and onset of isometric ventricular relaxation; 5, opening of A-V valves and onset of rapid ventricular filling; and 6 and 7, slow ventricular filling or diastasis, ending with atrial contraction.

Atrial inflow during ventricular contraction is particularly effective in the presence of tachycardia in which the time available for diastolic inflow is shortened. The pistonlike downward movement of the atrioventricular junction during ventricular systole enlarges the atria and vena cava and attracts blood to them. The filling of the atria during ventricular systole depends on the quantity and pressure of blood available in the venous reservoir and the vigor with which ventricular systole moves the A-V junction. Thus, ventricular myocardial contraction is a very important means of actively filling the atria during systole and, therefore, in determining the extent of ventricular filling during the rapid filling phase.

Finally, attention is directed to the dashed and abruptly dipping line representing an alternate decline of the ventricular pressure and which, at times, indicates a negative intraventricular pressure has developed. Such a dip in the pressure curve of ventricular relaxation, although recorded for many years and considered an artefact, is now given more credence since (1) it can be recorded with a micromanometer (which is supposedly immune to artefacts); (2) recent experimental evidence indicates that the relaxing ventricle can develop suction under certain artificial experimental conditions. For example, in the beating mammalian heart, a moderate volume of fluid can be drawn into the ventricular cavity in the absence of a positive ventricular filling pressure and in the presence of an empty ventricle or one with some systolic residual volume. The time available during which suction could act is approximately 0.1 sec., i.e., the earlier part of the rapid inflow period. The quantitative contribution of the ventricle to ventricular filling under normal conditions is still unknown and, hence, the physiological significance of diastolic suction for the return of blood to the heart cannot be evaluated. Wiggers, in summarizing the problem, states "crucial evidence is still required that the small remnant of elastic recoil still operative at the end of relaxation can create sufficient suction to be of significance in filling the normally beating heart. Dynamically it must be shown that the concordant declines of atrial and ventricular pressures are due to a more rapid rate of ventricular relaxation than of filling from the atrium."

Diastasis, or the period of slowed ventricular filling, begins when the atrial pressure begins to rise during diastole (6). The end of diastasis (7) is marked by the onset of atrial contraction ("a" wave) which is reflected in the ventricle since the atrial and ventricular cavities are now continuous.

The dynamic interval of atrial systole lasts until the peak of the atrial contraction wave while the inflow phase that follows ends at the onset of ventricular isometric contraction and completes the cardiac cycle.

ATRIAL CONTRACTION. The dynamic importance of atrial contraction on ventricular filling has been much debated. The older view that the chief function of the atria is filling the ventricles is not now acceptable since it is known that such filling occurs chiefly during the earlier portion of diastole when the difference between atrial and ventricular pressure is maximal. However, in hearts slowed by vagal stimulation to separate atrial and ventricular contraction and in hearts with 2:1 or more block, it can be demonstrated that atrial contraction has a small but significant effect on the ventricular volume curve obtained with a cardiometer.

PRESSURE AND TIME VALUES OF DYNAMIC AND ELECTRICAL EVENTS AND THEIR TEMPORAL RELATIONSHIP IN THE LEFT AND RIGHT HEART. For full details original articles should be consulted. However, certain features are obvious. The following table gives the approximate figures for the duration of the chief phases of the cardiac cycle of the left heart when the heart rate approximates 70 per minute in the human.

|  | Seconds |
| --- | --- |
| Atrial systole | 0.11 |
| Atrial diastole | 0.71 |
| Ventricular systole (total) | 0.27 |
|    Isometric contraction period | 0.06 (right ventricle, .02) |
|    Ejection period | 0.21 |
| Ventricular diastole (total) | 0.56 |
|    Protodiastolic period | 0.02 |
|    Isometric relaxation period | 0.05 (right ventricle, .02) |
|    Rapid inflow period | 0.16 |
|    Diastasis | 0.23 |
|    Atrial systole | 0.10 |

*A. Pressure pulse values.* Aortic pressure throughout the cardiac cycle is uniformly higher than in the pulmonary artery. The peak aortic pressure during systole of 120 mm. Hg is approximately five times that of 25 mm. Hg in the pulmonary artery; the relative end-diastolic pressures are 80 mm. Hg versus 10 mm. Hg; the relative pulse pressures are 40 mm. Hg versus 15 mm. Hg. The diastolic pressure in both cavities is quite low with a small pressure gradient from the left ventricle (5 mm. Hg) to the right ventricle (2 to 3 mm. Hg). The atrial pressure values are only a few mm. Hg and are uniformly somewhat higher in the left atrial than in the right atrial curve.

*B. Asynchronisms of pressure pulses.* While dynamic events on the two sides of the heart are generally similar, there is considerable asynchronism and some difference in duration of parts of the cardiac cycle. The onset of contraction of the right atrium precedes that of the left atrium while the onset of contraction of the right ventricle follows that of the left ventricle. Right ventricular ejection begins earlier and is completed later than left ventricular ejection.

*C. Electrocardiogram versus onset of pressure events.* In man the interval between the onset of electrical and mechanical activity in the left atrium (rise of P wave versus onset of rise of atrial A wave) is of the order of 0.06 sec.; for the right atrium, the interval approximates 0.08 sec. For the left ventricle, the interval between the onset of ventricular depolarization (Q wave) and onset of left ventricular contraction (onset of pressure rise) approximates 0.04 sec.; for the right ventricle, the interval is about 0.05 sec. The T wave has a variable relation to the end of systole but terminates usually before the incisura of the aortic pressure curve.

### The Movements of the Heart Valves

The chief factor concerned in the opening and closing of the valves is, as already indicated (p. 242), the difference in pressure upon their opposite surfaces. Some additional features of the valvular mechanisms must now be considered.

THE ATRIOVENTRICULAR VALVES (TRICUSPID AND MITRAL). The valve leaflets or cusps, three in number on the right and two on the left side, are attached by their bases to the fibrous rings surrounding the atrioventricular openings. Their free margins are connected through delicate tendons (chordae tendineae) to the papillary muscles which prevent inversion of the valves into the auricle during ventricular systole. The chordae tendineae are tightened at the commencement of systole by the contraction of the papillary muscles. The leaflets are composed mainly of a double layer of the endothelial lining of the heart, strengthened by a few connective tissue fibers. Their attached bases are thicker and contain more connective tissue, small blood vessels and delicate strands of smooth muscle. The latter, however, play no part in valve closure

which is effected, as mentioned above, in a passive manner.

*A. The mechanism of valve closure.* According to traditional concept, an advancing gush of blood thrusts the A-V valves widely open during early ventricular diastole. During atrial systole the leaflets do not lie back against the ventricular wall but occupy a midposition as a result of two opposing currents. The inflowing blood pressing upon their atrial surfaces keeps them open, while eddies reflected in the reverse direction from the ventricular walls strike their ventricular surfaces and tend to close them. Thus, they float in a position of delicate balance. When, as a result of the fall in intra-atrial pressure at the end of atrial systole, the incoming jet is diminished in force and finally ceases, the back eddies persisting for a brief space and being unopposed, approximate the valves or bring them gently into apposition (fig. 20.3). The fact that the first heart sound has been found to be significantly delayed in the absence of atrial systole supports this view that normally the atrioventricular valves are closed or nearly so, before ventricular systole. They are not, however, firmly closed. This is effected by the rise in pressure in the ventricle when it contracts. Dean has shown by attaching a hair to the septal leaf of the valve and recording its movements, that if ventricular systole does not follow almost instantly upon the cessation of the flow of blood from the atrium, the valves start to reopen. In instances, therefore, in which ventricular systole is delayed, that is, when the A-V interval is prolonged, the reopening of the valves proceeds for an appreciable time. Then, when ventricular contraction occurs, a small amount of blood regurgitates into the atrium before the valves are swung closed by the

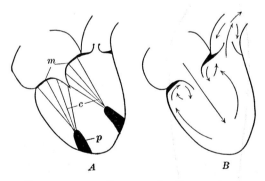

FIG. 20.3. Two diagrams showing mechanisms concerned in valve closure. *A*, showing relations of papillary muscles and chordae tendineae to valve flaps; *B*, partial closure due to eddy formation (after Wiggers, 1954.)

rising intraventricular pressure. The backward flow of blood through the orifice may then give rise to a murmur just preceding the first heart sound (presystolic murmur).

These concepts have been derived mainly from observations and direct photography of valve action in isolated hearts and from correlation of heart sound with mechanical and electrical events of the cardiac cycle. However, cinefluorographic observations of the motions of the mitral valve cusps by means of attached radiopaque markers in intact anesthetized dogs, showed the edges of the valve cusps to be only slightly separated during ventricular filling. Since in both instances, it is not possible to rule out certain experimental artefacts, at present no choice can be made between the concept of wide valve excursion in isolated hearts and restricted valve movements in intact animals.

THE SEMILUNAR VALVES. The dynamics of aortic and pulmonary closure are essentially the same in principle as those described for the A-V valves. The valves form three small pockets open toward the arterial lumen. Back eddies which are set up during the ejection phase of systole prevent the contact of the valves with the arterial wall. When ejection ceases, the centripetal currents carry the valves into apposition and firm closure is effected by the higher pressure at this time upon their arterial surfaces.

### Heart Sounds

METHODOLOGY. The sounds produced by the heart during a cardiac cycle consist of waves of greatly varying frequency. To pick these up, a simple form of stethoscope is used in which a

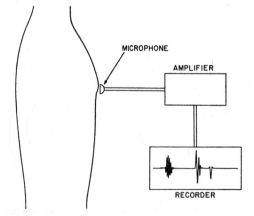

FIG. 20.4. Schematic diagram illustrating the recording of heart sounds. The signal from the microphone goes through an amplifier to give it the necessary amplitude to drive a recorder.

small bell or disk placed over the chest conducts the sound waves through rubber tubes to ear pieces. Because of the intervening tissue, the intensity of the sounds is generally decreased and some components are accentuated and others depressed. The stethoscope itself does not amplify sounds accurately or conduct them accurately to the ear, the size and shape of the end pieces and the pressure exerted affecting the auditory characteristics of the sounds. Despite this, the sounds heard thus by ear give more practical information than is obtained by any other approach. The heart sounds have also been picked up by a microphone applied to the chest wall over the heart, amplified, and the frequency selectively filtered before it reaches the ear or is conducted to a loudspeaker. This is didactically helpful since many can listen simultaneously, but it does not give a better appreciation of the sounds as they actually occur.

Graphic registration of the heart sounds has been used to give a permanent record for study and to permit precise relations to be established between them and the events of the cardiac cycle, as recorded by other graphic methods such as the electrocardiogram and intracardiac and intravascular pressure curves. As already mentioned, this provides an accurate method of measuring the duration of ventricular systole. In the classical direct method, heart sounds at the chest level are conducted by a stethoscopic bell by means of a short rubber tube to a sound recorder, the coarsest vibrations being allowed to escape through a lateral opening. The recorder consists of a very fine rubber membrane with attached mirror whose movements are recorded on photographic paper. Einthoven introduced an indirect method in which the sounds picked up by a stethoscope fastened to the chest were transmitted to a microphone the movements of the disk of which produced changes in a simple electric circuit recordable by a string galvanometer (fig. 20.4). With the development of crystal microphones and proper vacuum tube amplification, a number of devices are available commercially in which the heart sounds are converted at the chest level into electrical variations which are amplified and recorded by high frequency oscillographs. In this electronic apparatus, the lower frequencies have generally been severely attenuated or filtered to resemble the effect of the human hearing mechanism with a stethoscope. The records are used to increase the acumen of clinical auscultation; the advantage is mainly in appreciating the timing and relation to each other of heart sounds and murmurs. But in the matter of increase in perception of faint murmurs, phonocardiography does not compare with the remarkable sensitivity and selectivity of the human ear.

For obvious reasons, sounds picked up from the surface of the thorax are not a true representation of the actual vibrations of the cardiac valves and walls. Thus, attempts have been made to move the pick-up device closer to the source of sound by placing microphones in the esophagus, by suturing microphones to the myocardium in experimental animals, by applying suction microphones directly to the surface of the human heart, and finally, by introducing the microphone into the cardiac chambers themselves. The latter technique aids in locating the site of production of normal heart sounds and serves as a valuable diagnostic tool in disease states in locating the origin of abnormal sounds and murmurs. However, use of data obtained thereby must be tempered by knowledge of the fact the catheter mounted device may itself, through the motion imparted to it in the cardiac cavities, produce sounds which are recorded as naturally occurring.

CHARACTERISTICS OF HEART SOUNDS. Two distinct sounds are heard by direct auscultation and occasionally a third is also audible during a cardiac cycle. A fourth sound is revealed by graphic methods. The first two sounds occur mainly during ventricular systole, the other two sounds take place during ventricular diastole (fig. 20.2).

A. *Origin of heart sounds and time relations.* These vibrations arising in the heart are fundamentally the result of sudden displacement of blood (acceleration) or abrupt stoppage of blood (deceleration).

The temporal realtions of human heart sounds to central hemodynamic events are illustrated schematically in figure 20.2. The large vibrations of the first sound begin with the rapid rise in intraventricular tension and by the beginning of ejection they have already reached a maximum. The beginning of the second sound coincides with the trough of the incisura of the aortic pressure. The third sound occurs near the end of the rapid inflow phase of diastole of the ventricles. The fourth sound begins near the middle of the atrial pressure wave and extends to the isometric phase of ventricular contraction.

B. *First heart sound.* The first sound is of relatively long duration, soft in quality and low in pitch. The second sound is shorter, sharper and of higher pitch. These characteristics are best imitated vocally by the syllables "lub" and "dup" separated by a brief pause. The two heart sounds

mark the beginning and end of ventricular systole and the determination of the interval between their commencements (as determined by the phonocardiogram) is a reliable method for arriving at the length of ventricular systole in man. The pause between the end of the second sound and the beginning of the first coincides with ventricular diastole.

The first sound is heard most clearly and at maximum intensity over the 5th left intercostal space, i.e., with an area centered over the "apex beat." Here the mitral element of the sound predominates. Any abnormal sound produced at the tricuspid valve is detected by listening over the lower end of the sternum.

The principal factors entering into the production of the first sound are: (1) the closure of the atrioventricular valves and the tension set up in the valve leaflets and chordae tendineae as the intraventricular pressure rises (valvular element), (2) the rush of blood from the ventricles and the shock transmitted to the walls of the aorta and pulmonary artery (vascular element), and (3) contraction of the ventricular muscle. Vibrations set up by the atrial muscle at the end of its systole may sometimes contribute to this sound.

The vibration of the valves is the most important element of the first sound. Some have claimed that the first sound is not prolonged into the ejection period, and therefore, the impact of the blood upon the walls of the large vessels cannot contribute to the sound. But the observations of Straub and of Orias and Braun-Menendez indicate that the first sound does extend beyond the isometric period and that the vascular element is an important component. Of the three, the muscular element appears to add least to the sound. Dock has questioned whether the ventricular muscle produces a sound at all. He recorded the sound vibrations by means of a phonocardiograph applied to the surface of the heart and reported that no sound was produced when the empty heart contracted, valve action being abolished. Although he concluded from this that the normal first sound contained no muscular element, evidence from other sources is strongly opposed to such a conception. Wiggers and Dean, previously had recorded sound vibrations from an isolated strip of myocardium. It has also been shown that when free movement of the valves of the beating heart is prevented, the booming character of the first sound still persists.

Phonocardiographic records from the chest over the heart show, as a rule, no vibrations before the onset of ventricular contraction thus indicating that the presystolic apposition of the valves is silent. The sound commences 0.008 second before the peak of the R wave of the electrocardiogram. Its duration is about 0.18 sec. Sometimes, however, the phonocardiogram records a few small presystolic vibrations which are attributed to auricular systole; occasionally a faint sound is heard at this time.

The record of the first sound is composed chiefly of a series of from 9 to 13 vibrations, and has a duration of from 0.9 to 0.16 sec. These are of small amplitude to start with but rise to a "crescendo" which reaches its maximum at the end of the isometric period and is followed by a "diminuendo" of about the same duration. This main series of vibrations is sometimes, as mentioned above, preceded by a couple of small introductory vibrations which occur before the ventricular pressure rise. These are possibly of atrial origin. The main series is also followed by a few final vibrations, variable in number. The vibrations are in general irregular, which places the sounds in the category of noises rather than of muscial tones. The frequency is low varying from 33 to 110 per sec.

*C. The second sound* results from the vibrations set up in the blood column and arterial walls as the aortic and pulmonary valves are placed under tension following their closure. The duration of the second sound is about 0.10 sec. It commences about 0.09 sec. after the summit of the T wave of the electrocardiogram. The average frequency is about 50 per sec. It is heard best over the pulmonary and aortic areas—the upper part of the sternum adjacent to the 2nd left intercostal space, and the 2nd right costosternal junction, respectively.

*D. The third heart sound.* Sometimes a faint third sound is heard in normal hearts which follows the second sound by about 0.08 sec. and lasts for about 0.04 sec. It is heard at the apex and is commonly found in young adults. Thayer found it present in 65 per cent of normal individuals. It may be made to appear or is intensified by procedures which increase the venous flow into the atria, e.g., exercise, recumbent position, etc. The sound was first described by Gibson and independently by Herschfelder; several explanations have since been given to account for it. (1) Some have considered it to be due to the asynchronous closure of the aortic and semilunar valves, but the interval between it and the second sound is too great for the acceptance of this explanation. (2) White considers that it is due most probably to the opening snap of the A-V valves

or to the vibration of the ventricular walls as the blood rushes into the ventricle. (3) Another view is that the sound is simply due to prolonged after-vibrations of the aortic valves which have become separated from the earlier vibrations as a silent interval. None of these explanations is entirely saisfactory in all instaces.

*E. Variations in the intensity of the heart sounds.* It is the general belief that the first sound varies in intensity with the force of ventricular systole and the loudness of the second sound with the height of the arterial blood pressure. The experiments of Wiggers bear this out. The sounds were recorded graphically and correlated with the intraventricular and aortic pressure curves. It was found that the vibrations of the first sound were increased in amplitude and number when the tension developed by the cardiac muscle was increased. The intensity of the first sound is directly related to the rate of the pressure rise within the ventricle during the isometric period. The intensity of this sound is not dependent upon the volume of the systolic discharge but rather upon the diastolic pressures in the pulmonary and systemic circuits. Wiggers found that when the heart was slowed and the systolic discharge consequently increased but the diastolic pressure lowered, the intensity of the first heart sound was reduced while acceleration of the heart (reduced systolic discharge with raised diastolic pressure) increased its intensity. These experiments together with the observations that the first heart sound is believed to be largely on a valvular basis and is intensified with prolongation of the P-R interval, strongly suggest that the intensity of the sound is ultimately conditioned by the position of the A-V valves at the onset of ventricular systole.

The intensity of the second sound in the aortic or pulmonary area is increased by an elevation in the systemic or pulmonary pressures, respectively. Among the cardiovascular conditions associated with intensification of the second sound are, mitral stenosis and failure of the left ventricle which raise the pulmonary arterial pressure, and arterial hypertension which raises the aortic pressure.

### REFERENCES

BAKOS, A. C. P. The question of the function of the right ventricular myocardium: an experimental study. Circulation, 1950, **1**, 724.

BERGLUND, E., SARNOFF, S. J., AND ISAACS, J. P. The pericardium in regulation of cardiovascular dynamics. Circulation Res., 1955, **3**, 133.

BERGLUND, E. AND SARNOFF, S. J. Role of the pericardium in regulation of ventricular stroke work
and output when the left ventricle is acutely
challenged. Am. J. Physiol., 1952, 171, 708.

BING, R. J., HEIMBECKER, R. AND FALHOLT, W.
An estimation of the residual volume of blood
in the right ventricle of normal and diseased
human hearts *in vivo*. Am. Heart J., 1951, 42,
483.

BOYER, N. H. Studies of the third heart sound.
Am. Heart J., 1942, 23, 797.

BRAUNWALD, E., MOSCOWITZ, H. L., AMRAM, S. S.,
LASSER, R. P., SAPIN, S. O., HIMMELSTEIN, A.,
RAVITCH, M. M., AND GORDON, A. J. Timing of
electrical and mechanical events of the left side
of the human heart. J. Appl. Physiol., 1955, 8,
309.

BRAUNWALD, E., MOSCOWITZ, H. L., AMRAM, S. S.,
LASSER, R. P., SAPIN, S. O., HIMMELSTEIN, A.,
AND RAVITCH, M. M. The hemodynamics of the
left side of the heart as studied by simultaneous
left atrial, left ventricular and aortic pressures:
particular reference to mitral stenosis. Circulation, 1955, 12, 69.

BRAUNWALD, E., FISHMAN, A. P., AND COURNAND,
A. Time relationship of dynamic events in the
cardiac chambers, pulmonary artery and aorta
in man. Circulation Res., 1956, 4, 100.

BRECHER, G. A. Cardiac variations in venous return studied with a new bristle flow meter. Am.
J. Physiol., 1954, 176, 423.

BRECHER, G. A. AND KISSEN, A. T. Ventricular
diastolic suction at normal arterial pressures.
Circulation Res., 1958, 6, 100.

COBLENTZ, B., HARVEY, R. M., FERRER, M. L.,
AND COURNAND, A. The relationship between
electrical and mechanical events in the cardiac
cycle of man. Brit. Heart J., 1949, 11, 1.

COUNIHAN, T., MESSER, A., RAPPAPORT, M. B.,
AND SPRAGUE, H. B. The initial vibrations of the
first heart sound. Circulation, 1951, 3, 730.

DOCK, W. Mode of production of the first heart
sound. Arch. Int. Med., 1933, 51, 737.

DOCK, W. The forces needed to evoke sounds from
cardiac tissues, and the attenuation of heart
sounds. Circulation, 1959, 19, 376.

ECKSTEIN, R. W. Sounds due to muscular contraction and their importance in the ausculatory
quality of the first heart sound. Am. J. Physiol.,
1937, 118, 359.

GOULEY, B. A. The aortic valvular lesion associated with Austin Flint murmur. Am. Heart J.,
1941, 22, 208.

HENDERSON, Y. AND BARRINGER, T. B. The conditions determining the volume of the arterial
blood stream. Am. J. Physiol., 1913, 31, 288.

HENDERSON, Y. AND JOHNSON, F. E. Two modes of
closure of the heart valves. Heart, 1912, 4, 69.

HOCHREIN, M. AND ECKHARDT, W. Dynamik Ver-
schiedener Klappen-Fehler insbesandere der
Mitral Stenose und Aorten Insuffizenz. Klin.
Wchnschr., 1930, 9, 12.

HOLT, J. P., ALLENWORTH, J., DIANA, J., COLLINS,
D., AND HINES, H. Estimation of the residual
volume of the right ventricle of the dog's heart.
Circulation Res., 1957, 5, 323.

HOLT, J. P. Estimation of residual volume of

ventricle of the dog's heart by two indicator
dilution technics. Circulation Res., 1956, 4, 187.

JOCHIM, K. The contribution of the auricle to
ventricular filling in complete heart block. Am.
J. Physiol., 1938, 122, 639.

KAGAN, A. Dynamic responses of the right ventricle following extensive damage by cauteriza-
tion. Circulation, 1952, 5, 816.

KOUNTZ, W. B., GILSON, A. S., AND SMITH, J. R.
The use of the cathode ray for recording heart
sounds and vibrations: I. Studies on the normal
heart. Am. Heart J., 1940, 20, 667; II. Studies on
the muscular element of the first heart sound.
Am. Heart J., 1941, 21, 17.

LITTLE, R. C., HILTON, J. G., AND SCHAEFFER, R.
D. The first heart sound in normal and ectopic
ventricular contractions. Mechanism of closure
of the A-V valves. Circulation Res., 1954, 2, 48.

MCCLURE, J. A., LACY, W. W., LATIMER, P., AND
NEWMAN, E. V. Indicator dilution in an atrioventricular system with competent or incompetent valves. A complete analysis of the behavior
of indicator injected instantaneously or continuously into either chamber. Circulation Res.,
1959, 7, 794.

MCKUSICK, V. A., TALBOT, S. A., AND WEBB, G. N.
Spectral phonocardiography; problems and
prospects in the application of the Bell sound
spectrograph to phonocardiography. Bull.
Johns Hopkins Hosp., 1954, 95, 90.

MOSCOVITZ, H. L. AND WILDER, R. J. Pressure
events of the cardiac cycle in the dog. Circulation Res., 1956, 4, 574.

NYLIN, G. On the amount of and changes in the
residual blood of the heart. Am. Heart J., 1943,
25, 598.

RAPPAPORT, M. B. AND SPRAGUE, H. B. Physiologic
and physical laws that govern auscultation and
their clinical application. Am. Heart J., 1941,
21, 257.

RAPPAPORT, M. B. AND SPRAGUE, H. B. The
graphic registration of the normal heart sounds.
Am. Heart J., 1942, 23, 591.

ROBB, J. S. AND ROBB, R. C. Normal heart. Anatomy and physiology of the structural units. Am.
Heart J., 1942, 23, 455.

RUSHMER, R. F. AND THAL, N. The mechanics of
ventricular contraction: a cinefluorographic
study. Circulation, 1951, 4, 219.

RUSHMER, R. F., CRYSTAL, D. K., AND WAGNER,
C. The functional anatomy of ventricular contraction. Circulation Res., 1953, 1, 162.

RUSHMER, R. F. Continuous measurements of left
ventricular dimensions in intact, unanesthetized
dogs. Circulation Res., 1954, 2, 14.

RUSHMER, R. F. Length-circumference relations
of the left ventricle. Circulation Res., 1955, 3,
639.

RUSHMER, R. F. Anatomy and physiology of ventricular function. Physiol. Rev., 1956, 36, 400.

RUSHMER, R. F., FINLAYSON, B. L., AND NASH,
A. A. Movements of the mitral valve. Circulation Res., 1956, 4, 337.

SAMET, P., BERNSTEIN, W. H., AND LITWAK, R. S.
Electrical activation and mechanical asynchron-
ization in the cardiac cycle of the dog. Circulation Res., 1959, 7, 228.

SIECKE, H. AND ESSEX, H. E. Relation of the difference in pressure across the mitral valve to the amplitude of the first heart sound in dogs with atrioventricular block. Am. J. Physiol., 1958, **192**, 135.

SLOAN, A. W. AND WISHART, M. The effect on the human third heart sound of variations in the rate of filling of the heart. Brit. Heart J., 1953, **15**, 25.

SMITH, H. L., ESSEX, H. E., AND BALDES, E. J. A study of the movements of heart valves and of heart sounds. Ann. Int. Med., 1950, **33**, 1357.

SMITH, J. R., EDWARDS, J. C., AND KOUNTZ, W. B. The use of the cathode ray for recording heart sounds and vibrations. III. Total cardiac vibrations in 100 subjects. Am. Heart J., 1941, **21**, 228.

STARR, I., JEFFERS, W. A., AND MEADE, R. H. The absence of conspicuous increments of venous pressure after severe damage to the right ventricle of the dog, with a discussion of the relation between clinical congestive heart failure and heart disease. Am. Heart J., 1943, **26**, 291.

WIGGERS, C. J. AND DEAN, A. L. The movements of the mitral cusps in relation to the cardiac cycle. Am. J. Physiol., 1916, **40**, 206.

WIGGERS, C. J. AND DEAN, A. L. The nature and time relations of the fundamental heart sounds. Am. J. Physiol., 1917, **42**, 476.

WIGGERS, C. J. AND KATZ, L. N. The contour of the ventricular volume curves under different conditions. Am. J. Physiol., 1922, **58**, 439.

WIGGERS, C. J. Factors determining the relative intensity of the heart sounds in different auscultation areas. Arch. Int. Med., 1919, **24**, 471.

WIGGERS, C. J. Cardiac mechanisms that limit operation of ventricular suction. Science, 1957, **126**, 1,236.

WOLFERTH, C. C. AND MARGOLIES, A. The influence of auricular contraction on the first heart sound and the radial pulse. Arch. Int. Med., 1930, **46**, 1048.

*Monographs and Reviews*

BRECHER, G. A. Critical review of recent work on diastolic suction. Circulation Res., 1958, **6**, 554.

GREEN, H. D. Circulatory system. In Methods in Medical Physics. Vol. **2**, p. 209. The Year Book Publishers, Chicago, Illinois, 1950.

LEATHAM, A. Auscultation of the heart sounds. Lancet, 1958, **2**, 703.

LEATHAM, A. Auscultation of the heart murmurs. Lancet, 1958, **2**, 757.

LEVINE, S. A. AND HARVEY, W. P. Clinical auscultation of the heart. Ed. 2. W. B. Saunders Company, Philadelphia, 1960.

LEWIS, T. Diseases of the heart, described for practitioners and students. The MacMillan Company, London, 1933.

McKUSICK, V. A. (guest ed.). Symposium on cardiovascular sound. I. Mechanisms. Circulation, 1957, **16**, 270.

McKUSICK, V. A. (guest ed.) Second Symposium on cardiovascular sound. Circulation, 1958, **18**, 946.

ORIAS, O. AND BRAUN-MENENDEZ, E. The heart sounds in normal and pathological conditions. Oxford University Press, London, 1939.

WIGGERS, C. J. Physiology in health and disease. Ed. 5. Lea & Febiger, Philadelphia, 1954.

WIGGERS, C. J. Pressure pulses in the cardiovascular system. Longmans, Green & Company, Inc., New York, 1928.

WIGGERS, C. J. Circulation in health and disease. Ed. 2. Lea & Febiger, Philadelphia, 1923.

# 21

# REGULATION OF PRESSURE AND FLOW IN THE SYSTEMIC AND PULMONARY CIRCULATION

If all the vascular beds of the body were to open simultaneously to their full capacities, the total peripheral resistance would disappear and the cardiac output and blood pressure would be reduced to zero. In order, therefore, to permit the circulation pumps and vessels to carry out their functions, most blood vessels must be partially constricted much of the time. To effect this, vascular constriction must be precisely balanced against vascular dilation so as to permit the requisite cardiac output for tissue needs.

Body economy requires that blood flow through some organs or regions be dictated by their local function. In some tissues with a high metabolic rate, such as active skeletal muscle and the myocardium, the volume of blood flow is very high and the arteriovenous (A-V) oxygen difference may be 70 per cent or more. In other tissues, such as skin, kidney, and the brain, blood flow is not determined by local metabolic demands. Here, with rather low metabolic requirements, the blood flow is high with a small A-V oxygen difference, because the specialized functions of temperature regulation, urinary secretion and neural activity require a very large blood flow beyond their oxygen requirements.

The size of vessels can be varied passively because of their content of elastic and collagenous tissue, and of smooth muscle, each of which can be stretched by an intravascular pressure. The walls of most vessels such as the aorta, arteries, arterioles, venules and veins, contain involuntary muscle fibers arranged in circular fashion. The walls of the arterioles are composed almost exclusively of this smooth muscle. Vascular contractility is dependent only on these smooth muscle cells. Such contractility is based on their local "tone" and on their response to blood borne substances. In addition, like the cardiac muscle, the musculature of these vessels is supplied by two types of nerve fibers—inhibitory and excitatory. Those which cause contraction of the mus-

culature are called vasoconstrictor; those which inhibit, and in consequence, cause relaxation of the muscle rings, are termed vasodilator. Both sets together are referred to as vasomotor nerves.

Since, according to Poiseuille's law, pressure, flow and resistance are intimately associated, it is necessary for proper study, as pointed out in chapter 15, to be able to measure the blood flow in the presence of a constant perfusion pressure, or to measure the blood pressure change in the presence of a constant blood flow. In no other way can one determine whether a change in peripheral resistance arises through a change in blood flow from a primary change in heart action or through a change in state of vasomotion of peripheral vessels induced by local mechanisms, or by nervous and humoral mechanisms, operating locally. Ever since Poiseuille introduced the mercury manometer, in 1828, and later Ludwig added a float and a writing point, it has been easy to make pressure measurements, whereas, because of the slowness in development of methodology, flow measurements have not been too plentiful. However, enough information is at hand to consider the subject briefly.

## Local Control of Vascular Smooth Muscle

The smallest blood vessels have an inherent, myogenic automaticity or basal degree of contraction of their contained smooth muscle which is independent of blood borne substances or nervous influences, but which can be altered by stimulation of nerve fibers, local electrical stimulation, or by changing the physical and chemical environment. The mechanism of this inherent vasomotion is unknown. Presumably, it arises from locally produced metabolites whose effects can be complex. Locally, in the arterioles, precapillaries and capillaries, there are normally released 5 hydroxytryptamine, noradrenaline, acetylcholine, histamine, $CO_2$, lactic acid, products of nuclear metabolism and presumably many

251

other substances, each of which could act differently on these vessels. The extent of such basal vasomotion has been evaluated in sympathectomized, vascular areas where neurohumoral, circulatory, constrictor influences are eliminated. Although large quantitative differences exist in different parts of the vascular tree, generally speaking, there is an inverse relation between the local, inherent activity of smooth muscle cells and the extent of neurohumoral control in any given vascular bed. The cutaneous arteriovenous anastomoses, such as in the paw of the cat, which are strongly controlled from the hypothalamic heat loss center, are maximally dilated when neurohumoral agents are eliminated, while elimination of the vasomotor nerves serving vitally important metabolic areas, such as the brain and myocardium, has scarcely any effect on the local blood flow. In areas such as skeletal muscle, neural elimination still leaves a very strong vessel tone in the dog and man, which is increased with time. Indeed, some investigators have expressed the belief that in skeletal muscle, blood flow is mainly under local control by metabolites, and not nerves, since sympathectomized people do as well running (athletes and normals) before and after sympathectomy. This difference may apply in the same vascular bed, for evidence suggests that reactivity to local metabolic effects is stronger in the metarterioles and precapillary sphincters, whereas constrictor fibers predominantly affect the arterioles. Presumably, in all beds, there is some locally produced vasodilation which counteracts the centrally induced reduction in blood flow by constrictor nerves and protects the tissue against ischemia.

### The Sympathetic Vasoconstrictor Fibers

DISTRIBUTION. These were discovered in 1852 by Claude Bernard, who stimulated the cervical sympathetic nerve in the rabbit and observed constriction of the vessels of the ear. They belong to the thoracicolumbar (sympathetic) division of the involuntary nervous system. The constrictor fibers arise from groups of nerve cells situated in the lateral horns of the spinal gray matter, extending in man from the 1st thoracic to the 2nd or 3rd lumbar segment, inclusive. All the arterioles of the body whereever situated are supplied with filaments whose ultimate source is in this relatively limited region of the central nervous system. They are distributed to the periphery in the manner elsewhere described for the thoracicolumbar outflow in general (see also ch. 71).

The vascular nerves of the limbs, as shown by Todd and Kramer and by Woollard, are distributed by two distinct modes. (1) A *proximal* innervation which arises in the case of the vessels of the upper limb directly from the cervical part of the sympathetic chain—middle and inferior cervical ganglia. The fibers pass to the subclavian artery and are conveyed in a plexiform manner along the outer coat of this vessel and its branches, and into the arm along the axillary artery. The corresponding supply to the vessels of the lower limb is derived by extension from the aortic plexus in the abdomen. The fibers follow the common and external iliac arteries into the thigh. The sympathetic fibers derived in the manner just described do not extend beyond the larger vessels of the limbs—proximal portions of the brachial and femoral. (2) A *distal* innervation which is carried to the peripheral vessels via the spinal nerve trunks. These reach the arteries at different levels and, penetrating the vascular wall, form a nerve net surrounding the muscular coat; the highest level of this type of innervation probably overlaps the region innervated by the proximal group of fibers mentioned above. The lowest levels supply the arterioles and capillaries. It is solely through such sympathetic fibers traveling with somatic nerve trunks that constrictor impulses are conveyed to the minute vessels of the limbs. Ganglion cells are absent from the vessels of the limbs. Section of a peripheral nerve, therefore, causes complete degeneration of vasoconstrictor fibers in the area of its distribution.

Vasoconstrictor fibers to the head and neck are conveyed from the sympathetic chain through plexuses investing the blood vessels, but also via peripheral nerve trunks (cervical and certain cranial nerves). The vessels of the abdomen and pelvis are supplied with fibers which pass along the vascular walls from plexuses surrounding the aorta and its branches. The sympathetic fibers to the heart arise chiefly in 5 upper dorsal segments of the cord, pass to the stellate ganglia and upper dorsal ganglia as white rami, and proceed to the heart by a complex plexus. There is no certainty that these fibers should be included here. They are included, however, because with their stimulation noradrenaline is released in the heart, but no good evidence exists to prove that stimulation *per se* causes dilation since each stimulation is overshadowed by a massive metabolic response and associated dilation.

SITE AND MODE OF ACTION. These nerve fibers

constitute a group of powerful vasoconstrictor mechanisms which are available and in constant function. The physiological discharge rate of the vasoconstrictor fibers is 1 to 2 per sec. to maintain normal vessel tone and reaches 10 impulses per sec., with maximal physiological excitation. The chemical transmitter released at the smooth muscle cell is probably norepinephrine, since almost pure norepinephrine is released into the blood stream on intense sympathetic stimulation. However, such an overflow does not usually occur at physiological discharge rates. These constrictor fibers exert control over the resistance vessels (arterioles and adjacent smaller blood vessels) where the main drop in blood pressure occurs. This can be observed by noting the marked increase in blood flow in a limb of man or animal with sympathetic block to that area. Predominantly, the true arterioles are controlled by constrictor fibers while the capillaries are mainly regulated by local factors.

In addition, these fibers exert strong control over the heart size and the capacity vessels, mainly the veins, which can alter greatly the venous return to the heart and, thus, markedly influence cardiac output. To establish this capacitance action, pressure changes occurring in functionally isolated parts of the superficial and deep venous system of dog and man were used to indicate changes in venous constriction, and evidence of a reflex constriction to a variety of stimuli was obtained. Isolated venous segments in the intact forearm constrict after reflex sympathetic stimulation by cold, excitement, etc. Venoconstriction in the forearm occurs in response to pooling of blood in the leg. Similar observations have been made on the capacity vessels of the splanchnic area. These effects are abolished by constrictor fiber blockade by hexamethonium. Possibly the most clear-cut experiments in dogs on the quantitative importance of the sympathetic system in adjusting total vascular volume, and hence, venous return and cardiac output, are those in which a pump, with output which remained constant under marked variations of peripheral resistance, was substituted for the left ventricle of a dog. The pulmonary drainage of blood was carried to a reservoir by means of a plastic tube in the left auricle. The blood was pumped from the reservoir through a T tube in the descending thoracic aorta. Under equilibrium conditions (reservoir level remaining constant), if norepinephrine (which simulates sympathetic vasoconstriction in physiological dosages) was injected into the dog, there was not only an increase in vascular pressures but also approximately 250 cc. (⅕ of the dog's blood volume) was forced into the pulmonary drainage reservoir feeding the mechanical left ventricle. This could only come from the venous system and the right heart. When hexamethonium (simulating a functional sympathectomy) was injected instead of norepinephrine, the pressures fell and the dog took up 200 to 300 cc. of blood from the reservoir. Further work has extended these findings to man. In normal man, removal of large amounts of blood in 50 cc. increments produces little change in vascular pressure or hemodynamics. But, if done following inhibition of sympathetic vasoconstrictor reflexes with hexamethonium, then with each 50 cc. of blood redrawn, there is a perceptible decline in blood pressure. After removal of only 350 to 500 cc. of blood, the arterial pressure falls, by decrements, to collapse levels. During reinfusion, the process is reversed. Thus, sympathetic vasoconstrictor inhibition has converted the vasculature into a static system. In addition, using the pressure-volume apparatus of Litter and associates, which can be applied to the extremities of man, it is calculated that infused epinephrine and norepinephrine can shift as much as 500 ml. of blood from the veins of dependent limbs in a short period of time.

These effects of constrictor fibers on venous volume can considerably change venous return by very small changes in vein caliber. For example, if the veins contain 60 per cent of blood volume of which 1 to 2 per cent make up the stroke volume of the ventricles, a 1 to 2 per cent shortening of venous vascular smooth muscle would be estimated to double diastolic inflow to the heart; this same amount of constriction of the resistance vessels would only insignificantly increase the peripheral resistance.

Excitation of sympathetic vasoconstrictor fibers affects somewhat the aortic smooth muscle cells and possibly other arteries. Presumably, the effect is mainly a change of vascular distensibility and, only secondarily, on mild pressure changes along the arterial tree (see also ch. 26). In general, however, the effect is small. In vessels from the root of the aorta down to arteries of 1 mm., induced changes in diameter are probably less than 5 per cent of total diameter even with marked vasoconstriction or vasodilation. Even a 30 to 50 per cent change of intravascular pressure will only alter diameter within 5 per cent.

FUNCTIONAL SIGNIFICANCE. Experimental evidence now indicates that these vasoconstrictor fibers are responsible for blood pressure homeostasis (vascular adjustments derived from the baro and chemoreceptors), and for the regulation of heat loss by the skin blood flow. Thus, the commonest type of centrally induced vasodilation is caused simply by an inhibition of vascular tone. In fulfilling their role as the main neurogenic adjustors of the peripheral circulation, they may show a generalized, strictly segmental or regional function, depending upon the type of stimulus.

CENTRAL CONTROL. The control of the degree and sites of vasoconstriction depends predominantly on the influence of hormonal action and on the action of the central nervous system. In discussing the central control of the cardiovascular system, it should be emphasized that, in the past, relatively little work has been done in this field. This has been true ever since the discovery and location of the medullary vasomotor centers by Oswjannikow and by Dittman in 1873. It was not until 1916 that Ransom and Billingsley published further significant work. Practically all the work in the field has been done by neurophysiologists with the result that generally only blood pressure and heart rate have been measured. More recently, circulatory physiologists have become interested in the problems, and with teams of neuro and circulatory physiologists in operation, regional blood flows and direct effects on the heart have been studied with some progress.

However, at times, interpretation of results is difficult because of the types of central nervous changes that are necessarily induced experimentally. For such studies these include stimulation of outlying nerve fibers, ganglionic blockade, electrical exploration of the central nervous system, ablation of areas and chronic implantation of stimulating electrodes. Each has its drawbacks in a physiological system. Ganglionic blockade is a pharmacological test used to identify vasomotor activity. Its action may be incomplete or not entirely selective. An electric shock is an artificial stimulus and its frequency and intensity may bear no relation to a physiological stimulus. Such stimulation experiments, in general, demonstrate what can happen in nerve fibers, and that in the central nervous system there are excitable areas in the region of the electrodes which, in turn, have synaptic continuity with the cardiovascular outflows. They do not necessarily indicate what role the excitable areas play in the intact human or animal. Ablation experiments

obviate some of these difficulties but there is no surety that the cardiovascular changes induced by ablation are not in part due to injury to surrounding areas. Attempts have recently been made with the use of chronically implanted electrodes to simulate the hemodynamic responses normally occurring in excitement and exercise and then to show, by ablation of such areas, that the cardiovascular response disappears. This approach has considerable promise.

*A. The spinal cord.* The preganglionic sympathetic neurons may, under some circumstances, exhibit spontaneous activity independent of an excitatory drive from afferent fibers or central levels. This spontaneous discharge may arise from a changed oxygen and $CO_2$ tension which is prone to occur in a spinal preparation in which neuronal respiration and blood supply are without doubt considerably altered.

Various afferent impulses are able to call forth spinal vasomotor reflexes when the vasoconstrictor neurons form the efferent link. Pain or cold stimulation in the skin induces a segmentally arranged constriction of the intestinal vessels in such spinal animals. Vasodilation occurs when the skin is moderately heated. More intense and widespread effects are seen in human beings with chronic transverse lesions of the spinal cord. Guttman and Whiteridge showed the existence of powerful reflexes, in the spinal man, arising from the hollow viscera. In patients with high spinal transection, distension of the bladder would raise the blood pressure from normal levels to 300/140 mm. Hg. This is ascribed to the action of reflexes initiated by the tension in the bladder wall and mediated by the isolated spinal cord and the sympathetic outflow. There could also be demonstrated vasoconstriction in the hand and a fall in calf blood flow. These phenomena are consistent with a very widespread vasoconstriction as a result of afferent impulses which spread to an unusual extent in the isolated spinal cord.

*B. Medulla.* The constrictor sympathetic vascular effects are controlled primarily by areas in the medulla oblongata situated in the floor of the 4th ventricle. Local electrical stimulation has revealed a lateral "pressor area" and a medial "depressor area" causing vasoconstriction and vasodilation, respectively. The vasodilation is caused by inhibition of vasoconstrictor tone, specific vasodilator fibers not being involved. This area is defined simply as the vasomotor center. These areas do not represent the highest centers of this system. The latter are situated in the hypothalamus and in the cerebral cortex. In the intact mammal, complicated afferent influences integrated in the cerebral cortex and hypothalamus modify and control the action of the vasomotor center.

The state of activity of the medullary vasomotor center depends upon afferent nerve impulses received from various organs and regions of the body, as well as from other nervous centers, respiratory centers, etc., and upon the chemical composition of the body. In turn, the contractility of the heart, the relative peripheral resistance and, hence, the cardiac output, with its distribution to the various organs, are all mainly controlled by the medulla oblongata responding to impulses from all tissues of the body, including the spinal cord and other portions of the brain itself.

The vasomotor center exhibits inherent automaticity, since its continuous discharge goes on even after elimination of all incoming nerve influences. Section of the brain stem above the medulla does not affect blood pressure, indicating that upper areas do not dominate vasomotor outflow from the sympathetic nervous system. However, such control may be demonstrated by sectioning the cord in the lower cervical region. This interrupts the stream of vasoconstrictor impulses passing from the medullary to the spinal centers; the vessels dilate and the blood pressure falls. After a time, however, the blood pressure rises again; the spinal centers exhibit their inherent power of autonomous action, and assuming the duties hitherto exercised by the medullary centers, restore the vessels to their previous state of tonic constriction. The time required for the vessels to regain their tone after section of the cord varies considerably in different species.

The high degree of vasoconstrictor tone which is normally maintained is shown by the fact that section of the splanchnics doubles the flow in the vessels of the denervated area (Burton-Opitz). After the tone resulting from cord section has been restored it falls again if the splanchnics are sectioned, but after a time a certain degree of tone is regained. This resides in the vascular muscle itself—*peripheral tone*. Apparently, a long period is required for the development of the intrinsic arteriolar tone.

*C. The hypothalamus.* In the hypothalamus, electrical stimulation shows the existence of both excitatory and inhibitory neurons which, presumably, have much to do with blood pressure regulation. It must be remembered that drastic redistribution of blood flow following extensive changes in the discharge of the constrictor fibers to some areas, is often concealed behind slight blood pressure changes and, hence, blood pressure change alone is not a reliable guide. Recently, the hypothalamic area has been explored for structures from which a pure inhibition of sympathetic activity could be induced. Such a structure, of very restricted dimensions, has been localized in the anterior part of the hypothalamus, only a few millimeters from the relay station of the sympathetic vasodilator fibers (see next section). From this area, topical stimulation induces a generalized, often very marked, inhibition of sympathetic discharge affecting both resistance and capacitance vessels.

An immediate and persistent lowering of blood pressure in both normotensive and renal hypertensive dogs occurs following large bilateral coagulations involving the hypothalamic area. This lowering of blood pressure is small in magnitude but is as marked as that resulting permanently from bilateral sympathectomy and low cervical transection. Whether this lowering in blood pressure has a neural or an endocrine basis has not been determined. It is not due to the absence of the neurohypophysial antidiuretic principle because precipitation of a maximal diabetes insipidus (functional neurohypophysectomy) has been accomplished without affecting blood pressure. It is believed not to be due to a neighboring adenohypophysial hypofunction because the lowering of pressure following adenohypophysectomy is delayed rather than immediate as is the case following hypothalamectomy. It is perhaps associated with the immediate and marked decrease in basal energy metabolism which supervenes following appropriate hypothalamectomies.

In addition, there is a "heat loss center" in the anterior parts of the hypothalamus which controls the discharge to the vasoconstrictor fibers of the skin and blood vessels, and, thus, plays an important role in adjusting blood pressure. Electrical stimulation or local cooling of this area brings about a fall in blood pressure while direct warming of this region produces a rise in blood pressure. The cutaneous arterioles and precapillary vessels, and, especially, the arteriovenous anastomoses (shunts), are the vessels most sensitively engaged in the control of heat loss. However, Keller has marshalled evidence to indicate that vasoconstrictor impulses responsible for the maintained contraction of cutaneous blood vessels *do not take* origin from the hypothalamus as evidenced by the following experiments. An asymmetry in the ear vessels and in skin temperature (Horner's syndrome) does not follow unilateral lesions in the hypothalamus or hemisection of the brainstem at a midbrain, pontile or upper medullary level; nor does a complete transection of the midbrain or pons result in generalized cutaneous vasodilation. Ipsilateral vasodilation does occur following hemisection of the lower medulla and this approximates in magnitude and duration that which follows hemisection of the cervical cord.

*D. Cerebral cortex.* Quite a number of studies of cortical vasoconstrictor fiber control are available but relatively little is known about the circulatory adjustments. Stimulation of the motor and premotor cerebral cortex results in marked elevation of blood pressure with constriction of the cutaneous, splanchnic and renal vessels, and, at the same time, a considerable vasodilation in the skeletal muscle. It is believed that these higher centers play significant roles in blood pressure response to pain and anxiety.

### The Vasodilator Fibers

Dilator impulses emerge from the central nervous system by (1) the thoracicolumbar outflow, (2) the cranial outflow of the parasympathetic division reaching the periphery by way of the chorda tympani, glossopharyngeal and vagus nerves, (3) the sacral outflow of the pelvic nerve, and (4) the posterior spinal nerve root's—antidromic impulses.

THE SYMPATHETIC VASODILATOR FIBERS. The question of dilator fibers in the sympathetic system has been much debated. About 10 years ago, it was generally believed that they took an active part in regulation of vascular tone, their activity being governed by the medulla, and that such fibers were distributed to the skeletal muscles, the facial muscles, the buccal mucosa, the coronaries, the intestines, and to certain skin areas, such as the ear. These findings were based on direct stimulation of sympathetic fibers and the recording of blood flow by plethysmography. The advent of direct measurement of blood flow (volume changes by plethysmography do not always mean change in blood flow), and location of an area of central control has led to considerable clarification. The control of the degree of vasodilation of blood vessels is, indeed, supplemented by a system of efferent dilator nerves transmitting from the central nervous system, but this seems to be distributed only to skeletal muscle. Electrical stimulation of the sympathetic

fibers usually brings about vasoconstriction in the innervated area, since the action of the vasoconstrictor influence usually predominates over that of vasodilation. But, if the vasoconstrictor response is first blocked by ergotamine, then, if the sympathetic outflow contains vasodilator fibers, electrical stimulation produces vasodilation. The existence of a sympathetic vasodilator innervation to skeletal muscle of the dog and cat has been established by this technique. The vasodilator nerves may also be activated by topical stimulation in the brain (hypothalamus), using the Horsley-Clarke technique with the result that venous outflow from skeletal muscle of the hind leg of the dog may increase 4 to 5 times (as does the local lactic acid production), but the oxygen usage may decrease, suggesting that shunts are being utilized. In addition, such stimulation results in release of norepinephrine from the adrenal glands. This increased rate of blood flow approximates maximum dilation achieved by other means, such as acetylcholine injection. This may be a potent means of dilation in the human, since blood flow in the human forearm increases during fainting. Also, since the blood pressure falls, and the blood flow is greater in the normal forearm than in a nerve-blocked forearm during syncope, this might be explained by active vasodilation in the normal forearm excited by sympathetic fibers to the muscles. The transmitter is believed to be acetylcholine and the fibers are exclusively cholinergic; i.e., they are blocked by small amounts of atropine. They take their origin in the motor cortex, pass to the hypothalamus as a thin bundle in the ventrolateral portion of the medulla oblongata, and down to the lateral horn of the spinal medulla where they are relayed to lower motor neurons. This pathway is anatomically and functionally separate from the medullary vasomotor center which mediates vasoconstrictor activity. Their functional significance is unknown, but it has been suggested that they are activated in response to cerebral activity, presumably in association with, or in anticipation of skeletal muscle activity.

PARASYMPATHETIC VASODILATOR FIBERS. The parasympathetic vasodilator fibers run to restricted cranial and sacral areas such as the cerebral vessels, tongue, salivary glands, external genitalia and, possibly, to the bladder and rectum. These fibers are probably not concerned with baro and chemoreceptor control of blood vessels, nor are they tonically active. It is generally believed that these fibers are cholinergic, although their vasodilator effect is very resistant to atropine. Their distribution to a few areas with highly specialized functions makes it probable that their function is associated with the special tissue in which they are located.

ANTIDROMIC VASODILATOR IMPULSES. Stricker, many years ago, reported that stimulation of the peripheral segments of the cut posterior roots of the sacral nerves caused dilation of the vessels of the dog paw. This observation was at variance with the Bell-Magendie law which states that the posterior roots convey only centripetal impulses. However, in subsequent years, the former view has been fairly well documented. Since such fibers do not convey the induced impulses to the central nervous system, but rather the vasodilator impulses are conveyed along the fibers in a direction opposite to that in which ordinary sensory impulses travel, they are called antidromic.

The effective stimulus leading to vessel dilation may arise in or around dorsal root ganglia, or it may arise in the skin, to be conveyed antidromically to superficial blood vessels. The latter are sometimes called axon reflexes, but they are obviously not true reflexes since no nerve cell is involved. The efferent and afferent limbs of the axon reflex are formed by the branching of a single nerve fiber. A stimulus applied to one branch sets up an impulse which travels centrally to the point of division where it is reflected down the other branch to an effector organ. The most familiar type of axon reflex is that which involves a sensory nerve fiber and through which vasodilator effects are effected.

Dorsal dilation is of significance only in tissues with a relatively rich distribution of pain fibers, such as the skin and mucous membranes. Various substances have been indicated as the transmitter—a histaminelike substance, acetylcholine, and adenosine triphosphate. This local axon reflex in the skin is induced by any factor which causes damage to surface tissues—trauma, cooling, heating, frostbite. Thus, this local mechanism contributes to local defense and repair in surface tissues by creating an increase of local blood flow in response to the majority of harmful stimuli.

## Adrenal Medulla versus Neural Control of Blood Vessels

Aside from direct neurogenic connections to the blood vessels, the presence in the blood stream of circulating catecholamines raises the question of their role in controlling the circulation. Presumably they appear through some form of hypothalamic stimulation. It has been widely assumed, but never proved, that the hormones secreted from the adrenal medulla markedly contribute to the vasomotor control of the blood vessels. Using a method that allowed a direct comparison of the individual actions of the hormone and vasomotor fiber on peripheral resistance in representative vascular beds, it has been found that the blood vessels are completely dominated by their vasoconstrictor fibers, the contribution by the adrenal secretion being negligible, except in skeletal muscle, in which small physiological concentrations of epinephrine caused almost maximal vasodilation. On the basis of adrenal catecholamine secretion following maximal excitation of the vasomotor center, it is estimated that the maximal secretion is 2 to 3 $\mu$ per g. per kg. per min. Such concentrations of epinephrine and norepinephrine (probably 10 times the normal concentration), when injected intravenously, dilate the vessels of the skeletal muscles and probably those of the liver, but have insignificant vasoconstrictor effects in other regions when compared with the constrictor fibers.

The importance of the catechol hormones for the motor control of the blood vessels is next to insignificant as compared with direct vasomotor innervation. However, a moderate secretion of epinephrine may induce extensive metabolic effects in skeletal muscle and liver cells which lack direct sympathetic innervation. Norepinephrine secretion from the adrenal gland has relatively little influence on the blood vessels, either directly or indirectly, through metabolic dilation.

The vasomotor system of nerves discussed above is the main adjustor of the peripheral circulation, whereby the blood pumped by the heart is distributed throughout the body according to the needs of each individual tissue and of the organism as a whole. This vital role is accomplished by constant, moment-to-moment adjustments of the resistance in the local vascular beds, and it is mediated and regulated by the central nervous system through various reflex mechanisms (fig. 21.1).

Our knowledge and understanding of these reflex mechanisms is far from complete: the function of some of them is fairly well established; the existence of others is known without any certainty regarding their function; and it is safe to assume that there exist still others, totally unknown to us at the present time. Inevitably, in the ensuing parts, the lengthiest considerations will be given to the most completely studied

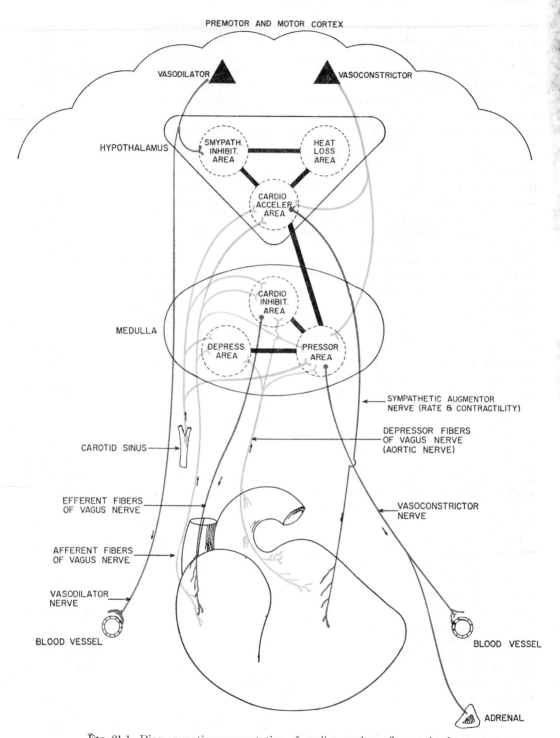

Fig. 21.1. Diagrammatic representation of cardiovascular reflex mechanisms.

mechanisms, but it should be clear that this is not necessarily proportional to their respective physiological importance.

Vasomotor reflexes can be elicited by the stimulation of practically any afferent nerve—somatic or visceral.

### Vascular Reflexes Resulting from the Stimulation of Somatic Nerves

Historically, these are among the earliest vascular reflex mechanisms known, although their importance in overall circulatory regulation is relatively minor.

Stimulation of the central end of a nerve, such as the sciatic, the median or a sensory cranial nerve, may result in either a rise or a fall in the arterial blood pressure according to the strength and type of the stimulus employed. The components of the reflex arc upon which the responses depend are, (1) afferent fibers in the peripheral nerve, (2) the vasomotor centers, and (3) the efferent vascular nerves, i.e., the vasoconstrictors, or vasodilators. In order to elicit a pressor reflex, a stimulus much stronger than that necessary to provoke a depressor response must, as a rule, be applied; that is, one which would elicit pain in a conscious animal. In the elicitation of either reflex, the magnitude of the response is apparently dependent upon the number of afferent fibers involved. For example, stimulation of various nerves of the brachial or lumbar plexus causes practically equivalent depressions or elevations in the blood pressure when the number of afferent fibers in the respective nerves is taken into account.

It must be re-emphasized that not all the pressor or depressor impulses ascend to the medulla but that reflex arcs exist which have their centers within the cord; both vasoconstrictor and vasodilator reflexes can be elicited in an animal whose cord has been divided in the lower cervical region a short time previously.

From the results of experiments upon animals, it is to be expected that in the human subject a painful stimulus applied to a somatic nerve will be followed by a pressor response. The excitation of psychic centers and, also, the liberation of adrenaline are additional factors which play an important part in the pressor response resulting from painful stimuli. On the other hand, there are numerous afferent fibers in the hollow viscera which respond to stretch and result in a decreased blood pressure. Stimulation of the mesentery, peritoneum and abdominal viscera or of certain regions such as the anus, vagina, and spermatic cord may be followed by a fall in blood pressure. Finally, there may be obvious reflex effects which may or may not be associated with blood pressure changes. For example, in normal persons with bladder distention, there may be facial flushing but with evidence of widespread venous constriction. Following inflation of balloons placed in the esophagus, rectum or in an ileostomy, regional venoconstriction also can be demonstrated.

### The Presso or Baroreceptors

Experiments have shown that the fundamental regulations of systemic blood pressure is reflexly controlled by the action of the arterial pressure itself on pressure sensitive receptors located in the vascular walls, especially of the aortic arch and carotid sinus areas.

THE AORTIC OR CARDIAC DEPRESSOR NERVE. The branch of the vagus which is known as the *aortic* or *cardiac depressor* nerve was first described by Cyon and Ludwig (1866). It is purely afferent and depressor in function; when sectioned, and its central (cerebral) end stimulated, a pronounced fall in pressure occurs (fig. 21.2); excitation of the cardiac end, on the other hand, causes no effect. Two factors are involved in the depressor response following stimulation of the depressor fibers. (*1*) *Slowing of the heart rate and increased force of the ventricular contraction.* The efferent fibers of the vagus of the same and of the opposite side constitute the efferent limb of the reflex arc through which this response is chiefly brought about; for its full elicitation at least one vagus must, therefore, remain intact. (*2*) *Vasodilation.* The vasomotor pathways constitute the efferent limb of this reflex. Vasoconstrictor tone is reduced and vasodilator tone increased. The reflex effect upon the vessels cannot, therefore, be elicited af-

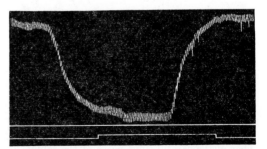

FIG. 21.2. Fall in arterial blood pressure resulting from stimulation of the central end of the cardiac depressor (aortic) nerve. The drum was stopped in the middle of the curve and the excitation maintained for 17 minutes. The line of zero pressure should be 30 mm. lower than here shown. (From Bayliss.)

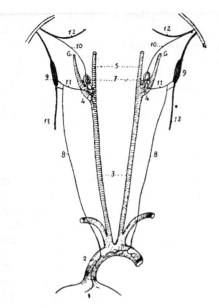

FIG. 21.3. Innervation of the carotid sinus and arch of aorta. 1, Heart; 2, arch of aorta; 3, common carotid; 4, carotid sinus; 5, external carotid; 6, internal carotid; 7, carotid bodies; 8, cardiac depressor nerve; 9, ganglion of vagus; 10, sinus nerve, branch of the glossopharyngeal nerve; 11, nerve branch connecting the carotid sinus with the vagus ganglion; 12, glossopharyngeal nerve; 13, vagus nerve. (After Heymans.)

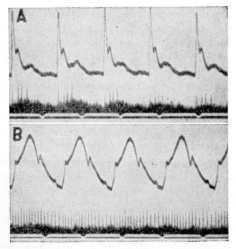

FIG. 21.4. The upper curve in each record represents the arterial blood pressure registered by a membrane manometer; the lower curve of each record shows the electrical discharge from a single fiber of the carotid sinus nerve of the rabbit. In the upper record (A) the mean arterial pressure was 55 mm. Hg; even at this low level a discharge of 4 impulses accompanied each ventricular systole. In the lower record (B) the mean arterial pressure was 135 mm. Hg; in this instance there was a more rapid and more continuous discharge from the end-organ. (Bronk and Stella.)

ter section of the spinal cord in the lower cervical region.

The receptors of the reflex (the terminals of the aortic nerve) are situated in the aortic arch and upper part of the thoracic aorta, in the ventricles and possibly also, according to Daly and Verney, in the coronary and pulmonary vessels (see fig. 21.3).

The fall in pressure is due mainly to dilation of the splanchnic vessels. The dilation is not, however, confined to these vessels but includes those of the skin and muscles. Cardiac slowing plays a minor role in the production of the fall in blood pressure, for almost as great an effect can be obtained after both vagi have been cut. The depressor reflex can be elicited by mechanical or electrical stimulation of the aortic wall itself wherein the special proprioceptors are located; stretching is an especially effective type of stimulus. It was shown that action currents ascend the nerve synchronously with the heart beats (fig. 21.4). The normal stimulus is, therefore, quite evidently the pulsatile expansion of the aortic wall, a rise in general blood pressure increasing the intensity of the stimulus, a fall in pressure causing the reverse effect.

THE CAROTID SINUS MECHANISM. The carotid sinus is the term applied to the slight enlargement of the common carotid artery where it bifurcates into the internal and external carotids (fig. 21.3). The carotid sinus was shown by Hering in 1923 to play an important role in the regulation of the cardiac rate and arterial blood pressure. Compression of the carotid at its bifurcation (so as to raise the pressure within the sinus) causes a marked slowing of the heart rate, vasodilation and a fall in blood pressure; these effects result even though mechanical stimulation of the vagus is carefully avoided. Electrical stimulation of the sinus wall produces similar effects. Pressure upon the common carotid some distance below the sinus (so as to reduce the blood pressure within the sinus itself) causes cardiac acceleration, vasoconstriction and a rise in arterial pressure together with, as shown by Heymans, the liberation of adrenaline. The carotid sinus therefore constitutes a mechanism whereby both pressor and depressor effects are mediated. The effects are brought about through the following neural mechanism.

THE SINUS REFLEX ARC. The afferent fibers of the reflex arc are contained in the *sinus nerve*, a branch of the glossopharyngeal. This delicate filament descends between the internal and external carotids to the sinus where its fibers terminate in sensory organs (proprioceptors) situated between the connective tissue fibers in the adventitia of the sinus wall. Centrally the fibers of the sinus nerve make connections with the cardio-inhibitory and vasomotor centers. The efferent limb of the cardiac part of the reflex is, of course, the vagus. The efferent limbs of the vasodilator and vaso-constrictor reflexes are apparently sympathetic fibers, for these reflexes are abolished by complete removal of the sympathetic chains.

Study of the action currents passing along the sinus nerve shows that ordinary arterial pressures impulses are discharged throughout the cardiac cycle, their frequency increasing during systole and decreasing during diastole. A rise in general blood pressure increases the rate of impulse discharge as well as the number of sense organs excited. The latter show slow adaptation so that though the stimulus (distension of the arterial wall) persists the impulse discharge shows little reduction in frequency, and when the pressure is very high, they extend with little reduction in rate throughout diastole. At low pressures, impulses are discharged only during systole.

The sinus reflexes have been studied exhaustively by Heymans and his associates. They carried out cross-circulation experiments which speak conclusively for the physiological importance of these reflexes in cardiovascular regulation (see fig. 21.5). The sinus of one dog (B) was isolated from the general circulation and perfused with the blood of another animal (A) in the manner shown in the figure. The nerve supply to the sinus was left intact. When the arterial pressure of dog A was raised, that of dog B, recorded in the femoral artery, fell. Conversely, a reduction in blood pressure of dog A caused a rise in the blood pressure of dog B. In the latter instance, adrenaline liberation also occurred which was a contributory factor in the blood pressure elevation as indicated by its pressor effect upon the circulation of dog C, connected to the suprarenal vein of B. These effects could not be obtained after denervation of the sinus.

The sinus and aortic nerves, or so-called "buffer" nerves, constitute a mechanism of the utmost importance in controlling the arterial blood pressure and in maintaining the circulation to the brain. The rise in diastolic pressure and the increase in heart rate which occur when the body changes from the recumbent to the sitting position or from the sitting to the standing position, are apparently brought about through these nerves; they therefore play an essential part in

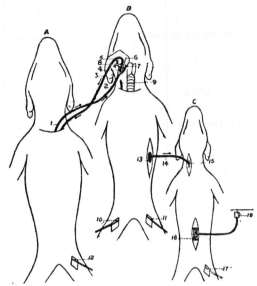

FIG. 21.5. Scheme of perfusion of the isolated carotid sinus of dog B, by dog A, and an anastomosis between the suprarenal vein of B and the jugular vein of dog C. 1, left carotid artery of dog A; 2, right carotid artery of B, anastomosed with carotid of A; 3, left external jugular vein of A; 4, isolated right carotid sinus of B; 5, lingual artery of B, anastomosed with jugular vein of dog A; 6, nerve supply to carotid sinus of B. The blood from dog A flows through the carotid sinus of dog B and back to A via the lingual artery of B and the external jugular of A. 7, internal carotid; 8, facial and maxillary arteries; 9, common carotid; 10, 11, 12 and 17, femoral arteries to manometers; 13, adrenal gland; 14 and 15, suprarenal-jugular anastomosis; 16, decapsulated spleen in plethysmograph; 18, piston recorder for plethysmograph. (After Heymans.)

compensating for the effect of gravity upon the circulation.

An underfilled state of the vessels, as may result from hemorrhage or shock, or any other condition which tends to cause a fall in blood pressure, will call these mechanisms into play. A generalized vasoconstriction results to adjust the vascular capacity to the reduced blood volume and thus maintain the blood pressure. Excessive elevation of the blood pressure, on the other hand, is countered by a depressor reflex (see diagram fig. 21.1). The great importance of these reflex mechanisms in hemorrhage is shown by the fact that in an animal in which all four buffer nerves have been sectioned the rapid loss of only about $1/10$ of the blood volume proves fatal, whereas usually a reduction in blood volume of from 35 to 45 per cent is required to cause death. Mayerson found that tilting anesthetized dogs from the horizontal to the upright position caused a sharp drop in blood pressure followed within 10 sec.

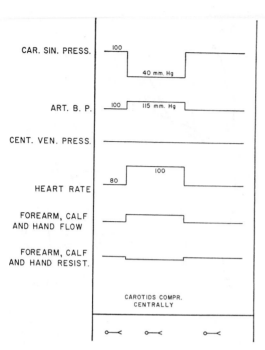

CAR. SIN. PRESS.

ART. B. P.

CENT. VEN. PRESS.

HEART RATE

FOREARM, CALF
AND HAND FLOW

FOREARM, CALF
AND HAND RESIST.

CAROTIDS COMPR.
CENTRALLY

Fig. 21.6. Bilateral carotid artery compression in supine man producing carotid sinus hypotension, reflexly causes a rise in systemic pressure, a tachycardia and an increase in peripheral flow with concomitant decrease in peripheral resistance.

by a compensatory rise. After section of both sets of buffer nerves the compensatory rise did not, as a rule, occur.

Several (European) workers have reported the occurrence of permanent hypertension in animals following bilateral section of the sinus aortic nerves. Pressures as high as 200 mm. Hg lasting over a period of 3 years have been reported. Other investigators who have carried out similar experiments find that the hypertension so produced is not permanent in the majority of animals, but tends to return to normal after a variable period. Such a result may be due to the regeneration of the sectioned nerves or to the reflex control of the circulation being assumed by some other mechanism.

Mechanism of action. The mechanism of action of the blood pressure on the baroreceptors is complex and only partially understood. If deformation of the baroreceptive arterial walls from a raised arterial pressure is prevented, the baroreceptors no longer re-spond to the pressure change. Local application of drugs, such as epinephrine or norepinephrine, increases the smooth muscle tension in the arterial wall of the isolated carotid sinus preparation which, in turn, is

associated with a large increase in impulse traffic along the baroreceptor fibers throughout the cardiac cycle, and a resetting of the baroreceptive mechanisms at a higher level, with resultant blood pressure adjustment. Sodium nitrite, which relaxes smooth muscle, reduces the intramural tension in these sensitive regions, decreases the impulse traffic and resets the blood pressure regulation at a lower level. These experiments indicate that under normal conditions, the response of the baroreceptor area and the level of blood pressure maintained depend not only on the level of arterial pressure, but, possibly, even more so on the resistance of the baroreceptive arterial walls to deformation by the intravascular pressure.

### Possible Other Arterial Baroreceptors

Possible additional arterial baroreceptor types have been studied in the common carotid artery, the thoracic, and mesenteric arteries. Experiments in which a sudden rise in intracranial pressure causes systemic hypertension, and sudden reduction in intracranial pressure leads to systemic hypotension, suggest, but do not prove, that pressure sensitive receptors are present in the cranial cavity. Such responses could be due to asphyxia of the medullary centers. However, the fact that chronic constriction (flow effect not known) of the internal carotid arteries by plastic clamps above the sinus area in dogs causes chronic systemic hypertension enduring up to four years, is not so easily explained. Impulse output in the mesenteric baroreceptors exists throughout the cardiac cycle, and, if pressure is changed in the mesenteric artery or the artery is clamped, vasomotor reflexes are induced. These reflexes do affect the systemic blood pressure even when the sino aortic nerves are cut. It is a segmental, reflex adaptation of the circulation and vasomotor state related to pressure changes in a given area. It apparently exists in the cat but not in the dog. Reflex responses can also be obtained in the innervated perfused hind leg of the open-chest dog, when the descending aorta between the left subclavian artery and the diaphragm is isolated and perfused at varying pulsatile pressures, or when adrenaline is added.

The importance of these afferent mechanisms in control of the circulation is not known.

### Balanced and Reciprocal Vascular Reactions

In the intact animal the height of the blood pressure at any moment, insofar as the nervous control of the peripheral vessels is concerned, is apparently the algebraic sum of the effects of afferent impulses impinging upon the vasomotor centers. Under ordinary circumstances impulses arising from the carotid sinus and aortic arch play the most prominent roles, but impulses from skin, muscles and viscera and from higher nervous centers also exert an important influence. That pronounced effects upon the peripheral vessels can be produced by the irradiation of impulses from higher centers is evidenced by such phenomena as blushing, pallor, erection and certain types of syncope (fainting). Similar vascular changes can be observed in the mucosa of the exteriorized colon of the dog when the animal is excited and in splenic volume. Even very mild excitation of psychic centers exerts an influence upon the vascular mechanisms. The psychogalvanic reflex (due to changes in the electrical resistance of the skin) has a vascular basis. A reciprocal relationship also exists between splanchnic and cutaneous vascular areas on the one hand and the vessels of the muscles on the other. Adrenaline, for example, causes dilation of the latter vessels accompanied by vasoconstriction in the skin and abdominal viscera. Stimulation of the wall of a large vein or distension of the duodenum causes reflex constriction of the cutaneous vessels, and stimulation of the skin results in an increase of the blood in the liver and in the renal cortex. Furthermore, the muscular and cutaneous tissues may show opposite vascular reactions. Thus, in the dog, cooling of the body causes constriction of the skin vessels and vasodilation in the muscles.

A mechanism also exists in the experimental animal whereby afferent impulses arising within an organ, although leading to generalized vasoconstriction, result locally in dilation and increased blood flow.

An interesting example of the complex nature of the reflex vascular adjustments has been described. An electrical record obtained from a nerve twig coming from a Pacinian corpuscle in the mesentery during perfusion of the mesenteric vessels showed an increase in the frequency of the afferent impulses when the perfusion pressure was raised. The impulse frequency was reduced by bleeding the animal and increased again when the blood was reintroduced into the body. It is suggested that the Pacinian corpuscles which lie in close relation to the vessels are stimulated when the latter dilate. Messages pass to the vasomotor center which then discharges vasoconstrictor impulses to the vessels of the area from which the afferent impulses arose. Thus, undue distention of the vessels and pooling of blood in the splanch-

nic region is prevented. It has also been shown that stimulation of the peripheral end of the splanchnic nerve causes a much greater rise in blood pressure than usual if the carotid sinuses have been excluded from the circulation (by clamping the carotids). This observation indicates that ordinarily the pressor effect of splanchnic stimulation is largely counteracted by a depressor reflex initiated from the sinus.

## The Extraresistance (Cardiac) Effects of the Baroreceptor Reflexes

Too much attention has been paid in the past to the effects of baroreceptor reflexes on the level of blood pressure itself. The action of the baroreceptors is not confined to effects on arteriolar resistance. Much of the preoccupation with peripheral resistance has stemmed from the difficulty in measuring capacity and total flow of the vascular system, a situation which is now being alleviated. The ease of measurement of arterial blood pressure and the dramatic effects thereon from stimulation of the baroreceptor afferents have resulted in identifying circulation changes in terms of blood pressure and, hence, in terms of alterations of peripheral resistance. If vasoconstriction of arterioles were the sole result of baroreceptor stimulation, it is debatable whether any benefit would be conferred on the circulation as a whole. The last few years have seen considerable development in flow methodology and evidence, thus far, from such studies indicates that we have been too prone to describe changes in the circulation to blood pressure and arteriolar resistance alterations. The most important changes during reflex, systemic hypertension of sinoaortic origin are those of venoconstriction (effects on the capacity vessels) and direct sympathetic stimulation of the heart. Occlusion of the common carotid arteries causes systemic hypertension with resultant decrease in the plethysmographic volume of spleen, limb, kidney, and other parts of the circulation. If the systemic hypertension is ascribed to widespread arteriolar vasoconstriction, cardiac output would be expected to fall or, at least, not to increase. However, total pulmonary, muscle and kidney blood flow have been shown to increase during carotid occlusion. There is always some increase in peripheral resistance but it is of less quantitative significance, since the cardiac output increases.

There is evidence that the sympathetics (from the stellates), and parasympathetics (vagal) to the heart, can significantly alter the atrial and ventricular contractility and that this occurs naturally by way of reflexes. In the open chest dog, stimulation of the cardiac nerve fibers previously isolated from the left stellate ganglion, increased systolic blood pressure, cardiac output and stroke volume with a decrease in heart size. The heart rate did not necessarily change. Since stellate stimulation largely elevated arterial blood pressure and cardiac output in the presence of a constant heart rate, after all known connections to the peripheral vasculature had been severed, it follows that the rise of blood pressure was caused by the augmented force of contraction giving an increased cardiac output and not by increased peripheral resistance. These results with cardiac fiber stimulation are similar to those obtained with carotid sinus hypotension. In the open chest dog, when both carotid sinuses were independently perfused under controlled conditions, in the presence of a high, but constant, heart rate, and the mean perfusion pressure and pulse pressure were greatly decreased, the arterial blood pressure, cardiac output and stroke volume rose appreciably. The calculated stroke work increased about 10 times, while the peripheral resistance was only about doubled. This indicates that the circulatory response to carotid sinus baroreceptor stimulation can be, dominantly, an increased cardiac action and, secondarily, an increase in peripheral resistance. Repetitive stimulation at different levels of carotid sinus hypotension produced a shift of the ventricular function curve to the left (more external work at a lower filling pressure). The reverse is also true, i. e., carotid hypertension reduces arterial blood pressure, cardiac output, stroke volume, and shifts the ventricular function curve to the right. The effector portion of this reflex appears to be the sympathetic fibers from the stellate ganglia to the heart, since, following their section these effects disappeared or could not again be induced.

In the open-chest dog with an electrically driven heart (and, therefore, at a constant high heart rate), distal stimulation of the cut vagi decreased mean atrial pressure, arterial pressure, cardiac output and stroke volume, while the ventricular function curve was shifted to the right. Carotid sinus hypertension (produced by the method described in the previous paragraph) gave similar findings. Carotid sinus hypotension enhanced the atrial pressure, arterial pressure, cardiac output and stroke volume. All responses were abolished by atropine. The change in response of atrial contractility is presumed to be reflexly induced, while the ventricular changes arise secondary to the changing, atrial contribution to ventricular end diastolic pressure and fiber length.

Finally, observations in man are instructive. Pressures within the carotid sinus regions were directly measured with indwelling catheters in conscious, supine man while the internal pressure was lowered by central, bilateral, carotid artery compression. As the carotid sinus pressure dropped from a mean of 100 to 40 mm. Hg., the arterial blood pressure and heart rate increased only mildly. There is no evidence that the pressor response is secondary to reduction in caliber of the limb and skeletal muscle vessels. The resistance to flow which they offer is actually slightly less than in the control state as the result of a mild increase in systemic blood pressure and in blood flow through the limbs. Simultaneous measurement of cardiac output would have been helpful here, since the increase in arterial blood pressure could arise from the increased cardiac output or from increased vessel resistance in another area.

## Cardiovascular Reflexes of Chemoreceptor Origin

Just as the receptors in the root of the aorta and in the carotid sinus serve as outposts of the brain, testing the blood for its pressure level so that the vasomotor center may be advised, so, in similar fashion, the adjacent carotid and aortic bodies contain epitheloid cells and nerve endings sensitive to the chemical composition of the arterial blood. The fibers of the aortic body run in the vagus while the fibers of the carotid body are branches of the glossopharyngeal nerves. The aortic body is connected with a branch of a fine artery arising from the aorta beyond its arch. The carotid body (glomus caroticum) is a small structure situated upon a branch of the occipital artery or upon a small vessel arising directly from the external carotid just above the bifurcation of the common carotid. It is composed of rounded clumps of polyhedral cells, and possesses a rich network of capillaries of sinusoidal character. These chemoreceptors sample the blood for its $pO_2$, $pCO_2$, pH, and possibly for other qualities. Blood flow through the carotid body appears to be by far the largest for any body tissue. Calculations based on direct flow measurements indicate a flow of 2,000 ml. per 100 g. per min. (left ventricle = 80 to 100 ml. per 100 g. per min.) while the oxygen usage of 9 ml. per 100 g. per min., compares with that of the left ventricle. This flow can be cut to ⅓ by stimulation of the cervical sympathetics. Reflex vasomotor effects evoked by chemoreceptor stimulation have been extensively studied. In general, the chemoreceptors are stimulated by anoxia, hypercapnia, and acidosis. The mechanism by which changes in blood chemical composition effect a response in these two structures is not clearly understood nor has the chemoreceptor intermediate that stimulates the nerve endings been identified, but it has been shown that electroneurographic evidence of chemoreceptor activity exists at $CO_2$ tensions above 30 mm. Hg and $O_2$ tensions approximately 90 mm. Hg or less. With increasing $CO_2$ and decreasing $pO_2$, discharge of the chemoreceptors is diffuse, but the discharge with increasing $CO_2$ tension is rarely as great as that from anoxia. According to Heymans, "it is doubtful that chemoreceptors exert any significant effects on the circulation at rest." However, acute hypoxia (inhalation of low oxygen mixtures or of nitrogen) causes systemic hypertension and increased vasoconstriction (decreased blood flow) in the limbs and initestine, but responses are abolished if the chemoreceptor areas are blocked. It is unlikely that chemoreflexes cause systemic hypertension only by inducing an increase in arteriolar resistance, but there are no studies of the reflex effects of such stimulation on cardiac output or on the capacitance vessels. It is certain, however, that they contribute to the maintenance of the circulation following depletion of the blood volume. The latter can be shown in an animal in which, following massive hemorrhage, the blood pressure decreased to 70 mm. Hg. There was intense firing of the chemoreceptors which could be stopped by raising the oxygen tension while resection of the sinus nerves caused a further fall of blood pressure. The latter can only be due to withdrawal of chemoreceptor reflex vasoconstriction since the baroreceptors are not operative at this blood pressure level. Presumably the capacitance vessels (veins) are involved here as well as the resistance vessels, but this remains to be determined.

### The Vascular Effects of Normal Variations in Blood Oxygen, Carbon Dioxide and pH

The positive cardiovascular effects of large changes in blood $pO_2$ and $pCO_2$ and in temperature, have been discussed in chapter 21. It is generally stated that both $CO_2$ and oxygen have dual effects. Although $CO_2$ may have a minor reflex effect through the aortic and carotid body chemoreceptors, it may also have a large direct central effect on the medullary centers which leads to peripheral vasoconstriction with rising blood $CO_2$ concentrations, while with decreasing blood $CO_2$ the center will ultimately cease giving out its normal tonic influence. It also may have a large direct peripheral vessel effect, an increasing blood $CO_2$ causing peripheral dilation and a decreasing peripheral $CO_2$ leading to local vasoconstriction. Similarly, the central effects of oxygen lack are supposedly largely through the sinus and aortic bodies, a decrease in oxygen leading to reflex peripheral vasoconstriction, while in the periphery, local hypoxia has the effect of vasodilation. While these statements based on experimental data have been perpetuated, it is very difficult to make such a functional separation and yet retain some reasonable degree of normalcy in the experimental approach to the problem. Aside from the effects mediated through the chemoreceptors, it is doubtful that it is known what the relative effects are of variations in blood gases and pH, within a physiological range, on the vasomotor centers and the general peripheral circulation. However, for some individual organs or regions, one can distinguish between the local effects of chemical changes in the blood on the state of peripheral vessels as compared to their central neural effects at physiological levels of stress and under normal conditions. For example, the main body of evidence indicates that small increases in carbon dioxide have a direct vasodilating action on cerebral and skin vessels in animals and in humans.

The complexity of the problem, even in individual regions, is indicated when one compares the effect of carbon dioxide on the vasomotor state in the extremities of an abnormal and normal preparation. The hindlimb of an animal perfused with blood from a heart-lung preparation shows vasodilation (greater blood flow at the same perfusion pressure) when the lungs are ventilated by air containing a small amount of carbon dioxide, or by air with some reduction in its oxygen content. These reactions must result from local chemical reactions. However, in human subjects with hypercapnia alone induced from breathing a small concentration of carbon dioxide in the inspired air, the forearm's vascular resistance (mainly muscle) is greatly increased, for systemic blood pressure is increased with little or no change in local blood flow. In the same subjects in whom hypoxia was produced by breathing 5 to 10 per cent oxygen in nitrogen, forearm blood flow increases 100 per cent in the presence of a constant systemic arterial and venous pressure so that vascular resistance in the forearm is considerably reduced. Since the same results are observed in the nerve-blocked arm, the local change in vasomotor state is due to a humoral mechanism and not to a nervous mechanism. When the increased elimination of $CO_2$ during hypoxia is prevented by adding enough $CO_2$ to the oxygen poor gas mixture to maintain the alveolar $pCO_2$ constant, vascular resistance in the forearm is not significantly changed. This indicates that marked hypoxia does not affect local overall vessel resistance. Thus, in man, a humoral vasoconstriction occurs with hypercapnia, and a humoral vasodilation occurs with hypoxia in the muscles of the forearm which is due more to the hypocapnia resulting from the hypoxia than directly to the lack of oxygen. But the exact mechanism is not clear. The $CO_2$ or altered pH could have had a local effect, but it is just as probable that a rapid change in arterial $pCO_2$ evoked biochemical changes in the blood which caused local vasoconstriction or dilation. Of several possible humoral vasodilators which are known, the lowered $pCO_2$ might have led to the release of adrenaline which is known to cause vasodilation in skeletal muscle.

In the past, it has been debatable whether the circulatory effects observed with respiratory or metabolic acidosis come from the elevated $pCO_2$, the fall in pH, or a combination of both. This has been because there has not been any good way of separating these effects. However, with the use of the organic buffer Tris (hydroxymethyl) amino methane, reasonable experimental separation has been performed with the finding that the cardiovascular effects arise from the decrease in pH and not from the associated change in blood $PaCO_2$ (fig. 21.7). To make this study, the effects of metabolic acidosis were observed in dogs under apneic oxygenation with and without Tris injection. Apneic oxygenation is a condition of ventilatory arrest during which oxygenation of the blood is maintained while acute hypercapnia develops. This condition is produced by ventilating the dog with 100 per cent oxygen in an open circuit for one hour. During this time, oxygen replaces nitrogen throughout the body. After this period of denitrogenation, apnea is induced by succinylcholine, and the lungs are left connected to a reservoir of oxygen. Thus, the blood is maintained in full oxygen saturation, but blood $CO_2$ accumulates slowly. Without the presence of Tris in such dogs, there is a rise in $CO_2$, arterial, pulmonary artery and central venous blood pressures, $PaCO_2$, and plasma norepinephrine and epinephrine; the blood pH drops precipitously,

the heart rate mildly. In similar dogs treated with intravenous drip of Tris, all these physiological variables remain close to their control values except $PaCO_2$ which rises from 38 to 82 mm. Hg. Since such a $pCO_2$ increase in the intact animal does produce the above circulatory changes when it is accompanied by a parallel fall in pH, the $H^+$ concentration increase during hypercapnia seems to be a determinant factor in the stimulation of the cardiovascular system. This type of experiment, however, still does not clearly separate the effects of $CO_2$ and pH, for the latter does change (7.45 to 7.31), and the vascular system may be very sensitive to it.

## Reflexes from the Heart and Lungs

Despite considerable lacks in our knowledge concerning their functions, the carotid and aortic baroreceptor and chemoreceptor reflexes are the most completely studied and understood of vasomotor regulatory reflex mechanisms.

From various intrathoracic vessels (including the chambers of the heart) arise other reflexes affecting vasomotor tone. Although their importance in the regulation of the circulation may possibly be comparable to that of the previously mentioned reflexes, much less is known about their function. As a matter of fact, our present state of knowledge permits little more than an enumeration of various cardiopulmonary reflexes discovered up to date.

It is much more difficult to investigate cardiopulmonary reflexes than those related to the baroreceptors in the systemic circuit. This is because the operative procedures necessary to make interpretable experiments are so extensive and traumatic, and it is almost impossible to denervate the heart and/or lungs. Despite this, the usual technique so successful in other vascular beds, of eliciting reflexes by change of perfusion pressure in an isolated vascular bed, has been used with some success to indicate qualitatively, if not quantitatively, cardiopulmonary reflexes.

### Right Heart Reflexes

Observations have shown conclusively that in the walls of the atria and great veins, there are receptors which have fairly large afferent nerve fibers and which respond to change of pressure in the atria by firing during atrial contraction (Type A), and during passive distention during atrial diastole (Type B). These afferent fibers are in the vagi.

The existence of a right atrial reflex has been

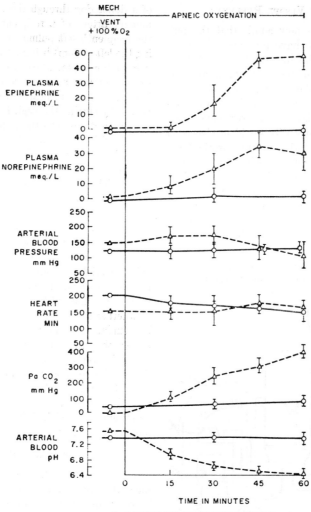

FIG. 21.7. Comparative changes in pH, $pCO_2$, blood pressure and catecholamine levels during apnoeic oxygenation with and without TRIS administration. (Nahas, Am. J. Physiol., 1959, **197**, 1308.)

shown as follows: Blood returning through both venae cavae was collected and pumped into the right atrium, whence it passed through the right ventricle to the pulmonary artery, where it was collected and pumped into a donor dog's veins for oxygenation and returned by a pump to the recipient's left atrium. Increase of perfusion pressure in the right heart gave bradycardia and systemic hypotension which were abolished after vagotomy. Since atropine prevented the bradycardia resulting from the perfusion pressure elevation but did not affect the associated hypotension, a reflex peripheral dilation had occurred. The receptors were found to be in the atrium and not in the ventricle.

In 1915, Bainbridge showed that the intravenous injection of saline or blood produced tachycardia in the anesthetized dog and that this was abolished only by bilateral vagotomy. This is the one reflex which is known to most medical students. Yet, he left unanswered the question of the nature of the effective stimulus to the receptors and their location in the great veins or right side of the heart. Many subsequent investigators using more refined techniques have tried to pin-point the receptors involved and their location. Many are of the opinion that the receptors are in the right atrium, others that no such reflex exists. The answer must await the use of better techniques.

## PULMONARY VESSEL REFLEXES

Most investigators now admit that the pulmonary blood vessels have tone and, therefore, the possibility that this tone can be altered. Daly has found evidence in the anesthetized dog that the pulmonary vascular resistance can be altered be extrinsic vasomotor nerves. Both vasoconstrictor and vasodilator responses have been demonstrated. Recently, direct evidence has been produced that stimulation of the carotid body chemoreceptors by perfusion with venous blood decreases pulmonary vascular resistance. This response was abolished by cutting the carotid sinus nerve or cervico vagosympathetic trunks, or by injection of atropine. However, localization of the vascular area involved in the dilation was not possible.

A. *Pulmonary depressor reflex.* In perfusion experiments, blood is pumped from the right atrium

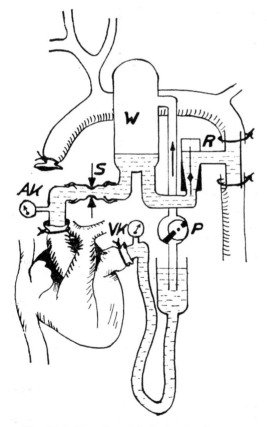

FIG. 21.8. Experimental device to show presence of left ventricular pressure (stretch) receptors by aortic compression. *S*, clamp; *AK* and *VK*, aortic and left atrial pressure manometers, respectively; *W*, constant pressure buffering chamber; *R*, systemic flow meter; *P*, pump. (Doutheil and Kramer, Pflüger's Arch. ges. Physiol., 1959, **269**, 114.)

of a donor dog through the cannulated left pulmonary artery of a recipient, the outflow from the recipient's left pulmonary vein (thus excluding the left atrium) being returned to the jugular vein of the donor. Marked elevation of the perfusion pressure at times decreases the systemic blood pressure and heart rate which effect is removed by cutting the vagi. In addition, injection of certain drugs into the pulmonary artery also causes a fall in systemic blood pressure and heart rate which is prevented by previous vagal section. This suggests a pulmonary depressor chemoreflex. The receptors concerned are believed to lie in the pulmonary veins.

B. *Reflexes from the smaller pulmonary vessels.* Despite a tremendous amount of investigation, it is problematic whether reflexes are initiated from the smaller vessels of the pulmonary circuit—arterioles, capillaries and venules. Embolization by clots, starch grain, glass and plastic beads, have not led to conclusive experiments as to whether the results have a mechanical or a reflex explanation. From the work of Daly, it is known that the sympathetic innervation of the vessels is largely vasoconstrictor and that stimulation of the stellates may, at times, reduce lung blood flow by as much as 30 per cent. Despite this, there is no knowledge that pulmonary vasoconstriction can be elicited from stimulation of pulmonary vascular receptors.

## LEFT HEART REFLEXES

A. *Left ventricle.* Daly and Verney were first to show that pressor receptors existed in the left heart. In an innervated heart-lung preparation in which the aortic pressure was kept constant, an increased pressure in the left side of the heart caused cardiac slowing. More recently, it has been shown that when the pressure is elevated in a vascularly isolated left heart, reflex bradycardia, systemic hypotension, and vasodilation of the leg vessels result. Since left atrial pressure elevation alone was ineffective, it is concluded the receptors were in the left ventricle. Upon vagal blockage the effect disappeared. These effects may also arise from pressoreceptors of the aortic arch which are known to extend into the left side of the heart. Informative experiments are those of Doutheil and Kramer, who varied the left ventricular stretch and pressure by an adjustable clamp on the aorta, while the systemic flow was metered, and its perfusion pressure was maintained constant during aortic constriction by a very large pressure buffering chamber attached to the aorta. It can be observed (fig. 21.8) that within 4 sec. after elevation of left ventricular pressure by mechanical constriction, the aortic flow starts to rise and is almost doubled, indicating massive peripheral dilation arising in the beginning of the aorta or in the left heart. The afferent pathway for this reflex was demonstrated to be the vagus nerve, for following its cervical section, the effect disappeared. To what extent this reflex is invoked under normal conditions is problematic, since a rather large increase in ventricular pressure (and presumably, therefore, stretch) is necessary to elicit a systemic flow response.

*B. Coronary chemoreflex (Bezold-Jarish reflex).* In the dog or cat, the peripheral ends of the major coronary artery branches have been separately connected to systemic arteries. Injection of veratrine peripherally into the left circumflex artery causes a fall in blood pressure and heart rate. The systemic hypotension was shown to be independent of the bradycardia, being due to reflex vasodilation. This does not occur if the vagi are first cut. This does not occur upon injection into the right coronary artery or into the coronary artery branches supplying the atrial appendages. Thus, there are receptors in the left ventricular wall supplied by the left circumflex artery.

*C. Left atrial receptors.* Recent work has shown that left atrial vagal receptors (and also possibly in the pulmonary veins) may be the sensory endings of a reflex which controls blood volume. It was first shown that negative pressure breathing causes diuresis. This was then related to the congestion of the thoracic blood vessels which arise from this procedure. Since the effect was removed by vagotomy, it was reasoned that pulmonary or cardiac vessel receptors of vagal origin exist which are responsive to stretch or pressure. Experimentally, it was shown that procedures which lead to an increase of the intrathoracic blood volume (negative pressure breathing), congestion of the pulmonary vascular bed by mitral stenosis through snares, embolization of the pulmonary capillary bed, or an inflated balloon in the left atrium, all cause marked diuresis which, in the balloon experiments, is prevented by previous cooling of the vagus nerves. However, in general the physiological purpose and quantitative effects remain unknown.

### RESPIRATORY REFLEXES

*A. Vasoconstriction in the finger.* Vasoconstriction occurs in a finger after voluntary deep inspiration or passive deep inflation of the chest with air under positive pressure. The vasoconstriction was determined by a finger plethysmo-graph in which a blood flow decrease was noted with inspiration which bore no relation to the respiratory fluctuations of systemic blood pressure. The receptors and afferent pathways of this reflex are unknown except that without doubt, they arise within the lungs.

*B. Respiratory arrhythmias.* Changes in heart rate caused by respiration can be demonstrated. Most investigations show that mild inflation causes cardiac acceleration and that this can be abolished by vagal section. It is believed, therefore, that the lungs are a constant source of impulses which exert an inhibitory influence on the cardiac vagal center, this influence being maximal during lung inflation and minimal during lung deflation. Presumably, the respiratory arrhythmia of the pulse has also a central initiating mechanism since increase of the carbon dioxide tension in the cerebral vessels augments the heart rate during each period of inspiratory discharge. But it has not been established whether this central arrhythmia is due to diminution of vagal activity during inspiration, or augmentation of sympathetic accelerator activity.

### PERIPHERAL VASCULATURE REFLEXES

Although little is known, recent interest has been aroused in sensory mechanisms that may lie in the peripheral vasculature. Haddy and Gilbert, using anesthetized dogs in which pressures were measured in the brachial artery, cephalic vein, small artery and small veins of the paw, and with maintenance of a constant brachial artery flow by a pump, found that elevation of cephalic vein pressure, although the arteries and veins dilated, was completely compensated for by constriction in the small vessel segment. However, after procaine nerve block the vessels did respond like a passive elastic system. Therefore, the observed small vessel constriction must have been of venous origin. However, this local veno-vasomotor reflex has not been confirmed by Greenfield and Patterson using the plethysmograph.

### LOW PRESSORECEPTORS IN MAN

Most of the previously described intrathoracic vascular reflexes were studied exclusively in experimental animals and their significance in the human remains to be confirmed. It is, therefore, of interest to mention recent experiments in man which have functionally implicated low pressoreceptors in the thoracic portion of the central blood pool in adjustments of the circulation (fig. 21.9). When the legs of a recumbent man are passively raised, the blood flow through the skele-

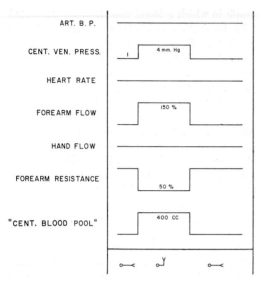

ART. B. P.

CENT. VEN. PRESS.                4 mm. Hg

HEART RATE

FOREARM FLOW                     150 %

HAND FLOW

FOREARM RESISTANCE
                                 50 %

"CENT. BLOOD POOL"               400 cc

Fig. 21.9. Passive elevation of the legs in recumbent man produces elevations in the central blood pool and central venous pressure with increased peripheral flow, while heart rate and systemic arterial pressure are unchanged. The decreased peripheral resistance is felt to be secondary to reflex dilation.

tal muscles of the forearm is increased greatly as is the central pool of blood. Since at this time, the arterial blood pressure is at the same or lower level, it suggests that this dilation in the forearm is not a consequence of arterial baroreceptor stimulation. While the precise nature of the stimulus and accurate location of the receptors concerned in the reflex have not been determined, it seems likely that forearm dilation is due to stimulation of receptors in the low pressure area of the thoracic vascular bed. This is so, since application of leg cuffs before trunk and leg elevation, or the use of sympathetic blockade to the forearm, eliminates the flow response. Rapid positive and negative pressure breathing causes a similar augmentation of blood flow in forearm and calf without changes in arterial blood pressure and heart rate. Presumably, this response is also to be explained through stimulation of low pressoreceptors in the chest.

### Summary

Change in activation of the vasoconstrictor fibers is responsible for blood pressure homeostasis and heat loss regulation of the skin blood flow. Centrally induced vasodilation is caused almost entirely by inhibition of constrictor tone. They may show a generalized or a strictly segmental or regional engagement, depending upon the type of stimulus. Together with the sympathetic vaso-

dilator fibers to skeletal muscles, they may affect specific vascular areas in a discharge pattern causing marked distribution of blood flow. The vasoconstrictor fibers are, therefore, looked upon as the main neurogenic adjustors of the peripheral circulation showing prompt and regional adjustments of their impulse discharge to any change in environment, especially those changes that affect the hypothalamus and the vasoconstrictor center in the medulla.

In the nerves from the pressure or stretch sensitive vascular walls of the aorta and carotid sinus, a burst of impulses occurs with each rise of blood pressure; the impulse frequency and systemic blood pressure and heart rate can be varied at will when these areas are artificially perfused at different pressures and pulse pressures; section of the nerves results in a persistent hypertension. These presso or baroreceptors are joined by the aortic and carotid sinus nerves with the nerve centers in the medulla oblongata which maintain systemic blood pressure at normal levels. Any arterial blood pressure deviation causes compensatory reflexes through the baroreceptors to reestablish a normal blood pressure. The efferent pathways for the heart for these baroreceptor vasomotor reflexes are the vagus and the sympathetic; in addition, the sympathetic vasoconstrictor fibers adjust the size of the "resistance" and "capacity" vessels in control of peripheral resistance to blood flow and the return of blood to the heart. The sympathetic fibers which control secretion of epinephrine and norepinephrine by the adrenal glands also stimulate these secretions and add a blood-borne hormone to the nervous influence, but as already indicated, this humoral influence is almost insignificant compared to that of the direct nerve effect.

The baroreceptors also react to nonspecific pharmacological agents. Baroreceptors exist in several other tissues—common carotid artery, thoracic and mesenteric arteries; these are probably not related to blood pressure homeostasis but may be engaged in local reflex adjustments of peripheral resistance and blood flow. Baroreceptor nerve endings are in the walls of the caval veins, heart (mainly the atria), and in the pulmonary circulation. Presumably, these receptors are primarily engaged in the reflex adjustment of venous return, heart rate, blood volume, and cardiac output. Chemoreceptors in the carotid and aortic bodies are excited to induce vasoconstriction in the resistance and capacitance vessels through the sympathetic constrictor fibers in the presence of marked hypotension from hemorrhage. Chemoreceptors are also in the pulmonary and coronary circulations, but the physiological stimuli adequate for their activation are not known.

## REFERENCES

ALEXANDER, R. S. Tonic and reflex functions of medullary sympathetic cardiovascular centers. J. Neurophysiol., 1946, 9, 205.

ALEXANDER, R. S. Studies on the venomotor system. Circulation Res., 1954, 2, 405.

AVIADO, D. M. AND SCHMIDT, C. F. Cardiovascular and respiratory reflexes from the left side of the heart. Am. J. Physiol., 1959, 196, 726.

BACH, L. M. The reflex activation of the vasodilator fibers of the dorsal roots and their role in vasodilator tone. Am. J. Physiol., 1946, 145, 474.

BARCROFT, H., BONNAR, W. M., EDHOLM, O. G., AND EFFRON, A. S. On sympathetic vasoconstrictor tone in human skeletal muscle. J. Physiol., 1943, 102, 21.

BLACK, J. E. AND RODDIE, I. C. The mechanism of the changes in forearm vascular resistance during hypoxia. J. Physiol., 1958, 143, 226.

BRONK, D. W., PITTS, R. F., AND LARRABEE, M. G. Role of hypothalamus in cardiovascular regulation. Res. Publ. A. Nerv. & Ment. Dis., 1940, 20, 323.

BRONK, D. W. AND STELLA, G. J. Afferent impulses in carotid sinus nerve; relation of discharge from single end organs to arterial blood pressure. J. Cell. & Comp. Physiol., 1932, 1, 113.

BRONK, D. W. AND STELLA, G. J. Response to steady pressures of single end organs in isolated carotid sinus. Am. J. Physiol., 1935, 110, 708.

BURCH, G. E. AND MURTADHA, M. A study of the venomotor tone in a short intact venous segment of the forearm of man. Am. Heart J., 1956, 51, 807.

CELANDER, O. The range of control exercised by the sympathico-adrenal system. Acta physiol. scandinav., 1954, (suppl. 116), 1.

CELANDER, O. AND FOLKOW, B. A comparison of the sympathetic vasomotor fiber control of the vessels within the skin and the muscles. Acta physiol. scandinav., 1953, 29, 241.

COMROE, J. H. The location and function of the chemoreceptors of the aorta. Am. J. Physiol., 1939, 127, 176.

CROUCH, R. L. AND THOMPSON, G. K. Autonomic functions of cerebral cortex. J. Nerv. & Mental Dis., 1939, 89, 328.

DALY, I. DE B. AND VERNEY, E. B. Cardiovascular reflexes. J. Physiol., 1926, 61, 268.

DALY, I. DE B. AND DALY, M. DE B. The effect of stimulation of the carotid sinus baroreceptors on the pulmonary vascular bed in the dog. J. Physiol., 1959, 148, 270.

DALY, M. DE B., LAMBERTSEN, C. J., AND SCHWEITZER, A. Observations on the volume of blood flow and oxygen utilization of the carotid body in the cat. J. Physiol., 1954, 125, 67.

DAWES, G. S. Studies on veratrum alkaloids; receptor areas in coronary arteries and elsewhere as revealed by veratridine. J. Pharmacol. & Exper. Therap., 1947, 89, 325.

DITTMAR, C. Vasomotor centre, location. Ber. sächs. Ges. (Acad.) Wiss., 1873, 25, 449.

DOUTHEIL, U. AND KRAMER, K. Über die Differenzierung kreislaufregulierender Reflexe aus dem linken Herz. Pflüger's Arch. ges. Physiol., 1959, 269, 114.

ECKSTEIN, J. W. AND HAMILTON, W. K. The pressure-volume responses of human forearm veins during epinephrine and norepinephrine infusions. J. Clin. Invest., 1957, 36, 1663.

ELIASSON, S., LINDGREN, P., AND UVNÄS, B. Representation in the hypothalamus and the motor cortex in the dog of the sympathetic vasodilator outflow to the skeletal muscles. Acta physiol. scandinav., 1952, 27, 18.

ELIASSON, S., FOLKOW, B., LUNDGREN, P., AND UVNÄS, B. Activation of sympathetic vasodilator nerves to the skeletal muscles in the cat by hypothalamic stimulation. Acta physiol. scandinav. 1951, 23, 333.

ELIASSON, S. AND STRÖM, G. On the localization in the cat of hypothalamic and cortical structures influencing cutaneous blood flow. Acta, physiol. scandinav., 1950, 20, (suppl. 70), 113.

ELIASSON, S., LINDGREN, P., AND UVNÄS, B. The hypothalamus, a relay station of the sympathetic vasodilator tract. Acta physiol. scandinav., 1953, 31, 290.

EULER, U. S. VON, LILJESTRAND, G., AND ZOTTERMAN, Y. Excitation mechanism of chemoreceptors of carotid body. Skandinav. Arch. Physiol., 1939, 83, 132.

FOLKOW, B. Impulse frequency in sympathetic vasomotor fibers correlated to the release and elimination of the transmitter. Acta physiol. scandinav., 1952, 25, (Suppl. 89–92) 49.

FRIEDEN, J. AND KELLER, A. D. Blood pressure in normotensive and renal hypertensive dogs following hypothalamic ablations and neurohypophysectomy. Army Medical Research Laboratory, Fort Knox, Kentucky, Project 6-64-12-028, Report 172, March 1955.

GILLIATT, R. W. Vasoconstriction in the finger after deep inspiration. J. Physiol., 1947, 107, 76.

GILMORE, J. P., MITCHELL, J. H., AND SARNOFF, S. J. The carotido-vago-atrial and carotido-sympatho-atrial reflexes. Fed. Proc., 1960, 19, 119.

GREENFIELD, A. D. M. AND PATTERSON, G. C. On the capacity and distensibility of the blood vessels of the human forearm. J. Physiol., 1956, 131, 290.

GRUHZIT, C. C. AND MOE, G. K. Reflex vasodilatation induced by epinephrine. Am. J. Physiol., 1952, 171, 730.

GUTTMAN, L. AND WHITTERIDGE, D. Effects of bladder distension on autonomic mechanisms after spinal cord injury. Brain, 1947, 70, 361.

HADDY, F. J. AND GILBERT, R. P. The relation of a venous-arteriolar reflex to transmural pressure and resistance in small and large systemic vessels. Circulation Res., 1956, 4, 25.

HEYMANS, C. Abdominal baro and chemosensitivity in dogs. Circulation Res., 1960, 8, 347.

HEYMANS, C. AND VAN DEN HEUVEL-HEYMANS, G. New aspects of blood pressure regulation. Circulation, 1951, 4, 581.

HOFF, E. C., KELL, J. F., HASTING, N., SHALES,

D. M., AND GRAY, E. H. Vasomotor, cellular, and functional changes produced in kidney by brain stimulation. J. Neurophysiol., 1951, **14**, 317.

KINMONTH, J. B., SIMEONE, F. A., AND PERLOW, V. Factors affecting the diameter of large arteries with particular reference to traumatic spasm. Surgery, 1949, **26**, 452.

KUNTZ, A. J. Anatomic and physiologic properties of cutaneo-visceral vasomotor reflex arcs. J. Neurophysiol., 1945, **8**, 421.

LANDGREN, S. AND NEIL, S. The contribution of carotid chemoceptor mechanisms to the rise of blood pressure caused by carotid occlusion. Acta physiol. scandinav., 1951, **23**, 152.

LINDGREEN, P. AND UVNÄS, B. Activation of sympathetic vasodilator and vasoconstrictor neurons by electrical stimulation in the medulla of the cat and dog. Circulation Res., 1953, **1**, 479.

MAGOUN, H. W., RANSON, S. W., AND HETHERINGTON, A. Descending connections from hypothalamus. Arch. Neurol. & Psychiat., 1938, **39**, 1127.

MANN, M. AND WEST, G. B. Nature of hepatic and splenic sympathin. Brit. J. Pharmacol., 1950, **5**, 173.

MARTIN, D. A., WHITE, K. L., AND VERNON, C. R. Influence of emotional and physical stimuli on pressure in isolated vein segment. Circulation Res., 1959, **7**, 580.

MAYERSON, H. S. Effect of gravity on the blood pressure of the dog. Am. J. Physiol., 1942, **135**, 411.

MCCUBBIN, J. W., GREEN, J. H., AND PAGE, I. H. Carotid sinus participation in experimental renal hypertension. Circulation, 1958, **17**, 791.

NAHAS, G. G. Effects of acute exposure to low oxygen tension on the circulation of vagotomized non-narcotized dogs. J. Appl. Physiol., 1956, **9**, 65.

NAHAS, G. G., JORDAN, E. C., AND LIGOU, J. C. Effects of a "$CO_2$ buffer" on hypercapnia of apneic oxygenation. Am. J. Physiol., 1959, **197**, 1308.

PAINTAL, A. S. A study of ventricular pressure receptors and their role in the Bezold reflex. Quart. J. Exper. Physiol., 1955, **40**, 348.

PAINTAL, A. S. A study of right and left atrial receptors. J. Physiol., 1953, **120**, 596.

RANDALL, W. A., AND ROHSE, W. G. The augmentor action of the sympathetic cardiac nerves. Circulation Res., 1956, **4**, 470.

RANSON, S. W. AND BILLINGSLEY, P. R. Vasomotor reactions from stimulation of the floor of the fourth ventricle. Studies in vasomotor reflex arcs. Am. J. Physiol., 1916, **41**, 85.

RICHIUS, C. A. AND BRIZZE, K. Effect of localized cutaneous stimulation on circulation in duodenal arterioles and capillary beds. J. Neurophysiol., 1949, **12**, 131.

RODDIE, I. C., SHEPHERD, J. T., AND WHALEN, R. F. Reflex changes in human skeletal muscle blood flow associated with intrathoracic pressure changes. Circulation Res., 1958, **6**, 232.

RODDIE, I. C. AND SHEPHERD, J. T. The effects of carotid artery compression in man with special reference to changes in vascular resistance in limbs. J. Physiol., 1957, **139**, 377.

ROSE, J. C. AND FREIS, E. D. Alterations in systemic vascular volume of the dog in response to hexamethonium and norepinephrine. Am. J. Physiol., 1957, **191**, 283.

ROTTA, A., CANEPA, A., HURTADO, A., VELASQUEZ, T., AND CHAVEZ, R. Pulmonary circulation at sea level and at high altitudes. J. Appl. Physiol., 1956, **9**, 328.

SARNOFF, S. J. AND YAMADA, S. I. Evidence for reflex control of arterial pressure from abdominal receptors with special reference to the pancreas. Circulation Res., 1959, **7**, 325.

SARNOFF, S. J. et al. The influence of carotid sinus pressure on myocardial contractility. Fed. Proc., 1959, **18**, 137.

SHIPLEY, R. AND GREGG, D. E. Cardiac response to stimulation of the stellate ganglion and cardiac nerves. Am. J. Physiol., 1945, **143**, 396.

STRÖM, G. Vasomotor responses to thermal and electrical stimulation of frontal lobe and hypothalamus. Acta Physiol. scandinav., 1950, **20** (70), 83.

TODD, T. W. AND KRAMER, J. G. The distribution of nerves to the arteries of the arm, with a discussion of the clinical value of results. Anat. Rec., 1914, **8**, 243.

WAKERLIN, G. E., CRANDALL, E. E., FRANK, M. H., JOHNSON, B., POMPER, L., AND SCHMID, H. E. Experimental hypertension produced by constriction of carotid sinus area. Circulation Res., 1954, **2**, 416.

WILLIAMS, M. H. Mechanical vs. reflex effects of diffuse pulmonary embolism in anesthetized dogs. Circulation Res., 1956, **4**, 325.

### Monographs and Reviews

ADAMS, W. R. AND VEITH, I. (editors). Pulmonary circulation. An international symposium. Grune & Stratton, Inc., New York, 1959.

AVIADO, D. M., JR. AND SCHMIDT, C. F. Reflexes from stretch receptors in blood vessels, heart and lungs. Physiol. Rev., 1955, **35**, 247.

BARCROFT, H. AND SWAN, H. J. C. Sympathetic control of human blood vessels. Edward Arnold & Company, London, 1953.

DAWES, G. S. AND COMROE, J. H. Chemoreflexes from heart and lungs. Physiol. Rev., 1954, **34**, 167.

DAWES, G. S. Reflex factors in the regulation of the circulation. Josiah Macy Foundation. Transactions of the Third Conference on Shock and Circulatory Homeostasis, 1953.

FOLKOW, B. Nervous control of the blood vessels. Physiol. Rev., 1955, **35**, 629.

FOLKOW, B. Structural, myogenic, humoral and nervous factors controlling peripheral resistance. Proceedings of the Conference on Hypotensive Drugs and Control of Vascular Tone in Hypotension. Pergamon Press, London, 1956.

GAUER, O. H., AND HENRY, J. P. Beitrag zur Homöostase des extraarteriellen Kreislaufs. Klin. Wchnschr., 1956, **34**, 356.

GREGG, D. E. Coronary circulation in health and disease. Lea & Febiger, Philadelphia, 1950.

HEYMANS, C. AND NEIL, E. Reflexogenic areas of

the cardiovascular system. J. & A. Churchill, Ltd., London, 1958.

LANDIS, E. M. AND HORTENSTINE, J. C. Functional significance of venous blood pressure. Physiol. Rev., 1950, **30,** 1.

LUND, A. Significance of the cerebral cortex to the vasomotor reaction of the extremities. Ejnar Munksgaards Forlag, Copenhagen, 1943.

PERIFIELD, W., AND RASMUSSEN, T. The cerebral cortex of man. The Macmillan Company, New York, 1950.

RUSHMER, R. F. AND SMITH, O. A. Cardiac control. Physiol. Rev., 1959, **39,** 41.

SCHMIDT, C. F. The cerebral circulation in health and disease, Charles C Thomas, Publisher, Springfield, Illinois, 1950.

EICHNA, L. W. AND McQUARRIE, D. G. (editors). Symposium. Central Nervous System Control of Circulation. Physiol. Rev., 1960, **40** (suppl. 4).

UVNÄS, B. Sympathetic vasodilator outflow. Physiol. Rev., 1954, **34, 608.**

VON EULER, U. S. Noradrenaline. Chemistry, physiology, pharmacology and clinical aspects. Charles C Thomas, Publisher, Springfield, Illinois, 1956.

ZWEIFACH, B. W. Structural make-up of the capillary wall. Ann. New York Acad. Sc., 1955, **61,** 670.

# 22

# REGULATION OF PRESSURE AND FLOW IN THE SYSTEMIC AND PULMONARY CIRCULATION

## Arterial Blood Pressure

The first determination of arterial blood pressure was in 1733 when the Reverend Stephen Hales inserted a brass cannula into the central end of the femoral artery of a horse, connected it to a long vertical glass tube, and observed that a column of blood filled the tube to a height of 8 ft., 3 in. (185 mm. Hg).

SPECIES DIFFERENCES. The arterial blood pressure varies moderately between different warm-blooded species, and there is little or no relationship between the size of an animal and the height of its blood pressure. The blood pressure, in general, is higher in birds than in mammals, whereas that of cold-blooded animals is only about one-third as great. The carotid blood pressure (mean) of the unanesthetized, basal dog approximates 110 mm. Hg. The domestic cow has a mean blood pressure of about 135 mm. Hg. The following systolic pressures (mm. Hg.) have have been reported: mouse, 113; rat, 130; canary, 220; robin, 118; frog, 43; turtle, 44; and carp, 43. Of considerable interest is the arterial pressure in the carotid artery of the giraffe, because of the very long, vertical distance from heart to brain. In experiments performed on 4 standing, unanesthetized giraffes, the carotid pressure, corrected to heart level, ranged from 280/150 to 344/194 mm. Hg. The walls of the giraffe's left ventricle and the aorta are extraordinarily thick.

### ARTERIAL BLOOD PRESSURE IN MAN

A. *Normal values.* The average systolic pressure of young male adults at mental and physical rest in the sitting position (as usually measured in a routine medical examination) is usually given as 120 mm. Hg; the diastolic as 80, the mean pressure as 100, and the pulse pressure as 40. However, the range of normal blood pressures may be from 90 to 120 mm. Hg systolic, and 60 to 80 mm. Hg diastolic. Slight diurnal variations in blood pressure of from 5 to 10 mm. Hg systolic occur, the peak being in the afternoon and the lowest level in the early hours of the morning.

B. *Age, sex and build.* Age exerts a definite influence upon the blood pressure levels. At birth the systolic pressure measures from 20 to 60 mm. with an average of 40 mm. It rises rapidly, however, and has an average value of about 70 mm. at the end of a fortnight and 80 mm. at the end of a month. A slow steady rise takes place from this time until about the 12th year when it averages 105 mm. With the onset of puberty, a more sudden rise occurs which in boys reaches 120 mm. at about the age of 17. A steady though not great rise in blood pressure, from adolescence to old age, is the rule in health, the averages for the age of 60 being given as about 140 systolic pressure and 87 diastolic. In women up to the time of the menopause, the systolic pressure is from 4 to 5 mm. lower than for men of the same age. At the menopause, however, there is a somewhat abrupt rise, and the pressure remains a little above the male average from then on (table 22.1).

Comparing groups of markedly obese and normal persons, the former have a rather pronounced increase of systolic pressure. The incidence of abnormally high blood pressure (hypertension) is also definitely greater in overweight persons.

C. *The effects of digestion, emotion, exercise and posture.* The systolic pressure is influenced to a small but definite extent by meals. A rise of from 6 to 8 mm. is the usual effect, and this lasts for an hour or so. There is little change in the diastolic pressure; if anything, it is reduced, presumably as a result of vasodilation in the digestive organs and skin.

Quiet, restful sleep may be accompanied by a fall of from 15 to 30 mm. in the systolic pressure. The fall is most marked during the first hours, rising gradually again after this until the time of waking. If the sleep is disturbed and accompanied by imaginary motor activities, there may be no depression of the pressure, but rather an elevation, in some instances to as high as 200 mm. systolic and 105 mm. diastolic. Excitement, fear,

274

worry, etc., markedly affect the arterial blood pressure, especially the systolic. The effects are brought about through increased cardiac action and changes in the state of the vessels through impulses playing upon the cardiac and vasomotor centers in the medulla. The liberation of adrenaline into the blood stream may also be a factor.

Of all physiological conditions, exercise, if of a strenuous nature, has the most powerful effect upon the arterial blood pressure. During the muscular effort or even immediately before, i.e., at the instant that the exertion is contemplated, the systolic pressure commences to rise and may reach a height of 180 or 200 mm. Hg. Except in well trained persons or athletes, this is invariably associated with a large increase in heart rate to 150 or 180 per minute. In the trained individual, the blood pressure rise may be quite mild. The diastolic pressure shows a less pronounced rise (100 to 110) so that the pulse pressure is increased. In light exercise the diastolic pressure may remain at the normal level while the systolic rises several millimeters. Immediately after the exercise the pressure drops momentarily to normal or even slightly below. It then mounts rapidly to its previous high level, from which it gradually declines again, and in a healthy person reaches the normal within from 1 to $4\frac{1}{2}$ minutes. The evanescent drop in pressure is explained as being due to the sudden relaxation of the abdominal muscles. The blood is drained into the venous reservoirs. These when deprived of their support (abdominal muscles) have their capacity increased and the blood flow into the right heart is temporarily curtailed. It is not until an appreciable time has elapsed to enable the increased venous capacity to become filled again by blood pouring in from the recently active muscles that an adequate flow into the right heart is restored.

The diastolic pressure is somewhat higher in the standing than in the sitting position and lowest in recumbency. This change is found to occur whether the postural change is brought about actively or passively and is evidently an overcompensation for the gravity effect. The systolic pressure usually rises but to a less extent than the diastolic, so the pulse pressure is reduced. Pressures, however, taken at as short an interval as 10 seconds after the erect position has been assumed show that the initial effect is a fall of from 6 to 22 mm. Hg in the systolic pressure. This is sufficient to stimulate the carotid sinus and aortic mechanisms and cause increased vascular tone with a consequent compensatory rise in pressure. Compensation is usually complete

TABLE 22.1

*The average variations of blood pressure (after Hunter's compilation of observations on a quarter million healthy Americans)*

(After Gager)

| Age | Systolic Pressure | Diastolic Pressure | Pulse Pressure |
|---|---|---|---|
| 10 | 103 | 70 | 33 |
| 15 | 113 | 75 | 38 |
| 20 | 120 | 80 | 40 |
| 25 | 122 | 81 | 41 |
| 30 | 123 | 82 | 41 |
| 35 | 124 | 83 | 41 |
| 40 | 126 | 84 | 42 |
| 45 | 128 | 85 | 43 |
| 50 | 130 | 86 | 44 |
| 55 | 132 | 87 | 45 |
| 60 | 135 | 89 | 46 |

within 30 seconds. Reverting from the standing to the sitting or recumbent position has the reverse effect, fall in diastolic pressure and rise in pulse pressure. In persons with an abnormally and habitually low blood pressure, the systolic pressure may actually rise in the lying-down position and fall when the subject stands. The diastolic, on the other hand, is always lowered in recumbency and raised in the erect posture.

THE SYSTOLIC, DIASTOLIC, MEAN AND PULSE PRESSURES. Hales, in describing his experiment, speaks of the blood column after it had ceased to rise further in the tube, oscillating above and below a mean level. To quote his own words, "When it (the blood) was at its full height, it would rise and fall at, and after, each pulse, 2, 3 or 4 inches." By recording with an adequate pressure manometric system, these fluctuations are seen as waves synchronous with the heart beats (see fig. 22.4). The crest of the wave represents the maximal pressure, corresponding to the contraction or systole of the ventricle, and is called the systolic pressure. The trough of the wave, i.e., the point of minimal pressure, coincides with the end of the resting phase or diastole of the cardiac cycle, and is called the diastolic pressure. The mean pressure is usually given as half the sum of the values for the systolic and diastolic pressures. This would be strictly accurate only if the pulse wave inscribed a perfect triangle which, however, is not the case. The average pressure throughout the cardiac cycle, i.e., the true or geometric mean, is generally somewhat lower than this, lying nearer the diastolic than the systolic pressure. This can be obtained by integration of the curve.

The difference between the diastolic and systolic pressures is the pulse pressure. This is caused by the ejection of blood into the aorta during systole. Its magnitude, other things being equal, will vary with the quantity of blood ejected by the heart at each beat.

The systolic pressure reflects mainly the distensibility characteristics of the arterial system as it receives blood from the left ventricle. It would be expected to undergo wider variations under the stresses of every day life than the diastolic pressure. The latter represents the constant load which the arterial walls are called upon to bear and the resistance which the ventricular contraction must overcome to throw open the aortic valves. It shows a steady but slight decline from the larger to the medium sized vessels. The systolic pressure shows a fall between the larger and the smaller arteries which, though not great, is much more pronounced than that which occurs in the diastolic. On this account, the two pressures tend to become more nearly equal toward the periphery, the pulse pressure being reduced. Since the pulse pressure is the difference between the systolic and diastolic pressures, it may be reduced by an alteration in one or other of these. A rise in the systolic or a fall in the diastolic, will cause the pulse pressure to increase, while a fall in the systolic or a rise in the diastolic will lower the pulse pressure. If both systolic and diastolic pressures rise or fall to an equal extent, the pulse pressure remains unchanged. The mean pressure will rise as a result of a rise in either the diastolic or systolic pressure, or of both together, and will fall when a reduction of either or of both of these pressures occurs.

### DETERMINANTS OF NORMAL ARTERIAL BLOOD PRESSURE

Several factors combine to maintain normal arterial blood pressure. They are, (a) the pumping action of the heart, (b) the peripheral resistance, (c) the quantity of blood in the arterial system, (d) the viscosity of the blood, (e) the elasticity of the arterial walls.

A. *The pumping action of the heart.* The means by which the cardiac contraction exerts its effect upon the arterial blood pressure is, obviously, through the *quantity* of blood which it is capable of discharging into the aorta in a unit period of time, i.e., upon the output of the heart per minute or stroke volume times heart rate. When more blood is forced into the already filled arterial system, it cannot escape at once from the system in the same amount as it is thrown into the aorta, so the arterial walls become stretched. The pressure rises until the velocity of flow through the arterioles is great enough to balance again the outflow from the system with the inflow. Hales grasped this fundamental fact when he wrote, "the real force (pressure) of the blood in the arteries depends on the proportion which the quantity of blood thrown out of the left ventricle in a given time bears to the quantity which can pass through the capillary arteries (arterioles) into the veins at that time."

B. *The peripheral resistance.* The peripheral resistance is dependent upon the caliber of the small vessels, mainly of the arterioles and, to a less extent, of the capillaries, and upon the viscosity of the blood. It has also been demonstrated by Haddy, that the macroscopic vessels (smaller arteries and veins) contribute significantly to resistance across systemic vascular beds. By far the greater part of the peripheral resistance of the circulatory system is constituted by the minute vessels of the muscles and of the abdominal structures. The importance in this connection of the latter—the so-called splanchnic area—can be demonstrated by tying off all branches of the aortic arch, except the carotids, and the abdominal aorta below the inferior mesenteric branch, when little or no change in peripheral resistance results; whereas an increase in the latter at once occurs when the blood supply to the splanchnic area is reduced by ligating the superior mesenteric artery. Stimulation of the great splanchnic nerve, which innervates the rings of muscle fibers in the walls of these vessels, causes their constriction, and consequently a reduction in the outflow from the arterial system. The pressure will continue to rise until inflow and outflow are again balanced. In the absence of compensatory changes in the other factors concerned in the maintenance of the pressure this remains at the higher level so long as the constriction persists. Dilation of the vessels, i.e., reduction in peripheral resistance, will of course be followed by the opposite effect. When the vessels of the splanchnic area are fully dilated they are capable of accommodating almost all the blood in the body; in such an event the blood pressure would fall to zero. The peripheral resistance might be compared to a dam in a river. If the dam is raised or lowered, and no change occurs in the supply of water flowing down the river to the dam, the water continues to rise or fall respectively (and its pressure in consequence increases or diminishes) until it reaches the new level. From then on the quantity of water which overflows in a given time is the same as it was at the original level.

The total peripheral resistance in animals or in man can be calculated from the mean blood pressure (M) and the cardiac output (F), since all blood entering the aorta must, of course, pass through the peripheral vessels. This can be derived for the whole body from the simultaneously measured arterial pressure and cardiac output, and for an organ or region from the local arterial pressure and flow, but interpretation is valid only under strictly controlled conditions which have already been discussed. In general, in isolated organs, either pressure or flow should be kept constant while the other is varied. For total circulation, either this arrangement or possibly a complete pressure-volume curve for the systemic circulation can be used, before and after a test stimulus, with subsequent comparison of the two curves. There is a curvilinear relationship between pressure and flow in the aorta (fig. 22.1). This is also true in separate vascular beds where pressure and flow have been measured but the shape of the curves may be quite different.

Various terminologies have been used to define peripheral resistance. Green has used a unit of peripheral resistance (PRU) as equal to 1 mm. Hg./1 ml/min. Many authors take such a ratio and by expressing P in dynes per square centimeter and F as milliliters per second, the peripheral resistance can be given in absolute units of force. Thus,

$$\text{Peripheral resistance (R)} = \frac{\text{M(mm. Hg)} \times 1332}{\text{F(ml./sec.)}}$$

$$R = \frac{\text{dynes/cm.}^2}{\text{cm.}^3\text{/sec.}}$$

$$R = \frac{\text{dyne sec.}}{\text{cm.}^5}$$

1332 is a figure for the conversion of pressure to dynes.

The peripheral resistance so calculated is found to vary inversely with the size of the animal, i.e., directly with the surface area. It amounts normally to from about 600 to 2,000 absolute units in man, but may be over 5,000 in arterial hypertension in which F shows little change. The values for the dog and rabbit range from 2,000 to 9,000 and from 11,500 to 12,000, respectively. This means that the minute vessels in a large animal offer less resistance than do the fewer number in a smaller animal, even though the

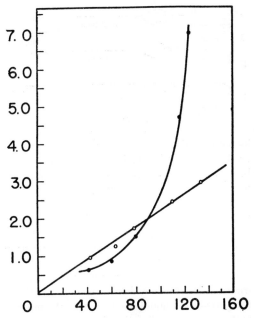

FIG. 22.1. Relationship between mean arterial pressure in millimeters of mercury (abscissa) and cardiac output in liters per minute (ordinate) in a typical experiment. Solid circles represent values observed with buffer nerves intact; open circles, values obtained after bilateral vagotomy and while a constant pressure of 210 mm. Hg. was exerted upon the isolated, innervated carotid sinuses (From Levy, Circulation Res., 1954, 2, 372.)

vessels of both are constricted to the same degree. This is due to the fact that the rate of flow in the smaller animal is greater in relation to the size of its vascular bed (cardiac output bearing a constant relationship to surface area which varies inversely with body weight).

*C. The quantity of blood in the arterial system.* In any closed system of rigid tubes fluid must fill it to capacity in order that a pressure can be developed within it. The arterial walls are distensible and elastic, and a certain degree of stretching of these must occur before any considerable pressure is created. The arterial system must be actually over-filled, and the greater the extent of the over-filling, the greater will be the blood pressure. Loss of blood, either of all its elements, as in hemorrhage, or of the fluid portion alone, if not compensated for sufficiently by readjustment of the other factors concerned in blood pressure maintenance, must inevitably result in a fall of pressure. Increasing the total amount of circulating fluid artifically as by the transfusion of blood or blood substitute will elevate the pressure again. In animals the blood pressure may be lowered by hemorrhage to half

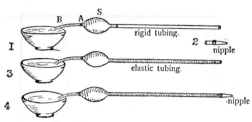

FIG. 22.2. Description in text.

its normal value and restored again to its original level by re-introducing into the circulation the blood which has been removed or by the infusion of an effective blood substitute.

*D. The viscosity of the blood.* The greater the viscosity or "thickness" of any liquid the greater is the pressure required to force it along a length of narrow tube in a given time; or if the pressure remains constant the longer will be the time required for the liquid to traverse the tube. The frictional resistance which is developed between the parts of the liquid itself, that is, the internal friction is greater when the viscosity is high than when it is low. Viscosity depends upon the degree to which the molecules or particles of a fluid cohere. Blood is some 5 times more viscous than water.[1] With regard to the influence of viscosity upon the blood pressure, it is again a matter of outflow through the arterioles. If the driving force remains constant and the caliber of the vessels is unchanged, then the greater the viscosity the greater will be the frictional resistance developed in this region and the less will be the quantity of fluid that will pass through in a unit of time.

The blood owes its viscosity to its colloids (plasma proteins) and to an even greater extent its suspended corpuscles; friction is developed between the surfaces of the latter and the surrounding fluid. Changes in the concentration of the blood as a result of changes in its protein content or in the number of its corpuscles will therefore alter its viscosity; venesection by removing a quantity of blood and causing dilution of the remainder causes a fall in viscosity which may materially relieve the work of the heart. For these reasons the viscosity is low in anemia and high in polycythemia, leukemia and anhydremia. Also changes in its chemical composition or in its gas content may alter the viscosity of the blood. Carbon dioxide increases the viscosity, oxygen lowers it; venous blood is, in consequence, more viscous than arterial, and high blood viscosity is usual in congestive heart failure with cyanosis. Chloro-

form anesthesia and narcotization with morphine are said to increase the blood viscosity. It is also raised in hyperglycemia, hypercalcemia and in acidosis.

The viscosity of most liquids is reduced by a rise of temperature—hot syrup flows more freely than cold. In muscular exercise and in fever the blood temperature is raised, the viscosity of the blood is lowered, and the work which the heart is called upon to do in overcoming the frictional resistance in the smaller vessels is thereby appreciably reduced. Blood concentration, however, which occurs to some extent under these circumstances, tends to offset the effect of temperature.

*E. The elasticity of the vessel walls.* This is concerned mainly with the origin and maintenance of the diastolic pressure and with sustaining the mean pressure at a higher level than would be possible in a rigid system under otherwise identical conditions.

The elasticity of arterial tissue does not come into play to any notable extent with a pressure below from 30 to 40 mm. of mercury. Below this level there would be little stretching of the walls of the arteries which would then behave like a system of rigid tubes. At the usual diastolic pressure that exists, however, the walls are stretched and by virtue of their elasticity tend to recoil against the distending force. We have seen that the flow of blood is pulsatile in the arteries. Beyond the arterioles, i.e., in the capillaries and veins, the flow is continuous. The conversion of the pulsatile flow to a uniform one depends upon the existence of a diastolic pressure. The physical principles involved in the maintenance of the diastolic pressure and the disappearance of the pulse beyond the arterioles may be best illustrated by a simple artificial model similar in principle to one devised by Borelli for the same purpose some 300 or more years ago.

In figure 22.2 is represented a bulb syringe, S, valved at A, and having a short tube, B, which dips into a basin of water. Leading from the opposite pole of the bulb is a longer tube, C. When the bulb is alternately compressed and released fluid is drawn from the basin and discharged from the mouth of the tube. If the walls of the latter are composed of some rigid material (fig. 22.2, 1), it will be found that when the pump is worked the fluid issues from the tube in spurts or jets synchronous with each stroke, but no flow occurs between the strokes. An increase in the frequency or force of the strokes does not alter the intermittent character of the flow nor does lengthening the tubing. If the peripheral re-

---

[1] This is an average figure. Values obtained by different observers for the viscosity of blood, taking distilled water as unity, vary considerably but the majority range between 4.5 and 5.5.

sistance of the vascular system be imitated by attaching a nipple of small bore to the mouth of the delivery tube so as to increase the resistance to the outflow of fluid, the issuing stream is finer and its velocity is increased, but it still remains intermittent (fig. 22.2, 2). Let the elasticity of the arterial wall now be imitated by replacing the rigid tube by one of rubber, yet let the mouth of the tube be left free and not constricted in any way (fig. 22.2, 3). The intermittent character of the stream is unaffected. However, if the small-bored nipple representing the peripheral resistance be fixed into the mouth of the elastic tubing the stream will be found to have lost its pulsatile character and to have become continuous (fig. 22.2, 4). Two factors are therefore necessary to produce this result, (a) *resistance to the outflow* and (b) *elastic tubing*. The reasons for this are clear. If the fluid has free egress from the tube most of that which enters it from the pump is discharged from the open end before the next beat occurs; the pressure, in consequence, does not rise to a sufficient height to distend the rubber wall, i.e., elasticity is not called into play, over-filling of the tube does not occur, and in consequence the latter acts simply as though it were composed or rigid material.

The foregoing facts apply directly to the arterial system. The elasticity of the vascular walls and the peripheral resistance are both essential for the maintenance of the diastolic pressure. As the contents of the ventricle are thrown into the already over-filled system during systole the added pressure which is then exerted upon the vascular walls causes their further distension. After the completion of systole the elastic walls rebound and, pressing upon the blood within their embrace, force it onwards through the peripheral vessels. In other words, the arterial lumen returns to its previous diameter and the energy that had been stored up during the stretching of the elastic tissue is in this way gradually expended during diastole.

The elastic recoil of the arterial wall thus acts in a sense as a subsidiary pump to drive the blood onwards in a continuous stream between the heart beats. Otherwise the pressure would fall to zero after each systole.

It is clear then that any increase in the elasticity of the arteries, other factors remaining unchanged, will tend toward a lowering of the diastolic pressure. If the aorta and its larger branches are stiffened (as a result of sclerotic changes), they cannot expand to the same degree as can healthy, resilient vessels, and therefore do not so readily accommodate the blood (60–100 cc.) ejected from the heart during systole. Such a state will lead to a rise in the systolic pressure. Normally, however, the cross-sectional area of the aorta increases considerably with age, so that it needs to expand much less to accommodate the systolic discharge.

## THE INFLUENCE WHICH VARIATIONS IN SOME OF THE FOREGOING FACTORS EXERT UPON THE DIFFERENT PHASES OF THE ARTERIAL PRESSURE

*A. Change in heart rate* unaccompanied by an alteration in any of the other factors, e.g., output of heart per minute, peripheral resistance, etc., will cause a change in the diastolic pressure but relatively little change in the systolic thus giving a smaller pulse rate. During cardiac acceleration, for example, the diastolic period is shortened and less time is therefore allowed for the energy stored in the elastic walls during systole to become converted into energy of flow during diastole. In other words, the fall in pressure during diastole is halted at a higher level by the earlier arrival of the next beat. A decrease in heart rate will have the opposite effect; with the longer diastole the slope of pressure is enabled to reach a lower level. Since the quantity of blood entering the arteries per minute remains constant the quantity entering at each beat must vary inversely with the change in rate, which accounts for the relatively small change in the systolic pressure.

*B. Alterations in the quantity of blood discharged per minute by the ventricle.* If little change should occur in the heart rate and other factors remain unaltered, increase in the output per beat of the heart causes a rise chiefly of the systolic pressure. The diastolic pressure is raised less noticeably, consequently the pulse pressure is increased. The explanation for the less pronounced rise in the diastolic pressure is that, as a result of the high pressure at the end of the ejection period, the pressure gradient throughout diastole is steeper and more energy is expended in giving velocity to the blood; of the blood pumped into the arterial system during systole a larger proportion than ordinarily will therefore have passed through the arterioles by the end of diastole.

*C. Changes in the peripheral resistance* while other factors remain constant. Though these affect both systolic and disatolic pressures they show their influence predominantly upon the latter phase. The diastolic period is considerably longer even in a rapidly beating heart than the ejection period of systole and, as we have seen, the peripheral resistance is an important factor in the maintenance of the diastolic pressure. It follows therefore that any increase or decrease in the outflow from the arterial system will affect this pressure to a greater degree than the systolic. The mean pressure and pulse pressure vary accordingly. Aortic regurgitation produces an effect upon diastolic pressure similar to that caused by a reduction in the peripheral resistance but greater in degree. The mechanical principles involved are similar; an increased quantity of blood passes from the arterial system during diastole as a result of leakage through the incompetent aortic valves. The peripheral vessels are also usually dilated, which, combined with the high pulse pressure, may cause the appearance of a pulse in the capillaries especially if their emptying be aided by holding the arm above the heart level. Slight pressure upon a superficial capillary area such as at the base of the finger nail may then show alternate blanching and flushing synchronous with the heart beat. In aortic regurgitation the pulse pressure attains a magnitude seen in no other condition (80 or 110 mm. Hg) for not only is the diastolic pressure much reduced but the systolic pressure is raised as well, owing to the greater volume of blood ejected at each heart beat—that which has regurgitated through the aortic valves plus that received from the auricle. For these reasons, the carotids throb visibly. The pulse is of the collapsing type (water hammer or Corrigan's pulse). An arteriovenous aneurysm produces somewhat similar effects upon the arterial system.

D. *A rise or a fall in blood viscosity.* Other factors remaining unchanged, tend to affect the diastolic pressure in a manner similar to changes in the calibers of the peripheral vessels.

E. *Increase in blood volume* will raise both pressures, as a result of the overfilling of the arterial system and greater stretching of the elastic walls.

F. *Increase in elasticity of the arterial walls.* Obviously a condition such as arteriosclerosis, which renders arteries less resilient and more like rigid tubes will, tend toward a lowering of diastolic pressure. Yet as a matter of fact, in arteriosclerosis the diastolic pressure may be raised rather than lowered, since there is frequently an associated narrowing of the peripheral vessels which more than offsets the hardening of the walls of the larger arteries. When, however, the sclerosis is confined to the larger vessels and their branches while the peripheral vessels are free from proliferative changes which narrow their lumina the diastolic pressure is lowered. Diminished distensibility of the walls of the aorta and the larger arteries tends to increase the systolic pressure.

In the foregoing paragraphs variations in the several blood pressure factors and their effects have each been considered as being the only variable in a particular instance. The object of this was to disclose the value of each and the manner in which it acted. Yet it must be remembered that such a description is more or less artificial and that in health and even to a large extent

under pathological conditions the various factors interact with one another—there is a give and take among them. When a change in the value of one factor occurs, readjustments of others take place to regulate the blood pressure and keep it within the normal limits. For instance, dilation of the vessels in one area may be accompanied by vasoconstriction in another. Reduction in blood volume as by hemorrhage, is followed by constriction of the peripheral vessels, while increased blood volume or a rise in viscosity will likely be followed by the opposite effect upon the vessels.

THE ARTERIAL PRESSURE PULSE. Pressure waves in the heart cavities, the aorta and almost any of its branches, and in the systemic venous system, can be readily recorded in the experimental animal and in humans by use of appropriate combinations of catheters or needles with pressure manometers of adequate frequency (see ch. 19). The form or pattern of the pressure curves can also be recorded from superficial vessels such as the radial artery, subclavian artery and vein, carotid artery, jugular vein, etc., by overlying cup-tambour arrangements or microphones (for details see ch. 19, and Wiggers).

A. *Velocity.* The pulse is the pressure change created by the ejection of blood from the heart into the already full aorta, and propagated as a wave through the blood column and arterial wall to the periphery. If the walls of the system were absolutely rigid, since liquids are incompressible, an impact delivered at one end would cause a pressure change to be transmitted almost instantaneously. In the case of elastic tubing, such as composes the vascular system, the pressure change is accompanied by an expansion of the tube's wall. From the equation of Bramwell and Hill ($Vp = K\sqrt{\Delta pV/\Delta V}$ in which Vp is pulse wave velocity and V is vessel volume, it is obvious that the velocity with which a pressure wave is transmitted peripherally, is largely determined by the elasticity of the vessel wall.

Because of their accessibility, pressure pulse wave velocities are generally measured in the brachial, radial or femoral arteries, although many measurements exist for the aorta. The usual order of time of arrival of the pressure pulse is brachial, femoral, radial. The velocity of the pulse wave can be determined by noting the difference in the time of arrival of the naturally occurring pulse wave at a near and at a far point of the vascular system. This can be done roughly by means of a pair of tambours overlying points on the two arteries and which are connected to writing levers or recorders. A more accurate way is to record directly the arterial pressures at the two points from indwelling needles connected to pressure manometers, or to record the transit time of a mechanically induced external impact wave. The time difference divided into the distance traveled between two points gives the velocity of propagation of the wave. Thus,

Distance in millimeters
———————————————
  Time in seconds

= velocity in millimeters per second.

The rate of propagation of the pulse wave peripherally depends on the degree of vessel distention by internal pressure, and on its distensibility characteristics. Thus, the level of blood pressure, the basic structure of the vessel wall and its alteration by function or disease are the important determinants of pulse wave velocity. The normal velocity in the aorta approximates 3 to 4 meters per second; in the arteries of the limbs, it is 7 to 14 meters per second, the velocity of the pulse in the femoral artery being somewhat greater than in the brachial artery. In hypertension resulting from muscular exercise, the walls of the vessels are more strongly stretched and the pulse wave is transmitted at a higher speed. Vasodilation or low pressure from many causes reduces the velocity of the pulse wave. Figure 22.3 shows this strong relation between the pulse wave velocity and ambient intraarterial pressure in the brachioradial artery segment of normal individuals. (Pressures below diastolic were obtained by temporary digital occlusion of the axillary or subclavian artery). This fact must be taken into account in the comparison of velocities at different ages and in different disease states. In addition, since the rate of transmission alters with the state of elasticity of the vessel wall, the velocity is increased with old age or when the elasticity is increased by disease, such as arteriosclerosis. In the brachial artery, speeds have been recorded of 5 meters per second at age of 5 years, 6 meters per second at middle age, and 8.6 meters per second at age of 84 years.

In the aorta (and arterial tree), the acceleration of the blood occurs almost simultaneously with the rise of the pressure pulse. This is to be expected since the latter causes the former. However, whereas the pressure wave travels in terms of meters per second, the movement of the red cells or plasma is much slower, at 10 to 20 cm. per second. Thus, although the pressure wave may reach the vessels of the foot in 0.2 second,

it requires several heart beats for the blood entering the ascending aorta to reach the foot vessels. This is because the speed of the blood depends upon such factors as the blood pressure gradient, cross-sectional area of the vessel and viscosity, while the velocity of the pulse wave is determined almost entirely by the elasticity of the wall of the vessel.

*B. Characteristics and transformation of the pressure pulse.* Pressure curves simultaneously recorded from the aortic arch and a peripheral artery of the dog are shown in figure 22.4. It is obvious that the pressure pulse patterns are quite different. The aortic pressure rises quite abruptly, and after an anacrotic shoulder (abrupt change in gradient), rises still further to a systolic rounded peak. The pressure then drops slowly during the last half of systole until closure of the aortic valves, which is occasioned by a sharp incisura. During diastole, the pressure is first sustained and then drops smoothly. The extra-arterial forces which affect the aortic pulse pattern are by impact from the contracting atrium and the bulging of the aortic valves during the isometric contraction period. These waves appear on the aortic pulse preceding the main wave and are noticeable in the immediate aortic branches, but not beyond. A series of internal free vibrations are added at the incisura and at

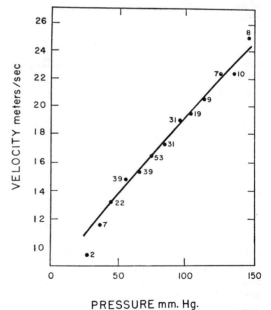

PRESSURE mm. Hg.

FIG. 22.3. Curve showing the relation between arterial blood pressure (abscissa) and pulse wave velocity (ordinate). (From Landowne, J. Appl. Physiol., 1958, **12**, 93.)

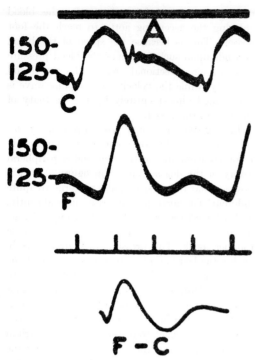

FIG. 22.4. Arterial pressure pulses recorded from the central aorta, *C*, and the femoral artery, *F*, in the anesthetized dog. Curve F-C beneath pulse tracings obtained by coordirectographic subtraction of the aortic pulse from the femoral pulse. This represents the reflected or standing wave in the distal portion of the arterial tree. Time 0.1 second; ordinate pressures in millimeters of mercury (after Alexander, R. S., Am. J. Physiol., 1949, **158**, 287).

the first steep rise during ejection, as the pressure pulse reaches the main aortic branches. In the simultaneously recorded peripheral pulse, the onset of the pressure rise is delayed and rises a little more slowly but to a very peaked, earlier, and larger maximum, being about 30 mm. Hg higher than that in the aorta. The drop of pressure in the latter half of systole and in early diastole is much quicker. The dicrotic notch and its after wave are quite large. The remainder of the diastolic curve is uneventful. Thus, in the peripheral vessel the net effect is to augment the peak amplitude of the pulse wave, obscure the incisura, and to depress the remainder of the pulse curve. Pressure curves recorded from arteries intermediately situated such as the renal, mesenteric, and carotid, show a lesser augmentation of the peak systolic pressure and a smaller dicrotic wave; pulses recorded from more peripheral arteries such as the dorsalis pedis, show an exaggeration of these phenomena. The effects of the extra-arterial forces are gradually damped

in the extensions of the aorta and are lost in the radial artery.

The pressure pulse just described at the root of the aorta is basically triangular. This original pattern is largely retained as the pressure wave is transmitted down the aorta and into some of its immediate branches. The temporal distortions of the pressure pulses in their transit from the central to the peripheral arteries are effected mainly as the result of damping from friction of the blood with the vessel wall, hysteresis of the vessel wall, differences in the distensibility of the vessels, and summation of reflected pressure waves. The viscosity of the blood in the smaller arteries acts to smooth out the abruptness of pressure changes; in arteries such as the femoral, there is a possibility of considerable lag in the response of its wall to internal pressure such as occurs in isolated vessel strips; and the greater distensibility of these arteries, taken *in toto*, gives the system a low natural frequency (3 to 5 cycles per second), which tends to smooth out or make less angular the basic central pressure pattern, slow down the rate of pressure elevation, and lessen the pressure peak obtained.

In addition to damping, the other major factor controlling the peripheral pattern is wave summation. The pressure wave leaving the aortic arch rebounds from areas of increasing resistance in the peripheral arteries and arterioles, and travels retrogradely along the arterial tree. These centrally reflected pressure waves can be obliterated by damping or may summate with or be subtracted from the peripherally directed pressure wave, depending upon the phasic relationships. They do not, in general, materially alter the central aortic pattern. The magnitude and pattern of such a reflected wave can be roughly ascertained by substraction of the peripheral pulse pattern from the central aortic pattern (see fig. 22.4). This reveals that the waves occur in both systole and diastole. The points of change in resistance and pressure reflection have not been firmly established, but best opinion favors a locus in the abdominal aorta, just below the diaphragm, and a point in the femoral system. Reflected components from these areas can be either negative or positive.

*C. Determinants of aortic pulse pressure pattern.* The aorta and its larger branches can be regarded as a large elastically distensible compression chamber with cardiac ejection entering at one end and drainage occurring at the other end. The chamber possesses varying degrees of distensibility, conforming to those existing in various portions of the aorta and its branches. The generated pulse pressure is caused by an imbalance between the ventricular outflow entering the aorta, and the peripheral run-off leaving the aorta with each systole. The systolic portion largely expresses input into the aorta; the diastolic portion expresses decompression of the aorta or peripheral run-off, since, at this time, it is disconnected functionally from the ventricle. Four factors are of major importance in determining the pressure and increments of pressure from moment to moment: the elasticity or distensibility of the vessel walls, the volume of contained blood, the volume increment from cardiac ejection, and the decrement in volume caused by peripheral drainage. These relations are expressed by the equation:

$$E = \frac{\Delta P}{\Delta v} \cdot V$$

in which E = volume-elasticity coefficient, p = change in pressure, v = change in volume, and V = capacity of aorta in diastole. If the aorta and arteries constituted a simple elastic chamber, the pressure-volume relations (P/V) should be predictable from the preceding, and if P is known, V should become available. It would be helpful if such a relation could be used to indicate what is happening to the blood and whether the effect is centrally or peripherally induced. However, difficulties in such an approach are: (1) there is no way to quantitate V; (2) the pressure-volume relation of any part of the aorta is linear over only a limited pressure range; (3) distensibility is different in various regions of the arterial tree; and (4) changes have been revealed in the distensibility characteristics of the aorta by reflex stimulation and adrenalin injection.

*D. Usefulness of aortic or central artery pulse patterns.* Despite the difficulties in elucidating the pressure volume relations in the aorta, pressure pulses from the large arteries, depicting fairly well the pattern of the central aortic pulse pressure, have been found useful in predicting hemodynamic changes. Such interpretation and extrapolation is based on experiments in dogs in which changes in peripheral resistance and cardiac activity have been deliberately induced and their effects on the pressure pulses separately determined. Figure 22.5 shows the human subclavian pulse obtained indirectly. The duration of systole and diastole can be determined. In the presence of a high peripheral resistance and in a normal vessel, the pulse shows a much steeper rise throughout systole. In the presence of a low aortic resistance but with good vascular volume, the curve has an initial early spike followed by a lower systolic tip, a rapid decline and a greatly reduced slope during diastole. When the stroke volume is low, as in hemorrhage, the systolic part is small, smooth and rounded, and diastole is almost flat. Decreased distensibility of the aorta is revealed by a rapid, sustained and large elevation of the pulse, a high incisura and a gradual decline during diastole. Distinctive pulse patterns caused by lesions of the aortic valves are also shown. These are considered in detail in chapter 28. Attempts to use central arterial pressure

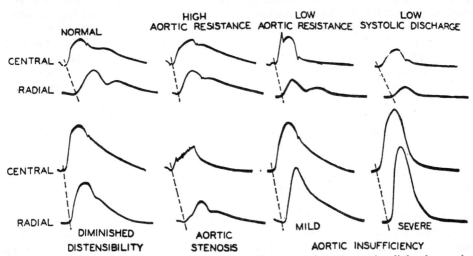

Fig. 22.5. Illustration of changes in contour and amplitude of subclavian and radial pulses under abnormal cardiovascular conditions. Discussion in text. Note changes in transmission rates. (Wiggers, Circulatory dynamics, Grune and Stratton, Inc., New York, 1952.)

pulses to estimate stroke volume have been numerous but none have been successful (see ch. 23).

## Arterial Blood Flow

With contraction of the human ventricle, a stroke volume or systolic discharge of 60 to 70 cc. is ejected into the distensible aorta within less than 0.25 seconds. Of this, at least 45 cc. is pushed into the aorta within the first 0.1 second. Space for this volume in the aortic arch is made by distending it and by removing some of its blood. The resulting pressure change travels as a wave throughout the length of the aorta and its branches to the capillaries (and sometimes through them), and expands the entire arterial tree radially and longitudinally. This enlargement results in a forward movement of blood from aortic valves to capillaries before the end of ventricular systole. As yet, too few studies of phasic flow have been made to justify a statement pertaining to the factors which determine the major characteristics of the flow patterns in the aorta. It is, however, worthwhile describing and considering them briefly.

PHASIC AORTIC FLOW. Aortic flow pulses have been measured in dogs and, also, incidentally in a number of human subjects at the time of surgical exposure of the aorta. The former will be considered since it has been possible to record simultaneously both pressure and flow pulses, and, at times, to record at least two flow pulses at different aortic levels. The phasic flows were recorded with an electromagnetic flow meter or sonar meter. Examples are shown in figure 22.6. The phasic flow in the ascending aorta is roughly triangular in shape 22.6A. Acceleration reaches a peak ejection rate early in systole following which there is a rapid deceleration ending in a momentary, small, high frequency backflow at the time of closure of the aortic valves. The flow curve is flat with almost zero velocity during most of diastole. The considerable modifying effect of the aorta upon the left ventricular ejection pulse is seen in figure 22.6B, taken near the terminus of the aorta. The flow pulse is now a series of smooth, highly damped oscillations of a frequency of 3 to 4 cycles per second which continue to extinction, but which are renewed with each heart beat. There is quite a large backflow in very early diastole. Flow pulses in the isthmal area of the aorta (proximal portion of descending aorta) are intermediate in pattern between the central and abdominal patterns. In figure 22.6C are the calculated blood velocity curve and the aortic differential pressure curve, the latter taken by a

double lumen catheter with pressure pick up holes 6 cm. apart. This shows the positive and negative acceleration waves which act on the aortic blood column to produce the flow pulsations. The effects of inertia are seen throughout the cardiac cycle. The beginning upstrokes of both pressure and flow curves coincide quite well, but when the first positive wave of the $\Delta P$ reaches its peak, flow acceleration is maximal, and when $\Delta P$ is maximally negative, flow deceleration is maximal. This represents about a 90° phase lag.

PHASIC FLOW IN PERIPHERAL ARTERIES. Flow patterns and simultaneous intraarterial pressure curves characteristic of several peripheral arteries are illustrated in figure 22.7. There are certain distinguishing characteristics. A flow pattern is made up of waves whose directional changes have a qualitative correspondence with gradient changes in the simultaneously recorded intravascular pressure pulse and which may be characteristically distinctive for that artery and vascular bed. Since the flow velocity varies with the differential pressure existing at the site of the flow meter, similarity in contour of the flow and applied pressure pulse is one criterion for the comparison of flow curves from different arteries. Certain patterns, especially those of the superior mesenteric and renal arteries, have a well-rounded and sustained systolic portion in relative conformity to that of the pressure pulse. Those of the hepatic and common carotid arteries are less well-rounded; those of the brachial and femoral arteries have a sharp systolic peak. The flow pulse pressure is generally small in the renal and axillary patterns, and somewhat larger in the superior mesenteric and hepatic, while the femoral may be quite large. Backflow components are consistently found in the femoral and axillary patterns and, on occasion, in the common carotid, while the renal, hepatic and superior mesenteric flow curves exhibit only forward flow. However, the main feature which permits a separation of the flow curves is the variable relation of the early diastolic to presystolic flow rates. Comparison of this relation with similar early diastolic and presystolic points on the corresponding pressure curve, shows that the superior mesenteric, renal, hepatic, common carotid, and femoral patterns have, on this basis, a progressively graded dissimilarity to their respective pressure curves.

While a method of analysis and interpretation is not yet available by means of which the probable determinants of, and interrelated influences upon phasic flow can be quantitatively evaluated, a partial attempt has been made in at least one

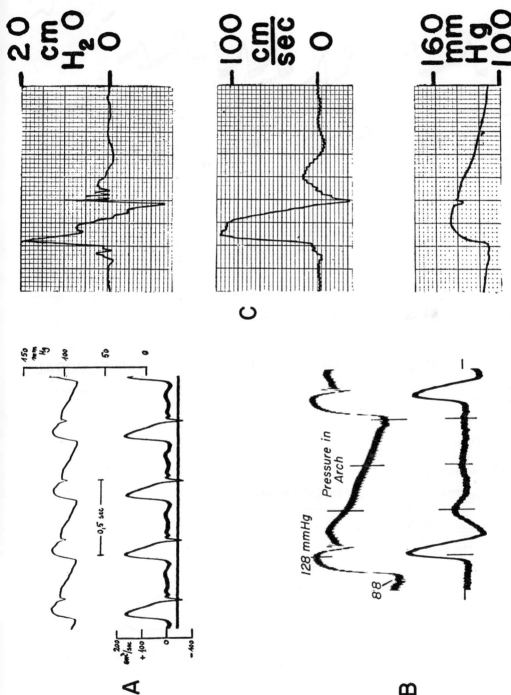

Fig. 22.6A. Tracings from bottom to top: flow in the ascending aorta, pressure in the aorta (from Wetterer, Minnesota Med., 1954, 37, 79). B. Tracing from top to bottom: pressure in aortic arch, flow in terminal aorta (from Spencer, Circulation Res., 1958, 6, 492). C. Simultaneous recording of (1) aortic axial pressure drop between two points 6 cm. apart, at level of subclavian artery, (2) computed blood velocity at this level, and (3) aortic blood pressure at subclavian artery junction (from Fry, Circulation Res., 1957, 5, 75).

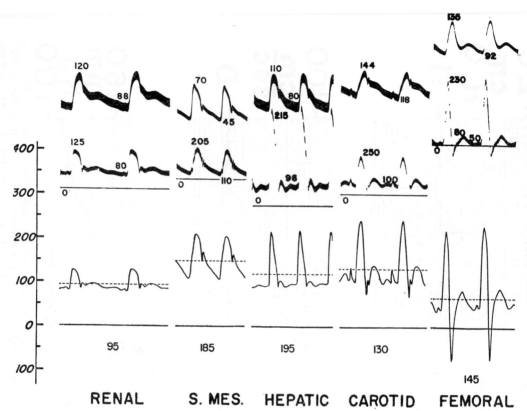

FIG. 22.7. Phasic flow in peripheral arteries obtained by orifice meter (Shipley and associates, Am. J. Physiol., 1943, **138**, 718.

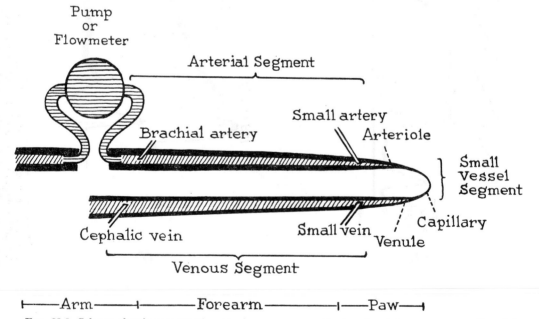

FIG. 22.8. Schema showing means of measuring pressure gradient and resistance across small peripheral vessels. (Haddy, Minnesota Med., 1958, **41**, 162).

artery. The approach is too technical to be considered here and the interested reader is referred to the paper of Shipley et al.

ARTERY TO VEIN PRESSURE AND FLOW. Pressure gradients across the very small vessels of the periphery have been difficult to establish in reasonably normal, biological situations. Possibly the closest approach to this is based upon the experimental approach of Haddy, in which arterial and venous pressure are measured in the quite small vessels (0.2 mm. diameter) of the dog forepaw, while constant blood flow is maintained by a pump (fig. 22.8). It can be seen that with the environmental temperature at 20° C., the pressure drop from small artery to small vein approximates 40 mm. Hg, and, from small vein to large vein, 6 mm. Hg. (fig. 22.9). Upon exposure to 0° C., the increase in pressure gradient is almost entirely through the small vessels with little gradient change between the small and large veins. Since the blood flow was maintained constant, the increase in pressure gradient represents directly active vasomotor resistance changes. Unfortunately, at present it is not possible by this technique to differentiate between changes in resistance of the arterioles and venules. Expansion, however, of this type of investigation would be most fruitful.

### Venous Pressure

The functional importance of the venous blood pressure has long interested physiologists and clinicians. The superficial veins, which can be observed and whose pressure values and pulse pressure contours can be easily measured, have been considered to serve as reliable indicators of the functional status of the less accessible and deeper lying portions of the systemic venous system.

THE VENOUS PRESSURE PULSE. The venous pressure pulse is best determined with the subject in the recumbent position. Venous pressure is measured directly with an indwelling needle or catheter or indirectly (without pressure values) by applying a cup over a vein external to the chest, such as the jugular, and connected to a manometer or a microphone receiver. The venous pulse waves are usually timed against an electrocardiogram, arteriogram or phonocardiogram (see ch. 20). Two distinct types of pulsations, respiratory and cardiac, are seen in the peripheral and central veins. With inspiration, blood is aspirated into the chest and the external veins tend to collapse while internal veins expand; with

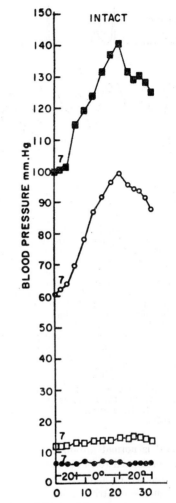

FIG. 22.9. Effect of temperature changes upon vascular pressures in the foreleg of the dog, flow rate being maintained constant (from Haddy, Circulation Res., 1957, 5, 59).

expiration, venous inflow is impeded and the external veins become distended while the chest veins tend to become smaller. These changes make up the respiratory venous pulse. The cardiac venous pressure pulse represents a retrograde reflection of a somewhat distorted version of the right atrial pulse pattern (see ch. 20). These a, c, v, waves are clearly seen in the record obtained from a peripheral vein in figure 22.10.

Valuable information concerning the events of the cardiac cycle, both from the experimental and clinical point of view, can be obtained by a study of the jugular pulse records. The length of the P-R interval can be roughly estimated by noting the time interval between the jugular and c waves. It is not difficult to decide whether the

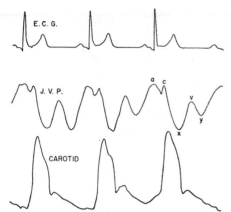

FIG. 22.10. The jugular venous pulse pattern (JVP) of a normal subject. An electrocardiogram (ECG) and carotid pulse tracing were simultaneously recorded. The presystolic "a" wave is caused by atrial contraction. The "c" peak is secondary to closure of the tricuspid valve although it may also represent transmission of the arterial pulse to the vein. The descending limb of the pulse tracing after the "c" wave is secondary to emptying of the vein into the right atrium. The negative "x" wave occurs during lowering of the atrioventricular septum and tricuspid valve during ventricular systole. Then the pressure rises, as the right atrium fills, to form the "v" wave. The second negative depression, the "y" wave represents the fall in jugular venous pressure as the tricuspid valve opens and the right atrium empties. (From Wood, P., Diseases of the heart and circulation, J. B. Lippincott Company, Philadelphia, 1956.)

a-c interval is normal (around 0.16 second), or obviously prolonged (0.24 second or more). The orderly sequence of a, c, v, waves indicates a normal sequence of atrial and ventricular beats. With partial or complete heart block, the number of a waves is greater than the number of c-v complexes. With atrial fibrillation, the a waves are absent. Premature ventricular beats of atrial origin are preceded by an a wave; those arising in the ventricle are not. A giant a wave can arise from tricuspid stenosis, severe pulmonary hypertension, pulmonary stenosis, tricuspid atresia,

nodal rhythm and partial heart block. The powerful right atrial contraction causing the giant a wave is due to the increased resistance to right ventricular filling. In tricuspid insufficiency, giant ventricular systolic (v) waves are seen. The systolic wave rises rapidly to a summit upon which vibrations of the murmur are superimposed.

NORMAL VENOUS BLOOD PRESSURE AND ITS VARIATIONS. Using the techniques previously described, mean blood pressure in the large, superficial veins of unanesthetized man at rest and in the supine position, is found to be a function of distance from the right atrium. The average value decreases from 13.8 mm. Hg (188 mm. $H_2O$) in the dorsal venous arch of the foot to about 5.2 mm. Hg (70 mm. $H_2O$) in the jugular vein. The pressure change from the surface veins to the central veins and along the central veins has been precisely determined. Great care must be taken in measuring the peripheral venous pressure since, under some conditions in the supine position, the peripheral veins may become partially collapsed and, as a result, the peripheral venous pressure becomes independent of right atrial pressure. It is generally advisable to make the measurement with the arm well below heart level to prevent this venous collapse. With this precaution, the average pressure of 7.1 mm. Hg (97 mm. $H_2O$) in the antecubital vein drops to about 4.6 mm. Hg (63 mm. $H_2O$) in the vena cava opposite the right atrium (fig. 22.11). Thus, the over-all venous pressure gradient approximates 9.2 mm. Hg (125 mm. $H_2O$) with a pressure difference of only a few mm. $H_2O$ occurring between the upper thoracic veins and the right atrium. Although venous pressure measurements in the same subject are quite constant, considerable variation (up to 100 mm. $H_2O$) may occur in the venous pressure from the same area in different persons.

Peripheral and central venous pressures are

FIG. 22.11. Comparison of central venous pressure (CVP) and the peripheral venous pressure (PVP). After release of occluding cuffs at the thighs, the pressures return to control levels without a change in the pressure gradient. (From Gauer, O. H. and Sieker, H. O., Circulation Res., 1956, 4, 75).

altered in the same direction under many circumstances. They do not appear to be related to age, sex or hypertension, but they are decreased in severe hemorrhage and surgical shock. They are increased by positive pressure breathing, the Valsalva maneuver, tilting, the excitement stage of anesthesia, the apneic phase of asthmatic attacks and in Cheynes-Stokes breathing. The main pathological condition in which central and peripheral venous pressures are elevated, sometimes as high as 22 mm. Hg (300 mm. $H_2O$) in the antecubital vein, is congestive heart failure.

DETERMINANTS OF VENOUS PRESSURE. The interplay of factors which determine systemic venous pressure and venous flow can be briefly stated. The veins are placed between the capillaries or the A-V anastomoses, and the right heart. The blood enters the venules with an appreciable pressure residuum (vis a tergo) from the arterial side, after it has passed through the capillaries. This pressure is met by the resistance to flow from the veins themselves and from the heart itself (the vis a fronte). The venous pressure is affected by internal factors which control the relation between the contained venous volume and the state of distensibility of its vessel walls. Finally, there are various external or extramural factors (vis a latere) such as the actions of respiration, muscle and gravity, which together represent the pressure effect of the surrounding tissues. Because their interplay is so complex, and flow methodology is generally so inadequate for normal situations, it is difficult to estimate their relative effect on venous pressure and flow. However, before considering the details of operation of these determinants, it must be emphasized that they act to insure that the pressure in the veins can never be less than the right atrial pressure, and whenever right atrial pressure increases, the peripheral venous pressure increases. This excess of pressure (10 to 12 mm. Hg or 125 mm. $H_2O$) in the various veins, over that in the right atrium, is an expression of the pressure gradient ($P_1$-$P_2$ in Poiseuille's formula). This, together with a reasonable venous cross-section, causes blood to flow from vein to atrium.

*A. The contraction of the left ventricle (the "vis a tergo")*. The energy of the ventricular contraction (the "vis a tergo") is expended in driving blood through the arterioles and onward through the capillaries and veins to the right atrium. By the time the blood reaches the venules, the remaining pressure may approximate 7 to 8 mm. Hg. When it reaches the right atrium, the energy has been almost entirely dissipated in overcoming the frictional resistance offered by the vascular channels; at this point, the pressure may be less than 1 mm. Hg.

*B. Quantity of blood flowing through the arterioles in relation to capacity of the veins*. Although the details are largely unknown, generally speaking, the more blood which is received from the arterial side, the greater will be the venous pressure. That is, with dilated arterioles, the difference between the arterial pressure on the one hand and venous pressure on the other, tends to be reduced; with constricted vessels the pressure difference will be increased. Rough estimates based on the volume-elasticity of the various compartments of the vascular system indicate that if a liter of blood is transfused into the circulation of man at rest, only 10 to 20 cc. would be found in the arterial tree and about 980 cc. in the extra-arterial system (systemic venous and pulmonary circuits), and that the pressure elevation in the whole system would be only 4 or 5 mm. Hg. In bleeding and transfusion experiments in man, the circulation behaves like an elastic container (ch. 15); with pooling of blood in the extremities by occlusive cuffs, the central venous pressure falls without any apparent sign of counter-veno motor control. This emphasizes the view that normal stresses to which the circulation is exposed, if they are not too abrupt or excessive, lead to only passive change in the resistance vessels and systemic venous system, and do not cause relaxation or strong contraction of the peripheral capacitance vessels.

This relationship, however, does not always hold because the veins are capable of adjusting their capacity to the quantity of blood received from the arterial system by reflex vasomotor activity. The smaller vessels may expand to accommodate the extra blood so that little change in venous pressure results, or they may reduce their capacities and maintain pressure in spite of a reduced volume of received blood.

The participation of venomotor tone in the control of the venous pressure and venous blood flow can be shown in animal experiments in which oxygen want, high $CO_2$, stimulation of the carotid sinus and excessive hemorrhage are effective in reducing the size of the capacitance vessels, but proper interpretation is difficult because of the often, unphysiological strength of the stimulus. In man, using strong stimuli such as the Valsalva maneuver, asphyxia, high G, or large blood losses, the veins constrict in what may be called an emergency reaction. In the latter case, the central venous pressure may be normal or even increased.

It is significant that the central and peripheral venous pressures do not necessarily shift in the same direction. The pressure gradient from very small veins (0.5 mm. diameter or less) to large central veins, is not necessarily constant and can be markedly affected by various states. With cold, hyperventilation and moderate exercise, only the peripheral venous pressure may rise significantly. This often independent action of local venous pressure and central venous pressure indicates that reflex venomotor activity of the capacitance vessels in normal persons is highly selective and regional in operation and that local small vein or venule pressure is not necessarily an index of happenings in the central venous system. Hence, the state of distensibility of the arterioles, venules and small veins, and large central veins, are not necessarily related, and net effects are unpredictable.

*C. The action of the right side of the heart upon the blood flow in the veins.* Obviously, if the blood is not passed on again by the right heart as quickly as it is carried to it by the great veins, the venous pressure will rise. That is, there will be a tendency for the blood to be "dammed back." When the heart is beating vigorously and output and inflow are balanced, no rise in venous pressure occurs. In health the force of the ven-

tricular contraction is nicely adjusted to the quantity of blood which pours into the atrium from the veins, and no accumulation occurs. If, however, the heart fails, the venous pressure rises and back pressure effects ensue.

There now appears to be good experimental proof that the activity of the right ventricle itself actually increases greatly vena caval flow into the right atrium. This is illustrated in the vena caval flow curves of figure 22.12, in which it can be seen that there is a larger forward flow of blood during right ventricular systole than during diastole. Thus, venous inflow into the right atrium is large in the presence of closed tricuspid valves. The responsible force is believed to be right ventricular contraction itself. During such contraction, the descent of the atrioventricular junction enlarges the great venous reservoir which comprises the atria and venae cavae. Obviously, this could be a very useful mechanism for maintaining venous return during tachycardia. In slow hearts, most of atrial inflow occurs during the long ventricular diastole, but during a rapid heart rate the proportion of atrial inflow due to active systolic "injection" of blood from the veins into the right atrium, is greatly increased.

The influence of cardiac action upon the movement of blood in veins and atria does not necessarily imply that the ventricles exert an aspirat-

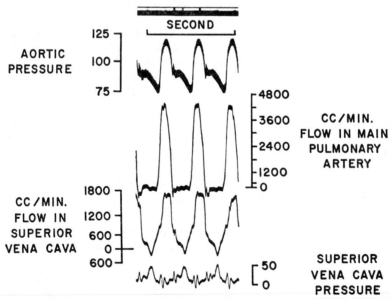

FIG. 22.12. Simultaneous recording in open chest dog of aortic pressure, superior vena cava pressure, and pulmonary artery pressure and superior vena cava flow with bristle flowmeter. Note acceleration of venous return during systolic ejection. (From Brecher, Venous Return, p. 111, Grune & Stratton, Inc., New York, 1956.)

ing action during diastole. This problem has been debated many years and is considered in chapter 20 in some detail. In general, it can be said that under strictly controlled experimental conditions, there is some positive evidence for this. However, one must remember that there is no good quantitation of this and it would take place only in very early diastolic relaxation, which is a very short time period.

Sometimes when vigorous respiratory efforts are made, slight fluctuations of the venous pressure can be detected in the peripheral veins of the human subject. These variations rarely amount to more than 10 mm. of $H_2O$ but may be considerably higher than this when dyspnea resulting from obstruction to the free entrance and egress of air from the lungs exists. Owing to the inertia of the blood column the aspirating effect is less evident the nearer to the periphery at which the pressure measurements are made.

The respiratory effects upon venous pressure and also presumably upon venous flow, can also be exaggerated in normal subjects by the following procedures. If a forced expiration is made with the glottis closed (Valsalva's experiment)

the negative intrathoracic pressure can be abolished and a positive pressure of several millimeters of mercury substituted. The veins of the neck, face and limbs become distended with blood as a result of the impediment to the flow into the right auricle. The peripheral venous pressure under these circumstances may rise to 400 mm. $H_2O$ or more. In the converse experiment of Mueller in which a forced inspiration is made with the glottis closed, the powerful suction effect may cause a fall of 50 mm. $H_2O$ or so in the venous pressure of a peripheral vein. The increase in negative intrathoracic pressure may be seen by means of the X-ray to exert an effect upon the ventricle which during diastole becomes somewhat enlarged beyond its usual size.

*D. External forces.* Natural and artificial respiration have a very large effect on central venous pressure and flow. Direct measurements of flow with the bristle flow meter in the closed-chest dog have shown flow to increase in both the superior and inferior vena cava during inspiration, and in turn, this effect is transmitted to the outlying veins (fig. 22.13). The interplay of mechanisms is as follows: the blood in the great

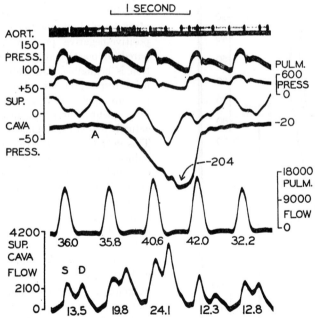

Fig. 22.13. Effect of spontaneous respiration on venous return and cardiac output (closed chest). Tracings from top to bottom: time and base line, aortic pressure in millimeters of mercury, pulmonary artery, superior vena caval and intrathoracic pressure in millimeters of water, pulmonary arterial and superior vena caval flows in cubic centimeters per minute A, beginning of inspiration, S, acceleration of superior vena caval flow during ventricular systole, D, acceleration of superior vena caval during ventricular diastole. Stroke volume (in cubic centimeters) under pulmonary arterial flow curve. Flow (in cubic centimeters) through superior vena cava during each cardiac cycle at bottom of record. Electrical frequency response of both flowmeters reduced from 400 to 40 cycles per second. Superior vena caval pressure curve damped. (Brecher, G. A., Venous Return, Grune & Stratton, Inc., New York, 1956.)

veins at their entrance into the atrium has a small, but definite pressure of about 5 mm. $H_2O$ transmitted from the arterial side. That is to say, if the thorax were opened so as to abolish the subatmospheric pressure within it, and a manometer placed in the inferior vena cava, a positive pressure of this magnitude would be registered. During inspiration, the pressure within the thorax is about −6 mm. Hg (81 mm. $H_2O$) below that of the atmosphere. During expiration it amounts to −2.5 mm. Hg (34 mm. $H_2O$). Their algebraic sum during inspiration (−6 mm. Hg ÷ 0.5 mm. Hg), and during expiration (−2.5 mm. Hg ÷ 0.5 mm. Hg), represents the transmural pressure expanding the intrathoracic structures and causing blood to enter the thorax. This especially expands the thin-walled intrathoracic veins. A similar effect but of less degree is exerted upon the walls of the atria. The diameters of the thick-walled ventricles, however, and the comparatively

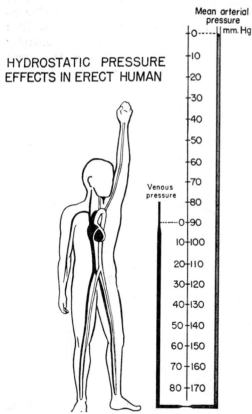

HYDROSTATIC PRESSURE EFFECTS IN ERECT HUMAN

FIG. 22.14. In erect position, arterial and venous pressures are both increased by about 85 mm. Hg. at the ankle. With the arm elevated over the head, the arterial pressure at the wrist is about 40 mm. Hg. and the effective venous pressure is zero down to a level just above the heart. (From Rushmer, Cardiac Diagnosis, W. B. Saunders Company, Philadelphia, 1955.)

rigid coats of the larger arteries remain practically uninfluenced by the "negative pressure" during ordinary breathing. During expiration, the intravenous pressure within the abdomen exceeds the intraabdominal pressure by only about 1 mm. Hg. However, descent of the diaphragm during the inspiratory phase compresses the abdominal contents and, since the outlying veins have valves, blood is forced into the thorax. The recent extensive use of artificial respiration in surgical and medical situations has focused attention on the effects of such procedures on the circulation. In the closed-chest dog, intermittent, positive-atmospheric-pressure, artificial respiration (expiration occurring passively against atmospheric pressure) reduces significantly venous return to the right heart over that occurring with natural respiration. Intermittent positive-negative pressure respiration (use of mild suction during expiration) augments vena caval flow over that occurring during positive-atmospheric pressure respiration. The use of positive-negative pressure respiration with particular attention to the negative pressure phase might be beneficial to patients in poor circulatory condition because it could be made to facilitate their venous return. In the presence of an open chest, the net caval flow increase of positive-negative pressure respiration as compared to positive-atmospheric pressure respiration is negligible. The untoward effects of artificial respiration arise because of the positive pressure applied during artificial inspiration; the intra pleural pressure, instead of decreasing, actually increases, and may even become positive. This decreases vena caval flow secondary to an induced increase in pulmonary vascular resistance and, in part, to the mechanical compression or "tamponade" of the heart and lungs caused by the expanding lungs. The mechanical aspects of respiration, however, are apparently not essential to maintenance of venous return or cardiac output, for in the presence of apneic oxygenation in dogs (a condition of induced ventilatory arrest with the trachea connected to a reservoir of oxygen), life continues and the cardiac output may even increase.

*E. Posture and exercise.* The venous pressure varies, of course, as a result of the gravity effect, i.e., with the position of the vein in relation to the right atrium, at which level, venous pressure is assumed to approximate zero (fig. 22.14). If man assumes the upright position and is motionless and relaxed, the measured pressure in an ankle vein approximates 85 to 90 mm. Hg. This is slightly more than the hydrostatic pressure from the vein to the heart level. This means that there is a continuous column of blood from the right atrium to the ankle. Similarly, the arterial blood pressure measured at the ankle will be increased over that at the heart level by an amount equal to the hydrostatic level. Thus, the arterial and venous pressures at the ankle are increased by the same amount, and the pressure difference between vein and artery is the same at ankle and heart level. This means that a favorable pressure gradient exists for venous flow. Below heart level, the veins increase in fullness and the venous pressure gradient responsible for venous return from periphery to the heart is the measured venous pressure minus the hydrostatic column. This is a small gradient but, since the veins are distended, resistance is quite low. In the upright position, veins from the upper part of the body empty towards the heart. These upper veins partially collapse and their intravascular pressure may approximate zero. Above heart level, the pressure gradient along the venous channels is the height of the hydrostatic column above heart level. This gradient is large but since the veins are partially collapsed, resistance is high.

There is, however, a special feature of the venous system which distinguishes it from the arterial system. This is the tendency of the veins to collapse. In the low pressure system, even in the recumbent position, the veins are not usually round but may be partially or fully, and intermittently collapsed. For surface veins, collapse arises from increase in atmospheric pressure; in the deeper veins, it is caused by the surrounding tissue pressure acting on the venous walls. This occurs during normal respiration in the neck veins and in the inferior vena cava below the diaphragm where this process is aided by the increased intra-abdominal pressure. With deep and prolonged inspiration, these veins may completely collapse. Such a collapse tendency may be greatly augmented by an increased gravitational stress. In the upright position, the pressure in the neck veins falls to 0 mm. Hg, and the atmospheric pressure on the outside of the neck causes these veins to collapse all the way up to the skull. This causes the pressure in these veins to remain at zero along their course. It is this tendency for collapse that causes resistance in the large veins for when distended, resistance is minimal. However, not all veins are collapsible, especially the venous sinuses in the skull, verte-

bral column, bones, liver and spleen, which are held open by firm-walled surrounding tissues. For example, the veins in the skull are in a noncollapsible chamber, and in the standing position a negative venous pressure of about 10 mm. Hg exists in the sagittal sinus because of the hydrostatic pressure difference between the top and base of the skull.

It is obvious from the preceding that the pressure gradient between two points in the venous system may give no information as to volume flow between the points, because of this tendency of the extrathoracic veins to collapse. Partial collapse can reduce blood flow despite an increase in pressure gradient along the vessel. Volume flow through partially collapsed veins is represented by a modification of Poiseuille's law to a tube with an elliptical cross-section. With venous pressure constant, volume flow in a partially collapsed vein is estimated to be about 25 per cent of that through the same vein when round.

Although a change in position does not alter the relative pressure gradients on the arterial and venous sides, still a normal return of venous blood is not necessarily insured. This would be the situation only if all the vasculature were made up of semi-rigid tubes and in which flow would depend only on the difference of artery and venous pressure at the level of the heart. This, however, is not true in a distensible system such as the veins. Owing to its much greater filling capacity, the volume on the venous side is greatly increased by this shift from horizontal to the erect position. In man, the decreased venous return under such conditions if of short duration because of a number of compensatory vasomotor mechanisms which operate very quickly. However, even with these compensations, the venous return is somewhat less than in the supine man. It is difficult to decide how effective are the active venomotor mechanisms in returning blood to the heart as man assumes the upright position. Direct information on venomotor control of the intestinal vessels, mostly in operated animals, indicates that they are capable of widespread constriction, but again, these situations can hardly be regarded as normal. In tilting the human subject into an upright posture, the blood pressure at the carotid sinus decreases mildly and the heart becomes smaller (fig. 22.15). About 400 cc. of blood leaves the thoracic compartment to accumulate mainly in the veins of the extremities (determined by leg plethysmographys). The pressure in them increases and the filling pressure of the heart drops. Cardiac output drops mildly; stroke volume de-

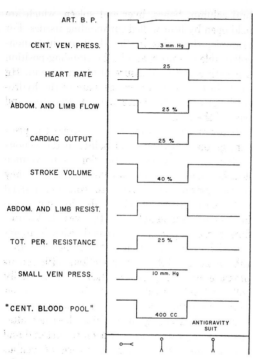

ART. B. P.

CENT. VEN. PRESS.        3 mm Hg

                         25
HEART RATE

ABDOM. AND LIMB FLOW     25 %

CARDIAC OUTPUT           25 %

STROKE VOLUME
                         40 %

ABDOM. AND LIMB RESIST.

TOT. PER. RESISTANCE     25 %

SMALL VEIN PRESS.        10 mm. Hg

"CENT. BLOOD POOL"
                         400 CC
                              ANTIGRAVITY
                              SUIT

FIG. 22.15. Effect on various cardiovascular parameters in man of changing from supine to the upright position.

creases considerably; the heart rate rises. There is also a decrease in blood flow through skin, skeletal muscle, liver and kidney. These changes are at least partially explainable on a mechanical basis, i.e., tipping into the erect posture might be regarded as a functional hemorrhage into the lower portions of the body. Since the pressure in a superficial arm vein maintained at heart level rises considerably (about 10 mm. Hg), possible widespread peripheral venous constriction has taken place to shift blood centrally to make more blood available to the heart for maintaining cardiac output, although its effect is not enough to maintain central venous pressure. That this limitation of peripheral blood flow is a reflex phenomenon has been shown by its absence in a sympathectomized extremity. The fact that application of a G suit before or after the subject has assumed the upright position, either prevents these changes, or re-establishes the original state of the circulation, mitigates against the role of the arterial baro-receptors and favors the stimulation of low pressor receptors. While their precise stimulus and accurate location are not known, they presumably belong to the many receptors demonstrated anatomically in the thoracic vascular bed.

Since man spends most of his life in the erect position, there is no doubt regarding the practical effectiveness of these compensatory mechanisms. It is especially evident when one compares their behavior with that in persons with naturally occurring, or drug-induced, hypotension, who lose very large quantities of blood into their extremities and lose consciousness upon standing up. Despite this, venomotor compensation is still far from perfect in normal persons since an excess of, at least, 400 cc. of blood still remains in their extremities.

The circulation of animals such as the domestic rabbit, eel and snake, which have not acquired a compensatory mechanism, are placed at great disadvantage when the vertical position is assumed. The eel and snake can be killed by immobilization in the vertical head-up position. They literally bleed to death into their veins. Thus, in the human subject if, upon assuming the erect posture after a protracted confinement to bed, the muscles of the abdomen and limbs are weak and the tone of the nervous mechanism governing the peripheral vessels lowered, the hydrostatic effect is overcome with difficulty. The blood subsides into the capacious abdominal veins and capillaries and the right heart is no longer adequately supplied with blood. The arterial pressure falls and the cerebral blood flow becomes inadequate. The subject turns pale, sweats freely and feels giddy or perhaps nauseated, and in a complete faint loses consciousness (syncope). In this situation, and in various circulatory disorders, baths can obviously have a beneficial effect on venous return. Body immersion up to the heart level increases the pressure exerted on the body and reduces pooling in the abdomen and dependent parts. In man, increased gravitational stress in the head-foot direction (positive acceleration) leads to practically no venous return to the right heart. The increased hydrostatic pressure distends the veins so much that they contain almost all the blood volume, and active vasomotor influences are not sufficient to combat this very high hydrostatic pressure. Again this can be effectively combated by wearing an inflated pressure suit to compress the extrathoracic parts of the body and to force blood to flow centrally.

In exercise, a much greater volume of blood enters the central veins from the arterial side. The various mechanical assists already mentioned, that increase the venous pressure gradient and venous blood flow toward the heart and decrease the venous reservoir, now operate even more effectively. In addition, the act of muscle shortening propels blood toward the heart. In animal experiments in which skeletal muscle is perfused with blood under a constant pressure, the arterial inflow decreases and venous outflow increases during muscle shortening; upon relaxation, the arterial inflow increases and the venous outflow decreases; the net result is to augment flow. The pressure within the active muscles surrounding the veins is thus a potent factor in regulating venous pressure and flow. Intra muscle pressure rises from a resting level of 2 to 5 cm. $H_2O$ to as high as 50 cm. $H_2O$ during exercise. The venous pressure in the ankle veins which, in the standing position approximate 80 to 90 mm. Hg, is now greatly reduced. By rhythmical action of the muscle, the venous valves are activated and the blood column broken up, and venous pressure at the ankle may decrease to as low as 30 mm. Hg (40 cm. $H_2O$). Although helpful, the presence of venous valves is not essential for this beneficial action of active muscle on venous return. Extravascular vessel compression will promote flow equally in both directions only if flow resistance is equal in both directions. Without the presence of valves, the resistance in the vessels on the capillary side of the venous system is lower than in the veins on the right cardiac side. Hence, rhythmical vein compression per se will drive blood toward the heart, and this has been shown experimentally to occur. It can also be observed clinically that in advanced age and under pathological conditions with incompetent or no venous valves, muscle movements improve venous return. Information on active changes in venomotor action in man is limited and is essentially contained in the observations that there is a drastic reduction in splanchnic blood volume with exercise and the pressure in the superficial veins (within a nonexercising area) increases by 10 to 13 mm. Hg over that in a standing position only.

## Regulation of Pulmonary Pressure and Flow

Uniquely interposed between the right and left heart and entirely enclosed within the negative pressure confines of the thorax, the pulmonary circulation exhibits certain peculiarities uncommon to the other organ-perfused systems. For instance, (1) it is the only circuit in the body to receive the total cardiac output, (2) it operates at a perfusion pressure $\frac{1}{4}$ to $\frac{1}{8}$ that of the systemic circuit, (3) its mean transit time is equal to the systemic, albeit across a much reduced linear distance, reflecting the enormous surface area of the pulmonary capillary bed, (4) it is predominantly controlled by the beat to beat pressure differential between the pulmonary artery (right ventricle) and the left atrium upon which phasic, intrathoracic respiratory variations are superimposed, and (5) it is the only arterial circuit which carries desaturated hemoglobin and which, by virtue of the alveolar-capillary pressure difference, the desaturated hemoglobin and the huge surface area participates in large instantaneous gas exchanges.

PULMONARY RESISTANCE. To determine the mechanisms controlling pulmonary flow, it is necessary to know the resistance to flow. Classically, this should be simply the ratio of the difference of pressure across any portion of a vascular bed to the blood flow that develops; it is a convenient factor by which the pressure drop can be multiplied to give the flow. Such resistance gives information regarding the two factors upon which it depends, the viscosity and geometry of the vascular bed. Since, however, the relation of pressure and flow is not a straight line and when plotted does not pass through the origin, the mechanisms involved are not determinable from a single point relationship. To make the results interpretable, a vascular bed must be perfused in the control state and in the presence of a variable at the same pressure while flow is measured, or at the same flow while pressure is measured. In no other way can it be even roughly determined that a calculated change in resistance (Pressure/Flow) reflects vasomotor activity produced by the stimulus, or reflects only the passive change in resistance caused by alteration in left atrial pressure or in pulmonary flow. There is also an additional difficulty in measuring changing resistance in the pulmonary circulation, for here the relationship between pressure and flow is quantitatively quite different from that in the systemic circulation. The difference is that with the same volume perfusing both circuits, the pressure drop from the pulmonary artery to the left atrium is only about one-fifth that from the aorta to the right atrium. This is illustrated in figure 22.16 where the differential pressure between the pulmonary artery and the pulmonary veins is only about 15 to 20 mm. Hg. With present pressure methodology, figures of this magnitude can only be roughly determined. This means that while the systemic resistance at the arterioles is high and made up of relatively thick muscle cuffs, the resistance at the outlet of the small pulmonary artery branches has quite thin muscular coats with relatively large luminae. The tone of the terminal pulmonary vessels is thereby relatively low so that a rise in pulmonary venous pressure is readily transmitted to the arterial side, or so that a rise in blood volume injected into the arterial side will increase greatly the volume in the lungs. As a result of the high degree of distensibility of the pulmonary vascular bed, secondary to the opening up of fresh capillaries or further opening of those being used, the blood contained within the lungs shows wide variations under different conditions and on a passive basis.

PRESSURE PULSE IN THE PULMONARY CIRCUIT. Pressures in the pulmonary circuit are determined by means of intracardiac catheterization or by indwelling tubes already described. Pulmonary circuit pressures are much lower than those in the systemic arterial circuit. For the curves of figure 22.16, angiostomy cannulas were placed in the central pulmonary artery and pulmonary veins. Phasic pressure from the two vessels and also their differential pressure were recorded some days postoperatively in the unanesthetized dog. The results showed that the pulmonary artery pressure is 40/10 mm. Hg and the pulmonary vein pressure is 2 to 12 mm. Hg. The pattern of the pulmonary arterial pressure is distinctive showing a marked incisura low on the anacrotic limb. In late diastole, the pressure descent almost ceases and becomes horizontal. The pulse contours of the peripheral and central portions of the pulmonary artery display differences somewhat like those of the systemic circuit. The pulse wave velocity in the pulmonary artery under essentially normal conditions is about 4 meters per second, or about the same as in the aorta at normal intra-aortic pressure. This suggests that the aorta may be even more distensible than the pulmonary artery since the pulse velocity is inversely related to distensibility. The contour of the pulmonary vein pressure curve clearly shows a, c, and v waves, and closely resembles pressure pulses taken from the left atrium.

PHASIC BLOOD FLOW IN THE PULMONARY CIRCUIT. Figure 22.13 demonstrates that the flow through the main pulmonary artery is almost entirely during systole, the diastolic flow being flat and close to zero. This strongly suggests that there is little or no diastolic run-off of blood into the pulmonary capillaries. By the ingenious method of DuBois and associates, measurements of cyclic change in flow through the pulmonary capillaries has revealed that this is quite pulsatile with a very high peak flow during systole. By the end of diastole, pressures in the vascular bed are equilibrated and capillary flow practically ceases (figure 22.17). Flow curves in the pulmonary veins are not available.

THE EFFECTS OF THE RESPIRATION UPON THE PULMONARY AND SYSTEMIC BLOOD PRESSURES AND FLOWS. The effects of natural respiration on the hemodynamics of the pulmonary circulation are illustrated in figure 22.13. The pulmonary arterial pressure falls during inspiration and rises during expiration. One should expect that, as a result of the increased flow of blood into the right ventricle during inspiration (see superior caval flow) and the greater systolic discharge, both the pulmonary pressure and pulmonary flow would rise during this phase of respiration. However, only the pulmonary flow rises. Because of the traction exerted upon the circumference of the pulmonary vessels by the surrounding lung tissue, their capacity is increased. This more than compensates for the lack of change in the pressure gradient and for the greater amount of blood entering the pulmonary circuit during the inspiratory phase. During expiration these effects are reversed. The right systolic discharge is less but the capacity of the vascular bed of the lungs is at the same time reduced; an upward swing in pulmonary arterial pressure occurs. With maximal expansion of the lungs, or during a forced expiration with the glottis closed (Valsalva's experiment), the vessels are strongly compressed by the surrounding lung tissue, and the pulmonary arterial pressure rises sharply.

The increased capacity of the pulmonary vessels during inspiration reduces, momentarily, the flow of blood into the left atrium; the consequent reduction in the systolic discharge of the left ventricle causes a fall in aortic pressure (figure

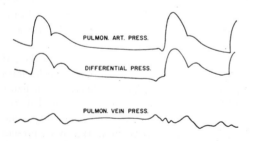

FIG. 22.16. Record from the unanesthetized dog showing the pressure pulse contours in the pulmonary artery, *upper curve*; pulmonary vein, *lower*; and the differential pressure between the two, *middle curve*. Pulmonary artery pressure, 28/10 mm. Hg.; mean pulmonary vein pressure, 10 mm. Hg.; differential pressure 5 to 10 mm. Hg. (From Hamilton, Am. J. Physiol., 1939, **125**, 130.)

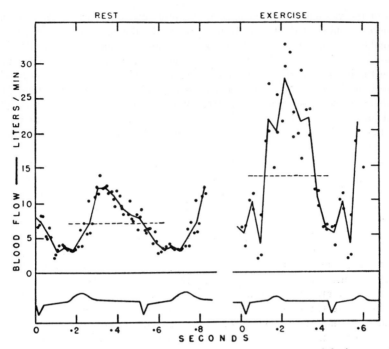

FIG. 22.17. Simultaneous pulmonary capillary blood flow curves at rest and during exercise. (DuBois, J. Clin. Invest., 1957, **36**, 1566.)

22.13). After a few beats of the right ventricle, the greater capacity of the pulmonary vessels again becomes filled and the flow of blood into the left chambers of the heart increases; the aortic pressure rises. The succeeding expiration, by reducing the capacity of the pulmonary vessels, drives blood to the left side and further increases the discharge into the aorta; the systemic pressure, in consequence, continues its rise until near the end of the expiratory phase. The large undulations which appear in the blood pressure tracings of animals are due to these effects. If the respiratory movements and the systemic blood pressure are recorded simultaneously, it is found that the blood pressure commences to fall at the commencement of inspiration and reaches its lowest point in the latter half of this phase; the blood pressure tracing then commences to rise and reaches its maximum toward the latter part of expiration. In this situation, it is presumed that the decrease and increase in peripheral resistance are on a passive basis but this has not been proved.

EFFECTS OF EXERCISE ON THE PULMONARY CIRCULATION. The general form of the curve relating pulmonary artery pressure and pulmonary blood flow in man and the intact dog at rest and exercise, is shown in figure 22.18. The curve indicates that pulmonary artery pressure is main-

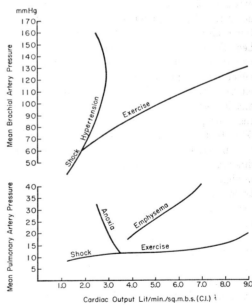

FIG. 22.18. The relationship of pressure to flow in the systemic circulation and pulmonary circulation in normal and abnormal states. Note the difference in response of the two circulations to exercise.

tained below the upper limit of normal until the flow exceeds at least three times the base level whereupon it increases progressively. This absence of pressure rise with increased flow implies an expansion of the vascular bed from opening of new channels, widening of those already perfused, or a combination of both. Thus, the resistance decreases. It is believed (without proof) that this is on the basis of passive distension of the lungs, especially since the same relation holds when attempts are made to denervate the heart, when isolated lung lobes are perfused, or when variations in the quantity of blood in the lungs is induced by different procedures.

As pointed out earlier, to understand what is happening hemodynamically in the pulmonary circulation, it is more important here than in any other vascular bed to know both the pulmonary artery pressure and pulmonary vein (or left atrial pressure). This is because the pressure gradient is only a few millimeters of mercury, and a 5 mm. Hg-change in the pulmonary venous pressure could be transmitted back as a 5-mm. Hg rise on the pulmonary artery side without any active change in peripheral resistance in the lung vessels. So, unless it is known what is happening in the pulmonary veins, one is at a loss to ascribe the cause of a change in pulmonary artery pressure. Keeping this in mind, little or no evidence exists in the dog that various procedures that actively affect peripheral resistance in the systemic circuit have any effect in the pulmonary bed. For example, epinephrine injection in small or large doses into the pulmonary artery, has no effect on the pulmonary circulation in its first circuit. After it has entered the systemic circuit and increased pulse pressure and cardiac output, then the pulmonary vein pressure may increase 50 to 60 mm. Hg, but so does the pulmonary artery pressure by a like amount, so the pressure difference is not changed. Acetylcholine, aminophylline, histamine and stellate ganglion stimulation are also without effect on the differential pressure. Hence, the passive bag theory of pulmonary function has arisen.

EVIDENCE FOR AND AGAINST VASOMOTOR CONTROL OF THE PULMONARY CIRCULATION. The pressure in the pulmonary artery may increase as the result of back pressure from the left heart, an increase in pulmonary blood flow and vasoconstriction in the pulmonary vascular bed. Also, pressure changes follow alteration of intrathoracic pressure.

The pulmonary vasculature could respond to active vasoconstriction and contribute to an increase of pulmonary artery pressure. The small pulmonary vessels possess muscular coats and are equipped with dual nerve supply—sympathetic and parasympathetic; stimulation of the baroreceptors gives increased pulmonary flow and decreased pulmonary arterial pressure; casts of the two sides of a lung are markedly different if one side is perfused with noradrenaline up to the time of plastic injection (the latter showing marked constriction in the vessels of less than 25 microns ($\mu$) in diameter). However, since there is little doubt that wide variations in vascular resistance can normally occur in a purely passive way, and since it is impossible to establish accurately the pressure gradient when it is so very low, demonstration of an active part played by smooth muscle under normal conditions, in the walls of the small vessels, is difficult.

In the presence of left heart failure resulting from mitral stenosis, the pulmonary capillary pressure rises, distends the capillary bed and leads to pulmonary edema. It has been postulated that as soon as the edema occurs from high back pressure, a reflex occurs giving rise to local, arterial constriction and accounts, in part, for the pulmonary artery pressure elevation, at times even to 100 mm. Hg, and the minimization of the pulmonary edema. Presumably, however, the mechanism for increased pulmonary resistance is not an adaptive reflex but a life saving effect of pathological changes in the small pulmonary vessels.

In normal subjects, anoxia, induced by breathing 12 per cent oxygen in nitrogen, considerably increases pulmonary arterial pressure, mildly increases cardiac output, and is without effect on left atrial pressure or central blood volume. This suggests that the vasoconstriction induced is on an active basis. Although generalized, such vasoconstriction of the pulmonary bed would seem to serve no useful purpose; local hypoxia, however, could be helpful in regulating the distribution of blood by causing vasoconstriction which, in turn, diverts blood from the affected region to vessels in better aerated parts of the lung. In experiments in man and animals in which one lung was respired with an hypoxic mixture, the lung probably developed vasoconstriction, since the arterial saturation returned to normal. This would be the case if the vessels in the hypoxic lung constricted and forced the blood normally flowing through them into well-oxygenated channels. Final proof, however, that hypoxia induces active vasoconstriction in man is contained in the experiments in which acetylcholine (a drug with strong vasodilating effects on the systemic circulation) was infused into the right atrium, but in such quantities that no systemic effects were produced. In the presence of hypoxia induced by breathing a low oxygen mixture, infusion of acetylcholine decreased the elevated pulmonary arterial pressure but did not change the left atrial pressure, cardiac output, systemic blood pressure, or heart rate. This seems to indicate than an active vasoconstriction caused by hypoxia is relieved by the drug. This view is further substantiated by the observation that in emphysematous patients who represent a chronic and more limited form of hypoxia with some degree of arterial unsaturation, acetylcholine infusion lowers still further the arterial oxygen saturation. The site and mechanism of action are unknown but they could be many—a local reflex from alveoli or pulmonary veins, chemoreceptor stimulation of the sinus or aortic body, direct local action on pulmonary bed, and shift of systemic blood into the pulmonary circuit, etc. Presumably, the action is not related to sympathetic nervous control since the vasoconstrictor effect of hypoxia can be observed in man with a total sympathectomy.

In summary then, experimental evidence demonstrates that human pulmonary vessels can constrict and dilate, but these functions have have been shown only under extreme conditions. Hence, the role played by active vasomotion in controlling the pulmonary circulation is not known, and since the present methods available for such study have serious limitations, this problem will be difficult to solve.

## REFERENCES

ALEXANDER, R. S. Transformation of the arterial pulse wave between the aortic arch and the femoral artery. Am. J. Physiol., 1949, 158, 287.

ALEXANDER, R. S. Standing wave components in arterial pulses of hypothermic dogs. Circulation Res., 1958, 6, 580.

BRAMWELL, J. C. AND HILL, A. V. The velocity of the pulse wave in man., Proc. Roy. Soc. 93B, 298, 1922.

BRECHER, G. A. Mechanism of venous flow under different degrees of aspiration. Am. J. Physiol., 1952, 169, 423.

BRECHER, G. A. AND HUBAY, C. A. Pulmonary blood flow and venous return during spontaneous respiration. Circulation Res., 1955, 3, 210.

BRIGDEN, W., HOWARTH, S., AND SHARPEY-SCHAFER, E. P. Postural changes in the peripheral blood flow of normal subjects with observations on vasovagal fainting reactions as a result of tilting, the lordotic posture, pregnancy and spinal anesthesia. Clin. Sc., 1950, 9, 79.

CHIDSEY, C. A., FRITZ, H. W., ZOCCHE, G. P., HIMMELSTEIN, A., AND COURNAND, A. Effect of acetylcholine on the distribution of pulmonary blood flow in chronic pulmonary emphysema. Malattie Cardiovascolari, 1960, 1, 15.

COURNAND, A. Some aspects of the pulmonary circulation in normal man and in chronic cardiopulmonary diseases. Circulation, 1950, 2, 641.

CULBERTSON, J. W., WILKINS, R. W., INGELFINGER, AND BRADLEY, S. E. The effect of the upright posture upon hepatic blood flow in normotensive and hypertensive subjects. J. Clin. Invest., 1951, 30, 305.

DOYLE, J. T., PATTERSON, J. L., WARREN, I. V., AND DETWEILER, D. K. Observations on the circulation of domestic cattle. Circulation Res., 1960, 8, 4.

DuBois, A. B., AND MARSHALL, R. Measurements of pulmonary capillary blood flow and gas exchange throughout the respiratory cycle in man. J. Clin. Invest., 1957, 36, 1566.

FISHMAN, A. P., McCLEMENT, J., HIMMELSTEIN, A., AND COURNAND, A. Effects of acute anoxia on the circulation and respiration in patients with chronic pulmonary disease studied during the "steady state." J. Clin. Invest., 1952, 31, 770.

FRANKLIN, D. L., ELLIS, R. M., AND RUSHMER, R. F. Aortic blood flow in dogs during treadmill exercise. J. Appl. Physiol., 1959, 14, 809.

FRITTS, H. W., HARRIS, P., CLAUSS, R. H., ODELL, J. E., AND COURNAND, A. The effect of acetylcholine on the human pulmonary circulation under normal and hypoxic conditions. J. Clin. Invest., 1958, 37, 99.

FRY, D. L., NOBLE, F. W., AND MALLOS, A. J. An electric device for instantaneous and continuous computation of aortic blood velocity. Circul. Res., 1957, 5, 75.

GAUER, O. H., HENRY, J. P. AND SIEKER, H. O. Changes in central venous pressure after moderate hemorrhage and transfusion in man. Circulation Res., 1956, 4, 79.

GAUER, O. H. AND SIEKER, H. O. The continuous recording of central venous pressure changes from an arm vein. Circulation Res., 1956, 4, 74.

GREEN, H. D., LEWIS, R. N., NICKERSON, N. D., AND HELLER, A. C. Blood flow, peripheral resistance and vascular tonus with observations on relationship between blood flow and cutaneous temperature. Am. J. Physiol., 1944, 141, 518.

GREGG, D. E., ECKSTEIN, R. W., AND FINEBERG, M. H. Pressure pulses and blood pressure values in unanesthetized dogs. Am. J. Physiol., 1937, 118, 399.

HADDY, F. J., FLEISHMAN, M., AND SCOTT, J. B., JR. Effect of change in air temperature upon systemic small and large vessel resistance. Circulation Res., 1957, 5, 58.

HAMILTON, W. F., WOODBURY, R. A., AND VOGT, E. Differential pressures in the lesser circulation of the unanesthetized dog. Am. J. Physiol., 1939, 125, 130.

HAMILTON, W. F. AND DOW, P. An experimental study of the standing waves in the pulse propagated through the aorta. Am. J. Physiol., 1939, 125, 48.

HELLEBRANDT, F. A., CRIGLER, E. F., AND KELSO, E. A. Variations in intramuscular pressure during postural and phasic contraction of human muscle. Am. J. Physiol., 1939, 126, 247.

HICKHAM, J. B. AND CARGILL, W. H. Effect of exercise on cardiac output and pulmonary arterial pressure in normal persons and in patients with cardiovascular disease and pulmonary emphysema. J. Clin. Invest., 1948, 27, 10.

HOLT, J. P. The effect of positive and negative intrathoracic pressure on peripheral venous pressure in man. Am. J. Physiol., 1943, 139, 208.

HUBAY, C. A., WALTZ, R. C., BRECHER, G. A., PRAGLIN, J., AND HINSON, R. A. Circulatory dynamics of venous return during positive-negative pressure respiration. Anesthesiology, 1954, 15, 445.

INOUYE, A. AND KOSAKA, H. A study with the electromagnetic flow meter of flow patterns in carotid and femoral arteries of rabbits and dogs. J. Physiol., 1959, 147, 209.

JOHNSON, V., HAMILTON, W. F., KATZ, L. N., AND WEINSTEIN, W. Studies of the dynamics of the pulmonary circulation. Am. J. Physiol., 1937, 120, 624.

KRAMER, K., OBAL, F., AND QUENSEL, W. Untersuchungen über den Muskelstoffwechsel des Warmbluters; die sauerstoffaufnahme des Muskels wahrend rhythmischer Tätigkeit. Arch. ges. Physiol., 1939, 241, 717.

LAGERLOF, H., ELIASCH, H., WERKO, L., AND BERGLUND, E. Orthostatic changes of the pulmonary and peripheral circulation in man. A preliminary report. Scandinav. J. Clin. & Lab. Invest., 1951, 3, 85.

LANDOWNE, M. Characteristics of impact and pulse wave propagation in brachial and radial arteries. J. Appl. Physiol., 1958, 12, 91.

LEVY, M. N., BRIND, S. H., BRANDLIN, F. R., AND PHILLIPS, F. A. The relationship between pressure and flow in the systemic circulation of the dog. Circulation Res., 1954, 2, 372.

McDONALD, D. A. The relation of pulsatile pressure to flow in arteries. J. Physiol., 1955, 127, 533.

MOTLEY, H. L., COURNAND, A., WERKO, L., HIMMELSTEIN, AND DRESDALE, D. The influence of short periods of induced acute anoxia upon pulmonary artery pressures in man. Am. J. Physiol., 1947, 150, 315.

OCHSNER, A., COLP, R., AND BURCH, G. E. Normal blood pressure in the superficial venous system of man at rest in the supine position. Circulation, 1951, 3, 674.

PAGE, E. B., HICKHAM, J. B., SIEKER, H. O., McINTOSH, H. D., AND PRYOR, W. W. Reflex venomotor activity in normal persons and in patients with postural hypotension. Circulation, 1955, 2, 262.

PATEL, D. J. AND BURTON, A. C. Active constriction of small pulmonary arteries in the rabbit. Circulation Res., 1957, 5, 620.

POLLACK, A. A. AND WOOD, E. H. Venous pressure in the saphenous vein at the ankle in man during exercise and changes of posture. J. Appl. Physiol., 1949, 1, 649.

RILEY, R. L., HIMMELSTEIN, A., MOTLEY, H. L., WEINER, H. M., AND COURNAND, A. Studies of pulmonary circulation at rest and during exercise in normal individuals and in patients with chronic pulmonary disease. Am. J. Physiol., 1948, 152, 372.

RYAN, J. M., STACY, R. W., AND WATMAN, R. N.

Role of abdominal aortic branches in pulse wave contour genesis. Circulation Res., 1956, 4, 676.

SHIPLEY, R. E., GREGG, D. E., AND SCHROEDER, E. F. An experimental study of flow patterns in various peripheral arteries. Am. J. Physiol., 1943, 138, 718.

SPENCER, M. P., JOHNSTON, F. R., AND DENISON, A. B., JR. Dynamics of the normal aorta: "inertiance" and "compliance" of the arterial system which transforms the cardiac ejection pulse. Circulation Res., 1958, 6, 491.

SPENCER, M. P. AND DENISON, A. B., JR. The aortic flow pulse as related to differential pressure. Circulation Res., 1956, 4, 476.

STEAD, E. A., WARREN, J. V., MERRILL, A. J., AND BRANNON, E. S. The cardiac output in male subjects as measured by the technique of right atrial catheterization. Normal values with observations on the effect of anxiety and tilting. J. Clin. Invest., 1945, 24, 326.

SWANN, H. G., MONTGOMERY, A. U., DAVIS, J. C., AND MICKLE, E. R. A method for rapid measurement of intrarenal and other tissue pressures. J. Exper. Med., 1950, 92, 625.

WADE, O. L., COMBES, B., CHILDS, A. W., WHEELER, H. O., COURNAND, A., AND BRADLEY, S. E. The effect of exercise on the splanchnic blood flow and splanchnic blood volume in normal man. Clin. Sci. 1956, 15, 457.

WALLACE, G. M. AND STEAD, E. A. Spontaneous pressure elevations in small veins and effects of epinephrine and cold. Circulation Res., 1957, 5, 651.

WARREN, J. V., PATTERSON, J. L., DOYLE, J. T., GAUER, O. H., KEEN, E. N., MC GREGOR, M., AND GOETZ, R. H. Circulation and respiration in the giraffe. Circulation, 1957, 16, 947.

WARREN, J. V., BRANNON, E. S., WEENS, H. S., AND STEAD, E. A. Effect of increasing blood volume and right atrial pressure on circulation of normal subjects by intravenous infusion. Am. J. Med., 1948, 4, 193.

WARREN, J. V., BRANNON, E. S., STEAD, E. A., AND MERRILL, A. J. The effect of venesection and the pooling of blood in the extremities on the atrial pressure and cardiac output in normal subjects with observations on acute circulatory collapse in 3 instances. J. Clin. Invest., 1945, 24, 337.

WEISSLER, A. M., WARREN, J. V., ESTES, E. H., McINTOSH, H. C., AND LEONARD, J. J. Vasodepressor syncope. Factors influencing cardiac output. Circulation, 1957, 15, 875.

WEISSLER, A. M., LEONARD, J. J., AND WARREN, J. V. Effects of posture and atropine on cardiac output. J. Clin. Invest., 1957, 36, 1656.

WILKINS, R. W., CULBERTSON, J. W., AND INGELFINGER, F. J. The effect of splanchnic sympathectomy in hypertensive patients upon estimated hepatic blood flow in the upright as contrasted with the horizontal position. J. Clin. Invest., 1951, 30, 312.

WOMERSLEY, J. R. Method for the calculation of velocity, rate of flow and viscous drag in arteries when the pressure gradient is known. J. Physiol., 1955, 127, 553.

WOODBURY, R. A. AND HAMILTON, W. F. Blood pressure studies in small animals. Am. J. Physiol., 1937, **119**, 663.

*Monographs and Reviews*

BRECHER, G. Venous return. Grune & Stratton, Inc., New York, 1956.

BURCH, G. E. A primer on venous pressure. Lea & Febiger, Philadelphia, 1950.

BURTON, A. C. The relation between pressure and flow in the pulmonary bed. Pulmonary circulation, Grune & Stratton, Inc., New York, 1958.

COURNAND, A. Control of the pulmonary circulation in normal man. In Circulation. Proceedings of the Harvey Tercentenary Congress, London, 1957. Edited by J. McMichael. Blackwell Scientific Publications, Oxford, 1958.

DuBois, A. B. Instantaneous pulmonary capillary blood flow. Pulmonary circulation, Grune & Stratton, Inc., New York, 1958.

FRITTS, H. W. AND COURNAND, A. Physiological factors regulating pressure, flow and distribution of blood in the pulmonary circulation. Pulmonary circulation, Grune & Stratton, Inc., New York, 1958.

GAUER, O. H. AND HENRY, P. Beitrag zur homeostase des extra-arteriellen Kreislaufs. Volumenregulation als unabhangiger physiologischer Parameter. Klin. Wchnschr., 1956, **34**, 356.

GAUER, O. H. Homeostasis of the extra-arterial circulation. First International Symposium on Submarine and Space Medicine, New London, Connecticut, 1958.

GREGG, D. E. Homeostasis of the arterial circulation. First International Symposium on Submarine and Space Medicine, New London, Connecticut, 1958.

HADDY, F. J. Vasomotion in systemic arteries, small vessels and veins determined by direct resistance measurements. Minnesota Med., 1958, **41**, 162.

HEYMANS, C. The regulation of blood pressure and heart rate. American Lecture Series ♯43, Charles C Thomas, Publisher, Springfield, Ill., 1950.

LANDIS, E. M. AND HORTENSTINE, J. C. Functional significance of venous blood pressure. Physiol. Rev., 1950, **30**, 1.

McWILLIAMS, J. A. Blood pressures in man under normal and pathological conditions. Physiol. Rev., 1925, **5**, 203.

OPDYKE, D. F., ALEXANDER, R. S., REMINGTON, J. W., PETERSEN, L. H., HUGGINS, R. A., AND SMITH, E. L. Panel discussion: interpretation and significance of alterations in central pulse form. Fed. Proc., 1952, **11**, 732.

RUSHMER, R. F. Cardiac diagnosis, W. B. Saunders Company, Philadelphia, 1955.

Sjostrand, T. Significance of the volume and distribution of the blood for the circulation. Physical Rev., 1953, **33**, 202.

WETTERER, E. Die Wirkung der Herztätigkeit auf die Dynamik des Arteriensystems. Verhandl. deutsch. Gesellsch. für Kreislaufforschung, 1956, **22**, 26.

WETTERER, E. Flow and pressure in the arterial system. Their hemodynamic relationship and the principles of their measurement. Minnesota Med., 1954, **37**, 77.

WIGGERS, C. J. Circulatory dynamics. Grune and Stratton, Inc., New York, 1952.

WOOD, P. Diseases of the heart and circulation. Ed. 2, J. B. Lippincott Company, Philadelphia, 1956.

# 23

# THE OUTPUT OF THE HEART AND THE
# REGULATION OF ITS ACTION

## Nervous Control of the Heart

### THE HEART RATE

In general, the rate of the heart bears an inverse relationship to the size of the animal, and a direct relationship to the metabolic rate. The heart rate in the canary, for example, is in the neighborhood of 1000 beats per minute, whereas that of the elephant is about 25. The average rate in adult man is around 70 per minute, but there is a rather wide variation between individuals, a rate considerably below or above this average being not uncommon. Muscular training tends to reduce the cardiac rate; athletes not infrequently having a pulse rate between 50 and 60. On the other hand, a rate between 80 and 90 is sometimes seen in other healthy persons. The rate diminishes progressively from birth, when it is around 130 per minute, to adolescence, but increases slightly again in old age. Among physiological conditions which temporarily increase the heart rate are *muscular exercise, emotional excitement and high environmental temperature*. It also increases somewhat during *digestion*. The rate is lowered during *sleep* (55 to 60). Among pathological conditions which cause an increase in cardiac rate are *hemorrhage, surgical shock, hyperthyroidism, fever* (an increase of 10 beats per 1° F. rise in temperature) and certain *cardiac arrhythmias*, e.g., paroxysmal tachycardia, atrial fibrillation, etc.

*Tachycardia* and *bradycardia* are general terms used to denote, respectively, any considerable increase in heart rate above, or reduction below the normal average.

Ordinarily the heart rate is not under voluntary control. However, several instances have been reported of individuals possessing the power of voluntarily accelerating the heart rate. In one such case the effect was brought about apparently through the discharge of impulses along accelerator nerves since other sympathetic manifestations, e.g., vasoconstriction, glycosuria and dila-

tion of the pupils accompanied the increased pulse rate.

The heart, as we know, beats rhythmically after its complete separation from the central nervous system, but in the intact animal this automatic action is under the continuous influence of nervous impulses. The nervous mechanism comprises groups of nerve cells in the medulla—the *cardiac centers*; various *afferent pathways* along which impulses are conveyed to these centers from numerous regions of the body; and the *vagus* and *accelerator* or *augmentor* nerves which transmit impulses from the centers to the heart.

### THE VAGUS NERVES

The vagus nerves are cardio-inhibitory. This action was discovered by the Weber brothers in 1845. They convey fibers, belonging to the parasympathetic division of the involuntary nervous system, from a center in the medulla (*cardio-inhibitor center*) to the special tissues of the heart. The medullary center was located by Miller and Bowman in the dorsal nucleus of the vagus situated in the floor of the 4th ventricle. Weak electrical stimulation of this area produced slowing of the beat, and stronger currents, complete arrest of the heart. The cardiac fibers of the vagus separate from the trunk of the nerve in the neck between the origins of its superior and inferior laryngeal branches. Intermingling with fibers of the accelerator nerves they enter into the formation of the deep and superficial cardiac plexuses whence they are continued to the atrial muscle. Here they make connection with ganglion cells. Postganglionic fibers pass to the specialized tissue of the sino-atrial and atrioventricular (A-V) nodes where they are prolonged between the muscle fibers. They form a rich plexus and are seen to end as ring-shaped or club-shaped structures ("boutons") upon the fibers of the specialized tissue. Many postganglionic fibers do not enter the nodal tissues but terminate in the atrial myocardium proper. Those which enter the atrioventricular node do not extend beyond the upper part of the bundle. None has been found to terminate in the ventricular myocadium (Nonidez), or in the lower part of the specialized conducting system.

### THE ACCELERATOR OR AUGMENTOR NERVES

The accelerator fibers were described by Von Bezold in 1863. They belong to the thoraco-lumbar division of the involuntary nervous system and arise from cells situated in the lateral horns of the upper thoracic segments of the spinal cord. These cells constitute a spinal cardio-accelerator center. The preganglionic fibers enter the gangliated cord of the sympathetic to connect with cells in the *inferior, middle* and *superior cervical ganglia.* In many animals and also often in the human subject the inferior cervical and the first thoracic ganglia are fused into an irregularly shaped structure called the *stellate ganglion* from which accelerator fibers pass directly to the heart. The heart also receives accelerator fibers *directly* from the sympathetic chain as far down as the 4th or 5th thoracic ganglion. In order, therefore, to remove all accelerator influence from the heart it is necessary, as shown by Cannon, Lewis and Britton, and by others in man, to interrupt these connections as well as to remove the stellate ganglia. The axons of the cells of the cervical ganglia (postganglionic fibers) form the *inferior, middle* and *superior cardiac nerves* (fig. 23.1). These fibers, especially those

forming the nerves of the right side, terminate in the sino-atrial node. Those of the left side are distributed mainly to the A-V node and bundle. According to Nonidez, the sympathetic efferent fibers which reach the heart are contained mainly in the middle cardiac nerve. The superior cardiac nerve is distributed to the large arteries at the base of the heart while the inferior cardiac nerve is mainly afferent. The spinal accelerator center is subordinate to higher centers. The precise locations of the latter are not known, but the experiments of Beattie, Brow and Long indicate the presence of a center in the posterior hypothalamic region; and Green and Hoff observed changes in heart rate, in blood pressure and in limb and kidney volumes upon stimulating the cerebral cortex (motor and premotor areas) in cats and monkeys. A medullary center also probably exists.

### TONIC ACTION OF NERVES

The separate effects of stimulation of the vagal and sympathetic fibers to the heart on the heart rate, conduction, distensibility and contractility of the heart have been considered in chapter 14. But their normal tone, reflex activation and control, and their interplay or balance remain to be considered.

*A. The tone of the vagus.* During the normal life of the animal the vagus nerves exert a continuous restraint upon the action of the heart. In other words the vagus, or rather the cardio-inhibitory center, possesses tone, impulses passing from it in a continuous stream to the heart. This effect, which may be compared to the action of a dragging brake, can be readily demonstrated in animals by cutting or freezing the nerves. The heart's action then immediately becomes greatly accelerated. The increase in rate following the removal of the vagal influence also occurs though the stellate ganglia have been previously excised; the result therefore cannot be due to an increased action of the accelerator nerves. The tonic action of the vagus nerves may be annulled by means of atropine, $\frac{1}{20}$ to $\frac{1}{15}$ grain being required in man to completely abolish their effects, the heart rate then increasing to 150 or 180 per minute. The difference between this rate and the normal resting rate of 70 per minute, therefore, represents the vagal effect which is being constantly exerted under ordinary circumstances. Various conditions, physiological and pathological, alter the tone of the vagus center. The tone is naturally higher in some species, e.g., the dog, which is

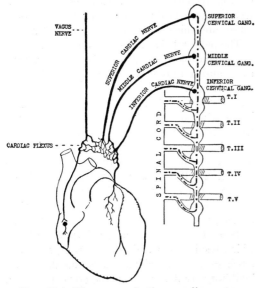

FIG. 23.1. Diagram of the cardiac nerves. *Broken lines* = preganglionic sympathetic fibers.

capable of feats of endurance, than in others, e.g., the domestic rabbit. It also shows individual variations in man, athletes usually showing a higher tone than those who lead sedentary lives.

Vagal tone is apparently reflex in nature and dependent upon afferent impulses flowing to the vagus center especially along the sinus and aortic nerves. Section of these nerves causes an increase in heart rate and little further acceleration occurs as a rule when the vagi themselves are subsequently severed.

*B. Accelerator tone.* The accelerators also exert a tonic action. This has been demonstrated by excision of the stellate ganglia when the heart rate is reduced. Gasser and Meek, for example, found that when the ganglia were removed but the vagi left intact, an immediate and marked fall in rate (about 40 per cent) occurred; further slowing occurred later which was attributed to a rise in vagal tone. Slowing of the rate is produced, however, by excision of the ganglia, even though vagotomy has been performed previously; this fact of course precludes the possibility of the immediate reduction in rate following excision of the stellate ganglia being due to increased vagal tone. Chapman and associates observed slowing of the heart in man after bilateral excision of the sympathetic ganglia from the 2nd to the 5th thoracic ganglia inclusive. In some instances a reduced cardiac response to exercise was observed after this operation.

Bronk and his associates have demonstrated the existence of accelerator tone in the cat by recording the action potentials from nerves leaving the stellate ganglion. A fairly continuous discharge of impulses at a rate of from 5 to 20 per second was observed. Stimulation of the central end of an afferent nerve (e.g., sinus or aortic nerve) caused a discharge of impulses in the efferent fibers of the same frequency as those in the afferent impulses.

### Cardiac Reflexes

Under ordinary conditions, the activities of the cardio-inhibitory and cardio-accelerator centers which result in the continuous discharge of impulses along the corresponding cardiac nerves are in turn dependent to a very large extent, if not entirely, upon the reception of impulses by afferent paths. In other words, the maintenance of the tone of the centers, and so of the normal resting rate of the heart, and the alterations in rate which occur under various physiological conditions are in large measure either reflex in nature or due to impulses received from cerebral

centers. The impulses which stream into the nervous centers arise in all parts of the body, the heart itself included. By these influences the tone of either center may be exalted or depressed, and corresponding changes produced in the cardiac rate. If the cardiac vagus on one side be cut and its central portion (i.e., the end leading to the brain) stimulated, a reflex through the cardio-inhibitory center and the opposite vagus occurs which alters the cardiac rate. The nature of the change in rate—whether acceleration or inhibition—which will result from stimulation of the central end of the vagus or of most other afferent nerves cannot always be foretold. Reflex slowing of the pulse can usually be demonstrated in the human subject by pressure upon the eyeball at the outer canthus (oculo-cardiac reflex), or by the stimulation of nasal branches of the 5th nerve. Stimulation of afferent fibers in the respiratory passages as by the inhalation of irritating vapors, e.g., anesthetics, is particularly likely to cause reflex inhibition of the heart. Extrasystoles and bradycardia have been demonstrated electrocardiographically in man during abdominal operations, the irregularities being the consequence, apparently, of visceral stimulation. Excitation of the central end of various peripheral nerves, e.g., the sciatic, causes reflex changes in the pulse rate. In these last instances acceleration is more readily obtained than inhibition. The irradiation of impulses on to the cardiac centers from the cerebral centers, e.g., from the motor area at the commencement of muscular exercise or from regions concerned with emotional manifestations, are held responsible for the changes in pulse rate which occurs under these conditions.

The pulse rate is generally inversely related to the arterial blood pressure, a rise or fall in pressure causing respectively a decrease or increase in heart rate. These adjustments are believed to be subserved by (1) a reflex whose afferent limb is constituted of afferent vagal fibers (aortic nerve) ending in the aortic arch and heart, (2) a reflex in which the sinus nerve forms the afferent limb. These mechanisms have been considered in chapter 21. Presumably, such changes in heart rate are brought about not simply by an increase or a decrease in tone of one or the other cardiac centers, but by reciprocal variations in the tone of both. For example, the slowing of the heart which results from a rise in arterial pressure is much less pronounced if impulses from the cardio-inhibitory center have been prevented from reaching the heart by section of the vagi. After removal of the stellate ganglia, on the other hand, the cardiac response to a rise in blood pressure is reduced to a less extent. Obviously, the mechanisms concerned are not too well understood since a fall in blood pressure causes an increase in the rate of the heart even after it has been completely denervated.

## Cardiac Output and Cardiac Work

The most important external manifestation of the heart is its output of blood and the work it performs. These measurements are obtained by the Fick procedure, by the dilution principle, and in some instances, by the foreign gas methods (ch. 18).

### Definitions and General Considerations

The output of the heart per beat is spoken of as the *systolic discharge* or the *stroke volume*, and the output per minute as the *minute volume*. The value of the latter is simply the product of the stroke volume and the pulse rate (pulse rate times stroke volume = minute volume); the minute volume divided by the pulse rate, therefore, gives the stroke volume. The quantity of blood ejected by each beat of the left ventricle in the average healthy man during rest is from 70 to 80 cc. An equal quantity is, of course, discharged at the same time by the right ventricle, making a total for the whole heart of from 140 to 160 cc. The contents of the left ventricle are ejected against a much higher mean arterial pressure than the contents of the right; the mean pressure in the pulmonary artery being about $\frac{1}{6}$ of that in the aorta. The minute volume is expressed in terms of one ventricle. The output of one ventricle obviously represents the quantity of blood flowing through the lungs, or through the systemic vessels, during the same period. An adult of sedentary occupation pumps at least 5500 liters of blood through his body daily—from left to right ventricle through the systemic vessels, and from right to left through the lungs.

The heart cavities are not believed to completely empty themselves during the resting state, but contain around 100 cc. of residual blood at the end of systole. Each ventricle has a normal capacity of approximately 200 cc.

The portion of the energy output of the left ventricle that appears as useful work can be roughly calculated from the product of mean aortic blood pressure and cardiac output. The work done by the right ventricle can be similarly calculated except that the mean pressure is that in the pulmonary artery. The end diastolic pressure in the left or right ventricle should be subtracted from the measured aortic pressure or pulmonary arterial pressure since the end diastolic ventricular pressure does not have its origin from ventricular systole. Preferably, the transmural pressure should be subtracted but this is difficult to obtain in man. Ordinarily the end diastolic pressure is small approximating up to 5 mm. Hg in the right ventricle and up to 10 mm. Hg in the left ventricle. However, under some conditions of heavy ventricular loading such as an A-V fistula, or congestive heart failure, the value may reach 30 to 40 mm. Hg, and hence, the correction is important. The simpler calculation also assumes that the velocity factor is but a very small part of the external work of the heart. Normally, this is of the order of 1 to 2 per cent. When cardiac output is quite large in the presence of a decreased systemic pressure, or especially if aortic or pulmonary stenosis occurs, the kinetic factor can be up to 50 per cent of the cardiac work. For a somewhat precise evaluation of the work done by either ventricle, the following formula may be used,

$$W = QR + \frac{wV^2}{2g}$$

in which W is work in gram meters; Q is cardiac output in cc. per beat; R is mean aortic blood pressure in meters Hg; w is mass of blood ejected in grams; and g is 9.8. The mean velocity (V) during systolic ejection in centimeters per second at the root of the aorta or pulmonary artery is equal to stroke volume (cross sectional area in square centimeters at the aortic or pulmonary root times the duration of ejection). The aortic or pulmonic diameter is obtained from cadavers. The kinetic factor is assumed to be the same for both ventricles since the cross-sectional areas of aorta and pulmonary artery are about the same.

To better compare cardiac output and cardiac work in different individuals, the values are generally expressed in terms of surface area and are spoken of as flow or work indices. Thus, the cardiac index (CI), stroke volume index (SVI), cardiac work index (CWI), and stroke work index (SWI) are obtained by dividing the cardiac output, stroke volume, cardiac work, and stroke work by the surface area of the body. An average surface area is 1.7 square meters. Normal values for the right and left heart obtained in man during catheterization studies are in Table 23.1.

TABLE 23.1

*Hemodynamic studies in man of the right and left heart during rest and exercise both at sea level and at high altitude*

| Condition | Treadmill Exercise kg. m./min./m.² | Heart Rate | Mean BP* mm. Hg | CI* L./min. | TPR* (Press.)/(Flow) | CWI* kg.-m./min./m.² | SVI* cc. | SWI* gm. m./min. m.² | O² usage L./min. m.² | A-VO₂ cc./100 cc. |
|---|---|---|---|---|---|---|---|---|---|---|
| Right heart (average surface area, 1.83 m.²) | | | | | | | | | | |
| Rest | | 73 | 16 | 3.4 | 2.6 | 0.63 | 47 | 8 | 0.132 | 4.1 |
| Exercise | Leg movements | 152 | 35 | 9.2 | 2 | 3.94 | 67 | 26 | 1.047 | 11.32 |
| Left heart (average surface area, 1.74 m.²) Lima | | | | | | | | | | |
| Rest | | 81 | 92 | 2.8 | 19 | 3.6 | 33 | 41 | | |
| Exercise | 704 to 986 | 163 | 109 | 8.1 | 8 | 12.1 | 51 | 75 | 1.353 | 16.9 |
| Left heart (average surface area, 1.62 m.²) Morococha | | | | | | | | | | |
| Rest | | 83 | 101 | 4.2 | 15 | 6.0 | 51 | 72 | 0.209 | 5.7 |
| Exercise | 490 to 580 | 156 | 118 | 7.5 | 10 | 12.3 | 49 | 79 | 1.072 | 13.9 |
| Exercise | 695 to 749 | 175 | 125 | 15.2 | 5 | 26.4 | 88 | 151 | | |

* BP, blood pressure; CI, cardiac index; TPR, total peripheral resistance; CWI, cardiac work index; SVI, stroke volume index; SWI, stroke work index.

THE OUTPUT OF THE HEALTHY HEART. NORMAL STANDARDS. PHYSIOLOGICAL VARIATIONS. The minute output of the heart under basal conditions[1] for the average size male adult is about 5.5 liters, and the CI is 3.2 liters. The CI is slightly lower for the female and considerably higher for children. Cardiac output can be quite variable in the same person from day to day unless extreme precautions are used to maintain the resting state.

A. Conditions in which cardiac output is not changed. The cardiac output is apparently the same when a person is asleep as when he is awake and in the horizontal position. It is unaffected by menstruation and by moderate variations in the external temperature although it may be increased up to 30 per cent at environmental temperatures above 30°C., or by low temperatures that are associated with shivering. The native indigenous to high altitude undergoes considerable acclimatization by changes in his cardiovascular and respiratory systems so that at altitudes of, at least, 15,000 feet, the cardiac output is normal as are his heart rate and systemic blood pressure and systemic A-VO₂.

[1] Body recumbent, at rest and at 20°C. for 15 to 20 minutes and 12 hours after food and drink.

However, the slightest exertion will increase his cardiac output which will be considerably higher in the sitting rather than in the reclining position, whereas in persons indigenous to sea level, such change in posture at sea level may decrease cardiac output.

B. Conditions in which cardiac output decreases. Normal. The cardiac output is decreased about 30 per cent in changing from the recumbent to the upright posture.

Pathological states. Atrial fibrillation and a very rapid heart rate may reduce cardiac output up to 50 per cent. In complete heart block and with an efficient myocardium, the output may be approximately normal, but when this exists in the presence of coronary sclerosis, myocardial degeneration, or after open heart surgery (cutting of the A-V bundle), the output may be greatly reduced. In other subjects, although the output at rest is normal, the inability of the heart to accelerate properly prevents an adequate output during muscular exertion. In congestive heart failure, cardiac output very often is reduced, and the increase in cardiac output which normally follows muscular effort does not occur or is slight. This type of failure is to some extent compensated for by a greater increase in the systemic A-VO$_2$ difference than occurs in healthy persons doing a similar amount of external work.

*C. Conditions which increase cardiac output.* Cardiac output may be increased 50 to 100 per cent by anxiety and excitement and, at least, 30 per cent by eating (during first 3 hours). Anxiety, apprehension, and excitement may increase cardiac output greatly presumably through the release and action of catecholamines. Pregnancy (in the later months) and low oxygen or high CO$_2$ in the inspired air are conditions which increase cardiac output up to 100 per cent. Presumably, the elevation is again related to the high level of circulating catecholamines which stimulate the myocardium. If prolonged or too severe, the output declines due to the injurious effect upon the heart muscle. In maximum exercise the cardiac output may be increased ninefold.

*D. Effects of drugs upon the cardiac output. Adrenaline* and *histamine* increase the oxygen consumption and the cardiac output; the effect upon the minute volume is, however, proportionately greater than that upon the oxygen consumption. *Acetylcholine,* whose effects in general are very evanescent, causes a slight increase in the minute volume. A decided rise in the cardiac output is produced by *nitrites* which, like acetylcholine, cause arteriolar dilation. The increase in the cardiac output caused by nitrites is probably a compensatory effect of the lower peripheral resistance, whereby the blood pressure is maintained near the normal level. *Digitalis* produces no immediate effect upon the minute volume in normal persons. In subjects with congestive heart failure and atrial fibrillation the output is as a rule, though not invariably, increased as the cardiac condition improves. *Strophanthin* acts similarly to digitalis. *Atropine* which increases the heart rate to 150 or 180 beats per minute does not increase, as a rule, the cardiac output. *Alcohol* in moderate dosage (35 cc.) causes no more than a slight rise in the cardiac output.

### Regulation of Cardiac Output and Cardiac Work during Exercise and Excitement

Reliable determinations of cardiac output and cardiac work during exercise and excitement are not too numerous. For mild to moderate exercise, measurements are generally made by the Fick procedure with the subject in the supine position and with indwelling cardiac catheters while he pushes bicycle pedals with his feet operating against a mechanical frictional resistance. For heavy as well as light external work, cardiac output is determined with the dilution technique while the subject runs on a treadmill. In strenuous exercise, the cardiac output may reach 35 to 45 liters per minute (table 23.1) or increase 7 to 9 times, while the body oxygen usage may increase 10 to 12 times.

Exercise and excitement make up the most important and continuous stress impacts of every day life. With present knowledge, it is impossible to portray sequentially the responses of the heart and circulation to these stimuli. A description of present information is, however, possible and some of it will stand a reasonable degree of integration. Many parameters of importance have been measured.

*A. Heart rate.* At the transition from rest to work, the pulse frequency rises very rapidly with heavy exercise, reaching levels of 160 to 180 per minute. During short exhaustive work, heart rates as high as 240 to 270 have been recorded in normal young people. This increase in heart rate is attributed to some form of autonomic control, but the mechanisms have not been established. The suspect Bainbridge reflex probably does not apply since this requires for its operation cardiac distension from increased venous return. As we shall see later, the heart is more apt to decrease in size. The tachycardia during exercise is attributed to a reflex through the carotid sinus and aortic baroreceptors resulting from a reduced arterial pressure as the result of vasodilation in the active muscle. However, the systemic blood pressure rises, not falls, during exercise. Finally, tachycardia is explained as related to direct regulation from the higher centers.

*B. Ventricular pressure-volume relations.* It has long been believed that the output of the heart is governed by its venous blood supply and that the increase in minute output during muscular work requires a regulating mechanism by which venous return is augmented. To effect this, the venous blood supply and pressure in the central veins must increase to such a height that the increased venous flow and ventricular filling pressure will dilate the heart and increase the length of its fibers during each diastole and by this stretch cause a greater ventricular response in the following systole.

A very large amount of experimental work has stressed this viewpoint. Howell and Donaldson (1884) first showed the intrinsic adaptation of the heart of the dog to an artificially increased venous return. Frank in 1895, in the frog heart, came to the conclusion that the magnitude of ventricular contraction is determined by the intra-cavity

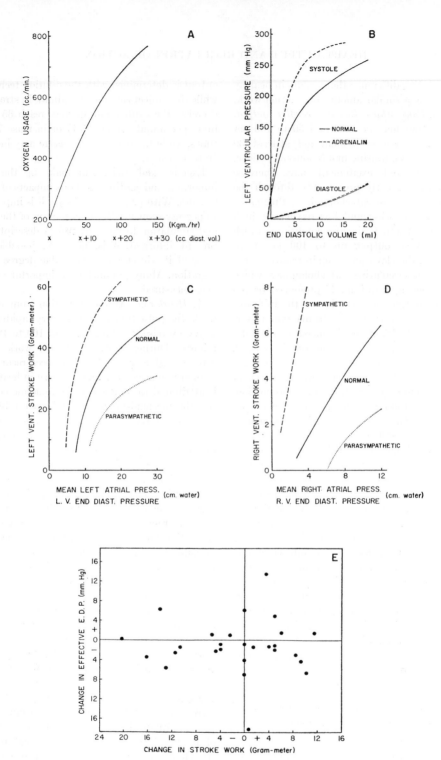

Fɪɢ. 23.2. Performance characteristics of the heart. A. Relation of $O_2$ usage to cardiac work and diastolic volume, i.e., the energy output of the heart, utilizing the "heart'lung preparation." (Starling and Visscher, J. Physiol., 1926, **62**, 243.) B. Pressure-volume function curves of the left ventricle in the open-chest dog. C. Effect of sympathetic and parasympathetic cardiac nerve stimulation on the relation between mean left atrial pressure and left ventricular stroke work and relation between left ventricular end diastolic pressure and left ventricular stroke work. Note lack of depressant effect of vagal stimulation upon end diastolic pressure-stroke work relations. (Sarnoff, Am. J. Cardiol. 1960, **5**, 579.) D. Response of right ventricular stroke work to mean right atrial pressure and to ventricular end diastolic pressure, and the effects of autonomic stimulation. The parasympathetic response is presented only for direction and does not indicate magnitude. (Sarnoff, Am. J. Cardiol. 1960, **5**, 579.) E. Change in effective end diastolic pressure (*EDP*) versus stroke work in the normal dog before and within 1 minute after exercise. (From Gregg, *et al.* Physiol. Rev., 1955, **35**, 130.)

volume at the end of systole. In 1914, Patterson, Piper and Starling measured the pressure and volume of both ventricles with a cardiometer in a heart-lung preparation of the dog while the venous return was passively and progressively increased by elevating a blood infusion reservoir connected to the right atrium. As the atrial pressure or ventricular filling pressure rose, the heart dilated and with each systole ejected a greater stroke volume at a greater ventricular pressure. This relationship called "Starling's Law of the Heart" indicated in a more formalized way that "the energy of contraction, however measured, is a function of the length of the muscle fibers," before contraction (fig. 23.2A). As these investigators indicated, this relationship is little more than the application to cardiac muscle of what was already known about skeletal muscle by Blix

in 1895 and Flick in 1882. This relationship of ventricular pressure and volume has been confirmed for the whole heart in the open chest dog and for the left ventricle in the open and closed chest dog (fig. 23.2B).

Because of the difficulty of estimating volume of a single ventricle and the relative ease of pressure measurement, attempts have been made to correlate mean atrial pressure or end diastolic pressure of the associated ventricle with the stroke volume or stroke work. An elegant experimental preparation for this type of study by Sarnoff is in figure 23.3. At the outset it might be expected on mechanical and other grounds that neither mean atrial pressure nor end diastolic pressure would be a reliable substitute for the ventricular volume as a guide to the response of the ventricle. First of all, the two pressures do not

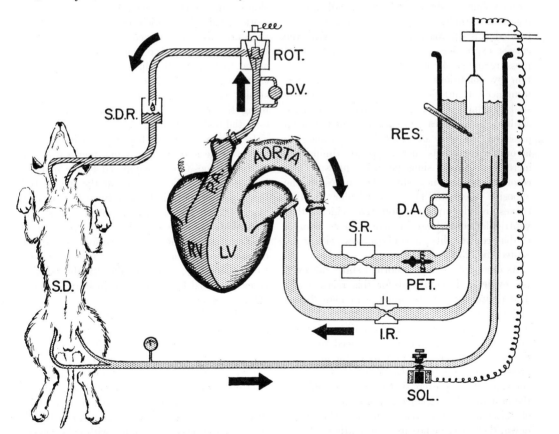

FIG. 23.3. Modern version by Sarnoff of isolated heart or heart-lung preparation. The coronary venous return is passed through a donor dog to maintain the blood at a normal biochemical environment before it is infused into the coronary system of the isolated heart. In older versions of the Starling isolated heart or heart-lung preparation in which the coronary venous blood circulating through the myocardial wall was simply reoxygenated and returned to the coronary system, progressive deterioration in performance characteristics developed within 60 to 90 minutes. *S-D*, support dog; *S-D-R*, support dog reservoir; *SOL*, solonoid valve electrically operated by microswitch at top of reservoir float; *S-R*, air-filled Starling resistance; *PET*, Potter electroturbinometer; *D-A*, arterial densitometer; *RES*, reservoir; *I.R.*, water-filled inflow Starling resistance; *D.V.*, venous densitometer; *ROT*, rotameter. (Sarnoff, *et al.* Am. J. Physiol., 1958, **192**, 141.)

always follow each other. They represent only an approximation to one of the variables that determine the end diastolic volume of a ventricle. The end diastolic volume is determined not only by the filling pressure but by its duration, the resistance of the ventricle to filling (its tone), and by the systolic volume of blood remaining in the heart after systole has ended (its systolic residue). Both the latter are independent of these pressures. Finally, the relationship between these pressures and the end diastolic volume is almost flat in the physiological range, i.e., it takes large changes in diastolic volume to induce almost no change in atrial or ventricular end diastolic pressure. Despite this, most experimenters found that under ordinary circumstances, mean atrial pressure or ventricular end diastolic pressure and the succeeding ventricular response of pressure, stroke volume or stroke work were usually altered together. Sarnoff, in particular, has greatly expanded this approach and has found that the curves expressing the relation of mean atrial pressure and stroke work are shifted in one direction by conditions improving myocardial performance (stimulation of cardiac fibers from the stellate ganglia, reflex stimulation of the myocardium by a decrease in carotid sinus perfusion pressure, injection of epinephrine), while unfavorable conditions such as vagal stimulation, increase in carotid sinus perfusion pressure and coronary insufficiency shift the curves in the opposite direction. These ventricular function curves provide important objective evidence that ventricular control can involve changes in myocardial contractility, a concept now widely accepted (fig. 23.2C and D).

As one approaches the normal state, however, the evidence is equivocal for this relationship. The peripheral venous pressure in man during heavy work (2.8 liters oxygen per minute) can increase up to 7 mm. Hg. Variations of filling pressure, however, cannot be deduced from peripheral venous pressure because of the unknown pressure gradient from the periphery to central veins. In the dog exercising on the treadmill, in the human following injection of a small amount of epinephrine or exercising mildly while lying down, there may be no direct correlation between the increased cardiac output or cardiac work and the atrial or ventricular end diastolic pressure. On the other hand, in subjects with an artificial pneumothorax, a linear relation was found between effective or transmural atrial pressure and stroke volume with an increase of 2 mm. Hg providing an increase in stroke volume of 40 per

cent. This relationship also apparently holds in patients with high output failure and very large ventricular volumes.

*C. Ventricular volume and stroke volume.* As already indicated, comparisons of direct measurements of ventricular volume with pressure or with stroke volume or stroke work have not been made in the normal state in which the aggregate complications of venous resistance, intrathoracic pressure, vascular volume, changing heart rate, neurogenic factors, and humoral influences exist. However, highly suggestive evidence has been obtained by estimating the ventricular volume in systole and diastole. In dogs, this has been done by measuring the cyclic changes in an external ventricular dimension (using the mercury filled tube of Whitney or the sonar technique); or by measuring a changing internal ventricular dimension by an induction gauge. A limited amount of work is available in which stroke volume has been simultaneously determined by the sonar or electromagnetic flow meter technique applied to the aorta. In humans, the diastolic volume has been estimated from the X-ray silhouette while the stroke volume has been directly determined using the Fick or dye dilution principle. The essential findings follow:

In man and the dog, the left ventricular diastolic volume and stroke volume increase in the recumbent position as compared to the more or less upright position. Concurrently the central blood pool or thoracic blood volume increases by about 400 cc. The cardiac output and heart rate change in opposite directions on alteration of position, i.e., in the supine position the cardiac output increases and the heart rate decreases. Correspondingly, assuming the upright position is accompanied by a reduction in heart size and stroke volume.

In the resting dog, an increase in venous return induced by a rapid infusion of blood or by displacing blood from the splanchnic area into the thorax by abdominal compression increases the left ventricular dimension without significantly altering stroke volume or stroke work. Excitement or startle or the anticipation of exercise just before treadmill activity can lead to a transitory increase in stroke volume with enlargement of the left ventricle.

Nonexhaustive exercise by healthy dogs and normal untrained human subjects may be accompanied by increased cardiac output, primarily resulting from tachycardia with little or no progressive increase in stroke volume as the level of exertion increases. Stroke volume during such exertion may only occasionally exceed the resting recumbent values in healthy dogs or untrained human subjects. Concurrently, the left ventricular dimension of the dog's heart remains the same or becomes smaller. However, trained athletes and patients with chronic volume loads such as in valvular insufficiency may increase cardiac output with a significant augmentation of stroke volume and a lesser degree of tachycardia. The relatively small hearts of untrained persons may show a tendency to reduce their diastolic size during exercise but the end diastolic size of the large hearts of athletes gets much smaller.

Evidence for increased contractility of the myocardium during exercise is in the increasing rate of tension development, rate of blood ejection and rate of relaxation as seen in the ventricular pressure curves and the aortic flow curves.

The preceding evidence suggests, but does not offer quite certain proof, that the fundamental property of cardiac muscle of a relation between end ventricular diastolic size and energy release is not dominant, but rather that in the normal dog and man, an increase in cardiac output during exercise is achieved mainly by an increase in heart rate with a constant or slightly increased stroke volume. A little reflection will indicate, however, that this is a self-regulating mechanism and cannot alone explain the observed changes in cardiac output. When the heart accelerates, the output per beat can be kept constant only if the venous inflow is adequate; only under such circumstances can the minute volume be increased. If, for example, the beat of the heart has occurred at the end of a period of rapid filling, i.e., before or at the moment that the heart chambers are filled, simply increasing the heart rate will cause the beat to fall earlier in the period of rapid filling. Reduction in the stroke volume in proportion to the increase in rate must result and no increase in the minute volume can, therefore, occur. At very rapid heart rates, as in paroxysmal tachycardia, a point is reached at which the heart does not relax sufficiently between beats to take on an adequate load of blood, and the minute volume is actually reduced.

The contribution which cardiac acceleration can make toward the minute volume is, therefore, strictly limited, for rates from 180 to 200 are about the maximums to which the healthy heart can be speeded up. This is only about $2\frac{1}{2}$ to 3 times the normal rate. With a constant stroke volume, therefore, cardiac acceleration could not increase the minute volume more than about 3 times. Yet reliable data have shown that the

cardiac output of untrained man doing strenuous exercise may increase ninefold (from 5 to 6 liters per min. at rest to 35 to 45 liters) and the oxygen consumption 12 times (from 250 cc. oxygen at rest to 3,000 cc.). In this circumstance, it must be concluded that the stroke volume increases 2 to 3 times (even at a maximum pulse rate) to account for up to 50 per cent of the cardiac output increase.

This is borne out by some of the data in table 23.1. The left ventricular response to treadmill exercise of natives of the Morococha, Peru region (elevation 14,900 ft.), and of natives of the Lima, Peru region (elevation 500 ft.), was studied at the elevation where they had always lived. It can be seen that at sea level, on the average, about half the increase in cardiac output comes from an increase in stroke volume from 41 to 75 cc. In one group at Morococha, exercising at a somewhat lower level of treadmill activity (490 to 580 kg.-m. per min. per m.²), the cardiac output and cardiac work were almost entirely explainable by the increase in heart rate and systemic blood pressure. The data in the second group at Morococha obtained at a higher level of treadmill activity (650 to 749 kg.-m. per min. per m.²) represents an attempt to stress the left ventricle to maximum external effort. Each of the five persons in this group stated at the end of the exercise that he was "completely exhausted." Two of them attained a cardiac output approximating 35 liters per min. and a stroke volume of about 200 cc. On an average, the stroke volume increased from 53 to 88 cc., and accounted for about 66 per cent of the increase in cardiac output.

The preceding also indicates that the cardiac size decreases in exercise. If the ventricle does become smaller during diastole and systole, then the heart must possess an adequate residual volume to effect an increased stroke volume or a constant stroke volume. Presumably, as already pointed out, the human heart at the end of systole contains about 400 cc. blood divided equally among the four cavities. This will give each ventricle a residual volume of 100 cc. in the recumbent position and about 45 cc. in the upright position and which is used as the ventricle becomes smaller with exertion. This diminishes the volume reserve of the ventricles in severe exercise. Presumably, it is replenished during each diastole from the blood volume in the thoracic pool. The mechanisms for this are not understood, but it can be demonstrated that the stroke volume is directly, and the heart rate indirectly, related to the volume of blood in this central compartment.

In summary, it can be stated that both changes in stroke volume and heart rate contribute significantly to regulation of cardiac output in man, but no firm conclusion can be drawn as to the relative role that stroke volume, heart rate and diastolic and systolic volumes play under various conditions of stress. Proper understanding will follow the development of adequate methodology for determining cyclic changes in ventricular volume and stroke volume in animals and especially in man.

*D. Body A-VO₂ difference.* Since the body oxygen usage can increase 12 times in exercise, it is important to know the mechanisms by which this amount of oxygen is supplied to the tissues. Continuous measurements of A-V $O_2$ difference from the onset of exercise have not yet been made and so it is not known how early these changes occur. The A-V $O_2$ difference is generally calculated from the body oxygen usage divided by the cardiac output, the former being determined by collection and oxygen analysis of the expired air and the cardiac output by the dilution technique, which does not require cardiac catheterization. The oxygen extraction rises but considerably more slowly than does the cardiac output, reaching in very heavy exercise a calculated maximum of 13 to 16 cc. per 100 cc. of blood. Since most of the increase in blood flow is presumably through the exercising muscle, this means that the oxygen extraction at times must be very nearly complete in the latter, a situation similar to that which has been observed in the heart muscle with maximal activity. In well trained subjects, it appears that the rise in A-V $O_2$ difference, as well as heart rate, are somewhat smaller, while the stroke volume is larger.

*E. Other hemodynamic variables in exercise.* In addition to the heart rate and stroke volume alterations occurring in exercise, many other changes are involved which may be mild or almost insignificant in light exercise, or which may be massive in strenuous activity (table 23.1). In the presence of heavy exercise and a very large increase in cardiac output, the CWI of the left ventricle may increase 4 times; the systemic blood pressure may increase considerably; the arterial pressure pulse may increase from 50 to 100 mm. Hg; the total peripheral resistance may decrease greatly. Presumably, the latter results mainly from vasodilation in the metabolically active beds for, since splanchnic blood flow in man is decreased in the presence of an elevated systemic

blood pressure, resistance in the splanchnic bed must be increased. In the pulmonary circulation, the arterial pressure rises moderately, while the resistance undergoes very little change. Finally, as pointed out earlier, the central venous, atrial, and ventricular end diastolic pressure do not necessarily increase. The alterations in many hemodynamic parameters during exercise is indicated in figure 23.4.

The cause, sequence and relative importance of these and other factors in the control of cardiac output during excitement and muscular exercise is still an enigma. Following the discovery of the baroreceptors, it was quite natural that they be invoked as the major mechanism controlling cardiac output during exercise. This was especially felt to be so since, as already mentioned, it has been established experimentally in the dog that if the blood pressure in the carotid sinus is lowered, there results reflexly an increased heart rate, decreased systemic peripheral resistance, increased peripheral venomotor tone, increased cardiac contractility (presumably *via* catecholamine release in the heart) and increased cardiac output. This presupposes a fall in arterial blood pressure caused by the vasodilation in the working muscles as the factor which initiates the hemodynamic changes resulting in an augmented cardiac output. However, intra-arterial blood pressure in man and dog at the transition from rest to work has been shown not to fall and, of course, later in the working period it increases. Another important experiment has indicated that the output of the heart in exercise is not related to the extent of vasodilation for, if pneumatic cuffs are placed on the exercising extremities of man so that about 50 per cent of the working musculature is cut off, the oxygen usage may be halved, but the cardiac output and heart rate are not decreased.

*F. Simulated exercise.* Finally, attempts have been made to simulate in the normal animal the cardiovascular events which are known to occur in exercise with the hope that one might serve as the proper experimental substitute for exercise. These include increased venous return (already considered), decreased peripheral resistance through injection of isoproterenol, injection of autonomic hormones, electrically induced tachycardias at rates existing in exercise, chronic stimulation of the sympathetic nerves to the heart and chronic stimulation of the central nervous system. Left ventricular performance during exercise could be fairly accurately reproduced by iso-

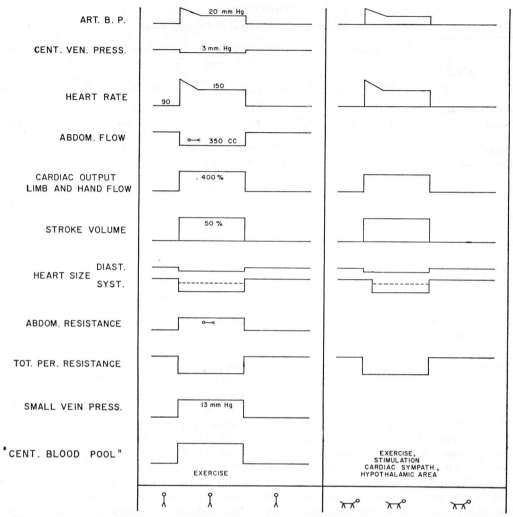

FIG. 23.4. *Left side,* hemodynamic responses in exercising man and *right side,* hemodynamic responses in the unanesthetized dog to exercise to stimulation of the cardiac sympathetic fibers and of the hypothalamic area. Dotted lines represent the less usual responses.

proterenol infusion and stimulation of the hypothalamic region in the unanesthetized dog.

REGIONAL DISTRIBUTION OF $O_2$ CONSUMPTION AND BLOOD FLOW. The preceding discussion indicates that despite much study of long familiar functions, their operation in the adjustments of oxygen and cardiac output to exercise is poorly understood. The response of oxygen usage and blood flow, of course, represents the average requirements of organs and regions of the body. At present, adequate knowledge is not available of the allocation of cardiac output in the resting or exercising animal, let alone man. Simultaneous measurements of flow through major regions or organs such as the heart, kidney, brain, liver, intestines, cannot be made in the same person at the same time. Even in the experimental animal, the only method available (based on the dilution principle) involves anesthesia and/or excitement so as to vitiate the interpretation of the findings. Despite this, table 23.2 is presented showing data on distribution of flow and oxygen consumption in resting and exercising man, obtained by different types of measurement by different observers on different subjects. (In some instances, values are extrapolated from animals). The values are certainly not absolute but the general pattern of distribution may be right. The kidney blood flow of 400 cc. per 100 grams of tissue is about 6 times greater than that of any other organ (nearest is the heart with a flow of 70 cc.). The heart per unit of tissue, on the other hand, uses consider-

TABLE 23.2

*Distribution of cardiac output and oxygen usage*

| Region | Weight | | Blood Flow | | | Oxygen Usage | | | O₂ Extraction | |
|---|---|---|---|---|---|---|---|---|---|---|
| | Kg. | % Total | L./min. | % Total | cc./100 gm./min. | cc./min. | % Total | cc./100 gm./min. | Venous O₂ cc./100 cc. blood | A-VO₂ |
| Total | 70 | 100 | 5.4 | 100 | | 250 | 100 | | 14.5 | 4.5 |
| Brain | 1.54 | 2.2 | 0.83 | 15 | 54 | 63 | 23 | 3.7 | 12.5 | 6.5 |
| Convulsion | | | 1.15 | 20 | 75 | | | | | |
| Heart | 0.33 | 0.5 | 0.22 | 4 | 70 | 23 | 9 | 7.0 | 7 | 12 |
| Liver, Intestines | 2.86 | 4.0 | 1.54 | 29 | 54 | 55 | 20 | 1.95 | 15 | 4.0 |
| Kidney | 0.33 | 0.5 | 1.43 | 27 | 430 | 20 | 7 | 6.0 | 17 | 2.0 |
| Skeletal muscle | 34.0 | 50.0 | 0.92 | 17 | 2.7 | 55 | 20 | 0.16 | 12.5 | 6.5 |
| Exercise | | | 35.0 | 80 | 100 | 2700 | 90 | 7.9 | 3 | 16.0 |

ably more oxygen than any other organ. Four organs—brain, heart, liver and intestine, and kidney, make up about 7 per cent of body weight but receive 65 to 70 per cent of the output of the heart and account for 60 per cent of the total oxygen used at rest. The skeletal muscles representing 50 per cent of body weight receive only 20 per cent of cardiac output at rest and account for only 15 per cent of body oxygen usage, but during exercise they may account for 80 to 90 per cent of the oxygen consumption and cardiac output. The brain which is only 2 per cent of body weight requires more than 20 per cent of the total oxygen used by the body and during convulsions (observed in monkeys), this fraction may increase to 40 per cent and the brain fraction of cardiac output from 14 to 20 per cent. Thus, the cardiovascular response is not limited to an adjustment of the cardiac pump, complicated as this may be. Certainly, real changes occur in the distribution of the output of the pump. There is, however, no integrated picture of the circulatory responses that occur and the underlying involvement of the central nervous system and peripheral mechanisms in the allocation of oxygen and cardiac output is unknown.

## Cardiac Reserve

HEART RATE, VENTRICULAR VOLUME, BLOOD
FLOW, CORONARY VENOUS O₂,
VENTRICULAR EFFICIENCY

Present knowledge of the reserves available to the heart to cope with various stress impacts permits little more than their enumeration. The potential reserves are its heart rate, its systolic and diastolic volume, its blood flow, the oxygen content of the body mixed venous blood, the, cardiac work, the changing efficiency of the heart, and possibly the stores of catecholamines.

The reserve in heart rate is about 130 to 140 beats per min., resulting in a maximum heart rate of 210. The reserve in stroke volume is 80 to 100 cc. since each ventricle normally contains about 150 to 170 cc., of which 60 to 70 cc. is ejected during systole. This figure is somewhat lower than the measured figure of 190 cc. for maximum stroke volume in Peruvian natives in the mountains, exercising to exhaustion on a treadmill. Attainment of such an increased stroke volume indicates an increased contractility of the myocardium. The reserve in blood flow approximates 30 liters per min., since maximum cardiac output is about 35 liters per min. in man working to exhaustion, and the resting cardiac output is about 5 liters. The potential reserve of oxygen within the body is about 900 cc. This is based upon the fact the body mixed venous blood contains 15 to 16 cc. oxygen per 100 cc. blood, and the blood volume is 5500 cc. However, neither normal persons nor persons with heart disease utilize this oxygen to the full. With maximum exertion, the oxygen extraction approximates 14 to 16 volumes per cent. This is supplemented by the ability of the human body to take up a maximum of 3000 cc. oxygen per min., or an excess of about 2700 cc. over that in the basal state. The reserve work of the heart is at about 75 kg. per min., since the maximum left ventricle work recorded is about 80 kg. per min., and the resting left ventricle work approximates 5 to 6 kg. per min.

In the whole body, the efficiency value for performing external work is fairly easily obtained by measuring the external work performed by the subject and dividing this by the energy equivalent of the difference between total body oxygen consumption and the oxygen usage of the body during rest. For the beating left ventricle, the efficiency is calculated in a similar way by dividing the external work of the ventricle by the difference between the energy equivalent of its oxygen usage while beating and while at rest. The external work of the ventricle is determined by the method already indicated; the oxygen usage of the left ventricle is determined from the product of coronary blood flow through the left myocardium and the coronary A-V oxygen difference. This is converted to kilogram meters of work per minute by multiplying by 2.057 which is the energy equivalent of 1 cc. oxygen in kg.-m.

Accurate determination of ventricular efficiency in man is not possible since left ventricular weight cannot be determined and, hence, total left ventricular flow is not available. In the unanesthetized dog, efficiencies of 31 per cent are reported. In the anesthetized dog with good cardiac output and systemic blood pressure, efficiencies have been found to vary from 7 to 54 per cent.

By definition, mechanical efficiency is work done per unit of energy output. The work of the heart is performed during the first part of the period of systole, but as in skeletal muscle, energy is released by the heart (oxygen used) when it is doing no work. Oxygen is used before, during, and after ventricular systole. A certain amount of oxygen can be used during the early part of systole from the onset of the elevation of intraventricular pressure to the time of opening of the pulmonary and aortic valves (isometric contraction period) during which time no blood is moved and no external mechanical work is done. Also, during diastole, oxygen can be used but the muscle fibers are relaxed and not shortening. The cardiac efficiency will, therefore, vary in part with the extent of contribution of the oxygen consumption during the resting and isometric contraction periods to the total oxygen usage. In general, the former will tend to lower the calculated efficiency at low levels of work and to increase efficiency as the work is increased.

Published data on myocardial efficiency are of particular interest because they do not include oxygen values for the resting ventricle or ventricle doing no external work. The myocardium takes up considerable oxygen in diastole as well as systole. With our present poor methodology, separation can only be made by measuring oxygen uptake, first in the beating heart during repetitive systoles and diastoles, and then in the relaxed heart or during prolonged diastole, and finally, obtaining the oxygen usage during systole by difference. To do this, the coronary arteries are perfused with blood under constant pressure while coronary A-V oxygen difference and left coronary inflow are measured continuously, first in the beating heart and then in the heart stopped by vagal stimulation or removal of an arterial pacemaker, until a new equilibrium had been established, usually within 20 to 25 seconds. The resting metabolism (absence of heart rate, blood pressure and cardiac output) during cardiac arrest approximates 2.5 ml. oxygen per 100 grams left ventricle per min., or about 25 to 30 per cent of the value at the prior working level. This value during diastole averages about one-third that during systole for the same time period. These values in the vagal stopped heart have some interesting characteristics. Oxygen uptake is unaffected by ventricular diastolic size. They are not fixed but vary greatly with the control metabolic level in the beating heart before it is stopped. Under some circumstances, the oxygen usage in the resting heart may equal 50 per cent of that in the beating heart. In addition, in the nonworking but beating heart which has been emptied by hemorrhage and suction, the metabolism of 3.4 ml. per 100 grams of left ventricle per min., is considerably greater than that with vagal asystole. Adjustments of the mechanical efficiency taking into account the usual oxygen usage in the vagal arrested heart and in the beating empty heart, are in table 23.3. The apparent efficiency is increased thereby from an assumed efficiency of 15 per cent to 26 per cent. While it cannot be stated that alteration of the mechanical efficiency by these amounts is correct, the data do emphasize that until the oxygen usage of the myocardium doing no external work is known under various physiological conditions, calculation of or reference to figures for cardiac efficiency is premature.

THE ROLE OF CATECHOLAMINES. The findings that the heart contains significant stores of noradrenaline, and that stimulation of the cardiac sympathetic fibers (isolated from the stellate ganglia) may increase stroke volume and stroke

## TABLE 23.3

*Effect of oxygen usage in the nonworking left ventricle on the calculated left ventricular efficiency*

$$\text{Efficiency} = \frac{\text{Left ventricular work (kg.-m./min.) (100)}}{\text{(Total left ventricular O}_2 \text{ used} - \text{resting O}_2 \text{ used) 2.057}}$$

$$\text{Efficiency} = \frac{1.2\ (100)}{8.1} = 15\%$$

$$\text{Efficiency} = \frac{1.2\ (100)}{8.1 - 2.3} = 22\%$$

$$\text{Efficiency} = \frac{1.2\ (100)}{8.1 - 3.4} = 26\%$$

work without change in heart rate, has stimulated interest in the catecholamines as a possible powerful reserve mechanism. The role played by local stores of catechol hormones in circulatory regulation at various points of the cardiovascular system is now the subject of much current investigation.

The presence of catecholamines has been demonstrated in the mammalian heart (von Euler, 1946) and in the walls of blood vessels (Schmiterlow, 1948). Noradrenaline forms over 90 per cent of the total tissue catecholamines, adrenaline less than 10 per cent.

The noradrenaline content of these organs is closely related to the number of adrenergic fibers supplying them, and it disappears almost completely following postganglionic sympathetic denervation (Goodall, 1951). Similarly, administration of reserpine to the experimental animal results in practically complete disappearance of noradrenaline from the heart (Bertler and associates, 1956), and the walls of arteries (Burn and Rand, 1958a).

It was shown that isolated atria of animals previously treated with reserpine exhibit a slower rate and lesser amplitude of contractions than control animals (Burn and Rand, 1958b). Based on this observation, it is suggested that the stores of catecholamines normally present in the heart contribute to the regulation of cardiac activity by accelerating the spontaneous rate. As of now, however, there is no direct evidence confirming this view.

Isolated aortic strips of animals previously treated with reserpine were shown to be more sensitive to adrenaline and noradrenaline than strips taken from aortae of control animals (Burn and Rand, 1958a). The lesser sensitivity of normal (as compared to reserpine treated) vessels is tentatively interpreted as indicating that the catecholamine stores contained in them are "functional" and contribute to the mainte-

nance of normal vascular tone. Again, more direct evidence is needed before any firm conclusions may be drawn regarding the physiological significance of these stores.

In the adrenal medulla, catecholamines are secreted by chromaffin cells. Cells containing chromaffin granules exist also outside the adrenals, in various tissues. They were recently discovered in the skin (Adams-Ray and Nordenstam, 1956). It is suggested that they produce catecholamines which play a role in the local control of the peripheral circulation. The administration of reserpine results in a decrease of the noradrenaline content of the skin, accompanied by the disappearance of chromaffin granules (Burn and Rand, 1958a). The chromaffin reaction, however, is not specific for catecholamines and their presence will have to be confirmed by other means.

The above investigations point out the various possible roles that local stores of catechol hormones may play in the regulation of the circulatory system. At the present time, all of these mechanisms must be regarded as hypothetical, awaiting further experimental confirmation.

## REFERENCES

Adams-Ray, J. and Nordenstam, H. Un systeme de cellules chromaffines dans la peau humaine. Lyon chir., 1956, **52**, 125.

Barger, A. C., Richards, V., Metcalfe, J., and Gunther, B. Regulatoin of the circulation during exercise. Cardiac output (direct Fick) and metabolic adjustments in the normal dog. Am. J. Physiol., 1956, **184**, 613.

Barratt-Boyes, G. B. and Wood, E. H. Hemodynamic response of healthy subjects to exercise in the supine position while breathing oxygen. J. Appl. Physiol., 1957, **11**, 129.

Beattie, J., Brow, G. R., and Long, C. N. H. Physiological and anatomical evidence for the existence of nerve tracts connecting the hypothalamus with spinal sympathetic centres. Proc. Roy. Soc., 1930, **106B**, 253.

Bertler, A., Carlsson, A., and Rosengren, E.

Release by reserpine of catecholamines from rabbits' hearts. Naturwissenschaften, 1956, **43**, 521.

BRONK, D. W., FERGUSON, L. K., MARGARIA, R., AND SOLANDT, D. Y. The activity of the cardiac sympathetic centers. Am. J. Physiol., 1936, **117**, 237.

BURN, J. H. AND RAND, M. J. Noradrenaline in artery walls and its dispersal by reserpine. Brit. M. J., 1958a, **1**, 903.

BURN, J. H. AND RAND, M. J. Action of nicotine on the heart. Brit. M. J., 1958b, **1**, 137.

CHAPMAN, E. M., KINSEY, D., CHAPMAN, W. P., AND SMITHWICK, R. H. Sympathetic innervation of the heart in man. Preliminary observations of the effect of thoracic sympathectomy on heart rate. J. A. M. A., 1948, **137**, 579.

DEXTER, L., WHITTENHOGER, J. L., HAYNES, F. W., GOODALE, W. T., GORLIN, R., AND SAWYER, C. G. Effect of exercise on circulatory dynamics of normal individuals. J. Appl. Physiol., 1951, **3**, 439.

DONALD, K. W., BISHOP, J. M., CUMMING, G., AND WADE, O. L. The effect of exercise on the cardiac output and circulatory dynamics of normal subjects. Clin. Sc., 1955, **14**, 37.

VON EULER, U. S. Presence of a sympathomimetic substance in extracts of mammalian heart. J. Physiol., 1946, **105**, 38.

FRANKLIN, D. L., ELLIS, R. M., AND RUSHMER, R. F. Aortic blood flow in dogs during treadmill exercise. J. Appl. Physiol., 1959, **14**, 809.

GASSER, H. S. AND MEEK, W. J. A study of the mechanisms by which muscular exercise produces acceleration of the heart. Am. J. Physiol., 1914, **34**, 48.

GOODALL, McC. Studies of adrenaline and noradrenaline in mammalian heart and suprarenals. Acta physiol. scandinav., 1951, **24**, suppl. 85.

GREEN, H. D. AND HOFF, E. C. Effects of faradic stimulation of the cerebral cortex on limb and renal volumes in the cat and monkey. Am. J. Physiol., 1937, **118**, 641.

HICKHAM, H. D. AND CARGILL, W. H. Effect of exercise on cardiac output and pulmonary artery pressure in normal persons and in patients with cardiovascular disease and pulmonary emphysema. J. Clin. Invest., 1948, **27**, 10.

McKEEVER, W. P., GREGG, D. E., AND CANNEY, P. C. Oxygen uptake of the nonworking left ventricle. Circulation Res., 1958, **6**, 612.

McMICHAEL, J. AND SHARPEY-SCHAFER, E. P. Cardiac output in man by direct Fick method; effects of posture, venous pressure change, atropine and adrenaline. Brit. Heart J., 1945, **6**, 33.

MILLER, F. R. AND BOWMAN, J. T. The cardioinhibitory center. Am. J. Physiol., 1915, **39**, 149.

NAHAS, G. G. AND CAVERT, H. M. Cardiac depressant effect of $CO_2$ and its reversal. Am. J. Physiol., 1957, **190**, 483.

NONIDEZ, J. F. The structure and innervation of the conductive system of the heart of the dog and rhesus monkey as seen with a silver impregnation technique. Am. Heart J., 1943, **26**, 577.

PATTERSON, S. W., PIPER, H., AND STARLING, E.

H. The regulation of the heart beat. J. Physiol., 1914, **48**, 465.

RILEY, R. L., HIMMELSTEIN, A., MATLEY, H. L., WEINER, H. M., AND COURNAND, A. Studies of the pulmonary circulation at rest and during exercise in normal individuals and in patients with chronic pulmonary disease. Am. J. Physiol., 1948, **152**, 372.

ROTTA, A., CANEPA, A., HURTADO, A., VELASQUEZ, T., AND CHANEZ, R. Pulmonary circulation at sea level and at high altitudes. J. Appl. Physiol., 1956, **9**, 328.

RUSHMER, R. F., SMITH, D. A., AND FRANKLIN, D. Mechanisms of cardiac control in exercise. Circulation Res., 1959, **7**, 602.

RUSHMER, R. F. Constancy of stroke volume in ventricular responses to exertion. Am. J. Physiol., 1959, **196**, 745.

SARNOFF, S. J. AND BERGLUND, B. Ventricular function. I. Starling's law of the heart studied by means of simultaneous right and left ventricular function curves in the dog. Circulation, 1954, **9**, 706.

SARNOFF, S. J. Certain aspects of the role of catecholamines in circulatory regulation. Am. J. Cardiol., 1960, **5**, 579.

SARNOFF, S. J., CASE, R. B., WELCH, G. A., BRAUNWALD, E., AND STAINSHY, W. H. Performance characteristics and oxygen debt in a non-failing metabolically supported, isolated heart preparation. Am. J. Physiol., 1958, **192**, 141.

SCHMITERLOW, C. G. The nature and occurrence of pressor and depressor substances in extracts from blood vessels. Acta physiol. scandinav., 1948, **16**, suppl. 56.

STARLING, E. H. AND VISSCHER, M. B. Regulation of energy output of the heart. J. Physiol., 1927, **62**, 243.

THIELEN, E. O., GREGG, D. E., AND ROTTA, A. Exercise and cardiac work response at high altitude. Circulation, 1955, **12**, 383.

WIGGERS, C. J. AND KATZ, L. N. Contour of the ventricular volume curves under different conditions. Am. J. Physiol., 1922, **58**, 439.

*Monographs and Reviews*

ASMUSSEN, E. AND NIELSEN, M. Cardiac output during muscular work and its regulation. Physiol. Rev., 1955, **35**, 778.

BEST, C. H. AND TAYLOR, N. B. Physiological Basis of Medical Practice, Ed. 6, 1955.

BING, R. J. AND MICHEL, G. Myocardial efficiency in metabolic factors in cardiac contractility. Ann. New York Acad. Sci., 1959, **72**, 555.

GREGG, D. E., SABISTON, D. C., AND THEILEN, E. O. Performance of the heart: changes in left ventricular end-diastolic pressure and stroke work during infusion and following exercise. Physiol. Rev., 1955, **35**, 130.

GREGG, D. E. Homeostasis of the arterial circulation. First International Symposium on Submarine and Space Medicine, New London, Connecticut, 1958.

HAMILTON, W. F. The Lewis A. Connor memorial lecture. The Physiology of the Cardiac Output. Circulation, 1953, **8**, 527.

KATZ, L. N., SARNOFF, S. J., GUYTON, A. C.,

GREGG, D. E., SABISTON, D. C., THEILEN, E. O., LORBER, V., RUSHMER, R. F., GAUER, O. H., RICHARDS, D. W., AND HAMILTON, W. F. Symposium on the regulation of the performance of the heart. Physiol. Rev., 1955, **35,** 91.

PICKERING, G. Starling and the concept of heart failure. Circulation, 1960, **21,** 323.

RUSHMER, R. F. AND SMITH, O. A. Cardiac control. Physiol. Rev., 1959, **39,** 41.

SCHMIDT, C. F. The adjustment of oxygen supply to oxygen demand in organs. Symposium on Stress. Army Medical Service Graduate School, WRAMC, 1953.

STARLING, E. H. Linacre lecture on law of the heart. Longmans, Green & Company, Inc., Cambridge, 1915; New York, 1918.

WIGGERS, C. J. Determinants of cardiac performance. Circulation, 1951, **4,** 485.

# 24

# THE CORONARY CIRCULATION

## General Consideration

Beginning with Harvey in the seventeenth century, the anatomical and dynamic details of this system have been gradually elucidated.

ANATOMICAL. Two coronary arteries, the right and left, carry blood to the myocardium. About 2 mm. from its ostium, the left coronary artery divides into the left circumflex and the anterior descendens branch. The former runs in the atrioventricular (A-V) groove to the left, ending in a posterior descending branch. The anterior descending branch runs downward in the interventricular groove toward the apex. Near its origin, septal branches are given off. The right coronary descends in the right (A-V) sulcus and ends posteriorly as several descending branches on the right and left ventricles. The subdivisions of the main coronary rami descend superficially in the general direction of the apex and give off myocardial branches which course directly into the ventricular muscle. At or near the apex, where the superficial muscles form a spiral and penetrate to form the innermost (subendocardial) layer of muscle, the terminal coronary arteries go along with the muscle to supply the inner layer of both ventricles and the papillary muscles. Anatomical studies in both the dog and human heart indicate that vessel branching within the myocardium is related to muscle bundles, but numerous communications exist between the different muscle layers.

As in any other vascular system, each of the two coronary arteries connects with its capillary bed, its superficial myocardial venous bed, and eventually with the right atrium (fig. 24.1). The epicardial branches of the coronary arteries and coronary veins also anastomose with each other and with extracardiac arteries and veins. There are numerous arteriovenous shunts. In addition to these pathways, the arterioles as well as the capillaries and superficial veins connect directly with both ventricular cavities by discrete, deep drainage channels, the arterioluminal, the arteriosinusoidal, and the Thebesian vessels which together comprise the deep coronary drainage circuit.

In man, approximately 50 per cent of hearts have the right coronary artery predominant; 30 per cent have a balanced coronary circulation; and 20 per cent have the left coronary artery predominant. The arterial pattern of the dog heart compares with the situation in man in which the left coronary artery is predominant. In the latter, the left coronary artery nourishes about 85 per cent of the heart muscle, supplying the whole of the left heart as well as portions of the right ventricle.

### PREPARATION AND METHODOLOGY

The objective of studies of the coronary circulation is knowledge of the determinants of coronary flow, of the oxygen uptake (coronary flow times the coronary arteriovenous oxygen difference) by the myocardium, and of their relation to the work of the heart in states of normalcy, of increased or decreased stress, and of disease in man. This objective is far from being realized.

The Pitot tube, orifice meter, rotameter, bubble flowmeter, and thermostromular are used to measure coronary flow by insertion between the cut ends of a coronary vessel. The thermostromular also measures flow in the intact coronary artery. The electromagnetic flow meter has also been used successfully to quantitate coronary flow in the anesthetized and unanesthetized exercising dog. In addition, the nitrous oxide method can be used in the normal dog and human being, and if used with care, reasonably accurate values for human beings can be obtained. All except the bubble flowmeter and nitrous oxide methods permit continuous recording of flow. All measures mean flow; the orifice meter, Pitot tube, and electromagnetic flow meter can be used for recording phasic flow. The oxygen saturation of coronary arterial and venous blood is obtained by continuous withdrawal of aliquots of the respective bloods through indwelling tubes and their analyses by the Van Slyke, Beckman, or by

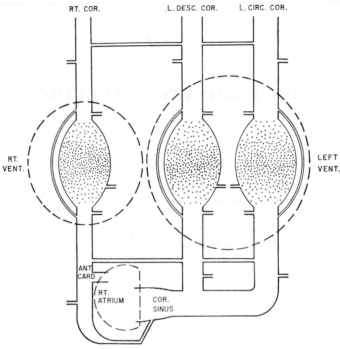

FIG. 24.1. Schematic representation of the coronary circulation. The areas enclosed within the circles depict the capillary beds, collateral communications and A-V shunts (Gregg and Sabiston, Circulation, 1956, **13**, 916).

oximeter techniques. The first two methods give average oxygen values over a period of time; the last permits continuous recording of the arterio-venous oxygen difference.

UTILIZATION OF THE SUPERFICIAL VERSUS THE DEEP DRAINAGE CIRCUITS IN THE NORMAL HEART. As determined by clamping of the coronary arteries all blood in the superficial veins of the heart arises in the two coronary arteries and none comes from the deep-lying connections within the cardiac cavities. Despite the presence of these deep channels and the existence of a favorable pressure gradient during diastole for flow through them into the ventricular cavities, they are not used. Balance studies of coronary inflow and outflow have shown that most of the blood entering the left coronary artery drains into the coronary sinus. The remainder of left coronary inflow is recovered in the superficial (anterior cardiac) veins of the right myocardium that drain into the right atrium. Most of the right coronary artery inflow appears in these anterior cardiac veins and the remainder (10 to 20 per cent) drains into the coronary sinus. Thus, essentially all coronary inflow can be collected in the superficial veins of the heart leaving little or no blood to drain by the deep channels into the heart cavities. Presumably a similar utilization of anatomical path-

ways exists in man. However, in man, it is reported that 16 per cent of left coronary flow enters the left ventricular cavity by the deep drainage channels. This has not yet been confirmed.

The deep drainage channels could have an important functional role if they served as arterial channels from the left ventricle to the myocardium during coronary artery constriction or occlusion, or as venous channels for the whole myocardium in the presence of extensive superficial vein constriction or occlusion. Regarding the first situation, although essentially complete occlusion of the coronary arteries in human beings has been found at autopsy, the presence or extent of development of extracardiac arterial collaterals is not known. In addition, with functional separation of one or both coronary arteries from the aorta, no blood flow from the ventricles into the superficial coronary venous system can be demonstrated and the hearts do not survive. Regarding the second situation with acute closure of all visible superficial coronary veins, although such hearts may survive, large intra- and extracardiac superficial venous channels quickly appear. Hence, known observations are conflicting and any conclusion regarding the utilization of deep coronary venous drainage channels in diseased hearts is difficult.

USE OF LEFT CORONARY ARTERY FLOW TO-
GETHER WITH THE CHEMICAL COMPOSITION OF
CORONARY SINUS BLOOD AS AN INDEX OF LEFT
VENTRICULAR METABOLISM. It is not possible to
quantitate accurately the metabolism of the right
ventricle in the dog because its superficial anterior
cardiac veins have many exits into the right
atrium and their contained blood is grossly contaminated by blood from the left coronary artery.
However, drainage of the left myocardium is
accessible. In most instances quantitative changes
in the metabolism of the left ventricle can be
obtained from measurement of the chemical composition of the coronary sinus blood together with
the left coronary inflow. This is because (1) coronary sinus blood is almost entirely from the left
coronary artery; (2) by means of a special cannula which permits collection of all blood draining
into the coronary sinus, the percentage of left
coronary artery inflow recovered in the coronary
sinus is quite high (80 to 90 per cent) and reasonably constant during the induction of a variety
of physiological variables and drug injections;
(3) the $O_2$ content of the venous blood from the
left coronary artery not draining into the coronary sinus is generally only slightly less than that
in the coronary sinus. This is a very important
and practical consideration because of the widespread use of these measurements in man and dog
for just this purpose.

BASAL DATA. In the resting state, the coronary
data for dog and man agree. With the left ventricular cardiac work index approximately 3.5 to 4.6
Kg.M left coronary flow approximates 72 to 85
ml. per 100 grams of left ventricle per minute.
Correct values for left coronary flow during natural maximal stress, such as exercise, are not yet
available but in the anesthetized open chest dog
values as high as 600 ml. per 100 grams of left
ventricle per minute have been recorded. Although the heart can remove essentially all oxygen from the coronary blood in its passage
through the myocardium, normally about two-
thirds is extracted with an arteriovenous difference of 12 to 14 ml. and a coronary sinus value of
4 to 5 ml. This extraction changes little with increased stress, signifying that the oxygen supply
is well balanced with metabolic demands.

Oxygen uptake per 100 grams of left ventricle
is 8 to 10 ml. per minute. Oxygen consumption
during systole averages about 3 times that in
diastole for the same time period.

MYOCARDIAL RESPONSE TO ANOXIA. The coronary vascular bed is very reactive to the stimulus
of anoxia; occlusion of a coronary artery for as
short a time as 5 seconds results in a temporary
increase in blood flow. Reactive hyperemia is
considered to be the excess blood flow (over the
control flow that normally would have occurred)
following release of an arterial occlusion (fig.
24.2). The reactive hyperemic blood flow and its
duration increase with lengthening periods of left
circumflex artery occlusion up to 120 sec.; peak
flows also increase but in smaller amounts. The
theoretical blood flow "debt (control blood flow
multiplied by the duration of occlusion) is usually
greatly overpaid. Reactive hyperemia in skeletal
muscle vascular beds shows these same characteristics except the blood flow "debt is variably
under or overpaid (ch. 25). Coronary vasodilator
agents do not consistently affect myocardial reactive hyperemia while Pitressin usually decreases
the response.

The oxygen consumption during myocardial
reactive hyperemia is measured by determining
the left coronary artery blood flow (rotameter)
and the oxygen saturation of the coronary sinus
blood (measured continuously with a densitometer). The theoretical oxygen "debt" (control
oxygen consumption times duration of left coronary artery occlusion) is overpaid for 15 and 30
sec., but slightly underpaid for 10-second occlu-
sions. In contrast to skeletal muscle, where the
arteriovenous oxygen (A-V $O_2$) difference decreases during reactive hyperemia, the myocardial A-V oxygen difference increases during the
period of increased blood flow. The rate of oxygen
consumption during the increased blood flow
period is greater than in the control state, showing that the myocardium has been stimulated to
take up more oxygen. The basic hypothesis
governing the calculation of the oxygen "debt"
in these studies is erroneous, for the oxygen in the
blood in the coronary vascular bed during arterial
occlusion, the metabolic rate during the circulatory stasis, and changes in cardiac work are not
considered. As further evidence that the myocardium develops an oxygen deficit, i.e., anaerobic
metabolism occurs, it was found that lactic acid
increases in the coronary sinus blood, often in
comparison to pyruvic acid levels, following the
period of anoxia.

The *contracting* myocardium can withstand
much shorter periods of arterial occlusion and
oxygen deficit than *resting* skeletal muscle, and
repays its oxygen "debt" with an increased blood
flow but a decreased A-V oxygen difference.

# 15, 30, 60 AND 90 SECONDS OCCLUSIONS AND REACTIVE HYPEREMIAS OF LEFT CIRCUMFLEX ARTERY

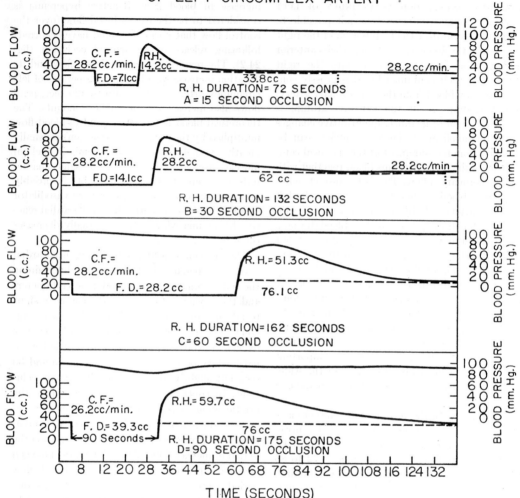

C.F.= CONTROL FLOW
F.D.= FLOW DEBT
R.H.= REACTIVE HYPEREMIA

Fig. 24.2. Myocardial response to anoxia. Tracings redrawn from original experiment (Coffman, personal communication).

## The Determinants of Coronary Flow

Consideration of the mechanisms that control the blood supply to the myocardium involve certain difficulties not encountered in similar investigations in other organs of the body. The myocardial wall of the left ventricle not only furnishes the pressure head for driving blood into the coronary arteries but also may either offer phasic resistance to coronary flow or actually aid flow by its muscular contraction around the coronary vascular bed. Similarly, the right ventricle rapidly changes resistance to right coronary flow at the same time that left ventricular contraction presents blood to it under a pulsatile head of pressure. However, coronary flow is related to the pressure difference (effective pressure) between the central coronary artery (identical to aortic pressure) and the right atrium divided by the sum of the viscous resistances to flow in the epicardial portion of the artery and in the peripheral coronary bed. Viscous resistance to flow (aside from change in hematocrit) is mainly governed by the mean caliber of the coronary vascular bed. Since the arterial resistance is negligible, the mean coronary diameter and, hence, flow are controlled by the effective intravessel pressure and by two peripheral mechanisms, i.e., active changes in the state of the small mass of intravascular smooth muscle built into the coronary vessels, and the mechanical or passive effect on flow exerted during ventricular systole by the large muscle mass around the coronary vessels. The peripheral mechanisms are regarded as more important in controlling coronary flow than the central coronary or aortic pressure which does not change greatly even in exercise. It is estimated that doubling the aortic pressure might double the coronary flow, but doubling the average radius of the coronary bed might increase coronary flow about 16 times.

Insight into the complexity of the integrating action of these three flow determinants has been obtained from recording of the peripheral coronary pressure and the phasic, or moment-to-moment changes, in coronary inflow and outflow in the epicardial arteries and veins (fig. 24.3). At the onset of isometric contraction of the left ventricle, there is an abrupt decrease in left coronary inflow (*solid line*) or even the appearance of backflow. With the rise in aortic pressure, forward flow increases initially and rapidly, only to decrease to a new intermediate level in late systole. With the onset of isometric relaxation, coronary flow increases significantly, peaking at early diastole and then declining progressively. The velocity of coronary inflow differs somewhat from the estimated intramyocardial flow (*dotted line*). The deficit during isometric contraction is caused by the compressing action of the myocardium on the coronary capillaries, forcing blood into the superficial vessels. Early in the period of ejection, the flow excess is caused by the uptake of blood in the superficial coronary arteries; in diastole, the excess is caused by the uptake of blood to fill the previously compressed capillaries. These demarcations of flow are much less obvious in the right coronary inflow pattern, which roughly resembles the prevailing aortic pressure

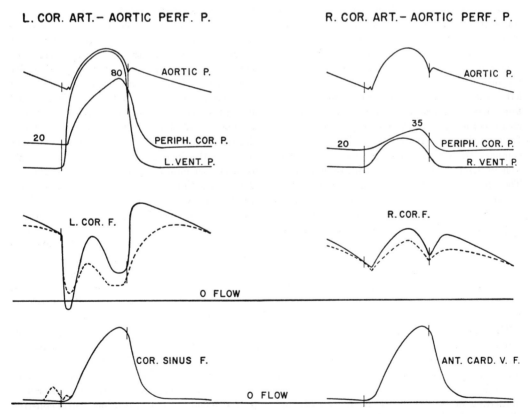

FIG. 24.3. Series of curves relating phasic variations in left and right coronary inflow and coronary sinus-anterior cardiac vein outflow to aortic pressure, ventricular pressure and peripheral coronary pressure. Coronary inflow (*solid lines*) and anterior coronary vein flow obtained with orifice meter, coronary sinus flow with pitot tube. *Broken lines*, estimated intramural velocity curves. (Gregg, D. E. Coronary Circulation. Encyclopedia of Cardiology, Vol. 1, Ch. 23, McGraw-Hill-Blakiston, New York, 1959).

curve. Thus, blood is flowing through the myocardium throughout the cardiac cycle, except possibly for a brief period in early systole in the left coronary artery. In the left coronary artery, the systolic rate of flow is less than that during diastole; in the right coronary artery, the systolic rate equals or exceeds the diastolic. In contrast to the left coronary inflow pattern, the flow curves in the coronary sinus and anterior cardiac veins rise and fall smoothly, with most flow occurring during systole and very little during diastole.

The preceding account indicates that the coronary bed has a fluctuating resistance to coronary flow. In the left coronary artery, the peripheral coronary maximal systolic and minimal diastolic pressure values approximate 80/20 mm. Hg, respectively, and inflow is cut off at these pressure levels when the left coronary artery is perfused under constant pressure. In the right coronary artery, the contour and time relations of the peripheral coronary pressure curve are similar, but the values for systole and diastole and for the cutoff of flow are considerably lower.

Elevation of right atrial pressure must increase coronary venous pressure and decrease the flow of blood in the coronary arteries provided no compensatory mechanisms set in. Such studies have not been made. However, mild elevation of the pressure in the coronary veins, draining the left coronary artery by coronary sinus constriction, may only decrease coronary flow and increase coronary arteriovenous oxygen difference. Even marked constriction of, or clamping of, the coronary sinus may cause only moderate reduction in arterial pressure and left coronary flow. The smallness of the effect on coronary flow, despite elevation at times of the coronary venous pressure to near aortic systolic level, is presumably caused by the compensatory increased functioning of collateral venous communications with the anterior cardiac veins, whose flow increases considerably. Similarly, right coronary inflow is not greatly reduced by clamping most of the anterior cardiac veins, presumably for the same reason.

The relation of coronary perfusion pressure to coronary flow $(P/CF)$ is generally such that the calculated coronary resistance decreases as the coronary flow rises. This holds for almost any dynamic state of the coronary system (excised fibrillating or beating heart, heart *in situ*) and also exists in the pulmonary artery, peripheral vascular beds, and in an artificial set of rigid tubes. In the heart, it is impossible to say what fraction of the flow change is caused by passive dilation from the perfusion pressure per se, since the oxygen consumption per minute and per heart beat is elevated without any other observable systemic dynamic change. Accordingly, if a physiological variable alters coronary pressure and flow by about the same amount and hence the ratio is unaltered, it is impossible to know whether the change in coronary flow is due to a change in effective head of pressure alone or whether the variable directly affected resistance. However, a gross change in the vasomotor state of the bed occurs when coronary flow changes considerably with a constant pressure, or when flow and pressure change considerably in opposite directions.

Separation and quantitation of the determinants of coronary flow lying within the myocardial wall, i.e., the intravascular and extravascular muscle, are of extreme importance. To do this, continuous measurements are made in the open-chest dog while the left coronary artery is perfused with blood under a constant pressure; first it is done in the beating heart, and then during ventricular asystole induced by vagal stimulation or by disconnecting an external pacemaker which drives the ventricles, the latter manifesting complete atrioventricular heart block which had been surgically produced earlier. By either means, the mechanical effects of ventricular contraction are largely removed. Figure 24.4 illustrates that induction of ventricular asystole by vagal stimulation always increases immediately (within 1 second) left and right coronary inflow, in this instance from 56 to 78 and from 9 to 11 cc. per minute respectively. Thus, ventricular contraction acts to impede coronary flow through the ventricular wall. The extent of the rise of flow is taken to represent the magnitude of the mechanical or passive factors limiting coronary flow. The magnitude of this mechanical throttling effect on coronary flow during systole normally varies from 31 to 300 per cent and averages about 50 per cent. The new flow level represents that state of coronary dilation related to the condition of the intrinsic smooth muscle of the coronary vessels at the prevailing coronary pressure. The relative contribution of extravascular and intravascular resistance to an increase of coronary flow has been tested under the different conditions of increasing heart rate, decreased arterial blood oxygen saturation, aortic constriction, transfusion and drug injections. In all instances, the major portion of a flow increase is through active dilation and not through reduction in extravascular resistance. The largest reduction (40 per cent) in extravascular resistance came from a decrease in arterial oxygen saturation.

### Determinants of Normal Cardiac Metabolism

METABOLIC PATTERNS IN THE HEART. The ability of the heart to do work depends basically on its biochemical activity leading to muscular contraction. Cardiac muscle has been found to have basic chemical patterns similar to those of skeletal muscle. The catabolism of fat, carbohydrate and protein produces free energy, about half of which is dissipated as heat and half is captured as phosphate bond energy which is used for muscle cell work and for various anabolic activities such as synthesis of glycogen, lipids, proteins and enzymes. These catabolic and anabolic reactions proceed simultaneously under the influence of a complex system of enzymes, coenzymes (from the vitamin B complex), and hormones.

Coronary sinus catheterization studies in man and dog have indicated that the heart is able to choose its fuel from a variety of foodstuffs. These include mainly glucose, lactate, pyruvate, fatty acids (nonesterified) and to a lesser extent, acetate, ketone bodies and amino acids. To determine their quantitative contribution to the energy production of the heart, i.e., its oxygen consumption, measurements have been made of their cardiac extraction (coronary artery − coronary sinus difference), their total uptake [coronary flow times (coronary artery − coronary sinus difference of substance)], and the myocardial respiratory quotient (coronary sinus − arterial carbon dioxide difference) divided by (coronary artery − coronary sinus oxygen difference). Excellent correlation has been demonstrated between the myocardial respiratory quotient and the myocardial uptake of substance. The extent to which each substrate contributes to the energy requirement of the heart *in vivo* is influenced by its concentration (above threshold) in arterial blood. In addition, the state of nutrition of the organism markedly influences the kind of substrate used for energy production of the heart. Under postprandial conditions, or after glucose infusion, myocardial metabolism is mainly glucose, lactate and pyruvate, since its respiratory quotient approximates 0.9 with a high extraction of carbohydrate and a negligible uptake of amino acids. Even the substitution of 5 to 10 per cent oxygen for the normal 21 per cent in the inspired air does little to change carbohydrate uptake by

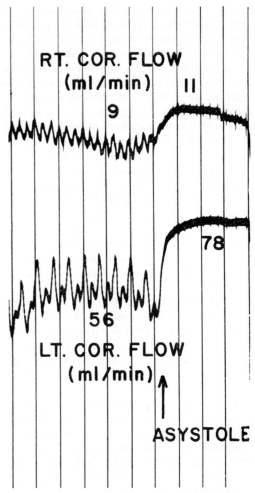

FIG. 24.4. Response of left and right coronary flow to vagal induced asystole. Note the prompt increase with the induction of asytole. Time lines are 1 sec. apart. (Sabiston and Gregg, Circulation, 1957, **15**, 14.)

the normal heart. During overnight fasting, the heart derives much of its energy from fat, as indicated by a myocardial respiratory quotient of 0.80 with a low extraction and uptake of carbohydrate. With prolonged fasting, the extraction coefficient for carbohydrate practically disappears, those for fatty acids and ketones are maximal, and the respiratory quotient is 0.70. As regards the uptake of oxygen, the coronary A-VO$_2$ differences in man vary linearly with the arterial oxygen content through a range from mild anemia to marked polycythemia, so that the myocardial extraction coefficient (A-V)/(A) is constant.

In addition to patterns of myocardial metabolism in the normal heart, other metabolic changes have been reported in some pathological and diseased states. Patients with heart failure and decreased cardiac work due to valvular disease show an increased carbohydrate uptake by the heart with a normal extraction of lactate and pyruvate and increased glucose extraction. The heart in the patient with diabetes appears to derive most of its energy from fat even in mild cases with a postabsorptive respiratory quotient of about 0.7 and an increased uptake of fatty acids and a decreased carbohydrate uptake.

Thus, the heart demonstrates broad flexibility in the utilization of substrate for energy production without a change in work performance or work capacity. This makes it largely independent of fluctuations in its chemical environment. There is no evidence that substrate lack occurs in any clinical situation to the extent that it embarrasses the cardiac work capacity. Similarly, the metabolic disturbances such as diabetes mellitus which alter the fuel mixture available to the heart do not also alter cardiac function. It is, however, well to defer detailed consideration of other data because an interpretation must be based on the assumption that oxidation of foodstuffs to carbon dioxide and water is the sole factor in the determination of the myocardial respiratory quotient and of the myocardial extraction and uptake of these compounds including oxygen. Without doubt, storage of and/or conversion into other compounds is occurring concurrently, and these activities are especially prominent in the presence of a changing cardiac level of activity or changing levels of blood substrate.

DETERMINANTS OF $O_2$ USAGE OF THE MYOCARDIUM. Our knowledge is only sufficient to introduce the subject. With present poor methodology, separation can only be made by measuring oxygen uptake, first in the beating heart during repetitive systoles and diastoles, and then in the relaxed heart or during prolonged diastole and, finally, obtaining the oxygen usage during systole by difference. Estimation of the metabolism of the myocardium in the absence of a heart beat, that is, during prolonged diastole has been made in the vagal arrested heart as previously described under determinants of coronary flow. The oxygen saturation of the arterial blood and coronary sinus blood is also measured continuously. This permits left coronary arteriovenous oxygen difference as well as coronary-inflow to be measured continuously first in the beating heart and then in the stopped heart until a new equilibrium is established, usually within 20 to 25 seconds.

Typical results are shown in figure 24.5. As coronary inflow rises immediately with asystole from 70 to 90 cc. per minute, the oxygen saturation of blood in the coronary sinus also rises from a low control value of 44 per cent to a very high value of 81 per cent, thus greatly reducing the coronary arteriovenous oxygen difference. The $O_2$ usage at rest is 35 per cent of that in the beating heart. Calculations in many experiments show that as the result of the combination of increased coronary flow and decreased coronary arteriovenous oxygen difference, the average oxygen usage per 100 grams of left ventricle per min., decreases from the average control level of 8.1 in the beating heart to 2.3 ml. in the resting heart, or to 30 per cent of the control. Individual values ranged from 1.0 to 4.0 ml. This oxygen consumption in diastole is about one-third that in systole for an equivalent time period.

Attention is also directed to the values for oxygen usage obtained in the same type of preparation but in which the external work of the heart is reduced to zero by other means. In the potassium stopped heart, the oxygen usage of 2 cc. during diastole is about the same. In the beating heart emptied by suction and hemorrhage, and in the heart with induced ventricular fibrillation the oxygen usages of 3.4 and 3.8 cc. are much greater. These oxygen values have some interesting characteristics. The oxygen uptake during vagal arrest or removal of the artificial pacemaker is unaffected by the ventricular diastolic size. In any one experiment, the value is not fixed but varies greatly with the control metabolic level in the beating heart. With intracoronary artery epinephrine or norepinephreine injection, the values are especially high and may equal 50 per cent of those in the control state. The implications of such experiments in relation to ventricular efficiency have already been considered in chapter 14.

## Patterns of Response of the Coronary Circulation

The preceding gives some idea of the fractionation of the control of coronary flow and oxygen uptake within the myocardium during a cardiac cycle. There are certain general patterns of hemodynamic responses of the heart and coronary circulation which follow primary changes in stress. The information has been obtained from both humans and animals and has been assembled from many laboratories (Table 24.1).

METABOLITES. The coronary flow is greatly increased and the coronary arteriovenous oxygen

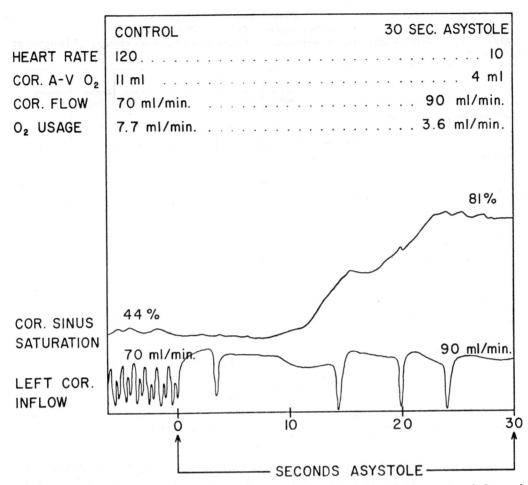

Fig. 24.5. Reproduction of tracing from original record showing changes in left coronary inflow and coronary sinus oxygen saturation during prolonged ventricular asystole. (Gregg, D. E. Verh. Dtsch. ges. Kreislaufforschg. 1955, **21**, 22.)

difference decreased by some chemical constituents of the blood, but this response does not occur with others; in both cases there is little or no change in systemic dynamics (blood pressure, cardiac work, heart rate) or myocardial oxygen consumption. The coronary response to carbon dioxide and decreased pH is minimal; intracoronary injection of intermediate metabolites will increase coronary flow and decrease oxygen extraction, but it is doubtful that the normal concentration of these chemicals within the coronary vessels effectively alters flow, since it has not been possible to demonstrate in the coronary sinus blood substances having vasoactive or chronotropic action on the coronary circulation or myocardium. However, coronary flow is markedly increased, coronary resistance and arteriovenous oxygen difference are decreased by mild anemia, by short periods of ischemia, by

reduction of the oxygen content of the inspired air and by coronary perfusion with reduced blood but without effect on myocardial metabolism, cardiac work, heart rate, or systemic dynamics.

HEART RATE. When the heart rate is increased considerably by electrical stimulation of the myocardium, aortic blood pressure, minute cardiac output, and work increase while the stroke volume and stroke work decrease. Simultaneously, minute coronary flow and oxygen usage increase, coronary resistance decreases, oxygen extraction is unchanged, but the coronary flow and oxygen consumption per beat decrease. Since acceleration of the heart means proportionally greater time per beat and per minute in systole than in diastole and since in systole coronary flow is less than in diastole, it would be anticipated that increased heart rate per se should reduce coronary flow. Since it does not, it must be that increased

## TABLE 24.1
*Circulatory responses to stress states*

Arrows merely indicate direction of response, not magnitude, i.e., → no change, ↗ increase or ↘ decrease.

| CONDITION | Cardiac Work | Cardiac Output | Coronary Flow | Cor. Press. Cor. Flow | Oxygen Usage | Coronary a-v O2 |
|---|---|---|---|---|---|---|
| ↗ Blood $CO_2$, ↘ blood pH | → | → | → | → | → | → |
| Ischemia, mild anemia and anoxia, metabolites | → | → | ↗ | ↘ | → | ↘ |
| ↗ Heart rate, ↗ CO (transfusion) ↗ C.W. / Aortic coarctat. (mild)[1], thyrotoxicosis / Cardiac sympathetic nerves, epinephrine and norepinephrine i.v. / Severe anemia[2] and anoxia[2] | ↗ | ↗ | ↗ | ↘ | ↗ | → |
| Hypothermia, shock (hemorrhagic) / Heart failure (extreme)[3] | ↘ | ↘ | ↘ | | ↘ | → |
| Aortic coarctation (complete) | ↘ | ↘ | ↗ | ↘ | ↗ | → |
| Hypertensive cardiovascular disease | ↗ | → | → | ↗ | → | → |

[1]Cardiac output → or ↘    [2]Cor. a-v O2 ↘    [3]Cor. a-v O2 ↗

flow is due to arteriolar dilation from the increased metabolic activity. The same trend of flow and oxygen usage per beat and per minute also occurs at the faster heart rate when minute cardiac work is held constant or when comparisons are made at the same stroke work. This means that cardiac acceleration can augment the energy metabolism of the myocardium without manifestations of the extra energy as work.

TRANSFUSION. Augmentation of ventricular load by increasing venous return and hence circulating blood volume through infusion has a clinical counterpart in the load placed upon the human heart by transfusion or by an aortacaval fistula. The increasing coronary flow is partially explainable on a mechanical basis, since the slowing of the heart should increase coronary flow per beat and per minute by increasing diastolic time in which flow is greater. However, presumably active dilation results from the increasing local chemometabolic activity associated with the increased cardiac work. The coronary flow and oxygen are used economically, for the ratio of cardiac work to oxygen consumption increases.

AORTIC COARCTATION. With simulation of clinical coarctation by acute mechanical constriction of the thoracic aorta just beyond the left subclavian artery, venous return to the heart by way of the inferior vena cava is decreased, but compensatory flow through various branches of the aortic arch may increase, with a resultant maintained cardiac output and elevated left ventricular work load. With greater aortic constriction, the net cardiac output decreases, causing the cardiac work to decrease. In either case the coronary dilation and increased flow arise in large part from *active* changes in the bore of the coronary bed related to the metabolic demands and in part passively from the increased blood pressure and moderately decreased heart rate. The cardiac oxygen consumption is increased much more by this augmentation of pressure work than with an equal increase of volume work following transfusion. No chronic studies of aortic coarctation have been made, because, owing to development of collateral circuits, the aorta may be first partially and then completely constricted at the arch without permanent development of hypertension proximal to the occlusion. In human coarctation not much change is reported in coronary flow and oxygen uptake, but this might be expected because systemic pressure was only mildly elevated. However, if true, the deviation might be explained by the fact that in these hearts, which are hypertrophied, there are fewer capillaries per unit of muscle to carry the oxygen and flow.

HORMONES. *A. Thyroid.* The myocardium participates in the increase in oxygen consumption characteristic of all body tissues in thyrotoxicosis. This hypermetabolism is accompanied by an increase in coronary blood flow, a decrease in coronary vascular resistance, and an increase in oxygen consumption per minute and per beat. Since there is an increase in oxygen usage per beat, cardiac oxygen utilization is presumably related not only to the increase in heart rate but to the general hypermetabolism of the myocardium as well.

*B. Epinephrine.* The response of the systemic and coronary circulation to intracoronary artery injection of a minimal amount of epinephrine is similar to that indicated for stellate stimulation. Probably the coronary changes can be similarly explained. With doses of 0.0002 mg. or less, coronary flow may increase without any change in blood pressure or heart rate and with an increased coronary arteriovenous oxygen difference. With the same or larger doses, as the systemic effects of the substance (increased aortic blood pressure, cardiac output, and changing heart rate) become evident, the coronary effects are exaggerated. In those instances in which it has been tested, norepinephrine affects the coronary circulation similarly. The circulatory responses to cigarette smoking, i.e., increased heart rate, systemic blood pressure, cardiac work, left coronary blood flow, oxygen consumption, and decreased coronary vascular resistance, parallel those with epinephrine injection and are presumably related to its release.

*C. Acetylcholine.* This hormone, intraarterially, increases coronary blood flow in the anesthetized dog. If the dose is properly chosen, this response in the beating heart occurs without a significant change in blood pressure or heart rate. The increased flow response is completely abolished after atropine. This then increases the mean bore of the coronary vessels, since the flow is elevated in the presence of a normal or lower central coronary blood pressure. Its effect on cardiac metabolism has not been determined and whether its effect is directly on the intrinsic smooth muscle of the coronary vessels or is induced through metabolic changes of the heart is unknown.

*D. Pitressin.* Of the hormones used clinically, Pitressin alone increases coronary resistance to flow. Coronary flow decreases, the reduction occurring throughout the cardiac cycle in the presence of an increased central coronary pressure. It is believed that this drug acts by direct effect on the coronary arterioles, but the possibility of a reduced metabolic influence has not been ruled out.

NERVOUS INFLUENCES. No critical evidence has been adduced that stimulation of vagal fibers to the heart causes coronary flow changes not explainable on some other basis, such as a change in heart rate. However, stimulation of the cardiac fibers from a stellate ganglion increases mean left coronary flow as the resultant of a decrease in systolic flow and a large increase in diastolic flow. Concurrently, left ventricular metabolism, cardiac output, and cardiac work increase while the systolic and diastolic size of the heart decrease. The decreased ratio of pressure to flow indicates an increased mean coronary bore. The major part of the dilation is explained by active changes in the coronary bed resulting from the release of an epinephrine-like substance which directly enhances myocardial metabolism. This process is very wasteful because the oxygen uptake is greatly increased even when cardiac work is not permitted to rise. The fact that the central coronary pressure and heart rate do not necessarily change rules them out as a necessary part of the flow-controlling mechanisms. About 30 per cent of the flow increase is due to the marked shortening of systole and lengthening of diastole. When the heart rate and blood pressure are elevated, the systemic and coronary effects are greatly accentuated.

Reports have appeared suggesting that coronary flow can be influenced reflexively and adversely by impulses arising in various body regions, especially the heart lungs, and abdominal viscera, but the importance of these reports is doubtful because of the methodology used.

ANEMIA. The coronary system participates actively in the circulatory adjustments to anemia. For hemoglobin values of 10 grams or more, the systemic circulation is essentially unaltered, and the compensation of the coronary system to the decreased oxygen-carrying capacity is similar to that with hypoxia, i.e., an increased coronary flow without change in oxygen uptake. When the hemoglobin values reach 6 to 8 grams, the response of the systemic circulation is manifested by tachycardia, increased cardiac output, cardiac work, and a fall in peripheral resistance. The coronary flow may now triple, coronary venous blood may contain less than 2 volumes per cent oxygen, the coronary arteriovenous oxygen difference may be 4 ml. or less, and oxygen uptake is considerably increased. The increase in coronary flow is related in part to the decreased blood viscosity and in larger part to the active dilation associated with myocardial hypoxia, which in turn arises from the low hematocrit and from the increased metabolism. Ultimately, myocardial failure will occur in severe anemia when the coronary vessels have approached maximal dilation and cannot further compensate for the decreased oxygen-carrying capacity of the blood either by increased flow or by increased oxygen extraction. In the presence of coronary stenosis associated with anemia, the effect of coronary arteriolar dilation in increasing coronary flow is minimized by the high fixed resistance of the stenotic artery, and myocardial depression and failure occur at lesser degrees of anemia.

VALVULAR LESIONS. Acute elevation of right ventricular pressure by pulmonary artery constriction initially decreases right coronary flow, to be followed quickly by a maintained increase in systolic, diastolic, and mean flow in the right coronary artery and, to some extent, in the left coronary artery. Upon release, right coronary flow temporarily increases still further. During the sustained response, the systemic blood pressure can be fairly well maintained. At the same time the right ventricular work declines and its metabolism increases, the former arising from the increased pulmonary artery pressure and cardiac output, the latter from a combination of increased right coronary flow and a greater oxygen extraction from the coronary blood. The coronary response to elevation of left ventricular pressure by aortic constriction central to the coronary ostia is similar to that with pulmonary artery stenosis. In both instances, the sustained flow increase indicates a dominant influence of active coronary dilation over the increased mechanical flow-inhibiting effect of increasing extravascular compression which earlier was dominant. These maintained changes in the coronary circulation could well be the early response in the human being to gradual moderate stenosis of the corresponding valves.

HEART FAILURE. The heart shares with other types of muscle the characteristic that an optimum exists beyond which further stretching reduces the force of contraction and leads to myocardial failure. In acute heart failure with progressive deterioration of the myocardium from pulmonary artery stenosis, the changes in coronary flow and oxygen usage per minute and per beat may be in the same direction as those

described for the right myocardium but of lesser magnitude. If the heart failure is severe enough, extravascular compression can become dominant over any active coronary dilation from metabolic processes, and coronary flow and oxygen usage may be normal or decrease, with the oxygen extraction at times reaching 90 per cent. The coronary circulation in the heart failing with severe aortic stenosis undergoes similar changes. When acute heart failure and chronic congestive failure simulating the human condition are induced by surgical complete heart block, changes in left coronary flow and ventricular oxygen consumption also rather closely parallel alterations in the reduced left ventricular work. In chronic left heart failure due to rheumatic, arteriosclerotic, and hypertensive heart disease, the coronary circulation apparently responds by a slight increase in oxygen usage through maintenance of the left coronary flow and an increased coronary arteriovenous oxygen difference. This corresponds with the changes indicated above for the right heart in one stage of failure. Such hearts have considerable difficulty in transforming released energy into realizable work. Studies of the coronary circulation in high-output failure from excessive transfusion or a chronic aortacaval fistula are not available.

HYPOTHERMIA. The circulatory and metabolic adjustments of the heart during hypothermia have been partially explored. The associated changes that occur which tend to reduce the coronary flow are a diminution in blood and muscle temperatures, cardiac output, heart rate, cardiac work, oxygen usage by the heart, an increased blood viscosity, and a greatly lengthened period of ventricular systole. Opposing these factors are the relaxation of the major coronary vessels, which is known to occur with hypothermia, and dilation of the coronary bed caused by the hypotension per se. As a resultant of these determinants, coronary flow is decreased at low temperature. However, the percentage of reduction in cardiac output is greater than in coronary flow, which results in an increase in the coronary fraction of cardiac output at temperatures of 25 to 26°C. There is little change in peripheral resistance in the coronary bed, whereas in the systemic bed an increase in peripheral resistance occurs. Myocardial function appears to be adequate. However, many hearts are apparently not too far from failure, because if total venous inflow occlusion (which decreases coronary flow close to zero) is now added to permit open cardiotomy, myocardial failure supervenes, as evidenced by elevation in mean right atrial pressure and post-mortem findings. This trend can be reversed by perfusion of the coronary system with small volumes of oxygenated blood.

SHOCK. Standardized oligemic shock in dogs is characterized during the hypotensive phase by a decrease in cardiac output, systemic blood pressure, cardiac work, stroke volume, stroke work, and by an increase in heart rate and an adequate central venous pressure. Coronary flow and coronary resistance are greatly decreased. Coronary flow is generally greater and the resistance generally less than can be accounted for by a simple decline in arterial blood pressure. At the same time, the oxygen uptake decreases, and the coronary arteriovenous oxygen difference is generally unchanged. The coronary response to sustained hypotension through spinal anesthesia or injection of procaine and *Etamon* is similar. With restoration to normal systemic blood pressure by reinfusion (intraarterial and intravenous routes are equally effective), coronary flow is greater and flow resistance is less than at an equivalent arterial blood pressure in the preshock state, and the augmented flow is maintained after circulatory failure subsequently intervenes.

The fact that early in the hypotensive phase ventricular end diastolic pressure does not rise indicates that the functional capacity of the heart is adequate for the work performed. However, that myocardial depression or failure is partially responsible for the hemorrhagic shock syndrome is suggested by the fact that at times after prolonged hypotension there may be evident cardiac dilation and elevated left and right atrial pressures with the heart eventually proceeding to ventricular fibrillation or standstill. Gross and microscopic evidence of myocardial injury appears in both reversible and irreversible shock. Such myocardial depression could be caused by an insufficient coronary flow during either the hypotensive or the posthemorrhagic periods. The high coronary flow during the restoration period would seem to preclude an inadequate coronary flow as an adequate explanation. During the hypotensive period, the actual coronary flow is greatly curtailed. The problem is whether the associated sizable reduction in coronary resistance is sufficient to permit enough blood to reach the myocardium to prevent it from failing. In some instances, at least, this loss of myocardial contractility is consequent upon an insufficient coronary flow, since the relation of atrial pressure to cardiac size can be reversed by increasing mildly

with a pump left coronary flow without change to either the hypotension or blood volume.

HYPERTENSIVE CARDIOVASCULAR DISEASE. An exception to the general picture of coronary compensation to increased systemic stress appears to be the response of the chronically hypertensive heart. In essential hypertension with a normal cardiac output and elevated systemic blood pressure, the coronary flow and oxygen consumption are unaltered while coronary resistance increases. This increased resistance is shared with the renal and cerebral circulations. Since these hearts are generally hypertrophied, total coronary flow and oxygen usage are increased. This deviation is explainable if it is assumed that such hearts with known coronary artery disease have an increased amount of perfused fibrotic tissue.

Correct values for left coronary flow and myocardial oxygen consumption during natural maximal stress, such as exercise, are not available because of technical difficulties of instrumentation and application. However, the data suggest that with a normal hematocrit and normal arterial oxygen content, maximal work is determined by factors within the muscle and not by limitation of coronary flow and oxygen supply.

Is there one over-all unifying mechanism controlling coronary flow? Is there a similar mechanism controlling the oxygen usage of the myocardium? The answer has been sought for many years. From the preceding discussion, it is apparent that when the primary change in stress is an increased heart rate, increased venous return (whole blood transfusion), increased cardiac work, aortic coarctation (moderate), thyrotoxicosis, cardiac action of fibers from the sympathetic nerves, intravenous injection of epinephrine or norepinephrine, severe anemia or anoxia, there is an increase in cardiac work and cardiac oxygen usage. Concurrently, coronary flow increases while coronary vascular resistance decreases. In situations of primary decrease in stress such as hemorrhagic hypotension, hypothermia, and extreme heart failure, the cardiac work and oxygen consumption decrease as does the coronary inflow. An exception to this general picture of coronary compensation to changing stress is that of complete aortic coarctation which may be characterized by a reduction in the output and work of the heart but an increased left coronary flow and oxygen usage. A second exception is that of chronic hypertension in which the cardiac work is increased, but cardiac output, oxygen usage and left coronary flow are unaltered while coronary resistance to flow increases. Thus, in most instances, coronary flow follows a primary change in cardiac stress. However, correlation of coronary flow is best with $O_2$ usage. This relationship is understandable since the oxygen consumption is derived from the product of the coronary flow and the coronary arteriovenous oxygen difference. Normally, most oxygen is removed from the coronary blood, and the level of coronary sinus oxygen is usually fairly constant under stress, i.e., it does not change more than 10 to 15 per cent. In those instances in which the coronary arteriovenous oxygen difference increases or decreases by this amount, it does not greatly affect the relation of coronary flow to oxygen usage since the change is very small relative to the magnitude of the coronary flow change.

No final answer has been obtained as to the control of coronary flow. It has been variously related to the oxygen tension of the arterial blood, oxygen tension within the myocardium, and the action of local metabolites or vasodilating substances. Ultimately, at the cellular level, presumably, it is related to the rate of reduction of cytochrome oxidase and the needs of the hydrogen transport system.

It would be expected that the oxygen consumption during systole when ventricular muscle is shortening and developing tension, would depend in some way on the dynamic adaptation of the ventricle to its work. The presence of some such correlation was first illustrated by the experiments of Evans and Matsuoka, and of Starling and Visscher, indicating in the isolated heart a linear relation between diastolic volume and oxygen usage. More recently, it has been found that oxygen usage correlates best with the total tension developed by the left ventricle.

Most of the information thus far considered is based upon observations in the open-chest dog. It is not known to what extent it applies to normal situations since it has been obtained under conditions far removed from normal as the result of insults from anesthesia, surgery and trauma. It is true that semiquantitative values for coronary flow and oxygen usage are available in the resting human and dog. No information exists, however, in normal humans and animals as to the regulation of the coronary circulation exposed to the stresses of every day life such as exercise and excitement.

A start is being made in alleviating this situation. Successful direct measurements of coronary flow have been made in normal unanesthetized dogs by applying chronically an appropriate electromagnetic flow meter (a somewhat modified Kolin type) directly to the circumflex branch of the left coronary artery. Although this gives correct flow values, very often it causes thrombosis within a few days because of the violent heart action. To remove the probe to a quiet area, it is applied to the left internal mammary artery just above the site of its chronic anastomosis to the peripheral end of the left circumflex coronary artery (see section on coronary artery collaterals in this chapter). Illustrated in figure 24.6 are the changes in phasic and mean coronary flow in such a dog 15 months after construction of the anastomosis and 7 weeks after implantation of the electromagnetic flow meter probe. First, he stood on a treadmill, then ran for 3 minutes at 12 miles per hour at a 5 per cent grade, and finally, he stood at rest. Although not measured, the blood pressure and cardiac output obviously rose in this dog as they have in other dogs. A pulse pressure pattern has been sketched in for orientation purposes. The control flow is 46 cc. per minute, with most of this occurring during diastole. Within 15 to 20 seconds after the onset of exercise, the changes in the coronary flow response are complete and do not change further during the 3-minute period of exercise. The changes include an increase in heart rate from 80 to 220 per minute, a reduction in duration of both systole and diastole per beat, an increase in mean flow from 46 to 111 cc. per minute, as the result of a large reduction in systolic flow and an increase in diastolic flow per beat, and accentuation of back flow during systole. Calculation shows that the flow per heart beat is midlly decreased, and, hence, the mean flow increase is entirely on the basis of the increase in heart rate. Within 5 seconds after sudden stoppage of the treadmill, the patterns and flow have started to revert toward normal; the return to normal is completed within about 7 minutes. The last record was taken so that a comparison could be made between the maximum diastolic rate of flow during exercise and that during reactive hyperemia. It was taken shortly after the 7-minute recovery period and immediately following a 5-second occlusion by a pneumatic cuff of the coronary artery in which flow was being measured. Despite the slower heart rate, maximum diastolic flow during reactive hyperemia is about the same as that during exercise. This coronary flow response to exercise shown is not that which one observes when the workload of the heart is increased by transfusion or elevation of aortic pressure by aortic constriction. It does, however, resemble a combination of the effects resulting from a mechanical increase in

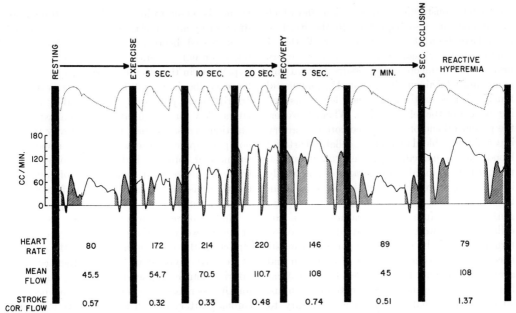

FIG. 24.6. Response of the unanesthetized, intact dog to exercise. Curves are redrawn from the original experiment. Phasic flow curves obtained with an electromagnetic flow meter monitoring an internal mammary-circumflex coronary anastomotic shunt. *Upper curve*, aortic pressure. *Lower curve*, phasic circumflex coronary flow. (Gregg, D. E. unpublished data).

heart rate by means of an artificial pacemaker and from the augmentation of cardiac contractility resulting from stimulation of the cardiac fibers from the left stellate ganglion or following the intracoronary injection of epinephrine or levarterenol. The ultimate interpretation remains to be determined.

### The Coronary Artery Collateral Circulation

The state of the human heart in the presence of naturally occurring coronary insufficiency or occlusion, or the state of the dog's heart in which coronary insufficiency has been experimentally induced, can be improved by augmentation of the coronary artery collateral circulation which naturally functions, by retrograde perfusion of the ischemic coronary bed with arterial blood, or by elevation of the ventricular fibrillation threshold, thus giving time for collaterals to develop. In addition, in man, positive and subjective benefit could arise through psychogenic effects which are not necessarily related to the heart.

Information on the coronary collateral circulation is no better than the method used to obtain it and experimental tools for study of the collateral circulation are admittedly crude. These are concerned with measurements of the effects of various prophylactic and postcoronary occlusion procedures on the electrocardiogram, mortality,

size of infarcts, exercise tolerance, and finally, on the injectable and functional collaterals in the presence of coronary occlusion or insufficiency. All are difficult to evaluate because of the considerable variability of the size of the naturally occurring collateral circulation.

The measurement which is most important, least subject to error, and which has yielded most information, is that of the collateral flow. This is determined by collecting the volume of blood that flows externally from a tube inserted into the peripheral end of an occluded coronary artery. This is done acutely in the open-chest dog before, and sometime after, a variable has been chronically induced to improve collateral flow. This is collateral flow before it passes through a capillary bed. Collateral flow can also be measured after it has passed through a capillary bed and has appeared in the coronary sinus. This can be done when extracardiac tissue with a vascular stalk has been previously placed on the heart to stimulate collateral development. The coronary sinus flow is measured before and after clamping the potential extracardiac source of collateral blood. The difference in flow represents that which has traversed the capillary bed.

NATURAL RESPONSE OF THE CORONARY COLLATERAL CIRCULATION. The natural responses of the coronary system during experimental coronary artery constriction and occlusion, and which presumably are also happening in the heart of man, have been studied extensively. Within 1 minute after occlusion of a left coronary artery branch, the intracoronary pressure beyond this point drops to about $35/25$ mm. Hg and useful function is lost, for the muscle now lengthens during systole of the left ventricle. When, however, the peripheral end of this ligated coronary artery is permitted to bleed externally, collateral arterial blood appears immediately, averaging about 3.0 ml. per minute for about 50 grams of potentially infarcted myocardium. Probably not more than 2.4 ml. of this blood (containing 0.5 ml. of oxygen) would perfuse the myocardial bed if the collateral flow were not permitted to bleed externally. This is because of the peripheral resistance existing beyond the point of occlusion and averaging 23 mm. Hg. This level of collateral flow and oxygen content is estimated to be up to 40 per cent of that calculated as necessary to maintain indefinitely the viability of this myocardium, since the oxygen uptake of 50 grams of a heart with perfused coronary arteries at rest and doing no external work approximates 1.2 ml. as compared to the immediately available collateral oxygen supply of 0.5 ml.

Hence, it is important to try to increase immediately this collateral flow or backflow. The level of backflow does not naturally increase and cannot be made to increase for 8 to 10 hours by drugs or by any known physiological means such as increased heart rate, increased flow in the other coronary arteries, induction of hypoxia or hypoxemia in the other coronary arteries. It can, however, be increased by passive elevation of arterial blood pressure (fig. 24.7). Why the collateral flow remains fixed, why the anastomoses function as a set of inert tubes, and why they do not participate in the vasodilatory response of the normal coronary bed is not known. It contrasts with the rapid development of collaterals in other vascular beds such as the femoral and carotid arteries.

This retrograde flow can be greatly reduced by at least two conditions, namely, by excessive stretch of the myocardium and by the presence of reactive hyperemia in the other coronary arterial branches. One suspects that the reason for the decreased collateral flow in an occluded coronary artery branch while reactive hyperemia exists in the other coronaries is also the excessive stretch of the normal myocardium. Thus, the improvement that occurs in the human heart with drugs such as Neo-Synephrine in the presence of coronary insufficiency and infarction arises because of a good dynamic response in the normal but over-stretched myocardium. This would increase the collateral flow by increasing the coronary perfusion pressure and by making a smaller heart.

Most hearts with an occluded coronary artery branch die within a number of hours. Others are more fortunate collateral-wise for, if they survive the first few hours, then, for some completely unknown reason, within 12 hours collateral flow starts to rise, doubling within 2 days and within 3 to 4 weeks it may approximate 40 to 100 per cent of normal inflow into that coronary artery. At the same time the peripheral coronary pressure pulse beyond the point of ligation of the coronary artery branch may approximate in pattern and ordinate values the aortic pressure pattern, simultaneously recorded.

These are the ordinary hearts. In other hearts, stresses, some known but mostly unknown, prophylactically enhance the potential collateral circulation without the stimulus of coronary insufficiency or occlusion (Table 24.2). These are exemplified in man by the increase in the incidence of the injectable collateral bed in the presence of hypertrophy, valvular disease, cor pulmonale, and anemia, and probably high altitude. This is exemplified in animals by an increase in both the injectable and functional collaterals in

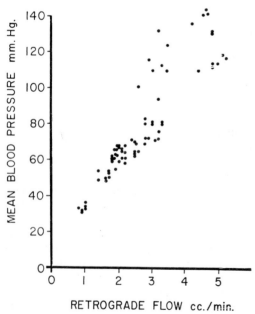

Fig. 24.7. Relation of retrograde coronary flow to mean arterial perfusion pressure in dogs. (Kattus and Gregg, Circulation Res., 1959, **7**, 628.)

TABLE 24.2

*Prophylactic augmentation of coronary artery collaterals by natural stimuli*

| | Known stimuli | Incidence of injectable collaterals % | Retrograde flow ml./min. |
|---|---|---|---|
| Man | None | 9 | — |
| | Hypertrophy | 26 | — |
| | Valvular disease | 28 | — |
| | Cor pulmonale | 73 | — |
| | Anemia | 39 | — |
| | Coronary constriction | 11 – 63 | — |
| | Coronary occlusion | 90 – 100 | — |
| | High altitude (man & pig) | ↗ | ↗ |
| Pig | Anemia | 100 | — |
| Dog | Transfused anemia | ↗ | 9 art. |
| Dog | Mild coronary constriction and exercise | → | 3 art. |

the presence of high altitude and transfused anemia. No good experimental evidence exists to indicate that physical exercise per se augments prophylactically the collateral flow as measured in a normal coronary artery immediately after its occlusion. Even with a combination of moderate coronary artery constriction and exercise, the retrograde flow does not increase.

DRUGS VERSUS CORONARY COLLATERAL FUNCTION. Since the vascular bed beyond an occluded coronary artery is presumably maximally dilated by anoxia, it is unlikely that a drug could improve a heart by immediately increasing flow to this area. Actually, the best experimental evidence offers no support for the belief that any drug penetrates the connecting collaterals or exerts any beneficial influence in the ischemic bed. It has not been possible to increase the flow of blood into this ischemic area within a short time after coronary artery occlusion, or to retain myocardial shortening by the use of drugs that are known to dilate the normal coronary bed, such as papaverine, nitroglycerine, epinephrine, aminophylline, coramin, and khellin. In chronic experiments, cortisone and ACTH do not promote collateral flow or reduce the size of infarcts. The hypothesis that coronary occlusion reflexively decreases flow in the nonoccluded coronary artery to a fatal level, it is not borne out by the experimental fact that flow in the nonoccluded coronary artery generally rises with coronary artery ligation. The alleged favorable effect on survival of prophylactic and therapeutic drugs, such as papaverine and quinidine, is better explained by their known action in raising the fibrillation threshold and in reducing the excitability of the myocardium.

NATURAL RESPONSE OF THE NORMAL BUT OVERSTRESSED PORTION OF THE MYOCARDIUM. Since the collateral flow does not increase for some hours, any early natural compensation must occur, not by improvement of the circulation in the affected area, but through enhanced action of the normal myocardium which is not involved. Deletion of contracting muscle blocks following coronary artery occlusion not only reduces the total myocardial force available for raising intraventricular tension, but some of this pressure is spent in stretching the ischemic area and thus is lost for expelling blood into the aorta. The immediate consequences of this which lead to a hypodynamic ventricle are a reduction in left ventricular systolic pressure, aortic pulse pressure, systolic and diastolic pressures, duration of systole, and in stroke volume and stroke work. In this situation, left coronary inflow decreases considerably because of the mechanical reduction in size of the peripheral vascular bed. However, within a few minutes, the normal portion of the heart puts into operation compensatory mechanisms by means of which dynamic conditions are largely restored to normal, provided the normal myocardium is in a good responsive condition. Briefly, as the result of the lesser expulsion of blood with hypodynamic beats, the accumulating systolic remainder added to the oncoming blood stretches the viable muscle more and raises the ventricular end diastolic pressure or left atrial pressure. This combination of increased pressure in and increased radius of the ventricular cavity, causes the normal muscle to contract more vigorously, thereby restoring normal hemodynamics. In this situation of increased cardiac work per unit of functioning myocardium, coronary flow, arteriovenous oxygen difference, and metabolism of the left ventricle increase. The increase in oxygen uptake is equal to, and at times can be much more than that lost by the deletion of noncontractile muscle.

However, not all hearts react as well because the viable portion of the myocardium may not respond to stretch, or the same lack of response may occur later after an initial salutary response. This has been especially studied when the coronary obstruction has been induced by intracoronary injection of microspheres. This leads to acute or progressive heart failure associated with a profound hypotension with a decreased cardiac output, and the clinical signs and symptoms of a shocklike state similar to that which occurs following the loss of blood or plasma. The clinical inference that this is due to the supervention of peripheral circulatory failure has not received heavy experimental support. On the contrary, experimental work favors the view that in this situation, circulatory failure not due to severe ireegularity of the heart beat is due, successively, to defection of useful contractions in the ischemic area, a loss of contractile energy through expansion of the affected area, and failure of the still viable fractions to compensate adequately.

EFFECTS OF DRUGS AND AN EXTRACORPOREAL CIRCULATION IN THE PRESENCE OF MYOCARDIAL INFARCTION WITH SHOCK. Since protracted hypotension can, at times, lead to myocardial damage and failure, and since experimentally, the coronary collateral flow varies passively with the systemic blood pressure, attempts have been made to improve such hearts experimentally and clinically by drugs and a veno-arterial perfusion.

The state of the heavily stressed normal myocardium could be improved with drugs either by increasing its oxygen supply or by using the available oxygen more economically. The major mechanism for increasing the oxygen supply is by increased coronary flow since, normally, the oxygen is largely extracted from blood passing through the myocardium. The drugs would have to promote coronary flow in the heavily loaded normal myocardium in which oxygen usage, coronary flow and coronary A-VO$_2$ difference are already at a high level. Whether any drug has the desired type of dilation (active myocardial vessel relaxation, decreased extravascular compression, minimal increase in metabolism and cardiac work, minimal effect on other vascular beds), and whether it also increases ventricular efficiency, remains to be determined. In the normal dog, drugs such as papaverine, nitroglycerine, epinephrine, aminophylline, coramine, the adenosine nucleotides, and khellin augment the myocardial oxygen supply, but generally at a considerable expense to the heart, through decreased coronary sinus oxygen (with nitroglycerine coronary sinus oxygen is increased), and increased cardiac work and metabolism. In normal man, sublingual nitroglycerine leads to an increased myocardial oxygen usage (increased coronary flow and constant coronary A-VO$_2$ difference), with little or no change in cardiac output and cardiac work, and with a decreased efficiency. In patients at rest with coronary artery disease, coronary flow is normal. Following nitroglycerine, coronary flow and oxygen usage are unchanged, but systemic blood pressure, cardiac work and cardiac output are reduced; hence, coronary resistance is not changed, while efficiency is decreased. It would thus seem that the dilator capacity of the coronary tree with coronary artery disease is exhausted. The mechanism whereby nitroglycerin relieves pain is not that of general coronary dilation and is unknown.

The incidence of cardiogenic shock complicating acute myocardial infarction has been reported as 12 per cent. Mortality associated with this complication may be in excess of 80 per cent. Vasopressor drugs have been widely employed in this situation. The improvement that occurs in the human heart with drugs such as neosynephrine, in the presence of coronary insufficiency and infarction, arises because of a good dynamic response in the normal but overstretched myocardium. This presumably augments the coronary collateral flow by increasing the coronary perfusion pressure and by making the heart smaller.

Although the use of vasopressor agents reduces mortality in myocardial infarction with shock, at least half fail to respond. In such patients, extracorporeal circulatory support is being tried whereby blood is pumped from a convenient vein to an artery. The major objective is to produce a sustained increase in aortic pressure and, hence, an increase in coronary, cerebral, and other important regional circulations, and yet without an increase in left ventricular work that might cause further cardiac deterioration. Conclusive evidence of the benefit of this procedure has not yet been obtained.

ATTEMPTS TO IMPROVE CORONARY COLLATERAL CIRCULATION. The state of such hearts can be improved considerably by various physiological and surgical procedures. The principles of the procedures used together with the surgical manipulations are portrayed (Table 24.3). These include section of the cardiac sympathetic nerves, induction of myocardial hypoxia by various manipulations of the coronary venous system, production of chronic epicardial granuloma by mechanical and chemical means, application of extracardiac tissue to the heart, internal mammary artery ligation, sham operations, coronary endarterectomy and coronary artery bypass.

*A. Animals.* Many of these procedures in the experimental animal are of positive benefit to the heart and give immediate or sustained protection against subsequent ligation of a major coronary artery ramus. This is illustrated in the data obtained in many laboratories (Table 24.4). Ligation of a major ramus of the left coronary artery causes about a 70 per cent mortality within the first 1 to 2 hours, and chronically there is considerable infarction. When partial or complete occlusion of the coronary sinus precedes coronary artery ligation, or when a portion of the coronary bed is perfused in retrograde fashion by connecting the coronary sinus to an artery, the immediate mortality is reduced considerably. With the exception of section of cardiac sympathetic fibers and internal mammary artery ligation, all other procedures listed—chronic coronary venous maneuvers, application of various chemical and mechanical irritants, separately or in combination, and application of extracardiac tissue to the heart lead to a significant reduction in mortality and infarction. There is an increase in the injectable and functional collaterals with the chronic coronary venous maneuvers and with the application of mechanical and chemical irritants to the heart. The level of collateral flow, 5 to 12 cc. in

TABLE 24.3

*Procedures for improving coronary function (man and animal)*

| Approaches | Tissue |
|---|---|
| Section cardiac sympathetic fibres | |
| Myocardial hypoxia | Coronary sinus constriction or ligation, aorta - cor. sinus shunt pulmonary artery-left atrial shunt |
| Chronic pericardial granuloma via mechanical and chemical means | Talc, powdered bone, asbestos, mica, gelatin, sponge, silver nitrate, mechanical burrs |
| Application extra cardiac tissue to the heart | Spleen, omentum, fat, muscle, skin flap, intestine, lung, arterial implants |
| Internal mammary artery ligation | |
| Sham operation | |
| Coronary by-pass and endarterectomy | Internal mammary and carotid arteries |

TABLE 24.4

*Physiological effects of prophylactic procedures on coronary collaterals (dog)*

Directional arrows merely indicate direction, not magnitude, i.e., → no change, ↗ increase or ↘ decrease.

| Experiment | Procedures prior to ligation of coronary artery ramus | Acute ligation of coronary artery ramus | | | | |
|---|---|---|---|---|---|---|
| | | Mortality % | Infarction | Injectable collaterals | Retrograde flow ml./min. | Persistence of collaterals |
| Acute | None | 70 | — | — | 3 art. | — |
| Chronic | None | 70 | Gross | — | 50 art. | — |
| Chronic | Section cardiac sympathetic fibres | → | → | → | → | — |
| Acute | (Cor sinus constriction or ligation) (Aorta-coronary sinus shunt) | ↘ | — | — | 15 ven. | — |
| Chronic | (Cor sinus constriction or ligation) (Aorta-coronary sinus shunt-Beck#2) | ↘ | ↘ | ↗ | 7-12 art. | yes |
| Chronic | Irritants applied to heart -- Talc, asbestos, mechanical abrasion, mica, phenol, silver nitrate, etc. | ↘ | ↘ | ↗ | 5-8 art. | yes |
| Chronic | Mechanical abrasion, asbestos, cor sinus reduced to 3 mm., fat-Beck #1 | ↘ | ↘ | ↗ | 8 art. | yes |
| Chronic | Extracardiac tissue -- muscle, lungs, intestine, omentum, pedicle, skin flap, internal mammary artery | ↘ | ↘ | ↗ | 2 art. | — |
| Chronic | Ligation internal mammary artery | → | → | → | 3 art. | — |
| Chronic | Sham operation | ↘ | ↘ | ↗ | 7 art. | — |
| Chronic | Cor by-pass and coronary endarterectomy | — | — | — | — | — |

most instances, considerably exceeds the control flow of 3 cc. with acute artery ligation alone, and approximates that necessary to maintain viability in the potentially infarcted area. There is as yet no evidence that the protection of the heart afforded by "arterialization" of the coronary sinus arises from passage of blood retrogradely from vein to capillary. Such a procedure reduces left coronary inflow, hence, it is more likely that the benefit arises from the increased collateral flow which is associated with the induced myocardial hypoxia. In general, the over-all protection to the heart by the various procedures is probably on a collateral flow basis, but since sham operations involving manipulation of the heart also increase collateral flow, the possibility must be entertained that there may be no specific effect of some of the maneuvers; they may act by raising the ventricular fibrillation threshold, thus giving time for collaterals to develop.

In some procedures that apply extracardiac tissue to the heart, such as a pedicle skin flap, internal mammary artery ligation or its myocardial implantation, the collateral flow does not increase. These studies, however, are incomplete.

Further work should be done to determine, in addition to the usual arterial collateral flow measurements, whether blood brought in by the extracardiac tissue actually flows through the capillary bed of the myocardium in the presence of chronic as well as acute coronary occlusion. If it does, then it should be possible to demonstrate its presence in the coronary sinus flow. Preliminary experiments indicate, however, that clamping of the extracardiac source of a myocardially imbedded artery, pedicle skin flap, etc., does not usually affect coronary sinus flow.

*B. Man.* All of the procedures listed in Table 24.3, designed to promote collateral development, including the sham operation, have been applied to the heart of man suffering from coronary artery disease. All appear to increase to some extent the work and exercise tolerance and to decrease the cardiac pain. These observations are not necessarily explained on the same basis of the improvement in the collateral circulation of the dog which follows such procedures. This is because in the dog, surgery precedes coronary artery ligation, whereas in the human, surgery follows coronary artery occlusion. Surgery in the dog is designed to promote collaterals in the presence of a normal coronary circulation. Surgery in the human is designed to promote collateral circulation after the coronary insufficiency has been naturally established. In man, hypoxia, the greatest known vessel dilator, and a natural stimulus to collateral development, has already been working for many months. To be effective, the surgical procedure must supply a stimulus to collateral development far more potent than hypoxia. This has never been demonstrated in animals in which coronary insufficiency has previously been induced.

The explanation of the results in man are not clear. Undoubtedly, some subjects are protected and live longer because of the known experimental fact that handling the heart enhances the ventricular fibrillation threshold. Some may be improved by procedures such as de-epicardialization which could obliterate the afferent pathways for pain. However, results of the sham operation of Lillehei, Adams and of others, involving only a skin incision, strongly suggest that much of the positive benefit is on a psychogenic basis.

Coronary endarterectomy, which has been applied to man, is on a sound physiological basis, and its purpose is entirely different from the preceding. The surgeon directly re-establishes coronary flow through the original coronary artery by removing its atherosclerotic plug. It does not require collateral development and should be effective provided there exists a gross coronary insufficiency of blood beyond the obstruction, provided the vessel remains patent and thrombi do not form, and provided there are no sizeable atherosclerotic lesions beyond the region of the occluded coronary artery. Although initial operations were apparently favorable to the patients, relieving their angina, improving their electrocardiograms and work tolerance, a later report is not so sanguine. Many more operations will have to be done to establish the possible merit of this procedure in humans.

Finally, bypass of a length of an occluded coronary artery by anstomosis of its peripheral patent end to a systemic artery has not yet been attempted in man. In dogs, a nonsuture anastomosis by intima to intima contact between the left coronary artery and the left internal mammary artery has been highly successful. In almost all of the dogs, the anastomoses have been demonstrated to be patent and without myocardial infarction, as evidenced by gross observation, angiography, and measurement of coronary blood flow through the anastomosis up to the time of dog sacrifice (12 to 24 months after operation).

Since such an operation is almost always successful and without sequelae in the dog in which the anastomosed vessels are only 2 to 2.5 mm. diameter, there should be no difficulty at all in the human heart in which the coronary artery branches have a much greater diameter. This procedure could, therefore, have a very practical application in the creation of a permanent new blood supply in the presence of coronary artery disease in man.

There is, however, a probable late complication to successful coronary endarterectomy or coronary bypass in man which must not be overlooked. In the presence of such a large new blood supply, the existing collateral flow might disappear. If another coronary occlusion subsequently occurs, the patient would be in difficulties because he had lost his collaterals.

## Summary

From the preceding, it would appear that in the normal heart a moderate collateral circulation exists which functions immediately following a coronary artery occlusion. Different prophylactic procedures are successful experimentally in preserving life either by compensating for a deficit in the supply of collateral oxygen or by preventing ventricular fibrillation. This protection against occlusion of a coronary artery may be associated with a collateral development on the arterial side of the order of magnitude of that essential for viability. Human coronary surgery which follows coronary insufficiency has no counterpart in animal experiments and these human coronary experiments cannot as yet be interpreted on a physiological basis.

## REFERENCES

ABRAMSON, D. I., TUCK, S., JR., AND BELL, Y. Blood flow and oxygen uptake responses to short periods of arterial occlusion. Fed. Proc., 1960, **19**, 95 (Abstract).

ADAMS, R. Internal mammary-artery ligation for coronary insufficiency. An evaluation. New England J. Med., 1958, **258**, 113.

BAROLDI, G., MANTERO, O., AND SCOMAZZONI, G. The collaterals of the coronary arteries in normal and pathologic hearts. Circulation Res., 1956, **4**, 223.

BARONOFSKY, I. D., SPROFKA, J. L., AND NOBLE, J. F. Use of intestinal loops for revascularization of the heart. Circulation Res., 1954, **2**, 506.

BERNE, R. M. The effect of immersion hypothermia on coronary blood flow. Circulation Res., 1954, **2**, 236.

BERNE, R. M., BLACKMON, R. J., AND GARDNER, T. H. Hypoxemia and coronary blood flow. J. Clin. Invest., 1957, **36**, 1101.

BING, R. J., CASTELLANOS, A., GRADEL, E., SIEGEL, A., AND LUPTON, C. Enzymatic, metabolic, circulatory and pathologic studies in myocardial infarction. Tr. A. Am. Physicians, 1956, **69**, 170.

BLUMGART, H. L., ZOLL, P. M., PAUL, M. H., AND NORMAN, L. R. The experimental production of intercoronary arterial anastomoses and their functional significance. Circulation, 1950, **1**, 10.

BRACHFELD, N., Bozer, J., AND GORLIN, R. Action of nitroglycerin on the coronary circulation in normal and in mild cardiac subjects. Circulation, 1959, **19**, 697.

CANNON, J. A., LONGMIRE, W. P., AND KATTUS, A. A. Considerations of the rationale and technic of coronary endarterectomy for angina pectoris. Surgery, 1959, **46**, 197.

CASE, R. B., BERGLUND, E., AND SARNOFF, S. J. Ventricular function. II. Quantitative relationship between coronary flow and ventricular function with observation on unilateral failure. Circulation Res., 1954, **2**, 319.

COFFMAN, J. D. AND GREGG, D. E. Blood flow and oxygen debt from coronary artery occlusion. Clin. Res., 1960, **8**, 179.

COFFMAN, J. D. AND GREGG, D. E. Reactive hyperemia flow characteristics of canine myocardium. Fed. Proc., 1960, **19**, 91 (Abstract).

DAY, S. B. AND LILLEHEI, C. W. Experimental basis for a new operation for coronary artery disease. A left atrial-pulmonary artery shunt to encourage development of interarterial intercoronary anastomoses. Surgery, 1959, **45**, 487.

DENISON, A. B., JR., BARDHANABAEDVA, S., AND GREEN, H. D. Adrenergic drugs and blockade on coronary arterioles and myocardial contraction. Circulation Res., 1956, **4**, 653.

DUFF, F., BERGLUND, E., AND BORST, H. Effects of heart rate on ventricular function and coronary circulation in dogs. Am. J. Physiol., 1955, **183**, 611.

ECKENHOFF, J. E., HASKENSHIEL, J. H., LANDMESSER, C. M., AND HARMEL, M. Cardiac oxygen metabolism and control of the coronary circulation. Am. J. Physiol., 1947, **149**, 634.

ECKSTEIN, R. W., STROUD, M., III., ECKEL, R., DOWLING, C. V., AND PRITCHARD, W. H. Effects of control of cardiac work upon coronary flow and oxygen consumption after sympathetic nerve stimulation. Am. J. Physiol., 1950, **163**, 539.

ECKSTEIN, R. W. Development of interarterial coronary anastomoses by chronic anemia. Disappearance following correction of anemia. Circulation Res., 1955, **3**, 306.

ECKSTEIN, R. W. Effect of exercise and coronary artery narrowing on coronary collateral circulation. Circulation Res., 1957, **5**, 230.

ECKSTEIN, R. W. AND LEIGHNINGER, D. S. Chronic effects of aorta-coronary sinus anastomosis of Beck in dogs. Circulation Res., 1954, **2**, 60.

EVANS, C. L. AND MATSUOKA, Y. The effect of various mechanical conditions on the gaseous metabolism and efficiency of the mammalian heart. J. Physiol., 1915, **49**, 378.

FOLTZ, E. L., PAGE, R. G., SHELDON, W. F., WONG, S. K., TUDDENHAM, W. J., AND WEISS, A. J. Factors in variations and regulations of coronary blood flow in intact anesthetized dogs. Am. J. Physiol., 1950, **162**, 521.

FREIS, E. D., SCHNAPER, E. W., JOHNSON, R. L., AND SCHREINER, G. E. Hemodynamic alterations in acute myocardial infarction. Cardiac output, mean arterial pressure, total peripheral resistance, "central" and total blood volumes, venous pressure and average circulation time. J. Clin. Invest., 1952, **31**, 131.

GOODALE, W. T., OLSON, R. E., AND HACKEL, D. B. The effects of fasting and diabetes mellitus on myocardial metabolism in man. Am. J. Med., 1959, **27**, 212.

GORLIN, R., BRACHFELD, N., MacLEOD, C., AND BOPP, P. Effect of nitroglycerin on the coronary circulation in patients with coronary artery disease or increased left ventricular work. Circulation, 1959, **19**, 705.

GREEN, H. D. AND WEGRIA, R. Effects of asphyxia, anoxia and myocardial ischemia on the coronary circulation. Am. J. Physiol., 1942, **135**, 271.

GREEN, H. D., WEGRIA, R., AND BOYER, N. H. Effects of epinephrine and pitressin on the coronary artery inflow in anesthetized dogs. J. Pharmacol. & Exper. Therap., 1942, **76**, 378.

GREGG, D. E. AND SHIPLEY, R. E. Studies of the venous drainage of the heart. Am. J. Physiol., 1947, **151**, 13.

GREGG, D. E. AND GREEN, H. D. Registration and interpretation of normal phasic inflow into a left coronary artery by an improved manometric method. Am. J. Physiol., 1940, **130**, 114.

GREGG, D. E. AND SHIPLEY, R. E. Changes in right and left coronary artery inflow with cardiac nerve stimulation. Am. J. Physiol., 1944, **141**, 382.

GREGG, D. E. AND SHIPLEY, R. E. Augmentation of left coronary inflow with elevation of left ventricular pressure and observation on the mechanism for increased coronary inflow with increased cardiac load. Am. J. Physiol., 1944, **142**, 44.

GREGG, D. E., PRITCHARD, W. H., SHIPLEY, R. E., AND WEARN, J. T. Augmentation of blood flow in the coronary arteries with elevation of right ventricular pressure. Am. J. Physiol., 1943, **139**, 726.

GREGG, D. E., THORNTON, J. J., AND MAUTZ, F. R. The magnitude, adequacy and source of the collateral blood flow and pressure in chronically occluded coronary arteries. Am. J. Physiol., 1939, **127**, 161.

HACKEL, D. B., SANCETTA, S. M., AND KLEINERMAN, J. Effect of hypotension due to spinal anesthesia on coronary blood flow and myocardial metabolism in man. Circulation, 1956, **13**, 92.

HALL, R. J., KHOURI, E. M., AND GREGG, D. E. Non-suture internal mammary-coronary artery anastomosis. (abstract). Circulation, 1959, **20**, 791.

HARKEN, D. E., BLACK, H., DICKSON, J. F., III, AND WILSON, H. E., III. De-epicardialization: A simple, effective surgical treatment for angina pectoris. Circulation, 1955, **12**, 955.

JACOBS, H. I., ROSEN, V., AND AGRESS, C. M. Further evidence for a critical vessel caliber in experimental coronary shock. Circulation Res., 1953, 1, 466.

JELLIFE, R. W., WOLF, C. R., BERNE, R. M., AND ECKSTEIN, R. W. Absence of vasoactive and cardiotropic substances in coronary sinus blood of dogs. Circulation Res., 1957, 5, 382.

KATTUS, A. A. AND GREGG, D. E. Some determinants of coronary collateral blood flow in the open chest dog. Circulation Res., 1959, 7, 628.

KATZ, A. M., KATZ. L. N., AND WILLIAMS, F. L. Regulation of coronary flow. Am. J. Physiol., 1955, 180, 392.

KUHN, L. W., GRUBER, F. L., FRANKEL, A., AND KUPFER, S. Hemodynamic effects of extracorporeal circulation on coronary shock. Circulation Res., 1960, 8, 199.

LEIGHT, L., DEFAZIO, V., TALMERS, F. M., REGAN, T. J., AND HELLEMS, H. K. Coronary blood flow, myocardial oxygen consumption and myocardial metabolism in normal and hyperthyroid human subjects. Circulation, 1956, 14, 90.

McKEEVER, W. P., GREGG, D. E., AND CANNEY, P. C. Oxygen uptake of the non-working left ventricle. Circulation Res., 1958, 6, 612.

LEWIS, F. B., COFFMAN, J. D., AND GREGG, D. E. The effect of heart rate and intracoronary isoproterenol, levarterenol and epinephrine on coronary flow and resistance. Circul. Res. 1960 (In Press)

OPDYKE, D. F. AND FOREMAN, R. C. A study of coronary flow under conditions of hemorrhagic hypotension and shock. Am. J. Physiol., 1947, 148, 726.

OSHER, W. J. Pressure-flow relationship of the coronary system. Am. J. Physiol., 1953, 172, 403.

PAUL, M. H., THEILEN, E. O., GREGG, D. E., MARSH, J. B., AND CASTEN, G. G. Cardial metabolism in experimental ventricular fibrillation. Circulation Res., 1954, 2, 573.

RAYFORD, C. R., KHOURI, E. M., LEWIS, F. B., AND GREGG, D. E. Evaluation of the use of the left coronary artery inflow and the oxygen content of the coronary sinus blood as a measure of left ventricular metabolism. J. Appl. Physiol., 1959, 14, 817.

ROWE, G. G., HUSTON, J. H., MAXWELL, G. M., WEINSTEIN, A. B., TUCKMAN, H., AND CRUMPTON, C. W. The effects of 1-Hydrazinophthalazine upon coronary hemodynamics and myocardial oxygen metabolism in essential hypertension. J. Clin. Invest., 1955, 34, 696.

SABISTON, D. C. AND GREGG, D. E. Effect of cardiac contraction on coronary blood flow. Circulation, 1957, 15, 14.

SABISTON, D. C., THEILEN, E. O., AND GREGG, D. E. The relation of coronary blood flow and cardiac output and other parameters in hypothermia. Surgery, 1955, 38, 498.

SABISTON, D. C., FAUTEUX, P. J., AND BLALOCK, A. An experimental study of the fate of arterial implants in the left ventricular myocardium. Ann. Surg., 1957, 145, 927.

SARNOFF, S. J., BRAUNWALD, E., WELCH, G. H., JR., CASE, R. B., STAINSBY, W. N., AND MACRUZ, R. Hemodynamic determinants of oxygen consumption of the heart with special reference to

the tension-time index. Am. J. Physiol., 1958, 192, 148.

SCHLESINGER, M. J. Significant variations in the anatomic pattern of the coronary vessels. Blood, heart and circulation. Publ. Am. Ass. Advance. Sci., 1940, 13, 61.

SHIPLEY, R. E. AND GREGG, D. E. The cardiac response to stimulation of the stellate ganglia and cardiac nerves. Am. J. Physiol., 1945, 143, 396.

STARLING, E. H. AND VISSCHER, M. B. The regulation of the energy output of the heart. J. Physiol., 1927, 62, 243.

THEILEN, E. O., PAUL, M. H., AND GREGG, D. E. A comparison of the effects of intra-arterial and intravenous transfusions in hemorrhagic hypotension on coronary blood flow, systemic blood pressure and ventricular end-diastolic pressure. J. Appl. Physiol., 1954, 7, 248.

VASTESAEGER, M., VAN DER STRAETEN, P. P., FRIART, J., CANDAELE, G., GHYS, A., AND BERNARD, R. M. Les anastomoses intercoronariennes telles qu'elles apparaissent a la coronarographie postmortem. Acta cardiol., 1957, 12, 365.

VIDONE, R. A., KLINE, J. L., PITEL, M., AND LIEBOW, A. A. The application of an induced bronchial collateral circulation to the coronary arteries by cardiopneumonopexy. II. Hemodynamics and the measurement of collateral flow to the myocardium. Am. J. Pathol., 1956, 32, 897.

VINEBERG, A. AND WALKER, J. Six months to six years experience with coronary artery insufficiency treated by internal mammary artery implantation. Am. Heart J., 1957, 54, 851.

WARTMAN, W. B., CAMPBELL, L. A., AND CRAIG, R. L. The effect of ACTH on experimental myocardial infarcts. Circulation Res., 1955, 3, 496.

WEGRIA, R. AND NICKERSON, N. D. The effect of papaverine, epinephrine, and quinidine on the fibrillation threshold of the mammalian ventricle. J. Pharmacol. & Exper. Therap., 1942, 75, 50.

WIGGERS, C. J. AND GREEN, H. D. The ineffectiveness of drugs upon collateral flow after experimental coronary occlusion in dogs. Am. Heart J., 1936, 11, 527.

WOLF, M. M. AND BERNE, R. M. Coronary vasodilator properties of purine and pyrimidine derivatives. Circulation Res., 1956, 4, 343.

YONCE, L. R. AND HAMILTON, W. F. Oxygen consumption in skeletal muscle during reactive hyperemia. Am. J. Physiol., 1959, 197, 190.

ZOLL, P. M., WESSLER, S., AND SCHLESINGER, M. J. Interarterial coronary anastomoses in the human heart with particular reference to anemia and relative cardiac anoxia. Circulation, 1951, 4, 797.

*Monographs and Reviews*

AGRESS, C. M., KITCHELL, J. R., SCHERF, D., BINE, R., JR., BROTMAN, I., AND GOFMAN, J. W. Symposium on treatment of myocardial infarction. Am. J. Cardiol. 1958, 1, 224.

ALELLA, A., BRETSCHNEIDER, H. J., DELIUS, L., GIESE, W., HARDERS, H., HAUSS, W. H., LUBBERS, D., MATTHES, K., MEESMANN, W., MERCKER, H., MOLBERT, E., MULLER-MOHNSSEN, H.,

SCHMIER, J., SCHOEDEL, W., SCHOENMACKERS, J., AND WITZLEB, E. Probleme der Coronardurchblutung, Bad Oeynhausener Gesprache II, Springer-Verlag, Heidelberg, 1958.

BECK, C. S., BROFMAN, B. L., AND MAUTZ, F. R. Symposium on coronary artery disease. Dis. Chest, 1957, **31**, 243.

BING, R. J. The coronary circulation in health and disease as studied by coronary sinus catheterization. Bull. New York Acad. Med., 1951, **27**, 407.

BING, R. J. The Harvey Lectures, p. 27, The Academic Press, New York, 1956.

BLUMGART, H. L. Anatomical and functional importance of intercoronary arterial anastomoses (ed.) Circulation, 1959, **20**, 812.

GREGG, D. E. Coronary circulation in health and disease. Lea & Febiger, 1950.

GREGG, D. E. Regulation of the collateral and coronary circulation of the heart. Lecture, Harvey Tercentenary Congress, London, 1957.

GREGG, D. E. The coronary circulation, Encyclopedia of Cardiology, Vol. I, Ch. 23, McGraw-Hill-Blakiston, New York, 1959.

GREGG, D. E. Coronary flow and energetics of the normal heart. Ann. New York Acad. Sc., 1960.

GREGG, D. E. Physiopathology of different surgical approaches to human coronary atherosclerosis. Acta cardiol., 1959, **14**, Suppl. 8, 3.

GREGG, D. E. Some problems of the coronary circulation. Verh. der Deutsch. Gesellsch. fur Kreislaufforschg. 1955, **21**, 22.

GREGG, D. E., AND SABISTON, D., JR. Current research and problems of the coronary circulation. Circulation 1956, **13**, 916.

KARDESCH, M., HOGANCAMP, C. E., AND BING, R. J. The survival of excitability, energy production and energy utilization of the heart. Clinical progress. Circulation, 1958, **18**, 935.

OLSON, R. E. AND PIATNEK, D. A. Conservation of energy in cardiac muscle in metabolic factors in cardiac contractility. Ann. New York Acad. Sci., 1959, **72**, 466.

# 25

## SPECIAL FEATURES OF THE CIRCULATION IN DIFFERENT REGIONS. BRAIN, SKELETAL MUSCLE, SKIN.

### The Cerebral Circulation

The cerebral circulation has been investigated extensively in various experimental animals in the past. The traumatic procedures necessary for obtaining blood flow measurements, however, prohibited the study of the circulation in the human brain. This became possible only since the introduction, recently, of a method permitting indirect measurement of cerebral blood flow in unanesthetized human subjects.

The nitrous oxide method (Kety and Schmidt, 1948) is based on the Fick principle (see ch. 18). The subject breathes a gas mixture containing 15 per cent $N_2O$, while blood samples are obtained from a peripheral artery and from the internal jugular vein (representing mixed cerebral venous blood). Cerebral blood flow per unit weight of brain may be calculated from the arterial and venous gas concentrations and the partition coefficient for nitrous oxide between brain and blood. Results are usually expressed as milliliters of blood per 100 grams of brain per minute; in resting, normal young men the mean value is 54 ml. Assuming a weight of 1400 grams for the brain, total cerebral blood flow is about 750 ml. per minute.

In experimental animals, where it is possible to check the results obtained by this method against direct cerebral blood flow measurements, there is good agreement between the two. Consideration of the cerebral circulation here will be limited to information derived from studies in man.

Cerebral blood flow is determined by two opposing sets of forces: the effective perfusion pressure and cerebral vascular resistance (see fig. 25.1). Effective perfusion pressure is the gradient between arterial blood pressure and internal jugular venous pressure; cerebral vascular resistance is defined here as the sum of all factors opposing the flow of blood through the brain, such as intracranial pressure, blood viscosity and vascular diameter.

Internal jugular venous pressure for all practical purposes is negligible as compared to arterial pressure. Even the obstruction of the vein by means of a tourniquet placed on the neck, producing pressures up to 300 mm. of water, has no effect on cerebral blood flow (Moyer and associates, 1954a). Thus, arterial blood pressure is the sole important determinant of the driving force of blood flow across the brain.

The relation of arterial blood pressure to cerebral blood flow is determined by the level of the blood pressure itself. A lowering of the mean arterial pressure to a level of about 60 to 70 mm. Hg by means of high spinal anesthesia, paralyzing most of the sympathetic vasoconstrictor nerves has no effect on cerebral blood flow, which remains constant (Kleinerman and associates, 1958). This indicates a compensatory lowering of vascular resistance in the brain (see below). Similarly, an elevation of blood pressure is without effect on blood flow due to a secondary increase in resistance (Moyer and associates, 1954b). This autoregulation of the cerebral circulation becomes ineffective, however, when mean blood pressure falls below 60 mm. Hg. In this hypotensive range, a lowering of blood pressure results in a reduction of blood flow. Initially, this is compensated for by increased oxygen extraction by the tissues, but at mean pressure levels of about 30 mm. Hg, when cerebral blood flow is reduced to about 30 ml. per 100 grams of tissue per minute, signs of cerebral ischemia appear (Finnerty and associates, 1954). Conversely, raising the blood pressure under these conditions increases blood flow, unlike in the normotensive range.

As seen in figure 25.1, several extravascular factors contribute to "cerebral vascular resistance". Intracranial pressure, exerted upon the freely collapsible capillaries of the brain is a force opposing the flow of blood. Any increase in this pressure, resulting from an expansion of the contents of the rigid cranial box (such as a brain

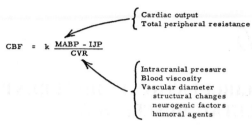

$$CBF = k \frac{MABP - IJP}{CVR}$$

Cardiac output
Total peripheral resistance

Intracranial pressure
Blood viscosity
Vascular diameter
    structural changes
    neurogenic factors
    humoral agents

FIG. 25.1. Factors determining the cerebral blood flow. CBF, cerebral blood flow; MABP, mean arterial blood pressure; IJP, internal jugular venous pressure; CVR, cerebral vascular resistance. (From Kety, S. S., in Circulation, Proceedings of Harvey Tercentenary Congress, p. 329, 1958.)

tumor) elevates cerebral vascular resistance in a direct, linear manner (Kety and associates, 1948). In spite of this, cerebral blood flow does not diminish until intracranial pressure reaches very high levels (about 450 mm. of water). The maintenance of normal flow is due to an increase of systemic blood pressure brought about by peripheral vasoconstriction. It has been suggested that the stimulus for the latter is ischemia of the medullary vasomotor center.

Viscosity of the blood increases resistance to flow: in polycythemia cerebral blood flow is considerably reduced; it is restored to normal levels after correcting the increased viscosity by phlebotomies (Nelson and Fazekas, 1956). In anemia, on the other hand, cerebral blood flow is increased in proportion to the decreased red cell mass; transfusion produces a return to normal flow (Robin and Gardner, 1953).

The most important component of cerebral vascular resistance is the diameter of the cerebral blood vessels. Their adjustment is responsible for the remarkable constancy of blood flow over a wide range of perfusion pressures, discussed above. The exact mechanism of vasomotor regulation in the brain is not known. Although the cerebral vessels are supplied by sympathetic fibers, there is no evidence to show that they are physiologically active in man. Bilateral blocking of the stellate ganglia fails to produce any change in cerebral vascular resistance or blood flow, contrary to what might be expected if these nerves were normally contributing to the maintenance of cerebral vascular tone.

In contrast to this is the marked sensitivity exhibited by the cerebral vasculature to changes in arterial concentration of carbon dioxide and oxygen. Carbon dioxide is the most powerful cerebral vasodilator known. Inhalation of a gas mixture containing 5 or 7 per cent $CO_2$, which

raises arterial $pCO_2$ by 9 mm. Hg, causes a 75 per cent increase in cerebral blood flow. Systemic blood pressure rises without any change in cardiac output, indicating a peripheral vasoconstrictor effect, but cerebral vascular resistance falls, showing the specific vasodilator action of carbon dioxide on the cerebral vessels (Kety and Schmidt, 1948). Hyperventilation, which lowers arterial $pCO_2$, reduces cerebral blood flow.

These effects of carbon dioxide are not related to associated changes in hydrogen ion concentration. Intravenous infusion of sodium bicarbonate, which produces an increase of the total carbon dioxide content of the blood and a systemic alkalosis, has the same qualitative effect on cerebral vascular resistance as inhalation of 5 per cent $CO_2$, which also raises total blood carbon dioxide but results in acidosis. Conversely, an infusion of $NH_4Cl$ duplicates the cerebral effects of hyperventilation: both procedures reduce the total carbon dioxide content of the blood, but the accompanying pH changes are in the opposite directions (Schieve and Wilson, 1953).

The vasodilator effect of carbon dioxide is a threshold phenomenon. No change in cerebral vascular resistance is detectable for arterial $pCO_2$ increases of up to 4.5 mm. Hg; beyond this point there is progressive vasodilation with further arterial $pCO_2$ increments (Patterson and associates, 1955).

In view of the pronounced cerebral vasomotor activity of carbon dioxide on the one hand, and the absence of any demonstrable neurogenic control on the other, it is logical to postulate that cerebral blood flow is regulated, at least in part, by local carbon dioxide concentrations. It was calculated that a reduction in blood flow of about 30 per cent would be required for capillary carbon dioxide tension to reach the average vasodilator threshold level of 4.5. In all likelihood, however, a reduction of this magnitude is not necessary, since under physiological conditions any increase in carbon dioxide concentration would be accompanied by hypoxia (see below).

The cerebral vasomotor action of oxygen is qualitatively the direct opposite of that produced by carbon dioxide. Inhalation of a gas mixture containing 10 per cent oxygen, which reduces arterial oxygen content by about one-third, causes a 35 per cent increase in cerebral blood flow, despite a fall in systemic blood pressure and a decreased arterial $pCO_2$ and pH (due to increased pulmonary ventilation) (Kety and Schmidt, 1948). The net effect of this degree of hypoxia on cerebral vascular resistance equals that produced by the inhalation of 5 to 7 per cent $CO_2$. Inhalation of high concentrations of oxygen which increase arterial $pO_2$, causes a reduction of cerebral blood flow, but recently it was stated that this does not occur if care is taken to prevent concomitant hypocapnia (Turner and associates, 1957).

If, as it may seem plausible, hypercapnia and hypoxia act synergistically on cerebral vascular resistance, possibly in combination with other metabolic products resulting from a diminished blood supply, this could well explain the mechanism of autoregulation exhibited by the cerebral circulation. Any impairment of blood supply resulting from a drop in perfusion pressure would automatically lead to an accumulation of metabolic products which, when present in sufficient concentrations, would act to restore blood flow by producing vasodilation. At the present time, however, this is still an unproved hypothesis.

Whatever is the exact mechanism of cerebral vasomotor regulation, cerebral blood flow shows a remarkable constancy under a variety of physiological conditions studied so far. Mild exercise (Kleinerman and Sancetta, 1955) produces a slight increase in cerebral vascular resistance, probably due to the concomitant drop in arterial $pCO_2$ secondary to hyperventilation. Intellectual efforts, such as mental arithmetics, have no effect on cerebral blood flow (Sokoloff and associates, 1955). Anxiety also seems to be devoid of influences on cerebral hemodynamics (Scheinberg and Stead, 1949). Natural sleep induces cerebral vasodilation and a small increase in blood flow without changes in arterial oxygen or carbon dioxide tensions (Mangold and associates, 1955). Eating does not affect cerebral blood flow (Rowe and associates, 1959). The effects of tilting from the supine to the upright position depend on the degree of tilting. Moderate elevations (20° from horizontal) have no effect on cerebral blood flow (Shenkin and associates, 1948), but more near-vertical positions which lower the mean arterial pressure at head level below 60 mm. Hg cause, as it might be expected, a reduction in blood flow despite a decrease in cerebral vascular resistance (Scheinberg and Stead, 1949).

## The Cutaneous Circulation

### The Anatomy of the Cutaneous Circulation and Skin Color

The architecture of the vessels of the skin has the general pattern already described on page 158. The arterioles upon approaching the bases of the

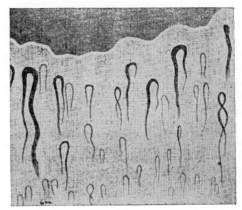

Fig. 25.2. The bed of the finger nail in a healthy subject, showing the capillary loops and the summits of the skin papillae. (After Lewis.)

papillae (i.e., the layer of the corium immediately underlying the epidermis) turn horizontally, and give rise to metarterioles from which originate, in turn, hairpin-shaped endothelial tubes—the *capillary loops*. The proximal or arterial limb of the capillary loop ascends in the papilla and then turns upon itself to form the venous limb. The latter on reaching the base of the papilla joins with the venous limbs of neighboring loops to form a *collecting venule*. The collecting venules anastomose with one another to form a rich plexus—the *subpapillary venous* plexus—which runs horizontally beneath the bases of the papilla. It drains into deeper veins. The capillary loops can be seen readily in the living skin under the low power of the microscope. The vessels at the base of the human fingernail are shown diagrammatically in figure 25.2.

The color of the skin is not dependent normally upon the most superficial vessels, i.e., the capillary loops but upon the subpapillary venous plexus. The vessels of the plexus, though more deeply placed, present a greater area parallel to the skin, whereas the capillary loops are disposed chiefly at right angles to the skin surface.

When the skin is unusually pale and little blood is contained in the superficial vessels (subpapillary venous plexus), the skin is more transparent, and the deeper venous plexuses then contribute largely to the color of the skin, often adding a leaden tint to the pallor. When the overlying vessels are open and the skin is well supplied with blood, these deeper vessels are hidden from view.

Apart from pigmentary effects, and assuming the general arterial blood to be normal, the *color* of the skin, i.e., the dominance of the reddish or of the bluish hue, depends upon the extent to which the oxyhemoglobin becomes reduced during the passage of the blood through the cutaneous vessels. The degree of reduction will depend entirely, as a rule, upon the rate of blood flow. When the flow is rapid or slow the blood is, respectively, more arterial or more venous in character. The tint of the skin varies accordingly.

The *depth* of the skin color, i.e., the intensity of color apart from hue is dependent upon the diameters and the degree of engorgement with blood of the superficial vessels.

So, taking into account both the hue and the depth of color, an intense scarlet color of the skin indicates a normal or increased blood flow and dilated vessels; a deep blue color accompanies a slowed blood flow and dilated vessels (such as would result from obstruction to the venous trunks), or arterial desaturation (cyanosis). Pallor or a light pink color of the skin is seen when the vessels are constricted or of moderate tone, and the blood flow normal or rapid. A slowed cutaneous blood flow and constricted superficial vessels tend to produce a leaden or ashen type of cyanosis for, as mentioned above, the dark blood in the deeper venous plexuses then becomes faintly visible.

EXPERIMENTAL INVESTIGATION OF SKIN BLOOD FLOW. Blood flow in the skin serves two main functions: (1) the regulation of body temperature, and (2) nourishment of the skin. The investigation of the regulation of skin blood flow has been through the effects produced by direct or indirect warming or cooling, by pharmacological agents which act similarly to nervous system transmitters, by drugs which block the nervous supply, or by direct stimulation of nerves, baroreceptors or specific areas of the brain. Since the skin of animals (except for the paws) differs from human skin in possessing probably only vasoconstrictor fibers, data obtained from humans will be presented unless only animal studies are available. The skin of dogs and cats lacks eccrine glands, and sweating is absent (except in the paws). Techniques of blood flow measurement in human skin include plethysmography, continuous temperature recording, calorimetry, clearance rates of readioactive materials, oxygen polarography, blood oxygen saturation of cutaneous veins, pulse volume studies, and direct microscopic inspection of the vessels (ch. 15). It must be emphasized that clearance rate studies do not always agree with plethysmographic measurements. The reason for this disparity is unknown although it has been suggested that the former measures only

capillary flow while the latter determines total flow (capillary and shunt flow). The limitation of human skin studies is the lack of a direct method of blood flow measurement.

THE CONTROL OF SKIN BLOOD FLOW AND THE REGULATION OF BODY TEMPERATURE. The skin blood blow in regional areas reacts and is, evidently, innervated differently. Cutaneous vessels are regulated by the sympathetic nervous system; a parasympathetic supply has not been shown in any area. Usually the sympathetic innervation is demonstrated by blocking its effects with adrenergic or ganglionic blocking agents or sympathectomy. This presumably rules out a somatic or parasympathetic nervous system control of the vasomotor reflex being studied. The type of end-organ transmitter involved in the sympathetic responses is determined by the use of adrenergic or cholinergic (atropine) blocking agents. It should be pointed out that the sympathetic fibers travel with the main somatic nerves in the extremities so that both are blocked by anesthetization of the deep nerves.

### A. *Cutaneous Blood Flow in the Hand and Foot*

Only a vasoconstrictor nerve supply with adrenergic sympathetic fibers has been identified in the hand or foot to be of importance in the reflex control of body temperature. The demonstration of specific cholinesterases by histochemical methods in the digital arteriovenous anastomoses suggests they may be cholinergically controlled. Also, it has been postulated that the sympathetic nerve supply to human fingers exerts a tonic dilator influence on vessels through the release of acetylcholine. The indirect evidence for this theory includes the dilation of vessels by extracts of human digital arteries, its prevention by atropine, and the possession of a pseudo-cholinesterase activity. More recently, a substance called "bradykinin" has been suggested as an important factor causing active vasodilation in human forearm skin and, evidently, in any skin area containing eccrine sweat glands (palms and soles). During activity of the sweat glands, a proteolytic enzyme is released into the tissues where it acts on an unknown protein to produce the polypeptide, bradykinin (fig. 25.3). The latter substance is a powerful vasodilator, and its concentration has been demonstrated to increase in forearm skin, reflexly vasodilated by body warming, even before sweating or a rise in skin temperature have occurred. The eccrine glands are presumably activated by a cholinergic substance *via* the sympathetic nervous system. This pathway is not

SCHEMATIC DIAGRAM OF BRADYKININ FORMATION IN HUMAN SKIN

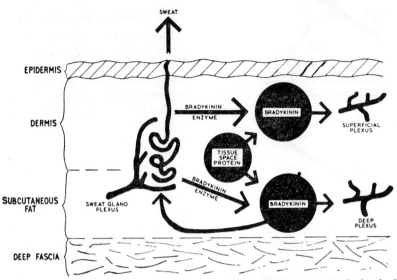

Fig. 25.3. Schematic diagram of bradykinin formation in human forearm skin during body warming. Sympathetic stimulation of the sweat gland releases a proteolytic enzyme which acts on a tissue fluid protein to form a polypeptide (bradykinin). The polypeptide has a vasodilator action of the cutaneous vasculature (from Barcroft *et al.*).

believed to account for all reflex vasodilation for the vasodilation has been observed without an apparent change in sweat gland activity, and *vice versa.*

Body warming elicits a reflex vasodilation in the hand or foot which has been shown to correlate with a release of vasoconstrictor tone (a decreased number of impulses traveling over the sympathetic nerve fibers). The reflex may originate either in cutaneous receptors or by central nervous system stimulation. The vessels, themselves, are also evidently sensitive to warm temperature for the dilation following vasomotor nervous inhibition (by blocking agents) can be augmented by local heating of the hand. When the human body is cooled, the toe temperature approaches environmental temperature, whereas the finger tips cool but show more fluctuation in temperature and blood flow. Similar cooling of the hands and feet occurs reflexly to cold applied to one area of the body, such as the forehead. The transmitter substance involved in the cutaneous vasoconstriction mediated by the sympathetic nervous system has been shown to be adrenergic in nature, but whether epinephrine, norepinephrine or a related amine is involved is not known.

Since vasoconstrictor tone develops earlier and is more stable and less readily reversed by body warming in the feet than in the hands, it has been suggested that the lower extremities are concerned with gross adjustments while the upper extremities provide the fine regulation of body temperature.

If a finger is immersed in cold water, its temperature falls rapidly to the bath temperature and blood flow slows; the vessels then fluctuate in cycles of constriction and dilation. Both the sympathetic vasoconstrictive reflex and the local direct effect of cold on the vessels are involved in the reduction of blood flow. The vasodilatory mechanism during the cyclic changes remains partially unexplained. It is probably an effective protection against cold injury. Lewis thought it was secondary to a local or axon reflex (*via* the dorsal root vasodilator fibers), but the absence of sensory fibers only reduces, not abolishes, the response. As mentioned before, there is evidence for an active vasodilator innervation of the arteriovenous anastomoses which may take part in this cold vasodilation.

Arteriovenous anastomoses are communications between smaller arteries and arterioles and the corresponding venous channels, through which the blood may be shunted and capillary areas short circuited (figure 25.4). Included in the shunt definition of arteriovenous anastomoses should be the presence of a direct or indirect regulatory mechanism. These communications have been studied mostly in animals, especially the rabbit. In the rabbit ear, arteriovenous

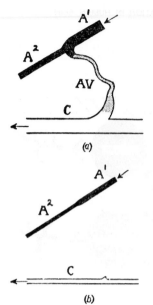

FIG. 25.4. Reaction of anastomosis and associated vessels to lowering of body temperature. A¹, artery; A², arteriole; AV, arteriovenous anastomosis; C, vein. Upper figure (*a*), anastomosis, open; lower figure (*b*), anastomosis closed. (After Grant.)

anastomoses have been shown to be very effective in controlling the body's temperature. When open, these channels would offer very low resistance vessels through which large volumes of blood could flow. It has been demonstrated by a method involving the injection of microspheres that more than one-third of the total flow through the rabbit ear or dog paw may pass through such shunts. The microspheres are suitably selected in size to pass through anastomotic vessels but not capillaries. Animal arteriovenous communications are presumably supplied by constrictor sympathetic fibers and constrict or dilate to a variety of stimuli. Human digits and palms (glomus areas) and ears have large numbers of these potential shunts. The glomus areas contain muscular tufts of arteriovenous anastomoses and receive a rich nervous innervation. In man, little information, except that mentioned previously, exists regarding the control or function of the arteriovenous anastomoses. Although they have been postulated as playing a large role in the regulation of body temperature by increasing or decreasing the radiation of heat, their participation in such reflexes has not been shown in man. The high rates and wide, rapid variations in digital blood flow (1 to 150 ml. per 100 ml. of skin per minute) are often attributed to these channels. It is evident that

new methods of study are needed to further our knowledge of these interesting communications.

### B. *Cutaneous Blood Flow of the Forearm*

The blood flow of the forearm skin has been estimated to vary from 0 to 70.5 ml. per 100 ml. of skin per minute using rates determined plethysmographically before and after abolition of flow by iontophoresis of the skin. The skin of the forearm has been shown to possess both a sympathetic vasoconstrictor and vasodilator nerve supply in contrast to that of the hand and foot. It was demonstrated that the increase in forearm blood flow secondary to body heating occurred in the skin and not in the muscles by the following: (1) iontophoresis of the forearm skin with epinephrine abolishes the increased forearm flow response, (2) venous oxygen saturation from cutaneous superficial veins rises while that from muscle veins remains stable during body heating, and (3) the temperature of the skin rises with body heating but that of muscle does not. By blockage of the forearm skin nerve supply with local ring anesthesia or deep nerve blocks, the vasodilation reflex was prevented. The vasodilation could be blocked partly by atropine indicating cholinergic sympathetic fibers were involved. The experiments demonstrating the bradykinin mechanism and its activation by sympathetic sudomotor stimulation (as explained above) were performed in the forearm skin. Bradykinin vasodilation, the release of vasoconstrictor tone, and the direct effect of heat in relaxing the blood vessels may all play a part in the vasodilation which occurs in forearm skin during total body warming. A parasympathetic innervation has not been demonstrated.

The skin temperature and blood flow of the forearm decrease in response to body cooling. A longitudinal temperature gradient from the warmer trunk to the cooler hands and feet is maintained. The cooling of the forearm skin is evidently *via* sympathetic constrictor fibers as in the hands and feet.

It has also been demonstrated that subcutaneous injections of $CO_2$ in humans causes a vasodilation probably of the small resistance vessels. In dogs, low pH solutions intra-arterially elicit a marked increase in cutaneous blood flow while alkaline solutions reduce flow.

Human skin studies utilizing the oxygen polarograph have shown that the oxygen tension increases with temperature elevations up to, but not over, about 43° C. It is postulated that heating causes an increased blood flow, dissociation of oxygen from hemoglobin, and increased supply of oxygen and blood to the skin. At higher temperatures, the oxygen utilization would outstrip the increased supply. The role of skin metabolism in the regulation of its blood flow has received little investigation.

### C. Cutaneous Blood Flow to Other Skin Areas

Skin areas, other than the extremities, have received little study because of the lack of techniques for measuring blood flow. Most available studies have utilized the qualitative measurements of blood flow determined by the photoelectric plethysmograph or surface temperature changes. The forehead skin is believed to have a weak or absent vasoconstrictor nerve supply. During cold exposure, the surface temperatures of the head and trunk fall relatively little and high rates of blood flow continue. This has been an important finding leading to the use of head gear to prevent heat loss in cold weather. Vasomotor reflexes to noise or distal application of cold, which severely decrease hand flow, have only a slight effect on forehead blood flow. India ink injections show the vascular plexus of the forehead to be very extensive while the rapid clearance of radioactive sodium and volume pulse measurements demonstrate the blood flow to exceed that in the skin of the calf, forearm and trunk. The forehead and cheek evidently do not possess glomi so this flow is all through the capillary beds. Pharmacological agents (nicotinic acid, histamine and others) increased the skin temperature in these areas but not in the toes or fingers. Adrenergic and ganglionic blocking agents had no effect on forehead skin temperature. It has been suggested that cholinergic sympathetic fibers maintain vasomotor tone in the forehead and cheek areas but experimental evidence for this is too indirect.

### D. The Effect of Perfusion Pressure on Skin Blood Flow

The mechanical effects of perfusion pressure on blood flow were measured in isolated cutaneous beds of dog hind limbs. The *in situ* vascular bed was perfused *via* the saphenous artery from a reservoir whose height could be varied to change perfusion pressure. When the rate of flow was plotted against changes in perfusion pressure, a parabolic curve (fig. 25.5) was obtained instead of a straight line. There was a progressive decrease in resistance to flow in the vessels as the perfusion pressure rose. With an increase of vasomotor tone in the vascular bed, the flow for any given

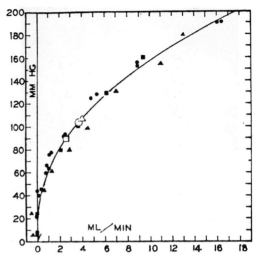

FIG. 25.5. Plot of relationship between perfusion pressure and blood flow through the skin supplied by the saphenous artery, in the hindlimb of a dog in which vasomotor activity remained practically constant at a high level. *Solid symbols* represent data obtained at different times during a 7-hour interval. *Hollow symbols* represent the animal's mean arterial blood pressure at these times. Ordinate scale represents the perfusion pressure in mm. Hg, expressed as the difference in pressure between arterial and venous pressures. Abscissal scale represents the blood flow in milliliters per minute. (Slightly modified from Green, Lewis, Nickerson and Heller.)

pressure decreased. The nonlinear relation between flow and perfusion pressure may be secondary to a progressive decrease in viscosity of blood (because of a more axial flow of red cells) or to a mechanical dilation of blood vessels with the rising perfusion pressure.

### E. The Cutaneous Veins

In dogs and cats, it has been shown that the superficial large and small veins of the skin have a nerve supply, undergo rhythmic changes in diameter, and respond to pharmacological agents. The small veins may contract separately and independently from the large veins or arterial vessels during sympathetic nerve stimulation. Since the small veins (and large veins) constrict, an increase in pressure results. Thus, a reduced blood flow may occur through the vascular bed without a mechanical obstruction being present. In humans, forearm cutaneous vein segments, which were isolated *in situ* by pressure, have been demonstrated to constrict following a variety of normal and noxious stimuli. The venoconstriction was blocked by chemical or surgical sympathectomy or infiltration of an anesthetic solution around the vein. Venous tone decreased during the vaso-

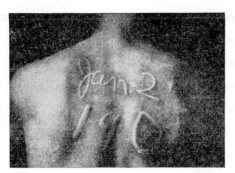

Fig. 25.6. Dermographism. (From Adami's textbook of Pathology, after Hyde and Ormsby.)

vagal syndrome and by stroking the skin over the vein. The fact that cutaneous veins constrict by cooling and are not affected by warming is evidence for the existence of only a vasoconstrictor nervous supply. The active innervation of veins is evidently very important in response of the cutaneous circulation to ordinary and abnormal stimuli, and also in determining the color of the skin.

*F. Vascular Responses of the Skin to Stimulation by Mechanical and Other Agencies. Dorsal Root Vasodilator Fibers*

1. THE WHITE REACTION. If the surface of the skin is stroked lightly with a blunt "pointed" instrument, a line of pallor appears in 15 to 20 seconds which traces the path taken by the instrument. The line attains its maximal intensity in from ½ to 1 minute, and then gradually fades to disappear in from 3 to 5 minutes. The white reaction proper is due to *direct stimulation of the capillary wall and has not a nervous basis.* It has been shown by Lewis to be due to the tension exerted upon the walls of the minute vessels—capillary loops, collecting venules and especially of the subpapillary venous plexus—which respond to the stimulus by contraction. The sharply delineated character of the white line, and the fact that it can be obtained after the circulation through the region has been occluded by compression of the larger vessels, show that it is an active capillary response, and not the result of arteriolar constriction.

2. THE TRIPLE RESPONSE. This comprises: (a) *the red reaction*, (b) *the flare*, and (c) *the wheal.*

(a) *The red reaction.* If the pointed instrument be drawn more firmly across the skin, especially of the forearm or back, a red instead of a white band appears after a somewhat shorter latent period (3 to 15 seconds), reaches its maximum in from ½ to 1 minute, and then gradually fades.

Like the white reaction it is strictly localized to the line of stroke; it is due to *dilation* of the capillary vessels. The red reaction can be induced in its full intensity in the skin from which the circulation has been occluded, so it is due to active dilation of the latter vessels and not merely a passive result of arteriolar dilation. *The red reaction is not dependent upon nervous mechanisms since it occurs after section and degeneration of the cutaneous nerves.*

(b) *The spreading flush or flare.* If the stimulus is unusually strong, or is repeated often enough, the reddening of the skin is not confined to the line of stroke but surrounds it for a variable distance (1 to 10 cm.) according to the intensity of the injury inflicted. The temperature in the suffused area is definitely raised. This flare reaction appears a few seconds (15 to 30) after the local red line, and fades sooner but remains a bright arterial color throughout. It is due to dilation of the arterioles, since it does not appear after the circulation of the part has been occluded by means of a tourniquet; also, unlike the red reaction, *the flare is dependent upon local nervous mechanisms (axon reflex). It occurs after the nerves are divided but not after they have degenerated.*

(c) *Local edema or wheal.* When the stimulus is still more intense, the skin along the line of the injury becomes blanched and raised above the surrounding area to a height of 1 or 2 mm. or even more. Such a wheal or welt is commonly produced in a normal person by the lash of a whip and other types of strong localized stimulation. In susceptible individuals, even light stimulation, such as drawing a pencil with moderate pressure over the skin of the back, will produce linear wheals surrounded by a diffuse red halo along the pencil's track. In this way letters or other designs may be embossed upon the skin (fig. 25.6). This phenomenon is spoken of as *dermographism or factitious urticaria.* The wheal is preceded by and completely replaces the usual red reaction. It makes its appearance in from 1 to 3 minutes from the time of injury and is at its maximum height in 3 or 5 minutes. It is surrounded by the flare described above. The raised patch at first is clearly demarcated, but as time passes it increases in diameter and decreases in height, loses its sharpness and finally, though perhaps not for some hours, disappears. The wheal is due to the transudation of fluid from the minute vessels involved previously in the red reaction; it is, therefore, a localized edema. Increased permeability of the capillary wall is judged to be the immediate cause of the localized edema which constitutes the wheal. Increased intracapillary pressure, distension of the capillary lumen, or reduction in pressure in extracapillary spaces have been shown by Lewis to be not responsible. That increased permeability rather than simply a rise in the filtration pressure is the dominating feature is also manifest by the high protein content of the transuded fluid. This more nearly approaches that of blood serum than the fluid of ordinary edema. Wheal production does not depend upon a nervous mechanism.

A considerable weight of indirect evidence has been presented by Lewis to support the conception that a diffusible substance is responsible for the three reactions comprising the triple response. This material, which he calls *H-substance*, is thought to be literated by the injured cells of the epidermis lying beneath the horny layer and superficial to the papillae. The possibility that more deeply lying tissues, when subjected to injury, may release the substance is not excluded, but a needle which does not penetrate beyond the epidermis elicits the typical threefold reaction. The chemical substance closely resembles *histamine* in its action. It apparently causes the red reaction and the wheal by a direct action upon the capillary wall. The flare is believed to be due to chemical stimulation of the sensory endings of the skin, thus bringing about arteriolar dilation through the mechanism of the axon reflex. Although the evidence for this theory is indirect and actual proof of the existence of such a humoral mechanism is lacking, the results of Lewis's various ingenious experiments carry conviction.

The cutaneous reactions following injuries of various sorts, e.g., burning, freezing, electrical stimulation, are believed to be produced by the same humoral mechanism. The cardinal signs of inflammation—redness, heat and to some extent the swelling and pain—can be similarly explained, namely, direct action of the dilator H-substance upon the minute vessels, and an indirect effect through the medium of the axon reflex, upon the arterioles of the surrounding area. The ultraviolet light reaction in man is evidently secondary to a different mechanism. It has been shown that the ultraviolet light erythema is not reduced by pretreatment with antihistamines. Also histamine introduced into areas of ultraviolet erythema produces its usual triple response. Thus, Lewis's theory of all cutaneous inflammatory processes being secondary to release of the H-substance is not universally applicable.

The dorsal root of the spinal cord contains vasodilatory fibers supplying mostly the cutaneous vessels. They do not convey impulses to or from the higher central nervous system centers for control of the cutaneous circulation. No true cutaneous vasomotor reflexes are seen after sympathectomy. Experiments have shown that the dorsal root vasodilator fibers do not engage in the baro- or chemoreceptor control of vascular tone, nor in the regulation of heat loss from the skin. The transmitter substance of these fibers is unknown but they probably act in an axon reflex arrangement to affect regional blood vessels. These are probably the fibers that, upon damage to the superficial tissues, are involved in the vasodilator (flare) reaction of the triple response. Any stimulus causing damage to the skin activates these fibers, such as *severe* cooling, heating or pain. It was mentioned previously that an axon reflex may be involved in the cyclic vasodilation occurring when a finger is placed in cold water. Severe cooling would elicit the axon reflex in these fibers from the dorsal root with a consequent vasodilation in the finger. The latter would warm the finger stopping the axon reflex discharge and then vasoconstriction would recur.

### G. Central Nervous System Control of Cutaneous and Muscle Blood Flow

The central nervous system regulation of blood flow is through the sympathetic fibers.

A variety of stimuli affecting peripheral receptors elicit spinal vasomotor reflexes whose efferent limbs are the cutaneous sympathetic vasoconstrictor fibers. These reflexes are usually segmentally or regionally arranged. Also, in certain animal preparations, the preganglionic sympathetic neurons in the lateral horns of the spinal medulla may exhibit spontaneous activity independent of afferent stimuli.

The vasomotor center located in the oblongate medulla is believed to be the primary controlling factor of cutaneous and muscle vessel vasoconstrictor tone. Experiments on dogs and cats have shown that stimulation of the midline of the oblongate medulla leads to vasodilation in both skin and muscle. This vasodilatory response is not blocked by atropine and, therefore, is secondary to a release of vasoconstrictor tone. Stimulation lateral to this vasodilator area elicits vasoconstriction in the same areas. Both these responses are absent in sympathectomized animals. The vasodilator and vasoconstrictor areas may act as an integrated unit and, evidently, are primarily involved in vascular reflexes arising from the baroreceptors in the carotid sinus and aorta. A decrease in blood pressure causes reflex

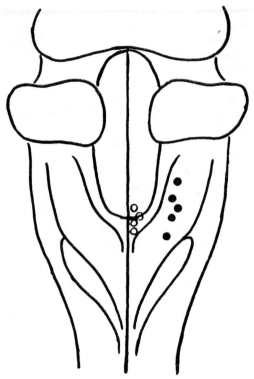

Fig. 25.7. Schematic drawing of the oblongate medulla showing the situation of points yielding skeletal muscle vasodilation secondary to inhibition of vasoconstrictor tone (*open circles*), and points yielding sympathetic vasodilator discharges (*black dots*). (From Lindgren and Uvnäs.)

vasoconstriction in the dog hindlimb *via* the carotid sinus baroreceptors while stimulation of the carotid sinus nerve induces vasodilation in skin and muscle.

The vasomotor center possesses automaticity for it continues discharging impulses without apparent afferent stimuli from the periphery or higher autonomic centers. The marked fluctuations from moment to moment that occur in the digital and forearm arteries and veins, and that disappear following sympathectomy, are thought to be secondary to the activity of the vasomotor center. The patterns of these continuous variations in pulse volume of the fingers, toes and ears, appear to correlate with the personality types (emotional stability or lability) of the human studied.

Stimulation of a more lateral area to the vasomotor center invokes a vasodilation in skeletal muscle through the activity of the cholinergic (blocked by atropine) sympathetic fibers (fig. 25.7). The vasodilatory area of the vasomotor center has no anatomical or apparent functional connection with these cholinergic fibers which pass through the oblongate medulla.

The anterior hypothalamus is often referred to as the "heat loss center" for it controls the vasoconstrictor fibers in association with the vasomotor center. Local heat applied to this area inhibits vasoconstrictor fiber discharge (vasodilation) while electrical stimulation excites the fibers (vasoconstriction). This center is thought to predominantly regulate the cutaneous vessels and, maybe, the arteriovenous anastomoses. Sympathectomy, also, abolishes these effects of the hypothalamus. Stimulation of certain areas in the hypothalamus may elicit a vasodilation in muscle *via* the cholinergic fibers which synapse in this area. This muscle vasodilation is often associated with a vasoconstriction of the skin.

Many areas of the cerebral cortex have been found that influence, by excitation or inhibition, vasoconstrictor fiber discharge. For example, stimulation of the motor or premotor cortical areas results in cutaneous vasoconstriction. A muscle vasodilation also occurs but is evidently secondary to a baroreceptor reflex from a rise in blood pressure. The cholinergic vasodilator fibers to skeletal muscle are also represented near the motor cortex. These fibers, which are distributed probably only to muscle, synapse in the hypothalamus and mesencephalon and pass through the oblongate medulla as described above. Their function in man is not completely understood, but they appear to be involved in the control of the blood flow needs of muscle and not in the regulation of blood pressure.

### Skeletal Muscle Circulation

Resting forearm skeletal muscle blood flow has been estimated to normally range from 1.8 to 9.6 ml. per 100 ml. of muscle per minute (compare to forearm skin flow on p. 348). The blood flow in skeletal muscle is affected and controlled by a multitude of factors. Many of these regulations are poorly understood and their relative importance in the normal functioning of skeletal muscle is not known. Investigation of skeletal muscle blood flow is performed in man by similar techniques outlined under skin blood flow. The plethysmograph measures both the skin and muscle blood flow; the forearm is considered representative of muscle while the hand or foot, of skin (because of the relative amounts of each tissue in these regions). The skin is often iontophoresed with epinephrine to limit or abolish its blood flow in order to obtain forearm muscle determinations. In animals, blood flow may be measured by more direct methods and the results of central nervous system manipulations may be studied.

NERVOUS SYSTEM CONTROL OF SKELETAL MUSCLE BLOOD FLOW. Vasoconstrictor fibers have been shown to supply skeletal muscle by the demonstration of an increased blood flow in human forearms following nerve blocks, and by other indirect procedures. The transmitter substance for these constrictor fibers is not known but adrenergic blocking agents remove the vasoconstrictor tone. Intra-arterial epinephrine has both a vasodilator and vasoconstrictor effect on human skeletal muscle vessels, while norepinephrine has only a vasoconstrictor action. Vasodilator cholinergic sympathetic fibers also supply skeletal muscle as demonstrated by a responsiveness of the bed to acetylcholine, blocking of the vasodilatory response with atropine, and the results of studies performed during vasovagal syncope. Despite a fall in blood pressure in the latter, the forearm blood flow increases (and hand flow decreases). If the patient had a sympathectomy, the forearm blood flow does not increase demonstrating that an active vasodilation *via* sympathetic nerve fibers had presumably occurred in the intact extremity. These vasodilator fibers appear to be activated by higher brain centers and do not participate in reflex blood pressure adjustments.

At present, the vasoconstrictor fibers are believed to be primarily concerned in postural and other homeostatic blood pressure adjustments. When the legs of a subject are raised, an increased blood flow occurs in the forearm but not the hand. This reflex has been shown to be secondary to an increased volume of blood in the thorax and an elevated central venous pressure which probably stimulates receptors in the low pressure vascular bed of the thorax. Since atropine does not abolish the forearm vasodilation, it is considered to be a result of a release of vasoconstrictor tone.

HUMORAL FACTORS IN SKELETAL MUSCLE BLOOD FLOW. Recent studies in humans have shown that the increase in forearm blood flow during hyperventilation is prevented by breathing an air mixture containing 5 per cent $CO_2$, occurs only in the muscles and not in the skin, and is not abolished by blocking the nerve supply to the limb. This evidence points to a humoral mechanism, involving a low $CO_2$ tension, which causes the increased forearm blood flow by a direct action on peripheral vessels.

An elevation or a decrease in the pH of blood perfusing a dog's hind limb elicits a vasodilation.

Lactic acid increases the blood flow, but sodium lactate titrated with a buffer to a pH of 7.4 does not. There is indirect evidence that the vasodilatory effect of epinephrine may be through the action of released lactic acid.

MECHANICAL EFFECTS ON SKELETAL MUSCLE BLOOD FLOW. When perfusion pressure is plotted against skeletal muscle blood flow (as determined in isolated muscle beds of the hindlimb of a dog), a parabolic-shaped curve is found in the upper and lower ranges (fig. 25.8), as in the skin vascular bed. These two normal relationships of pressure to flow are joined in the intermediate range by a sigmoid curve (a large drop in perfusion pressure changes blood flow little). It was postulated that the reason for the sigmoid curve was a reactive dilation at perfusion pressures below mean normal aortic pressure to maintain blood flow to the muscular bed. The two parabolic areas on the curve would represent perfusion pressures during two states of vasomotor activity of the vessels. Because of the shape of the curve, changes in vasomotor activity, secondary to a variable being tested, cannot always be predicted from the perfusion pressure and blood flow.

METABOLITES AND SKELETAL MUSCLE BLOOD FLOW; EXERCISE AND REACTIVE HYPEREMIA. The skeletal muscle vascular bed is subjected to very active and widely ranging fluctuations in blood flow. The idea has often been expressed that the formation of metabolites by the muscle cells is the main factor in controlling the bed. Since direct stimulation of an animal's curarized muscle still elicits an increased blood flow, while motor nerve excitation does not, it is felt that the hyperemia of contracting muscle is secondary to a local physicochemical change. Also, humans with sympathectomized extremities can perform as well as those with an intact innervation. Local or reflex warming or cooling has little effect on the intrinsic vasomotor tone of muscles. It has been suggested that the metabolites, accumulated from muscle cell metabolism, may act directly on the smooth muscle cells of vessels or indirectly *via* a local nervous mechanism, such as peripheral ganglion cells or an axon reflex. The existence of ganglion cells among the muscle fibers has not been proven.

In the dog, muscular activity induces a dilation of the femoral artery which is mediated by an axon reflex (elicitable by acetylcholine). This mechanism, if it was shown to be present in the smaller arterial branches, could account for the vasodilation. In the cat limb, post exercise, muscle hyperemia is blocked by substances (cocaine, botulinum toxin) which are likely to abolish such

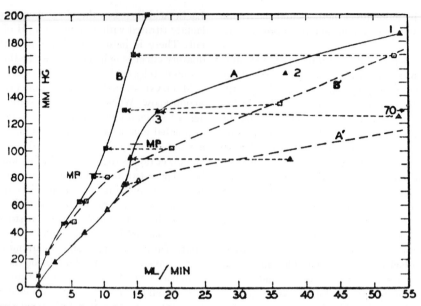

F<small>IG</small>. 25.8. Plots of relationship between perfusion pressure and blood flow in the portion of the canine quadriceps muscle supplied by the branches of the femoral artery between the inferior epigastric and saphenous branches. Plots $A$ and $B$ were obtained 6 hours apart in the same animal. $A^1$ and $B^1$, dashed lines, flow during first 2 seconds of perfusion at each pressure; $A$ and $B$, solid lines, stabilized flows after maintenance of perfusion pressure for 10 to 20 seconds. Arrows indicate change of flow with time at each perfusion pressure. MP, represents the level of mean arterial pressure. Ordinate scale represents the perfusion pressure in mm.Hg, expressed as the difference between arterial and venous pressures; abscissal scale, blood flow in milliliters per minute (from Green, Lewis, Nickerson and Heller).

axon reflexes. The vascular reactivity is not paralyzed by these agents for the vessels continue to respond to epinephrine and acetycholine. Since botulinum toxin specifically paralyzes cholinergic nerve endings, the fibers in the axon reflex may be cholinergic. However, a strong argument against this theory is that the vasodilation of exercise hyperemia is not blocked by atropine (although atropine has been found not to block cholinergic fibers in all areas).

The role that local metabolites play in stimulating such axon reflexes is not known. Anoxia, increased $CO_2$ tension, lactic acid, hydrogen ions, histamine, acetylcholine, adenosine triphosphate, adenylic acid, and potassium ions, have been suggested as the local determinant eliciting exercise vasodilation. Most of the metabolites have been studied by infusion into the muscular vascular bed or by examination of venous blood leaving the muscle following exercise hyperemia. Each has received little support as the dilator metabolite, but a combination of two or more of these factors may provide the answer.

The circulation in human skeletal muscle has been studied during sustained muscular contraction by indirect methods. It was found that below a certain critical strength of sustained contraction

of the calf muscle, blood flow was not decreased, but, above this critical point, the vessels were evidently compressed, for a hyperemia followed release of the contraction.

During rhythmic contraction of calf muscles, blood flow was increased during and immediately following exercise. It was felt that increased flow (vasodilator metabolite mediated) alternating with decreased flow (mechanical compression of vessels) paralleled the relaxation and contraction of the muscle. Mechanical obstruction, metabolite formation, and the action of muscles on the venous flow are probably all intricately involved in the muscular blood flow of exercise. It has been shown that an increase in venous pressure may alter arterial inflow to muscle. The sympathetic nervous system probably does not have a significant effect on the circulatory changes during exercise, for vasodilation is similar during and after exercise in normal and sympathectomized limbs. Also, the vascular bed of the exercising hindlimb of the dog is not responsive to sympathetic stimulation.

Following a period of complete occlusion of the arterial supply to a limb, the blood flow increases markedly and then returns to the control level. This phenomenon has been named "reactive hyperemia." Actually, it is the blood flow in excess of that expected (the control blood flow) which is usually referred to as reactive hyperemia. The response occurs both in skin and muscle and can be decreased by cooling, epinephrine, or tobacco smoking. The reactive hyperemic blood flow and its duration correlate with the previous length of occlusion of the artery. This has been shown to be true for occlusion periods up to 10 minutes.

The blood flow and oxygen debt incurred during the period of occlusion are calculated by multiplying the control blood flow or oxygen usage before circulatory arrest by the duration of occlusion. Of course, this assumes that the blood flow and oxygen usage of the muscle would have remained at the previous control rates if the blood flow had not been occluded and that the metabolic rate of the muscle is not affected by the circulatory arrest. In the isolated, gracilis muscle of dogs and in the human forearm, the oxygen debt was approximately repaid for different periods of occlusion, while the blood flow debt repayment ranged from 50 to 200 per cent of that expected. It appears probable that the muscle blood flow is at least partially controlled by the need for oxygen.

The metabolites incriminated as the cause of exercise hyperemia have also been postulated as eliciting reactive hyperemia. Since reactive hyperemia occurs in sympathectomized and denervated limbs, nervous system control is not considered as important. The mechanical effect of the lack of pressure in the vessels during the period of occlusion has been demonstrated to play a role in the dilation. If the forearm is "packed" with venous blood before the circulatory arrest, the ensuing reactive hyperemia is decreased. However, the peak flows of the reactive hyperemias are not altered so that intravascular pressure cannot be the entire cause of the dilation. Lewis and Grant postulated that H-substance was involved in the production of reactive hyperemia, and some observers (others have not) found an increased histamine concentration in the venous blood after circulatory arrest. However, antihistamines do not decrease or abolish the reactive hyperemia response. As in exercise hyperemia, the vasodilator metabolites and effects of pH cannot be ruled out by studying only the venous blood; tissue studies would probably be more informative. Failure to discover the causative agent of vasodilation in muscular exercise and following arterial occlusion has been a major obstacle to the understanding of muscle physiol-

ogy and the diseases involving a decreased blood supply to human limbs. It seems likely that the study of aerobic and anaerobic tissue metabolism of skeletal muscle will be more profitable than blood flow studies, which evidently do not correlate with oxygen usage.

ARTERIOVENOUS ANASTOMOSES IN SKELETAL MUSCLE. The question of whether arteriovenous shunts actually exist as functional units in skeletal muscle is still unsettled to most physiologists. Microscopic studies on the circulation of rat skeletal muscle revealed many communications between small arteries and veins which did not enter the muscle proper. During inactivity, most of the flow was through these anastomoses and not to the muscle fibers. When the rats were bled in small amounts, the muscular arterioles closed and flow in the capillaries ceased while it persisted in the anastomotic channels. However, that such communications actually function in man and possess a means of shunt regulation, has not been demonstrated. Indirect evidence for the existence of functional anastomoses are decreased oxygen consumption and increased lactic acid production during vasodilation; such findings would occur if capillary flow was reduced.

## SUMMARY

Although much investigative work has been performed, wide gaps still exist in our knowledge of the physiology of the cutaneous and muscle circulations. Most of the information concerning the control of these vascular beds has been gained from indirect and circumstantial evidence. The important limiting factor is the lack of a good technique for the direct measurement of blood flow in human skin and muscle. The indirect methods, currently in use, all have their inadequacies. Another drawback is the difficulty in distinguishing the many variables (metabolic, nervous, temperature, bradykinin, arteriovenous anastomoses) that affect the cutaneous and muscle circulation. In human experiments, skin and muscle flow cannot be satisfactorily studied individually, and the contribution of the blood flow in bone, fat and subcutaneous tissue cannot be evaluated. The central nervous system control of the peripheral circulation has been investigated in animals only; much is known about efferent fibers but little concerning afferent pathways. The study of the metabolic control of blood flow in skin has been neglected while that of muscle has not advanced far enough. In conclusion, many isolated facts are known concerning the mechanisms controlling cutaneous and muscle vascular reactivity, but little is apparent of their integration in the homeostasis of these tissues.

## Peripheral Vascular Disease

### RAYNAUD'S PHENOMENON AND RAYNAUD'S DISEASE

A distinction must be drawn between *Raynaud's phenomenon* and *Raynaud's disease*. Raynaud's phenomenon is understood to be the intermittent spasm of the small arteries of the extremities. The affected members, the fingers and less commonly the toes, become cold, numb, waxy pale (dead fingers) or cyanotic. The attacks are precipitated by exposure to cold. It is secondary to some other abnormal state, e.g., thromboangiitis obliterans, arteriosclerosis, cervical rib, etc.

*Raynaud's disease* is the occurrence of Raynaud's phenomenon as a primary affection, i.e., not associated with some other arterial condition. It is a vascular spasm of the digital arterial bed and is bilaterally symmetrical. The disease, which is rare as compared with Raynaud's phenomenon, was first described by Raynaud in 1862. Young women are predominently affected. The fingers, sometimes the toes, or rarely the ears and nose, are the seat of periodic attacks of vascular spasms. The attack lasts as a rule for a few minutes, but may persist for an hour or two. The color change commences in the finger tips and spreads toward the bases of the fingers. As the attack passes off the part again becomes cyanotic, then red and hot; the numbness is replaced by burning pain. The pulse at the wrist or ankle persists during the attack. Thrombosis of small arteries may lead to ulcers, sclerodactyly, rarefaction of the terminal phalanges, and other trophic changes. Gangrene sometimes results.

The disease has been generally attributed to hyperactivity of the vasomotor (vasoconstrictor) nerves. Sympathetic ganglionectomy is, therefore, frequently resorted to in an effort to abolish the attacks. Lewis has shown, however, that a typical attack may be induced in a subject upon whom this operation has been performed, by exposing the affected part to cold (as by immersing it in cold water). He concludes therefore that the fault lies not in the nervous control but in the vascular wall itself. The following observations cited by Lewis substantiate his view.

(1) If one finger of a subject of the disease be immersed in cold water, an attack confined to this finger may be induced. Such a localized result cannot be explained upon the basis of a nervous reflex.

(2) Anesthetization of the ulnar nerve of a normal person by means of novocaine causes dilation of the vessels of the little finger (removal of vasoconstrictor tone). The vascular spasm in Raynaud's disease cannot be released in this way.

(3) If a subject suffering from Raynaud's disease affecting both hands, and upon whom a unilateral ganglionectomy had been performed, be seated in a cool room with both hands placed in cold water, the vascular spasm which results is more pronounced on the nonsympathetonized side. If, however, the rest of the body is warmed while the hands are immersed in cold water, the attack is more pronounced on the sympathectomized side. In the first experiment the greater degree of spasm on the nonoperated side is attributed to the added effect of a vasoconstrictor reflex. The lesser degree of spasm on the nonoperated side in the second experiment could be attributed to the inhibition of vasoconstrictor impulses. Though a nervous influence is evident in these observations the essentially local nature of the fault is also indicated.

Simpson and associates do not consider that Raynaud's disease is due *primarily* to a fault of the vascular tissue. These observers maintain that only in the advanced stages of the disease is the vascular wall itself abnormal and that in milder cases the fault is essentially vasomotor in character. They point out that Lewis' crucial experiments were performed upon severe or complicated cases of the disease.

Ganglionectomy, even though it may not remove the fundamental cause of the condition, does often exert a decidedly beneficial effect. The attacks are less frequent and intense after the operation; normal vasoconstrictor tone and, as just indicated, the reflex response to cold having been abolished, a more intense reaction of the arterial wall itself must occur before arrest of the circulation to the part can result. However, relapses often occur 1 to 2 years following the operation in those who were benefited.

### ERYTHROMELALGIA

Erythromelalgia is a rare but interesting condition characterized by attacks of painful redness of one or both feet, or occasionally of the hands. The pain is burning in character and is induced by warming or exercising the part; or by allowing it to hang down. Rest, elevation of the part or the application of cold tends to relieve the pain. Erythromelalgia has been attributed to vasodilation resulting from some abnormality of the vascular nerves. Lewis finds, however, that the essential abnormality in these cases is not vasodilation, for an equivalent degree of vasodilation may occur in normal subjects in response to warmth or exercise, yet pain does not result. Erythromelalgia, or *erythralgia* as Lewis prefers to call the condition, is probably not of vasomotor origin. The abnormality in these cases is apparently a hypersensitive state of the cutaneous pain fibers to heat or tension. This "susceptible state" of the skin in erythralgia is altogether analogous to that seen in inflammation, and to that which can be induced in any normal person by certain types of cutaneous injury—exposure to ultraviolet light, repeated rubbing or stretching, burns, etc. It is well known that the pain endings of skin injured in these ways are very sensitive to warmth or to tension. Warming the part either by increasing the blood flow through its vessels, or by the application of heat causes burning pain. Pain also results when the part is dependent, the engorged vessels then causing tension upon the hypersensitive nerve endings.

Lewis suggests that in the pain associated with erythralgia and with the types of cutaneous injury just mentioned, a chemical substance liberated in the skin serves as the immediate stimulus to the nerve endings. The observation that the pain which follows repeated rubbing or stretching of the normal or of the erythralgic skin is prolonged and intensified by arresting the circulation to the part, supports this conception.

### ACROCYANOSIS

In this disorder, the hands and less commonly the feet, are persistently cold, blue and sweaty. Exposure to cold intensifies the cyanotic color. In the case of the hands the cyanosis commences at about the level of the wrist and deepens as it is traced toward the fingers. There is puffiness of the fingers, but trophic disturbances are unusual. The milder forms of the disorder are closely allied, according to Lewis, to chilblains. The disorder is presumably due to increased tone of the cutaneous *arterioles* resulting from hypersensitivity to cold. The condition does not have a nervous basis; the fault is in the vascular wall itself, the cyanosis persisting unchanged after anesthetizing the ulnar nerve with novocaine. In acrocyanosis the cutaneous circulation is slowed as a result of arteriolar constriction; capillary dilation occurs with an increase in the quantity of blood in the skin. The slower blood flow, by allowing the hemoglobin to give up a greater part of its oxygen store, is responsible for the blue tint of the skin.

### THROMBOANGIITIS OBLITERANS (BUERGER'S DISEASE)

This is an *organic* vascular disease involving, as a rule, the medium and small arteries (and to a less extent the veins) of the extremities. The condition in the majority of cases is confined to the lower limbs. However, coronary, cerebral, renal and other systemic arterial involvement occurs. The vessels are stiffened and hard. The adventitia is thickened; the media shows atrophy of its muscle and an increase in connective tissue; and, active proliferation of the intima occurs, several layers of cells being formed. The marked narrowing of the vascular lumen which results is followed by thrombosis. This and not the intimal proliferation itself is responsible for the final obliteration of the vessel. Organization of the thrombus, i.e., its invasion by fibroblasts and its conversion into fibrous tissue, follows. Some restoration of the circulation through the vessel may occur later as a result of the formation of new channels within the substance of the organized thrombus; but whether or not such a process of revascularization results, the blood supply to the part is always greatly reduced.

Among some of the earlier manifestations of the condition are: fatigue of the limbs upon exertion; intermittent claudication; hypersensitivity of the vasoconstrictor reactions of the extremities to cold resulting in attacks of pallor or cyanosis, coldness and numbness or a dull ache; superficial migratory phlebitis. A definite reduction in blood flow through the part may be demonstrated by plethysmographic or calorimetric methods. Extreme variations in the color of the limb result from altering its position in relation to the level of the heart; when the affected member is dependent, undue redness or cyanosis results, whereas when raised above heart level it becomes intensely pale and waxy in appearance.

As the pathological changes progress, the pulse disappears from the wrist or ankle, or even from the popliteal or brachial artery; ulcers and other trophic disorders appear and ultimately gangrene of the toes or fingers sets in, requiring amputation. The vascular obliteration tends, however, to creep upwards necessitating amputation at successively higher levels.

The cause of the disease is unknown; some believe it to be of infective origin. Excessive use of tobacco is strongly suspected of being a predisposing factor. Buerger and others have remarked upon the very high incidence of the condition in Jews; of a series of 150 cases reported by Brown and Allen from the Mayo Clinic, over 50 per cent were Jews. The disease occurs almost exclusively in males, whereas Raynaud's disease with which it is likely to be confused, especially in its early stages, affects females predominantly. Another feature distinguishing it from Raynaud's disease is that in the latter, the color of the skin is affected little or not at all by elevation of the limb; and the pulse in the larger arteries does not disappear.

It is, of course, only during the earlier stages of the condition, i.e., when spasm due to increased vasoconstrictor reactivity is a contributing factor, and before organic changes have progressed to the point where they have occluded the vessels, that treatment can be expected to bring about any real benefit. When a spastic factor can be demonstrated, sympathectomy frequently results in very notable improvement. Even when the larger arterial vessels are obliterated, sympathectomy, by removing the vasoconstrictor tone of collateral vessels, may be followed by a definite improvement in the blood supply to the part. Remarkable improvement often follows the withdrawal of tobacco smoking. It has been reported that discontinuation of smoking, in thromboangiitis obliterans causes a decrease in platelet adhesiveness.

There are several methods to choose from for the detection of vascular spasm. The temperature of the part may be taken by means of a skin thermometer or a thermocouple before and after one or other of the following procedures, which, normally, causes vasodilation and raises the temperature of the part: (a) heating the entire body by a warm environment; (b) local anesthesia of sympathetic ganglia (or by the ganglionic blocking agents); (c) spinal anesthesia which temporarily paralyzes the vasoconstrictors; (d) anesthetization of a peripheral nerve; and (e) general anesthesia. A rise in temperature of the part, following one of these procedures, indicates the previous existence of a spastic element. The greater the degree of spasm the more pronounced and rapid is the temperature rise. If the occlusion is entirely organic in nature, no change in temperature results.

Instead of recording the skin temperature, the blood flow through the affected part may be estimated by the plethysmographic or calorimetric method before and after one of the procedures just enumerated.

## INTERMITTENT CLAUDICATION

This is a condition (described by Charcot in 1856) in which, as a result of organic (usually athrosclerotic) narrowing of the arteries of a limb (usually the lower limb, *claudicare*, to limp) and consequent restriction of its blood supply, severe pain is experienced in the muscles during exercise. This pain occurs after the same amount of exercise on each occasion and disappears with rest. The pain has been attributed to a muscular cramp or to spasm of the vessels. Neither of these explanations can be entertained, for the muscles are flaccid during the attack. The abnormal stiffness of the arteries seems to preclude the possibility of their being narrowed appreciably by spasm and the smaller vessels are in all likelihood dilated rather than constricted during the attack.

The essential cause of intermittent claudication is a relative anoxia of the muscles—they are called upon to perform work for which the oxygen supply is inadequate. Lewis has shown that pain identical in character with that occurring in this condition can be induced by exercising any normal limb during the arrest of its circulation. When the circulation is restored, an immediate increase in the volume of the limb occurs which is taken to indicate that the vessels were dilated during the pain. In a patient suffering from the disease in one limb it was shown that the pain occurring in the limb during exercise was practically the same with regard to its time of onset, development and duration as that induced by exercising the sound limb during circulatory arrest.

The fundamental importance of anoxia in the production of the pain is also evident from the observations of Pickering and Wayne who found that exercising the muscles of an anemic subject, in whom there was no evidence of arterial disease, caused the characteristic pain of intermittent claudication. Kissin also showed that exercise performed by normal persons during anoxia (induced by breathing an air mixture containing a low percentage of oxygen) caused the typical cramplike pain. The clinical experiments of Lewis indicate that the direct cause of the pain is not oxygen lack itself but the stimulation of sensory nerves by the metabolic products of muscular activity. Ordinarily these are removed by oxidation, but they accumulate when the blood supply is inadequate. He refers to the pain stimulus as "factor P". The evidence supporting this concept is as follows:

(1) The pain does not vary with the individual contractions but is a steady ache.

(2) Using a standard test (maximal grip exerted by thumb and index finger, recorded isometrically, and repeated at the rate of one per second) it was found that in normal subjects with the circulation to the arm arrested, the pain commenced in about 35 seconds after the commencement of the exercise and took another 53 seconds to reach the point where it became intolerable. The pain disappears within 3 seconds after restoring the circulation—presumably as a result of the removal of "factor P". If, on the other hand, occlusion of the vessels is maintained, the pain persists.

(3) Lewis found that the time of onset of the pain is determined by the total amount of work performed rather than by the length of the exercise period. Thus, when the circulation of a normal limb is arrested, pain ensues after the same number of contractions of equal strength whether they are repeated in rapid or in slow succession. On the other hand, if a constant rate is maintained, the pain follows sooner with strong than with weak contractions. If, however, the circulation to the part is only partially obstructed (Katz and associates) or if air containing a low percentage of oxygen is breathed (Kissin), the amount of work necessary to cause pain is lessened by increasing the rate at which the contractions are repeated—the chemical factor presumably accumulating more rapidly as a result of the shorter time intervals allowed for its removal.

(4) If, after the pain has been relieved by restoring the circulation to the part, the vessels are again occluded and the limb exercised, the time of onset of the pain ensues earlier, the shorter the period during which the blood had been permitted to flow. This result suggests that products accumulated during the previous exercise period, if not given sufficient time to be removed, are carried over to the second period and the concentration necessary for stimulation is reached sooner.

The nature of the chemical pain factor is unknown; Katz and associates believe it to be acid in character and nonvolatile. The ingestion of sodium bicarbonate was found to increase the amount of exercise required to cause pain.

#### "Immersion Foot"; "Trench Foot"

During the Second World War this name was given to a state of the vessels and tissues of the feet brought on by severe and prolonged chilling of the feet by cold water. It was seen most frequently in persons who had been shipwrecked and immersed for hours in the sea at northern lati-tudes. But it may also result if the feet alone are kept cold and moist; sailors working under the stress of wartime conditions in wet boots, or soldiers during duty in wet trenches (trench foot) may then suffer. In cases of immersion foot the feet during the period of exposure are swollen, numb and pulseless. Their color varies with the temperature from bright red to deep blue or waxy white, or may be mottled with areas of blue and white or blue and red. Within a few hours (2 to 48) after removal from the water, the feet become hyperemic and severely painful, the pain often being described as burning, scalding or stabbing in character. The swelling increases; blistering, ulceration, local wasting of muscles and, in the worst cases, gangrene result. Capillary damage permits fluid of high protein content to leak into the tissues. These effects are likely to be most severe if the temperature of the members has been quickly restored to normal. The hyperemic stage, after 6 to 10 weeks may merge into one in which the feet are pale and cold and very sensitive to exposure to cold. Damage to peripheral nerves and sympathetic fibers is a regular occurrence in severe clinical immersion foot. Anesthesia, motor weakness, and muscular atrophy may last for many weeks.

The hands may be affected by cold water in the same way as the foot but much less commonly, since they are rarely exposed to conditions of such extreme severity.

While the members are actually exposed to the cold water, the vessels are in strong constrictor spasm and a decreased blood flow results. A decrease in tissue oxygen tension is found, most likely secondary to the lessened dissociation of oxygen from hemoglobin (the oxyhemoglobin dissociation curve is displaced to the left by cold). The metabolism of the tissues both as a result of the cold and the anoxia is greatly reduced. It is believed, therefore, that a minor degree of tissue damage occurs at this time and the greater part after removal from the water, when the temperature of the parts rises. The vasoconstriction is a reflex response due to the action of cold on the general body surface, as well as to its local effect upon the vascular walls, and also probably to the absence of vasodilator metabolites. In the hyperemic stage there is maximum dilation of the vessels, the warming of the body having overcome the vascular spasm.

Since the intensity of the hyperemia and the tissue damage are enhanced by a rise in temperature, every effort is made to prevent rapid warming of the affected members. Ice bags or blasts of cold air are, therefore, applied locally to maintain the skin temperature of the feet around 21° C. It is also necessary to keep the entire body at as low a temperature as is consistent with comfort; this is achieved preferably by means of some form of cool cabinet.

*Frost bite.* Prolonged exposure to severe cold causes vasoconstrictor spasm, and when freezing occurs the circulation in the small vessels of the part becomes completely arrested. After the part has thawed, intense hyperemia usually follows, and most of the tissue damage is believed to be caused at this time. The increased capillary permeability secondary to the freezing together with the high capillary pressure of the hyperemic stage causes edema and swelling of the part. This of itself may cause strangulation of the circulation, but thrombosis also occurs. If the resulting ischemia is extreme, gangrene follows. Measures are directed toward the reduction of these effects by thawing the part rapidly and by the administration of an anticoagulant, e.g., dicoumarol or heparin.

## REFERENCES

ABRAMSON, D. I., TUCK, S., JR., AND BELL, Y. Blood flow and oxygen uptake responses to short periods of arterial occlusion. Fed. Proc., 1960, **19**, 95.

ALEXANDER, R. S. Tonic and reflex functions of medullary sympathetic cardiovascular centers. J. Neurophysiol., 1946, **9**, 205.

ALLWOOD, M. J. AND BURG, H. S. Effect of local temperature on blood flow in the human foot. J. Physiol., 1954, **124**, 345.

ANREB, G. B., BARSOUM, G. S., SALAMA, F., AND SOUIDAN, Z. Liberation of histamine during reactive hyperemia and muscle contraction in man. J. Physiol., 1944, **103**, 297.

ANREP, G. B. AND VON SAALFELD, E. Blood flow through skeletal muscle in relation to its contraction. J. Physiol., 1935, **85**, 375.

ARMIN, J., GRANT, R. T., THOMPSON, R. H. S., AND TICKNER, A. An explanation for the heightened vascular reactivity of the denervated rabbit's ear. J. Physiol., 1953, **121**, 603.

BARCROFT, H., DARNHORST, A. C., McCLATCHEZ, H. M., AND TANNER, G. M. On the blood flow thru rhythmically contracting muscle before and during release of sympathetic constrictor tone. J. Physiol., 1952, **117**, 391.

BROWN, G. E. AND ALLEN, E. V. Thrombo-angiitis obliterans; clinical, physiologic and pathologic studies. W. B. Saunders Company, Philadelphia, 1928.

BURCH, G. E., COHN, A. E., AND NEUMANN, C. A study by quantitative methods of the spontaneous variations in volume of the finger tip, toe tip, and postero-superior portion of the pinna of resting normal white adults. Am. J. Physiol., 1942, **136**, 433.

CELANDER, O. The range of control exercised by the sympathico-adrenal system. Acta physiol. scandinav., 1954, **32**, suppl., 116.

CELANDER, O. AND FOLKOW, B. The nature and the distribution of afferent fibers provided with axon reflex arrangement. Acta physiol. scandinav., 1953, **29**, 359.

COFFMAN, J. D., WOOD, J. E., JR., AND WILKINS, R. W. Effect of cooling and of smoking tobacco upon the blood flow of reactive hyperemia of the foot. Circulation, 1958, **18**, 177.

COOPER, K. E., EDHOLM, O. G., AND MOTTRAM, R. F. The blood flow in skin and muscle of the human forearm. J. Physiol., 1955, **128**, 258.

DEAL, C. P., JR., AND GREEN, H. D. Effects of pH on blood flow and peripheral resistance in muscular and cutaneous vascular beds in hind limb of pentobarbitalized dog. Circulation Res., 1954, **2**, 148.

DIJI, A. AND GREENFIELD, A. D. M. The local effect of carbon dioxide on the blood vessels of the human skin. J. Physiol., 1958, **140**, 42P.

DAWES, G. S. Vasodilator action of potassium. J. Physiol., 1941, **99**, 224.

DOLE, V. P., JR. AND MORISON, R. S. A note on the question of reflex activation of dorsal root dilators. Am. J. Physiol., 1940, **130**, 304.

DUFF, F., PATTERSON, G. C., AND WHELAN, R. F. Effect of intra-arterial antihistamines on hyperemia following temporary arrest of circulation in the human forearm. Clin. Sc., 1955, **14**, 267.

DUGGAN, J. J., LOVE, V. L., AND LYONS, R. H. A study of reflex venomotor reactions in man. Circulation, 1953, **7**, 869.

EDHOLM O. G., MOREIRA, M. F., AND WERNER, A. Y. The measurement of forearm blood flow during a raised venous pressure. J. Physiol., 1954, **125**, 41.

EDHOLM, O. G., FOX R. H., AND MACPHERSON, R K. The effects of cutaneous anesthesia on skin blood flow. J. Physiol., 1956, **132**, 159.

EDHOLM, O. G., FOX, R. H., AND MACPHERSON, R. K. Vasomotor control of cutaneous blood vessels in human forearm. J. Physiol., 1957, **139**, 455.

EICHNA, L. W. AND WILKINS, R. W. Blood flow in the forearm and calf. II. Reactive hyperemia. Bull. Johns Hopkins Hosp., 1941, **68**, 450.

EISEN, M. E., TYSON, M. C., MICHAEL, S. R., AND BAUMANN, F. Adhesiveness of blood platelets in arteriosclerosis obliterans, thromboangiitis obliterans, acute thrombophlebitis, chronic venous insufficiency and arteriosclerotic heart disease. Circulation, 1951, **3**, 271.

ELIASSON, S., FOLKOW, R., LINDGREN, P., AND UVNAS, B. Activation of sympathetic vasodilator nerves to the skeletal muscles in the cat by hypothalamic stimulation. Acta physiol. scandinav., 1951, **23**, 333.

FINNERTY, F. A., JR., WITHIN, L., AND FAZEKAS, J. F. Cerebral hemodynamics during cerebral ischemia induced by acute hypotension. J. Clin. Invest., 1954, **33**, 1227.

FOLKOW, B., STRÖM, G., AND UVNÄS, B. Efferent nervous pathways involved in cutaneous vasodilatation induced by activation of hypothalamic heat loss mechanisms. Acta physiol. scandinav., 1950, **21**, 145.

FOLKOW, B., STRÖM, G., AND UVNÄS, B. Do dorsal root fibers convey centrally induced vasodilator impulses? Acta physiol. scandinav., 1949, **17**, 327.

FOLKOW, B., HAEGER, K., AND KAHLSON, G. Reactive hyperemia as related to histamine; drugs antagonizing vasodilatation induced by histamine; vasodilator properties of adenosinetriphosphate. Acta physiol. scandinav., 1948, **15**, 264.

FOX, R. H. AND HILTON, S. M. Bradykinin formation in human skin as a factor in heat vasodilatation. J. Physiol., 1958, **142**, 219.

FROESE, G. AND BURTON, A. C. Heat losses from the human head. J. Appl. Physiol., 1957, **10**, 235.

FRUMIN, M. J., NGAI, S. H., AND WANG, S. C. Evaluation of vasodilator mechanisms in the canine hind leg; question of dorsal root participation. Am. J. Physiol., 1953, **173**, 428.

GRANT, R. T. Observations on local arterial reactions in rabbit's ear. Heart, 1930, **15**, 257.

GRANT, R. T. Observations on blood circulation in voluntary muscle in man. Clin. Sc., 1938, **3**, 157.

GREEN, H. D. AND HOFF, E. C. Effects of faradic stimulation of the cerebral cortex on limb and renal volumes in the cat and monkey. Am. J. Physiol., 1937, **118**, 641.

GREEN, H. D., LEWIS, R. N., NICKERSON, N. D., AND HELLER, A. C. Blood flow, peripheral resistance and vascular tonus, with observations on relationship between blood flow and cutaneous temperature. Am. J. Physiol., 1944, **141**, 518.

GREENFIELD, A. D. M., SHEPHERD, J. T., AND WHELAN, R. F. Circulatory responses to cold in fingers infiltrated with anesthetic solution. J. Appl. Physiol., 1952, **4**, 785.

HARMEL, M. H., HAFKENSCHIEL, J. H., AUSTIN, G. M., CRUMPTON, C. W., AND KETY, S. S. The effect of bilateral stellate ganglion block on the cerebral circulation in normotensive and hypertensive patients. J. Clin. Invest., 1949, **28**, 415.

HARPUDER, K., BYER, J., AND STEIN, I. D. Effect of intra-arterial injection of adrenalin on blood flow of human forearm. Am. J. Physiol., 1947, **150**, 181.

HERTZMAN, A. B. Relative responses of dorsal metacarpal, digital and terminal arteries of the hand in vasoconstrictor reflexes. Am. J. Physiol., 1941, **134**, 59.

HERTZMAN, A. B. AND ROTH, L. W. Absence of vasoconstrictor reflexes in the forehead circulation. Effects of cold. Am. J. Physiol., 1942, **136**, 692.

HILTON, S. M. Experiments on the postcontraction hyperemia of skeletal muscle. J. Physiol., 1953, **120**, 230.

HILTON, S. M. The effects of nicotine on the blood vessels of skeletal muscle in the cat. An investigation of vasomotor axon reflexes. J. Physiol., 1954, **123**, 289.

HILTON, S. M. Femoral artery dilatation and postcontraction hyperemia of the leg muscles. J. Physiol., 1956, **131**, 31.

HILTON, S. M. AND HOLTON, P. Antidromic vasodilatation and blood flow in the rabbit's ear. J. Physiol., 1954, **125**, 138.

KATZ, L. N., LINDNER, E., AND LANDT, H. J. On the nature of the substances producing pain in contracting skeletal muscle: It's bearing on the problem of angina pectoris and intermittent claudication. J. Clin. Invest., 1935, **14**, 807.

KELLEY, W. D. AND VISSCHER, M. Effect of sympathetic nerve stimulation on cutaneous small vein and small artery pressures, blood flow and hindpaw volume in the dog. Am. J. Physiol., 1956, **185**, 453.

KETY, S. S., SHENKIN, H. A., AND SCHMIDT, C. F. The effects of increased intracranial pressure on cerebral circulatory functions iu man. J. Clin. Invest., 1948, **27**, 493.

KETY, S. S., AND SCHMIDT, C. F. The effects of altered arterial tensions of carbon dioxide and oxygen on cerebral blood flow and cerebral oxygen consumption of normal young men. J. Clin. Invest., 1948, **27**, 484.

KETY, S. S. AND SCHMIDT, C. F. The nitrous oxide method for the quantitative determination of cerebral blood flow in man: Theory, procedure and normal values. J. Clin. Invest., 1948, **27**, 476.

KISSIN, M. J. The production of pain in exercising skeletal muscle during induced anoexmia. J. Clin. Invest., 1934, **13**, 37.

KLEINERMAN, J., ET AL. Effects of high spinal anesthesia on cerebral circulation and metabolism in man. J. Clin. Invest., 1958, **37**, 285.

KLEINERMAN, J. AND SANCETTA, S. M. Effect of mild steady state of exercise on cerebral and general hemodynamics of normal untrained subjects. J. Clin. Invest., 1955, **34**, 945.

LEE, J. S. AND VISSCHER, M. B. Microscopic studies of skin blood vessels in relation to sympathetic nerve stimulation. Am. J. Physiol., 1957, **190**, 37.

LEWIS, T. Experiments relating to the peripheral mechanism involved in spasmodic arrest of the circulation in the fingers, a variety of Raynaud's disease. Heart, 1929, **15**, 7.

LEWIS, T. Raynaud's disease, with special references to the nature of the malady. Brit. M. J., 1932, **2**, 136.

LEWIS, T., Clinical observations and experiments relating to burning pain in the extremities and to so-called "erythromelalgia" in particular. Clin. Sc., 1933, **1**, 175.

LEWIS, T. AND PICKERING, G. W. Observations upon maladies in which the blood supply to digits ceases intermittently or permanently, and upon bilateral gangrene of digits; observations relevant to so-called "Raynaud's disease." Clin. Sc., 1934, **1**, 327.

LEWIS, T. AND GRANT, R. Reactive hyperaemia. Heart, 1925, **12**, 73.

LINGREN, P. AND UVNÄS, B. Vasoconstrictor inhibition and vasodilator action—two functionally separate vasodilator mechanisms in the skeletal muscles. Acta physiol. scandinav., 1955, **33**, 108.

LUND, A. Significance of the cerebral cortex to the

vasomotor reaction of the extremities. Ejnar Munksgaards Forlag, Copenhagen, 1943.

LUND, A. Function of cortical vasomotor centers elucidated through experimental studies on animals. Acta psychiat., et neurol., 1945, **20**, 213.

MANGOLD, R., SOKOLOFF, L., CONNER, E., KLEINERMAN, J., THERMAN, P. G., AND KETY, S. S. The effects of sleep and lack of sleep on the cerebral circulation and metabolism of normal young men. J. Clin. Invest., 1955, 34, 1092.

MESCON, H., HURLEY, H. J., JR., AND MORETTI, G. Anatomy and histochemistry of the arteriovenous anastomoses in human digital skin. J. Invest. Dermat., 1956, **27**, 133.

MONTGOMERY, H. Oxygen tension of peripheral tissue. Am. J. Med., 1957, **23**, 673.

MOYER, J. H., MILLER, S. I., AND SNYDER, H. Effect of increased jugular pressure on cerebral hemodynamics. J. Appl. Physiol., 1954, 7, 245.

MOYER, J. H., MORRIS, G., AND SNYDER, M. A comparison of the cerebral hemodynamic response to aramine and norepinephrine in the normotensive and the hypotensive subject. Circulation, 1954, **10**, 265.

NELSON, D. AND FAZEKAS, J. F. Cerebral blood flow in polycythemia vera. A. M. A. Arch. Int. Med., 1956, **98**, 328.

PAGE, E. B., HICKAM, J. B., SIEKER, H. O., AND McINTOSH, H. D. Reflex venomotor activity in normal persons and in patients with postural hypotension. Circulation, 1955, 11, 262.

PARTINGTON, M. W. The vascular response of the skin to ultra-violet light. Clin. Sc., 1954, 13, 425.

PATTERSON, G. C. AND WHELAN, R. F. Reactive hyperemia in the human forearm. Clin. Sc., 1955, 14, 197.

PATTERSON, G. C. Role of intravascular pressure in causation of reactive hyperemia in the human forearm. Clin. Sc., 1956, 15, 17.

PATTERSON, J. L., HEYMAN, A., BATTEY, L. L., AND FERGUSON, R. W. Threshold of response of the cerebral vessels of man to increase in blood carbon dioxide. J. Clin. Invest., 1955, 34, 1857.

PICKERING, G. W. AND WAYNE, E. J. Observations on angina pectoris and intermittent claudication in anemia. Clin. Sc., 1934, 1, 305.

REMENSNYDER, J. P., MITCHELL, J. H., AND SARNOFF, S. J. Control of peripheral vascular beds during exercise. Fed. Proc., 1960, 19, 95.

ROBIN, E. D. AND GARDNER, F. H. Cerebral metabolism and hemodynamics in pernicious anemia. J. Clin. Invest., 1953, 32, 598.

RODDIE, I. C., SHEPHERD, J. T., AND WHELAN, R. F. Contribution of constrictor and dilator nerves to skin vasodilatation during body heating. J. Physiol., 1957, 136, 489.

RODDIE, I. C., SHEPHERD, J. T., AND WHELAN, R. F. Humoral vasodilation in forearm during voluntary hyperventilation. J. Physiol., 1957, 137, 80.

RODDIE, I. C., SHEPHERD, J. T., AND WHELAN, R. F. Reflex changes in vasoconstrictor tone in human skeletal muscle in response to stimulation of receptors in a low pressure area of intrathoracic vascular bed. J. Physiol., 1957, 139, 369.

RODDIE, I. C., SHEPHERD, J. T., AND WHELAN, R.

F. The vasomotor nerve supply to the skin and muscle of the human forearm. Clin. Sc., 1957, 16, 67.

RONDELL, P. A., KEITZER, W. F., AND BOHR, D. F. Distribution of flow through capillaries and arteriovenous anastomosis in the rabbit ear. Am. J. Physiol., 1955, 183, 523.

ROWE, G. G., MAXWELL, G. M., CASTILLO, C. A., FREEMAN, D. J., AND CRUMPTON, C. W. A study in man of cerebral blood flow and cerebral glucose, lactate and pyruvate metabolism before and after eating. J. Clin. Invest., 1959, 38, 2154.

SCHEINBERG, P. AND STEAD, E. A., JR. The cerebral blood flow in male subjects as measured by the nitrous oxide technique. Normal values for blood flow, oxygen utilization, glucose utilization, and peripheral resistance, with observations on the effect of tilting and anxiety. J. Clin. Invest., 1949, 28, 1163.

SCHIEVE, J. F. AND WILSON, W. P. The changes in cerebral vascular resistance of man in experimental alkalosis and acidosis. J. Clin. Invest., 1953, 32, 33.

SHENKIN, H. A., ET AL. The effects of change of position upon the cerebral circulation of man. Am. J. M. Sc., 1948, 216, 714.

SNELL, E. S. Relationship between vasomotor response in the hand and heat changes in the body induced by intravenous infusions of hot or cold saline. J. Physiol., 1954, 125, 361.

SIMPSON, L. S., BROWN, G. E., AND ADSON, A. W. Raynaud's disease, evidence that is type of vasomotor neurosis. Arch. Neurol. & Psychiat., 1931, 26, 687.

SOKOLOFF, L., MANGOLD, R., WECHSLER, R. L., KENNEDY, C., AND KETY, S. S. The effect of mental arithmetic on cerebral circulation and metabolism. J. Clin. Invest., 1955, 34, 1101.

SPEALMAN, C. R. Effect of ambient air temperature and of hand temperature on blood flow in hands. Am. J. Physiol., 1945, 145, 218.

STRÖM, G. Influence of local thermal stimulation of the hypothalamus of the cat on cutaneous blood flow and respiratory rate. Acta physiol. scandinav., 1950, 20, Suppl. 70, 47.

STRÖM, G. Vasomotor responses to thermal and electrical stimulation of frontal lobe and hypothalamus. Acta physiol. scandinav., 1950, 20, Suppl. 70, 83.

TURNER, J., LAMBERTSEN, C. J., OWEN, S. G., WENDEL, H., AND CHIODI, H. Effects of .08 and .8 atmospheres of inspired $pO_2$ upon cerebral hemodynamics at a "constant" alveolar $pCO_2$ of 43 mm.Hg. Fed. Proc., 1957, 16, 130.

WOOD, J. E., JR., LITTER, J., AND WILKINS, R. W. Mechanism of limb segment reactive hyperemia in man. Circulation Res., 1955, 3, 581.

WOLL, P. D. AND DAVIS, G. D. Three cerebral cortical systems affecting autonomic function. J. Neurophysiol., 1951, 14, 507.

WANG, S. C. AND BORISON, H. L. An analysis of the carotid sinus cardiovascular reflex mechanism. Am. J. Physiol., 1947, 150, 712.

WERTHEIMER, L., REDISCH, W., HIRSCHHORN, K., AND STEELE, J. M. Patterns of surface temperature response to various agents. Circulation, 1955, 11, 110.

YONCE, L. R. AND HAMILTON, W. F. Oxygen consumption in skeletal muscle during reactive hyperemia. Am. J. Physiol., 1959, 197, 190.

YOUMANS, P. L., GREEN, H. D., AND DENISON, JR., A. B. Nature of vasodilator and vasoconstrictor receptors in skeletal muscle of the dog. Circulation Res., 1955, 3, 171.

ZWEIFACH, B. W. AND METZ, D. B. Selective distribution of blood through the terminal vascular bed of mesenteric structures and skeletal muscle. Angiology, 1955, 6, 282.

*Monographs and Reviews*

ABRAMSON, D. I. Vascular responses in extremities of man in health and disease. University of Chicago Press, Chicago, 1944.

BARCROFT, H. The circulation in the limbs. In Circulation, edited by J. McMichael. Blackwell Scientific Publications, Oxford, 1958.

BARCROFT, H., AND SWAN, H. J. C. Sympathetic control of human blood vessels. Edward Arnold & Company, London, 1953.

CLARK, E. R. Arterio-venous anastomoses. Physiol. Rev., 1938, 18, 229.

FOLKOW, B. Nervous control of the blood vessels. Physiol. Rev., 1955, 35, 629.

GREEN, H. D. AND KEPCHAR, J. H. Control of peripheral resistance in major systemic vascular beds. Physiol. Rev., 1959, 39, 617.

HERTZMAN, A. B. Vasomotor regulation of cutaneous circulation. Physiol. Rev., 1959, 39, 280.

LEWIS, T. The blood vessels of the human skin and their responses. Shaw, London, 1927.

LEWIS, T. Vascular disorders of the limbs. Macmillan & Company, Ltd., London, 1936.

LEWIS, T. Clinical Science, illustrated by personal experiences. Shaw, London, 1934.

LEWIS, T. Observations on some normal and injurious effects of cold upon the skin and underlying tissues. Brit. M. J., 1941, 2, 795, 837, 869.

MARTIN, P., LYNN, R. B., DIBLE, H. J., AND AVID, I. Peripheral vascular disorders. E. S. Livingston, Ltd., Edinburgh, 1956.

MERYMAN, H. T. Tissue freezing and local cold injury. Physiol. Rev., 1957, 37, 233.

MONTGOMERY, H. Experimental immersion foot. Review of the physiopathology. Physiol. Rev., 1954, 34, 127.

SHEARD, C. Temperature of skin and thermal regulation of the body. In Medical Physics, edited by O. Glasser. p. 1523. Year Book Publishers, Inc., Chicago, 1944.

SHELLEY, W. B. AND ARTHUR, R. P. The Physiology of the Skin. In Annual Review of Physiology, edited by V. E. Hall. Annual Reviews, Inc., Palo Alto, California, 1958.

UVNÄS, B. Sympathetic vasodilator outflow. Physiol. Rev., 1954, 34, 608.

## 26

# SPECIAL FEATURES OF CIRCULATION IN DIFFERENT REGIONS. SPLANCHNIC CIRCULATION; RENAL CIRCULATION

### The Splanchnic Circulation

The splanchnic circulation may be represented as consisting of three parts: (1) the mesenteric bed, supplying the gastrointestinal tract, (2) the splenic bed, and (3) the hepatic bed.

A unique feature of this circulatory system is that the combined outflow from two of the components (mesenteric and splenic) constitutes the major portion of the inflow of the third one (hepatic), through the portal vein. In its hemodynamic implications, this anatomical arrangement has been compared to the Wheatstone bridge in an electrical circuit (Bradley, 1958), because of the placement of the resistance vessels (fig. 26.1). This serves mainly to emphasize the large number of variables that influence blood pressure and flow in any one point of the system, and the potential fallacy of conclusions based upon measurements of a single variable, such as portal venous pressure.

As in other regions of the circulation, it is the measurement of blood flow that presents the greatest source of difficulties. Direct methods to this date can only be applied at the cost of considerable surgical and anesthetic trauma, and with various degrees of interference to flow (particularly venous flow) due to cannulation procedures. This latter obstacle has been eliminated by the application of noncannulating electromagnetic flow meters (Green and associates, 1959). Indirect methods, based on the Fick principle and the ability of the liver to clear certain dyes, such as bromsulphalein from the blood stream (Bradley and associates, 1945), do not have these disadvantages, but—aside from their failure to meet strictly the criteria of the Fick principle—can be used only for measurement of total splanchnic outflow (i.e., hepatic venous flow), not for that of its various components.

### THE MESENTERIC CIRCULATION

Hemodynamically the intestinal circulation has both certain features in common with other vascular regions and others peculiar to itself. Perfusion studies on isolated denervated intestinal loops in the dog show that the pressure-flow relationships in the mesenteric bed are essentially similar to those in other areas, such as the skin or skeletal muscle (Selkurt and associates, 1958). There exists a "critical closure" pressure of the order of 15 mm. Hg below which flow ceases; above this point, progressive increments of pressure result in greater and greater increments of flow: in other words, vascular resistance decreases with increasing perfusion pressure. The reasons for this deviation from Poiseuille's law (dilatation of blood vessels with increased intraluminal pressure and the opening up of "dormant" capillaries) have been fully discussed in chapter 25.

The hemodynamic characteristics peculiar to the mesenteric circuit derive from the location of these vessels in the walls of viscera capable of actively or passively changing their intramural tension. Isolated, perfused intestinal loops exhibit two sorts of spontaneous contractile activity: rhythmic segmental contractions, and alterations of the muscular tone. Each of these has a definite influence on blood flow within the loop (Sidky and Bean, 1958). During segmental contractions, there is an increase in venous outflow and decrease in arteriolar inflow, proportional to the strength of the contraction; reverse changes occur during relaxation. In addition to these phasic changes associated with individual contractions, there is close relationship between mean blood flow per unit time and the frequency of rhythmic segmental activity. All other things being equal, the minute volume flow increases

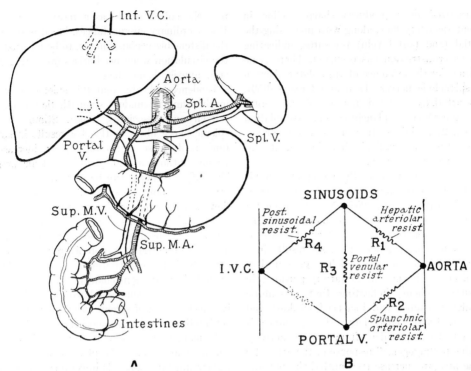

**A**                          **B**

Fig. 26.1. The Splanchnic Circuits. The vascular resistances in the splanchnic bed (*A*) are shown here in diagrammatic form (*B*). The resistances indicated are determinants of pressures in the portal vein and in the liver sinusoids, and of flows through the portal vein and hepatic artery. $R_1$, hepatic arteriolar resistance; $R_2$, splanchnic (i.e., mesenteric, pancreatic, gastric and splenic) arteriolar resistance; $R_3$, portal venular resistance; $R_4$, postsinusoidal or hepatic venular resistance. The dotted line represents a fifth resistance lying in the direct communications between the portal vein and inferior vena cava. (From S. E. Bradley, *Circulation*, Proceedings of the Harvey Tercentenary Congress, p. 356, 1958.)

with increasing frequency of contractions. Changes in the gut's muscular tone are of longer duration and involve greater lengths of intestine than segmental contractions. An increase of tonus results in reduction of both arterial inflow and venous outflow. Following cessation of tonic contraction, blood flow temporarily increases above precontraction levels, in a manner analagous to the reactive hyperemia observed in skin, skeletal muscle and myocardium (see ch. 25). Since segmental and tonic contractions occur independently from one another and may be more or less superimposed, their effect on intestinal blood flow can be quite complex. If these processes observed in the isolated loop also operate in the intact animal or man, the musculature of the intestine may emerge as a factor in the regulation of splanchnic and systemic blood flow.

   Passive changes in intramural pressure, such as those occurring in acute distension, also influence intestinal circulation (Noer and associates, 1951). It was shown in serosal vessels of rabbit's intestine, that at intraluminal pressures of 15 to

20 mm. Hg, segmental contractions cease, accompanied by slowing of blood flow in the venules. With progressive rising of the pressure, circulation slows, then ceases, first on the venous, then on the arterial side. While such levels of intra-intestinal pressures are clearly outside the physiological range, these circulatory changes are the basis of the massive trapping of blood and leakage of plasma into the wall and lumen of the gut observed during acute intestinal obstructions.

   In the maintenance of normal mesenteric circulation, the hemodynamic characteristics of the local vascular bed and the possible influence thereon of the intestinal smooth musculature are supplemented by a rich network of vasomotor nerves. These nerves belong to the sympathetic nervous system; their preganglionic fibers are contained in the splanchnic nerves; the postganglionic fibers form large plexuses around the abdominal aorta and accompany its branches to all the viscera. The function of vasomotor nerves has been discussed in detail in chapters 21 and 25. Electrical stimulation of the splanchnic nerves in anesthetized dogs produces sharp decline in mesenteric artery flow, along with increasing the arterial (and portal vein) pressures, indicating that vasoconstriction has occurred. There is no evidence for the existence of vasodilator fibers in the splanchnic nerves (Deal and Green, 1956). Intra-arterially injected norepinephrine reproduces the effect of splanchnic nerve stimulation (see ch. 21), while section of the nerves or administration of ganglionic blocking agents increases mesenteric flow.

Vasomotor reactions in the mesenteric circuit are of considerable importance in various circulatory adjustments (see p. 253). Not all vasomotor activity, however, is necessarily mediated by the nervous system. In the dog, experimental elevation of the portal venous pressure results in a reduction of mesenteric blood flow greater than the decrease in mesenteric artery-portal vein pressure gradient, indicating that mesenteric vascular resistance had increased (Selkurt and Johnson, 1958). This change in resistance is shown to be independent from nervous activity and due to "myogenic" response of the arterioles to the pressure increase transmitted through the capillaries (Johnson, 1959). It is not known what role, if any, this venous-arteriolar response plays in the intact animal.

## THE SPLENIC CIRCULATION

The nature of the intrasplenic circulation is a long-standing, unsettled controversy. Lack of agreement is centered around the manner of connection between arterial and venous capillaries: whether their lumina are continuous with one another ("closed circulation") or is arterial blood discharged directly into the meshwork of the splenic pulp from which it seeps back into the venous capillaries ("open circulation"). The basis for suspecting a discontinuity of the circulatory bed (unparalleled elsewhere in the body) is the presence of blood cells and intra-arterially injected foreign material in the splenic pulp, seen on histological examination; this is attributed to experimental artefacts by adherents of the "closed circulation" theory. Microscopic transillumination studies in the living animal (Whipple and associates, 1954) suggest that both open and closed circulatory patterns function simultaneously ("combined circulation"), but it is debatable whether these observations on mouse spleen are applicable to the human organ in view of the demonstrated structural differences between the two (Snook, 1950).

In certain mammals (dog, cat, horse, guinea

pig) the spleen serves as a reservoir of blood. Under ordinary circumstances, blood is stored in the distensible venous sinuses, to be released into the circulation when need arises (as during exercise, anoxia, hemorrhage).

Evidence indicates that this splenic emptying mechanism is under sympathetic regulation (Green and associates, 1960). Stimulation of splenic nerve fibers in the dog results in simultaneous decrease in arterial inflow, increase in venous outflow, and decrease of splenic weight. The inflow response can be reproduced by intra-arterial norepinephrine injection, while the outflow response can best be reproduced by injection of epinephrine. This suggests the existence of separate mechanisms for the control of splenic inflow and outflow: a norepinephrine-mediated arteriolar inflow constriction and an epinephrine-mediated emptying mechanism. This latter might be due either to venular relaxation causing passive elastic recoil of splenic tissues, or to primary contraction of splenic smooth muscle fibers.

In man, there is no evidence to indicate that splenic contractions take place under physiological circumstances, nor do injections of adrenaline raise the circulatory plasma or red cell volumes (Parsons and associates, 1948) as one would expect if the spleen served as an important blood depot.

## THE HEPATIC CIRCULATION

In addition to receiving its arterial blood supply through the hepatic artery, the liver is also perfused by the mesenteric and splenic venous outflow through the portal vein. As pointed out earlier, this unique circulatory arrangement leads to considerable complexity of splanchnic hemodynamics, and information regarding the various factors determining blood flow through the liver is still fragmentary. The following may illustrate the difficulties encountered.

The hemodynamic properties of the portal venous bed of the isolated liver show a great deal of similarity to those of other vascular beds, such as the mesenteric described earlier. There is, in particular, a progressive decrease of vascular resistance with increase of perfusion pressures throughout the physiological pressure range (up to 12 to 13 cm. of $H_2O$) (Breuer and associates, 1956). This would indicate that relatively small changes of portal pressure are associated with marked flow effects and that, consequently, portal venous pressure is an important determinant of total hepatic flow.

As may be seen from figure 26.1, however,

portal venous pressure is under the influence of a variety of factors. Mesenteric and splenic arteriolar tone regulate inflow, while the outflow is determined by venular tone and hepatic sinusoidal pressure. The latter, in turn, is dependent upon hepatic arteriolar tone and hepatic venous pressure (determined by inferior vena caval pressure) which regulate inflow and outflow in the sinusoids. Active contractions of the portal and hepatic veins are possible additional factors, all capable of altering portal venous pressure and thus influencing total hepatic flow.

Experimental separation of all these variables has not been possible up to now; nonetheless, certain important observations have been made.

Continuous simultaneous direct measurements of hepatic arterial and portal venous flows in anesthetized dogs show the contribution of the portal vein to total hepatic flow as being approximately 65 per cent in one study (Selkurt and Brecher, 1956), and 80 per cent in another (Green and associates, 1959). The effective portal perfusion pressures under these circumstances are 6 and 8 mm. Hg, respectively. In such preparations, splanchnic nerve stimulation causes an increase in both hepatic arterial and portal venous pressures, with a concomitant reduction in the corresponding flows. The calculated increases in resistance of the portal venous and hepatic arterial beds approximately equal one another, suggesting an equal degree of splanchnic vasomotor innervation. Compared to the mesenteric bed, they are both less sensitive to vasomotor stimulation. The effects of epinephrine and norepinephrine are similar to those of splanchnic nerve stimulation, causing, however, a less marked increase in the resistance of the portal bed. Thus, even though portal vein and hepatic artery pressures increase and hepatic arterial blood flow diminishes, portal flow does not change much and may even increase (Green and associates, 1959). In fact, the net effect of epinephrine in the resting, nonanesthetized human is an increase of total hepatic flow, as estimated by indirect Bromsulphalein retention (BSP) measurements, along with an elevation of portal venous pressure (Bradley, 1952). Norepinephrine under similar conditions causes a decrease of estimated liver flow in man (Bearn and coworkers, 1951), while in normal, anesthetized dogs, it has no flow effect (Smythe and associates, 1953).

The hemodynamic properties of the hepatic vascular bed and the nervous and humoral controls exerted on it play an important part in circulatory homeostasis by adjusting splanchnic blood flow in response to varying body needs. Blood flow through the splanchnic bed is sufficiently large to enable it to serve as a reservoir. The circulating splanchnic blood volume in man at rest and in the anesthetized dog, measured by isotope dilution techniques, forms approximately 20 per cent of the total blood volume (about 1000 cc. in man) (Bradley and coworkers, 1953). Splanchnic blood flow (i.e., the total amount of blood perfusing the liver through the hepatic artery and portal vein), estimated by the BSP method, amounts to approximately 1,500 cc. per minute in man, or about 20 per cent of the resting cardiac output.

Changes in splanchnic hemodynamics occur under various physiological and pathological conditions. In man, occupation of the erect position is associated with widespread reflex vasomotor adjustments opposing the hydrostatic forces which would lower the blood pressure in the upper half of the body (see ch. 22). The splanchnic bed is an important effector end organ in these reflexes. Passive tilting of human subjects from supine to upright position causes a decrease of splanchnic blood flow without similar changes of mean blood pressure, indicating that an increase in splanchnic vascular resistance has occurred (Culbertson and associates, 1951). This channels blood to other vascular areas, notably those in the upper regions of the body. In subjects with previous splanchnicectomy, the same tilting procedure causes arterial hypotension and a proportional decrease of splanchnic blood flow without changing the vascular resistance (Wilkins and coworkers, 1951). This would indicate that the vasoconstriction is normally mediated through the splanchnic sympathetic nerves.

Vasomotor adjustments and redistribution of circulating blood are also prominent during exercise. In normal human subjects, performing light exercise in the recumbent position, circulating splanchnic blood volume and splanchnic blood flow decrease significantly (Wade and associates, 1956). As exercise is usually associated with an increase in arterial blood pressure and cardiac output (see ch. 18 and 23), the reduction in splanchnic flow must be caused by increased vascular resistance. The advantages for the organism of such vascular adjustments are evident; vasoconstriction diverts blood flow to those organs that need it most (e.g., the exercising muscles). Moreover, the extra blood derived from the reduction in circulating splanchnic blood volume serves to boost venous return, thereby contributing to the elevation of cardiac output.

Finally, the splanchnic circulation plays an important role in the response of the organism to a reduction of circulating blood volume, such as occurs after hemorrhage. This response is conditioned to a great extent by the amount of blood lost, and it may vary, accordingly, from transient vasomotor changes to a state of irreversible circulatory collapse resulting in death.

It might be expected from the splanchnic responses to tilting and to exercise that blood loss would produce vasoconstriction in the splanchnic bed, in order to maintain flow in other parts of the body such as the brain and heart. This is not the case, however, as shown by animal experiments.

Aucte removal of about one-third of the total blood volume of the anesthetized dog results in a fall of cardiac output, mean arterial pressure, splanchnic flow (as measured by the BSP method) and splanchnic blood volume. The changes following this degree of blood loss are, in general, reversible. Splanchnic flow decreases in proportion to the fall of blood pressure, without significant change in splanchnic resistance. Thus, the splanchnic bed, unlike the vasculature of skin, skeletal muscle and kidneys, does not participate in the systemic vasoconstriction following hemorrhage. On the other hand, splanchnic blood volume diminishes to a greater extent, proportionally, than the reduction in total blood volume (Reynell and associates, 1955). Removal of larger amounts of blood, resulting in irreversible shock, produces more marked but qualitatively similar changes in hemodynamic parameters. The metabolic consequences, however, are quite different. Splanchnic oxygen consumption is not affected by the moderate blood loss; the diminished flow is compensated for by increased oxygen extraction by the tissues (Hamrick and Myers, 1955). With more massive hemorrhage, however, blood flow is so reduced that this compensation is inadequate and splanchnic oxygen consumption falls, resulting in hepatic hypoxia.

Thus, the splanchnic hemodynamic response to hemorrhage is a reduction of splanchnic blood volume rather than an increased resistance to flow. Diminishing the store of blood contained in the splanchnic bed amounts to an "auto-transfusion" and tends to re-establish the circulating blood volume. On the other hand, the failure to increase local vascular resistance indicates the priority given to the maintenance of adequate splanchnic oxygenation. The latter seems to be of great importance for the organism, as a factor in determining the outcome of hemorrhagic shock. Indeed, it was shown that oxygenation of the liver (Frank and associates, 1946), or of the intestine (Lillehei, 1956), by perfusion through the splenic vein or superior mesenteric artery protects dogs from the otherwise fatal outcome of shock induced by massive hemorrhage. The exact mechanism whereby splanchnic hypoxia contributes to the irreversibility of shock is not known. One current hypothesis postulates the elaboration of vasotoxic substances by the hypoxic intestine, and the failure of their removal or detoxification by the hypoxic liver (Selkurt, 1959).

## Renal Circulation

Renal circulation and renal function are so closely interrelated that reference to only one without consideration of the other always has to be artificial and incomplete. Also, much of our knowledge about renal blood flow stems indirectly from the behavior of some special functions of the kidney. The reader is referred to the chapter on "Urine Formation" where renal function, the anatomy and the clearance method for renal blood flow measurements are considered in detail.

METHODOLOGY OF RENAL BLOOD FLOW. The renal blood flow in man is usually measured by the clearance technique. There are some restrictions necessary in connection with this method: (1) rapid changes in the renal blood flow cannot be detected since a single clearance period covers 5 to 15 minutes and gives only average values during this time; (2) determinations can be carried out only when urine is produced at the same time, since, for the calculation of renal blood flow, it is necessary to know the amount of the clearance substance (usually paraminohippuric acid) which is excreted in the urine. For example, in shock and in certain renal diseases, when no urine is produced, renal blood flow cannot be evaluated by this method. (3) The urine formation is also stopped when the arterial blood pressure is less than 50 mm. Hg, since the hydrostatic pressure in the glomerular capillaries is insufficient to produce a glomerular filtrate.

In order to get a more exact picture of the renal hemodynamics, it was necessary, therefore, to turn to animal experiments. Nearly all the direct and indirect methods for the measurement of blood flow described in chapter 18 have been applied in these animal experiments. However, these methods fail to elucidate the pattern of distribution of the *intrarenal* blood flow. During the last two years, two methods have been developed to separately determine the blood flow of the renal cortex and medulla. (1) Under certain circumstances the accumulation rate of a substance in a tissue can be used as a measure of the blood flow. This method has been applied to the determination of blood flow to the different renal areas. When radioactive albumin is introduced into the arterial circulation, the radioactivity builds up in the tissue. The rate of accumulation of the radioactivity is a function of the blood flow to the region. (2) The other method utilizes the translumination of the different parts of the kidney by implanted micro light sources. The intensity of the transmitted light is measured by micro-photo cells which are either inserted under the renal capsule for measurement in the cortex, or placed against the papilla for measurement in the medulla. After a single injection of dye (Evans blue) into the renal artery, dye dilution curves can be recorded in different areas (fig. 26.4), permitting calculation of the mean circulation time ($\bar{t}$). In addition, blood volume (V) in the different areas can be calculated in accordance with the spectral characteristic of hemoglobin. The logarithm of the ratio $(I_{oxy})/(I_{reduc})$[1] is proportional to the hemoglobin concentration in the tissue ($Hb_{tissue}$). Knowing the local intravascular hemoglobin concentration ($Hb_{vasc}$), the ratio $(Hb_{tissue})/(Hb_{vasc})$ therefore represents the blood volume (V) in the tissue. According to the Stewart-Hamilton formula, the ratio $(V)/(\bar{t})$ represents the blood flow in different areas.

NORMAL RENAL BLOOD FLOW. Under resting conditions, in the recumbent position, and with a normal mean arterial blood pressure, about 1,200 cc. of blood per minute pass through both human kidneys, or about 20 per cent of the cardiac output. This is called the renal fraction of the cardiac output. Since the average weight of both kidneys is about 300 gm., normally 1 gm. of kidney is perfused by 4 cc. of blood per minute. However, this value is only an average for the whole kidney since there are great differences in the distribution of the blood supply within various renal areas. Blood flow values per gram of tissue have been found to be similar in dogs (4 to 5 cc. per gm. per minute). However, smaller animals have a greater renal perfusion rate. Values up to 10 cc. per gm. per minute have been obtained in rate by the PAH clearance method. For a better comparison

[1] $I_{oxy}$ = transmitted light during 100 per cent oxygen saturation of hemoglobin. $I_{reduc}$ = transmitted light during 0 per cent oxygen saturation of hemoglobin.

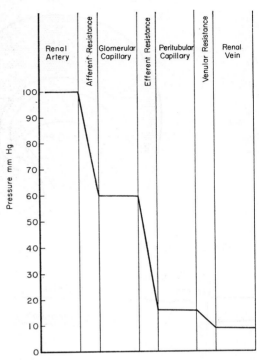

FIG. 26.2. Pressure gradients in the mammalian renal circulation.

of values obtained from different laboratories, it has become the custom to express renal blood flow in cc. per gm. per minute.

In the kidney, there are two capillary beds connected in series: the glomerular capillaries and the peritubular capillaries. They are separated by the vasa efferentia, which functionally and anatomically behave like arterioles. The main resistance to flow in the kidney is divided almost equally between the vasa afferentia (preglomerular) and vasa efferentia (postglomerular), and thus the main pressure drop occurs in these segments (fig. 26.2). It has been demonstrated by micropuncture studies in the cortex of mammalian kidney, that the hydrostatic pressure in the peritubular capillaries is usually 14 to 18 mm. Hg, and is about the same as the hydrostatic pressure in the proximal tubules. At the present time, there are no direct measurements of the hydrostatic pressure in mammalian glomerular capillaries. However, by indirect calculations, this pressure has been assumed to be normally in the range of 60 to 70 mm. Hg.

Ever since the investigations of Wirz and associates showed the significance of the renal medulla upon the concentrating mechanism of the kidney, and the functional difference of this area from the renal cortex, interest has grown in

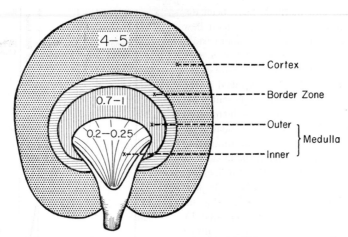

FIG. 26.3. Blood flow rates (cc. per gram per minute) in different areas of the dog kidney.

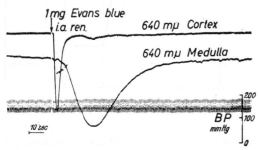

FIG. 26.4. Dye-dilution curves in the renal cortex and medulla of the dog after rapid injection of Evans blue into the renal artery ( ↓ i. a. ren.). The passage of Evans blue was measured by small photocells, which separately picked up reflected light from the cortex (*upper curve*) and transmitted light through the medulla (*middle curve*). The photocells were sensitive at the Evans blue absorption wave length (640 mμ). The lower curve represents systemic blood pressure (BP). (From Kramer, K., and associates, Pflüger's Arch. ges. Physiol., 1960, **270**, 251.)

the distribution of total renal blood flow to the component parts of the kidney. Up to the present, all the data on the intrarenal distribution of blood flow are the results of experiments in dogs because of the operative procedures involved in obtaining these measurements. The results show that the perfusion rate in the renal cortical tissue is much greater than in the medulla (fig. 26.3), and indicate that only 1 to 2 per cent of the total renal blood flow passes through the inner medulla. This low blood flow in the inner medulla is associated with a low velocity of the blood in the vasa recta of the medulla. The mean circulation time of the blood through the vasa recta is about 50 seconds, and only about 2.5 seconds through the cortical capillaries (fig. 26.4). On the other hand, the vascular volume in the cortex and in the medulla seems to be the same; in both areas, the vascular volume has been calculated to be about 20 to 22 per cent of the tissue volume. More than one factor is known to cause this low velocity of blood in the vasa recta. The resistance to flow in these vessels is very high because of the unusual length (as compared to other capillaries) of the vasa recta, which may be as long as 20 mm. The composition of the blood is changed as it passes through the medulla, especially when the end urine is highly concentrated. The medullary blood becomes more and more dehydrated as it reaches the tip of the papilla, by transmembrane shunting of water from the descending to the ascending limb of the vasa recta. This water-shunt mechanism results in a diminution of the intravascular blood volume and in an increase of the blood viscosity. Thus, the unusual length of the vasa recta, the decreasing intravascular blood volume and increasing blood viscosity all contribute to the low velocity of medullary blood flow.

INTRARENAL HEMODYNAMICS AND RENAL FUNCTION. Intrarenal hemodynamics and renal function are so interrelated that change in one will always affect the other. An increase in the cortical blood flow, if correlated with elevated glomerular capillary pressure, causes an increase in the glomerular filtration rate. In these circumstances, the excretion of osmotically active substances will be increased. This latter effect is partially caused by an increase in the tubular load, i.e., a greater amount of osmotically active substances offered to the tubules by the increased glomerular filtration rate. On the other hand, in the presence of an increase in cortical blood flow, there is a concomitant increase in the peritubular capillary pressure which, by itself, may affect the total excretion by means of decreased proximal tubular reabsorption.

Medullary blood flow seems to be important for the concentrating ability of the kidney. In the renal medulla, the osmotic pressure progressively increases from the base to the tip of the medulla and becomes a determinant in the concentration of the final urine delivered to the renal pelvis. An increase of blood flow in the medulla tends to wash out the osmotically active substances from this area, decreasing the osmotic pressure and causing a lower concentration of the final urine. In this manner, renal function is affected by primary changes in medullary blood flow and, conversely, medullary blood flow may be affected by primary changes in renal function. In water diuresis, the medullary blood flow is greater than in antidiuresis. The cortical blood flow and the glomerular filtration rate are unchanged under these circumstances.

AUTOREGULATION OF RENAL BLOOD FLOW. The blood flow (F) in an organ is directly proportional to the arteriovenous pressure gradient (Pa-v), and inversely proportional to the resistance (R), i.e., $F = (Pa-v)/(R)$. In most organs, when only the arteriovenous pressure gradient increases, the blood flow increases more than the increase in pressure gradient, meaning that there has been a concomitant decrease in the resistance caused by the passive distention of the vessels with pressure. The pattern of behavior of the renal blood flow is different; it reacts in the manner just described at perfusion pressures only up to 90 mm. Hg. However, when the arterial perfusion pressure rises above 90 mm. Hg, the resistance increases so that the total blood flow in the kidney remains nearly constant (fig. 26.6, curve N). Above 250 mm. Hg, the blood flow again becomes directly dependent on the arterial pressure. This phenomenon is known as the autoregulation of renal blood flow because it is also present after cutting the renal nerves, after injecting ganglioplegic drugs, and in the isolated perfused kidney.

Simultaneous measurements of blood flow in the cortex and inner medulla of the kidney have shown that autoregulation is present solely in the cortex. Since only about 1 to 2 per cent of the total renal blood flow passes through the inner medulla, a solitary increase in medullary blood flow does not actually cause a measurable increase of total renal blood flow. Therefore, in the presence of a rising arterial perfusion pressure, the total renal blood flow remains nearly constant in spite of an increasing medullary blood flow.

Hence, it is more accurate to limit discussion of autoregulation solely to the cortical blood flow.

There are at the moment, three theories which attempt to explain this special behavior of the renal blood flow.

*A. Myogenic theory.* When the arterial perfusion pressure is increased, the vessels become distended. The smooth muscles, especially in the preglomerular vessels, react to this distention by shortening, thereby constricting the vessels so that a new high resistance is established. This implies that the tonus of the vessels is increased by an autonomic myogenic reaction to increasing arterial perfusion pressure.[2] It has been demonstrated in the dog kidney that when the arterial perfusion pressure is suddenly increased, the blood flow is only increased passively during the first 3 to 4 seconds. Following this, the resistance in the vascular bed increases to such an extent that the blood flow nearly ceases at about 15 seconds. After 20 to 30 seconds, the blood flow increases to the normal level of the autoregulation (fig. 26.5). This initial latency and the phasic changes of the resistance are in accord with the contracting properties of smooth muscle. The autoregulation can be abolished by drugs which paralyze the smooth muscles (potassium cyanide, papaverine, and procaine (novocaine) in high concentration). Likewise, the phasic changes of the resistance, caused by rapid pressure increases, are removed by these drugs (fig. 26.5).

There are experimental indications that the autoregulatory mechanism resides within the preglomerular vessels. The glomerular filtration rate is controlled, among other things, by the intraglomerular capillary pressure. The constancy of the glomerular filtration rate and its independence from arterial perfusion pressure changes above 90 mm. Hg, constitutes indirect evidence of a constant, intraglomerular capillary pressure. Furthermore, by paralyzing the vascular smooth muscles with papaverine, the glomerular filtration rate now becomes directly proportional to the arterial perfusion pressure. Thus, there is strong evidence to support the contention that the auto-

---

[2] Contraction of the smooth muscles as the result of elevated intravascular pressure has been described for many vascular systems. In contrast to the kidney, these myogenic reactions are not powerful enough to constrict the vessel to such an extent that blood flow remains constant in spite of an elevated perfusion pressure. It is not necessarily true that the single muscle cell of the renal vessel reacts differently than in other organs. A spatial arrangement of the muscle cells, specially oriented, can increase the net effect of the single cell contraction on the diameter of the vessel.

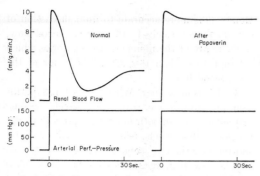

Fig. 26.5. Pattern of flow in the renal artery of dogs following sudden increase in the arterial perfusion pressure from 0 to 150 mm. Hg before and after vascular muscle paralysis by papaverine. The phasic changes in renal blood flow in the normal kidney, indicating a concomitant, inverse change in resistance can be abolished by papaverine. The steady state blood flow of 4 cc. per gram per minute at 150 mm. Hg in the control (autoregulated kidney) is increased under papaverine to about 9 cc. per gram per minute. (See also figure 26.6, difference between curve N and curve O at 150 mm. Hg). (Modified after Thurau, K. and Kramer, K. Pflüger's Arch. ges. Physiol., 1959, **269,** 77.)

regulatory mechanism depends upon the integrity and reactivity of the preglomerular vascular muscles.

*B. Cell separation theory.* In a vascular system in which small vessels branch off from a large one, the small vessels receive cell poor plasma from the outer zone of blood in the large vessel, because the erythrocytes remain in the axial stream of the large vessel. This separation of plasma and erythrocytes at the bifurcation of vessels is called plasma skimming or cell separation. For the kidney, it is assumed that this cell separation takes place to an unusual degreee at the origin of the afferent arterioles. The blood remaining in the interlobular arteries becomes more and more concentrated with erythrocytes and flows through special erythrocyte-shunts directly into the veins without flowing through the peritubular capillaries, which are perfused only by cell poor plasma. The degree of the cell separation is supposed to be dependent on the arterial perfusion pressure, so that blood with a hematocrit up to about 80 per cent in the distal part of the interlobular arteries can be produced. In this range of hematocrit, the viscosity of the blood is high and varies greatly with small changes in hematocrit. This variable viscosity which is dependent on the arterial blood pressure, is believed to be the cause of the variable resistance responsible for the autoregulation. According to this theory, a cell-free perfusion of the kidney should not show any

autoregulation. However, it has been demonstrated by different investigators that autoregulation does occur even when the kidney is perfused by dextran, a cell-free plasma, or blood with a very low hematocrit. It would, furthermore, be expected that the oxygen saturation of the blood in the distal peritubular capillaries should be lower than that in the mixed venous blood. However, investigations have shown that the oxygen saturation in this area is not different from that in mixed venous blood. Also, the passage times of plasma and erythrocytes from the renal artery to the renal vein are the same, but, according to the cell separation theory, they should differ.

*C. Intrarenal pressure theory.* By insertion of a 24 gauge needle into the renal tissue, it was found that the intrarenal tissue pressure measured in this way increases disproportionately with increasing arterial perfusion pressure. From this data, it is calculated that the elevated tissue pressure has a clamping effect on vascular geometry and resistance to flow. This assumes that the needle pressure selectively measures only normal tissue pressure and that no vessels have been ruptured by the needle insertion. In any case, measurements of the intracapillary and intratubular pressures in the rat kidney by the micropuncture technique have shown that these pressures do not change when the arterial perfusion pressure is elevated above 90 mm. Hg.

The present great interest in the investigation of autoregulation of renal blood flow may introduce some new theories in the future. At the present time, however, the myogenic theory is the most favored.

NERVOUS CONTROL OF RENAL BLOOD FLOW. The highly developed plexus renalis contains sympathetic and parasympathetic fibers. However, under normal physiological conditions, not too much is known of the significance of this rich nerve supply to the kidney. The interpretation of the results of experiments with regard to the nervous control of renal blood flow is complicated by the fact that the vascular system of the kidney has an autonomic and variable tonus which is independent of any innervation (see autoregulation of renal blood flow) and may interfere with nervous vascular reactions. For a better understanding of this vascular behavior, see figure 26.6, which shows pressure flow curves resulting either from change of nervous vascular tonus or from autonomic tonus.

Much investigation has been going on to gain information about the nervous control of the renal blood flow under *resting conditions.* Renal blood flow has been measured before and after denervation of the kidney.

In *unanesthetized* man and animals in recumbency, the renal blood flow of the denervated kidney does not differ from that of the innervated kidney. This implies that under resting conditions there is no sympathetic nervous influence in the renal vascular bed. Furthermore, the nonexistence of a sympathetic tone of the renal vascular bed, under resting conditions, has been confirmed by animal experiments in which depressor reflexes in the systemic circulation were produced. Stimulation of the reflexogenic areas of the carotid sinus and aortic arch causes vasodilation in the kidney only when a sympathetic tonus of the renal vessel has been *previously* produced by asphyxia or by anesthesia.

In anesthetized animals, it has been shown that the renal blood flow may increase after denervation; but, since the sympathetic tone in the peripheral vascular bed is usually augmented during anesthesia, the denervation, therefore, eliminates only the unphysiological sympathetic stimulation produced by the anesthesia, and thereby permits return of the blood flow to normal values. Accordingly, in a dog where one kidney is denervated, the renal blood flow decreases only in the innervated kidney during pentobarbital injection. The blood flow of the denervated kidney shows no change.

Neurogenic vasoconstriction of the renal vessels is produced by severe hypoxia, i.e., arterial oxygen saturation below 50 per cent. However, in the range of decreasing arterial oxygen saturation between 100 and about 50 per cent, there seems to be no change in renal blood flow, and this is true either in anesthetized dogs or in unanesthetized man. The vasoconstrictor effect of severe hypoxia can be eliminated in the dog by abolishing the chemoreceptors in the carotid sinus and aortic arch, indicating that the constrictor response to hypoxia is induced by stimulating the peripheral chemoreceptors.

Vasoconstriction in the dog kidney also occurs during hypercapnia while breathing a mixture of 5 to 30 per cent $CO_2$ in oxygen. In these experiments, the pH of the blood simultaneously decreased from 7.49 to 7.21. Since the constriction is abolished by renal denervation, hypercapnia and this degree of acidosis seem to produce only neurogenic rather than local vasoconstriction.

A decreased discharge rate of the pressoreceptors in the carotid sinus or aortic arch in dogs, caused by lowering the intrasinusal or intra-aortic blood pressure, or by damping the pulse pressure

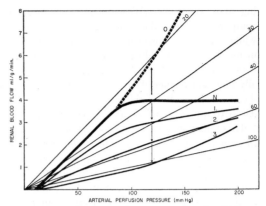

FIG. 26.6. Pressure-flow curves in the kidney. The thin lines through the origin of the graph represent equal resistances to flow expressed in terms of $\frac{mm.\ Hg}{cc.}$ per gram per minute.

*Curve N.* Pressure flow curve under normal conditions. The increase of resistance above 80 mm. Hg is independent of extrinsic factors (see autoregulation of renal blood flow). *Curves 1 to 3.* Pressure flow curves with increasing vascular tone secondary to various extrinsic factors such as increase sympathetic stimulation or epinephrine. With increasing extrinsically induced vascular tone, the pressure flow curves become more and more linear simultaneous to a decrease in autoregulation. *Curve O.* Pressure flow curve after paralyzing the smooth muscles of the renal vessels. Note the abolition of autoregulation; also note that under normal conditions (*curve N*), there is no myogenic tone in the renal vessels between 0 to 80 mm. Hg.

in these areas, leads to neurogenic vasoconstriction in the kidney as well as in other organs.

In connection with the nervous control of the renal blood flow, the question also arises as to whether or not there exists a nervous control of the function of the tubular cells. After denervation of the kidney, an increase of sodium excretion is often found, suggesting a decreased absorptive capacity of the tubular cells. However, in nearly all these experiments, the glomerular filtration rate simultaneously increased. It is well known that this increase of the glomerular filtration rate can cause an elevated sodium excretion without altered tubular function. Moreover, those experiments in which the excretion of electrolytes was increased *without* a corresponding increase in the glomerular filtration rate, by no means prove a primary changed tubular function after denervation. As yet, it is still unknown whether changes of the intrarenal distribution of blood flow occur after denervation since, for example, even small changes in medullary blood flow can affect the composition of the end urine.

*Exercise, posture and central blood volume. Effects on renal blood flow.* In the upright exercising man, renal blood flow is diminished when compared to blood flow under resting conditions while supine. If, however, exercise is performed in recumbency, the blood flow in the kidney remain nearly unaffected. Also, the dog, which usually does not change its posture during exercise, shows no change in renal blood flow when running 5.6 to 10 mph at a 15° slope on a treadmill.

These findings give rise to the supposition that the upright position *per se*, in which exercise is usually performed, leads to the decrease in renal blood flow. Indeed, it has been found that the usual response on changing from the recumbent to the standing position is a decrease in renal blood flow. Under the extreme conditions of prolonged standing, the renal blood flow may decrease by about 50 per cent of the control value. These changes are accompanied by similar reductions in glomerular filtration rate and urine output. Since the arterial blood pressure is little or unchanged, the reduction in renal blood flow is primarily caused by an elevated resistance to flow. This is only part of a generalized elevation in total peripheral resistance secondary to the upright position. This enhanced peripheral resistance is caused by an augmented neural vasoconstriction rather than by a humoral mechanism. The afferent mechanisms involved are poorly understood, but it is believed that this can be effected through reduction of central blood volume. The central blood volume in the thorax can be reduced to subnormal values by means of positive pressure breathing. It has been shown, that under these circumstances, the renal resistance to flow increases. Since the blood volume in the chest is also diminished in the upright position, this reduction in central blood volume, induced by changing from the recumbent to the standing position, may be one factor involved in the renal constrictor mechanism. Conversely, an increase in central blood volume above normal by blood infusion, tilting of the body to the head down position, or negative pressure breathing, should produce an neurogenic vasodilation in the kidney. But, as pointed out in the preceding section on nervous control of renal blood flow, under normal resting conditions there are *no* sympathetic discharges to the renal vessel, and hence a neurogenic vasodilation is nonexistent. It is not surprising, therefore, than an increase in central blood volume fails to result in a renal vasodilation. However, there is another interesting effect of an increased central blood volume upon the kidney which should be briefly mentioned here. It has been found that elevation of central blood

volume simultaneously increases the urine output. Since renal blood flow and also the glomerular filtration rate are not altered under these conditions, and, since the resultant diuresis is caused primarily by an increased free water excretion (i.e., without concomitant excretion of osmotically active substances), there is strong evidence that an increase in central blood volume inhibits antidiuretic hormone (ADH) secretion of the neurohypophysis. It is suggested that this ADH-inhibition is reflexly induced by stimulation of stretch receptors located predominantly in the left atrial wall and sensitive to an increase in central blood volume. Whether this mechanism has any significance in the regulation of the total blood volume, is the subject of present investigations.

Returning to the discussion of renal blood flow during exercise in man, there is no doubt that the change to the upright position *per se* is one factor involved in the decreased renal blood flow. But, reductions in renal blood flow down to 20 per cent of the control value, as measured in severe exercise in man, can hardly be explained by this orthostatic mechanism alone. It is a matter for further investigations to establish the other factors which determine the changes in renal blood flow during exercise.

*The effect of some pharmacological agents upon renal circulation.* Epinephrine and norepineph-rine both have powerful vasoconstrictor effects upon the renal vessels. Each drug acts upon smooth muscles, and its action can be abolished by adrenergic blocking agents. Single intravenous injection of 2 $\mu$g. per kg. of epinephrine causes complete cessation of renal blood flow. During continuous intravenous infusion of low doses (10 to 15 $\mu$g. per minute) of epinephrine or norepinephrine in man, there occurs a 30 per cent decrease in renal flow without change in the glomerular filtration rate. The result indicates that low concentrations of the pressor agents predominantly produce efferent arteriolar constriction. Since the systemic arterial pressure is concomitantly elevated, a small rise in resistance must also occur in the afferent arterioles or, otherwise, there would occur an increase in the glomerular filtration rate. Similar results have been found in the denervated kidney in man. The effect of 2 to 10 $\mu$g. per minute of 1-norepinephrine, given intravenously, has been studied in the homo-transplanted kidney of an identical twin recipient and in the innervated kidney of the donor. In both kidneys the renal blood flow decreased 25 per cent, when given 2 $\mu$g. 1-norepinephrine, and

50 per cent, when given 10 μg., without changes in the glomerular filtration rate, revealing the similarity in the response of the innervated and denervated kidney to 1-norepinephrine in unanesthetized man. Despite the decrease in renal blood flow following minute doses of epinephrine, there occurs a moderate swelling of the kidney. Experiments in dogs have shown a simultaneous increase in renal blood volume. It has, therefore, been concluded that an increase in resistance to flow also occurs in postcapillary segments (probably venular) which leads to an elevated intracapillary pressure and a resultant distention of the renal capillaries.

Pitressin is an extract of the posterior pituitaries of oxen and hogs with an antidiuretic-vasopressor action. Infusions of 1 to 2 mV per kg. per hour, with which significant antidiuretic effects can be produced, have no effect upon the renal blood flow in man. Higher, nonphysiological doses, increase the resistance to flow in the kidney by direct action on the renal vessels. Repeated injections elicit tachyphylaxis.

The injection of serotonin (5-hydroxytryptamine) into the renal artery in dogs, produces constriction of the renal vessels. This constrictor effect has been shown in innervated as well as in denervated kidney and persists after the application of sympatholytic agents. Thus, serotonin probably acts directly on the smooth muscles. However, *intravenously* injected serotonin may be followed by a renal vasodilation reflexly induced by the action of this drug upon depressor receptors whose afferent fibers arise within the chest and are mediated through the vagus nerve. In patients with malignant carcinoid, the urinary excretion of serotonin or its metabolic products is elevated secondary to the high circulating blood level. In these patients, the glomerular filtration rate and renal blood flow are usually diminished.

1-Hydrozinophthalazine (Apresoline) produces a vasodilation in the kidney which persists for hours following a single injection. The mechanism of the vasodilatory effect is still unknown. It seems that Apresoline has no direct paralyzing effect upon the renal vessels since injection into the renal artery produces an initial vasoconstriction, followed in several minutes by the onset of vasodilation, the latter becoming more marked during the next 30 minutes and persisting for 2 to 3 hours.

REACTIVE HYPEREMIA. In both cardiac and skeletal muscles, and in some other organs, the blood flow temporarily increases over the control value after releasing an arterial clamp. This overshoot of blood flow, lasting from several seconds to several minutes, depends upon the duration of occlusion and may exceed the estimated blood flow debt incurred during the occlusion period. If the term reactive hyperemia is restricted to this overshoot, then by definition, the renal circulation does not show this phenomenon. After releasing an occlusion of the renal artery, there occurs a brief 3 to 5-second overshoot of blood flow (fig. 26.5), which, however, is independent of the duration of occlusion and is, in no instance, greater than the estimated blood flow debt. Furthermore, after interruption of the renal blood flow for several minutes, the re-established blood flow, following the initial overshoot, usually decreases temporarily to subnormal values.

HYPOTHERMIA AND RENAL BLOOD FLOW. At the onset of the cooling phase, as the body attempts to maintain a normal temperature (shivering phase), the renal blood flow increases 20 to 45 per cent above the control value. This has been observed utilizing para-aminohippurate (PAH) clearances in both anesthetized and unanesthetized man and animals. This initial increase in renal blood flow can be abolished by inhibiting shivering with d-tubocurarine. As the rectal temperature falls below 32° C. (90° F.), the renal blood flow progressively decreases and, at 27° C. (80° F.) is only 50 per cent of the normal value. This decrease in blood flow is also observed in the isolated dog kidney which was perfused by cooled blood, and in which the renal blood flow was directly measured. A major part of the decreased blood flow is caused by an increased resistance related to the augmented viscosity of cooled blood, but this factor alone, however, is insufficient to explain the degree of change in blood flow. It is still unknown which other nervous or humoral factors are involved.

Regional cooling such as the immersion of an extremity into ice water for some minutes, sufficient to produce a painful sensation, in man is attended by a 20 per cent decrease in renal blood flow. This is probably caused by a nervous reflex, stimulating sympathetic discharges to the renal vessels.

ARTERIOVENOUS OXYGEN DIFFERENCE AND OXYGEN UPTAKE OF THE KIDNEY. The oxygen difference between arterial and venous blood in the human kidney (A-V oxygen difference) is about 1.7 cc. per 100 cc. of blood, which is small compared with an A-V oxygen difference of 4 to 5 cc. per 100 cc. of blood between arterial blood and mixed venous blood of the right heart. From the renal A-V oxygen difference and the total renal blood flow (1,200 cc. per minute), the oxygen up-take of both human kidneys is calculated to be about 21 cc. per minute. In isolated dog kidney, as well as in dogs' kidneys *in situ*, the A-V oxygen difference has been found to be fairly constant in spite of renal blood flow changes, which means that the oxygen consumption in the kidney parallels the blood flow. Up to the present, little information is available concerning this phenomenon, but data from recent experiments suggest that the increase of oxygen consumption accompanying elevated blood flow is caused by an increase of reabsorbtive activities, especially for sodium, which is believed to be an active oxygen consuming mechanism. The renal oxygen uptake has often been related to 100 gm. of renal tissue. Assuming a total weight of 300 gm. for the two kidneys, the oxygen uptake rate would be 7 cc. per 100 gm. per minute. However, for this latter calculation of oxygen uptake, the same restrictions as mentioned for the similar calculation of renal blood flow, have to be considered since the different renal areas have also different oxygen uptake rates.

In the renal cortex of anesthetized dogs, the oxygen uptake has been calculated to be 8 to 9 cc. per 100 gm. of tissue per minute, in the inner medulla only 0.3 to 0.4 cc. per 100 gm. of tissue per minute. Since oxygen uptake and blood flow in the medulla, compared to the cortex, are diminished by about the same factors, the A-V oxygen difference, therefore, may be the same in both areas and, consequently, no different than the A-V oxygen difference of the kidney in toto.

The A-V oxygen difference in the renal medulla of anesthetized dogs has also been indirectly calculated by means of the oxygen tension of the final urine, which is assumed to be in equilibrium with the medullary venous blood. Usually, the oxygen tension in the urine is less than in the mixed renal venous blood and in these experiments, the difference during air breathing was $25 \pm 3$ mm. Hg. Thus, by this method, the A-V oxygen difference in the medulla has been calculated to be 8.5 cc. per 100 cc. of blood, which would indeed be very high. However, there are indications that oxygen pressure in the medulla may also be influenced by the counter-current exchange mechanism. In this case, oxygen pressure would progressively decrease to the tip of the medulla by transmembral shunting of oxygen from the descending to the ascending limb of the vasa recta. The low oxygen tension of the final urine would represent only the low oxygen pressure at the tip of the medulla rather than the

oxygen pressure of the medullary venous blood and, therefore, could not be used for calculations of the medullary A-V oxygen difference.

For the outer zone of the renal medulla, there exist only determinations of oxygen uptake in excised tissue slices incubated in Warburg vessels. Under these circumstances, an oxygen uptake of about 4 cc. per 100 gm. of tissue per minute has been found.

## CONCLUSIONS

Renal hemodynamics exhibit certain peculiarities which need re-emphasis. Under basal conditions, there exists no neurogenic tone in the renal vessels, and the kidney is protected against elevations of arterial blood pressure by an autonomic mechanism which usually maintains the cortical blood flow, the glomerular filtration rate and the intrarenal capillary pressure at constant levels. A neurogenic vasodilation is generally nonexistent and only vasoconstriction can be produced via the nervous system. This behavior is absolutely contrary to that of the coronary circulation where the experimental physiology, up to the present time, has demonstrated only dilatory reflex mechanisms. Renal hemodynamics are poorly understood by solely using measurements of the *total* renal blood flow. The renal artery supplies blood at varying flow rates to the differently functioning areas, and function and blood flow seem to be mutually interdependent; this has only been demonstrated in animals. The human kidney, however, still holds secret its distribution of intra-renal blood flow since, at the present time, techniques applicable for use in humans have not been developed.

## REFERENCES

AVIADO, D. M., JR., WUNCK, A. L., AND DEBEER, E. J. Effect of sympathomimetica on blood flow in anesthetized dog. J. Pharmacol. & Exper. Therap., 1958, **124**, 238.

BEARN, A. G., BILLING, B., AND SHERLOCK, S. The effect of adrenaline and noradrenaline on hepatic blood flow and splanchnic carbohydrate metabolism in man. J. Physiol., 1951, **115**, 430.

BERGER, E. Y., GOLDSTONE, M., AND HORWITZ, S. A. The effect of anoxic anoxia on the human kidney. J. Clin. Invest., 1949, **28**, 648.

BERGSTRAND, A. AND STERKY, G. Renal function in hypothermia. Acta physiol. scandinav., 1954, **31**, 13.

BERLINER, R. W. AND DAVIDSON, D. G. Production of hypertonic urine in the absence of pituitary antidiuretic hormone. J. Clin. Invest., 1957, **36**, 1416.

BERNE, R. M. Hemodynamics and sodium excretion of denervated kidney in anesthetized and unanesthetized dogs. Am. J. Physiol., 1952, 171, 148.

BLATTEIS, C. M. AND HORVATH, S. M. Renal, cardiovascular and respiratory responses and their inter-relations during hypothermia. Am. J. Physiol., 1958, 192, 357.

BOYLAN, J. W. AND ANTKOWIAK, D. E. Mechanism of diuresis during negative pressure breathing. J. Appl. Physiol., 1959, 14, 116.

BRADLEY, S. E., MARKS, P. A., REYNELL, P. C., AND MELTZER, J. The circulating splanchnic blood volume in dog and man. Tr. A. Am. Physicians, 1953, 66, 294.

BRAUER, R. W., LEONG, G. F., McELROY, R. F., JR., AND HOLLOWAY, R. J. Hemodynamics of the vascular tree of the isolated rat liver preparation. Am. J. Physiol., 1956, 186, 537.

BRICKER, N. S., STRAFFON, R. A., MAHONEY, E. P., AND MERRILL, J. P. The functional capacity of the kidney denervated by autotransplantation in the dog. J. Clin. Invest., 1958, 37, 185.

BRICKER, N. S., GUILD, W. R., REARDEN, J. B., AND MERRILL, J. P. Studies on the functional capacity of a denervated homotransplanted kidney in an identical twin with parallel observations in the donor. J. Clin. Invest., 1956, 35, 1364.

BRODWALL, E. K. A study of renal function in orthostatic hypotension. Circulation, 1960, 21, 38.

CARLIN, M. R., MUELLER, C. B., AND WHITE, H. L. Effects of exercise on renal blood flow and sodium excretion in dogs. J. Appl. Physiol., 1950, 3, 291.

CHAPMAN, C. B., HENSCHEL, A., MINCKLER, J., FORSGREN, A., AND KEYS, A. Effect of exercise on renal plasma flow in normal male subjects. J. Clin. Invest., 1948, 27, 639.

CHARGILL, W. H. AND HICKAM, J. B. The oxygen consumption of the human kidney. J. Clin. Invest., 1948, 27, 528.

CARGILL, W. H. AND HICKAM, J. B. The oxygen consumption of the normal and the diseased human kidney. J. Clin. Invest., 1949, 28, 526.

CHASIS, H, RANGES, H. A., GOLDRING, W., AND SMITH, H. W. The control of renal blood flow and glomerular filtration in normal man. J. Clin. Invest., 1938, 17, 683.

CORCORAN, A. C., BROWNING, J. S., AND PAGE, I. H. Renal hemodynamics in orthostatic hypotension. J. A. M. A., 1942, 119, 793.

CULBERTSON, J. W., WILKINS, R. W., INGELFINGER, F. J., AND BRADLEY, S. E. The effect of the upright posture upon hepatic blood flow in normotensive and hypertensive subjects. J. Clin. Invest., 1951, 30, 305.

DEAL, C. P., JR. AND GREEN, H. D. Comparison of changes in mesenteric resistance following splanchnic nerve stimulation with responses to epinephrine and norepinephrine. Circulation Res., 1956, 4, 38.

EMANUEL, D. A., SCOTT, J., COLLINS, R., AND HADDY, F. J. Local effect of serotonin on renal vascular resistance and urine flow rate. Am. J. Physiol., 1959, 196, 1122.

FOLKOW, B. Intravascular pressure as a factor regulating the tone of small vessels. Acta physiol. scandinav., 1949, 17, 289.

FORSTER, R. P. AND MAES, J. P. Effect of experimental neurogenic hypertension on renal blood flow and glomerular filtration rates in intact denervated kidneys of unanesthetized rabbits with adrenal glands demedullated. Am. J. Physiol., 1947, 150, 534.

FRANK, M. A., SELIGMAN, A. M., AND FINE, J. Traumatic shock. XIII. The prevention of irreversibility in hemorrhagic shock by viviperfusion of the liver. J. Clin. Invest., 1946, 25, 22.

FREEMAN, O. W., MITCHELL, G. W., WILSON, J. S., FITZHUGH, F. W., AND MERRILL, A. J. Renal hemodynamics, sodium and water excretion in supine exercising normal and cardiac patients. J. Clin. Invest., 1955, 34, 1109.

GOTTSCHALK, C. W. AND MYLLE, M. Micropuncture study of pressures in proximal tubules and peritubular capillaries of the rat kidney and their relation to urethral and renal venous pressures. Am. J. Physiol., 1956, 185, 430.

GRECO, DEL F., MASSON, G. M. C., AND CORCORAN, A. C. Renal and arterial effects of serotonin in the anesthetized rat. Am. J. Physiol., 1956, 187, 509.

GREEN, H. D., LOCKSLEY, S. H., SEXTON, J., AND DEAL, C. P. Autonomic vasomotor responses in the canine hepatic arterial and venous beds. Am. J. Physiol., 1959, 196, 196.

GREEN, H. D., OTTIS, K., AND KITCHEN, T. Autonomic stimulation and blockade on canine splenic inflow, outflow and weight. Am. J. Physiol., 1960, 198, 424.

GRUPP, G. AND HEIMPEL, H. Zum Problem der reaktiven Hyperämie der Niere. Pflüger's Arch. ges. Physiol., 1958, 267, 426.

HADDY, F. S., SCOTT, J., FLEISHMAN, M., AND EMANUEL, D. Effect of change in blood flow rate upon vascular resistance. Am. J. Physiol., 1958, 195, 111.

HAMRICK, L. W., JR. AND MYERS, J. D. The effect of hemorrhage on hepatic blood flow and splanchnic oxygen consumption of the dog. Circulation Res., 1955, 3, 65.

HINSHAW, L. B., BALLIN, H. M., DAY, S. B., AND CARLSON, C. H. Tissue pressure and autoregulation in the dextran perfused kidney. Am. J. Physiol., 1959, 197, 853.

HULET, W. H. AND SMITH, H. W. Negative pressure respiration, water diuresis and natriuresis in normotensive, hypertensive and prehydrated normotensive subjects. J. Clin. Invest., 1959, 38, 1972.

JOHNSON, P. C. Myogenic nature of increase in intestinal vascular resistance with venous pressure elevation. Circulation Res., 1959, 7, 992.

KAPLAN, S. A., WEST, C. D., AND FOMON, S. J. Effects of unilateral division of splanchnic nerve on the renal excretion of electrolytes in unanesthetized and anesthetized dogs: the mechanism of crossed stimulation. Am. J. Physiol., 1953, 175, 363.

KRAMER, K., AND WINTON, F. R. The influence of urea and of change in arterial pressure on the oxygen consumption of the isolated kidney in dog. J. Physiol. 1937, **96,** 87.

KRAMER, K. AND ULLRICH, K. O₂-Saettigung und Hb-Gehalt des Capillarblutes der Nierenrinde. Pflüger's Arch. ges. Physiol., 1958, **267,** 251.

KRAMER, K., THURAU, K., AND DEETJEN, P. Hämodynamik des Nierenmarks. I. Capilläre Passagezeit, Blutvolumen, Durchblutung, Gewebshämatokrit und O₂-Verbrauch des Nierenmarks in situ. Pflüger's Arch. ges. Physiol., 1960, **270,** 251.

LASSEN, N. A., LONGLEY, J. B., AND LILIENFIELD, L. S. Concentration of albumin in renal papilla. Science, 1958, **128,** 720.

LAUSON, H. D. AND THOMPSON, D. D. Effects in dogs of decrease in glomerular filtration rate on cation excretion during intravenous administration of unreabsorbable anions. Am. J. Physiol., 1958, **192,** 198.

LEVY, M. N. Oxygen consumption and blood flow in the hypothermic perfused kidney. Am. J. Physiol., 1959, **197,** 1111.

LILIENFIELD, L. S. AND ROSE, J. C. Effect of blood pressure alterations on intrarenal red cell-plasma separation. J. Clin. Invest., 1958, **37,** 1106.

LILIENFIELD, L. S., ROSE, J. C., AND LASSEN, N. A. Diverse distribution of red cells and albumin in dog kidney. Circulation Res., 1958, **6,** 810.

LILIENFIELD, L. S., BAUER, M. H., AND MAGANZINI, H. C. Plasma flow in renal medulla. Circulation, 1959, **20,** 729.

LILLEHEI, R. C. Prevention of irreversible hemorrhagic shock in normal and Eck fistula dogs by controlled cross perfusion of the superior mesenteric artery. Am. J. Physiol., 1956, **187,** 614.

MAILLET, M. Innervation sympathique du rein: son role trophique. Acta neuroveg., 1959, **20,** 155.

MARSON, F. G. Effect of noradrenaline on urine and renal blood flow. Brit. J. Pharmacol., 1956, **11,** 431.

MEHRIZI, A. AND HAMILTON, W. F. Effect of levarterenol on renal blood flow and vascular volume in dogs. Am. J. Physiol., 1959, **197,** 1115.

MILES, B. E., VENTOM, M. G., AND deWARDENER, H. E. Observations on the mechanism of circulatory autoregulation in the perfused dog's kidney. J. Physiol., 1954, **123,** 143.

NOER, R. J., ROBB, H. J., AND JACOBSON, L. F. Circulatory disturbances produced by acute intestinal distension in the living animal. A. M. A. Arch. Surg., 1951, **63,** 520.

OCHWADT, B. Zur Selbststeuerung des Nierenkreislaufes. Pflüger's Arch. ges. Physiol., 1956, **262,** 207.

OCHWADT, B. Durchflusszeiten von Plasma und Erythrocyten, intrarenaler Hamatokrit und Widerstandsregulation der Isolierten Niere. Pflüger's Arch. ges. Physiol., 1957, **265,** 112.

PABST, K. AND THRON, H. L. Kaltediurese beim unnar kotisierten Hund. Pflüger's Arch. ges. Physiol., 1960, **270,** 585.

PAGE, I. H. AND McCUBBIN, J. W. Renal vascular and systemic arterial pressure responses to nervous and chemical stimuation of the kidney. Am. J. Physiol., 1953, **173,** 411.

PAGE, L. B., BAXTER, C. F., REEM, G. H., SCOTT-BAKER, J. C., AND SMITH, H. W. Effect of unilateral splanchnic nerve resection on the renal excretion of sodium. Am. J. Physiol., 1954, **177,** 194.

PAGE, L. B. Effects of hypothermia on renal function. Am. J. Physiol., 1955, **181,** 171.

PAPPENHEIMER, J. P. AND KINTER, W. B. Hematocrit ratio of blood within mammalian kidney and its significance for renal hemodynamics. Am. J. Physiol., 1956, **185,** 377.

PARSON, W., MAYERSON, H. S., LYONS, C., PORTER, B., AND TRAUTMAN, W. V., JR. Effect of the administration of adrenalin on the circulating red cell volume. Am. J. Physiol., 1948, **155,** 239.

RENNIE, D. W., REEVES, R. B., AND PAPPENHEIMER, J. R. Oxygen pressure in urine and its relation to intrarenal blood flow. Am. J. Physiol., 1958, **195,** 120.

REUBI, F. C. Renal hyperemia induced in man by a new phthalazine derivative. Proc. Soc. Exper. Biol. & Med., 1950, **73,** 102.

REYNELL, P. C., MARKS, T. A., CHIDSEY, C., AND BRADLEY, S. E. Changes in splanchnic blood volume and splanchnic blood flow in dogs after hemorrhage. Clin. Sc., 1955, **14,** 407.

RHOADS, C. P., VAN SLYKE, D. C., HILLER, A., AND ALVING, H. S. Effects of novocainization and total section of the nerves of the renal pedicle on renal blood flow and function. Am. J. Physiol., 1934, **110,** 392.

RITTER, E. R. Pressure-flow relations in the kidney alleged effects of pulse pressure. Am. J. Physiol., 1952, **168,** 480.

SARTORIUS, O. W. AND BURLINGTON, H. Acute effects of denervation on kidney function in the dog. Am. J. Physiol., 1956, **185,** 407.

SCHER, A. M. Mechanism of autoregulation of renal blood flow. Nature, 1959, **184,** 1322.

SELKURT, E. E. Effect of pulse pressure and mean arterial pressure modification on renal hemodynamics and electrolyte and water excretion. Circulation, 1951, **4,** 541.

SELKURT, E. E. Intestinal ischemic shock and the protective role of the liver. Am. J. Physiol., 1959, **197,** 281.

SELKURT, E. E. AND BRECHER, G. A. Splanchnic hemodynamics and oxygen utilization during hemorrhagic shock in the dog. Circulation Res., 1956, **4,** 693.

SELKURT, E. E., SCIBETTA, M. P., AND CULL, T. E. Hemodynamics of intestinal circulation. Circulation Res., 1958, **6,** 92.

SELKURT, E. E. AND JOHNSON, P. C. Effect of acute elevation of portal venous pressure on mesenteric blood volume, interstitial fluid volume and hemodynamics. Circulation Res. 1958, **6,** 592.

SHIPLEY, R. E. AND STUDY, R. S. Changes in renal blood flow, extraction of inulin, glomerular filtration rate, tissue pressure and urine flow with acute alterations of renal artery blood pressure. Am. J. Physiol., 1951, **167,** 676.

SIDKY, M. AND BEAN, J. W. Influence of rhythmic and tonic contraction of intestinal muscle on blood flow and blood reservoir capacity in dog intestine. Am. J. Physiol., 1958, **193,** 386.

SIEKER, H. O., GAUER, O. H., AND HENRY, J. P. The effects of continuous negative pressure breathing on water and electrolyte excretion by the human kidney. J. Clin. Invest., 1954, **33**, 572.

SMITH, H. W., ROVENSTINE, E. A., GOLDRING, W., CHASIS, H., AND RANGES, H. A. The effects of spinal anesthesia on the circulation in normal, unoperated man with reference to autonomy of arteries, and especially those of the renal circulation. J. Clin. Invest., 1939, **18**, 319.

SMYTHE, C. M., NICKEL, J. F., AND BRADLEY, S. E. The effect of epinephrine (USP), I-epinephrine, and 1-norepinephrine on GFR, RPF and urinary excretion of sodium, potassium and water in normal man. J. Clin. Invest., 1952, **31**, 499.

SMYTHE, C. M., GILMORE, J. P., AND HANDFORD, S. W. The effect of 1-norepinephrine on estimated hepatic blood flow in the normal anesthetized dog. J. Clin. Invest., 1953, **32**, 605.

SNOOK, T. A comparative study of the vascular arrangements in mammalian spleens. Am. J. Anat., 1950, **87**, 31.

STONE, J. E., WELLS, J., DRAPER, W. B., AND WHITEHEAD, R. W. Changes in renal blood flow in dogs during the inhalation of 30% carbon dioxide. Am. J. Physiol., 1958, **194**, 115.

SURTSHIN, A., MUELLER, C. B., AND WHITE, H. L. Effect of acute changes in glomerular filtration rate on water and electrolyte excretion: mechanism of denervation diuresis. Am. J. Physiol., 1952, **169**, 159.

SURTSHIN, A., HOELTZENBEIN, J., AND WHITE, H. L. Some effects of negative pressure breathing on urine excretion. Am. J. Physiol., 1955, **180**, 612.

SWANN, H. Intrarenal pressure and renal blood flows. p. 76. Josiah Macy, Jr. Foundation III. Conference, 1951.

THOMPSON, D. D., KAVALER, F., LOZANO, R., AND PITTS, R. F. Evaluation of the cell separation hypothesis of autoregulation of renal blood flow and filtration rate. Blood flow, filtration rate and PAH extraction as functions of arterial pressure in normal and anemic dogs. Am. J. Physiol., 1957, **191**, 493.

THURAU, K., KRAMER, K., AND BRECHTELSBAUER, H. Die Reaktionsweise der glatten Muskulatur der Nierengefässe auf Dehnungsreize und ihre Bedeutung für die Autoregulation des Nierenkreislaufes. Pflüger's Arch. ges. Physiol., 1959, **268**, 188.

THURAU, K. AND KRAMER, K. Weitere Untersuchungen zur myogenen Natur der Autoregulation des Nierenkreislaufes. Aufhebung der Autoregulation durch muskulotrope Substanzen und druckpassives Verhalten des Glomerulusfiltrates. Pflüger's Arch. ges. Physiol., 1959, **269**, 77.

THURAU, K., DEETJEN, P., AND KRAMER, K. Hämodynamik des Nierenmarks: Wechselbeziehung zwischen vasculärem und tubulärem Gegenstromsystem bei arteriellem Drucksteigerungen, Wasserdiurese und osmotischer Diurese. Pflüger's Arch. ges. Physiol., 1960, **270**, 270.

ULLRICH, K. AND PEHLING, G. Activer Natriumtransport und Sauerstoffverbrauch in der äus-

seren Markzone der Niere. Pflüger's Arch. ges. Physiol., 1958, **267**, 207.

VAN SLYKE, D. D., RHOADS, C. P., HILLER, A., AND ALVING, A. S. Relationships between urea excretion, renal blood flow, renal oxygen consumption, and diuresis. The mechanism of urea excretion. Am. J. Physiol., 1934, **109**, 336.

WADE, O. L. ET AL. The effect of exercise on the splanchnic blood flow and splanchnic blood volume in normal man. Clin. Sc., 1956, **15**, 457.

WARREN, J. V., BRANNON, E. S., AND MERRILL, A. J. A method of obtaining renal venous blood in unanesthetized persons with observations on the extraction of oxygen and sodium paraaminohippurate. Science, 1944, **100**, 108.

WAUGH, W. H. Myogenic nature of autoregulation of renal flow in the absence of blood corpuscles. Circulation Res., 1958, **6**, 363.

WAUGH, W. H., AND SHANKS, R. G. Cause of genuine autoregulation of the renal circulation. Circul. Res. 1960, **8**, 871.

WEISS, S., PARKER, F., JR., AND ROBB, G. P. A correlation of the hemodynamics, function and histologic structure of the kidney in malignant arterial hypertension with malignant nephrosclerosis. Ann. Int. Med., 1932, **6**, 1599.

WHITE, H. L. AND ROLF, D. Effects of exercise and some other influences on the renal circulation in man. Am. J. Physiol., 1948, **152**, 505.

WHIPPLE, A. O., PARPART, A. K., AND CHANG, J. J. A study of the circulation of the blood in the spleen of the living mouse. Ann. Surg., 1954, **140**, 266.

WILKINS, R. W., CULBERTSON, J. W., AND INGELFINGER, F. J. The effect of splanchnic sympathectomy in hypertensive patients upon estimated hepatic blood flow in the upright as contrasted with the horizontal position. J. Clin. Invest., 1951, **30**, 312.

WINTON, F. R. Present concepts of the renal circulation. A. M. A. Arch. Int. Med., 1959, **103**, 495.

WIRZ, H. Druckmessung in Kapillaren und Tubuli der Niere durch Mikropunktion. Helvet. physiol. et pharmacol. acta, 1955, **13**, 42.

WIRZ, H., HARGITAY, B., AND KUHN, W. Lokalisation des Konzentrierungsprozesses in der Niere durch direkte Kryoskopie. Helvet. physiol. et pharmacol. acta, 1951, **9**, 196.

YAMADA, S. I. AND ASTIOM, H. Critical closing pressure and vasomotor tone in the hind leg and the kidney of the cat. Am. J. Physiol., 1959, **196**, 213.

*Monographs and Reviews*

BRADLEY, S. E., INGELFINGER, F. J., BRADLEY, G. P., AND CURRY, J. J. The estimation of hepatic blood flow in man. J. Clin. Invest., 1945, **24**, 890.

BRADLEY, S. E. Methods for the evaluation of the splanchnic circulation. Circulation. Proceedings of the Harvey Tercentenary Congress, p. 355. Blackwell Scientific Publications, Oxford, 1958.

BRADLEY, S. E., INGELFINGER, F. J., AND BRADLEY, G. P. Determinants of hepatic hemodynamics. Visceral circulation, A Ciba Foundation Symposium, p. 219. J. & A. Churchill, Ltd., London, 1952.

KRAMER, K. Die Stellung der Niere im Gesamt-kreislauf Verhandl. deutsch. Ges. inn. Med., 65. Kongress, 1959.

PAGE, I. H. Serotonin (5-hydroxytryptamine); the last four years. Physiol. Rev., 1958, 38, 277.

SELKURT, E. E. Der Nierenkreislauf. Klin. Wchnschr., 1955, 33, 359.

SMITH, H. W. The kidney. Structure and function in health and diseases. Oxford University Press, New York, 1951.

WINTON, F. R. Physical factors involved in the activities of the mammalian kidney. Physiol. Rev., 1937, 17, 408.

# 27

# REGULATION OF THE CIRCULATION UNDER STATES OF STRESS

## Dilation and Hypertrophy of the Heart

CARDIAC DILATION. Dilation is an increased capacity of the cardiac chambers brought about by the elongation of the myocardial fibers. This increased capacity may result from many physiological or pathological factors. The force of ventricular contraction increases with increments in diastolic volume until overdistension occurs, and the force of contraction then decreases with a rise in diastolic pressure. An increased diastolic volume is a physiological means automatically brought into play to increase the cardiac work and to mobilize the energy reserves of the heart. The nearer the fibers approach their maximal physiological length during diastole, the greater will be the encroachment upon the heart's reserve. It has also been shown that the oxygen consumption of the heart muscle is proportional to its end diastolic volume (or its fiber length, fig. 27.1). Thus, the heart which is supporting a greater load expends a greater amount of energy to attain its cardiac output.

From the above discussion, it can be seen that cardiac dilation can be a compensatory mechanism of the heart in meeting everyday stresses although other factors (humoral and neurogenic) are also important. Dilation also occurs when an increased diastolic volume is secondary to a pathological state. An increased venous return to the heart, an increased outflow resistance, a reflux into the heart chambers, or intrinsic myocardial disease impairing the contractility of the muscle may induce dilation. However, the heart cannot continue to dilate indefinitely with an increase in work. A point is reached beyond which further dilation leads to a decline in work. The heart is unable to expel sufficient blood from its chambers, and the activity of the heart is no longer adequate to supply the peripheral tissues with their needs. Therefore, beyond this certain point, dilation becomes detrimental. It is claimed that the diseased heart reached this detrimental

point of dilation with less stretch of the myocardial fibers than the normal heart, but the experimental evidence for this is not adequate. Dilation can be a reversible phenomenon even when caused by pathological states. However, this is not always so, and the heart may continue to fail even when the underlying cause is removed.

CARDIAC HYPERTROPHY. The average weight range of the human adult heart is approximately 250 to 350 grams. In disease, 500 grams is not an unusual weight, and hearts weighing 1,000 gms or more are seen. The increased weight of the ventricular muscle is due to an increase in length and diameter of the individual muscle fibers. Linzbach, in 1947, found this was true of hearts hypertrophied up to 500 grams but, contrary to previous studies, reported a splitting of fibers longitudinally, and thus, an increase in the number of fibers in hearts weighing over 500 grams. With the increase in size of fibers, there is not a corresponding increase in the number of capillaries. Hypertrophy, then, differs from normal growth for, in the latter, the capillaries multiply and keep pace with the muscle as it grows; in hypertrophy the capillaries do not multiply and, per unit of muscle, actually decrease. This could become a limiting factor in the extent of development of hypertrophy especially in hearts with an already compromised blood supply.

The biochemical alterations in the myocardium in hypertrophy have received little study. The electrolyte and fluid concentrations in the intra and extracellular spaces have a normal relationship in the hypertrophied heart of rabbits following the production of aortic insufficiency. In rats exposed to reduced atmospheric pressure and increased environmental temperature to produce hypertrophy, the total protein of the heart increased by 42 per cent. An increase in the fractions containing myoglobin, contractile protein and metachondria was found. The latter increase may indicate an expansion of the oxygen trans-

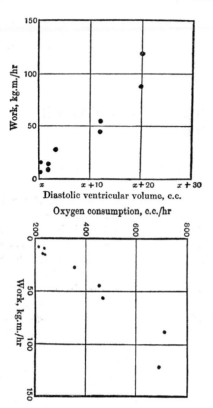

Fig. 27.1. Lower chart shows the work done plotted against the oxygen consumed. In calculating the work of the heart the velocity factor (p. 23) was neglected. Upper chart gives data from the same experiment, work being plotted against the diastolic volume of the ventricles. The volumes are expressed as $x$ plus known values. The $x$ represents the lowest value of the volume during the experiment, which is impossible to measure when a cardiometer is used to record heart volume. The cardiometer enables one to measure only an increase over this minimum value. The figure shows a direct correspondence between work done and ventricular volume. (After Starling and Visscher.)

porting and utilizing systems. The increased fractions in hypertrophy differ from those found in normal growth. This fact, plus the absence of capillary growth, indicate that hypertrophy is not caused by the same process which induces the left ventricle to become the more muscular of the two ventricles after birth.

The mechanical factors leading to hypertrophy are the same myocardial stresses mentioned for dilation; hypertension and valvular disease lead the list of actual diseases. As in dilation, the chamber undergoing the stress may be the only one involved or all chambers may become hypertrophied, including the atria.

The factors which actually induce the cardiac muscle to hypertrophy are unknown. Experi-

ments by Eyster and associates on the production of aortic insufficiency or stenosis in dogs illustrate the basis for the injury theory. These animals showed an early dilation of the heart (by roentgenograms) which disappeared within a few days and was followed by the development of hypertrophy. In dogs relieved of their aortic stenosis during the dilation phase, hypertrophy still developed. The sudden dilation of the heart was theorized to injure the myocardial fibers which led to their hypertrophy. Recently, these experiments have been criticized and repeated. An increase in the heart weight-body weight ratio was found only when the cause of the heart stress was continued and not if the stress was removed during the dilation phase. Also, the theory does not agree with clinical findings which often show dilation not followed by hypertrophy in patients. Other experiments in rats have shown that dilation of the heart caused by a reduced ambient pressure after explosive decompression was reversible and not followed by hypertrophy.

Another explanation for hypertrophy invokes the greater surface area of the muscle as supplying a greater area for nutrition which leads to fiber growth. A defective blood supply, either by a deficient coronary circulation or by an anemia, has been postulated as the cause of hypertrophy. A fourth theory would explain hypertrophy as essentially of hormonal origin in which the somatotrophic hormone of the anterior pituitary plays the leading role. Experiments on rats showed that this hormone produces an increased heart mass in the absence of an increased work load. Thyroxine was found to possess a lesser degree of this activity while cortisone inhibited the effect of the somatotrophic hormone. The work theory holds that hypertrophy is primarily due to the increased load on the heart, and experiments demonstrating a hypertrophy of experimental animals' hearts under the stimulus of exercise are cited as evidence.

The above theories and our knowledge of the factors involved in the production of myocardial hypertrophy are inadequate. Animal experimentation is very difficult to evaluate since hypertrophy is usually judged on the basis of the heart weight to body weight ratio. The animals have often gained or lost weight during the experimental period. The degree of myocardial edema must also be taken into consideration as a cause of the increased bulk of the heart. Moderate hypertrophy must be present before microscopic findings are present; animal experiments usually deal with minimal hypertrophy. The most valid method would seem to be a long term study of a very large group of control and experimental animals of the same weight and breed with a comparison of their heart weights and microscopic findings. A definition of cardiac hypertrophy must take into account the presence of muscle edema, fat, and fibrotic tissue in the muscle being weighed.

In human disease there is a marked difference in the degree of hypertrophy found in response to similar pathological stresses. Some patients with serious hypertensive disease demonstrate little or no hypertrophy at autopsy. Also, the clinical course of patients with heart disease has not been proven to vary from those with, as compared to those without hypertrophy. A disease entity exists called "idiopathic" myocardial hypertrophy in which young people succumb to congestive heart failure and the only autopsy finding is myocardial hypertrophy.

Hypertrophy has been called a compensatory mechanism of the heart in response to an increased load whereby the increased mass of the heart permits it to release more energy. Several studies have shown that a hypertrophied animal heart has the ability to react to a further stress; i.e., it has a reserve. Rats who developed cardiac hypertrophy due to aortic constriction were able to raise their cardiac output more than control animals in response to overloading of their circulatory systems. From this experiment, it was concluded that a hypertrophied heart had a greater reserve power than the normal heart. However, the fact that hypertrophy is beneficial to the heart has been questioned. It has been pointed out that the ST-T changes in the electrocardiogram in hypertrophy are similar to those of coronary insufficiency, that hypertensive patients without hypertrophy fare as well as those with increased mass of heart muscle, and that hearts developing hypertrophy after acute cardiac insults do not always improve.

Hypertrophy of the heart may be preceded or accompanied by dilation of the heart. It is claimed that dilation is the immediate response of the heart to stress while hypertrophy is a more gradual developing phenomenon to chronic stress. Experimental data, with the above criticisms in mind, show hypertrophy developing as early as 2 days in rats, and in 2 to 3 weeks in dogs subjected to the stress of hypertension or valvular disease. However, the hypertrophy was based on heart weight to body weight ratios. There is no adequate explanation why some hearts show neither hypertrophy nor dilation, some only one, and some both of these phenomena under the same pathological conditions. Both have been shown to be occasionally reversible in animals and humans when the stress is removed.

The importance of hypertrophy lies in the fact that it is the response of the heart to most forms of stress. Our limited knowledge concerning the etiology and development of hypertrophy is a major stumbling block in the understanding of the physiology of the heart. It is apparent that improved methods of investigation and measurement of myocardial hypertrophy are needed.

## Arterial Hypertension

The blood pressure may be persistently above or below the normal range. These departures from the normal are termed *hypertension* and *hypotension*, respectively. It is difficult to make a sharp separation of the normal from the abnormal, but an elevation above the average normal for a particular age group may be considered to be definitely abnormal. In the adult, elevations of systolic pressure above 140 mm. Hg and of diastolic pressure above 90 mm. Hg are usually considered hypertensive levels, although such a sharp distinction is not reliable unless considered in relation to age. The clinical syndrome of hypertension appears to be a result of the elevated diastolic pressure. Usually, the systolic pressure is also raised, but it need not be. Also systolic hypertension may occur without a diastolic pressure elevation. Systolic hypertension alone is not believed to be clinically important unless very high levels threaten the integrity of the blood vessels. Systolic hypertension with a decreased diastolic pressure often accompanies a variety of diseases such as hyperthyroidism, heart block with a slow rate and aortic insufficiency. A reduction of blood pressure below the normal range for the age group (systolic below 90 to 110, and diastolic below 60 in adults is usually termed hypotension).

### Experimental Renal Hypertension

Experimental hypertension most similar to essential (of unknown etiology) human hypertension is that following renal artery constriction. Moderate to severe chronic constriction by a special clamp of a renal artery in the dog, which causes a definite and immediate reduction in renal blood flow, is followed by a rise in systemic blood pressure. However, this hypertension usually persists for only a few weeks. (In the rabbit, rat, goat and sheep, hypertension lasting many months generally follows constriction of one renal artery). In the dog, permanent (years) systemic hypertension follows constriction of both

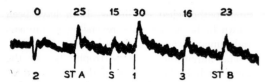

FIG. 27.2. Demonstration of renin in the blood of a patient with acute glomerulonephritis and hypertension. Blood pressure curves are those of a cat under dial anesthesia. The figures above the curves indicate the rise in blood pressure in mm. Hg. 2—Response to injection of unincubated control equivalent to 10 cc. serum. This response, it will be observed, is about the same as that given by the saline control (1). St. A—Response to 0.75 cat unit of standard hypertensin. S—Response to 10 cc. physiological saline. 1—Response to incubated sample equivalent to 5 cc. serum. When calculated for renin, this is equivalent to 2.4 cat units of renin per 10 cc. serum. 3—Response to sample incubated with hypertensinase. Note that this gives approximately the same rise as the saline control. St. B—Response to 1.2 cat units of standard hypertensin (after Dexter and Haynes).

renal arteries, constriction of one renal artery with subsequent removal of the other kidney, or wrapping of both kidneys in silk or cellophane. The latter is presumably the result of ischemia induced by compression of the renal parenchyma by the thick membrane of connective tissue which develops under the silk or cellophane. This type of hypertension is benign and lasts for years. Its manifestations are almost identical with those seen in the benign phase of human essential hypertension, for there is an increase in systemic blood pressure, total peripheral resistance and left ventricular hypertrophy, but a normal heart rate, cardiac output, blood volume and renal excretory function (by the usual tests which may not be sensitive enough to detect early changes). By more extensive constriction of both main renal arteries, there results hypertension, impairment of renal function, and appearance of some chemical substance in the blood which causes development of a fulminating type of hypertension, closely resembling the malignant phase of essential human hypertension, characterized by arteriolar hyaline degeneration and necrosis in all vascular beds. Even the kidney with the constricted renal artery may show severe vascular damage when the blood pressure is greatly elevated (in rats). By severely constricting one renal artery and tying off the ureter of the other kidney, these lesions develop in the arterioles of the kidney with intact renal artery and with its ureter tied off.

HUMORAL FACTORS. The pathogenesis of the early phase of sustained hypertension is not clearly understood but a neural reflex from the ischemic kidney is not the cause since renal denervation, splanchnic, and total sympathectomy fail to interfere with development of hypertension from renal artery constriction. The early phase of hypertension is caused by some humoral mechanism since release of the clamp or excision of the kidney, in an animal hypertensive because of constriction of one renal artery, restores a normal blood pressure.

The humoral pressor mechanism for the early period of hypertension is explained either by failure of the kidney to produce an essential agent in the absence of which hypertension develops, or by the release of a pressor substance from the ischemic kidney. Pressor substances may not only arise from an ischemic kidney but pressor enzymes and polypeptides may have a nonrenal origin.[1] An abundance of evidence supports the view that the pressor mechanism of acute renal ischemia is mediated by the release of a humoral substance, renin. Renin is a proteolytic enzyme free from any direct pressor effect. It acts on an alpha 2 globulin substrate in plasma to produce angiotensin (angiotonin or hypertensin). The alpha 2 globulin is produced, apparently, in the liver, since it disappears from the blood after hepatectomy. Two different chemical forms of angiotensin have been obtained in purified form. The decapeptide, angiotensin I, is the initial product of the action of renin on its substrate, and lacks pressor activity. This decapeptide is transformed to the vasoconstrictor octapeptide, angiotensin II, by a chloride activated enzyme of the plasma. The octapeptide has been synthesized. Failure to consistently find renin by assay methods in humans or animals who have renal hypertension of long standing, has caused doubt that this theory explains the chronic phase of the disorder. However, Dexter and Haynes, (fig. 27.2) and Skegg and his associates have demonstrated circulating angiotensin in the peripheral blood of hypertensive patients; large amounts were found in dogs with acute renal hypertension and in patients with malignant hypertension but barely increased levels in patients with benign essential hypertension. Possibly the methods are too insensitive for accurate assay since renin and angiotensin can either not be recovered or only in small amounts from the blood of an animal that has been made acutely hypertensive due to

---

[1] A vasoconstrictor substance (pepsitensin) closely resembling angiotensin in its effects has been obtained by the action of pepsin upon plasma globulin.

TABLE 27.1

*Summary of effects of injections of renin on blood pressure and antirenin titer in 61 renal hypertensive dogs with hypertension of 4 to 36 months' duration*

Each symbol represents treatment results in one renal hypertensive dog. 0, no antihypertensive effect; +, decrease in blood pressure one-third toward normotension; ++, decrease in blood two-thirds toward normotension; +++, decrease in blood pressure to normotension. Four different preparations of hog renins were used. Antirenin titer is expressed in antirenin units per milliliter. (From Wakerlin, G. E., Circulation, 1958, 17, 653.)

| Maximum antirenin titer | Antihypertensive Effect of Hog Renin | | | |
|---|---|---|---|---|
| | Crude, from cortex | Semipurified, from cortex | Crude, from whole kidney | Semipurified, from whole kidney |
| *AU per ml.* | | | | |
| 0 | | | 0000000 | |
| 1 | 00 | 0 | 0 | |
| 2 | | + | 0 | |
| 3 | ++ +++ | + | 00 | |
| 4 | 0 | + | | |
| 5 | +++ | | 0000 | |
| 6–7 | 0 ++ | ++ +++ | | 0 0 + |
| 8–10 | ++ +++ +++ | +++ | 0 0++ | 0 |
| 11–14 | +++ +++ | ++ ++ ++ +++ +++ | 0 | + ++ |
| 15–20 | | ++ +++ | 000 ++ | |
| 21–30 | | ++ | 0 | |
| 31–40 | | | 0 | |
| 41–60 | | | | ++ |
| 61–100 | | | | |
| 101–125 | +++ | | | |

renin or angiotensin infusion. However, the blood pressure of a dog hypertensive for months to years from constriction of the renal arteries can be returned to normal by repeated injections of renin resulting in the development of antirenin in the blood (table 27.1). This is convincing evidence that the humoral mechanism is still active in elevating the blood pressure. Unfortunately, this procedure is not effective in humans.

Renin is confined to the cortex of the kidney. Although previous studies supported a tubular origin of renin, recent reports demonstrated renin only in areas of the kidney which contained glomeruli and not in purely tubular areas. As postulated many years ago, by Goormatigh, the juxtaglomerular cells may be the source of renin. These cells contain granules which exhibit histochemical properties similar to those of renin. There was a good correlation between the number of these granules and the renin content of the kidney (Marshall and Wakerlin). More recent studies by the Hartrofts and by Tobian demonstrated that the granularity of the juxtaglomerular cells increased or decreased when renin would be expected to be increased or decreased, respectively, according to the animal's blood pressure. Also, fluorescent antirenin antibodies have been demonstrated to attach to these granules.

The stimulus for the production or liberation of renin by the kidney is not known. It is denied by Page that ischemia of the kidney is itself responsible, for, though the immediate effect of constriction of the renal artery is a fall in pressure in the vessels of the kidney, and a reduction in blood flow, later on the renal blood flow may return to normal. Nor did anoxia of the renal tissue seem to be a necessary condition for the development of renal hypertension, because no increase over the normal was found in the arteriovenous oxygen difference of the ischemic kidney (Levy and associates). Moreover, anoxia induced by cyanide does not cause renin to appear in the circulation although a kidney so poisoned produces renin when the renal artery is clamped.

Kolff and his associates have shown that the production of a "renin" response from constriction of canine renal arteries occurs irrespective of a pulsatile or nonpulsatile (by use of a depulsating chamber) renal blood flow. It has been postulated that the release of renin from the kidney may be secondary to changes in the transmural pressure affecting renal vascular baroceptors. The latter theory has been elaborated with the juxtaglomerular cells as the baroceptors, for the granularity of these cells varies with changes in perfusion pressure.

Ischemia of one kidney without interference with the kidney of the opposite side is not followed by permanent hypertension, nor is the elevation of blood pressure, even while it lasts, as great if a normal kidney is present; the return of the blood pressure to normal after excision of an ischemic kidney is much less rapid if the opposite kidney is also removed. Also, in order to demonstrate the maximum effect of the pressor substance liberated by the ischemic kidney, a recipient animal must first be nephrectomized. Finally, if both kidneys are removed from rats, hypertension will develop if the animals are kept alive. These facts show that the presence of a normal kidney evidently has a protective effect, and are the basis for the "renoprival" theory of hypertension. The normal kidney may produce some material which lowers the blood pressure, or it may destroy or excrete a pressor substance. Excretory removal is not likely, for the diversion of urine into the bloodstream does not result in hypertension. The fact that removal of a unilateral ischemic kidney causes the blood pressure to return to normal, and that antirenin, which lowers the blood pressure in chronic renal hypertension, has no effect when both kidneys are absent, show that renoprival and chronic renal hypertension are probably unrelated in etiology.

Braun-Menendez and his associates demonstrated the presence in normal kidney tissue of an enzyme which inactivates the pressor principle (angiotensin). This enzyme, called *hypertensinase* by its discoverers, and angiotonase by Page and his colleagues, is possibly responsible for the effect exerted by normal kidney tissue upon the development and severity of renal hypertension. Hypertensinase is also found in intestinal mucosa, pancreas, as well as in the erythrocytes; minimal amounts are present in liver and in serum. Attempts to obtain a material from extracts of normal kidney tissue which would neutralize or inactivate the pressor substance responsible for clinical hypertension have not, so far, been very successful.

Two other possible humoral pressor systems in the kidney warrant brief mention. Helmer and associates found an increased concentration of sustained pressor substance (SPS) in the renal vein blood of chronic renal hypertensive rats. The relation between SPS and renin is not clear, but it may be a precursor or derivative of renin.

Shorr and his colleagues suggest that hepatorenal factors enter into the mechanism of renal hypertension. They demonstrated that constriction of the renal artery by a clamp caused the appearance in the blood of the renal vasoexcitatory material (VEM) which normally cannot be detected. A little later, the hepatic vasodepressor material (VDM) was found in low concentration in the blood; it increased progressively until in the chronic hypertensive phase, it counteracted the action of VEM. More evidence is needed before the VEM-VDM system can be assigned a pathogenetic role in renal hypertension.

In the latter stages of the benign phase of experimental hypertensin, although renal pressor substances may circulate in diminished but sufficient amounts to maintain elevated blood pressure, evidence suggests that other mechanisms are involved. Following injection of ganglionic blocking agents, a reduction in blood pressure does not occur in early renal hypertension or during renin infusion but does develop in late renal hypertension. This fits in with the established fact that in late renal hypertension the baroreceptor mechanism is reset at the higher blood pressure level, possibly due to changes in the walls of the carotid sinus from prolonged exposure to high blood pressure. The carotid-aortic reflex is the principal depressor response to elevations of blood pressure. In chronic renal hypertension, it still responds to acute pressor stimuli but, presumably, not to the sustained renal pressor stimulus. In addition, there now occur generalized morphological vascular changes secondary to the hypertension which may act to perpetuate the disorder.

THE ENDOCRINES IN RELATION TO EXPERIMENTAL HYPERTENSION. Although the evidence points to angiotensin as acting directly upon the vessels, the possibility must be considered that it exerts its effect by stimulating a ductless gland, such as the pituitary or adrenal, to secrete a vasoconstrictor substance. The endocrine glands could also cause hypertension by stimulating the kidney to produce a pressor agent.

The adrenal medulla probably does not play a role in experimental renal hypertension, for the hypertension is not prevented or modified in any way by bilateral excision of all medullary tissue. Tumors of the adrenal medulla, called pheochromocytomas, do produce a clinical syndrome in which hypertension is the outstanding feature. The elevated blood pressure is secondary to the excess production of catecholamines (which can be measured in the blood and urine).

Goldblatt has found that constriction of the renal arteries fails to cause a rise in blood pressure after bilateral removal of the adrenal cortex, even though the animal is maintained in good condition by a high salt and low potassium diet (ch. 58). But if cortin is administered to the adrenalectomized animals, renal ischemia is followed by the usual hypertensive response. The blood pressure of hypertensive rats is lowered by adrenalectomy and is only partially restored by the administration of *desoxycorticosterone*. Since hypertension is not sustained, and evidently, vascular tone and responsiveness are decreased when the adrenals are absent, the adrenal cortex is said to have a "permissive" action in renal hypertension. There may also be an "additive" effect of the kidney and adrenal cortex, for the administration of desoxycorticosterone to uninephrectomized rats, or of desoxycorticosterone and renin to normal rats, produces a more severe hypertension with more intense vascular damage than either procedure alone. It is of interest that renin has been found to stimulate growth of the zona glomerulosa of the adrenal cortex in rats. However, these results should not be taken to imply that the renal principle mediates its action *through* the adrenal cortex, for Houssay and his colleagues found that in short term experiments in which an ischemic kidney was transplanted into a nonhypertensive animal, complete adrenalectomy of the latter or ligation of the adrenal veins did not prevent the rise in blood pressure.

Desoxycorticosterone is capable itself of inducing hypertension in normal animals, provided that the diet contains adequate amounts of salt. It is ineffective upon a salt poor diet. Damage to the renal vessels (nephrosclerosis) is caused by the administration of this hormone; it also increases the retention of salt (enhanced tubular reabsorption) and an increase in the volume of the extracellular fluids. Both the renal effect and that upon water and salt metabolism are probably responsible for the hypertension caused by this cortical hormone.

In this regard, it is pertinent that Tobian has found an increased concentration of water, sodium, potassium and magnesium in the aortic tissue of renal and desoxycorticosterone hypertensive rats; renal arteries from hypertensive patients also showed an increased sodium and water content. It is postulated that the electrolyte and fluid changes may lead to edema of the vessel walls. The narrowing of the vascular bed by this process could cause an elevated blood pressure secondary to the increased peripheral resistance.

Other authors have reported a low serum magnesium and a high plasma sodium with a normal potassium in hypertensive patients. These studies have been stimulated by the recent discovery of a clinical hypertensive syndrome associated with an excess production of the adrenal cortical electrolyte hormone, aldosterone. Patients with hyperaldosteronism show an elevated serum sodium with a low potassium; one patient has been reported with a low serum magnesium level. The hypertension in this syndrome may be cured by removal of the aldosterone producing tumor, hyperplasia or normal appearing adrenal cortex.

There is no evidence that the posterior lobe of the pituitary plays a role in the development of renal hypertension, but the anterior lobe appears to be implicated through its action upon the adrenal cortex. Ablation of the anterior lobe in animals with renal hypertension lowers the blood pressure, which is raised to its previous level by the administration of adrenocorticotrophin or of a crude anterior lobe extract. So far as is known neither the thyroid nor the sex glands are in any way responsible for renal hypertension.

NEUROGENIC FACTORS IN EXPERIMENTAL HYPERTENSION. Hypertension has been produced in animals by a variety of neurological manipulations. Russian researchers especially emphasize the problems of vasomotor control by the central nervous system. They postulate that a disturbance in the central nervous system is the primary factor in the pathogenesis of essential hypertension, and renal involvement is only secondary. In animals, they were able to produce stable hypertension by conflicting conditioned signals resulting in experimental neurosis. By indirect tests, early involvement of the central nervous system in essential and experimental hypertension was shown. This has led to the theory that, in man, excess nervous strain weakens the functional capacity of the brain cortex which is reflected in a decreased effectiveness of the cortical inhibitory centers controlling blood pressure. The nervous and emotional strain of modern civilization has frequently been suggested as an underlying factor in the development of essential hypertension; many groups have studied hypertensive patients in relation to emotional instability and strain, but conclusions cannot be drawn because of the presence of many experimental variables and the inconsistency of the results.

Denervation of the carotid sinus and aortic vasosensory areas in dogs produces chronic arterial hypertension (200 to 250 mm. Hg) for

1 to 3 years, and considerable tachycardia with extreme lability of the pressure and rate. In some dogs, the blood pressure and heart rate tend to return toward normal during sleep. Hypertension caused in this way differs from essential or renal hypertension, for cardiac output and limb blood flow are elevated (since stroke volume is unchanged, the rise in output is secondary to the increased heart rate), and total peripheral resistance is relatively unchanged.

Constriction of the internal and external carotid arteries bilaterally above the carotid sinus to approximately one-third normal size gives a high level of hypertension in a large percentage of dogs for at least 4 years. The pathogenesis is not known. Hypertension has also been produced in animals by subjecting them (rats) to loud noises, by stimulation of the hypothalamus or of certain areas of the cerebral cortex.

In dogs completely sympathectomized except for the renal innervation, cutting of the buffer nerves increases sympathetic vasomotor discharge to the kidney, resulting in chronic hypertension. Subsequent renal nerve section relieves the elevated blood pressure. Electrical stimulation of the renal sympathetic nerves induces hypertension as long as the stimulus is maintained (3 months). Blood pressure returns to normal levels upon cessation of stimulation.

A high blood pressure often accompanies an increased intracranial pressure in patients. The heightened blood pressure is apparently due to a generalized vasoconstriction resulting from the reduced oxygen supply to the vasomotor center. Cushing pointed out that the increased pressure within the cranial cavity caused compression of and slowing of the blood flow through the vessels supplying the medulla. In animals, sudden occlusion of the common carotids, after the vertebrals and other branches of the subclavian have been ligated, causes a pronounced rise in blood pressure. Even though the carotid sinus has been excised, chronic hypertension may be produced in dogs by cerebral ischemia produced in a similar way. Permanent hypertension has been produced by the injection of an inert substance such as kaolin into the cisterna magna of rabbits (Dixon and Heller) and thus interfering with the blood supply to the medullary centers; and cerebral anemia produced by ligation of the carotids and vertebrals causes hypertension in the dog. Even some of these apparently purely neurogenic types of hypertension appear to be, in part at least, of renal origin. For example, renal denervation corrects the hypertension caused by cisternal injection of kaolin.

## PRIMARY OR ESSENTIAL HYPERTENSION (HYPERPIESIA)

The immediate cause of the raised blood pressure in this disease is also an increase in the peripheral resistance, i.e., a vasoconstriction or narrowing in some way of the peripheral vessels. As implied in the name "essential" or "primary", the etiology of this abnormality is unknown. The disease is more common in women than men, shows a familial tendency, and usually has its onset from the 3rd to the 5th decade. The systolic and diastolic pressures are elevated although the latter is the characteristic finding in diagnosis, and the former may be within normal limits.

The hemodynamic effects of hypertension primarily involve the left heart. The left ventricle must compensate for the increased load imposed by the elevated peripheral resistance which tends to limit its stroke output. A greater residual volume causes stretching of the myocardial fibers with an increased initial tension which leads to an augmented force of contraction to restore the stroke output. Humoral and neurogenic influences undoubtedly play a part in increasing the stroke volume (ch. 23). The work of the left heart increases as measured by cardiac output and mean arterial pressure in large series of catheterized patients. These calculations probably underestimate the situation for the kinetic energy of ejection becomes a large factor in the work of the left ventricle in hypertension. The work of the heart is nearly proportional to the blood pressure elevation for the cardiac output has usually been normal when measured in patients. The oxygen consumption per unit weight of left ventricle of patients with chronic hypertension is normal. Due to the hypertrophy of the left ventricle seen in most hypertensives, the total weight, and therefore, the total oxygen consumption of the heart is increased. The pressures in the pulmonary circulation and right heart are normal unless failure of one of the ventricles is present. Most hypertensive patients have an increased total peripheral resistance which is probably uniformly distributed both in the splanchnic area and extremities. The distribution of cardiac output and the level of blood flow to various body regions remains essentially normal.

The pressure in the capillaries and small veins is within normal limits, and the slope of pressure through these vessels is not materially different from that in health. The fall in pressure through

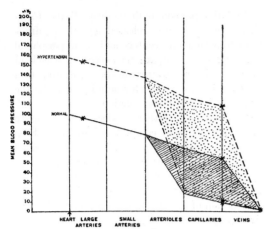

FIG. 27.3. Diagrammatic representation of fall in blood pressure in vascular circuit in subjects with hypertension compared with the normal. Shaded and stippled areas represent alteration in the pressure relationships in the skin vessels after the injection of histamine. The lower boundaries of these areas represent the pressure gradient under natural conditions; the upper boundaries this gradient after the injection of histamine (after Ellis and Weiss, modified).

the arterioles is much greater than in health (fig. 27.3). Ellis and Weiss found mean pressures of 155 and 12 mm. respectively in the brachial artery and in the capillaries—a fall of over 140 mm. Of this about 125 mm. must have occurred in the arterioles. Normally the fall of pressure in the latter vessels is less than half this figure (approximately 50 or 60 mm.).

In most cases of hypertension, there is no significant change in venous pressure, circulation time, blood volume or viscosity. With strenuous exercise, patients without cardiac symptoms show a normal increase in cardiac output and oxygen consumption, but no change in pulmonary artery or wedge pressures.

In hypertensive subjects the reactivity of the peripheral vessels to nervous stress or to cold, as by the immersion of a hand in icewater, is usually greater than normal. The latter procedure—the so-called *cold pressor test*—is employed for investigating the vascular responses. In most hypertensives the reaction is excessive; a sharp and inordinate rise in diastolic pressure occurs without an increase in cardiac output or pulse rate, which is taken as indicating a hypersensitive vasoconstrictor mechanism. Hines has studied this reaction in normal as well as in hypertensive subjects over a period of years, and has classed them into three groups, *hyper-reactors*, who respond to the test by a rise over 20 mm. Hg *normoreactors*, who give a rise of between 10 and

## TABLE 27.2

*The reaction of the diastolic pressure to the cold-pressor test, correlated with the subsequent development of hypertension (Hines)*

| Classification* | Cases | Hypertension 15 Years Later | |
|---|---|---|---|
| | | Cases | Percentage |
| Hyporeactors........... | 36 | 0 | 0 |
| Normoreactors.......... | 48 | 8 | 17 |
| Hyper-reactors.......... | 57 | 31 | 54 |

* Blood pressure normal, less than 100 mm. Hg diastolic.

20 mm. Hg, and *hyporeactors*, with whom the rise was less than 10 mm. Hg. The subjects with normal blood pressures and who were hyper-reactors, showed a definite susceptibility to the development of hypertension in later life (see table 27.2). In these, as well as in the hypertensive hyper-reactors, the magnitude of the response tends to increase progressively after 40 years of age. Actually the cold pressor test elicits a complex response of reflex vasoconstriction, pain perception and possibly an adrenergic discharge. Ganglionic blocking agents abolish this abnormal reaction.

SUMMARY. Dr. Goldblatt's view is that the primary cause of essential hypertension in man is intrarenal obliterative vascular disease from any cause, usually arterial and arteriolar sclerosis, or any other condition that brings about the same disturbance of intrarenal hemodynamics. Although essential human hypertension is supposedly unassociated with obvious disturbance of renal function, this does not mean there is no functional disturbance of any kind; it refers specifically to the usual tests for excretory function. One of the strongest supports for the idea that the hypertension is the result of renal vascular disease and not its cause, is the finding that evidence of severe renal arteriolar sclerosis was not found at autopsy in individuals who had had normal blood pressure, and that moderate to severe renal arterial and arteriolar sclerosis occurred in almost 100 per cent of cases in which hypertension had existed. The recently published reviews of human unilateral renal hypertension confirm that interference with the renal blood supply can cause a form of human hypertension similar to that created experimentally (25 to 50 per cent permanently cured by excision of the kidney). The recent report of the ability to arrest the course of hypertension by transplanting a normal kidney and removing two diseased kidneys is a further verification.

The popular assumption that essential hypertension is mediated by a neurogenically maintained increase in peripheral arteriolar resistance lacks substantial experimental proof. Failure of total sympathectomy to cure essential hypertension is the strongest argument that the autonomic nervous system is not primarily involved in maintenance of increased peripheral resistance.

If Goldblatt's mechanism applies, either ischemia must be functional and inapparent at autopsy or biopsy, or the release of renal pressor enzymes in early stages is secondary to an enzymatic defect not detectable with the microscope.

The treatment of essential hypertension is predominantly medical, with the use of various pharmacological agents. Surgical treatment ranging from subdiaphragmatic splanchnicectomy to "total" (thoracolumbar and accessory ganglia) sympathectomy is usually reserved for selected patients; such surgery removes the sympathetic vasomotor tone from a large segment of the systemic vascular system resulting in a decreased peripheral resistance and an increased capacity of the vascular bed. Since sympathectomy does not offer better results than medical treatment, its popularity has declined. The ganlgionic blocking agents, by reducing cholinergic transmission in the autonomic ganglia, produce a "chemical sympathectomy" and have the most profound effects of the pharmacological agents used. The blocking agents probably reduce both arteriolar and venous tone, producing an increased systemic vascular volume and a decreased cardiac output by a combination of venous pooling and failure of reflex vasoconstriction. Because of postural hypotension and the side reactions from a concomitant parasympathetic blockade (constipation, urinary retention, mydriasis), these drugs are being used less frequently and in smaller doses, in combination with less potent antihypertensive agents.

Alkaloids of the plant, Rauwolfia serpentina Benth, are widely used antihypertensive preparations. Their action is very complex. Besides a sedative effect, Rauwolfia derivates presumably decrease sympathetic nervous tone, probably by an action directly or indirectly on the hypothalamus. Serotonin has been shown to be displaced from its binding sites in the brain which may lead to the reduction in sympathetic outflow

and relative parasympathetic overactivity. Catecholamines are also released by these drugs from hypothalamic centers and from peripheral postganglionic sympathetic nerves. The lack of sympathetic transmitter substance, leading to a decrease in vasoconstrictor activity, may be the drug's main hypotensive action.

Hydralazine, another moderate hypotensive agent, possess many complex actions. It has been shown to inactivate pressor materials derived from renin, to inactive some decarboxylase enzymes, and to probably stimulate monamine oxidase, the enzyme involved in inhibition or destruction of catecholamines and serotonin. The drug produces a prolonged dilation of constricted blood vessels and, unlike other hypotensive agents, increases renal plasma flow despite the decrease in blood pressure. Schroeder maintains that the relaxation of vasoconstriction is not due to sympatholytic activity but to a direct effect on the vascular smooth muscle cell which may be related to the drug's chelating action on trace metals.

The veratrum alkaloids are not widely used in the treatment of hypertension for the hypotensive dose approximates the emetic dose. The therapeutically used veratrum alkaloids or mixtures, produce a vasodepressor reflex by means of the baroreceptors of the carotid sinus, aortic arch and left ventricle, and not by their parasympathetic stimulatory effects. Some veratrum alkaloids do have an action directly on higher vasomotor centers.

Recently, diuretics of the benzothiadiazine family (such as chlorothiazide) have been found to have hypotensive properties. Their action has been assumed to be similar to the hypotensive effect of a low sodium diet (which is still a very useful treatment for hypertensive patients). The antihypertensive mechanism of these diuretics is believed to be a result of a decreased plasma volume with loss of sodium, chloride and water from the body and a subsequent decreased cardiac output and blood pressure. Restoration of the blood volume with dextran, early in treatment, restores the blood pressure towards normal levels. However, the blood pressure reduction has been shown to be maintained even when the plasma volume, exchangeable sodium and cardiac output return to normal levels with more prolonged treatment. Therefore, other mechanisms may be operative in the antihypertensive action of these drugs besides a purely diuretic effect.

A large number of new agents are being tested in the treatment of hypertension, most of which are either serotonin, monoamine oxidase or catecholamine inhibitors. One of the latter drugs, guanethidine, had been found to inhibit the peripheral release of catecholamines from postganglionic sympathetic nerve fibers. A predominantly postural hypotension is produced, as with ganglionic blocking agents, but without the parasympathetic side effects. The role of serotonin in hypertension is unclear. Enigmatically, both inhibitors of monoamine oxidase (which destroys serotonin) and of serotonin lower blood pressure in hypertensive patients and are receiving clinical trials in treatement. There is indirect evidence that monoamine oxidase inhibitors may possess some ganglionic blocking activity.

The above-mentioned drugs are usually used in combination, in dosages necessary to reduce the blood pressure to reasonable levels for the patient concerned. Each agent seems to have an additive or potentiating effect on the other so that together smaller doses can be used with fewer side effects or toxic reactions than when either drug is used alone. Although the life of the patient may be prolonged by these agents, there is no definite evidence that the underlying process is reversed.

MALIGNANT HYPERTENSION. Malignant or "accelerated" hypertension is a more severe, progressive form of arterial hypertension, characterized by rapidly advancing renal damage, usually, but not always, accompanied by retinal hemorrhages, exudates and papilledema. The papilledema (elevation of the optic disks) has been related to the marked diastolic pressure elevation inducing an increase in cerebrospinal fluid pressure. The clinical course is one of rapid degeneration with early demise due to cerebral, cardiac, or renal complications.

ECLAMPSIA GRAVIDARUM. Eclampsia is a state occurring in pregnancy in the last trimester characterized by hypertension, headache, nausea and vomiting, albuminuria, edema, tremors, or convulsions ending in coma. The blood pressure may be extreme and of rapid development. The diastolic pressure shows the more pronounced rise, indicating a generalized vasoconstriction. The cause of the arteriolar spasm is unknown. The blood pressure, as a rule, falls after evacuation of the uterus, which points to the uterine contents being in some way responsible for the symptoms. Since death of the fetus does not result in an abatement of the condition, and it develops in association with a hydatidiform mole, placental tissue is certainly incriminated. Beyond these facts nothing is known for certain with respect to the causative mechanisms in eclampsia.

## Hypotension

Hypotension is usually considered to be present in an adult when the systolic pressure is persistently below 110 mm. Hg, although such a definition is arbitrary, since hypotensive symptoms may not be experienced at lower levels. On the other hand, patients with arterial hypertension may develop symptoms at higher systolic pressures.

PRIMARY HYPOTENSION. In the absence of an underlying disease, low blood pressure is referred to as "primary" or "essential" hypotension. The subjects with primary hypotension (who are usually emotionally labile, asthenic, young females) often suffer no ill effects beyond fatigue and weakness. The nonspecific symptoms may be more related to the individual's personality than to the hypotension. These patients are more likely to be free from cardiac and renal disease, the condition, for this reason, being said to forecast longevity. Except for a hereditary predisposition, the etiological factors in primary hypotension are unknown.

SECONDARY HYPOTENSION. Low blood pressure may occur either as a temporary or persistent phenomenon in numerous disease states, such as hemorrhage, traumatic shock, acute fever, myocardial infarction, tuberculosis, adrenal or pituitary insufficiency and debilitating diseases. The symptoms of secondary hypotension usually result from the underlying disease rather than the low blood pressure. The determining factors are not well understood, but the hypotension is usually due to an inadequate cardiac output, a decreased peripheral resistance or blood volume, or a combination of these factors.

ORTHOSTATIC OR POSTURAL HYPOTENSION. In this interesting condition, the reflex mechanisms normally operating to maintain the blood pressure against the effect of gravity are apparently in abeyance, or their sensitivity greatly depressed. A profound fall in blood pressure occurs on assumption of the standing position; the systolic pressure may fall to 40 mm. Hg, and the diastolic to zero (as determined by the usual ausculatory method). The subject experiences dizziness and/or syncope. This syndrome may occur idiopathically with no known underlying disease secondary to various nervous system diseases (diabetes mellitus with neuropathy, tabes dorsalis, myasthenia gravis, syringomyelia), following surgical sympathectomies, or during treatment with adrenergic or ganglionic blocking agents. Idiopathic orthostatic hypotension is believed to be a definite syndrome usually accompanied by anhidrosis and impotence; the male between 40 and 70 years of age is more often affected. Since anhidrosis and failure of a reflex tachycardia on standing accompanies the postural hypotension, the abnormality is believed to be in the sympathetic nervous system. However, indirect evidence also implicates involvement of the parasympathetic system so that the name "primary autonomic insufficiency" has been suggested.

Experimental studies on patients with chronic orthostatic hypotension have shown that they do not pool more blood in the lower extremities on assumption of the erect position than normals, but that there is an abnormal response to the usual shift in blood volume. The abnormality consists in the last of reflex arteriolar and venous constriction which usually occurs on standing. The drop in blood pressure may be augmented by a fall in cardiac output, but the latter may not decrease excessively (also, a large postural cardiac output fall may occur without a significant change in blood pressure). The demonstration of low plasma or urinary levels of catecholamines in patients with postural hypotension offers direct evidence of an abnormality in the sympathico-adrenal system. It is interesting that vasopressin, which lacks a pressor effect in man, raises the blood pressure in these patients.

Treatment of primary hypotension is usually unnecessary, while correction of the underlying disease should be attempted in secondary hypotension. Abdominal binders, elastic stockings, various sympathomimetic pressor agents, vasopressin, adrenal cortical sodium retaining hormones, or a high salt diet are often, but not always, helpful in chronic orthostatic hypotension. Sodium retaining hormones or a high salt intake are believed to act by increasing the blood volume and, hence, the blood pressure; however, the underlying abnormality is not corrected.

### Hyperventilation, Hypoventilation, Hypercapnia, etc.

Circulatory adjustments result when the $pCO_2$ of arterial blood is increased or decreased. A decrease in $pO_2$ of arterial blood also elicits changes in the cardiovascular system, but a rise in $pO_2$ above that which is present in normal resting subjects at sea level has little or no effect. The patterns of response which need to be analyzed, therefore, are those related to hypocapnia (acapnia), hypercapnia, hypoxia (anoxia) and a combination of hypercapnia and hypoxia (asphyxia).

Hypocapnia can be produced by voluntary hyperventilation or by artificial respiration of anesthetized animals. Carbon dioxide depletion causes a lowering of the tonic activity of the vasoconstrictor center; arteriolar dilation results and the blood pressure falls. The heart rate may be accelerated reflexly from the fall in pressure in the sinoaortic zones. The *direct* effect of carbon dioxide lack upon the peripheral vessels is to increase their tone, but this effect is not evident in the pressence of the reduction in arteriolar tonus related to the central effects.

Dale and Evans found that when cats were severely over ventilated the blood pressure fell to around 40 mm. Hg within a minute or two, and the depressor effect did not occur or was quite evanescent when a mixture of 5 per cent $CO_2$ in air was substituted for air as the ventilating gas. Depressor effects of hyperventilation with air also were present in decapitated animals thus indicating that the spinal vasomotor centers also are sensitive to changes in carbon dioxide tension. After destruction of the spinal cord hypocapnia caused a rise in blood pressure, as would be expected in view of the direct effects on peripheral vessels which in this case are not opposed by the central influences.

In the majority of human subjects in the standing position forced ventilation causes a fall in arterial blood pressure. The fall is attributed in part, at least in some subjects, to interference with the venous return which occurs as a result of the forcible expiratory movements (Vincent and Thompson), since the fall may occur when the subject breathes a mixture containing $CO_2$. Severe prolonged hyperventilation in some subjects may cause enough pooling of blood in dependent parts of the body to cause dizziness or even fainting since cerebral blood flow is decreased.

According to earlier views (Y. Henderson) shock could be produced by prolonged hyperventilation, however this does not appear to be the case in experimental animals if a method is used which does not obstruct flow of blood in the lungs. Although arterial pressure is lowered peripheral resistance also is lowered so that blood flow through most organs is maintained or even increased, and blood pressure is restored quickly when the hyperventilation is discontinued.

Hypercapnia causes increased tone of the vasoconstrictor center. Local effects of a rise in

$pCO_2$, as when metabolism in the tissues is increased are vasodilator, but this effect is not evident in the presence of moderate increases in $pCO_2$ achieved by rebreathing or adding $CO_2$ to the inhaled mixture. Mathison reported that when an animal breathed an air mixture containing 10 per cent $CO_2$ with an adequate percentage of oxygen the arterial blood pressure rose within less than a minute to double its previous height and intestinal volume fell. Injections of lactic acid or other organic acids into the blood stream produced effects similar to those of carbon dioxide excess.

In a decapitated animal a rise in blood pressure in response to $CO_2$ occurs when the percentage in respired air is increased to 20, whereas breathing air mixed with 5 per cent $CO_2$ may be sufficient to excite the medullary vasomotor center.

A moderate degree of hypoxia as produced by ascent to altitude or by breathing at sea level a gas mixture containing about 12 to 15 per cent $O_2$ causes a moderate increase in heart rate and elevation of the blood pressure. Breathing is stimulated so that a mild decrease in $pCO_2$ also occurs. A brief severe bout of hypoxia produced by breathing nitrogen for about 30 seconds causes marked cardiac acceleration while changes in blood pressure are somewhat variable. Breathing is stimulated, hence influences related to hypocapnia make the interpretations difficult. Heymans (1950) stated that cardiac acceleration in response to oxygen lack is due mainly "to reflex stimulation of the sympathetic centers (cardiac and adrenalinic centers) by way of the chemoreceptors", and that oxygen want effects these centers directly only if very marked. However, in experiments involving perfusion of the carotid bodies a lowering of the $pO_2$ in the perfused blood failed to elicit cardiac acceleration, and this was true when the systemic-arterial blood pressure was kept constant by the use of a mechanical compensator (Bernthal). Intravenous injection of sodium cyanide in the smaller doses which stimulate breathing also causes cardiac acceleration, however the effect of cyanide on heart rate is not exerted reflexly from the chemoreceptors (see Heymans, 1958).

In experiments on intact animals subjected to severe anoxia before and after adrenalectomy it is demonstrated that liberation of epinephrine is a factor in the production of cardiac acceleration (Van Loo and associates), however neural acceleration also is concerned. At present it must be concluded that the mechanism which sets off the acceleration in response to hypoxia is not known.

Cardiac output is increased in man as much as 50 per cent while breathing a gas mixture containing 8 per cent oxygen (Doyle and associates, 1952). Also, increases in cardiac output are produced by hypoxia in unanesthetized dogs (Nahas and associates, 1954).

In hypoventilation or asphyxia the combined effects of increased $pCO_2$ and decreased $pO_2$ are seen. Blood pressure is elevated; heart rate usually is increased. Cardiac output is elevated. The changes in the blood and the respiratory effects are described elsewhere (ch. 32 and 33). As asphyxia is prolonged blood pressure falls as a consequence of decreased strength of cardiac contractions and conduction in the atrioventricular portion of the conducting system may be impaired.

As asphyxia is progressive in an anesthetized dog which is allowed to rebreathe air from a small rubber bag the blood pressure progressively becomes higher until it may reach a level double that in the period before asphyxia. Shortly, as rebreathing continues, the blood pressure suddenly falls. This is attributed to a weakening of the cardiac contractions due to anoxemia and not to release of arteriolar tonus, for if the volume of the kidney is recorded at this time, it is found that no change occurs.

As described above, the local effect of a deficiency of $O_2$ and an excess of $CO_2$ or rise in $cH$ is to cause vasodilation while the effect of these changes in the vasomotor center is to promote vasoconstriction. In exercise large increases in $pCO_2$ and $cH$ and decreases in $pO_2$ occur in the active muscles, and these changes promote a greater blood flow. Changes in $pCO_2$ and $pO_2$ in systemic arterial blood during exercise are not prominent since equilibrium with alveolar air of essentially normal composition still occurs (see question of control of pulmonary ventilation during exercise p. 499 and of vasomotor reactions during exercise).

The persistent elevation of the blood pressure which results from a rise in intracranial pressure is attributed to compression of medullary vessels and hence interference with blood supply to the vasomotor centers. The rise in $pCO_2$ and $cH$ in the vasoconstrictor center causes an increase in vasoconstrictor tonus and therefore a rise in arterial blood pressure to a level sufficient to restore blood flow to the brain. When the rise in intracranial pressure is rapid, as in the case of cerebral hemorrhage in man or when it is produced in experimental animals by introducing fluid, the rise in blood pressure is rapid and a decrease in heart rate is elicited from pressoreceptors. Hence, repeated recording of blood pressure and heart rate provides information concerning whether the rise in intracranial pressure is continuing.

### Circulatory Adjustments to Climatic Conditions

Changes in environmental temperature elicit characteristic alterations in circulation. Adjustments in cutaneous blood flow, blood volume and cardiac output occur as a part of the process of heat regulation (see ch. 52). At present there is interest in the use of lowered body temperature to prevent or treat shock and to permit surgery on patients who might not be able to tolerate the stress of anesthesia and operations at normal body temperature. Therefore, it has become necessary to consider the circulatory effects of severely lowered body temperature.

Any mammal if exposed to a sufficiently low temperature will react by conserving its heat and increasing heat production; but if the cold is intense enough for a sufficiently long period the animal begins to cool. At a critical level of body temperature death occurs, but this level is lower for hibernators than for mammals which do not hibernate (Lyman and Chatfield, in *Physiology of Induced Hypothermia*). Species which hibernate evidently undergo adaptations which do not occur, at least in similar degree, in nonhibernators. If a nonhibernator is cooled progressively, death usually occurs due to ventricular fibrillation or asystole when the body temperature has reached the vicinity of 20 to 15° C. The heart of a hibernator (ground squirrel) can beat effectively at rates of 5 to 10 beats per minute at low temperatures and will continue to beat when removed from the animal and placed in cold unoxygenated saline, but the heart of a nonhibernator (white rat), under similar conditions, stops beating within a few minutes (Dawe and Landau, 1960).

As shown by Hook and Stormont (1941), and Hegnauer and associates (1950), heart rate in the dog decreases almost linearly with decreases in body temperature down to about 20 beats per minute at about 18 to 20° C. Blood pressure showed a progressive decrease but not as much as the decrease in heart rate down to about 24° C. Then as temperature was lowered further, the decrease in blood pressure paralleled the decrease in heart rate. Similar results have been obtained by others. As the heart rate decreases in hypother-

mia the durations of both systole and isometric relaxation as well as duration of diastole increase greatly (as much as 2½ times). When heart rate is decreased comparably by vagal stimulation, most of the lengthening of the cycle is related to prolongation of diastole.

The cardiac output of dogs at a body temperature of 20° C. is about 15 per cent of normal due almost entirely to the decrease in heart rate since stroke volume may be normal. The tissues use less oxygen and the coefficient of oxygen utilization is increased. Although coronary blood flow is reduced it is adequate for the needs of the heart in the presence of reduced metabolism (Berne, 1954). During rewarming signs of circulatory inadequacy are noted and have been attributed to the peripheral vasodilation and to adrenal insufficiency related to lack of adrenal response to trauma during hypothermia.

Much attention has been given to the question of what causes ventricular fibrillation in hypothermic animals, and no definite conclusions have been reached. Absolute and relative refractory periods of cardiac muscle are lengthened and conduction is slowed. Excitability changes of the heart in hypothermia are varied. In some cases changes in threshold are not prominent while in others there is an abrupt loss of excitability. It is possible that the latter change is related to failure of repolarization of the fibers of the conducting system which sometimes occurs during cooling. The problem is discussed in detail by Hoffman (Symposium, *Physiology of Induced Hypothermia*). Covino (1958) reported that in hypothermic dogs which were about to fibrillate, calcium was shifting into the heart and potassium was leaving. He suggests a cause and effect relationship between these changes and ventricular fibrillation in hypothermic dogs, however several other factors including sympathetic neural activity, hydrogen ion shifts, and type of anesthetic agent also are considered to have an effect on the incidence of fibrillation.

### Circulatory Responses to Gravitational Stress

THE EFFECTS OF ACCELERATION. A constant speed, however great, has in itself no effect upon the circulation. As pointed out by Armstrong, we are travelling through space quite unaware of a speed of over 18 miles per second caused by the motion of the earth. But acceleration, that is, a change in velocity either in the line of our motion (*linear acceleration* and *deceleration*), or the movement of the body in a circular or curved course (*centripetal* or *central acceleration*), may cause profound effects upon the body as a result of the inertia of the blood and viscera. A third type of accelerated movement, known as *angular acceleration*, takes place when the body rotates about its own axis, as when a plane rolls or spins. The rate of angular acceleration is rarely great enough to cause any serious physiological disturbance, but this form of acceleration causes effects on equilibrium and orientation. The development of the modern airplane and maneuvers of military flying have brought prominently to the fore the importance and hazards of acceleration in relation to the circulation. According to Newton's Law, F = MA where F = force, M the mass and A the linear acceleration. Therefore, A = F/M.

The effects of *horizontal linear acceleration* upon the body of a pilot are seen in catapulted take-offs, or in picking up personnel from the ground or in gliders by high speed planes. Deceleration, i.e., a sudden reduction in velocity, occurs in crash landings, parachute landings, or from parachute opening (especially at very high altitudes), etc. Vertical acceleration, as when the plane falls or pitches, owing to changes in air density, causes motion sickness.

*Centripetal acceleration* is the type which in military flying causes serious effects upon the circulation. It is defined as the acceleration of a body toward the center of a circle in the circumference of which it is moving at uniform velocity. The central force producing the acceleration (*centripetal force*) is resisted by an equal and opposite, radially acting force, generally called *centrifugal force*. This may be expressed, thus:—

$$F = MV^2/r$$

in which M is the mass, V the velocity and r the radius of the circular movement. At a linear or centripetal acceleration equal to that of gravity, namely, 32.2 ft. per second, per second the force exerted is equal to that of gravity. Gravitational force, like centrifugal force, is proportional to mass and is exhibited as weight. The force due to acceleration is, therefore, conveniently expressed in units of gravitational force and designated by the letter G. Thus an acceleration amounting to 2G indicates a force double that of gravity, i.e., a body acted upon by such a force would be doubled in weight. The centrifugal force is proportional to the square of the velocity. It can be calculated in G units from equation $G = V^2/32 \cdot 2 \cdot r$, where V is the velocity in feet, r the radius in feet of the curved course which the moving body takes, and G units of gravitational force per pound of mass.[2] Thus, the weight of a pilot's body subjected to a force of 2G is doubled, is tripled at 3G, and quadrupled at 4G, and so on.

Acceleration which produces a force acting upon the airman in the long axis of the body from head to seat is called positive (+G); that acting from seat to head is called negative (−G). A pilot pulling out of a power dive, that is, changing direction at high velocity to a horizontal and upward direction in a banking maneuver has his head directed inward toward the center of the circular movement and is therefore subjected to a positive centripetal acceleration. If the force amounts to from 5 to 6 + G or more, and lasts for longer than 3 or 4 seconds, the phenomenon now generally referred to as "blackout" results, for his blood being acted upon by a force 5 or 6 times that of gravity "falls" or is "thrown" into the lower part of the body (the large vessels, it will be recalled, run in the general direction of the long axis of the body); the weight and, consequently, the hydrostatic pressure of the blood is increased (see fig. 27.4). In animal experiments it has been shown that as a result of the very high capillary pressure a marked increase in filtration of fluid from the blood into the extravascular spaces with hemoconcentration occurs. In man the skin of the lower parts of the legs may show numerous blood extravasations (petechiae). The movement of blood toward the feet reduces the venous return of blood to the heart, and, as a consequence, the pressure of blood in the cerebral and retinal vessels falls. Vision is temporarily lost and the pilot may become unconscious. The abdominal viscera are forced downwards and drawing upon the diaphragm may embarrass respiration. X-ray photography shows elongation of the heart and a reduction in cardiac volume.

"Negative" acceleration, as when a turn is made at high velocity with the plane in the inverted position, the pilot's head being directed outward, causes opposite effects upon the circulation and is likely to produce more serious injury, but fortunately, unlike positive acceleration, does not come into play in any necessary maneuver. "Negative" acceleration also occurs in spins resulting from some structural damage to the

[2] From the following equation the force developed during linear acceleration or deceleration can be calculated.
$$G = (V_x^2 - V_y^2)/32.2 \times 2 \times S$$
where $V_y$ is the initial velocity, $V_x$ the final velocity and S the distance travelled during the period of acceleration.

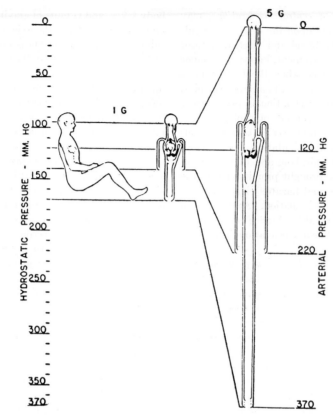

Fig. 27.4. Diagrammatic representation of the hydrostatic pressures in the vascular system of a man in the sitting position at 1 G and at 5 G. (Wood and associates.)

plane, when the tremendous force created may, through the increased weight of their bodies, prevent the pilot and other occupants of the plane from moving. In a turn with the head directed outward, the blood is driven toward the head resulting in effects sometimes called "red-out". The vessels of the head and neck become engorged, there may be small cutaneous hemorrhages, severe throbbing pain in the head is experienced and the eyes feel as though they were being extruded from their sockets. The abdominal viscera are pushed upwards against the diaphragm. The venous return to the heart is increased and the blood pressure in the cerebral vessels is raised considerably (as much as 65 mm. Hg). There may be mental confusion for a time. Cerebral hemorrhage may result, but since the hydrostatic pressure of the cerebrospinal fluid is also increased, it acts as a buffer which, to a large extent, protects the delicate walls of the small cerebral veins and capillaries, which are the most likely to rupture.

Large centrifuge machines have been devised for subjecting the body to positive acceleration and studying the effects produced. Instruments

record blood pressure, cardiac action and blood content of the drum membrane automatically. Thus the tolerance of a pilot to +G can be measured (see fig. 27.5).

In order to prevent the physiological effects of positive acceleration, several types of double-walled suits have been designed which, by containing water or air under pressure, oppose a force to resist a rise in the hydrostatic pressure of the blood. The first suit of this kind to be employed in actual air combat was invented by Franks of the Royal Canadian Air Force. It envelops the abdomen and lower limbs; water is introduced into the space between its walls. During the development of centrifugal force a hydrostatic pressure, automatically graded to that exerted upon the blood, is applied through the tissues to the vascular walls. Thus, distension of the vascular bed of the lower part of the body and the accumulation of blood is prevented.

The effects of centripetal acceleration may also be minimized by the pilot assuming a crouching position with the trunk bent well forward and the thighs strongly flexed at the hips. The direc-

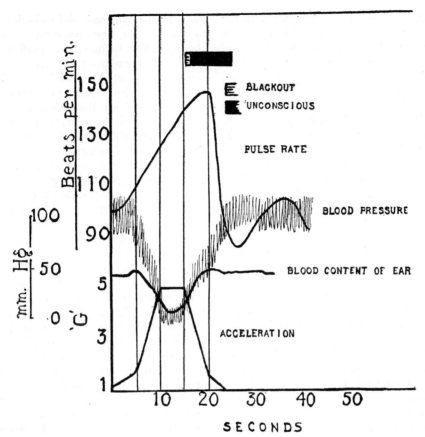

FIG. 27.5. Records of pulse rate, blood pressure and blood content of the ear of a normal subject exposed in the human centrifuge for 5 seconds to 5 G. (Drawn in part from graphs kindly furnished by Dr. W. R. Franks.)

tion of the centrifugal force is then across the great vessels of the trunk rather than in line with them, and runs from knee to hip more or less parallel to the vessels of the thigh; the movement of the blood along the veins of the thigh toward the heart is thus actually aided.

MAN UNDER GRAVITY-FREE CONDITIONS. Gravity is omnipresent and is the only environmental factor which cannot be eliminated experimentally on the earth for any prolonged period of time. This is why our knowledge of the effects of gravity on the circulation is so small. Apart from the few seconds in a free fall, such as in an airplane undergoing a dive of an almost vertical drop, there is only one way to escape gravity, and that is to leave the earth in a space ship. Such an experiment, once a fantastic dream of the future, has now come close to reality with the travel of dogs into space and their recovery. Man is next.

The acceleration due to take offs and landings of space ships presents no fundamental physiological difficulties, for in test subjects, the limit of tolerance to centrifugal forces in the direction of chest to back, corresponds to an acceleration of 17 G for 4 minutes, and in the direction of back to chest, to an acceleration of 11 G for 3 minutes. This is compatible with the acceleration due to take-offs and landings of space ships. When the interplanetary ship has left the atmosphere of the earth and its propulsion is discontinued, it will behave like a celestial body in its orbit through the solar system. The orbit must lead the ship to its goal following the laws of gravitation. Consequently, during the greater part of the interplanetary flight, a gravity-free or a near gravity-free state is encountered. Its duration will vary from days (trip to moon) to months (trip to Venus or Mars).

Projection of things to come in space is precarious and must depend more or less on assumptions and conclusions by analogy. Mechanical effects from the surrounding tissues can alter the circulation mildly. The circulatory changes caused by gravity are due to elastic deformation which body organs and blood vessels undergo. In the weightless state, the organs are without support and, hence, this might lead to mild derangement of body organs as they seek slightly altered positions. Direct disturbances of the circulation, however, by absence of gravity would not be anticipated. The circulation operates by elastic forces delivered by the heart and the elasticity of the blood vessels. Although the blood loses its weight, it retains its mass, inertia, and other properties of a liquid. In general, it is believed it would resemble that of a man at sea level in the horizontal position except that flattening of the veins would not occur and the distribution of the blood would be the same in the horizontal and vertical head up or down position, or indeed, in any position. Finally, it might be expected that absence of gravity would lead to diminution of activity of the vasomotor system and of reflexes that have so much to do with normal compensatory responses of the circulatory system to stress. This is so, since the execution of locomotion takes place under continuous guidance of a complex system of sensory receptors widely distributed over the body. Since the degree of activation of muscle is related to the weight of the body, and since this depends mainly on muscle proprioceptors, one could expect that muscle tonus will be reduced and the limbs relaxed and flaccid. In addition, since it will take no more energy to move a large object than a small object, and very little energy in either case, one might expect a further reduction in skeletal muscle activity with a fall in cardiac output and even atrophy of the heart and skeletal muscle. Some form of standard exercise might be needed to prevent this.

## Cardiovascular Effects of Ionizing Radiations

The effects of ionizing radiation upon the circulation of the skin and upon arteries and veins have been recognized and studied intensively over the past 60 years. It has been recognized only recently that whole-body radiation produces dysfunction of the entire cardiovascular system and that some form of cardiac failure may be a factor in causing radiation death in some species of animals. What role cardiovascular changes play in causing radiation death in man has not been studied in detail.

Ionizing radiation produces a variety of abnormalities of the cardiovascular system. These are caused by (1) a direct effect of radiation upon the tissues, (2) effects produced by the ionization of water by radiation, (3) effects produced by metabolites from damaged tissue, (4) effects pro-duced by the autonomic and endocrine reactions to radiation, (5) effects produced by the marked changes in fluid balance of the irradiated animal, and (6) effects produced by other ill-defined but perhaps important abnormalities of the irradiated animal. Insufficient experimental data exist to define with precision the complete sequence of changes in the cardiovascular system or the exact mechanism by which these abnormalities are produced by ionizing radiation.

REACTION OF SKIN TO RADIATION. When the skin of man and animals is exposed to a sufficient dose of ionizing radiation (300 to 600r, depending upon the wave length) a characteristic sequence of changes is observed. There is usually an initial erythema during the 1st day which rapidly subsides, followed by a 2nd wave of erythema in the 2nd or 3rd week; a 3rd wave may be seen after 6 weeks. During the later waves of erythema the skin temperature is increased suggesting that a marked vasodilation with increased blood flow has occurred although there is no perceptible change during the latent periods. These changes in cutaneous circulation have been attributed to a combination of the direct effect of irradiation on the component cells of the blood vessels; by modification in the neuromuscular control of the peripheral vascular system (directly or indirectly produced by irradiation); and by the release of histamine and other tissue hormones by the damaged tissue surrounding the blood vessels. The relative importance of each of these in producing damage and dysfunction to the vascular system of the skin remains to be determined.

VASCULAR PHYSIOLOGY. Ionizing radiation produces diffuse and irregular damage to the arteries, capillaries, and veins of man and animals. It has been recognized only recently that, in addition to producing obliterative vascular lesions, irradiation produces significant physiological abnormalities of blood vessels. Arteries from irradiated dogs (total-body 300r) have an abnormal pressure volume curve, these vessels being more spastic than is normal upon removal from the body. Vessels from irradiated dogs likewise have a decreased vasoconstriction to 1-epinephrine and 1-norepinephrine when compared to control arteries. When a normal artery is irradiated *in vitro* two effects are noted. A slight constriction of the arterial wall occurs immediately upon beginning of irradiation, which is completed in 30 to 45 seconds. This is a direct effect of the radiation. The flow through the vasa vasorum is decreased. This latter effect is secondary to ionization of the solution surrounding the specimen. Alterations in capillary permeability produced by irradiation play a significant role in producing changes in the red and white cell content of the peripheral blood. These studies have shown that ionizing radiations produce a variety of physiological abnormalities of the peripheral vascular system which are only beginning to be delineated.

CARDIOVASCULAR EFFECTS OF TOTAL-BODY RADIATION. The threshold dose of total-body X-ray or gamma radiation required to produce significant abnormalities of the cardiovascular system is below 300r and probably above 100r. Because of the tremendous species variation in these responses to irradiation it will be necessary to consider the response of man, when known, and other species separately.

*Arterial blood pressure.* Patients who are receiving x-ray therapy may develop a hypotensive episode shortly after irradiation which returns to normotensive levels within an hour or two. Rabbits develop hypotension immediately following total-body irradiation of as little as 50r. There is no change in blood pressure, cardiac output or total peripheral resistance of dogs during or for 5 hours following exposure to 1500r of gamma radiation. In the rat an initial hypotensive episode which occurs within the first 2 hours has been described. In both the rat and rabbit there is a rise in plasma histamine which is related in time to the initial hypotensive episodes in these species. This relation may be only fortuitous as there is evidence that the initial hypotension following irradiation is, in part, mediated by reflex mechanisms.

In most species recovery from an initial hypotension is prompt and blood pressure falls again only in the terminal period. VDM and VEM have been found in the blood of rats 6 to 10 days following irradiation.

*Cardiac physiology and biochemistry.* The isolated hearts of animals tolerate ionizing radiation in doses 10 times greater than the lethal dose for man without showing significant functional abnormalities. These data are strong evidence that irradiation does not directly injure the myocardium and the conduction system of the heart.

However, a series of changes in cardiac biochemistry and function following whole-body irradiation (700r) of the rat have been carefully defined by Caster and associates. These are most readily summarized by considering these changes chronologically: *0 to 2 days.* During the first 3 to 12 hours there are significant increases both in venous pressure and in the plasma volume of the tissues. By the 2nd day there is a loss in deoxyri-

bonucleic acid (DNA) and lipid from the heart, a decrease in the area of the heart shadow and in the total body plasma volume, and the peripheral venous pressure has returned to normal. Electrocardiographic changes begin to appear. *3 to 5 days.* Both venous pressure and plasma volume drop to a minimum. Four days following radiation shows the beginning of a lineal decrease in DNA and actomyosin in the heart. *6 to 14 days.* By the 6th day the venous pressure increases abruptly and continues high until death. The plasma volume of the heart is increased by 50 per cent. The potassium, DNA and actomyosin concentrations of the heart reach minimum values and the percentage of fluid in the heart and lung increases. Cardiac arrythmias appear more frequently by the 8th to 10th day and deaths occur frequently. The mechanical action of the heart (as indicated by the heart sounds) changes, and there is a significant shift in the electrical axis of the heart.

*Electrocardiographic observations.* Abnormalities in the T waves (depression and/or inversion), S-T segments (lowering) and miscellaneous arrythmias have been observed in most species following total-body irradiation. The sequence of changes in the electrocardiogram of the rat following irradiation (700r) have been described by Caster and associates. In these studies the decrease in plasma volume rather than direct damage to the myocardium apparently played a major role in producing these changes.

*Postmortem evidence.* In many species the terminal findings include a marked pulmonary edema and enlargement of the right side of the heart. Blood vessel walls are diffusely and irregularly damaged.

## Effects of Aging on the Circulation

With advancing age significant reductions occur in the functional capacities of many different organ systems. Oftentimes these changes are secondary to alterations in the circulation which result in impaired blood flow to specific organs and tissues. Because of its increased prevalence among the elderly, the disease process, arteriosclerosis, plays an important role in the functional impairments which accumulate with age. There are, however, progressive changes in the circulation which occur independently of the development of this disease. These changes will be described in this section.

*Heart.* Progressive changes take place in the heart which are not related to coronary artery disease, the most frequent cause of death in in-

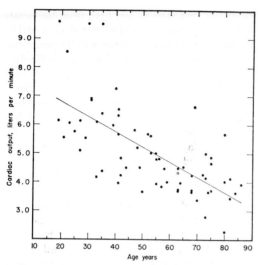

FIG. 27.6. Age changes in basal cardiac output in normal males. Each point represents an individual subject.

dividuals over the age of 65. For example, there is a gradual accumulation of insoluble granular material in cardiac muscle fibers (Strehler et al., 1959). These granules make their first appearance at about the age of 20 and increase gradually so that by age 80 they may occupy as much as 5 to 10 per cent of the myocardial volume. Animal experiments have shown that at higher ages the activity of important intracellular enzymes of the myocardium, such as succinoxidase, is significantly reduced (Barrows and associates, 1958).

Although average values for resting heart rate tend to diminish slightly with increasing age (Howell, 1950), the increased incidence of irregularities in rhythm in the aged offers evidence of impairment in the mechanisms regulating rate.

Cardiac output under basal conditions diminishes by approximately 50 per cent between the ages of 20 and 80 years (Brandfonbrener and associates, 1955). Fig. 27.6 illustrates a series of measurements made on normal subjects by the dye injection technique. This curve illustrates the wide individual differences in the effects of age which are also found in observations on many other physiological variables. Thus, there are 80-year-old persons with cardiac outputs as high as the average 40-year-old. Cardiac outputs, calculated by an empirical formula from ballistocardiographic records, also show a significant reduction with age (Tanner, 1949).

Statistical analysis of resting blood pressure measurements in a sample of 79,757 apparently healthy people aged 20 to 106 years indicates a gradual rise in systolic pressure up to the age of

70 (Lasser and Master, 1959). After this age systolic pressure remains constant in men and declines in women. There is only a small rise in diastolic pressure (table 27.3).

In experiments where simultaneous measurements of blood pressure and cardiac output were made it is possible to calculate left ventricular work from the equation $W = 14.3 \ \bar{p}_s$ stroke volume gm.-m./beat and stroke power from the equation $P = 1.40 \times 10^{-4} \times \bar{p}_s \times$ stroke volume/$t_s$ watts where $\bar{p}_s$ = mean pressure during systole and $t_s$ = duration of systole. Both ventricular work and power or rate of work diminish significantly with age (Landowne and associates, 1955). These observations reflect a decrease in left ventricular work since the calculated pressure increase is not proportional to the decrease in cardiac output. The duration of systole increase results in a decrease in calculated rate of work or power of the heart.

Other evidence of decreased power of the heart in advanced age is found in ballistocardiograph tracings. Starr and Hildreth (1952) recorded a second ballistocardiogram after an interval of 10 to 14 years in 80 normal persons aged 20 to 60+. With increasing age, the I plus J amplitude diminished by roughly 50 per cent over the age span tested. These results are interpreted as a reduc-

TABLE 27.3

*Mean blood pressure and standard deviation in apparently healthy persons, 20 to 106 years of age*

| Age Group | Males | | Females | |
|---|---|---|---|---|
| | Systolic | Diastolic | Systolic | Diastolic |
| 20–24 | 123±13.7* | 76± 9.9 | 116±11.8 | 72± 9.7 |
| 25–29 | 125±12.6 | 78± 9.0 | 117±11.4 | 74± 9.1 |
| 30–34 | 126±13.6 | 79± 9.7 | 120±14.0 | 75±10.8 |
| 35–39 | 127±14.2 | 80±10.4 | 124±13.9 | 78±10.0 |
| 40–44 | 129±15.1 | 81± 9.5 | 127±17.1 | 80±10.6 |
| 45–49 | 130±16.9 | 82±10.8 | 131±19.5 | 82±11.6 |
| 50–54 | 135±19.2 | 83±11.3 | 137±21.3 | 84±12.4 |
| 55–59 | 138±18.8 | 84±11.4 | 139±21.4 | 84±11.8 |
| 60–64 | 142±21.1 | 85±12.4 | 144±22.3 | 85±13.0 |
| 65–69 | 143±26.0 | 83± 9.9 | 154±29.0 | 85±13.8 |
| 70–74 | 145±26.3 | 82±15.3 | 159±25.8 | 85±15.3 |
| 75–79 | 146±21.6 | 81±12.9 | 158±26.3 | 84±13.1 |
| 80–84 | 145±25.6 | 82± 9.9 | 157±28.0 | 83±13.1 |
| 85–89 | 145±24.2 | 79±14.9 | 154±27.9 | 82±17.3 |
| 90–94 | 145±23.4 | 78±12.1 | 150±23.6 | 79±12.1 |
| 95–106 | 146±27.5 | 78±12.7 | 149±23.5 | 81±12.5 |

* ± indicates standard deviation

From R. P. Lasser and A. M. Master, Geriatrics, 1959, 14, 345.

tion in the force of ejection and a slowing of the contractile response of the ventricle. Such an adaptation would permit a weak heart to secure the maximum cardiac output possible.

The speed of circulation of the blood as measured by decholine, or by the mean transit time of dyes injected for the estimation of cardiac output, shows a significant slowing with age. The mean transit time of T-1824 from the antecubital vein to brachial artery increases from 19.0 seconds to 28.7 seconds between the ages of 23 and 82 years (Landowne and associates, 1955).

Age changes are also apparent in the electrocardiogram. The P-Q, P-R and QT intervals show a slight tendency toward prolongation, especially at low frequencies, in elderly subjects. The voltages of P, R and T waves decline after the age of 60. The mean electrical axis of the P wave, which is deviated to the left at birth, becomes vertical by the age of 40 and then shifts progressively to the left as age advances. The mean electrical axis of the QRS complex behaves in an opposite manner indicating a more horizontal position of the heart at advanced ages (Mezzasalma and Morpurgo, 1958; Simonson and Keys, 1952). Vector analysis of conventionally recorded electrocardiograms show similar age changes. Both the QRS and T vector are rotated more anteriorly (larger azimuth angle), are smaller in magnitude and show a smaller angle between the vectors in old than in young men (Simonson and Keys, 1956). At present it is not possible to determine the relative importance of alterations in the electrical activity of the heart and anatomical and positional changes in producing the age changes in the electrocardiogram.

*Blood vessels.* With advancing age the chemical composition of certain blood vessels changes. Lansing and associates (1951), have shown that the elastin of the aorta undergoes an increase in specific gravity, calcium content and proportion of amino acids containing free carboxyl groups. There is an underlying shift in the amino acid composition of elastin, with an increase in aspartic and glutamic acid and a decrease in glycine, proline and valine. The deposition of collagen increases in the intimal and medial layers of blood vessels. Furthermore, the collagen in old blood vessels increases in resistance to solubilization by chemical treatment. It shows a denser aggregation of strands with increased chemical cross-linking. The average circumference of the human aorta increases gradually from 45.0 mm. at age 20 to 29 to 81.0 mm. at age 80 to 89, whereas the cross-sectional area of the media increases from

62.0 mm.$^2$ to 133.5 mm.$^2$ over the same age span (Wellman and Edwards, 1950). It is clear, therefore, that, as the aorta ages, some substance is added to the media.

These structural and chemical changes form the basis for the increased rigidity of old blood vessels with an attendant increase in pulse wave velocity. Between the ages of 20 and 70 years the pulse wave velocity in the aorta increases from about 5 m. per second to 11 m. per second (Hallock, 1934; Karnbaum, 1957). At lower intra-arterial pressures (diastolic) the pulse wave velocity in the brachial artery also increases with age, but at higher pressures (systolic) the age difference is much less. Thus, in older subjects, the artery behaves as if its fibers were initially more completely extended than in the young (Landowne, 1958).

The peripheral vascular system also shows significant age changes. Flow through a number of vascular beds is significantly reduced in old age. For example, plethysmographic studies of blood flow through the fingers show a fall from 4.77 to 2.76 ml. per 10 ml. finger volume per minute between the ages of 40 and 60 years (Ring and coworkers, 1959).

There is a rapid fall in the circulation to the brain from childhood through adolescence followed by a more gradual but progressive reduction throughout the remainder of life (Kety, 1956). Between the ages of 25 and 95 years the average fall in blood flow to the brain is approximately 25 per cent of the mean value at age 25.

Kidney blood flow, determined by the clearance of Diodrast or para-aminohippuric acid (PAH), falls by about 60 per cent of the mean value at age 25 between the ages of 25 and 90 (fig. 27.7).

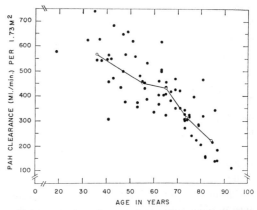

FIG. 27.7. Age changes in resting renal plasma flow in normal males, determined by clearance of PAH. Each point represents the mean of three 10-minute clearance periods on an individual.

Although the total amount of blood available for perfusion, as indicated by the cardiac output, diminishes with age, there is not a proportional reduction in flow to all organs. As indicated above, the age reduction in blood flow to the kidney is greater than the reduction in cardiac output, or flow to the brain. Ideally, we should have simultaneous measurements of cardiac output and flow through different organ systems in subjects of different ages. In the absence of such data, we must rely on average measurements made on different subjects at different times.

The simplest explanation of the differences in blood flow through different organ systems is to assume differences in the degree of structural changes such as arteriosclerosis in the vascular beds involved. However, this hypothesis is not in accord with observations which indicate that the reduction in blood flow in certain vascular beds is produced by a functional vasoconstriction that can be reduced by vasodilating agents. For example, the intravenous administration of a vasodilating agent (pyrogen) produces proportional increases in renal blood flow in both young and old subjects (Shock, 1952). This increase in flow results from a decrease in renal arteriolar constriction. In the aged person, under resting conditions, a functional increase in vascular resistance reduces blood flow to the kidney, which makes a great proportion of the cardiac output available for perfusion of other organs such as the brain.

The response of peripheral blood vessels to both heat and cold shows a reduction with age. However, the primary change is in the speed of response, rather than the final degree of vasodilation or constriction attained.

Thus the marked increase in peripheral resistance calculated from measurement of blood pressure and flow which accompanies aging is due, at least in part, to functional changes in the degree of vasoconstriction of individual vascular beds, and not entirely to the increasing degree of sclerosis of the blood vessels.

*Age changes in circulatory response to stress.* Age changes in all organ systems become much more apparent when the individual is subjected to a physiological stress. Exercise places extra demands, especially on the circulatory system, which are met less effectively in the old than the young.

One of the factors limiting physical performance in older subjects is their diminished ability to transport oxygen. Robinson (1938) showed that the increase in oxygen uptake during work proceeds at a slower rate in old than young subjects. He also found that the maximum amount of oxygen transported from the lungs falls from 53 to 26 cc. per kg. body weight per minute between the ages of 17 and 75. Furthermore, old subjects require more oxygen per kg. m. of work performed than do young at high or low work rates (Norris and Shock, 1960). There is a greater accumulation of lactic acid in the blood during and after exercise in old subjects than in young, which indicates a greater degree of muscular anoxia in old than young.

The rate of recovery of oxygen consumption and carbon dioxide elimination following exercise also diminishes with age. Thus, advancing age places a limitation not only on total performance, but also on the rate of readjustment of physiological displacements produced. One of the characteristics of older subjects is their inability to increase their heart rate after severe exercise to as great an extent as younger people. Young men are able to increase their heart rate to a mean value of 200 beats per minute whereas by the age of 65 the maximum rate attained after exercise is only 160 on the average. Since the increment in cardiac output during exercise is controlled primarily by increase in rate rather than stroke volume, the aged individual is unable to maintain adequate blood flow to exercising muscles. It is therefore not surprising that the arteriovenous oxygen difference increases more in old than young under conditions of heavy exercise.

Performance on the standard Master step-test also shows impairment in normal aged subjects. Old subjects increase their systolic blood pressure and heart rate more after exercise and require a longer time to return to pre-exercise levels than do young.

Changes in posture also offer a challenge to the cardiovascular system. When subjects are passively tilted from supine to the upright position, older subjects showed a greater decrease and slower recovery of diastolic blood pressure and smaller increase in heart rate than do the young (Norris and associates, 1953).

The stress of a pain stimulus (Hardy-Wolf thermal stimulator) results in significant increments in heart rate. However, the variability of heart rate from beat to beat under these circumstances diminishes significantly with increasing age (Malmo and Shagass, 1949). It appears that the factors controlling heart rate are less sensitive to environmental changes in the old than in young.

## SUMMARY

In addition to the increased incidence of arteriosclerosis, age imposes gradual impairments in the functional capabilities of the cardiovascular system. Structural and metabolic changes occur in the myocardium. There is a gradual reduction in cardiac output as age advances. The systolic blood pressure rises with age, but there is little change in diastolic pressure. Mechanisms for the control of heart rate are less effective in old than young. In old subjects the duration of systolic is lengthened, and there is a decrease in left ventricular work even under resting conditions. There is a reduction in the force of ejection and a slowing of the circulation time.

The peripheral vascular system undergoes changes in structure, chemical composition and function. Large blood vessels become more rigid. The distribution of blood flow among different organs shifts with increasing age. Some organs, such as the kidney, show a functional vasoconstriction that diverts a greater proportion of the falling cardiac output to other organs such as the brain.

The reduced capacity for physical work in the aged is related to their inability to increase their heart rate, and thereby to increase cardiac output to meet the increased tissue demands for oxygen. Light exercise produces greater increments in heart rate and blood pressure in old than young. The rate of recovery of heart rate, oxygen uptake and carbon dioxide elimination after exercise, is slower in old than young subjects. Aging results in a general reduction in the reserve capacities of the cardiovascular system and an impairment in the effectiveness of mechanisms controlling heart rate and vasomotor tonus.

## REFERENCES

ANDERSON, E., PAGE, E. W., LI, C. H., AND OGDEN, E. Restoration of renal hypertension in hypophysectomized rats by administration of adrenocorticotrophic hormone. Am. J. Physiol., 1944, 141, 393.

BARROWS, C. H., JR., YIENGST, M.J., AND SHOCK, N. W. J. Gerontol., 1958, 13, 351.

BERNE, R. M. The effect of immersion hypothermia on coronary blood flow. Circulation Res., 1954, 2, 236.

BERNTHAL, T., GREENE, W., AND REVIN, A. M. Proc. Soc. Exp. Biol. & Med., 1951, 76, 121.

BERNTHAL, T. AND WOODCOCK, C. C. Am. J. Physiol., 1951, 166, 45.

BEZNAK, M. The role of anterior pituitary hormones in controlling size, work and strength of heart. J. Physiol., 1960, 150, 251.

BEZNAK, M. Effect of growth hormone preparations on cardiac hypertrophy and blood pressure of hypophysectomized rats. Am. J. Physiol., 1956, 184, 563.

BEZNAK, M. Cardiac output during development of cardiac hypertrophy. Circulation Res., 1958, 6, 207.

BING, R. J., HAMMOND, M. M., HANDELSMAN, J. C., POWERS, S. R., SPENCER, F. C., ECKENHOFF, J. E., GOODALE, W. T., HAFKENSCHIEL, J. H., AND KETY, S. S. The Measurement of coronary blood flow, oxygen consumption and efficiency of the left ventricle in man. Am. Heart. J., 1949, 38, 1.

BRANDFONBRENER, M., LANDOWNE, M., AND SHOCK, N. W. Changes in cardiac output with age. Circulation, 1955, 12, 557.

BRAUN-MENENDEZ, E. AND VON EULER, U. S. Hypertension after bilateral nephrectomy in the rat. Nature, 1947, 160, 905.

BRAUN-MENENDEZ, E., ET AL. J. Physiol., 1940, 98, 283. The substance causing renal hypertension.

CASTER, W. O. in Proceedings of the Second International Conference on the Peaceful Uses of Atomic Energy, 1958, 22, 228.

CASTER, W. O., ARMSTRONG, W. D., AND SIMONSON, E. Am. J. Physiol., 1957, 188, 169.

CONN, J. W. Primary aldosteronism: a new clinical syndrome. J. Lab. & Clin. Med., 1955, 45, 6.

CONWAY, J. AND LOUWERS, P. Hemodynamic and hypotensive effects of long-term therapy with chlorothiazide. Circulation, 1960, 21, 21.

COVINO, B. G. In cold injury, Transactions of the Fifth Conference, edited by M. Irene Ferrer, Josiah Macy, Jr., Foundation, New York, 1958.

CUSHING, H. Some experimental and clinical observations concerning states of increased intracranial tension. Am. J. M. Sc., 1902, 124, 375.

DALY, M. DE B. AND SCOTT, M. J. J. Physiol., 1958, 144, 148.

DAWE, A. R. AND LANDAU, B. R. Am. Heart J., 1960, 59, 78.

DEGRANDPRÉ, R. AND RAAB, W. Interrelated hormonal factors in cardiac hypertrophy. Experiments in nonhypertensive hypophysectomized rats. Circulation Res., 1953. 1, 345.

DEXTER, L. AND HAYNES, F. W. Relation of renin to human hypertension with particular reference to eclampsia, pre-eclampsia, and acute glomerulonephritis. Proc. Soc. Exper. Biol. & Med., 1944, 55, 288.

DIXON, W. E. AND HELLER, H. Experimentelle hypertonic durch Erhohung desintrakraniellen Druckes. Arch. f. Exp. Path. Pharmakol. 166, 265, 1932.

DOYLE, J. T., WILSON, J. S., AND WARREN, J. V. Circulation,1952, 5, 263.

DRIPPS, R. D. AND COMROE, J. H., JR. Am. J. Physiol., 1947, 149, 277.

ELLIS, L. B. AND HAYNES, F. W. Postural hypotension with particular reference to its occurrence in disease of the central nervous system. Arch. Int. Med., 1936, 58, 773.

ELLIS, L. B. AND WEISS, S. J. The measurement of capillary pressure under natural conditions and after arteriolar dilatation; in normal subjects and in patients with arterial hypertension and with arteriosclerosis. J. Clin. Invest., 1930, **8**, 47.

EYSTER, J. A. E., MEEK, W. J., AND HODGES, F. J. Cardiac changes subsequent to experimental aortic lesions. Arch. Int. Med., 1927, **39**, 536.

FASCIOLO, J. C. ET AL. La hypertensinassa: su dosaje y distribucion. Rev. Soc. argent. biol., 1940, **16**, 643.

FREIS, E. D. Treatment of hypertension with chlorothiazide. J. A. M. A., 1959, **169**, 105.

FREIS, E. D., ROSE, J. C., PARTENOPE, E. A., HIGGINS, T. F., KELLEY, R. T., SCHNAPER, H. W., AND JOHNSON, R. L. The hemodynamic effects of hypotensive drugs in man. III. Hexamethonium. J. Clin. Invest., 1953, **32**, 1285.

GOLDBLATT, H., LYNCH, J., HANZAL, R. F., AND SUMMERVILLE, W. W. Studies on experimental hypertension: I. The production of persistent elevation of systolic blood pressure by means of renal ischemia. J. Exper. Med., 1934, **59**, 347.

GRIMSON, K. S., BOUCKAERT, J. J., AND HEYMANS, C. Production of a sustained neurogenic hypertension of renal origin. Proc. Soc. Exper. Biol. & Med., 1939, **42**, 255.

GRIMSON, K. S. Role of the sympathetic nervous system in experimental neurogenic hypertension. Proc. Soc. Exp. Biol. & Med., 1940, **44**, 219.

GROLLMAN, A., MUIRHEAD, E. E., AND VANATTA, J. Role of the kidney in pathogenesis of hypertension as determined by a study of the effects of bilateral nephrectomy and other experimental procedures on the blood pressure of the dog. Am. J. Physiol., 1949, **157**, 21.

GROLLMAN, A., WILLIAMS, J., AND HARRISON, T. R. Reduction of elevated blood pressure by administration of renal extracts. J. A. M. A., 1940, **115**, 1169.

HALEY, T. J., RILEY, R. F., WLILIAMS, I., AND ANDEM, M. R. Am. J. Physiol., 1952, **168**, 6268.

HALLOOK, P. Arch. Int. Med., 1934, **54**, 770.

HARTROFT, P. M. AND HARTROFT, W. S. Studies on renal juxtaglomerular cells. I. Variations produced by sodium chloride and desoxycorticosterone acetate. J. Exper. Med., 1953, **97**, 415.

HARTROFT, P. M. The juxtaglomerular cells and their influence on sodium metabolism. Presented at the Hahnemann Symposium on Edema, Philadelphia, December 7, 1959.

HEGNAUER, A. H., SCHRIBER, W. S., HATERIUS, H. O., FLYNN, J., AND WOLFF, R. C. Am. J. Physiol., 1950, **161**, 455.

HICKAM, J. B. AND PRYOR, W. W. Cardiac output in postural hypotension. J. Clin. Invest., 1951, **30**, 401.

HICKLER, R. B., THOMPSON, G. R., FOX, L. M., AND HAMLIN, J. T., III. Successful treatment of orthostatic hypotension with 9-alpha-fluorohydro-cortisone. New England J. Med., 1959, **261**, 788.

HINES, E. A., JR. The significance of vascular hyperreaction as measured by the cold-pressor test. Am. Heart J., 1940, **19**, 408.

HITCHINGS, G. H., DAUS, M. A., AND WEARN, J. T. Chemical changes in rabbit heart during hypertrophy. Am. J. Physiol., 1943, **138**, 527.

HOOK, W. E. AND STORMONT, R. J. Am. J. Physiol., 1941, **133**, 334.

HOWARD, J. E., BERTHRONG, B., GOULD, D. M., AND YENDT, E. R. Hypertension resulting from unilateral renal vascular disease and its relief by nephrectomy. Bull. Johns Hopkins Hosp., 1954, **94**, 51.

HOWELL, T. H. Old age; some practical points in geriatrics and gerontology. Ed. 2. H. K. Lewis & Co., Ltd., London, 1950.

KARNBAUM, S. Z. Kreislaufforsch., 1957, **46**, 709.

KATZ, L. N. The mechanism of cardiac failure. Circulation, 1954, **10**, 663.

KERR, A., JR. Cardiac dilatation and hypertrophy. Am. Heart J., 1957, **54**, 23.

KETY, S. S. Human cerebral blood flow and oxygen consumption as related to aging. In The Neurologic and Psychiatric Aspects of the Disorders of Aging, Ch. 4, p. 31. Williams & Wilkins Company, Baltimore, 1956.

KOLFF, W. J. AND PAGE, I. H. Blood pressure reducing function of the kidney: Reduction of renoprival hypertension by kidney perfusion. Am. J. Physiol., 1954, **178**, 75.

LANSING, A. I., ROBERTS, E., RAMASARMA, G. B., ROSENTHAL, T. B., AND ALEX, M. Proc. Soc. Exper. Biol. & Med., New York, 1951, **76**, 714.

LANDOWNE, M. J. Gerontol., 1958, **13**, 153.

LANDOWNE, M., BRANDFONBRENER M., AND, SHOCK, N. W. Circulation, 1955, **12**, 567.

LASSER, R. P. AND MASTER, A. M. Geriatrics, 1959, **14**, 345.

LINZBACH, A. Micrometric and histologic studies of cardiac hypertrophy. Virchows Arch. path. Anat., 1947, **314**, 534.

LUFT, R. AND VON EULER, U. W. Two cases of postural hypotension showing a deficiency in release of norepinephrine and epinephrine. J. Clin. Invest., 1953, **32**, 1065.

MALMO, R. B. AND SHAGASS, C. J. Appl. Physiol., 1949, **2**, 181.

MASON, W. B., ALPERT, S., AND SMITH, D. J. University of Rochester Report ♯ UR-278, 1953.

MERRILL, J. P., MURRAY, J. E., HARRISON, J. H., AND GUILD, W. R. Successful homotransplantation of the human kidney between identical twins. J. A. M. A., 1956, **160**, 277.

MEZZASALMA, G., AND MORPURGO, M. Gior. gerontol. (Suppl. 14), 1958, 9.

McCUBBIN, J. W., GREEN, J. H., AND PAGE, I. H. Baroceptor function in chronic renal hypertension. Circulation Res., 1956, **4**, 205.

NAHAS, G. G., VISSCHER, M. B., MATHER, G. W., HADDY, F. J., AND WARNER, H. R. J. Appl. Physiol., 1954, **6**, 467.

NEIL, E. Arch. internat. pharmacodyn., 1956, **105**, 477.

NORRIS, A. H., AND SHOCK, N. W. Exercise in the advanced years. In Science and Medicine of Exercise and Sports, W. R. Johnson (Editor). Harper & Brothers, New York, 1960.

NORRIS, A. H., SHOCK, N. W., AND YIENGST, M. J. Circulation, 1953, **8**, 521.

PAGE, E. B., HICKAM, J. B., SIEKER, H. O., McINTOSH, H. D., AND PRYOR, W. W. Reflex venomotor activity in normal persons and in patients with postural hypotension. Circulation, 1955, 11, 262.

PAGE, I. H. AND SWEET, J. E. The effect of hypophsectomy on arterial blood pressure of dogs with experimental hypertension. Am. J. Physiol., 1937, 120, 238.

PAGE, I. H. Production of persistent atrerial hypertension by cellophane perinephritis. J. A. M. A., 1939, 113, 2046.

PENROD, K. E. Am. J. Physiol., 1951, 164, 79.

QUINBY, W. C., DEXTER, L., SANDMEYER, J. A., AND HAYNES, F. W. Renal humoral pressor mechanism in man: Effect of transitory complete constriction of human renal artery on blood pressure and on concentration of renin, hypertensinogen and hypertensinase of renal arterial and venous blood, with animal observations. J. Clin. Invest., 1945, 125, 69.

RATHER, L. J. Experimental cardiac hypertrophy: Rate of development and effect of adrenalectomy. Am. J. Physiol., 1949, 159, 153.

RING, G. C., KURBATOV, T., AND SHANNON, G. J. J. Gerontol., 1959, 14, 189.

ROBERTS, J. T. AND WEARN, J. T. Quantitative changes in the capillary-muscle relationship in human hearts during normal growth and hypertrophy. Am. Heart J., 1941, 21, 617.

ROBINSON, S. Arbeitsphysiologie, 1938, 10, 251.

ROSECAN, M., GLASER, R. J., AND GOLDMAN, M. L. Orthostatic hypotension, anhidrosis and impotence. Circulation, 1952, 6, 30.

SHOCK, N. W. Age changes in renal function. In Cowdry's Problems of Ageing, edited by A. I. Lansing, Ed. 3, p. 614. Williams & Wilkins Company, Baltimore, 1952.

SHORR, E. In Hypertension, a Symposium, edited by E. T. Bell, p. 79, University of Minnesota press, 1951.

SIMONSON, E. AND KEYS, A. Circulation 1952, 6, 749.

SIMONSON, E. AND KEYS, A. Circulation, 1956, 14, 100.

SMITH, D. J., PARKER, R. C., HANNA, C., AND CURLEY, H. E. Am. J. Physiol., 1959, 197, 725.

SOBEL, H. AND COHEN, F. M. Proteins of heart in experimental cardiac hypertrophy in the rat. Proc. Soc. Exper. Biol. & Med., 1958, 99, 656.

STARLING, E. H. AND VISSCHER, M. B. The regulation of the energy output of the heart. J. Physiol., 1926, 62, 243.

STARR, I. AND HILDRETH, E. A. Circulation, 1952, 5, 481.

STEAD, E. A., JR. AND EBERT, R. V. Postural hypotension; a disease of the sympathetic nervous system. Arch. Int. Med., 1941, 67, 546.

STICKNEY, J. C., NORTHRUP, D. W., AND VAN TIERE, E. J. Cardiac dilatation without hypertrophy from reduced ambient pressure in rats. Circulation Res., 1956, 4, 217.

STREHLER, B. L., MARK, D. D., MILDVAN, A. S., AND GEE, M. V. J. Gerontol. 1959, 14, 430.

TANNER, J. M. J. Clin. Invest., 1949, 28, 567.

TAYLOR, R. D. AND PAGE, I. H. Production of prolonged arterial hypertension in dogs by chronic stimulation of the nervous system. Circulation, 1951, 3, 551.

TOBIAN, L., JR. AND BINION, J. T. Tissue cations and water in arterial hypertension. Circulation, 1952, 5, 754.

TOBIAN, L., JR. AND BINION, J. Artery wall electrolytes in renal and DCA hypertension. J. Clin. Invest., 1954, 33, 1407.

WAGNER, H. N., JR. AND BRAUNWALD, E. The pressor effect of the antidiuretic principle of the posterior pituitary in orthostatic hypotension. J. Clin. Invest., 1956, 35, 1412.

WAKERLIN, G. E., BIRD, R. B., BRENNAN, B. B., FRANK, M. H., KREMEN, S., KUPERMAN, I., AND SKOM, J. H. Treatment and prophylaxis of experimental renal hypertension with "renin." J. Lab. & Clin. Med., 1953, 41, 708.

WAKERLIN, G. E., CRANDALL, E., FRANK, M. H., JOHNSON, D., POMPER, L., AND SCHMID, H. E. Experimental hypertension produced by constriction of the carotid sinus area. Circulation Res., 1954, 2, 416.

WAKERLIN, G. E., BRANNICK, T. L., OSGOOD, B., G., AND BURNS, R. O. Treatment of experimental renal hypertension with anti-renin. Am. J. Physiol., 1950, 163, 701.

WAKERLIN, G. E. Antibodies to renin as proof of the pathogenesis of sustained renal hypertension. Circulation, 1958, 17, 653.

WEBER, R. P. AND STEGGARDA, F. R. Proc. Soc. Exper. Biol., 1949, 70, 261.

WELLMAN, W. E. AND EDWARDS, J. E. A. M. A. Arch. Path., 1950, 50, 183.

WILKINS, R. W., CULBERTSON, J. W., AND HALPERIN, M. H. The hemodynamic effects of sympathectomy in essential hypertension. Ann. Int. Med., 1949, 30, 291.

WOOD, E. H., LAMBERT, E. H., BALDES, E. J., AND CODE, C. F. Effects of acceleration in relation to aviation. Fed. Proc., 1946, 5, 327.

VAN LOO, A., SURTSHIN, A., AND KATZ, L. N. Am. J. Physiol., 1948, 154, 397.

*Monographs and Reviews*

ARMSTRONG, H. G. Principles and practice of aviation medicine. Ed. 3. The Williams & Wilkins Company, Baltimore, 1952.

BREST, A. N. AND MOYER, J. H. Newer approaches to antihypertensive therapy. J. A. M. A., 1960, 172, 1041.

DESJARDINS, A. U. Action of roentgen rays and radium on the heart and lungs; experimental data and clinical radiotherapy. Am. J. Roentgenol., 1932, 27, 149, 303, 477; 28, 127, 271, 421, 567, 699, 843.

DRIPPS, R. D. (chairman and editor) The physiology of induced hypothermia symposium. National Academy of Sciences, National Research Council, Washington, D. C., 1956.

FREIS, E. D. Hemodynamics of hypertension. Physiol. Rev., 1960, 40, 27.

GAUER, O. The physiological effects of prolonged acceleration. German Aviation Medicine, 1950, 1, 554.

GAUER, O. AND HABER, H. Man under gravity-free conditions. German Aviation Medicine, 1950, 1, 641.

GOLDBLATT, H. Factors regulating blood pressure.

Fifth Conference, Josiah Macy, Jr., Foundation, New York, 1951.

GRANT, R. P. Aspects of cardiac hypertrophy. Am. Heart J., 1953, **46**, 154.

HEYMANS, C. AND NEIL, E. Reflexogenic areas of the cardiovascular system. J. & A. Churchill, Ltd., London, 1958.

HOOBLER, S. W. (editor). Proceedings of Conference on Basic Mechanisms of Arterial Hypertension. Circulation, 1958, **17**, 641.

KORNER, P. I. Circulatory adaptations in hypoxia. Physiol. Rev., 1959, **39**, 687.

KRAYER, O. AND ACHESON, G. H. The pharmacology of the veratrum alkaloids. Physiol. Rev., 1946, **26**, 383.

LANSING, A. I. (editor). The arterial wall. The Williams & Wilkins Co., Baltimore, 1959.

MICHAELSON, S. J. Hemodynamic effects of ionizing radiation; vertebrates. Handbook of Circulation, p. 196. W. B. Saunders Company, Philadelphia, 1959.

MOYER, J. H. (editor). Hypertension, the first Hahnemann symposium on hypertensive disease. W. B. Saunders Company, Philadelphia, 1959.

PATT, H. M. AND BRUES, A. M. The pathological physiology of radiation injury in the mammal. II. Specific aspects of the physiology of radiation injury. Radiation Biology, Vol. 1: High Energy Radiation Part II. p. 976. McGraw-Hill Book Company, New York, 1954.

SCHROEDER, H. A. AND PERRY, H. M., JR., Current status of therapy in hypertension. J. A. M. A., 1956, **162**, 1382.

SIMONSON, E. AND BROZEK, J. Russian Research on Arterial Hypertension. Ann. Int. Med., 1959, **50**, 129.

SMITH, D. J., MACMILLAN, W. H., SAUNDERS, H., AND DANIELL, H. W. Effects of ionizing radiation upon the cardiovascular, biochemical and hematological systems of man and animals: A review. Report No. 1, Contract AF 19(604)-1093, School of Aviation Medicine, USAF, 1955.

STRUGHOLD, H. Bioastronautics. Advances in research. School of Aviation Medicine, USAF, Randolph Air Force Base, Texas, 1959.

STARLING, E. H. The Linacre lecture on the law of the heart. Longmans, Green & Company, New York, 1918.

TOBIAN, L. Physiology of the juxtaglomerular cells. Ann. Int. Med., 1960, **52**, 395.

WAKERLIN, G. E. Endocrine factors in renal hypertension. Physiol. Rev., 1955, **35**, 555.

WARREN, S. Effects of radiation on normal tissues: VI. Effects of radiation on the cardiovascular system. Arch. Path., 1942, **34**, 1070.

WIGGERS, C. J. Cardiac adaptation in acute progressive anoxia. Ann. Int. Med., 1941, **14**, 1237.

WILKINS, R. W. New drugs for the treatment of hypertension. Ann. Int. Med., 1959, **50**, 1.

ZWEIFACH, B. W. AND SHORR, E. Factors regulating blood pressure. Fifth Conference, Josiah Macy, Jr., Foundation, New York, 1951.

# 28

# REGULATION OF THE CIRCULATION
# UNDER STATES OF STRESS

## Shock and Hemorrhage

### Bases and Principal Characteristics

The state which commonly develops several hours after a severe tissue injury is referred to either as traumatic, or surgical, or wound, or secondary shock. The last designation contrasts it with primary shock which may supervene immediately following the injury. Primary shock has mainly a neural basis and, therefore, is also called neurogenic shock.

It is believed that the most characteristic feature of traumatic shock is a disparity between the circulating blood volume and the capacity of the circulatory system. When such a disparity develops, for any reason, the pressure in the great veins and right atrium becomes reduced and consequently the filling of the ventricles is inadequate. This leads to a decrease in stroke volume, cardiac output and arterial blood pressure. The fall in blood pressure elicits cardiac acceleration and vasoconstriction. The pale cold skin which is typical of shock is a manifestation of the cutaneous vasoconstriction. Also, the decreased rate of blood flow results in the hypokinetic type of hypoxia and associated cyanosis of the ears and finger tips. The acceleration of the heart rate results in encroachment on time for ventricular filling and this, along with the lowered venous pressure, contributes to lowering of the stroke volume and pulse pressure. A pulse pressure of less than 20 mm. Hg is not uncommon in shock.

Oliguria or anuria may occur in shock since there is inadequate pressure to maintain the glomerular filtration rate (GFR). Renal blood flow is decreased even more than the reduction in GFR. The nonprotein nitrogen of the blood increases and the alkali reserve falls.

The initiating mechanisms in traumatic shock are those which promote either a decrease in blood volume or an increase in the capacity of the cardiovascular system. Trauma may cause actual blood loss of varying degree, but in addition, it may cause extravasation of fluid into the dam-aged part. The importance of the loss of blood or plasma volume in the production of the signs and symptoms of shock is made evident by the dramatic improvement in the condition of the patient which occurs when the circulating blood volume is restored early after shock has developed. Later on when circulation has been inadequate for awhile the beneficial effect of transfusions is less, or the blood pressure may not be restored by this method.

Early in traumatic shock it appears that there is no serious defect in the heart itself as indicated by the response to transfusions; inadequate cardiac filling is the main problem. In so-called cardiogenic shock the circulatory failure is central, i.e., in the heart, and the right atrial pressure is not reduced. Obviously, the problem in this case is quite different than in traumatic shock.

If the essential feature in traumatic shock is the reduction in circulating blood volume then the severity will be related both to the amount of reduction and to the time which has elapsed since the reduction occurred. The production of shock by withdrawal of blood has been studied extensively in experimental animals, and it has been demonstrated that removal of a certain fraction of the blood volume for a certain time will result in the appearance of shock and subsequent death even though the blood be reinfused.

### Stages of Shock

Wiggers (1950) differentiates between four stages in the progression of shock to the phase in which treatment is ineffective. In the *initial* or developing stage circulating blood volume is decreased but not sufficiently to cause serious symptoms. Next is the *compensatory* stage in which blood volume is reduced further, but blood pressure tends to be maintained within the normal range through vasoconstriction. At this stage blood flow through the skin and, perhaps, the kidneys is decreased while flow to the central nervous system and myocardium tend to be maintained. The volume of the spleen and other blood reservoirs typically is decreased. The *progressive* stage of shock is characterized by the fact that unfavorable changes are becoming more and more prominent: falling blood pressure, increasing vasoconstriction, accelerated heart rate, decreased pulse pressure, oliguria, etc. Progression indicates that compensatory mechanisms are unable to cope with the reduced blood volume so as to maintain the status quo. When the blood pressure is reduced to the range of 60 to 70 mm. Hg myocardial depression, a decrease in heart rate and, perhaps, a decrease in arteriolar tonus may become factors in promoting the hypotension. The last, or *irreversible*, stage is so designated because treatment no longer is successful in saving the life of the patient. Arterial blood pressure is not restored by the infusion of blood. Apparently, both a loss of arteriolar tonus and myocardial depression are factors in the inability of the circulatory system to respond to transfusions in a beneficial manner. The infused blood tends to remain in the capillary beds.

## Theories Concerning the Cause of Shock

Shock can be produced in experimental animals by mechanical trauma which does not break the skin (e.g., pounding the limb of an anesthetized animal with a mallet) and by bleeding the animal to the extent of 40 to 60 per cent of its calculated blood volume. Blalock, using these methods, concluded that there is no essential difference between the shock induced by the two methods. He favored the view that fluid loss at the *site* of trauma was sufficient to set off the train of events leading to shock. However, Moon believed that a stage is reached in animals in shock when hypoxia of capillary walls causes increased permeability and thus promotes fluid loss into the tissues at sites remote from the injury. This theory seems to be losing ground.

The results of numerous studies of shock in animals can be summarized by stating that the decrease in blood flow in vital structures such as the myocardium, central nervous system and, perhaps, the liver which occurs when blood volume is inadequate leads to the development of changes which can not be reversed by present methods of treatment. It is possible that in irreversible shock vital cells have become irreparably damaged. However, the possibility remains that if the nature of the changes in the late stages of shock were understood better effective treatment could be achieved. Contrary to earlier theories shock does not appear to be due to hypocapnia (as suggested by Y. Henderson) or to paralysis of the vasomotor

center (Crile) or to adrenal exhaustion (Swingle) or to fat embolism from damaged tissues (Porter). It is true that the adrenal cortex, adrenal medulla and the vasomotor system are subjected to increased demands in a patient in shock, but failure of any of these is not demonstrated to be the basis for irreversibility.

In the period from 1914 to 1921 Dale and Laidlaw, Cannon and Bayliss, and others searched for a toxic factor in the production of shock and gave special attention to histamine. This substance is produced in damaged tissues and causes certain changes in the cardiovascular system similar to those which are found in shock. However, it does not appear that enough histamine is produced over a long enough period in traumatized tissues to cause irreversible shock.

Shorr, Zweifach and associates reported the liberation of a depressor substance from the liver in animals in shock. This substance, initially called VDM (vasodepressor material) and later identified as ferritin, was considered to be responsible for the irreversible stage of shock. However, subsequent studies cast doubt on this interpretation. Injection of ferritin in very large doses does not cause symptoms of shock.

It has been suggested that bacterial toxins are concerned in the irreversibility of traumatic shock. Fine (1954) states that irreversibility to transfusion is present from the onset in septic shock whereas it does not develop until after a long delay in hemorrhagic shock. Even in hemorrhagic shock, according to Fine, a bacterial factor is encountered since antibiotics delay or prevent the development of irreversibility. Therefore, he believes that administration of antibiotics is important as a part of the therapy of both traumatic and hemorrhagic shock.

### Burn Shock

Secondary shock results from extensive burns. In this case loss of fluid and plasma constituents into the damaged area is considered to be the initiating factor. Since blood cells, for the most part, are retained hemoconcentration is characteristic. Transfusion of plasma is quite beneficial under these conditions. The amount of loss of plasma volume is related to the extent of the burn. The possibility of a toxic factor in burn shock is even greater than in traumatic shock, however no specific substance has been demonstrated to be responsible for development of irreversibility. It seems that considerable amounts of histamine are produced in tissues and liberated following burns.

Barsoum and Gaddum found the histamine content of patients suffering from extensive burns to be several times higher than the normal. Also, it is not uncommon for a patient with extensive burns to develop ulceration of the duodenum (Curling's ulcer) which is attributed to the stimulating effect of histamine on gastric secretion. However, no clear correlation in time was found between the histamine concentration in blood and the onset of shock. Rose and Brown observed that the course of blood histamine concentration following burns could be divided into three stages (1) an early increase in some cases, (2) a marked decrease during the period of edema and plasma loss, i.e., during the time when shock was evident, and (3) a return to normal or above normal levels as the edema subsided and the patient was improving. These results do not support the view that histamine is the responsible agent in the development of shock following burns.

### *"Crush Syndrome"*

A person who has had a limb compressed for some time, for example by a beam or pile of rubble, may pass into a state resembling shock. In the *crush syndrome* impairment of renal function is a prominent factor. The urine is brownish in color, contains dark granular casts and gives a positive test for myoglobin derived from the damaged muscles. In severe cases anuria develops, and death is due to the failure of renal function. The renal tubules are considered to be damaged by myohematin. The anuria, therefore, would be caused in a manner analogous to that resulting from the transfusion of incompatible blood, the difference being that in one the pigment is liberated from muscle and in the other from erythrocytes.

It appears that the blood flow to the renal cortex becomes reduced in the *crush syndrome* which seems to render the tubules more susceptible to the action of the blood pigment. Trueta and his associates found that the renal cortex had a reduced blood flow in tourniquet shock and stimulation of afferent nerves from the limb also causes renal vasoconstriction.

The renal pathological changes seen in the *crush syndrome* are described as lower nephron nephrosis (ch. 35). This consists of extensive degeneration or necrosis of tubular epithelium and is characteristic of a number of different conditions in which toxic substances reach the kidney in considerable quantities or when the renal

blood flow is decreased severely for a relatively prolonged period.

### *Anaphylactic Shock*

The anaphylactic reaction is one which follows administration of a foreign substance (usually protein in nature) to an animal which has been sensitized to it by a previous dose. The second dose may be quite small as compared with the initial dose. The first dose acts as an antigen; that is, it induces the production of antibody by the animal. Usually about 2 weeks must elapse between doses in order that the second dose may produce maximum effects. The severe form of the anaphylactic reaction is called anaphylactic shock. This shows different manifestations in different species. *In the dog* the primary change which may cause the death of the animal is constriction of the hepatic veins. This holds the blood back in the splanchnic organs and all of the manifestations of failure of venous return consequently appear. Cardiac output, arterial blood pressure and pulse pressure fall. Heart rate is accelerated. Respiration is stimulated. Salivation and vomiting are induced. *In the guinea pig* the most serious feature of the anaphylactic reaction is the contraction of bronchiolar smooth muscle. This leads to extreme dyspnea and death from asphyxia. The effect can be demonstrated in the perfused isolated lungs of a sensitized animal by the addition of antigen to the perfusion fluid. Histamine may be concerned, at least in part, in this reaction since the amount of this substance in the lungs and blood is increased during the anaphylactic reaction, and it has a potent stimulant action on the bronchiolar smooth muscle.

*In the rabbit,* the reaction may be general or purely local. When the foreign substance is injected subcutaneously into a sensitized animal, the skin and subcutaneous tissue at the site of the injection become edematous and swollen; a sterile abscess or slough appears. This was originally described by Arthus and is known as the Arthus phenomenon. When the antigen is administered intravenously, the blood pressure falls abruptly and the respirations become rapid. The bladder and intestine are evacuated. The animal may die within a few minutes from dilation and failure of the right ventricle. The failure of the heart is secondary to the increased resistance in the pulmonary circuit caused by constriction of the arterioles. The arterioles in other parts of the vascular system are also constricted and emboli composed of clumps of leukocytes may be seen blocking the pulmonary and systemic capillaries.

The evidence indicates, with little doubt, that, in anaphylactic shock, the antibody-antigen reaction takes place in or on the tissue cells and not in the blood plasma. Dale showed for example, that when the uterus was removed from a sensitized guinea pig and its vessels freed from all traces of blood, it gave the typical anaphylactic contraction when the antigen was added to the bath in which it was immersed. Manwaring also found that the blood of the sensitized animal could be replaced by blood from a normal animal without affecting the first animal's sensitivity.

It is now generally accepted that the antigen-antibody reaction in some way brings about the liberation of histamine from the affected tissues and that the action of this amine is responsible for some of the anaphylactic manifestations. Nearly all the features, as seen in these three species, can be explained upon such a basis. In the dog and guinea pig, anaphylactic shock is associated with a rise in the histamine concentration of the blood and, although the whole blood of the rabbit shows no increase and is often reduced, the amine passes from the white cells (which contain it in especially large amounts) into the plasma. The species peculiarities of the anaphylactic manifestations can be accounted for largely by the amount of smooth muscle in the reactive tissues of these three species and by its susceptibility to the action of histamine. In the dog, the smooth muscle of the hepatic veins is especially well developed. In the guinea pig, the bronchioles are particularly susceptible to stimulation by histamine and, in the rabbit, the pulmonary arterioles show unusually thick muscular coats.

Though histamine liberation appears to be a major factor in the production of the phenomena of anaphylaxis, certain observations indicate that some other factor or factors are involved. Minute doses of histamine, for example, cause contraction of the isolated rat's uterus, whereas large doses of antigen are required to produce even a weak contraction. Also, the isolated guinea pig's uterus, poisoned by high concentrations of histamine, responds to a further dose by relaxation, but by contraction to a further dose of antigen.

Peptone solution, injected intravenously, produces in the dog effects almost identical with those of anaphylactic shock, including incoagulability of the blood due to the liberation of heparin from the liver. Sensitization by a previous dose is not necessary, however. Adding peptone to rabbit blood *in vitro* causes the liberation of histamine from the cells into the plasma.

In man, fatal anaphylactic shock may follow the injection of horse serum into a person who has been sensitized by a previous administration. Allergic reactions, in general, show many similarities to anaphylactic reactions and many observations suggest that the two are fundamentally allied, although in the case of allergic reactions, sensitization by an earlier exposure cannot always be demonstrated, the reaction appearing upon the first known contact with the foreign substance.

## Congestive Heart Failure

Heart failure occurs when the heart muscle is weak or if the heart ceases to pump blood because of arrest or ventricular fibrillation or if cardiac filling is prevented. The heart may fail suddenly as a result of occlusion of a coronary artery or following rapid accumulation of fluid or blood in the pericardial sac, or failure may result from sudden overloading of a heart already weakened by chronic disease. In acute heart failure there is a sudden reduction in or cessation of cardiac output. Arterial blood pressure decreases, the pulse weakens or is not palpable, and vasoconstrictor reflexes are elicited from the pressoreceptors. The patient is in shock as far as conditions on the arterial side of the systemic circuit are concerned, but the venous pressure is not lowered as in shock related to decreased blood volume.

### Chronic Congestive Heart Failure

A number of chronic diseases eventually lead to weakening of the heart muscle, and this results in the development of the syndrome which is known as chronic congestive heart failure. It is important to recognize that heart failure designates a clinical syndrome rather than any specific defeat in the heart.

Weakness of the heart is not necessarily expressed as decreased cardiac output, since homeostatic mechanisms operate which tend to maintain whatever cardiac output is needed to meet the metabolic requirements of the tissues. Hence, in many cases of chronic congestive heart failure a normal cardiac output under resting conditions is observed in the presence of a moderately elevated venous pressure (Espersen; Altschule; McMichael, 1938 and 1947; Richards, 1949). The weakness of the heart is evident in that it pumps less blood than a normal heart would pump if it were subjected to the same (elevated) filling pressure. It will be noted that the definition of cardiac weakness implied in the preceding statement is that a weak heart is one which will show a lower than normal increase in output in response to a given increase in the venous pressure. Thus if cardiac output at various venous pressures is graphed, a curve would be obtained which lies somewhere below that for a ventricle of normal strength, and the weaker the ventricle, the lower will be this curve (see Youmans and Huckins, 1951).

Another way of thinking about the strength of the heart is in terms of its *reserve*. Although the moderately weakened heart can achieve a normal output under resting conditions or during mild exercise it has less reserve. As the level of muscular activity is increased a point would be reached at which cardiac output could not increase further, whereas the normal heart could continue to increase its output well beyond this amount as muscular activity is increased (Nielsen). Thus, the first indication of cardiac weakness is a reduction in the cardiac reserve, as determined by suitable exercise tests, and the severity of cardiac "disability" would be related to the degree of loss of the cardiac reserve.

When the cardiac reserve is diminished as a result of disease cardiovascular adjustments occur to maintain adequate output, and the heart and circulation are said to be in a state of compensation. When such adjustments are inadequate as manifested particularly by a considerable rise in venous pressure, increase in heart size (dilation) and other signs of congestion the condition is referred to as cardiac decompensation.

Congestive heart failure may develop in any person whose heart has been working for a more or less prolonged period against a high peripheral resistance (e.g., essential hypertension) or if the work of the heart has been above normal because of cardiac valvular defects (rheumatic fever) or because of prolonged continuous demands for increased cardiac output (hyperthyroidism, arteriovenous fistula). When the work of the heart is increased chronically, for any reason, a sequence of changes in heart muscle is induced which terminates eventually in its weakening. On the other hand, weakness of the myocardium may result from more specific causes such as inadequate blood supply, damage by certain toxins, etc.

## Sequence of Changes in Congestive Heart Failure

The chief manifestations of chronic congestive heart failure are: increased extracellular fluid volume; increased blood volume; elevated venous pressure; dyspnea; cyanosis in some cases; enlargement of the liver and spleen; edema of the dependent parts of the body; and in some cases hydrothorax and ascites. The cardiac output in classical congestive heart failure in the patient at rest is within the normal range or decreased. However, in a group of conditions commonly referred to as "high output" heart failure specific stimuli are present which cause an elevated basal cardiac output.

Until a few years ago most discussions of the mechanisms involved in the development of the characteristic changes seen in congestive heart failure presented either or both of two theories: the "backward failure" theory, and the "forward failure" theory; however, it no longer seems profitable to describe these theories as such but rather to present the sequence of events now reasonably well established.

One of the most characteristic features of congestive heart failure is the increase in volume and pressure of blood in the pulmonary circuit and in the right atrium and systemic veins (Landis and others, 1946; McMichael, 1947). What causes these changes? According to the earlier theories a decrease in output of the left ventricle would, on purely hemodynamic bases, allow the pulmonary circuit to become congested to the extent that it occurs in congestive heart failure. Likewise, the rise in systemic venous pressure was attributed entirely to failure of the right ventricle to respond to its filling pressure in such a way as to keep the pressure down to normal levels. At the time of the actual onset of failure it was visualized that blood was returning to the corresponding ventricle more rapidly than it was being pumped out, and therefore, the pressure upstream from the ventricle was being permitted to progressively increase until the relatively high levels which occur in congestive heart failure were reached. In some explanations the ventricle was referred to as "damming back" the blood or causing "back pressure". It is apparent, however, that a cardiac ventricle behaves as a force pump and not as a dam (Starr, 1949). The ventricles do not create a back pressure by failing to pump; they allow the pressure to rise as they fail to force the blood on. Therefore, the term "back pressure" does not seem to be suitable to describe any of the hemodynamic changes associated with congestive heart failure. For example, the rise in pressure in a cistern which occurs as water runs into it faster than it is lifted out by a pump would not be called back pressure.

The concept that venous pressure can increase to very high levels as a consequence of failure of the ventricle to pump the blood which is flowing in by the venous system implies a continuing venous return in the presence of decreased cardiac output. However, the venous return is the same as the cardiac output for any prolonged period except as a shift of volume out of the arterial tree occurs when cardiac output and mean arterial blood pressure decrease. As arterial pressure falls the volume in the systemic arterial tree decreases and this is associated with a slight increase in pressure in the "low pressure" portions of the cardiovascular system (i.e., the great veins, atria and pulmonary circuit). The maximum increase in pressure which could occur in the atria, on purely hemodynamic bases, when ventricular output decreases is that which would occur following ventricular arrest. When this occurs flow from the arterial tree into the systemic veins and pulmonary system continues until equalization of pressure occurs at the static blood pressure level which is only about 8 to 10 cm. of water. Thus, a rise in venous pressure to the levels which commonly are seen in congestive heart failure is not produced simply by failure of the ventricles to pump the blood returning to them. The large rises in venous pressure are dependent in part upon elevation of the blood volume. Starr (1940) reported that the static blood pressure, i.e., that found throughout the circulatory system shortly after the heart ceases to beat, was considerably higher in patients who had died of heart failure than in those who died from other causes. The elevation of static blood pressure can be attributed to any of three changes: reduced capacity of the cardiovascular system; reduced distensibility; or increased volume of blood in the system. There is no reason for considering that either of the first two changes is characteristic of congestive heart failure. Blood volume, on the other hand, has been found to be elevated in congestive heart failure by most investigators who have studied it (Altschule, Borst).

The initial change in the cardiovascular system which leads to the classical syndrome of congestive heart failure must be assumed to be the decrease in left ventricular output related to weakening of the left ventricle or lack of filling of the left ventricle secondary to such changes as right ventricular failure or compression of the left ventricle from without (as from pericardial effusion). Then a series of changes is initiated which in mild or moderate cases leads to restoration of the cardiac output. Hence, when congestive heart failure is diagnosed some of the measurable changes are those which have occurred to counter a decrease in cardiac output. When cardiac output is found to be decreased in the patient at rest this indicates that the condition is so severe that compensatory mechanisms which serve to maintain cardiac output have been overtaxed. In other words a subnormal cardiac output in the patient at rest indicates virtual absence of cardiac reserve.

Patients with congestive heart failure usually have a decreased renal blood flow while the glomerular filtration rate is reduced to a lesser degree (Merrill, Bradley and Blake, Davies and Kilpatrick, Mokotoff and others). The load of sodium and chloride filtered at the level of the glomerulus is decreased in direct proportion to the reduction in glomerular filtration. This alone, if sodium reabsorbing capacity of the tubules were unaltered, would lead to a considerable reduction in in NaCl excretion. However it appears that tubular reabsorption of sodium also is stimulated. This change has been attributed to the action of aldosterone which is reported to be produced in increased amounts (Parrish, Lasche and others, Singer and Wener). Regardless of the mechanism, the ability of the kidney to excrete NaCl is markedly impaired in patients with congestive heart failure as indicated by the fact that they may show a positive salt and water balance despite a greatly restricted salt intake.

The decreased renal blood flow and glomerular filtration rate in congestive heart failure in the presence of an arterial blood pressure within the normal range indicates that the tonus of renal arterioles is increased. The increased filtration fraction (see ch. 34) may be related to efferent arteriolar constriction; since a change of this type causes a lowered renal blood flow without producing a corresponding decrease in glomerular filtration rate.

Patients with congestive heart failure do not show impairment of ability to excrete water in a degree that makes it necessary for them to restrict their water intake. The defect which leads to the increase in the amount of NaCl and water in the body and the corresponding rise in volume of the extracellular fluid compartment is the failure of the kidney to excrete NaCl. As the salt is retained water is held back with it. As a part of this secondary process the increased production of antidiuretic hormone (ADH) may be involved. It has been postulated that the reabsorption of sodium ion from the tubules is the primary change and that the chloride ion moves along with sodium because of its opposite charge. It is significant that the amount of edema in a patient with congestive heart failure can be controlled by directing attention to lowering the total amount of NaCl in the body, by any of several methods, while allowing him to drink water *ad libitum* (Futcher and Schroeder, Schroeder). In the reaction against the severe restriction of water intake, which occurred when it was recognized that there is no physiological basis for such a regimen, it was reported that forcing fluids was of benefit in treating congestive heart failure

(Schemm, 1942 and 1944). It now appears that a low fluid intake is disadvantageous but that high fluid intake is not of value except to correct the ill effects of dehydration produced by a period during which fluid intake had been severely restricted.

### High Output Circulatory Failure

Some patients who are diagnosed as having congestive heart failure have a basal cardiac output well above the normal range. Furthermore, effective treatment leads to a lowering of the basal cardiac output to normal levels. It is not reasonable to consider that cardiac weakness as such would lead to an increase in the basal cardiac output; therefore, in patients who have the high output type of circulatory failure it is reasonable to postulate a source of cardiac stimulation which is not present in normal persons.

The similarities between simple congestive failure, described in the preceding section, and high output failure are related to the fact that retention of NaCl and water occurs in both. The increase in extracellular fluid volume leads to many of the signs and symptoms which are common to the two syndromes. The two principal differences between the syndromes are (1) that in high output failure the peripheral resistance typically is low while in simple congestive heart failure it tends to be elevated, and (2) that the level of the basal cardiac output, by definition, is elevated in high output failure. Since a low peripheral resistance, as produced for example by an arteriovenous shunt, will elicit an increase in cardiac output, it is logical to consider that the decreased peripheral resistance is a primary change in the cardiovascular system in patients with high output failure and is the basis for the cardiac stimulation (Youmans and Huckins, 1951; Youmans, 1954 and 1957). Associated with the increased cardiac output there is a shortened circulation time, decreased arteriovenous oxygen difference, increased heart rate in some cases and, commonly, a widening of the pulse pressure.

There are several reasons for postulating that the decrease in peripheral resistance in high output failure is the initial change in the cardiovascular system that leads to the other changes characteristic of the syndrome. (1) In arteriovenous fistula, which may lead to high output failure, perhaps in its purest form (see Elkin and Warren, Holman, Cohen and others), the initial hemodynamic alteration obviously is the reduced resistance to outflow of blood from the systemic arterial tree. (2) Decreased peripheral resistance

occurs in beriberi, severe anemia, hyperthyroidism, Paget's disease, patent ductus arteriosus, hyperthyroidism and certain types of chronic pulmonary disease, all of which may lead to high output failure. (3) The high cardiac output can be explained as a compensatory response to the low peripheral resistance. (4) The renal retention of salt and water may be caused by a shunting of blood away from the kidney by a disproportionately large decrease in resistance in the extrarenal portion of the systemic circuit.

In 1937 Weiss and Wilkins emphasized the similarities between the effects of systemic arteriovenous fistula and chronic thiamine deficiency, and they observed that circulatory changes produced by large doses of thiamine in patients with beriberi heart disease are similar in important respects to those associated with closure of an arteriovenous fistula. The pattern of cardiovascular changes in beriberi heart disease is the typical high output failure syndrome (Porter and Downs, Weiss and Wilkins, Burwell and Dexter).

Davies and Kilpatrick found renal blood flow and glomerular filtration rate reduced in patients with high output failure due to chronic cor pulmonale. The average for 10 patients was about one half the average for normal individuals. If the renal blood flow in these patients is expressed as the per cent of the cardiac output, the range is 2.0 to 15 per cent with an average of 7 per cent as compared with an average of around 22 per cent in normal subjects. It is evident that the kidneys do not share in the increased circulation in high output failure associated with beriberi or cor pulmonale. This demonstrates that the extrarenal fraction of the peripheral resistance is disproportionately lowered in these diseases, just as it is in systemic arteriovenous fistula.

It seems probable that chronically increased demands upon the heart caused by a low peripheral resistance would lead eventually to development of cardiac weakness just as when increased cardiac work is related to other types of changes in the circulatory system. If this should occur, the sequence of changes seen in simple congestive heart failure would be expected to be superimposed upon those changes related to low peripheral resistance to produce the final picture in prolonged severe high output failure. In other words, early in high output failure the changes seen could be related entirely to compensation for low peripheral resistance while later the factor of cardiac weakness also probably would be present.

## Consequences of Hypervolemia in Congestive Heart Failure

It is visualized that hypervolemia to some extent has a compensatory role in simple congestive heart failure and in the high output failure syndrome; however, the increase in blood volume may be great enough to lead to difficulties. The principal dangers in hypervolemia are, first, the possibility that the weakened left ventricle may become dilated to the extent that the dilation per se contributes to an acute decrease in cardiac output, and second, that the pressure in the pulmonary capillary bed may become increased to the point of producing transudation into the alveoli. The dangers of fluid administration to patients with hypervolemia are obvious, but the consequences of administration of vasoconstrictor drugs are less apparent. The ill effects of such drugs in hypervolemia are related to the fact that they promote a shift of blood from the systemic circuit into the already engorged pulmonary circuit, and this may cause a rise in pulmonary capillary pressure sufficient to produce pulmonary edema.

The degree of pulmonary congestion in a patient with chronic hypervolemia is least in the orthostatic position, but is increased when the patient lies down. Immediate transfer of blood from the systemic to the pulmonary circuit occurs as a result of the effects of gravity when the recumbent position is assumed. However, there is also a gradual increase in blood volume while the patient remains recumbent, as edema fluid moves from the interstitial space through the capillary walls; thus the blood volume shows nocturnal increases in patients with chronic hypervolemia and edema. The rise which occurs during the night, and the consequent increase in pulmonary engorgement, perhaps may explain the development of acute dyspnea.

## Hemodynamics

The following is a discussion of the effects of arrhythmias, valvular disease, cardiac tamponade, and congenital heart disease on the hemodynamic function of the heart. In less than two decades, tremendous advances have been made in the study of these pathological entities by the development of catheterization techniques (including pressure measuring devices) for use in humans. Reference will at times be made to pertinent animal studies, but, mainly, the more important human data will be presented. However,

it must be remembered that large variables are inherent in flow measurements on human subjects even when obtained by cardiac catheterization. In addition to the difficulties in measuring cardiac output by the Fick principle (including dye methods (ch. 18), true controls are lacking (except those from a series of catheterized, normal subjects) for the patient cannot be his own control. As an example, an end diastolic ventricular pressure of 4 mm. Hg may be elevated since the patient's normal level (before compensation of the heart to the pathological stress) may have been 1 mm. Hg. This small pressure elevation could represent a significant diastolic volume increase. Since catheterization may be a frightening experience to most patients, another variable is the failure to attain a resting, steady state. Anesthesia cannot be used because it produces hemodynamic changes such as an increased cardiac output. When variables are measured "following exercise," the exertion is performed with the patient in the supine position (with catheter in place); therefore, the amount of exercise is usually mild.

Formulas have been derived for the calculation of flow through shunts and stenotic and regurgitant valves. These formulas often use the cardiac output, pulmonary wedge pressure, completely mixed venous blood samples and other measurements or calculations which possess their own errors. Clinically the information derived from these catheterizations is very practical and important, but physiologically it may represent only directional and semiquantitative hemodynamic changes. Therefore, the precise measurements obtainable in animal experiments are often lacking.

The pulmonary wedge pressure and the extent to which it may or may not represent the events in the pulmonary capillary bed, or the left side of the heart, has been discussed. The term "pulmonary circulation pressures" includes the pulmonary venous, wedge, and arterial pressures. The "filling pressure gradient" is the difference in pressure between the atrium and ventricle causing blood to flow from the former to the latter. Often a gradient cannot be measured across a normal or pathological valve by the techniques in present use. Yet a pressure gradient must exist in order for blood to flow. There is evidence that small pressure differences (which may not be measurable by modern equipment) can lead to large blood flows (ch. 22). An important technique for measuring these pressure gradients by withdrawal of the catheter from one chamber to another with continuous measurements of pressures, is being replaced by the use of a double lumened catheter with an opening in each chamber.

### HEMODYNAMICS IN ARRHYTHMIAS

The investigation by graphic methods, the etiology and the treatment of disorders of the heart beat have already been considered in chapter 23. In this section, the hemodynamic effects of arrhythmias on the circulatory system will be discussed. Stress on the heart is caused by arrhythmias possessing one of the following characteristics: (1) a very rapid rate, (2) an irregular rhythm with disruption of the normal atrial and ventricular coordination, or (3) a very slow rate. Whether the arrhythmia develops in a normal or diseased heart is often very important to the hemodynamic effects produced and, hence, must be considered in determining the actual alterations caused by the heart rhythm. Also, if drugs, like digitalis (inotropic effect on the heart), quinidine (decreased peripheral resistance and increased cardiac output), or procaine amide (decreased blood pressure probably due to peripheral vasodilation) are used to revert the arrhythmia,

the corrected hemodynamic effects cannot be attributed only to reversion of the arrhythmia. A consideration of the role of atrial contraction in the normal functioning of the heart becomes important in those arrhythmias interfering with atrial systole. Atrial systole brings the atrioventricular (A-V) valves into closer apposition and may add some blood volume to the ventricles. However, there is no adequate evidence that a normal heart cannot function properly without contraction of its atria. On the other hand, improperly timed atrial systoles, occurring when the atrioventricular valves are closed, can lead to hemodynamic abnormalities.

TACHYCARDIAS. The results of animal experiments by Starzl and associates on normal hearts in closed-chest animals showed that electrically induced atrial tachycardias at rates up to 190 per minute for short periods usually caused no alterations in cardiac output, systemic arterial blood pressure or systemic venous pressure, whereas the the stroke volume and radiographic size of the heart decreased (fig. 28.1). If on the other hand, the ventricles were electrically stimulated to a tachycardia (made possible with stimulatory rates above the existing sinus rate), the cardiac

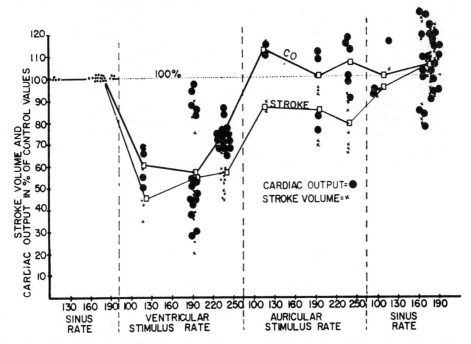

FIG. 28.1. The effect of atrial and ventricular tachycardia in the dog. Changes in cardiac output and stroke volume from the initial sinus rate values are shown with increasing rates of atrial and ventricular electrical stimulation. The changes are depicted as percentages of control values. Experiments were performed in closed chest dogs. In contrast to atrial stimulation, ventricular driving, irrespective of ventricular stimulation site, resulted in a reduction in cardiac output and stroke volume. (From Starzl, T. E. and associates, Circulation, 1955, **11**, 952.)

output, stroke volume, and blood pressure decreased. The resultant atrioventricular asynchronism produced discordant positions of the A-V valves at the time of ventricular systole, varying from fully open to fully closed, thereby altering the end-diastolic ventricular volume. The strongest beats (largest stroke volumes) would occur after the longest diastoles (largest end diastolic volumes), whereas shorter diastoles would produce weaker beats. If the atrioventricular conduction pathways were then blocked and the ventricles driven at rates up to 190, the results resembled those described for atrial tachycardia.

Clinically the supraventricular tachycardias (atrial and nodal) cause circulatory disturbances if there is underlying heart disease, or if the tachycardia is prolonged in time. However, heart rates over 200 per minute were tolerated for hours and sometimes days in patients without heart disease. Ferrer and associates studied two patients during paroxysms of nodal tachycardia by right heart catheterization. An unaltered cardiac output with a decreased stroke volume was found. Right atrial pressure was elevated while blood pressure and peripheral resistance were normal. Since atrial systole followed ventricular contraction in these patients, the atrioventricular valves were probably not tightly opposed during ventricular systole. This could lead to tricuspid regurgitation and explain the elevated right atrial pressure.

Patients with atrial flutter have been studied in the same manner as above. Those without underlying heart disease, and one patient with a slow ventricular rate, were found to have normal cardiac outputs. When heart disease was present, atrial flutter with a rapid ventricular rate induced a marked decrease in cardiac output and stroke volume concomitant with a small systemic arterial pulse pressure, prolonged circulation time, dilated heart by roentgenograms, and a raised venous pressure in some patients. In all instances, after reversion to sinus rhythm, the resting cardiac output rose. This was found to be true in 2 patients after all medication had been discontinued. Since this rise in cardiac output occurred without a change in heart rate in 2 patients, and the ventricular diastolic filling time therefore remained constant, it was suggested that atrial flutter contributed to reduced blood flow by the continuous, rapid atrial contractions impeding venous inflow. Pulmonary circulation pressures (pulmonary artery and pulmonary wedge pressures) were normal during atrial flutter in those without circulatory insufficiency. It is of interest,

and unexplainable, that patients with atrial flutter and congestive heart failure had a lower pulmonary artery pressure than those with cardiac failure and sinus rhythm.

IRREGULAR RHYTHM. Atrial fibrillation contrasts with the above tachycardias by having an irregular ventricular rhythm and absent atrial contractions. The distinguishing characteristics of atrial fibrillation from the regular tachycardias are beat to beat variations of ventricular rate, or ventricular filling and emptying, and of arterial blood pressure (a changing resistance to ventricular ejection). It has been shown in animals and patients that the beat to beat changes were related not only to the previous diastolic filling time and end-diastolic volume, but also to the arterial pressure, end-systolic volume and the duration of systole of the preceding beat. In closed-chest dog experiments, acutely induced atrial fibrillation with rapid ventricular rate decreased cardiac output and blood pressure, and increased central venous pressure and the arteriovenous oxygen difference. Dilation of the heart could be seen by roentgenograms. On reversion to sinus rhythm the previous status of the circulatory state returned. In patients, reversion to sinus rhythm is usually beneficial if the ventricular rate is rapid and if drugs that affect the circulatory system are used. Most show an increased cardiac output with shortened circulation time and decreased right atrial pressure. Exercise tolerance is often improved. However, most of the patients studied had underlying heart disease and had evidence of cardiac failure. In 2 patients without heart disease, cardiac output was not changed on reversion to sinus rhythm.

In summary, it can be said that atrial fibrillation with a rapid ventricular rate can lead to circulatory failure in diseased hearts or sometimes in normal hearts. Despite the demonstration of some atrioventricular valvular regurgitation with atrial fibrillation, evidence is lacking that the arrhythmia with a slow ventricular rate is definitely detrimental to the circulatory status of a patient. The effect of the lack of atrial contraction has been discussed above. Since many patients in chronic congestive heart failure are benefited, and since the development of blood clots in the fibrillating atria is dangerous, most cardiologists recommend at least one attempt at reversion to normal rhythm.

BRADYCARDIAS. Up to this point, the arrhythmias which cause a rapid heart rate have been considered. Very little hemodynamic data is available concerning sinus bradycardia and partial heart block. A decreased cardiac output but a marked increase in stroke volume was present in one patient studied with sinus bradycardia. It is generally held that when the heart rate slows, there is an increase in end-diastolic volume due to the longer diastolic period. This increases the myocardial fibers' length and leads to a greater stroke volume. In this manner, the cardiac output is maintained at slow heart rates, probably as low as 30 to 40 beats per minute. Slower rates often lead to circulatory insufficiency secondary to a decreased cardiac output.

In experimental dogs, complete heart block can be produced by tying or cutting the atrioventricular conduction pathway. This usually results in average heart rates of 40 to 55. These dogs acutely manifest a decreased cardiac output proportional to the decrease in heart rate, an increased pulse pressure secondary to a decreased diastolic but normal systolic arterial blood pressure, a greater systemic arteriovenous oxygen difference and a rise in right atrial pressure. Within hours each of these factors tends to return toward normal. If the dog's ventricles are electrically stimulated to the preblock heart rate, the cardiac output and other abnormalities return immediately to normal levels. However, these dogs, especially if allowed normal exercise, usually develop severe cardiac failure within 3 months. In this respect they differ from humans who appear to better tolerate complete heart block. (Patients with congenital heart block may have a normal life span.)

Patients with complete heart block have been studied with right heart catheterization and by rapid biplane angiography. In patients without circulatory insufficiency, an elevation is found in right atrial systolic and mean pressure, right ventricular systolic and end-diastolic pressure, and pulmonary and systemic artery pressure and pulse pressure. A decreased cardiac output and cardiac index (cardiac output per square meter of body surface) with an increased stroke volume is present. However, the cardiac output (and cardiac index) was reported as normal, despite the above abnormal cardiac pressures, in some patients without underlying heart disease. Angiographic studies with timed electrocardiography have contributed to the understanding of the hemodynamic data in complete heart block. The timing of atrial systole in relation to ventricular systole determines the size of the atria and whether or not reflux of blood occurs into the great or pulmonary veins. When the atria contract against closed valves, or if more than one atrial systole occurs before a ventricular systole empties the

ventricle, the right atrial pressure rises and reflux may occur.

In summary, complete heart block without underlying heart disease is compatible with a long and active life despite the presence of abnormal chamber pressures. Often such patients, especially if the heart block is of congenital origin, have a small increase in heart rate with exercise. If there is underlying heart disease, the prognosis is quite poor (despite available treatment) due to eventual circulatory failure from a chronic overload on the heart. Treatment consists of epinephrine, isoproterenol, sodium lactate, methamphetamine or atropine, and more recently the corticosteroids have been recommended. Isoproterenol is the only drug which has been studied and has been shown to augment the cardiac output not only by an increase in heart rate in some patients but also by a direct myocardial effect with an increased stroke volume in others. Recently, platinum electrodes of miniature, battery-operated, mechanical stimulators have been inserted into the ventricles by percutaneous probe or at open thoracotomy and have met with some favorable success.

## HEMODYNAMICS IN VALVULAR HEART DISEASE

Rheumatic endocarditis is the most frequent disease leading to abnormalities of the heart valves. The mitral valve is most commonly affected followed by the aortic, and then the tricuspid valve. The pulmonic valve leaflets are rarely affected. Pulmonic valvular disease will be considered in the following section, Congenital Heart Disease. Other causes of valvular disease include syphilis, bacterial endocarditis, calcification of the valves and trauma.

When the valves become deformed by disease, they impede the flow of blood or allow leakage to occur. If there is narrowing of one of the orifices of the heart, the condition is spoken of as "stenosis." Stenosis of the valves is caused by fusion of the leaflets, rigidity of the cusps due to fibrosis and/or shortening and adherence of the chordae tendinae. When the valves are incapable of closing tightly, they are said to be "incompetent," "regurgitant," or "insufficient." They now allow blood to regurgitate in the opposite direction to that of the normal flow. Insufficiency of a valve may be due to deformity, rigidity, retraction, fusion of the cusps or chordae tendinae, or to a dilation of the ring of the valves. If the leaflets are deformed sufficiently to produce stenosis of a particular orifice, they may also be incapable of closing properly and regurgitation will occur as well. Therefore, stenosis and incompetence of a valve often occur together.

HEART MURMURS. When the valves become deformed, abnormal heart sounds appear. Such sounds are spoken of as murmurs or bruits. Presumably, heart murmurs result from the development of turbulence in rapidly flowing blood. The flow of blood through most cavities and channels is silent because the flow is laminar. Turbulence will appear when the Reynolds' number is exceeded (ch. 15). Practically speaking, cardiac murmurs appear in the presence of the following conditions, separately or in combination: high rates of flow through normal or abnormal valves; forward flow through a constricted, or an irregular valve or into a dilated vessel; back flow through a valve, septal defect or patent ductus arteriosus; presence of a loose, vibrating structure, such as a chordae tendinae. The impression should not be gained that all murmurs denote underlying cardiac pathology. Early systolic murmurs can be detected in a majority of children, especially those with thin chest walls. These murmurs are called functional and are most often heard at the pulmonary area. Early systolic murmurs are also audible in many normal persons following exercise and, presumably, arise from the increased flow rate. Hemic murmurs develop in anemic patients as the result of decreased blood viscosity and increased blood velocity in the presence of an augmented cardiac output.

TIME RELATIONS. The particular valve involved is determined from the relation of the murmur to the events of the cardiac cycle and from the point upon the chest wall where the sound is transmitted with the greatest intensity. For instance, the aortic valves should open fully during the ejection phase of ventricular systole so as to offer little or no resistance to the outflow of blood at this time. At the end of the period of ejection they should close tightly. If however the orifice is stenosed, the obstruction causes a murmur to be heard during ventricular systole which replaces or modifies the clear first sound. This is referred to as a *sys-*

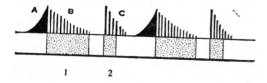

FIG. 28.2. Diagram showing the time relations of heart murmurs to the heart sounds. *A*, presystolic murmur; *B*, systolic murmur; *C*, early diastolic murmur. Numbers refer to normal heart sounds.

*tolic murmur* (fig. 28.2). If, on the the other hand, the valves are incompetent and do not come together at the end of the systolic discharge, a rush of blood from the aorta into the ventricle occurs in diastole, and a murmur modifies the normal second sound—diastolic murmur. The murmur may appear in early, mid-, or late diastole or may persist throughout almost the entire period. When stenosis and incompetence co-exist a murmur may be produced at the aortic orifice during both systole and diastole, in which event the two normal sounds are replaced by a to and fro blowing sound. A systolic murmur will also be caused by incompetence of the A-V valves (mitral or tricuspid) since the rise in pressure during ventricular systole will drive blood backwards into the atrium and cause abnormal vibrations to be set up.

GALLOP RHYTHM. In certain conditions, three distinct sounds are heard which give rise to a rhythm not unlike the gallop or canter of a horse. In addition to the clearly audible first and second heart sounds of each cardiac cycle, a third and even a fourth diastolic sound may be heard. All four sounds are often seen in phonocardiographic tracings. Gallop rhythms appear to be the pathological counterparts of the third and fourth heart sounds.

In some cases, the abnormal sound precedes the first sound—the presystolic (atrial) type of gallop rhythm. Two sounds are heard in rapid succession followed by a pause, and then by the second sound (fig. 28.3). This type is associated with depressed atrioventricular conduction (ch. 16), bundle branch block, myocardial infarction or, most commonly, hypertensive cardiovascular disease. The extra sound is usually attributed to the actual muscular contraction of the atrium; more recent evidence favors a forceful movement of the ventricular wall apparently resulting from atrial ejection into the partially filled ventricle. Normally, the ventricular contraction follows so closely upon atrial systole, that any sound that may be produced merges into the first heart sound. When, as a result of slowed conduction, the atrial and ventricular systoles are separated by an appreciable interval, the sound resulting from contraction of the atrium may become audible.

In other instances, the abnormal sound follows shortly after the second heart sound—early diastolic (protodiastolic) type of gallop rhythm (fig. 28.4). Most commonly, this gallop rhythm is associated with incipient or actual cardiac failure, therefore, it has a different clinical significance than the presystolic gallop. The cause of

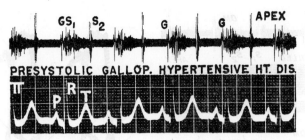

FIG. 28.3. Phonocardiogram (and electrocardiogram) demonstrating a presystolic gallop ($G$) in a patient with hypertensive heart disease. A systolic murmur is also present between the first ($S_1$) and the second heart sounds ($S_2$). (From Levine and Harvey.)

the protodiastolic gallop is unknown. It is not secondary to an asynchronous closure of the pulmonary and aortic valves. The sound occurs at the end of the period of rapid ventricular filling (as shown by correlative studies with intracardiac pressure curves). Most likely it is either produced by vibrations set up in the walls of the relaxed dilated ventricle by the shock of blood as it rushes from the atrium, or by a temporary reclosure of the atrioventricular valves (Dock).

Two variations of these gallop rhythms may occur. When both gallop sounds are present, a quadruple rhythm is produced. When the heart rate becomes very fast, a single, very loud sound may occur in mid-diastole. This is a result of the fusion of the two gallop waves. It is probably not just an addition of the two sounds but is a new sound produced as a result of atrial contraction actually augmenting the phase of rapid ventricular filling.

In some instances, an abnormal sound is heard between the first and second heart sounds—the systolic type of gallop. In contrast to diastolic gallops, the systolic gallop is usually of little clinical significance. The origin of the extra sound is uncertain although it may be secondary to vibration set up in a dilated vessel, pleuropericardial adhesions, or to other extracardiac factors.

MITRAL STENOSIS. Mitral stenosis is the most common valvular abnormality resulting from rheumatic involvement of the heart. Some degree of mitral regurgitation is also often present. The hemodynamic effects are due to the obstruction to flow between the left atrium and the left ventricle. The normal mitral valvular orifice in man varies between 4 and 6 cm.$^2$ When this is reduced to about 1.5 cm.$^2$, hemodynamic abnormalities may be found and at 1 cm.$^2$, they are severe enough to cause symptoms in most patients.

Mitral stenosis, by offering an obstruction to the flow of blood from the atrium into the ventricle, may cause a murmur to be heard at any time

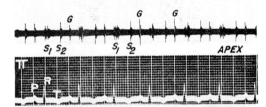

FIG. 28.4. Phonocardiogram (and electrocardiogram) demonstrating an early diastolic gallop ($G$). Note that the gallop sound occurs in early diastole nearer the second ($S_2$) than the first heart sound (from Levine and Harvey).

between the second and the first heart sounds (fig. 28.5). Since intensity of the murmur is dependent on both amount of flow and stenosis, it is not an indication of the degree of stenosis. The duration of the murmur is recognized as correlating better with the size of the stenotic valve since a longer ventricular filling period must be accompanied by a longer murmur. Though the murmur may extend throughout diastole, it tends to be more intense toward the beginning and the end of this phase; it may be heard only during these times or be confined to one or the other of them. The late diastolic murmur (presystolic) disappears when auricular fibrillation supervenes and abolishes the propulsive action atrial systole.

Braunwald and his associates have defined the hemodynamics of the cardiac cycle in mitral stenosis by catheterization of the left chambers of the heart in patients. Simultaneous inscription of atrial and ventricular pulse pressures (fig. 28.6) show that the crossing of the left atrial and ventricular curve and the onset of the atrial "c" wave are delayed. Since the left atrial pressure at the end of diastole is higher than the ventricular pressure, the mitral valve cannot close until the ventricular pressure reaches that of the left atrium. Presumably, isometric contraction may begin while the valve is still open and left ventricular filling continuing. When the mitral valve reopens, the left atrial and ventricular curves di-

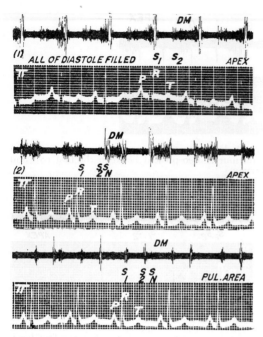

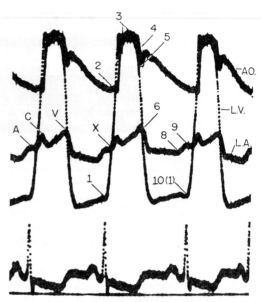

FIG. 28.5. Phonocardiogram (and electrocardiogram) depicting the murmur of mitral stenosis. Tracing (1) shows an apical diastolic murmur (*DM*) filling all of diastole with presystolic accentuation. The systolic interval between the first ($S_1$) and second ($S_2$) heart sounds demonstrates no murmur. Tracing (2) also is a diastolic murmur recorded at the apex and pulmonic areas from a patient with mitral stenosis. $S_n$ denotes the "opening snap" of the mitral valves which is often heard in mitral stenosis. (From Levine and Harvey.)

FIG. 28.6. The cardiac cycle of the left side of the heart in mitral stenosis. *A.O.*, aortic pressure curve; *L.V.*, left ventricular curve; *L.A.*, left atrial pressure curve; lower tracing is the electrocardiogram. 1, ventricular contraction onset; 2, end of isometric contraction period; 3, end of maximum ejection period; 4, end of reduced ejection period; 5, end of protodiastole (aortic valve closure); 6, end of isometric relaxation period; 8, onset of atrial contraction (the period of diastasis is absent); 9, peak of atrial contraction wave; and 10, onset of ventricular isometric contraction. See text for explanation (from E. Braunwald and associates, Circulation, 1955.)

verge (instead of normally coinciding) for a pressure gradient is maintained to force blood across the stenotic valve. This pressure gradient results in a slight shortening of the isometric relaxation period and allows an early onset of mitral valve opening. Thus, the time for left ventricular filling may be increased by small amounts at either end of the ventricular filling period. The period of diastasis is usually absent and the atrial pressure curve shows a continuous decline in pressure during diastole until atrial contraction occurs. In the normal heart, left ventricular filling takes place early in diastole for the most part, but in mitral stenosis it is believed that filling continues throughout diastole.

Although little is understood concerning the sequence of hemodynamic events which may occur in any one patient, much data has been accumulated from animal experiments and from catheterization studies in patients with mitral stenosis in different phases of the disease. Such data cannot take into account the effects of a concomitant, unmeasurable amount of mitral

insufficiency, other valvular disease or myocardial insufficiency which are often present in the patients studied. In general, the asymptomatic patients show a normal cardiac output, a normal pulmonary artery and pulmonary wedge pressure and a normal pulmonary resistance at rest. The filling pressure gradient between the left atrium and the left ventricle is the only consistent abnormality in those patients that have had left heart catheterization. Often there is an abnormal response to exercise by an inadequate increase in cardiac output and a rise in pulmonary artery pressure. Since filling of the ventricle may take place during the entire period of diastole when a stenotic valve is present, an increased heart rate could decrease the cardiac output by shortening the period of diastole. Exercise results in an increased venous return to the right side of the heart. The increased right ventricular work load in pumping the blood through the raised pulmonary resistance may lead to decompensation and a decrease in cardiac output.

Most patients with severe, symptomatic mitral

stenosis show the following abnormalities at catheterization: a decreased cardiac output, stroke volume and vital capacity; an increased left atrial, pulmonary wedge, and pulmonary artery pressure; an increased left ventricular filling pressure gradient and an increased pulmonary arteriolar resistance. The right atrial mean, and the right and left ventricular end-diastolic, pressures are normal unless myocardial failure has supervened. With exercise, the abnormalities in these patients are usually further intensified.

From the above data, a scheme can be postulated for the hemodynamics in a patient with gradually increasing mitral stenosis. It has been shown by Gorlin and his associates that the dynamic effect of mitral stenosis is not linearly proportional to its degree but tends to be curvilinear. As the stenosis becomes tighter, a more than proportional rise in pressure is necessary to produce equivalent increases in flow across the valve. The left atrial pressure rises in order to produce the necessary pressure gradient that forces blood into the left ventricle across the resistance created by the stenotic valve. There must be a corresponding increase in pulmonary vein, capillary, and finally, pulmonary artery and right ventricular systolic pressure to maintain the flow of blood to the left atrium from the right side of the heart. As the mitral valve narrows further, blood flow into the normal sized left ventricle is decreased despite a large pressure gradient from the enlarged left atrium, and cardiac output diminishes. The tissues of the body compensate for the decreased cardiac output by extracting more oxygen from each cubic centimeter of blood, creating an increased arteriovenous oxygen difference. When the hydrostatic pressure in the pulmonary capillaries exceeds that of the plasma osmotic pressure, there will be transudation of fluid into the alveoli from the capillaries producing pulmonary edema.

The increased pulmonary artery pressure is not entirely due to the mitral valve obstruction. Parker and Weiss described a thickening of the pulmonary arterioles secondary to intimal proliferation. Necrotizing arteriolitis was also present along with pulmonary capillary elongation, dilation and basement membrane thickening. Whether these findings are related to the increased pressure and congestive phenomena of long standing mitral stenosis or represent changes from rheumatic involvement of the lung has not been settled. Curti and associates found no consistent correlation between the calculated pulmonary arteriolar resistance and the degree of disease of the pulmonary arterioles in lung biopsies. They postulated that active vasoconstriction may play a large role in the pulmonary resistance present in cases of mitral stenosis. Whatever the cause of the lung pathology, the changes add another obstruction to the circuit in addition to the stenotic valve.

With the pulmonary artery pressure rise, the systolic pressure, and thus the work of the right ventricle, increases. When the right ventricle can no longer maintain its output against the increased pulmonary resistance, its end diastolic pressure rises, leading to right atrial and eventual systemic venous pressure elevations. Then, signs and symptoms of right heart failure appear.

Enlargement of the mitral orifice in mitral stenosis by finger fracture or incision has been performed in thousands of patients. Hemodynamic studies before and after operation have demonstrated dramatic changes in some patients from such commissurotomies while others have been unimproved. The symptomatic improvement is often more impressive than the hemodynamic changes. The pulmonary vascular resistance has been reported to decrease over a period of 6 months to a year in many patients. Evaluation of this operation is difficult for the knowledge of the natural history of mitral stenosis in untreated and medically treated patients is inadequate. Also, a prolonged follow-up of the operated patients is needed.

MITRAL INSUFFICIENCY. Mitral insufficiency often coexists with a stenotic mitral valve but may occur in the "pure" form. The magnitude of the regurgitant stream is not only determined by the mitral valve area but also by the pressure relationships on both sides of the valve. Rodbard and Williams have suggested that contraction of the muscular ring at the base of the mitral valve decreases the size of the mitral leak during ventricular systole. The fact that simultaneous flow through two orifices favors the larger orifice also lessens the amount of mitral regurgitation. However, since the pressure gradient from the left ventricle to the left atrium is much less than from the left ventricle to the aorta, regurgitation is favored. The amount of reflux into the left atrium has been calculated in patients to sometimes exceed the aortic flow and, in animal experiments, with the production of acute mitral insufficiency, the heart has been able to compensate for large amounts of regurgitant flow. Wiggers and Feil demonstrated that reflux may occur during the entire period of systole, including isometric contraction, continuing into protodiastole in dog hearts with surgically produced acute mitral insufficiency. This explains why the murmur of mitral incompetence is pansystolic in time and often obscures the second heart sound (fig. 28.7). However, sometimes the murmur is maximal late in systole and may even be confined to late systole. The mechanism of this late systolic crescendo murmur is not understood.

Ross and associates studied the dynamics of the cardiac cycle in patients with mitral insufficiency by left heart catheterization. Left atrial pressure (fig. 28.8) rises little during isometric contraction followed by a rapid increase to a peak ("v" wave) during late ejection by the ventricle. The left atrial pressure slightly exceeds the left ventricular pressure during the "y" descent. An abnormally rapid fall in ventricular pressure during late ejection is coincident with the atrial "v"

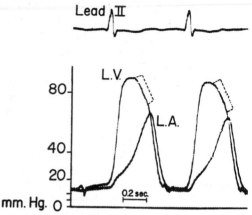

FIG. 28.8. Simultaneous left atrial and left ventricular pressures recorded at operation in a patient with mitral insufficiency. The atrial pressure curve rises to a high peak during ventricular ejection secondary to the regurgitation. An abnormally rapid fall in ventricular pressure (indicated by the brackets) is noted during late ventricular ejection. End diastolic pressures are elevated in both chambers; there is no diastolic pressure gradient across the mitral valve (from Ross, Braunwald, and Morrow).

wave. The rapid fall is evidently due to the inability of the ventricle to maintain its ejection pressure when regurgitant flow is maximal. Reflux of blood most likely begins during isometric contraction. The forward aortic output cannot begin until the intraventricular pressure exceeds the aortic pressure. It should be mentioned that the large "v" wave is not characteristic of mitral regurgitation for it has also been seen in predominant mitral stenosis. The "v" wave is responsible for a systolic atrial pulsation often seen in mitral insufficiency by fluoroscopy.

Patients with mitral insufficiency usually show a decreased cardiac output but some are normal or low normal. Since the left ventricle pumps blood into the left atrium and aorta, the total left ventricular stroke volume must increase or the aortic output will fall. The left ventricular tension and systolic pressure are increased by a greater diastolic volume leading to an elevated stroke output. Large regurgitant flows may exist without measurable increase in left ventricular end diastolic pressure. Braunwald and associates shunted blood from the left ventricle to the left atrium in dogs and suggested that the increased stroke volume was related to a more complete emptying of the ventricle, however, normal dog hearts are quite different from the hypertrophied, dilated, left atrium and ventricle seen in patients with diseased mitral valves.

The greater left ventricular diastolic volume

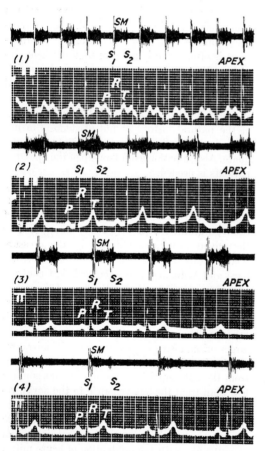

FIG. 28.7. Phonocardiogram (and electrocardiogram) demonstrating the murmur of mitral insufficiency. These 4 tracings show loud systolic murmurs (*SM*) at the apex in patients with mitral insufficiency. $S_1$ and $S_2$ denote the first and second heart sounds. The diastolic interval ($S_2$ to $S_1$) is clear (from Levine and Harvey).

may be brought about by a considerable increase in left atrial pressure. The left atrial pressure rises during ventricular systole but may be normal during diastole; the mean pressure is usually elevated. There may or may not be abnormal pulmonary circulation pressures. When present, they are of less severe intensity than seen in mitral stenosis, and may be secondary to left ventricular failure, pathological pulmonary changes (as described for mitral stenosis), or to an elevated left atrial pressure (to maintain sufficient diastolic blood flow through the mitral valve).

When the left ventricular end diastolic pressure rises to maintain the cardiac output in the presence of mitral incompetence, it may be due only to the inability of the ventricle to maintain its stroke volume through the two orifices or, also, to intrinsic myocardial disease with impaired contractility. Whichever mechanism predominates, the end result is a further rise in left atrial pressure, eventually reflecting back to increase the peripheral venous pressure, as described for mitral stenosis.

Operative procedures to correct mitral insufficiency have consisted of suturing of the valves, insertion of prostheses, or of decreasing the size of the atrioventricular annulus with a circumferential suture. That no one procedure has been widely accepted is evidence of the lack of success with these techniques.

AORTIC STENOSIS. Stenosis of the aortic valves may be classified as noncalcific or calcific. The former is predominantly due to rheumatic fever, but the etiology of the latter remains in doubt. Although the general opinion favors rheumatic endocarditis, atherosclerosis of the valves and even brucellosis have been incriminated. The clinical picture and hemodynamic abnormalities of aortic stenosis may be imitated by a congenital, circular narrowing of the aorta just above the valves, called "supravalvular stenosis," or by a subaortic stenosis due to a fibrous ridge attached to the myocardium below the aortic valve. Brock has described an entity which causes functional subvalvular stenosis and pathologically shows only an enormous hypertrophy of the outflow tract of the ventricle. Recently, the latter has been found to have a high familial incidence. The normal area of the aortic valve is about 3 cm.². Gorlin and associates estimated the "critical" orifice (below which significant hemodynamic changes take place) to be 0.5 cm.². Aortic stenosis produces a small orifice through which blood is ejected at high velocity during systole, presumably resulting in turbulent flow. The

murmur (fig. 28.9) is usually mid-systolic for there is an interval between the first heart sound and the onset of the murmur determined by the time needed by the ventricle to raise its pressure sufficiently to open the aortic valve. The murmur increases to a maximum about midsystole and then diminishes to cease before the second heart sound. It is usually heard loudest over the aortic area and is transmitted into the neck vessels, but can also be loud at the apex.

Those patients with aortic stenosis who are asymptomatic usually have a normal cardiac output and stroke volume. The systolic gradient of pressure between the left ventricle and aorta (by left heart catheterization) is the diagnostic feature present in all cases (fig. 28.10). This gradient may reach as high as 150 mm. Hg so that the brachial artery pressure is much lower than the ventricular systolic pressure. The left ventricular end diastolic pressure is usually normal. Musser and associates found an elevated left ventricular end diastolic pressure in patients who were thought not to be clinically in failure. They postulated that the concentric hypertrophy of the

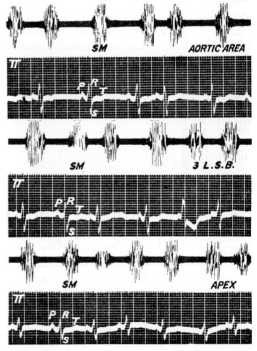

FIG. 28.9. Phonocardiogram (and electrocardiogram) showing the systolic murmur of aortic stenosis. The systolic murmur, with a midsystolic accentuation (often called "diamond-shaped") was recorded in three areas (aortic, left sternal border in the 3rd interspace, and apical). Note absence of diastolic murmur (from Levine and Harvey).

chamber decreased its capacity and perhaps small volume changes then led to large pressure changes. The workload of the left ventricle in patients with aortic stenosis has been calculated to be usually twice that of normals but may reach six times normal. Gorlin and coworkers found that, although the ventricular filling pressure rose in their patients, there was no change in effective or total stroke work or cardiac output with exercise. They suggested that this was secondary to the hydraulic obstruction rather than myocardial failure and that the hearts were on the plateau of their ventricular function curves.

The brachial artery pressure curve (which is similar to the aorta curve shown in fig. 28.10) in patients with aortic stenosis, shows a prolongation of the systolic upstroke time (end of diastole to peak of systole). There is an incisura on the ascending limb referred to as the "anacrotic notch." The latter has been shown by Katz and associates to be present in the central aortic pressure curve. They postulated that the vibration created by the suction action on the aortic walls of the suddenly produced rapid axial stream beyond the constriction was its cause.

With the above data in mind, a hemodynamic picture can be postulated for aortic stenosis. Because of the obstruction between the left ventricle and aorta, the left ventricular systolic pressure must rise to force blood through the stenosed

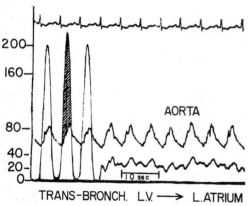

FIG. 28.10. Simultaneous pressure recordings in the left ventricle (*L.V.*) and aorta in a patient with aortic valvular stenosis. Catheterization of the left heart was *via* the transbronchial route. The electrocardiogram is shown above the pressure tracings. Note the very high left ventricular systolic pressure and systolic pressure gradient (hatched area) across the aortic valve. The aortic curve shows a small pulse pressure, prolonged systolic upstroke time, and an "anacrotic" notch. See text for further explanation (courtesy of E. Braunwald, Section of Cardiology, Clinic of Surgery, National Heart Institute).

valves. The period of ejection is prolonged and blood is expelled at a high velocity. The percentage of the left ventricular work spent in giving velocity to the blood rises sharply. An increased diastolic volume causes a more forceful systolic contraction with restoration of normal cardiac output. Left ventricular hypertrophy develops to compensate for the increased workload and may be the reason the left ventricle is able to sustain such high systolic pressures without failure.

The left ventricular systolic pressure may rise very high but finally the end diastolic ventricular pressure must increase in an attempt to maintain cardiac output. One of the reasons for failure of the left ventricle may be a decreased coronary supply. Animal experiments have demonstrated a significant reduction in coronary blood flow during ventricular systole which was due to increased coronary bed resistance associated with a very high intraventricular pressure. Also, since the aortic stenotic heart cannot usually increase its cardiac output with exercise, there would probably not be an increase in coronary flow. Elevation of the left ventricular diastolic pressure may eventually lead, through the increased left atrial pressure, to a rise in the pulmonary circulation pressures, an increased workload for the right ventricle and right-sided heart failure.

Patients with aortic stenosis may have their valves opened by a surgical approach through the ventricle or aorta, often with the help of an extracorporeal pump-oxygenator. A dilator, finger, or knife is used as in mitral stenosis. Clinical improvement has been excellent in many patients and a reduction in the left ventricular to aortic systolic pressure gradient has been found immediately after operation.

AORTIC REGURGITATION. Incompetent aortic valves most often result from rheumatic fever or syphilis; rarer causes are bacterial endocarditis, trauma, dissecting aneurysm of the aorta or congenital defects of the valves. The murmur (fig. 28.11) of aortic regurgitation is pandiastolic, beginning early after closure of the aortic valves, swelling quickly to a crescendo and then diminishing with the falling diastolic pressure. It is continuous throughout diastole because of a persistent pressure difference between the aorta and ventricle. This murmur is high pitched and usually of a very low intensity; it is often difficult to hear. An apical presystolic murmur is sometimes heard in aortic incompetence resembling that of mitral stenosis. This murmur was described originally by Austin Flint and bears his name. According to the most generally accepted explanation, it is due to vibrations set up in the anterior leaflet of the mitral valve as blood regurgitates through the aortic orifice into the path of the stream entering from the left atrium.

The hemodynamic effects of aortic incompetence are due to the regurgitation of blood from the aorta into the left ventricle. Wiggers and Maltby, in animal experiments, demonstrated that the magnitude of backflow varied with the size of the leak and could be 50 per cent or more when the cusps were totally deficient. The pressure gradient existing in diastole between the left ventricle and the aorta, and the duration of the diastolic filling period are also important factors determining the amount of regurgitation. The left ventricle is called upon to accommodate, in diastole, not only the blood from the atrium, but that regurgitated as well. This leads to a high initial tension at the end of diastole and a greater stroke volume during systole; in time, dilation and hypertrophy develop to give a very large left ventricle. Welch and associates in dog experiments, have produced aortic regurgitation by a shunt from the aorta to the ventricle. Since the left ventricular end-diastolic pressure rose to higher levels than the left atrial pressure, they postulated that the mitral valve protected the pulmonary circulation and allowed a high left ventricular end-diastolic pressure to produce a more forceful contraction.

The left ventricle with aortic reflux demonstrates a much shorter isometric period and its pressure curve (fig. 28.12) rises abruptly. As the semilunar valves open, an "explosive" ejection of the large volume of blood into the unfilled aorta causes the abrupt increase in systolic pressure. A much greater proportion than usual of the ventricular contents is discharged during the first half of systole, and a much smaller proportion during the period of reduced ejection. It is at this time—the period of reduced ejection—that the .sharp fall in pressure occurs and *not during diastole.* The pressure fall continues steeply into the period of isometric relaxation. Little further decline during the remainder of diastole occurs. Other factors contributing to the low diastolic pressure are the regurgitation itself and a peripheral dilation causing a rapid run-off of the blood. Gorlin and coworkers claim that peripheral vasodilation is a basic characteristic of aortic insufficiency which disappears when congestive heart failure develops with its usual systemic vasoconstriction. The pulsation in the capillaries seen in aortic regurgitation has been attributed by Lewis and Drury to dilation of the arterioles. Wiggers found

that peripheral signs of aortic insufficiency could be produced in an artificial model when central regurgitation was produced and the peripheral resistance kept constant. He, therefore, considered that it was due primarily to the low diastolic pressure and high pulse pressure. However, Myerson and associates have been able to produce all the peripheral phenomena of aortic insufficiency in a single extremity by the intra-arterial injection of mecholyl to cause vasodilation. Most cardiologists agree that peripheral vasodilation is a characteristic of aortic insufficiency.

The sudden ejection of a large volume of blood in early systole and the peripheral vasodilation

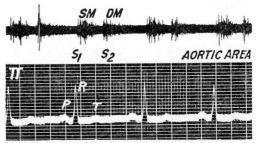

FIG. 28.11. Phonocardiogram (and electrocardiogram) demonstrating the murmur of aortic insufficiency. $S_1$ and $S_2$ denote the first and second heart sounds. An early, decrescendo diastolic murmur (*DM*) is recorded at the aortic area. A systolic murmur (*SM*) is also present (from Levine and Harvey).

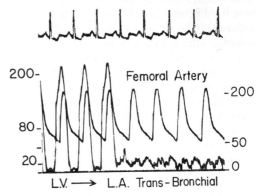

FIG. 28.12. Simultaneous recordings of the pressures in the left ventricle (*L.V.*) and femoral artery in a patient with aortic valvular insufficiency. The electrocardiogram is shown at the top of the figure. The calibration of the pressure for the left ventricle is on the left side and for the femoral artery on the right side. Note that the systolic pressures of the left ventricle and femoral artery are similar. The catheter has been withdrawn into the left atrium to obtain its pressure curve. The transbronchial route for left heart catheterization was used. See text for description of pressure curves (courtesy of E. Braunwald, Section of Cardiology, Clinic of Surgery, National Heart Institute).

also provide an explanation for the high-peaked character of the pulse tracing, and for the low position or absence of the dicrotic wave on the catacrotic limb (fig. 28.12). Also, the collapsing or water hammer, character of the radial pulse (Corrigan's pulse), and the sound resembling a pistol shot, heard when a stethoscope is applied over an artery, are attributed to these phenomena causing the very wide peripheral pulse pressure.

Catheterization studies show the effective cardiac output (aortic blood flow) to be normal in most patients studied and usually to rise with exercise. The latter is in contrast to patients with aortic stenosis. Exercise may decrease the magnitude of the regurgitation by increasing the heart rate. In animal experiments, after production of acute aortic insufficiency, an increase in heart rate reduced the regurgitant flow probably by a decrease in the diastolic filling time. The work of the left ventricle in patients with aortic valve incompetence is increased two to three times, and the left ventricular systolic pressure rises, as does stroke work, with exercise, again constrasting with aortic stenosis. Left heart catheterization usually reveals a normal left ventricular end-diastolic pressure but an increased left atrial pressure. Pulmonary wedge pressures, however, are normal in some patients but rise on exercise. No gradient of pressure is found across the aortic valve when aortic stenosis is absent. Patients have lived normal lives for years with aortic insufficiency. The reason for left ventricular failure occurring after a long asymptomatic period (except for those related to the wide pulse pressure and peripheral vasodilation) is not clear, but may be secondary to many factors, such as, over-stretching of the myocardial fibers, associated degenerative disease, or any added stress calling for an increased cardiac output. At this point, the left ventricular end-diastolic pressure rises and a pressure increase gradually occurs back through the pulmonary circulation to the right ventricle. Stretching of the mitral ring (with resultant regurgitation) by a greatly dilated left ventricle may play a large role in the final picture.

Hufnagel and associates have devised an operative approach to this disease by insertion of a rigid prosthetic plastic ball valve in the descending aorta. Clinical improvement has been satisfactory in many of the operated patients, but emboli often form in the aorta, seeding to various parts of the body. The valve is also a noise nuisance to the patient. Bailey and coworkers have inserted a nylon ball in the aorta, at the valve level, and have reported success in several patients.

TRICUSPID STENOSIS. Stenosis of the tricuspid valve is usually the result of rheumatic involvement but may also be congenital in origin. As an isolated lesion, it is rare; mitral stenosis is most often associated with it and, also, some degree of tricuspid insufficiency usually occurs through the stenotic valve. The murmur of a stenotic tricuspid valve resembles that of mitral stenosis, but is located parasternally in the 4th or 5th intercostal space. It is low-pitched, rumbling, and is like the mitral stenotic murmur in its diastolic timing. Distinguishing features of the tricuspid murmur from a mitral stenotic murmur are its increase with inspiration and a soft or normal pulmonic component of the second heart sound.

Right heart catheterization studies on patients with tricuspid stenosis have helped to define the hemodynamics of the lesion. It must be remembered that few of the cases studied had "pure" tricuspid stenosis and that mitral disease often complicated the picture by raising the pulmonary circulation pressures. As in mitral stenosis, the main hemodynamic abnormality is that the atrium does not empty its contents normally into the ventricle. The increased resistance at the stenotic valve leads to an increased diastolic volume in the right atrium, the latter becoming dilated and hypertrophied. In order to propel the blood into the right ventricle, the pressure in the right atrium must be elevated. In patients, a high right atrial pressure is observed which exceeds the right ventricular pressure throughout diastole and, thus, creates a diastolic filling gradient across the tricuspid valve (fig. 28.13). The right atrial pressure is higher than the ventricular diastolic pressure even at the end of diastole. The latter chamber must raise its pressure to atrial level before the valve can close, causing a prolonged isometric contraction period. Because of the increased right atrial pressure, the peripheral venous pressure rises and, eventually, signs of right-sided heart failure (edema, hepatomegaly, and ascites) appear.

With exercise, patients show an increased right atrial pressure and an increase in the diastolic filling gradient. The right ventricular diastolic pressure would most likely be normal at rest and with exercise, but is usually elevated because of an associated mitral lesion in these patients. The cardiac output and stroke volume are decreased and, with exercise, a subnormal increase occurs. The low cardiac output is usually explained by the inability of the thin-walled, dilated right atrium to adequately fill the right ventricle. The lack of a normal increase in cardiac output during exercise may be secondary to a decreased diastolic filling time with an increased heart rate.

In tricuspid stenosis, the atrial pulse pressure (fig. 28.14) exhibits a very large "a" wave due to the contraction of a hypertrophied atrium dilated by a large diastolic residual volume against a narrowed outlet. These giant "a" waves propagate retrogradely through the venous system, causing a presystolic, pulsating liver, and can often be seen clearly in the jugular veins of the neck. Such giant "a" waves are not diagnostic of tricuspid stenosis for they may also be seen in other diseases, such as severe pulmonary hypertension. The peak atrial systolic pressure wave is thus very high and falls very rapidly with atrial relaxation The "v" wave is usually small while the "c" wave may be absent. The right atrial pressure does not decrease greatly when the tricuspid valves reopen, indicating impaired emptying of the right atrium, and ventricular filling probably takes place throughout diastole, as described for mitral stenosis.

The accentuation of the tricuspid stenosis murmur with inspiration is usually explained by the increased venous return to the right atrium secondary to the fall in intrathoracic pressure. The right

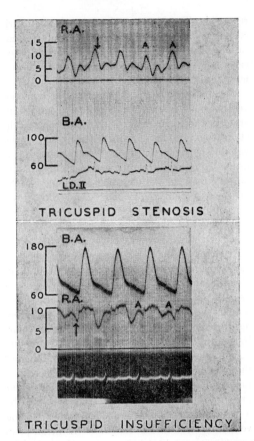

TRICUSPID STENOSIS

TRICUSPID INSUFFICIENCY

FIG. 28.14. Pressure tracings of the right atrium (*R.A.*) and brachial artery (*B.A.*) in a patient with tricuspid stenosis (*upper tracing*), and in a patient with tricuspid insufficiency (*lower tracing*). The electrocardiogram is shown in the lower section of each tracing. The *arrows* indicate the onset of ventricular systole and the letter *A* marks the peak of atrial systole. For discussion of atrial curves, see text (from Ferrer and associates, 1953.)

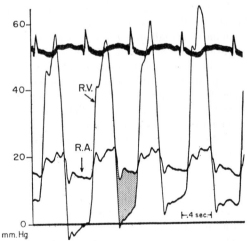

FIG. 28.13. Simultaneous pressure curves from the right atrium (*R.A.*) and right ventricle in a patient with tricuspid stenosis. The electrocardiogram is shown at the top of the tracing. Note that the right atrial pressure exceeds the right ventricular pressure throughout diastole creating the pressure gradient depicted by the hatched area. The right ventricular systolic pressure is elevated secondary to pulmonary hypertension from a concomitant mitral stenosis. For discussion of the pressure curves, see text (courtesy of E. Braunwald, Section of Cardiology, Clinic of Surgery, National Heart Institute).

ventricular pressure also falls with the decrease in intrathoracic pressure, and an increased pressure gradient and flow occur across the valve.

Tricuspid commissurotomy is now performed in this disease as in mitral stenosis. If the latter disease is also present, both valves may be opened at the same operation, but the mitral should be done first to avoid pulmonary congestion from a suddenly increased right ventricular output as the tricuspid stenosis is relieved.

TRICUSPID INSUFFICIENCY. Organic tricuspid insufficiency is predominantly functional or rheumatic in origin, but trauma and bacterial endocarditis are rarer etiologies. It is sometimes present congenitally or in the syndrome associated with malignant carcinoid tumors. Functional tricuspid incompetence may occur whenever there is dilation of the right ventricle, and it is usually reversible. The murmur of an incompetent tricuspid valve resembles that of mitral regurgitation, being pansystolic. It is often accentuated early in systole and is heard loudest at the lower, left, sternal edge.

The pulse pressures of the right atrium and ventricle have been simultaneously and separately studied in patients by right heart catheterization. The mean right atrial pressure is elevated. The right ventricular systolic pressure is usually very high while the end diastolic pressure may or may not be elevated depending on the presence of right ventricular failure, often from concomitant mitral disease. The atrial pressure curve (fig. 28.14) often shows a sharp spike at the onset of ventricular systole, probably due to the force of the contracting ventricle. Next a plateau-elevated curve, representing regurgitation of blood from the ventricle, occurs; the "x" wave is usually absent. This plateau curve may so resemble the ventricular pressure curve in severe insufficiency that it is spoken of as "ventricularization" of the atrial curve. The atrial pressure during the ventricular systolic period is higher than that of the presystolic period and is sustained to the end of isometric relaxation. The ventricular pressure then falls below the atrial level and the A-V valves open. The pressure in the relaxing ventricle continues to drop while the atrial pressure decreases at a slower rate and reaches its lowest value after the right ventricular pressure is minimal. Emptying of the right atrium reverses the decreasing ventricular pressure and the two chambers equalize their pressures, rising rapidly to complete the early diastolic dip. The diastolic dip, which is not always present in tricuspid insufficiency, is also seen in right ventricular failure and constrictive pericarditis but not with the characteristic plateau pressure curve of the right atrium.

The cardiac output is decreased in most patients with tricuspid insufficiency and rises, although subnormally, with exercise. The peripheral arteriovenous oxygen difference is usually abnormal and increases further with exercise as the tissues extract more oxygen per unit of blood to compensate for the decreased blood flow. Patients with tricuspid insufficiency are often said to have a lower cardiac output than those with mitral incompetence because there is no ventricular pump to compensate for the tricuspid regurgitation of blood.

The enlarged right atrium, with its increased pressure, may never completely empty in tricuspid insufficiency and eventually cannot compensate despite the presence of hypertrophy and dilation. This leads to a high peripheral venous pressure with the development of edema, hepatomegaly, and ascites. In contrast to tricuspid stenosis, the enlarged, congested liver pulsates during systole. The usual explanation for the pulsating liver is that the reflux of blood into the atrium transmits a pulse wave to the organ, but Bloomfield and associates have measured in some patients a pressure gradient from the right atrium to the peripheral veins suggesting there may actually be a reflux of blood into the inferior vena cava and into the liver. The right atrium may reach gigantic size in tricuspid insufficiency, as in stenosis, but, in contrast to the latter, the right ventricle also hypertrophies and/or dilates because of the increased workload imposed by pumping blood into both the right atrium and pulmonary artery.

### HEMODYNAMICS IN CARDIAC TAMPONADE

Pericardial effusions may develop during the course of an inflammation of the pericardium (pericarditis) due to a multitude of etiologies. Large amounts of fluid, up to a liter or more, accumulating slowly may not embarrass the heart, while acute effusions of much smaller amounts may compress the myocardium and interfere with its function (often referred to as "tamponade"). Chronic constrictive pericarditis is a fibrous, sometimes calcified thickening of the pericardium which adheres to the epicardium. Both conditions interfere with the normal cardiac action by restricting the ventricles, one by an increased intrapericardial pressure (effusion), the other by a stiffened pericardium (constrictive pericarditis). They produce a clinical syndrome characterized by systemic and pulmonary venous congestion with signs and symptoms of left and right sided heart failure. There is an absence of cardiac murmurs, but a prominent heart sound may be heard early in diastole. According to McKusick, this protodiastolic sound is probably related to the rapid ventricular filling and/or the abrupt halt in ventricle filling.

The hemodynamic abnormalities of cardiac tamponade have been studied in both animal experiments and in patients. Pericardial effusion in dogs has been produced by infusion of air or saline into the pericardium while irritative substances, such as cellophane, have been used to incite chronic constrictive pericarditis. The syndrome produced in the dog is very similar to that seen in man. Metcalfe and associates, and Isaacs and co-workers, have shown that the main hemodynamic abnormality is a hindrance to the diastolic expansion of the heart and not a restriction of blood flow into the right atrium secondary to constriction of the venae cavae at their orifices. As successive amounts of saline or air were injected into the pericardium to raise the intrapericardial pressure, the systemic and pulmonary venous, the mean atrial, and the pulmonary wedge pressures increased while peripheral blood pressure fell slowly at first and then precipitously. The cardiac output decreased secondary to a progressive fall in stroke volume and was insufficiently maintained by a concomitant rise in heart rate. The intravascular pressures (pulmonary and systemic, venous and arterial) tended to approach each other as the intrapericardial pressure increased. Isaacs and colleagues explained the restricted cardiac output by the pressure-volume curve of the pericardium which showed that large volume changes gave small increases in pressure when pressures and volumes were small, but as the curve rose, small volume increases caused large pressure increases (fig. 28.15). Thus, the circulatory effect would be due to a limitation of space available for expansion of the ventricle. Isaacs and associates also produced generalized and localized constrictive pericarditis in dogs by placing plastic casts in the pericardium. Hemodynamic changes were identical to those described for tamponade from effusion only when one or both ventricles were constricted. Isolated atrial involvement proved to be unimportant.

Catheterization studies in patients with chronic constrictive pericarditis and/or effusion have produced data comparable to that in the animal experiments. The mean atrial, systemic, pulmonary wedge, pulmonary artery diastolic and right ventricular end diastolic pressures tend to be similarly elevated in severe cases. Hemodynamic events are the same for both sides of the heart, and the right mean atrial pressure is approximately equal to that of the left atrium showing that the distensibility of the heart is determined by the thickened pericardium.

The ventricular pulse pressure curve is of low amplitude with a slightly elevated, normal or decreased systolic pressure. After the systolic pressure rise, there is a rapid fall almost to or even below the baseline (? zero pressure), for the ventricle empties normally creating a steep pressure gradient between the high atrial mean pressure and the ventricle. As a result, blood rushes into the ventricle causing a steep rise of the pressure curve to a higher than normal plateau for the remainder of diastole. This sharp fall and rise is

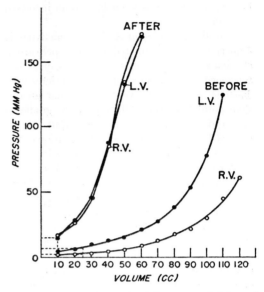

Fig. 28.15. Volume-elasticity curves of right and left ventricles before and after total pericardial constriction. These are volume-pressure curves obtained immediately after death from the right (*R.V.*) and left (*L.V.*) ventricles of the dog's heart within a normal pericardium (before) and from right and left ventricles within a generalized pericardial constriction (after). Increments of 10 cc. of saline were injected *via* the pulmonary artery or aorta into the closed ventricles while intraventricular pressures were recorded. It can be seen that, if the pericardium is thickened by scar so that it offers more resistance than usual, as the right ventricle volume increases against this increased resistance, greater than usual corresponding pressures are required (from Isaacs, Carter, and Haller).

called the diastolic "dip" (p.244). Since the ventricular end diastolic (and mean diastolic) pressure approximates the mean atrial pressure (for the ventricle is prevented from distending by the thickened pericardium), filling of the ventricle occurs during the first part ("dip") of diastole with little further increase during the plateau phase. The atrial pressure curve shows two sharp drops to give a characteristic "M" shape: a large pressure decrease during the rapid ventricular filling, which coincides with the "dip" of the ventricular curve in time, amplitude and shape, and a smaller drop associated with ventricular ejection ("X" wave). Atrial systole is of high amplitude for the atrium is contracting against a nearly completely filled ventricle. Cardiac output and stroke volume have been normal in some patients but are usually decreased. With exercise, all elevated pressures rise further. In those that show some increase in cardiac output with exertion, the stroke volume did not increase indicating that the rise in cardiac output was secondary to an increased heart rate.

From the data presented above, hemodynamic sequelae can be postulated for both pericardial effusion and chronic constrictive pericarditis. The thickened pericardium or effusion interferes with diastolic filling of the ventricle so that greater than normal diastolic filling pressure gradients are needed to maintain cardiac output. As explained before (pp. 146 and 309), dilation of the ventricle normally leads to an increase in stroke output by increasing the myocardial fiber length resulting in a greater force of contraction. Presumably, such dilation is prevented by a constricting scar. Systemic and pulmonary venous pressure rise by unknown mechanisms, to increase the venous return to the heart and maintain cardiac output. The increased venous pressures lead to serous cavity effusions, anasarca, hepatomegaly and pulmonary congestion. The compensatory mechanisms probably become inadequate as scarring progresses, and cardiac output and stroke volume fall.

The treatment of pericardial effusion is drainage of the fluid by needle tapping or surgery to create a pleuropericardial window. In chronic constrictive pericarditis, the two ventricles are decorticated of their thickened pericardium; the atria may be left alone. Following the surgical procedures, all pressures may return to near normal with a disappearance of the diastolic "dip", but most patients continue to show abnormal hemodynamics despite clinical improvement. The failure to attain normality is postulated to be due to incomplete decortication of the ventricles, persistent abnormalities of the lungs, or myocardial fibrosis. It should also be mentioned that the entire clinical and hemodynamic picture of chronic constrictive pericarditis and pericardial effusion can be produced by other conditions, the most common of which is diffuse myocardial fibrosis.

### HEMODYNAMICS IN CONGENITAL HEART DISEASE

The development of intracardiac catheterization to measure the pressures and oxygen contents of the various chambers of the heart has led to a better understanding of the hemodynamic effects of congenital lesions upon the heart. Various formulas have been developed for measurement of cardiac output, and systemic, pulmonary and shunt flows from the data obtained. It must be borne in mind in this section that many assumptions must be made in these formulas and that adequately mixed blood is often difficult to obtain when a shunt is present. Only the more common congenital entities involving the heart will be discussed. It is hoped that from the data presented, the main hemodynamic effects of the less common anomalies can be surmised.

PULMONIC STENOSIS. Cardiac catheterization studies have shown that isolated pulmonary stenosis is a much more common congenital heart lesion than it was formerly considered. Acquired stenosis, due to rheumatic fever, bacterial endocarditis, or carcinoid tumors, is quite rare. The obstruction to right ventricular outflow usually occurs at the valves but is not uncommon in the outflow tract of the right ventricle (infundibular stenosis), and even occurs in the pulmonary artery or one of its main branches. The outflow tract may be narrowed by muscular hypertrophy, but often, a diaphragmatic stenosis is also present. The murmur of pulmonary valvular stenosis is located in the second or third left costal inter-

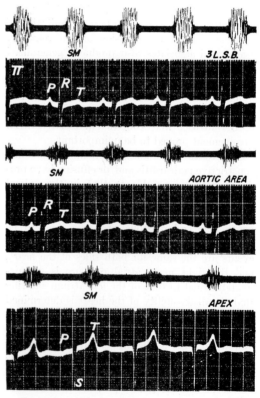

FIG. 28.16. Phonocardiogram (and electrocardiogram) showing the murmur of pulmonic stenosis. *Upper tracing* recorded in the 3rd left interspace at the sternal border; *middle tracing*, at aortic area; and *lower tracing*, at apical area. The systolic murmur (*SM*) is loudest at the pulmonic area and fills all of systole. The diastolic interval shows no murmur (from Levine and Harvey).

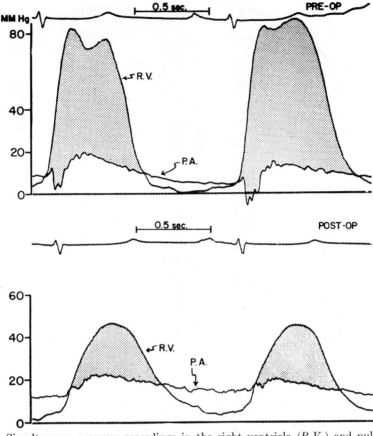

Fig. 28.17. Simultaneous pressure recordings in the right ventricle (*R.V.*) and pulmonary artery (*P.A.*) in a patient with valvular pulmonic stenosis. The electrocardiogram is shown above each pressure tracing. *Upper tracing* is preoperative and *lower tracing* is postoperative. The mean pulmonic valve systolic gradient is shown by the stippled area and fell from 45 to 19 mm. Hg postoperatively. Note the elevated right ventricular systolic pressure which decreased, but not to normal, following surgery (from Tanenbaum, Braunwald, and Morrow).

space, parasternally. It is often loud and rough with a pansystolic duration (fig. 28.16). Infundibular stenosis most often produces the same type of murmur over one or two lower interspaces. Multiple catheterization studies of patients with the various forms of pulmonic stenosis have been reported (fig. 28.17). The characteristic finding is an increased systolic pressure gradient across the stenotic area. Usually, there is little or nor measurable gradient in this area. The right ventricular systolic pressure and work are elevated, presumably depending on the degree of stenosis. Right ventricular and diastolic pressure is normal until failure intervenes. The right atrial mean pressure is normal to high.[1] The pulmonary

artery pressure is normal or decreased, while pulmonary wedge pressure and vascular resistance are normal. The pulmonary blood flow is less than normal, but this has been shown not to cause arterial desaturation since saturation of pulmonary venous blood is within the normal range. Cardiac output is normal or low, although increases are found in the presence of minimal stenosis. Oxygen consumption increases with mild exercise showing that pulmonary artery flow can increase.

The pathophysiology of pulmonic stenosis is due to the obstruction to flow from the right ventricle to the pulmonary artery (fig. 28.18) leading to an increased volume of blood retained in the former. This increases the myocardial fiber length, the systolic pressure, and the work of the right ventricle, resulting in a compensatory increase in output to maintain the pulmonary blood flow and venous return to the left heart.

[1] The mean right atrial pressure may be high because of a large atrial pulse pressure (giant "a" wave) with an elevated systolic but normal diastolic level. The giant "a" wave is related to the contraction of the normal sized or enlarged atrium against the increased resistance to filling offered by the right ventricle.

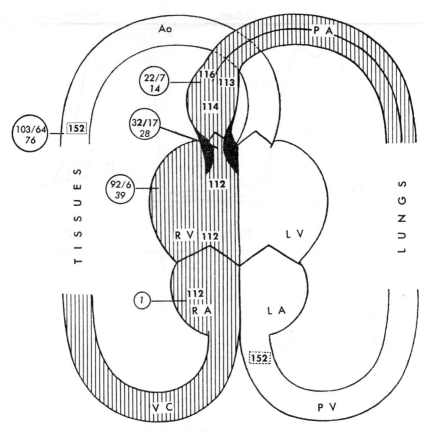

Fig. 28.18. Pulmonic Stenosis. Figures within vessels or chambers denote the blood oxygen content in cubic centimeters per liter of blood. Circled figures indicate the blood pressure; systolic over diastolic and mean pressures are shown. The black shadow shows the area of pulmonic stenosis, infundibular in this patient. The pressure changes from the pulmonary artery to the right ventricle were determined by catheterization and localized the area of stenosis. The pulmonary artery is dilated as often seen in cases of pulmonic stenosis. Notice the marked degree of systolic hypertension in the right ventricle with a normal pulmonary artery pressure (from Cournand, Baldwin, and Himmelstein).

Such dynamic changes lead to right ventricular hypertrophy; the work of the left ventricle is not increased. The right atrial pressure rises in order to maintain a filling pressure for its ventricle. With increasing degrees of stenosis, the right ventricular output falls and its end diastolic volume and pressure rise. The latter is reflected in the peripheral venous system by the development of right heart failure signs. Animal experiments and data from patients suggest that the presence of an atrial septal defect or patent foramen ovale in pulmonic stenosis acts as an escape valve for the increased load on the right heart by allowing a shunting of blood to the left atrium. Such cases, of course, may develop cyanosis.

The surgical approach to correction of pulmonary stenotic valves is an incision or excision of the valves by means of a transarterial or transventricular approach. Extracorporeal pump-oxygenators are now used more frequently in order to view the valve directly. Infundibular stenosis may be corrected by excision of the stenotic area or by an actual reaming out of the hypertrophied muscle. Following the operation, the chamber pressure may return to normal but often remains elevated. Most patients have improved markedly whether their pressures returned to normal levels or not.

PULMONIC INSUFFICIENCY. Insufficiency of the pulmonic valves, acquired or congenital, is a very rare lesion. Functional incompetence from dilation of the valvular ring is often seen in pulmonary hypertension secondary to mitral stenosis or pulmonary disease. A soft, blowing, diastolic, decrescendo murmur, which can sometimes be loud and harsh, is located in the second or third left costal interspace parasternally, and may be transmitted to the apex. When present in mitral stenosis, it has been named the "Graham Steell" murmur.

Several series of dog experiments with partial or complete pulmonic valvectomy or bypassing the pulmonic valve (shunting of the total right ventricular output into the pulmonary artery) did not produce myocardial decompensation, even with strenuous exercise, for periods up to 18 months. The pulmonary artery diastolic and systolic pressures were found to approximate those of the right ventricle in these dogs. Changes in cardiac output were not consistent. The right ventricle was dilated (by fluoroscopy or at autopsy) or sometimes hypertrophied (at autopsy by heart weight to body weight ratios).

A few patients with isolated pulmonic insufficiency were studied by catheterization of the right heart. The right ventricular and pulmonary artery systolic and diastolic pressures were approximately equal (fig. 28.19). Mean right atrial pressures were normal. No evidence of right ventricular decompensation was shown unless pulmonary hypertension or another lesion co-existed. The pulmonary artery pulse pressure curve resembled the tracing seen in aortic insufficiency.

According to the above clinical and experimental data, pulmonic insufficiency evidently is easily compensated by the right ventricle. Usually there is not sufficient functional disturbance to produce symptoms or signs as evidenced by the few clinical reports. The patients, whose catheterization data are reported above, were asymptomatic for many years despite their incompetent pulmonic valves. However, insufficiency of pulmonary valve may become significant if pulmonary hypertension is present. The increased diastolic pulmonary artery pressure in the latter condition would lead to larger regurgitant flow. Right ventricular volume, stroke output and work would increase. Right ventricular hypertrophy was found in patients showing a combination of pulmonic insufficiency and hypertension.

ATRIAL SEPTAL DEFECT. Often referred to as the most frequent congenital heart lesion, atrial septal defect most often involves the foramen ovale and includes part of the septum secundum. Defects in the septum primum are less common and usually lie in the caudal part of the septum, involving the valvular rings. A patent foramen ovale (called "probe patent") is often found at autopsy, consisting of only a slit-like aperture which is functionally closed during life by the left to right atrial pressure gradient. Defects less than 0.5 cm. in diameter are usually hemodynamically insignificant, while those greater than 2 cm. almost always produce signs and symptoms. A loud systolic murmur, usually heard in the second or third

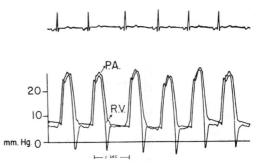

FIG. 28.19. Simultaneous pulmonary artery (*P.A.*) and right ventricular (*R.V.*) pressures obtained at right heart catheterization in a patient with congenital pulmonic valvular insufficiency. The pressures in the right ventricle and pulmonary artery are identical (28/7 mm. Hg). A diastolic pressure gradient is not present across the pulmonic valve indicating the absence of pulmonary stenosis (from Collins, Braunwald, and Morrow).

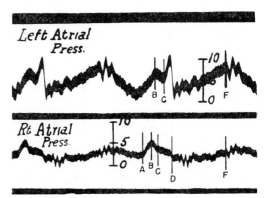

FIG. 28.20. Simultaneously recorded left and right atrial pressures in the open-chest dog. Vertical intercepts at *A*, *C*, *F*, beginning of atrial systole, onset of ventricular isometric contraction period, closure of aortic and pulmonary valves, respectively. For discussion, see text (from Opdyke and associates).

costal interspace, but also present in other areas, is the common finding and is felt to be caused by the large right ventricular outflow. An apical or pulmonic diastolic murmur may also be audible, presumably due to the large blood flow through the tricuspid valves or pulmonic insufficiency.

Opdyke, Little and associates, have studied the hemodynamic effects of the normal atria in dogs, with and without an atrial septal defect. They found that during the cardiac cycle, the left consistently surpassed the right atrial pressure by a small, but significant, difference except for an occasional brief period before atrial systole (fig. 28.20). When intravenous infusions were given, the pressure differential between the two atria was maintained. In another group of dogs, after

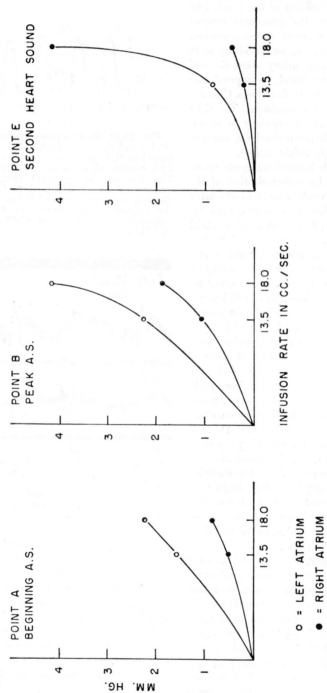

Fig. 28.21. Semi-volume elastic curves of right and left atriovenous-ventricular cavities at various points of the atrial cycle (*A. S.*, atrial systole). For discussion, see text. (Slightly modified from Opdyke and associates.)

creation of an atrial septal defect, the same left to right pressure differential existed. By tying the veins entering both atria, it was demonstrated that the left atriovenous system was less distensible than the right; more blood could be added to the right atrial chamber before a pressure rise occurred (fig. 28.21). This difference in distensibility could account for the pressure differential between the two atria. It was concluded that the pressure differential was solely a dynamic event since an equalization of pressures in the two atria occurred when ventricular asystole was produced; the gradient was then reestablished with the resumption of ventricular action. Two other reasons have been postulated for the differ-

ence in atrial pressures: (1) right atrial contraction slightly earlier than left atrial systole may transmit pressure to the left chamber, (2) an increased resistance to filling by the thicker left ventricle as compared to the right ventricle may result in a higher left atrial pressure.

Catheterization studies in patients have agreed with the above animal findings. When the catheter passes through the atrial septal defect, left and right atrial pressures can be compared. Findings vary, of course, with the size of the defect and with the presence or absence of pulmonary hypertension, which will be discussed below. In the absence of the latter, catheterization studies show (fig. 28.22): (1) the left exceeds the right

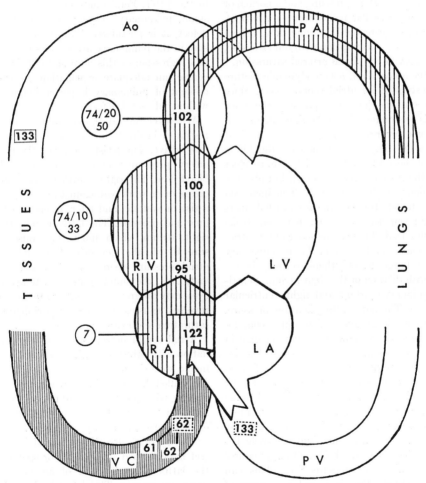

Fig. 28.22. Atrial septal defect. Numerical figures within vessels or chambers denote the blood oxygen content in cubic centimeters per liter of blood. Circled figures indicate the blood pressure; systolic over diastolic and mean pressures are shown. The presence of a shunt of well-oxygenated blood into the right atrium is diagnosed by the large difference in oxygen content between the blood samples from the venae cavae and the right atrium. Since the findings do not differentiate between an atrial septal defect and anomalous drainage of pulmonary veins into the right atrium, the shunt (denoted by the *arrow*) is depicted in an intermediate position. The pulmonary flow was calculated to be over twice the systemic flow. Pulmonary hypertension and an elevated right ventricular end diastolic pressure are also present (from Cournand, Baldwin, and Himmelstein).

atrial mean pressure, the actual pressures being normal or elevated, (2) right atrial and ventricular oxygen saturations are higher than that of the superior vena caval blood due to the left to right shunt, (3) a left to right shunt flow which often is 3 times the systemic flow, (4) a normal or increased right ventricular systolic pressure; the latter may be due to a functional pulmonic stenosis from the excessive pulmonary blood flow in addition to the increased stroke volume of the right ventricle, (5) an increased workload of the right ventricle, especially in imparting velocity to the increased flow, (6) a markedly increased pulmonary blood flow which may be 2 to 4 times the systemic flow, but a normal or slightly elevated pulmonary artery pressure, and a normal or low pulmonary vascular resistance, (7) a normal, but sometimes decreased, systemic flow, (8) an increased oxygen consumption with mild exercise, and (9) a normal peripheral arterial saturation.

From the above data, a hemodynamic picture can be postulated for atrial septal defect. Since the left exceeds the right atrial pressure, the shunt of blood is predominantly to the right atrium, although some reverse flow may occur. The right atrial pressure may rise to increase the filling pressure of the ventricle for the latter must eject not only the systemic venous return but also the large amount of shunted blood. The increased volume of blood stretches the myocardial fibers of the right ventricle to give an increased stroke output; this leads to an increased right ventricular workload and to a very large pulmonary blood flow. Large defects, therefore, may be associated with dilation of the right atrium, ventricle and pulmonary artery and right ventricular hypertrophy. The normal lung is a low pressure, highly distensible system which can accommodate the large excess flow with little change in pressure and a decrease in resistance. The increased venous return to the left heart is divided between the shunt and the systemic blood flow, which may be normal or decreased. With large shunts, right ventricular output is augmented, but may not continue proportional to the increase in right atrial pressure; the right ventricle becomes less efficient at the higher filling pressures as the end diastolic pressure rises. This can eventually lead to the signs and symptoms of right heart failure since the peripheral venous pressure reflects the right chamber pressure elevations.

Pulmonary hypertension usually does not develop until the third decade in patients with atrial septal defects. The increased pulmonary

vascular resistance is due to narrowed arterioles by medial hypertrophy and endothelial proliferation, and probably, in some patients, to an increased vascular tone. The etiology of the development of these changes has not been elucidated despite much investigation. They appear earlier in ventricular septal defect but evidently are not only secondary to an increased pressure in the pulmonary vessels, for this would not explain their development in atrial septal defects. In dogs, similar pulmonary vascular changes can be produced by end-to-end anastomosis of a systemic arterial vessel to a pulmonary artery. This is more effective than a side-to-end anastomosis and could be explained by the lack of direct pressure thrusts in the latter. Fetal lungs show highly muscular, small, pulmonary vessels; in ventricular septal defect, it is postulated that the increased pressure in the pulmonary artery does not allow normal regression of this fetal state. This is not, of course, an adequate explanation for the development of pulmonary hypertension in patients with atrial septal defects.

Whatever the cause, once pulmonary vascular resistance begins to increase in septal defects, it is progressive. The resistance raises the pulmonary artery pressure and decreases the pulmonary blood flow. The right ventricle has a further increase in its workload against pressure and shows a rise in systolic, and later, in end diastolic volume and pressure. The latter is reflected in the right atrium which must then raise its pressure to fill the ventricle. The elevated right atrial pressure decreases the pressure gradient and, thus, the shunt from the left atrium. This cycle may progress to a point where the shunt flow reverses, causing a decreased peripheral arterial saturation and cyanosis.

Atrial septal defects are also seen in combination with other congenital lesions, such as pulmonic stenosis, mitral stenosis (usually acquired and called Lutembacher's syndrome), Ebstein's disease, tricuspid atresia, and many others. These all affect the hemodynamic findings but, because of their rarity, will not be discussed.

The surgical correction of an atrial septal defect is performed by a closed or open technique, the latter with the aid of an extracorporeal pump-oxygenator. The defect is closed by direct suturing. After complete closure, a shunt flow is not measurable, systemic blood flow often increases, pulmonary blood flow is markedly reduced, and right ventricular work and pressures are reduced. The pulmonary vascular resistance often increases in the postoperative period along with the decreased pulmonary flow. If severe pulmonary hypertension was present, results are not so good, for the pulmonary vascular changes usually do not regress and right heart failure may develop. Patients with high pulmonary vascular resistance are refused operation for this reason. An idea of the reversibility of the pulmonary hypertension may be gained by having the patient breathe pure oxygen or by administration of a pulmonary vasodilator agent, although such a correlation with postoperative results has not been extensively studied.

VENTRICULAR SEPTAL DEFECT. Ventricular septal defect is probably the second most common congenital heart lesion. Approximately 90 per cent of the defects occur in the membranous septum lying in the outflow tract of the left ventricle beneath the base of the aortic valve, separated usually from the latter by a band of connective tissue. Less common are defects of the muscular septum which are often multiple perforations, not usually functionally open because of the contraction of the musculature during systole. A pansystolic, loud, often coarse murmur is heard in the third to fourth costal interspace parasternally. A mid-diastolic apical murmur may also be present, resulting either from a functional mitral stenosis or from rapid ventricular filling.

The hemodynamic effects of a ventricular septal defect are determined by the size of the defect, the pressure gradient across the valve, and the relative resistances to flow of the pulmonic and systemic circulations. Small defects are usually asymptomatic with the murmur as the only sign present; such uncomplicated cases are called Roger's disease, after the man who first described the murmur. Because of the pressure differential, which may be over 100 mm. Hg between the left and right ventricle, large defects have much more profound hemodynamic effects than those seen in atrial septal defects.

Catheterization findings in patients with ventricular septal defect depend on the size of the opening and on the presence or absence of pulmonary hypertension. Pulmonary hypertension is often present from birth in these patients, or may develop later and progress in severity. Small to medium defects (fig. 28.23) (less than 1 cm. per M² of body surface) show a pressure gradient across the defect, an elevated right ventricular systolic pressure, an increased oxygen content of right ventricular blood compared to right atrial blood, a shunt flow which may reach several liters per minute, and a large pulmonary blood flow with a normal or slightly elevated pulmonary

artery pressure. The left and, also, the right heart have an increased workload and are usually hypertrophied. The left ventricle must pump blood into both the right ventricle and the aorta; it increases its output in order to maintain systemic blood flow. Mean right atrial and pulmonary wedge pressure are normal, while pulmonary vascular resistance may be normal or low in the absence of pulmonary hypertension.

With very large ventricular septal defects, the systolic pressures tend to equalize between the right and left ventricle. The shunted blood flow into the low resistance right ventricular system is enormous in amount. There is a very large pulmonary blood flow and decreased pulmonary vascular resistance. Such defects usually lead to early failure of one or both ventricles unless pulmonary hypertension develops to decrease the amount of shunted blood. In patients with pulmonary hypertension (fig. 28.24), the pulmonary artery pressure is increased but the pulmonary wedge pressure is normal (in the absence of left ventricular failure) demonstrating that it is an arteriolar resistance. There is a decreased pulmonary blood flow and an increased pressure workload of the right ventricle, leading to pressure elevations in this chamber which tend to decrease the shunt flow. As this cycle progresses, the shunt flow may be reversed causing a decreased peripheral arterial saturation and cyanosis. The latter syndrome is indistinguishable from that described below as Eisenmenger's complex.

In summary, the amount of flow through a ventricular septal defect depends on the size of the defect and the resistances of the systemic and pulmonary circulation. Small defects present a large resistance to flow, meaning that a high pressure differential continues to exist between the two ventricles. Large defects allow a very large shunt flow which is decreased only by the development of increased pulmonary vascular resistance. However, the latter increases the workload of the right ventricle so that now both ventricles are severely hemodynamically involved.

Eisenmenger's complex, consisting of a ventricular septal defect, an aorta which overrides the ventricular septum and is therefore open to both ventricles, and right ventricular hypertrophy, will be briefly discussed, for it is often considered to be a severe form of ventricular septal defect. Substituting the word "syndrome" for "complex," Wood and others list any reversed shunt flow due to pulmonary hypertension (such as occurs in patent ductus arteriosus, ventricular and atrial septal defects) under this classification. Since the

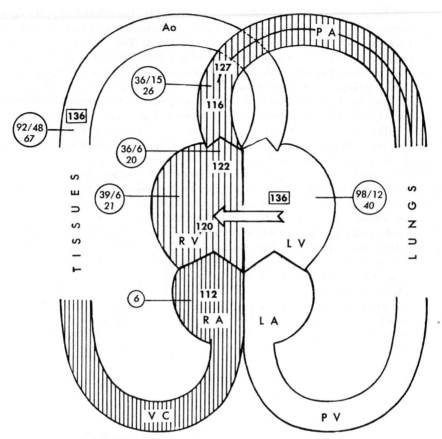

Fig. 28.23. Interventricular septal defect. Figures within vessels or chambers denote the blood oxygen content in cubic centimeters per liter of blood. Circled figures indicate the blood pressure; systolic over diastolic and mean pressures are shown. The increase in oxygen content in the right ventricle (compared to the right atrium) indicates a shunt of oxygenated blood (shown by the arrow) from the left ventricle. The estimated systemic and pulmonary blood flows were 3.57 and 6.14 liters per minute, respectively. This indicated a shunt flow of 2.57 liters per minute. Note the moderate elevation of right ventricular and pulmonary artery systolic pressures secondary to the shunt flow (from Cournand, Baldwin, and Himmelstein).

upper portion of the ventricular septum has a spiral course whereby the aortic root may come in contact with both ventricular cavities, a large ventricular septal defect located below the aortic valve may cause an apparent overriding of the aorta, i.e., the second component of the Eisenmenger's complex. The right to left shunt in this cyanotic disorder is probably not related to the dextroposition of the aorta but to the pulmonary hypertension which is always present. The aorta, unless it rises almost directly from the right ventricle, would receive little blood from the right side as long as the right ventricular systolic pressure remained well below that of the left ventricle. In patients with a large ventricular septal defect and an over-riding aorta, catheterization studies show a tremendous increase in pulmonary vascular resistance, an elevated right ventricular

and pulmonic systolic pressure equal to the systemic systolic pressure, evidence of a right to left shunt by decreased arterial oxygen saturation, and a normal or low pulmonary blood flow. The oxygen saturation of the right ventricular blood is higher than that of the right atrial blood indicating that an admixture occurs through the septal defect. The right ventricular work is markedly increased; this is reflected in the hypertrophy of this chamber. There is an increased oxygen consumption with mild exercise, although the cyanosis may deepen due to increased right to left shunting of blood.

The surgical correction of ventricular septal defect has been greatly enhanced by the use of extracorporeal pump-oxygenators and/or hypothermia. Under direct vision, the defect is sutured closed with or without the use of a synthetic

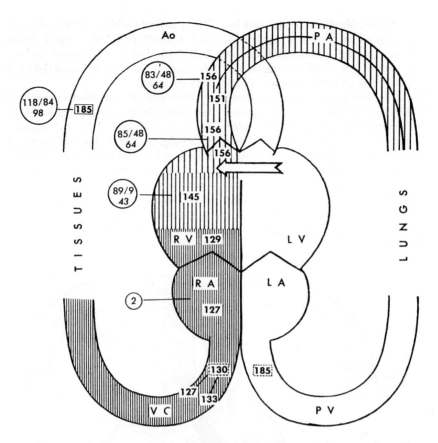

Fig. 28.24. Interventricular septal defect with marked pulmonary hypertension. Figures within vessels or chambers denote the blood oxygen content in cubic centimeters per liter of blood. Circled figures indicate the blood pressure; systolic over diastolic and mean pressures are shown. The increase in oxygen content in the right ventricle (compared to the right atrium) indicates a shunt of oxygenated blood (shown by the arrow) from the left ventricle. The lack of a systolic pressure gradient across the pulmonic valve rules out pulmonic stenosis. The high pressure in the pulmonary artery must be secondary to pathological changes in the pulmonary vasculature causing an increased resistance to flow. Note that the end diastolic right ventricular pressure is elevated slightly, indicating the presence of decompensation. The estimated systemic blood flow is 3.7 liters per minute and the pulmonary flow 6.95 liters per minute, giving an estimated shunt flow of 3.25 liters per minute (from Cournand, Baldwin, and Himmelstein).

patch. The ideal candidate for surgery would have a large shunt volume with a high pulmonary blood flow but normal or only slightly increased pulmonary vascular resistance. Small defects with minor hemodynamic changes are usually not corrected because of the surgical risk. Cyanotic patients with right to left shunts from severe pulmonary hypertension including Eisenmenger's complex, do not benefit from closure of the defect. Following operation, patients who had an elevated pulmonary vascular resistance show little decrease when catheterized several months later. Patients with severe pulmonary hypertension who have undergone surgery have fared very poorly.

TETRALOGY OF FALLOT. The tetralogy of Fallot is the most common of the cyanotic congenital heart diseases. Classically, it has been described as a combination of pulmonary stenosis, ventricular septal defect, right ventricular hypertrophy and dextroposition of the aorta, the latter overriding the ventricular septum. A right-sided aortic arch is also present in about a quarter of the cases. The pulmonary stenosis is most commonly of the infundibular type. Since the advent of cardiac catheterization studies, the concept of tetralogy as a single entity has been undermined. It is now considered that a spectrum of patients exists, ranging from severe tetralogy, with a large ventricular septal defect and severe pulmonic stenosis, to patients with either a large ventricular septal defect *or* a severe pulmonic stenosis as the dominant lesion. Between these two extremes are milder combinations of the two lesions. The dextroposition of the aorta is not considered as an important determinant in the hemodynamic picture (see ventricular septal defect). The right ventricular hypertrophy is not congenital in origin but results from the stress imposed on this chamber. There is usually a loud, harsh, systolic murmur in the second or third costal interspace parasternally, presumably due to the pulmonary stenosis, but it is not pansystolic, ending before the aortic second sound.

Patients with large ventricular septal defects, but mild pulmonic stenosis, show a left to right shunt without cyanosis and the reader is referred to the above discussion of ventricular septal defects for the hemodynamic abnormalities. Sim-

ilarly, patients with a severe pulmonic stenosis and a small ventricular septal defect behave hemodynamically as discussed under pulmonic stenosis but, in addition, have a right to left shunt with cyanosis.

When both the ventricular septal defect and the pulmonic stenosis are significant, the following catheterization data and calculations are found (fig. 28.25): (1) the pulmonary artery pressure is reduced as is the pulmonary blood flow, (2) the pulmonary capillary flow is often greater than the pulmonary artery flow from collateral circulation to the lungs, however, the effective pulmonary flow is still below normal, (3) the right ventricular systolic pressure is elevated, but the end diastolic pressure is usually normal;

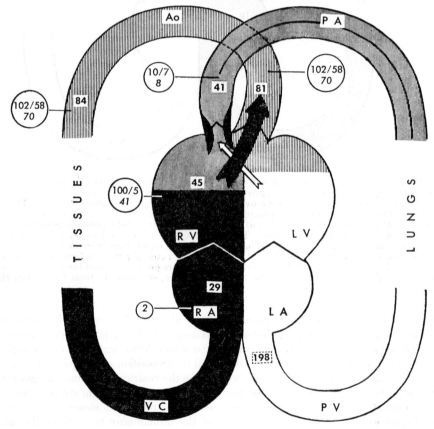

Fig. 28.25. Tetralogy of Fallot. Numerical figures within vessels or chambers denote the blood oxygen content in cubic centimeters per liter of blood. Circled figures indicate the blood pressure; systolic over diastolic and mean pressures are shown. Dark areas represent very low blood saturation as compared to white areas denoting high blood saturation. The large systolic gradient of the right ventricle to the pulmonary artery indicates a marked degree of stenosis. The systolic pressures in the right ventricle, aorta, and brachial artery are almost identical. From analysis of the oxygen data, it can be calculated that the left to right ventricular shunt is small, but the *right to left ventricular shunt* is large (indicated by *arrows*). Calculation of the systemic blood flow shows it to be somewhat reduced; the pulmonary blood flow is about half the systemic flow. Note that the aorta overrides both ventricles (from Cournand, Baldwin, and Himmelstein).

the right ventricular systolic pressure approximates the aortic systolic pressure, (4) right and left mean atrial pressures are similar, (5) the arterial oxygen saturation is decreased; left atrial samples of blood are usually more saturated than left ventricular samples showing that the shunt is mostly interventricular and not from the right ventricle into the aorta, and (7) the oxygen consumption with mild exercise does not rise but decreases, as does the peripheral arterial saturation, deepening the cyanosis.

In summary, a hemodynamic picture can be postulated for tetralogy of Fallot. The resistance offered by pulmonic stenosis causes the right ventricle to shunt blood mostly through the ventricular septal defect and somewhat into the dextropositioned aorta. The right ventricle hypertrophies in response to the increased workload but rarely dilates, for it can easily empty into the left ventricle or aorta. The systolic pressure of the right ventricle rises to the level of that in the left ventricle in order to eject its blood into the systemic circulation through the least resistant available opening, i.e., the aortic valve *via* the septal defect. The aortic blood is desaturated by the shunted venous blood. The pulmonary artery pressure and blood flow are markedly decreased because of the pulmonic stenosis, but the pulmonary capillary circulation may be augmented by a collateral flow from systemic arteries. The fact that some reversed shunt also occurs is established by the higher blood oxygen content of the right ventricle compared to that in the atrium. These patients cannot increase their oxygen consumption during mild exercise, probably because of the limited, circulating volume of mixed venous blood that can be propelled across the stenosed valve in to the lungs.

The surgical correction of tetralogy of Fallot has grown through three stages. The Blalock-Taussig operation, creating a channel similar to a patent ductus arteriosus between the aorta (subclavian artery) and the pulmonary artery, supplies more blood to the lungs, but the results, although often good, are not excellent. The next procedure attempted was an indirect correction of the pulmonic stenosis (see p. 430). This produced slightly better results but with a higher operative mortality. The use of the extracorporeal pump-oxygenator has recently made a direct open approach possible to correct both the ventricular septal defect and the pulmonic stenosis. Since these patients do well without a correction of the dextropositioned aorta, this is further proof

that it is probably not a significant hemodynamic determinant in this anomaly.

PATENT DUCTUS ARTERIOSUS. Patent ductus arteriosus is next in frequency, after the septal defects, among congenital heart diseases. It is the persistence of a patent channel, joining the left pulmonary artery to the aorta (distal to the subclavian artery), which is normally found in the fetus and which closes within a few weeks after birth. The exact mechanism of the normal obliteration of the ductus is not understood although it has been shown that the ducti constrict, when perfused with oxygenated blood, and dilate, if nitrogen replaces the oxygen; another theory asserts that high pressures maintain the ductus patent while low pressures lead to its closure. Classically, a "machinery" murmur (fig. 28.26) is heard throughout systole and diastole due to the continuous shunting of blood and is located in the second or third costal interspace, parasternally. This murmur is harsh in quality, increasing toward the end of systole, and waning during diastole.

The hemodynamic effects of a patent ductus arteriosus are secondary to the shunting of blood from the high pressure system of the aorta to the low pressure circulation of the pulmonary artery (fig. 28.27). The amount of blood shunted depends upon the size of the ductus and the pressure difference between the aorta and the pulmo-

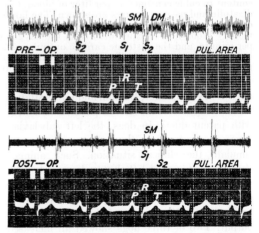

FIG. 28.26. Phonocardiogram (and electrocardiogram) demonstrating the "machinery" murmur of patent ductus arteriosus. *Upper tracing* (recorded preoperatively) at the pulmonic area shows loud systolic (*SM*) and diastolic (*DM*) components of the continuous murmur. $S_1$ and $S_2$ denote the first and second heart sounds. *Lower tracing* (recorded after ligation of the ductus) shows persistence of a soft pulmonic systolic murmur (from Levine and Harvey).

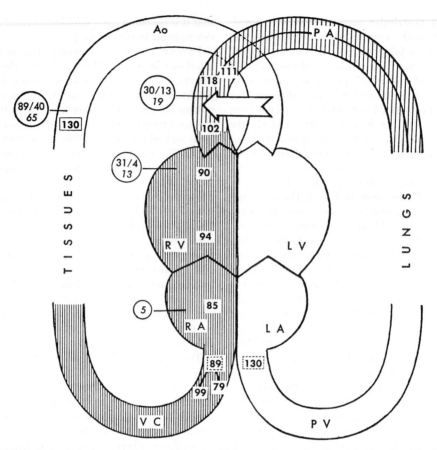

Fig. 28.27. Patent ductus arteriosus. Figures within vessels or chambers denote the blood oxygen content in cubic centimeters per liter of blood. Circled figures indicate the blood pressure; systolic over diastolic and mean pressures are shown. The large increase in oxygen content in the pulmonary artery demonstrates a shunt of oxygenated blood (indicated by the *arrow*) from the aorta. The estimated pulmonary blood flow as calculated from the oxygen content of the left pulmonary artery was 4.98 liters per minute, and the systemic cardiac output was 2.38 liters per minute. This means a shunt flow of 2.6 liters per minute existed. The slight increase in pulmonary artery pressures indicates the presence of a mild degree of pulmonary hypertension (from Cournand, Baldwin, and Himmelstein).

nary artery. Eppinger, Burwell and Gross studied the hemodynamic changes in patients and dogs with patent ducti. In dogs, the left subclavian artery was sutured to the pulmonary artery to simulate the clinical situation. Such animals showed an increased left, but a decreased right, ventricular output. The shunted blood from the aorta to the pulmonary artery was calculated to be more than 50 per cent of the left ventricular output. Two of three dogs showed an increased mean pulmonary artery pressure, probably from the large pulmonary blood flow rather than an increased pulmonary resistance. Patients with patent ductus were studied, while under anesthesia and during thoracotomy, before the ductus was tied. The oxygen content of the pulmonary artery was greater than that of the right ventricle. Blood flows through the shunt varied from 4 to 19 liters per minute, which was 45 to 75 per cent

of the left ventricular output. The total pulmonary blood flow (right ventricular plus shunt flow) was 10 to 25 liters per minute. The left was 2 to 4 times the right ventricular output. Arterial blood pressure showed a low diastolic level with a wide pulse pressure. Studies in unanesthetized subjects by other groups have demonstrated similar findings. The mean right atrial pressure was normal, while the right ventricular and pulmonary artery systolic pressures were normal or elevated. The pulmonary vascular resistance was increased when pulmonary hypertension was present.

In summary, the higher aortic pressure shunts blood through a patent ductus arteriosus to the low pressure pulmonary circuit during the entire cardiac cycle. Depending on its size, some shunts have been calculated to deliver up to 30 liters per minute to the pulmonary artery. This leads to an excess pulmonary blood flow and venous return to the left side of the heart. The increased volume return to the left ventricle results in a stretch of the myocardial fibers, whereby the left ventricle increases its output in order to maintain systemic blood flow at or near normal levels. This increased workload of the left ventricle may lead to its hypertrophy. The escape of blood from the aorta to the pulmonary artery causes a sharp fall in diastolic pressure, producing an increased pulse pressure and most of the peripheral signs of aortic insufficiency.

Patients with a patent ductus arteriosus may develop pulmonary hypertension, for unknown reasons, as discussed under atrial septal defect. As the pulmonary vascular resistance increases, the pulmonary artery and right ventricular systolic pressures rise. This causes a decrease in the pressure differential between the aorta and pulmonary artery and a decrease in the shunt flow. When the pulmonary hypertension is more severe, the shunt flow may become partially, and then completely, reversed, producing a hemodynamic picture similar to Eisenmenger's complex, except that the cyanosis is limited to the lower body. Such patients usually have a very large ductus, right ventricular hypertrophy, secondary to the increased work of the right ventricle, and an atypical or absent murmur.

The surgical treatment of patent ductus arteriosus consists of cutting the ductus and suturing the aortic and pulmonary ends closed. After operation, the arterial diastolic pressure rises, the left ventricular output decreases and, in the majority of patients, the murmur disappears. Operation is usually not recommended for patients with severe pulmonary hypertension and reversal of ductal flow, since the ductus serves as an escape valve for the excess right ventricular pressure and output. Delayed closure, in such cases, by partial ligation or by a two-stage shunting operation has been suggested, but not tested in a sufficient number of patients.

COARCTATION OF THE AORTA. Coarctation of the aorta is a congenital defect which is usually subdivided into an "infantile" and "adult" form. Infantile coarctation consists of a long segment of narrowing in the distal aortic arch, from the left subclavian artery to the ductus arteriosus insertion, while the adult form is a shorter, more localized constriction at or distal to the ductus attachment. Since these two variations are often seen in different age groups than their label implies, it has been suggested that such a classification be discarded because it serves no useful purpose to the surgeon who is attempting to correct the defect. A loud systolic murmur, due probably to the turbulence at the constricted area, extends from early systole slightly into diastole. It is most often loudest at the base of the heart but is also heard in the left interscapular area.

The hemodynamics of coarctation of the aorta involve an increased pressure workload on the left ventricle which has to pump its output through the narrowed area. This strain, which often leads to left ventricular hypertrophy, is somewhat relieved by the development of an extensive collateral circulation between the subclavian artery and its branches above the constriction, and the branches of the descending aorta below (fig. 28.28). In patients studied by catheterization techniques, the cardiac output is normal or increased. The blood flow to the upper body is normal or elevated and, due to the extensive collateral circulation, normal to the lower body. An elevated blood pressure occurs above the coarctation. There is a delay in onset of the femoral pulse (fig. 28.29) which normally precedes the radial pulse slightly. This delayed onset may not be palpable but the late systolic peak of the femoral pulse, as compared to the radial, is very noticeable. The femoral pulse curve shows a slow rise and fall with a decreased pulse pressure and an absent dicrotic notch.

Patient and animal studies purport to show that the upper body hypertension can be explained on a purely mechanical basis related to the degree of aortic constriction. Gupta and Wiggers thoroughly studied, in dogs, the hemodynamics of aortic constriction just beyond the left subclavian artery. As the degree of constriction was increased, systolic, diastolic and pulse pressures increased in the aorta above the constriction and decreased in the femoral artery. They postulated that the hypertension above the constriction was not only secondary to the increased resistance but also to the reduced capacity and distensibility of the aortic compression chamber, into which the left ventricle empties, and to the physiological reactions of the left ventricle, whereby its systolic discharge is increased. They explained the slow rise and fall and the maintenance of diastolic pressure of the femoral pulse to the damping effect on the aortic pressure wave in its passage through the constricted area. In dogs with a constricted aorta, but with a subclavian to aorta shunt imitating the collaterals found in man, the systolic and diastolic pressures of the aorta above the constriction were decreased, while those of the femoral artery were increased when compared to the findings in coarcted dogs without such a

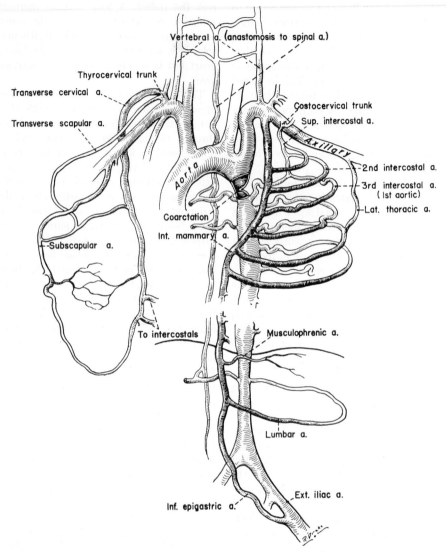

Fig. 28.28. Diagrammatic representation of routes of collateral circulation in coarctation of the aorta. The extensive collateral circulation between the subclavian arteries and their branches above the constriction and the branches of the descending aorta below the coarctation is shown. (From Edwards and associates. An atlas of congenital anomalies of the heart and great vessels. Charles C. Thomas, Publisher, Springfield, Illinois, 1954.)

shunt. The pulse pressure increased, but the contour of the femoral pulse wave did not return to normal. Thus, an artificial collateral circulation reduced the workload on the left ventricle and the elevated blood pressure of the upper body while increasing the blood flow to the lower extremities.

Experimentation on dogs has produced evidence for and against renal ischemia being a factor in the upper body hypertension. Also, Painter and associates have demonstrated hypertrophy of the media and endothelial proliferation of arterioles in organs of patients above and below

the constricted aorta. The fact that hypertension does not exist in the lower body was explained by the metabolic need for blood dilating its narrowed arterioles. This increased peripheral resistance could explain the finding of normal or even increased femoral artery diastolic pressures in many coarctation patients.

Coarctation of the aorta has been corrected in hundreds of patients by excision of the involved area and anastomosis of the proximal to the distal end. If a long area of the aorta is involved, a graft is inserted. Following operation, the upper extremity hypertension may either decrease to nor-

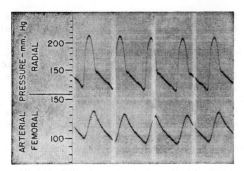

FIG. 28.29. Tracings of the intraradial and intrafemoral arterial pressures from a patient with coarctation of the aorta. The following points should be noticed: (1) the elevation of the systolic and diastolic pressures in the radial artery, (2) the smaller femoral systolic and pulse pressures, (3) the slight delay in onset of the femoral pulse wave compared to that of the radial pulse wave, and (4) the late peak of the femoral pulse as compared to that of the radial pulse (from Brown, Clagett, Burchell, and Wood).

mal levels or remain elevated. The persistence of this hypertension after removal of the constricted aortic area would argue for a renal etiology except that the increased pressure may have induced permanent arteriolar changes, thereby increasing the peripheral resistance.

## REFERENCES

BAILEY, C. P. AND LIKOFF, W. The surgical treatment of aortic insufficiency. Ann. Int. Med., 1955, 42, 388.

BARGER, A. C., ROE, B. B., AND RICHARDSON, G. S. Relation of valvular lesions and of exercise to auricular pressure, work tolerance, and to development of chronic, congestive failure in dogs. Am. J. Physiol., 1952, 169, 384.

BING, R. J., VANDAM, L. D. AND GRAY, F. D. Physiological studies in congenital heart disease. III. Results obtained in five cases of Eisenmenger's Complex. Bull, Johns Hopkins Hosp., 1947, 80, 323.

BING, R. J., VANDAM, L. D., AND GRAY, F. D., JR. Physiological studies in congenital heart disease. II. Results of preoperative studies in patients with Tetralogy of Fallot. Bull. Johns Hopkins Hosp., 1947, 80, 121.

BLOOMFIELD, R. A., LAUSON, H. A., COURNAND, A., BREED, E. S., AND RICHARDS, D. W., JR. Recording of right heart pressures in normal subjects and in patients with chronic pulmonary disease and various types of cardio-circulatory disease. J. Clin. Invest., 1946, 25, 639.

BLOUNT, S. G., JR., McCORD, M. C., MUELLER, H., AND SWAN, H. Isolated valvular pulmonic stenosis: clinical and physiologic response to open valvuloplasty. Circulation, 1954, 10, 161.

BLOUNT, S. G., JR., MUELLER, H. AND McCORD, M. C. Ventricular septal defect. Am. J. Med., 1955, 18, 871.

BRAUNWALD, E., MOSCOVITZ, H. L., AMRAM, S. S., LASSER, R. P., SAPIN, S. O., HIMMELSTEIN, A.,

RAVITCH, M. M. AND GORDON, A. J. The hemodynamics of the left side of the heart as studied by simultaneous left atrial, left ventricular and aortic pressures; particular reference to mitral stenosis. Circulation, 1955, 12, 69.

BRAUNWALD, E., WELCH, G. H., AND SARNOFF, S. J. Hemodynamic effects of quantitatively varied experimental mitral regurgitation. Circulation Res., 1957, 5, 539.

BRECHER, G. A. AND OPDYKE, D. F. Effect of pulmonic stenosis upon the circulation in the absence and presence of an interatrial septal defect. Am. J. Physiol., 1950, 163, 701.

BRENT, L. B., ABURANO, A., FISHER, D. L., MORAN, T. J., MYERS, J. D., AND TAYLOR, W. J. Familial muscular subaortic stenosis. Circulation, 1960, 21, 167.

BRÖCK, R. C. Functional obstruction of the left ventricle (acquired aortic subvalvular stenosis). Guy's Hosp. Rep., 1957, 106, 221.

BROWN, G. E., JR., CLAGETT, O. T., BURCHELL, H. B., AND WOOD, E. H. Preoperative and postoperative studies of intraradial and intrafemoral pressures in patients with coarctation of the aorta. Proc. Staff Meet. Mayo Clin., 1948, 23, 352.

BURWELL, C. S., EPPINGER, E. C., AND GROSS, R. E. The effects of patency of the ductus arteriosus on the circulation. J. Clin. Invest., 1940, 19, 774.

BURWELL, C. S. AND DEXTER, L. Tr. A. Am. Physicians, 1947, 60, 59.

COHEN, S. M., EDHOLM, O. G., HOWARTH, S., McMICHAEL, J., AND SHARPEY-SCHAFER, E. P. Clin. Sc., 1948, 7, 35.

COLLINS, N. P., BRAUNWALD, E., AND MORROW, A. G. Isolated congenital pulmonic valvular regurgitation. Am. J. Med., 1960, 28, 159.

COURNAND, A., MOTLEY, H. L., HIMMELSTEIN, A., DRESDALE, D., AND BALDWIN, J. Recording of blood pressure from the left auricle and the pulmonary veins in human subjects with interauricular septal defect. Am. J. Physiol., 1947, 150, 267.

CULBERTSON, J. W., ECKSTEIN, J. W., KIRKENDALL, W. M., AND BEDELL, G. N. General hemodynamics and splanchnic circulation in patients with carctation of the aorta. J. Clin. Invest., 1957, 36, 1537.

CURTI, P. C., COHEN, G., CASTLEMAN, B., SCANNELL, J. G., FRIEDLICH, A. L., AND MYERS, G. S. Respiratory and Circulatory studies of patients with mitral stenosis. Circulation, 1953, 8, 893.

DAMMANN, JR., J. F., THOMPSON, W. M., JR., SOSA, O., AND CHRISTLIEB, I. Anatomy, physiology and natural history of simple ventricular septal defects. Am. J. Cardiol., 1960, 5, 136.

DAVIES, C. E. AND KILPATRICK, J. A. Clin. Sc., 1951, 10, 53.

DENIE, J. J. AND VERHEUGT, A. P. Supravalvular aortic stenosis. Circulation, 1958, 18, 902.

DEXTER, L., HARKEN, D. E., COBB, L. A., JR., NOVACK, P., SCHLAUT, R. C., PHINNEY, A. D., AND HAYNES, F. W. Aortic stenosis. A. M. A. Arch. Int. Med., 1958, 101, 254.

DEXTER, L., HAYNES, F. W., BURWELL, C. S., EPPINGER, E. C., SOSMAN, M. C., AND EVANS, J. M. Studies of congenital heart disease. III.

Venous catheterization as a diagnostic aid in patent ductus arteriosus, Tetralogy of Fallot, VSD and ASD. J. Clin. Invest., 1947, 26, 561.

DOCK, W., GRANDELL, F., AND TAUBMAN, F. The physiologic third heart sound: its mechanism and relation to protodiastolic gallop. Am. Heart J., 1955, 50, 449.

DODGE, H. T., KIRKHAM, F. T., JR., AND KING, C. F. Ventricular dynamics in atrial fibrillation. Circulation, 1957, 15, 335.

DONOVAN, T. J., HUFNAGEL, C. A., AND EASTCOTT, H. H. G. Techniques of endocardial anastomosis for circumventing the pulmonic valve. J. Thoracic Surg., 1952, 23, 348.

DOW, J. W., LEVINE, H. D., ELKIN, M., HAYNES, F. W., HELLEMS, H. K., WHITTENBERGER, J. W., FERRIS, B. G., GOODALE, W. T., HARVEY, W. P., EPPINGER, E. C., AND DEXTER, L. Studies of congenital heart disease. IV. Uncomplicated pulmonic stenosis. Circulation, 1950, 1, 267.

ELKIN, D. C. AND WARREN, J. V. J.A.M.A., 1947, 134, 1524.

EPPINGER, E. C., BURWELL, C. S., AND GROSS, R. E. J. Clin. Invest., 1941, 20, 127.

ESPERSEN, T. Acta med. scandinav., 1941, 108, 153.

FERGUSON, D. J. AND VARCO, R. L. The relation of blood pressure and flow to the development and regression of experimentally induced pulmonary arteriosclerosis. Circulation Res., 1955, 3, 152.

FERRER, M. I., HARVEY, R. M., WEINER, H. M., CATHCART, R. T., AND COURNAND, A. Hemodynamic studies in two cases of W-P-W syndrome with paroxysmal A-V nodal tachycardia. Am. J. Med., 1949, 6, 725.

FERRER, M. I., HARVEY, R. M., KUSCHNER, M., RICHARDS, D. W., JR., AND COURNAND, A. Hemodynamic studies in tricuspid stenosis of rheumatic origin. Circulation Res., 1953, 1, 49.

FERRER, M. I., HARVEY, R. M., CATHCART, R. T., COURNAND, A., AND RICHARDS, D. W., Hemodynamic studies in rheumatic heart disease. Circulation, 1952, 6, 688.

FISH, R. G., TAKARO, T., AND CRYMES, T. Prognostic considerations in primary isolated insufficiency of the pulmonic valve. New England J. Med., 1959, 261, 739.

FOWLER, N. O., MANNIX, E. P., AND NOBLE, W. Some effects of partial pulmonary valvectomy. Circulation Res., 1956, 4, 8.

FUTCHER, P. H. AND SCHROEDER, H. A. Am. J. M. Sc., 1942, 204, 52.

GORLIN, R. AND GOODALE, W. T. Changing blood pressure in aortic insufficiency. New England J. Med., 1956, 255, 77.

GORLIN, R. AND GORLIN, S. G. Hydraulic formula for calculation of the area of the stenotic mitral valve, other cardiac valves, and central circulatory shunts. I. Am. Heart J., 1951, 41, 1.

GORLIN, R., HAYNES, F. W., GOODALE, W. T., SAWYER, C. G., DOW, J. W., AND DEXTER, L. Studies of the circulatory dynamics in mitral stenosis II. Am. Heart J., 1951, 41, 30.

GORDON, A. J., JENKINS, G., GRISHMAN, A., AND NABATOFF, R. A. Tricuspid stenosis. Am. J. Med., 1957, 22, 306.

GORLIN, R., LEWIS, B. M., HAYNES, F. W.,

SPIEGL, R. J., AND DEXTER, L. Factors regulating pulmonary "capillary" pressure in mitral stenosis. IV. Am. Heart J., 1951, 41, 834.

GORLIN, R., McMILLAN, I. K. R., MEDD, W. E., MATHEWS, M. B., AND DALEY, R. Dynamics of the circulation in aortic valvular disease. Am. J. Med., 1955, 18, 855.

GORLIN, R., SAWYER, C. G., HAYNES, F. W., GOODALE, W. T., AND DEXTER, L. Effects of exercise on circulatory dynamics in mitral stenosis III. Am. Heart J., 1951, 41, 192.

GREEN, H. D. The coronary blood flow in aortic stenosis, in aortic insufficiency and in arteriovenous fistula. Am. J. Physiol., 1936, 115, 94.

GROSS, R. E. The patent ductus arteriosus. Am. J. Med., 1952, 12, 472.

GROSS, R. E. Coarctation of the aorta: Surgical treatment of 100 cases. Circulation, 1950, 1, 41.

GUPTA, T. C. AND WIGGERS, C. J. Basic hemodynamic changes produced by aortic coarctation of different degrees. Circulation, 1951, 3, 17.

GUPTA, T. C. The effects of arterial and pulmonary shunts on the dynamics of aortic coarctation. Circulation, 1951, 3, 32.

HANDELSMAN, J. C., BING, R. J., CAMPBELL, J. A., AND GRISWOLD, H. E. Physiological studies in congenital heart disease. V. The circulation in patients with isolated septal defects. Bull. Johns Hopkins Hosp., 1948, 82, 615.

HANSEN, A. T., ESKILDSEN, P., AND GOTZACHE, H. Pressure curves from the right auricle and the right ventricle in chronic constrictive pericarditis. Circulation, 1951, 3, 881.

HANSEN, W. R., McCLENDON, R. L., AND KINSMAN, J. M. Auricular fibrillation: Hemodynamic studies before and after conversion with quinidine. Am. Heart J., 1952, 44, 499.

HARVEY, R. M., FERRER, I., CATHCART, R. T., RICHARDS, D. W., AND COURNAND, A. Mechanical and myocardial factors in chronic constrictive pericarditis. Circulation, 1953, 8, 695.

HARVEY, R. M., FERRER, I., SAMET, P., BADER, R. A., BADER, M. E., COURNAND, A., AND RICHARDS, D. W. Mechanical and myocardial factors in rheumatic heart disease with mitral stenosis. Circulation, 1955, 11, 531.

HARVEY, R. M., FERRER, M. I., RICHARDS, D. W., AND COURNAND, A. Cardiocirculatory performance in atrial flutter. Circulation, 1955, 12, 507.

HIMMELSTEIN, A. AND COURNAND, A. Cardiac catheterization in the study of congenital cardiovascular anomalies. Am. J. Med., 1952, 12, 349.

HUFNAGEL, C. A., HARVEY, W. P., RABIL, P. S., AND McDERMOTT, T. F. Surgical correction of aortic insufficiency. Surgery, 1954, 35, 673.

ISAACS, J. P., CARTER, B. N., AND HALLER, J. A. Experimental pericarditis: The pathologic physiology of constrictive pericarditis. Bull. John Hopkins Hosp., 1952, 90, 259.

ISAACS, J. P., BERGLUND, E., AND SARNOFF, S. J. Ventricular function. III. The pathologic physiology of acute cardiac tamponade studied by means of ventricular function curves. Am. Heart J., 1954, 48, 66.

KATZ, L. N., RALLI, E. P., AND CHEER, S. The cardiodynamic changes in the aorta and left ventricle due to stenosis of the aorta. J. Clin. Invest., 1927–8, **5**, 205.

KILLIP, T., III, AND LUKAS, D. S. Tricuspid stenosis. Circulation, 1957, **16**, 3.

KOHOUT, F. W., AND KATZ, L. N. Pulmonic valvular regurgitation. Am. Heart J., 1955, **49**, 637.

LANDIS, E. M., BROWN, E., FAUTEUX, M., AND WISE, C. J. Clin. Invest., 1946, **25**, 237.

LASCHE, E. M., PERLOFF, W. H., AND DURANT, T. M. Am. J. M. Sc., 1951, **222**, 459.

LEVINSON, D. C., GUNTHER, L., MEEHAN, J. P., GRIFFITH, G. C., AND SPRITZLER, R. J. Hemodynamic studies in five patients with heart block and slow ventricular rates. Circulation, 1955, **12**, 739.

LEWIS, T. AND DRURY, A. N. Observations relating to arteriovenous aneurism. Part I. Circulatory manifestations in clinical cases with particular reference to arterial phenomena of aortic regurgitation. Heart, 1923, **10**, 301.

LIND, J., WEGELIUS, C., AND LICHTENSTEIN, H. The dynamics of the heart in complete A-V block. An angiographic study. Circulation, 1954, **10**, 195.

LITTLE, R. C., OPDYKE, D. F., AND HAWLEY, J. G. Dynamics of experimental atrial septal defects. Am. J. Physiol., 1949, **158**, 241.

MARAIST, F., DALEY, R., DRAPER, A., JR., HEIMBECKER, R., DAMMANN, F., JR., KIEFFER, R., JR., KING J. T., FERENCZ, C., AND BING, R. J. Physiological studies in congenital heart disease. X. The physiological findings in 34 patients with isolated pulmonary valvular stenosis. Bull. Johns Hopkins Hosp., 1951, **88**, 1.

McCORD, M. C. AND BLOUNT, S. G., JR. The hemodynamic pattern in tricuspid valve disease. Am. Heart J., 1952, **44**, 671.

McCORD, M. C., VAN ELK, J., AND BLOUNT, S. G., JR. Tetralogy of Fallot: Clinical and hemodynamic spectrum of combined pulmonary stenosis and ventricular septal defect. Circulation, 1957, **16**, 736.

McDONALD, L., DEALEY, J. B., JR., RABINOWITZ, M., AND DEXTER, L. Clnical, physiological and pathological findings in mitral senosis and regurgitation. Medicine, 1957, **36**, 237.

METCALFE, J., WOODBURY, J. W., RICHARDS, V., AND BURWELL, C. S. Studies in experimental pericardial tamponade: effects on intravascular pressures and cardiac output. Circulation, 1952, **5**, 518.

McKUSICK, V. A. Chronic constrictive pericarditis. I. Some clinical and laboratory observations. Bull. Johns Hopkins Hosp., 1952, **90**, 3.

MOKOTOFF, R., ROSS, G., AND LEITER, L. J. Clin. Invest., 1948, **27**, 1.

MOSCOVITZ, H. L., GORDON, A. J., BRAUNWALD, E., AMRAM, S. S., SAPIN, S. D., LASSER, R. P., HIMMELSTEIN, A., AND RAVITCH, M. M. The use of simultaneous left heart pressure pulse measurements in evaluating the effects of mitral valve surgery. Am. J. Med., 1955, **18**, 406.

MUSSER, B. G., BOUGAS, J., AND GOLDBERG, H. Left heart catheterization. II. With particular reference to mitral and aortic valvular disease. Am. Heart J., 1956, **52**, 567.

MYERSON, A., LOMAN, J., RINKEL, M., AND LESSES. M. F. Human autonomic pharmacology.

XVIII. Effect of intra-arterial injection of acetylcholine, acetyl-beta-methylcholine chloride, epinephrine and benzedrine sulfate. Am. Heart J., 1938, **16**, 329.

NIELSEN, H. E. Acta med. scandinav., 1937, **91**, 223.

OLESEN, K. H. AND FABRICIUS, J. Pulmonic valvular regurgitation during 27 years after gonorrheal endocarditis: report of case with catheterization data. Am. Heart J., 1956, **52**, 791.

OPDYKE, D. F., DUOMARCO, J., DILLON, W. H., SCHREIBER, H., LITTLE, R. C., AND SEELY, R. D. Study of simultaneous right and left atrial pressure pulses under normal and experimentally altered conditions. Am. J. Physiol., 1948, **154**, 258.

PAINTER, R. C., HINES, E. A., JR., AND EDWARDS, J. E. Measurements of arterioles in coarctation of the aorta. Circulation, 1952, **6**, 727.

PARKER, F., JR. AND WEISS, S. The nature and significance of the structural changes in the lungs in mitral stenosis. Am. J. Path., 1936, **12**, 573.

PARRISH, A. E. J. Clin. Invest., 1949, **28**, 45.

PERRY, T. M. Brucellosis and heart disease. IV. Etiology of calcific aortic stenosis. J. A. M. A., 1958, **166**, 1123.

PORTER, R. R. AND DOWNS, R. S. Ann. Int. Med., 1942, **17**, 645.

RICHARDS, D. W., JR. Am. J. Med., 1949, **6**, 772.

RODBARD, S. AND WILLIAMS, F. The dynamics of mitral insufficiency. Am. Heart J., 1954, **48**, 521.

ROSS, J., JR., BRAUNWALD, E., AND MORROW, A. G. Clinical and hemodynamic observations in pure mitral insufficiency. Am. J. Cardiol., 1958, **2**, 11.

RYTAND, D. A. The renal factor in arterial hypertension with coarctation of the aorta. J. Clin. Invest., 1938, **17**, 391.

SAWYER, C. G., BURWELL, C. S., DEXTER, L., EPPINGER, E. C., GOODALE, W. T., GORLIN, R., HARKEN, D. E., AND HAYNES, F. W. Chronic constrictive pericarditis: further consideration of the pathologic physiology of the disease. Am. Heart J., 1952, **44**, 207.

SCHEMM, F. R. Ann. Int. Med., 1942, **17**, 952; ibid., 1944, **21**, 937.

SELZER, A. Defects of the cardiac septums. J. A. M. A., 1954, **154**, 129.

SEPULVEDA, G. AND LUKAS, D. S. The diagnosis of tricuspid insufficiency. Circulation, 1955, **XI**, 552.

SHEPHERD, J. T., WEIDMAN, W. H., BURKE, E. C., AND WOOD, E. H. Hemodynamics in patent ductus arteriosus without a murmur. Circulation, 1955, **11**, 404.

SINGER, B. AND WENER, J. Am. Heart J., 1953, **45**, 795.

STARR, I. Am. J. M. Sc., 1940, **199**, 40.

STARR, I., JEFFERS, W., AND MEADE, R., JR. Am. Heart J., 1943, **26**, 291.

STARZL, T. E. AND GAERTNER, R. A. Chronic heart block in dogs. A method for producing experimental heart failure. Circulation, 1955, **12**, 259.

STARZL, T. E., GAERTNER, R. A., AND BAKER, R. R. Acute complete heart block in dogs. Circulation, 1955, **12**, 82.

STARZL, T. E., GAERTNER, R. A., AND WEBB, R.

C., JR. The effects of repetitive electric cardiac stimulation in dogs with normal hearts, complete heart block and experimental cardiac arrest. Circulation, 1955, 11, 952.

STEWART, H. J., DIETRICK, J. E., CRANE, N. F., AND THOMPSON, W. P. Studies of the circulation in the presence of abnormal cardiac rhythms. Observations relating to (Part I) rhythms associated with rapid ventricular rate and to (Part II) rhythms associated with slow ventricular rate. J. Clin. Invest., 1938, 17, 449.

STACK, M. F., RADER, B., SOBOL, B. J., FARBER, S. J., AND EICHNA, L. W. Cardiovascular hemodynamic functions in complete heart block and the effect of isopropylnorepinephrine. Circulation, 1958, 17, 526.

TANENBAUM, H. L., BRAUNWALD, E., AND MORROW, A. G. Determination of cardiac output and pressure gradients at operation; a technic for the immediate assessment of the results of operations for stenotic valvular disease. New England J. Med., 1958, 258, 527.

WARREN, J. V., LEONARD, J. L., AND WEISSLER, A. M. Gallop rhythm. Ann. Int. Med., 1958, 48, 580.

WELCH, G. H., JR., BRAUNWALD, E., AND SARNOFF, S. J. Hemodynamic effects of quantitatively varied experimental aortic regurgitation. Circulation Res., 1957, 5, 546.

WEISS, S. AND WILKINS, R. W. Ann. Int. Med., 1937, 11, 104.

WIGGERS, C. J. AND FEIL, H. Cardiodynamics in mitral insufficiency. Heart, 1922, 9, 149.

WIGGERS, C. J. The magnitude of regurgitation with aortic leaks of different sizes. J. A. M. A., 1931, 97, 1359.

WIGGERS, C. J. AND MALBY, A. B. Further observations on experimental aortic insufficiency. IV. Hemodynamic factors determining the characteristic changes in aortic and ventricular pressure pulses. Am. J. Physiol., 1931, 97, 689.

WINCHELL, P. AND BASHOUR, F. Some physiological features of aortic septal defect. Am. J. Cardiol., 1958, 2, 687.

YOUMANS, W. B. Mod. Concepts. Cardiovas. Dis., 1957, 26, 389.

*Monographs and Reviews*

ALTSCHULE, M. D. The pathological physiology of chronic cardiac decompensation. Medicine, 1938, 17, 75.

BEECHER, H. K. Early care of the seriously wounded man. J. A. M. A., 1951, 145, 193.

BOLTON, C. The pathology of cardiac dropsy. Brit. Med. J., 1917, 1, 642.

BORST, J. G. G. The maintenance of an adequate cardiac output by the regulation of the urinary excretion of water and sodium chloride: an essential factor in the genesis of oedema. Acta med. scandinav., 1948, Suppl., CCVII (207), 130.

BRADLEY, S. E. AND BLAKE, W. D. Pathogenesis of renal dysfunction during congestive heart failure. Am. J. Med., 1949, 6, 470.

COURNAND, A., BALDWIN, J. S. AND HIMMELSTEIN, A. Cardiac catheterization in congenital heart disease. The Commonwealth Fund, New York, 1949.

ERSKINE, J. M. The relation of the liver to shock. Internat. Abstr. Surg., 1958, 106, 207.

FINE, J. The bacterial factor in traumatic shock. Charles C Thomas, Springfield, Illinois, 1954.

FRIEDBERG, C. K. Diseases of the heart. Ed. 2. W. B. Saunders Company, Philadelphia, 1956.

GREEN, H. H. Editor, Shock and circulatory hemeostasis. Josiah Macy, Jr. Foundation, New York, Transactions of five annual conferences, 1952 to 1957.

GREGERSEN, M. I. Shock. Ann. Rev. Physiol., 1946, 8, 335.

GREGERSEN, M. I. Blood volume. Ann. Rev. Physiol., 1951, 13, 397.

HOLMAN, E. Arteriovenous aneurysm; abnormal communication between the arterial and venous circulations. Macmillan Company, New York, 1937.

HOLMAN, E. Clinical and experimental observations on arteriovenous fistulae. Ann. Surg., 1940, 112, 840.

LEATHAM, A. Auscultation of the Heart. Lancet, 1958, 2, 703, 757.

LEVINE, S. A., AND HARVEY, W. P. Clinical auscultation of the heart. W. B. Saunders Company, Philadelphia, 1950.

McMICHAEL, J. Output of heart in congestive failure. Quart. J. Med., 1938, 7, 331.

McMICHAEL, J. Circulatory failure studied by means of venous catheterization. Advances Int. Med., 1947, 2, 64.

MERRILL, A. J. Mechanisms of salt and water retention in heart failure. Am. J. Med., 1949, 6, 357.

SCHORR, E., ZWEIFACH, B. W., FURCHGOTT, R. F., AND BAEZ, S. Hepatorenal factors in circulatory homeostasis. Circulation, 1951, 42, 1951.

SHEPHERD, JOHN T. The pulmonary circulation in the presence of interatrial, interventricular and interarterial communications. Pulmonary Circulation, edited by W. Adams and I. Veith. Grune & Stratton, Inc., New York, 1959.

STARR, I. Our changing viewpoint about congestive failure. Ann. Int. Med., 1949, 30, 1.

STEAD, E. A., JR. Edema of heart failure. Bull. New York Acad. Med., 1948, 24, 607.

WARREN, J. V. AND STEAD, E. A., JR. Fluid dynamics in chronic congestive heart failure. An interpretation of the mechanisms producing the edema, increased plasma volume and elevated venous pressure in certain patients with prolonged congestive failure. Arch. Int. Med., 1944, 73, 138.

WIGGERS, C. J. Physiology of shock. The Commonwealth Fund, New York, 1950.

WOOD, P. Diseases of the heart and circulation. Ed. 2. J. B. Lippincott Company, Philadelphia, 1956.

YOUMANS, W. B. Renal function in congestive heart failure. Ann. Int. Med., 1954, 41, 739.

YOUMANS, W. B. Mechanism of high output circulatory failure. Ann. Int. Med., 1954, 41, 747.

YOUMANS, W. B. AND HUCKINS, A. R. Hemodynamics in failure of the circulation. Charles C Thomas, Springfield, Illinois, 1951.

SECTION THREE
*Respiration*

# 29

# UPTAKE AND DELIVERY OF THE RESPIRATORY GASES

## The Physical Principles Governing the Respiratory Exchanges

The cells of higher animals continually use oxygen and produce carbon dioxide as a waste product. Movement of oxygen into the lungs of mammals is promoted by breathing movements. Oxygen diffuses into the blood in the pulmonary capillaries to be carried to all parts of the body where it diffuses from the capillary blood into the interstitial fluid and on to the cells. Carbon dioxide diffuses from the cells to the interstitial fluid and then to the blood in the systemic capillaries to be carried to the lungs where it diffuses into the alveolar air.

The major problems to be considered under the heading of respiratory physiology are 1) the uptake of oxygen from alveolar air and its delivery to the tissues, 2) the uptake of carbon dioxide from tissues and its delivery to the alveolar air, 3) the mechanism of rhythmic inspiration and expiration, and 4) the mechanisms by means of which the amount of air breathed per minute is adjusted to the needs of the body. The actual chemical processes by which the oxygen is utilized in the cells (cellular respiration), will not be discussed. This subject is considered in detail in texts in biochemistry. Some of the derangements of respiration are considered under the appropriate major headings, while others which are of a more general nature are described in the final chapter of the section.

It is assumed that the reader already will have knowledge of elementary biochemistry and human anatamy. Further, it is essential that the relation of carbon dioxide to the acid-base balance (ch. 13), the physiology of nerve, muscle, and reflex action (ch. 63) and the physiology of the autonomic nervous system (ch. 71) should

be studied in advance in order to understand the chemical and neural control of respiration.

## The Kinetic Theory of Gases—Diffusion, Partial Pressures, Absorption Coefficients

Any quantity of a gas when placed in a container of whatever size expands its volume until limited by the boundaries of the confining vessel. This fact is explained upon the theory that the gas molecules are in continuous motion, moving through space at high velocity and being deflected from their course only upon coming into collision with other gas molecules or with the boundaries of the space itself which they strike and from which they rebound repeatedly. Such movements constitute a bombardment upon the confining walls which is responsible for what is called the pressure or tension of the gas. The greater the number of molecules in any given space the more frequent, obviously, will be the bombardments. So, if the capacity of the space is reduced the molecules are brought closer together. The rate of bombardment upon a unit of surface will increase and the pressure of the gas will rise (see *Boyle's Law* below). A rise in temperature increases the velocity of the molecular movements, increases the rate of bombardment and the force of the impacts. The pressure in consequence increases (*Charles' Law*).

In all circumstances, the gas molecules as a result of their movements will in time distribute themselves evenly throughout the space in which they are confined, and consequently, the pressure will be the same upon all parts of the limiting

TABLE 29.1

*Absorption coefficients of various gases in distilled water at different temperatures*

| Tempera-ture | Oxygen | Carbon Dioxide | Carbon Monoxide | Nitrogen |
|---|---|---|---|---|
| 0 | 0.049 | 1.71 | 0.035 | 0.024 |
| 20 | 0.031 | 0.87 | 0.023 | 0.016 |
| 40 | 0.023 | 0.53 | 0.018 | 0.012 |

surface. In other words, although at the start the molecules may be in greater concentration in one part of the space than in another, even distribution is soon brought about, and the pressure throughout all parts of the space becomes equal. This behavior of a gas whereby the equalization of its molecular concentration occurs is spoken of as *diffusion*. If we should deal with a mixture of two or more different gases instead of with a single gas it would be found that each component in the mixture behaved as though present alone. Its molecules would become distributed evenly throughout the mixture, and its pressure would depend upon its concentration without regard to the concentrations of the other component gases (*Law of partial pressures*).

If two samples of a gas, of different concentrations, be placed one on each side of a membrane permeable to that gas, diffusion also occurs until the tensions on the two sides of the membrane are equal; as in the case of a gas mixture each gas behaves as though present alone.

When a gas or a mixture of gases lies in contact with the surface of a liquid, the molecules of each gas penetrate the liquid and become dissolved in it until the tensions of that particular gas within and without the liquid are equal. The gas is then said to be equilibrated with the liquid (*Law of solubility of gases*). On the other hand, if the liquid be now exposed to a lower pressure of the gas the molecules which had undergone solution at the higher pressure escape until equilibrium is restored at the lower level. Soda water, for example, is water which has been equilibrated with carbon dioxide at a high pressure. When the cork is removed from the bottle containing the surcharged liquid, effervescence occurs. Molecules of carbon dioxide are given off until the pressure of the dissolved gas equals that of the carbon dioxide in the atmosphere. A gas at different tensions in two liquids also comes into equilibrium whether the liquids are in direct contact or are separated by a membrane permeable to the gas. Also the actual *amount* of gas which will undergo solution at a given pressure varies with the particular gas and

with the liquid. If distilled water for example be exposed to oxygen at a pressure of 760 mm. and a temperature of 0°C. each 100 cc. will take up 4.9 cc. of the gas. Oil, on the other hand, under the same conditions of pressure and temperature will absorb a great deal more. Therefore, if samples of water and oil are exposed to the atmosphere though the gas pressures in the three media are identical, the volumes of the atmospheric gases in 100 cc. (volumes per cent) of each medium will be widely different.

The quantity of a gas (measured at standard temperature and pressure) which can be absorbed by 1 cc. of a liquid at 760 mm. Hg is called the *absorption coefficient* of the gas for that particular liquid. Thus the absorption coefficient of oxygen in water at 0°C. is 0.049 and of carbon dioxide 1.71; the coefficient varies inversely with the temperature (see table 29.1). The presence of dissolved solid substances in the water will reduce the absorption coefficient of these gases. The values for the body fluids are, therefore, slightly less than those given above. Thus the coefficient of absorption of oxygen in plasma at body temperature (37°C.) is 0.024 and of carbon dioxide 0.510.

The rate of diffusion of a gas through a liquid is in direct proportion to the absorption coefficient of the gas in that liquid and inversely proportional to the square root of its molecular weight. The diffusion rate of carbon dioxide through a wet membrane is about 30 times greater than that of oxygen when the two gases are under identical conditions. For general physiological work the *diffusion coefficient* of oxygen has been defined by Krogh as the number of cubic centimeters of the gas which will diffuse 0.001 mm. distance over a square centimeter of surface, per minute, at a pressure of 1 atmosphere. It varies for different tissues and body fluids and increases 1 per cent per degree Centigrade.

The diffusion coefficients for oxygen through the following materials at body temperature were found:

Water . . . . . . . . . . . . . . . . . . . . . . . . . . . . . . 0.51
Gelatin 15 per cent . . . . . . . . . . . . . . . . . . . . 0.45
Muscle . . . . . . . . . . . . . . . . . . . . . . . . . . . . . 0.31
Connective tissue . . . . . . . . . . . . . . . . . . . . . 0.18

Certain diseases that cause thickening of the pulmonary membrane, destroy lung capillaries, or interfere with diffusion within the blood itself, will reduce the rate of gas diffusion between the blood and the alveolar air. Among such conditions are edema of the lung, emphysema, pulmonary fibrosis, mitral stenosis, and congestive heart failure.

## Summary of the Gas Laws

(1) *Boyle's Law.* When the volume of a gas is altered, the temperature remaining constant, the pressure varies inversely, i.e., the product of the pressure and the volume remains constant. If the space wherein a certain gas is confined be reduced by half, the gas pressure is doubled and vice versa.

(2) *Law of Charles (or Gay-Lussac).* For each rise in temperature of 1°C a gas kept at constant pressure expands by $\frac{1}{273}$ of its volume at 0°C. The volume of a gas at constant pressure is therefore proportional to its absolute temperature (−273°C.).

(3) *The Law of Partial Pressure (Dalton's Law).* The pressure exerted by a gas in a mixture of gases is equal to the pressure which the same quantity of that gas would exert were no other gases present. It follows that the total pressure of a mixture of gases is equal to the sum of the pressures of its component gases. For example, the atmosphere (dry) exerts a pressure of 760 mm. Hg. The gases of which it is composed—oxygen, nitrogen (including other inert gases), and carbon dioxide are present in the proportions of 20.96 per cent, 79 per cent and 0.04 per cent respectively. The partial pressure exerted by oxygen is therefore (20.96/100) × 760 = 159.2 mm. Hg and of carbon dioxide (0.04/100) × 760 = 0.30 mm. Hg.

Air in contact with water is continually receiving water molecules from the surface of the liquid. This water vapor follows Dalton's Law exerting a pressure independently of the other gases, and proportional to the quantity present in the air. The higher the temperature the greater is the quantity of water which the air will hold before becoming saturated and the greater consequently will be the tension of aqueous vapor.

The air in the lungs has a temperature of about 37°C and is usually stated to be fully saturated with water vapor; the latter, therefore, exerts a pressure of 47 mm. Hg.[1] The air after leaving the lungs falls in temperature, some of the water vapor condenses and the latter in consequence is much less. The tension of water vapor in room air (18°C) would be no more than 15.5 mm. Hg, even though the air were fully saturated, and is usually around 4 or 5 mm. Hg. The aqueous tensions of air (saturated) at various temperatures are given in table 29.2.

In the measurement of the respiratory gases the *volumes* are expressed dry (i.e., less the aqueous vapor, though actually no correction for this is

[1] Christie and Loomis from direct measurements have obtained a lower value for the aqueous tension of alveolar air than the usually accepted one of 47 mm. Hg, (namely 45 mm. Hg). They claim that the alveolar air is not fully saturated and that the temperature of the lung is lower than has been assumed. Hyperpnea they found reduced the aqueous tension by as much as 7 mm. Hg. Holding the breath increased it by 0.5 mm. Hg.

### TABLE 29.2

*Tension of aqueous vapor and water in grams in moisture-saturated air at different temperatures*

| Temperature | Tension of Aqueous Vapor | Water per Cubic Meter of Air |
|---|---|---|
| °C | mm. Hg | grams |
| 0 | 4.6 | 4.9 |
| 5 | 6.5 | 6.8 |
| 10 | 9.1 | 9.4 |
| 15 | 12.7 | 12.8 |
| 20 | 17.4 | 17.2 |
| 30 | 31.6 | 30.1 |
| 37 | 47.1 | |

required) and at standard temperature and pressure (S.T.P.)—760 mm. Hg and 0°C. The individual gases, carbon dioxide or oxygen, are then expressed as percentages of this dry volume.

In order to arrive at the *tension* of one or other gas from its percentage in dry air, the figure for the barometric pressure less the aqueous tension must of course be used as the basis for calculation. For example, if the carbon dioxide percentage in a sample of alveolar air (dry) is 5.6 per cent and the barometric pressure, (and so of course the total gas pressure of the alveolar air) is 760 mm. Hg, then the tension of carbon dioxide in the alveolar air must be

$$(5.6/100) \times (760 - 47) = 39.9 \text{ mm. Hg}$$

Similarly when the $O_2$ percentage in dry alveolar air is 14.2 the oxygen tension is

$$(14.2/100) \times (760 - 47) = 101.2 \text{ mm. Hg}$$

(4) *Henry's Law of the Solution of Gases.* If the temperature remains constant, then the quantity of a gas which goes into solution in any given liquid is proportional to the partial pressure of the gas.

## The Exchange of Gases in the Lungs

### THE PARTIAL PRESSURES OF THE GASES IN THE LUNG AIR

In table 29.3 are given average figures for the partial pressures of oxygen, carbon dioxide and nitrogen including argon and other inert gases in inspired, expired and alveolar airs. The fall in oxygen pressure from inspired to alveolar air and in the reverse direction for carbon dioxide will quite evidently promote the free interchange of these gases across the pulmonary epithelium. The interchange of gasses between inspired and alveolar airs is reflected in the intermediate values shown for the gas pressures in the expired air.

The alveolar oxygen and carbon dioxide tensions tend to vary with the minute volume.

### TABLE 29.3

*Composition of atmospheric air, inspired air, and alveolaran at pressure of 1 atmosphere*

| Barometer 760 mm. Hg | Partial Pressure* | | |
|---|---|---|---|
| Gas | Inspired air | Expired air | Alveolar air |
| | mm. Hg | mm. Hg | mm. Hg |
| Oxygen............... | 158.25 | 116 | 100 |
| Carbon dioxide....... | 0.30 | 28 | 40 |
| Nitrogen, argon etc.... | 596.45 | 569 | 573 |
| Aqueous vapor........ | 5.00 | 47 | 47 |
| Totals.............. | 760.00 | 760 | 760 |

\* These are general figures. There is considerable variation between individuals and under different conditions. The range of gas pressures in the alveolar air for man at rest is from 97 to 108 mm. Hg of oxygen, and from 35 to 45 mm. Hg for carbon dioxide.

Minute amounts of argon, helium, neon and other rare gases, are present in the atmosphere and are included in the figure given for nitrogen. They are inert in so far as respiration is concerned, nor do they appear to be essential for any physiological process.

During voluntary hyperpnea the $CO_2$ tension falls and the $O_2$ tension rises. When the breath is held or during periods of apnea, changes of a reverse order occur.

Nitrogen, so far as respiration is concerned is inert. Argon and other inert gases are included along with nitrogen and all of these together ordinarily are designated as "nitrogen", since no distinction needs to be made in discussions of respiratory physiology.

A small but constant amount (about 0.83 volume per cent) of nitrogen is taken up and dissolved in the plasma but it is neither used nor produced within the body, hence, the quantities in arterial and in venous blood are identical. It will be noted, however, that the *percentage* of this gas is higher in alveolar and expired airs than in inspired air. This is due not to any absolute increase in the quantity of nitrogen but to the reduction of the total volume of the respiratory gases resulting from the greater quantity of oxygen absorbed than of carbon dioxide put out.

#### PARTIAL PRESSURES OF OXYGEN AND CARBON DIOXIDE IN BLOOD

In table 29.4 are given the tensions of oxygen and carbon dioxide in arterial and in venous blood. The venous blood, it will be seen, has a lower tension of oxygen (by 60 mm.) than the alveolar air but a higher tension of carbon dioxide

### TABLE 29.4

*Gas tensions in arterial and in venous blood*

| | Tension | |
|---|---|---|
| | Venous blood | Arterial blood |
| | mm. Hg | mm. Hg |
| Oxygen............ | 37 | 100[3] |
| Carbon dioxide...... | 46 | 40 |
| Nitrogen............ | 573 | 573 |
| Water vapor........ | 47 | 47 |
| Totals ............ | 703 | 760 |

(by 6 mm.). It is to be remembered that the pulmonary capillaries and the air in the alveoli are separated by delicate membranes freely permeable to these gases. The pressure gradients are favorable to a rapid inward diffusion of oxygen (from alveolar air to blood) and an outward diffusion of carbon dioxide (from blood to alveolar air). Equilibrium is quickly established between the respiratory gases in the alveolar air and in the blood of the pulmonary capillaries. Since the diffusion coefficient of carbon dioxide through the pulmonary membrane is much higher than that of oxygen, the pressure gradient of the former gas need not be so high for this to occur. It will be seen from tables 29.3 and 29.4 that the tension of carbon dioxide in the blood leaving the lungs, i.e., in the mixed arterial blood, is the same as that in the alveolar air. Indeed, it is the usual practice, when one wishes to know the arterial $CO_2$ tension, to determine that of the alveolar air and assume that the two are identical. It has been shown, however, by Bock and associates that a slight difference (0.5 mm. Hg) does exist.

The oxygen tension of the mixed arterial blood returned from the lungs of man is only slightly lower than that of the alveolar air. Comroe and Dripps, in a series of normal human subjects, obtained a value of 97.4 Hg for the alveolar air and 97.1 Hg for the arterial blood[2]—an *alveolar air-arterial difference* of only 0.3 Hg. Comparable values for man were obtained by Lileinthal and associates.

Gaseous equilibrium is attained not instantaneously but progressively along the course of the pulmonary capillary. Diffusion is rapid at the venous end but as blood and alveolar air approach equilibrium the diffusion process necessarily be-

[2] Since virtually no oxygen is released from the blood in the arterial system, a sample taken from an artery will have the same $O_2$ tension as that in a pulmonary vein.

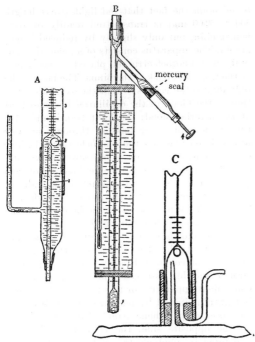

FIG. 29.1. Krogh's microtonometer. *A* is an enlarged view of an equilibration chamber constituting the lower part of *B(1)* but which is shown only in part in the latter drawing. *A* is filled with saline solution through the side tube. *1*, a narrow tube into which the specimen of blood is introduced; *2*, an air bubble. The lower end of *1* is connected by rubber tubing to a cannula inserted into a blood vessel; the blood issues from a narrow opening at the upper end of the tube *1* in a fine jet and plays upon the bubble. After the gases in blood and bubble have come into equilibrium the latter is drawn into the graduated capillary tube shown in *B*, by means of the screw-plunger (*4*), and analyzed according to the following procedure. The volume of the bubble is first measured, it is next drawn into a solution of KOH which absorbs the $CO_2$, then returned to the graduated tube and measured again; the difference between the two measurements gives the amount of $CO_2$ which it contained. The bubble is then passed through a solution of potassium pyrogallate, to absorb the $O_2$, and its volume measured a third time. *C* is a model with an attached cannula which can be inserted directly into a blood vessel.

comes slower. The length of the capillary and the rate of the blood flow through it are factors which must determine the extent to which equilibrium occurs. Roughton obtained a figure of 0.75 seconds for the time of passage of the blood through the pulmonary capillaries for normal men at rest; this was shortened to 0.34 seconds during heavy work. The total volume of blood in the pulmonary capillaries at any moment is also, owing to their distension, much greater than during rest; during arduous exercise the quantity of blood in the lungs may be double that during rest.

The tensions of oxygen and carbon dioxide in human arterial blood may be determined by bringing a small bubble of air into contact with a sample of the blood obtained by arterial puncture. The method employed for the purpose is an adaptation to man (Barcroft and Nagahashi) of a method originally invented by Krogh for animals (see fig. 29.1). After the gases in the air have come into equilibrium with those dissolved in the blood, the small bubble is analyzed and its composition determined. The gas tensions are then calculated from their percentages. Since no gaseous exchanges occur across the walls of the arteries, the tensions so determined are those of the blood leaving the pulmonary capillaries. It has already been mentioned that the arterial carbon dioxide tension is usually obtained from an analysis of alveolar air. The gas tensions of the blood coming to the lungs—the *mixed venous blood*—may be determined in man by direct or indirect methods. In animals mixed venous blood may be obtained from the right ventricle by puncturing the chest wall with a hollow needle attached to a syringe.

### The Volumes of Oxygen and Carbon Dioxide in Blood

Knowing the respective absorption coefficients for oxygen and carbon dioxide in plasma, and the gas pressures, the volume of each gas in *simple solution* in 100 cc. of plasma can be readily calculated (table 29.5). For example, the absorption coefficient of oxygen in plasma is 0.023 at body temperature and at a pressure of 760 mm. Hg. At the partial pressure of oxygen in arterial blood the plasma should hold in solution (100/760) × 0.023 = 0.003 cc. of oxygen per cubic centimeter or 0.3 volume per cent. The absorption coefficient of carbon dioxide in plasma (0.51) or of whole blood (0.48) is higher than that of oxygen, but the partial pressure of carbon dioxide to which arterial blood is exposed in the lung is lower (40 mm.

### TABLE 29.5

*Volumes per cent (cubic centimeters of gas per 100 cc. blood) of oxygen and carbon dioxide in arterial and in venous blood*

| Gas | Venous Blood | | Arterial Blood | |
|---|---|---|---|---|
| | Total | In simple solution | Total | In simple solution |
| Oxygen......... | 12–14 | 0.1 | 19.5 | 0.3 |
| Carbon dioxide... | 58 | 3.0 | 48 | 2.5 |

Hg) than that of oxygen. The quantity of the former gas in simple solution in whole blood is therefore $(40/760) \times 48 = 2.5$ volumes per cent.

About 19.5 volumes per cent of oxygen and from 40 to 50 volumes per cent of carbon dioxide can be removed from arterial blood. The proportions of these gases present in simple solution are, therefore, only a small fraction of the quantities held in the blood in other ways. They are present in chemical combination—oxygen with hemoglobin and carbon dioxide mainly as bicarbonate (see p. 459).

Blood normally contains about 15 grams of hemoglobin per 100 cc. Since 1 gram of hemoglobin carries a maximum of 1.34 cc. of oxygen, arterial blood would, therefore, when saturated to its full capacity, contain about 20 cc. of oxygen. Blood as it leaves the lungs is about 97.5 per cent saturated with oxygen so that the hemoglobin holds at this degree of saturation about 19.5 cc. of oxygen per 100 cc. of blood.[3]

*The photoelectrical determination of the oxygen saturation.* In man, the oxygen saturation can be determined in the blood as it circulates through a translucent part such as the pinna of the ear, by means of the *oximeter*. This instrument, originally suggested by the work of Squires, has been developed by Goldie and by Millikin. The method is

[3] Since the blood in passing through the capillaries of an air sac comes into equilibrium with the air of that air sac as described previously the statement that the arterial blood has a tension less than that of the alveolar air and is only from 94 to 96 per cent saturated, requires explanation. The discrepancy is explained as follows. The air sacs are not all ventilated to the same extent; in some the $O_2$ tension is higher, in some lower than that of the alveolar air as determined upon a sample. In other words the $O_2$ tension of a sample of alveolar air is an average of the $O_2$ tensions of the air in all the air sacs. But when we come to consider the blood coming, not from a single air sac, but from the lung as a whole—i.e., the *mixed arterial blood*—it becomes evident that while an under-ventilated air sac will lower the oxygen tension and so the oxygen saturation of the hemoglobin, an overventilated one cannot compensate this effect to any significant extent. The $O_2$ in solution (upon which the $O_2$ tension directly depends) is in equilibrium with that combined in hemoglobin, and it is evident from the shape of the $O_2$ dissociation curve of hemoglobin that a rise in oxygen tension above 100 mm. Hg will saturate the blood very little more, whereas a fall of 20 mm. Hg or so will reduce the saturation very materially.

The variation between individuals in the $O_2$ saturation of the arterial blood is attributed to the different degrees to which uneven ventilation of the air sacs occurs and also to slight differences in the shapes of the dissociation curves. It was first shown by Barcoft that the $O_2$ dissociation curve is not precisely the same for all persons. The dissimilarities are due apparently to slight differences in the chemical constitution of the globin part of the hemoglobin molecule.

based upon the fact that red light (wave-length 600 to 7500 m$\mu$) is transmitted readily by oxyhemoglobin, but only slightly by reduced hemoglobin. The apparatus consists of an electric light bulb and a photoelectric cell placed, respectively, at the front and back of the pinna. The heat of the bulb dilates the vessels so that the oxygen saturation of the blood in the capillaries becomes that of the arterial blood; the light transilluminates the tissue and, after passing through suitable filters, is received by the photoelectric cell. The electric current set up is measured galvanometrically, and the actual percentage of oxygen saturation is calculated by means of the calibrations of the instrument with values established by the Van Slyke method. This method has proved of great value in determining the oxygen saturation of the blood drawn by catheter from the right auricle, ventricle and pulmonary artery in the diagnosis of congenital cardiac defects (p. 522). Groom and his associates have devised a more convenient apparatus for this purpose. The blood is transilluminated by passing it through a tube composed of polythene attached to the catheter; on the opposite side, the transmitted light is registered by photoelectric cells, placed, respectively, behind red and near infrared (wave-length 750 to 900 m$\mu$) filters. The oxyhemoglobin concentration is calculated from the value registered by the first cell; the total hemoglobin from that given by the second cell. From the ratio of these values the oxygen saturation is estimated.

The quantity of oxygen or of carbon dioxide contained in a given sample of blood (*oxygen or carbon dioxide content*) is determined by transferring the sample to a blood-gas apparatus (Haldan or Van Slyke) and then freeing all the oxygen from the hemoglobin by the addition of potassium ferricyanide, or all carbon dioxide from combination by the addition of acid. Precaution must be taken not to permit the sample to come in contact with air. Since the cell wall is not freely permeable to $K_3Fe(CN)_6$ the corpuscles should be first laked by ammonia or saponin solution. Haldane showed that all the oxygen in blood is liberated by this procedure and the oxyhemoglobin is turned into methemoglobin (p. 57). The *oxygen capacity* of a sample of blood is calculated by exposing it to air or oxygen and determining the amount which it then contains, that is, when the hemoglobin is completely saturated. The ratio of oxygen content to oxygen capacity $\times$ 100 gives the percentage saturation of the blood with oxygen. Since the quantity of oxygen (1.34 cc.) which will combine with 1 gram of hemoglobin is known, the hemoglobin content of a specimen of blood may be calculated from the quantity of $O_2$ in the blood when fully saturated, i.e., from its oxygen capacity. For example, if a sample of blood has an oxygen capacity of 10 volumes per cent, its hemoglobin content is $(10/1.34 =)$ 7.5 grams per cent or about 50 per cent of the normal.

## The Transport and Delivery of Oxygen to the Tissues

The small amount of oxygen in simple solution (about 1 per cent of the total) is negligible when one considers the oxygen requirements of the tissues even during rest (250 cc. per minute). If the blood could hold no more than this it would be necessary for some 120 liters to circulate through the tissues each minute, even assuming that all the oxygen were given up during each circulation. Nevertheless, the gas in simple solution is of the utmost importance since it is in equilibrium with the alveolar air on the one hand and on the other determines the quantity of oxygen which shall be held in combination with the hemoglobin. This will be made clear from a study of the oxygen dissociation curve for hemoglobin.

### The Dissociation Curve of Hemoglobin

Oxygen enters into chemical combination with the iron of the hemoglobin molecule (see ch. 6) to form *oxyhemoglobin*. Each atom of the metal unites with two atoms of oxygen. The remarkable feature of the union of oxygen with hemoglobin is the readiness with which the gas is released from combination when its tension in the surrounding medium is reduced. Hemoglobin from which the oxygen has dissociated is called *reduced hemoglobin*. The relationship between the partial pressure of oxygen and the percentage saturation of the hemoglobin with the gas—i.e., the proportion of oxyhemoglobin to reduced hemoglobin—can be shown in the form of a curve—the *oxygen dissociation curve of hemoglobin*. The curve for a solution of hemoglobin in distilled water is obtained in the following manner. Several samples of the hemoglobin solution are placed each in a separate closed vessel known as a tonometer (fig. 29.2). The respective samples are then exposed to known oxygen tensions: 0, 10, 20, 40 and 100 mm. Hg. The tonometers are rotated continuously in a water bath at body temperature. The solution is thus spread out as a thin film over the interior surface of the vessel. After equilibrium has been attained, the proportion of oxy- to reduced hemoglobin is determined. When 100 per cent saturated—that is, when the hemoglobin has taken up oxygen to its full capacity—the solution contains about 20 volumes per cent of oxygen. When a quarter or half saturated it therefore contains 5 or 10 volumes respectively. The results are plotted on a chart with the oxygen tensions along the

abscissae and the percentage saturation along the ordinates as shown in figure 29.3.

Huffner obtained such a curve for hemoglobin from calculations based upon the law of mass action (see below).

If the foregoing procedures are carried out with blood instead of with a hemoglobin solution a different type of curve is obtained as shown in figure 29.4 It is S-shaped.

The dependence of the oxygen saturation of hemoglobin in an aqueous solution upon the partial pressure of the gas is in accordance with the law of mass action which states that "the velocity of chemical change is proportional to the product of the concentrations of the reacting substances." In this case the reacting substances are reduced hemoglobin and oxygen. The reaction is reversible and is represented thus:

$$Hb \ + \ O_2 \ \rightleftarrows \ HbO_2$$

Reduced                     Oxyhemoglobin
Oxyhemoglobin

It is evident that in the foregoing procedures the tension of oxygen in the hemoglobin solution, or in the plasma in the case of whole blood, came into equilibrium with the oxygen pressure of the atmosphere introduced into the tonometer. Then, the concentration of the dissolved oxygen must be proportional to the partial pressure of the gas to which the solution was exposed. So, if $C_0$ = concentration of $O_2$, $C_R$ = concentration of reduced hemoglobin and $C_H$ = concentration of oxyhemoglobin, then the velocity of the reaction of Hb with $O_2$ to form $HbO_2$ will be proportional to the product of $C_0$ and $C_R$ multiplied by

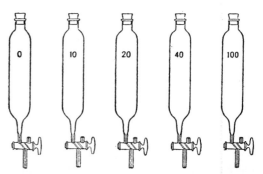

FIG. 29.2. Series of tonometers. The numbers denote the pressure of oxygen in mm. (After Barcroft.)

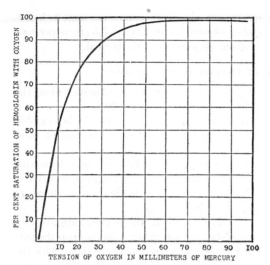

FIG. 29.3. Oxygen dissociation curve of a solution of pure hemoglobin. (After Barcroft.)

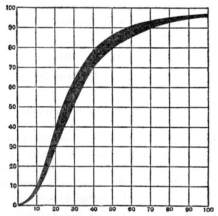

FIG. 29.4. Composite curve to show the degree of variation in the oxygen dissociation curve of human blood as determined upon a number of persons. In each case the blood was exposed to an atmosphere containing the same percentage of $CO_2$ as that of the alveolar air of the individual examined. Ordinates, percentage saturation; abscissae, oxygen pressure. (After Barcroft.)

a constant k, and the reverse reaction, the dissociation of oxyhemoglobin ($HbO_2$) to reduce hemoglobin (Hb) and oxygen, will be proportional to $C_H$ multiplied by another constant $k_1$. Thus:

$$k(C_0 \times C_R) \rightleftharpoons k_1(C_H)$$

At any given tension of oxygen in the opposed reactions, the formation of oxyhemoglobin and its dissociation proceed simultaneously until equilibrium becomes established. A simple reaction of this nature will explain the dissociation curve of a hemoglobin solution but the S-shaped curve of blood is thought to be due to a series of reactions.

It will be recalled that natural hemoglobin has a molecular weight (about 64,000) four times greater than was previously supposed. It may therefore be given the symbol $Hb_4$. It is thought that each molecule of hemoglobin combines with four molecules of oxygen, $Hb_4 + 4O_2 \rightarrow Hb_4O_8$. The oxygen dissociation curve calculated by the application of the law of mass action to this equation has a more pronounced S-shape than any actually observed for blood. On the other hand, the curve calculated from the equation $Hb_4 + O_2$ is hyperbolic (fig. 29.3). It is believed, therefore, that in the combination of oxygen with hemoglobin under physiological conditions, four separate but simultaneous reactions take place.

$$Hb_4 + O_2 = Hb_4O_2$$

$$Hb_4 + 2O_2 = Hb_4O_4$$

$$Hb_4 + 3O_2 = Hb_4O_6$$

$$Hb_4 + 4O_2 = Hb_4O_8$$

The combination of all these reactions, it has been suggested, is responsible for the special S-shape of the oxygen dissociation curve (figs. 29.4 and 29.5).

Certain features associated with the shape of the dissociation curve of whole blood as shown in figure 29.4 are of the utmost physiological importance. It will be seen that with the partial pressure of oxygen in arterial blood (97 mm. Hg) the hemoglobin is already nearly (98 per cent) saturated with the gas. Exposing the hemoglobin to a higher oxygen tension, therefore,

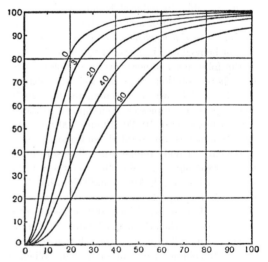

FIG. 29.5. Dissociation curves of human blood, exposed to 0, 3, 20, 40 and 90 mm. $CO_2$. Ordinates, percentage saturation. Abscissae, oxygen pressure. (After Barcroft.)

will cause a negligible increase in the total quantity of oxygen taken up by the blood, and to gain even the ultimate 2 or 3 per cent the oxygen pressure would require to be raised to over 300 mm. Hg. The flattening out of the upper part of the curve means that relatively little reduction in the percentage saturation of the hemoglobin occurs until the oxygen pressure falls to about half its normal value. At pressures above 60 mm. Hg, relatively wide variations in alveolar oxygen pressure can occur with minimal changes in the total oxygen load of the blood. At an oxygen tension of 70 mm. Hg the hemoglobin is still about 90 per cent saturated. The slope of the lower part of the curve is such that a given fall in oxygen pressure causes a much greater desaturation of the hemoglobin. The behavior of hemoglobin as indicated by the shape of the curve, therefore, favors a nearly maximum uptake of oxygen in the lungs so long as the oxygen pressure is above 80 mm. Hg. and a rapid release of the gas at the lower oxygen pressures which prevail in the tissues (1 mm. or less to 60 mm. Hg). It will be realized from a glance at the hyperbolic curve shown in figure 29.3 how unsuitable hemoglobin would be as a carrier of oxygen if it behaved in the manner indicated by such a curve. The hemoglobin would show a great avidity for oxygen in the lungs but would not yield up its oxygen load until the partial pressure in the tissues had fallen to a very low level. At the pressures which exist in the tissues the rate of dissociation of oxyhemoglobin would be many times slower than the rate of its formation. Hemoglobin would thus be worthless as an oxygen carrier. As it is, the oxygenation of hemoglobin in the lungs and its reduction in the tissues proceed at practically equal rates.

### The Effects of Reaction and of Temperature upon the Shape of the Oxygen Dissociation Curve

A *change in the reaction* of the blood toward the acid side causes the dissociation curve to flatten toward the right, i.e., the affinity of hemoglobin for oxygen is reduced. Carbon dioxide and lactic acid liberated during tissue activity will exert this effect. The influence exerted by $CO_2$ was discovered by Bohr and is usually referred to as the Bohr effect[4] (see fig. 29.5).

[4] The oxygen dissociation curve of hemoglobin is so sensitive to acid that it has been used by Barcroft and his associates as a basis of a method for measuring changes in blood reaction. A shift of the curve to the right, i.e., when the blood absorbs less oxygen at a given $O_2$ pressure, would

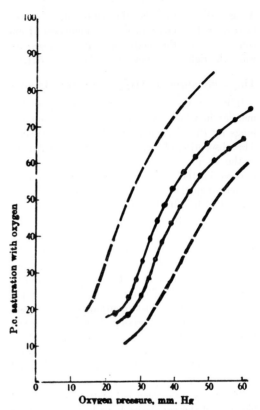

Fig. 29.6. Oxygen dissociation curves of goats' blood; *fetal*, two curves on left, *maternal*, two curves on right. *Beaded lines*, about 10th week of pregnancy; *interrupted lines*, about 18th week. (Drawn from data of Barcroft and associates.)

*Temperature* exerts a similar effect upon the dissociation curve. These agencies, therefore, cause the hemoglobin to liberate its oxygen more readily at the lower oxygen tensions but exert little effect upon the uptake of oxygen at the higher tensions. They cause the reactions involved in the breakdown of oxyhemoglobin to be speeded up, the equilibria shown on page 456 being shifted to the left. Alkalis and a fall in temperature will of course have the reverse effect.

The oxygen dissociation curve of fetal hemoglobin differs from that of postnatal hemoglobin in being steeper as shown in figure 29.6; that is, at a given oxygen tension it takes up more oxygen than does adult blood. Yet, since the passage of oxygen from mother to fetus is simply a matter of diffusion, the tension of oxygen in the blood of the umbilical vein is the same as that in the maternal venous blood of the placenta.

indicate an increase in H ion concentration, and a shift to the left the reverse change.

As gestation proceeds, the fetal curve moves farther to the left, and due to increased H-ion concentration, the maternal curve moves toward the right. (See Fetal Circulation, p. 521.)

## The Unloading of Oxygen in the Tissues

It is now possible to give a summary of the manner in which oxygen is taken up from the lungs by the blood and supplied to the tissues. The absorption of oxygen from the alveolar air is the result simply of diffusion. The oxygen tension in the arterial blood is lower (never higher) than that of the alveolar air. This is so, even at high altitudes where the alveolar oxygen tension is greatly reduced (ch. 33). There is no reason, therefore, to believe that the pulmonary epithelium actually secretes oxygen into the blood.[5] The percentage saturation of the hemoglobin is dependent upon the oxygen tension of the blood, i.e., the amount of the gas in simple solution, which, as just mentioned, is governed in turn by the oxygen pressure in the alveolar air. We have seen that the hemoglobin in the blood leaving the lungs is about 98 per cent in the form of oxyhemoglobin (i.e., it is 98 per cent saturated with oxygen).

Practically no oxygen is lost from the arterial blood until the capillaries have been reached, so the blood reaches the periphery with a high pressure head of oxygen. The oxygen tension of the tissue fluids and cells is relatively low, but varies with the functional activity at the moment between 1 and 60 mm. Hg; a flow of oxygen from the plasma across the capillary membrane results. This, of course, will tend to lower the oxygen tension of the capillary blood plasma and upset the equilibrium between it and the oxyhemoglobin. Dissociation of the latter occurs to sustain the partial pressure of the plasma oxygen. In other words a steady flow of oxygen from red cell to tissue cell is maintained as a result of the slope in partial pressure of the gas. The rise in temperature and liberation of carbon dioxide and lactic acid in the tissues, as we have seen, shifts the oxygen dissociation curve to the right and so accelerates the decomposition of the oxyhemoglobin.

## Coefficient of Oxygen Utilization

Depending upon the particular tissue and its activity at the moment, the blood in its passage

[5] The view that the pulmonary epithelium does not always play the role of a passive membrane but is capable of actively secreting oxygen into the arterial blood was advanced by Bohr and later elaborated by Haldane.

through the capillaries loses from a fifth to nearly all of its oxygen load. The mixed blood coming to the lungs, i.e., blood from all organs of the body, during rest is somewhat more than 75 per cent saturated with oxygen, containing about 4.5 volumes per cent less than does the arterial blood. The figure used to express the proportion of the total oxygen content of the blood which is given up to the tissue is called the *coefficient of oxygen utilization*. Thus, if the oxygen content of the arterial blood is 19.5 volumes per cent and that of the venous blood 15 volumes per cent (i.e., an arteriovenous oxygen difference of 4.5 volumes per cent) the coefficient is $[(4.5)/(19.5)] = 0.23$. As indicated above, the coefficient varies considerably for different tissues and for the same tissue in accordance with the degree of its activity.

### The Respiratory Quotient

The ratio of the volume of carbon dioxide produced by a tissue to the volume of oxygen absorbed

$$\frac{\text{Volumes } CO_2 \text{ produced}}{\text{Volumes } O_2 \text{ absorbed}}$$

is called the respiratory quotient of that particular tissue. The ratio of these volumes as determined from the expired air will be the respiratory quotient of the body as a whole.

## The Manner in Which the Call of the Tissues for Oxygen is Met

Increased activity of any tissue always entails an increased oxygen consumption which may be several times the resting value. Increase in the oxygen supply to the tissue above its requirement, on the other hand, does not increase the oxygen usage. The tissue takes what oxygen its activity at the moment demands but no more.

There are two ways in which a greater demand of the tissues for oxygen may be met. By (1) increasing the total blood flow through the tissue and maintaining a high intracapillary oxygen pressure, and (2) raising the coefficient of oxygen utilization, i.e., increasing the quantity of oxygen abstracted from a given volume of blood.

Both these factors come into play but the extent to which each operates is not the same for different tissues. The coefficient of oxygen utilization is increased by establishing a steep oxygen pressure gradient between the plasma within the capillaries and the tissue cells. That is, the quantity of oxygen used (Q) will, other things being equal, be proportional to the difference in intra-capillary and intracellular pressures ($P_C$ and $P_T$ respectively), thus:

$$Q \propto P_C - P_T$$

The pressure gradient of oxygen from blood to tissue cells acts in a sense as a force to drive oxygen through the tissues. The farther the cells are from the source of supply—the blood—the lower the oxygen pressure will be and the less oxygen will they receive. During activity or any pronounced fall in oxygen tension of the blood, the cells most distant from the source of supply may suffer anoxia unless more capillaries open up, and thus reduce the radius along which oxygen diffuses. Some tissues, however, such as cardiac muscle, take up oxygen at a pressure as low as 5 mm. Hg (Keilin). An increase in the pressure gradient is brought about, (a) by the action of acids (carbonic and lactic) and a rise in temperature both of which accelerate the decomposition of oxyhemoglobin and so maintain a high intracapillary oxygen pressure, (b) by lowering the oxygen tension within the tissue cells, and (c) by shortening the distance through which the oxygen must diffuse, i.e., by opening up more capillaries and so reducing the radius of the cylinder of tissue supplied by each capillary.

During activity more oxygen is consumed and the oxygen tension in the tissues tends to fall, thus increasing the pressure gradient from blood to tissue cells.

As mentioned above, during arduous work the coefficient of oxygen utilization is much increased, and, since the blood flow through the muscles is greatly increased, as well, the oxygen supply to the contracting muscles is augmented several fold. In man the oxygen consumption of the muscles may actually be increased by from twenty to thirty times or in an athlete even fifty times. The increase in oxygen consumption is brought about in part by the removal of more oxygen from each unit of blood.

The circulation rate (ch. 25) in man may increase tenfold or more during muscular exercise. It is certain, however, that there is also a *redistribution* of the blood, that is, a greater proportion of the total blood volume is driven through the muscles than during rest. The actual blood flow through the active muscles may, for this reason, be twenty times or more greater than the flow during rest. Nevertheless, though the red cell has a shorter stay in the capillary it unloads more of its oxygen, as indicated by the increase in the coefficient of oxygen utilization. The actual speed of the red cell through the capillary is not, however, as great as might be thought from the increased volume of blood flowing through the muscles, for the opening up of more capillary channels and the consequent increase in the total cross section of the blood stream tends to prevent excessive acceleration of the red cell's passage.

## The Carriage of Carbon Dioxide by the Blood

BY PROFESSOR J. K. W. FERGUSON

The total carbon dioxide content of blood means the amount of $CO_2$ which can be extracted from a given volume of blood by exposure to a vacuum after the addition of acid. The results are usually expressed as volumes per cent (v.p.c.) by which is meant cc. of $CO_2$ (measured at S.T.P.) per 100 cc. of blood. The methods of Van Slyke and his coworkers are now most commonly used for the measurement of $CO_2$ in blood and other fluids. In Van Slyke's manometric apparatus a known volume of blood is acidified and subjected to a partial vacuum in which $CO_2$ and other gases are rapidly extracted. The gases are then compressed to a known volume and their pressure measured. The $CO_2$ is removed by introducing NaOH, and the pressure at the same volume is again measured. Fom the change in pressure the amount of $CO_2$ can be calculated. By such a method then, it is found that human blood normally contains 50 to 60 v.p.c. of $CO_2$, the venous

blood usually containing 5 to 10 v.p.c. more than the arterial.

It was first shown by Pflüger (1864) that, if whole blood were very thoroughly evacuated, all the $CO_2$ could be removed without the addition of acid. On the other hand, all the $CO_2$ in plasma could not be removed by vacuum alone. After very thorough evacuation the addition of acid or of red blood corpuscles allowed the liberation of more $CO_2$. These facts suggested that, in plasma, $CO_2$ is present mainly as bicarbonate; for on exposure to a vacuum $NaHCO_3$ loses a part of its $CO_2$ according to the equation,

(A)   $2NaHCO_3 \rightarrow CO_2 + H_2O + Na_2CO_3$.[6]

To liberate the $CO_2$ in $Na_2CO_3$ it is necessary to add acid. These results suggested, too, that the red cells contain something which can act as an acid.

[6] At a given temperature ($H_2CO_3$) is a constant fraction of the dissolved $CO_2$, and hence does not require separate representation in the formula.

*Solubility of $CO_2$ in physiological fluids at body temperature*

| Fluid | Absorption Coefficient[2] |
|---|---|
| Water............... | 0.545 |
| Plasma.............. | 0.510 |
| Red cells........... | 0.44 |
| Whole blood........ | 0.48 |

The amount of dissolved $CO_2$ in blood can be calculated from its solubility coefficient in blood (table 29.6), when the pressure of carbon dioxide with which the blood is in equilibrium is known (p. ...). The dissolved $CO_2$ consists in part of carbonic acid ($H_2CO_3$). Although the actual amount of $H_2CO_3$ is extremely small (being only about 0.1 per cent of the dissolved $CO_2$) it is of great importance. When $H_2CO_3$ enters the blood, which is a slightly alkaline solution, it combines with base to form bicarbonate ($BHCO_3$) until an equilibrium is reached between the three forms of $CO_2$:

(B) $\qquad CO_2 \rightleftharpoons H_2CO_3 \rightleftharpoons BHCO_3$ .

The relative amounts of these three forms at equilibrium depend upon the pH of the solution and can be calculated from the Henderson-Hasselbalch equation:

(C) $\qquad pH = pK_1 + \log \dfrac{(BHCO_3)}{(CO_2)\ \text{dissolved}^7}$

$pK_1$ is a composite constant which in normal plasma has a value of about 6.1. The pH of plasma is normally about 7.4. Hence we may write:

(D) $\qquad 7.4 = 6.1 + \log \dfrac{\text{Bicarbonate } CO_2}{\text{Dissolved } CO^1}$

or

$$\frac{\text{Bicarbonate } CO_2}{\text{Dissolved } CO_2} = \frac{20}{1} .$$

If the pH of the plasma is abnormal this ratio will, of course, be different.

The interior of the red cell is more acid than the plasma. Consequently, the ratio of bicarbonate to dissolved $CO_2$ will be smaller. Furthermore, since the water content of the red cell is less than that of plasma, the amount of dissolved $CO_2$ will be less too. For these two reasons then,

[7] Cubic centimeters $CO_2$ (measured at S.T.P.) dissolved in 1 cc. fluid at a pressure of $CO_2$ of 760 mm. Hg.

at the same tension of $CO_2$, the cell contains *less* total carbon dioxide than the plasma. Yet, as we shall soon see, the red cells play the dominant role in the transport of carbon dioxide.

## THE ROLE OF HEMOGLOBIN IN CARBON DIOXIDE TRANSPORT

When carbon dioxide enters the blood from the tissues it combines with water to form $H_2CO_3$. This reaction is relatively slow in most solutions with a pH close to neutrality. In the blood, however, the reaction is catalyzed by an enzyme, carbonic anhydrase, which is found in the red cell but not in the plasma. The $H_2CO_3$ is thus formed within the cells. Nearly all of the $H_2CO_3$ thus formed then combines with base to form bicarbonate. The base available for combination is that which is already combined with weaker acids, mainly proteins, which are displaced by carbonic acid according to the equation,

(E) $\qquad H_2CO_3 + KHb \rightleftharpoons HHb + KHCO_3$ .

Hemoglobin is used as the example in this equation because it does, in fact, furnish directly and indirectly, the greater part of the base used. It does so for a number of reasons. In the first place, it comprises about three-quarters of the total protein in blood. Secondly, it holds in combination an even greater proportion of the base held by weak acids in the blood, because it has so many weak acid groups in its molecule. Thirdly, it has the remarkable property of changing its acid strength with its degree of oxygenation. When the blood is in the tissues, it loses its oxygen, and the hemoglobin becomes a weaker acid and able to yield more base to carbonic acid. In the lungs the hemoglobin is oxygenated and becomes a stronger acid. This assists in displacing carbonic acid from combination with base and in turning it out of the blood. Figure 29.7 shows the titration curves of oxyhemoglobin and hemoglobin. It will be seen that at the same pH, oxyhemoglobin is combined with more base than is hemoglobin, i.e., oxyhemoglobin is the stronger acid.

That hemoglobin behaved in this peculiar way was first suggested by Christiansen, Douglas and Haldane (1914), who investigated the *carbon dioxide dissociation curve* of reduced and oxygenated whole blood. As in the construction of an oxygen dissociation curve, samples of oxygenated or reduced whole blood are brought into equilibrium in a series of saturating vessels, called tonometers, with different pressures of

$CO_2$. The $CO_2$ contents of the equilibrated bloods are then determined by analysis and plotted against the corresponding gas tensions. Christiansen, Douglas and Haldane found that the curve for oxygenated blood was lower than that for reduced blood. In other words, reduced blood could carry more $CO_2$ at the same tension of $CO_2$ than oxygenated blood (fig. 29.8). For many years it was thought that this phenomenon was due entirely to the change in acid strength of hemoglobin on oxygenation. Reduced hemoglobin, being a weaker acid, would yield more base to carbonic acid and hence, at equal pressures of $CO_2$, more bicarbonate would be formed. It now appears, however, that 50 per cent or more of this greater $CO_2$-combining power of reduced blood is due to the greater power of reduced hemoglobin to combine directly with $CO_2$.

Leaving aside the question of how the greater $CO_2$-combining power of reduced blood is effected, let us consider the physiological importance of the phenomenon. By examining figure 29.8, it will be seen that if the blood, represented by point A on the curve, took up 5 v.p.c. of $CO_2$, from the tissues and no reduction of the hemoglobin occurred, the tension of $CO_2$ in the blood would rise by about 14 mm. Hg. If, however, about 6 v.p.c. of $O_2$ are lost from the capillary

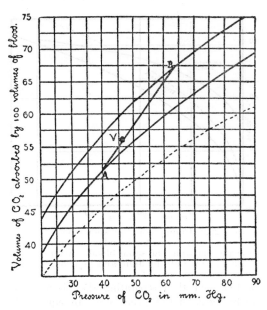

FIG. 29.8. Carbon dioxide dissociation curves of fully reduced human blood (upper solid line) in presence of hydrogen, and fully oxygenated human blood (lower solid line), in presence of air. Volumes of $CO_2$ along the ordinates; $CO_2$ tension along the abscissae. Line AVB is the so-called physiological dissociation curve of $CO_2$, i.e., as a result of the reduction of hemoglobin the relation of volumes of $CO_2$ to $CO_2$ tension is indicated at points along this line and not along the lower curve for oxygenated blood. At *A* (arterial point) are indicated the volume and tension of $CO_2$ in arterial blood. Point *B* indicates the conditions in fully reduced blood. Point *V* (venous point) represents the degree of reduction of hemoglobin which normally occurs in the body during the passage of the blood through the systemic capillaries. The position of the line AVB varies with the respiratory quotient, moving to the right or left, respectively, with a rise or fall in the R.Q. Its position in the figure corresponds to a respiratory quotient of about 0.8. The interrupted line below is the $CO_2$ dissociation curve for oxygenated dog's blood. (Modified from Christiansen, Douglas and Haldane.)

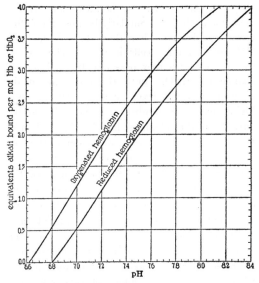

FIG. 29.7. Curves to show the amounts of base (K) bound by oxygenated and reduced hemoglobin at varying pH. The slopes of the curves represent the buffer values, in terms of the equivalent of base required to cause unit pH increase (from Peters and Van Slyke, *Quantitative Clinical Chemistry*, Vol. 1, 1932, from data of Hastings, Van Slyke, Neill, Heidelberger and Harington).

blood (as indicated by point V) the extra $CO_2$ can be taken on with a rise of only 7 mm. Hg in the $CO_2$ tension. As the change in $CO_2$ tension is minimized, so too is the change in the pH of the plasma, because at the lower pressure of $CO_2$ less free carbonic acid is present. In the lungs the reverse reactions occur. Here oxygenation of the hemoglobin reduces the $CO_2$-combining power of the blood, and a smaller fall in $CO_2$ pressure is effective in removing the excess $CO_2$.

The dominant role of the red cells in $CO_2$ transport can be further demonstrated by contrasting the $CO_2$ dissociation curves of *separated* plasma and *true* plasma. The latter is constructed by exposing whole blood to different pressures

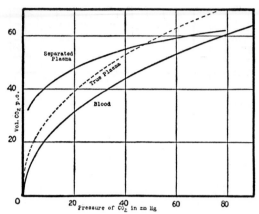

FIG. 29.9. Comparison between the $CO_2$ dissociation curves of blood and of separated and true plasma from the same blood. (After Evans, redrawn from data by Joffe and Poulton.)

of $CO_2$ and then separating the plasma and analyzing it for $CO_2$ ; the former by equilibrating plasma in the absence of red cells (fig. 29.9).

It is apparent that the curve for *separated* plasma is much flatter than that of *true* plasma which signifies that much larger changes in $CO_2$ pressure and pH accompany a given change in $CO_2$ content in *separated* plasma. Evidently separated plasma is not as well buffered as true plasma. The greater buffer power of true plasma must be due to the red cells. We know, however, that base ions, e.g., $K^+$ and $Na^+$ cannot pass from the red cell into the plasma, because the red cell membrane is impermeable to cations with the exception of $H^+$. Consequently, the red cells must increase the buffer power of the plasma indirectly. They do so by means of the *chloride shift* or *Hamberger phenomenon*.

If $CO_2$ is added to whole blood and the corpuscles and plasma are analyzed separately, it will be found that:

(1) The bicarbonate content of both plasma and corpuscles has increased.

(2) The chloride content of the corpuscles has increased.

(3) The chloride content of the plasma has decreased.

(4) The metallic cation content of the corpuscles and plasma has not changed.

(5) The water content and volume of the corpuscles has increased.

The reverse changes occur when $CO_2$ is removed from blood by evacuation. Evidently, there is a transfer of the chloride from plasma to cells when $CO_2$ enters the blood, and the reverse process when $CO_2$ leaves the blood; hence the name, chloride shift. A simple qualitative ex-

planation of this phenomenon can be given. When $CO_2$ enters the blood, more $HCO_3^-$ is formed in the corpuscles than in the plasma, because they contain more available base for neutralizing $H_2CO_3$. These excess $HCO_3^-$ ions tend to diffuse out into the plasma, but, owing to the electrostatic attraction of the cations within the cells, can only do so if an equal number of $Cl^-$ ions enter to take their place. Thus $HCO_3^-$ from the cells enters the plasma in exchange or $Cl^-$ which enters the corpuscles. This process will continue until an equilibrium is reached which has been found to agree (very nearly) with the distribution required by Donnan's theory of membrane equilibria (p. ...). This requires the following relations:[8]

(F) $$\frac{[H^+]}{\text{cells}} \times \frac{[Cl^-]}{\text{cells}} = \frac{[H^+]}{\text{plasma}} \times \frac{[Cl^-]}{\text{plasma}}$$

$$\frac{[H^+]}{\text{cells}} \times \frac{[HCO_3^-]}{\text{cells}} = \frac{[H^+]}{\text{plasma}} \times \frac{[HCO_3^-]}{\text{plasma}}$$

or

$$\frac{[H^+] \text{ plasma}}{[H^+] \text{ cells}} = \frac{[Cl^-] \text{ cells}}{[Cl^-] \text{ plasma}} = \frac{[HCO_3] \text{ cells}}{[HCO_3^-] \text{ plasma}}$$

The phenomenon can, in fact, be explained very precisely in terms of the Donnan theory. When $CO_2$ enters the blood the ratio $(HCO_3^-)$ cells/$(HCO_3^-)$ plasma increases because more base is available in the cells. Similarly because the buffer power of plasma is less than that of the cells $(H^+)$ plasma/$(H^+)$ cells increases. The $Cl^-$ of the plasma must now pass into the cells in exchange for $HCO_3^-$ until the ratios are again equalized at a new level. Since the new ratio is a higher one, the number of osmotically active particles in the cells must now be higher than in the plasma. Consequently, water enters the corpuscles to equalize the osmotic pressures of the corpuscles and plasma and the volume of the corpuscles increases. If stasis of blood occurs during the withdrawal of blood from a vein, an abnormal amount of $CO_2$ may accumulate and the relative volumes of corpuscles and plasma may be appreciably altered. Hence stasis is undesirable when the blood is required for purposes where the relative volumes of corpuscles and plasma must be measured, e.g., in the estimation of blood volume.

[8] In applying the Donnan equilibrium to the red cell, the only cation which can be regarded as diffusible through the red cell membrane is the $H^-$ ion.

## The Evolution of Carbon Dioxide in the Lungs

The pressure of $CO_2$ in the alveoli is kept by respiratory activity at a lower level than it is in venous blood; hence $CO_2$ diffuses from the blood into the alveoli. This disturbs the equilibrium between the three forms of $CO_2$ and causes reactions to proceed in the direction indicated below:

$$BHCO_3 \rightarrow H_2CO_3 \rightarrow CO_2 + H_2O$$

(G)                          $\downarrow$

(diffuses out)

It has been known for a long time that the reaction $H_2CO_3 \rightleftharpoons CO_2 + H_2O$ is inherently a slow one. It is known too that the blood spends only about one second in the capillaries of the lung and about the same time in the capillaries of active tissues. The velocity constants of these reactions in solutions other than blood are known too, and it can be calculated that if blood had not certain peculiar properties, the time which it spends in the lungs would scarcely allow the escape of 10 per cent of the $CO_2$ which we know does escape. Rapid loading and unloading of $CO_2$ by the blood is accomplished in two ways. The first, which has been mentioned already, is the action of the enzyme, carbonic anhydrase, which accelerates enormously, in either direction, the reversible reaction $H_2CO_3 \rightleftharpoons CO_2 + H_2O$. As the carbonic anhydrase of the blood is found only in the red cells and not in the plasma, we may deduce that the rapid changes in $CO_2$ content occur primarily in the red cells while the plasma comes more slowly into equilibrium with the cells, perhaps after the blood has left the capillaries.

Carbonic anhydrase is present in a number of other animal tissues besides the erythrocytes, e.g., in gastric mucosa and the mucosa of the small intestine as well as in the renal cortex, pancreas, lens and retina, brain, spleen, red muscle, liver, testes, in the oviducts of hens, where its function appears to be concerned in the deposition of calcium in the eggshell, and in saliva. Its physiological significance in most of these situations is unknown. Carbonic anhydrase is a protein, and zinc, as shown by Keilin and Mann, is an important constituent of its molecule. The action of the enzyme is destroyed by an inhibitor in plasma, which has been identified as a pseudoglobulin. It is also inhibited by sulfanilamide, cyanide, sulfocyanate, and by heavy metals. Different sulfonamide drugs differ in their ability to inhibit carbonic anhydrase. The ones most commonly used therapeutically are weak inhibitors of this enzyme. Some, however, have been developed for this special purpose, such as, acetazolamide (Diamox). It is used particularly as a diuretic in cardiac failure. It acts on the kidney to increase the excretion of sodium and potassium, an action which seems to depend on the inhibition of carbonic anhydrase.

The other mechanism for the rapid combination and dissociation of $CO_2$ in blood is the direct combination of $CO_2$ with hemoglobin. This reaction does not go through the stage of carbonic acid and is very rapid. For many years past the existence of such a compound has been generally denied. It is now accepted however. About 25 per cent of the $CO_2$ liberated in the lungs under normal resting conditions is carried in the blood in direct combination with hemoglobin. Nevertheless, the total amount of $CO_2$ in the blood combined in this way is small; probably it never amounts to more than from 8 to 10 per cent of the total $CO_2$. But the fact that reduced hemoglobin combines with more $CO_2$ than does oxyhemoglobin gives the compound an enhanced importance in the transport of $CO_2$; it accounts for from 20 to 25 per cent of the gas freed in the lungs.

Carbon dioxide does not combine with the hemoglobin molecule in the same way that $O_2$ and CO do. It apparently combines with an $NH_2$ group to form a so-called carbamino-acid. Hence, one name suggested for this compound is hemoglobo-carbamic acid (Hb-NHCOOH). Another name less descriptive but possessing the virtue of brevity is carbhemoglobin.

Carbamino-compounds of $CO_2$ with amino-acids are well-known and the technique of estimating these simpler compounds has been adapted for determining carbhemoglobin. Other forms of combined $CO_2$, such as $NaHCO_3$, can be precipitated as $BaCO_3$ by the addition of alkaline $BaCl_2$. The barium salts of the carbamino-acids are soluble and remain in the supernatant fluid after centrifuging. The affinity of Hb for $CO_2$ diminishes with pH, and with strong acidification all the $CO_2$ dissociates off. Consequently, the Van Slyke technique for estimating total $CO_2$ can be applied to the supernatant fluid to measure the carbhemoglobin.

An increase in the $CO_2$ pressure of the blood should, *per se*, cause the formation of a greater amount of carbhemoglobin, but since an increase in $CO_2$ pressure is always accompanied by an increased acidity, which lowers the affinity of

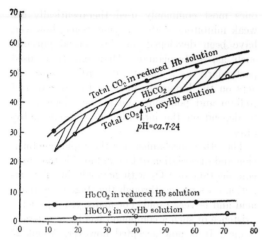

FIG. 29.10. Upper curves, showing the proportions of the difference in $CO_2$ capacity of reduced and of oxyhemoglobin which is due to the higher carbamino content of reduced hemoglobin. The shaded area represents the proportion due to carbamino $CO_2$. Lower curves, showing the negligible effect of a rise in $CO_2$ tension upon the carbhemoglobin content of blood. (After Ferguson and Roughton, modified.)

Hb for $CO_2$, variations in $CO_2$ pressure over physiological ranges have actually little effect on the carbhemoglobin content of the blood. That is to say, the dissociation curve of carbhemoglobin is practically flat over physiological ranges of $CO_2$ pressure. The main factor of physiological importance in displacing $CO_2$ from Hb is oxygenation of the Hb (fig. 29.10).

### SUMMARY

About 5 per cent of the total $CO_2$ in blood is physically dissolved. Two to ten per cent, depending on the degree of oxygenation of the hemoglobin, is combined directly with hemoglobin (carbhemoglobin). The remainder is present as bicarbonate and, as such, is combined with base which has been yielded to $H_2CO_3$ by the weak acids of the blood; the most important of these is hemoglobin.

The $CO_2$-combining power of reduced blood is greater than that of oxygenated blood, (1) because reduced hemoglobin is a weaker acid than oxyhemoglobin; and (2) because reduced hemoglobin can combine directly with more $CO_2$ to form carbhemoglobin than can oxygenated hemoglobin.

Base yielded by hemoglobin participates indirectly in the carriage of $CO_2$ by the plasma by means of the *chloride shift*. Base within the cells neutralizes the $Cl^-$ ions which enter the red cells, thereby leaving base in the plasma free to neutralize $HCO_3^-$ ions.

As the blood passes through the lungs it loses a small part of its total $CO_2$ (i.e., about 10 per cent). The elimination of $CO_2$ is accomplished with minimal change in pH and in $CO_2$ tension by the concurrent oxygenation of the bood which decreases the $CO_2$-combining power of blood in the two ways mentioned above.

The transfer of $CO_2$, to and from the blood while it is in the capillaries, can be accomplished

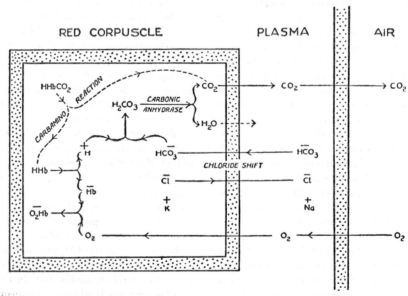

FIG. 29.11. Showing main processes occurring in the blood during the output of carbon dioxide and uptake of oxygen in the lung (after Roughton).

in less than one second, because (1) carbonic anhydrase catalyzes the slow reaction $H_2CO_3 \rightleftharpoons CO_2 + H_2O$ and (2) because the formation and dissociation of carbhemoglobin is inherently rapid (fig. 29.11).

## REFERENCES

ATWELL, R. J., RYAN, J. M., HULL, H. B., AND TOMASHEFSKI, J. F. Am. J. Physiol., 1955, **183**, 451.

BARCROFT, J., AND NAGAHASHI, M., J. Physiol., 1921, **55**, 339.

BOCK, A. V., DILL, D. B., EDWARDS, H. T., HENDERSON, L. J., AND TALBOTT, J. H. J. Physiol., 1929, **68**, 277

CHRISTIANSEN, J., DOUGLAS, C. G., AND HALDANE, J. S. J. Physiol., 1914, **48**, 244.

CHRISTIE, R. V., AND LOOMIS, A. L. J. Physiol., 1932, **77**, 35.

DAVENPORT, H. W. Physiol. Rev., 1946, **26**, 574.

FERGUSON, J. K. W., AND ROUGHTON, F. J. W. J. Physiol., 1934, **83**, 68, 87.

GROOM, D., WOOD, E. H., BURCHELL, H. B., AND PARKER, R. L. Proc. Staff Meet. Mayo Clin., 1948, **23**, 601.

JOFFE, J., AND POULTON, E. P. J. Physiol., 1920, **54**, 129.

KROGH, A. Skandinav. Arch. Physiol., 1908, **20**, 259.

KROGH, A. AND KROGH, M. Skandinav. Arch. Physiol., 1910, **23**, 179.

LILIENTHAL, J. L., JR., RILEY, R. L., PROEMMAL, D. D., AND FRANKE, R. E. Am. J. Physiol., 1946, **147**, 199.

MILLIKAN, G. A. Rev. Scient. Instruments, 1942, **12**, 434.

PAPPENHEIMER, J. R., FISHMAN, A. P. AND BORRERO, L. M. J. Appl. Physiol., 1952, 4, 855.

RAHN, H. Am. J. Physiol., 1949, **158**, 21.

RILEY, R. L., AND COURNAND, A. J. Appl. Physiol., 1949, **1**, 825. Ibid., 1951, **4**, 77.

ROUGHTON, F. J. W. Am. J. Physiol., 1945, **143**, 594.

WILLIAMS, M. H. Am. J. Physiol., 1953, **173**, 77. Ibid., 1956, **184**, 109.

*Monographs and Reviews*

BAINBRIDGE, F. A. The Physiology of Muscular Exercise. Ed. 3, rewritten by A. V. Bock, and D. B. Dill. Longmans Green & Company, Inc., London, 1931.

DAVENPORT, H. W. The ABC of Acid-base Chemistry: The Elements of Physiological Blood-gas Chemistry for Medical Students and Physicians. Ed. 4. University of Chicago Press, Chicago, 1958.

HALDANE, J. S., AND PRIESTLEY, J. G. Respiration, Clarendon Press, Oxford, 1935.

HENDERSON, L. J. Blood. A Study in General Physiology. Yale University Press, 1928.

PETERS, J. P., AND VAN SLYKE, D. D. Quantitative Clinical Chemistry, Vol. II. The Williams & Wilkins Company, Baltimore, 1932.

ROUGHTON, F. J. W. Respiratory functions of the blood. *In* Handbook of Respiratory Physiology, edited by W. M. Boothby, p. 51. United States Air Force School of Aviation Medicine, Randolph Field, Texas, 1954.

# 30

# THE MECHANICS OF BREATHING

---

## PHYSIOLOGICAL ANATOMY

Air entering through the nasal openings is warmed, and some of the grosser impurities are retained by the fine hairs around the nostrils and by the mucous secretion. The nasal cavity just within the external nares (vestibule) is lined with skin. The remaining parts of the nasal cavities are lined with mucous membrane which is covered by a layer of ciliated columnar epithelial cells and scattered "goblet" cells; it is continuous with the membrane lining the accessory nasal sinuses. The nasal lining is very vascular; it contains a venous plexus whose channels anastomose freely and give the mucosa an appearance suggestive of erectile tissue. The vascular channels are dilated by several conditions, e.g., infections, local irritants, certain anaphylactoid states and a rise in temperature of the inspired air or of the environment, or by local heating of the skin; the mucosa swells and the airway is narrowed in consequence. Cooling the inspired air or skin causes vasoconstriction, as will also the application of adrenaline or ephedrine to the mucosa. The vascularity of the mucosa is also influenced reflexly by the application of heat or cold to the skin of remote regions of the body. The pharynx is, of course, a common pathway for food and air. As the food passes the laryngeal opening this is closed by reflex action and respiration is inhibited. The surface epithelium of the nasal part of the pharynx is provided with cilia and goblet cells. In the oral part of the pharynx the epithelium is of the stratified squamous type. The epithelium of the bronchial tree presents very definite changes as one proceeds from the larynx to the terminal bronchioles. The stratified squamous covering of the upper part of the larynx changes to ciliated in the lower part of the vestibule of this organ. The vocal cords are covered with squamous epithelium, but ciliated cells again line the trachea. The epithelium of the trachea contains also goblet cells and mucous and serous glands. The large bronchioles are similar to the trachea in this respect, but in the bronchioles the goblet cells and deep glands are lost.

CILIA. The nasal secretions are moved toward the nostrils largely by the action of cilia. The sinuses are kept clear, under normal conditions, by the beating action of the cilia with which the epithelium is very plentifully supplied. As stated above, ciliated cells are found in the nasal part of the pharynx, in the lower part of the vestibule of the larynx and in the trachea. The cilia beat with a motion which propels material toward the mouth. They become even more abundant when the large bronchioles are reached, but are largely replaced by cuboidal or flattened cells in the respiratory bronchioles.

The efficiency of the ciliated cells of the trachea and large bronchioles in propelling mucus and waste material orally is, under normal conditions, of a high order. The cilia are not influenced by nerve impulses, but are very susceptible to chemical changes in the blood and to substances applied locally. Certain general anesthetics depress their activity and many sedatives exert the same effect. Ciliary action is depressed by cold and increased when the temperature of the cells is raised slightly above normal. The efficiency of the cilia depends in part on the viscosity and stickiness of the material which is in contact with them. Their effectiveness may be varied by changing the properties of this material as well as by an increase or decrease in the rate or force of their beating. The motion of the cilia is wavelike and has been well compared to the undulation of a field of windswept grain. The individual cilium moves, in the direction in which its force is exerted, with a whiplike motion and then relatively slowly returns to its former position.

ELASTIC TISSUE. The bronchial tree is rich in elastic tissue, most of the fibers being disposed longitudinally in the tunica propria. This elastic membrane, which extends throughout the trachea, bronchi and bronchioles to the alveoli, is responsible for the recoil of the bronchial tree during expiration and probably in large part for the recoil mechanism of the whole lung. In the larynx, cartilage supports the special structures necessary for the attachment of the vocal cords and the functioning of the glottis. The cartilaginous rings in the trachea are incomplete on their posterior aspect. This arrangement provides for some contraction of the trachea, but the lumen cannot be obliterated as is the case with the small bronchioles. The tracheal lumen is narrowed somewhat when it is elongated during inspiration.

MUSCLE. The ends of the cartilaginous rings of the trachea may be approximated by the action of the transverse smooth muscle fibers. In the bronchi the bands of fibers tend to become circular and this is seen even more definitely in the bronchioles. The amount of muscle is reduced in the respiratory bronchiole and does not extend beyond this subdivision of the bronchial tree.

BLOOD SUPPLY. The bronchial tree, as far as and including the respiratory bronchioles, is supplied by a rich plexus of vessels derived from the bronchial arteries—branches of the thoracic aorta. The blood is collected by the bronchial veins which in the case of the right lung empty into the azygos vein. Those from the left lung are tributary to the left superior intercostal vein (or sometimes to the accessory hemiazygos vein), but a part of the blood brought to the lungs by the bronchial arteries is returned directly to the pulmonary veins, and some, as mentioned below, enters the pulmonary vascular bed. The respiratory part of the lung receives its blood from the pulmonary artery, the blood being returned via the pulmonary veins to the left side of the heart. Anastomoses between the pulmonary and systemic systems of vessels occur, however, in the walls of the respiratory bronchioles, so that the blood from this region of the bronchial tree is returned in part to the right side of the heart and in part to the left. Such anastomoses are more numerous in certain inflammatory pulmonary conditions, and it has been thought possible that an abnormal increase in the amount of blood entering the pulmonary vascular bed through such channels might raise the pressure in the capillaries sufficiently to overbalance the colloid osmotic pressure of the plasma and lead to pulmonary edema. It has been suggested that certain types of paroxysmal pulmonary edema may be produced in this way, as a result of reflex vasodilation of the anastomosing channels of the bronchial arteries. However, the greatest quantity of bronchial artery blood which enters the pulmonary system has been calculated to be not more than 1 per cent of the total pulmonary circulation, even with maximal vasodilation. It appears unlikely that this would be sufficient to seriously alter the hydrostatic-osmotic balance in the pulmonary capillaries. Not quite all the blood of the pulmonary artery traverses the capillary bed of human lungs; a portion is shunted through arteriovenous anastomoses, a fact which accounts for the passage of relatively large parasites through the lungs.

NERVE SUPPLY OF THE BRONCHIOLES. Excitor (bronchoconstrictor) fibers to the bronchiolar muscle are derived from the vagus, and inhibitor (bronchodilator) fibers from the sympathetic. Afferent fibers from the lungs run in the vagus. The nerve supply to the pulmonary vessels is considered in ch. 28. The bronchioles are constricted by acetylcholine, pilocarpine, histamine and by certain foreign proteins (anaphylactic reactions). They are dilated by adrenaline, ephedrine and atropine (figs. 30.1 and 34.5, p. 518).

THE BRONCHIOLES AND AIR SACS. Macklin divides the bronchial tree into two parts. The first part which extends from the trachea to the *terminal bronchiole* inclusive, serves simply as an air-conduit and, like the branches and twigs of a tree, possesses no respiratory function. The terminal bronchiole is simply the last of a series of subdivi-

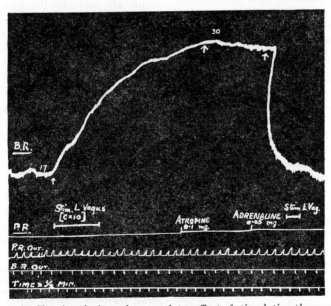

FIG. 30.1. Guinea pig. Showing the bronchoconstrictor effect of stimulating the vagus of the same side. The effect lasts after stimulation has ceased. Atropine in moderate dose had a very slight dilator action; adrenaline in small quantity caused marked bronchodilation. During this action further stimulation of the vagus had an almost negligible effect. (After Thornton.)

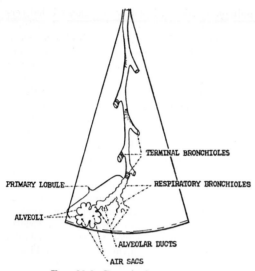

TERMINAL BRONCHIOLES

PRIMARY LOBULE

RESPIRATORY BRONCHIOLES

ALVEOLI

ALVEOLAR DUCTS

AIR SACS

Fɪɢ. 30.2. Description in text

sions of these nonrespiratory bronchioles. The muscle in its wall is more highly developed than in any other part of the bronchial tree and when fully contracted exerts a sphincterlike action which can completely shut off the air supply to the air chambers beyond. The structures lying distal to the terminal bronchiole are the "leaves" of the bronchial tree. They are respiratory in function, i.e., an interchange of gases between lung air and blood occurs across their walls. This part consists of (a) the *respiratory bronchioles*, (b) *alveolar ducts*, (c) *alveolar sacs*, and (d) *pulmonary alveoli*. The cluster formed of these structures together constitutes a *lung-unit* or *primary lobule* (i.e., the group of structures which like the nephron or renal unit carries out the specific function of the organ). It is the distensible or bellows part of the lung.

*The respiratory bronchiole* has the same diameter as the terminal bronchiole, of which it appears as a branch or a continuation. The *alveolar ducts*, five or six in number, arise from each respiratory bronchiole (fig. 30.2). Each alveolar duct after a variable number of rebranchings gives rise to from 3 to 6 dilations, the *alveolar sacs*. The bays in the walls of the latter constitute the *pulmonary alveoli* which are lined by a single layer of flattened epithelial cells cemented together. The alveolar walls contain elastic fibers and a rich network of capillaries. Frequently a single capillary channel alone intervenes between the walls of adjacent alveoli. The blood in the capillaries is therefore separated from the air in the alveoli by two membranes of the utmost delicacy—the alveolar and capillary walls—so the greatest freedom is afforded for the diffusion of gases from the blood to the alveolar

air and from the alveolar air to the blood (Willson; Macklin).[1]

The bronchioles, as they are traced toward the periphery of the lung, branch and rebranch repeatedly, diminishing in length with each subdivision. The first branchings are about 1.5 mm. in length and from 0.3 to 0.4 mm. in diameter. The terminal and respiratory bronchioles are from 0.2 to 0.5 mm. in length, but of about the same diameter as the earlier subdivisions. That is, the bronchioles, though becoming shorter, show practically no decrease in diameter as they pass toward the periphery. The alveolar sacs, however, are considerably wider than the respiratory bronchiole or than the alveolar duct from which they arise. The diameter of each pulmonary alveolus which has a semiglobular form is from 0.075 to 0.125 mm., and the total number in the lungs has been estimated by Zuntz at 750 millions. Willson estimates the total epithelial surface of the lungs at 70 square meters. Of this, probably 55 square meters is respiratory; this is over 25 times the surface area of the skin.

### The Expansion of the Lungs at Birth

Before birth the alveoli contain a small quantity of fluid; the thorax is unexpanded and completely filled by the quite airless lungs. At this time the smaller proportion of the blood of the right heart passes through the lungs. The remainder passes by the ductus arteriosus into the aorta and via the foramen ovale in the interauricular septum to the left heart. Respiratory movements are made by the fetus *in utero*, a fact clearly demonstrated by the work of Barcroft and of Snyder and Rosenfeld. In man, they can be induced by suitable stimulation after the 17th week. India ink injected into the amniotic sacs of rabbits was found in the alveoli. The significance of the latter observation is debatable. Windle states that he has observed the aspiration of amniotic fluid into the alveoli of experimental animals only under asphyxial conditions. Davis and Potter, on the contrary, injected thorotrast (a radio-opaque material) into the amniotic sacs of ten women about to be delivered by Caesarian section and were able to demonstrate the presence of the material in the lungs of half of the newborn infants.

The fetal respiratory movements are readily

[1] The results of Joselyn's studies on the anatomy of the alveoli strongly suggest that the alveolar lining may be a discontinuous membrane and that the capillaries are uncovered. In certain areas, therefore, the air in the alveoli would be separated from the blood only by the capillary endothelium and a small amount of fluid.

induced by tactile stimulation. Either anoxia or carbon dioxide excess alone causes strong movements. Asphyxia, caused by clamping the umbilical cord, brings about gasping respirations. The fetal respirations are depressed by anesthetics, narcotics, or by carbon dioxide deficit. In experimental animals the sensitivity to anoxia and $CO_2$ (inhaled by mother) has been observed to vary with the age of the fetus.[2] Barcroft and Karvonen found that anoxia, induced in sheep fetuses by cyanide, had no effect upon the respirations, except between the 58th and 91st days; before and after this time, no effect was observed. They believe that the effects are brought about through the carotid body (ch. 32). The commencement of breathing at birth they attribute to cutaneous nerve stimulation, rather than to mild asphyxia.

At the moment of birth the respiratory movements become more forceful, the diaphragm descends and the external intercostal muscles contract with the result that the diameters of the thoracic cavity are very considerably increased. A large proportion of the venous blood is now conveyed through the lungs. The general enlargement of the capacity of the thorax—a closed cavity—tends to reduce the pressure on the outer (pleural) surfaces of the lungs. The greater the degree of enlargement of the chest, the greater will be the reduction in the pressure upon the outer pleural surfaces. The interior of the lungs, however, is in direct communication, through the air passages, with the atmosphere. The visceral and parietal pleurae being inseparable the lungs follow the thoracic wall as it enlarges, and therefore must expand. The reduced pressure of the pulmonary air as a result of the expansion results in a flow of atmospheric air into the lungs. Full expansion of the lung is not attained until some few days after birth. The lung throughout the individual's life remains in the expanded position—pressed as it were against the thoracic framework as a result of the greater pressure exerted upon the alveolar than upon the pleural aspects of the pulmonary tissue.

Rhythmically alternating increases and reductions of the expanded state of the lungs initiated at birth continue throughout life and constitute

respectively the *inspiratory* and *expiratory* phases of respiration. The alternate inflations and partial deflations of the lung are the direct result of corresponding changes in the capacity of the thoracic cavity occasioned by the movements of the diaphragm and other respiratory muscles. Changes in pressure within the lung—the *intrapulmonary pressure*—and upon its pleural surfaces—the *intrapleural pressure*—occur coincidently with the alterations in lung volume.

INTRAPULMONARY PRESSURE. The mean intrapulmonary pressure is atmospheric, but there are rhythmic variations with the phases of respiration. These variations may be demonstrated by connecting one nostril with a manometer and breathing with the mouth closed. The pressure will be found to be about $-2$ mm. Hg during the inspiratory phase and to rise to $+3$ or $+4$ mm. Hg during the expiratory phase of ordinary quiet respiration.[3] The variations are accentuated considerably during forced respiration. The maximal negative pressure capable of being developed within the lungs by a forced inspiration, as when a strong sucking effort is made, is from $-40$ to $-50$ mm. Hg. When expiratory efforts are made against a closed glottis, as in coughing, during muscular effort with straining, or during defecation or micturition the intrapulmonary pressure becomes raised by from 10 to 40 mm. Hg above the pressure of the atmosphere. If the free flow of air into and out of the lungs is hindered as a result of some diseased condition the intrapulmonary pressures will be increased beyond the normal range.

THE PLEURAL CAVITIES. The lungs are invested by the visceral layer of the pleural membrane. The membrane is reflected from the root of each lung on to the inner aspect of the walls of the chest and upper surface of the diaphragm—this is the parietal layer of the pleura. The two layers thus form a closed membranous sac on each side of the chest. The potential space enclosed by the pleural membranes is spoken of as the pleural cavity. In health *no actual space exists; the two membranes are in apposition* except for a thin film of fluid which serves as a lubricant to allow the surfaces to glide over one another during the respiratory movements. This potential cavity may, however, as the result of disease become an actual one. Serous fluid (hydrothorax), pus (pyothorax or empyema), blood (hemothorax) or air (pneumothorax) may collect and separate the

[2] Windle has drawn attention to the serious effects upon the central nervous system of fetal anoxia, even of short duration, and suggests that asphyxia of the newborn, even though of short duration, may be responsible in some instances for nervous and mental conditions, e.g., subnormal mentality, or even feeble-mindedness, in the adult.

[3] As a result of the obstruction to breathing offered by the apparatus, these values are somewhat greater than actually exist during normal breathing.

two layers. Between the two pleural compartments lies the *mediastinum*, a space which is subdivided by the heart with its pericardial investment into an anterior and a posterior part—the *anterior* and *posterior mediastina*.

INTRAPLEURAL PRESSURES. It has already been mentioned that the pressure on the pleural surfaces of the lungs is less than that upon their alveolar surfaces, i.e., the intrapleural pressure is subatmospheric. We must now consider the manner in which this "negative" pressure is produced. As stated above (p. 469) when the chest cavity is first expanded, the lungs are carried outwards by the inflow of air to fill the enlarged space. If this were all that occurred, the pressure within the lung and in the pleural cavity would be equalized and in the expanded position of the thorax after birth, as in the unexpanded state in the unborn animal, the pressure in the pleural cavity would not be subatmospheric. The expansion of the thorax, however, and the consequent inflation of the lungs puts the pulmonary tissue upon the stretch. In other words, the closed thoracic box, as a result of the first breath, becomes too large for the lungs to fill by a simple unfolding and distention of the walls of the air spaces. The elastic tissue of the bronchial tree, blood vessels and of the air sacs themselves is put under stress. The pull or recoil of the elastic lung amounts, in the adult when the chest is about midway between inspiration and expiration, to a pressure of from −4 to −5 mm. of mercury. The existence of such a pressure can be demonstrated indirectly by connecting a manometer with the trachea of a dead subject and puncturing the chest wall. Thus the negative pressure in the pleural cavity is abolished, and the lungs are permitted to recoil, i.e., to collapse. Air is expelled from the alveoli, and the manometer registers a pressure of +4 mm. Hg. This represents the pull which had been exerted before the puncture was made and is just equal in amount to the negative (suction) pressure in the pleural cavity. In the newborn the lungs fill the thoracic cavity with comparatively little stretching. The distension of the lungs increases, however, in later years since the thoracic cage grows more rapidly than the lungs; the elastic pull in consequence also increases and with it the intrapleural negative pressure. The intrapleural pressure may be demonstrated directly by plunging a cannula connected with a manometer into the pleural cavity in such a way as to prevent leakage between it and the margins of the puncture. The manometer registers a negative pressure equivalent in amount to the positive

pressure recorded in the previous experiment. In other words, the mercury is "sucked" toward the pleural cavity until the pressure within the latter just equalizes that of the atmosphere.

Another and apparently a more important factor in preventing the separation of the pleural surfaces, and maintaining the lungs normally in the expanded state against their own elastic pull, is the "hydraulic traction" (West) exerted by the film of fluid between the layers of the pleura. This so-called hydraulic traction depends upon the tensile strength of water (as is exhibited when an attempt is made to pull apart two wet, smooth surfaces, e.g., two apposed moist glass slides). A film of water is capable of withstanding a pull of 3600 mm. Hg per square centimeter. The introduction of air into the pleural cavity permits shear to take place, just as the two glass slides can be easily separated if a small quantity of air is allowed to enter between them. That inequality of pressure on the two sides of the two aspects of the lung is not the sole, nor perhaps the most important, factor holding the pleural layers in close apposition is evident from the fact, pointed out by Burns, that the intrapulmonary pressure can be reduced far below the intrapleural pressure without the lungs collapsing.

The intrapleural pressure (and the pressure throughout the thoracic cavity generally) is always subatmospheric under ordinary circumstances,[4] even after death. This "negative" pressure is increased during inspiration—since then the distention of the elastic lungs is greater—and reduced during expiration. During the former phase of quiet respiration (human) it amounts to about −6 mm. Hg, during an ordinary expiration is about −2.5 mm. Hg. In the midposition as stated above it is about −4.5 mm. Hg. When the movements are forced it may be very greatly increased or diminished in the respective respiratory phase. During a strong inspiratory effort with the closed glottis it may amount to −40 mm. Hg. and in forced expiration under the same circumstances it is abolished and a positive pressure of 50 mm. Hg. or so substituted. These changes in intrathoracic pressure exert an influence upon other thoracic structures. An increase in the "negative" pressure causes the thin-walled veins and auricles to expand and fill with blood drawn from extrathoracic regions (fig. 30.3). On the other

[4] The intrapleural pressure may be measured in the human subject by inserting a hollow needle into the pleural cavity, injecting a small quantity (40 cc. or so) of air and connecting the needle with a water manometer and a recording system.

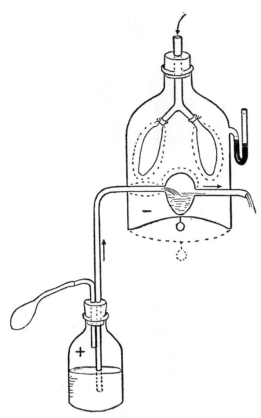

FIG. 30.3. Model to illustrate the manner by which changes in thoracic capacity cause corresponding changes in the volume of air in the lungs and affect the return of blood to the heart. The large glass chamber represents the thorax; it is hermetically sealed and has a flexible bottom or diaphragm. The Y-tube, which is in communication with the atmosphere, represents the trachea and bronchi; the lungs are represented by the attached balloons composed of thin rubber. The pressure within the chamber, i.e., surrounding the balloons, is subatmospheric to start with; the balloons are therefore partially expanded. When the diaphragm is drawn down (as indicated by the dotted lines) the pressure within the chamber is further reduced. The rubber balloons are distended to a corresponding extent by atmospheric air entering through the Y-tube. As the diaphragm is allowed to rise again, the "negative" pressure within the chamber returns to its previous value and the elastic balloons recoil to their original dimensions.

The bottle shown in the lower lefthand part of the drawing contains fluid upon which pressure can be exerted to cause a steady flow up the tubing into the small oval chamber within the larger one. The oval chamber may be taken to represent the heart; the tubing connecting it with the pressure bottle represents the large veins, and the tubing leading from its right side the arteries. If the tubing on the left, as well as the upper part of the oval chamber (which corresponds to the auricles) be composed of some thin resilient material, then during the inspiratory reduction in intrathoracic pressure they will undergo expansion (dotted lines). A greater body of fluid will in consequence

hand, in forced expiration against the closed air passages the thoracic walls press powerfully upon the air-filled lungs. The rise in pressure which results is transmitted to structures lying in the mediastinum. Blood is thus expelled from the large intrathoracic veins and auricles into the veins of the abdomen and neck.

## The Respiratory Movements

What has been said in the foregoing paragraphs should have made it clear that the flow of air into and from the lungs depends entirely upon changes in the capacity of the thoracic cavity. The air is not drawn in and expelled by active dilation and contraction of the pulmonary passages, as was the belief at one time. Air is drawn in or forced out strictly in accordance with the pressure differences between the atmosphere and the lung air caused by the expansion or contraction of the thoracic boundaries. The principles are well illustrated by the model shown in figure 30.3. We will now consider how these changes are brought about.

The respiratory cycles of an adult person occur normally at the rate of from 16 to 18 per minute. In the newborn infant during quiet breathing the rate is between 30 and 40 per minute.

During inspiration the thoracic cavity is enlarged in all diameters, vertical, anteroposterior and transverse. The enlargement, however, is not equal in all directions. The upper part of the thorax increases much less in capacity than does the lower part; and since the position of the spinal column remains relatively fixed, the increase in the anteroposterior diameter of the thorax is due mainly to an expansion forwards. The increase in the vertical diameter is due to the downward elongation resulting from the descent of the diaphragm.

Unequal enlargement of the thoracic box entails unequal expansion of the lungs. The lung is not distended equally from a center as in the inflation of an elastic-walled globe. Keith distinguished three zones in the expanding lung.

(a) A nonexpansile *root zone* containing the bronchus, pulmonary vessels and lymphatics and their main divisions.

(b) An *intermediate zone* in which the vascular and bronchial branches radiate outwards toward the lung surface. Between these rays lies expansile

be transferred from the bottle to the small chamber representing the heart.

The manometer inserted into the wall of the large chamber registers the pressure changes (indicated by dotted lines) occurring during the descent and ascent of the flexible diaphragm.

pulmonary tissue. This zone, therefore, consists of tissue of varying degrees of expansibility, that lying near the periphery of the rays being more expansile than that situated more centrally.

(c) An *outer* or *subpleural zone*, from 1 to $1\frac{1}{4}$ inches deep, of maximal distensibility.

Those regions of the lung lying in relation to the relatively immobile regions of the thoracic walls, namely (a) the dorsal surface of the lung apex, (b) the posterior surfaces of the lungs in contact with the spinal column and attached segments of the ribs, and (c) the mediastinal surface lying in relation to the pericardium and other structures of the mediastinum, are expanded *indirectly*. The parts of the lung which are *directly* expanded during inspiration are those lying in contact with the freely movable boundaries of the thorax, namely (a) the sternum and ribs and (b) the diaphragm.

It is evident that those portions of lung in contact with practically stationary regions of the thoracic walls can only be expanded indirectly, that is, when other parts of the lung move out of the way. This could not occur did the root of the lung remain fixed. As a matter of fact the lung root moves downwards, forwards and laterally during inspiration (fig. 30.4) and, as shown by Macklin by X-ray studies upon human subjects,

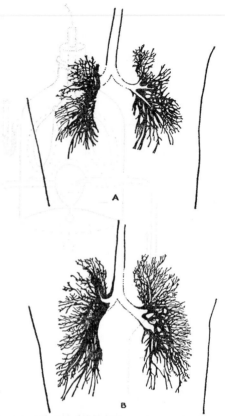

FIG. 30.5. X-ray photographs (retouched) of the bronchial tree of a young woman: A, in full expiration; B, in full inspiration. (After Macklin.)

the bronchial tree becomes elongated (stretched) during the inspiratory phase. The trachea becomes stretched and the apex of the lung actually descends as it expands. During expiration the highly elastic bronchial tree recoils to its previous length and the lung root ascends (fig. 30.5). If the root of the lung were fixed, little expansion of a region such as the apex or of other regions classed as expanding indirectly could result. Nor could anything but a very moderate expansion of other regions (e.g., costosternal and diaphragmatic, etc.) occur if the bronchial tree were unable to lengthen. It is the *elongation* of the rays as described above rather than the widening of the spaces between them at their original lengths, like the separation of the sticks of a fan, that is of importance in permitting the expansion of the intervening pulmonary tissue.

The effect of the enlargment of the thorax is exerted first and to the greatest extent upon lung tissue in relation to the movable parts of the chest walls. The inspiratory decrease of intrapleural pressure in the diaphragmatic regions of

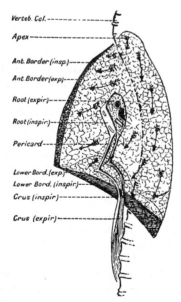

Verteb. Col. - - - - - - - - - - - - - -

Apex - - - - - - - - - - - - - - - -

Ant. Border (insp.) - - - -

Ant. Border (exp) - - -

Root (expir) - - - -

Root (inspir) - - -

Pericard - - -

Lower Bord. (exp) - -

Lower Bord. (inspir) - - -

Crus (inspir) - - - - - - - - -

Crus (expir) - - - - - - - - - -

FIG. 30.4. Mediastinal aspect of the light lung to show the respiratory movement of the lung root. The crus of the diaphragm is also indicated, and its attachment to the root of the lung through the pericardium. The arrows indicate the direction of the inspiratory movement of the various parts of the lung. (After Keith.)

the thorax is considerably greater than that in the region of the apex or in other parts of the lung which are expanded indirectly. As a result of the greater negative pressure in the lower part of the thorax, a horizontal groove is sometimes developed here (Harrison's sulcus) when the framework, as in ricketts, is soft and yielding. The restricted expansion of the air sacs of the apex and other regions of the lung which are expanded indirectly has been held responsible for their being so commonly the primary site of tuberculous infection.

## The Enlargement of the Thoracic Cavity during Inspiration

This is effected, according to Keith, by four distinct mechanisms which consist of the movements of:

(a) The *thoracic lid* or *operculum* (1st rib and manubrium sterni).

(b) The *upper costal series* (2nd to 5th ribs inclusive).

(c) The *lower costal series* (6th to 10th ribs inclusive) and the *diaphragm*.

(d) The *floating rib series* and *the muscles* of the abdominal wall.

### The Thoracic Lid or Operculum

The thoracic lid or operculum is formed by the first pair of ribs and the manubrium sterni. It is jointed behind to the spinal column and in front to the sternum by the manubrio-sternal joint. During the elevation of the thorax in inspiration the thoracic lid moves as a single piece upon the body of the sternum, assuming a more horizontal position (by from 1° to 16°). That is, the manubrium is pushed upward and forward (fig. 30.6). Thus, the upper part of the thorax is increased in its anteroposterior diameter. The anterior por-

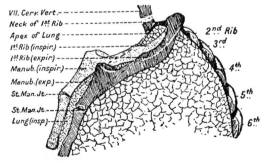

FIG. 30.6. Diagram to show the respiratory movements of the first pair of ribs and manubrium sterni, and the effect of these movements of the expansion of the apex of the lung. (After Keith.)

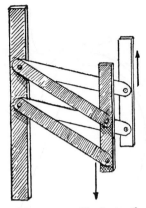

FIG. 30.7. Diagram to illustrate the action of the external intercostal muscles during inspiration; ↓, expiration and ↑, inspiration.

tion of the lung apex is directly expanded to some extent by this mechanism. The extent of the movement of the thoracic lid varies considerably in different individuals and with the depth of inspiration. It is very slight in quiet breathing. The manubrio-sternal joint becomes ankylosed in later life but rarely before the 60th year.

### The Upper Costal Series

The 2nd, 3rd, 4th, 5th and 6th ribs slope obliquely from behind downwards and forwards. Each rib is longer, its direction more oblique and it makes a fuller sweep outwards than its neighbor immediately above. During inspiration these ribs (with the exception of the 2nd) assume a more horizontal position, their anterior portions moving upward and forward. That is, each rib rotates around an oblique horizontal axis parallel to its neck (fig. 30.8CD). The sternum is thrust forward and upward, executing a movement at the manubrio-sternal joint. These movements increase the anteroposterior diameter of the thorax. The elevation of the ribs is effected by the external intercostal muscles. The muscle fibers pass obliquely downwards and forwards from the lower border of one rib to the upper border of the rib below. When the muscle contracts it exerts a pull upon these attachments which tends to depress the upper rib of the pair and to raise the lower. The first rib, however, acts through the contraction of the scalene muscles, as a fixed point above, so that contraction of the external intercostals can only result in an elevation of the ribs. Owing also to the obliquity of the fibers which are attached below to the anterior end of the long arm of a lever and above to the posterior end of the long arm, a distinct mechanical advantage is

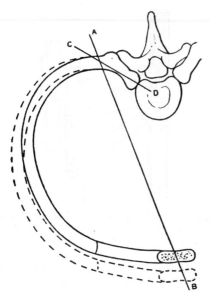

FIG. 30.8. A diagram showing the axis of movement (AB and CD) of the ribs from the 2nd to the 6th. The ribs from the 7th to the 10th also make a movement around an anteroposterior axis but not around the axis CD. The interrupted lines indicate the position of the rib in inspiration. (After Gray.)

given to the upward movement (fig. 30.7). In general the internal intercostal muscles are expiratory in function. The internal and external intercostals receive impulses alternately along the intercostal nerves (Bronk and Ferguson).

The strongly bowed midportion of the body of each rib from the 2nd to the 6th also becomes elevated, in relation to its two ends, rotating around an oblique anteroposterior axis. This movement, which is compared to the raising of a bucket handle to a more horizontal position, increases the transverse thoracic diameter (fig. 30.8AB).

### The Lower Costal Series and the Diaphragm

The ribs from the 7th to the 10th also swing outwards and upwards (bucket handle movement) during inspiration, rotating around an oblique anteroposterior axis which passes through the midline in front and the necks of the ribs behind. The subcostal angle is widened by this movement and the transverse diameter of the lower part of the thorax increased; the anteroposterior diameter is slightly reduced.

The diaphragm is the chief muscle of respiration, its movements being responsible during deep breathing for about 60 per cent of the total amount of air breathed. It consists of a musculo-

tendinous sheet arched toward the thoracic cavity. The tendinous portion is centrally placed (central tendon) and is adherent to the pericardium. The muscular tissue is placed circumferentially. The diaphragm consists of two parts which differ from one another in their actions.

(a) The *costosternal* part arises from the back of the xiphoid and the cartilages and adjacent portions of the six lower pairs of ribs. It is attached to the anterior edge of the central tendon.

(b) The *lumbar* or *crural part* arises from the fibrous arches over the quadratus lumborum and psoas muscles and by two fleshy bundles (the crura of the diaphragm) from the bodies of the upper lumbar vertebrae. These fibers are inserted into the posterior margin of the central tendon.

ACTION OF THE DIAPHRAGM. The diaphragm descends during inspiration and ascends during expiration. In full expiration its upper limit lies at a level situated between the costal cartilages of the 4th and 5th ribs. In quiet breathing the range of its movement is about 1.2 cm. and in forced breathing about 3.0 cm. The total diaphragmatic surface is about 270 sq. cm. A descent of 1.0 cm. therefore (assuming that all regions descend practically to the same extent) will increase the thoracic capacity by 270 cu. cm. and cause a corresponding volume of air to enter the lungs.

As the diaphragm descends its domed shape alters very little; it may be seen by means of the fluoroscope to move up and down like a piston (fig. 30.9). At the end of expiration a considerable proportion of the diaphragmatic surface is in contact with the chest wall as high as the 6th or 7th rib, but during inspiration it is "peeled off" the thoracic boundary, while the base of the lung expands to fill the space (pleural sinus). As a result of the slight indrawing of the intercostal spaces caused by this movement, a faint shadow may be seen to move down the side of the chest wall in most normal persons. This is known as Litten's sign. The *costosternal* part of the diaphragm, (using the lower ribs, which through the action of the external intercostals, serve as fixed points) moves downward and forward, depressing the abdominal viscera. Thus, the capacity of the lower part of the thorax is increased. The abdominal wall distends but when, as a result of the resistance offered by the abdominal muscles, the downward movement of the viscera becomes arrested, the latter act as a fixed point for the continuing contraction of this part of the diaphragm; its force is now spent in raising the lower ribs to which it is attached. Through this action the ster-

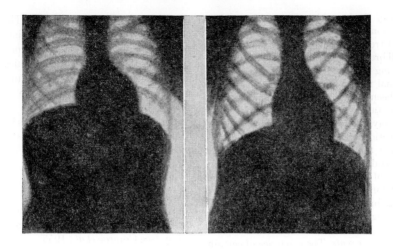

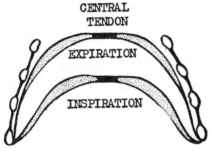

FIG. 30.9. *Upper,* radiogram showing the position of the diaphram during expiration and inspiration. Note the effect upon the position and shape of the heart. (After Norris and Landis.) *Lower,* diagram showing the expiratory and inspiratory positions of the diaphragm.

num is thrust forward and upward. The *spinal* or *crural* part in its descent acts solely in increasing the vertical diameter of the thorax.

The excursions of the diaphragm and consequently its midposition as well are influenced by (a) the upward pull of the subatmospheric intrathoracic pressure, and (b) the abdominal viscera. In the standing position the weight of the latter aids the descent of the diaphragm but hinders its ascent; the mean or midposition of the diaphragm is therefore taken up at a lower level than in recumbency. (c) The abdominal muscles: these, when lax and the body in the standing position, allow the viscera to subside to a lower level and so to increase the downward pull upon the diaphragm.

### THE FLOATING RIBS AND THE ABDOMINAL MUSCLES

Functionally the floating ribs (11th and 12th) must be considered with the abdominal muscles which are the antagonists of the diaphragm. The recti and oblique muscles undergo a decrease in

tonus as the diaphragm descends; they regain tonus with its ascent.

### Expiration

Expiration is to a large extent a passive movement; in quiet breathing, or *eupnea,* it is probably entirely so. That is, as the contraction of the inspiratory muscles ceases, the thoracic framework tends through its own weight and inherent elasticity to resume its former position, the elastic lungs recoil and the relaxed diaphragm is drawn upwards toward the thoracic cavity by the "negative" intrathoracic pressure. There is, however, also a definitely active element. As mentioned above, the abdominal muscles regain tonus and by pressing upon the viscera aid the ascent of the diaphragm.

Under conditions which require a considerable increase in lung ventilation (*hyperpnea*) or an increased muscular effort to maintain ventilation (*dyspnea*), the expiratory muscles contract to accelerate the expulsion of air from the lungs.

*Movements of the bronchial tree during respiration.* In addition to the inspiratory elongation of the bronchial tree mentioned above, the bronchioles and small bronchi dilate during inspiration and constrict during expiration. Whether these rhythmical bronchial movements are purely passive in nature has been debated. The bronchioles also exhibit a peristaltic movement which can be detected by X-ray photographs of the bronchioles after the injection of Lipiodol[5] or other material that is opaque to the X-ray. It is not thought that the peristaltic movement plays any part in the movement of air, but it appears to assist in the movement of foreign material towards the larger air tubes. This bronchiolar peristalsis is said to be increased in lung abscess and diminished in bronchiectasis. It is decreased by morphine.

*Pulmonic alveolar vents.* The existence of certain pores in the alveoli (pores of Kohn) have long been recognized, but the difficulty of being certain that they are not artefacts produced by the method of preparing the sections has prevented their wide acceptance as normal structures. Macklin, however, has been able to demonstrate the presence of such vents in thick sections prepared from the lungs of many species including man. Examination of the sections justifies the belief that they are normal communications between the alveoli. While the function of the vents is not as yet completely understood, it appears probable that they play a significant part in the equalization of pressures in groups of the alveoli, particularly perhaps during forced inspiration. The vents are opened wide during inspiration and may be entirely closed in expiration.

## The Work of Breathing

In recent years methods have been devised to obtain quantitative information about the forces and resistances involved in breathing. The action of muscles during inspiration opposes forces which can be analyzed into three components, the force required (a) to overcome elastic resistance, (b) to move nonelastic tissue, and (c) to overcome resistance to air flow through the tracheobronchial tree.

### Elastic Resistance

The tissues of the lungs and thorax behave somewhat like springs in that they are stretched during inspiration and recoil to assume their previous state when the stretching force is removed. The slope of a line that is obtained when a distending force, namely pressure, is plotted against increase in volume of the system indicates

[5] A preparation of iodized oil.

the stiffness or the distensibility. The less the increase in volume with a given increase in the pressure applied, the more rigid or the less distensible is the system. The mechanical *compliance* of the lungs is defined as the volume change per unit pressure change, where the former is expressed in liters and the latter in centimeters of water. The compliance of the lungs is decreased in disorders such as pulmonary congestion secondary to chronic cardiac failure and in diseases which lead to pulmonary fibrosis.

The respiratory system actually consists of two sets of elastic elements; those in the lungs and those in the thoracic wall. Methods have been devised whereby these may be evaluated separately (see Comroe *et al.*, 1955).

### Force to Move Nonelastic Tissues

This is for the most part the force required to overcome friction within those tissues which move during inspiration. The amount of force required is greater with more rapid inspiration. It is to be noted that the work involved in moving nonelastic tissues becomes zero at the termination of inspiration while at this point the elastic force is maximal since the maximal enlargement of the thorax has been reached.

### Resistance to Air Flow

The total airway resistance depends on the number, length and cross-sectional area of the tubes through which the air passes. The amount of work required to move air through the air passages is determined by the resistance related to the structure of the airway itself and by the amount of air moved per unit of time. If air flow is at a velocity great enough to cause turbulence more work is required than when flow is laminar. If gases of lower density than air are breathed (e.g., helium) work involved in moving the gas is lowered correspondingly. The resistance to the flow of air is relatively greater at the bronchiolar level than elsewhere in the respiratory tree; and, since the bronchioles can undergo considerable changes in caliber, large changes in resistance can develop in this region of the bronchial tree. The major problem in bronchial asthma is the increase in resistance to passage of air through the bronchioles. When resistance in the airway is increased by bronchiolar constriction, it is compensated for by a more forceful inspiratory effort so that the normal volume of air if moved. On expiration, if only elastic recoil were operating, air would pass out more slowly than under normal conditions, but active expiration develops to produce a sufficiently rapid egress of air.

## The Cough Reflex

There are three mechanisms for the expulsion of foreign material from the larynx, trachea and lower air passages as far as the terminal bronchioles. First, the action of the cilia; second, the peristaltic motion of the bronchioles; and third, the cough reflex. The peristaltic movement has been referred to above. The cough reflex is most commonly initiated by the stimulation of afferent nerve endings in the region of the tracheal bifurcation, the most sensitive area, or in the laryngeal mucosa. It may also be initiated from the excitation of vagal afferents from the lungs, or from nerve endings in the pleura. Ear disease, through the stimulation of terminals of the auricular branch of the vagus (Arnold's nerve), may also cause coughing. The act itself consists of a short inspiration followed immediately by closure of the glottis and a forcible expiratory effort. A considerable degree of pressure is thereby developed within the lung. The glottis then opens suddenly and offending material is moved a variable distance along the air passage. During the subsequent inspiration the irritating particle, if not large enough to seriously obstruct the air passage, remains in its new position, from which it is carried forward again during succeeding expulsive efforts until it is swept away from sensitive areas.

Inert, nonirritating foreign matter of a particulate nature which has entered the alveoli, is removed by large ameboid cells—the alveolar macrophages, or "dust cells". Normally, a few of these cells are to be seen in the alveoli, but they are attracted in large number by the presence of foreign particles. The origin of these cells is a controversial question. Some are thought to originate from the monocytes of the reticuloendothelial system; others, from cells in the alveolar septa (septal cells). The foreign material is conveyed by the macrophages into the lymph channels draining the alveoli. In city dwellers or those who work in dust laden atmospheres, e.g., coal miners, the lymph nodes are dark with the scavenged material. Irritating matter, especially pathogenic bacteria, are attacked as in other situations by the neutrophilic phagocytes of the blood.

*Hiccup or singultus* is a spasmodic and purposeless contraction of the diaphragm which results from many causes or may occur without known cause; it occurs rarely in epidemic form. It is usually reflex in nature being initiated by some abnormal stimulation of the afferent nerve terminals in the diaphragm or viscera in the upper part of the abdominal cavity. The fibers of the phrenic nerve constitute the efferent limb of the reflex. Hiccup following abdominal operations may be most intractable and endanger the life of the patient. The inhalation of an air mixture containing 6 or 7 per cent of carbon dioxide (or simply breathing and rebreathing from a bag for a number of respirations) has been reported to be a valuable means of terminating an attack.

## Pneumothorax

Air may enter the pleural cavity through a penetrating wound of the chest (*open pneumothorax*), as a result of the rupture of an emphysematous vesicle on the surface of the lung or from the extension through the pleura of a lesion of the pulmonary tissue (e.g., tuberculous) or of some other air-containing organ such as the esophagus or stomach. When the intrapleural space contains air but communication with the atmosphere has become occluded the pneumothorax is said to be *closed*.

If the opening through the thoracic wall were large and the mediastinum acted as a more or less rigid partition, the pleural cavity of the affected side could be considered quite separate from that of the sound side. The lung on the open side would exhibit its elastic properties and recoil; the air would be expelled and the lung in the collapsed state. The opposite lung would be unaffected. Actually, the mediastinum, as a rule, is mobile, so the two pleural cavities, though anatomically separate, act so far as the distribution of pressure is concerned, almost as if they were a single cavity. Consequently when an opening exists in the thoracic wall the yielding mediastinum with its contents—heart and great vessels—moves toward the sound side. The negative pressure on the sound side of the chest is therefore reduced, and the lung on that side also tends toward collapse. The response to the pneumothorax is deepening of the respirations. That is, the thorax enlarges and the lungs expand to a greater degree to create a negative pressure despite the communication between the chest cavity and the atmosphere. It therefore becomes a matter of competition between the amount of air entering the lungs through the trachea and that entering through the opening in the chest during inspiration. The chest may be compared

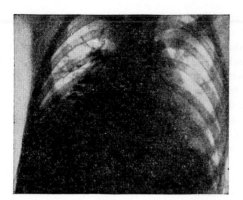

Fig. 30.10. Bronchiectasis. X-ray photograph after injection of bronchial tree with Lipiodol. (After Moll, retouched.)

to a bellows with a hole in its wall; when the bellows is opened (inspiration) the volume of air entering through the leak and that through the nozzle (which is analogous to the trachea) will depend upon the sizes of the respective openings. From this it will be realized that with a small opening pulmonary ventilation of practically normal value could be maintained. Even with a large opening a normal tidal volume of air might be drawn in during inspiration. The reason for this is, of course, that the tidal volume is only a small fraction of the vital capacity. When, however, the opening is quite large the thorax, even when the inspiration is maximal might fail to expand the lung sufficiently to maintain the tidal volume at its normal value. As a result of the work of Graham and his associates the following summary may be made.

(a) Both lungs are affected in a pneumothorax. If the opening is small or if in a closed pneumothorax the pressure is low, the effect upon the two lungs is nearly equal.

(b) A bilateral open pneumothorax may not be fatal if the openings are small.

(c) The size of the opening compatible with life bears a relation to the vital capacity of the subject. Any pneumothorax, unless the opening is very small, would be fatal to a person who before the pneumothorax occurred had possessed a vital capacity little greater than his tidal air.

(d) The reduction in the intrathoracic "negative" pressure caused by a pneumothorax tends to impede the filling of the right heart and to produce stasis in the venous system.

When the mediastinum has been rendered stiff and resistant by previous disease some of the foregoing statements obviously will not apply. Also, if the pleural surfaces on the side of the opening are adherent and so hold the lung out

against the thoracic wall a pneumothorax will not result. Or if, as a result of such adhesions the pneumothorax is limited in extent, only a part of the lung is affected.

*Pleural shock.* Marked slowing of the pulse and a profound fall in blood pressure, which may lead to fatal syncope, sometimes follow puncture of the chest wall for the withdrawal of fluid or during the production of pneumothorax. The cardiovascular reaction is apparently due to a pleural reflex since a similar effect upon heart rate and blood pressure can be induced in animals by stimulating the pleura. It is more commonly seen when the chest is punctured for the withdrawal of fluid than during the injection of air in the production of pneumothorax, a fact among others which argues against its being due to air embolism. Injury to the visceral pleura or to the underlying layer of pulmonary tissue appears to be a factor essential for the production of this type of circulatory collapse.

### Bronchiectasis

This is the term applied to an abnormal dilation of the bronchi or bronchioles. The dilation may be localized or widespread, fusiform, saccular, beaded or uniform in distribution. The contour of the bronchial tubes is readily demonstrated by X-ray after the injection of Lipiodol (fig. 30.10). Secretion may collect within the dilated lumina and be expectorated at intervals as large quantities of a foul-smelling sputum. This classical sign of the condition is only seen in its advanced stages. More commonly the sputum is small in amount and in the form of yellow "chunky" pieces (Warner).

Bronchiectasis is practically always secondary to some other affection of the lungs. The primary change leading to the condition is weakening of the bronchial wall as a result of infective processes. The elastic and muscular tissues are atrophic. As we have seen the bronchial tree dilates during inspiration and constricts during expiration. The latter movement is, in part at least, an elastic recoil. With the gradual deterioration of the elastic tissue of the bronchial wall, the latter's resiliency becomes progressively less. The lumen of the tube does not regain its normal caliber after inspiration but remains more or less dilated. According to the most widely held view, further dilation is induced because the pressure within the bronchial lumen during inspiration is higher than the pressure in the surrounding pulmonary tissue and in the pleural space. During expiration, however, the intrabronchial pressure cannot rise above the pressure in the surrounding tissue; the bronchial walls are supported. Coughing or other conditions causing a general rise in intrapleural pressure cannot, therefore, induce bronchiectasis. On the other hand, conditions which increase the negative pressure within the thorax, such as the collapse of an area of lung (atelectasis), of a lobe or of entire lung (massive atelectasis), will increase the tendency to bronchiectasis. Incomplete obstruction of a bronchus especially if it exerts a valvelike action, by permitting inspiration but hindering expiration, favors the development of bronchiectasis. The latter is, therefore, not an uncommon result of the lodgment of a foreign body in a bronchus. On the other hand, it is thought by some (Roberts and Blair) that retention of secretions, as originally suggested by Laennec, combined with inflammatory weakening of the bronchial wall are the important causative factors, and deny the significance of atelectasis and an increase in pleural negative pressure. Whitwell, in an examination of 200 lungs removed at operation, found atelectasis in only 10 per cent.

*Fibrosis* of a lung or portion of lung is considered by some as a potent cause of bronchial dilation. It is thought that the fibrosing lung as it shrinks makes equal circumferential traction upon the bronchi or bronchioles and thus leads to their dilation. It is probable that even in these instances previous weakening of the bronchial wall is the primary fault since bronchiectasis commonly occurs in the absence of fibrosis.

## Pressure Breathing

Pressure breathing refers to breathing against a pressure greater than the ambient pressure. This has been utilized, for example, in pilots flying at altitudes such that the $pO_2$ in inspired air is insufficient even when breathing 100 per cent $O_2$ by mask; and also it has been used as a therapeutic measure in patients with pulmonary edema. In the latter case the rationale is to provide pressure such as to counteract the transudation of fluid into the alveoli. A subject can breathe against a pressure of around 20 mm. Hg for relatively prolonged periods and against somewhat higher pressures for a few minutes. An immediate effect of pressure breathing is the increased resistance to flow of blood through the pulmonary capillaries which results in a decreased flow of blood to the left side of the heart and consequently in a reduction of left ventricular output and of systemic arterial blood pressure. Since the return of blood to the right atrium is unimpeded, the pressure here increases, and as the right ventricular volume

increases, the strength of the ventricular contraction becomes stronger with the result that the flow through the pulmonary circuit is soon restored despite the greater resistance. When pulmonary blood flow is restored, the left ventricular filling also is restored, and arterial pressure is brought back up to approximately normal levels. At the new steady state circulation is essentially normal but is being maintained at the expense of increased right ventricular work. Some degree of vasoconstriction (both arteriolar and venous), set off reflexly from the sinoaortic pressoreceptors, also appears to be involved in maintaining the arterial blood pressure and contributing to elevated venous pressure (on the basis of decreased holding capacity of the systemic circuit) during pressure breathing.

## The Valsalva Maneuver

By voluntarily closing the glottis and performing a strong expiratory effort one can produce an intrathoracic pressure of well over 80 mm. Hg., and this pressure is reflected in a similar rise in the alveoli and also in the blood vessels and other structures within the chest. Actually, this maneuver (which has an effect similar to that of the method described by Valsalva for blowing air into the middle ear and hence is known as the Valsalva maneuver) also involves contraction of the abdominal muscles and, consequently, there is a considerable rise in intra-abdominal pressure. A similar type of muscular activity is utilized in defecation, during which there may be a considerable rise in intrathoracic and intra-abdominal pressure. The Valsalva maneuver has the effect of preventing the return of blood from the four extremities and head just as if blood pressure cuffs were applied and inflated to a pressure level corresponding to that produced in the body cavities. Thus when the act is commenced, venous pressure in the extremities and head rises, venous return decreases sharply, cardiac output decreases, and arterial blood pressure falls. The heart rate is increased reflexly as a result of the fall in pressure in the sinoaortic zones. As soon as the expiratory effort is released, the blood, which has accumulated in the veins, rushes into the right ventricle which now suddenly becomes quite enlarged and contracts forcibly to pump its contents through the pulmonary circuit and into the left side of the heart. The surge of blood into the left ventricle causes a sudden increase in the amount of blood pumped into the systemic arterial tree, and the concomitant rise of arterial pressure elicits reflexly from the pressoreceptors a brief period of bradycardia, following which the conditions that existed prior to the maneuver are re-established. The normal heart can withstand the strain put upon it by the sudden rise in venous return which is seen on terminating the Valsalva maneuver; but in patients with chronic congestive heart failure, the heart is weakened and may be distended even under basal conditions; in such cases the influx of blood may produce overdistention of a degree which results in acute cardiac decompensation. This is considered to be the mechanism of some of the sudden deaths occuring in patients with chronic congestive heart failure during straining efforts.

## REFERENCES

ARCHIBALD, E., AND BROWN, A. Am. Rev. Tuberc., 1927, **16, 111**.

ARMSTRONG, B. W., AND SMITH, D. J. Am. J. Physiol., 1955, **182, 599**.

BARCROFT, J., AND MARVONEN, M. J. J. Physiol., 1948, **107, 153**.

BRONK, D. W., AND FERGUSON, L. K. Am. J. Physiol., 1935, **110, 700**.

BURNS, D. J. Physiol., 1940, **26P**.

CHRISTIE, R. V., AND McINTOSH, C. A. J. Clin. Invest., 1934, **13, 279**.

DAVIS, M. E., AND POTTER, E. L. J. A. M. A., 1946, **131, 1194**.

ELLIS, M. J. Physiol., 1936, **87, 298**.

HILDING, A. C. Am. J. Physiol., 1957, **191, 404**.

JOSSELYN, L. E. Anat. Rec., 1935, **62, 147**.

LOOFBOURROW, G. N., WOOD, W. B., AND BAIRD, I. L. Am. J. Physiol., 1957, **191, 411**.

MOLL, H. H. Quart. J. Med., 1932, **1, 457**.

NEGOVSKI, V. A. Am. Rev. Soviet Med., 1945, **2**, 303. Ibid., **3**, 45, 147, 243, 399.

NICHOLSON, T. R., AND TRIMBY, R. H. Am. J. Physiol., 1940, **128, 276**.

ROBERTS, J. C., AND BLAIR, L. G. Lancet, 1950, **1**, 386.

ROBERTSON, O. H. Physiol. Rev., 1941, **21, 121**.

SNYDER, F. F., AND ROSENFELD, M. Am. J. Physiol., 1937, **119**, 153. Anat. Rec., 1937, **67**, Supp. 3, p. 47.

THORNTON, J. W. Quart. J. Exper. Physiol., 1931, **21, 305**.

WARNER, W. P. Quart. J. Med., 1934, **3, 401**.

WARNER, W. P., AND GRAHAM, D. Arch. Int. Med., 1933, **52, 888**.

WEST, S. Brit. Med. J., 1887, **1, 393**.

WHITWELL, F. Thorax, 1952, **7, 213**.

WILLSON, H. G. Am. J. Anat., 1922, **30, 267**.

*Monographs and Reviews*

BARCROFT, J. Physiol. Rev., 1936, **16, 103**.

BRECHER, GERHARD A. Venous Return. Grune & Stratton, Inc., New York, 1956.

CAMPBELL, E. J. M. The Respiratory Muscles and the Mechanics of Breathing. Lloyd-Luke, London, 1958.

GRAHAM, E. A. Harvey Lectures, 1923–24, **19, 123**. Medicine, 1924, **3, 417**.

KEITH, A. The Mechanism of Respiration in Man, Further Advances in Physiology. Edward Arnold & Company, London, 1909.

MACKLIN, C. C. Physiol. Rev., 1929, **9, 1**.

MILLER, W. S. The Lung. Charles C Thomas, Springfield, Ill., 1937.

WINDLE, W. F. Physiology of the Foetus. W. B. Saunders Company, Philadelphia, 1940. Harvey Lectures, 1944–45, **40, 236**.

# 31

# LUNG VOLUMES AND PULMONARY VENTILATION

## The Lung Volumes

The amount of gas moved into the lungs and out during a single respiratory cycle is known as the *tidal volume*. The position of the chest at the cessation of expiration in eupnea (which is reached as a result of inactivity of the respiratory muscles) is known as the *resting end-expiratory position*. The amount of gas that can be exhaled beyond this position is the *expiratory reserve volume*, while the *inspiratory capacity* is the amount of gas that can be inhaled starting from this position. *Inspiratory reserve volume* is the amount of gas that can be inhaled beyond the tidal volume that is recorded in quiet breathing. Since tidal volume and inspiratory capacity are measured easily, inspiratory reserve volume can be obtained by subtracting the former from the latter. (see fig. 31.1). *Vital capacity* is the maximal amount of gas that can be expelled from the lungs following a maximal inspiration. Not all of the air of the lungs can be forced out by a maximal expiratory effort, and that which remains is the *residual volume*. *Total lung capacity* is the vital capacity plus the residual volume. Another volume which is of interest since it represents the amount of gas in the lungs to which the tidal volume is added on inspiration is the *functional residual capacity*. It may be seen in the table that this is the residual air plus the expiratory reserve volume. All of the names of the different volumes and capacities are abbreviated by the use of the first letters of the words employed. Mean figures for the various volumes in 50 young men were found to be:

$$\left.\begin{array}{l} \text{TV---0.5 L} \\ \text{IRV---3.3 L} \\ \text{ERV---1.0 L} \end{array}\right\} = \text{VC---4.8 L}$$
$$\underline{\text{RV---1.2 L}}$$
$$\text{TLC---6.0 L}$$

In 50 young women the mean VC was found to be 3.14 or about two-thirds of the figure for men.

## VITAL CAPACITY AND ITS VARIATIONS

A relationship between certain body measurements and vital capacity has been shown by several investigators. Hutchinson, a pioneer in the field, invented the spirometer and studied the vital capacity in a large number of individuals, normal and diseased. He demonstrated a relation of vital capacity to height and weight. The most consistent relationship, as shown by Dreyer and by West, exists between vital capacity and surface area (see table below).

A fairly close relationship between total height and vital capacity was also found, the latter expressed as cubic centimeters being 25 times the height in centimeters for men, 20 times for women and 29 times for athletes. For example, an average adult male 170 cm. tall would have a vital capacity of (170 × 25 =) 4250 cc. The surface area of the same individual assuming an average weight for his height, namely, 70 kg., would be 1.80 square meters. Therefore, his vital capacity should be (1.80 × 2500 =) 4500 cc. The difference in the results of the two methods of calculation of the normal standard is therefore around 5 per cent.

The ratios of vital capacity to height and surface area respectively, as found by West, are shown in the following table:

|  | Men | Women | Ath-letes |
|---|---|---|---|
| Vital capacity, cc. per cm. height.......... | 25.0 | 20.0 | 29.0 |
| Vital capacity, cc. per square meter of body surface.............. | 2500 | 2000 | 2800 |

Occupation as shown by Dreyer and others exerts a potent influence upon the vital capacity, the normal standard of persons employed in sedentary work being considerably lower than of those pursuing more arduous occupations. Dreyer divided his subjects into three classes A, B and C. Class A are those with the maximum vital capac-

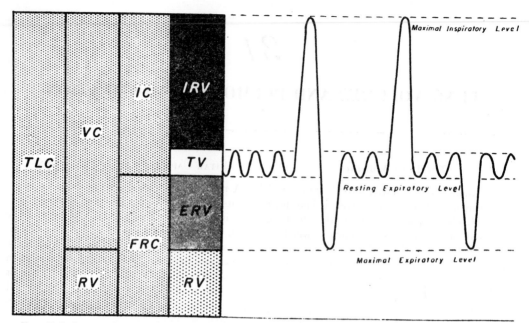

Fig. 31.1. Lung volumes indicated as they would appear on a spirographic tracing. See text for meaning of letters. (Reproduced by permission from Comroe *et al.* The Lung. Year Book Publishers, Inc., Chicago, 1955.)

ities. Classes B and C have values 90 per cent and 85 per cent respectively of those of Class A. He considered a reduction of 15 per cent below the standard of the class to which the subject belongs as an almost certain indication of some abnormality. It should be mentioned that measurements of chest expansion, as by means of a tape-measure may bear little relation to the vital capacity. A subject with powerful muscles can enlarge his thoracic cage to a capacity greater than his lungs are able to fill. His diaphragm instead of taking a full downward stroke is drawn upwards while the viscera are forced into the extrathoracic space by a strong contraction of the abdominal muscles.

The vital capacity is reduced in many diseased conditions especially those involving the respiratory and cardiovascular systems. Among these are:

(a) Conditions which directly involve the lungs, e.g., pneumonia, pulmonary tuberculosis, emphysema, etc.

(b) Mechanical interference with the enlargement of the thoracic cavity, e.g., as by abdominal conditions impeding the movements of the diaphragm or abnormalities of the thoracic walls. The movements of the thoracic walls may be seriously restricted by abdominal or pleuritic pain.

(c) Intrathoracic conditions which encroach upon the space normally occupied by the lungs, e.g., pericardial or pleuritic effusions, pneumothorax, tumors, etc.

(d) Heart disease. Engorgement of the pulmonary vessels and pulmonary edema involving especially the lung bases lead to a reduction of the vital capacity in cardiac cases. Peabody found that when in heart disease the vital capacity reached 40 per cent of the normal, the subjects were almost constantly dyspneic or showed dyspnea upon the slightest exertion.

The vital capacity, the functional residual capacity and the residual volume, and consequently the total lung capacity are reduced in the recumbent posture.

## MEASUREMENT OF FUNCTIONAL RESIDUAL CAPACITY (FRC) AND RESIDUAL VOLUME (RV)

The residual volume is the only one of the primary lung volumes that can not be measured directly. It can be estimated by indirect methods which involve diluting a known volume of gas with the residual volume and determining the amount of dilution which occurs. Both open and closed circuit methods have been used.

Using a closed circuit, helium can be used as the test gas. A known volume of a gas mixture containing 10 per cent helium is introduced into a spirometer. The initial concentration of helium in the lungs is zero, and in the spirometer it is 10 per cent. Beginning from either the resting end-expiratory position (in which case FRC is measured) or from the position of maximal expiration (in which case RV is measured), the subject breathes from the spirometer until mixing is complete so that the concentration of helium in the lungs and spirometer becomes equal. Then the concentration of helium in the spirometer is determined.

The volume of gas in the lung with which the helium was mixed is calculated on the assumption that the same number of molecules of helium is present at the end of the test as at the beginning. This assumption is permissible since only a short time is involved in rebreathing and helium is only slightly soluble in water. The lung volume is calculated as follows:

$$V_L F_{IN,L} + V_S F_{IN,S} = (V_L + V_S) F_{END,S}$$

where $V_L$ = initial volume in lung — unknown FRC or RV depending on position.

$F_{IN,L}$ = initial concentration of test gas in lung.

$V_S$ = initial volume in spirometer.

$F_{IN,S}$ = initial concentration of test gas in spirometer.

$F_{END,S}$ = final concentration of test gas in spirometer (and in lungs).

Suppose the initial volume of the gas mixture in the spirometer was 1000 ml. and the initial and final concentrations of helium in the spirometer were 10 per cent and 5 per cent respectively. The calculation is as follows:

$$0 + (1000 \times 0.10) = (V_L + 1000) \, 0.05$$
$$100 - 50 = 0.05 \, V_L$$
$$V_L = 1000 \text{ ml.}$$

In practice it is preferable to measure FRC, because the resting end-expiratory position is a more constant point to work from than the position of maximal expiration. Then the ERV is determined experimentally, and this is subtracted from the FRC to obtain RV.

### Tests of Mechanical Factors in Breathing

In the measurements of lung volumes neither the effort involved nor the time factor in movement of air is evaluated. Records of normal breathing, forced inspiration, forced expiration from the position of forced inspiration (*timed vital capacity*) and *maximal breathing capacity* obtained on a moving drum provide information concerning the rate of movement of gas. In figure 31.2 a spirogram obtained from a normal subject is shown for comparison with those characteristic of patients with pulmonary fibrosis, asthma and emphysema. In fibrosis the major change is seen to be the decrease in vital capacity. In asthma, which is characterized by increased resistance in the airway, the rate of expulsion of air and rate of inhalation are greatly decreased; and, since air can not be moved as fast as in the normal, maximal breathing capacity also is greatly decreased. In emphysema the defects though similar to those seen in asthma, are of greater degree.

For these tests the instructions to the subject are very important if comparisons of records are to be made. First the subject breathes normally, then he is told to inspire maximally, and then to blow out as hard and fast as he can. Next he should inhale as quickly as possible to the position of maximal inspiration. Following this, to obtain maximal breathing capacity (MBC), he is instructed to breathe as deeply and rapidly as he is able for 15 seconds. For this he is allowed to set his own frequency and amplitude.

The normal person can exhale about 83 per cent of the vital capacity in one second, 94 per cent in two seconds, and 97 per cent in three seconds. In patients with pulmonary fibrosis the vital capacity is below normal but the per cent exhaled per second may be normal.

The MBC is low in many types of cardiopulmonary diseases. It is not diagnostic of any single disease and is not as specific in evaluating the type of defect as simpler tests utilizing a single respiratory maneuver. However, it may be of considerable value in individual cases having impairment of breathing if repeated records are obtained for comparison in order to determine whether the patient is showing improvement under treatment.

### RESPIRATORY MINUTE VOLUME (RMV) AND PULMONARY VENTILATION

The volume of gas moved in and out of the respiratory passages per minute, the *respiratory minute volume*, is the product of the mean tidal volume and the respiratory rate. It can be measured directly by having the subject exhale through a gas meter for a given period or the individual tidal volumes recorded during a minute can be added. The upper portions of the respiratory tree serve as conduits; since no exchange of gas occurs at these levels, it is evident that a correction needs to be made to determine how much of the RMV is available for alveolar ventilation. The latter also is known as pulmonary ventilation. As emphasized by Gray it is this

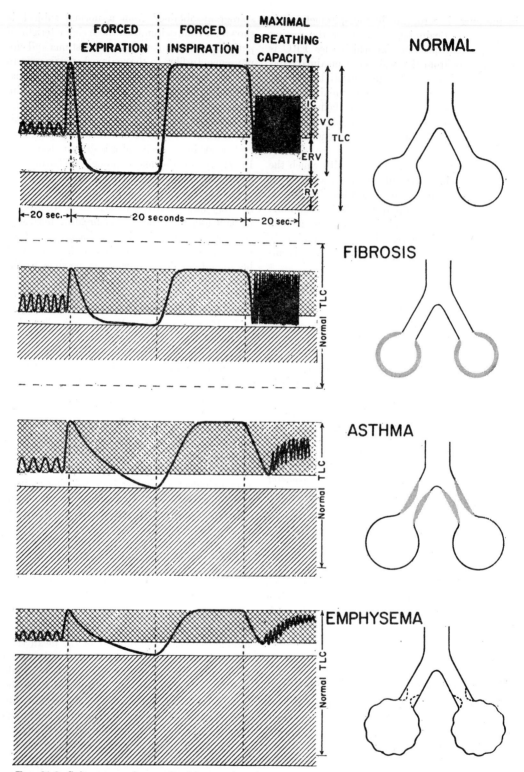

Fig. 31.2. Spirograms of normal subject and patients with pulmonary fibrosis, asthma, and emphysema. (Reproduced by permission from Comroe *et al*, *The Lung*. Year Book Publishers, Inc., Chicago, 1955.)

figure which may be expected to be of physiological significance rather than the RMV.

The volume of the air passages from the nose and nasopharynx down to that level of the respiratory tree where interchanges of oxygen and carbon dioxide with the blood occur is known as the *anatomic* dead space. The volume of this space can be determined on the basis of the fact that expired gas is a mixture of gas from the dead space and from the alveoli. This method involves analysis of expired air and alveolar air samples, and representative samples of the latter are difficult to obtain. Another method for determining the dead space is to inhale pure oxygen from a spirometer and then to exhale through a continuous gas analyzer. At the beginning of the expiration the first gas to leave the airway is pure oxygen which has been in the dead space without any admixture with other gases; then as expiration proceeds, the gas shows a progressive increase in nitrogen until it reaches the concentration found in alveolar air. Beginning with the point at which the nitrogen concentration in expired air becomes constant, alveolar air is expired. Thus there are three phases in the nitrogen concentration curve (see fig. 31.3): (a) no nitrogen present; (b) progressively increasing nitrogen concentration; and (c) maximal and constant nitrogen concentration. From the data obtained by such an analysis of a single exhalation the dead space can be computed. (Examples of the calculation

are given by Comroe *et al.* 1955.) Mean values for the dead space in persons in the supine or in a semi-recumbent position range around 150 ml.

The alveolar ventilation is calculated by subtracting the volume of the dead space from the tidal volume and multiplying this by the respiratory rate. If volume of expired air has been measured directly by means of a gas meter the product of respiratory rate times 150 ml. can be subtracted to convert to the figure for alveolar ventilation. Since the dead space is about 0.3 of the tidal volume under resting conditions alveolar ventilation is about 0.7 of the RMV. Average values for normal young men under resting conditions are 3 to 4 liters per min. per square meter for RMV and 2 to $2\frac{1}{2}$ liters per min. per square meter for alveolar ventilation. As tidal volume increases, since dead space remains constant, the figure for alveolar ventilation becomes a larger fraction of the RMV. Conversely, shallow breathing is relatively inefficient in producing alveolar ventilation, since the dead space becomes a larger fraction of the tidal volume.

The *ventilation ratio* (VR) which will be considered further in the discussion of the regulation of pulmonary ventilation, is the ratio of the alveolar ventilation under a given set of conditions to the alveolar ventilation under resting conditions. Thus it is the times increase in ventilation, produced by a given set of conditions, over that observed at rest.

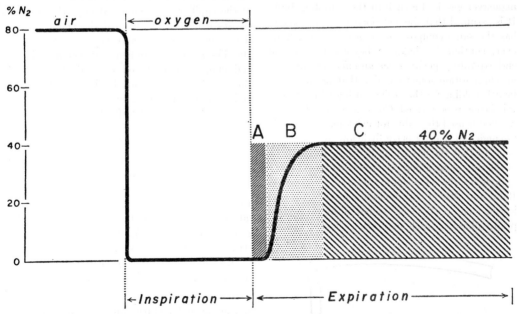

FIG. 31.3. Single breath analysis using rapid, continuous gas analyzer. See text for explanation. (Reproduced by permission from Comroe *et al.*, The Lung. Year Book Publishers, Inc., Chicago, 1955.)

## ALVEOLAR AIR

This is the air contained in the air sacs and alveoli. Its gases come into equilibrium with those in the blood of the pulmonary capillaries. The alveolar air continually is being renewed largely as a consequence of the respiratory movements; but since the lungs are not emptied during expiration, it is quite clear that complete renewal of the air cannot be effected by a single respiration. The ventilation of the lungs occurs by the mechanical mixing of the inspired air with the volume of air known as the FRC and by the slower process of diffusion. During expiration the air of the upper respiratory passages is first expelled; then follows a part of the air of the bronchial tree. At the end of expiration the air which has been in the distended alveoli, since these have been reduced in capacity, now overflows into the bronchioles and bronchi. At the next inspiration this air is swept back again into the air sacs, its place being taken by fresh atmospheric air. The latter as compared with the alveolar air has a high oxygen pressure and a low pressure of carbon dioxide. Oxygen, therefore, diffuses from the inspired to the alveolar air and carbon dioxide diffuses from the alveolar air to the inspired air.

*Methods of obtaining alveolar air samples.* One method of obtaining alveolar air is as follows. The subject, after a normal expiration, makes a forced expiration through a Haldane tube of the type shown in figure 31.4. Toward the end of this maneuver gas is drawn into the sampling bulb. It is assumed that the last portion of air exhaled has the same composition as alveolar air; however, continued exhalation beyond the normal end-expiratory position has an effect on alveolar air composition somewhat like that produced by breath-holding for the period during which forced exhalation is performed. Consequently, when this method is used the value for $pCO_2$ may be a little too high and that for $pO_2$ a little low. Rahn (1954) believes that the gas which is exhaled four-fifths of the way along a normal expiration most nearly approaches the mean composition of alveolar air. Rahn and Otis (1949) devised a method for collecting small portions of expired air at the appropriate phase of each expiration. The device is

FIG. 31.4 Haldane tube and sampling bulb

referred to as an end-tidal sampler. Samples collected by this method have a mean $pCO_2$ which is about 2.5 mm. Hg lower than those obtained from the same subjects by the Haldane-Priestley method and a $pO_2$ which is $4.3 \pm 0.6$ mm. Hg higher. The alveolar $pCO_2$ values obtained by the end-tidal sampler are reported to approach more closely those for arterial $pCO_2$, and this is presented as further evidence for the accuracy of the method on the grounds that it seems reasonable to assume that equilibration between alveolar $pCO_2$ and capillary $pCO_2$ in lungs is complete.

The average volumes per cent of $O_2$ in alveolar air, reduced to standard temperature and pressure, is around 14.2 and the figure for $CO_2$ is around 5.5. The percentage in the lungs is reduced, however, as a result of dilution with water vapor of which about 6.2 volumes per cent is present. The $pCO_2$ of alveolar air usually is around 39 to 40 mm. Hg in normal resting subjects at sea level and under the same conditions the alveolar $pO_2$ is around 100 mm. Hg.

Atmospheric air at STP contains 20.94 volumes per cent of $O_2$ and 0.04 volumes per cent of $CO_2$. This gives a $pO_2$ of about 160 mm. Hg and a $pCO_2$ of about 0.3 mm. Hg.

### Alveolar-Capillary Diffusion and Diffusing Capacity

With a normal alveolar $pO_2$ of 100 mm. Hg the diffusion gradient for oxygen at the arterial end of the capillary is around 60 mm. Hg. and decreases exponentially toward the venous end of the capillary where it may be only 0 to 10 mm. Hg. The *mean* $pO_2$ gradient between alveolar air and lung capillary blood was calculated by C. Bohr (1909) to be 15 mm. Hg in resting subjects and 30 mm. Hg during severe exercise. Bohr developed the concept of "diffusion constant" of the lung which is now known as "diffusing capacity." This quantity is written $D_{O_2}$ or $D_{L_{O_2}}$ and is defined as the number of milliliters of oxygen which are taken up by the blood per minute at an average $pO_2$ gradient of 1 mm. Hg between the alveolar air and the lung capillary blood. Since rate of diffusion is proportional to the pressure gradient, $O_2$ uptake $(V_{O_2})$ = diffusing capacity $(D_{O_2}) \times$ average $pO_2$ gradient.

*Measurement of diffusing capacity.* To measure the diffusing capacity for oxygen three measurements are necessary: (1) ml of $O_2$ passing from alveolar air to blood per minute, (2) mean alveolar $O_2$ pressure, and (3) mean pulmonary capillary $O_2$ pressure.

$$D_{O_2} = \frac{\text{ml. of } O_2 \text{ passing from alveolar air to blood per minute}}{\text{mean alveolar } pO_2 - \text{mean capillary } pO_2}$$

Item number 1 is measured as in the BMR test. For item 2 the most accurate figure is obtained by use of the alveolar air equation. (This equation applies the principle that the total pressure of the four gases in the alveoli equals the barometric pressure. Hence if the partial pressures of $CO_2$, $N_2$ and $H_2O$ vapor are known the oxygen tension can be obtained by subtraction. Water vapor is assumed to be 47 mm. Hg, $pCO_2$ is determined for arterial blood which is assumed to be in equilibrium with the $pCO_2$ of alveolar air, and $pN_2$ can be calculated accurately if the respiratory exchange ratio is determined.) Item 3 has been computed by Bohr's integration procedure from the following: (1) $pO_2$ of mixed venous blood (which is what enters the pulmonary capillaries), (2) $pO_2$ in alveolar air, (3) $pO_2$ in the blood at the end of the pulmonary capillaries, and the physiological oxygen-hemoglobin dissociation curve. Forster emphasizes the point that the most difficult problem is the measurement of end-capillary $pO_2$, since there is no way of obtaining a sample to analyze. It is apparent that indirect methods for obtaining this figure involve the introduction of the experimental errors of the several tests involved and also the setting up of several assumptions some of which probably are unwarranted. Furthermore, it is probable that the value for $pO_2$ in mixed end-capillary blood, even if it were determined accurately, would be of no real use, since in a large proportion of the pulmonary capillaries the alveolar-capillary $pO_2$ gradient most likely becomes zero before the blood reaches the end of the capillary. The relatively slight difference in alveolar $pO_2$ and that of blood returning to the left atrium may be attributed to mixing of blood from poorly aerated portions of the lung with that from well aerated alveoli where equilibrium may be presumed to be complete well before the blood reaches the venular end of the capillary. It seems quite possible that the values calculated for the mean alveolar-capillary $pO_2$ difference in the resting subject may be as much as two to three times that which actually is present. It is probable also that the amount of the error which is introduced in postulating that equilib-

rium between alveolar air and pulmonary capillary blood is not reached until the blood arrives at the end of the capillary is much greater at rest than during exercise, when rate of blood flow is increased; and this could explain a large part of the increase in the figure for $D_{L_{O_2}}$ in exercise as compared with that of the subject at rest.

Forster (1957) states that certain facts which he tabulates "make it apparent that each method of measuring $D_L$ actually measures something different." The methods referred to are the $D_{L_{O_2}}$ steady state method, the $D_{L_{CO}}$ steady-state method (three modifications) and the $D_{L_{CO}}$ breath-holding method (two modifications). Obviously if each measures something different, only one could measure the specific membrane properties which physiologists wish to measure, and it is possible at present that none of the methods in use measures any single specific aspect of lung function.

To summarize the situation with references to measurements of $D_L$, it would seem that one of the factors needed in the calculations, namely the mean alveolar-capillary $pO_2$ difference has not been determined accurately, and consequently the errors involved probably are quite large.

## REFERENCES

CHRISTIE, R. V. J. Clin. Invest., 1932, **11**, 1099.
COMROE, J. H., AND DRIPPS, R. D. Am. J. Physiol., 1944, **142**, 700.
DREYER, G. Lancet, 1919, **2**, 227.
HENDERSON, Y., CHILLINGWORTH, F. P., AND WHITNEY, J. L. Am. J. Physiol., 1915, **38**, 1.
HUTCHINSON, J. *In* Todd's Cyclopaedia of Anatomy and Physiology, 1850, **4**, p. 1016.
LILIENTHAL, J. L., JR., RILEY, R. L., PROEMMAL, D. D., AND FRANKE, R. E. Am. J. Physiol., 1946, **147**, 199.
VAN SLYKE, D. D., AND BINGER, C. A. S. J. Exper. Med., 1923, **27**, 457.
WEST, H. F. Arch. Int. Med., 1920, **25**, 306.
*Monographs and Reviews*
ARNETT, J. H. J. Clin. Invest., 1935, **14**, 543.
COMROE, J. H., JR., FORSTER, R. E., DUBOIS, A. B., BRISCOE, W. A., AND CARLSEN, E. The Lung. Clinical Physiology and Pulmonary Function Tests. The Year Book Publishers, Inc., Chicago, 1955.
FORSTER, R. E. Physiol. Rev., 1957, **37**, 391.
FOWLER, W. S. Physiol. Rev., 1952, **32**, 1.
HALDANE, J. S., AND PRIESTLEY, J. G. Respiration. Clarendon Press, Oxford, 1935.
HENDERSON, Y. Adventures in Respiration. The Williams & Wilkins Company, Baltimore, 1938.
OTIS, A. B. Physiol. Rev., 1954, **34**, 449.

# *32*

# THE CONTROL OF BREATHING

## Control of Inspiration and Expiration

As described in chapter 30, inspiration during eupnea is accomplished by contraction of certain muscles, such as the diaphragm and external intercostals, which may be called *primary* muscles of inspiration; while expiration is the result of the elastic recoil of the lungs and thoracic cage, and the action of gravity when the inspiratory muscles relax. With increased demands for ventilation, additional muscles, collectively called *accessory* muscles of inspiration, are activated to produce a more rapid and deeper inspiration; certain muscles also contract during expiration to accelerate the return of the chest to the resting end-expiratory position. In eupneic breathing, therefore, for inspiration and expiration to occur it is necessary simply for the motor neurons supplying the primary muscles of inspiration to show intermittent bursts of activity.

The initial observation which is important in considering regulation of breathing is that apnea occurs when the $CO_2$ tension of the blood is below certain levels if at the same time the $O_2$ tension is above certain levels. This situation can be produced simply by hyperventilating with atmospheric air, or an even longer period of apnea can be produced by hyperventilating with oxygen. After hyperventilation is terminated apnea will supervene until $CO_2$ tension becomes elevated to a certain level or until $O_2$ tension becomes lowered below certain levels. Thus it is seen that the initiation of breathing after hyperventilation depends upon stimuli which derive either from a rise in $CO_2$ tension or from a fall in $O_2$ tension or from an interaction of these changes.

The relative importance of $CO_2$ and $O_2$ in influencing breathing in an individual at sea level (ambient pressure of 760 mm. Hg) is illustrated when the percentages of these gases in inspired air are altered. If the $O_2$ percentage is increased above the amount normally found, even up to 100%, negligible influences on rate and depth of breathing are observed. Also, if the amount of $O_2$ in inspired air is moderately lowered, namely,

down to about 18%, typically, little or no change in breathing is observed. Some persons will show stimulation of breathing as the $O_2$ is lowered to around 16% and levels of 10 to 12% regularly cause hyperpnea. From these facts it is apparent that reduction in $O_2$ tension is not an important factor in regulation of breathing until the tension is reduced below some critical level which is somewhat lower than that found in normal resting subjects breathing air at a pressure of one atmosphere. Any slight increase in the $CO_2$ tension of arterial blood, on the other hand, causes an increase in breathing and a decrease in $CO_2$ tension is associated with apnea even when the $O_2$ tension is moderately below that which is found normally at sea level. Such facts provide a basis for the interpretation that the inspiratory process at sea level in normal subjects is related to the action of $CO_2$ on certain neurons in the respiratory center in the medulla oblongata, causing them to discharge; and the termination of inspiration, resulting in expiration, occurs as a result of "feedback" of inhibitory influences to these neurons. This mechanism serves to keep the $CO_2$ tension of arterial blood at a constant level of about 38 to 40 mm. Hg in the presence of wide fluctuations in $O_2$ tension of arterial blood as long as the latter are at levels from about 80 to 90 mm. Hg and up.

## The Respiratory Center

It is customary and convenient to speak of the collections of nerve cells in the brain stem which are concerned with the integration of the activity of the muscles of respiration as the *respiratory center*. But the use of the term should not be taken to imply that the controlling nervous elements are a compact circumscribed mass, or confined to a closely restricted area. Section through the brain at any level rostral to the upper border of the pons usually does not alter significantly the respiratory rhythm. But sections at various levels behind this cause pronounced disturbances in respiration. If a cut is made through the medulla caudal to the tip of the calamus scriptorius, all breathing ceases.

Legallois (1824) located the respiratory center in the lower part of the medulla oblongata, and Flourens (1842, 1858) found a small spot about the size of a pin's head just beneath the forepart of the *calamus scriptorius* in the floor of the fourth ventricle, on either side of the midline. He showed that after bilateral destruction of this area, which he named *noeud vital* (vital knot), the respirations ceased. It appears, however, that the respiratory failure in these animals could have been secondary to circulatory failure related to loss of vasomotor tone.

Markwald (1887) described powerful and prolonged tonic inspiratory movements or "cramps" which supervened after bilateral section of the vagus nerves and division of the brain stem immediately behind the posterior colliculi. He concluded that a center inhibitory to inspiration was located in the latter situation, but that the vagi also had an inhibitory action, consequently the inspiratory "cramps" appeared only after vagal influence had been abolished as well. Markwald's observations were confirmed shortly afterwards by other experimenters. The subject was studied further by Lumsden (1932), who found that the prolonged inspiratory movements occurred only if the section passed through the pons a few millimeters behind its anterior border and occurred whether or not the vagi were divided. The inspiratory cramps or *apneuses*, as Lumsden preferred to call them, last for several seconds. He postulated their dependence upon an *apneustic* or *inspiratory center* at the level of the striae acusticae, which was dominated normally by an inhibitory or *pneumotaxic center* situated in the upper part of the pons. The duty of the latter center was, through its inhibitory influence, to help to transmute the apneustic movements into the rhythmical movements characteristic of normal respiration. After section of the brain stem behind the striae acusticae, the respirations consisted of a series of gasps occurring at relatively long intervals. Lumsden concluded that these represented the activity of a primitive *gasping center* situated in the lower part of the medulla from which the two higher centers had evolved. It was considered to be of little importance in higher animals.

Lumsden's results were confirmed in the main by Stella and by Pitts, Magoun and Ranson. Stella, however, found in contradiction to Lumsden, that section through the pons (i.e., separation of the pneumotaxic center) did not result in

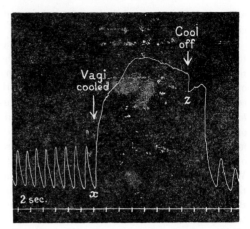

FIG. 32.1. Showing apneusis. Section of the brain stem along a plane passing dorsally immediately behind the posterior colliculi; and ventrally 2.5 mm. below the upper border of the pons. Between *x* and *z* the vagi were blocked by cold. Time: 2 sec. (After Stella.)

apneusis unless the vagal influence was abolished also (see fig. 32.1). The results of Pitts and his associates are in essential agreement with those of Stella. They found that animals decerebrated through the upper part of the pons maintained a normal type of respiration which responded in the usual way to chemical and peripheral nerve stimulation so long as the vagi were intact, but immediately developed apneustic respiration and a complete cessation of rhythmical movements when both vagi were severed. Stimulation of the central end of one of the cut vagi temporarily restores the respiratory rhythm. The apneustic center is, therefore, under a double inhibitory influence, either one of which is capable of converting the apneustic type of respiration to the rhythm of normal or nearly normal respiration. The vagal impulses influencing the apneustic center are initiated by the stretch of the lung towards the latter part of the inspiratory phase of normal breathing. Studies by Cohen (1958) indicate that the pneumotaxic center shows rhythmic activity synchronous with breathing when its connections with the respiratory center are intact but fails to show rhythmicality when these pathways are cut.

The apneuses, like normal respirations, are affected powerfully by the $CO_2$ tension of the blood, being increased in depth by having the animal breathe an air mixture containing a high concentration of $CO_2$ and reduced in depth, or prevented from occurring, by carbon dioxide lack. According to Stella, the pneumotaxic center is bilateral but its connections with the apneustic center are mainly homolateral, i.e. un-crossed.

Pitts, Magoun and Ranson describe the respiratory center in the cat, which they locate in the reticular formation of the medulla, as consisting of an inspiratory and an expiratory division; both centers are bilaterally represented. The *inspiratory center* occupies the rostral half or two thirds of the reticular formation overlying the olivary nuclei on both sides, i.e., beneath the caudal third of the floor of the fourth ventricle (fig. 32.2). When stimulated a maximal co-ordinated inspiration results, involving both diaphragm and thorax. If stimulated during apneusis, the magnitude of the inspiratory movement is increased; if stimulated during an interval between apneuses, an apneustic movement is produced. The expiratory center lies in the reticular formation dorsal to the inspiratory center. Electrical stimulation within this area causes expiration; if stimulated during inspiration or during apneusis, these movements are inhibited. Regular respirations—inspiration alternating with expiration—are induced by rhythmical stimulation of the inspiratory center; expiration then occurs passively. Rhythmical stimulation of the expiratory center also produces regular respiration, spontaneous inspirations then alternating with the expiratory movements. Intimate synaptic connections exist between the diffusely distributed neurons within each center and between the two oppositely act-

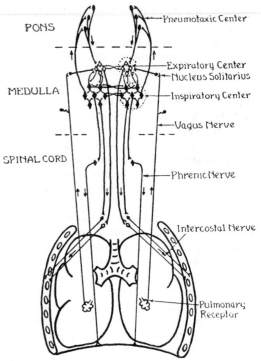

FIG. 32.3. Diagram illustrating the chief nervous connections responsible for the control of the respiratory rhythm. Inspiratory and expiratory centers in the medulla on the right side surrounded by dotted circles. (After Pitts, slightly modified.)

ing centers on the same side, as well as between similarly acting centers on opposite sides of the medulla. Thus, unilateral stimulation of a small area of the inspiratory center causes maximal contraction of all the inspiratory muscles. Excitation of one center causes simultaneous activation of its fellow of the contralateral side, accompanied by reciprocal inhibition of both oppositely acting centers. Thus, the alternating rhythm of inspiration is established and sustained, and the respiratory movements synchronized on the two sides of the body. The functional importance of the bilateral connections is demonstrated in a striking manner by making a deep longitudinal cut through the midline of the caudal part of the medulla; then the respiratory rhythms on the two sides of the body become asynchronous (see fig. 32.3).

The similarity in the effects of stimulation of the expiratory center and of the central end of the vagus, namely, inhibition of inspiration and of apneusis, has led Pitts and his colleagues to the conclusion that the vagal respiratory effects are mediated through the expiratory center. The influence of the pneumotaxic center probably is exerted in the same way.

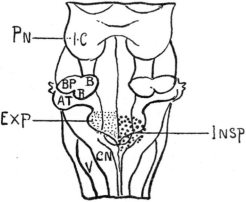

FIG. 32.2. Dorsal view of lower brain stem of cat showing location of pneumotaxic (Pn.), inspiratory (Insp.) and expiratory (Exp.) centers. Extent of expiratory center shown in light stippling, inspiratory center in heavy stippling. Though the centers are bilateral each is outlined on one side only, for the sake of simplicity. IC, inferior colliculus; AT, acoustic tubercle; B, brachium conjunctivum; B.P., brachium pontis; R, restiform body; CN, cuneate nucleus. (Redrawn from Pitts, Magoun and Ranson.)

The respiratory center is connected with the motor neurons of the phrenic and intercostal nerves in the cervical (C. 3, 4 and 5) and upper thoracic segments of the cord (T. 2-6) by descending tracts which run in the anterior columns and in the ventral parts of the lateral columns of the spinal cord.

## THE SPONTANEOUS ACTIVITY OF THE MEDULLARY RESPIRATORY CENTERS

This has been a subject of interest to physiologists for many years. Some investigators, such as Coombs and Pike, and Schafer, have denied that the center is capable of spontaneous activity, maintaining that afferent impulses, especially those set up in the lung by the stimulus of stretch and conveyed by the vagus, and those initiated from proprioceptors in the respiratory muscles and travelling by the posterior nerve roots, were essential. However, the results secured within recent years by means of improved methods of investigation leave little reason to doubt that, in certain species at least, the brain stem continues to discharge impulses to the respiratory muscles after all or nearly all afferent paths have been severed. For example, rhythmical bursts of impulses can be recorded from the central stump of the phrenic nerve of a decerebrate animal after section of the vagi, glossopharyngeal and other cranial nerves entering the pons and medulla, and division of the spinal cord below the level of the 7th cervical segment. Such an extensive operation would certainly interrupt all important afferent paths including those from the carotid sinus and the aortic arch. It is not to be supposed, of course, that the respirations would be normal after such a radical procedure, for even if not essential for maintaining the activity of the center, afferent nerve influences are of the utmost importance in the regulation of that activity and the production of the normal respiratory rhythm. Evidence for automaticity of the respiratory center of a cold-blooded species has been secured by Adrian and Buytenijk. They succeeded in re-

cording rhythmical action potentials from the excised brain stem of the gold-fish; the potential changes had the same range of frequency as the respiratory movements (fig. 32.4).

The spontaneous respiratory activity is apparently dependent primarily upon the inspiratory center, the expiratory center playing an inhibitory role to interrupt intermittently the inspiratory discharge. As shown by Cohen (1958) impulses are not discharged spontaneously from the pneumotaxic center. Pitts and his colleagues suggest that the pneumotaxic center is excited from the inspiratory center, that a proportion of the impulses discharged from the latter region ascend to the pontine center whence impulses descend to the expiratory center; a discharge of *inhibitory* impulses is transmitted from the latter to the inspiratory center. As the discharge of impulses from the expiratory center ceases, the inspiratory center resumes its activity, and the cycle is repeated. A rise in the rate of discharge of the inhibitory impulses will increase the rate of breathing, while a reduction in the frequency of the discharge will be followed by slowing of the respirations.

It appears, then, that in the intact animal the automatic alternating rhythm of the medullary centers is maintained largely by inhibitory impulses from the pneumotaxic center and vagal afferents impinging upon the expiratory centers, which in turn inhibit, intermittently, the activity of the inspiratory centers. The vagal influence is evoked by inflation of the lungs (i.e., by inspiration); expiration, a passive act, follows (ch. 30). Under ordinary physiological conditions the vagal regulating influence appears to play the dominant role.

Of the two main methods which have been used for localizing inspiratory and expiratory centers, namely stimulation versus "sounding" for action potentials, the latter would seem to be somewhat more suitable. Stimulation serves to expose only a dominant or major influence. Neurons having opposite effects could be present and could be

FIG. 32.4 Comparison of electrical potential wave rhythm and rhythm of respiratory movements. (After Adrian and Buytendijk.)

stimulated simultaneously, but the effects of the dominant one of the two groups would be expected to appear. Hence, inspiration elicited from a given site would not rule out the possibility that expiratory neurons are present in this region, nor could an expiratory response elicited from a specific site prove that no inspiratory neurons were being stimulated simultaneously. According to Brookhart (1940) lower strengths of stimuli applied to the regions in which the inspiratory center and expiratory center are supposed to be located will elicit various types of effects, and somewhat stronger stimuli are required to produce the effects reported by Pitts and coworkers. On the other hand the recording of a burst of impulses only during one phase of the respiratory

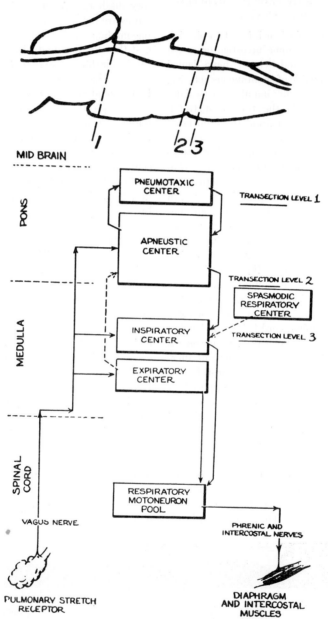

Fig. 32.5. Schematic representation of organization of central respiratory mechanisms in the brain-stem of the cat. Key to transection levels is indicated above. In vagotomized cats transection rostral to level 1 allows eupnea to be present; transection between level 1 and 2 causes apneustic breathing to appear; transection between 2 and 3 results in eupneic breathing or gasping or occasionally Biot's breathing, and transection caudal to level 3 is followed by absence of respiration (reproduced by permission from Wang, Ngai, and Frumin).

cycle would constitute evidence that only the
inspiratory or expiratory neurons, depending on
the time relations, were activated at that site
under the conditions of the experiment. When the
"sounding" method is used, according to Gesell,
Bricker and Magee (1936), for the most part,
impulses are recorded from a given site during
both inspiration and expiration. This would indicate that expiratory and inspiratory neurons are
intermingled and would tend to make one doubt
that there are anatomically discrete expiratory
and inspiratory centers.

A difficulty with the "sounding" method for
determining the location of inspiratory and expiratory neurons of the respiratory center is
that impulses may be picked up directly from
motor neurons. Achard and Bucher (1954) investigated the region of the respiratory center
with needle electrodes and determined by subsequent histological examination the precise cells
from which recordings were obtained. Any purely
inspiratory activity obtained by them was from
*motor neurons* involved in inspiration, while action
currents recorded from numerous other electrodes
located in the area of the respiratory center did
not permit a distinction between respiratory
rhythms and the continuous asynchronous "background" activity in the reticular substance. It
must be concluded, therefore, that the question
of the precise location of inspiratory and expiratory neurons within the medulla has not yet been
answered.

The relative importance of the pneumotaxic
center in maintaining rhythmic breathing after
vagotomy seems to differ according to the species
of animal studied and the conditions of the experiments. According to Hoff and Breckenridge
(1954) in dogs, and under certain conditions in
cats, midpontine section combined with bilateral
vagotomy does not cause cessation of breathing.
This has been confirmed by Wang and coworkers.
In fact vagotomy has been reported to have no
effect on breathing in some instances in animals
having the brain stem sectioned in the midpontine
region. Hoff and Breckenridge have returned to
the view that the cause of the rhythmic discharge
of respiration lies within the medulla itself. "Just
how the rhythm of respiration develops within
the medulla is still problematical, and it may well
be possible that within the confines of the medulla
itself anatomical pathways are to be found
wherein reciprocating self-limiting circuits, akin
to those postulated between medulla and pons in
earlier hypotheses, determine the rhythm of
breathing."

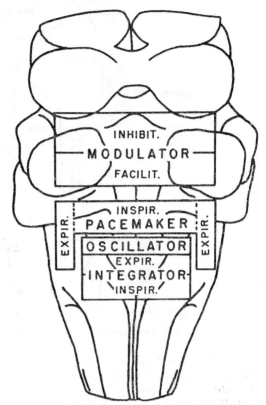

FIG. 32.6. Schematic representation of functional concept of central regulation of respiration.
Relative locations in the brain-stem of a cat of the
regions which subserve the various functions are
indicated (reproduced by permission from Brodie
and Borison).

The situation at present can be summarized
by stating that the presence of a respiration-
regulating group of neurons in the upper pontine
region, the so-called pneumotaxic center, has been
clearly demonstrated and has an important role
in regulation of rhythmic breathing in the intact
animal. However, it seems to be clearly demonstrated, also, that rhythmic breathing still can
occur when both this mechanism and the vagal
reflexes are eliminated. Finally, the precise manner in which the pontine elements influence respiration has not been determined. In figures 32.5
and 32.6 are shown two recent attempts to explain the organization of the respiratory center.

### Hering-Breuer Reflexes

The Hering-Breuer reflexes are effects on the
respiratory cycle which are elicited by inflation
and deflation of the lungs. The receptors concerned are in the lungs, and the afferent pathways
are in the vagus nerves. The function of these
reflexes apparently is to regulate the respiratory

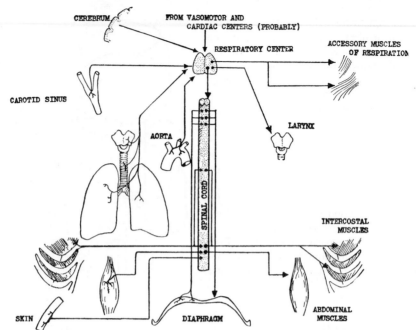

FIG. 32.7. Diagram to illustrate the reflex and chemoreflex control of respiration

cycle rather than to alter significantly the pulmonary ventilation for any prolonged period. The observations made by Hering and Breuer in 1868 were that inflation of the lungs causes arrest of inspiration, expiration then ensuing, and deflation of the lungs has an inspiration-exciting effect. They found that these effects were abolished when the vagus nerves were sectioned. Another way to demonstrate the effects of lung

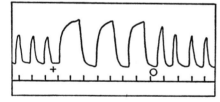

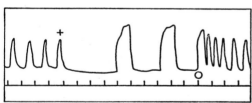

FIG. 32.8. Record of contractions of isolated slip of a diaphragm of a rabbit to illustrate Hering-Breuer reflexes. Upstroke is produced by contraction of the slip, i.e., inspiration. *Above* at + the trachea was occluded at the end of expiration, and at 0 the obstruction was removed. *Below* at + the trachea was occluded at the end of inspiration, and at 0 the obstruction was removed (after Head).

distention is to block the airway at the beginning of either inspiration or expiration. When inflow of air is prevented, a stronger inspiratory effort results than in the preceding cycle, and when egress of air is blocked at the end of inspiration a longer interval than the preceding one occurs before the onset of the next inspiratory effort. In eupnea apparently the inflation effect during inspiration alone is a factor. As inspiration proceeds, distention of the lungs occurs, and impulses are carried by vagal afferents to the respiratory center where they cause inhibition of the inspiratory neurons, thus terminating inspiration. Once the lungs begin to deflate impulses are no longer set up in the vagal afferents and, consequently, the inspiratory neurons again are free to discharge in response to their local chemical environment.

The mechanical problem in studying the Hering-Breuer reflexes can be circumvented in the case of the rabbit since this animal has a slip of muscle on the posterior surface of the diaphragm which can be dissected free and recorded from separately from the remainder of the diaphragm (fig. 32.7). This diaphragmatic slip can be used as an indicator of the degree of activation of inspiratory muscles. If the lungs are distended, the rate and amplitude of contraction of the slip decrease, and if the lungs are deflated, an increase in rate and amplitude of contraction of the slip is observed (fig. 32.8).

The stimulating effect of lung deflation on

inspiration is related under ordinary conditions to failure in the production of the normal amount of inspiration-inhibiting influence at the end of inspiration. However, severe deflation, as from pneumothorax, results in activation of other receptors, and reflex stimulation of inspiration follows. Finally, if lung inflation is severe, not only is inspiration inhibited but active expiration is elicited reflexly. This may not require a third type of receptor, but may be simply the result of greater degree of activation of the same kind of receptors which are concerned in the reflex inhibition of inspiration. The role of vagal reflexes in regulating inspiration and expiration has been described in detail by Wyss (1954).

A physiological role of the Hering-Breuer reflexes is to regulate the extent of lung inflation so that the tidal volume tends to fall within a certain range. Also, these reflexes serve to insure filling and emptying of the lungs despite a considerable increase in resistance in the airway. As would be expected, the typical result following bilateral vagotomy is an increase in the depth of breathing. The inspiratory act under these conditions is seen to be unnecessarily long since the chest tends to remain in the inspiratory position for a short period after ingress of air has stopped. This is an inefficient process since muscular work is being done while no air is being moved. Also, a decrease in respiratory rate develops in most animals after vagotomy. This probably is a compensatory change, secondary to the increased depth, which results in an amount of pulmonary ventilation similar to that which was present before vagotomy. An increased depth of breathing without a decrease in rate would soon wash out $CO_2$ so that the stimulus to the respiratory center would be removed, hence the rate soon would decrease to cause restoration of normal $CO_2$ levels. It should be mentioned, however, that the effects of vagotomy on rate and depth of breathing vary greatly depending upon the anesthetic agent which is used; and furthermore, changes are progressive for a prolonged period following vagotomy.

The effects on respiration of direct stimulation of the central end of the vagus nerve sectioned at the cervical level are somewhat unpredictable since the nerve contains several types of afferent fibers which carry impulses to the respiratory center. These include (1) aortic arch afferents, (2) aortic body afferents, (3) inspiration-inhibiting fibers activated normally during lung inflation, (4) inspiration-exciting fibers activated

physiologically by excessive lung deflation, (5) fibers concerned with visceral pain, and possibly still other types of fibers. However, strong stimulation of the central end of the vagus nerve usually causes apnea, and this may persist for a few seconds after cessation of stimulation. This result could be elicited if the effects of stimulation of (1) and (3) above were sufficient to override the effects of stimulation of (2) and (4).

The Hering-Breuer reflexes are basically proprioceptive in nature. In this case contraction of skeletal muscle not only increases the tension in muscles and shortens them but elastic objects, the lungs, also are put under greater tension. The lungs also are supplied with receptors from which information is carried back to the same neurons that activated the muscles. The muscles of respiration, like skeletal muscle in general, are supplied with proprioceptive innervation through which their contraction is regulated in the same way as described for the limb musculature. After vagotomy, breathing is still possible, although it is altered considerably, and some degree of proprioceptive control still is retained.

### Reflex Effects from Pressoreceptors

A sudden rise in pressure in the sino-aortic zones elicits reflexly a decrease in rate and depth of breathing. If the pressure rise is considerable, apnea may be produced. Typically, adaptation is rather rapid so that breathing is restored even though the new pressure level is maintained. Part of the recovery of respiration is related to adaptation in the receptors themselves, but also it occurs as a consequence of the rise in $pCO_2$ during apnea. The opposite change, a sudden fall in pressure in the sino-aortic zones, elicits hyperpnea. Thus, any sudden change in blood pressure per se tends to elicit respiratory responses. During rapid bleeding or following injection of vasodilator drugs, such as nitroglycerin or bethanechol (a choline derivative), respiration is stimulated (fig. 32.9), and the effect is prevented in considerable part by sino-aortic denervation (Schopp, Gilfoil and Youmans, 1957). The respiration-stimulating effect of nitroglycerin which still remains after denervation can be partly or completely prevented if a device is used to prevent the fall in arterial blood pressure.

Schmidt in 1941, and recently Aviado and Schmidt (1955) have suggested that the effects on respiration elicited from the pressoreceptors serve no physiological purpose; however, this mechanism probably is of importance in influenc-

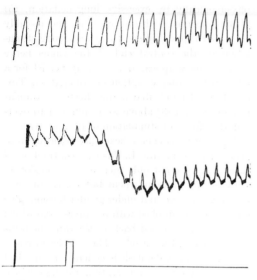

Fig. 32.9. Effects on blood pressure (*below*) and respiration (*above*) following injection of 0.1 mg. per kg. of nitroglycerin into dog anesthetized with alpha-chloralose. The respiratory stimulation can be prevented if the fall in arterial blood pressure is counteracted by means of rapid infusion of blood from a pressure-regulating device (from studies by Schopp, Gilfoil and Youmans).

ing the venous return (Youmans, 1958). Vasodilation promotes pooling of blood, especially in the abdominal viscera, and increased respiratory activity promotes the movement of blood from the abdominal portion of the inferior vena cava on into the thoracic portion. The concept of the respiratory pump, as a factor in aiding venous return, introduced by Donders in 1859, seems accurate according to the studies reviewed by Brecher (1956). Conversely, the respiratory inhibition during a rise in blood pressure, especially in a person in the orthostatic position, would favor pooling of blood in the splanchnic region so that venous return would be decreased; thus cardiac output would be lowered, and the rise in blood pressure would be counteracted. In short, one may interpret the respiratory responses from pressoreceptors, along with effects on heart rate and arteriolar tonus elicited at the same time, as being concerned with the stabilization of arterial blood pressure. The characteristics of these reflexes are such that they are useful in counteracting sudden changes of brief duration; they are not concerned with counteracting prolonged changes.

## Regulation of Pulmonary Ventilation

### Respiratory Adjustments to $CO_2$

The $CO_2$ content of inspired air is negligible, as far as human physiology is concerned, and can be increased somewhat without causing an increase in RMV. Its concentration at sea level can be increased by about 1% (7.6 mm. Hg) before a measurable increase in pulmonary ventilation occurs. If 4% $CO_2$ is breathed, the RMV is approximately doubled on the average, but the effect may be scarcely noticed by the subject. Any further increase in $CO_2$ from 4% up to 10% produces a correspondingly greater RMV, and at the latter level it may be 8 to 10 times the resting level. Also the subject may have symptoms of dizziness, faintness and headache. Increasing the $CO_2$ percentage beyond 10 does not result in significantly greater increases in RMV, and at levels above 20% the RMV may begin to show a decrease. Also, these levels cause convulsive seizures. From the practical standpoint it would appear that if $CO_2$ is to be administered to stimulate breathing, there would be little use for any mixture containing less than 5% or more than 10% $CO_2$.

It is generally agreed that the primary site of action of $CO_2$ in producing effects on breathing is in the inspiratory division of the respiratory center. Cells in a respiratory center that has been isolated from extrinsic neural influences show alterations in rates of discharge in response to corresponding changes in $pCO_2$ of the blood reaching them, and injection of bicarbonate directly into the respiratory center causes an increased activity of these neurons. Considerable attention has been given to the question of the precise mechanism by means of which $CO_2$ exerts its stimulant action on the respiratory center. It has been debated whether $CO_2$ per se has such an effect or whether the effect is exerted indirectly as a consequence of the concomitant increase in cH. There is evidence that both a rise in $pCO_2$ and in cH in the respiratory center contribute to and supplement each other in causing an increase in pulmonary ventilation.

Another mechanism, reflex in nature, is available for the stimulation of breathing as a consequence of a rise in the $pCO_2$ of arterial blood. The chemoreceptors, already described as concerned with producing circulatory adjustments in response to changes in $pO_2$ and $pCO_2$, when subjected to a sufficient rise in $pCO_2$ will elicit an increase in RMV. The extensive literature dealing with chemoreceptors has been summarized by Heymans and Neil (1958). The fact of reflex stimulation of breathing in response to rises in $pCO_2$ of the blood flowing to the aortic and carotid bodies has been demonstrated by a number of methods and is generally accepted. A question which has been vigorously disputed, however, is whether the respiratory center in the intact subject is more sensitive than the chemoreceptors. In other words does the chemoreceptive reflex mechanism constitute the first line of defense against a rising $pCO_2$ in arterial blood or does the respiratory center have the greater sensitivity. Heymans has supported the view that the chemoreceptors are concerned with reflex drive of breathing even under resting conditions at sea level, while Schmidt and Comroe favor the interpretation that these receptors are activated in significant degree only after considerable increases in arterial $pCO_2$. The details of the argument are reviewed by Heymans and Neil, who conclude that the question remains open as to how much the chemoreceptors participate in the response to moderate hypercapnia in the intact animal. However, the majority viewpoint seems to be that the normally sensitive respiratory center responds to rising $CO_2$ and through increased ventilation prevents a rise in $pCO_2$ of arterial blood sufficient to elicit a response from chemoreceptors. If, on the other hand, the respiratory center is rendered relatively insensitive to $CO_2$, for example, by anesthetic agents and narcotic drugs, respiration is depressed, and $pCO_2$ rises to a level sufficient to set up chemoreceptive drive of breathing. According to the latter interpretation the $CO_2$-induced chemoreflex constitutes a secondary line of defense to help insure pulmonary ventilation when the sensitivity of the respiratory center is reduced.

The lowering of $pCO_2$ in arterial blood can be achieved by voluntary hyperventilation or by excessive artificial ventilation of anesthetized subjects. Following hyperventilation, apnea is observed, and breathing is resumed when either $pCO_2$ rises to approximately the level found in the subject under resting conditions or when the $pO_2$ of arterial blood drops to a level sufficient to set up reflex drive of breathing on an $O_2$ lack basis, whichever occurs first. After one has hyperventilated moderately with atmospheric air, oxygen lack develops quickly as the store of oxygen in the lungs is absorbed and utilized; breathing is resumed in sequence to the oxygen lack stimulus before the $pCO_2$ has been restored to the normal resting level. Then the oxygen lack is relieved by a few breaths, and apnea appears again. Gradually, the $pCO_2$ level becomes restored and takes over as the sole drive. This is the basis for the appearance of a few cycles of periodic breathing after hyperventilation. As would be expected if one hyperventilates with 100% $O_2$, rather than air, just as much $CO_2$ is blown off as before, with a given degree of respiratory activity, but the $pO_2$ in alveolar air is quite high at the end of the period of hyperventilation. Consequently a longer time will be required for the $O_2$-lack stimulus to appear than for the $pCO_2$ level to be restored. Therefore, following hyperventilation with 100% $O_2$ the elevation of $pCO_2$ may be the initial factor in the restoration of breathing.

## Respiratory Adjustments to $O_2$

The $pO_2$ in inspired air can be reduced by lowering the atmospheric pressure in a decompression chamber in which the subject has been placed, or he may breathe prepared gas mixtures having various ratios of $O_2$ to $N_2$. Since $O_2$ tension is lowered in proportion to the decrease in barometric pressure with altitude, one may indicate the altitude at which the experimentally induced $pO_2$ would be encountered. Thus a certain altitude, as far as $pO_2$ is concerned, is simulated by the experimental conditions. For example, if one breathes a mixture of 10.5 per cent $O_2$ and 89.5 per cent $N_2$ at 760 mm. Hg pressure, the $pO_2$ is about $\frac{1}{2}$ that in atmospheric air at the same pressure. This approximates the $pO_2$ found in atmospheric air at an altitude of 18,000 feet where the barometric pressure is about 380 mm. Hg. The details concerning respiratory responses to $pO_2$ lower than that of room air at sea level have been described by Dripps and Comroe (1947) and by Rahn and Otis (1949). The major observations may be summarized as follows. Some subjects show a slight stimulation of breathing when the $O_2$ is lowered to 16 per cent to 18 per cent; while others do not respond until a level in the range from 16 per cent down to 12 per cent, or even lower in occasional subjects, is reached. At levels of 10 per cent or below, breathing is stimulated but irregularities may develop. As the $O_2$ tension in inspired air is lowered and respiratory minute volume increases, the $CO_2$ tension in alveolar air and arterial blood falls. Thus at the same time that the oxygen-lack stimulus is operating to cause an increased RMV, the $CO_2$ and cH drives of breathing are being withdrawn. It is apparent, therefore, that the stimulating effects of oxygen-lack *per se* on breathing could be recorded if the fall in $CO_2$ tension were prevented, as by adding the appropriate amount of $CO_2$ to the inspired air. In the discussion of hyperventilation it was noted that a relatively slight reduction in $CO_2$ tension (3 to 4 mm. Hg) results in apnea when there is no accompanying $O_2$ lack. At altitude, therefore, where the $CO_2$ tension is lowered more than this (secondary to increased RMV), it must be assumed that respiratory drive is entirely on an oxygen-lack basis or that a readjustment in sensitivity to $CO_2$ tension has occurred. Acutely, the former seems to be true, while after prolonged exposure to low oxygen tension the latter change apparently occurs.

Papers on respiration written before the discovery of the chemoreceptors of the carotid bodies refer to a stimulant action of oxygen-lack on the respiratory center. It is now believed that a lowered $O_2$ tension in the medulla does not result in stimulation of breathing; and decreases in $O_2$ tension of arterial blood, within ranges that the animal can tolerate for significant periods, do not cause stimulation of breathing if the carotid and aortic bodies have been denervated. Thus, the only sensitive mechanism which responds to oxygen-lack and elicits an increase in RMV is the chemoreceptor reflex. Here, too, as in the case of the $CO_2$ effect, the precise level at which a lowered arterial $O_2$ tension elicits stimulation of breathing is disputed. Comroe and Schmidt (1938) first reported that the $O_2$ tension in blood perfusing the carotid bodies was lowered to about 50 mm. Hg before the receptors were activated, but others have reported the threshold to be above 100 mm. Hg $pO_2$. Experiments showing the effects on RMV of blocking the chemoreceptors do not serve to establish the level of activity under normal resting conditions if anesthetic agents are used, since, as already explained, these substances usually cause depression of the respiratory center so that some part of the drive of breathing is transferred to the chemoreceptors. If oxygen lack stimulates breathing only through activation of chemoreceptors, then depression of breathing should be produced as a result of breathing mixtures containing more $O_2$ than that found in atmospheric air. To be relevant to the question the experiment must be performed on normal, resting subjects at a barometric pressure of approximately one atmosphere, and the gas to be tested should differ from the control only in that an inert gas, such as nitrogen, is substituted for oxygen. Loeshke (1953) reported an 8 per cent reduction of RMV for about a minute when 32 per cent $O_2$ in $N_2$ was substituted for room air in unanesthetized man, and this was followed by a rise until equilibrium was reached after about 4 minutes.

On returning to room air, RMV increased a little for a few minutes and then returned to the control level. Dripps and Comroe (1947), however, reported only 3.1 per cent reduction in RMV caused by inhalation of 100 per cent $O_2$, whereas Baker and Hitchcock (1957) found an increase in ventilation in response to 100 per cent $O_2$. The results cited indicate that if there is any drive of breathing related to $O_2$-tension effects in normal subjects at sea level it is so small that it can be detected only by very careful measurements. Furthermore, it is possible that even the slight increases in ventilation which have been reported are not related to the removal of chemoreceptor drive, but rather to a rise in $pCO_2$ tension in the respiratory center secondary to the vasoconstriction produced by high $O_2$ tension in the arterioles of the brain. (See Kety, S. S. and Schmidt, C. F., 1948.)

### Effects of Hydrogen Ion Concentration and the Interactions between Respiratory Drives

Since changes in $pCO_2$ are accompanied by changes in pH, a question may be raised whether changes in hydrogen ion concentration as such have an influence upon breathing. Gray (1950) has emphasized the point that in metabolic acidosis pulmonary ventilation is greatly increased while arterial $pCO_2$ is below normal. Obviously then if it is true to begin with that only three drives ($pO_2$, $pCO_2$, cH) operate to control breathing, increased acidity per se is capable of stimulating breathing since neither of the other two factors has changed in a direction which would cause such stimulation. Gray further states that an increase in RMV is not regularly associated with an increase (and in fact may occur in the presence of a decrease) in drive related to any one of the three factors considered to be concerned with the control of pulmonary ventilation, however, at least one of three changes must be present: (1) rise in arterial $pCO_2$, (2) decrease in arterial $pO_2$, or (3) increase in arterial cH. It is envisaged that any one of these may assume the major role in driving respiration under certain circumstances. In the case of administering $CO_2$ the arterial cH increases almost linearly with the increase in arterial $pCO_2$ so that, according to Gray's multiple factor theory, the stimulation of breathing is greater than would be produced by either the rise in $pCO_2$ alone or the rise in arterial cH alone.

The evidence seems to be sufficient to establish

that the level of pulmonary ventilation in subjects at rest is determined by either the arterial $pCO_2$ tension, the arterial $pO_2$ tension, the arterial cH or by interaction of these three drives. The relationship between each of these drives and the other two has been discussed at length in physiological literature. Gray advanced the hypothesis that effects of the three factors are simply *additive*; and, in line with this view he presents an equation for calculation of the ventilation ratio (ratio of alveolar ventilation under new conditions to alveolar ventilation under control conditions) from the changes in $pCO_2$, $pO_2$ and cH of arterial blood.

According to Gray's theory if $pCO_2$ is lowered further below the level which leads to apnea because of lack of a $CO_2$ stimulus to the respiratory center, the $pCO_2$ effect is further subtracted. Stated in another way, if breathing is put on an oxygen-lack drive, the lower the $pCO_2$, the lower will be the amount of respiratory stimulation because of the lesser $pCO_2$ effect to be added to the oxygen-lack drive. In experiments by Nielsen and Smith (1952) the alveolar $pO_2$ tension was maintained at constant low levels, eliciting $O_2$-lack drive, while the effects of adding $CO_2$ were tested. It was found that $CO_2$ had no effect, or only a slight effect, on the ventilation under these conditions until a threshold value of arterial $pCO_2$ of about the same magnitude as that which causes initiation of breathing under normal conditions was reached. Hence, it appears that the $CO_2$ level does not at all influence the level of ventilation when breathing is being maintained by the hypoxic stimulus. Christensen (1954) comments that it is difficult to see how Gray's multiple factor theory can explain an unchanged ventilation when the alveolar and arterial $pCO_2$ are changed between 21 and 33 mm. Hg at a constant alveolar $pO_2$. It seems possible that just as $pO_2$ is not a factor in respiratory regulation when it is above a certain level, $pCO_2$ may not be a factor at all when it is below a certain level.

Immediate respiratory responses to exposure to a given reduction in $pO_2$ in inspired air are of lesser degree than those which are seen after chronic exposure. Acclimatization occurs so that during prolonged exposure pulmonary ventilation is increased, as indicated by a further lowering of the alveolar $pCO_2$ beyond that observed initially. Rahn and Otis (1949) suggest that a rise in alkalinity of the blood due to decreased oxyhemoglobin saturation inhibits the respiratory stimulation that would be expected to result from the decrease in $pO_2$ *per se*. Regardless of the mechanism of acclimatization which occurs during chronic exposure to lowered $pO_2$ in inspired air, when it has occurred, there is increased pulmonary ventilation, lowered alveolar $pCO_2$, increased alveolar $pO_2$ beyond that observed initially, and a lowered alkali reserve. During the process of acclimatization, alkali is removed by urinary excretion. The pH of the blood is within the normal range. It appears that other more complex changes in respiratory control are involved in the gradual adjustments to hypoxia. For example, the alveolar $pCO_2$ which is lowered initially may return to or even exceed the level in normal subjects at sea level, hence sensitivity of the regulatory mechanism to $CO_2$ must have become readjusted. In short, in acute hypoxia the $CO_2$ drive may be largely or completely eliminated, but it must be assumed that the $CO_2$ drive is in some degree restored during acclimatization.

## Mechanisms of Hyperpnea during Exercise

During exercise pulmonary ventilation increases, and the rise is quite proportionate to the amount of increase in muscular activity. Since an increased rate of production of $CO_2$ and of acid metabolites and an increased rate of utilization of oxygen occur as a consequence of increased muscular activity, *a priori* it is logical to think that the respiratory stimulation is induced by the same three factors which are considered to operate in the resting subject. However, a number of studies show that muscular exercise is not regularly associated with either a decrease in arterial $pO_2$, or a rise in arterial $pCO_2$ or cH. In individual experiments none of these factors shows a change during exercise in the direction needed to elicit increased respiratory activity (Grodins, 1950).

The $pCO_2$ of *mixed venous* blood is increased and the $pO_2$ decreased during exercise, but no respiration-influencing receptor located on the *venous* side of the systemic circuit has been demonstrated. (The presence of bodies similar to the aortic bodies around the pulmonary artery and receiving a blood supply from it have been described, and if such receptors exist they might be expected to elicit stimulation of breathing during exercise). There is evidence that respiration is stimulated reflexly by impulses arising in the working muscles or the joints which are acted upon by these muscles. Still another possibility is that during voluntary activity impulses are directed in descending nerve tracts into the respiratory center to exert a stmulant effect. In any case it appears that accessory respiratory drives are brought into play during exercise so that increased ventilation may occur even before a change in $pCO_2$, $pO_2$ or cH have had time to occur at the sites upon which these stimuli act. The factors which are concerned in the stimulation of breathing, which most respiratory physiologists believe must be present in exercise over and above that related to the three chemical stimuli which operate under resting conditions, are referred to by Grodins (1950) as the *exercise stimulus*. It is probable that afferent influences from various sources are concerned and also that chemical excitants not yet identified play a role.

### Periodic Breathing

Under certain conditions irregular or "periodic" breathing may develop. There are two major types: Biot's breathing and Cheyne-Stokes breathing. In Biot's breathing there are periods of variable length during which breathing is present, and these alternate with apneic periods of different lengths. The transitions from the periods of activity to apnea and back are abrupt. In contrast to this in Cheyne-Stokes breathing, although periods of respiratory activity alternate with apneic periods, the amplitude of breathing increases gradually to a maximum and then decreases gradually until the next period of inactivity. Biot's breathing has been observed in meningitis and other pathological conditions affecting the medulla. Cheyne-Stokes respiration has been observed in a number of different circumstances, some of which are pathological and some physiological (fig. 32.10).

Cheyne-Stokes breathing occurs in some normal subjects at moderately high altitudes, (for example, 12,000 to 15,000 feet) and it may be seen in normal sleeping infants. Experimentally, it may be produced in normal subjects following a prolonged period of voluntary hyperventilation, and it can be produced by having the subject breathe deeply through a tube of a certain length. In the latter case, the dead space is increased by a specific amount, and if there is too little or too much increase in dead space, Cheyne-Stokes breathing will not develop. Several drugs, notably morphine, will cause the appearance of Cheyne-Stokes breathing if given, in adequate doses. The condition is commonly seen in persons suffering from chronic congestive heart failure, and in such cases the periodicity tends to be aggravated by sedation or during sleep.

The basis for Cheyne-Stokes breathing after hyperventilation, as explained on page 497, appears to be that oxygen-lack drive makes its appearance and is relieved several times before the $pCO_2$ finally is built back up to levels sufficient to drive normal respiration. The oxygen-lack drive presumably is via the chemoreceptors. However, there is evidence that two or more types of initial defect may cause Cheyne-Stokes breathing. For example, during periodic breathing there also are cyclic changes in the blood pressure level; and in some instances, the rise in mean arterial blood pressure occurs during the phase of respiratory activity while in other cases the rise in blood pressure is during the apneic phase. These two types most likely are related to quite different basic mechanisms. The former has been demonstrated to occur in dogs having the sino-aortic pressoreceptors and the carotid and aortic bodies denervated or isolated (Youmans and Schopp, 1957) hence chemoreceptive drive could not have been a factor. It is still probable, however, that the other type of periodicity is dependent upon a seesawing between reflex and central drives. Guyton (1956) has described experiments in which he found that Cheyne-Stokes breathing was produced if the time required for blood to flow from the heart to the brain was prolonged by increasing the length of the channels. Since circulation time is increased in chronic heart failure, this may be the change that initiates periodic breathing in patients suffering from this condition.

Eyster (1906) produced periodic breathing in dogs by elevating the intracranial pressure. His records show that breathing occurred when blood

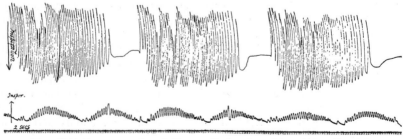

FIG. 32.10 Two examples of Cheyne-Stokes breathing. (After Lewis.)

pressure rose above the level of the intracranial pressure, and apnea was present when the pressure was below this level. In clinical cases with increased intracranial pressure, Eyster observed the same pattern of cyclic changes in respiration and blood pressure as that produced experimentally in dogs.

### Reflexes Initiated in Other Parts of the Body

The experiments of Churchill and Cope show that a reflex increase in the respiratory rate results from distention of the pulmonary vascular bed. When the vessels of the lung, which was isolated from the body except for its nerves, were injected with fluid to cause overfilling of the vascular bed, rapid shallow breathing immediately ensued. Section of the vagal fibers abolished the response.

Stimulation of almost any afferent nerve may bring about a reflex change in respiration. Stimulation of pain fibers is especially potent in this regard, and the respiratory effects of the excitation of the cutaneous nerves by extremes of heat or cold are well known. The thermal effect upon respiration is apparent in the panting of the dog. The increased pulmonary ventilation in fever is also partly due to the stimulation of receptors (*thermoreceptors*) responsive to a rise in temperature. The thermoreceptors are situated peripherally, especially in the skin, and centrally in the hypothalamus; the latter, being stimulated through the rise in temperature of the blood, set up impulses which are transmitted to the respiratory centers, the pneumotaxic center in particular. The great increase in pulmonary ventilation occurring in muscular exercise is dependent in part upon reflexes originating in the active muscles and moving joints. Proprioceptive impulses from the diaphragm and other respiratory muscles during one respiratory movement exert an important influence upon the succeeding movement. Stimulation of sensory nerves in the respiratory tract, as by ether anesthesia, or of the abdominal viscera, either during surgical operations or as the result of disease may cause profound changes in breathing. Also, as pointed out by Harrison and his associates, stimulation of afferent nerve endings in the great veins and right auricle by the rise in venous pressure is a possible factor in the hyperpnea of exercise or in the dyspnea of cardiac failure. The glossopharyngeal nerve contains afferent fibers which inhibit respiration during the second stage of the act of swallowing. Abrupt inhibition of respiration is also caused by the inhalation of an irritant gas through stimulation of nasal branches of the 5th nerve. In other instances irritation of these endings may cause sneezing—a modified respiratory act (see fig. 32.7). Coughing, though it can be brought about by a voluntary effort, is most commonly reflex in character, and initiated by the stimulation of afferent nerve endings in the trachea and larynx (p. 477).

## Dyspnea

Dyspnea literally means difficult breathing. When the respirations from whatever cause cannot be carried out with ease and practically unconsciously, the individual is said to be dyspneic. The term therefore implies a subjective element. Dyspnea thus differs from hyperpnea. The latter term means simply increased pulmonary ventilation, and this may occur quite unconsciously or if the subject is aware of the augmentation of the breathing, there is not necessarily any sensation of difficulty or distress. When the hyperpnea becomes extreme and yet leaves the need for which it has been instituted unsatisfied, discomfort or distress is experienced, and the term dyspnea is applicable. Meakins offers the following concise definition: "Dyspnea is the consciousness of the necessity for increased respiratory effort."

### Causes of Dyspnea

Since the respiratory and circulatory functions are directed toward the acquisition of oxygen and the elimination of carbon dioxide, dyspnea may result if either of these functions be disturbed to such an extent that the normal gaseous exchanges cannot be accomplished. On the other hand, the oxygen requirement and the carbon dioxide production may be so great that the *normal* respiratory and circulatory mechanisms find difficulty in meeting the demands of the moment. Or again the supply of oxygen itself may be inadequate as a result of a low oxygen tension in the atmosphere (e.g., high altitudes). In considering the causes of dyspnea we must, therefore, in many instances look beyond the lungs themselves. The lungs are the bellows, but it is the tissues which consume oxygen and produce carbon dioxide; and it is the heart and the blood which are concerned with the carriage of these gases between lungs and tissues. The height of the hyperpnea at which dyspnea appears is called the *dyspneic point*. There is a relationship between the latter and the *vital capacity*. A person with a large vital capacity obviously can breathe a larger volume of air without discomfort than can one with a smaller vital capacity. There is a close relationship however between the onset of dyspnea and the ratio of the *functional residual capacity* to the *total lung capacity*. The more nearly equal are the functional residual capacity and the total lung capacity, the greater will be the tendency toward dyspnea.

The fundamental or immediate causes of dyspnea can in most instances be reduced to the following categories. (1) Stimulation of the respiratory center either (a) reflexly from the carotid and aortic bodies (anoxia or increase in H-ion concentration due to fixed acids), (b) directly, by $CO_2$ excess, (c) a combination of (a) and (b) as in asphyxial states, or (d) by impulses from cerebral centers or by afferent impulses, especially of a painful character, from abdominal or peripheral regions. (2) Hypersensitivity of the Hering-Breuer reflex, thus bringing about earlier inhibition of the inspiratory phase and causing, as a consequence, a more rapid shallow type of breathing.

The abnormal conditions chiefly associated with dyspnea are:

(1) Prevention of adequate oxygenation of the blood in the lungs (arterial hypoxia, ch. 33).

(2) Interference with the transport of the respiratory gases. Anoxia of the hypokinetic or anemic type (a) slowing of the circulation as in cardiac failure, (b) severe anemia, breathlessness chiefly on exertion.

(3) Restriction of the action of the diaphragm or intercostals.

(4) *Acidosis*, reduced alkali reserve or retention of $CO_2$.

(5) Increased metabolism.

(6) *Nervous conditions*, e.g., emotional disturbance, neurasthenia, hysteria, encephalitis, or the direct stimulation of the respiratory center by cerebral tumor, hemorrhage or edema.

### Dyspnea due to Pulmonary Diseases

Dyspnea is a feature of various respiratory diseases.

(a) In some instances, e.g., laryngeal or bronchial obstruction and asthma, the dyspnea is due to a combination of anoxia and $CO_2$ retention.

(b) In other instances owing to the reduced distensibility of the lungs resulting from edema, congestion, inflammation, fibrosis, etc., the Hering-Breuer reflex is thought to be abnormally sensitive.

(c) Limitation of the movements of the diaphragm and chest wall. In emphysema, for example, owing to the loss of lung elasticity the resting position of the chest is one of nearly full inspiration. The diaphragm is fixed and the thorax elevated. Any further enlargement of the chest entails unusual effort on the part of the intercostal muscles (see also ch. 30) and the enlistment of the accessory muscles of respiration. Expiration involves active contraction of the expiratory muscles.

### Cardiac Dyspnea

Dyspnea upon exertion is a feature of certain chronic pulmonary and heart lesions, e.g., mitral stenosis. Stimulation of the carotid and aortic bodies by oxygen want or of the respiratory center by carbon dioxide excess is not, *in the absence of cardiac failure*, responsible for the dyspnea, since the oxygen saturation of the arterial blood may not be reduced to any important degree, and the carbon dioxide tension is within or even below the normal range. Pulmonary engorgement leading to diminished distensibility of the lung is considered by Meakins, Christie and associates to be the prime cause of cardiac dyspnea. Though the reduction in the vital capacity may be roughly proportional to the dyspnea, the two do not bear the relationship of cause and effect, since the subject's vital capacity is always greater than the volume of air required for the exertion which causes the dyspnea. Due, however, to the diminished distensibility—the stiffness of the lung—a greater inspiratory effort is expended in breathing the extra volume of air which the muscular exertion demands. The lung might be compared to stiffened bellows leather; more force is required to distend it. The elasticity of the lung is also moderately reduced so that expiration instead of being a passive act brought about largely by the recoil of the lung now requires the aid of the contraction of expiratory muscles in order to "squeeze" the air from the chest. The intrapleural pressure, therefore, instead of remaining "negative" throughout the respiratory cycle becomes positive toward the end of expiration (Christie and Meakins). The decreased distensibility of the lung, for the same reason that it increases the difficulty of enlarging the volume of tidal air, reduces the vital capacity. In other words the dyspnea and reduced vital capacity are due to a common cause. The reduced distensibility will also have the effect, as already mentioned, of increasing the sensitivity of the Hering-Breuer reflex with the production of shallow breathing.

*In congestive heart failure* with marked slowing of the circulation there is commonly hyperpnea and dyspnea even during rest, and then there may be added to the pulmonary factor itself the stimulating effect of carbon dioxide excess upon the respiratory center. But, according to Christie and Meakins, this is of minor importance. When pulmonary edema supervenes, interference with the absorption of oxygen and the production of arterial hypoxia (stimulation of carotid body) may possibly be a factor. Hindrance to the absorption of oxygen, caused by the presence of exudate in the alveoli and the edematous swelling of the alveolar walls, is accompanied by little or no interference with the elimination of carbon dioxide; this is probably due in part to the much greater solubility of carbon dioxide than of oxygen and, in consequence, to the freer diffusion of the former gas through the edema fluid. In congestive heart failure arterial hypoxia with a normal or even a subnormal carbon dioxide content of the arterial blood may exist even in the absence of pulmonary edema.

Experimental support can be cited for the view that reduced distensibility of the lungs as a result of congestion is an important factor in cardiac dyspnea. It has been mentioned elsewhere (p. 502) that distension of the pulmonary bed causes rapid shallow breathing. The production of multiple emboli in the pulmonary capillaries by the intravenous injection of starch granules causes congestion of the lungs and rapid shallow breathing, and Partridge found that after rapid breathing has been induced in this way, the impulses recorded from the vagus nerve are of higher frequency than those resulting from inflation of normal lung to an equal degree. It has also been shown that in man pulmonary congestion does actually reduce the distensibility of the lung tissue.

Harrison and his colleagues found in subjects of cardiac failure the $CO_2$ content of the jugular blood to be within normal limits and observed no significant reduction in the cerebral blood flow (i.e., through the respiratory center).

Though there is much to be said for the reflex origin of cardiac dyspnea, not all are agreed as to its paramount importance. McMichael, for example, in a clinical study found a reduction in cardiac output in those subjects showing hyperpnea (which is always associated with the dyspnea) during rest. The hyperpnea showed a closer correlation with the cardiac output than with the vital capacity which, he points out, is contrary to what

might be expected were congestion of the lungs the dominant causative factor. He is inclined to believe that the hyperpnea and dyspnea of the cardiac patient *during rest* is due to reduced blood flow through the center, resulting in a high $CO_2$ tension, and possibly to the accumulation of acid products of its own metabolism.

*Orthopnea.* In congestive heart failure with dyspnea at rest the breathlessness is usually more pronounced in the recumbent than in the sitting position. When propped up with pillows, the patient may be quite comfortable but becomes dyspneic when he lies down. Many theories have been advanced in attempts to explain the less difficult breathing in the upright position. Among these are:

(a) Removal of the weight of the abdominal viscera which interferes with the descent of the diaphragm in the recumbent position.

(b) Reduction in the intracranial venous pressure and the improved draining of blood from the medulla and in consequence, augmentation of the flow through the respiratory center. Mere bending of the head forward (when recumbent) which reduces the cerebral venous pressure, but not the pulmonary engorgement, reduces the volume of respired air in the orthopneic patient (Battro and Labourt).

(c) Draining of blood from the chest and the relief of pulmonary congestion. This is probably the most important factor. The vital capacity is less in the recumbent than in the sitting posture. This is true even for the normal person but in cardiac cases the effect is accentuated by the vascular engorgement and decreased distensibility of the lung induced by recumbency.

*Cardiac asthma (paroxysmal nocturnal dyspnea).* In some patients with severe chronic congestive heart failure acute dyspnea which may terminate in pulmonary edema comes on during the night. The patient has a feeling of suffocation. He assumes the upright position and may go to the window for air. These attacks are related to excessive engorgement of the lungs with blood so that pulmonary capillary pressure rises to the point of producing transudation into the alveoli. As indicated above the volume of blood in the lungs increases when one changes from the upright to the recumbent position. Patients with chronic heart failure already have an elevated venous pressure which increases further when they recline. The key question is with regard to the fact that paroxysmal nocturnal dyspnea comes on after a delay usually of several hours since the effects of changing from the upright to the recumbent position insofar as they are related to gravity might be expected to occur within seconds or minutes. The clue to this problem probably is provided in the observation that edema fluid in patients with congestive heart failure is transferred from the interstitial spaces into the blood, and a rise in blood volume occurs slowly during the night. This could lead to a further elevation of venous and pulmonary capillary pressure. The paroxysm could be set off in two ways. The pressure in the pulmonary capillaries could rise to the point of producing transudation and hence impairment of exchange of $O_2$ and $CO_2$. On the other hand, the venous pressure might reach the critical level at which overdistention of the heart would result in a decrease in the output of the heart. Once this occurs a vicious cycle is produced: decreased output leads to further elevation of venous pressure, and elevation of venous pressure leads to further overdistention of the heart and decreased output. In either case the change to the orthostatic position would be beneficial in that the blood would tend to remain in the dependent part of the body and thus decrease the volume and pressure of blood in the heart and lungs. Also, it should be noted that acute cardiac decompensation, produced by exceeding the critical pressure on the curve which relates cardiac output to venous pressure, leads to a rise in pulmonary capillary pressure and hence to acute pulmonary edema.

### Dyspnea in Anemia

When at rest, the anemic subject as a rule is not dyspneic. The hemoglobin, though reduced in amount, becomes fully saturated with oxygen in the lungs. The oxygen tension and consequently the quantity of the gas in simple solution in the arterial blood are normal. The arterial blood of a patient whose hemoglobin is 30 per cent of the normal value will, however, contain only a little over 6 volumes per cent of oxygen. In the healthy resting body the blood in its passage through the capillaries gives up about 5 volumes per cent. If the velocity of blood flow through the tissues in anemia were the same as during health, a unit volume of blood would give up an equivalent amount of oxygen. This would leave a reserve of only 1 volume per cent, i.e., the venous blood would be almost completely reduced. The tissues, including the carotid and aortic bodies, would suffer at all times from anoxia. The circulation rate (cardiac output) is, however, increased in

anemia so that each unit of blood gives up a smaller proportion than this of its oxygen load. The chemoreceptors apparently are not stimulated, and the patient is not dyspneic while resting even though his hemoglobin is greatly reduced. Fahr and Ronzone reported a case in which the hemoglobin was 12 per cent of the normal and the arterial blood contained only 2.2 volumes per cent of oxygen. There was no dyspnea during rest. Not only is the output of the heart increased, but a redistribution of the blood occurs. The vessels of the skin are constricted, and a greater proportion of the total blood volume is driven through other regions. The extent to which the circulatory readjustments can compensate for the blood defect is limited, therefore during exertion the extra demand for oxygen cannot be met. Oxygen want follows, the respiratory mechanism is stimulated; hyperpnea and dyspnea result.

It is to be remembered that in anemia the carriage of carbon dioxide may also be interfered with since hemoglobin constitutes an important part of the mechanism provided for the transport of this gas (see ch. 29).

### Dyspnea due to Increased Metabolism

Muscular exercise is an outstanding cause of a great increase of metabolism. Reflexes initiated in the active muscles, and from the walls of the great veins as a result of the high pressure of blood entering the right side of the heart, and possibly as well the irradiation of impulses from the motor cortex, are thought to play an important part in the hyperpnea of exercise (p. 499). As the severity of the exercise is increased, hyperpnea merges into dyspnea. The athlete and the untrained person differ widely in respect to the degree of muscular exertion which will produce this physiological type of dyspnea. The difference depends upon the following factors:

(a) *Vital capacity.* In the average normal man the pulmonary ventilation increases from 4- to 5-fold before the dyspneic point is reached. The athlete on the other hand, since his vital capacity is greater, shows a correspondingly greater increase in his pulmonary ventilation before dyspnea supervenes. The existence of any pulmonary condition which reduces the vital capacity will depress the level of the dyspneic point.

(b) *Circulation rate.* The trained man's circulation rate increases to a greater degree than the untrained, and so more oxygen is delivered to his tissues.

(c) *Neuromuscular integration.* Co-ordination

of the several muscles in a given muscular act is more precise in the trained than in the untrained man. There is thus less waste of effort. In the performance of a given amount of work, therefore, the untrained man consumes a greater volume of oxygen, i.e., he is a less efficient machine. Yet his respiratory center appears to be more sensitive to nervous influences—impulses from the contracting muscles and from the cerebral cortex.

A pathological increase in metabolism, e.g., hyperthyroidism, fever, etc., cannot apparently in the absence of some respiratory or circulatory abnormality cause dyspnea during rest. The increase in metabolism would need to be around 300 per cent before dyspnea might be expected to occur and such a metabolic level is never reached in these or any other pathological condition. Nevertheless, in hyperthyroidism dyspnea will follow upon a degree of exertion which would cause no distress in a healthy person, for the greater metabolic rate, due to the disease, added to that of the exercise will increase the metabolism sufficiently to raise the pulmonary ventilation above the dyspneic point. The dyspnea of hyperthyroidism, when pulmonary and cardiovascular complications are absent, therefore, is like that of anemia in that it is evident only upon exertion.

### Dyspnea due to Acidosis

The importance of the part played by pulmonary ventilation in resisting a rise in the hydrogen ion concentration of the body fluids has been dealt with elsewhere (ch. 13). Little more need be said here. Nonvolatile acids, e.g., lactic in muscular exercise, β-Hydroxybutyric and acetoacetic acids in diabetes, and retained acids in nephritis, react with bicarbonate. The alkali reserve becomes reduced, but the ratio,

$$\frac{H_2CO_2}{NaHCO_3} = \frac{1}{20}$$

is maintained through the stimulating effect of $CO_2$ upon the respiratory center. It is thus that the $CO_2$ of the alveolar air (and so of the arterial blood) is kept at a level proportional to the reduction in the denominator of the equation. When this can no longer be effected, i.e., when the hydrogen ion concentration of the blood rises, the acidosis being then uncompensated, the center is stimulated both directly and through reflexes initiated from chemoreceptors of the carotid and aortic bodies.

J. B. S. Haldane produced a severe acidosis and dyspnea in himself by the ingestion of acid-forming salts ($CaCl_2$ and $NH_4Cl$). But as a matter of fact, the production of fixed acids in diseased conditions rarely causes such a high degree of hyperpnea that dyspnea results, unless the circulatory and respiratory mechanisms are very inefficient or the metabolic rate is increased. According to Means the "alkali reserve" must drop to around 12 volumes per cent before dyspnea supervenes as a result of the acidosis itself. In milder grades of acidosis, however, dyspnea occurs upon exertion. The hyperpnea due to the increased metabolism of the exercise is then added to that due to the acidosis, with the result that the dyspneic point is soon reached.

In severe diabetic acidosis *air hunger*, or Kussmaul breathing, may be seen in the comatose patient.

Carbon dioxide retention may, as in emphysema, be accompanied by a compensatory rise in bicarbonate and a normal blood reaction (compensated $CO_2$ excess); dyspnea is not a notable feature in this condition. In other instances of $CO_2$ retention, compensation is incomplete (uncompensated $CO_2$ excess or gaseous acidosis) and dyspnea results. In others, again, the $CO_2$ retention is due to the depression of the respiratory center itself, as in morphine narcosis; in such instances, although compensation is incomplete, dyspnea of course does not occur.

### REFERENCES

Adrian, E. D. J. Physiol., 1933, 79, 332.

Adrian, E. D., and Bronk, D. W. J. Physiol., 1928, 66, 81.

Adrian, E. D., and Buytendijk, F. J. J. J. Physiol., 1931, 71, 121.

Archer, O., and Bucher, V. Helv. Physiol. Acta, 1954, 12, 265.

Baker, S., and Hitchcock, F. J. Appl. Physiol., 1957, 10, 363.

Barcroft, J., and Margaria, R. J. Physiol., 1931, 72, 175. Ibid., 1932, 74, 156.

Battro, A., and Labourt, F. E. Rev. argent. cardiol., 1943, 10, 83.

Baxter, D. W., and Olszewski, Jerzy. J. Neurophysiol., 1955, 18, 276.

Bean, John W. Am. J. Physiol., 1952, 171, 522.

Breckenridge, C. G., and Hoff, H. E. Am. J. Physiol., 1953, 175, 449. Ibid., 1954, 178, 521.

Brodie, D. A., and Borison, H. L. Am. J. Physiol., 1957, 188, 347.

Chatfield, P. O., and Purpura, D. P. Am. J. Physiol., 1953, 172, 632.

Christie, R. V., and Meakins, J. J. Clin. Invest., 1934, 13, 323.

Churchill, E. D., and Cope, O. J. Exper. Med., 1929, 49, 531.

COLLIP, J. B. J. Physiol., 1920–21, **54**, 58.

COMROE, J. H. Physiol. Rev., 1944, **24**, 319.

COMROE, J. H., AND SCHMIDT, C. F. Am. J. Physiol., 1938, **121**, 75. Ibid., 1943, **138**, 536.

COOMBS, H. D., AND PIKE, F. H. Am. J. Physiol., 1918, **45**, 569.

CROMER, S. P., AND IVY, A. C. Proc. Soc. Exper. Biol. & Med., 1931, **28**, 565.

DALE, H. H., AND EVANS, C. L. J. Physiol., 1920, **54**, 167.

DAVIS, H. L., FOWLER, W. S., AND LAMBERT, E. H. Am. J. Physiol., 1956, **187**, 558.

DOUGLAS, C. G., AND HALDANE, J. S. J. Physiol., 1909, **38**, 401. Ibid., 420.

DRINKER, C. K. Am. Rev. Tuberc., 1948, **58**, 1.

DRIPPS, R. D., AND COMROE, J. H. Am. J. Physiol., 1947, **149**, 277.

EYSTER, J. A. J. Exper. Med., 1906, **8**, 565.

FAHR, G. AND RONZONE, E. Arch. Int. Med., 1922, **29**, 331.

FIELD, H., JR., AND BOCK, A. V. J. Clin. Invest., 1925, **2**, 67.

FINLEY, K. H. Arch. Neurol. & Psychiat., 1931, **26**, 754.

FLOURENS, J. P. M. Compt. rend. Acad. sc., Paris, 1858, **47**, 803.

FREY, J. S., AND GESELL, R. Proc. Soc. Exper. Biol., 1947, **6**, 106.

GESSELL, R. Physiol. Rev., 1925, **5**, 551.

GESSELL, R., BRICKER, J., AND MAGEE, C. Am. J. Physiol., 1936, **117**, 423.

GESELL, R., BRASSFIELD, C. R., AND LILLIE, R. H. J. Comp. Neurol. 1954, **101**, 331.

GRAY, J. S. Pulmonary Ventilation, Am. Lecture Series. Charles C Thomas, Springfield, Ill., 1950; Science, 1946, **103**, 739.

GUYTON, A. C., CROWELL, J. W., AND MOORE, J. W. Am. J. Physiol., 1956, **187**, 395.

HABER, EDGAR, KOHN, KURT W., NGAI, S. H., HOLADAY, D. A., AND WANG, S. C. Am. J. Physiol., 1957, **190**, 350.

HALDANE, J. B. S. J. Physiol., 1921, **55**, 265.

HALDANE, J. S. J. Physiol., 1895, **18**, 201, 430.

HALDANE, J. S., AND POULTON, E. P. J. Physiol., 1908, **37**, 390.

HALDANE, J. S., AND PRIESTLEY, J. G. J. Physiol., 1905, **32**, 225.

HARRISON, T. R. AND ASSOCIATES. Arch. Int. Med., 1932, **50**, 690. J. Clin. Invest., 1932, **11**, 133.

HARROP, G. A. J. A. M. A., 1923, **80**, 1641.

HEAD, H. J. Physiol., 1889, **10**, 1:279.

HENDERSON, V. E., AND GRAIGIE, E. H. Am. J. Physiol., 1936, **115**, 520.

HENDERSON, V. E., AND SWEET, T. A. Am. J. Physiol., 1929, **91**, 94.

HERING, E., AND BREUER, J. Sitz. Akad. Wiss., Wien, 1868, **57**, 672. Ibid., **58**, 909.

HEYMANS, C., AND BOUCKAERT, J. J. J. Physiol., 1930, **69**, 254. Ibid., 1933, **79**, 49.

HEYMANS, C., BOUCKAERT, J. J., AND DAUTREBANDE, L. Compt. rend. Soc. biol., 1931, **107**, 54.

HEYMANS, J. F., AND HEYMANS, C. Arch. internat. pharmacodyn., 1927, **33**, 273.

HOFF, H. E., AND BRECKENRIDGE, C. G. A.M.A. Arch. Neurol. & Psychiat., 1954, **72**, 11.

JACOBS, M. H. Am. J. Physiol., 1920, **51**, 321. Ibid., **53**, 457.

KAO, F. F. Am. J. Physiol., 1956, **185**, 145.

KAO, F. F., AND RAY, L. H. Am. J. Physiol., 1954, **179**, 249.

KETY, S. S., AND SCHMIDT, C. F. J. Clin. Invest., 1948, **27**, 484.

LILJESTRAND, G. Acta. physiol. scandinav., 1951–54, **23–24**, 225.

LILJESTRAND, A. Acta physiol. scandinav., 1953, **29**, 321, Suppl. 106.

LOESHKE, G. C. Pflüger's Arch. ges. Physiol., 1953, **257**, 349.

LUMSDEN, T. J. Physiol., 1932, **58**, 81, 111.

MARKWALD, M., Ztschr. Biol., 1887, **23**, 149. Ibid., 1890, **26**, 259.

MCMICHAEL. J. Clin. Sc., 1939, **4**, 19.

MEAKINS, J. C. J. A. M. A., 1934, **103**, 1442.

METZ, B. Am. J. Physiol., 1958, **192**, 101.

MONNIER, M. Rev. neurol., 1938, **69**, 517.

MORGAN, D. P., KAO, F., LIM, T. P. K., AND GRODINS, F. S. Am. J. Physiol., 1955, **183**, 454.

NGAI, S. H. AND WANG, S. C. Am. J. Physiol., 1957, **190**, 343.

NIELSEN, M., AND SMITH, H. Acta. physiol. scandinav., 1951–52, **23–24**, 293.

NIELSON. M. Skand. Archinav. Physiol. (Suppl. 10), 1936, **74**, 87.

PARTRIDGE, G. J. Cell. & Comp. Physiol., 1933, **2**, 367. Canad. M. A. J., 1935, **33**, 11.

PEMBREY, M. S., AND ALLEN, R. W. J. Physiol., 1950, **21**, xviii.

PITTS, R. F. Physiol. Rev., 1946, **26**, 609.

PITTS, R. F., MAGOUN, H. W., AND RANSON, S. W. Am. J. Physiol., 1939, **126**, 673, 689. Ibid., **126**, 654.

PORTER, W. T. J. Physiol., 1895, **17**, 455.

RAHN, H., AND OTIS, A. B. Am. J. Physiol., 1949, **157**, 145.

ROSENTHAL, J. Hermann's Handb. der Physiol., 1882, **4**, (2) 157.

SCHMIDT, C. F., DUMKE, P. L., AND DRIPPS, R. D., JR. Am. J. Physiol., 1939, **128**, 1.

SCHOPP, R. T., GILFOIL, T. M., AND YOUMANS, W. B. Am. J. Physiol., 1957, **189**, 117, 123.

SCOTT, R. W. Am. J. Physiol., 1918–19, **47**, 43. Ibid., 1917, **44**, 196.

SEEGERS, W. H. J. Biol. Chem., 1940, **136**, 103.

SHARPEY-SCHAFER, E. J. Physiol., 1932, **75**, 130.

SMITH, D. L., MAASKE, C. A., AND JULIAN, F. Am. J. Physiol., 1955, **181**, 341.

STELLA, G. J. Physiol., 1938, **93**, 10, 263.

STEWART, G. N., PIKE, F. H., AND GUTHRIE, C. C. J. Exper. Med., 1908, **10**, 490.

TANG, P. C. Am. J. Physiol., 1953, **172**, 645.

VON EULER, U. S., LILJESTRAND, G., AND ZOTTERMAN, Y. Skandinav. Arch. Physiol., 1939, **83**, 132.

WANG, S. C., NGAI, S. H., AND FRUMIN, M. J. Am. J. Physiol., 1957, **190**, 333.

WATT, J. G., DUMKE, P. R., AND COMROE, J. H., JR. Am. J. Physiol., 1943, **138**, 610.

WEISS, S., AND ROBB, G. P. J. A. M. A., 1933, **100**, 1841.

WHALEN, W. J. Am. J. Physiol., 1955, **183**, 445.

WINTERSTEIN, H. Pflüger's Arch. ges. Physiol., 1911, **138**, 167.

WITZLEB, E., BARTELS, H., BUDDE, H., AND MOCHIZUCKI, M. Pflüger's Arch. ges. Physiol., 1955, **261**, 211.

YAMAMOTO, W. S. Am. J. Physiol., 1957, **191**, 423.

YOUMANS, W. B. Anesthesiology, 1958, **19**, 552.

YOUMANS, W. B., AND SCHOPP, R. T. Proc. Soc. Exper. Biol. & Med. 1957, **95**, 100.

*Monographs and Reviews*

AVIADO, D. M., JR., AND SCHMIDT, C. F. Physiol. Rev., 1955, **35**, 247.

BRECHER, G. Venous Return. Grune & Stratton, Inc., 1956.

BJURSTEDT, H. Ann. Rev. Physiol., 1957, **19**, 151.

CHRISTENSEN, H. The chemical and nervous control of respiration in Handbook of Respiratory Physiology. p. 103, United States Air Force School of Aviation Medicine. Randolph Field, Texas, 1954.

CORDIER, D., AND HEYMANS, C. Le centre respiratoire. Hermann, Paris, 1935.

DAWES, G. S., AND COMROE, J. H., JR. Physiol. Rev., 1954, **34**, 167.

DRIPPS, R. D., AND SEVERINGHAUS, J. W. Physiol. Rev., 1955, **35**, 741.

GESELL, R. Physiol. Rev., 1925, **5**, 551. Ann. Rev. Physiol., 1939, **1**, 185.

GRAY, J. S. Pulmonary Ventilation and Its Regulation. Charles C Thomas, Springfield, Ill., 1950.

GRODINS, F. S. Physiol. Rev., 1950, **30**, 220.

HALDANE, J. S., AND PRIESTLY, J. G. Respiration. Oxford University Press, 1935.

HARRISON, T. R. Failure of the Circulation. Williams & Wilkins Company, Baltimore, 1939.

HEEMSTRA, H. Ann. Rev. Physiol. 1956, **18**, 121.

HEYMANS, C. New England J. Med., 1938, **219**, 157.

HEYMANS, C., AND BOUCKAERT, J. J. Le sinus carotidien et la zone homologue cardioaortique. Doin, Paris, 1933.

HEYMANS, C., AND NEIL, E. Reflexogenic Areas of the Cardiovascular System. J. A. Churchill, Ltd., London, 1958.

KROGH, A. The Comparative Physiology of Respiratory Mechanisms. University of Pennsylvania Press, Philadelphia, 1941.

MEANS, J. H. Dyspnea. Medicine, 1924, **3**, 309.

MILLIKAN, G. A. *In* Handbook of Respiration Data in Aviation. National Res. Council, Washington, D. C. W. B. Saunders Company, Philadelphia, 1958.

O'LEARY, J. L., AND COBEN, L. A. 1957. Physiol. Rev., 1958, **38**, 243.

OTIS, A. B. Ann. Rev. Physiol. 1958, **20**, 159.

PI-SUÑER, A. Physiol. Rev., 1947, **27**, 1.

ROSSI, G. F., AND ZANCHETTI, A. The Brain Stem Reticular Formation: Anatomy and Physiology. Arch. Ital. de Biol., 1957, **115**, 199 (see pages 263–265).

SCHMIDT, C. F., AND COMROE, J. H., JR. Physiol. Rev., 1940, **20**, 115. Ann. Rev. Physiol., 1941, **3**, 151.

WINTERSTEIN, H. Ergebn. Physiol. 1955, 328.

WYSS, O. A. M. Respiratory center and reflex control of breathing. Helvet. physiol. et pharmacol. acta, 1954, Supplement 10.

# 33

# HYPOXIA, ASPHYXIA, DYSBARISM, OXYGEN THERAPY, AND RESUSCITATION

## Types of Hypoxia

The terms *hypoxia* and *anoxia* are synonymous, although the former etymologically is more suitable. Both terms are in common use and will be used interchangeably in the following discussion. The most useful definition of hypoxia is that it refers to any condition in which there is an inadequate *supply* of oxygen to the tissues. According to this definition it is synonymous with *oxygen lack* or *oxygen want*. Upon the basis of three quite different categories of causes Barcroft classified anoxia into *anoxic, anemic* and *stagnant* types. The categories described by him still need to be differentiated, but changes in the names of two of them seem to be preferable. A fourth type, caused by cyanide and known as histotoxic anoxia, was added by Peters and Van Slyke; however, there is no oxygen lack in this case, but rather inability of the cells to utilize the oxygen brought to them, with the result that oxygen tension of the tissues is actually elevated. Hence it would seem to be preferable not to classify cyanide poisoning as a form of hypoxia. For reasons which will become apparent in the subsequent discussion *arterial hypoxia* is preferable to anoxic anoxia in Barcroft's classification, and *hypokinetic hypoxia* is a better term for stagnant anoxia. The three major types of oxygen lack, together with the principal causes of each, are listed below. Also, it should be realized that two or more of these types or causes can be present simultaneously, and each type may be acute or chronic.

OXYGEN LACK: MAJOR TYPES AND CAUSES

ARTERIAL HYPOXIA *is characterized by a lower than normal* $pO_2$ *in arterial blood.* (Oxygen capacity of blood and rate of blood flow are normal or elevated).

A. Low $pO_2$ in inspired air
1. Altitude
2. Breathing in closed space[1]

[1] Arterial $pCO_2$ is increased.

3. Breathing artificial gas mixture containing lower $pO_2$ than that found in atmospheric air.
B. Decreased pulmonary ventilation
1. Airway obstruction[1]
2. Weakness or paralysis of respiratory muscles[1]
3. Depression of respiratory center by drugs[1]
4. Pneumothorax
C. Inadequate oxygenation in (abnormal) lungs.
1. Poor mixing[1]
2. Impaired diffusion (alveolar-capillary block)
3. Bronchiolar constriction (asthma)[1]
4. Filling of alveoli with fluid. Pulmonary edema, pneumonia, pulmonary hemorrhage, drowning.[1]
D. Venous-arterial shunts. Various types of cardiac or vascular abnormalities in which unoxygenated blood is mixed with oxygenated blood.

ANEMIC HYPOXIA *is characterized by a lowered oxygen capacity of the blood.* (The $pO_2$ of arterial blood and rate of blood flow are normal or elevated)

A. Less than normal hemoglobin content. *Anemias* of all types.
B. Hemoglobin combined with something other than oxygen, e.g. *carbon monoxide.*
C. Hemoglobin altered so that it can not combine with $O_2$. *Methemoglobin* found after poisoning with chlorates, nitrites, ferricyanides, acetanilid, etc.

HYPOKINETIC HYPOXIA *is characterized by a decreased rate of blood flow.*

A. Generalized. Congestive heart failure, hemorrhage, shock, etc.
B. Localized. Vasospasm, thrombosis, embolus.

Some confusion has arisen in the use of the term *anoxemia*. In some of the medical dictionaries and textbooks it is defined as synonymous with arterial hypoxia while some authors (Comroe and Dripps, 1950) use it as referring to a diminution of oxygen in the blood whether it be related to decreased $pO_2$ or decreased hemoglobin. In any case it would seem to be preferable to use the more specific terms, arterial hypoxia and anemic hypoxia, since these are not ambiguous.

ASPHYXIA. *Asphyxia* refers to conditions in which hypoxia is combined with *hypercapnia*—an increased $CO_2$ tension in the arterial blood and hence in the tissues also. It will be noted that a number of the causes of arterial hypoxia also lead to hypercapnia, while in some cases, notably at altitude, hypercapnia is not a factor. The opposite change, a lowered $CO_2$ in the body, is referred to as *hypocapnia* or *acapnia*. The reactions in asphyxia are related to effects of decreased arterial and tissue $pO_2$ and increased arterial and tissue $pCO_2$. Asphyxia of some degree is present in a number of those conditions listed in the classification of causes of oxygen lack, since elimination of $CO_2$, as well as uptake of oxygen, is impaired. Respiratory stimulation and dyspnea are prominent, and although the stimulation is derived from both the lowered $pO_2$ and increased $pCO_2$, the latter is more important. Cyanosis, being related to the presence of an increased amount of reduced hemoglobin in the blood in the cutaneous capillaries (p. 524), also is characteristic of asphyxial states as well as those in which arterial anoxia is present without hypercapnia. Blood pressure tends to be elevated due to the stimulant action of $CO_2$ on the vasoconstrictor center, except in the terminal stages. Chronic adjustments to asphyxia include the increase in erythrocyte count, hematocrit, hemoglobin and oxygen capacity of the blood, which are induced by the lowered $pO_2$ tension, and renal excretion of acid to compensate for the rise in cH produced by retention of $CO_2$.

### Tensions and Volumes Per Cent of Oxygen in the Blood in Hypoxia

In the *arterial* type of hypoxia both the $pO_2$ and the volumes per cent of $O_2$ are lowered. The blood has a normal or elevated $O_2$ capacity (20 volumes per cent or more), but it is not exposed to $pO_2$ which is high enough to produce the usual degree of saturation (95 + per cent). However, even though the blood is carrying less than a full load of $O_2$, when it reaches the capillaries in tissues which are functioning at a lower than normal oxygen tension it can unload as much oxygen per 100 ml. of blood as occurs normally. That is, normally about 20 volumes per cent would be present in the arterial blood and 15 volumes per cent in mixed venous blood, while in arterial hypoxia arterial blood capable of holding 20 volumes

per cent would actually contain 15 and give off 5 so that the mixed venous blood would contain only 10 volumes per cent. In the latter case 50 per cent desaturation of hemoglobin would be produced at the tissue level as compared with 25 per cent in the normal.

In *hypokinetic* hypoxia both the $pO_2$ and volumes per cent of $O_2$ in the arterial blood are normal; however, as the blood flow through the tissues is slower than in the normal state and the cells continue to use oxygen at an essentially normal rate, the $pO_2$ in the tissues becomes lowered, and this causes the unloading of more $O_2$ per unit volume of blood flowing through the tissues. In very active tissues which are subjected to a severely deficient blood flow, virtually all of the oxygen in the blood delivered to the tissue may be extracted. This indicates that the $pO_2$ in such tissues approaches zero. Such a situation can not exist for more than a very short time before damage to the tissue results.

In *anemic* hypoxia the arterial $pO_2$ is normal so that saturation of hemoglobin approaches 100 per cent, but the volumes per cent of $O_2$ carried is reduced in proportion to the reduction in the amount of hemoglobin. Hence if blood carrying, for example, 10 volumes per cent of $O_2$ at full saturation of the hemoglobin gives up 5 volumes per cent per 100 ml. of blood flowing through the tissues, it is apparent that the $O_2$ in the tissues is so low as to cause 50 per cent desaturation. Again this is to be contrasted with the normal state in which, on the average, only about 25 per cent desaturation occurs as blood flows through the tissues.

### Arterial Hypoxia at Altitude

Arterial hypoxia, uncomplicated by hypercapnia, is observed in individuals breathing air at high altitudes or in decompression chambers. Knowledge of both the acute and chronic adjustments to altitude is of great interest since man ascends rapidly in airplanes or resides for years at levels of 15,000 to 18,000 feet.

The per cent composition of atmospheric air is the same at altitude as at sea level. But the barometric pressure decreases with altitude. It is noteworthy that at an altitude of 18,000 feet the barometric pressure is about 380 mm. Hg or one-half of that at sea level. The oxygen tension, therefore, is diminished to one-half of that at sea level, since the $pO_2$ at any altitude is calculated by multiplying the barometric pressure by .2094. Thus, a second vertical scale showing oxygen tension could be derived simply by multiplying each of the figures in the barometric pressure scale by .2094.

At altitude as one breathes air containing a lower $pO_2$ than that of air at sea level the alveolar $pO_2$ becomes lowered. The decrease in alveolar $pO_2$ at altitude if severe enough is counteracted in part by an increase in pulmonary ventilation, although this response is not as prominent immediately as it is after some delay.

Conditions at altitude can be simulated in an air tight chamber from which the air has been partially evacuated. At a given barometric pressure a certain altitude is simulated as far as gas tensions are concerned. Chambers have been constructed in such a way that they may be very rapidly, i.e., explosively, decompressed and the reactions of the subject followed from moment to moment. During acute exposure to simulated altitude, produced by rapid decompression of a chamber containing the subject, alveolar ventilation is increased so that alveolar $pCO_2$ is lowered, and the amount of decrease is proportional to the reduction in ambient pressure (increase in altitude). For example, shortly after decompression to a simulated altitude of 18,000 feet the alveolar $pCO_2$ is in the range of $27 \pm 2$ mm. Hg, and the alveolar $pO_2$ is in the range of $42 \pm 3$ mm. Hg. The alveolar $pO_2$ is less than half that found at sea level. At this point it should be noted that the water vapor tension in alveolar air, being determined by body temperature which is constant, remains at 47 mm. Hg at all altitudes, and when expressed in terms of per cent, it increases in direct proportion to the decrease in total pressure in the alveoli. For example, at sea level the per cent of water vapor is $47/760 \times 100$ whereas at 18,000 feet it is $47/380 \times 100$. At an altitude where the barometric pressure is only 74 mm. Hg, water boils at body temperature and the alveoli are filled with water vapor.

Immediately after sudden exposure to altitude, respiratory adjustments occur; however, conditions continue to change from one 5-minute period to the next for a period of 30 to 60 minutes (Riley, Otis and Houston, 1954). Some of the bases for these changes already have been discussed.

The immediate circulatory adjustments to acute arterial hypoxia are an increase in heart rate and blood pressure, and the onset of cyanosis as a result of an increase in the amount of reduced hemoglobin in arterial blood. The amount of desaturation can be estimated from the alveolar $pO_2$ and the oxygen-hemoglobin dissociation curve.

In the normal subject breathing air (about 21 per cent $O_2$), about 95 per cent saturation of the hemoglobin of arterial blood with oxygen is attained. In a person breathing air at any given altitude somewhat less than 95 per cent saturation would occur but could be achieved if the $O_2$ per cent in inspired air were increased sufficiently. It is found that at 18,000 feet it would be necessary to breathe about 45 per cent $O_2$ in order to attain 95 per cent saturation, and at about 34,000 feet, 100 per cent $O_2$ is needed. It follows that at altitudes higher than 34,000 feet some degree of arterial hypoxia will occur even when the subject breathes pure $O_2$, and at very high altitudes intolerable degrees of oxygen lack would be experienced even when breathing 100% $O_2$. The limit at which aviators can fly in nonpressurized cabins breathing 100 per cent $O_2$ is in the range of 40,000 to 45,000 feet. Above this level cabins containing gases under pressures higher than that of the ambient air are required.

Several mountain climbing expeditions have been made in the past by different groups of physiologists for the purpose of studying the effects of low oxygen tensions upon the respiratory functions and of determining the factors underlying the phenomen of acclimatization. An expedition was made to Monte Rosa (15,000 feet) in 1894 by Mosso and by others subsequently; to the peak of Teneriffe (12,000 feet) in 1910 by Zuntz, Barcroft and associates, and in 1911 to Pike's Peak (14,100 feet) by the Anglo-American expeditions of which Haldane, Douglas, Henderson and Schneider were members. In 1921 to 1922 Barcroft headed a party to Cerro de Pasco (14,200 feet) in the Peruvian Andes. A Himalayan expedition was led by Hartman in 1931, and in 1935 Dill led a party to the Chilean Andes. Recently, Pugh (1957) has reported observations made on Mt. Everest during the successful British expedition of 1952.

## GENERAL SIGNS AND SYMPTOMS

Airplane ascents, if made rapidly without the use of oxygen, may result in sudden loss of consciousness due to the reduction in oxygen supply to the brain. When the ascent is made more slowly, or the altitude is not so great as to cause immediate loss of consciousness, the aviator may at first experience sensations of excitement, exhilaration and well being. As higher altitudes are reached effects of a more serious nature develop, often insidiously. Mental and sensory dullness, muscular weakness, headache, vomiting, cyanosis, dyspnea and perhaps a tendency toward periodic breathing may be induced. A common and dangerous effect is the development of fixed ideas which may result in the performance of foolhardy and ill-judged actions.

When a person climbs to a mountain height, the time taken in the journey allows a certain degree of physiological readjustment to take place, and the symptoms are usually less intense. But, as in the case of the aviator, mental features, e.g., a feeling of elation, exhilaration, talkativeness and sometimes emotional outbursts, laughing or crying, quarrelsomeness or the development of fixed ideas are prominent. Mental tasks, e.g., calculations, memory tests, and telling the time from the mirror image of a clock face are performed less efficiently. Similar effects upon the mind are produced upon persons exposed to low oxygen pressures within a steel cabinet. The mental effects as pointed out by Barcroft are not unlike those caused by drunkenness. To quote his words,

"Alcohol affects different persons in different ways; so on my journeyings in high altitudes I have seen most of the symptoms of alcoholism reproduced. I have seen men vomit, I have seen them quarrel, I have seen them become reckless, I have seen them become morose. I have seen one of the most disciplined of men fling his arms about on the ledge of a crevasse to the great embarrassment of the guide. I have seen the most loyal companion become ill-tempered and abusive to the point at which I feared international complications would arise."—Lessons from High Altitudes.

Complete prostration may follow the earlier symptoms. If the individual remains at the high altitude the symptoms pass off after a time, as he becomes acclimatized to the low oxygen tension.

At a simulated altitude of about 20,000 feet (i.e., in a decompression chamber) most subjects experience failing vision, incoordinations, and inability to write or to execute simple mental tasks within 15 minutes or so after the extra oxygen supply has been cut off; at 26,000 feet none are able to retain "effective consciousness" for this length of time without oxygen.

### CHANGES ASSOCIATED WITH ACCLIMATIZATION

At an altitude of 14,200 feet as at Cerro de Pasco where Barcroft and his party carried out their investigations, the barometric pressure is around 440 mm. Hg. The partial pressure of oxygen is therefore about 92 mm. Hg. The oxygen tension of the alveolar air is not as far below that of the atmosphere as at sea level, and varied among the greater number of the party from 55 to 60 mm. Hg. The closer approximation of the atmospheric and alveolar oxygen tensions at high altitudes is due to the increased breathing which results in a more effective ventilation of the air sacs. The increased respiration is brought about through the action of the lowered oxygen tension in the blood. The oxygen tension is slightly lower in the arterial blood than in the alveolar air which indicates that the passage of the gas is due purely to diffusion and not to an active secretion by the pulmonary epithelium. If this occurred, as has been suggested (Haldane), one would expect the arterial oxygen tension to be higher than that of the alveolar air. Alveolar carbon dioxide tension also, as a result of the increased pulmonary ventilation, is lower than that at sea level; it varied in different individuals of Barcroft's party from 23 to 29 mm. Hg. At 14,200 feet the arterial blood is from 85 to 88 per cent saturated with oxygen (see fig. 29.4, p. 456).

A marked increase in the number of red cells (see ch. 6) and a corresponding increase in hemoglobin content of the blood occur at high altitudes. The blood volume is also augmented. The natives of mountainous regions have a red cell count of from 6 to 8 million per cubic millimeter. The greater quantity of hemoglobin of course raises the oxygen capacity of the blood and so tends to compensate for its lowered oxygen saturation. That is, the *total* oxygen content of the arterial blood tends in spite of the low saturation to rise. Nevertheless, it may not be evident at first sight how a rise in the oxygen capacity is of advantage, for blood of normal hemoglobin content even when only 80 per cent saturated possesses a quantity of oxygen which is quite adequate for the needs of the tissues. It has already been pointed out, however, that the important factor in supplying the tissues is the oxygen pressure gradient between the plasma in the capillaries and the tissue cells. So then, if there are a greater number of red cells, each will be required to give up less of its oxygen store in passing through the capillaries to furnish a given quantity of oxygen (see anoxia due to anemia, p. 509). Consequently the saturation and the oxygen tension of the venous blood will be maintained at a higher level than otherwise would be possible. This means that the mean intracapillary oxygen pressure will also be higher, and as a result the tissues are more effectively supplied with oxygen.

The reduction in the alveolar carbon dioxide results in a corresponding decrease in the carbon dioxide tension of the arterial blood. The ratio $H_2CO_3/NaHCO_3$, which tends to be altered by the loss of carbon dioxide, is adjusted by a decrease in the excretion of acid and ammonia in the urine, a consequent lowering of the "alkali reserve" and depression of the $CO_2$ dissociation curve (p. 461). The actual pH of the plasma changes little if at all. Up to about 12,000 feet if any change occurs it is toward the alkaline side; above this level the blood reaction shows little further change or tends to return to normal. Lactic acid, which was thought at one time to be produced in excess as a result of the anoxia is actually formed in smaller amounts at high altitudes than at sea level. Even during severe exercise at 15,000 feet and higher altitudes the lactic acid concentration in the blood is lower than during exercise of comparable severity at sea level.

Barcroft and his party observed a shift to the left in the oxygen dissociation curve of hemoglobin, i.e., the affinity of hemoglobin for oxygen was increased. The shift in the dissociation curve is ascribed by Barcroft to an increased alkalinity of the *interior of the red cell*. This increased alkalinity is in turn a direct result of the rise in the number of red cells. The buffering power of the blood is increased through the greater facility offered for the action of the "chloride shift" mechanism (ch. 13 and 29). In other words, when a given amount of carbon dioxide is liberated by the tissues, it is distributed among a greater number of red cells than under normal circumstances; therefore, the alkalinity of each cell is reduced to a proportionately less extent. There have been conflicting reports concerning this question of the shift in the oxygen dissociation curve. Some observers have been unable to confirm Barcroft's finding, while others claim that a shift to the right occurs. The truth appears to be that up to about 14,000 feet the affinity of hemoglobin for oxygen increases, but at higher levels the dissociation curve tends to assume the form found at sea level, and at altitudes of 19,000 feet there is a definite shift to the right.

One might suppose that an increased circulation rate would be an important adjustment to the rarefied atmosphere whereby an adequate oxygen supply to the tissues would be maintained, but except for a temporary increase during the first few days no change in cardiac output occurs at altitudes of less than 14,000 or 15,000 feet. Above 15,000 feet the greater degree of anoxia results in an increase in the minute output of the heart. Before acclimatization, the pulse rate during rest increases by from 15 to 20 beats per minute at altitudes between 15,000 and 18,000 feet. At greater altitudes, especially in persons

in poor physical condition, the increase in rate may be greater than in the normal. The acceleration of the pulse, according to Barcroft, is a signal of distress flown by the heart laboring under the effects of the anoxia, rather than an indication of an increased minute volume. The blood pressure shows little or no change up to 15,000 feet; a small rise may occur at higher altitudes. For an account of the effect of anoxia on the coronary circulation.

Those who have lived all their lives at very high altitudes (around 14,000 feet) have a larger vital capacity than dwellers at sea level. Barcroft reports that a native of Cerro de Pasco of 5 feet, 3 inches in height had a chest of a man of 6 feet. Moderate altitudes, up to about 7500 feet, appear to have little or no effect upon the chest development.

Although anoxia is the most serious effect of high altitudes with which the mountain climber or aviator has to contend, rapid ascents, as by airplane, cause other important physiological disturbances which should be mentioned, namely: (1) expansion of gases in the gastrointestinal tract, (2) aeroembolism (see below) and (3) pressure disturbances in the ears (ch. 78).

*Expansion of gases in the gastrointestinal tract.* Like the gases of the atmosphere those in the stomach and intestine increase in volume in proportion to the reduction in pressure. Gas having a volume of 1 liter at sea level expands to 2 liters at the pressure (375 mm. Hg) existing at 18,000 feet, to 4 liters at 34,000 feet to 6 liters at 42,000 feet (pressure 128 mm. Hg). Distention of stomach and intestine will result unless the abdomen is supported by a belt or other means, or the gases are freely evacuated. In rapid ascents distress or even severe pain results if there is any hindrance, as by an obstruction in the colon, to the ready passage of flatus.

## Dysbarism

The term *dysbarism*, or decompression sickness, refers to the signs and symptoms which result when the total pressure of ambient gases suddenly is reduced. It refers to the effects of reduction in pressure as such rather than to those caused by a lack of oxygen. Dysbarism is seen in deep sea divers or caisson workers when they pass too quickly from the high pressure in which they have been working to the ordinary pressure of the atmosphere, hence the name *caisson* disease has been used. The "bends" is a popular name for the condition. In dysbarism the *percentage* reduction in pressure is a more important factor than the absolute amount of decrease. A sudden reduction in pressure to approximately 45 per cent of the pressure with which the subject was equilibrated ordinarily is necessary in order to cause dysbarism. Therefore, an aviator who flies rapidly from sea level to an altitude where the pressure is one-third of an atmosphere would have about the same chance of developing decompression illness as a diver who is decompressed quickly from three atmospheres to one. A diver who has been exposed to a pressure of, for example, 8 atmospheres usually can be subjected to a quick reduction in pressure to 4 atmospheres without developing symptoms, then after he has been at this pressure long enough to approach equilibrium with the surrounding pressure he can be quickly lowered to 2 atmospheres where he remains for a time and next the pressure can be lowered to 1 atmosphere.

The cause of symptoms during rapid decompression is the formation of bubbles of gas in fatty tissues and blood. The gas is mainly nitrogen. The total amount of nitrogen dissolved in the body when one is exposed to a gas mixture having the same percentage composition as atmospheric air is several times that of $O_2$ and double that of $CO_2$. Also nitrogen diffuses less readily and, unlike $O_2$, it is not used in metabolic processes. When body fluids are saturated with $N_2$ at a given pressure and the ambient pressure suddenly is lowered, $N_2$ is evolved in gaseous form just as $CO_2$ is evolved from carbonated water when the cap is removed from the bottle containing it. Bubbles in the blood tend to lodge in the smaller vessels and obstruct the flow of blood. Symptoms vary depending upon the sites where the bubbles lodge. Fatty tissue usually is the site of bubble formation since $N_2$ is 5 times more soluble in oil than in water. The involved tissues include subcutaneous tissue, bone marrow, adrenal cortex, myelin sheaths, etc. Bubbles in the myelin sheats of sensory nerves cause pain (bends), paresthesias, itching, etc., and those in myelin sheaths of motor nerves may cause temporary paralysis. It has been recognized for many years that obese persons are more susceptible to "the bends" than lean persons.

In rapid ascents in airplanes dysbarism is not a problem up to 20,000 feet since the reduction in pressure is less that 55 per cent; and, in fact, symptoms ordinarily do not appear below 30,000 feet. Above this level, however, dysbarism is common. The tendency to develop decompression illness is greater the more rapid the ascent. The most effective way to prevent or diminish the effects of rapid decompression is to have the aviator breathe 100 per cent oxygen or an oxygen-helium mixture for a time before the flight and thus wash much of the nitrogen out of the body. When this is done the aviator should be able to ascend quite rapidly to 40,000 feet (continuing to breathe 100 per cent $O_2$) without discomfort.

The effects of aeroembolism in flyers during rapid ascent take the form most commonly of severe pain in one or more of the large joints and itching of the skin or cutaneous sensations of heat or cold. Other more serious symptoms such as paralysis, intense burning pain in the chest, or pulmonary edema may, though rarely, occur. The symptoms are rarely as severe as in compressed air illness, since the amount of gas which can be released is not as great in the decompression which occurs in ascent to altitude.

The *explosive decompression* technique which is used to study adjustments to lowered $pO_2$ in the inspired air also is useful in the study of dysbarism. A rate of ascent can be simulated in this way which is much faster than any which has been attained even in rockets. Many thousands of flying personnel have been subjected to explosive decompression as a routine procedure during the past fifteen years. The subject is instructed to breathe with mouth open. As the gas in the lungs expands during decompression it rushes out through the open airway. Gas in the sinuses also expands suddenly and exhausts through the natural channels, but if these openings are not patent severe pain is produced.

Experimental animals have been found to have an astonishingly high tolerance to explosive decompression at simulated high altitudes (from sea level to 50,000 feet—750 to 87 mm. Hg). The rate of decompression in the experiments of Whitehorn and his associates ranged from about 1100 mm. Hg per second to as high as 33,000 mm. Hg or more per second. That is to say, decompression from 750 mm. Hg to 87 mm. Hg was brought about in the latter instance in 0.02 second. Then the animal was quickly recompressed and the effects of anoxia thus prevented. The chief effects observed in these experiments were distension of the hollow viscera and lungs, fixation of the expanded thorax in the inspiratory position and of the diaphragm in the expiratory position, due to upward pressure of the distended stomach and intestines, sharp but temporary fall in blood pressure with cardiac slowing, hemorrhages into lungs and hollow organs, or rupture of the latter. The fall in blood pressure, which does not occur for a heart beat or two, seems to be due to decreased cardiac filling caused by the increased intrathoracic pressure, due in turn to the rise of the diaphragm. The cardiac slowing does not occur after bilateral section of the vagus nerves. In no instance out of some 700 decompressions on several different species of laboratory animal did a fatality occur from a single decompression. The injuries which are most likely to occur from explosive decompression are damage to ears and lungs, though rupture of the stomach or intestine may result.

### Respiration in a Sealed Cabin

In flight beyond the earth's atmosphere the passengers must be in a sealed compartment. The total pressure of gases in the compartment could be reduced quickly to one half that at sea level without causing any difficulty in normal subjects providing the $pO_2$ were kept up to a level sufficient to prevent arterial hypoxia. This could be done if the per cent of $O_2$ were about 35 to 40 at a cabin pressure of 380 mm. of Hg. It would be necessary to release the oxygen from a container, and there would be no point in permitting a lower oxygen tension than that which produces full saturation of hemoglobin in arterial blood, since oxygen can not be saved simply by reducing the supply. Also, there would be no advantage in providing a higher oxygen tension than that breathed at sea level.

The sealed cabin must contain apparatus for absorbing the $CO_2$. A rise in $CO_2$ content up to 2 per cent at 380 mm. Hg pressure would appear to be permissible even for indefinitely long periods. Circulation of the gas in the cabin through cannisters, such as are used in the closed $CO_2$-absorption methods of administering anesthetic gases, could accomplish $CO_2$ removal quite readily. (Chemicals could be used which could be regenerated by exposing them to the exterior of the cabin by some sort of double-window arrangement or in a hollow sphere in the wall of the cabin which would be equipped with a window, providing exposure for part of the time to the inside of the cabin and part time to the exterior). The cabin would need to be equipped with instruments for continuous monitoring of $pO_2$ and $pCO_2$. For long term space flight the idea of using the photosynthetic process to take up $CO_2$ and produce $O_2$ has been advanced.

Average values for the daily metabolic turnover of a "standard" man are presented below (compiled by H. G. Clamann, United States Air Force School of Aviation Medicine, Randolph Field, Texas). Calculations of what supplies must be taken in a sealed cabin for trips of any duration can be made on the basis of such data (table 33.1).

Perhaps it is worth mentioning that if a passenger in a sealed cabin were provided with a pressure suit which could withstand an internal pressure about one-fourth of an atmosphere greater than that on the outside and which was equipped with an oxygen source he could put this on, establish a pressure in the suit with oxygen at 160 mm. Hg, and then open the cabin to allow evacuation of all gases from it. Such a suit would be of the same type as that needed if one were to leave a space ship when beyond the earth's atmosphere.

TABLE 33.1

*Daily metabolic turnover*

(Man 70 kg. RQ = 0.82. Food: Protein 80 grams, Carbohydrate 270 grams, Fat 150 grams)

| | Input | | | Output | | |
|---|---|---|---|---|---|---|
| | *grams* | % | | *grams* | % | |
| Gases | 862 | 24.04 | (Oxygen) 603 l. | 982 | 27.39 | (Carbon Dioxide) 496 l. |
| Liquid | 2200 | 61.37 | (Water) | 2542 | 70.91 | (Water) |
| Solids | 500 | 13.95 | (Food) | 27 | 0.75 | (Urea) |
| | 23 | 0.64 | (Salts) | 23 | 0.64 | (Salts) |
| | | | | 11 | 0.31 | (Unaccounted for) |
| | 3585 | 100.00 | | 3583 plus 2830 Kcal | 100.00 | |

## Pneumonia

In *lobar pneumonia* the oxygen saturation of the arterial blood varies in different cases from normal to less than 70 per cent. The signs and symptoms of anoxia usually appear when the saturation is around 85 per cent. Cerebral symptoms, e.g., sleeplessness and delirium, cyanosis and dyspnea increase with the oxygen desaturation, and a saturation of less than 80 per cent is associated with a very high mortality. In 33 cases reported by Stadie with a saturation as low or lower than this only 1 recovered. In lobar pneumonia the carbon dioxide content of the arterial blood is reduced on the average by about 15 per cent (Meakins and Davies). The "alkali reserve", however, is normal or only slightly reduced. The blood pH may in some cases be shifted slightly toward alkalinity. From these findings it appears that there exists a partially compensated alkalosis, induced by the hyperventilation (blowing off of carbon dioxide).

The increased ventilation of the alveoli also increases the percentage of oxygen in the alveolar air, but this fact cannot, as we shall see presently, increase appreciably the oxygen in the arterial blood.

In *bronchopneumonia* a higher degree of oxygen desaturation of the arterial blood is usually present than in the lobar type. The cyanosis may be extreme. There is often *retention* of carbon dioxide when a rise in plasma bicarbonate results, to compensate, in part at least, the gaseous acidosis. The carbon dioxide content of the arterial blood may be 80 volumes per cent or more and the carbon dioxide dissociation curve well above the normal level.

*The causes of hypoxia in pneumonia.* The main factors concerned in the production of the hypoxia are (a) the passage of blood through unaerated (consolidated) portions of the lung and (b) shallow breathing. The oxygen unsaturation is not due to any change in the hemoglobin itself (e.g., the formation of methemoglobin) since the blood of pneumonia patients has a normal oxygen capacity. The oxygen dissociation curve at a given carbon dioxide tension is not appreciably different from that of normal persons.

In *lobar pneumonia* during the stages of engorgement and red hepatization the alveoli of the affected portion of the lung are poorly aerated. Mucus blocks the bronchioles and the *air spaces* are filled or their walls coated with exudate. But a large proportion of the vessels of these unaerated regions are still pervious. Consequently blood traversing such areas must remain poorly oxygenated or entirely venous. This blood with a low oxygen saturation and a high carbon dioxide content mixes with blood which has passed through aerated regions. The general arterial blood therefore has its oxygen saturation reduced in proportion to the amount of unsaturated blood with which it is mixed (see also Shunt, p. 521). When the pneumonic area passes into the stage of gray hepatization the vessels of the affected lobe become obliterated to a large extent and the pulmonary blood then passes through aerated regions (fig. 33.1). That is, the arterial blood is no longer vitiated by blood from non-aerated areas. Therefore in a typical case of lobar pneumonia when the disease is confined to a single large area and the breathing is not shallow, there is little anoxemia at this stage. If however, bronchopneumonic areas co-exist, the respiratory functions will be affected as described below. (See Oxygen Therapy, p. 526).

In *bronchopneumonia*, patches of lung tissue are cut off from their air supply. The fine bron-

Fig. 33.1. X-ray photograph of lung (injected with barium) from a case of lobar pneumonia (after Gross). *Upper right hand area.* Consolidated area—red hepatization. The main vessels are constricted and the finer vascular structure is less dense than in the normal lung. *Lower right hand area.* Consolidated area—gray hepatization. The main vessels are patent but the finer vessels have been occluded. *Lower left hand area.* Healthy portion of lung except for compensatory congestion; the vessels are dilated.

chioles become plugged with mucus, groups of alveoli become filled with exudate and the alveolar walls are edematous and thickened. Yet, obliteration of the vessels to any great extent does not occur. Blood continues to flow through unaerated areas. This blood which has a low $pO_2$ on mixing with that from aerated alveoli lowers the saturation of the general arterial blood.

SHALLOW BREATHING. In pneumonia breathing is frequently very rapid and shallow. Instead of the tidal air being around 500 ml. as in health it may be reduced to 250 ml. or less. It will be recalled that 150 ml. are required to fill the anatomical dead space, therefore only 100 ml. will enter the air sacs of the healthy parts of the lung. We have seen that the expansion of the lungs is not equal in all its parts (p. 471). The alveoli towards the hub of the radiating rays expand less than those near the periphery. Those parts, such as the apex, which are indirectly expanded have even in health a tendency to be ventilated less than those which are directly expanded. In shallow breathing, these differences are greatly exaggerated. Although the tidal volume is only half the normal, the total quantity of air breathed per minute (minute volume) is, as a result of the increased respiratory rate, much greater than normal. Since a proportion of the alveoli are very

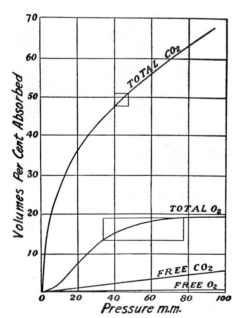

FIG. 33.2. Carbon dioxide and oxygen dissociation curves. The small rectangles indicate the extent of the variation of the $O_2$ and $CO_2$ of the subject's blood when at rest. (From L. J. Henderson.)

poorly ventilated or not at all, owing to the unequal expansion of the lung, those in other areas tend to be overventilated. The $O_2$ tension in the latter is therefore raised. But so far as the oxygenation of the blood is concerned the overventilation of some alveoli cannot make up for the underventilation of others. We know that the hemoglobin is nearly saturated already at the ordinary alveolar oxygen tension of 100 mm. Hg. As already mentioned the dissociation curve of hemoglobin in pneumonia does not differ appreciably from that in health, and the most, therefore, that could be expected from a rise in the alveolar $O_2$ tension would be an increase of 2 per cent or less in oxygen saturation of the blood traversing overventilated regions and a slight increase in the amount of $O_2$ held in simple solution. In other words, the blood flowing through the poorly ventilated parts of the lung will have a low saturation since the $O_2$ tension is low, while that flowing through the overventilated parts will be little above the normal. The net result will be a low oxygen saturation of the mixed arterial blood

Matters are different in the case of $CO_2$ elimination. The shape of the $CO_2$ dissociation curve which shows a progressive slope throughout the entire range of $CO_2$ tensions is quite unlike that for oxyhemoglobin (fig. 33.2). The greater total ventilation results in a lowering of $CO_2$ tension in the overventilated parts of the lung and, consequently, in a "blowing off" of $CO_2$ from the blood circulating through these regions. $CO_2$ is retained in the blood circulating through poorly ventilated regions. In the patient with lobar pneumonia the amount of $CO_2$ blown off may exceed that retained; the net result will be a lowering of the $CO_2$ content of the arterial blood. In bronchopneumonia a larger proportion of the pulmonary blood circulates through non-aerated areas. As a consequence, $CO_2$ retention is greater, and a normal or a higher than normal $CO_2$ content of the blood is more usual.

*The cause of shallow breathing in pneumonia.* Pleuritic pain, by restricting the respiratory excursions, may result in this type of breathing. In other instances it appears to be of a reflex nature resulting from the inflammatory process which, through a reduction in the distensibility of the pulmonary tissue, exalts the sensitivity of the afferent vagal endings in the alveolar walls. Thus the inspiratory movement is terminated before a full excursion has been completed (see Hering-Breuer reflex, p. 493). In support of a reflex origin may be mentioned the experiments of

Dunn and of Binger, Brow and Branch who produced this type of breathing in animals by the intravenous injection of potato starch granules. These, acting as small emboli, plugged the pulmonary capillaries. The rapid shallow breathing was immediately abolished by section of the vagi or prevented if the nerves had been cut before the injection. Breathing a mixture rich in carbon dioxide with intact nerves also restored the respiratory rate and depth to normal—the action of carbon dioxide upon the respiratory center itself overcoming the afferent nervous influence. Also, in pneumonia it has been found that oxygen inhalations, even though they may restore the oxygen saturation of the arterial blood to normal, do not necessarily abolish the shallow breathing— further evidence for the existence of a nervous element in the production of this type of breathing. Shallow breathing may also result from other diseases involving the alveoli, e.g., inflammation by irritant gases (phosgene and chlorine), pulmonary edema, miliary tuberculosis and pulmonary emboli, which would be expected to stimulate afferent nerve endings. It also occurs in certain nervous states, hysteria, certain forms of neurasthenia and sometimes in encephalitis lethargica, but is not seen in lesions involving the bronchi or bronchioles alone, e.g., bronchitis and asthma.

Severe arterial hypoxia, however produced, tends itself through its damaging effect upon the respiratory center to induce rapid shallow breathing, and in any event will exaggerate this type of breathing, since it also tends to increase the sensitivity of the Hering-Breuer reflex. Thus a vicious circle—shallow breathing inducing anoxemia and the latter reacting to enhance the former —is set up. Owing to the narrowed state of the cutaneous vessels the cyanosis is of the pale leaden-gray type (p. 526), and if the anoxia is not relieved, failing circulation adds to the oxygen want (anoxia of the hypokinetic type).

### Bronchial Asthma

This is a paroxysmal disease in which acute oxygen want is caused by a spasm of the smooth muscles of the finer bronchioles. Edema of the bronchiolar mucosa is probably also present. The alveoli are poorly ventilated, and some may be completely cut off from their air supply. The high percentage of carbon dioxide and low percentage of oxygen in the alveolar air result in a low oxygen saturation of the arterial blood and the retention of carbon dioxide. The acidosis related to $CO_2$ retention is met by the excretion of a highly acid

urine and a rise in the "alkali reserve". An intense plum-colored cyanosis may develop. The continued stimulating effect of oxygen want and carbon dioxide excess upon the respiratory mechanisms causes severe dyspnea.

Difficulty is experienced both in inspiration and expiration, but since there is a natural tendency for the bronchioles to narrow during expiration and dilate during inspiration, the greatest respiratory effort is exerted during expiration. The respiratory muscles contract with great force, and the accessory muscles of respiration are brought into play. The expiratory muscles compress the chest; the abdominal muscles contract in the attempt to squeeze the air from the lungs. The intrapulmonary pressure is greatly elevated, and the air escapes through the constricted tubes with a distinct wheezing sound. Due to the difficulty and prolongation of the expiratory phase normal deflation of the lungs cannot occur before the next inspiration ensures. The lungs, therefore, remain somewhat expanded even at the end of expiration. That is, during the asthmatic paroxysm a very large volume of residual air is present in the lungs (fig. 33.3). The tidal volume and the vital capacity are greatly reduced. The changes in volume of the overdistended lung are small and not commensurate with the excursions of the thoracic walls. As a consequence, the high value of the intrathoracic negative pressure induced during inspiration causes the structures at the root of the neck to be drawn toward the thoracic cavity to take up the space which the lungs are unable to fill. During expiration the veins of the neck and face become engorged. The restricted movements of the lung also greatly reduce the effect of mechanical mixing upon the lung air, the process of diffusion being depended upon to a larger extent for the freshening of the alveolar air.

### Causation

Asthma often shows a strong hereditary tendency. The bronchiolar spasm may be (a) of a *reflex nature* and due to the stimulation of hypersensitive afferent vagal endings in the larynx, or of trigeminal fibers by some nasal abnormality; the bronchoconstrictor impulses travel via efferent vagal fibers, (b) an *allergic phenomenon*, i.e., the result of sensitization to some foreign protein. This is the most common cause of the condition. It is then frequently associated with other allergic conditions, e.g., hay fever, urticaria or eczema either in the patient himself or in members of his family. The foreign protein may be inhaled. Pollens of various grasses and flowers, the dandruff of animals, e.g., horse, cat or dog, or feathers are among the most common excitants; the exciting cause may be some kind of food or the protein of bacteria within the respiratory tract itself may be responsible. The sensitivity of certain individuals to foreign proteins presents many features resembling those of anaphylactic shock in animals. Sudden death may result from the injection of horse serum (e.g., diphtheria antitoxin or antitetanic serum) into an asthmatic subject. A guinea pig when injected with a protein to which it has previously been sensitized dies rapidly from anaphylactic shock. The bronchiolar muscle is strongly contracted. The air is trapped so that the lungs are maximally distended and do not collapse when the thorax is opened. Even when the pulmonary tissue is deeply incised the air does not escape from the distended lung. This manifestation of anaphylaxis is associated with, perhaps due to, the liberation of histamine. It is well known that anaphylaxis and histamine administration produce almost identical effects in the guinea pig (fig. 33.4). Histamine-producing bacteria

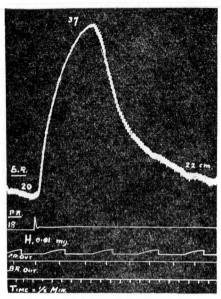

Fig. 33.4. Guinea pig. Reaction of bronchial muscle to 0.01 mg. histamine. (After Thornton).

have been reported in the bronchial secretions of asthmatics.

The *treatment* of asthma resolves itself into the relief of the paroxysm and the removal of the underlying cause. Adrenaline or ephedrine acts by inhibiting the bronchiolar muscle during the attack. Atropine paralyzes the bronchoconstrictor (vagal) fibers. Of the three drugs, adrenaline is the most effective. In the allergic form of the disease every effort is made to identify the offending protein. Antihistamine drugs have been employed with varying degrees of success.

## Chronic Emphysema

The lungs in emphysema (Greek *em* + *physema*, a blowing) are in a state of extreme distention as a result of the enlargement of the air sacs. The latter, however, show fewer alvoli in their walls owing to the atrophy of the interalveolar septa. Contiguous air sacs within a lobule coalesce or even adjacent lobules may fuse to form large air spaces. For this reason the total respiratory surface is reduced. The alveolar and capillary walls become thickened and the interstitial pulmonary tissue increased. Many capillaries become occluded. The pulmonary elastic tissue is reduced in amount so that the lungs, when removed from the thorax, do not collapse normally but remain in an overexpanded state. The peripheral lobules, which in health expand to the greatest extent, are those mainly affected in emphysema, the

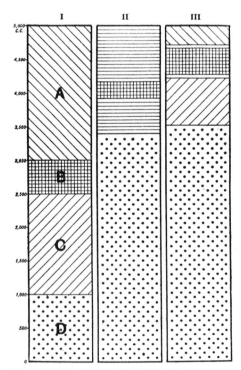

Fig. 33.3. Diagram showing subdivisions of the lung air in asthma (*II*) and emphysema (*III*) compared with the normal (*I*). *A*, Inspiratory reserve volume; *B*, tidal volume; *C*, expiratory reserve volume; and *D*, residual volume. (After Coke.)

enlarged lobules appearing as blebs upon the surface of the lung.

The chest is what is known as barrel-shaped. The ribs are more horizontal than normally, the thoracic spine is bowed backwards (kyphosis) so that the anteroposterior diameter of the chest is as great as or exceeds the transverse. The position of the chest is one of nearly full inspiration. The midposition of the diaphragm is at a much lower level than usual and its excursions above and below this level are restricted. The respiration is therefore mainly costal. In some instances the diaphragm is practically fixed or indeed may be drawn up during inspiration (paradoxical movement). As in the paroxysm of asthma the residual air is 2 or 3 times the normal, and the complemental air is reduced. The tidal volume is normal or only moderately reduced and the vital capacity (fig. 33.3) is lowered by from 20 to 60 per cent. Owing to the loss of the elasticity of the lung, expiration is no longer simply a passive movement but is aided by a forcible contraction of the expiratory muscles. When the patient is asked to make a deep inspiration, he does not expel all the air during the next expiration. Several respirations occur before the chest returns to its original size. Expiratory reserve volume is greatly decreased, and residual volume is markedly increased (fig. 33.3). These phenomena are due to the fact that the inelastic lungs have been overstretched and are brought back to their original volume with difficulty.

In emphysema there are anoxemia and retention of carbon dioxide. The oxygen saturation of the arterial blood runs from a little below normal to around 75 per cent or even less. The carbon dioxide tension in the alveolar air in well marked cases is from 50 to over 60 mm. Hg (7 to 8 per cent) and the carbon dioxide content of the arterial blood correspondingly high.

Owing to the obliteration of many capillaries in the lungs, the resistance in the pulmonary circuit is increased, a greater burden being thus put upon the right ventricle.

The cause of the impaired gaseous exchange is not altogether clear. Thickening of the alveolar and capillary walls and the obliteration of capillaries have been considered to be factors. Yet if this were so one would not expect the retention of carbon dioxide which, owing to its greater solubility (30 times that of oxygen) has a much higher rate of diffusion through the pulmonary membrane, to be so much more pronounced than the anoxia. The sharp rebound at the end of inspira-

tion which occurs in the healthy lung causes mechanical mixing of the lung air and is an important factor in the efficient ventilation of the alveoli. The absence of this effect in the emphysematous lung and its greater dependence, in consequence, upon the slower process of diffusion is probably an important factor leading to the defective aeration of the blood. According to Christie, the impaired gaseous exchange is due mainly to the fact that, as a result of the loss of elasticity, the intrathoracic pressure is not distributed evenly throughout the lung. As a consequence, the outlying alveoli which are largely functionless with obliterated vessels are ventilated to a greater extent than the relatively healthy ones more centrally placed. Owing to the shapes of the respective dissociation curves such underventilation of the functioning alveoli will tend to have a greater effect in preventing the elimination of $CO_2$ than in interfering with the absorption of oxygen. Other factors which are probably of importance are the slower rate of diffusion of $CO_2$, owing to its larger molecule, in the alveolar air, and the increased residual volume.

The red cell count, hemoglobin percentage, and consequently the oxygen capacity of the blood, are increased above the normal in emphysema. The cyanosis (p. 524) is often pronounced, yet the patient's dyspnea is less than might be expected from his color and from the carbon dioxide retention which exists. This is explained by the well established fact that in emphysema the respiratory center is relatively insensitive to carbon dioxide. A normal person when breathing a carbon dioxide rich mixture (8 per cent) increases his pulmonary ventilation by 300 per cent or more; the breathing of the emphysematous patient, on the other hand, shows relatively little change as a result of breathing a much stronger mixture (see fig. 33.5).

### Causation

Two factors are concerned in the production of emphysema (a) reduction in the elastic tissue of the lung and (b) increased distention of the alveolar spaces.

It is very questionable whether, in the absence of some abnormality of the lung tissue itself, emphysema can result from increased intrapulmonary pressure, such as occurs in those following certain occupations, e.g., glass blowers and the players of wind instruments. The study of groups of men following such occupations does not indicate that emphysema is produced in this way.

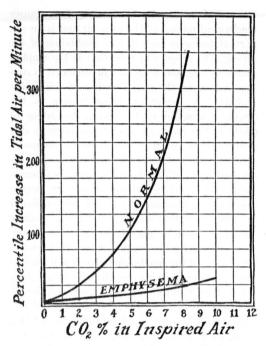

FIG. 33.5. Chart showing the percentile increase in tidal air per minute as the percentage of inspired carbon dioxide is raised. Note that when the normal subject inspires air containing 8 per cent carbon dioxide, the tidal volume is increased about 300 per cent, whereas in the emphysematous subject it is increased only about 25 per cent. (After R. W. Scott.)

Emphysema has, however, been induced in animals by stenosis of the trachea or bronchi or by the insertion of a valved apparatus into the trachea which allowed the free ingress of air but offered an obstruction to expiration. It is probable that in these instances the persistently high intraalveolar pressure by stretching the lung structures during *inspiration* first caused atrophy of the elastic tissue. During inspiration the air spaces are dilated by the negative pressure upon their outer surfaces. The trapped inspired air causes an ever-increasing distending pressure to be exerted upon the alveolar walls. Inasmuch as the intrathoracic pressure is "less negative" during expiration, a reduction rather than an enlargement of alveolar capacity would result at this time. Asthma and chronic bronchitis which frequently are forerunners of emphysema also, probably, exert their damaging effect upon the alveolar structure during the inspiratory phase. In the former condition the spasm of the bronchiolar muscle exerts a valvelike action. In chronic bronchitis mucous plugs would act similarly. Coughing, it has been supposed, places a strain upon the alveolar walls. But during the phase of coughing when the glottis is closed the alveolar walls are supported. When the

glottis opens, the air escapes from the alveoli if the obstructing material has been dislodged, and no strain upon the alveolar wall would result. If, however, the air remains entrapped its sudden re-expansion (rebound), as the pressure in the surrounding pulmonary tissue falls at the end of a cough, may injure the alveolar membrane and start the emphysematous process.

What may be termed a physiological or *compensatory* emphysema occurs when part of the pulmonary surface is reduced as by the collapse of a part or the whole of one lung. This is more in the nature of an hypertrophy. A similar enlargement of both lungs occurs at high altitudes.

A type of emphysema also occurs in the elderly—*senile or postural emphysema*—and is secondary to the change in the shape of the thorax which becomes more barrel-shaped and increased in capacity. The lungs enlarge to fill the increased space. This condition is associated with few symptoms. There is little reduction in the vital capacity, and the oxygen saturation of the arterial blood is practically normal.

### Atelectasis

Any condition which lowers the pressure within the alveoli or increases the pressure upon the lung surface, i.e., reduces the "negative" intrapleural pressure, may lead to collapse of the lung. Thus pleural effusions, pneumothorax, tumors, etc., pressing from without or the isolation of the alveoli from their air supply by the obstruction of a bronchus will therefore result in collapse of the lung or of the portion of the lung affected. Atelectasis (Greek *ateles*, incomplete; *ektasis*, distention) is also the term applied to the condition in the newborn in which, as a result of the blockage of a bronchus or of a group of bronchioles by mucous secretion, or owing to weak inspiratory movements, a portion of the lung fails to become distended with air.

*Absorption of air from isolated alveoli and other closed spaces.* When a bronchus or bronchiole in a previously distended lung is obstructed the imprisoned air soon becomes absorbed from the affected alveoli. Collapse of the air sacs cannot take place until this has occurred. Absorption is brought about in the following way, as pointed out by Henderson. The air in the isolated alveoli has a total pressure of 760 mm. Hg. The partial pressures are in round numbers, $O_2$, 100 mm.; $N_2$, 570 mm. $CO_2$, 40 mm. and aqueous vapor, 47 mm. In the venous blood the total pressure is 703 mm., the nitrogen and aqueous vapor being the same as that of the alveolar air, but the partial pressure of oxygen is only 40 mm.

and of carbon dioxide 46 mm. An interchange of the latter gases therefore occurs between the alveolar air and the venous blood. It might be thought that the imprisoned air would then be in equilibrium with the blood and no further absorption occur. But the alveolar air loses more oxygen than it gains carbon dioxide whereupon its volume is reduced. The atmosphere acting upon the body surface and through the yielding soft tissues compresses the air so as to maintain its total pressure practically constant at 760 mm. As a result of the absorption of oxygen the percentage and consequently the partial pressure of carbon dioxide and of nitrogen are increased. These gases now diffuse into the blood. The volume of the alveolar air is further reduced thereby but its total pressure still remains unaltered. The percentage and therefore the partial pressure of oxygen rises and more of this gas passes into the blood. The process continues in this manner until no air remains, and the walls of the original space are ultimately approximated by the pressure of the atmosphere. Air is absorbed from the pleural cavity or from any other closed cavity of the body in the same way (Henderson and Henderson). The absorption of the air confined within the pleural cavity permits the lung, if the air pressure had caused its collapse, to re-expand (see also p. 477).

The collapse and shrinkage of the lung which results from blockage of a bronchus increases the intrathoracic negative pressure, since the closed thoracic box is less completely filled. The diaphragm is therefore drawn upwards and uncollapsed portions of the lungs are expanded to a greater extent (compensatory emphysema) in order to fill the unoccupied space.

### Shunt

In the fetus the vessels of the airless lungs are bypassed by the greater part of the blood brought to the heart. That is to say, most of the blood is shunted to the arterial side through channels which normally close at, or shortly after, birth. It is clear that if one or more of these channels should persist after birth, or if the interventricular septum is defective so that a large part of the venous blood does not traverse the lungs, but is short circuited from the right to the left heart or directly into the aorta, the oxygen saturation of the arterial blood will be seriously reduced. Arterial hypoxia evidenced by cyanosis (p. 524) and dyspnea (p. 501) will result (fig. 33.6). These will be especially pronounced upon exertion since the

unsaturation of the polluting venous blood will be thereby increased.

*The fetal circulation.* Before the congenital abnormalities are described, the fetal circulation and the circulatory readjustments which occur at birth, or shortly thereafter, will be briefly reviewed.

In the fetus the oxygenated blood from the placenta is carried by the *umbical vein* to the liver, where it separates into two streams, one of which is distributed to the left ⅔ or so of the liver; the

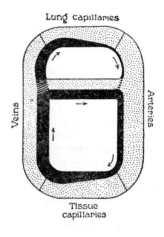

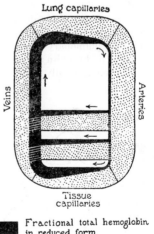

■ Fractional total hemoglobin in reduced form

▒ Fractional total hemoglobin in oxygenated form

FIG. 33.6. Diagram (upper) showing the proportion of oxyhemoglobin to reduced hemoglobin in different parts of the circulation in an instance where a portion of the blood passes through unaerated channels (shunt) from the venous to the arterial system. Lower diagram represents a case in which the oxygen unsaturation of the blood is abnormally high in a part of the peripheral capillaries but normal in the arterial blood (stagnant type of anoxia). (After Lundsgaard and Van Slyke.)

remainder passes directly via the *ductus venosus* into the inferior vena cava, thus mixing with blood returning from the lower part of the body. The portal vein supplies the rest of the liver. That portion of the blood from the umbilical vein which has traversed the vessels of the liver is also delivered by the hepatic veins into the inferior vena cava. The hepatic veins are a number of small vessels and two much larger ones; the latter form a junction with the ductus venosus just before the latter joins the inferior vena cava. The blood in the vena cava beyond this point is, therefore, partly oxygenated (from placenta via umbilical vein and ductus venosus) and partly reduced, having traversed the tissues of the lower limbs, intestines and liver. The caval blood, upon reaching the right auricle, separates into two unequal parts. The much larger stream passes directly through the foramen ovale (*via sinistra*) into the left auricle; the smaller stream enters the right ventricle. The blood which has reached the left auricle, after being joined by a small but by no means inconsiderable volume of blood returned from the pulmonary tissue, flows into the left ventricle, and is discharged into the aorta and distributed to the brain by the brachiocephalic artery, and to the myocardium by the coronary arteries. The remainder flows down the aorta.

The blood returned from the head and entering the right auricle by the superior vena cava, together with the small fraction of blood of the inferior vena cava which was not directed through the foramen ovale, enters the right ventricle and is ejected into the pulmonary artery. A smaller part, yet, as shown by Franklin and his associates, more than has been generally supposed is conveyed to the lungs by two branches of the latter vessels. The main stream, discharged from the right ventricle, passes by a wide vessel, the *ductus arteriosus*, into the aorta, and mixing with the blood coming from the left ventricle, is distributed throughout the body. That portion which is supplied to the lower limbs is returned by two vessels—the *umbilical arteries*—to the placenta.

During birth, or very shortly after, the three umbilical vessels close (even though the cord has not been tied or broken) by the contraction of smooth muscle in the vascular walls. The flow through the ductus venosus ceases as a result of contraction of a smooth muscle sphincter at the point where it leaves the umbilical vein. This occurs in the sheep fetus, according to Franklin and his associates, in from 5 to 25 minutes after the umbilical vessels have closed. Within 5 minutes or so after the commencement of breathing the foramen ovale closes, and a little later (apparently never before the obliteration of the foramen ovale) the ductus arteriosus becomes occluded. All the blood from the right side of the heart is normally from now on directed through the lungs. Franklin and his associates found, however, in the case of the new-born lamb, that should the general condition of the latter seriously deteriorate, the ductus arteriosus may open again. The mechanism of closure of the ductus appears to be initiated in some way by the action of the oxygenated blood upon the vascular muscle and not through a nervous mechanism. In the lamb this channel has never been observed to close before occlusion of the umbilical vessels.

### Congenital Cardiac Defects

Patent ductus arteriosus, or foramen ovale interventricular septal defects, stenosis of the pulmonary artery and coarctation of the aorta (narrowing of aorta in the neighborhood of the ductus arteriosus) are among the congenital defects most commonly met with.

The development of the direct Fick method (catheterization of the right side of the heart) for determining the cardiac output has provided means of the greatest value in diagnosing congenital defects of the circulation. It is now possible to obtain samples of blood for gas analysis from the right ventricle or from the pulmonary artery. (See fig. 33.7.)

*Patent foramen ovale or other defect in the interauricular septum.* In patency of the foramen ovale, the opening is guarded by a valvelike membrane which prevents blood from passing from the left to the right auricle, and none passes in the opposite direction unless the pressure in the right auricle is high. With other defects of the interauricular septum, a shunt from right to left with cyanosis may occur, but if there is mitral stenosis and a large defect (*Lutembacher's syndrome*) the high

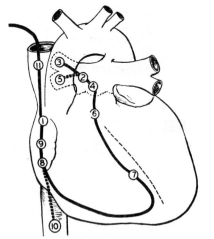

Fig. 33.7. Numbers from 1 to 11 indicate the positions from which blood samples may be taken by means of the intracardiac catheter. (After Groom and associates.)

pressure in the left auricle causes a shunt from left to right.

*Patent ductus arteriosus.* Blood enters the pulmonary system from the arterial side; the oxygen content in the pulmonary artery is increased, but is normal in the right auricle and ventricle.

If a *defect of the interventricular septum* exists alone, the oxygen content of the blood in the right ventricle and pulmonary artery is increased but not of that in the right auricle.

Neither of these last two defects, if it exists alone, will cause cyanosis, since the shunt is from left to right (arteriovenous shunt). Rarely, however, in the case of a patent ductus arteriosus, the direction of flow is reversed temporarily at certain times (during crying or coughing), blood passing from the pulmonary artery into the aorta.

Often the abnormalities are multiple. For example, a patent foramen ovale, together with stenosis of the pulmonary artery, results in the passage of venous blood to the arterial side, i.e., through the auricular defect; slight or moderate cyanosis is seen. The combination of congenital defects, originally described by John Hunter and later by Fallot, and now generally known as the *tetralogy of Fallot*, consists of, (a) an interventricular septal defect, (b) narrowing of the pulmonary artery, or stenosis of its orifice, and (c) dextroposition of the aorta, the orifice of this vessel being shifted to the right to straddle the septal defect. (d) The fourth element making up the tetrad is right ventricular hypertrophy. The blood flow through the lungs and the pulmonary pressure are reduced. Owing to the high pressure developed in the right ventricle blood is driven through the defect into the overriding aorta. If the pulmonary stenosis is very severe, the ductus arteriosus must be patent in order to provide sufficient blood flow through the lungs to support life. Cyanosis and dyspnea are usually pronounced. Blalock and Taussig have devised an operation for the correction of the chief effects of these conditions. It consists of anastomosing a large branch of the aortic arch (usually carotid or subclavian) to the right or left pulmonary artery.

Another combination of defects has three features of the tetralogy of Fallot, namely, defect of the intraventricular septum, dextroposition of the aorta and right ventricular hypertrophy, but pulmonary stenosis is absent. It is known as *Eisenmenger's complex*. The shunt is from left to right in early life, but later, when as a result of the large volume of blood entering the right ventricle from the left side as well as through the normal channels this chamber enlarges and hypertrophies, the high pressure developed may force venous blood into the overriding aorta; cyanosis then appears.

In those congenital cardiac anomalies showing cyanosis, the arterial oxygen saturation is found to be, during rest, from 45 per cent in severer degrees of cyanosis to 90 per cent in the milder cases. The red cell count, however, is likely to be increased, and the hemoglobin concentration may be high as 26 grams per cent. The arterial oxygen content, i.e., the volumes of oxygen per 100 cc. of blood, in those with the higher hemoglobin concentration is, consequently, much higher than normal and may reach a value of 29 volumes per cent, as against the normal maximum of 22 volumes per cent (see Cyanosis, p. 524). Exercise, which in normal subjects causes little or no change in arterial oxygen saturation, produces a profound fall in the congenital heart cases, amounting in some to a reduction of over 30 per cent.

## Carbon Monoxide Poisoning

References to carbon monoxide poisoning are contained in the earliest medical writings. This gas was used by the Greeks and Romans for the execution of criminals and as a means of committing suicide. Carbon monoxide is today the most important gaseous poison against which physicians have to contend. During times of peace it accounts for more deaths than all the other gases combined. Carbon monoxide combines with the hemoglobin of the blood and thus renders it unavailable for oxygen carriage. The affinity of hemoglobin for carbon monoxide is approximately 300 times its affinity for oxygen. Therefore, when the atmosphere contains only a very small percentage of CO, the hemoglobin takes up the poisonous gas and in so doing prevents its combining with an equivalent volume of oxygen.

Recovery from carbon monoxide poisoning is usually complete when the exposure has not been too long or the concentration too high. It is important that the carbon monoxide hemoglobin should be broken up as soon as possible since injury to the tissues is produced by the anoxia. It is possible to displace the carbon monoxide by oxygen if the tension of oxygen is sufficiently high and that of carbon monoxide low. Mixtures with a high percentage of oxygen and from 6 to 7 per cent carbon dioxide combined with artificial respiration are used in the treatment of CO poisoning. The carbon dioxide, as well as acting as a respiratory stimulant, reduces the affinity of hemoglobin for carbon monoxide. Intravenous injections of methylene blue have been advocated but are valueless. Carbon monoxide, as well as its action in displacing oxygen from hemoglobin, has histotoxic properties, inhibiting the tissue respiratory enzymes. This fact has no practical bearing, however, upon carbon monoxide poisoning in man, for the concentrations at which such action occurs is many times greater than could ever occur in the body.

## Cyanide Poisoning

No interference with oxygen carriage is caused by cyanide, but there is inhibition of tissue respiration. Cyanide inhibits the action of cytochrome oxidase, carbonic anhydrase and probably of other enzyme systems. It follows from this that any antidote for cyanide poisoning must have one of two actions. Either the cyanide must be removed or detoxified or the inactivated catalyst must be replaced. Methylene blue does act as a catalyst for certain biological oxidations, and this led to its use as an antidote for cyanide poisoning. When methylene blue is given to the intact animal, there is a marked rise in body temperature which is due to increased metabolism. Methylene blue permits inhibiting effects of cyanide on cellular oxidations. This fact has been established from investigation on a great number of tissues. Sahlin in 1926 provided the first experimental demonstration that methylene blue antagonizes the action of cyanide in the intact animal. He used rats and the observation as been confirmed on other animals—dogs, rabbits, mice. The evidence suggests that methylene blue acts by removing the cyanide from tissue. Methylene blue and cyanide do not combine directly, but methylene blue forms methemoglobin which combines with the cyanide to form cyanmethemoglobin. The cyanmethemoglobin is relatively nontoxic and is broken down slowly, the detoxification probably being brought about by conversion of the cyanide to thiocyanate (Smith and Malcolm). Other substances which form methemoglobin (Hug; Wendel) such as sodium nitrite, amyl nitrite, pyrogallol, etc., are also effective in the treatment of cyanide poisoning. Such methods of course are limited by the quantity of hemoglobin that can safely be converted to methemoglobin.

A number of sulphur compounds have been found effective in cyanide poisoning. Chen, Rose and Clowes showed that sodium thiosulphate and sodium tetrathionate may protect dogs against as much as three lethal doses of cyanide.

## Cyanosis

Cyanosis (Greek, *cyanos*, blue) may be defined as the diffuse, dusky or bluish color of the skin and mucous membranes caused by the presence in the blood of the superficial capillaries (subpapillary venous plexus) of reduced hemoglobin above a certain definite amount.[2] Cyanosis

[2] The presence of abnormal compounds of hemoglobin, e.g., methemoglobin and sulfohemoglobin, resulting from the action of various toxic substances, causes a type of cyanosis (enterogenous cyanosis), but these will not be considered

is seen in the arterial and hypokinetic types of anoxia but not in the anemic or histotoxic forms. It seems scarcely necessary to state that the retention of carbon dioxide in the blood has no *direct* effect upon the production of cyanosis. The blue color of the skin depends fundamentally upon the *absolute* amount of reduced hemoglobin in the capillary blood and *not* upon the *relative proportions* of reduced hemoglobin and oxyhemoglobin. For example, in anemia the hemoglobin content of the blood may be only 20 per cent of the normal. In the capillary blood all of this could be in the reduced form, yet cyanosis would not result, since the absolute amount of reduced hemoglobin (i.e., "blue" pigment) would be insufficient to produce any blue discoloration. On the other hand, in polycythemia the hemoglobin may be 100 per cent above normal. Cyanosis will occur when the hemoglobin of the capillary blood is only 20 per cent reduced, for the absolute concentration of reduced hemoglobin will then be raised to threshold value. The greater quantity of the bright-colored oxyhemoglobin present exerts little or no influence; that is, it does not, as might be expected, tend to neutralize the color effect of the reduced hemoglobin.

Normal blood contains about 15 grams of hemoglobin per 100 cc. Lundsgaard found that the capillary blood must contain approximately 5 grams of reduced hemoglobin per 100 cc. before cyanosis will appear. When fully saturated (20 volumes per cent), ¾ gram of hemoglobin will take up 1 cc. of oxygen. Five grams of hemoglobin, therefore, hold about 6.7 cc. of oxygen, and 5 grams of reduced hemoglobin are formed when the blood contains 13.3 volumes per cent of oxygen. Cyanosis may therefore be expected to appear when the blood in the capillaries is on the average around 7 volumes per cent unsaturated. As a result of certain modifying factors (p. 526) the precise level of capillary unsaturation at which cyanosis makes its appearance varies in different cases between 6 and 7 volumes of oxygen per cent.

The oxygen unsaturation of the capillary blood does not of course occur abruptly at the arterial end but is progressive from point to point along the course of the vessel. The loss of oxygen may

here (see p. 57). Cyanosis may result from anoxia of either the arterial or hypokinetic type. It obviously cannot occur in the anemic type, which is due essentially to a low hemoglobin concentration, in the histotoxic type in which the hemoglobin gives up less of its oxygen store than in health, nor in the arterial and hypokinetic types if a severe grade of anemia exists.

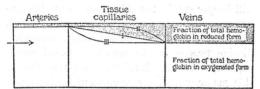

FIG. 33.8. Diagram showing hypothetical variations in the shape of the reduction curve of oxy-hemoglobin during the passage of the blood through tissue capillaries. (After Lundsgaard and Van Slyke.)

be uniform from the arterial to the venous end of the capillary as shown in Curve I, figure 33.8, or the desaturation may occur mainly toward the venous end (Curve II) when the capillary blood would approximate arterial blood in its content of reduced hemoglobin. Under other circumstances the greatest oxygen loss may occur toward the arterial end (Curve III) when the unsaturation of the capillary blood throughout would approach that of venous blood. It is difficult to obtain data from which the true curve may be drawn. The simplest of these curves (Curve I) is assumed and the average unsaturation of the capillary blood is taken as midway between that of arterial and venous bloods respectively. Thus

$$\frac{1}{2}(A + V) = C$$

where A and V represent the unsaturation in volumes per cent of arterial and venous bloods respectively and C the average unsaturation of the capillary blood.

For example, in a normal person the arterial unsaturation is 0.5 volume per cent (19.5 volumes per cent saturation), another 5 volumes per cent are given up in the capillary, the venous unsaturation is therefore 5.5 volumes per cent. So

$$\frac{1}{2}(0.5 + 5.5) = 3.0 \text{ volumes per cent average}$$
unsaturation of capillary blood

$$(3.0 \times 0.75) = 2.2 \text{ gram reduced Hb}$$

We have seen that the average unsaturation of the capillary blood must be between 6 and 7 volumes per cent (approximately 5 grams of reduced Hb) before cyanosis appears. This degree of unsaturation of the capillary blood may be brought about either by an increase in the arterial unsaturation (arterial type of anoxia) or as a result of a greater amount of oxygen being lost from the blood in its passage through the capillaries (hypokinetic type of anoxia). That is, by an increase in the venous unsaturation (V) alone. In order to produce an average unsaturation of from 6 to 7 volumes per cent in the capillary blood the arterial unsatura-

tion would need to be from 4 to 4.5 volumes per cent, or the unsaturation of the venous blood—that in the arteries being normal—11 to 13 volumes per cent. Meakins and Davies found that when the veins of the arm were obstructed in normal individuals cyanosis was just detectable when the venous blood reached an unsaturation of 11.4 volumes per cent.

These facts may be clarified by examples. If the blood as it leaves the lungs contains only 15.5 volumes per cent of oxygen, i.e., if it has an unsaturation of 4.5 volumes per cent and the tissues abstract the usual quantity of oxygen, namely 5 volumes per cent, the unsaturation of the venous blood will be 9.5 volumes per cent and that of the capillary blood

$$\frac{1}{2}(4.5 + 9.5) = 7 \text{ volumes per cent}$$

$$(7 \times 0.75 = 5.2 \text{ grams Hb}).$$

If on the other hand the arterial unsaturation is around the normal value of 0.5 volume per cent but as a result of slowing of the circulation each unit volume of the blood gives up a greater quantity of oxygen, and the venous unsaturation is increased to say 13 volumes per cent, the average unsaturation of the capillary blood will be

$$\frac{1}{2}(0.5 + 13) = 6.7 \text{ volumes per cent.}$$

In either of these instances slight cyanosis would be expected to appear.

Let us now consider what occurs when the hemoglobin percentage is above or below the normal value.

In *anemia* the amount of hemoglobin is below normal, and the oxygen capacity of the blood is correspondingly lowered. If the hemoglobin content be only 30 per cent of the normal, the volumes per cent of oxygen in the arterial blood, though the latter be fully saturated, will be only about 6 volumes per cent, i.e., the quantity of hemoglobin in 100 cc. of blood is less than 5 grams. It is obvious that such a person could not become cyanotic even if, as a result of defective oxygenation of the blood or of slowing of the circulation, all his hemoglobin were in the reduced state. A patient whose hemoglobin was, say, 60 per cent (oxygen capacity 12 volumes per cent) would, like one with a normal hemoglobin content, become cyanotic when his arterial blood reached an unsaturation of about 4.5 volumes per cent, that is when his capillary blood had an average unsaturation of around 7 volumes per cent. But the oxygen want of the anemic subject would be greater than that of the subject with a normal hemoglobin content since in the case of the former 4.5 volumes per cent constitute nearly 40 per cent of the oxygen capacity of his blood. In a less enlightened age when bleeding was resorted to for the relief of cyanosis, the brilliant success of that procedure is not to be wondered at—nor that the patient died. In the hypokinetic type of anoxia the unsaturation of the venous blood of a subject with 60 per cent hemoglobin content could not reach the value necessary to produce cyanosis until all the hemoglobin was in the reduced state. Thus $\frac{1}{2}(1 + 12) = 6.5$ volumes per cent unsaturation of the capillary blood.

In *polycythemia*, in which the hemoglobin content is, say, double the normal (oxygen capacity 40 volumes per cent), cyanosis occurs in very mild degrees of anoxemia. At an arterial unsaturation of 4.5 volumes per cent the polycythemic subject would have the same degree of cyanosis as an ordinary person with this quantity (5 grams) of reduced hemoglobin in his blood. But in the polycythemic subject with a hemoglobin content of 200 per cent, 4.5 volumes per cent is only 11 per cent of the oxygen capacity of his blood; in the person with a normal hemoglobin content it constitutes 22.5 per cent. The oxygen want in the former would be relatively slight as compared with that of the latter. Or put in another way and including the anemic subject—if the anoxemia were of the same degree in each, the anemic person would show little or no cyanosis; the polycythemic, a cyanosis of high degree and the normal subject a color intermediate in intensity. In a person with an abnormally high blood count a degree of slowing of the peripheral blood flow which would be without effect upon one possessing a normal hemoglobin content will result in cyanosis. Thus in regions such as the face, ear lobes and hands, where the cutaneous vessels are well filled with blood, cyanosis is readily induced in the polycythemic subject by exposure to cold. In certain conditions associated with arterial anoxemia, e.g., emphysema (p. 518) and congenital heart disease the red cell count is increased, and the cyanosis, in consequence, enhanced. It will be evident from these examples that the presence of cyanosis indicates anoxia but the absence of cyanosis does not rule out the possibility of anoxia.

## THE FACTORS WHICH INFLUENCE THE DEPTH OF CYANOSIS CAUSED BY A GIVEN QUANTITY OF REDUCED HEMOGLOBIN

(a) *The state of cutaneous capillaries.* When these are dilated more of the dark colored blood will be present in the skin than when they are constricted. In the former instance cyanosis will of course be more pronounced. Increased carbon dioxide tension in the peripheral blood causes capillary dilation, therefore, when retention of this gas accompanies oxygen want, as in venous congestion of superficial regions, etc. the cyanosis is intense. If the peripheral vessels are strongly constricted, as in shock, cyanosis may be inconspicuous.

(b) *Pigmentation and thickness of the skin.* These factors obviously will modify the depth of the cyanotic color. Cyanosis is more clearly evident in regions where the skin is thin and unpigmented. The yellow discoloration of the skin caused by an excess of bilirubin in the blood (jaundice) tends to modify the cyanotic tint, but since the former stains the skin itself, while the discoloration due to reduced hemoglobin is confined to the capillary vessels, jaundice is likely to be just as intense in regions where the skin is thick as in those where it is thin. The cyanotic discoloration can be temporarily abolished by pressure upon the skin whereas the icteric staining cannot. Cyanosis does not appear in the conjunctivae but these are deeply colored in jaundice.

## OXYGEN THERAPY

Oxygen administration is of great value in combating acute arterial anoxia as may occur in pneumonia, pulmonary edema, or obstruction to breathing, as well as in states such as congestive heart failure, or coronary thrombosis when, though the arterial blood contains the usual amount of oxygen, the tissues, owing to impairment of the peripheral circulation, suffer from a deficiency of oxygen.

The chronic anoxia due to anemia, in which the hemoglobin is saturated with oxygen to the normal degree, is treated preferably by measures directed to the disease itself rather than by oxygen therapy. In failure of the peripheral circulation, the inhalation of 100 per cent oxygen will increase the oxygen content of the blood to revive a flagging respiratory center. But the anoxia due to a shunt of blood from the right to the left side of the heart (p. 522) or through a similarly completely unaerated portion of the lung will not be much benefited by oxygen inhalations; it is not possible to make the blood supplying healthy and well aerated alveoli absorb any important amount of *extra* oxygen and so compensate for the shunted blood.

When, however, the diffusion coefficient of oxygen (ch. 29) through the alveolar membrane is reduced as a result of edema, thickening or a coating of fluid, oxygen administration by raising the pressure of the gas in the alveolar air will increase its rate of diffusion across the pulmonary epithelium. The oxygen saturation of the blood flowing through the damaged pulmonary tissue is increased.

Consequently, in broncho- or lobar pneumonia when such changes are responsible for the anoxemia, in emphysema or in pulmonary edema whether from cardiac or pulmonary disease or from gas poisoning, the success of oxygen administration is often spectacular. Anoxemia increases the permeability of the pulmonary epithelium to fluids and, consequently encourages edema formation. In other words, a vicious circle is established—edema inducing anoxemia and the latter increasing the edema—which is broken by oxygen administration.

Anoxemia due to rapid *shallow breathing* is relieved by oxygen treatment since the oxygen tension of poorly ventilated alveoli is raised thereby. The shallow breathing itself is likely to persist since it is primarily due to the local process in the lung acting upon the nerve endings rather than to the anoxemia. Therefore this type of breathing could, no more than the pulmonary lesion itself, be expected to be abolished by oxygen treatment.

It has been said that when the arterial blood contains the normal quantity of oxygen, namely about 19.5 volumes per cent (saturation 97.5 per cent) as in the hypokinetic type of anoxia of congestive heart failure, oxygen inhalation cannot be of any great value, since the oxygen saturation can be raised only to 100 per cent, and the total oxygen content increased by 2.2 volumes per cent (an increase of 1.7 volumes in simple solution together with 0.5 volumes combined with hemoglobin). That is, the total oxygen content of a person breathing 100 per cent oxygen will be 21.7 volumes per cent. But this increase of 2.2 volumes per cent (representing an increase in $O_2$ content of 11 per cent) is as pointed out by Comroe and Dripps of the highest importance in anoxia, for it raises very considerably the pressure at which oxygen is delivered to the tissues. For example, when a patient is breathing ordinary air, every 100 cc. of blood in passing through the capillaries loses 7 volumes of $O_2$ (normal about 5 vols.), and, therefore, leaves the venous end of the capillary with a content of 12.5 vols. per cent, is 63 per cent saturated, and has a $pO_2$ of around 32 mm. Hg. Now when 100 per cent oxygen is breathed the extra 2.2 volumes per cent in the arterial blood is given up on entering the capillaries, which reduces the oxygen saturation only to that existing under ordinary conditions in the arterial blood, namely, 97.5 per cent. But the tissues owing to the slowing of the circulation abstract a further 4.8 volumes per cent to satisfy their need of 7 volumes per cent. The venous blood, therefore, contains 14.7 volumes per cent of oxygen, and is over 73 per cent saturated, instead of about 63 per cent without oxygen administration; the $pO_2$ is nearly 40 mm. Hg. Thus the tissues are supplied with oxygen at a virtually normal head of pressure. In congestive heart failure, therefore, especially if there is generalized edema, the administration of oxygen is often of great benefit.

### METHODS OF ADMINISTRATION

Oxygen is given usually by means of a nasal or oral-nasal catheter, by a specially designed face mask, or the patient is placed in a hood-tent or airtight cabinet in which the $O_2$ percentage is maintained at the required concentration. Carbon dioxide (5 to 10 per cent) is sometimes added, especially in CO poisoning, persistent hiccough and postoperative atelectasis, in order to encourage lung expansion. In an oxygen tent the patient's own breath may raise the $CO_2$ to the range of 1 to 2 per cent.

In normal persons the breathing of 100 per cent oxygen often causes a slight initial reduction of breathing of about 3 per cent. If the administration is continued, the respirations are stimulated possibly as a result of afferent impulses set up in the respiratory tract by the inhalation and conveyed to the medullary center. In anoxia, a much more pronounced depression or even complete cessation of breathing may occur. This so-called *oxygen apnea* may be very alarming, especially during anesthesia. But it is a sure indication of the existence of anoxia and the need for oxygen therapy, for it shows that the respiratory center has been profoundly depressed to the direct stimulating action of $CO_2$. Before oxygen administration the center had been driven by impulses from the peripheral chemoreceptors; the relief of the anoxia has abolished this source of stimulation. In chronic anoxia, such as may be seen in congestive heart failure and pulmonary emphysema, especially when there is also carbon dioxide retention, the patient may pass into coma when oxygen is administered. The unfavorable effects following administration of $O_2$ under these conditions are attributable to the further rise in $pCO_2$ which occurs as a result of the depression of breathing.

Another effect of oxygen inhalation is the elimination of nitrogen. A man of average weight (70 kg.) breathing oxygen eliminates about 18 ml. of nitrogen per minute. The rate of removal of the gas from all tissues is not however the same; it is removed most rapidly from the blood and the most vascular parts of the brain. Pure oxygen is, therefore, administered to divers to prevent decompression sickness, and to pilots before high altitude flights.

Helium (atomic weight 4, $\frac{1}{7}$ density that of nitrogen) is lighter than any other gas except hydrogen. Barach has applied this physical fact to reduce the respiratory effort in asthmatic attacks, in those suffering from laryngeal or tracheal obstruction and in certain other types of dyspnea. A gas mixture is used in which helium is substituted for nitrogen (oxygen, 21 per cent; helium, 79 per cent). For the relief of anoxemia the oxygen percentage may be increased to 60 or 70 per cent.

*Effects of prolonged breathing 0.5 to 1 atmosphere of $O_2$.* Ill effects other than the "oxygen apnea" described above may result from prolonged administration of oxygen. Commonly subjects complain of substernal distress in 4 to 16 hours after beginning to breathe 100 per cent $O_2$ at sea level. The symptom usually persists for some hours after the patient resumes breathing of atmospheric air. The pain evidently is related to tracheobronchitis, and it is not a problem unless oxygen tension in inspired air is in excess of 0.5 of an atmosphere. Other manifestations of toxicity produced by breathing 70 to 100 per cent $O_2$ at a pressure of 1 atmosphere include fatigue, paresthesias in the hands and feet, joint pain, anorexia, nausea and vomiting. The causes of these symptoms are unknown (Comroe and Dripps, 1950).

In the ordinary clinical management of patients when oxygen is given in a tent or by nasal catheter oxygen toxicity does not become a factor since the $O_2$ content in inspired air is rarely, if ever, increased to above 50 per cent. Higher levels can be achieved if a close-fitting mask is used in the absence of rebreathing or if the subject is placed in an enclosure into which oxygen is introduced.

*Effects of oxygen pressures greater than one atmosphere.* When oxygen is breathed at pressures around 2 to 4 atmospheres severe symptoms indicating dysfunction of the higher central nervous system are experienced. These include mood swings, indifference, loss of judgment, somnolence, irrational apprehension and finally convulsions of the grand mal type. The latter are followed by automatism and amnesia. Vertigo also is a common symptom of oxygen poisoning. The cause of the symptoms is not clear. Reduction in the $CO_2$ carrying capacity of the blood, with a corresponding rise in $CO_2$ tension and cH in the tissues and venous blood, has been shown to occur in experimental animals; but it is not known if the symptoms in man are related entirely to these changes (Bean, 1945).

Mice die within 20 to 25 minutes when exposed to an oxygen tension of 8 atmospheres, whereas a pressure of 8 atmospheres of air is tolerated well.

*Effects of breathing air at very high pressures (nitrogen narcosis).* The inert gases, including nitrogen, at certain pressures display the typical properties of anesthetic agents. Whereas surgical anesthesia is produced in patients breathing 80 per cent of an atmosphere of nitrous oxide or xenon, about 38 atmospheres of nitrogen has been calculated to be necessary to have this effect. In experimental animals a pressure of 30 atmospheres of nitrogen is required to abolish righting reactions. However, symptoms referrable to impairment of function of the central nervous system occur in an individual exposed to 6 atmospheres of nitrogen (the equivalent of about 200 feet below the surface of water). Helium-oxygen mixtures have less anesthetic action than nitrogen-oxygen mixtures, hence divers breathing helium-oxygen can descend to much greater depths without the development of mental aberrations. The theories of how anesthesia is produced by nitrogen are the same as for the anesthetic actions of other gases. These are discussed in textbooks of pharmacology.

### Resuscitation

Until the last few years Schafer's prone pressure method of artificially inflating the lungs was most widely practiced. But today either the *Holger-Nielson* or the *mouth-to-mouth method* is preferred.

HOLGER-NIELSON OR BACK-PRESSURE-ARM-LIFT METHOD. After loosening the clothing around the neck and chest, drawing the tongue well forward, and wiping fluid, mucus, etc., from the mouth and throat in order to allow free passage of air, the subject is laid in the prone position (chest down). The arms are abducted at the shoulders to lie at right angles to the trunk and bent at the elbows (see fig. 33.9). The head is turned to one side with a cheek resting on the hands. The operator places himself in front of the subject with one knee resting beside his head and near his forearm. The

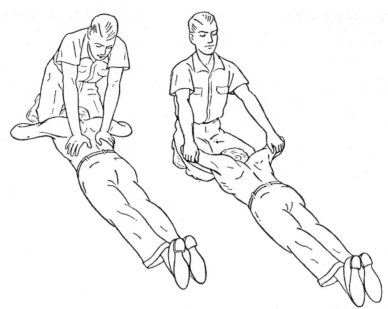

FIG. 33.9. Illustrating the Holger-Nielsen method of resuscitation. (From *First Aid. Metropolitan Life Insurance Company.*)

foot of the operator's other side is planted near the subject's opposite forearm. Then the operator places his hands, with fingers spread apart, upon the subject's back, thumbs touching, and on an imaginary line joining the axillae. He then sways forward, bringing his weight to bear through his arms and hands upon the subject's back. The operator should hold his arms straight at the elbows. This movement compresses the chest and imitates natural expiration. The operator then seizes the subject's arm above the elbows and draws them forward, at the same time as he himself straightens up. This position which expands the chest and simulates natural inspiration is held for two seconds. He then swings forward again and repeats the first phase. The double movement is repeated about 12 times a minute.

MOUTH-TO-MOUTH METHOD. In a symposium published in the May, 1958 issue of the Journal of the American Medical Association it is stated that mouth-to-mouth resuscitation is superior to all manual methods for all age groups. It is reported to be the only technique which produces adequate ventilation in all cases. The single most important factor in this and other methods in assuring adequacy of the ventilation is proper extension of the neck and elevation of the jaw. To perform mouth-to-mouth resuscitation the subject is placed in the supine position with the head extended and the rescuer at the side of the head. The rescuer grasps the lower jaw of the subject between his thumb and index finger and

lifts it vertically upward. The other thumb and index finger are used to clamp off the nostrils. The rescuer then places his mouth over the subject's mouth and exhales into the airway a volume about two times the normal tidal volume (fig. 33.10). Volume and pressure required are easily judged by the rescuer. He inflates the subject's

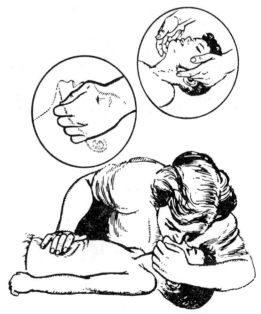

FIG. 33.10. Mouth-to-mouth method of artificial respiration. (Courtesy of Dr. John Henderson and Duell, Sloan, Pierce and Company Publishers, New York.)

lungs and thorax and notes the expansion of the chest. The rescuer then removes his mouth from that of the subject to allow him to exhale. The procedure should be performed about 12 to 20 times per minute.

The effectiveness and ease of performance of this type of resuscitation is improved by the use of an anesthesia face mask, or an oropharyngeal airway or an endotracheal tube.

During recent years several methods have been developed for the long continued application of artificial respiration by various mechanical devices. This work was begun by Thunberg in Lund who devised an apparatus called the barospirator. The subject was placed inside a metal chamber in which the pressure was raised and lowered rhythmically by means of the stroke of a large piston. The interchange of air within the lungs was caused by a rise and fall of pressure of the air in the external atmosphere. This apparatus was effective and a model was built large enough to accommodate patient, nurse and doctor. All three were ventilated without movement of the chest. A certain amount of discomfort was experienced in this cabinet due to the change in pressure on the two sides of the eardrum during the increase and decrease of air pressure. A more generally applicable model was produced by Drinker at Harvard. In this type the patient's head remains outside the cabinet (fig. 33.11). The chest is expanded by reducing the pressure within the cabinet and as the pressure is raised again, the natural elasticity of the lung causes expiration. Forced expiration, however, may be produced by raising the pressure above atmospheric. Patients have been adequately ventilated with this apparatus for many months. Some difficulty is occasionally encountered in the regulation of the rate and depth of respiration, but by determining the oxygen saturation of the arterial blood or watching for signs of cyanosis an observer can usually regulate the ventilation quite satisfactorily.

Two other types of apparatus should be mentioned; (1) the jacket model of Sahlin which operates like the Drinker machine but is applied only to the chest, and (2) the Bragg-Paul pulsator which consists of a hollow elastic bandage placed around the chest. The bandage, when inflated by an electrically driven bellows, compresses the chest, which returns to the midposition by virtue of its own elasticity during the intervals between the compressions.

The pulmotor and other similarly devised resuscitators, which force air into the chest and suck it out again as though the lungs were rubber bags, though so appealing in their mechanical efficiency, are physiologically unsound. They are not only less effective than other methods but may be actually harmful. The pulmonary tissue may be torn. Those machines which inflate the lungs with an oxygen-carbon dioxide mixture, and permit expiration to take place simply by interrupting the air current and thus permitting collapse of the thorax, are much sounder in principle.

A mixture of oxygen and carbon dioxide (5 per cent or 10 per cent of the latter) commonly is used for resuscitation. The high tension of $CO_2$ combined with the rhythmical inflation and deflation of the lungs, which presumably cause the discharge of afferent impulses, encourages the return of spontaneous breathing.

*Resuscitation of the newborn.* Asphyxia in the newborn infant is usually due to the failure of the lungs to expand fully, alveoli in areas of the pulmonary tissue remaining in the fetal state (atelectasis). The methods of resuscitation which may be effective in the adult are likely to fail. Cutaneous stimulation, e.g., slapping, hot or cold

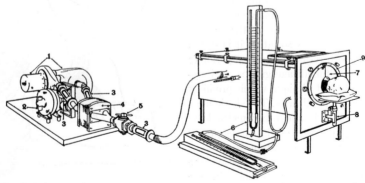

Fig. 33.11. The Drinker respirator. *1*, pumps; *2*, motor; *3*, vents; *4*, alternate; *5*, valves; *6*, manometers; *7*, external shutters; *8*, adjustment for head rest; *9*, adjustable ring to hold collar in place. (After Shaw and Drinker).

water, are time honored devices which are usually unsuccessful. The object aimed at should be the expansion of the collapsed alveoli, and when the infant makes no respiratory effort this is best accomplished by the insufflation of the lungs with a carbon dioxide-oxygen mixture, carried out by the passage down the trachea of a tube, to the outer end of which a rubber bag filled with the gas mixture is attached. When the breathing is not completely suspended but is weak, and the infant cyanosed, inhalations of a carbon dioxide-oxygen mixture are employed. Also mouth-to-mouth resuscitation is quite effective in infants.

## REFERENCES

BARACH, A. L. Ann. Int. Med., 1931, **5**, 428.

BARACH, A. L., AND RICHARDS, D. W. Arch. Int. Med., 1931, **48**, 325.

BARCROFT, J., BINGER, C. A., BOCK, A. V., DOGGART, J. H., FORBES, H. S., HARROP, G., MEAKINS, J. C., AND REDFIELD, A. C. Phil. Trans. Roy. Soc., 1923, **B211**, 351.

BINGER, C. A. L., AND MOORE, R. L. J. Exper. Med., 1927, **45**, 633.

BLALOCK, A., AND TAUSSIG, H. B. J. A. M. A., 1945, **128**, 129.

BOYCOTT, A. E., DAMANT, G. C. C., AND HALDANE, J. S. J. Hyg., 1908, **8**, 342.

CHEN, K. K., ROSE, C. L., AND CLOWES, G. H. A. Am. J. M. Sc., 1934, **188**, 767.

CHRISTIE, R. V. J. Clin. Invest., 1934, **13**, 295.

DALY, I. DEB. Tr. Med.-Chir. Soc., Edinburgh, 1936, 139.

DUNN, J. S. Quart. J. Med., 1920, **13**, 129.

GROOM, D., WOOD, E. H., BURCHELL, H. B., AND PARKER, R. L. Proc. Staff Meet. Mayo Clin, 1948, **23**, 601.

GROSS, L. J. A. M. A., 1919, **9**, 632.

HARROP, G. A. J. A. M. A., 1923, **80**, 1641.

HENDERSON, Y. J. A. M. A., 1924, **83**, 758. Ibid., 1928, **90**, 583. Ibid., 1929, **93**, 96. Brit. Med. J., 1931, **2**, 687. New England J. Med., 1932, **206**, 151.

HENDERSON, Y., AND HENDERSON, M. C. Arch. Int. Med., 1932, **49**, 88.

HENDERSON, Y., HAGGARD, H. W., CORYLLOS, P. N., AND BIRNBAUM, G. L. Arch. Int. Med., 1930, **45**, 72.

HUG, E. Compt. rend. Soc. biol., 1933, **112**, 511.

LUFT, U. L. Physiological aspects of pressure cabins and rapid decompression. *In* Handbook of Respiratory Physiology, p. 129. United States Air Force School of Aviation Medicine, Randolph Field, Texas, 1954.

MEAKINS, J., AND DAVIES, H. W. J. Path. & Bact., 1920, **23**, 451.

PUGH, L., J. Physiol., 1957, **135**, 590.

RILEY, R. L., OTIS, A. B., AND HOUSTON, C. S. Respiratory features of acclimatization to altitude. *In* Handbook of Respiratory Physiology, p. 143. United States Air Force School of Aviation Medicine, Randolph Field, Texas, 1954.

SAHLIN, B. Skandinav. Arch. Physiol., 1926, **47**, 284.

SCOTT, R. W. Arch. Int. Med., 1920, **26**, 545.

SMITH, R. G., AND MALCOLM, R. L. J. Pharmacol. & Exper. Therap., 1930, **40**, 457.

STADIE, W. C. J. Exper. Med., 1922, **35**, 377.

WARNER, W. P., AND GRAHAM, D. Arch. Int. Med., 1933, **52**, 888.

WENDEL, W. B. J. A. M. A., 1933, **100**, 1054.

WHITEHORN, W. V., LEIN, A., AND EDELMANN, A. Am. J. Physiol., 1946, **147**, 289.

WHITEHORN, W. V., LEIN, A., EDELMANN, A., AND HITCHCOCK, F. A. Am. J. Physiol., 1947, **148**, 253.

WHITEHORN, W. V., LEIN, A., AND HITCHCOCK, F. A. J. Aviation Med., 1947, **18**, 102.

*Monographs and Reviews*

ABBOT, M. E. S. Atlas of Congenital Cardiac Disease. American Heart Association, New York, 1936.

BALDWIN, E. DEF., COURNAND, A., AND RICHARDS, D. W., JR. Medicine, 1948, **27**, 243.

BARCLAY, A. E., FRANKLIN, K. J., AND PRICHARD, M. M. L. The Foetal Circulation and Cardiovascular System. Blackwell Scientific Publications, Oxford, 1946.

BARCROFT, J. The Respiratory Functions of the Blood. Cambridge University Press, London, 1925.

BLALOCK, A. Harvey Lectures, 1945–1946, **41**, 90.

BURCHELL, H. B., PARKER, R. L., DRY, T. J., WOOD, E. H., PENDER, J. W., AND PUGH, D. G. Proc. Staff Meet. Mayo Clinic, 1948, **23**, 482.

CATCHPOLE, H. R., AND GERSH, I. Physiol. Rev., 1947, **27**, 360.

COMROE, J. H., AND DRIPPS, R. D. The Physiological Basis of Oxygen Therapy, Am. Lecture Series. Charles C Thomas, Springfield, Ill., 1950.

COURNAND, A., BALDWIN, J. S., AND HIMMELSTEIN, A. Cardiac Catheterization in Congenital Heart Disease. Commonwealth Fund, New York, 1949.

FRANKLIN, K. J., AND ASSOCIATES. The Circulation in the Foetus. Blackwell Scientific Publications, Oxford, 1946.

FULTON, J. F. (Ed.) Decompression Sickness. W. B. Saunders Company, Philadelphia, 1951.

HALDANE, J. S., AND PRIESTLEY, J. G. Respiration. Clarendon Press, Oxford, 1935.

HARVEY, N. E. Harvey Lecture, 1943–44, **40**, 41.

HILL, L. Caisson Sickness. Edward Arnold & Company, London, 1912.

IVY, A. C. High altitude problems in aviation. Fed. Proc., 1946, **5**, 319.

KOUNTZ, W. B., AND ALEXANDER, H. L. Emphysema. Medicine, 1934, **13**, 251.

LUNGSGAARD, C., AND VAN SLYKE, D. D. Cyanosis. Medicine, 1923, **2**, 1.

MEAKINS, J. C., AND DAVIES, H. W. Respiratory Function in Disease. Oliver, Edinburgh, 1925.

SCHNEIDER, E. C. Physiol. Rev., 1921, **1**, 631.

STONE, LL. J. Advances Int. Med., 1955, **VII**, 243.

VAN LIERE, E. J. Anoxia; Its Effect on the Body. University of Chicago Press, 1942.

WHITTENBERGER, J. L. Physiol. Rev., 1955, **35**, 611.

# *34*

# URINE FORMATION

## The Structure of the Kidney; Theories of Renal Function

### THE STRUCTURE OF THE HUMAN KIDNEY

The functional unit of the kidney is the *nephron*, each kidney being composed of approximately one million such units. The nephron begins at a blind end enclosing a leash of capillaries. In this structure, known as the *glomerulus* (*renal corpuscle, Malpighian corpuscle*), urine formation begins by the separation, from the blood perfusing the glomerular capillaries, of an essentially protein-free filtrate of plasma. The glomerular space or *Bowman's capsule* is continuous with the lumen of the *renal tubule*, a long coiled structure structurally and functionally divisible into three segments: proximal convoluted tubule, loop of Henle and distal convoluted tubule. The nephron as an individual unit ends with the distal convoluted tubule but groups of distal convoluted tubules empty into a series of *collecting tubules*, which in turn coalesce to form *collecting ducts*. The collecting ducts in turn empty into the short *papillary ducts of Bellini* which open into the renal calyces at the tips of the papillae.

THE GLOMERULUS consists of a leash of capillaries interconnected by short anastamotic channels. These capillaries are invaginated into and covered on their outer surfaces by the visceral layer of the epithelium of Bowman's capsule. This layer of flattened cells is continuous with the parietal layer of epithelium and with the lining cells of the renal tubules. Blood enters the glomerulus from the short afferent arteriole, and the coalescence of the glomerular capillaries forms the efferent arteriole; the glomerular capillaries are thus unique in being interposed between two arterioles.

The glomerulus averages about 200 $\mu$ in diameter and the total surface of glomerular capillaries in the two human kidneys is estimated to be about 1.5 square meters. The glomeruli are found only in the cortex.

THE PROXIMAL CONVOLUTED TUBULE is a tortuous structure averaging about 55$\mu$ in diameter and 14 mm. in length. It lies in the renal cortex usually in close proximity to the glomerulus to which it is conjoined. It is lined with a single layer of cuboidal cells, each interdigitated with the adjoining cells in a highly complex manner. The border facing the tubule lumen is characterized and distinguished from that of other segments by delicate striations perpendicular to the free edge and known as the brush border. The terminal portion of the proximal tubule becomes straight and dips toward the medulla to become the loop of Henle.

THE LOOP OF HENLE commences with a descending limb which dips down into the medulla. As it does so, the cuboidal cells are suddenly replaced by the flattened cells of the *thin segment*. The loop penetrates into the medulla for a varying distance, the depth depending upon the location of the glomerulus from which the tubule is derived. Those loops derived from tubules with glomeruli situated near the surface of the kidney penetrate only a short distance into the medulla before turning back toward the cortex; those arising from tubules with glomeruli close to the cortico-medullary junction (*juxtamedullary glomeruli*) penetrate deeply to near the tip of the papilla before turning back (see fig. 34.1). The first part of the ascending limb does not differ in appearance from the thin portion of the descending limb, but as the ascending limb reaches the

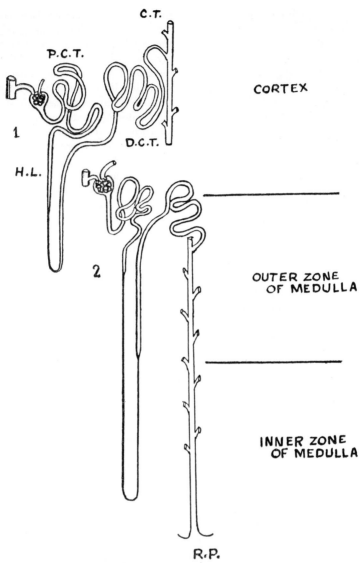

C.T.

P.C.T.

CORTEX

1

D.C.T.

H.L.

2

OUTER ZONE
OF MEDULLA

INNER ZONE
OF MEDULLA

R.P.

FIG. 34.1. Diagram of a cortical (1) and of a juxtamedullary (2) nephron. P.C.T., proximal convoluted tubule; D.C.T., distal convoluted tubule; C.T., collecting tubule; H.L., Henle's loop; R.P., renal pelvis.

outer medullary zone it widens and becomes lined with a cuboidal epithelium which continues into the distal tubule. The tubule continues into the cortex and comes into contact with the glomerulus from which it arose, this contact being marked by a region of closely packed nuclei designated as the *macula densa*.

THE DISTAL CONVOLUTED TUBULE may be defined as beginning at the macula densa. Like the proximal tubule with which its loops are generally entwined, the distal convoluted tubule lies in the cortex. It is distinguished by the fact that its lining epithelium is somewhat lower, less complex and lacks the brush border. The distal convoluted tubules empty into collecting tubules. The collecting tubules empty into collecting ducts which pass through the medulla and papilla to empty into the pelvis.

BLOOD SUPPLY. The renal artery upon entering the hilum of the kidney breaks up into numerous branches, the *interlobular arteries*, which pass outward between the renal pyramids to the junction of the cortex with the medulla. Here they turn to follow a more horizontal course and form arterial arches (the *arcuate arteries*) across the bases of the pyramids. From the arcuate arteries arise

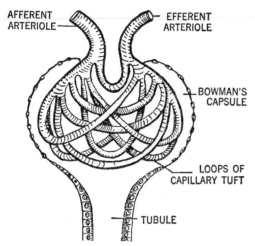

AFFERENT ARTERIOLE

EFFERENT ARTERIOLE

BOWMAN'S CAPSULE

LOOPS OF CAPILLARY TUFT

TUBULE

Fig. 34.2. Diagramatic representation of the glomerulus.

the *interlobular arteries* which run outward through the cortex. From the interlobular arteries the afferent arterioles carry blood to the glomeruli.

The short muscular *afferent arteriole* enters the glomerulus and breaks up into the leash of glomerular capillaries. The latter again coalesce to empty into the *efferent arteriole* which is usually appreciably smaller in diameter than the afferent arteriole (fig. 34.2).

The efferent arterioles derived from most glomeruli break up into a network of capillaries surrounding the convoluted tubules as they lie in the cortex. This capillar network is drained by veins which follow a course close to the arteries and empty into the renal vein (fig. 34.3).

The efferent arterioles derived from the *juxtamedullary glomeruli* close to the cortico-medullary junction do not feed into the peritubular capillary plexus. Instead each divides into a group of straight vessels, the *vasa recta* which descend into the medulla, following a course similar to the loops of Henle, and then turn to return to the cortex and enter the venous system. As they pass through the cortico-medullary junction, the vasa recta tend to become gathered into groups, the *vascular bundles*, and in these groups the descending and ascending limbs of the vasa recta lie closely intermingled in an arrangement ideally suited for diffusional exchanges between inflowing and outflowing blood.

### SUMMARY OF DEVELOPMENT OF CURRENT CONCEPTS

The development of our present understanding of the function of the kidney can be considered

to date from 1842 when Bowman described the structure of the glomerulus, particularly showing the continuity of the space of the Malpighian corpuscle with the lumen of the tubule. Bowman recognized the structural characteristics which suggested its function as a filter. He supposed that the filtration process provided only the urinary water and that the solutes of the urine were added by the secretory activity of the cells of the renal tubules. The process of glomerular filtration thus served merely to wash through the solutes.

Ludwig in 1844 proposed that glomerular filtration provided all of the water and solutes of the urine and that the function of the tubules was to concentrate the solutes by the reabsorption of water. It was recognized that this concentration would lead to some loss of solute by diffusion. Heidenhain (1874) from observations on the accumulation of dyes in the renal tubule cells returned to a theory close to that of Bowman, placing the burden of urinary excretion on secretion of solutes by the tubule cells.

In 1917, Cushny, in an attempt to simplify what had by then become a complex and confused subject, proposed what he termed the "modern theory of renal function." Totally rejecting any secretion by the renal tubules, Cushny hypothesized that urine formation began with the formation of a protein-free ultrafiltrate of plasma in the glomeruli. From this flow of fluid the tubules were assumed to reabsorb a solution of constant and unvarying composition. This solution was presumed to have the composition of an ultrafiltrate of normal plasma and Cushny proposed that the

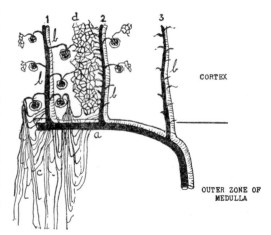

CORTEX

OUTER ZONE OF MEDULLA

Fig. 34.3. Diagram of the renal circulation; *a*, arcuate vessels; *b*, interlobular vessels (1, 2 and 3), arteries *black*, veins *shaded*; *c*, vasa recta; *d*, peritubular plexus of vessels. In 2 and 3 peritubular plexus and all but two glomeruli are omitted.

"fluid reabsorbed is always the same, whatever the needs of the organism at the moment."

The development of knowledge concerning the function of the kidney has shown that each of the above theories contains some parts which are correct and others which are not. The existence of secretion by the tubules was definitively shown by Marshall and his associates.

In the development of renal physiology which has taken place in the last 25 years, leading to the physiological picture presented in the following pages, two experimental techniques have played a central role. The micropuncture techniques developed by A. N. Richards and his many important associates provided means for collecting fluid from accurately located regions of the nephron and for the analysis of this fluid by microchemical methods. This has provided invaluable information on the nature and localization of events in the renal tubule. The clearance methods, with measurement of the rate of glomerular filtration, in connection with which the names of Rehberg, Homer Smith and Shannon stand out, has provided a tool for the evaluation of many processes in the intact unanesthetized animal or in man, under conditions approaching normal.

## General Nature of Urine Formation

Although the two human kidneys are made up of some two million nephron units, it is convenient for most purposes to consider the two kidneys as constituting a single huge nephron. Such a model is accurate to the extent that each nephron is similar in its functional proportions to every other and to the extent that each nephron functions in parallel with and independent of every other. These assumptions may be accepted as first approximations. The consequences of heterogeneity of nephron function and of interdependence of nephrons will be considered in subsequent sections. For present purposes we may speak of the glomerulus and the proximal convoluted tubule, etc., as if the kidneys represented a single unit, and referring to the sum of the functions of the several million units.

The processes of renal function are initiated in the glomerulus by the separation from the plasma of an essentially protein-free ultrafiltrate. The ultrafiltrate delivered from the glomerular capillaries into the space of Bowman's capsule enters the lumen of the proximal tubule. As the result of the net filtration pressure, the separated fluid flows through the tubule. As it passes through the various tubule segments, the fluid is drastically modified both in volume and composition by a series of operations performed upon it by the lining epithelium of the tubules. Many of the constituents of the fluid originally filtered into the glomerular space are removed from the fluid as it traverses the renal tubules and are returned to the blood to be retained within the body. Some components of the glomerular filtrate such as glucose and the amino acids are virtually completely reabsorbed, appearing in the final urine only under unusual circumstances. Other constituents such as urea, are reabsorbed to only a limited extent while still others are excreted and reabsorbed to an extent which is regulated so as to maintain the normal composition of body fluids. Among the substances reabsorbed to a major but variable extent is water itself, so that the volume flow of urine is always but a fraction of the flow of glomerular filtrate. In addition to reabsorbing many substances from the fluid flowing through the tubule the tubule epithelium also removes certain substances from the peritubular blood and deposits them in the fluid within the lumen. Thus three individual processes, glomerular filtration, tubular reabsorption (from lumen to blood) and tubular secretion (from blood to lumen) are involved in the process of urine formation. These three processes will be considered in detail in subsequent sections.

### GLOMERULAR FILTRATION

The idea that the glomerulus is a device for filtering fluid from the blood perfusing the glomerular capillaries goes back to Bowman who in 1842 first described the relationship of the glomerular capsule to the renal tubules. Bowman believed that only the water of the urine was contributed by this filtration process, the solutes being added by secretion in the tubule. Shortly thereafter Ludwig (1844) offered the view, which has since been amply confirmed, that the glomerulus acts as an ultrafilter, separating from the plasma a solution which contains all of the solutes of plasma except the proteins and each at a concentration identical to that in the plasma water except as modified by the absence of protein. The cornerstones of the evidence indicating that the glomerulus is indeed an ultrafilter were supplied by A. N. Richards and his associates who showed that the composition of fluid collected from glomeruli in amphibians was, with respect to an extensive list of constituents, that required of a plasma ultrafiltrate. (The studies were later extended, with respect to a limited number of substances, to fluid collected directly from mammalian glomeruli by Walker, Bott, Oliver and

MacDowell.) In addition it was shown that the hydrostatic pressure in the glomerular capillaries is sufficient to supply the driving force for the filtration process.

As in the case of other capillary beds, and in accord with the Starling hypothesis, the rate of filtration through the walls of the glomerular capillaries is determined by a balance of forces favoring and opposing filtration. The main driving force is the hydrostatic pressure—the intracapillary blood pressure ($P_b$). Opposing filtration is the osmotic pressure exerted by the plasma proteins ($\pi_b$) and the hydrostatic pressure of the fluid in Bowman's capsule ($P_c$). The rate of glomerular filtration (GFR) may thus be expressed as

$$GFR = K_p([P_b - P_c] - \pi_b) \qquad (1)$$

where $K_p$ is a constant relating net filtration pressure to filtration rate and thus related to the area and the permeability of the glomerular capillary walls.

The glomerular capillaries differ from those of other capillary beds in being interposed between two arterioles, in maintaining a higher hydrostatic pressure, and in having a higher permeability. Pappenheimer and his associates have estimated that the permeability of glomerular capillaries is approximately one hundred times that of the capillaries in the limbs (muscles); the difference is presumably largely in the fraction of the total capillary surface occupied by the pores through which filtration actually occurs. The membrane which constitutes the significant filtration resistance and which is penetrated by the pores of critical size is probably the capillary basement membrane.

Some idea of the size of the pores can be obtained from the characteristics of those solutes which are filtered through the glomerular capillary membrane as compared with those which are not. The normal glomerular membrane is virtually completely impermeable to the proteins of plasma. The smallest of these, albumin, has a molecular weight of about 70,000 and appears in the glomerular filtrate either not at all or at a concentration too low (less than 1 per cent of its concentration in plasma) to have been measured in the samples of mammalian glomerular filtrate which were examined. Hemoglobin (molecular weight 68,000) on the other hand is excreted at a rate which would indicate that it appears in glomerular filtrate at a concentration equal to about 5 per cent of its concentration in the plasma. (The concentration referred to is that not combined, in the plasma, with larger protein molecules.) The

hemoglobin molecule is somewhat less elongated than the albumin molecule, but the difference is relatively small. In any case, it is clear that the pores in the glomerular membranes can not be far removed in size from the dimensions of these molecules.

Also pertinent is the passage through the glomerular membrane of certain polysaccharides. Most important among these is inulin, a polymer of fructose, which has found a central role in the study of renal function. Its molecular weight is usually estimated to be 5200, but different inulin molecules probably differ in size, some being smaller, others larger. In addition, the molecule is greatly elongated, a characteristic which reduces its diffusibility and filtrability compared to a compact molecule of the same molecular weight. Nevertheless, the glomerular membrane appears to offer no hindrance to the passage of inulin, and its concentration in glomerular filtrate is the same as in the plasma from which the filtrate is derived. Dextrans (polysaccharides composed of glucose) of a molecular weight approximately equal to that of inulin have been found to pass the glomerular membrane freely, but their passage is progressively restricted as their molecular weight increases and those with molecular weights above 55,000 do not appear in the urine from normal kidneys (i.e., kidneys producing protein-free urine).

Although different theoretical treatments will yield different dimensions for the size of the pores in the glomerular membrane, the permeability can be interpreted as attributable to pores approximately 100 Å in diameter.

Equation (1) indicates that glomerular filtration is a function of three variables as well as the area and permeability of the glomerular membrane. It is important to consider the possible contribution of changes in each of these to the physiological regulation of glomerular filtration.

1. THE GLOMERULAR MEMBRANE. (a) *Permeability*. The permeability of the glomerular membrane per unit of functioning surface is presumably fixed by its anatomical nature and not subject to physiological variation. Although changes do occur with disease, the effect of change in permeability as opposed to change in effective filtering area is difficult to evaluate. The diseased membrane may permit the passage of molecules larger than those which normally penetrate, but the predominant effect appears to be a decreased permeability.

(b) *Area*. The effective area available for filtration depends upon the number of glomeruli active at any time and the number of functioning capillaries in each glomerulus. The weight of evidence favors the view that, in the mammalian kidney under physiological conditions, all glomeruli are continuously active. This interpretation is not universally accepted and there are those who believe that variation in the number of glomeruli contributing to urine formation is a major factor in determining the rate of glomerular filtration. Subsequent treatment of the subject in this section will be based on the assumption that all the glomeruli are continuously involved in the formation of glomerular filtrate.

2. CAPILLARY BLOOD PRESSURE ($P_b$). The major variable in the regulation of the rate of glomerular filtration is the pressure within the glomerular capillaries. The pressure at which blood enters the afferent arterioles is not much lower than that in the aorta; the decrease in pressure between aorta and glomerular capillaries is largely determined by the resistance of the afferent arterioles. Thus, other factors remaining equal, constriction of the afferent arterioles will decrease and dilatation will increase glomerular filtration. The effect of changes in the caliber of the efferent vessels is in general the converse of parallel changes in the afferent vessels.

It is to be noted that it is the *pressure, not the blood or plasma flow*, in the glomerular capillaries which determines glomerular filtration rate. Thus the rate of glomerular filtration need not bear any particular relationship to the cardiac output. A low level of cardiac output is, at least in theory, quite compatible with a normal rate of filtration provided this output is sufficient to maintain a normal blood pressure and provided that renal vasoconstriction is not a part of the general vasoconstriction necessary to maintain the normal arterial pressure.

Although the renal nerves play a role in the regulation of the renal arteriolar resistances and thus in the maintenance of a stable rate of glomerular filtration (and, particularly in man, this function is maintained at a remarkably constant level under normal conditions), the nerves are not essential to this stability. The kidney even when totally isolated, shows only slight changes in glomerular filtration rate (and blood flow) as perfusion pressure is varied over a wide range. This process, frequently designated by the term *autoregulation*, has attracted considerable interest among physiologists. It is probably attributable to spontaneous adjustments of the arteriolar resistances.

3. INTRACAPSULAR HYDROSTATIC PRESSURE ($P_c$). Under ordinary conditions variations in the pressure within Bowman's capsule probably contribute little to changing glomerular filtration rate. With ureteral obstruction this pressure may rise until the rate of filtration is reduced to negligible levels, but such obstruction does not, of course, occur under normal circumstances. It is also likely that in the extremes of solute diuresis produced experimentally the pressure required to drive the greatly increased flow of urine against the resistance offered by the tubules may be sufficient to reduce filtration.

4. COLLOID OSMOTIC PRESSURE OF THE PLASMA PROTEINS ($\pi_c$). The osmotic effect of the plasma proteins is the equivalent of a hydrostatic pressure of some 25 to 30 mm. Hg opposed to glomerular filtration. Glomerular filtration must, therefore, cease when the net hydrostatic pressure across the capillary membrane falls to this level. Although this osmotic effect is large enough for changes to exert appreciable effects on net filtration pressure, it is doubtful whether such changes contribute significantly to the physiological regulation of glomerular filtration. Experimentally, it can be shown that sudden dilution of the plasma proteins by the administration of isotonic sodium chloride solution produces an increase in glomerular filtration and urine flow (dilution diuresis), but the changes are small compared to those which can be produced experimentally in other ways.

*The Measurement of Glomerular Filtration Rate*

The difference between the rate at which a substance is filtered at the glomeruli and the rate at which it is excreted in the urine represents the rate at which the substance is removed from or added to the urine as the latter traverses the renal tubules. The rate at which a substance is filtered is given by the product of its concentration in the plasma (or more accurately, the concentration of unbound substance in the plasma water) and the rate of formation of glomerular filtrate. The rate of excretion is easily determined as the product of urine flow and the concentration in the urine of the substance in question. Thus the measurement of glomerular filtration rate plays a central role not only in the evaluation of glomerular filtration itself, but in the assessment of the processes of reabsorption and secretion as well.

The rate of glomerular filtration can be determined if there is some substance which is neither reabsorbed nor secreted by the tubules and if the concentration of this substance in the glomerular filtrate can be deduced from its concentration in the plasma. If a substance is neither reabsorbed nor secreted as the urine flows through the tubules, then, in the steady state, the rate of excretion of the substance must be the same as the rate at which it is filtered. Given the rate at which the substance is filtered and its concentration in the filtrate, the volume of the filtrate can be calculated.

For example, consider some substance X which we will assume has the requisite characteristics of (1) being freely filterable at the glomeruli, (2) being neither reabsorbed from nor excreted into the tubule lumen. Suppose we measure the flow of urine over a 10-minute period during which 20 ml. of urine are collected to yield a flow (V) of 2 ml. per minute.

The concentration ($U_x$) of substance X in the urine is determined and found to be 120 mg. per ml.

The rate of excretion, then, is given by the product of flow and concentration

$$U_x V = 120 \text{ mg./ml.} \times 2 \text{ ml./min.}$$

$$= 240 \text{ mg./min.}$$

Since for substances which are neither reabsorbed nor secreted the rate of excretion is equal to the rate of filtration, the rate of filtration of substance X is also 240 mg. per minute. But the rate of filtration of a substance is equal to the product of the rate of formation of filtrate (GFR) times the concentration of the substance in the filtrate which, in this case, is defined above as being the same as the concentration in the plasma ($P_x$). Assume the concentration in the plasma in this case is determined and found to be 2 mg./ml.

Thus the rate of filtration of X is the product GFR. $P_x = U_x V$ and

$$GFR = \frac{U_x V}{P_x} = \frac{240 \text{ mg./min.}}{2 \text{ mg./ml.}} = 120 \text{ ml./min.}$$

The desirability, for the evaluation of renal function, of a substance which fulfills the criteria for measuring glomerular filtration is apparent. It is now generally accepted that *inulin*, a starchlike polymer of fructose obtained from dahlia tubers, has the requisite characteristics and can be used for the measurement of glomerular filtration in all vertebrates including man.

THE USE OF THE TERM CLEARANCE. The expression $U_x V/P_x$ denotes a quantity which is generally referred to as the *clearance* of substance X and abbreviated $C_x$. As can be seen, it is the volume of plasma needed each minute to supply the substance in question at the rate at which it is excreted in the urine. It is thus a measure of the efficiency of the kidney in the excretion of a par-

ticular substance; the larger the value of its clearance, the more effectively it is excreted. The term is derived from the fact that one may consider the clearance to be that volume of plasma which completely yields its content for excretion and is thus cleared of the particular substance each minute. Some confusion arises when the latter concept of clearance is used since the volume cleared of a particular substance is usually virtual rather than real. The same clearance is obtained if 50 ml. of plasma yield all of their content, if 100 ml. lose half or 200 ml. yield one-fourth.

The clearance of a substance such as inulin is the volume flow of glomerular filtrate. By comparison of the clearance of any other substance with that of inulin we may infer the nature of the processes involved in its excretion. If it is filtered but neither reabsorbed nor excreted by the tubules, its clearance must be identical with that of inulin. If its clearance is lower, it must be reabsorbed from the tubules; if higher, it must be secreted by them.

Thus if $P_x$ is the concentration of X filterable in the plasma, $T_x$ the amount of X which is secreted into or reabsorbed from the tubule each minute and $C_{In}$ the inulin clearance taken as equal to the rate of formation of glomerular filtrate, then,

$$C_{In} P_x = \text{filtered X}$$

$$C_{In} P_x + T_x = \text{excreted X} = U_x V$$

(where $T_x$ will have a negative value if X is reabsorbed from the tubules).

Then

$$C_{In} + \frac{T_x}{P_x} = \frac{U_x V}{P_x} = C_x \qquad (2)$$

It can be seen from equation (2) that if for any reason the capacity of the tubule ($T_x$) to reabsorb or secrete a particular substance is limited, the clearance of that substance will approach the rate of glomerular filtration as the plasma concentration is progressively increased, since as $P_x$ approaches infinity, the term $T_x/P_x$ approaches zero. It will be shown that this is the case with most substances transported by the renal tubules.

THE RATE OF GLOMERULAR FILTRATION IN MAN. The clearance of inulin in a man of average size under normal basal conditions (except for the water usually administered during the determination of such clearances) averages slightly in excess of 125 ml. per minute. It is customary, in order to compare individuals of varying size, to normalize the clearance values by "correcting" them to what is generally considered an average normal value of body surface area, 1.73 square meters. Women have glomerular filtration rates some 10 per cent lower than those found in men even after "correction" to the same value of surface area.

The large value for the rate of formation of glomerular filtrate emphasizes the similarly great magnitude of many of the processes of reabsorption carried on by the renal tubules. Thus if we assume that the rate of 125 ml. per minute is maintained throughout the day we may calculate that some 7.5 liters are filtered each hour or 180 liters per day in an individual of normal size. Since ordinarily such an individual will excrete only a liter or two of urine, it is clear that an amount approaching 180 liters is also reabsorbed. The total body water of a 70 kilogram man is of the order of 45 liters, so that on the average all of the body water is filtered into the renal tubules and reabsorbed four times each day. On the same basis we may calculate that the extracellular fluid (approximately 12 liters) is filtered and reabsorbed some 15 times per day, the plasma volume (roughly 3 liters) some 60 times.

We may further multiply this volume by its content of the various filtrable solutes of plasma to estimate the amounts of these filtered and by comparison with the amounts excreted in the urine, calculate the amounts of each reabsorbed. Illustrative data are indicated in table 34.1. It is apparent from this table that very large quantities are turned over by the kidney each day and that only a small percentage departure from normal in the process of reabsorption could result in very large changes in excretion.

OTHER MEASURES OF GLOMERULAR FILTRATION. In man, except for inulin, no substance has been found which can be considered to give an accurate and reliable value for the rate of glomerular filtration. Approximations can be made using one of several substances, and such approximations are useful for comparative purposes but not for the evaluation of tubular reabsorptive and secretory processes. Most commonly the creatinine clearance is used and gives a value, under most conditions, not too different from the clearance of inulin.

This is probably the result of compensating errors, since creatinine is excreted into the lumen by the tubules of the human kidney. It is possible that it is also reabsorbed and in addition the methods usually used for determining the concentration of creatinine in plasma are not specific and include small amounts of other substances which apparently are reabsorbed. Under some

TABLE 34.1

*Filtration, reabsorption and excretion of certain normal constituents of plasma*

| | Filtered per 24 Hours | | Excreted* per 24 Hours | | Reabsorbed per 24 Hours | |
|---|---|---|---|---|---|---|
| | *grams* | *m.eq. or mmole†* | *grams* | *m.eq. or mmole* | *grams* | *m.eq. or mmole* |
| Sodium | 540 | 24,500 | 3.3 | 150 | 537 | 24,350 |
| Chloride | 630 | 17,850 | 5.3 | 150 | 625 | 17,700 |
| Bicarbonate | 300 | 4,900 | 0.3 | 1 | 300 | 4,900 |
| Potassium | 28 | 700 | 3.9 | 100 | 24 | 600 |
| Glucose | 140 | 780 | 0 | 0 | 140 | 780 |
| Urea | 53 | 870 | 25 | 410 | 28 | 460 |
| Creatinine | 1.4 | 12 | 1.4 | 12 | 0 | 0 |
| Uric Acid | 8.5 | 50 | 0.8 | 5 | 7.7 | 45 |

\* These are typical normal values. Wide variation is found depending on diet.

† Milliequivalents or millimoles.

conditions, particularly in the presence of renal disease, the departure of the creatinine clearance from the rate of glomerular filtration may be considerable.

Other substances which have been used to approximate the rate of glomerular filtration in man are certain hexitols (mannitol, sorbitol, dulcitol), particularly mannitol, and allantoin. The mannitol clearance is about 10 per cent lower than the clearance of inulin, indicating that about 10 per cent of the filtered mannitol is, on the average, reabsorbed.

In many lower mammals, as well as in amphibians, the creatinine clearance does not have the limitations which reduce its usefulness in man. The clearance of creatinine is, for practical purposes, identical with that of inulin in the dog, cat and rabbit.

TUBULAR REABSORPTION

The quantitative importance of the process of reabsorption in the renal tubules has been indicated above by the magnitude of the amounts of material involved. An understanding of the nature of the mechanisms by which this reabsorption is effected is essential to a grasp of the function of the kidney.

The processes involved in tubular reabsorption are divided into two categories, passive and active.

1. *Passive reabsorption.* It is clear that the volume of the urine is greatly reduced as it flows through the tubules. If, in the course of this re-

duction in volume, some solute is retained in the lumen to a greater extent than water, its concentration will rise above that in the glomerular filtrate and above the concentration in the plasma and interstitial fluid which surround the tubules. A concentration gradient for the substance is thus created between the lumen and the environment of the tubule and, provided the tubule is permeable to some extent to the substance in question, it will diffuse from the lumen of the tubule to interstitial fluid and blood. This type of process is designated by the term *passive reabsorption* and is typified by the reabsorption of urea, the excretion of which will be considered in more detail later.

More generally, the movement of any substance across a biological membrane (in this case the complex membrane is the renal tubule epithelium) is considered *passive* when it can be explained entirely by gradients of concentration and/or (in the case of charged particles) gradients of electrical potential. In such a context, the movement of urea is a passive process requiring no mechanism in the tubule cells specific for urea and no expenditure of energy by the tubule cells for the movement of urea itself. However, it should be noted that work must be done to raise the urea concentration so that it may diffuse out passively. It will be shown that in this instance the primary active process is the removal of salt from the lumen by the activity of the tubule cells; the movement of water is the passive consequence of the transport of salt and the movement of urea is in turn secondary to the movement of water.

2. *Active reabsorption.* The reabsorption of many substances from the renal tubules can not be explained by gradients of concentration or electrical potential. The process involved in the movement of these solutes is designated as *active reabsorption*. The best known and possibly simplest example of an active reabsorptive process is probably that for glucose. A consideration of glucose reabsorption will illustrate the characteristics of these mechanisms.

### Active Reabsorption: The Reabsorption of Glucose

Under normal conditions approximately 100 mg. of glucose are filtered at the glomerulus each minute. Of this, none but the merest trace is excreted in the urine. Clearly, the transport of glucose is effected against a *concentration gradient* and, since glucose carries no electrical charge, its transport is, by definition, *active*.

If the concentration of glucose in the plasma is progressively increased, it is found that, for a time, the urine remains free of glucose. However,

when a sufficiently high plasma glucose concentration is reached, glucose appears in the urine in appreciable quantities. Further increments in plasma glucose concentration are then accompanied by proportional increments of glucose excretion. The basis for the relationship of plasma glucose concentration and glucose excretion becomes clear when the glomerular and tubular events are analyzed by the simultaneous determination of glomerular filtration rate (inulin clearance). From the product of inulin clearance and plasma glucose concentration,[1] the filtered glucose is calculated; the difference between filtered and excreted glucose is the amount reabsorbed. It is then found that as the plasma glucose concentration increases (the filtered glucose, of course, increasing proportionately) the reabsorbed glucose increases, remaining equal to the filtered, until a limiting value of glucose reabsorption is reached. As the filtered glucose increases beyond this level there is no further increase in glucose reabsorption and the excess glucose is excreted in the urine. These relationships are illustrated in figure 34.4. The relationship among the various quantities is expressed by the equation:

$$U_G V = C_{In} P_G - T_G$$

where T represents the amount reabsorbed per minute from the tubule and the subscripts G and In refer to glucose and inulin respectively.

$T_G$ is seen to increase, remaining equal to the filtered glucose (frequently referred to as the *load* or *filtered load*), until $T_G$ reaches a maximum. This maximum, which represents the capacity of the tubules to transport glucose, is conventionally designated as the glucose $T_m$ or $T_{mG}$. The existence of such a limited capacity subject to saturation is a characteristic feature of active transport processes and is one of the criteria by which they may be identified.

The limitation which characterizes the transport mechanism involved in glucose reabsorption and other similar mechanisms is believed to derive from the involvement of a "carrier" in the process. In this view, the tubule cell membrane is virtually impermeable to glucose in the free state. However, the membrane contains certain molecules which can combine reversibly with

---

[1] In determining the amount filtered in the case of substances, such as glucose, which are rapidly metabolized by the tissues, it is important to measure the arterial plasma concentration, since the venous concentration may be appreciably lower and since it is arterial plasma from which glomerular filtrate is derived.

glucose, and in this state the glucose, now in combination with its carrier, is able to penetrate the membrane. Having reached the inside of the tubule cell, the carrier-glucose complex dissociates releasing free glucose which, we may assume, is free to diffuse out of the cell into the peritubular fluid and blood. The carrier is then available to repeat the process.

The reactions involved may be represented:

$$\overset{(1)}{A + B} \rightleftharpoons \overset{(2)}{AB} \rightarrow T + B$$

where A is glucose in the tubule lumen, B the carrier, AB the glucose-carrier complex and T the glucose which has been transported (e.g., into the tubule cell). Some step in the process requires an input of energy since the expenditure of energy is necessary to drive the reaction "uphill" from the low concentration in the lumen to the higher one in the cell. This energy might be involved in driving reaction (2) or possibly the carrier might be modified in the transport process and require activation before it can again combine with glucose in the lumen. When the mechanism is saturated all of the carrier is interpreted as in the combined state AB and the maximum rate of transport ($T_m$) reflects the total amount of carrier in the tubule cells and the rate constant for the dissociation of AB to yield B and T. Although, theoretically, the rate of such transport processes could be limited by the amount of energy available to drive them, there is no evidence that this actually occurs, and the same tubule cells are able simultaneously to carry out the transport of a number of solutes among which there is no mutual interference.

Although the existence of carriers with the properties described is fairly generally accepted, it should be noted that none has ever been isolated or identified chemically. The interaction between carrier and transported substance may be considered analogous to that between an enzyme and its substrate; in fact the reactions suggested above correspond to those to which the kinetic behavior of enzymatic reactions are attributed. Transport reactions also show certain other characteristics of enzymatic reactions, particularly in being subject to inhibition, both competitive and noncompetitive.

The glucose transport mechanism is fairly specifically inhibited by the glycoside, *phlorizin*. The administration of this inhibitor in adequate dosage completely abolishes glucose transport so that the clearance of glucose becomes equal to the glomerular filtration rate. This property is also

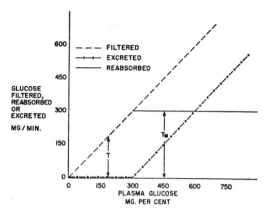

Fig. 34.4. Diagramatic and idealized representation of the relationship among filtration, reabsorption and excretion of glucose. The figures are calculated on the assumption that glomerular filtration rate was 100 ml per minute.

shared by the glycoside of the adrenocortical steroid, desoxycorticosterone. Several monosaccharides (e.g., xylose, fructose and galactose) are reabsorbed to some extent apparently by the same transport mechanism responsible for the reabsorption of glucose, and their reabsorption is also inhibited by phlorizin.

Micropuncture studies have clearly shown that the reabsorption of glucose occurs high in the proximal convoluted tubule and that when the plasma glucose concentration is normal the glucose has largely been removed before the urine reaches the middle of the proximal tubule.

In human beings, the normal capacity to reabsorb glucose (glucose $T_m$) averages approximately 375 and 300 mg. per minute per $1.73M^2$ of body surface area in men and women respectively. If we compare the capacity to reabsorb glucose with the rate of glomerular filtration we may deduce what concentration of glucose in the plasma would be required to yield enough filtered glucose to saturate the glucose $T_m$. Since the average normal rate of glomerular filtration is 125 ml. per minute it is apparent that a plasma glucose concentration of 3 mg. per ml. or 300 mg. per cent is required to yield a filtered load equal to reabsorptive capacity of 375 mg. per minute. From the idealized and oversimplified diagram of excretion and reabsorption versus load plotted in figure 34.4 it would be predicted that *no* glucose should appear in the urine until the plasma glucose is 300 mg. per cent; at that point, filtered load should be exactly equal to reabsorptive capacity and reabsorptive capacity should be fully saturated. Further increases in plasma glucose should give no increase in glucose reabsorption. In actual

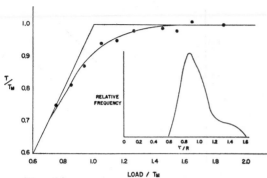

FIG. 34.5. Titration of the capacity to reabsorb glucose. Based on average data from ten normal individuals. The ordinate ($T/T_m$) is the ratio of glucose reabsorbed at a particular value of filtered glucose to the maximum capacity to reabsorb glucose in the same individual. It is thus the fractional saturation of glucose reabsorptive capacity. The abscissa (load/$T_m$) is the amount of glucose available for reabsorption, again related to the capacity of the individual to reabsorb glucose.

The frequency distribution curve shows the proportion of nephrons having various ratios (r) of filtration rate to reabsorptive capacity as related to the average of this ratio (R) for the two kidneys as a unit.

The data are those of Smith, Goldring, Chasis, Ranges and Bradley (J. Mt. Sinai Hosp., 10:59, 1943).

practice this is not the case. In figure 34.5 is reproduced the observed relationship between plasma glucose (filtered glucose) and excretion and reabsorption in normal man. It is seen that glucose begins to appear in the urine when the filtered glucose is only about three-fourths of the capacity of the tubules to reabsorb and that the reabsorption does not reach its maximum rate until the amount filtered is some 50 per cent greater than this maximum.

The departure from the idealized relationship is due to two factors. Two assumptions are implicit in the construction of the idealized relationship, and neither is completely valid: (1) Each tubule reabsorbs all the glucose presented to it until its capacity is fully saturated, and *none* of the filtered glucose escapes reabsorption until saturation is achieved; and (2) all of the tubules are functionally identical so that the kidney may be looked upon as a single nephron. We may now consider why these assumptions are valid only as first approximations.

1. The hypothetical basis of transport in terms of the formation of a substrate-carrier complex was presented above. The initial reaction is visualized as the reversible formation of the complex:

$$A + B \rightleftharpoons AB$$

If we write the mass action expression for this reaction, we obtain:

$$K = \frac{[A][B]}{[AB]}$$

where the brackets signify concentration and K is the dissociation constant for the substrate-carrier complex. The smaller the value of K, the greater the affinity of the carrier for the transported substance.

It is apparent from this that the residual (unreabsorbed) substrate will be very small only (1) if the value of K is very small or (2) when there remains an appreciable concentration of unsaturated carrier (B). Conversely (once the total A available is equal to the total transport capacity) there will be negligible unutilized transport capacity only (1) when K is very small or (2) when there remains a considerable amount of unreabsorbed substrate. Thus, the relationship will approach the ideal as the value of K becomes infinitely small and for any finite value of K there will be some departure from the ideal (fig. 34.4). Actually among the various substances actively reabsorbed by the renal tubules there are varying degrees of departure from ideality presumably reflecting differences in the value of K. The departure from ideality in the case of glucose is small compared to that for many other substances, suggesting a low value for the dissociation of the glucose-carrier complex.

The type of relationship plotted in figure 34.5 is commonly referred to as a *titration curve,* and the departure from the sharp break of the ideal relationship is called the *splay* of the titration curve.

2. The nephrons are clearly not all identical nor is it reasonable to expect them to be so. The heterogeneity of the nephron population which is pertinent to the shape of reabsorptive titration curves is heterogeneity of what is called *glomerulotubular* balance, that is, the relationship between the filtering capacity of the glomerulus and the reabsorptive capacity of the tubule attached to that particular glomerulus. Thus if we deal with a tubule with an average capacity to reabsorb glucose but a filtration rate of twice the average, it will become saturated with glucose when the plasma glucose concentration is only half that required to saturate the average nephron. Conversely nephrons with small glomerular filtering capacity and large reabsorptive capacity will become saturated only when the plasma glucose is much higher than that which would saturate the average nephron.

The titration curve in figure 34.5 can be analyzed to yield the distribution of glomerular activity in relation to glucose reabsorptive capacity if it is assumed that the titration curve in each individual nephron is ideal (that is, if the kinetic contribution to splay is disregarded). What is obtained is a distribution of the ratios of filtration to reabsorption for the nephron population as these ratios relate to the average ratio for the kidneys taken as a unit. This distribution curve, included in figure 34.5 indicates that in the normal human kidney no appreciable number of nephrons has a ratio of filtration to reabsorption of glucose departing more than 50 per cent from the average.

The earlier literature on the physiology of the kidney divides substances which may appear in the urine into *threshold* and *no-threshold substances*. A threshold substance was one which did not appear in the urine until its concentration in the blood exceeded some value, this value being designated as the renal threshold. No-threshold substances were those which appeared in the urine at all concentrations in the plasma. Clearly glucose (and most other substances actively reabsorbed by the tubules) would fall in the category of "threshold" substances. However, with improvements in the methods of study of renal function, this terminology has in large measure lost its usefulness, and it is greatly preferable to consider the specific mechanisms involved in the excretion of a particular substance and the quantitative aspects, formerly subsumed in the "threshold," in terms of the rates of filtration, reabsorption and secretion.

OTHER SUBSTANCES ACTIVELY REABSORBED BY THE TUBULES. The reabsorption of glucose is the prototype of a number of reabsorptive processes which are qualitatively similar. In several instances the site of reabsorption has been identified, and in each case the proximal tubule is the segment concerned. It is probable that, except for those mechanisms involved in the movements of the more important monovalent electrolytes and water (these will be considered separately later), the active reabsorptive (and secretory) processes are confined to the proximal convoluted tubules.

The normal urine contain only traces of *amino acids* although, of course, a number of amino acids are present in plasma. Several separate transport mechanisms are involved in their reabsorption. The basic amino acids arginine, lysine and histidine appear to share the same mechanism since elevation of the plasma concentration of any one depresses the reabsorption of the others. Reabsorptive $T_m$'s have been demonstrated for lysine and arginine but not for histidine, the reabsorption of which is still increasing at the highest levels produced experimentally. A second transport mechanism is responsible for the reabsorption of leucine and isoleucine which compete, but the capacity for reabsorption is so high that no $T_m$ has been demonstrated. Glycine appears to be reabsorbed by a separate mechanism. In those instances in which $T_m$'s have been demonstrated, there is considerable excretion of the amino acid when the reabsorptive capacity is far from saturated. Presumably this represents a relatively high degree of dissociation of the carrier-substrate complex. *Creatine* is reabsorbed by a mechanism closely related to, if not identical with, that involved in glycine reabsorption.

*Phosphate* is reabsorbed by an active process which can be saturated on elevation of the plasma concentration. The transport mechanism seems to be modified by a number of factors. It is probable, although not clearly established, that parathyroid hormone depresses the phosphate transport system. Acidosis increases phosphate excretion in part by what appears to be an increase in the splay of the titration curve.

*Sulfate* reabsorption is effected by a mechanism which becomes saturated with only a slight increase in the plasma concentration above the normal level. The reabsorption of sulfate can be depressed by the administration of thiosulfate which competes for reabsorption by the same mechanism.

*Uric acid* reabsorption is remarkable for the number of substances known to inhibit it. These include other reabsorbed compounds, such as glycine, and a number of drugs which inhibit the secretion of organic anions by the tubules (carinamide, probenecid, phenylbutazone). The reabsorptive capacity for uric acid is so great that it is certainly never saturated in the normal individual. Excretion occurs by virtue of the great splay in the titration curve. The excretion of urate at levels far below saturation of reabsorption has been attributed to the existence of a mechanism of low capacity capable of secreting urate into the tubules; the evidence for such a process is as yet inconclusive.

Among other substances actively reabsorbed by the tubules are *ascorbic acid* and *betahydroxybutyric* and *acetoacetic acids*.

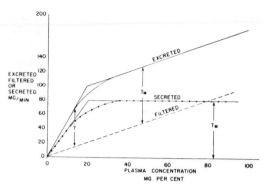

FIG. 34.6. Relationship between plasma concentration and filtered, secreted and excreted amounts of a substance excreted by tubule secretion. See text for details.

## TUBULAR SECRETION

The processes by which materials are removed from the peritubular fluid and transferred to the tubule lumen are designated by the term *tubular secretion*. The term *tubular excretion* is often used synonymously. In the present section the secretion of the monovalent ions potassium, hydrogen and ammonium will be omitted, and the discussion will be concerned with the somewhat simpler transport processes involved in the secretion of certain organic electrolytes.

The first substance for which tubular secretion was demonstrated was phenol red (phenolsulfonphthalein, PSP). The critical experiment was that of Marshall who showed that as much as 75 per cent of the phenol red contained in the arterial blood could be removed as the blood traversed the kidney, whereas, because of a high degree of binding of phenol red to plasma proteins, only 20 to 25 per cent of the phenol red in the arterial plasma is free and filterable. Clearly, no matter what fraction of the plasma was converted to glomerular filtrate, filtration alone could not account for the excretion of phenol red. These experiments put an end to a prolonged controversy over the existence of tubular secretory processes.

A large number of substances are now recognized to be transported into the tubules by the same mechanism responsible for the secretion of phenol red. Among these are *hippuric acid* and a variety of its iodo-, hydroxy-, and amino derivatives, *penicillin*, 5-hydroxyindoleacetic acid (a metabolite of serotonin), a number of *sulfonphthaleins* in addition to phenol red, several of the iodinated compounds which have been used for X-ray contrast study (intravenous pyelography) of the urinary tract (Diodrast, Iopax,

Neoiopax, Skiodan).[2] Also, although their tubular secretion in man has not been identified, it has been shown that glucuronides and ethereal sulfates are so transported in other animals, and the same is probably true in man. It is notable that the list contains no normal constituents of the body, but under normal conditions it seems likely that the mechanism serves for the rapid excretion of the conjugates of ingested foreign substances, these conjugates being in the form of hippurates, glucuronides and sulfates.

The tubular secretory process, which is also located in the proximal tubule, resembles those involved in reabsorption in many respects, except for the reversal of direction:

At low concentrations of the transported substance the mechanism is able to transport all of the material presented to it. The most commonly studied substance, p-aminohippuric acid (PAH) may be used, as an example. If PAH is administered intravenously in small amounts, so as to maintain a low concentration in the arterial plasma, it is found that the blood leaving the kidney in the renal vein may be almost free of PAH. An average of some 90 per cent of the PAH reaching the kidney in the plasma is removed. Since some of the blood reaching the renal vein has probably perfused tissue which does not transport PAH, it is apparent that very little can be left over from that plasma which passes through the active areas. This extremely effective *extraction* of PAH is the basis of the use of this substance for the estimation of renal plasma flow which is considered below.

As the plasma concentration of the transported substance is increased, the rate of tubular excretion increases until a maximum is reached and no further augmentation of secretion occurs. The relationship between plasma PAH concentration and PAH excretion in the urine is illustrated in figure 34.6. The dotted line passing through the intercept is the amount of PAH filtered at the glomeruli calculated from the product of inulin clearance and the plasma concentration of free PAH. (Since PAH is, to a small extent, bound to plasma albumin the total concentration must be corrected for this binding to obtain the filtered amount.) At every level of plasma PAH the rate of excretion exceeds the rate of filtration.

[2] While the iodine is important for X-ray density, it is not related to the susceptibility to transport which undoubtedly derives from the organic structures to which the iodine is attached. The first three of those mentioned are derivatives of pyridine-N-acetic acid; the last is an organic sulfate.

$$U_{PAH}V = C_{In}P_{PAH}f + T_{PAH}$$

where f is the fraction of the plasma PAH which is filterable. As the plasma PAH is increased the rate of excretion at first increases sharply, the slope of the line relating excretion to plasma concentration being equal to the renal plasma flow. When the plasma concentration is further increased, the rate of excretion increases less rapidly, and it is found that the excess of excreted over filtered has become constant. This excess represents the maximum rate of tubular secretion and is designated as $T_{mPAH}$.

If the rate of tubular secretion is determined by subtracting the filtered from the total excretion the relationship shown in figure 34.6 is obtained. Again, the actually observed titration curve differs from the idealized intersection of two straight lines and for reasons analogous to those involved in tubular reabsorption: (1) the dissociation of substrate-carrier complex and (2) heterogeneity of nephron function. The pertinent heterogeneity in this case, however, is in the ratio of perfusion to transport capacity since it is blood supply, rather than glomerular filtration, which along with plasma concentration will determine the amount available for secretion by the tubules.

Any of the various substances listed above as being secreted by this particular transport mechanism can be shown to compete with the others. Thus a high concentration of one will reduce the secretion of another and vice versa. Presumably they share a common carrier, and when some of the carrier sites are occupied by one, it has less capacity for the transport of another.

Several more or less specific inhibitors of this transport mechanism have been discovered (carinamide, probenicid, phenylbutazone). Actually these substances are probably also competitive inhibitors but are so poorly transported themselves that they occupy sites on the transport mechanism to the exclusion of the other transported substances. (It is interesting to note that these inhibitors have found their major practical application as inhibitors of the *reabsorption* of urate in the treatment of gout.)

The mechanism is inhibited noncompetitively by dinitrophenol and by mercurial diuretics. The effect of dinitrophenol, which has the property of uncoupling oxidation from phosphorylation, suggests that phosphate bond energy is important in the transport process. The effect of mercurial diuretics is striking in man, but, for unknown reasons, entirely absent in the dog.

The transport of PAH is enhanced by acetate and lactate and inhibited by a number of the dicarboxylic acid intermediates of the Krebs cycle.

All of the substrates of the secretory process responsible for the tubular excretion of PAH are weak organic anions. A separate and distinct mechanism is capable of transporting a variety of organic bases including N-methylnicotinamide, tetraethylammonium ion and priscoline. These compete with each other but show no interaction with the organic anions. The normal substrate for this mechanism has not been recognized.

### *The Utilization of Tubular Secretion for the Measurement of Renal Blood Flow*

As was noted above, several substances which undergo tubular excretion are very nearly completely removed from the blood which perfuses the kidney. This has made them singularly useful for the estimation of renal blood flow. Diodrast and p-aminohippurate (PAH), because they are well adapted to chemical analysis, have particularly been used for this purpose, and we will consider the use of PAH as an example.

In accord with the Fick principle, if the rate of removal of a substance from the blood as it flows through an organ is known, and if the concentration in the blood entering and leaving the organ can be determined, the blood flow can be calculated:

$$F = \frac{R}{A - V}$$

where F is the flow, R the rate of removal, and A and V the concentration in arterial and venous blood respectively.

In applying this to the measurement of renal blood flow using PAH, the following experimental facts are important: (1) there is no metabolism, production nor storage of PAH in the kidney; all of the PAH removed from the blood is excreted in the urine; (2) all of the PAH removed from the blood is removed from the plasma; the concentration in the red blood cells does not change significantly as blood passes through the kidney. Then the above equation can be modified to yield:

$$RPF = \frac{U_{PAH}V}{P_{PAH}^{A} - P_{PAH}^{RV}}$$

where RPF represents renal plasma flow and $P_{PAH}^{A}$ and $P_{PAH}^{RV}$ represent concentrations of PAH in arterial and renal venous plasma respectively.

Now, as it stands in this form the determination of renal plasma flow would require measurement of the rate of excretion of PAH and the concentrations in arterial and renal venous blood plasma. All of these are feasible in man, but the collection of renal venous blood is considerably more difficult than the remainder of the procedures. However, since we know that at low concentrations of PAH in the arterial plasma the removal of PAH as blood passes through the kidney is very nearly complete, we may as a first approximation consider the concentration in renal venous plasma to be zero and write

$$ERPF = \frac{U_{PAH}V}{P^A_{PAH}} = C_{PAH}$$

or that the *effective renal plasma flow* is equal to the PAH clearance. In practice it is not necessary to measure arterial plasma PAH since, when arterial concentration is constant, there is no measurable removal of PAH by peripheral tissues, and the PAH in peripheral venous plasma is the same as that in arterial plasma. Therefore, the effective renal plasma flow can be simply estimated by measurement of the plasma PAH clearance when the plasma PAH is maintained at a low level. (As plasma PAH is increased, the extraction becomes less complete and the clearance falls further below the true plasma flow.) From the effective renal plasma flow the corresponding renal blood flow can be calculated if the hematocrit is known.

$$ERBF = \frac{ERPF}{1 - H_{ct}}$$

It is interesting to note that Homer Smith and his associates deduced that the clearance of diodrast could be used to measure renal plasma flow in man before the technique for obtaining renal venous blood by venous catheterization had been devised and the virtually total extraction of diodrast confirmed.[3] This was based on the very high value (approximately 650 ml. per minute) of the diodrast clearance; thus plasma flow of at least 650 ml. per minute was required to supply the diodrast at the rate it was excreted. It was reasoned that this was already such a large volume flow that the true plasma flow could not be much higher.

[3] It should also be noted that if, for some reason, renal venous blood is collected so that true plasma and blood flow can be determined, PAH and similar substances lose their unique value. Then any substance which is removed by, but not produced, metabolized or stored in the kidney can be used for the measurement, since the Fick principle can be applied directly. A high degree of extraction, under these conditions, has only the virtue of minimizing experimental error.

## Renal Blood Flow and Filtration Fraction in Man.

The remarkably high value of the renal plasma flow has been mentioned above. A plasma flow of 650 ml. per minute corresponds to a blood flow of about 1200 ml. per minute, an amount approximately equal to one-fourth of the cardiac output under basal conditions. The ratio of the renal blood flow to cardiac output is frequently referred to as the *renal fraction* of the cardiac output.

The demonstrated equivalence of PAH clearance and (effective) renal plasma flow has made it possible to measure the renal blood flow in man with a minimum of manipulation and disturbance. Thus, it has been possible to measure changes in blood flow with disease as well as to determine the effects of various changes in physiological state and the effects of drugs, etc.

In considering changes in the renal plasma and blood flows, it is pertinent to take account of the fraction of the plasma lost as glomerular filtrate as the plasma flows through the glomerular capillaries. Since all of the renal blood flow under normal conditions passes through the glomeruli, the volume given up as glomerular filtrate is derived from the total plasma flow and the ratio of filtration rate to plasma flow (inulin clearance to PAH clearance) is a measure of the extent to which, in the average glomerulus, the plasma volume is reduced, and the plasma protein concentration increased by the process of glomerular filtration. The ratio of filtration rate to plasma flow is known as the *filtration fraction*.

While, as was noted in an earlier section, the rate of glomerular filtration is a remarkably stable function, the renal blood flow manifests a fairly marked degree of lability, and may be modified by any of a number of stimuli. Most of the changes are mediated via the sympathetic nerve supply and are in the direction of decreases. In fact, although the subject has long been debated and no consensus has been achieved, the only physiological effects clearly shown to be mediated by the nerve supply to the kidneys are vasoconstrictor, and the renal nerves have not been shown to play a significant role in the regulation of transport processes in the renal tubules.

The renal blood flow is diminished by fright, pain, exercise, epinephrine, norepinephrine and stimulation of several areas of the central nervous system, and by a number of other stimuli. In general, anything which lowers blood pressure will reduce renal blood flow, not so much because of the reduction in perfusion pressure, but because the kidney takes part in the general vasoconstriction which is the homeostatic response to a lowering of blood pressure. Thus there may be a marked decrease in renal blood flow with only a trivial reduction in aortic blood pressure. Drugs which reduce blood pressure also reduce the renal blood flow. However, in general, the reduction in flow is less than with equivalent reductions in blood pressure due to, for instance, hemorrhage or orthostasis, since the blood pressure reducing drugs usually inhibit renal as well as peripheral vasoconstriction. A special case appears to be hydrazinophthalazine which may increase renal blood flow while reducing systemic blood pressure, probably through a specific renal vasodilator action.

A more or less unique phenomenon is the marked renal vasodilation and hyperemia produced by the pyrogenic reaction. The latter phenomenon, the most striking clinical feature of which is chills and fever, is most often a response to bacterial products (certain bacterial polysaccharides, typhoid vaccine). It is accompanied by intense hyperemia of the kidney, and the renal blood flow may reach twice it normally very high value. Interestingly the renal response to pyrogenic materials is not abolished by the administration of antipyretic drugs although the latter may completely suppress the chills and fever.

With all of the above changes in renal blood flow there are frequently only slight changes in glomerular filtration rate and such changes are frequently entirely absent. Thus the changes in filtration fraction are the inverse of the changes in blood flow.

### The Reabsorption and Excretion of Water

One of the most striking features of the function of the mammalian kidney is the capacity to excrete urine differing in osmotic pressure from the blood from which it is derived. It is through this capacity to excrete concentrated or dilute urine that the solute concentration (osmotic pressure) of the body fluids is maintained within remarkably narrow limits despite wide variation in the intake of solute and water. When, because of water loss or solute gain, the solute concentration of body fluids rises, the urine becomes concentrated, solute is excreted with less than the equivalent amount of water, and the solute concentration of the body fluids is restored to normal. Conversely, when the body fluids become diluted by water intake or solute loss, a dilute urine containing an excess of water is excreted, and the osmotic pressure of body fluids is returned to normal. Before considering the mechanisms by which the renal tubules effect these changes, it may be helpful to digress briefly to review the concept of osmotic pressure and its measurement.

If two solutions containing different concentrations of solute are separated by a membrane permeable to the solvent (water in all cases with which we are concerned) but not the solute, there will be a movement of water from the more dilute to the more concentrated of the solutions. The movement of water is due to the fact that the presence of solute reduces the chemical activity of water, and water will move from the solution in which its activity (analogous to concentration) is high to one where it is lower. Water will move from dilute to concentrated solution until both have the same solute concentration or, if the movement of water is opposed by the application of a hydrostatic pressure, until the hydrostatic pressure balances the concentration difference. The hydrostatic pressure which would be required to maintain a solution at constant volume when it is separated by an ideal semipermeable membrane[4] from pure water is the osmotic pressure of that solution. The term osmotic pressure is applied although the osmotic pressure is never actually determined. Instead, some other property of the solution dependent upon total solute concentration is measured: most commonly the freezing point, occasionally the vapor pressure.

The *colligative properties* (osmotic pressure, freezing point depression, vapor pressure depression) depend on the ratio of the total number of solute particles to the number of mols of solvent. The nature of the solute is, to a large extent, indifferent; ideally, a protein molecule of molecular weight 100,000 has an effect equal to that of a sodium ion of weight 23, and a mol of sodium chloride, since it dissociates to yield two particles, has twice the effect of a mol of urea or glucose. One mol of ideal solute dissolved in a kilogram of water depresses the freezing point of the solution by 1.86°C. Such a solution is defined as an *osmolal* solution and is said to contain one osmol per kilogram of water. Since most biological fluids are considerably more dilute, it is convenient, in order to avoid decimals, to deal with *milliosmols* or *micro-osmols*, one milliosmol being one one-thousandth of an osmol, one micro-osmol one thousandth of a milliosmol. The milliosmolality of a solution is defined as its freezing point depression divided by 0.00186. Thus normal plasma

---

[4] An ideal semipermeable membrane is one permeable to solvent but impermeable to all solute.

is about 285 milliosmolal (abbreviated 285 mOs) and has a freezing point of about −0.53°C.[5]

It will facilitate consideration of the processes which take place between the filtration of an isotonic fluid (one which has the same osmotic pressure as blood plasma) and the excretion of dilute and concentrated urine, if we first consider the gross behavior of water excretion and its extrarenal control. Under basal conditions the urine is usually moderately concentrated and the urine flow is small. If under such conditions an individual ingests a moderately large volume of water, e.g., one liter, it is found that after an interval of some 15 to 20 minutes the urine flow begins to rise. The flow increases rapidly to reach a peak of some 12 to 15 ml. per minute at 40 minute to 1 hour, and, when an amount approximately equal to that ingested has been excreted, returns to the same low level as obtained before the water ingestion. (Of course, if the water ingestion is continued so that a positive balance is maintained, the high rate of flow may continue for prolonged periods.) If these events are analyzed more carefully, it is found (1) that the osmotic pressure of the blood shows a distinct drop (though only a few per cent) well before the onset of the increase in urine flow (*diuresis*); (2) that the change in urine flow is almost entirely due to a change in the amount of water excreted, manifested by a shift in urine osmolality from hypertonic to markedly hypotonic to plasma; solute excretion shows little or no change; (3) if glomerular filtration has been measured it is found that the increase in urine flow occurs without or with only trivial changes in the rate of formation of glomerular filtrate; the change in water excretion is due to a change in the absorption of water in the renal tubules; (4) if at the peak of the urine flow, additional water is ingested, the urine flow does not increase further but remains at a value of some 12 to 15 per cent of the volume of the glomerular filtrate; (5) if, at any point in the course of the diuresis, vasopressin, the antidiuretic hormone of the posterior pituitary, is administered, the diuresis is immediately interrupted, and the urine again becomes more concentrated than the blood.

The concentration of the urine is normally continuously regulated by the secretion of antidiuretic hormone (ADH) by the posterior lobe of the pituitary gland. This hormone is believed to be produced in the supraoptic nuclei of the hypothalamus and to migrate via the supraopticohypophyseal tracts to the posterior lobe of the pituitary where it is stored and released into the blood in response to stimuli mediated from the hypothalamus via the same tract system. Within the supraoptic nuclei certain cells (*osmoreceptors*) are believed to behave as tiny osmometers, taking up water and swelling when the osmotic pressure of the surrounding body fluids is reduced and giving up water as the osmotic pressure of the bathing fluid rises. The swelling and shrinking of these cells is believed to lead to the transmission of nervous impulses which modulate the release of antidiuretic hormone from the posterior pituitary. Thus a reduction of the osmotic pressure of the blood leads to inhibition of ADH release;[6] an increase of osmotic pressure stimulates ADH secretion. In turn, the ADH is carried by the blood to the kidney, and in the kidney ADH regulates the reabsorption and excretion of water.

The work of Verney, to whom we owe much of our understanding of the pituitary control of water excretion, showed that injection into the internal carotid artery of the dog of enough sodium chloride to raise the osmotic pressure of the blood by about 2 per cent resulted in immediate inhibition of water excretion. Injection of the same amount into a peripheral vessel had no such effect since it was then diluted with a large volume of blood before being delivered to the sensitive area in the brain. Injection of the osmotically equivalent amount of urea into the internal carotid was also virtually without effect. In this case the ineffectiveness is presumably due to the fact that urea readily penetrates cells. When the urea concentration of their environment is raised, the osmoreceptor cells take up urea rather than lose water. Since the receptors do not shrink, there is no induction of ADH secretion. Thus, *only those solutes to which cells are relatively impermeable make up the effective osmotic pressure in response to which ADH secretion is regulated.*[7]

Our knowledge of the location in the renal tu-

---

[5] Note that osmotic pressure depends on the number of solute particles per unit of solvent. The amount of water in a given *volume of solution* will vary with concentration as well as with the nature of the solute. There is, therefore, no simple way to convert from osmolality to a number of solute particles per unit volume of solution. It is, however, the practice to disregard the inaccuracy involved and multiply volume by osmolality to obtain the approximate amount of solute in a given volume.

[6] The latent period from water ingestion to onset of diuresis is attributable 1) to the time required for water absorption to produce sufficient dilution of the body fluids and thus inhibit ADH secretion, 2) for the circulating ADH to disappear.

[7] The above describes the normal control of ADH secretion. A number of other stimuli such as fear, trauma, nausea, certain drugs, and many others may produce secretion of ADH under conditions unrelated to the osmotic pressure of the body fluids.

bule and the nature of the processes by which water excretion is regulated is due largely to the application of the micropuncture technique—in amphibians by Richards and his associates and in mammals by Walker, Bott, Oliver, and Mac-Dowell and more recently and extensively by Wirz and Gottschalk.

The glomerular filtrate has the same osmotic pressure as the plasma except for the absence of the plasma proteins.[8] As the fluid flows through the proximal tubule, its volume is reduced to a fraction of that which enters the glomerular space. Although, because of inaccessibility from the kidney surface no samples have been collected from the last 40 per cent of the proximal tubule, it is generally estimated that approximately one-fifth of the filtered volume reaches the end of the proximal tubule and enters the loop of Henle. This reduction of volume occurs *without change in osmotic pressure* whether the urine being produced is dilute or concentrated. Thus the large fraction of fluid reabsorbed in the proximal tubule does not take part in the concentration and dilution processes, and, in fact, is lost to the process of osmoregulation. The water thus reabsorbed in the proximal segment has been termed by Smith *obligatory water reabsorption* to distinguish it from the *facultative water reabsorption* in the more distal portions of the nephron where water reabsorption is subject to regulation in accordance with the excess or deficit of water in the body fluids.

A considerable body of evidence indicates that the water reabsorption in the proximal tubule is entirely a passive process and that the active process which underlies it is the transport of salt (predominantly sodium salts) out of the tubule lumen. As sodium salts are transferred from lumen to peritubular fluid, there is a tendency to produce dilution of the tubule contents and hypertonicity of the surroundings. The proximal tubule is highly permeable to water and, in response to the osmotic gradient, water follows the salt out of the tubule. Within the limits of the determinations the proximal tubule contents are always isotonic with the blood.

The exact course of events in the loop of Henle

8 It is important to make a clear distinction between the total osmotic pressure, with which we are concerned in the processes of urine dilution and concentration, and the colloid osmotic pressure or oncotic pressure due to the plasma proteins which play such an important role in the distribution of fluid across capillary membranes (because the latter are so highly permeable to all the other solutes). The colloid osmotic pressure of plasma is equivalent to about 25 mm. Hg (1 to 2 mOs.) while the total osmotic pressure is of the order of 6 atmospheres (285 mOs.).

is not completely established because of inaccessibility to direct puncture (except at the tip). However, from more indirect evidence it is quite probable that the descending limb of the loop retains the high water permeability which characterizes the proximal tubule and that the fluid within the descending limb retains the same osmotic pressure as the surrounding interstitial fluid. The high water permeability is, however, lost in the ascending limb and now the continued removal of salt leaves the fluid dilute. The urine emerges into the distal convoluted tubule with its osmotic pressure reduced to about half that of plasma whether the final urine is to be dilute or hypertonic.

The changes which take place in the distal tubule depend upon whether a dilute or concentrated urine is to be produced. In the *formation of dilute urine*, the dilute fluid which enters the distal tubule is further diluted by the continued removal of salt, and the salt removal probably continues through the collecting system. The urine is thus rendered hypotonic by the active reabsorption of salt in a region which clearly has a low permeability to water. (Otherwise the osmotic gradient would be dissipated, as it is in the proximal tubule, by the escape of water to the more concentrated surroundings.) The low permeability to water which characterizes the distal convoluted tubule and collecting system during the formation of dilute urine is dependent upon the absence of ADH.

In the *formation of concentrated urine*, the events are similar up to the point at which the fluid enters the distal convoluted tubule. In the presence of antidiuretic hormone, however, the distal convoluted tubule and collecting ducts become permeable to water.[9] Consequently, as it flows through the distal tubule the osmotic gradient, established by the reabsorption of sodium and chloride, is dissipated, and, despite additional salt removal in the distal tubule, the dilute character of the urine is lost so that it regains isotonicity before it enters the collecting system. It is important to emphasize that it enters the collecting system isotonic, never hypertonic. The additional water loss which renders the urine more concentrated than blood occurs in the collecting system.

The nature of the mechanism by which urine is rendered hypertonic to the body fluids has long

9 Antidiuretic hormone has been shown to have the property of increasing water permeability in isolated membranes (frog skin, toad skin, toad bladder) by causing the dilation of water-filled pores. Presumably the effect on the distal tubule epithelium is similar.

been one of the more intriguing problems of renal physiology, and its apparent elucidation, largely through the efforts of Wirz and his associates, is one of the more important recent achievements. Although some of the details of the mechanism are relatively complex, the essentials are quite simple and directly related to the anatomical organization of the kidney. The convoluted tubules are cortical structures; the loops of Henle and the collecting tubules and ducts lie in the medulla. The latter structures are thus relatively isolated from the cortical structures in which most of the transport activity of the kidney takes place. In addition, the blood supply of medulla and papilla forms a looplike system derived from the efferent vessels of the juxtamedullary glomeruli, running down into the medulla, and looping back to the cortex. Thus both loop of Henle and the blood supply of the medullary region form *countercurrent* systems in which the outflowing fluid flows counter to and in proximity to inflowing fluid. We will for the moment defer consideration of the importance of this particular arrangement.

As was noted above, as fluid flows through the ascending limb of the loop sodium and chloride are removed while the water remains behind in the tubule lumen and the urine becomes diluted. The sodium and chloride removed are transferred to the interstitial fluid of the medulla, increasing the osmotic pressure of this fluid. The diluted urine emerges into the cortex where, in the pres-

ence of ADH, it loses its excess of water and is further reduced in volume as solute is removed in the distal tubule. This water loss occurs in the cortex, spatially separated from the salt left behind in the medulla, and in an area where, because of the very large flow of blood, the excess water produces only a minimal change in osmotic pressure. Now the remaining urine, greatly reduced in volume and isotonic with the blood, enters the collecting system and flows through the medulla. The interstitial fluid of the medulla, however, has a high osmotic pressure because of the salt transported by the loop and, the collecting duct being permeable to water in the presence of ADH, the urine loses water to attain the same osmotic pressure as the interstitial fluid. Thus the hypertonicity of the urine is produced. These events are illustrated diagramatically in figure 34.7. Because the volume flow through the loop is several times larger than that in the collecting ducts, a relatively small change in concentration in the loop is sufficient to yield enough solute to raise the concentration of the urine in the collecting ducts severalfold.

If the sodium salts transported into the medullary interstitial fluid are to raise the osmotic pressure of the latter, they must not be immediately carried away by the blood flowing through the area. The retention of excess solute in the medullary interstitial fluid is made possible by the arrangement of the blood flow which constitutes a countercurrent exchanger. The principle

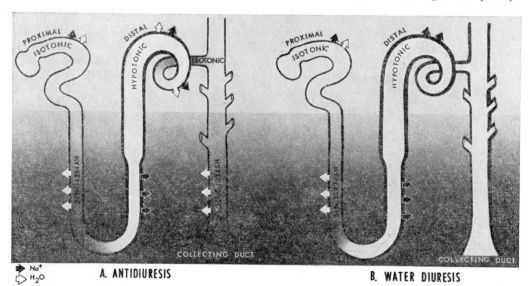

A. ANTIDIURESIS                   B. WATER DIURESIS

Fɪɢ. 34.7. Diagramatic representation of changes in the tonicity of fluid in the tubules during the formation of concentrated and dilute urine. Dark and light arrows indicate movements of sodium chloride and water respectively, and the relative permeability of the tubule wall to water is indicated by its thickness.

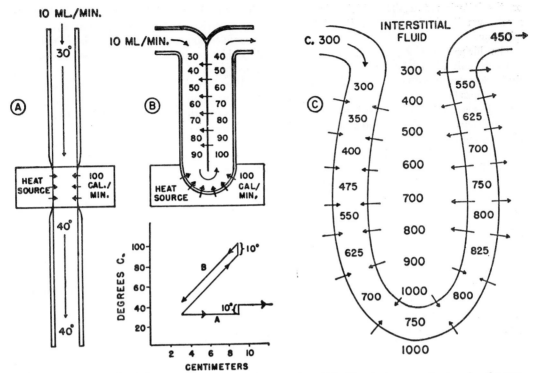

Fig. 34.8. Principle of the countercurrent exchanger. A and B, 100 calories per minute raise the temperature of 10 ml. per minute of water 10 degrees in both A (straight flow) and B (countercurrent flow). However, since the incoming water is heated by the outgoing water in B, the *maximum temperature* attained in the countercurrent system is considerably higher than with straight flow. The graph compares the temperature along the flow tubes in each system. C, countercurrent flow as applied to the capillary loop, showing that it is not necessary for the limbs of the loop to be in direct contact. In the *hypothetical* illustration given, both limbs are in contact with the same interstitial fluid, of progressively increasing concentration. Sodium salts (arrows) at first enter the capillary blood, later partly return to the interstitial fluid. Note the analogy between B, in which heat is recirculated, and C, in which sodium salts are similarly retained in an area.

of the countercurrent exchanger is illustrated in figure 34.8. Outflowing blood tends to lose its solute to the inflowing blood. As a result, solute is recirculated in the medulla. This characteristic makes it possible not only to retain sodium salts but to trap urea as well; the special role of urea in the concentration process is considered with the excretion of urea.

The loop arrangement has an additional physiological advantage. As the fluid flows down the descending limb of the loop of Henle into an environment made hypertonic by the activity of the ascending limb, it loses water so as to retain the same osmotic pressure as the environment. The loss of water raises the concentration of sodium salts in the loop contents so that the transport of sodium salts out of the ascending limb is against only a small gradient of concentration despite the very high concentration of sodium salts in the interstitial fluid surrounding the loop. This arrangement is that of a *countercurrent multi-*

*plier,* so called because the small concentration gradient from the loop contents to environment is multiplied in the longitudinal direction from cortex to tip of papilla.

The highest concentration achieved by the human kidney is generally about 1200 to 1400 mOs. (a relatively modest maximum compared with some other mammals, e.g., dog 2300 to 2500 mOs., rat 3000 to 3200 mOs., kangaroo rat over 5000 mOs.); the lowest concentrations observed are of the order of 30 to 40 mOs. Thus the kidney is able to produce urine four to five times more concentrated than or one-seventh to one-tenth as concentrated as the blood (roughly 300 mOs.).

In clinical practice, the specific gravity, rather than the osmolality, is generally used as an index of concentration and dilution. Urine of specific gravity 1.008 to 1.010 is approximately isotonic with plasma, but the two scales are not directly interchangeable since the specific gravity depends not only on the concentration of solute but also on the latter's nature. The chief value of the specific gravity lies in the simplicity of its determination.

The highest and lowest concentrations are produced only when solute excretion is at a relatively low level; as solute excretion increases dilute urines become less dilute and concentrated urines less concentrated. The basis for this change can be deduced from the mechanisms for dilution and concentration described above and is more easily understood if the urine flow is considered to be divided into two parts as suggested by Smith. One fraction is considered to contain all of the solute excreted at the same concentration as plasma; the other fraction is the amount of water contained in excess of this isotonic fraction. The isotonic fraction is calculated by dividing total solute excretion by the osmolality of plasma. Solute excretion is given by the product of urine flow and urine osmolality $U_{os}V$ and when this is divided by the plasma osmolality, the resulting value has the dimensions of a clearance and is generally called the osmolal clearance ($C_{os}$)

$$C_{os} = \frac{U_{os}V}{P_{os}}$$

*When the urine is dilute* the flow exceeds the osmolal clearance by an amount which Smith has designated the *free water clearance* ($C_{H_2O}$). This is the volume of water which must be removed from one minute's flow of urine to return the urine to isotonicity. Thus

$$V - \frac{U_{os}V}{P_{os}} = C_{H_2O}; \quad C_{H_2O} = V - C_{os}$$

From the mechanism described above it may be seen that, provided no water has escaped from distal tubule or collecting duct, $C_{H_2O}$ is the volume of water which originally contained the salt reabsorbed in ascending limb, distal tubule and collecting duct. The capacity of these segments to reabsorb sodium salts, therefore, sets the limit on the amount of water which can be excreted above that containing the urinary solutes in isotonic solution. It is this limited capacity to excrete water freed of solute which accounts for the increasing concentration of dilute urine as solute excretion increases, the isotonic portion of the urine flow ($C_{os}$) constituting an ever larger fraction of the total flow ($V$). Actually $C_{H_2O}$ may be less than maximal 1) because insufficient sodium salts are delivered to the distal portions of the tubule to saturate the reabsorptive capacity or 2) because some of the water "freed" by salt removal diffuses out of the distal tubule. Even in

the total absence of ADH some permeability to water persists, and this permeability may be increased by amounts of ADH which are too small to yield a maximal effect and thus a concentrated urine.

*When the urine is concentrated* the flow is smaller than the osmolal clearance; that is,—water must be *added* to the urine to render it isotonic. Thus $C_{H_2O}$ assumes a negative value; this has been designated as $T^c_{H_2O}$ by Smith. The driving force for the removal of water from urine flowing through the collecting ducts is provided by the salt transported out of the ascending limb of the loop of Henle. Therefore the amount of water thus removed ($T^c_{H_2O}$) can not be greater than the osmotic equivalent of the salt deposited in the medulla by the loop.[10] Since the value of $T^c_{H_2O}$ is limited, as solute excretion increases the urine concentration falls, again because the isotonic portion of the urine ($C_{os}$) constitutes an even greater fraction of the total ($V$). ($V = C_{os} - T^c_{H_2O}$.) The flows and concentrations of dilute and concentrated urines as solute excretion is varied are illustrated in figures 34.9a and 34.9b.

In considering the effects of antidiuretic hormone and the change from dilute to concentrated urine, it is important to emphasize that by far the most important effect is that in the distal tubule which involves the change from dilute to isotonic urine. The relative quantitative importance of the dilution and concentration processes can be illustrated in a person excreting enough solute to require the excretion of 2 liters of isotonic urine in 24 hours. If he were to produce maximally dilute urine for this period, he would excrete approximately 20 liters of urine. Therefore, if ADH were to effect a rise in urine concentration only to isotonicity with plasma, some 18 liters of water would be conserved. If, on the other hand, the same solute were to be excreted in a maximally concentrated urine, the volume would be reduced to about 500 ml., a further saving of about 1.5 liters. Clearly, the water saved in not putting out a dilute urine is quantitatively much more important than that conserved in forming a concentrated urine.

## THE REABSORPTION AND EXCRETION OF SODIUM AND CHLORIDE

The regulation of the osmotic pressure of body fluids tends to adjust the amount of water in the

[10] This is equivalent to saying that the production of a concentrated fluid (urine) in the medulla must be just balanced by the production of a dilute one (the fluid emerging from the ascending limb of the loop).

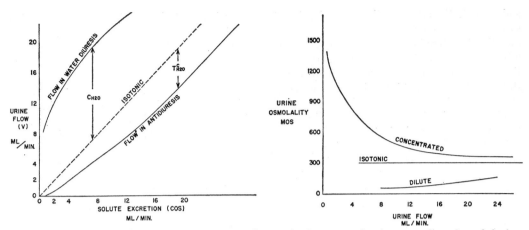

FIG. 34.9a (left). Relationship between urine flow and solute excretion in water diuresis and during the formation of concentrated urine.

FIG. 34.9b (right). Relationship between urine flow and urine osmolality when urine flow is modified by changing solute excretion. See text for explanation.

body to the amount of solute in the body fluids. Thus, so long as osmotic pressure regulation remains normal, the volume of the body fluids will depend on the amount of solute in the body. Since sodium salts constitute some 90 per cent or more of the solute of extracellular fluid, the volume of the extracellular fluid is largely dependent on the regulation of renal sodium excretion.

We have already considered, in relation to the regulation of water excretion, how sodium reabsorption is distributed in the renal tubule. It has been pointed out that a major fraction of the filtered solute and water are reabsorbed in the proximal tubule. Since most of this solute is composed of sodium salts and since the fluid remains isotonic in the process of this reabsorption, there is ordinarily little reduction of sodium concentration in the proximal tubule. However, the reabsorption involves active sodium transport since (1) the reabsorption occurs despite an electrical potential (20 mv., lumen negative to interstitial fluid) opposing the movement of sodium, and (2) if some nonreabsorbable solute (e.g., mannitol) is present, the sodium concentration does fall well below that of the peritubular fluid as sodium is reabsorbed. (However, because of a relatively high permeability the gradient of sodium concentration which can be established is limited because of diffusion from peritubular fluid.) Since chloride reabsorption is favored by the electrical potential, there is no reason to believe any specific transport mechanism for chloride is present. In essence, the chloride is pulled by its electrical charge as a result of the active transport of sodium.

The reabsorption of sodium in the more distal

segments of the nephron does result in the establishment of gradients of sodium concentration which may, indeed, be very steep since sodium may be virtually absent from the urine. The difference between proximal and distal tubules probably resides not in the character of the transport mechanism, but in the passive permeability of the tubule epithelium; there is less tendency, in the distal area, for the sodium to diffuse back into the lumen and dissipate the gradient.

In addition, in the distal tubule, not all of the reabsorption of sodium is accompanied by reabsorption of anion. Some of the sodium reabsorbed in the distal segment is replaced by potassium, and some is replaced by hydrogen and ammonium ions. These aspects of the sodium reabsorptive mechanism will be considered in relation to potassium excretion and the renal regulation of acid-base balance in later sections of this chapter.

The mechanism by which sodium is transferred from lumen to peritubular fluid is poorly understood. It is probably very closely related to that mechanism (also poorly understood) common to virtually every cell of the body, by which sodium is extruded from and potassium maintained at a high concentration in the intracellular fluid. The process probably involves a negatively charged carrier and an exchange of sodium ions for other cations (potassium and/or hydrogen), but no entirely satisfactory and generally applicable model is available.

### The Regulation of Sodium Excretion

A number of circumstances are known to influence the rate of sodium excretion. The way in which these factors are integrated to determine and regulate the rate of sodium excretion is not so well known. To say that the rate of sodium excretion is determined by the balance between filtration of sodium at the glomeruli and reabsorption of sodium by the renal tubules is merely to state the obvious. What is required is a knowledge of how these two processes are interrelated and modified to maintain a normal body sodium content. Although we can indicate qualitatively some of the determinants of sodium excretion, they can not be put together as, for instance, in the case of glucose, to predict the rate of salt excretion.

1. GLOMERULAR FILTRATION. Under average normal conditions only a very small fraction of the sodium contained in the glomerular filtrate is excreted in the urine—a person on an average salt intake puts out only about one-half of one per cent of the amount filtered. It is clear, therefore, that an increase of only one per cent in the rate of glomerular filtration[11] supplies enough additional sodium in the filtrate to double or triple the sodium excretion were none of the extra sodium reabsorbed by the tubules. It is also clear, however, that when the glomerular filtration rate increases, the increment of filtered sodium is never quantitatively excreted. In fact, unlike the situation with respect to the reabsorption of such substances as glucose and phosphate, changes in the rate of glomerular filtration are attended by parallel changes in the rate of sodium reabsorption. When glomerular filtration increases, sodium reabsorption increases; when filtration decreases, reabsorption likewise decreases. However, because these changes are not exactly proportional, changes in glomerular filtration are not accompanied by proportional changes in excretion. As a matter of fact, acute changes in the filtration of sodium produce relatively very large changes in sodium excretion. However, if the filtration rate changes are maintained for a protracted period compensatory changes in reabsorption occur so as to restore sodium balance.

These circumstances are very clearly demonstrated by the experiments of Mueller and his associates. In dogs operated upon to make it possible to collect the urine from each kidney separately, these investigators placed constricting clamps on one renal artery. It was found that if the artery was constricted so as to produce a

[11] Changes in the amount of sodium filtered are generally due largely to changes in the rate of glomerular filtration since the plasma sodium concentration is normally maintained within a very narrow range, reflecting the constancy of osmotic pressure to which sodium salts contribute such a major share.

barely detectable decrease in glomerular filtration rate, there was a marked drop in the amount of sodium excreted by the affected kidney. Such a kidney might excrete only 10 to 20 per cent of the daily sodium intake, the remainder being excreted by the normal control kidney so as to maintain sodium balance. This situation might persist indefinitely. If, however, the normal kidney was then removed there was a prompt increase in the salt excreted by the kidney with the constricted artery. When the full load of maintaining sodium balance was placed on the experimental kidney, compensatory adjustments of reabsorption overcame the effects of reduced glomerular filtration.

2. ADRENOCORTICAL STEROIDS. The best known of the influences which modify tubular reabsorption of sodium is that exerted by the steroid hormones of the adrenal cortex. The natural hormone with the greatest effect on sodium reabsorption is aldosterone, but similar effects are produced by desoxycorticosterone, cortisol, cortisone and others, as well as a number of synthetic steroids. All of the active steroids exert qualitatively identical effects on sodium transport by the renal tubules, increasing reabsorption in all its forms—that is, sodium reabsorption accompanied by chloride reabsorption as well as sodium exchange for potassium and hydrogen ions. However, the various steroids may produce differing effects on sodium *excretion* not only because they differ in potency with respect to their capacity to modify sodium transport, but because glucocorticoid activity is associated with the specific property of increasing the rate of glomerular filtration.

The control of salt excretion by the adrenal cortex is probably mediated by the secretion of aldosterone. The control of aldosterone secretion in turn is dependent upon some as yet unidentified receptor probably responsive to changes in effective intravascular volume and mediated by a trophic hormone probably secreted somewhere in the hypophyseal-hypothalamic area. Contraction of blood volume leads to increased secretion of aldosterone, increased reabsorption of sodium (and chloride) and secondarily, by an increase in the retention of water, to expansion of volume.

The mechanism by which the steroids modify sodium transport is unknown. It should be clearly understood that the transport process proceeds very well in the absence of the corticosteroids; the effect of the hormones is, in a sense, the fine adjustment of a process which is largely autonomous.

When adrenal salt-retention hormones are administered to normal animals there is a brief period of salt retention but the decreased salt excretion is relatively short-lived. After retaining a modest amount of salt, the animal comes back into balance. This does not indicate the development of resistance to the effect of steroid on sodium transport but compensation for this effect by other factors including, but probably not limited to, an increase in glomerular filtration.

3. OSMOTIC DIURESIS. The excretion of sodium is increased by any circumstance which leads to an increase in the excretion of solute. Perhaps the most common such event is elevation of the blood glucose to levels where the reabsorptive capacity of the tubules is saturated and glucose is excreted in the urine. The same effect may be produced by the administration of poorly reabsorbed substances such as urea or mannitol. This phenomenon is known as *osmotic diuresis*. Sodium excretion is increased because the presence of the other solute depresses sodium reabsorption in the proximal tubule. As sodium is reabsorbed, the other solute, which remains behind in the tubule, forms a larger and larger fraction of the total solute. Since the fluid retains the same total solute concentration as the blood, the sodium concentration must fall; the decrease in concentration impairs reabsorption.

4. EXCRETION OF POORLY REABSORBED ANIONS OR ANIONS SUBJECT TO TUBULAR EXCRETION. When large amounts of some anion are excreted in the urine, there must be an equivalent amount of cation excreted. To some extent sodium may be substituted for by potassium, ammonium or hydrogen ions, but the capacity to do this is limited. Thus under conditions where large amounts of sulfate, phosphate, p-aminohippurate (PAH), etc., are excreted, sodium excretion is increased.

5. SPECIFIC INHIBITION OF SODIUM TRANSPORT. The commonly used diuretics,—organic mercurials, chlorothiazide and related compounds, carbonic anhydrase inhibitors, etc., all owe their efficacy to the capacity to depress sodium transport by the renal tubules.

## THE EXCRETION OF POTASSIUM

Potassium holds a unique place among the normal constituents of the blood and urine in being subject to both reabsorption and secretion by the tubules. The average rate at which potassium is excreted in the urine is only about 15 per cent of the rate at which it is filtered at the glomeruli; on the other hand, if large amounts of potassium salts are administered, or if the secretion of hydrogen ion is inhibited, the rate of excretion of potassium may rise to levels equivalent to twice the rate at which it is filtered. There is considerable evidence to support the view that, even when the amount excreted is less than that filtered, the potassium in the urine is derived from tubular secretion.

The site and mechanism of potassium reabsorption are incompletely established, beyond the fact that reabsorption occurs more proximally than tubular secretion. It seems most likely that potassium reabsorption occurs in the proximal tubule and involves a specific active transport process since the urine potassium concentration may be considerably lower than the concentration in plasma and since all the electrical potential measurements which have been made have shown the lumen to be negative to the peritubular fluid. (An electrical potential oriented in the opposite direction would be required to produce passive movement against a concentration gradient.) It seems fairly certain that the reabsorptive mechanism is able to reabsorb all of the potassium delivered to it and that the filtered potassium makes no contribution to potassium excretion.

The potassium secretory process is located in the distal convoluted tubule, possibly extending into the collecting system. The tubular secretory mechanism operates by reabsorbing sodium ions in exchange for secreted potassium ions. Thus potassium excretion is limited to the amount of sodium which reaches the distal tubule segment in which exchange occurs.

The rate of potassium excretion is determined by several factors:

1. The concentration of potassium in cells, particularly the renal tubule cells. The concentration of potassium in the plasma has little influence on potassium excretion except insofar as cell potassium concentration tends to vary with plasma concentration. Such an arrangement is highly reasonable since potassium is primarily an intracellular ion, and it is, therefore, the cell potassium to which excretion should be related.

2. The amount of sodium delivered to the tubule site of sodium-potassium exchange is an important factor. Thus paradoxically, since sodium is reabsorbed as potassium is secreted, sodium and potassium excretion frequently vary in parallel rather than inversely.

3. The rate of tubular secretion of hydrogen ion or, possibly, the acidity of the secretory cells. The mechanism by which potassium is exchanged for sodium is also involved in exchanging hydrogen for sodium and there is competition between potassium and hydrogen in the process. Anything

which tends to enhance the secretion of hydrogen ion, depresses tubular excretion of potassium; anything which inhibits tubular secretion of hydrogen ion, enhances excretion of potassium.

4. The capacity of the exchange mechanism. Provided sufficient sodium is delivered to the exchange mechanism potassium excretion is enhanced by conditions which enhance sodium reabsorption (adrenocortical steroids) and depressed by inhibitors of the mechanism (mercurial diuretics).

5. Tolerance to potassium. For reasons that are not entirely clear potassium excretion is facilitated by repeated administration of potassium.

### Renal Regulation of Acid-base Balance

Under normal conditions the diet provides a number of sources of potential acid. The organic phosphorus of proteins and phospholipids is converted to phosphoric acid; the sulfur of the sulfur-containing amino acids is converted to sulfuric acid. When ammonium chloride is ingested, the ammonium ion is converted to urea and hydrogen ion leaving hydrochloric acid as the end product. If calcium chloride is ingested, the calcium may be excreted in the stool as the insoluble salts of organic acids (such as fatty acids), and hydrochloric acid is absorbed. Under abnormal conditions (starvation, diabetic ketosis) large amounts of organic acid may be produced, well beyond the capacity of the body to oxidize this acid to carbon dioxide.

In the usual dietary circumstances the dietary sources of acid predominate over the sources of alkali, but the latter may be in excess with certain intakes. Fruits and vegetables abound in the salts of organic acids. The organic anions are oxidized to $CO_2$ leaving the bicarbonates of sodium and potassium. In addition the intake may include sodium or potassium bicarbonate as such.

Acid or alkali entering the body fluids react with the buffers of these fluids and the pH change which occurs is thereby minimized. The most abundant buffer system of extracellular fluid is that made up of bicarbonate and carbonic acid and the bulk of the extracellular buffering is therefore involved with this system. Because it must provide the major part of the alkali to neutralize any acid gaining access to the extracellular fluid, the bicarbonate concentration has been designated the *alkali reserve* and can be considered a measure of the degree of acidosis or alkalosis (even though, by respiratory compensation, changes of

bicarbonate concentration may be accompanied by only minimal changes in pH).

Acid added to extracellular fluid reacts chiefly with bicarbonate to yield carbonic acid and the salt of the acid. The carbonic acid in turn yields $CO_2$ which is excreted in the lungs.

$$H^+A^- + Na^+HCO_3^- \leftrightarrows$$

$$NA^+A^- + H_2CO_3 \leftrightarrows H_2O + CO_2$$

The result is the replacement, in the extracellular fluid, of one equivalent of bicarbonate with one equivalent of the anion of the acid. The anion $(A^-)$ will eventually be excreted in the urine. If it is excreted as the sodium salt, the form in which it exists in plasma, the over-all result will have been the disappearance from the extracellular fluid of one mol of sodium bicarbonate for each mol of HA added.

The buffer capacity of the extracellular fluid can be restored only by regaining a mol of sodium bicarbonate. This might be done, if, instead of excreting the sodium salt (NaA) in the urine, the kidney were able to dispose of the free acid HA thus regenerating sodium bicarbonate. This would amount to a reversal of the reactions above:

$$H_2O + CO_2 \rightarrow H_2CO_3 + Na^+A^- \rightarrow$$

$$Na^+HCO_3^- + HA \rightarrow (urine)$$

This, in fact, the kidney is able to do by virtue of its capacity to produce urine considerably more acid (down almost to pH 4) than the blood (pH 7.40). Thus, to the extent that any acid is un-ionized at the pH of the urine, that acid may be disposed of directly, with regeneration and recovery of the bicarbonate by which it was temporarily buffered in the extracellular fluid.

The extent to which an acid is un-ionized at a given pH can be deduced from the Henderson-Hasselbalch equation

$$pH = pK + \log \frac{[A^-]}{[HA]}$$

This may be rearranged in the form $pK - pH = \log [HA] - \log [A^-]$ to indicate more clearly that when the pH is lower than the pK of the acid concerned there will be more un-ionized acid than salt. Thus any acid which has a pK higher, *or not much lower* than the pH of the urine,[12] can be excreted to an appreciable extent in un-ionized form. Acids with pK's high enough to appear in

[12] Although more acid urine *can* be formed, the urine pH is not often below 5.0 and is more commonly around 6.

the urine in undissociated form to an appreciable extent are monobasic phosphate ($H_2PO_4^- \leftrightharpoons HPO_4^- + H^+$), pK 6.80; $\beta$-hydroxybutyric acid, pK 4.7.

For most acids which enter the extracellular fluid, excretion as the undissociated acid is impossible. Hydrochloric and sulfuric acids are completely dissociated at all pH's. At a urine pH as low as 4.0, the concentration of hydrochloric or sulfuric acid would be only $10^{-4}$ N or 0.1 m.eq. per liter. Even *weak* acids having pK's much below 5 must be excreted almost entirely as salts. In the excretion of such acids, then, some other mechanism is required if bicarbonate is to be regained to replace that originally lost in neutralizing them. This is accomplished by the generation of ammonium ion from neutral precursors and the substitution of ammonium ion for sodium ion in the urine. The acids are excreted as ammonium salts; the sodium is returned to the extracellular fluid as sodium bicarbonate. The overall reaction may be considered to be the following:

$$RNH_2 + HOH \rightarrow NH_3 + ROH \text{ (which may}$$

then be oxidized to $CO_2$ and $H_2O$)

$$NH_3 + Na^+A^- + H_2CO_3 \rightarrow$$

$$NH_4^+A^- \text{ (to urine) } + Na^+HCO_3^-$$

Neither of these reactions nor those indicated above should be interpreted as indicating the actual processes which take place in the kidney. They represent the net results of a series of reactions.

Thus acids are disposed of without loss of alkali reserve (1) by excretion of weak acids in their unionized form and (2) by the substitution of ammonium ion for sodium ion in the excretion of their salts. The disposal of excess alkali is more direct. Alkali appears in the extracellular fluid as bicarbonate ($B^+OH^- + CO_2 \rightleftarrows B^+HCO_3^-$) and is excreted in the urine as that bicarbonate which escapes reabsorption in the tubules. This background concerning the nature of the overall processes will serve as an introduction to the renal mechanisms which determine the excretion of acid or alkali.

Three processes are important in regulating the amount of acid or alkali excreted: (1) the filtration of bicarbonate at the glomeruli, (2) the transport mechanism by which bicarbonate is reabsorbed and the urine rendered acid, and (3) the synthesis of ammonia by the cells of the renal tubule.

The glomerular filtrate contains bicarbonate at a concentration essentially identical to that in plasma.[13] Micropuncture studies by Gottschalk have shown that as the fluid flows through the proximal tubule in the mammal, its pH tends to fall somewhat (to as low as about 6.5).[14] Although the bicarbonate concentration of these fluids has never been measured, these pH determinations indicate that bicarbonate is extensively reabsorbed in the proximal tubules since some 80 per cent of tne glomerular filtrate is reabsorbed, and the bicarbonate concentration of the fluid which remains is lower than that of plasma.

The latter is inferred from the Henderson-Hasselbalch equation, pH = $6.1 + \log ([HCO_3^-]/[H_2CO_3])$ and the assumption that the denominator, $[H_2CO_3]$, remains constant. The assumption is justified by the very high diffusibility of carbon dioxide through all known biological membranes which would indicate that the carbon dioxide tension (concentration) and therefore the carbonic acid concentration must be very nearly equal to those of plasma.

In the distal tubule the urine is further acidified, and the process continues into the collecting ducts. The major reduction in pH occurs in the distal parts of the nephron, but this does not necessarily indicate that the reabsorption of base occurs predominantly in the latter segments. As bicarbonate is removed from the tubule lumen, changes in the pH of the remaining fluid will depend upon the changes in volume of the remaining fluid. If bicarbonate removal proceeds more rapidly than volume decreases, the bicarbonate concentration falls and the pH likewise falls since the concentration of carbonic acid remains constant (see above). If the volume of the remaining tubular fluid diminishes more rapidly than does the amount of bicarbonate remaining, the pH of the fluid will rise. Thus, the degree to which the urine is acidified depends not only upon the rate of bicarbonate removal, but on the relationship of the removal rate to the rate of removal of water. Consequently, the production of urine more alkaline than plasma requires only that a greater fraction of the filtered water than of the filtered bicarbonate be reabsorbed.

[13] Because the plasma proteins are nonfilterable anions, a Donnan equilibrium is set up across the glomerular membrane, and all monovalent filterable anions, including bicarbonate, are about 5 per cent more concentrated in glomerular filtrate than in plasma water. All monovalent filterable cations, including $H^+$, are about 5 per cent less concentrated.

[14] Measurements have been made only under conditions in which the fully elaborated urine was acid. It is not unlikely that when the final urine is alkaline, the pH does not decrease but may even rise in the proximal tubule.

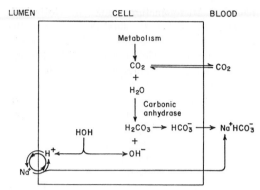

LUMEN          CELL          BLOOD

Fɪɢ. 34.10. Hypothetical cellular processes in the secretion of hydrogen ion in exchange for sodium.

### Mechanism of Urine Acidification

Largely as the result of the studies of Pitts and his associates the process by which bicarbonate removal is effected is generally accepted as being one in which hydrogen ion is secreted by the cells of the renal tubule in exchange for sodium ions. The mechanism may be conveniently depicted as follows (fig. 34.10): In the renal tubule cell, as a result of energy-requiring processes, hydrogen ion and hydroxyl ion are generated from water in spatially separated loci. The hydrogen ion enters the tubule lumen in exchange for a sodium ion which is taken into the cell. Meanwhile the hydroxyl ion is buffered within the cell by reacting with carbonic acid to yield bicarbonate ion and water. The bicarbonate and sodium ions are extruded into the extracellular fluid. The carbonic acid is regenerated by the hydration of carbon dioxide; the latter may be derived from either the metabolic processes within the cell or from the carbon dioxide of the blood and extracellular fluid.

The regeneration of the carbonic acid proceeds rapidly only in the presence of the enzyme *carbonic anhydrase* and this step may become rate-limiting in the overall process. When the production of carbonic acid is impaired by inhibition of the enzyme, the concentration of carbonic acid in the cell falls and with it the hydrogen ion concentration. Since the rate at which hydrogen ion is extruded in exchange for sodium ion is related to the hydrogen ion concentration in the cell, the rate of secretion of hydrogen ion is diminished. Thus *inhibition of carbonic anhydrase diminishes the secretion of hydrogen ion* and all of the processes dependent upon the secretion of hydrogen ion.

It should be noted that in the above process, for each hydrogen ion extruded one equivalent of

sodium as the bicarbonate is added to the extracellular fluid and this result is independent of the fate of the hydrogen ion in the tubule lumen (fig. 34.11). The fate of the hydrogen ion which enters the lumen in exchange for a sodium ion depends upon the composition of the fluid which it enters.

Acid added to any buffered solution is distributed among the buffers of that solution in a predictable way depending upon the relative concentrations of the buffers and their pK values. Any change in hydrogen ion concentration must affect all the buffers present since all must satisfy their ionization constants. The amount of hydrogen ion distributed to each buffer will be directly proportional to the concentration of the buffer and inversely related to the difference between the pH of the solution and the pK of the buffer.

We may consider as an example the secretion of hydrogen ion into the proximal renal tubule. The buffers contained in the glomerular filtrate may be considered to be bicarbonate (pK' 6.1) at a concentration of about 27 mmole per liter and phosphate (pK 6.8) at a concentration of about 1.5 mmole per liter. Because it is present in much higher concentration, bicarbonate will take up most of the hydrogen ion secreted even though the pH of the fluid (7.4) is closer to the pK of phosphate. Thus in the proximal tubule most of the added hydrogen ion reacts with bicarbonate.

$$H^+ + HCO_3^- \rightleftarrows H_2CO_3 \rightleftarrows H_2O + CO_2$$

The result of hydrogen ion addition, then, is the conversion of bicarbonate ion to $CO_2$ and water,

### MECHANISM OF URINARY ACIDIFICATION

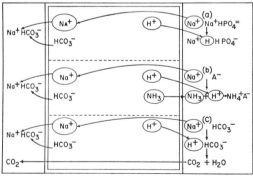

PLASMA          TUBULE CELL          URINE

Fɪɢ. 34.11. Fate of hydrogen ion secreted into tubule lumen in exchange for sodium. a) Formation of titratable acid; b) formation of ammonium ion; c) reabsorption of filtered bicarbonate. Modified from figure of Orloff (Yale J. Biol. & Med., 29:211, 1956).

and the $CO_2$ diffuses out of the tubule lumen to extracellular fluid. Thus the exchange of a mol of sodium ion for a mol of hydrogen ion has resulted in the removal of a mol of sodium bicarbonate from the glomerular filtrate even though no bicarbonate ion has crossed the membrane separating lumen from tubule cell. Instead, the bicarbonate ion which enters the extracellular fluid is generated independently in the tubule cell.

In the distal tubule the situation may be quite different. Suppose that the proximal tubule capacity for phosphate reabsorption has been saturated so that half of the filtered phosphate has escaped reabsorption and reaches the distal tubule. At the same time the volume of the fluid flowing through the tubule has been greatly diminished by the processes of reabsorption, so that we may assume that at some point in the distal tubule only 5 per cent of the glomerular filtrate remains. The phosphate concentration in the fluid will then have reached a value ten times that in the glomerular filtrate or 15 mmole per liter. Now the hydrogen ion secreted into the fluid will to a very considerable extent react with dibasic phosphate, converting it to monobasic phosphate:

$$H^+ + HPO_4^- \rightleftharpoons H_2PO_4^-$$

As the pH falls, the concentration of bicarbonate diminishing rapidly, a greater proportion of the hydrogen ion will be taken up by other buffers. At pH 6.1, the bicarbonate concentration will be only about 1.4 m.eq. per liter, at 5.1 about 0.14 m. eq. per liter.

It is important to note that as hydrogen ion reacts with bicarbonate the resulting undissociated acid ($H_2CO_3$) disappears from the urine (as $CO_2$). The hydrogen ion which reacts with other weak acids, however, remains and can be detected in the final urine in the form of *titratable acid*. The amount of the latter can be determined as the amount of alkali required to titrate the urine back to the pH of plasma, and is equal to the amount of hydrogen ion expended and sodium bicarbonate regenerated in the conversion of the buffer salt (as it existed in plasma) to the buffer acid as it appears in the urine. The titratable acid, therefore, is a very poor measure of the amount of hydrogen ion secreted by the renal tubules since most of the acid produced by this secretion is carbonic acid which is dissipated.

However, from the standpoint of the regulation of the acid-base balance of the body, the situation is reversed. That part of the secretion of hydrogen ion which is expended in reabsorbing bicarbonate from the glomerular filtrate serves an important conservative role in preventing loss of bicarbonate from the body, but its overall effect is only to return to the extracellular fluid that which it previously had lost for a time into the glomerular filtrate. The excretion of titratable acid, however, represents the addition of extra sodium bicarbonate to the extracellular fluid, replacing the neutral salt ($Na^+A^-$) which it had previously contained. This, then, is an addition to the alkali reserve and as such can be used to balance off the acid products of ingestion and metabolism.

The excretion of titratable acid is a process in which there is a net gain of alkali reserve, but it is a process of limited potentiality, limited by the capacity of the kidney to reduce the pH of the urine and by the amount of weak acid of suitable pK excreted in the urine. This process alone would be unable to maintain the alkali reserve against the continued addition to extracellular fluid of even most of those acids which can be excreted to a considerable extent in un-ionized form. Thus, β-hydroxybutyric acid can be excreted about half as the free acid, half as the salt. The excretion of titratable acid can therefore diminish the attrition of body buffer by about one-half, but the continued production of this acid would eventually exhaust the extracellular bicarbonate supply. Of course, the production of titratable acid contributes nothing to balancing off the effects of the ingestion or production of strong mineral acids. The latter effects are overcome by the production and excretion of ammonium ion in place of so-called "fixed cation" (largely sodium and potassium).

EXCRETION OF AMMONIA. The source of urinary ammonia was the subject of debate for many years. That the ammonia is produced in the kidney was established by the studies of Nash and Benedict who showed that more ammonia left the kidney in renal venous blood than entered in the arterial blood. The experiments of Van Slyke and his associates demonstrated that a major fraction of the urinary ammonia was derived from the amide nitrogen of glutamine.

$$\text{Glutamine} \rightarrow NH_3 + \text{glutamic acid}$$

Ammonia is also produced by the oxidative deamination of a number of amino acids (glycine, alanine, leucine, aspartic acid).

Ammonia, produced in the cells of the renal tubules, enters and accumulates in the renal tubules by simple diffusion. The nature of the process by which this accumulation takes place may be understood from a consideration of the nature of cell membranes and the solubility characteristics of weak electrolytes.

Most cell membranes that have been studied have the characteristics of lipid layers permeated by aqueous pores which occupy only a very small part of the total surface area. Substances which are highly soluble in lipid can penetrate the entire surface of the cell, while those which are highly water-soluble and lipid-insoluble can penetrate only through the aqueous pores. Lipid soluble materials, therefore, diffuse in and out of cells very much more rapidly than water soluble substances. Among the latter are most ions; ionized compounds are, in general, highly water soluble and poorly soluble in lipid. On the other hand many un-ionized substances are highly soluble in lipids (provided they are not highly polar compounds, e.g., sugars, urea, short-chain alcohols, etc.). In accord with these generalizations, the ammonium ion ($NH_4^+$) is highly water soluble and would be expected to penetrate cell membranes poorly; on the other hand, free ammonia ($NH_3$) is highly lipid-soluble and penetrates cells quite readily.

Now suppose we have two aqueous solutions of different pH separated by a membrane having the characteristics of the lipid layer discussed above. To such a system ammonia is added. The ammonia, being highly lipid soluble, will penetrate the membrane readily and will reach equilibrium when the concentration of the free ammonia ($NH_3$) is the same on both sides of the membrane. However, in each solution ammonia will react with hydrogen ion to yield ammonium ion:

$$NH_3 + H^+ \leftrightarrows NH_4^+$$

This reaction will be continuously at the equilibrium required by the dissociation equation:

$$K_A = \frac{[H^+][NH_3]}{[NH_4^+]}$$

or

$$pH = pK_A + \log \frac{[NH_3]}{[NH_4^+]}; \quad pK_A = 8.9$$

Since [$NH_3$] is the same on both sides of the membrane, the numerator of last term may be considered a constant and the log [$NH_4^+$] will vary inversely with the pH. Thus a decrease in pH of one unit will yield a tenfold increase in ammonium ion concentration. Since the free ammonia constitutes a very small part of the total ($NH_3 + NH_4^+$) the total will vary pretty much as the concentration of ammonium ion.

This model may be considered to approximate the situation in the kidney where the solution on one side of the membrane represents the contents of the renal tubule cells in which ammonia is produced and the other side of the membrane, the fluid in the lumen. We may consider the pH of the intracellular fluid and its ammonia concentration to be maintained relatively constant and ammonia to accumulate in the lumen until the free ammonia concentration is approximately the same on both sides and the ammonium ion concentration in the lumen that required by the urinary pH. The concentration of ammonium ion will therefore increase as urine pH decreases.

Because several assumptions involved in this model are only approximations, the actual ammonia excretion varies with pH appreciably less than would be predicted. A urinary pH change of two to two and a half units is required to yield a tenfold change in ammonia excretion. (The idealized model would indicate a tenfold change with each pH unit.) It should be noted that as $NH_3$ diffuses into the urine, hydrogen ion is titrated and the pH of the urine tends to become elevated; the pH difference would disappear if it were not maintained by the continuous secretion of hydrogen ion.

The formation of ammonia is believed to be a function of the distal portions of the nephron. In any case it is unlikely that the urine pH is low enough, in earlier parts of the tubule, for ammonia to play any essential role in the hydrogen ion secretion process. However, as urine pH approaches its minimum in the distal nephron, each hydrogen ion secreted into the lumen must be neutralized by capture of $NH_3$ to form an ammonium ion before another hydrogen ion can be secreted.

The excretion of ammonia like the excretion of titratable acid represents replenishment of the body's alkali reserve. Quantitatively it represents, under most conditions, the more important contribution to the maintenance of the acid-base balance of the body. The sum of titratable acid and urinary ammonium ion represent the net gain of sodium bicarbonate for the body fluids as a result of the process of urine formation. (In estimating body balance, it is necessary to subtract from this total any bicarbonate excreted in the urine.)

A striking and unique feature of ammonia formation and excretion is the phenomenon of *adaptation*. If an individual is given an acidifying regimen (such as the administration of ammonium or calcium chloride or the feeding of a strongly acid-ash diet), there is a gradual increase, over a period of three to five days, of the excretion of ammonia in the urine. This increase is independent of changes in urinary pH (which occur very much more rapidly) and the amount of ammonia in the urine is eventually greater at each pH than it was before the acidifying stimulus was started. The administration of alkali has an effect exactly the reverse of the administration of acid. Neither the nature nor the immediate stimulus to this adaptation are too clearly established. It undoubtedly involves a modification in the enzymatic mechanism by which ammonia is produced and presumably a rise in the concentration of ammonia in the cells in which it is produced.

In the rat, but not in the dog, it can be shown that glutaminase activity is increased. The overall behavior of ammonia excretion in man resembles that in the dog more closely than in the rat. For instance, if acidosis is produced by the administration of inhibitors of carbonic anhydrase which cause massive loss of bicarbonate in the urine, ammonia excretion and glutaminase activity increase markedly in the rat, but ammonia excretion remains at a level related only to urine pH in both man and dog. There is no evidence of adaptation of the sort produced by the administration of acidifying salts.

The stimulus to adaptation is also not clear. It is obviously in some way related to the intake of acid, but it does not appear to depend on the degree of acidosis, ammonia excretion remaining high when, as a result of the adaptation, plasma bicarbonate has been restored essentially to normal.

QUANTITATIVE ASPECTS OF URINE ACIDIFICATION. As with all processes of urinary excretion, the urinary acidification is dependent upon the balance between glomerular filtration and tubular reabsorption. In this case, the important characteristic of the filtrate is its bicarbonate concentration. We will postpone consideration of those factors which modify the secretion of hydrogen ion by the renal tubules and consider first the effect of changes in plasma bicarbonate concentration.

We must first take note of the fact that for reasons that have not been determined, the capacity of the tubules to reabsorb bicarbonate varies with the rate of glomerular filtration but not with the plasma bicarbonate concentration. The concentration of bicarbonate in the glomerular filtrate is therefore a far more important determinant of bicarbonate excretion than the total amount of bicarbonate filtered. To take this

into account and to present the reabsorption and excretion of bicarbonate as an orderly, predictable phenomenon, it is the practice to divide the amounts filtered, reabsorbed and excreted by the rate of glomerular filtration and to present the data as the amount reabsorbed, etc., per 100 ml. or per liter of glomerular filtrate.

When the plasma bicarbonate concentration is low the urine is acid and essentially free of bicarbonate; all of the filtered bicarbonate is reabsorbed. As the plasma bicarbonate concentration is increased, the urine remains essentially free of bicarbonate until the concentration approaches approximately 28 m.eq. per liter. Bicarbonate then begins to appear in the urine and as the plasma concentration increases further bicarbonate reabsorption remains virtually constant at 28 m.eq. per liter of glomerular filtrate, and the excess is excreted in the urine. This is illustrated in figure 34.12. This tends to produce stabilization of the plasma bicarbonate concentration at its normal level of 27 to 28 m.eq. per liter. When the plasma bicarbonate falls below this level, the filtered bicarbonate is completely reabsorbed and conserved. If the plasma bicarbonate rises appreciably above 28 m.eq. per liter, the excess is excreted and the plasma bicarbonate tends to return rapidly to normal.

It should be noted that, to the extent that the capacity of the tubule to secrete hydrogen ion is expended in the reabsorption of bicarbonate, no appreciable amount is available to appear as titratable acid or ammonia. Thus when the plasma bicarbonate is close to 28 m.eq. per liter, essentially all of the filtered bicarbonate will be reabsorbed but there will be little titratable acid and ammonia in the urine (reflecting the fact that the urine pH will not be very low). However, when the plasma bicarbonate drops lower the bicarbonate of the glomerular filtrate may be be exhausted before the capacity to secrete hydrogen ion is fully utilized, and a variable part of the remaining capacity will appear as titratable acid (depending on the rate of excretion of buffer acid) or as ammonium ion (depending upon the rate of production of ammonia).

It is also noteworthy that the amount of titratable acid and ammonia in the urine is a poor indication of the capacity of the tubules to secrete hydrogen ion because, if plasma bicarbonate is low, hydrogen ion secretion stops when the urine pH gets too low and before all the capacity for hydrogen-sodium exchange is utilized. Thus the *capacity* to secrete hydrogen ion can be evaluated

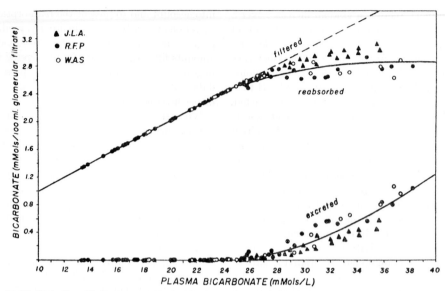

FIG. 34.12. Relationship between plasma bicarbonate and reabsorption and excretion of bicarbonate in man. (Pitts, Ayer and Schiess, J. Clin. Invest., **28**: 35, 1949).

only when there is bicarbonate left over from the process—that is, when the urine is alkaline.

FACTORS MODIFYING THE RATE OF SECRETION OF HYDROGEN ION. Under ordinary conditions of acid-base balance, with a normal carbon dioxide tension in the blood, a normal cell potassium concentration, etc., the capacity to secrete hydrogen ion in exchange for sodium is about 28 m.eq. per liter of glomerular filtrate as indicated in the preceding discussion. This tends to maintain the plasma bicarbonate concentration at about 28 m.eq. per liter. The capacity to secrete hydrogen ion may be varied in response to several factors:

*1. Carbon dioxide tension.* When the carbon dioxide tension is increased (respiratory acidosis) the plasma bicarbonate concentration increases by titration of the blood buffers, and the pH change attributable to the increased carbonic acid concentration is minimized. The elevated plasma bicarbonate concentration persists, and the maintenance implies an increase in bicarbonate reabsorption (hydrogen ion secretion) by the renal tubules. Indeed, such an increase in bicarbonate reabsorption is demonstrable immediately upon elevation of the carbon dioxide tension. If elevation of the carbon dioxide tension is maintained for extended periods there is a further increase in the capacity to secrete hydrogen ion; the nature of this further adaptation is unknown. Decreases in carbon dioxide tension (respiratory alkalosis) have exactly the opposite effects, reducing renal bicarbonate reabsorption (hydrogen ion secretion) and causing stabilization of the plasma bicarbonate concentration at a reduced level.

The effects of changes in carbon dioxide tension on hydrogen ion secretion are readily interpreted in terms of the hypothesis that the rate of secretion of hydrogen ion is directly related to the hydrogen ion concentration of the tubule cells. The concentration of dissolved $CO_2$ is directly related to the carbon dioxide tension ($pCO_2$) and the concentration of carbonic acid ($H_2CO_3$) is directly proportional to the $pCO_2$. Since cell membranes have a very high permeability to $CO_2$, all changes in extracellular $pCO_2$ are reflected by similar changes in intracellular $pCO_2$. Thus intracellular pH falls when extracellular $pCO_2$ is elevated and vice versa. (On the other hand, changes in extracellular bicarbonate concentration are probably *not* regularly reflected by parallel changes in intracellular bicarbonate and pH.)

*2. Potassium metabolism.* The secretion of hydrogen ion is depressed when potassium is administered so that the urine frequently becomes alkaline even though the plasma bicarbonate concentration is low. Conversely, in the presence of potassium depletion the rate of secretion of hydrogen ion is enhanced so that the plasma bicarbonate concentration becomes stabilized at an elevated level.

The effects of potassium on urine acidification reflect the fact that the mechanism by which hydrogen ion is secreted in exchange for sodium can also exchange potassium for sodium and that, as a result, there is competition between potassium and hydrogen ion for secretion. It may be that this apparent competition involves changes in cell hydrogen ion concentration rather than mutual exclusion from sites on a carrier. There is reason to believe that when cells lose potassium, they become more acid, and that when they gain potassium, they lose hydrogen ion. This interpretation has the advantage of placing the effects of potassium and of $CO_2$ tension on a similar basis,— the modification of cell hydrogen ion concentration.

3. *Carbonic Anhydrase.* The role of carbonic anhydrase and the effect of inhibition of this enzyme have been discussed earlier. Under normal conditions the activity of carbonic anhydrase is not rate-limiting in hydrogen ion secretion although it may become so when inhibited. There is no evidence that adaptation to acid loads involves an increase in kidney carbonic anhydrase.

4. *Adrenal steroids.* The secretion of hydrogen ion participates in the enhancement of sodium reabsorption produced by aldosterone and other steroids with similar effects on electrolyte metabolism.

### Passive Reabsorption; The Excretion of Urea

Because passive reabsorption is the result of the active reabsorption of other constituents of the glomerular filtrate, it is appropriate to consider this relatively simple mechanism last. The reabsorption of urea has long been considered a typical example of this process.[15] Certainly as the most abundant constituent of the urine and as one which fits in unique fashion into the formation of highly concentrated urine, urea requires separate consideration.

Cell membranes generally have a high permeability to urea. It is therefore not surprising that as the filtrate is reabsorbed from the renal tubules, tending to concentrate the urea in the remaining fluid, urea tends to diffuse out of the lumen. What is more remarkable is the very considerable extent to which the urea concentration can be raised in the urine. This appears to be due to two factors: (1) an unusually low permeability to urea of some or all of the cells lining the renal tubules (it is to be remembered that much of the tubule lining

---

[15] There is evidence that in ruminants (sheep, camel) there is some sort of active renal conservation of urea when the animal receives a low protein intake. While it has also been suggested that there is a similar mechanism in man, the evidence is not convincing, and for the sake of didactic clarity, any such process will be disregarded.

membrane also has a uniquely low permeability to water, especially in the absence of antidiuretic hormone); and (2) a mechanism for maintaining a high urea concentration in the interstitial fluid (of the medulla) surrounding those portions of the nephron containing fluid with the highest urea concentrations (the collecting ducts); in the latter case the concentration gradient driving the diffusion of urea out of the urine is minimized.

As is characteristic of substances excreted by mechanisms involving passive reabsorption, the fraction of the filtered urea excreted in the urine varies with the urine flow. The fraction of the filtered urea excreted is given by the ratio of the urea clearance $(C_U)$ to the glomerular filtration rate. At urine flows in excess of about 2 ml. per minute in individuals with normal renal function, there is relatively little further increase in the urea clearance with further elevation of urine flow up to the limits of *water diuresis*. At this time the urea clearance averages about 60 to 70 per cent of the inulin clearance, i.e., about 30 to 40 per cent of the filtered urea is reabsorbed. If *osmotic diuresis* is superimposed, the urine flow can be further increased, and under these conditions the excreted fraction of filtered urea increases further along a curve which may be extrapolated to suggest that no urea would be reabsorbed when no water was reabsorbed. Conversely, as urine flow decreases in antidiuresis the excreted urea diminishes to what may be only 15 or 20 per cent of the filtered. These phenomena are illustrated in figure 34.13 from the data of Shannon obtained in the dog.

As was noted earlier, in the discussion of water excretion and reabsorption, the change from the low flow of concentrated urine to the high flow of water diuresis involves primarily modifications in the flow in the distal portions of the nephron. The reabsorption of water which occurs in the proximal tubule is relatively unaffected. Thus, the additional urea which is reabsorbed when water diuresis is interrupted is logically considered to be reabsorbed in the distal tubule and collecting system. Furthermore, since in the absence of antidiuretic hormone these portions of the nephron have a low permeability to water they may be expected to have a low permeability to urea as well. It is thus logical to attribute the reabsorption of some 30 to 40 per cent of the filtered urea to losses from the proximal tubule as water is reabsorbed from that segment and to consider the losses from the distal portions of the nephron to be negligible in water diuresis. As the fraction of the filtrate reabsorbed in the proximal tubule is

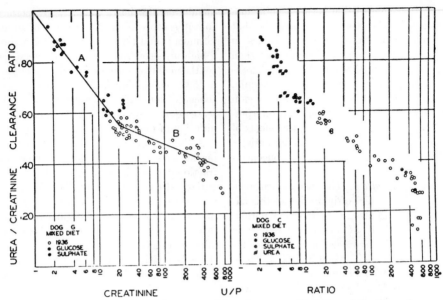

FIG. 34.13. The ratio of urea clearance to creatinine clearance. (Fraction of the filtered urea excreted in relation to the reabsorption of water as indicated by the U/P ratio of creatinine.) (Shannon, Am. J. Physiol., **122**: 782, 1938).

diminished in *osmotic* diuresis, the urea is concentrated to a lesser extent and less than the usual 30 to 40 per cent is reabsorbed.

In antidiuresis, the reabsorption of water in the distal tubule is markedly increased; at the same time, it is highly probable that the permeability to urea is also enhanced. Both of these factors lead to an increase in the diffusion of urea out of the urine in the distal portions of the nephron and account for the rapid falling off of the urea clearance as urine flow decreases to low levels.

Because the arrangement of the blood supply in the medulla constitutes a countercurrent exchanger, urea escaping from the collecting ducts is not easily carried away in the blood, as it is in the cortex. Instead, even a relatively slow leak of urea from the collecting ducts is sufficient to yield a high urea concentration in the peritubular region. As a result, the urea concentration in the interstitial space of the papilla is almost as high as in the urine. This has two important consequences: (1) the amount of urea lost from the urine is reduced because the concentration gradient is small, and (2) the osmotic effect of the urea in the collecting duct urine is counterbalanced largely by urea in the interstitial space; the sodium chloride of the interstitial space, which initiates the urine concentrating process can be utilized to balance the osmotic effect of the non-urea solute, the urea being simply added to both sides of the intervening membrane. Consequently the urine can be made considerably more concen-

trated when urea is a major part of the excreted solute, and urea, the major product of protein catabolism, and, in fact, by far the most abundant product of metabolism requiring urinary excretion can thus be excreted largely in water already obligated for the excretion of other urinary solutes.

Because the level of the blood urea and the urea clearance are frequently used for the clinical evaluation of renal function, a brief discussion of these clinical indices is warranted. Since the concentration of urea in red blood cell water is the same as in the plasma, the concentration of urea in whole blood is only slightly lower than in plasma, the difference being due to the larger fraction of solids in the red cells. Consequently, it has been the usual practice to base the clinical estimation of urea clearance on the measurement of urea in whole blood (although glomerular filtration operates only on plasma). Because of the variation of urea clearance with urine flow some account must be taken of this factor. The convention which has been adopted has been to arbitrarily divide urea clearances into two classes. When the urine flow exceeds 2 ml. per minute, the clearance of urea is calculated in the conventional fashion except for the substitution of B, the concentration in whole blood, for P, the concentration in plasma. The figure (UV)/B obtained is called the *maximal urea clearance* and a value of 75 ml. per minute is accepted as the average normal. It is customary to divide the clearance obtained by 75 and express the result as a per cent of normal.

When the urine flow is less than 2 ml. per minute, some correction is necessary to take into account the marked effect of urine flow change on urea excretion. It has been found empirically that, in normal individuals, if the clearance is divided by the square root of the urine flow ($\sqrt{V}$) the value obtained is relatively independent of urine flow provided the latter is less than 2 ml. per minute. This figure is referred to as the *standard urea clearance* and is equal to

$$\frac{UV}{B} \times \frac{1}{\sqrt{V}} = \frac{U\sqrt{V}}{B}.$$

It has an average normal value of 54 and, again, the result obtained is expressed as a per cent of the normal value.

When urea clearances are measured, every attempt should be made to assure a urine flow in excess of 2 ml. per minute since the maximal urea clearance is more clearly related to the value which one wishes to estimate, the rate of glomerular filtration.

The blood urea concentration is also, in a rough way, related to the rate of glomerular filtration. However, it is subject to modification by factors which do not affect the urea clearance, namely the intake and metabolism of protein and other nitrogen sources. For this reason the urea clearance is a much more reliable index of renal function.

For the individual in nitrogen balance, almost the entire nitrogen intake is excreted in the form of urea. The excretion of urea is in the long term equal to the formation of urea. Therefore, if we were to consider the daily excretion of urea as a sort of 24-hour determination of urea clearance we would have

$$C_U = \frac{UV}{B} = \frac{\text{rate of nitrogen turnover}}{B}$$

and

$$B = \frac{\text{rate of nitrogen turnover}}{C_U}$$

Thus we see that the blood urea is inversely related to the filtration rate to the extent that the urea clearance is related to the filtration rate, but in addition it is also directly proportional to the nitrogen turnover. The latter factor is eliminated when the urea clearance is determined.

NON-IONIC DIFFUSION. The excretion of weak electrolytes is frequently modified (or totally effected) by diffusion dependent upon the dissocia-tion characteristics of the substance concerned. The phenomenon is entirely analogous to that involved in the entrance of ammonia into the urine, a process which was discussed in some detail above. It was pointed out that un-ionized weak electrolytes frequently penetrate cell membranes very much more readily than their ions. As a result when cell membranes separate two aqueous phases of differing pH, the weak electrolyte accumulates in that phase in which the pH requires that the ratio of ionized to un-ionized weak electrolyte is higher. The same considerations apply to a number of other weak electrolytes, not only weak bases such as ammonia but weak acids as well. Most of the substances the excretion of which has been shown to involve this type of mechanism are foreign to the body, but it is highly probable that a number of normal constituents are also involved although they have not been studied in detail. Some of those drugs which have been shown to be excreted by mechanisms involving, entirely or in part, processes of non-ionic diffusion are: bases (quinine, atabrine, neutral red, mecamylamine) and acids (salicylates, phenobarbital). As opposed to the situation with respect to ammonia, which is produced in the tubule cells, the two phases of differing pH involved in excretion of these foreign materials are the urine and the peritubular interstitial space.

The effect of pH on the excretion of weak acids is exactly the opposite of its effect on that of weak bases. This is due to the fact that the ratio of ion to un-ionized fraction increases with pH in the case of weak acids, as indicated by the equation

$$pH = pK_A + \log \frac{[A^-]}{[HA]}$$

while in the case of weak bases the ratio of ionized to un-ionized decreases with rising pH as indicated by the dissociation equation for a base

$$pH = pK_A + \log \frac{[RNH_2]}{[RNH_3^+]}$$

The effect of pH on the excretion of weak bases is appreciable only when the pH of the urine is lower than the $pK_A$ of the base, since it is only when pH is less than pK that the amount of ion is the major fraction of the total. For similar reasons pH change has an appreciable effect on acid excretion only when the urine pH is higher than the pK of the acid.

It should be noted that the effect of changing pH is so great as to be compatible with net reabsorption (excretion of less than the filtered) at one urine pH and net secretion (excretion of more than the amount filtered) at another urine pH. It should also be noted that a substance may undergo active tubular secretion in the proximal tubule and nonionic diffusion in the distal, as appears to be the case with salicylates, and may be the case with a number of other weak electrolytes.

## REFERENCES

ANDERSEN, B. AND USSING, H. H. Solvent drag on nonelectrolytes during osmotic flow through isolated toad skin and its response to antidiuretic hormone. Acta Physiol. scandinav., 1957, **39**, 228.

BARTTER, F. C., LIDDLE, G. W., DUNCAN, L. E., JR., BARBER, J. K., AND DELEA, C. The regulation of aldosterone secretion in man: the role of fluid volume. J. Clin. Invest., 1956, **35**, 1306.

BERGER, E. Y., FARBER, S. J., AND EARLE, D. P., JR. Renal excretion of mannitol. Proc. Soc. Exper. Biol. & Med., 1947, **66**, 62.

BERLINER, R. W. Renal secretion of potassium and hydrogen ions. Fed. Proc., 1952, **11**, 695.

BERLINER, R. W., HILTON, J. G., YU, T. F., AND KENNEDY, T. J., JR. The renal mechanism for urate excretion in man. J. Clin. Invest., 1950, **29**, 396.

BERLINER, R. W. AND KENNEDY, T. J., JR. Renal tubular secretion of potassium in the normal dog. Proc. Soc. Exper. Biol. & Med., 1948, **67**, 542.

BERLINER, R. W., KENNEDY, T. J., JR., AND HILTON, J. G. Renal mechanisms for excretion of potassium. Am. J. Physiol., 1950, **162**, 348.

BERLINER, R. W., KENNEDY, T. J., JR., AND ORLOFF, J. Relationship between acidification of the urine and potassium metabolism. Effect of carbonic anhydrase inhibition on potassium excretion. Am. J. Med., 1951, **11**, 274.

BEYER, K. H., WRIGHT, L. D., SKEGGS, H. R., RUSSO, H. F., AND SHANER, G. A. Renal clearance of essential amino acids: their competition for reabsorption by the renal tubules. Am. J. Physiol., 1947, **151**, 202.

BRAZEAU, P., AND GILMAN, A. Effect of plasma $CO_2$ tension on renal tubular reabsorption of bicarbonate. Am. J. Physiol., 1953, **175**, 33.

CHASIS, H., RANGES, H. A., GOLDRING, W., AND SMITH, H. W. The control of renal blood flow and glomerular filtration in normal man. J. Clin. Invest., 1938, **17**, 683.

DAVIDSON, D. G., LEVINSKY, N. G., AND BERLINER, R. W. Maintenance of potassium excretion despite reduction of glomerular filtration during sodium diuresis, J. Clin. Invest., 1958, **37**, 548.

DAVIES, B. M. A., AND YUDKIN, J. Studies in biochemical adaptation. The origin of urinary ammonia as indicated by the effect of chronic acidosis and alkalosis on some renal enzymes in the rat. Biochem. J., 1952, **52**, 407.

DAVIS, J. O. Evidence for an aldosterone stimulating hormone. Recent Progr. Hormone Res., 1959, **15**, 298.

DAVIS, J. O., HOWELL, D. S., AND SOUTHWORTH, J. L. Mechanisms of fluid and electrolyte reten-tion in experimental preparations in dogs. III. Effect of adrenalectomy and subsequent desoxycorticosterone acetate administration on ascites formation. Circulation Res., 1953, **1**, 260.

FINDLEY, T., JR. AND WHITE, H. L. The response of normal individuals and patients with diabetes insipidus to the ingestion of water. J. Clin. Invest., 1937, **16**, 197.

GAMBLE, J. L., McKHANN, C. F., BUTLER, A. M., AND TUTHILL, E. An economy of water in renal function referable to urea. Am. J. Physiol., 1934, **109**, 139.

GOMEZ, D. M. Evaluation of renal resistances, with special reference to changes in essential hypertension. J. Clin. Invest., 1951, **30**, 1143.

GOTTSCHALK, C. W., AND MYLLE, M. Micropuncture study of the mammalian urinary concentrating mechanism: evidence for the countercurrent hypothesis. Am. J. Physiol., 1959, **196**, 927.

GOTTSCHALK, C. W. AND MYLLE, M. Am. J. Physiol., in press.

GUTMAN, A. B., YU, T. F., AND BERGER, L. Tubular secretion of urate in man. J. Clin. Invest., 1959, **38**, 1778.

HILGER, H. H., KLUMPER, J. D., AND ULLRICH, K. J. Wasserruckresorption und Ionentransport durch die Sammelrohrzellen der Saugetierniere. Arch. ges. Physiol., 1958, **267**, 218.

HOBER, R. Effect of some sulfanilamides on renal secretion. Proc. Soc. Exper. Biol. & Med., 1942. **49**, 87.

KANDEL, A. AND PETERS, L. Observations concerning the renal tubular transport characteristics of three quaternary bases in dogs. J. Pharmacol. & Exper. Therap., 1957, **119**, 550.

KOEFOED-JOHNSEN, V. AND USSING, H. H. The nature of the frog skin potential. Acta Physiol. scandinav., 1958, **42**, 298.

LEVINSKY, N. G. AND BERLINER, R. W. The role of urea in the urine concentrating mechanism. J. Clin. Invest., 1959, **38**, 741.

LEVINSKY, N. G., DAVIDSON, D. G., AND BERLINER, R. W. Effects of reduced glomerular filtration on urine concentration in the presence of antidiuretic hormone, J. Clin. Invest., 1959, **38**, 730.

LOTSPEICH, W. D. Renal tubular reabsorption of inorganic sulfate in the normal dog. Am. J. Physiol., 1947, **151**, 311.

MARSHALL, E. K., JR. AND VICKERS, J. L. The mechanism of the elimination of phenolsulphonphthalein by the kidney; a proof of secretion by the convoluted tubules. Bull. Johns Hopkins Hosp., 1923, **34**, 1.

MOLLER, E., McINTOSH, J. F., AND VAN SLYKE, D. D. Studies of urea excretion. II. Relationship between urine volume and the rate of urea excretion by normal adults. J. Clin. Invest., 1929, **6**, 427.

MONTGOMERY, H. AND PIERCE, J. A. The site of acidification of the urine within the renal tubule in Amphibia. Am. J. Physiol., 1937, **118**, 144.

MUDGE, G. H., AMES, A., FOULKS, J., AND GILMAN, A. Effect of drugs on renal excretion of potassium in the dog. Am. J. Physiol., 1950, **161**, 151.

MUDGE, G. H., FOULKS, J., AND GILMAN, A. The renal excretion of potassium. Proc. Soc. Exper. Biol. & Med., 1948, **67**, 545.

MUELLER, C. B., SURTSHIN, A., CARLIN, M. R., AND WHITE, H. L. Glomerular and tubular influences on sodium and water excretion. Am. J. Physiol., 1951, **165**, 411.

NASH, T. P. AND BENEDICT, S. R. The ammonia content of the blood and its bearing on the mechanism of acid neutralization in the animal organism. J. Biol. Chem., 1921, **48**, 463.

ORLOFF, J. AND BERLINER, R. W. The mechanism of the excretion of ammonia in the dog. J. Clin. Invest., 1956, **35**, 223.

ORLOFF, J., KENNEDY, T. J., JR., AND BERLINER, R. W. The effect of potassium in nephrectomized rats with hypokalemic alkalosis. J. Clin. Invest., 1953, **32**, 538.

PAPPENHEIMER, J. R., RENKIN, E. M., AND BORRERO, L. M. Filtration, diffusion and molecular sieving through peripheral capillary membranes. A contribution to the pore theory of capillary permeability. Am. J. Physiol., 1951, **167**, 13.

PITTS, R. F. A comparison of the renal reabsorptive processes for several amino acids. Am. J. Physiol., 1944, **140**, 535.

PITTS, R. F. AND ALEXANDER, R. S. The renal reabsorptive mechanism for inorganic phosphate in normal and acidotic dogs. Am. J. Physiol., 1944, **142**, 648.

PITTS, R. F. AND ALEXANDER, R. S. The nature of the renal tubular mechanism for acidifying the urine. Am. J. Physiol., 1945, **144**, 239.

PITTS, R. F. AND LOTSPEICH, W. D. Bicarbonate and the renal regulation of acid-base balance. Am. J. Physiol., 1946 **147**, 138.

PITTS, R. F., LOTSPEICH, W. D., SCHIESS, W. A., AND AYER, J. L. The renal regulation of acid-base balance in man. I. The nature of the mechanism for acidifying the urine. J. Clin. Invest., 1948, **27**, 48.

RECTOR, F. C., JR. AND ORLOFF, J. The effect of the administration of sodium bicarbonate and ammonium chloride on the excretion and production of ammonia. The absence of alterations in the activity of renal ammonia-producing enzymes in the dog. J. Clin. Invest., 1959, **38**, 366.

REHBERG, P. B. Studies on kidney function. I. The rate of filtration and reabsorption in the human kidney. Biochem. J., 1926, **20**, 447.

RELMAN, A. S., ETSTEN, B., AND SCHWARTZ, W. B. The regulation of renal bicarbonate reabsorption by plasma carbon dioxide tension. J. Clin. Invest., 1953, **32**, 972.

RICHARDS, A. N., BOTT, P. A., AND WESTFALL, B. B. Experiments concerning the possibility that inulin is secreted by the renal tubules. Am. J. Physiol., 1938, **123**, 281.

RICHARDS, A. N. AND WALKER, A. M. Methods of collecting fluid from known regions of the renal tubules of Amphibia and of perfusing the lumen of a single tubule. Am. J. Physiol., 1936, **118**, 111.

SARTORIUS, O. W., ROEMMELT, J. C., AND PITTS, R. F. The renal regulation of acid-base balance in man. IV. The nature of the renal compensations in ammonium chloride acidosis, J. Clin. Invest., 1949, **28**, 423.

SAWYER, W. H. Increased renal reabsorption of osmotically free water by the toad (*Bufo marinus*) in response to neurohypophysial hormones. Am. J. Physiol., 1957, **189**, 564.

SHANNON, J. A. The excretion of inulin by the dog. Am. J. Physiol., 1935, **112**, 405.

SHANNON, J. A. Glomerular filtration and urea excretion in relation to urine flow in the dog. Am. J. Physiol., 1936, **117**, 206.

SHANNON, J. A. Urea excretion in the normal dog during forced diuresis. Am. J. Physiol., 1938, **122**, 782.

SHANNON, J. A. Renal tubular excretion. Physiol. Rev., 1939, **19**, 63.

SHANNON, J. A. AND FISHER, S. The renal tubular reabsorption of glucose in the normal dog. Am. J. Physiol., 1938, **122**, 765.

SHANNON, J. A. AND SMITH, H. W. The excretion of inulin, xylose, and urea by normal and phlorizinized man. J. Clin. Invest., 1935, **14**, 393.

SHIPLEY, R. E. AND STUDY, R. S. Changes in renal blood flow, extraction of inulin, glomerular filtration rate, tissue pressure and urine flow with acute alterations of renal artery blood pressure. Am. J. Physiol., 1951, **167**, 676.

SMITH, H. W. The physiology of the kidney. Oxford University Press, New York, 1937.

SMITH, H. W. Lectures on the kidney. University Extension Division, University of Kansas, Lawrence, Kansas, 1943.

SMITH, H. W. Renal excretion of sodium and water. Fed. Proc., 1952, **11**, 701.

SMITH, H. W., FINKELSTEIN, N., ALIMINOSA, L., CRAWFORD, B., AND GRABER, M. The renal clearances of substituted hippuric acid derivatives and other aromatic acids in dog and man. J. Clin. Invest., 1945, **24**, 388.

SMITH, H. W., GOLDRING, W., AND CHASIS, H. The measurement of the tubular excretory mass, effective blood flow, and filtration rate in the normal human kidney. J. Clin. Invest., 1938, **17**, 263.

SMITH, W. W., FINKELSTEIN, N. AND SMITH, H. W. Renal excretion of hexitols (sorbitol, mannitol, and dulcitol) and their derivatives (sorbitan, isomannide, and sorbide) and of endogenous creatinine-like chromogen in dog and man. J. Biol. Chem., 1940, **135**, 231.

SULLIVAN, W. J. AND DORMAN, P. J. The renal response to chronic respiratory acidosis, J. Clin. Invest., 1955, **34**, 268.

TAGGART, J. V. Tubular transport mechanisms. Am. J. Med., 1950, **9**, 678.

TAGGART, J. V. Mechanisms of renal tubular transport. Am. J. Med., 1958, **24**, 774.

THATCHER, J. S. AND RADIKE, A. W. Tolerance to potassium intoxication in the albino rat. Am. J. Physiol., 1947, **151**, 138.

ULLRICH, K. J., HILGER, H. H., AND KLUMPER, J. D. Sekretion von Ammoniumionen in den Sammelrohren der Saugetierniere. Arch. ges. Physiol., 1958, **267**, 244.

USSING, H. H. The distinction by means of tracers between active transport and diffusion. The transfer of iodide across the isolated frog skin. Acta Physiol. scandinav., 1949, **19**, 43.

VAN SLYKE, D. D., PHILLIPS, R. A., HAMILTON,

P. B., ARCHIBALD, R. M., FUTCHER, P. H., AND HILLER, A. Glutamine as source material of urinary ammonia. J. Biol. Chem., 1943, **150,** 481.

VERNEY, E. G. Antidiuretic hormone and the factors which determine its release. Proc. Roy. Soc. London, 1947, **B135,** 25.

WALKER, A. M. Comparisons of total molecular concentration of glomerular urine and blood plasma from the frog and from Necturus. J. Biol. Chem., 1930, **87,** 499.

WALKER, A. M., BOTT, P. A., OLIVER, J., AND MACDOWELL, M. C. The collection and analysis of fluid from single nephrons of the mammalian kidney. Am. J. Physiol., 1941, **134,** 580.

WALKER, A. M., HUDSON, C. L., FINDLEY, T., JR., AND RICHARDS, A. N. The total molecular concentration and the chloride concentration of fluid from different segments of the renal tubule of Amphibia: the site of chloride reabsorption. Am. J. Physiol., 1937, **118,** 121.

WALLENIUS, G. Renal clearance of dextran as a measure of glomerular permeability. Acta Societatis Medicorum Upsaliensis, 1954, Supplement 4 to Volume 59.

WESSON, L. G., JR. AND ANSLOW, W. P. Excretion of sodium and water during osmotic diuresis in the dog. Am. J. Physiol., 1948, **153,** 465.

WILBRANDT, W. Secretion and transport of non-electrolytes. In Active Transport. SEB Symposia VIII, Academic Press, New York, 1954, p. 136.

WINDHAGER, E., WHITTEMBURY, G., OKEN, D. E., SCHATZMANN, H. J., AND SOLOMON, A. K. Single proximal tubules of the Necturus kidney. III.

Dependence of $H_2O$ movement on NaCl concentration. Am. J. Physiol., 1959, **197,** 313.

WIRZ, H. Der osmotische Druck in den corticalen Tubuli der Rattenniere. Helvet. Physiol. et Pharmacol. Acta, 1956, **14,** 353.

*Monographs and Reviews*

BERLINER, R. W., KENNEDY, T. J., JR. AND ORLOFF, J. Factors affecting the transport of potassium and hydrogen ions by the renal tubules. Arch. internat. pharmacodyn., 1954, **97,** 299.

BERLINER, R. W., LEVINSKY, N. G., DAVIDSON, D. G., AND EDEN, M. Dilution and concentration of the urine and the action of antidiuretic hormone. Am. J. Med., 1958, **24,** 730.

CUSHNY, A. R. The secretion of urine. Longmans, Green Co., London, 1926.

MARSHALL, E. K., JR. The comparative physiology of the kidney in relation to theories of renal secretion. Physiol. Rev., 1934, 14, 133.

ORLOFF, J. The role of the kidney in the regulation of acid-base balance. Yale J. Biol. & Med., 1956, **29,** 211.

PITTS, R. F. Renal excretion of acid. Fed. Proc., 1948, **7,** 418.

PITTS, R. F. Some reflections on mechanisms of action of diuretics. Am. J. Med., 1958, **24,** 745.

RICHARDS, A. N. The Croonian Lecture: Processes of urine formation. Proc. Roy. Soc. London, 1938, **126,** 398.

SMITH, H. W. The kidney. Structure and function in health and disease. Oxford University Press, New York, 1951.

# 35

# THE PATHOLOGICAL PHYSIOLOGY OF THE KIDNEY: MICTURITION

## The Clinical Evaluation of Renal Function

### Examination of the Urine

The first step in the evaluation of the functional status of the kidney and frequently the source of the first clue to the presence of renal disease is usually the clinical pathological examination of the urine. This has the unique advantage of extreme simplicity, requiring only a minimum of time and the simplest of equipment. Furthermore, the presence of renal disease is usually manifested by some abnormality of the urine. However, it is important to note that an apparently normal urine does not exclude the presence of certain diseases of the kidney nor impairment of renal function of even very marked degree.

Although the full routine examination of the urine includes several other tests usually intended to detect nonrenal metabolic abnormalities (diabetes, ketosis, etc.), those particularly related to diseases of the kidney itself are tests for protein and examination of the urinary sediment. In addition, determination of the specific gravity and acidity may, under certain conditions, be revealing of disorders of kidney function. Certain specific defects of renal function may be detected by analysis of urine for amino acids.

### Tests Involving Examination of the Blood Only

The most commonly used test intended to evaluate the functional state of the kidney is the determination of the blood urea. (The results of this determination are commonly reported as the blood urea nitrogen; since nitrogen makes up just under half of the molecular weight of urea, the blood urea concentration is approximately twice the concentration of blood urea nitrogen.) The concentration of urea in the blood is directly proportional to the nitrogen turnover and inversely proportional to the renal clearance of urea. Its relationship to the nitrogen turnover and to glomerular filtration are fully discussed on page 565 of the preceding chapter.

Since the blood urea concentration is only partially related to the rate of glomerular filtration and to the functional status of the kidney, it is hardly surprising that there is a wide range of normal values for the blood urea concentration and it is likely to be unequivocally elevated only when renal function is reduced by about half or more.

*Nonprotein nitrogen.* Under normal conditions urea contributes about half of the nonprotein nitrogen of plasma (or serum). The remainder is made up of the nitrogen of a heterogeneous group of substances: creatine, creatinine, uric acid, amino acids, etc. As renal function is depressed the nonprotein nitrogen concentration of plasma rises, largely because of increasing urea concentration, though some of the other components also accumulate. The nonprotein nitrogen determination is thus subject to very much the same interpretation and qualifications as the blood urea analysis.

*Creatinine.* The plasma creatinine concentration is a somewhat more reliable index of renal function than the blood urea concentration because the rate of formation of creatinine in the body is much more stable than the formation of urea. However, some reservation is required because the usual analysis of plasma for creatinine involves a chemical method affected by other constituents of the plasma.

### Tests Involving Collection of Urine

A general comment and caution concerning these tests as a group is warranted. These tests (except for the concentration test) involve determination of the rate of excretion of some substance. They thus require a *timed collection of urine* and can be no more accurate than the timing and completeness of collection. In the case of substances such as urea or creatinine which are normal constituents of the urine, the urine formed before the actual period of the test will contain the test substance and it is, therefore, just as important that the bladder be completely emptied at the start of the test period as that all of the urine be collected at the end. Failure to empty the bladder before the test period will give a result that is misleadingly high just as failure to empty at the conclusion of the test will give an erroneously low value. Failure to give due care and consideration to this point frequently vitiates the usefulness of what is fundamentally a valuable method for assessing kidney function.

*Urea clearance.* The mechanism of urea excretion has been considered in detail in the preceding chapter, and little need be added here. The test is useful for the information it gives concerning the level of glomerular filtration. In contradistinction to the simple determination of blood urea, the urea clearance is not dependent upon the rate of formation of urea so that this source of variation is eliminated. The urea clearance depends only upon the rate of glomerular filtration and the urine flow. When the test is carefully performed it is a very useful index of glomerular filtration rate.

*Creatinine clearance.* The clearance of endogenous creatinine is frequently a valuable index of glomerular filtration. As compared with the urea clearance it has the advantage of being unaffected by the rate of urine flow.[1] However, for reasons that have not been fully elucidated, the clearance of endogenous creatinine is sometimes considerably greater than the glomerular filtration rate and sometimes lower. This is particularly true in the presence of renal disease. The creatinine clearance can therefore be considered only a rough approximation of the rate of glomerular filtration.

*Excretion of phenolsulfonphthalein (PSP, phenol red).* Phenolsulfonphthalein (PSP) is one of that group of organic acids rapidly secreted into the urine by the renal tubules (see preceding chapter). In contrast to some of the other substances in this group, PSP is *not* completely removed from the blood which perfuses the kidney. Nevertheless, the rate at which it is excreted by the kidney is determined largely by the rate at which PSP is delivered to the kidney by the flow of blood. The excretion of PSP is, therefore, reduced when the renal blood flow is diminished. The greatest virtue of the test is its simplicity; PSP is a dye which, in alkaline solution, has an intense red color, and its concentration in the urine is easily estimated.

A number of different procedures for the performance of the PSP test have been used, involving various routes of administration of the dye and varying time periods for the collection of the urine. Procedures involving intravenous administration of the dye and relatively short periods for the collection of the urine are to be preferred as most sensitive to changes in kidney function. Low results can be obtained because of retention of PSP in the bladder as well as because of poor renal function.

*Concentration test.* The concentration test is a measure of the ability of the kidneys to form hypertonic urine. Because the test as usually performed involves determination of the urine specific gravity, it can be considered only a rather crude index of this particular function.[2] The determina-

tion of specific gravity is, however, such a simple procedure that it is unlikely that it will soon be replaced by an estimation of osmolality by the determination of the freezing point depression.

In the performance of the test, it is usual to determine the specific gravity of the urine formed after all fluids have been withheld for 10 to 24 hours. Normally the specific gravity should be greater than 1.025 although a specific gravity between 1.020 and 1.025 can not be interpreted as a clear indication of abnormality.

*Clearances of inulin and p-aminohippurate.* Properly performed these measurements yield accurate estimates of glomerular filtration rate and renal blood flow and hence are highly valuable in accurately defining the status of renal function. The theoretical basis of the measurements is discussed in the preceding chapter. Unfortunately the determination of inulin and p-aminohippurate clearances requires the administration of continuous intravenous infusions at constant rate. The desired and attainable accuracy can be achieved only with meticulous care in the collection of the urine, usually with bladder catheterization and washout of the bladder at the termination of each collection period. Finally, the chemical analysis, particularly that for inulin, is relatively involved. For these reasons these tests are rarely used for routine clinical purposes; for most such situations one or more of the approximation procedures discussed above will suffice.

### Measurement of Tubular Reabsorptive and Secretory Capacity

These indices of renal function determined, respectively, as the maximum capacity to reabsorb glucose ($Tm_G$) and to secrete p-aminohippurate ($Tm_{PAH}$) are, like the measurement of inulin and PAH clearances, more or less definitive measurements of renal function (see preceding chapter). Like the latter determinations, the procedures are involved, poorly suited to routine use, and rarely performed for purely clinical purposes.

### Disturbances of Renal Function

#### CLASSIFICATION

Disturbances of renal function may be separated into two groups—those due to disease of the kidney itself and those due to nonrenal disturbances. In the latter group fall abnormalities of renal function due to circulatory disorders and to disturbed hormonal balance with loss or excess of endocrine factors which modify the function

---

[1] However, as in any test involving the collection of urine, the *errors* due to incomplete or inaccurate collection of the urine are minimized if the rate of flow is high.

[2] In the formation of hypertonic urine the nature of the urinary solute is more or less a matter of indifference, the process being involved with

modifying the urine osmotic pressure to which each solute particle, independent of its nature, contributes equally. However, each solute particle does not modify the specific gravity in the same way; one molal solutions of different solutes may vary widely in specific gravity.

of the kidney. Among disturbances due to disease of the kidney itself two groups may be recognized: (1) disorders due to specific abnormalities of one or more of the transport mechanisms of the renal tubule; although these are particularly interesting from the point of view of clinicophysiological correlations, they are neither as frequent nor as important as (2) the inflammatory and degenerative diseases which involve the kidney more diffusely, affecting entire nephrons or nephron segments and their functions.

In the group of diseases which produce such diffuse involvement of the kidney, a few warrant brief discussion here to provide a background for some of the correlations between disturbances of physiology and renal disease. By far the most important of these from the standpoint of frequency of occurrence are glomerulonephritis, arteriolar nephrosclerosis, and pyelonephritis.

### Glomerulonephritis

Glomerulonephritis is a diffuse inflammatory disease involving primarily the glomeruli and secondarily, with loss of glomerular function, degeneration of the conjoined tubules. A number of classifications of glomerulonephritis, based largely on pathological distinction, have been proposed and a number of variants are recognized by some workers. For present purposes it is sufficient to note that glomerulonephritis can be divided into two forms which may or may not represent different stages of the same disease.

Acute glomerulonephritis is characterized by a more or less sudden onset with proteinuria and hematuria, and varying degrees of edema, hypertension and renal insufficiency. The onset of the disease can usually be related to an antecedent infection most often with Group A, $\beta$-hemolytic streptococcus. Glomerulonephritis is generally believed to be a disease involving, in some still obscure fashion, an antigen-antibody reaction which produces damage to the glomerular capillaries. Acute glomerulonephritis has a relatively low mortality. The great majority of cases recover completely, with no residual evidence of renal disease or of significant functional loss. A small proportion do not recover, but show persisting evidence of active renal disease and progressive loss of renal function with an eventually fatal outcome.

Chronic glomerulonephritis is a progressive disease characterized by proteinuria, hypertension and diminution of renal function. Whether or not it is the progressive form of the same disease recognized as acute glomerulonephritis is dis-

puted. In most patients with the chronic form no episode of acute glomerulonephritis is recognized. The rate of progress of the disease is extremely variable; some patients have a rapid downhill course with a precipitous decline in renal function. Others may, for years, have proteinuria as the only evidence of smoldering disease.

### The Nephrotic Syndrome

The nephrotic syndrome is characterized by massive proteinuria leading to a marked reduction of the plasma protein (particularly albumin) concentration, with edema, frequently massive, and generally a marked increase in the concentration of lipids, particularly cholesterol, in the plasma. Hematuria and hypertension are usually not prominent. A small proportion of instances of the nephrotic syndrome are clearly due to recognizable causes such as *amyloidosis* of the kidney, *lupus erythematosus, syphilis,* etc., but in most cases the underlying cause is not recognizable. No unanimity exists as to whether or not the idiopathic nephrotic syndrome represents a stage of chronic glomerulonephritis. A certain number of patients with the nephrotic syndrome do not recover, but show progressive loss of renal function with the development of hypertension and renal insufficiency in a fashion not distinguishable from chronic glomerulonephritis. On the other hand, with antibiotic treatment and prevention of intercurrent infection and with control of the disease with adrenocortical steroids, a considerable proportion of patients with the idiopathic nephrotic syndrome recover completely.

Whereas it was formerly believed that in true nephrosis the glomeruli were normal and the disease limited to degenerative changes in the tubule epithelium, this is now recognized as being the exact reverse of the true situation. The primary defect is in the capillary basement membrane, permitting the escape of protein into the glomerular filtrate. The striking changes in the appearance of the tubule cells on microscopic examination are probably secondary to the high concentration of protein in the glomerular filtrate with protein uptake from the tubule lumen.

### Arteriolar Nephrosclerosis

Arteriolar nephrosclerosis is the manifestation of renal damage due to hypertension. It is characterized by thickening and hyalinization and sometimes necrosis of the renal arterioles. There is progressive loss of glomeruli and the function of the tubules to which they are attached. Clinically it is characterized by proteinuria and progressive impairment of renal function which in some instances ("malignant nephrosclerosis") may be remarkably rapid. Some degree of nephrosclerosis occurs in most cases of hypertension of long standing. The progressive form leading to renal insufficiency occurs in some five to ten per cent of patients with so-called "essential" hypertension.

In contrast to the diffuse involvement of the kidney in *arteriolar*sclerosis (arteriolar nephrosclerosis) *arterio*sclerotic involvement of the larger vessels may lead to patchy ischemic degeneration of portions of the kidney. This type of involvement is relatively benign and rarely leads to significant functional disturbance.

## Pyelonephritis

Pyelonephritis is an inflammatory disease of the kidney resulting from infection of the urinary tract (pelvis) with invasion of the kidney interstitium. Single acute attacks may subside without significant sequelae, but repeated or long-standing infections lead to scarring and contraction of the kidney and what may be extensive loss of renal tissue. The loss of renal function may be accelerated as changes due to hypertension (itself initiated by the chronic pyelonephritis) are superimposed on the results of infection and scarring. Proteinuria is usually not prominent and may be absent.

### DISTURBANCES OF FUNCTION IN DIFFUSE RENAL DISEASE

PROTEINURIA (ALBUMINURIA). Perhaps the commonest manifestation of renal disease is the presence of increased amounts of protein in the urine. Normally only traces of protein are present in the urine, less than 100 mg. being excreted in a 24-hour period. In the presence of renal disease the amounts excreted may vary widely and reach figures of many grams. Whereas protein may gain access to the urine with exudation or bleeding into any part of the urinary tract, the glomeruli are the most pertinent source of urinary protein. Among the proteins of the urine albumin predominates, but despite the fact that urinary protein is frequently referred to as albumin, the other plasma proteins are also represented. However, it is true that the relative abundance of albumin is greater in the urine than the plasma.

An increased concentration of protein in the glomerular filtrate, the result of an abnormal increase in the permeability of the glomerular capillaries to plasma protein, is generally accepted as the cause of proteinuria in most instances of renal disease and is one of the major features of the nephrotic syndrome, of glomerulonephritis and of arteriolar nephrosclerosis.

It is worth noting that decreased reabsorption of normally filtered protein has been seriously considered as a possibly significant factor in producing proteinuria. Such a possibility, although not generally accepted, is compatible quantitatively with what is known about the composition of mammalian glomerular filtrate. The method used for examination of the micropuncture samples of glomerular filtrate would not have detected a protein concentration of 25 mg. per cent or less. Thus 250 mg. might have been present in each liter of glomerular filtrate and escaped detection. With a filtration rate of some 175 liters per day this would involve filtration of close to 45 grams of protein in each 24 hours.

On the other hand, there is good evidence not only that there is an increased filtration of protein in the presence of proteinuria but that there is also an increase in the reabsorption of protein by the tubules under these conditions and that, in all probability, it is this increased protein uptake that is responsible for the histological changes in renal tubule cells in such disorders as the nephrotic syndrome.

Aside from its importance as a clue to the presence of renal disease, proteinuria may, when of sufficient intensity, lead to significant depletion of the plasma proteins. In the nephrotic syndrome as a result of urinary losses, the plasma albumin concentration may be reduced to 20 per cent or less of its normal value. This is a significant factor in the development of nephrotic edema.

The presence of proteinuria is not always a sign of significant organic disease of the kidney. It may be produced in otherwise normal individuals, for example, by fever or by violent exercise. Particularly likely to be misleading is the benign condition known as *orthostatic albuminuria* or *postural proteinuria*. This is characterized by the occurrence, especially in young people, of proteinuria when the individual assumes the upright position. The urine, after a night's rest in bed, is protein free. The production of proteinuria is presumably attributable to some sort of circulatory disturbance associated with the erect posture. It is important chiefly because it is frequently mistakenly interpreted as indicating the presence of latent glomerulonephritis.

CYLINDRURIA. *Casts* are collections of protein which has precipitated in the tubules or ducts of the kidney and has been molded in the form of the structure in which it was precipitated. Cylindruria or the presence of increased number of casts in the urine is commonly associated with proteinuria of glomerular origin. Aside from the diagnostic information derivable from the nature of the casts, the detection of casts is most significant as an indication that the protein in the urine has arisen from the nephrons. The casts may consist of protein only (hyaline casts) or may have incorporated into them red or white blood cells, epithelial cells, etc. The normal urine does not contain more than 2000 casts per 24 hours.

HEMATURIA. Red blood cells may be present in the urine in increased numbers (normal: less than 130,000 per 24 hours) because of bleeding anywhere into the urinary tract. Of greatest importance in the present context is that, with inflammatory disease of the glomeruli, red cells as well as protein may penetrate the glomerular capillaries. Marked hematuria is particularly characteristic of acute glomerulonephritis.

IMPAIRMENT OF URINARY CONCENTRATION, POLYURIA, NOCTURIA. Two types of impairment of urine concentrating capacity are recognizable: (1) due to impairment of the process by which water is removed to produce urine hypertonic to plasma and (2) due to the excretion of increased amounts of solute per functioning nephron. Both types of defect contribute to the impairment of urine concentrating power observed in the presence of renal disease. Specific defects in the process which renders the urine hypertonic are present in *potassium depletion* and *hypercalciuria*. Since the processes responsible for rendering the urine more concentrated than plasma are located in the renal medulla, disease which disrupts the structure and/or function of this portion of the kidney, such as pyelonephritis and hydronephrosis, may be expected to have particularly marked effects on the concentrating process.

On the other hand, as renal function becomes progressively impaired by any nephron-destroying disease process, impaired ability to produce concentrated urine must inevitably result. Indeed, it has been shown experimentally that removal of one kidney and part of the other results in impaired ability of the remaining kidney to produce concentrated urine. The situation here is quite analogous to that observed as solute excretion is markedly increased (osmotic diuresis) in the individual with normal kidneys (see previous chapter, fig. 34.9b). As renal function becomes progressively diminished, the rate of excretion of solute must, over the long run, remain essentially unchanged reflecting the maintenance of salt balance and the excretion of products of metabolism.

However, as the number of nephrons involved in urine formation becomes smaller, the amount of solute excreted by each of those remaining becomes greater in proportion. Thus the volume of isotonic fluid in each nephron reaching the site of formation of hypertonic urine is increased and even the removal of a normal amount of water changes the concentration only to a limited extent.

As the ability to form concentrated urine is impaired, the volume of urine excreted must increase. The formation of increased volumes of urine is known as *polyuria*, a common manifestation of impaired renal function. The production of excessive amounts of urine may cause the patient to awake at night to void, a symptom designated as *nocturia*. (Of course, the ingestion of large volumes of fluid may lead to polyuria and nocturia in the absence of renal disease.)

OLIGURIA, ANURIA. Oliguria is the excretion of a markedly reduced volume of urine; anuria is the complete suppression of urine formation. Oliguria may, at times, be physiological—that is, a normal response to dehydration and the characteristic manifestation of the formation of highly concentrated urine. A particularly low urine flow is found when dehydration is accompanied by a low rate of solute excretion. This combination is likely to be encountered in the individual who is excreting very little salt because of a low salt intake, because of antecedent salt loss (sweating, diarrhea, vomiting, induced diuresis) or because salt excretion is suppressed for other reasons as in the individual who is developing edema (see discussion of edema).

On the other hand, oliguria or its extreme, anuria, may be a manifestation of a severe disorder of renal function. It may occur as a complication of severe acute nephritis or as a terminal event in chronic glomerulonephritis or other chronic renal disease. Most often, however, anuria or severe oliguria is a manifestation of some acute renal insult—a circumstance commonly known as *acute renal insufficiency* or *acute renal failure*. Such severe acute damage may be produced by a variety of injuries and nephrotoxic substances, particularly with traumatic shock (in which circumstance it has been called the *crush syndrome*), hemorrhagic shock, incompatible blood transfusion, and mercury or carbon tetrachloride poisoning. This list is far from inclusive, and acute renal insufficiency may be caused by any condition which produces prolonged hypotension and/or intense renal vasoconstriction. Renal ischemia seems a major factor in the production of acute renal insufficiency in those situations in which chemical nephrotoxins can not be implicated.

The methods by which glomerular filtration is measured are not applicable in the presence of anuria, so that it is not possible to say with certainty whether, in acute renal failure, glomerular filtration ceases, or whether it continues but that complete reabsorption of the filtered fluid occurs through disrupted tubule walls. Both theories have their supporters. In either case, it is clear, *effective* glomerular filtration is zero.

It has also been proposed that in the anuria following trauma the renal blood flow is not reduced, but actually increased, the blood being shunted away from the cortex and through the juxtamedullary and medullary regions by dilation in the latter areas. This concept has been largely discredited. In the presence of anuria there is a marked reduction in the renal blood flow. The preferential injection of the juxtamedullary circulation which can be demonstrated under these conditions (Trueta) is due to the lesser involvement of this part of the renal circulation in the generally intense renal vasoconstriction.

EDEMA. The accumulation of sufficient excess of extracellular fluid to produce detectable swelling of distensible tissues (edema) is a common feature of many renal diseases. Since edema fluid is extracellular fluid, it has the composition of plasma except for its lower protein concentration. Like plasma, then, its major constituents are sodium chloride and water. Except for localized and limited amounts of edema which can be produced by redistribution of the normal volume of extracellular fluid, the production of edema requires that an excess of both salt and water be retained within the body and, conversely, edema may be produced by any circumstance which yields a sufficient increase of the salt and water content of the body. Actually in the production of edema, it is the salt retention which is primary, water being retained to maintain the normal osmotic pressure of body fluids, and, further, in the salt, it is specifically the sodium ion which plays the predominant role; in the edematous individual, edema is increased by sodium bicarbonate (or, of course, sodium chloride) but not by ammonium or potassium chloride.

In patients with renal disease, edema may be traced to three types of disturbance: (1) to impairment of sodium excretion due to the direct effect of disease on renal processes involved in salt excretion, (2) to hypoproteinemia, and (3) to cardiac insufficiency, a common complication of renal disease particularly in the presence of long-standing hypertension.

The edema of acute glomerulonephritis is primarily of the first type, due to the effect of disease on the renal processes involved in salt excretion; salt intake exceeds the capacity of the kidney to excrete it, and edema results. The predominant mechanism is probably a sudden and sharp reduction in the rate of glomerular filtration without an equivalent impairment of the capacity of the tubules to reabsorb sodium salts, a condition frequently called "glomerulotubular imbalance." Through much of the course of chronic glomerulonephritis, a new balance is struck so that, despite reduction of the rate of glomerular filtration, sodium reabsorption by the tubules is reduced to an equivalent extent, and adequate excretion of salt is maintained. In the course of chronic glomerulonephritis, edema may appear as a result of any of the mechanisms noted above, because of the development of hypoproteinemia or, particularly late in the course of the disease, because glomerular filtration is reduced to such low levels that it is no longer possible to maintain more than a very low rate of salt excretion and finally because cardiac insufficiency may be superimposed.

In acute renal insufficiency the capacity to excrete salt may be entirely lost. Thus any salt and fluid intake is retained in the form of edema, except to the extent to which they may be lost by extrarenal routes. This situation represents the extreme of edema formation due to impairment of the renal processes for salt excretion.

The classic example of edema resulting primarily from hypoproteinemia is that which characterizes the nephrotic syndrome. In this disorder the continuous loss of large amounts of protein, particularly albumin, in the urine taxes the capacity of the body mechanisms to synthesize albumin and the plasma protein concentration falls. As the plasma protein concentration is reduced, the colloid osmotic pressure is lowered, particularly since most of the colloid osmotic pressure of plasma is normally attributable to its albumin concentration. The lowering of the plasma colloid osmotic pressure favors redistribution of fluid volume from plasma to interstitial space in accord with the Starling hypothesis (see ch. 3). It is important to note that although this series of events favors expansion of the interstitial fluid volume at the expense of the intravascular volume, no significant quantity of edema can be attributed to this series of events *alone*; the intravascular volume is not large enough to yield a significant volume of edema without disastrously compromising the circulation. The production of hypoproteinemic edema, then, requires, as does all edema formation, retention of excess salt and water. The reduced intravascular volume favored by the reduction of colloid osmotic pressure is, in all probability, the stimulus for renal salt retention mediated largely by the secretion of salt retention steroid (aldosterone) by the adrenal cortex. A low rate of glomerular filtration may be a contributory factor.

That hypoproteinemia alone is not a sufficient cause of edema in the nephrotic syndrome is indicated by the results of steroid treatment in this disorder. When fully successful, treatment with large doses of adrenocortical steroids produces disappearance of proteinuria, restoration of the plasma protein concentration, and diuresis with disappearance of the edema. However, in a number of instances in which the steroid is without apparent effect on proteinuria or plasma protein concentration, withdrawal of steroid therapy is accompanied by diuresis and loss of the edema, although the plasma protein concentration remains at its previous low level. Spontaneous diuresis without increase of the plasma protein concentration may also occur.

The edema of cardiac failure, whether a complication of renal disease (hypertension) or not, depends on renal retention of excess salt. Thus, edema of any origin is a manifestation of disordered kidney function, in the case of heart failure secondary to an abnormality of cardiac function. Although the sequence of events leading to edema in heart failure is disputed, the salt retention which occurs is the result of increased secretion of salt-active adrenocortical steroids, of some reduction of renal blood flow and glomerular filtration in many instances, and, almost certainly, of an additional poorly understood factor or factors as indicated by the following observations: The administration of salt-active steroids to normal experimental animals leads to only very little retention of sodium (much of which replaces potassium which is lost) and no edema. If, however, because of borderline cardiac insufficiency or elevation of venous pressure in a major segment of the circulation, the experimental animal is prone to the development of edema, sodium will be retained and edema will form—without reduction of the rate of glomerular filtration. The difference between edema formation and no edema formation in these two experimental situations is neither in glomerular filtration nor the amount

of adrenocortical steroid administered indicating involvement of additional unidentified factors.

ACIDOSIS. Inability to maintain a normal level of plasma bicarbonate (alkali reserve) in the face of an acidifying intake is a common feature of advanced renal disease of any type. The most important factor responsible for the acidosis is deficient ability to form and excrete ammonia and thus maintain the plasma bicarbonate concentration in the face of the acid load provided by the acidifying components of the normal diet. Usually there is no defect in the ability of the kidney to render the urine acid and highly acid urines are frequently observed in even the most advanced renal failure. Since there is no major change in the excretion of weak acids, the output of titratable acid is not depressed. However, the reduced number of nephrons is not adequate to form and put out ammonia at a normal rate in the face of even the usual, much less any increased, demands. Thus the strong acids derived from dietary sources are excreted as the sodium or potassium, rather than the ammonium salt and the blood bicarbonate (alkali reserve) is depleted. In some cases an additional factor may contribute to the acidosis in the form of a deficient ability to reabsorb bicarbonate completely when the plasma bicarbonate concentration is at normal or only slightly lowered levels.

If bicarbonate is added to render the intake effectively neutral, the acidosis of renal failure may be absent. In fact, if bicarbonate intake is much more than that necessary for a neutral intake, alkalosis may be relatively easily produced since the capacity to excrete bicarbonate at a rapid rate is limited as a consequence of the reduction of the rate of glomerular filtration.

As opposed to the tendency to the development of acidosis which is almost universal in advanced renal disease of any type, acidosis of renal origin may occur as the result of a more or less specific defect of renal function with renal function remaining relatively intact in other respects. This relatively uncommon condition is known as *renal tubular acidosis*. In contrast to the acidosis of renal insufficiency it appears to be due specifically to an inability to render the urine normally acid and not to a deficient capacity to form ammonia. The maximum capacity to secrete hydrogen ion in exchange for sodium can be shown to be normal, since there is a normal maximum rate of bicarbonate reabsorption when bicarbonate is administered. Under these conditions the urine is alkaline and the secretion of hydrogen ion which effects bicarbonate reabsorption occurs against only a very limited concentration gradient (see ch. 34, p. 559). However, as the bicarbonate concentration is reduced to normal or below, the tubules are unable to effect the complete removal of bicarbonate, this requiring that the urine be rendered highly acid. Hence bicarbonate escapes in the urine. The defect appears to be in the ability to secrete hydrogen ion against any considerable concentration gradient. Since the urine does not become acid, the excretion of ammonia remains low despite what is probably a normal ability to produce ammonia in the renal tubules (see p. 559).

RENAL INSUFFICIENCY; UREMIA. Renal insufficiency is the general term for reduction of the function of the kidney. It is manifested by many of those physiological disturbances already described—impaired concentrating capacity, polyuria, nocturia, acidosis and a general loss of flexibility in the maintenance of normal body composition in the face of the stress of departure of the intake from ideal. *Uremia* is the complex of symptoms and signs which accompany advanced renal insufficiency. It is characterized by anemia, nausea, vomiting, weakness, twitching, frequently convulsions and terminally stupor and coma. Although it derives its name from the elevated blood urea concentration which is a universal finding in the presence of the syndrome, the urea retention is not primarily responsible for the symptoms.

That urea itself is not responsible for the abnormalities associated with uremia is shown by several observations. Urea may be administered to normal individuals without producing significant disturbances. In the uremic individual, the blood urea can be considerably reduced by restriction of the protein intake without otherwise affecting the course of the disorder. The improvement which can be produced in the uremic patient by dialysis with the "artificial kidney" is not lost when urea is included in the dialysis bath so that the blood urea is not removed by the dialysis.

Disturbances of acid-base balance and fluid and electrolyte metabolism are also commonly present in uremia, and may, at times, contribute to or be responsible for certain of the symptoms. Nevertheless, these electrolyte imbalances can not be considered to be the major contributor to the picture of uremia, and the factor or factors primarily responsible for the symptoms and signs remains unidentified. It is generally believed that toxic products of metabolism may, in the presence of depressed renal function, accumulate in the body fluids till toxic concentrations are reached.

These substances, if they exist, have never been adequately identified.

### Intrinsic Defects of Renal Tubular Function

As opposed to the disturbances of renal function attributable to diffuse inflammatory or degenerative kidney disease, there are a number of abnormalities due to deficiency of certain transport mechanisms or groups of transport mechanisms. Many of these defects are familial or congenital though some may be acquired. They are for the most part uncommon, but warrant brief mention because of their unusual physiological interest.

One such defect, *renal tubular acidosis*, has been mentioned above and the impairment of sodium-hydrogen ion exchange described. The disorder is, at least in some instances, familial. It is frequently associated with nephrocalcinosis and pyelonephritis, but these are quite probably secondary rather than the cause of the renal abnormality.

NEPHROGENIC DIABETES INSIPIDUS is a rare congenital familial disorder most often encountered in males and characterized by the continuous obligatory excretion of dilute urine, and consequently intense polyuria and secondarily polydipsia. The abnormality is apparently due to inability of the distal portions of the renal tubules to respond to pituitary antidiuretic hormone by a decrease in the permeability to water. Thus the urine, diluted by salt removal in the distal portions of the nephron, fails to give up the excess of water in the tubules, and the water is lost in the urine. True or *pituitary diabetes insipidus* is characterized by the same symptoms and signs but is due to a lack of antidiuretic hormone secretion. The tubules are normally responsive to antidiuretic hormone in this disorder which is much more frequent than the nephrogenic type. Pituitary diabetes insipidus is usually an acquired abnormality secondary to injury to the pituitary and/or hypothalamus.

RENAL GLYCOSURIA is characterized by the excretion of glucose in the urine when the concentration in the plasma is normal or low. The abnormality is a defect in the mechanism by which glucose is reabsorbed in the proximal tubule; other proximal tubule functions may be normal. The specific nature of the derangement is not known. There is some depression of the maximum capacity to reabsorb glucose ($Tm_G$), but there is also considerable excretion of glucose when the concentration is below that required to saturate the reabsorptive mechanism. The possible interpretations of this "splay in the titration curve" are discussed on pages 540 to 543 of the preceding chapter.

RENAL HYPOPHOSPHATEMIA (or Vitamin D resistant rickets) is a familial disorder characterized by excretion of phosphate in the urine when the plasma concentration is low. It is attributable to a defect of the phosphate reabsorptive mechanism analogous to that for glucose in renal glycosuria.

AMINO-ACIDURIA. Defects of amino acid reabsorption occur as specific defects of certain transport mechanisms and as part of more generalized disorders of renal tubular function. An example of the specific type is that known as *essential cystinuria* in which the abnormality is limited to diminished reabsorption of cystine, lysine, arginine and ornithine. The chief hazard derives from the formation of stones from the poorly soluble cystine. Abnormalities involving certain other specific amino acids or groups of amino acids are also known. In addition defects of amino acid reabsorption may occur in several other disorders including, among others, Wilson's disease (fundamentally a disturbance of copper metabolism), heavy metal poisoning, and the Fanconi syndrome in which amino-aciduria is associated with defective reabsorption of glucose and phosphate and sometimes with renal tubular acidosis.

## DISTURBANCES OF RENAL FUNCTION OF EXTRARENAL ORIGIN

The function of the kidney is dependent, for the maintenance of glomerular filtration, on the adequacy of the circulation. The effect of shock, leading as it may to sustained damage to the kidney, has already been discussed. In addition several of the renal transport systems for electrolytes and water are regulated by the activity of endocrine organs. The function of these systems is therefore subject to disturbance through abnormal activity of the endocrine organs in the form of either deficient or excessive secretion of hormones acting on the kidney. Two such abnormalities have already been described in relation to intrinsic renal disorders which they resemble or to which they are related.

1. *Pituitary diabetes insipidus* in which, because of deficiency of antidiuretic hormone secretion, renal water reabsorption is diminished and a dilute urine is continuously formed. The converse of this disorder may occur and a concentrated urine be formed when a reduced osmotic pressure of body fluids would ordinarily lead to the formation of dilute urine; most often this is due to the induction of antidiuretic hormone secretion by non-osmotic stimuli.

2. The excessive reabsorption of salt which characterizes *edema formation* and the contribution of hypersecretion of aldosterone have been discussed in relation to edema. Excessive secretion of aldosterone leads to accumulation of edema only in the presence of factors predisposing to edema formation. In the absence of such factors, the increased sodium reabsorption is limited, and the major manifestation of hypersecretion of aldosterone is *potassium loss* resulting from stimulation of secretion of potassium ion in exchange for reabsorbed sodium. If potassium loss due to intrinsic renal disease with defective potassium reabsorption exists, it has not been demonstrated, and excessive renal potassium excretion appears to be due to excessive secretion of potassium by the renal tubules generally stimulated by excess adrenocortical hormone.

In the absence of adrenocortical hormones (*adrenal insufficiency*, Addison's disease) reabsorption of sodium and secretion of potassium by the renal tubules are defective. Sodium loss in the urine proceeds despite contraction of the extracellular fluid volume, which may become markedly reduced. The potassium concentration of body fluids becomes elevated. Abnormal loss of sodium in the urine despite sodium depletion may occasionally result from renal disease, and may be produced by inhibitors of sodium reabsorption (diuretics).

The reabsorption of phosphate by the renal tubules is regulated by parathyroid hormone. Excessive secretion of parathyroid hormone (*hyperparathyroidism*) is associated with loss of phosphate in the urine; loss of parathyroid function (*hypoparathyroidism*) leads to elevation of the plasma phosphate concentration without an equivalent increase in urinary excretion.

## Micturition

### Outline of the Anatomy of the Urinary Tract

The muscular coat of the *ureter* is arranged in three layers, an *external longitudinal*, a *middle circular* and an *internal longitudinal*.

The muscle of the *urinary bladder* is also disposed in three layers, an *external*, a *middle* and an *internal*. The fibers of the external layer run longitudinally, that is, in the long axis of the bladder. The fibers of the middle layer are thinly scattered; they have a circular arrangement and run both transversely and obliquely to the long axis of the viscus. The fibers of the internal layer follow a reticular pattern but for the most part run longitudinally.

The vesical mucous membrane is separated from the internal muscular layer by a submucous coat of loose areolar tissue. The mucosa is thin and, when the bladder is empty or contains only a small quantity of urine, has a corrugated appearance due to the presence of numerous folds or *rougae* which disappear when the bladder becomes distended. The epithelium is of the transitional type. When the bladder is empty the mucosa shows several cell-layers, but when distended only two strata of cells are to be seen, a deep stratum of cuboidal cells and a superficial one of large squamous cells.

The human bladder has a capacity of from 350 to 450 cc.

The *peritoneum* covers the superior surface of the bladder only.

The ureters pierce the wall of the fundus (or base) of the bladder very obliquely. From a half to three-quarters of an inch of their lower ends is embedded in the vesical muscle. During contraction of the bladder wall these portions of the ureters are compressed by the muscle fibers, thus preventing the reflux of urine as the intravesical pressure rises. The urethral orifice which is situated at the most dependent part of the bladder is guarded by the *vesical sphincter (internal sphincter)*, formed by the condensation of the muscle fibers of the circular layer. The triangular area marked out by the urethral orifice and the two ureteral orifices is called the *trigone (trigonum vesicae)*. The muscle of the bladder wall is referred to as the *detrusor urinae*. The male urethra is embraced in its membraneous portion by the *sphincter urethrae membranceae*, a striated muscle which is frequently referred to as the *external sphincter*. The *bulbocavernosus* muscle, which is applied to the urethral bulb and surrounds the corpora cavernosa penis, also exerts a constrictor action upon the urethra. The urethral wall itself contains two layers of smooth muscle, an outer circular and an inner longitudinal; in women (who do not possess an external sphincter of striated muscle) this serves to prevent the escape of urine after paralysis of the internal sphincter. The epithelial lining of the urethra is of the columnar type except near the bladder where it is of the transitional variety, and a short distance from the external urethral orifice where it is stratified and squamous.

### FILLING OF THE BLADDER

The ureters exhibit rhythmical peristaltic contractions which travel at a speed of from 20 to 25 mm. per second (rabbit) and at a frequency from 1 to 5 per minute, according to the volume of urine formed by the kidney. The peristaltic waves serve to propel the urine from the pelvis of the kidney to the bladder. The urine therefore enters the bladder not in a continuous stream but in separate squirts synchronous with the arrival of the peristaltic waves.

The detrusor muscle exhibits two types of activity, a sustained contraction or tonus, and intermittent contractions.

The bladder, in common with other hollow viscera, is capable of adjusting its tone and so of adapting its capacity to changes in the volume of its contents with relatively little alteration in internal pressure. It thus differs in its behavior from an elastic hollow sphere composed of a non-living material. For example, when a moderate quantity of fluids is run into the bladder through a catheter the intravesical pressure shows a transient rise, due to the tonic resistance offered by the bladder wall, but then declines again to near its previous level as adaptation occurs. As successive volumes of fluid are introduced the curve of intravesical pressure therefore shows a gradual step-like ascent until the bladder contents are unusually large. From then on further additions of fluid cause a much more abrupt rise in pressure. The adaptation is not to a constant pressure (15 cm. of water), as was previously taught, but is always to a pressure a little higher than that existing before the fluid was introduced. In the experiments of Denny-Brown and Robertson upon normal human subjects fluid was run into the bladder 50 cc. at a time. An increase in volume of the contents of the bladder from 50 cc. to 400 cc. caused little change in pressure (fig. 35.1). When completely paralyzed (as during the first two or three weeks following a transverse lesion of the cord) the bladder does not behave in this way, but simply as an inert elastic bag showing no tendency to respond to an increase in tension upon its walls or to adapt itself to its contents (Holmes); when successive quantities of fluid are introduced the curve of intravesical pressure rises along a smooth line.

Tension is the adequate stimulus for the sensory end organs in the bladder wall. When there-

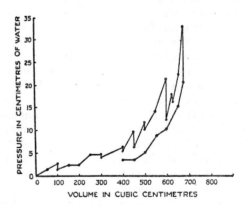

FIG. 35.1. Curve of pressure changes in the human bladder during filling (upper curve) and emptying (lower curve). (After Denny-Brown and Robertson.)

fore the bladder becomes distended by the accumulation of urine and the intravesical pressure reaches a certain value, rhythmical contractions of the detrusor muscle are set up. As the pressure rises further these culminate in the movements constituting the micturition reflex, namely, a strong contraction of the detrusor muscle accompanied by relaxation of the internal sphincter, and followed by opening of the external sphincter. It is usually stated that the reflex occurs at an intravesical pressure of from 15 to 18 cm. of water, but it may be activated by a pressure considerably lower than this. The urine is expelled with considerable force, the pressure within the bladder rising during the contraction of the detrusor to around 130 cm. of water. Since adaptation requires a certain time to take place, the reflex is activated at a lower urine volume than usual if the accumulation of urine is rapid. At the average rate at which urine forms, micturition occurs, unless restrained, after from 250 to 300 cc. have collected.

### The Voluntary Control of Micturition

The act of micturition, although essentially reflex in nature, is usually initiated by an effort of the will; it also can be voluntarily inhibited or be interrupted at any stage. The desire to urinate is accompanied by a vague feeling in the penis or perineum. The sensation appears when the urine volume is from 200 to 300 cc. If the act is long postponed a feeling of fullness and discomfort culminating in pain results. It is only in the infant or when, as a result of disease, the bladder is isolated from the control of the higher nervous centers, that micturition is a purely reflex act. Under ordinary circumstances in the adult, when the desire to micturate arises, the act is restrained until an opportunity for emptying the bladder presents itself. The restraint is then lifted and the reflex occurs automatically.

The voluntary restraint exerted upon micturition consists, according to Denny-Brown and Robertson, of inhibition of the detrusor with contraction of the external sphincter and perineal muscles. No evidence was obtained by these observers that the internal sphincter was under direct voluntary control, although a reciprocal increase in tone of the sphincter muscle accompanies inhibition of the detrusor. It was found that at a certain urine volume, contractions of the bladder and a consequent rise in intravesical pressure could be readily induced by an effort of the will; contraction of the abdominal muscles

was not necessarily associated with the performance of the act. The removal of restraint and the voluntary facilitation of the spontaneous bladder contractions are considered to be the important factors. At low urine volumes restraint is apparently exercised subconsciously. These observers therefore regard the act of micturition as being normally controlled through variations in voluntary and subconscious restraint of the reflex mechanism. Micturition therefore presents a very unusual feature in that movements innervated by autonomic nerves can be controlled by voluntary impulses. The higher centers from which the inhibitory impulses emanate are situated in the hypothalamus and cerebral cortex, probably in area 4.

Although the abdominal muscles play a nonessential part in micturition, the act, under ordinary circumstances, is started by the contraction of these muscles; and it is well known that the bladder can be emptied although it contains only a few cubic centimeters of urine. The flow of urine is also accelerated during micturition by the rise in intra-abdominal pressure induced by the voluntary contraction of the abdominal muscles. Relaxation of the muscles of the perineum occurs as an associated movement at the commencement of micturition. After the bladder has been emptied the bulbocavernosus muscle (ejaculator urinae) contracts and expels urine which had been left in the urethra.

Contractions set up in a distended bladder by sudden increases of intra-abdominal pressure acting upon the viscus, as in coughing, sneezing, defecation, etc., may, by forcing a little urine past the sphincter into the urethra, cause micturition unless a strong effort of the will is exercised. Psychic influences may also induce bladder contractions which evoke the act unless opposed by restraint. The lifting of voluntary inhibition, unless the bladder is fully distended, may on the other hand be prevented and the power to micturate be temporarily lost, as when a shy or nervous examinee is asked for a specimen of urine in the presence of another person.

### The Reflex Mechanisms of Micturition

Barrington describes six integrated reflexes as constituting the act of micturition in the cat, namely:

(1) *Contraction of the detrusor* evoked by distending the bladder; the afferent and efferent limbs of this reflex are in the pelvic nerves, its center in the hind-brain. Contraction of the detrusor is ac-

companied by reciprocal relaxation of the internal sphincter.

(2) *Contraction of the detrusor* caused by running fluid through the urethra. The afferent pathway for this response is in the pudendal (pudic) nerves, its efferent limb in the pelvic nerves and its center in the hind-brain. Through this reflex the contraction of the detrusor caused by the first reflex is sustained until the bladder is completely emptied.

(3) *Contraction of the detrusor* (transient and weak) when the proximal portion of the urethra is distended. The hypogastric nerves contain both afferent and efferent paths for this reflex; its center is in the sacral part of the cord.

(4) *Relaxation of the external sphincter* when fluid passes along the urethra. Afferent and efferent fibers are in the pudendal (pudic) nerves, the center is in the sacral part of the cord.

(5) *Relaxation of the external sphincter* when the bladder is distended. The afferent path is in the pelvic, the efferent in the pudendal nerves, its center in the sacral part of the cord.

(6) *Relaxation of the plain muscle in the proximal third of the urethra* caused by distending the bladder. Both afferent and efferent paths of the reflex are in the pelvic nerves; its center is in the sacral part of the cord.

In the normal act of micturition the first of these reflexes, namely, contraction of the detrusor in response to distention of the bladder, brings the others, with the exception of the third, automatically into action. It is questionable whether the third reflex is called into play under ordinary circumstances.

### THE INNERVATION OF THE URINARY TRACT

The *ureters* in their upper part receive sympathetic fibers from the renal plexus, in their middle part from the spermatic (or ovarian) plexus and near the bladder from the hypogastric nerves. The sympathetic fibers to the ureters exert a predominantly motor effect, although it appears that inhibitory fibers are also derived from the sympathetic. It is thought by some that the ureter receives fibers from the parasympathetic as well, since certain parasympathomimetic drugs cause motor effects. The existence of a parasympathetic innervation has not been demonstrated anatomically.

The *efferent nerves to the bladder* are the sympathetic and parasympathetic. The *sympathetic* furnishes inhibitory fibers to the detrusor muscle, and motor fibers to the trigone, internal sphincter, and the smooth muscle of the proximal part of the urethra.[3] These fibers arise from the lumbar

---

[3] The sympathetic also causes contraction of the ureteral orifices and of the muscle of the seminal vesicles, ejaculatory ducts and prostate.

spinal segments and pass through the inferior mesenteric plexus, the superior hypogastric plexus (presacral nerve) and the inferior hypogastric plexus to reach the hypogastric ganglion (fig. 35.2). Postganglionic fibers, which probably have their origins in the latter ganglion, enter into the formation of the vesical plexus; this lies in relation to the fundus of the bladder (the hypogastrics in some species apparently contain motor as well as inhibitory fibers).

When the hypogastric nerves are stimulated electrically, a brief contraction of the detrusor muscle precedes the inhibitory effect (fig. 35.3).

The *parasympathetic* supplies motor fibers to the detrusor muscle (which govern the tonus and contractile mechanisms) and inhibitory fibers to the internal sphincter. The sympathetic and parasympathetic nerves are therefore reciprocal in their actions. The parasympathetic fibers arise

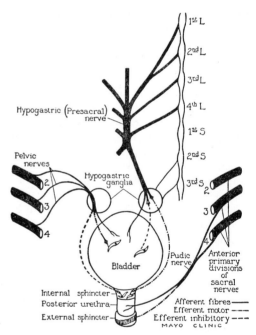

FIG. 35.2. To show innervation of the bladder. (After Learmonth.)

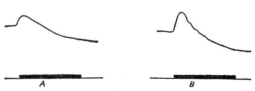

FIG. 35.3. Kymographic records showing initial contraction followed by inhibition of the detrusor muscle in response to faradic stimulation of the hypogastric nerves in a dog in which the sacral preganglionic parasympathetic outflow had been interrupted. (After Kuntz and Saccomanno.)

from the second and third sacral spinal segments and to some extent from the first and fourth. They are conveyed in the pelvic nerves (nervi erigentes) to connect with ganglion cells lying in close relation to the bladder wall (see also ch. 71). According to Henderson and Roepke, the tonus mechanism is cholinergic (ch. 71) but not the phasic contractions.

Both sets of autonomic nerves apparently exert a constant influence upon the tone of the detrusor and internal sphincter, the effect of one set being balanced against the other. Section of the sympathetic or parasympathetic causes, respectively, an increase or decrease in tone of the sphincter. In paresis of the bladder due to injury of the parasympathetic innervation, excision of the presacral nerve is sometimes performed with the object of removing the inhibitory influence of the sympathetic and thus enhancing the action of the pelvic nerves. Voluntary control of the detrusor is exerted apparently through the pelvic nerves.

The striated muscle constituting the external sphincter is innervated through the pudendal (pudic) nerves.

The *afferent* paths from the bladder travel in both *pelvic* and *hypogastric nerves*, those from the urethra in the *pudendal* nerves. The afferent fibers essential for the reflex movements of the bladder are contained in the pelvic nerves, those for the movements of the urethra in the pudendals. The hypogastric nerves contain no afferents for any of the important reflex mechanisms. The sensations set up by distension of the bladder are conveyed in both the pelvic and hypogastric nerves. The sensation of pain travels chiefly in the hypogastrics, but also in the pelvic nerves. Excision of the presacral nerve is practised for the relief of vesical pain. Tactile and thermal sensations and the sensation of pressure or filling of the bladder are conveyed mainly in the pelvic nerves (Learmonth).

## The Nerve Centers Governing Micturition

Centers for micturition are situated in the mid-brain, hind-brain and spinal cord. The observations cited in the section on the voluntary control of the detrusor muscle also indicate the existence of a center at the cortical level, and electrical excitation of the premotor area causes a rise in vesicle pressure followed by micturition. Increase in the tone of the bladder wall follows electrical stimulation of the anterior hypothalamic nuclei; stimulation of the posterior nuclei causes inhibition (Beatty and Kerr).

Barrington, experimenting with cats, found that destruction of a small area of the hind-brain (lying ventral to the internal edge of the superior cerebellar peduncle and extending forward from the level of the motor nucleus of the fifth nerve to the anterior end of the hind-brain) temporarily abolished the animal's ability to empty its bladder voluntarily. Destruction of an area in the mid-brain extending from the ventral part of the posterior end of the cerebral aqueduct to just beyond the mesencephalic root of the fifth nerve, was followed by permanent loss of voluntary micturition.

The reflex performance of the act was not, however, impaired. A more extensive lesion in the region of the mesencephalic root caused, in addition, frequency of micturition. Levin and Longworth observed that, in cats, injury to the tegmentum of the mid-brain was followed immediately by hyperactivity of the detrusor muscle to stretch. The capacity of the bladder becomes reduced as a consequence, and rhythmic waves of contraction appear. After a time, this increased activity diminishes and the bladder enlarges again.

The spinal centers lie in the second, third and fourth sacral segments. Only the third, fourth, fifth and sixth reflexes described in the section on reflex mechanisms are carried out through the spinal centers.

The descending and ascending paths conveying impulses to and from the spinal centers of micturition are situated in the dorsal half of the lateral column of the cord near its periphery, i.e., in close proximity to the pyramidal tract. The fibers of these paths show extensive crossing in the sacral segments (Barrington).

## The Effects of Nerve Section and of Cord Injuries on Micturition

Section of the hypogastric (presacral) nerves does not interfere with micturition; these nerves contain neither efferent nor afferent fibers essential for the performance of the act. Incontinence which might be expected to result (since motor fibers are conveyed by this nerve to the internal sphincter) does not occur. Indeed, incontinence does not follow a prostatectomy operation involving destruction of the internal sphincter, for the external sphincter is capable alone of preventing the escape of urine. Frequency of micturition was found by Barrington to follow section of the hypogastrics in the cat; it also occurs as a temporary effect of resection of the presacral nerve in the human subject. The phenomenon is due, apparently, to the loss of the inhibitory action of the sympathetic upon the tone of the detrusor and the impairment of the ability of the bladder to adapt its capacity to as large a volume of urine as usual.

Section of the pudendal nerves in the human subject is also, according to Learmonth, without any notable effect upon micturition, though of course paralysis of the external sphincter results.

Section of the pelvics causes paralysis of the bladder wall. The detrusor is atonic; the tone of the internal sphincter is raised. Retention of urine with overdistension of the bladder and overflow—dribbling—occurs. Barrington found that the tone of the sphincter diminished after a few days and the animal, apparently experiencing the sensation of fullness of the bladder, assumed the usual position for micturition and performed the act by a contraction of its abdominal muscles.

Severance of the posterior sacral nerve roots is followed immediately by the loss of all the important reflexes of micturition since the afferent paths (through the pelvics and pudendals) are interrupted; the bladder wall is flaccid and the resistance at the internal sphincter is increased. However, after a period of overdistension with overflow incontinence, the bladder may empty automatically at intervals. The sensations, except pain of overdistension (afferent fibers of hypogastrics intact) are retained.

Destruction of the sacral nerves (as in lesions of the cauda equina) or of the spinal centers will interrupt not only motor impulses to the bladder, but also the afferent impulses travelling by the pelvics and pudendals. The bladder is then completely isolated from central nervous control; but, after a period of retention of urine with overflow it may partially expel its contents automatically. The detrusor and internal sphincter act coördinately. Such an action suggests a neural mechanism of some sort. It occurs in animals even after the hypogastrics have been sectioned as well, and time allowed for degeneration to occur; it cannot therefore be due to preganglionic axon reflexes. Probably, in such and other instances in which motor impulses from the central nervous system have been interrupted, local reflex arcs through ganglion cells in the vesical plexus or bladder wall are responsible for the automatic action. The latter is only a makeshift for the normal micturition reflex since the bladder is not completely emptied but always retains a part of its contents (residual urine). McLennan draws attention to the fact that the state of the bladder after the afferent limb of the reflex arc is interrupted as in tabes is different from that following destruction of both afferent and efferent limbs. In the former the bladder is lax (hypotonic) and of large capacity, whereas in the latter it is hypertonic and of normal capacity. The reason for such a difference is obscure.

After transection of the cord above the sacral region, normal micturition cannot occur. Nevertheless, after a variable period of retention with overflow the spinal (sacral) centers assume control and the bladder empties at intervals automatically (see also mass reflex, ch. 65). Owing to the absence of the first and second reflexes of Barrington which, as just mentioned, are governed by higher centers, the bladder does not empty itself completely, but always contains a quantity of residual urine.

Bladder sensibility is completely lost following section of the hypogastrics and pelvic nerves or transection of the cord above the entrance of the afferent fibers of the hypogastrics. Injury or disease (e.g., tabes) of the posterior columns involving these fibers together with those from the sacral roots will have a similar effect.

Bilateral lesions of cortical areas 4 and 6 in man abolish voluntary control of the bladder; urinary incontinence results. Incontinence is seen not uncommonly in the aged, and may occur though no organic lesion is apparent; it is attributed to impairment of voluntary control by the cortical centers.

*Nocturnal enuresis*, or the passage of urine during sleep, occurs in young children up to an age which varies considerably, and may be attributed to the undeveloped state of the neural mechanism through which the act of micturition is voluntarily inhibited. But enuresis during sleep sometimes persists beyond the usual time and even to adult age. It may then be associated with some definite organic abnormality, e.g., in the lumbo-sacral vertebrae, e.g., spina bifida occulta, but nocturnal enuresis in the adult is usually related to some functional neurological disorder, or to psychological factors. Evidence of pelvic autonomic dysfunction or psychiatric conditions in the subject's immediate family are present in a large proportion of such persons. In others there is definite mental deficiency.

## REFERENCES

ADDIS, T. AND SHEVKY, M. C. A test for the capacity of the kidney to produce a urine of high specific gravity. Arch. Int. Med., 1922, **30,** 559.

BALDWIN, D. S., BERMAN, H. J. HEINEMANN, H. O., AND SMITH, H. W. The elaboration of osmotically concentrated urine in renal disease. J. Clin. Invest., 1955, **34,** 800.

BARRINGTON, F. J. F. The nervous mechanism of micturition. Quart. J. Exp. Physiol., 1914, **8,** 33. The effect of division of the hypogastric nerves on frequency of micturition. Ibid., 1916, **9,** 261. The relation of the hind-brain to micturition. Brain, 1921, **44,** 23. The nervous control of the urinary bladder in amphibians. Ibid., 1922, **45,** 126. The central nervous control of micturition. Ibid., 1928, **51,** 209. The component reflexes of micturition in the cat. Ibid., 1931, **54,** 177. The localization of the paths subserving micturition in the spinal cord of the cat. Ibid., 1933, **56,** 126.

BEATTIE, J. AND KERR, A. S. Brain, 1936, **59,** 302.

BULL, G. M. Postural proteinuria. Clin. Sc., 1948, **7,** 77.

CONN, J. W. Primary aldosteronism, new clinical syndrome. J. Lab. & Clin. Med., 1955, **45,** 3.

DENNY-BROWN, D. AND ROBERTSON, E. G. Brain, 1933, **56,** 149.

DENT, C. E. AND HARRIS, H. The genetics of "cystinuria." Ann. Eugenics, 1951, **16,** 60.

EARLE, D. P., JR., TAGGART, J. V., AND SHANNON, J. A. Glomerulonephritis. A survey of the functional organization of the kidney in various stages of diffuse glomerulonephritis. J. Clin. Invest., 1944, **23,** 119.

GOLDRING, W., CHASIS, H., RANGES, H. A., AND SMITH, H. W. Effective renal blood flow in subjects with essential hypertension. J. Clin. Invest., 1941, **20,** 637.

HAYMAN, J. M., JR., SHUMWAY, N. P., DUMKE, P., AND MILLER, M. Experimental hyposthenuria. J. Clin. Invest., 1939, **18,** 195.

HOLMES, G. Brain, 1933, **56,** 383.

LAUSON, H. D., BRADLEY, S. E., AND COURNAND, A. The renal circulation in shock. J. Clin. Invest., 1944, **23,** 381.

LEARMONTH, J. R. Brain, 1931, **54,** 147.

OLIVER, J. When is the kidney not a kidney? J. Urol., 1950, **63,** 373.

OLIVER, J., MacDOWELL, M., AND TRACY, A. The pathogenesis of acute renal failure associated with traumatic and toxic injury, renal ischemia, nephrotoxic damage and the ischemuric episode. J. Clin. Invest., 1951, **30,** 1307.

PHILLIPS, R. A., DOLE, V. P., HAMILTON, P. B., EMERSON, K., JR., ARCHIBLAD, R. M., AND VAN

SLYKE, D. D. Effects of acute hemorrhagic and traumatic shock on renal function of dogs. Am. J. Physiol., 1946, **145,** 314.

REYNOLDS, T. B. Observations on the pathogenesis of renal tubular acidosis. Am. J. Med., 1958, **25,** 503.

SCHWARTZ, W. B., HALL, P. W., 3RD, HAYS, R. M., AND RELMAN, A. S. On the mechanism of acidosis in chronic renal disease. J. Clin. Invest., 1959, **38,** 39.

SCHWARTZ, W. B. AND RELMAN, A. S. Acidosis in renal disease. New England J. Med., 1957, **256,** 1184.

VAN SLYKE, D. D., RHOADS, C. P., HILLER, A., AND ALVING, A. S. Relationships between urea excretion, renal blood flow, renal oxygen consumption, and diuresis. The mechanism of urea excretion. Am. J. Physiol., 1934, **109,** 336.

WRONG, O. AND DAVIS, H. E. F. The excretion of acid in renal disease. Quart. J. Med., 1959, **28,** 259.

*Monographs and Reviews*

DARMADY, E. M. Traumatic uraemia. A collective review. J. Bone & Joint Surg., 1948, **30B,** 309.

GOLDRING, W. AND CHASIS, H. Hypertension and hypertensive disease. The Commonwealth Fund. New York, 1944.

MUDGE, G. H. Clinical patterns of tubular dysfunction. Am. J. Med., 1958, **24,** 785.

RELMAN, A. S. AND SCHWARTZ, W. B. The kidney in potassium depletion. Am. J. Med., 1958, **24,** 764.

# 36

# THE SALIVARY GLANDS AND THE SECRETION OF SALIVA

### General Description of the Digestive Glands

Of the many secretions that are poured into the alimentary canal, some are formed by the cells of the mucous membrane lining the various hollow organs; others are formed by glands that may lie in the submucosa or entirely outside the digestive tube and are connected with it by means of ducts. The products of the glands are referred to as external secretions because the alimentary canal is considered to be an extension of the external surface of the body and its contents to be actually "outside" the body. The secreting cells are epithelial cells and, with the possible exception of some of the salivary gland cells, are derived from the entoderm.

Secreting cells are classified as *apocrine, holocrine,* or *merocrine,* according to the manner in which they discharge their secretion. In apocrine cells, secretory products become concentrated in the luminal end of the cell and are discharged into the lumen of the alveolus or duct along with the portion of the cell in which they have accumulated. Certain cells of the cat's submaxillary gland are said to secrete in this manner. In the case of holocrine cells, the entire cell along with its accumulated secretion is discharged into the lumen and forms the secretion of the gland; examples are the secreting cells of the sebaceous glands. A possible example in the gastrointestinal tract is the shedding of the intestinal epithelium described in chapter 40 under the head of *Intestinal Secretion*. A merocrine cell remains intact and discharges its secretory products through the cell membrane; examples are the acinous cells of the pancreas and most of the other digestive glands.

The glands themselves are classified according to their cellular composition as—homocrine, i.e., having secretory tubules lined with cells of one type only, or heterocrine, having secretory tubules lined with cells of more than one type. Most of the digestive glands are of the heterocrine type. Glands have also been classified as monoptychial or polyptychial depending upon whether the secreting cells are arranged in one layer or in more than one layer. The pancreatic acini are monoptychial and the submaxillary and sublingual glands are polyptychial according to this classification.

### Mechanisms of Secretion

The secretions of the digestive glands consist of water, other inorganic materials and organic substances. The organic matter consists principally of enzymes and mucoprotein. The water obviously comes from the blood by way of the tissue fluid since the total daily volume of the digestive secretions far exceeds the total volume of the glands. Unless the gland is one which secretes hydrochloric acid or sodium bicarbonate the inorganic constituents are those that are common to the body fluids and are usually present in approximately the same proportions in which they occur in these fluids. The osmolar concentration of most of the digestive secretions is considered to be the same as that of the blood plasma with the exception of saliva which is hypotonic. According to some observers gastric juice may be hypertonic when first secreted.

Since mucus is a protein and all the enzymes are protein in nature, secretion of organic matter by the digestive glands involves extensive protein synthesis. We recognize two stages in the production of the organic materials; first, a stage of synthesis or manufacture of the secretory products within the cell and, second, a stage of secretion in which the secretory products are discharged into the ducts, along with a certain amount of water and inorganic salts. So far as we know at present, the first or synthetic stage goes on continuously although it may be modified by secretory stimuli and is influenced by those environmental conditions which alter the general metabolism of the gland cell. Presumably, protein synthesis is a reversible process and subject to the law of mass action. That is to say, the rate of synthesis will be accelerated by increasing the concentration of the raw materials or reacting substances, amino acids chiefly, and will be retarded by accumulation of the synthesized protein, provided the protein remains in solution. The situation is so complicated, however, that such a simple scheme would probably need extensive alteration before it could be applied in a quantitative manner. Actually, in most instances, the synthesized material appears to be precipitated within the gland in the form of secretory granules.

The formation of secretory granules is a fascinating process which has been studied extensively but is still only imperfectly understood. Apparently the granules begin to form first in the vicinity of the Golgi apparatus, where they remain during the period of growth and maturation and when fully developed are transported toward the apical, or luminal portion of the cell where they tend to accumulate. When allowed to accumulate in sufficiently large numbers they may displace the nucleus of the cell toward the base and even invade the protoplasm between the nucleus and the base of the cell. Secretory granules accumulate in resting cells, that is, cells which have not been stimulated to discharge their secretion into the ducts of the gland. In the digestive glands this occurs in the fasting state or in the interdigestive periods. When the glands are stimulated to secrete, as the digestive glands are during digestion, the granular material is discharged into the ducts of the gland usually accompanied by water and inorganic salts. In spite of the existence of secretory granules most of the digestive enzymes appear to be present in the gland in diffusible form at some time in the process of synthesis. At any rate most of them may be found in the blood in measurable amounts, presumably having got there by diffusion from the secretory cells.

In the case of those enzymes which have the capacity to destroy tissue, e.g., the proteolytic enzymes, the material synthesized in the secreting cells is not the enzyme itself but a precursor called a zymogen; for example, pepsin is synthesized as pepsinogen, a proteolytically inactive protein, and trypsin as trypsinogen, which is inactive. The lipases are synthesized as such but are comparatively inactive except in the presence of surface active agents such as bile which are not normally present in the tissues. Another device by which the glands that secrete proteolytic enzymes are protected from digestion by their own secretory products is by the elaboration of antienzymes; for example, the pancreas contains an antitrypsin which inactivates trypsin and undoubtedly serves to protect the gland from digestion by the small amounts of active trypsin that may accidentally be formed in the acinous cells. An antitrypsin is also secreted into the pancreatic juice and probably serves to prevent activation of the trypsinogen within the ducts.

Since the digestive glands secrete water and salts as well as enzymes, the secretion of these two classes of products may be stimulated separately, at least in some of the digestive glands. One of the early physiologists to recognize this fact was R. Heidenhain (1878), who undertook to differentiate between the nerve fibers which, when stimulated, cause secretion of organic matter and those which cause secretion of water and salts; the former he designated as *trophic* fibers and the latter as *secretory* fibers. The terms are confusing, particularly since the word *trophic* more properly pertains to synthesis than to discharge from the cell of the organic matter in the secretion. Furthermore, the word *secretory* has become firmly fixed in the language as pertaining to the whole process of secretion (and will be used in that sense throughout this discussion). Babkin has suggested that the adjective *hydrelatic* be used in place of *secretory* and *ecbolic* in place of *trophic*. Babkin's terms, although more nearly correct, are not euphonious and perhaps for that reason have not come into general use.

## Salivary Glands

### General Form and Minute Structure

The first secretion encountered by the food is saliva. This fluid is secreted by three pairs of glands known as the parotid, submaxillary and sublingual glands, and by numerous smaller glands scattered throughout the mucous membrane of the mouth and pharynx. The parotid gland, the largest of the salivary glands, is situated at the side of the face below and in front of the ear and the mastoid process, and in front of the sternomastoid muscle. A process of the gland known as the retromandibular process, passes medially behind the ramus of the mandible. The parotid glands are swollen and therefore conspicuous in a person having mumps. The duct of the parotid gland, known as the parotid duct, also called Stensen's duct, after reaching the anterior border of the gland runs forward, external to the masseter muscle and crossing it, turns around the anterior border of this muscle and runs medialward through the fat of the cheek, at right angles to the first part of its course, to the buccinator muscle which it pierces to reach the mucous membrane of the check. After running for some distance under the mucous membrane, it forms a small papilla through which it communicates with the oral cavity. The opening is opposite the crown of the second upper molar tooth.

The submaxillary glands are next in size to the parotid; they are placed in the submaxillary triangle medial to the mandible. The posterior end of the gland lies very close to the sternomastoid muscle. The submaxillary duct, also known as Wharton's duct, runs from the deep surface of the gland along the mylohyloid muscle beneath the floor of the mouth on the medial side of the sublingual gland, to open on the floor of the mouth at the side of the frenulum linguae, on the summit of the soft papilla known as the caruncula sublingualis. The sublingual glands lie immediately below the mucous membrane of the floor of the mouth. These glands pour their secretion into the mouth, under the tongue, through a large number of ducts which arise near the upper borders of the glands and, after a short course, open upon a series of papillae along the summits of the plicae sublingualis.

Two types of cells, mucous and serous, can be recognized in microscopic sections of the salivary glands. The mucous cells have large translucent granules which readily transmit light so that in thin sections they appear transparent. The serous cells have small granules that are more opaque and appear darker in sections than the mucous cells. The serous cells secrete a thin, watery fluid containing the starch splitting enzyme, ptyalin. The mucous cells secrete mucus mainly.

In the salivary glands the cells of the glandular tissue are aggregated into a great number of small groups, with the individual cells arranged in a single layer around a small central cavity or alveolus. The cells are more or less wedge-shaped with their apices converging toward the central

cavity and their bases directed outwards. They discharge their secretion into the alveolus which is drained by a fine duct. Ducts from neighboring alveoli join to form ducts of larger caliber which unite again to form still larger trunks, until finally through a succession of junctions and the formation of channels of ever increasing size, the secretion flows into the mouth by a single large duct, in the case of the submaxillary and parotid glands, or by several of medium size, in the case of the sublingual. The general arrangement of the ducts reminds one of the stem branchings of a bunch of grapes—the rounded alveoli at the ends of the finest channels corresponding to the grapes. Glands showing such a pattern are, therefore, termed *racemose*. The ducts are named, in accordance with their location, *intralobular* or *interlobular*. The former drain a single alveolus or a group of alveoli. The latter lie between the lobules each being formed by the union of a number of intralobular ducts. The narrowed part of the intralobular duct lying nearer to the alveolus is known as the *isthmus*, or more usually the *intercalary* duct.

In addition to the two types of secreting epithelium, salivary glands have three different types of cells in their ducts. In the intercalary ducts that lead directly away from the alveoli, the epithelium is cuboidal in character. In the intralobular ducts it is columnar and presents a peculiar rod-shaped appearance, resembling in this respect some of the cells of the renal tubules. In the interlobular and sublobular ducts the epithelium is cylindrical. The fact that the cells differ in structure suggests that their functions may be different. The rod-shaped epithelium of the intralobular ducts is particularly suggestive of a secretory or reabsorptive function. Evidence presented later, under the head of *electrophysiology*, indicates that these cells reabsorb sodium from the saliva as it passes through the ducts.

Stimulation of the sympathetic nerves to the salivary glands sometimes causes a sudden gush of saliva from the gland. This suggests that some previously secreted saliva is being pressed out of the gland or its ducts as though by contraction of these structures, yet neither the secreting cells nor the duct cells have the structure of contractile tissue and there is no smooth muscle in the glands other than that of the blood vessels. The contractile elements are probably to be sought in what are known as "myoepithelial" cells or "basket" cells which have been described in detail by Zimmerman (1927). These are flat or star-shaped cells which lie between the basal membrane and the

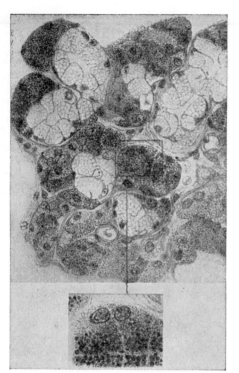

FIG. 36.1. Human submaxillary gland showing both mucous and serous groups of cells. Inserts are views with oil immersion, zymogen granules are clearly shown. (After Stormont, from Cowdry's *Special Cytology.*)

secretory cells. They are modified epithelial cells and they may have a contractile function although there is no clear evidence of such. They are distributed around the alveoli and the striated ducts; the latter are often somewhat dilated as though serving a reservoir function.

The alveoli of the parotid gland consist entirely of serous cells; parotid secretion, when collected separately from that of the other glands, has the characteristic watery character of serous secretion. The submaxillary gland contains some alveoli made up of mucous cells and others made up of serous cells; the two types may be seen side by side and in about equal numbers. In addition, many of the mucous alveoli have clusters of serous cells applied to their deep surface which appear to form caps; these, in section, are crescentic in shape and they have, therefore, been given the name of demilune cells. The secretion of these cells is believed to reach the lumen of the alveolus by means of small canaliculi between the mucous cells lining the alveolus. The sublingual glands have a similar structure, except that the serous elements are less prominent.

The cytoplasm of both the serous and mucous cells shows a granular structure. The fine granules of the serous cells are believed to furnish the enzyme of the secretion and are called zymogen granules. The mucinogen granules of the mucous cells provide the mucin that gives to the secretion of these cells its slimy character. When the glands are in the resting state the granules accumulate and the fine zymogen granules may load the cytoplasm to such an extent that the nucleus is almost obscured. When the glands enter upon secretory activity, the granules, whether zymogen or mucinogen, become less numerous as a result of their extrusion into the alveolar cavity. After a prolonged period of secretion, only a few remain; these are in the region of the cell bordering the cavity of the alveolus, the rest having been discharged along with the water and other constituents of the secretion. After a period of rest they accumulate again and gradually fill the cell.

## REGULATION OF SALIVARY SECRETION

Enough saliva is secreted continuously to keep the mucous membrane of the mouth and pharynx moist but during mastication and swallowing of food the amount of secretion is increased. Also it appears that the character of the secretion is adapted in some degree to the type of food undergoing mastication. As we shall learn later on, there are at least two ways of regulating the secretion of the digestive glands; one is through the nervous system and the other by means of hormones. In the case of the salivary glands it is believed that the regulation is exclusively through the nervous system. At any rate, all efforts to date to find a salivatory hormone have failed.

### *Innervation of Salivary Glands*

The glands are supplied with secretory nerves from two sources—the *bulbar* and the *thoracico-lumbar* divisions of the *autonomic nervous system* (ch. 71). The bulbar centers consist of a group of nerve cells which runs forward from the anterior end of the glossopharyngeal nucleus to the sensory nucleus of the facial nerve. The anterior (rostral) part is termed the *superior salivatory nucleus*, and governs secretion by the submaxillary gland; the posterior (caudal) part, called the *inferior salivatory nucleus*, controls secretion by the parotid gland.

The *submaxillary and sublingual glands* receive secretory impulses through the *chorda tympani nerve*. These fibers have the following course. Arising from the *superior salivatory nucleus* they leave the brain in the *nervus intermedius of Wrisberg* (ch. 65). They pass without interruption through the genicular ganglion of the facial nerve and descend with the facial to the point where its *chorda tympani* branch is given off. They enter this nerve which upon approaching the cavity of the mouth joins the lingual nerve. In the floor of the mouth the secretory fibers leave the lingual again to make connections with the nerve cells of small ganglia. From these, postganglionic fibers arise which terminate by fine arborizations around the secretory cells (fig. 36.2). The ganglia furnishing fibers to the submaxillary gland are small and numerous, and are situated in the hilum of the gland. The sublingual gland contains no ganglion cells, it receives its postganglionic fibers from a small ganglion—the *submaxillary ganglion* —situated in the course of the chorda fibers just beyond their point of separation from the lingual and before they enter the gland (see diagram fig. 36.3).

The *sympathetic supply* (postganglionic fibers) is derived from the superior cervical ganglion. The fibers reach the gland *via* the plexuses of the external carotid artery and its branches. The preganglionic fibers arise from the upper one or two thoracic segments of the cord. Fine filaments end in the secretory cells.

The chorda tympani also carries *dilator fibers* to the blood vessels of the gland; *vasoconstrictor fibers* are derived from the sympathetic.

The bulbar fibers to the *parotid* pursue the first part of their course in the glossopharyngeal, but they follow a devious path before finally terminating around the gland cells. They arise in the medulla from the *inferior salivatory nucleus.* At the jugular foramen they separate from the glossopharyngeal (petrous ganglion) in its *tympanic branch (Jacobson's N.)*, and after passing into the trunk of the *small superficial petrosal nerve* are conveyed to the *otic ganglion.* There they com-

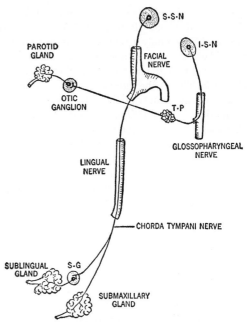

FIG. 36.3. Diagram of the parasympathetic nerve supply of the salivary glands. S-S-N, superior salivatory nucleus; I-S-N, inferior salivatory nucleus; S-G, submaxillary ganglion; T-P, tympanic plexus.

municate with ganglion cells from which postganglionic fibers arise. The latter are transmitted by the *auriculo-temporal* branch of the fifth nerve to the gland cells. The parotid also receives sympathetic secretory fibers. The cell stations of the latter as in the case of the submaxillary and sublingual lie in the superior cervical ganglion. The dilator fibers to the blood vessels travel with the bulbar fibers. The vasoconstrictor fibers are furnished by the sympathetic, and follow the blood vessels into the gland.

### *Stimulation of the Secretory Nerves—Electrophysiology*

Electrical stimulation of the nerves to the salivary glands produces different results in different species of animals. Stimulation of the parasympathetic nerves usually produces an abundant flow of quite watery saliva regardless of the gland or species studied, but stimulation of the sympathetic secretory fibers to the submaxillary or sublingual glands, although causing an abundant secretion in the cat, causes only a scanty and very viscid secretion in the dog. Even in the cat in which the secretion is fairly abundant, the composition of sympathetic saliva is different from that obtained on stimulation of the parasympathetic nerves. There is no clear proof that the

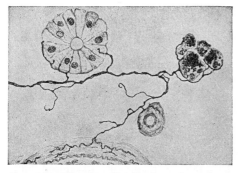

FIG. 36.2. Showing distribution of parasympathetic secretory nerves to cells and blood vessels of submaxillary gland of rabbit. (From Stormont in Cowdry's *Special Cytology.*)

sympathetic trunks contain secretory fibers for the parotid gland (Babkin, 1950). Stromblad (1955) obtained only a scanty secretion from the parotid gland of cats on administration of adrenalin or on stimulation of the sympathetic trunk in the neck. This is the more remarkable since the other salivary glands of the cat respond well to sympathetic stimulation. Stromblad suggests that the secretion observed on sympathetic stimulation may have been produced by stimulation of contractile elements in the glands, causing expression of saliva rather than a true secretion.

Stimulation of the autonomic nerves to the salivary glands causes characteristic changes in the electrical potentials that may be observed by placing electrodes in various positions on or within the gland and connecting them to a suitable recording device. With one electrode on the hilum and another on the outer surface of the submaxillary gland stimulation of either the sympathetic or parasympathetic nerves causes the hilum of the gland to become electropositive to the outer surface, after a comparatively long latent period. The latent period is 0.2 to 0.3 seconds with the parasympathetic and somewhat longer when the sympathetic is stimulated. Following parasympathetic stimulation the hilum positivity rapidly declines and may change to a negative potential; there is another sharp rise in hilum positivity when the current is turned off. The potential caused by sympathetic stimulation is more consistently hilum-positive.

Since the submaxillary gland is composed of several different types of cell, each of which may have its own electrical characteristics, it is doubtful what significance should be ascribed to the external secretory potential. More precise information may be obtained from the use of microelectrodes with the tip placed in the interior of a single cell. With these, Lundberg (1957), has obtained three types of response representing presumably three types of cells: alveolar cells, demilune cells, and duct cells. In all cases the interior of the cell was electronegative to the external medium. In the case of the alveolar cells, stimulation of either the parasympathetic or sympathetic caused a sustained increase in internal negativity or "hyperpolarization" of the cell membrane. This followed a time course roughly parallel to that already described for the external secretory potential. When the microelectrode was in what was believed to be a demilune cell the parasympathetic caused hyperpolarization but the sympathetic caused a decrease in the internal negativity of the cell (apparent depolarization). With the electrode in what was thought to be a cell of the striated ducts both sympathetic and parasympathetic nerves caused apparent depolarization.

In the sublingual gland microelectrodes picked up currents corresponding to those obtained from alveolar cells of the submaxillary but the external secretory potential was of a polarity opposite to that of the submaxillary gland, that is, the hilus became electronegative. This difference was believed to be due to differences in the cellular composition of the two glands and not to any difference in the electrical response of corresponding individual cells.

These electrical phenomena are remarkable in several respects. Evidently they are not analogous to the familiar action potentials of nerve and muscle. They appear not to be concerned with the excitatory process (which must be quite different in gland cells and in muscle cells) but are concerned with the functional work of the cell. Lundberg has presented good evidence that the hyperpolarization, associatd with secretory activity, is caused by an active transport of chloride ions through the outer cell membrane which is triggered by the release of a neurohormone at the autonomic nerve endings. The apparent depolarization, when it occurs, is not a self propagating disturbance of the cell membrane of the sort we are accustomed to associate with depolarization, but is probably due to the sustained activity of an ion transport mechanism in the duct cells opposite to that causing hyperpolarization in the alveolar cells.

As a corollary to these observations Lundberg (1958) has suggested that secretion of water and salt by the alveolar cells is accomplished through the activity of an active chloride ion transport mechanism in the outer cell membrane which "pumps" chloride ions into the cell from the surrounding interstitial fluid. Electrical forces cause sodium to accompany chloride and osmotic forces take in water. As a result of the increased hydrostatic pressure within the cell the salt and water escape through the inner membrane (where there may also be an ion pump) into the lumen of the alveolus. He has suggested further that the rodded epithelial cells of the ducts actively absorbs sodium from the secretion. Sodium absorption at this point would account for the apparent depolarization of these cells (decreased internal negativity) and also for the fact that saliva may be hypotonic with respect to the blood.

## Distribution of the Autonomic Nerves within the Glands

The fact that stimulating different nerves caused secretion of different types of saliva caused R. Heidenhain to elaborate his preivously mentioned theory of the differing functions of the autonomic nerves for the digestive glands. Since the chorda tympani nerve to the submaxillary gland usually causes an abundant, watery secretion, Heidenhain believed that it contained chiefly "secretory" fibers. The organic matter present in the saliva was, he believed, due to an admixture of "trophic" fibers. The fact that, in the dog, stimulation of the sympathetic causes only a very small amount of highly viscid secretion (containing a high concentration of organic matter) suggested that the sympathetic nerves consist mainly of "trophic" fibers, particularly in the dog, but with a greater admixture of "secretory" fibers in the cat. As a corollary to this hypothesis, it was assumed that one and the same secreting cell received two kinds of nerve fibers, "secretory" and "trophic."

Heidenhain's theory was challenged by Langley and Fletcher (1890), and later by Carlson and his coworkers (1907, 1908), who demonstrated the importance of the blood supply to a gland in determining the composition of its secretion. Langley came to the conclusion that there is only one kind of secretory nerve for the salivary glands and that the changes in composition seen on stimulating different nerves depends upon the effect which these nerves have on the blood vessels of the salivary glands. If stimulation of a particular nerve, for example, the sympathetic, caused not only secretion but constriction of the blood vessels so as to limit the blood supply of the gland, the gland then would put out the usual amount of solids but a smaller amount of water, resulting in a highly viscid secretion. If, on the other hand, in addition to secretory fibers the nerve contained vasodilator fibers so that an abundance of water was available for the secretion, the gland would put out a more watery fluid. This was in accordance with the fact that the parasympathetic nerves convey secretory and vasodilator fibers, whereas the sympathetics convey secretory and vasoconstrictor fibers to the salivary glands.

The combined physiological and histological studies of Stormont (1932), and more recently of Rawlinson (1933, 1935) in Babkin's laboratory have supported the concept that the individual cells of the salivary glands do not receive a double innervation but that each type of cell is inner-

vated by one or the other division of the autonomic nervous system but not by both. Rawlinson found, for example, that prolonged stimulation of the chorda tympani nerve, with the cervical sympathetic trunk cut, caused the mucous alveolar cells to decrease in size and to become irregular in shape and many of them to loose their ability to take the mucicarmine stain, whereas the alveolar lumen increased in size. The changes were greater the longer the stimulation of the chorda tympani and the more profuse the secretion. There were no definite or constant changes in the demilune cells which, it will be recalled, are serous cells. On the other hand, stimulation of the cervical sympathetic trunk caused no changes in the mucous alveolar cells but after prolonged stimulation the demilune cells were diminished in size and clear vacuoles appeared in their cytoplasm. If the ducts were blocked the vacuolation of the demilune cells became more pronounced, indicating that it was due to the accumulation of secretion. Furthermore, injection of massive doses of adrenaline caused marked changes in the demilune (serious) cells but had practically no effect on the mucous cells. These experiments strongly suggest that the chorda tympani, which is the parasympathetic nerve for the submaxillary gland in the cat, is distributed exclusively to the mucous cells in this species whereas the sympathetic nerve innervates the demilune cells.

On the basis of these and other experiments performed in his laboratory Babkin (1950, p. 869) proposed the following functions for the autonomic nerves to the cats submaxillary gland.

*Parasympathetic nerves:*

1. Hydrelatic effect (secretion of water and salts) on the mucous cells
2. Ecbolic effect (production of enzymes) on the same cells
3. Vasodilator effect

*Sympathetic nerves:*

1. Hydrelatic effect on the demilune cells
2. Motor effect on the myoepithelial cells
3. Vasoconstrictor effect

However, recent studies of the electrophysiology of the salivary glands by Swedish investigators cast serious doubt on these conclusions. Lundberg (1957, 1958) found, for example, that characteristic electrical changes could be produced in a single cell of the cat's submaxillary gland by stimulation of either the sympathetic or parasympathetic nerve. Although it might be possible to explain this fact as due to diffusion of neurohormones from adjacent cells, the straight-forward and probably correct explanation is that both nerves innervate one and the same cell. It has also been found (Emmelin, 1955) that once the gland is responding maximally to parasympathetic stimulation, stimulation of the sympathetic does not augment the secretion as it would do if it activated glandular elements not innervated by the parasympathetic.

It is not possible with our present knowledge to resolve these apparent contradictions but it should be kept in mind that Rawlinson was dealing with what Babkin called ecbolic nerves, that is nerves that caused discharge of organic matter from the cells; purely hydrelatic ("secretory") stimuli do not cause extensive histological changes in secreting cells. Lundberg, on the other hand, was dealing mainly with hydrelatic phenomena. There may be a diffference in the way in which the two types of nerves, ecbolic and hydrelatic, are distributed. At present we do not know how the individual cells of the cat's submaxillary gland are innervated.

*Limitations of electrical stimulation.* It is now possible to clarify the apparent species difference between dogs and cats with respect to the response of the salivary glands to stimulation of the sympathetic nerves. In both animals the sympathetic contains secretory fibers for the submaxillary and sublingual glands and it also contains vasoconstrictor fibers for the blood vessels supplying these glands. The difference lies in the relative effectiveness of the vasoconstrictor elements. In the cat, although vasoconstriction occurs, it lasts for only a short time even though the nerve may be continuously stimulated. Consequently the glands have an adequate blood supply throughout the major part of the period of stimulation. In the dog, on the other hand, the vasoconstriction persists throughout the period of stimulation so that although the secretory fibers to the serous cells are activated, there is an inadequate supply of fluid to form the secretion. The result is a small amount of highly concentrated saliva.

It should be remembered that electrical stimulation of a nerve trunk is highly artificial. All the fibers in the nerve are stimulated even though they may be wholly unrelated in function. This is a situation that never occurs under conditions of normal reflex stimulation. It may be assumed that when the secretory fibers are stimulated reflexly, whether these are sympathetic or parasympathetic, the blood supply to the gland is adjusted to the needs at the moment, whatever they may

be. Another point that should be clarified is the watery character of the secretion obtained on parasympathetic stimulation, in spite of the fact that these nerves are believed to cause secretion of mucus. Undoubtedly mucus is secreted even on artificial stimulation but secretion of water and mucus in the proper proportions to produce an ideal lubricant for the food must depend on normal reflex stimulation.

*Paralytic salivary secretion.* Claude Bernard observed in 1864, that if he cut the chorda tympani nerve in a dog or a cat, in about twenty-four hours the submaxillary gland began to produce a scanty secretion of thin, turbid saliva; the turbidity was due to the presence of leucocytes. The secretion increased until the seventh or eighth day, at which time it reached a plateau, and began to diminish about the third week. It stopped some six weeks after the nerve was cut. During this time the gland increased in size and no secretion could be obtained on stimulation of the mouth. Stimulation of the sympathetic, however, produced a flow of saliva. Division of the sympathetic nerve or extirpation of the cervical ganglion did not evoke a paralytic secretion. Rawlinson repeated these observations in Babkin's laboratory and found, on examination of the gland, that there was evidence of secretory activity during the paralytic secretion not, as one might suppose, in the mucous cells innervated by the chorda tympani but in the demilune cells. Moreover, these cells were more excitable than normal on stimulation by adrenaline or electrical stimulation of the sympathetic nerves. Evidently cutting the chorda tympani causes some alteration in the gland alveoli which greatly increases the excitability of the sympathetic nerve endings on the serous or demilune cells. This may be due to continuous activity of the postganglionic neurons of the chorda tympani when it is disconnected from its preganglionic fibers, thus causing a continuous release in small amounts of acetylcholine in the gland. The heightened irritability of the sympathetic innervation is thought to be due to this minute amount of neurohormone. Evidence of this relationship is seen in another phenomenon studied extensively also in Babkin's laboratory known as augmented salivary secretion.

*Augmented salivary secretion.* It has long been known that if one stimulates a secretory nerve to one of the salivary glands a subsequent stimulus of the same strength to the same nerve will evoke more saliva than the first stimulus, provided the second stimulus is applied within a few minutes after the first has ceased. Likewise, if one stimulates a parasympathetic nerve and then follows that by stimulation of the sympathetic, the sympathetic stimulation will produce more saliva than a sympathetic stimulus of the same strength, not preceded by parasympathetic stimulation. Similarly, stimulation of the sympathetic augments the response to parasympathetic stimulation. In the case of the submaxillary gland augmented secretion has been observed in the following situations by different investigators: chorda after chorda, chorda after sympathetic, sympathetic after chorda, and sympathetic after sympathetic. In short, augmented secretion is observed after any two successive stimulations of the same or of different secretory nerves of the salivary glands provided the second stimulus is not too long delayed.

The augmented secretion was studied extensively by Langley (1889) and more recently by Babkin (1950) and his coworkers. The explanation of this phenomenon is perhaps to be found in the interaction of the neurohormones of the parasympathetic and sympathetic nerves, acetylcholine and noradrenaline or adrenaline. Although these substances are considered generally to act antagonistically, it is nevertheless true that minute amounts of acetylcholine increase the excitability of sympathetically innervated structures to epinephrine or norepinephrine; likewise, minute amounts of epinephrine or norepinephrine increase the excitability of parasympathetically innervated structures to acetylcholine. In the salivary glands in particular, where there is reason to believe that many cells are activated by both adrenergic (sympathetic) and cholinergic (parasympathetic) nerves, adrenaline or noradrenaline and acetylcholine would appear to act synergistically. The augmented secretion observed on chorda after chorda or on sympathetic after sympathetic stimulation, would appear to be a simple case of summation. We may assume that whether the sympathetic or the chorda has been stimulated some neurohormone persists for a time after the stimulus has ceased, and this, added to the neurohormones released by subsequent stimulation augments the total amount of neurohormone present.

### *The Reflex Secretion of Saliva (Artificial Stimulation)*

The salivary glands can be readily excited by the artificial stimulation of afferent nerves supplying structures in the mouth. The reflexes are brought about through the salivary centers. The *efferent* limbs of the reflex arcs—the secretory fibers of the chorda tympani and the tympanic branch of the glossopharyngeal respectively— have been considered above. The *afferent* pathways are long fibers contained in the trunks of the chorda tympani and glossopharyngeal nerves, in the lingual, buccinator and palatine branches of the fifth nerve and in the pharyngeal branch of

the vagus. The fibers of the chorda tympani subserving the sensation of taste are distributed to the anterior two-thirds of the tongue. They arise from cells in the genicular ganglion; the central processes of the ganglion cells enter the pons in the *nervus intermedius of Wrisberg* to make connections with cells in the tractus solitarius from which impulses are relayed to the superior salivatory nucleus. The afferent fibers of the glossopharyngeal nerve concerned in the salivary reflex, carry sensations of taste from the posterior third of the tongue. They arise from cells in the petrous ganglion. The central processes of these cells enter the medulla to make connections through the tractus solitarius with the inferior salivatory nucleus (see also p. 1300). The lingual fibers (cells of origin in Gasserian ganglion) furnish the general buccal mucosa with common sensation—touch, pain, etc. Secretion of saliva may be induced by stimulation of the central end of any one of these three groups of afferent fibers. It can also be brought about by stimulating sensory nerves in other situations. For example, experimental stimulation of the central end of the vagus, sciatic or indeed of practically any sensory nerve of the body may cause salivation. According to some, stimulation of afferent nerves of the gastric mucosa is particularly likely to initiate a reflex secretion into the mouth. In disease, stimuli arising in the esophagus may cause profuse salivation (esophago-salivary reflex). Stimulation of trigeminal terminals in the nasal mucosa will also evoke a secretion of saliva (Babkin).

### *The Secretion of Saliva under Natural Conditions*

In the normal life of the animal the secretion of saliva is brought about reflexly in two ways, either through (a) the stimulation of the nerves of the mouth by the presence therein of food or other substances, or (b) by the stimulation of some organ of special sense other than that of taste. The former type of reflex is termed *unconditioned* or *inherent*, the latter, *conditioned* or *acquired*. A reflex of one type does not, of course, exclude the other, and as a matter of fact both are called into play together under ordinary circumstances.

*The unconditioned salivary reflex.* Materials placed in the mouth call forth, after a short latent period (two or three seconds), a secretion of saliva which varies in *quantity* and *quality* with the physical and chemical nature of the substance introduced. The effects which sensations of taste produce upon the secretion of saliva are well known. Among edible substances, those, generally speaking, which are the most palatable or arouse the sensation of taste with the greatest intensity, are the most potent salivary stimulants. Materials that are entirely inedible will, if unpleasant to the taste—acids especially—cause profuse salivation. In these instances the secretion depends mainly upon the stimulation of the taste fibers, and the stimulus is chemical in nature. But we have seen that stimulation, not only of the taste fibers (chorda tympani and glossopharyngeal) but of the fibers endowing the mucosa of the mouth with common sensibility (lingual nerve) as well, will produce a salivary flow. So, materials such as dry sand, inedible powders, whether soluble or insoluble, or any other material which is capable of stimulating these endings in a purely physical way will evoke a secretion. The mere movements of the jaws and of the tongue over the mucosa of the mouth will have such an effect, although there is no material present in the mouth. A secretion occurs when any substance is chewed, whether or not it is edible or possesses taste. The chewing of india rubber (or gum) for instance, the manipulations of the dentist, the contact of his instruments with the oral mucosa or the grinding of a tooth are familiar and potent causes of salivation.

The remarkable *adaptability* or *purposeful character* of the salivary reflex has been remarked upon by Pavlov. The physical and chemical qualities of the juice, as well as its quantity, are adapted to the physical or chemical characters possessed by the particular substance initiating the reflex. For instance, if clean pebbles be placed in a dog's mouth, they are expelled—merely allowed to drop out of their own weight. No secretion or very little occurs, since none is required; but if the stones are crushed and given as a powder, a profuse watery salivation follows to rid and cleanse the mouth of the useless material. The juice in this instance is poor in organic material and resembles that obtained upon electrical stimulation of the chorda tympani nerve or of the parasympathetic fibers to the parotid. Strong acid produces an abundant saliva which, according to Pavlov, is relatively rich in protein; this exerts a buffer action which reduces or annuls the injurious effect of the acid. The salivary response to the various foods is also adapted to their peculiar qualities. A chunk of meat, if given to a dog, is very quickly swallowed. Under the circumstances what is most required of saliva is a lubricant action. Accordingly, a highly viscous juice, rich in mucin, is produced. If the meat is first dried and powdered, or if dry biscuit is fed to the animal the secretion is characteristic of parotid or chorda saliva—e.g., watery and abundant, but poor in mucin. Milk

evokes the secretion of a saliva rich in mucin, and foods, in general, produce a saliva rich in organic material—mucin and ferments—whereas inedible substances tend to call forth a more watery juice. These adaptations are much less pronounced in man.

Professor Babkin (1950, p. 697) in whose laboratory at McGill University these observations were confirmed and extended, interpreted the results as follows: "It was evident from the facts observed that a salivary gland does not secrete as a unit, but that the different sets of epithelia of which the glands are composed contribute different components to the secretion and furthermore that local productivity depends on the intensity of the excitation received from the salivary center. The salivary center may be regarded as a compound structure consisting of several parts. Each peripheral stimulus, transmitted through the appropriate taste and other sensory nerves of the mouth cavity, acts on different parts of the salivary center and these in their turn excite reflexly and selectively the various epithelial groups in the salivary glands. Moreover it must not be forgotten that the brain possesses not one but two salivary centers— parasympathetic and sympathetic. The parts of these centers innervating different epithelial groups may be stimulated reflexly in various combinations and this will be reflected in the composition of the saliva secreted."

THE CONDITIONED OR ACQUIRED REFLEX. The secretion which flows into the empty mouth when "the mouth waters" is the result of a conditioned reflex. The stimulus which initiates such a reflex is not applied to the nerves of the mouth but is received by one or other of the organs of special sense, particularly those of sight and smell. A conditioned reflex may also be elicited through the sense of hearing or through sensory impressions arising from stimuli applied to the skin. In brief, a conditioned reflex is one in which the cerebral centers play an essential part, and in which training and experience are the basis for the development of the reflex process. Conditioned reflexes are taken up in detail in chapter 68.

## THE REACTION, QUANTITY AND COMPOSITION OF SALIVA

Human mixed saliva, according to the investigations of Starr, is slightly acid in reaction. In 86 per cent of a large series of normal persons the pH was found to vary between 6.35 and 6.85. The lowest pH found was 5.75 and the highest 7.05. Salivary reaction is dependent mainly upon the relative concentrations of free and combined $CO_2$, that is, upon the ratio $[H_2CO_3]/[NaHCO_3]$. So, in order that the true pH value be obtained the juice must be collected without loss of $CO_2$. The older figures in the literature are too high (7.50 to 8.00) since this precaution was not taken. The hydrogen ion concentration of the saliva was found to vary directly with the $CO_2$ content of the blood. This means that when the $CO_2$ tension in the blood is high, more $CO_2$ finds its way into the salivary secretion to lower its pH, and vice versa. Forced breathing causes a lessened amount of $CO_2$ in the saliva, and consequently a rise in its pH. On the other hand, conditions associated with a retention of $CO_2$ in the blood increase the loss of the gas in the saliva. Ingestion of $NaHCO_3$, although it reduces the acidity of the urine, increases that of the saliva, since a rise in the $CO_2$ tension in the blood results.

In man the amount of saliva secreted in 24 hours amounts to from 1000 cc. to 1500 cc.; but the output of the resting gland is only about 0.25 cc. per minute. The cow secretes some 60 liters daily. Ordinary mixed saliva contains about 99.5 per cent of water and 0.5 per cent total solids. It has a specific gravity between 1.002 and 1.012. Its main constituents are as follows:

  I. *Salts* (approximately 0.2 per cent).
    Sodium and potassium chloride.
    Sodium bicarbonate.
    Acid and alkaline sodium phosphates.
    Calcium carbonate and calcium phosphate.
    Potassium sulphocyanate.
  II. *Gases.*
    Carbon dioxide, oxygen and nitrogen.
 III. *Organic substances.*
    Ptyalin (salivary amylase), maltase, and
      lysozyme.
    Serum albumin and globulin.
    Urea, uric acid, creatine and amino-acids.
    Mucin, mainly in the submaxillary and sub-
      lingual secretions.
Glucose is absent, normally, and even in diabetes, none or only small amounts are found in the saliva.

The *bicarbonates* and to some extent the *phosphates* act as "buffers." The buffering action of saliva is such that its pH remains constant under all ordinary conditions and even though relatively strong solutions of acids or alkalis are introduced into the mouth, the reaction, except for a short period, is not altered. The "acid mouth," so glibly spoken of in dentifrice advertisements as an abnormal condition, and the possibility of altering the reaction of the oral secretions are figments of the imagination. Attempts to change the pH of the saliva experimentally by flooding the mouth with acid or alkaline solutions are followed by contrary effects upon the salivary reaction. Acid solutions cause a rise in pH, alkaline solutions a

fall. The changes last for about 10 minutes; the reaction then returns to normal.

The *chlorides* are necessary for the activation of the amylase. The *calcium salts* which are soluble in acid but insoluble in alkaline media tend to be thrown out of solution when the pH rises. The carbonate and phosphate of calcium may be deposited in the form of concretions (*salivary calculi*) within the ducts or, in combination with organic material, may be laid down upon the teeth as "tartar." A high salivary pH and a juice rich in mucin are believed to be conducive to tartar deposition and the development of calculi. The *potassium sulphocyanate* (KSCN) is an excretory product and is probably formed within the body from CN radicals derived from the metabolism of protein. Its production and excretion are thought to represent a detoxicating mechanism. It is said to be in excess in the saliva of habitual smokers, and has been shown by Sullivan and Dawson to be noticeably reduced during the course of pellagra, but returns to normal value during convalescence from this disease.

The bacteriocidal enzyme known as *lysozyme* has a destructive action upon staphylococci, streptococci, meningococci and other microorganisms. It is also present in the lacrimal secretion and is widely distributed in animal tissues and in egg white in which it is closely associated with the protein avidin (p. 928). It has a mucolytic action resembling that of hyaluronidase (Ch. 28) and probably owes its antibacterial activity to its ability to dissolve the polysaccharide in the capsule of the microorganisms.

## The Functions of Saliva

1. *Preparation of food for swallowing.* This is one of the most important functions of saliva. The food is moistened, thus enabling it to be rolled into a plastic mass, and given a lubricating coating of mucus. Claude Bernard showed that a horse with a parotid fistula had the utmost difficulty in swallowing dry hay or oats.

2. *Starch digestion.* The starch molecule is acted upon by salivary amylase and ultimately split into molecules of the dissacharide, maltose. The rapid passage of food through the mouth precludes the possibility that it is acted upon there to any great extent by the saliva. Whether the starchy food, after its thorough impregnation with saliva, undergoes any significant degree of digestion in the stomach, has been debated. The salivary amylase requires for its activity an alkaline, neutral, or but faintly acid medium; therefore, it was thought that the highly acid gastric juice would prevent, or soon teminate salivary digestion. It has been shown, however, that the latter part of the meal, which usually

consists of carbohydrate, may remain in the fundus of the stomach, protected for some time from the acidifying action of the gastric juice, by a layer of food ingested previously. For example, Walter Cannon (1911), noted that in cat stomachs that were carefully removed and frozen at various times after a meal, the inner layers of food in the cardiac end remained neutral or weakly alkaline for hours and only the outer layers were slightly acidified. For this reason it is likely that under favorable circumstances considerable digestion of starch is accomplished during this period. Bergheim found that 76 per cent of the starch of mashed potatoes was transformed into maltose in the human stomach.

When boiled starch is placed in a test tube in mixed human saliva and kept at body temperature, a slow conversion of the starch into maltose takes place. The chemical changes occur in a series of stages which may be distinguished by the manner in which the product of each reacts with iodine. Iodine gives a characteristic blue color with boiled starch. A short time after the saliva has commenced to act a physical change may be seen to have occurred in the starch; it loses its opalescent appearance and becomes soluble but it still gives a blue color with iodine. Presently, however, the starch begins to break down and is partially converted into a dextrin which now gives a red color with iodine and on this account is known as erythrodextrin. Small amounts of maltose may also be detected. Still later no color reaction occurs upon the addition of iodine; a colorless achroodextrin has been formed. In the body, starch is entirely converted into maltose and isomaltose which are later digested by maltase in the intestine and yield glucose. In the first stages, traces of glucose may also appear, due to the presence in the saliva of maltase in low concentration. The following scheme illustrates these changes:

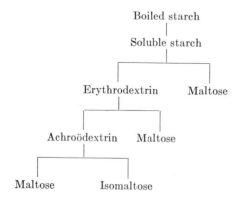

Salivary amylase has no action upon cellulose and for this reason starch for human consumption must be cooked in order that the cellulose envelopes surrounding the starch grains may be broken. Boiling also causes hydration of the starch molecule and renders it more easily digested by amylase.

3. *Solvent action.* Taste is a chemical sense; consequently, all swallowed substances, if they are to stimulate the taste buds, must be dissolved in saliva or other fluid.

4. *Cleansing action.* The constant flow of saliva exerts a very necessary cleansing effect on the mouth and teeth which are rinsed and kept comparatively free from food residues, shed epithelial cells, foreign particles, etc. In this way saliva inhibits the growth of bacteria by removing material which may serve as culture media. One has but to consider the foul condition of the mouth in certain fevers when the salivary secretion is suppressed, in order to realize how important are its cleansing and bactericidal properties. Under these conditions, decomposing organic material, swarming with bacteria (sordes), collects upon the teeth and lips and must be removed by artificial means.

5. *Moistening and lubricating action.* The saliva, by moistening and lubricating the soft parts of the mouth, pharynx, and esophagus, keeps them pliable and resilient; this action on the mouth and lips aids in articulation. Frequent sips of of water are almost essential for some public speakers in whom, as a result of evaporation from the mouth, during speech, the supply of saliva is insufficient.

6. *Excretory function.* Many substances, both organic and inorganic, are excreted in the saliva. Drugs such as mercury, potassium iodide, lead, etc., when introduced into the body, are excreted in part in the saliva. Severe inflammation of the oral mucous membrane (stomatitis) may be caused by the excretion of excessive amounts of mercury by this route. The blue line on the gum margins in lead poisoning is due to the metal having been excreted in the saliva and deposited as sulfide; sulfur is provided by organic materials contained in the tartar formed on the bases of the teeth; for this reason discoloration of the gums does not occur where teeth are absent. In chronic nephritis saliva contains a high percentage of urea; sugar sometimes appears in the saliva in severe diabetes. In parathyroid overdosage the calcium concentration of saliva is elevated. Several types of microorganisms, some intensely

virulent, for instance the viruses of hydrophobia and anterior poliomyelitis, are excreted in the saliva. The latter disease has been reproduced in monkeys by injecting the saliva of an infected person. In this connection, it may be added that mumps, which is usually looked upon as a specific inflammation of the parotid gland, is more likely a general disease since other organs, for example, the ovary, testicle, cerebral mengines, etc., unconnected with the salivary glands, are often seriously affected. The parotid inflammation may be incidental and result from the passage of the infectious agent through the gland into the saliva.

It should not be inferred that merely because the salivary glands are able to excrete certain substances when these are present in the blood that they provide an essential or important avenue of excretion. Doubtless all the excretory functions of the body could be carried on effectively in the absence of the excretory function of salivary glands.

7. *The role played by the salivary glands in the regulation of the water balance of the body.* When the water content of the body is adequate the saliva is secreted continuously. When, however, large quantities of fluid are lost from the body, either through sweat, the bowels, the kidneys, evaporation from the lungs, loss of blood, or when the water intake is curtailed, the salivary glands in common with the other tissues are subjected to the dehydrating effect. Injection into the veins or ingestion of strong salt solution has a similar effect. Salivary secretion is suppressed, drying of the oral mucous membranes and the constant stimulation of afferent nerves in the mouth and pharynx arouse the sensation of thirst (ch. 43). Thirst may be looked upon as an essential part of a protective mechanism against the depletion of body fluid. It serves to warn the individual that the body's water supplies require to be replenished.

### The Actions of Drugs and Chemicals upon Salivary Secretion

Serous secretion is stimulated by adrenaline and ephedrine; acetylcholine, muscarine, pilocarpine, physostigmine (eserine), and histamine increase the mucus secretion. Atropine which antagonizes acetylcholine, and ergotamine which paralyzes sympathetic effects, inhibit secretion. Quinine paralyzes the effects of both nerves.

### Disturbances of Salivary Secretion

Permanent suppression of the salivary secretion—*xerostomia* or *aptyalism* as it is termed—is an unusual condition; little is known regarding the mode of its production. Temporary suppression of salivary secretion is more common and occurs in emotional states and in fevers, or as already mentioned, when the water content of the tissues is lowered. Excessive salivation or *ptyalism* is not unusual and is often particularly troublesome in pregnancy, its cause in the latter state is unknown; it is possibly of reflex origin, or due to some metabolic product acting in a druglike manner upon the gland cells or the secretory nerves.

As a result of irritation of the gastric mucosa, in duodenal ulcer, or in lesions of the esophagus, such as carcinoma or spasm of the cardiac sphincter, salivation occurs as a reflex phenomenon, and may be pronounced (esophago-salivary reflex). The latter reflex is usually readily elicited in a normal person by the passage of a stomach tube or an esophageal sound. Since the glands respond to mechanical stimuli, painful or otherwise, the salivation associated with abnormal conditions in the mouth, e.g., a carious tooth, carcinoma of the tongue, etc. is not surprising.

When the reflex secretion is the result of stimuli arising in the stomach, esophagus or duodenum, and is excessive, the saliva may, without the individual's knowledge, pass down the esophagus and collect above the cardiac sphincter. The secretion occurs as a rule shortly after a meal and a short time later a large quantity of fluid may have accumulated, it may then be brought into the mouth in one or two gushes without any vomiting effort or even nausea. The condition is spoken of as *water-brash.*

### REFERENCES

BERNARD, C. Du rôle des actions réflexes paralysantes dans les phénomènes des sécrétions. J. Anat., Paris, 1864, 1, 507.

CARLSON, A. J., GREER, J. R. AND BECHT, F. C. The relation between the blood supply to the submaxillary gland and the character of the chorda and the sympathetic saliva in the dog and cat. Am. J. Physiol., 1907–1908, 20, 180.

EMMELIN, N. On the innervation of the submaxillary gland cells in cats. Acta Physiol. scandinav., 1955, 34, 11.

HEIDENHAIN, R. Ueber secretorische und trophische Drüsennerven. Pflüger's Arch. ges. Physiol., 1878, 17, 1.

LANGLEY, J. N. On the physiology of the salivary secretion V. The effect of stimulating the cerebral secretory nerves upon the amount of saliva obtained by stimulating the sympathetic nerve. J. Physiol., 1889, 10, 291.

LANGLEY, J. N. AND FLETCHER, H. On the secretion of saliva, chiefly on the secretion of salts in it. Phil. Trans. Roy. Soc. London, Ser. B. 1890, **180**, 116.

LUNDBERG, A. Secretory potentials in the salivary glands of the cat. Acta Physiol. scandinav., 1957, **40**, 21, 35 and 101.

RAWLINSON, H. E. Cytological changes after autonomic and adrenalin stimulation of the cat's submaxillary gland. Anat. Rec., 1933, **57**, 289.

RAWLINSON, H. E. The changes in the alveolar and demilune cells of the simple and stimulated paralytic submaxillary gland of the cat. J. Anat., Lond., 1935, **70**, 143.

STARR, H. E. Studies of human mixed saliva. I. The determination of the hydrogen ion concentration of human mixed saliva. J. Biol. Chem., 1922, **54**, 43.

STROMBLAD, S. Sensitivity of the normal and denervated parotid gland to chemical agents. Acta Physiol. scandinav., 1955, **33**, 83.

SULLIVAN, M. X. AND DAWSON, P. R. Sulfocyanate content of the saliva and urine in pellagra. J. Biol. Chem., 1921, **45**, 473.

*Monographs and Reviews*

BABKIN, B. P. Die äussere Sekretion der Verdauungsdrüsen. Springer, Berlin, 1928.

BABKIN, B. P. Secretory mechanism of the digestive glands, 2nd ed., pp. 664 to 824. Paul B. Hoeber, New York, 1950.

CANNON, W. B. The mechanical factors of digestion, p. 64. Longmans, Green & Co., Inc., New York, 1911.

HEIDENHAIN, R. Hermann's Handbuch der Physiologie, vol. 5, part 1. Leipzig, 1883.

LANGENSKEOLD, A. Component potentials of the submaxillary electrogram. Helsingfors, 1941.

LUNDBERG, A. Electrophysiology of salivary glands. Physiol. Rev., 1958, **38**, 21.

PAVLOV, I. P. The work of the digestive glands, 2nd ed., p. 71. Lippincott, Philadelphia, 1910.

STORMONT, D. L. The salivary glands. Cowdry's special cytology. 2nd ed., vol. 1, p. 91. Paul B. Hoeber, New York, 1932.

ZIMMERMANN, K. W. Die Speicheldrüsen der Mundhöhle und die Bauchspeichedrüse. Von Möllendorffs Handbuch der Mikroskopischen Anatomie des Menschen, Vol. 5, part 1, 161. J. Springer, 1927. Berlin. (Cited by Babkin, 1950.)

# 37

## GASTRIC DIGESTION

### Secretion of Gastric Juice

#### STRUCTURE OF THE MUCOSA

The stomach is lined with mucous membrane which is separated from the outer gastric wall by the muscularis mucosae and a supporting stroma of connective tissue. When the stomach is empty the mucous membrane is thrown into numerous longitudinal folds called rugae; these tend to disappear when the stomach is distended. The surface of the mucous membrane is marked by slight linear depressions, into small polygonal areas called *areae gastricae*, giving the surface a mammilated appearance; the areas measure from 1 to 6 mm in diameter. The surface layer of the mucous membrane is made up of tall columnar cells which secrete mucus. The surface is constantly covered by a thick layer of tough tenacious mucus secreted by these cells. The layer of mucus varies in thickness from $\frac{1}{2}$ mm to $2\frac{1}{2}$ mm. Beneath the surface layer are various types of tubular glands which differ in structure and in the composition of their secretion in different parts of the stomach. When the mucus is removed the gastric crypts may be seen. These depressions in the mucous membrane are just too small to be seen readily with the naked eye but are readily seen on moderate magnification. The mouths of the gastric glands open into the bottoms of the crypts.

The gastric mucosa can be divided into several areas, each of which contains a particular type of gland. In the narrow zone surrounding the cardiac orifice, known as the cardiac area, the glands are made up mostly of mucous cells, although a few pepsinogen cells are also present. Similar glands minus the pepsinogen cells are found in the esophagus. Between this area and the pyloric area is the zone of the fundus and corpus which contains the gastric glands proper, so called because they secrete the major constituents of the gastric juice. The lower limit of this area is marked by the incisura angularis on the lesser curvature, and a corresponding notch on the greater curvature. Between this limit and the

pylorus are the pyloric glands which resemble the cardiac glands and secrete mucus, although a small amount of pepsin is constantly present in their secretions.

#### The Gastric Glands Proper

The gastric glands are made up of three types of cells, mucous cells, pepsinogen or chief cells and parietal cells; the mucous cells may be further divided into isthmus cells and neck cells. The gland as a whole consists of three parts; an isthmus, a neck, and the body of the gland (fig. 37.1). The isthmus connects the gland with the gastric crypt; the neck joins the isthmus to the body; the body, which reaches nearly to the muscularis mucosae, ends blindly and is club shaped or branched. The total number of glands has been estimated at 35,000,000.

Although the isthmus cells are of the mucous type they probably secrete very little mucus inasmuch as they contain little of the granular material commonly considered to be converted into mucus. The cells of the neck are true mucus secreting cells but they secrete a different type of mucus from that of the surface epithelial cells. The mucus of the neck cells is soluble and constitutes a part of the soluble mucus of gastric juice. An important characteristic of the isthmus and neck cells is their frequent mitoses. It is believed that after birth these cells may develop into pepsinogen cells and thus replace chief cells that may have died or been destroyed. No mitoses are seen in the chief cells. In the neck region also are a great many parietal cells. These cells do not form part of the gland wall but appear to lie outside, giving the gland a nodular appearance (fig. 37.1). They can be distinguished from their neighbors not only by their location but by their staining reactions.

Most observers believe that the parietal cells secrete the hydrochloric acid and most of the water of the gastric juice and on this account they are also known as the "oxyntic" or acid secreting cells. Among the several observations which point to this conclusion is the direct corre-

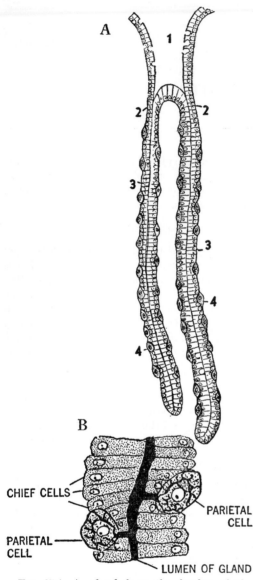

FIG. 37.1. *A*, gland from the fundus of the stomach. 1, crypt or foveola on the mucous surface connected to the neck (2) by the isthmus; 2, neck of gland containing mucin-secreting cells; 3, chief cells; 4, parietal cells. *B*, enlarged drawing showing intercellular and intracellular canaliculi.

CHIEF CELLS

PARIETAL CELL

PARIETAL CELL

LUMEN OF GLAND

lation between the number of the parietal cells and the titratable acidity and total chloride content of different regions of the gastric mucosa during secretion. Although separated from the lumen of the tubules by the chief or pepsinogen cells, the parietal cells transmit their secretion into the lumen through delicate canaliculi lying between the chief cells. These canaliculi are extensions of a system of exquisitely fine canals which lie within the protoplasm of the parietal

cells and possess definite walls. Coarse, transparent granules are seen in the protoplasm of the cells during rest. Depletion of this granular material occurs during activity.

The body of the gland, which makes up the remainder of the tubule, is composed principally of pepsinogen cells, called *chief cells*. Parietal cells are also present but in diminishing numbers as the fundus of the tubule is approached. In addition to pepsinogen the chief cells probably produce rennin which coagulates milk and is believed to be produced only in young animals, and a special gelatin splitting enzyme known as gelatinase, which liquifies gelatin at a rate 450 times that of pepsin. It is not known whether each of these enzymes is produced by a different type of chief cell of whether they are produced by one and the same cell. Since the chief cells appear to be morphologically identical there is no anatomical evidence for assuming that they differ from one another in their secretory products.

ORIGIN AND COMPOSITION OF GASTRIC JUICE

The major constituents of gastric juice are water, hydrochloric acid, enzymes and various types of mucus. In addition to the enzymes previously mentioned, the gastric juice contains a small amount of lipase. Additional inorganic constituents are the cations: sodium, potassium, and calcium, and the anions: phosphate and sulfate.

*Hydrochloric Acid and Neutral Chloride*

The concentration of hydrochloric acid in pure gastric juice varies from 0 to 150 m.eq. or more per liter. Other things being equal, the concentration of acid increases with increasing rates of secretion, up to a maximum of about 150 m.eq. per liter. A small part of the chloride of gastric juice is balanced against metallic ions, principally sodium. This constitutes the so-called neutral chloride. Since the concentration of other negative ions in the juice is negligible, its osmotic activity is primarily due to the acid, plus the neutral chloride. Since gastric juice is practically isotonic with blood, the ionic concentration of total chloride in the gastric juice differs but little from that of the total base of the blood; for example, in some experiments of Gilman and Cowgill (1933) the gastric chloride was 168 m.eq. per liter and the total base of the blood 160 m.eq. per liter.

In highly acid gastric juice the neutral chloride is present only in small amounts but in a less acid secretion it may constitute a major portion of the total chloride. When it is present in such large quantities its source becomes a matter of considerable interest. The source of the neutral chloride has been a matter of widespread discussion and controversy but current thinking tends to the view that it is secreted by the nonparietal cells, (mucous cells of the surface epithelium and chief cells of the gastric glands), along with the organic materials secreted by these cells; and that a certain amount, perhaps a smaller amount, enters the gastric contents by diffusion from the interstitial fluid. In impure gastric juice a large part of the neutral chloride represents swallowed saliva and regurgitated duodenal contents, or perhaps even salt taken with the food.

THE MECHANISM OF SECRETION OF HYDRO-CHLORIC ACID BY THE GASTRIC GLANDS. The precise manner in which the gastric mucosa secretes hydrochloric acid is still unknown, however, the following facts have been established which, taken together, point in a general way to the processes which must be involved in the secretion.

First, it is generally, although not universally, agreed that the acid is formed by the parietal cells of the gastric glands (Davies, 1951; for a dissenting opinion see Rehm and Dennis, 1957). It is not believed to be produced in the protoplasm of these cells but to appear first in the secretory canuliculi which communicate with the lumen of the gland. This conclusion is based on the observation that the parietal cell shows an alkaline reaction while secreting acid.

Second, the acid as secreted by the parietal cell, has a uniform concentration of approximately 0.17 molar. The theory of the constancy of the concentration of hydrochloric acid as secreted by the parietal cells was first put forward by Pavlov and has since been supported by many investigators, including Hollander and Cowgill (1931). This theory is mainly based on the observation that the nearer one approaches to a pure parietal secretion, the nearer the concentration of hydrochloric acid approaches 0.17 molar. The acidity when plotted against the neutral chloride gives a straight line expressing the inverse relationship between them. When extrapolated this line comes to a point representing a zero value for neutral chloride and an acidity of around 170 m.eq. per liter. Since neutral chloride and acid chloride are inversely related, the total chloride tends to remain relatively constant. However, since some of the nonparital secretion contains relatively little chloride, the total chloride increases somewhat with increasing rate of parietal secretion

and therefore with increasing total acidity (figs. 37.2, 37.3 and 37.4).

A somewhat different opinion was expressed by Fisher and Hunt (1950) who made a study of the extensive data of Ihre (1938) on gastric secretion in human subjects. They tested mathematically various assumptions regarding the composition of parietal secretion in the gastric juice and concluded that the most probable concentration of hydrochloric acid in human parietal secretion

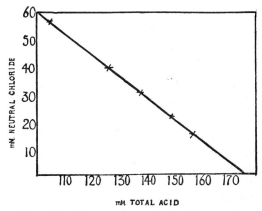

FIG. 37.2. Showing neutral chloride as a function of acidity. (After Hollander.)

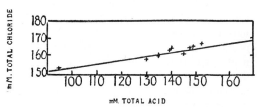

FIG. 37.3. Total chloride as a function of acidity. (After Hollander.)

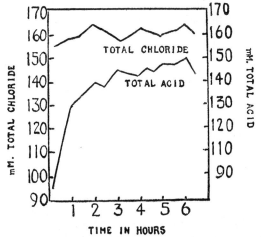

FIG. 37.4. Total chloride as a function of time. (After Hollander, redrawn.)

is 160 m.eq. per liter and that the secretion contains, in addition, 10 m.eq. per liter of neutral chloride. This does not necessarily mean that human parietal secretion differs from that of experimental animals but merely that different methods of estimation give different results. The precise values are, of course, not known.

Third, the secretion of hydrochloric acid involves expenditure of energy; that is to say, no simple chemical reaction which could proceed spontaneously can explain the formation of hydrochloric acid by the gastric glands. One estimate is that the secretion of one gram-molecular equivalent of hydrochloric acid requires expenditure of 10,000 gram-calories of energy.

Fourth, the energy is derived from oxidation, probably of glucose, and requires the activity of the enzymes ordinarily active in such oxidation.

Fifth, for every hydrogen ion produced, a bicarbonate ion is released into the interstitial fluid and ultimately into the blood. This requires a continuous supply of carbon dioxide. The carbon dioxide may be derived from the metabolism of the parietal cell itself if the secretory rate is low but at higher rates of secretion the metabolic carbon dioxide has to be supplemented with carbon dioxide derived from the circulating blood. The need for carbon dioxide arises from the fact that, whatever the reacting system may be, removal of hydrogen ions results in accumulation of an excess of hydroxyl ions; if these were not neutralized the resulting alkalinity would soon destroy the secreting cells. The fact that secretion of hydrochloric acid into the gastric juice results in secretion of an equivalent amount of bicarbonate into the blood explains the alkaline tide, so-called, seen in the urine during digestion (Bence-Jones, 1849).

Sixth, carbonic anhydrase (ch. 13 and 29) is present in high concentration in the parietal cells (Davenport, 1939) and participates in the overall process, though probably not directly in secretion of hydrogen ions. Its function apparently is to aid in the hydration of carbon dioxide to produce the carbonic acid that is utilized in neutralizing the hydroxyl ions produced during secretion. Secretion of hydrochloric acid is greatly depressed and in some subjects totally inhibited by the administration of large doses of Diamox, which is an inhibitor of carbonic anhydrase (Janowitz *et al.*, 1957). Although excised frog gastric mucosa will secrete in the absence of carbon dioxide, the tissue is destroyed by the alkalinity resulting from the loss of hydrogen ions (Davies and Longmuir, 1948). In the living animal, at least

in mammals, some mechanism apparently exists to prevent secretion under these circumstances and thus protects the secreting tissue from self destruction.

Seventh, the over-all reaction can be summarized in the following equation:

$$CO_2 + H_2O + NaCl \rightleftarrows HCl + NaHCO_3$$

This equation is not intended to describe the chemical reactions in detail but merely to indicate the beginning and end products and their quantitative relationships. It indicates that the ultimate source of the hydrogen ion is water, and the ultimate source of the chloride ions is the salt of the blood. Also that for each mole of hydrochloric acid produced a mole of sodium bicarbonate has to be formed. The intermediate steps, the source or sources of the energy, and the enzymes and substrates concerned in the intermediate reactions, all of which constitute the real problem of the secretion of hydrochloric acid, are not even suggested. The well known fact that the reactions of this equation would ordinarily progress to the left is a simple qualitative proof of the fact that energy is required for the secretion of hydrochloric acid.

Rehm (1950) and his coworkers have shown that there is a natural, maintained potential difference across the gastric mucosa, the secretory surface being negative in an external circuit to the nutrient surface. When the two sides of the mucosa are connected electrically a continuous current can be maintained representing about 10 per cent of the metabolic energy. The natural potential decreases with the onset of acid secretion. The rate of acid secretion can be increased or decreased by passing an electric current from a battery through the mucosa so as to increase or decrease respectively the potential difference across the tissue. Experiments with metabolic inhibitors show that most of the pathways of aerobic metabolism and the related phosphorylations are required to maintain the potential difference and the acid secretion. The facts prompted Rehm (1949, 1950) to propose a theory of acid secretion in which it is assumed that electrical energy is utilized in the separation of hydrogen ions during the secretion of hydrochloric acid. It seems more likely that here, as elsewhere, the potential difference is the result of —rather than the cause of—the activity.

As to the intermediate steps between carbon dioxide and water at one end of the reaction, and hydrogen ions and bicarbonate at the other end Davies (1951), after reviewing the history of research in this field from Claude Bernard's time until 1951, had this to say: "The available evidence shows that two related mechanisms of acid secretion are possible. In mechanism 1, the metabolic hydrogen atoms from glucose and water, which are transported by the dehydrogenases, become oxidized to hydrogen ions at the cytochrome level, and the electrons react with oxygen and water to form, first hydroxyl ions, and then bicarbonate ions by further reactions with carbon dioxide. This process uses the oxidation reduction energy from the level of atmospheric oxygen to that of the cytochromes. In mechanism 2, phosphate bond energy, generated by reactions at lower oxidation reduction levels is utilized to concentrate hydrogen ions, formed by ionization from water, in an electron cycle mechanism in which hydrogen ions are reduced to covalent hydrogen atoms, transported by a carrier system and oxidized to hydrogen ions at high concentration as a result of coupled phosphorylation. Kinetic and thermodynamic considerations show that the hydrogen carrier and electron transport systems could be oxaloacetate-malate and cytochrome $b$, or perhaps fumarate-succinate and cytochrome $c$. Both mechanisms require a spatial array of enzymes in the paracanalicular zone of the oxyntic cells, and in both cases chloride ions move in the opposite direction to, and as a result of, the movements of the electrons carried by the cytochromes."

Davenport (1957), writing six years later, had this to say: "In agreement with Conway" (1953) "and many others, I suspect that the secretory process itself is a cyclic oxidation and reduction. A carrier molecule within the cell combines with high energy phosphate. The product is oxidized and the energy contained within it is dissipated in transporting the newly released proton" (hydrogen ion) "against a concentration gradient into the gastric juice. Then the carrier is reduced by substrate and is ready to reenter the cycle. Two minor problems remain. For each proton secreted an electron must be taken up by oxygen, and the pH of the cell must be kept down by intracellular neutralization using the carbon dioxide mechanism" . . . "Carbonic anhydrase which occupies a peripheral position is involved, an enzyme behaving like succinoxidase is there, and it is likely that some sulfhydryl compound is essential." Davenport, like Davies, recognizes the need for assuming appropriate orientation of the various components involved in the reaction. (Dr. Davenport's concept is illustrated in figure 37.5.)

Davies (1951) considers that, "the rate of transport of water by the oxyntic cells is so enormous that it could not be handled molecule by molecule by any known enzyme systems. The water must be moved in bulk, and probably flows osmotically as a result of the secretion of the hydrogen and chloride ions by the oxyntic cells."

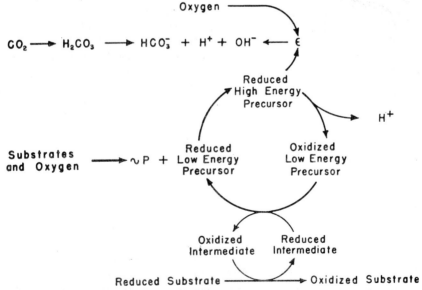

FIG. 37.5. Schema of a possible mechanism of gastric acid secretion showing the four essential parts: a) generation of high energy phosphate bounds from substrate and oxygen, b) cyclic oxidation and reduction generating hydrogen ions, c) removal of electrons to oxygen, and d) intracellular neutralization by carbon dioxide. From Davenport, 1957. (Courtesy of University of Wisconsin Press.)

### REGULATION OF GASTRIC SECRETION

#### *Methods of Study*

Studies of the regulation of gastric secretion offer some difficulty because of the fact that gastric juice is secreted in only small amounts in the fasting stomach and that secreted during digestion is always contaminated with food. This difficulty was overcome by Pavlov (1910) who devised a method for collecting pure gastric juice from the fed animal. This is accomplished by making an incompletely separated pouch of part of the stomach, now known as a Pavlov pouch. The stomach is divided by an incomplete incision into a larger and smaller portion. The mucous membrane is completely divided but an isthmus of the muscular wall is retained to connect the two parts and serve as a pathway for the vagus nerve fibers that supply the gastric glands. The cut edges of each part are then stitched together so as to restore the continuity of the main stomach wall and to make a closed cavity out of the smaller portion, or pouch, except for a small outlet that is brought out through the abdominal wall to provide drainage for the pouch secretions (fig. 37.6). The pouch usually consists of a part of the

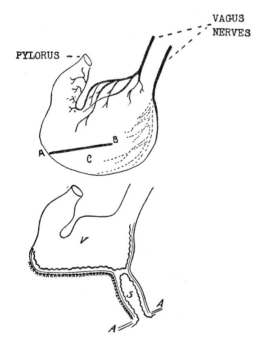

body and fundus of the stomach. Numerous modifications of the Pavlov pouch have been devised, most of them designed to retain a greater portion of the nerve supply to the pouch than did the original operation devised by Pavlov. A Pavlov pouch, or any one of its modifications, responds to all the nervous and humoral stimuli that affect the main stomach and makes possible the collection of pure gastric juice which can then be analyzed to determine the influence of various stimuli upon the volume and composition of the juice. Although a gastric pouch gives information regarding the secretory activity of only that particular portion of the stomach from which it is excised, pouches may be prepared from any region of the stomach; consequently the method makes possible investigation of the function of any part of the gastric mucous membrane.

If a pouch is completely separated from the main stomach by dividing the isthmus between the two, leaving only the blood supply intact, it is known as a Heidenhain pouch. The Heidenhain pouch is useful for investigating the secretion of a vagally denervated portion of the stomach; it continues to receive a sympathetic nerve supply through the periarterial nerve plexuses. If an attempt is made to cut the sympathetic fibers as well, by stripping the arteries, the pouch is known as a Bickel pouch (Bickel and Katsch, 1912).

Farrell and Ivy (1926) prepared a completely denervated pouch of the stomach by transplanting a portion of the stomach of a dog into the subcutaneous tissue of the animal's abdominal wall. After the pouch had established a new blood supply, they severed its connections with the original nerve and blood supply of the stomach. Such a preparation responds only to humoral stimulation and has been of fundamental importance in demonstrating the chemical nature of many of the stimuli which affect the stomach. "Pouches" have also been made of the entire stomach (the Fremont pouch, Pavlov, 1910), by cutting the stomach off from the esophagus and duodenum and connecting these two organs by means of an end to end anastomosis. The cut ends of the stomach are closed with sutures and a fistulous opening made from some part of the stomach through the abdominal wall.

In the human, gastric juice can be collected through a stomach tube; the secretion may be stimulated by means of a test meal or by use of one of the gastric secretagogues such as histamine. Similar methods can be used in unoperated animals but it is simpler and just as satisfactory for most purposes to prepare the animal with a

FIG. 37.6. The Pavlov pouch. Upper drawing shows line of incision to form a flap. C, cardiac part of stomach. Lower drawing shows the completed operation. S, pouch; the mucous membrane has been reflected to form a partition between the main cavity of the stomach and the miniature stomach. A, A, abdominal wall (after Pavlov).

gastric fistula and in this way avoid the use of a stomach tube.

Another of Pavlov's devices for the study of gastric secretion is esophagostomy. In this operation the esophagus is divided by a transverse incision and the cut ends brought to the outside through a wound in the neck (fig. 37.7). After healing, all the food which the animal eats escapes from the lower end of the upper segment of the esophagus and the animal can be fed by placing food in the lower segment through its exposed upper end. The maneuver of feeding such an animal with the consequent loss of food is known as sham feeding. The animal is able to experience all the sensations of eating without getting any food into its stomach.

THE INNERVATION OF THE GASTRIC GLANDS. Stimulation of the vagus nerve causes the secretion of juice high in peptic power and strongly acid. This action is mediated through acetylcholine. According to Alley and Babkin the glands of the lesser curvature respond more readily to vagal stimulation than do those of the greater curvature, and secrete a stronger juice. This fact may be of significance in the development of gastric ulcer (p. 621). Baxter has shown that stimulation of the sympathetic causes the secretion, mainly from the pyloric glands, of an alkaline mucoid juice which is very low in peptic power; this secretion is unaffected by atropine but is annulled by ergotamine (which paralyzes motor and secretory sympathetic fibers). Vineberg's results indicate that the vagus controls the secretion of mucin by the mucous neck cells and the surface epithelium of the gastric mucosa. The influence exerted by the sympathetic upon the peptic and oxyntic cells of the gastric body is not definitely known. According to some observers its effect upon these elements is inhibitory.

THE QUESTION OF THE CONTINUOUS OR INTERDIGESTIVE SECRETION OF GASTRIC JUICE. Pavlov found that the secretion of gastric juice in dogs was intermittent; beyond the secretion of some alkaline mucus the gastric glands in the absence of food or psychic influences (see below) remained at rest. This conclusion has been confirmed by the recent experiments of Babkin. But in man, juice is secreted continuously in fairly large amounts, though this fact does not necessarily indicate a fundamental difference between the activities of the glands of the human and canine stomachs. The shorter intervals between meals, and psychic influences which are impossible to eliminate in the case of the human subject, are probably responsible for the continuous and apparently spon-

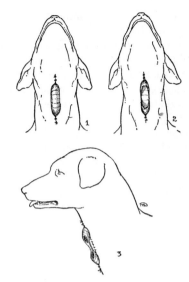

FIG. 37.7. A two-stage operation for making an esophageal fistula. 1. First stage, showing esophagus exteriorized. 2. Second stage, performed four or five days later, showing excision of elliptical segment of anterior esophageal wall. 3. Completed operation, lateral view. (After Dragstedt and associates.)

taneous secretion. This secretion is increased during sleep.

## THE PHASES OF GASTRIC SECRETION

### Cephalic or Initial Reflex Phase

The fact that there can be an abundant secretion of gastric juice even though there is no food in the stomach is readily demonstrated by means of sham feeding. When an animal provided with an esophagostomy is sham fed secretion of gastric juice begins within 5 minutes and may continue for as long as $1\frac{1}{2}$ hours. If the vagus nerves have been previously cut, sham feeding has no effect on the gastric secretion, proving that secretion in this instance is the result of reflexes for which the vagus serves as the efferent pathway. By collecting the juice from an innervated pouch, Pavlov was able to show that it contains a very high concentration of both hydrochloric acid and pepsin. A similar type of gastric juice is secreted by the empty stomach on electrical stimulation of the vagus nerves. The phase of gastric secretion which results from the sight, smell or taste of food or from the act of eating and which is prevented by section of the vagus nerves is known as the *cephalic*, or *initial reflex phase*. If the secretion results from the sight or smell of food without the food making actual contact with the mouth it is referred to as psychic secretion. Pavlov referred to the secretion produced during the initial reflex phase as "appetite juice."

THE PSYCHIC SECRETION IN MAN. In man, the cephalic phase causes the secretion of from 50 to 150 cc. within 20 minutes (Ivy). Richet (1878) observed long ago that in a subject who had suffered esophageal stricture and into whose stomach an artificial opening (fistula) had been made for feeding purposes, the secretion of gastric juice occurred when food was taken into the mouth. Within more recent years Carlson has carried out extended observations upon a subject who had had a similar operation performed on account of an obstructed esophagus resulting from the ingestion of a corrosive in childhood. This subject therefore was already prepared, like Pavlov's dogs, for sham feeding, the only difference being that there was no opening in the neck, it being necessary to spit out the food after chewing it. All the findings of Pavlov were, in the main, confirmed in the case of this subject. The influence of appetite or the desire for the food was particularly well brought out. The subject especially enjoyed the dessert, and the curve of gastric secretion showed the most pronounced rise when sweets or fruit, such as oranges, were chewed. The secretion, however, did not last for as long as in Pavlov's experiments, but commenced to decline as soon as the stimulation of the taste buds had ceased (fig. 37.8). Nor did the mere sight or smell of food (conditioned stimulus) evoke a response except when in one instance the subject was sent from the laboratory to select his meal from a nearby cafeteria. In this instance there was a very definite response to the sight and smell of the food. Several other observers have reported the existence of definite conditioned reflexes for gastric secretion in man.

The psychic effect upon gastric secretion has been demonstrated also by Bennett and Venables

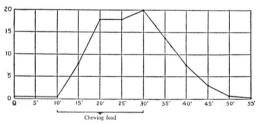

FIG. 37.8. Typical curve of secretion of gastric juice collected at 5-minute intervals during the mastication of palatable food for 20 minutes. The rise in secretion during the last 5 minutes of mastication is due to chewing the dessert (fruit) for which the person had an especial fondness. (After Carlson.)

(1920) upon subjects during hypnosis. A suggestion made to the subject that he was eating a savory food called for a secretion of juice. The mere suggestion of nauseating substances inhibited secretion (see below). In experiments upon medical students Hawk and his associates (1920) showed that a meal which had a disgusting appearance and a foul smell (indol was scattered over a dirty table-cloth) retarded digestion.

The application of these experimental results to dietetics is obvious. Foods agreeably flavored and attractive in appearance, impressions received from a meal prepared in a pleasing way, and, probably also, sensations aroused by the surroundings but not directly concerned with the food itself, have all an effect upon gastric secretion. The impulse which guides the gourmet is sounder physiologically than that which impels the glutton. The question of calories and the relative digestibilities of the various foodstuffs should not be allowed to obscure the psychic element entirely in these matters, for the "delights of the table" have true digestive value. These facts are expressed in the words of Pavlov "appetite spells gastric juice" or in the hospitable words of Macbeth "Now good digestion wait on appetite and health on both." Good gastronomical custom seems guided by this truth, for it has decreed that the meal shall begin and end with the more strongly flavored and appetizing dishes.

### The Chemical Phases of Gastric Secretion

THE GASTRIC PHASE. Pavlov also observed that if food were placed in the stomach without allowing the animal to smell or taste it, there was also a secretion of gastric juice beginning about 15 minutes after the food had been introduced; usually this required that the animal be fed through a gastric fistula while asleep. This, Pavlov considered to be the gastric phase of gastric secretion. It has more recently been described by Babkin (1950) as part of the second, or chemical, phase of secretion. The mechanism of stimulation in the second phase was at first thought to involve local reflexes within the gastric wall, since it occurred in the absence of extrinsic innervation, but after Bayliss and Starling discovered secretin Edkins (1906) suggested that a similar excitant for gastric secretion might be produced by contact of food with the gastric mucosa. Extracts of the pyloric mucous membrane prepared by Edkins did indeed stimulate secretion of gastric juice. He proposed that the stimulating substance be known as *gastrin*.

Gastrin was long believed to be a nonspecific tissue extract and to owe its activity to histamine (Sacks *et al.*, 1932), a common constituent of such extracts, but recent work has made it seem highly probably that it is a true hormone, somewhat similar in composition to secretin. It is elaborated by the pyloric mucous membrane of the stomach, and is absorbed and carried in the blood to the gastric glands, stimulating them to secrete (Komarov, 1942). The evidence on this point consists of the fact that extracts have been prepared in a number of laboratories both in America and in Europe which stimulate gastric secretion but do not depress blood pressure as histamine does. Furthermore, the activity of such preparations is not destroyed by histaminase, an enzyme which inactivates histamine. Active material is obtained only from the pyloric portion of the stomach, and, in lesser amounts, from the duodenum. None is obtained from the fundus or the body of the stomach, or from other tissues.

The controversy over the nature of gastrin is reminiscent of the efforts of Popileski during the early part of the century to prove that secretin is a nonspecific tissue extract. He did, in fact, come to the conclusion that secretin is identical with histamine. Although mistaken in his opinion, his efforts were not fruitless for they resulted in discovery of the gastric secretagogue action of histamine, a fact which has been of great service to physiology and medicine (Popileski, 1920).

Secretion formed by pure gastrin stimulation, excluding the nerves, contains less pepsin than that secreted during the initial reflex phase and resembles the secretion produced in response to histamine. Indeed the action on the gastric glands of the most highly purified preparations of gastrin so closely resembles the action of histamine as to suggest a close relationship between the two substances. Babkin (1938, 1950) has suggested that histamine is liberated in the vicinity of the parietal cells by vagus stimulation. Linde (1950) has gone even farther and concluded, on the basis of his experiments with an antihistamine, that gastrin as well as vagal stimulation acts by liberating histamine. According to this concept, both acetylcholine and gastrin possess the capacity to liberate histamine in the vicinity of the parietal cell, the histamine then acting as a stimulus to secretion of water and acid. Whether or not this is the correct explanation, the recent work of Ivy and his coworkers leaves little doubt that histamine or something very similar to it is involved in some way in the secretion of hydro-

chloric acid by the stomach (Ivy and Schayer, 1957; Schayer and Ivy, 1957, 1958).

The effective stimulus for the normal gastric phase of gastric secretion is the presence of food in the antrum. In addition to the chemical substances in the food, such as meat extractives, products of protein digestion and soaps, which excite gastric secretion when present in the antrum, mechanical stimulation of the pyloric portion is a highly effective stimulus. Simple distension with a balloon causes release of gastrin as does the presence of solid objects such as bone chips, or even brass or steel shavings. It is probable that the harmful effect of a coarse diet in peptic ulcer disease is caused more by the mechanical stimulation of the antrum by indigestible food particles than it is by irritation of the ulcer surface itself.

Considerable evidence has accumulated in recent years indicating that the gastric phase of gastric secretion is not a pure chemical phase but that its full functioning is dependent in some way upon the nervous system. Also Uvnäs (1942) and Linde (1950) in Sweden, have brought forward evidence suggesting that efficient functioning of the reflex phase is dependent to some extent on the presence of gastrin. Different investigators have suggested that (1) gastrin is released by stimulation of the vagus nerves; (2) that gastrin is necessary for the secretory effect of the vagus nerves on the gastric glands; (3) that a certain amount of vagal activity is necessary for the secretory effect of gastrin on the gastric glands; (4) that gastrin is released by a local reflex mechanism involving the presence of cholinergic nerve endings in the antral mucosa. Only the last is supported by enough experimental evidence to be considered a fact (Robertson *et al.*, 1950; Gregory and Ivy, 1941; Zeljony and Savich, 1911). Thomas (1952) after reviewing the experimental evidence came to the following conclusions:

1. Gastrin is released from the pyloric mucosa by local mechanical and chemical stimuli acting though a cholinergic nervous mechanism that probably comprises Meissner's plexus and its local and central connections.

2. Stimulation of the vagi facilitates the nervous mechanism involved in the release of gastrin and may cause the release of some gastrin in the absence of specific local stimuli.

3. Neither gastrin alone, nor vagus stimulation alone, can cause maximal stimulation of the gastric glands to secrete hydrochloric acid. Abundant

secretion is obtainable only when nervous and hormonal stimuli act simultaneously.

The importance of these considerations lies in the light they shed on the effects of the operations of vagotomy, on the one hand, and of subtotal gastric resection on the other. If the nervous and hormonal mechanisms of stimulation were independent of each other, we should expect that cutting the vagus nerves would influence only the initial reflex phase of gastric secretion and leave the gastric phase in full effect. This is not the result observed; all phases of gastric secretion are profoundly depressed by vagotomy and in a certain percentage of patients permanent achlorhydria results. Likewise, resection of the antrum, or subtotal gastric resection should affect only the gastric phase. Experience proves, however, that the cephalic phase is also profoundly influenced.

A fact first noted by Pavlov and since confirmed by many investigators (Wilhelmj *et al.*, 1936; Dragstedt *et al.*, 1951; Oberhelman *et al.*, 1952) is that the pyloric mucosa not only has the capacity to stimulate gastric secretion but also to inhibit it. Pavlov described the phenomenon as follows: "with the same dogs we also discovered a new form of autoregulation on the part of the stomach, which concerns the secretion of hydrochloric acid. It appears that acid prevents the further secretion of gastric juice when it has accumulated in any considerable quantity within the cavity of the organ." Dragstedt showed that hydrochloric acid in the stomach has to be in contact with the pyloric mucosa in order to produce inhibition. Whether it releases an inhibitory hormone or merely stops the production of gastrin by the pyloric mucosa is still unknown. Acid in the duodenum also inhibits gastric secretion (Wilhelmj *et al.*, 1934; Uvnäs *et al.*, 1956) provided the pH of the duodenal contents is lowered to 2.5 or below (Pincus *et al.*, 1942).

THE INTESTINAL PHASE. *The inhibitory effect of fat.* Pavlov observed also that the presence of certain food substances in the small intestine stimulated gastric secretion. This so-called intestinal phase has been extensively investigated by Babkin (1928, 1950) and his coworkers and others. The following substances have been found capable of exciting gastric secretion when placed in the small intestine: water, extractive substances of meat, products of protein digestion, (for example, peptone and amino acids), milk, alcohol, histamine, saponin, adrenaline, 1 : 10 normal hydrochloric acid, 10 per cent glycerine solution and magnesium sulfate. The intestinal phase

is regarded as being quantitatively unimportant and is somewhat temperamental, being present only under certain conditions. For example, in the experiments of Beamer *et al.* (1944), introduction of a peptone solution into the intestine caused no gastric secretion unless bile was present. In the presence of bile it caused a flow of gastric juice after a latent period of about 2 hours. The long latent period is also characteristic of the intestinal phase described by Webster and Armour (1932).

Most experiments on the intestinal phase of gastric secretion have been done, for obvious reasons, on animals in the fasting state with the stomach empty. The results may be quite different when the intestinal phase occurs in its proper sequence following a cephalic and a gastric phase. The known tendency of stimuli of different sorts to act synergistically in the gastrointestinal tract suggests, but does not prove, that the stimuli normally causing an intestinal phase may be much more effective in the presence of the residual stimuli of the cephalic and gastric phases.

The cause of the intestinal phase is unknown, except that it is due to chemical stimuli. The evidence on this point is due to the ingenious experiments of Gregory and Ivy (1941) who used a denervated pouch of the type described by Farrell and Ivy. This completely denervated gastric pouch secreted when food was placed in the intestine, proving that it was secreting in response to some chemical substance circulating in the blood. The stimulus may be a hormone or it may be secretagogues absorbed with the food from the intestine, as suggested by Babkin (1950).

Perhaps one reason for the somewhat erratic behavior of the intestinal phase of gastric secretion is the ease with which inhibition of secretion may be induced by placing certain substances in the intestine. The inhibitory effect of acid has already been mentioned. Although acid in certain concentrations may stimulate gastric secretion, if the intestinal pH is lowered to 2.5 or below it acts as an inhibitor. The most potent inhibitor of gastric secretion is fat in the intestine. Fat in the stomach is without inhibitory effects but as soon as it passes the pylorus gastric secretion begins to diminish and, if the quantity of fat is large, may cease all together. The inhibition lasts as long as the fat remains in the intestine but after the fat is absorbed the inhibition is followed by a pronounced increase in gastric secretion, the so-called rebound phase of fat inhibition. The inhibition and subsequent stimulation of secretion by fat is known as the *biphasic* effect of fat. The stage of increased secretion which follows the inhibition is believed to be due to release of gastrin by the soaps which have regurgitated into the stomach from the intestine during digestion of the fat. Were it not for the rebound phase, fat would be a most useful substance for controlling gastric secretion; even so, it can be used successfully if given in small amounts at frequent intervals over a long period of time. The use of cream in this way is the basis of one form of treatment of peptic ulcer.

*Enterogastrone.* The mechanism of inhibition of gastric secretion by fat was elucidated by Lim (1933; see also Kosaka and Lim, 1930), who showed that if the intestinal mucous membrane was exposed to fat, and then extracted, the extract caused inhibition of gastric secretion when given intravenously. Kosaka and Lim suggested that the inhibitory substance be called "enterogastrone." The substance has since been studied extensively by Ivy and his students in Chicago and it is to their work that we owe most of our knowledge of its chemical and physiological properties, as well as the first demonstration of the humoral nature of the inhibitory effect of fat on gastric *motility* (Farrell and Ivy, 1926; see also Ivy and Gray, 1937). Enterogastrone has never been obtained in pure form; hence, its chemical composition is unknown. Since it inhibits motility as well as secretion and the relative effect on the two functions differs in different preparations, it is probable that more than one substance is involved. Enterogastrone or some similar substance is excreted in the urine and is given the name "urogastrone."

### Regulation of Gastric Acidity

As we have seen, the hydrochloric acid of the gastric juice is probably secreted at a constant concentration of approximately 170 m.eq. per liter. Ordinary gastric juice, however, is considerably less acid than this and after a meal the gastric contents are still less acid. In dogs after a meal of raw meat, which is a powerful stimulas to gastric secretion in these animals, the contents of the body and fundus of the stomach usually have a pH between 1 and 2 and the contents of the pyloric portion between 2 and 3. The decrease in acidity is undoubtedly due to a combination of factors which may be classified for convenient discussion as intragastric and extragastric. Perhaps the first intragastric factor to become effective is exchange of hydrogen ions for sodium ions by diffusion through the gastric mucosa. This factor has been emphasized particularly by Teorell (1947). There is no doubt that such diffusion takes place but its relative importance in regulating gastric acidity has never been determined. Another intragastric factor is the nonparietal secretion of the gastric glands, including the fundic and pyloric glands and the surface epithelium of the stomach. All the cells, other than the parietal cells, secrete a fluid which is either neutral or alkaline. The neutral secretions dilute the acid; and the alkaline secretions, particularly those containing mucin, tend to neutralize some of it. In both cases the effect is to lower the acidity. Even though the nonparietal elements of the gastric glands, particularly the chief cells, may secrete very little water they do secrete protein which is an excellent buffering agent.

Among extragastric factors we recognize swallowed saliva and regurgitated duodenal contents as tending to reduce the acidity of the gastric contents. Very considerable quantities of saliva are swallowed with the food and although it may not be alkaline in reaction it does contain considerable quantities of mucin and other protein substances and so will tend not only to dilute but to buffer the gastric contents. Regurgitation of duodenal contents into the stomach occurs regularly after a fat meal and in the presence of high gastric acidity. It occurs at irregular and unpredictable intervals under other circumstances. The mechanism of duodenal regurgitation will be discussed in connection with gastric emptying in chapter 41. Since the regurgitated intestinal contents contain alkaline secretions from the pancreas and the intestinal mucosa they can exert a considerable influence on gastric acidity.

Undoubtedly the most important factor in lowering the acidity of the gastric contents after a meal is the food itself. Native protein, being an amphoteric substance, is an excellent buffer and as digestion progresses the number of amino groups available for neutralizing acid increases enormously. As the food becomes liquid and mixes with the gastric juice it also has a diluting effect so that during digestion of a normal meal the gastric mucosa is well protected from excess acidity. It may also be mentioned in this connection that the tough layer of mucus which adheres to the surface epithelial cells serves to protect these cells from the action of hydrochloric acid as well as from the mechanical trauma to which they might be subjected by coarse food or other swallowed substances.

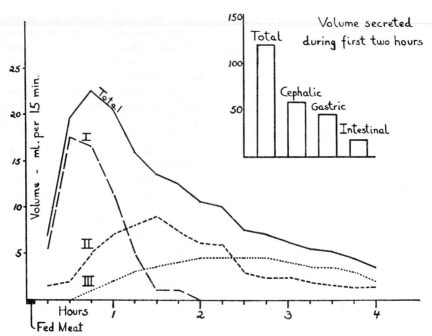

FIG. 37.9. Reconstructed curves to show the approximate distribution between the several phases of the gastric secretion in a dog after a meal of 300 grams of meat. I. Cephalic or initial reflex phase; II. Gastric or pyloric phase. III. Intestinal phase. Thomas and Friedman, 1951. (Courtesy of W. B. Saunders Co., Philadelphia.)

### The Normal Course of Gastric Secretion

With the above facts in mind we may consider the sequence of events affecting the secretion of gastric juice following a normal meal. First, there is the sight and smell, and the taste of food which, if agreeable and if the individual has an appetite, will initiate the psychic or cephalic phase of gastric secretion. This phase is augmented when the food is actually chewed and swallowed. The first juice secreted has powerful digestive action, particularly upon the protein constituents of the food, and releases from the food chemical excitants for the second or chemical phase of secretion. These, along with the mechanical action of such food particles as enter the pyloric antrum, cause the release of gastrin which augments and prolongs the secretion due to the cephalic phase and initiates the gastric phase. The gastric phase of secretion continues as long as food remains in the stomach. As soon as the stomach is empty and the buffering substances present during digestion are no longer available the pH of the antrum or duodenum falls to a point at which the inhibitory effect of acid becomes evident and that period of gastric secretion is brought to an end. If there is some defect in the mechanism that regulates the flow of hydrochloric acid so that it continues after the stomach is empty, a condition of hypersecre-

tion or continuous secretion is said to be present, and this may lead to ulceration of the gastric or duodenal mucous membrane.

The relative importance of the several phases of gastric secretion is indicated in figure 37.9.

REFERENCES

ALLEY, A. The secretory activity of the gastric mucosa in the region of the lesser curvature. Tr. Roy. Soc. Can., 1933, 27, Sec. V, 71. The effect upon the gastric juice secretion of various cooked preparations of haddock and of lobster. Am. J. Digest. Dis. & Nutrit., 1934, 1, 182.

ALLEY, A., MACKENZIE, D. W., JR. AND WEBSTER, D. R. Dissociation of the functional properties of the gastric glands under the influence of fat. Am. J. Digest. Dis. & Nutrit., 1935, 1, 333. Inhibitory effects of histamine. Am. J. Digest. Dis. & Nutrit., 1935, 1, 787.

BABKIN, B. P. The value of histamine as a test of gastric secretion from a physiological point of view. Canad. M. A. J., 1930, 23, 268. Does the stomach secrete gastric juice continuously? Contrib. to the Med. Sciences in honor of Dr. Libman, Internat. Press, New York, 1932, 1, 113.

BABKIN, B. P. Modes of stimulation of the gastric secretion. Nature, 1934, 134, 1005. The "chemical" phase of gastric secretion and its regulation. Am. J. Digest. Dis. & Nutrition, 1934, 1, 715.

BABKIN, B. P. The abnormal functioning of the gastric secretory mechanism as a possible factor in the pathogenesis of peptic ulcer. Canad. M. A. J., 1938, **38**, 421.

BABKIN, B. P. AND KOMAROV, S. A. The influence of gastric mucus on peptic digestion. Canad. M. A. J., 1932, **27**, 463. (See also, Webster, D. R. and Komarov, S. A. Mucoprotein as a normal constituent of the gastric juice. J. Biol. Chem., 1932, **96**, 133. Komarov, S. A., Isolation of muco-itinsulfuric acid from canine gastric juice. J. Biol. Chem., 1935, **109**, 177. The influence of mucoitinsulfuric acid on peptic digestion. Am. J. Digest. Dis. & Nutrition, 1936, **3**, 164.)

BAXTER, S. G. Sympathetic secretory innervation of the gastric mucosa. Am. J. Digest. Dis. & Nutrition, 1934, **1**, 40.

BEAMER, W. D., FRIEDMAN, M. H. F., THOMAS, J. E. AND REHFUSS, M. E. Factors responsible for the intestinal phase of gastric secretion. Am. J. Physiol., 1944, **141**, 613.

BENCE-JONES, H. Contributions to the chemistry of the urine. Paper III, Part I. (1849). On the variations of the acidity of the urine in the state of health. Phil. Trans. Roy. Soc. London, p. 235. Cited by Davies, 1951.

BENNETT, T. I. AND VENABLES, J. F. The effect of emotions on gastric secretion and motility in the human being. Brit. M. J., 1920, **2**, 662.

DAVENPORT, H. W. Gastric carbonic anhydrase. J. Physiol., 1939, **97**, 32.

DAVENPORT, H. W. Some reflections on gastric secretion. Gastroenterology, 1957, **33**, 15.

DAVIES, R. E. AND LONGMUIR, N. M. Production of ulcers in isolated frog gastric mucosa. Biochem. J., 1948, **42**, 621.

DRAGSTEDT, L. R., WOODWARD, E. R., OBERHELMAN, H. A., JR., STORER, E. H. AND SMITH, C. W. Effect of transplantation of antrum of stomach on gastric secretion in experimental animals. Am. J. Physiol., 1951, **165**, 386.

EDKINS, J. S. On the chemical mechanism of gastric secretion. Proc. Roy. Soc., London, Ser. B, 1905, **76**, 376. The chemical mechanism of gastric secretion. J. Physiol., 1906, **34**, 133.

EDKINS, J. S. AND TWEEDY, M. The natural channels of absorption evoking the chemical mechanism of gastric secretion. J. Physiol., 1909, **33**, 263.

FARRELL, J. I. AND IVY, A. C. Studies on the motility of the transplanted gastric pouch. Am. J. Physiol., 1926, **76**, 227.

FISHER, R. B. AND HUNT, J. N. The inorganic components of gastric secretion. J. Physiol., 1950, **111**, 138.

GILMAN, A. AND COWGILL, G. R. Osmotic relations between blood and body fluids II. The osmotic relation of blood and gastric juice. Am. J. Physiol., 1933, **103**, 143.

GREGORY, R. A. AND IVY, A. C. Humoral stimulation of gastric secretion. Quart. J. Exper. Physiol., 1941, **31**, 111.

HAWK, P. B., MILLER, R. J., BERGHEIM, O., AND REHFUSS, M. E. The psychic secretion of gastric juice in normal men. Am. J. Physiol. 1920, **52**, 1. See also Pro. Soc. Exper. Biol. & Med. 1920, **17**, 97.

HOLLANDER, F. The chemistry and mechanics of hydrochloric acid formation in the stomach.

Gastroenterology, 1943, **1**, 401. Studies in gastric secretion. IV, Variations in the chlorine content of gastric juice and their significance. J. Biol. Chem., 1932, **97**, 585. Current views on the physiology of gastric secretion. Am. J. Med., 1952 **13**, 453.

HOLLANDER, F. AND COWGILL, G. R. Studies in gastric secretion. I. Gastric juice of constant acidity. J. Biol. Chem., 1931, **91**, 151.

IHRE, B. Human gastric secretion. A quantitative study of gastric secretion in normal and pathological conditions. Acta med. scandinav. 1938: Suppl. 95, pp. 1–226.

IVY, A. C. Surgery, 1941, **10**, 861.

IVY, A. C. Enterogastrone. Am. J. Physiol., 1935, **113**, 53.

IVY, A. C. AND GRAY, J. S. Enterogastrone. Cold Spring Harbor Symposia, 1937, **5**, 405.

IVY, A. C. AND FARREL, J. I. The proof of a humoral mechanism. A new procedure for the study of gastric physiology. Am. J. Physiol., 1925, **74**, 639. Demonstration of stimulation of the gastric glands by mechanical distention of the stomach. Am. J. Physiol., 1925, **72**, 232.

IVY, A. C. AND FAULEY, G. L. Arch. Int. Med., 1930, **46**, 52.

IVY, A. C. AND DAWSON, A. B. Am. J. Physiol., 1926, **76**, 158.

IVY, A. C. AND KIM, M. S. J.A.M. A., 1931, **97**, 1511.

IVY, A. C. AND ASSOCIATES. Gastroenterology, 1944, **2**, 138.

IVY, A. C. AND SCHAYER, R. W. Fed. Proc., 1957, **16**, 65.

JANOWTIZ, H. D., DREILING, D. A., ROBBIN, H. L. AND HOLLANDER, F. Inhibition of formation of hydrochloric acid in the human stomach by Diamox. Gastroenterology, 1957, **33**, 378.

KOMAROV, S. A. Studies on gastrin. I. Methods of isolation of a specific gastric secretagogue from the pyloric mucous membrane and its chemical properties. Rev. Canad. Biol., 1942, **1**, 377.

KOSAKA, T. AND LIM, R. K. S. Demonstration of the humoral agent in fat inhibition of gastric secretion. Proc. Soc. Exper. Biol. & Med., 1930, **27**, 890.

LIM, R. K. S. Observations on the mechanism of inhibition of gastric function by fat. Quart. J. Exper. Physiol., 1933, **23**, 263.

LIM, R. K. S. AND ASSOCIATES. Chinese J. Physiol., 1934, **8**, 219.

LINDE, S. Studies on the stimulation mechanism of gastric secretion. Acta. physiol. scandinav., Suppl. 74, 1950, **21**, 1.

OBERHELMAN, H. A., JR., WOODWARD, E. R., ZUBIRAN, J. M., AND DRAGSTEDT, L. R. Physiology of the gastric antrum. Am. J. Physiol., 1952, **169**, 738.

PINCUS, I. J., THOMAS, J. E. AND REHFUSS, M. E. A study of gastric secretion as influenced by changes in duodenal acidity. Proc. Soc. Exper. Biol. & Med., 1942, **51**, 367.

POPIELSKI, L. Imidazolyläthelamin und die Organextracte. I. B-I als mächtigen erreger der Magendrüsen. Pflüger's Arch. ges. Physiol., 120, 178, 214.

REHM, W. S. A theory of the formation of hydrochloric acid by the stomach. Gastroenterology, 1950, **14**, 401. See also Am. J. Physiol., 1949, **159**, 586.

Ricket. J. Anat. et Physiol., 1878, p. 526. (Cited by Carlson, 1923.)

Robertson, C. R., Langlois, K., Martin, C. G., Slezak, G. and Grossman, M. I. Release of gastrin in response to bathing the pyloric mucosa with acetylcholine. Am. J. Physiol., 1950, **163**, 27.

Sacks, J., Ivy, A. C., Burgess, J. P. and Vandolah, J. E. Histamine as the hormone for gastric secretion. Am. J. Physiol., 1932, **101**, 331.

Schayer, R. W. and Ivy, A. C. Evidence that histamine is a gastric secretory hormone in the rat. Am. J. Physiol., 1957, **189**, 369.

Schayer, R. W. and Ivy, A. C. Release of C¹⁴ histamine from the stomach and intestine on feeding. Am. J. Physiol., 1958, **193**, 400.

Teorell, T. Electrolyte diffusion in relation to the acidity regulation of the gastric juice. Gastroenterology, 1947, **9**, 425.

Thomas, J. E. Some recent progress in gastrointestinal physiology. Rev. Gastroenterology, 1952, **20**, 174.

Uvnäs, B. The part played by the pyloric region in the cephalic phase of gastric secretion. Acta physiol. scandinav., 1942, **4**, Suppl. 13, 1.

Uvnäs, B., Anderson, S., Elwin, C. and Malm, A. The influence of exclusion of the antrum-duodenum passage on the hydrochloric acid secretion in Pavlov pouch dogs. Gastroenterology, 1956, **30**, 790.

Vineberg, A. M. The activation of different elements of the gastric secretion by variation of vagal stimulation. Am. J. Physiol., 1931, **96**, 363.

Webster, D. R. and Armour, J. C. Effect of pyloric obstruction on the gastric secretion. Tr. Roy. Soc. Canada, 1932, **26**, sec. V., 109.

Wilhelmj, C. M., Neigers, I. and Hill, F. C. A comparison of intragastric and duodenal factors in lowering the acidity of gastric contents. Am. J. Physiol., 1934, **107**, 490.

Wilhelmj, C. M., O'Brien, F. T. and Hill, F. C. The inhibitory influence of the acidity of the gastric contents on the secretion of acid by the stomach. Am. J. Physiol., 1936, **115**, 429.

Zeljony, G. P. and Savich, V. V. Concerning the mechanism of gastric secretion. Proc. Soc. Russ. Physicians, St. Petersburg, January–May, 1911. (Cited by Babkin, 1928.)

*Monographs and Reviews*

Babkin, B. P. The digestive work of the stomach. Physiol. Rev., 1928, **8**, 365.

Babkin, B. P. Die Äussere Sekretion der Verdauungsdrüsen. Springer, Berlin, 1928.

Babkin, B. P. Secretory mechanism of the digestive glands, 2nd ed., p. 72, Paul B. Hoeber, New York, 1950.

Bickel, A. and Katsch, G. (1912). Chirurgische Technik zur normalen und pathologischen Physiologie der Verdauungs apparates. (cited by Babkin, 1950.)

Carlson, A. J. The secretion of gastric juice in health and disease. Physiol. Rev., 1923, **3**, 1.

Conway, E. J. The biochemistry of gastric acid secretion. Am. Lecture Series. Charles C Thomas, Springfield, Ill., 1953.

Davenport, H. W. Metabolic aspects of gastric acid secretion. *In* Metabolic aspects of transport across cell membranes, p. 295. Q. R. Murphy, editor. University of Wisconsin Press, Madison, Wisconsin, 1957.

Davies, R. E. The mechanism of hydrochloric acid production by the stomach. Biol. Rev. Cambridge Phil. Soc., 1951, **26**, 87.

Davies, R. E. Gastric hydrochloric acid production—the present position. *In* Metabolic aspects of transport across cell membranes, pp. 227–293, University of Wisconsin Press, Madison, Wisconsin, 1957.

Grossman, M. I. The physiology of secretin. Vitamins and Hormones, 1958, **16**, 179.

Heinz, E. and Öbrink, K. J. Acid formation and acidity control in the stomach. Physiol. Rev., 1954, **34**, 643.

Michaelis, L. Some problems concerning the gastric juice. Harvey Lectures, 1926–1927, **22**, 59.

Northrop, J. H. and Herriott, R. M. Chemistry of crystalline enzymes. Ann. Rev. Biochem., 1938, **7**, 37.

Pavlov, I. P. The work of the digestive glands. Griffin, London, 1910.

Rehm, W. S. and Dennis, W. H. A discussion of theories of hydrochloric acid formation in the light of electrophysiological findings. *In* Metabolic aspects of transport across cell membranes, p. 303. University of Wisconsin Press, Madison, Wisconsin, 1957.

Wasteneys, H. and Boorsook, H. The enzymatic synthesis of protein. Physiol. Rev., 1930, **10**, 110.

# 38

## GASTRIC DIGESTION—*Continued*

---

### Applied Physiology

#### Gastric Analysis

Study of gastric secretion in the human subject requires use of a gastric tube unless one is fortunate enough to have access to a patient with a gastric fistula, such as Alexis St. Martin, who was studied by Beaumont. St. Martin was injured by the accidental discharge of a shotgun; the shot tore a hole in his side and carried away a part of his stomach. On recovering from this wound he was left with a permanent gastric fistula and much of our elementary knowledge of gastric function we owe to the careful observations that William Beaumont, who was at the time a military surgeon in the United States Army, made on his patient. Other studies on gastric fistula patients have since been made in physiological laboratories. A. J. Carlson (1923) had three such subjects available in his laboratory at the University of Chicago. More recently, Wolf and Wolff (1943) have reported their observations on the now famous Tom Little.

A great variety of stomach tubes have been used from time to time, the tendency in recent years being toward tubes of smaller size; number 12 French gage is a common size. Very recently plastic tubes have come into use, they have the advantage over rubber tubes that the wall can be thinner and the size of the lumen greater for a given outside diameter. Since they are cheap they need not be re-used and hence are thrown away and not resterilized. If the patient is unconscious or, for any other reason unable to swallow the tube, it may be passed through the nose. Passage of the tube through the nose has certain advantages, particularly if the tube has to remain in place for a long period of time. A tube in the nose will cause less discomfort over a period of time than one in the mouth and is less likely to be bitten or otherwise damaged by the patient.

The tube is usually passed when the stomach is empty, the patient being fasted for this purpose. The volume and acidity of the fasting gastric contents vary a great deal in normal individuals, but it is rare in the human to find the stomach completely empty or entirely devoid of hydrochloric acid. From 20 to 40 cc of gastric juice are commonly found in the fasting human stomach and the acidity of the fasting secretion will ordinarily range from 0 to 20 or 30 clinical units (m.eq. per liter) of so-called free hydrochloric acid. After the stomach has been emptied it is customary to give the patient a small meal called a test meal of which a great variety are in use. Typical test meals are: 300 ml. of oatmeal gruel; a piece of dry toast and a cup of tea; a shredded wheat biscuit or a piece of toast with 350 to 400 ml. of water; two slices of bread without the crusts; arrowroot biscuits with tea or water, (Machella, 1951).

### Fractional Gastric Analysis

Fractional gastric analysis was introduced by Rehfuss (1914) and his associates and is now in common use wherever gastric analysis is done. Beginning about 30 minutes after the test meal has been eaten, samples (usually 10 ml.) of gastric contents are removed from the stomach through the tube by suction at intervals which may be 15 or 30 minutes. Each sample is placed in a small flask and set aside for subsequent analysis. Taking of samples is continued for $2\frac{1}{2}$ hours at the end of which time the stomach is completely emptied through the tube. The samples are then analyzed for free and total acidity and for peptic activity. Other tests may be done as indicated.

The words *free acid*, *total acid* and *combined acid* were coined at a time when we had little understanding of the nature of acidity and little knowledge of ionization and the nature of buffers. They were based on the concept that a certain fraction of the hydrochloric acid exists free in solution, a certain other fraction exists in combination with protein or other acid absorbing substances and that these fractions could be distinguished by the use of indicators. We realize now that the indicators merely tell us when the solution has reached a certain pH.

It is customary to titrate the gastric contents first to pH 3.5 using dimethylamino-azobenzine as an indicator. This indicator changes from red to yellow somewhere between pH 3 and 3.5. The amount of acid indicated by titration to this level is spoken of as free hydrochloric acid. Free acid may be defined as the acid equivalent of the amount of standard alkali necessary to bring the pH of the solution to 3.5. It is expressed in clinical units (which is the number of milliliters of 0.1 normal base needed to titrate 100 ml. of gastric contents to the desired pH). Another sample is titrated with phenolphthalein as the indicator. This indicator changes to a pink color between pH 8 and 9. The amount of standard alkali needed to titrate to this pH is a measure of the total acidity also expressed in clinical units. The difference between free and total acidity is the combined acid. The combined acid is, of course, a measure of the buffering capacity of the gastric contents and will be influenced by the type of food and the amount of mucus and other buffers that happen to be present. Sometimes the acidity of the gastric contents is expressed in pH units; this is a useful notation when the acidity is low, but gives less information than the conventional notation when free acid (so-called) is present (James, 1957).

If no free acid appears in the gastric contents after a test meal it does not necessarily prove that the subject is achlorhydric, that is, one who secretes no hydrochloric acid. To detect true achlorhydria it is necessary to use a more powerful secretory stimulant such as histamine or one of its analogs.

## THE HISTAMINE TEST

As a test of gastric secretion the parenteral administration of histamine has certain very definite advantages over the ordinary test meal: (a) Histamine evokes a maximum secretory response and is often able to evoke a response when the test meal fails to do so (see below). It is thus of value in distinguishing false from true anacidity. (b) The response is not affected by conditions such as appetite and other psychic factors which influence the response to the test meal. (c) The test meal and salivary secretion (the latter cannot be measured) add to the volume of the contents; it is therefore impossible to determine accurately the quantity of juice secreted. (d) Swallowed saliva and the test meal itself partly neutralize the acid. (e) In the histamine test the glands respond promptly, maximal acidity being reached within 20 or 30 minutes; therefore, almost pure juice is obtained for analysis and neutralization factors and gastric evacuation exert a minimum influence. The test is usually performed the first thing in the morning with the subject fasting. In a subject of average weight about 0.25 mg. is injected.

## THE ISO-SECRETORY OR NORMAL CURVES OF GASTRIC ACIDITY

If in a normal person the free and total acidities of the gastric contents are determined every 15 minutes for a period of from 2 to 3 hours after the ingestion of a test meal, the results plotted against time along the base line with HCl percentages or clinical units in the vertical axis, a curve is obtained as shown in figure 38.1. The

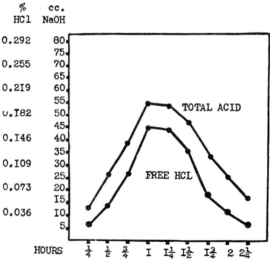

FIG. 38.1. Normal curves of gastric acidity following a test meal. (Redrawn from Maclean.)

curve for total acidity commences to rise a short time after the meal, and about 1 hour later reaches a maximum which varies from 35 to 70 in different persons. The curve maintains its maximal height for half an hour or less and then commences to decline reaching the resting level again in from 2½ to 3 hours after the ingestion of the test meal. The curve of free acidity runs parallel to, but at a lower level than that for the total acidity, the values ranging in different normal persons between 20 and 40 (0.07 to 0.15 per cent). Values are much higher after foods, such as meats, which stimulate gastric secretion more powerfully, averaging from 80 to 120 for total and from 60 to 100 for free acidity.

The figures given above represent the range of the great bulk of normal persons; but the gastric acidities show very wide individual variations in health, being influenced markedly by age and sex. The average free and total acidities (after a test meal) in young healthy males are about 40 and 65, respectively (see figs. 38.2 and 38.3). They are somewhat lower in females. They are also lower in children, the adult level being reached at about the age of 20 years. In men after 30 years and in women after 50 years a progressive decline in acidities (total and free) occurs and the incidence of anacidity and of subacidity increases sharply. A high normal value for gastric acidity is regarded by some as an index of physical fitness, the level tending to be low, it is said, in persons of sedentary habits and poor muscular development.

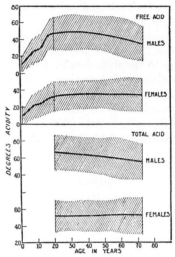

FIG. 38.2. Normal standards. The shaded areas represent the limits within which lay 80 per cent of the data for free and total acid at the different ages. The heavy lines represent modes. (After Vanzant, Alvarez and associates.)

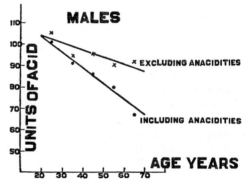

FIG. 38.3. Percentage decline of mean gastric acidity with advancing years (males). (After Polland.)

### HYPOCHLORHYDRIA (SUBACIDITY) AND ACHLORHYDRIA (ANACIDITY)

When the stomach contents give values persistently below 20 "clinical units" (0.05 per cent) for free HCl after test meals, the condition is spoken of as *hypochlorhydria* or *subacidity*. The complete absence of free HCl is referred to as *achlorhydria* or *anacidity*. Bennett and Ryle in a study of 100 healthy male subjects (medical students) found achlorhydria present in 4.0 per cent. In the general run of hospital cases without gastric disease or pernicious anemia 14 to 20 per cent show anacidity. It has already been pointed out that the absence of free hydrochloric acid from the stomach contents may be simply the result of excessive neutralization, and not of the suppression of acid secretion. Again, there may be no secretion of acid after a test meal yet the glands respond to the more powerful stimulus of histamine; anacidity of this character is called *false* or *apparent anacidity*. The failure of acid to appear after the injection of histamine is referred to as

*true anacidity*. The figures given above as reported by Bennett and Ryle for anacidity in healthy subjects as well as those given for hospital cases do not permit a distinction to be drawn between the two types of the condition, since test meals were used in the investigations. It is therefore impossible to say in what proportion of the cases true anacidity existed. The incidence of true anacidity appears, however, to be less than 1 per cent in young healthy male subjects and not more than 1 or 2 per cent in the case of young healthy females.

In cases of anacidity the peptic concentration of the gastric juice though usually low is in some cases not far below the normal value—further evidence that the secretion of acid and of pepsin are governed by independent mechanisms. Complete absence of both acid and pepsin from the gastric contents is called *achylia gastrica*.

The incidence of anacidity, both apparent and true, shows a definite increase with advancing years up to the sixth decade. Vanzant Alvarez, and associates, in an investigation of a large series of patients without gastric disease, found it present in from 25 to 35 per cent between the ages of 60 and 70 years. Females showed a higher incidence than males. After the sixth decade some reduction in the frequency of the condition was observed (see figs. 38.2 and 38.4).

Anacidity in the majority of instances gives rise to no gastric symptoms and is compatible with perfect health. In some cases it is associated with flatulent dyspepsia and occasionally a persistent diarrhea (gastrogenous diarrhea) which is relieved by the administration of acid.

The following are the chief pathological conditions associated with anacidity;

(a) *Pernicious anemia.* Achlorhydria is a constant phenomenon. Pepsin is also usually absent. Histamine is ineffective.

(b) *Carcinoma of the stomach.* There is anacidity in over 60 per cent of cases. It is due to the chronic gastritis and atrophy of glandular tissue. This, it is believed, precedes by a variable period the development of the growth. The anacidity may be either false or true.

(c) *Chronic gastritis* causes a gradual depression of the secretory function and may lead finally to its complete suppression.

(d) Hypochlorhydria or achlorhydria may also occur during *acute fevers*, in *malnutrition, gall-*

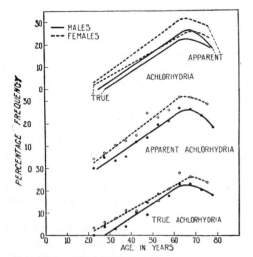

Fig. 38.4. Curves showing the relation between the incidence of achlorhydria and age. (After Vanzant, Alvarez, and associates.)

*bladder disease, Addison's disease, sprue, acne rosacea* and *chronic arthritis*.

## HYPERCHLORHYDRIA AND HYPERSECRETION

"There is no disease known capable of inducing true gastric hyperacidity" (A. J. Carlson, 1923). "The concept of hyperacidity unquestionably lacks actual foundation" (B. Ihre, 1938). Nevertheless "hyperacidity" is a clinical entity and should be defined. In clinical hyperacidity the free acid has a value of from 60 to 90 after a standard test meal, and may, instead of declining in the second hour, remain high or continue to rise. The high acidity of the gastric contents does not mean that the juice as secreted by the gastric glands is excessively acid. So far as is known the normal maximum of from 0.5 to 0.6 per cent of hydrochloric acid in the gastric secretion is never exceeded. The high acidity of the gastric contents is due either to the secretion of an abnormally large quantity of juice (hypersecretion) or to impairment of the factors regulating gastric acidity (p. 609), e.g., failure of the secretion rate to become reduced during the second hour, or delayed gastric evacuation.

Acute episodes of hyperacidity may be caused by dietary errors or alcohol. The worst offenders among the foods are the fats, since the secondary hypersecretion which they cause is apt to occur after most of the buffering agents have left the stomach. Dilute alcohol introduced into the gastrointestinal tract by any route of administration stimulates secretion of highly acid gastric juice (Beazell and Ivy, 1940). Strong solutions are said to stimulate mainly secretion of mucus (Babkin, 1950). Since alcohol has no capacity to buffer acid, it is very likely to cause some degree of hyperacidity unless taken with food or other buffering agents. Excessive use of coffee may also cause hyperacidity since caffeine has been shown to stimulate secretion of gastric juice (Roth and Ivy, 1944).

A much more serious problem is the chronic hypersecretion frequently associated with duodenal ulcer disease which is particularly evident when the gastric secretion is collected during the night (Kirsner *et al.*, 1959). The cause of continuous gastric secretion in the absence of food is one of the great unsolved problems of medicine. In general there are two main points of view, each with numerous variations. One is that hypersecretion is the result of duodenal irritation, either by a chronic ulcer or by some condition that may ultimately lead to ulcer (Ivy and Bachrach, 1940; Grossman, 1951). It has been suggested that duodenal irritation may cause release of histamine which, when carried by the blood to the stomach excites the parietal cells as does exogenous histamine. Opposed to this view is the evidence that in many ulcer patients hypersecretion is evident even when the ulcer is "inactive," that is, not causing symptoms.

A much more widely held theory is that the hypersecretion is primary and the duodenal irritation or ulceration, if it occurs, is secondary to the chronic hyperacidity (Dragstedt, 1944). In support of this view is the well known fact that duodenal ulcers heal only after the hyperacidity has been corrected. The argument is weakened somewhat by the fact that gastric ulcers are usually associated with hypoacidity and could not, therefore, be due to primary hyperacidity although they are, like duodenal ulcers, favorably influenced by antacid treatment. (Atkinson and Henley, 1955).

Among the possible causes of primary gastric hypersecretion, excessive use of tobacco, coffee or alcohol have been suggested (Ivy *et al.*, 1955). Proof of a significant association of these agents with chronic hypersecretion is lacking. Excessive use of coffee, tobacco or alcohol is often indicative of a state of nervous tension or anxiety which, of itself, may cause hypersecretion. Since they undoubtedly aggravate the disease in susceptible persons, limitation of their use is generally considered necessary in the treatment of diseases associated with so called hyperacidity.

Although the causes of primary hypersecretion are unknown, thinking in recent years has tended to crystallize on the concept that it represents a continuation of the cephalic or reflex phase of secretion into the interdigestive period (Dragstedt, 1942). This concept focuses attention on the central nervous system and its relations to the autonomic nerves. From this we derive the psychosomatic theory of gastric hypersecretion and ulcer disease, discussed in a later section.

*The neutralization test.* This test is of value in investigating the acid-regulating mechanism in duodenal ulcer, especially in determining the success or failure of an operation performed for its cure. Instead of stimulating gastric secretion by a test meal or histamine injection, 300 cc. of 0.5 per cent hydrochloric acid solution are introduced through a rubber tube, into the fasting stomach after its contents have been removed by aspiration. Samples of the acid solution are withdrawn from time to time as in the ordinary method of fractional gastric analysis, and the total acidities determined. The results are plotted and the curve compared with a normal standard curve. In the normal subject the total acidity falls from a value of 130 at the beginning of the test to around 40 within an hour or so. In cases of duodenal ulcer the total acidity falls more slowly and may be 70 or more after the lapse of 3 or 4 hours.

### ESTIMATION OF PEPTIC POWER

The earliest method of determining the peptic activity of a sample of gastric juice was introduced by Mett in 1889. Egg white is drawn into a glass tube of 1 mm. bore and a few inches long. The albumin is coagulated by placing the tubes in water at a temperature of 85°C. and leaving them until the water has cooled. The tubes are then broken into sections about an inch long, and immersed in the gastric juice diluted 1 to 15 with N/20 HCl and incubated at a temperature of 37°C. for 24 hours. After this time the length of the column of digested albumin at each end of the tubes is measured in millimeters under the low power of the microscope and the average of a number of measurements taken. The peptic power of the sample is expressed in accordance with Schutz's law which states that the amount of proteolytic enzyme present is proportional to the square of the number of millimeters of digested albumin. Therefore, if the average length of the digested columns is 2.5 mm. the peptic power of the undiluted juice will be $2.5^2 \times 16 = 100.0$. This is the average normal value.

Anson and Mirsky's method utilizes hemoglobin as the substrate. After the juice has acted upon the hemoglobin for 10 minutes, the undigested protein is precipitated with trichloracetic acid and removed by filtration. The quantity of protein split products, which is a measure of peptic activity, is estimated colorimetrically after the addition of phenol reagent.

### THE EFFECTS OF VARIOUS CHEMICALS AND DRUGS UPON GASTRIC SECRETION

*Alkalis* in general have been held to exert a depressing effect upon the secretion of gastric juice. Sodium bicarbonate, for instance, a favorite ingredient of digestive mixtures was investigated by Pavlov in dogs and found to be definitely inhibitory. This observation has been confirmed by Farrell, though others find that the inhibitory effect does not occur unless the dose is excessive, and that in small repeated doses it augments the secretion (Boyd). This seems to be true also of other alkalis, large doses depress but small doses, especially if repeated, may augment the flow of juice. Nor does the inhibitory effect of large doses persist after their discontinuance; on the contrary, hypersecretion not uncommonly follows ("acid rebound"). The value of alkalis in gastric disorders depends chiefly, however, upon their antacid properties, i.e., upon their ability to neutralize or buffer the acidity of the gastric contents rather than to depress secretion. For this purpose the unabsorbable alkalis, such as aluminum hydroxide and magnesium silicate are preferable to such substances as sodium bicarbonate and calcium carbonate which can be absorbed from the intestine. In the doses necessary to exert an appreciable effect on gastric acidity the soluble alkalis can cause profound changes in the acid-base balance of the body and have been known to produce severe alkalosis. The insoluble antacids do not affect the acid base balance of the body, and because of their slower and more prolonged action they are less likely to cause an acid rebound in the stomach. Incidentally, the acid rebound effect is now believed to be due to the temporary absence of the inhibitory effect of acid in the antrum following neutralization of the gastric contents by the alkali.

The various preparations of *bitters* are without any appreciable effect upon secretion unless they contain alcohol. *Acids* depress gastric secretion which is completely inhibited by the introduction into the stomach of a 1 per cent solution of hydrochloric acid (p. 609). Acid also exerts an inhibitory effect from the intestine upon gastric secretion. When introduced into the dog's intestine gastric secretion from a Pavlov pouch is inhibited. *Condiments* have little direct effect, but act indirectly in adding flavor to the food, stimulating the taste buds and thus encouraging the psychic secretion. *Histamine* is one of the most powerful stimulants of gastric secretion. Histamine liberated within the body, e.g., in dermographism or even by the immersion of the hand in cold water at a temperature of 10°C. causes a detectable secretory response within 15 minutes. Gastric secretion is not inhibited by such antihistamine drugs as *neoantergen* and *benadryl*, and most other agents of the same class; of the few which are antisecretory the dose required must be inordinately large. *Caffeine* and *alcohol* are strong secretory stimulants. The latter has a pronounced secretogogue action, causing the secretion of a juice of high acidity and rich in mucin. It is possible that alcohol exerts its secretory action through the liberation of histamine, for it has been shown that the histamine output of the perfused lung of the guinea pig is increased by the addition of alcohol (2 to 6 per cent) to the perfusion fluid. *Liver extract*, *meat*, and *vegetable extracts* generally are powerful excitants of the gastric glands, an action which they owe to the presence of secretagogues. *Insulin* (through its hypoglycemic effect on the vagus center), *acetylcholine* (usually), *mecholyl* (*acetyl-β-methylcholine chloride*), *pilocarpine* and *nicotine* are secretory stimulants, whereas *belladonna* or its alkaloids *atropine* and *hyoscine*, and *hyoscyamus* or its alkaloid *hyoscyamine* are secretory depressants. Atropine or vagus section depresses or abolishes the cephalic secretion; the drug reduces somewhat, but does not suppress, secretion due to histamine, alcohol, or caffeine.

Atropine, although it depresses gastric secretion, is not a practical drug to use for control of gastric acidity because, in the doses required to have an appreciable effect on the secretion of gastric juice, it has intolerable side actions such as acceleration of the heart, dilation of the pupil, paralysis of accommodation, etc. Recently a number of synthetic drugs with actions on the stomach similar to those of atropine have become available commercially. Many of these possess a greater action on gastric secretion and motility and have less effect on other peripheral structures than atropine so that their use for regulation of gastric secretion becomes feasible. These drugs are known generally as parasympatholytic drugs.

There is a widespread clinical impression that smoking tobacco increases gastric secretion and gastric acidity but the experimental evidence is not convincing. Conflicting results have been reported by equally competent investigators but the available evidence suggests that smoking one or two cigarettes increases gastric acidity in a majority of persons whereas smoking several cigarettes or smoking for a long time depresses gastric secretion. Such a result would be in accord with the known fact that nicotine in small doses stimulates autonomic ganglia whereas larger doses cause depression. The immediate effect of morphine is to depress gastric secretion but it causes gastric retention and hence tends to prolong the gastric phase and thus to increase the total secretion. Adrenergic blocking agents do not affect gastric secretion.

### Influence of Vitamins and Hormones on Gastric Secretion

#### *Vitamins*

Little is known of the effect of vitamins, or vitamin deficiency, on gastric secretion. Achlorhydria has been observed in severe thiamine deficiency (beri-beri) and the claim has been made that achlorhydria can be cured by administration of vitamin A (Földes and Vajda, 1941; Schödt,

1934, 1935). However, Dyer and Roe (1941) found that acute or chronic vitamin A deficiency had no effect on the ability of rats to secrete hydrochloric acid or mucin in their gastric juice when the amount of secretion was expressed in terms of body weight. Babkin and his associates (1940) found that vitamin D in excessive doses depressed gastric secretion but this was apparently due to the considerable increase in blood calcium concentration which resulted from administration of the vitamin. In their experiments only the reflex phase of secretion was effected by the hypercalcemia. Other studies on the effects of the blood calcium level on gastric secretion indicate that the normal blood calcium level of 10 mg. per cent is optimum for secretion of gastric juice, any considerable change in this level whether in the direction of increase or a decrease depresses gastric secretion.

*Hormones*

The effect of changes in blood calcium on gastric secretion has already been mentioned; these changes can be induced by administration of Parathormone as well as by administration of vitamin D and with the same results. Hypophysectomy causes characteristic changes in the chief cells of the gastric glands consisting of a decrease in the size of the nucleus, and loss of most of the pepsinogen granules. Adrenalectomy also causes involution of the zymogen cells and diminishes the output of pepsin in the gastric secretion (Baker and Abrams, 1954). Gastric acidity is diminished following adrenalectomy; indeed in human subjects adrenalectomy results in a very low level of gastric secretion (Gray, 1958). Secretion of hydrochloric acid is also reduced by hypophysectomy in rats (Jones and Harkins, 1958).

Great interest is attached to the possible effects of adrenocorticotrophic hormone (ACTH) and the adrenal steroids and the various synthetics that simulate the action of the steroids, on gastric secretion. Since these agents have come into general use and some instances of exacerbation of duodenal ulcers have been reported following their use, it is assumed that the ulcers are aggravated by an increase in the volume, acidity, or peptic activity or of all three in the gastric juice. The stimulating effect of these agents on gastric secretion has been emphasized by Gray and his associates (1955). They have noted particularly an increase in the output of uropepsin in circumstances in which it may be assumed that adrenal cortical activity is increased either through natural stimuli such as are involved in stress or

through the administration of ACTH or of the steroids themselves, or of their synthetic counterparts. Gray and others have also reported an increase in gastric acid secretion under similar circumstances but negative results have also been reported. Although the evidence is conflicting it appears that, when given in sufficiently large doses over a considerable period of time, these agents can, and do, increase the hydrochloric acid and pepsin secretion by the gastric glands and that in some cases at least this has been a factor in the aggravation of duodenal ulcer disease.

Serotonin is a subtance, possibly a hormone, secreted by certain enterochromaffin cells found principally in the intestinal mucosa which greatly augments intestinal motility when given intravenously. Among its numerous physiological actions it appears to exert an inhibitory effect on gastric secretion, particularly that produced by reflex stimulation or through the action of drugs that resemble acetylcholine. The effect of serotonin is of interest in connection with the action of reserpine which has been used as a tranquilizer and in the treatment of high blood pressure. Although therapeutic doses of reserpine are said not to influence gastric secretion, large doses given for a considerable time do increase the acid output of the gastric glands and it has been suggested that this might be due to serotonin, the production of which is increased by reserpine; evidently however, since serotonin inhibits gastric secretion, some other factor is operative in the reserpinized subject (Haverback *et al.*, 1957).

Insulin may be considered with the hormones although its effect on gastric secretion is not strictly a hormonal influence on the stomach. Insulin, in a dosage sufficient to lower the blood sugar to about 50 mg per cent, has an effect on the gastric glands similar to that of stimulation of the vagus nerves, that is the output of acid and pepsin is increased. The effect is due to the rapid decrease in blood sugar concentration which, through some mechanism not understood at present, has a stimulating action on autonomic centers of the brain stem. The effect on the stomach is due to stimulation of the vagus centers but sympathetic as well as parasympathetic centers are stimulated by the change in blood sugar. The well known insulin convlusions are merely a further manifestation of this general excitatory effect of rapidly induced hypoglycemia.

Since the effect of insulin on gastric secretion is dependent upon the integrity of the vagus nerves, the "insulin test" has been used as a means of determining the completeness of therapeutic vagotomy in human subjects (Hollander, 1946). A positive insulin test is proof of the presence of intact vagus fibers but a negative result is less conclusive since some subjects with intact vagi fail to secrete in response to insulin. The test has, nevertheless, been of great value in the surgical control of duodenal ulcer.

The inhibitory effect of enterogastrone on gastric secretion has already been referred to. It may be mentioned here that commercial preparations of enterogastrone have not been successful in the control of gastric hypersecretion in peptic ulcer disease. This may be due to the lack of a suitable commercial preparation or it may be that the hypersecretion of ulcer disease is a sign of the failure of the gastric glands to respond to normal inhibitory mechanisms of which enterogastrone is one. Enterogastrone is effective mainly against the chemical phases of gastric secretion. It has little influence on the initial reflex phase; as we shall see later on it is precisely the initial reflex phase which is believed to be prolonged and augmented in duodenal ulcer disease.

### Loss of Gastric Juice from the Body

When abnormally large quantities of gastric juice are lost from the body as in pyloric obstruction with persistent vomiting or in intestinal obstruction a profound effect upon the acid base balance of the body is produced. There is a fall in blood chloride leading to a state of compensated or uncompensated alkalosis. Because calcium salts are less soluble in alkaline body fluids, tetany due to calcium deficiency may occur in uncompensated alkalosis (ch. 13). Dragstedt and Ellis (1930) have shown that, in animals, drainage of the gastric juice to the exterior, through a fistula results in a reduction of blood chloride and alkalosis, marked dehydration and a rise in nonprotein nitrogen in the blood, leading to severe depression and death.

### Effect of Emotional States on Gastric Secretion

The effect of emotional experience on visceral function was discussed in popular vein by Walter B. Cannon in his book on "Bodily Changes in Pain, Hunger, Fear and Rage," (1915). He focused his attention on the inhibitory effects of acute emotions such as sudden fear and anger and for a long time this was considered to be the main effect of emotional states on gastric function. The fact that certain types of emotional disturbances could stimulate gastric function, specifically could increase secretion of hydrochloric acid, was

first demonstrated by Wolf and Wolff (1943) in their studies on their modern Alexis St. Martin, known as Tom. Tom had a gastric fistula which made it possible to observe changes in the gastric mucosa and to note increases and decreases in the secretion of hydrochloric acid. When exposed to sudden fear or pain, Tom's stomach became pale and ceased to secrete hydrochloric acid, in accordance with the concept popularized by Cannon; however, when a situation developed which caused prolonged resentment or deep seated chronic anger the opposite effects were observed; the gastric mucosa became congested and the secretion of hydrochloric acid was increased. Subsequently, similar results have been observed by a number of investigators on human subjects and on animals. Although there are individual variations, the weight of evidence indicates that chronic anxiety, anger, resentment and fear, if sufficiently prolonged, tend to produce effects on gastric function characteristic of increased activity of the parasympathetic division of the autonomic system including increased secretion of hydrochloric acid by the stomach.

The central mechanism for these effects is doubtless situated partly in the hypothalamus. This portion of the brain has been shown repeatedly to be a center for the coordination of impulses involved in emotional expression (Bard, 1928, 1929; Fulton, 1929). Clark (1932) refers to the hypothalamus as a visceral correlation center and Hess (1947) considers that "in the diencephalon the functions of the various autonomic organs are synthesized into cooperative action." MacDonald (1951), citing the work of Hess, concludes that the hypothalamus is "the head ganglion of the autonomic system."

It has long been known that stimulation of the posterior portion of the hypothalamus brings about visceral responses characteristic of the activity of the sympathetic division of the autonomic nervous system. Evidence that the vagi, or other parasympathetic nerves could be activated from the hypothalamus has not been so abundant but it is becoming increasingly apparent that parasympathetic effects can be obtained from various regions of the hypothalamus by appropriate stimulating techniques (Ström and Uvnäs, 1950). Thus we see that mechanisms exist for the alteration of visceral function, presumably including gastric secretion, as a part of the general phenomena associated with emotional expression.

Emotional feeling, as distinguished from emotional expression, involves the cortex. Widespread connections between various parts of the cerebral cortex and the hypothalamus are also known. Connections with the rhinencephalon are particularly abundant and are, no doubt, more deeply involved in our visceral responses to conscious experiences than are most of the other parts of the brain (MacLean, 1949). Since these areas are believed to be primarily concerned with emotional experience they may be of fundamental importance in visceral responses to emotional stimuli. The tracts that connect the hypothalamus directly or by way of the thalamus with the neopallium have been analyzed in detail by Murphy and Gellhorn (1945) who studied the distribution of action potentials resulting from the local application of strychnine to various points in the cortex, thalamus and hypothalamus. In discussing their results they state that certain of the conducting paths that they demonstrated may be said to be tracts of preferential discharge of low resistance. These were paths from the hypothalamus to the cortex and from the cortex to the hypothalamus, both by way of the thalamus; also included were two-way paths between the hypothalamus and the thalamus. The authors suggest that these two-way conduction paths between cortex and hypothalamus may constitute, under some circumstances, "reverberating circuits" by which they mean closed chains of neurons over which impulses may continue to circulate long after the exciting stimulus has subsided.

## Chronic Gastric and Duodenal Ulcer (Peptic Ulcer)

Epigastric pain coming on usually in from a half to one and a half hours after a meal and vomiting are the chief clinical features of gastric ulcer. In a certain proportion (about 20 per cent) of cases blood appears in the vomitus (hematemesis).

In duodenal ulcer, pain occurs usually within from 2 to 3 hours after a meal, that is, when the stomach is nearly emptly. The onset of the pain is therefore earlier after a light than after a heavy meal. The pain is relieved by taking food.

### Pathogenesis

It is generally agreed that the dominant factor in the development of gastric and of duodenal ulcer is the action of the pepsin-hydrochloric acid of the gastric juice. The term peptic ulcer is therefore well chosen. The importance of this factor is evidenced by the following facts.

(1) Apart from the ulcerations caused by some specific disease, e.g., tuberculosis, syphilis, carcinoma, etc., ulcer of the gastrointestinal tract is confined to those regions which are exposed to the action of acid (a) *Gastric ulcers* in the great majority of cases involve the pyloric part of the stomach; they are most frequently situated on the lesser curvature near the incisura angularis or on the anterior or posterior wall in close proximity to this limited area. They are never seen in the dome of the fundus and rarely on the upper part of the greater curvature; these regions, it will be noted, are not in contact with acid for any length of time. (b) The lower part of the esophagus into which highly acid juice frequently regurgitates, and the adjacent part of the stomach wall, i.e., the cardia, are sometimes the site of ulceration. (c) *Duodenal ulcer* occurs practically exclusively within the first inch or less of the duodenal cap (p. 692), and nearly always upon its anterior or posterior wall, that is, where the chyme before it has been neutralized by the alkaline juices of the duodenum comes into contact with the mucosa. (d) After gastrojejunostomy, the so-called *stomal ulcer* may occur in the jejunal mucosa in the region of the anastomosis, i.e., where the gastric juice first impinges. (e) In a Meckel's diverticulum which contains ectopic gastric glands an ulcer occasionally forms. The ulcer's site is either in that part of the mucosa of the diverticulum, which does not itself contain acid-secreting glands, or in the ileum at the point where the diverticulum opens into it. Matthews and Dragstedt (1932), experimenting with dogs, produced an "artificial Meckel's diverticulum" by transplanting a pouch of the gastric wall into the ileum; an ulcer developed in the ileum just beyond the transplant in every experiment. These observations emphasize a curious fact that the commonest situations of ulcer are not in the mucosa which secretes the acid, but in neighboring parts which normally secrete a neutral or alkaline fluid—the pyloric region, duodenal cap, cardiac region, esophagus, jejunum or ileum. The pyloric type of gland extends farther up the lesser curvature than up the greater curvature (fig. 38.5). It has even been suggested that the occurrence of ulcers in the body of the stomach, i.e., in the acid secreting part of the mucosa, is actually dependent upon the presence of patches of aberrant pyloric glands. (f) Mann and Williamson, employing dogs, excised the duodenum and transplanted it into the ileum, thus diverting its alkaline juices away from the region of the pylorus. The cut end of the jejunum was anastomosed to the pylorus. Fourteen out of sixteen animals upon which this operation was performed developed chronic ulcers

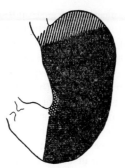

Fig. 38.5. Diagram showing the distribution of the parietal (acid-secreting) cells in the human stomach. In the black area the proportion of parietal cells was maximal and was taken as 100 per cent; in the cross-hatched area on lesser curvature the percentage of parietal cells was 75 per cent, in the shaded area at the fundus, 50 per cent, and in the white area 0 to 1 per cent. (After Berger, Amer. J. Anat., 1934, 54, 87.)

in the jejunum just beyond the pylorus. However, Fawley and Ivy found that this operation, if combined with excision of the fundus, or if the alkaline secretions are drained into the stomach, does not cause a jejunal ulcer.

Ulcers have also been produced by inducing continuous secretion of hydrochloric acid by implanting histamine in beeswax under the skin. This results in the continuous absorption of histamine and consequent continuous stimulation of the acid secreting cells of the stomach. Ulcers also occur in the duodenum. True peptic ulcer does not develop in the absence of hydrochloric acid. Although a small acute or subacute ulcer may sometimes develop in the absence of acid, a large chronic ulcer of the duodenum is almost never seen with anacidity, as, for example, in pernicious anemia.

(2) There is a definite tendency toward hypersecretion in most duodenal ulcer patients, though not in patients with gastric ulcer. The evidence on this point has been nicely summarized by Grossman (1951) as follows: "Patients with gastric ulcer show a distinct difference from those with duodenal ulcer in this regard. In gastric ulcer patients there is little or no tendency to secrete excessive amounts of acid, whereas this tendency is distinctly present in duodenal ulcer patients. Thus, both experimentally and clinically, the ulcer associated with hypersecretion of acid is duodenal in location. This hypersecretion of duodenal ulcer patients manifests itself in all types of gastric secretory studies, whether these studies are on the interdigestive secretion during the day or night, or on the secretion in response either to a meal or to drugs such as histamine, insulin or caffeine. The difference between normal persons and duodenal ulcer patients is greatest in studies on the basal or interdigestive secretion and in the response to caffeine. The response of the ulcer patient to caffeine deserves special mention because it is characterized by being abnormally prolonged as well as elevated.

"There is no sharp dividing line between the secretory level of duodenal ulcer patients and normal persons. Some duodenal ulcer patients secrete no more acid than the average normal person; some normal persons secrete as much acid as the average duodenal ulcer patient. Only a small percentage of duodenal ulcer patients secrete acid at rates higher than the highest level encountered in normal subjects. The difference between the acid secretory rates in normal persons and patients with duodenal ulcers is a statistical phenomenon; the *average* secretory rate of normal persons is distinctly below the *average* for patients with duodenal ulcer. The difference is statistically highly significant; that is the probability of its having occurred by chance or random sampling error is low."

In duodenal ulcer the typical findings upon gastric analysis are: a fasting juice of greater volume than normal and of high acidity; and a curve of gastric acidity after a test meal which rises well above (20 units or more) the normal maximum. In some cases the stomach empties more rapidly than usual as a result of exaggerated gastric motility, and the curve of acidity after reaching its maximum value falls steeply again. In other instances the stomach empties in the usual time but the curve of acidity is maintained at its maximum as a result of continued gastric secretion—the *plateau type of curve*. In still other instances the emptying of the stomach is delayed as a result of pylorospasm or achalasia (see below), and the curve of gastric acidity instead of falling at the usual time continues to rise—the so-called *climbing curve* (fig. 38.6). High gastric acidity is less commonly associated with gastric ulcer; according to Vanzant the acidity is actually a little below the normal average. True anacidity, however, is rarely, if ever, found.

Atkinson and Henley (1955) also found the acidity in gastric ulcer patients to be below the average of normal subjects but Ihre (1938) found it to be essentially normal. The relatively low gastric acidities found in gastric ulcer are probably the result of an associated gastritis and do not necessarily indicate that hyperchlorhydria did not precede the development of the ulcer.

(3) Stimulation of gastric secretion, as by the

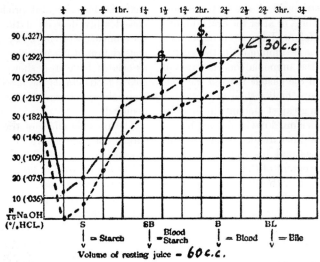

Fig. 38.6. Chart showing "climbing" type of curve of gastric acidity. (After Ryle.)

continued administration of histamine or of caffeine (p. 618), is one of the most effective experimental means of producing gastric ulcer. Although gastric ulcers are produced experimentally by means of a constant drip over the gastric mucosa of a solution of hydrochloric acid, some pepsin must be furnished by the stomach itself. Irrigation of a loop of jejunum with acid alone will not cause ulceration but this is readily produced by the addition of pepsin to the perfusion fluid.

(4) Measures directed toward the prevention of excessive gastric secretion and toward the neutralization of the acidity of the gastric contents are of outstanding value in encouraging the healing of the ulcer.

Though the importance of acid in the production of ulcer cannot be denied this factor cannot be solely concerned. For one thing, many persons who show hyperchlorhydria do not develop ulcer. "Why in these instances is the gastric mucosa immune to the action of the pepsin-hydrochloric acid?" Indeed, the question has often been asked, "Why does not the pepsin-hydrochloric acid of even normal gastric juice digest the gastric or duodenal mucosa?" It is also an extraordinary fact, firmly established by several workers, that the tissue of other parts of the intestinal tract or of other organs, though susceptible to the action of acid in their normal situations, are not digested when transplanted into the wall of the normal stomach. Dragstedt and Vaughn, for example, removed areas from the gastric wall of dogs and then sutured portions of the duodenum, ileum, jejunum, colon, spleen or kidney into the gaps.

In no case was the transplanted tissue digested. In the case of the kidney and spleen their gastric surfaces became covered with a layer of gastric epithelium. Sections of transplanted intestinal mucosa were found to be perfectly normal after a period of nine months.

On the other hand, as shown years ago by Claude Bernard (1859), the intact leg of a living frog is digested when introduced through a fistula into the stomach of a dog. Pavy (1923) showed the same thing for the rabbit's ear and Dragstedt and Vaughn have demonstrated that the intact limb of a live frog placed in an extract of frog's gastric mucosa is digested.

Until comparatively recently there has been no convincing or even very plausible answer to the question of why the stomach does not digest its own wall. One explanation offered was that the greater alkalinity of the blood coursing through the vessels of the gastric tubules as a result of the loss of H ions served to neutralize the effect of the acid juice. Others suggested that the immunity of the gastric mucosa to autodigestion is due to its containing an antipepsin. A possible explanation is the presence of ammonia in the gastric wall produced by the action of urease on urea.

UREA-UREASE-AMMONIA MECHANISM. The presence of ammonia in the gastric contents was observed many years ago (1852) by Bidder and Schmidt, but little significance was attached to the finding until Luck and Seth demonstrated its production in gastric tissue by the action of urease upon urea (urea + urease → $NH_3$ + $CO_2$), and pointed out the possible role of this mechanism in neutralizing gastric acid. A rise in blood urea as in renal insufficiency, or after the oral administration of urea is followed by a corresponding increase in the urea + ammonia in the gastric wall, and a rise in the ammonia concentration of the gastric juice. In the gastric mucosa the concentration of urease is higher than in any other tissue; it is found in greatest amounts in the cells of the surface epithelium. FitzGerald and his associates have made an extended study of this mechanism. Hastings and his colleagues found that the total urea content of the body (as determined by urea tagged with $C^{14}$ and an analysis of the expired air for $C^{14}O_2$) was 10 per cent per hour; this was reduced after gastrectomy.

Another factor which may be even more important is the presence of the protective layer of mucus which normally covers the entire gastric mucosa. Hollander (1951) has pointed out that the mucus "adheres to the underlying tissue with great tenacity, is capable of maintaining a considerable thickness instead of flowing off rapidly as the acid secretion does, is generally impermeable to destructive chemical agents because of its cohesiveness and is impermeable to pepsin because of its absorptive properties." Hollander also calls attention to the remarkable capacity of the surface layers of the gastric mucosa to regenerate and to secrete a fresh layer of mucus, should the mucous barrier be broken down at any point.

A CONSIDERATION OF OTHER FACTORS CONCERNED IN THE PRODUCTION OF ULCER. *Bacterial infection,* and interference with the *blood supply* to the mucosa, either as a result of emboli or thrombosis have been thought by some to be responsible for ulcer production. Except perhaps in rare instances, these are no longer believed to play a role. *Tobacco smoking* has been thought in some instances at any rate, to encourage ulcer formation or to interfere with the healing of an ulcer already formed; however, if smoking is conducive to gastric or duodenal ulceration the manner in which it acts is not clear. *Trauma,* although not essential to the production of ulcer is probably often a contributory factor. It is not difficult to believe that in the presence of other causative factors, rubbing of food against the gastric mucosa or the passage of coarse indigestible material into the duodenal cap, will encourage the production of ulcer, or retard the healing of an existing one. Mann and Bollman point out that the site of duodenal ulcer corresponds to the area of mucosa upon which the gastric contents impinge, and, when the gastric movements are energetic, this may occur with considerable force. They found

that the experimental production of ulcer was considerably delayed if the propulsive force of the stomach was reduced by making an hour-glass constriction in the prepyloric region. Ivy and his associates have also shown that in the rabbit coarse food retards the healing of an area of the stomach wall from which the mucosa has been denuded.

The possible effect of trauma upon the blood supply of the gastric mucosa is referred to elsewhere.

*The role of stress in the etiology of peptic ulcer—Psychovisceral disease.* As our knowledge of the control of visceral function has increased it has become more and more evident that experiences with a high emotional content can adversely affect visceral function to the extent of causing organic disease. Whether or not this takes place depends as much upon the individual and his reaction to his experiences as upon the experiences themselves, but in any case the emotional factor is predominant. Disease traceable to the individual's reactions to his environment, particularly his emotional reactions, are known as psychosomatic disease. They might better be called psychovisceral diseases (Thomas, 1955) because they generally affect some part of the viscera rather than the external body structures.

The fact that emotional states have an influence on gastric secretion has already been mentioned. The possibility is suggested that various forms of stress can, through this mechanism, cause gastric hypersecretion and thus promote the development of gastric or duodenal ulcers. In this connection some observations of Harvey Cushing (1932) are significant. He reported three cases of acute perforated ulcers with death following removal of cerebellar tumors which possibly had caused injury to the hypothalamus. He concluded that there was a parasympathetic center in the diencephalon, apparently situated near the tuber cinereum from which fibers passed backward to the medulla for relay to the vagus and other autonomic centers. He noted that experimental lesions anywhere in the intracranial course of these fibers were prone to cause gastric erosions, perforation, or ulcers. Similar observations have been reported by Keller (1933–1934) and his associates. It may also be recalled that the stimulation of the hypothalamus in the region of the tuber cinereum is followed by increased movements of the stomach and that hypersecretion and gastric hypertonus are frequently features of duodenal ulcers. That emotional stress is frequently associated with duodenal ulcer is well known. Dragstedt says "for a number of years many investigators have commented on the high incidence of ulcers in those persons whose occupations involve unusual anxiety, stress and strain and on the tendency for healed ulcers to recur during periods of great emotional tension." "On the basis of available experimental evidence on the genesis of ulcers—it seems most probable that the central nervous system plays an undoubted role in causing the disease through increasing the volume of gastric juice."

Reference should be made also to the probable role of the pituitary and adrenal hormones in the response of the viscera to environmental stimuli. These glands are surely involved in reactions of the body as a whole to stress. Specific effects on the gastrointestinal organs of the hormones that are probably released in these reactions are little known or understood, but it is known that acute gastrointestinal ulceration and mucosal hemorrhages are common occurrences in severe nonspecific types of stress. Although these have generally been interpreted as being due to activation of autonomic nerves, the work of Gray and his associates (1955) indicates that the adrenal hormones secreted in response to corticotrophin (ch. 58) may cause increased gastric secretion and thus play a part in causing duodenal ulceration.

The role of emotional factors (particularly emotionally induced hypersecretion) in gastric ulcer is not so evident although Dragstedt and associates (1954) believe that gastric stasis, which tends to cause a prolonged gastric phase of secretion, may be a factor in the production of gastric ulcers. There is no assurance that the etiology of gastric ulcer is the same as that of duodenal ulcer. Indeed there is reason to believe that the two may have quite different causations since gastric ulcer is about as common in women as in men whereas duodenal ulcer occurs with a much higher frequency (about 85%) in males.

### The Cause of Pain in Duodenal Ulcer

As mentioned previously duodenal ulcer is characterized by pain which appears several hours after a meal, most commonly at night or in the early morning. The pain is of a burning character and is usually felt somewhere in the epigastrium. Although it is evident that the pain appears at a time when the ulcerated surface is exposed to unneutralized acid from the stomach and, indeed, can be induced experimentally by introducing acid into the stomach or duodenum, the mechanism of its production is obscure. The viscera

are not supplied with pain fibers which can be demonstrated in the healthy subject by any of the ordinary methods of producing pain. The intestines can be cut, burned, or pinched without causing any other sensation than that due to contraction of the smooth muscle in the wall of the gut. Muscle spasm or stretching of the wall causes a characteristic type of pain which is different from that of ulcer pain.

One suggestion as to the cause of ulcer pain is that contact of acid with the ulcerated surface stimulates local reflex mechanisms which initiate muscle spasm in the smooth muscle in the vicinity of the ulcer. The difference in the quality of ulcer pain from ordinary muscle cramp may be due to the greater excitability of the sensory nerves induced by the inflammatory process. Another explanation utilizes this increased excitability and presumes that the threshold has been lowered sufficiently so that direct chemical trauma is capable of causing the sensation of pain, the pain in this instance being attributed to the action of acid on the exposed nerve endings or nerve fibers in the ulcer. One argument in favor of the direct acid irritation theory is that the pain is continuous and not intermittent as is the pain of muscle spasm, for example, intestinal or biliary colic. There is little to be urged against the direct acid irritiation theory except the seeming impossibility of the mechanism.

The pain is relieved by the administration of alkali and by such drugs as diminish the secretion or motility of the stomach; these are the belladonna alkaloids and the numerous synthetic parasympatholytic drugs. The pain is also relieved by sympathectomy or vagotomy. The former operation is effective because the visceral afferent fibers, including the pain fibers, from the abdominal organs accompany the sympathetic nerves. The latter has an effect like the parasympatholytic drugs; it diminishes gastric secretion and motility. It is interesting that pain can be induced in a vagotomized subject by introducing a large volume of acid into the stomach. Presumably the acid overflows into the duodenum and initiates the usual mechanism of ulcer pain. The success of this experiment is a strong argument in favor of the direct acid irritation theory, but it does not absolutely rule out spasm of the duodenal muscle as a cause of pain, since the vagi do not have a profound influence on the smooth muscle of the small intestine which may still respond by contraction to local irritation.

A point in favor of the muscle spasm theory is the fact that the parasympatholytic drugs relieve the pain of ulcer even when they fail to suppress greatly the secretion of acid. However this effect as well as the immediate effect of vagotomy may be due to the delayed emptying of the stomach which both induce, thus causing the acid to remain in the stomach where it does not make contact with the ulcer.

### Physiological Principles in Treatment of Peptic Ulcer

The treatment of peptic ulcer is directed toward the relief of pain, reduction of the acidity in the gastric and duodenal contents, protection of the ulcerated surface from mechanical trauma, and so far as possible elimination of environmental stress. Unless severe hemorrhage is a presenting symptom it is customary at present to use medical treatment first. Surgery is resorted to if the ulcer bleeds or if complications such as obstruction or perforation develop; it is also used in intractable cases that do not yield to medical treatment. Relief of pain and reduction of acidity are accomplished by administration of alkalis or other antacids such as ion-exchange resins. The parasympatholytic drugs are also effective. The judicious use of food can accomplish the same result. All protein containing foods act as antacids and the fat in milk inhibits gastric secretion. One difficulty is that any effective antacid is likely to be followed by an acid rebound, that is to say, when the effect of the antacid has passed off the gastric acidity tends to rise above its former level. For this reason, food, especially milk is given in small amounts at frequent intervals. The same principle applies to the use of antacids; indeed these are sometimes given by continuous intragastric drip (Winkelstein, 1951).

The diet for ulcer patients is selected with the idea of reducing so far as possible stimulation of gastric secretion and mechanical irritation of the ulcer. Stimulation of the cephalic phase of secretion is avoided by eliminating highly spiced foods and foods which make a strong appeal to the appetite such as broiled steaks; stimulation of the gastric phase as well a mechanical irritation of the ulcer is avoided by eliminating coarse and indigestible food such as raw vegetables and fruit. The use of tobacco and alcohol in moderation is permitted by some physicians and forbidden by others. On physiological principles they should both be eliminated. Rest and a placid way of life are desirable but cannot always be achieved.

Two different surgical approaches to the reduction of gastric acidity are in current use. The older method, known as subtotal gastric resection in which the pyloric portion and a large part of the body and fundus of the stomach are removed, is aimed primarily at the gastric phase of gastric secretion. Since experience has shown that removal of the antrum alone does not effect an adequate reduction in gastric acidity it is the custom now to take out a large part of the body and fundus of the stomach as well. More recently the operation of double vagotomy or vagectomy has come into use (Dragstedt, 1944, 1945, 1946). In this operation an attempt is made to sever completely the vagus nerves immediately above or below the diaphragm and to remove enough of the vagus trunks to prevent regeneration. The objective is to eliminate the cephalic phase of secretion which Dragstedt believes to be responsible for the hypersecretion in duodenal ulcer patients. The operation is not recommended for gastric ulcers.

Double vagotomy results in profound depression of gastric motility as well as secretion and the resulting gastric stasis proved to be a double hazard to the patient; there was danger of over distention and atony of the stomach and the retained food, acting in the antrum as a stimulus to the release of gastrin increased the gastric phase of secretion. These problems have been met by performing, at the same time as the vagotomy, a gastric drainage operation. Usually a gastroenterostomy is done in which an opening is made between the stomach and jejunum. This facilitates gastric emptying and encourages regurgitation of intestinal contents into the stomach thus tending further to lower gastric acidity. Although the two surgical approaches to the problem of peptic ulcer are based on quite different philosophies they are about equally effective; probably this is because of the interdependence of the gastric and cephalic phases of secretion mentioned in chapter 37.

### REFERENCES

ANSON, M. L. AND MIRSKY, A. E. J. Estimation of pepsin with hemoglobin. J. Gen. Physiol., 1932, **16**, 59.

ATKINSON, M. AND HENLEY, K. S. Levels of intragastric and intraduodenal acidity. Clin. Sc., London, 1955, **14**, 1.

BABKIN, B. P., KOMAROV, O. AND KOMAROV, S. A. Effect of activated ergosterol and of parathyroid hormone on gastric secretion in the dog. Endocrinology, 1940, **26**, 703.

BAKER, B. L. AND ABRAMS, G. D. Effect of hypophysectomy on the cytology of the fundic glands of the stomach and the secretion of pepsin. Am. J. Physiol., 1954, **177**, 409.

BARD, P. A diencephalic mechanism for the expression of rage with special reference to the sympathetic nervous system. Am. J. Physiol., 1928, **34**, 490. The central representation of the sympathetic system. Arch. Neurol. & Psychiat. 1929, **22**, 230.

BEAZELL, J. M. AND IVY, A. C. The influence of alcohol on the digestive tract. Quart. J. Stud. on Alcohol, 1940, **1**, 45.

BENNETT, T. I. AND RYLE, J. A. Studies in gastric secretion: V. A study of normal gastric function based on one hundred healthy men by means of the fractional method of gastric analysis. Guy's Hosp. Rep., 1921, **71**, 286.

BOYD, T. E. Influence of alkalis on secretion and composition of gastric juice, effect of prolonged administration of sodium bicarbonate and calcium carbonate. Am. J. Physiol., 1925, **71**, 455; (also see p. 464).

CLARK, W. E. LE GROS. The structure and connections of the thalamus. Brain, 1932, **55**, 406.

CUSHING, H. Peptic ulcer and the interbrain. Surg. Gynec. & Obst., 1932, **55**, 1.

DRAGSTEDT, L. R. Supradiaphragmatic section of the vagus nerves in the treatment of gastric ulcer. Gastroenterology, 1944, **3**, 450. Removal of the vagus nerves of the stomach in gastroduodenal ulcer. Surgery, 1945, **17**, 742. Section of the vagus nerves to the stomach in the treatment of peptic ulcer. Surg. Gynec. & Obst., 1946, **83**, 547.

DRAGSTEDT, L. R. Pathogenesis of gastroduodenal ulcer. Arch. Surg., 1942, **44**, 438.

DRAGSTEDT, L. R. Cause of peptic ulcer. J. A. M. A., 1959, **169**, 203.

DRAGSTEDT, L. R. AND ELLIS, J. C. The fatal effect of the total loss of gastric juice. Am. J. Physiol., 1930, **93**, 407.

DRAGSTEDT, L. R., OBERHELMAN, H. A., EVANS, S. O. AND RIGLER, S. P. Antrum hyperfunction and gastric ulcer. Ann. Surg., 1954, **140**, 396.

DRAGSTEDT, L. R. AND VAUGHN, A. M. Gastric ulcer studies. Arch. Surg., 1924, **8**, 791.

DYER, H. AND ROE, J. H. Relation of nutrition to gastric function; effect of vitamin A deficiency. Am. J. Digest. Dis., 1941, **8**, 833.

FARRELL, J. I. Contributions to physiology of gastric secretion; response of glands to substances applied to gastric mucosa. Am. J. Physiol., 1928, **85**, 672.

FAULEY, G. B. AND IVY, A. C. Fundusectomy prevents postoperative jejunal ulcer. Proc. Soc. Exper. Biol. & Med., 1926, **34**, 152.

FITZGERALD, O. Nature, 1946, **158**, 305; Biochem. J., 1950, **47**, ix. See also Conway et al. Gastroenterology, 1959, **37**, 449.

FITZGERALD, O. AND MURPHY, P., Lancet, 1949, **II**, 1107.

FÖLDES, F. AND VAJDA, G. Effect of vitamin A on the secretion of gastric juice in deficient hydrochloric acid production. Brit. M. J., 1941, **1**, 317.

FULTON, J. F. AND INGRAHAM, F. D. Emotional disturbances following experimental lesions of the base of the brain (pre-chiasmal). Am. J. Physiol., 1929, **90**, 35.

GRAY, S. J. The effect of steroids on the gastrointestinal tract. Am. J. Gastroenterology, 1958, **30**, 266.

GRAY, S. J., RAMSEY, C. AND REIFENSTEIN, R. W. Hormonal influences upon the stomach. Am. J. Gastroenterology, 1955, **24**, 244.

HARRIS, G. W. The hypothalamus and endocrine glands. Brit. M. Bull., 1950, **6**, 345.

HAVERBACK, B. J., BOGDANSKI, D. AND HOGBEN, A. Inhibition of gastric acid secretion in the dog by the precursor of serotonin (5-hydroxytryptophane). Gastroenterology, 1957, **34**, 188; (also see 1957, **32**, 1058).

HESS, W. R. Vegetative Functionen und Zwischenhirn. Helvet. Physiol. et Pharmacol. Acta, Suppl. IV, Ed. VII, pp. 1–65, 1947.

HOLLANDER, F. The insulin test for the presence of intact nerve fibers after vagal operations for peptic ulcer. Gastroenterology, 1946, **7**, 607.

IHRE, B. Human gastric secretion. A quantitative study of gastric secretion in normal and pathological conditions. Acta med. scandinav., Suppl., 1938, **95**, 1.

IVY, A. C. AND BACHRACH, W. H. An abnormal mechanism for the excitation of gastric secretion in the dog. Am. J. Digest. Dis., 1940, **7**, 76.

JONES, T. W. AND HARKINS, H. M. Evaluation of mechanisms involved in gastric acid secretion of pylorus ligated rats. Gastroenterology, 1958, **35**, 309.

KELLER, A. D., HARE, W. K. AND D'AMOUR, M. D. Ulceration in digestive tract following experimental lesions in brain stem. Proc. Soc. Exper. Biol. & Med., 1933, **30**, 772. Ulceration of the digestive tract following hypophysectomy. Am. J. Physiol., 1934, **109**, 63.

KIRSNER, J. B., LEVIN, E. AND PALMER, W. L. Observations on the excessive nocturnal gastric secretion in patients with duodenal ulcer. Gastroenterology, 1949, **11**, 598.

LUCK, J. M. AND SETH, T. N. Biochem. J., 1924, **18**, 227; **19**, 357.

MacDONALD, D. A. The control of the autonomic nervous system by the hypothalamus. Lancet, 1951, **1**, 627.

MacLEAN, P. D. Psychosomatic disorders and the visceral brain. Psychosom. Med., 1949, **11**, 338.

MANN, F. C. AND BOLLMAN, J. L. J. Experimentally produced ulcers; development and treatment. J. A. M. A., 1932, **99**, 1576.

MANN, F. C. AND WILLIAMSON, C. S. Experimental production of peptic ulcers. Ann. Surg., 1923, **77**, 409.

MATTHEWS, W. B. AND DRAGSTEDT, L. R. Surg. Gynec. Obstet. 1932, **55**, 265.

MURPHY, J. P. AND GELLHORN, E. Further investigations on diencephalic-cortical relations and their significance for the problem of emotion. J. Neurophysiol., 1945, **8**, 431.

POLLAND, W. S. AND BLOOMFIELD, A. L. Normal standards of gastric function. J. Clin. Invest., 1931, **9**, 651.

REHFUSS, M. E. A new method of gastric testing with a description of a method for the fractional testing of the gastric juice. Am. J. Med. Sc., 1914, **147**, 848.

ROTH, J. A. AND IVY, A. C. The effect of caffein on gastric secretion in the dog, cat and man. Am. J. Physiol., 1944, **141**, 454.

SCHÖDT, E. Über die behandlung Verschiedener

Magen-krankheiten mit Vitamin A. Ztschr. klin. Med., 1936, **130, 163**.

STROM, G. AND UVNÄS, B. Motor responses of gastrointestinal tract and bladder to topical stimulation of the frontal lobe, basal ganglia and hypothalamus in the cat. Acta Physiol. scandinav., 1950, **21, 90**.

THOMAS, J. E. The autonomic nervous system in gastrointestinal disease. J. A. M. A., 1955, **157**, 209.

VANZANT, F. R., ALVAREZ, W. C., EUSTERMAN, G. B., DUNN, H. L. AND BERKSON, J. The normal range of gastric acidity from youth to old age. Arch. Int. Med., 1932, **49, 345**.

*Monographs and Reviews*

BABKIN, B. P. Secretory mechanism of the digestive glands. Paul B. Hoeber, Inc., New York, 1950.

BEAUMONT, W. Experiments and observations on the gastric juice and the physiology of digestion. Facsimile edition reprinted on the occasion of the XIIIth International Physiological Congress. Boston, 1929.

BENNETT, T. I. Diseases of the upper alimentary tract. William Heinemann, Ltd., London, 1925.

BERNARD, CLAUDE. 1859. Cited by Dragstedt and Vaughn, 1924.

BIDDER, F. AND SCHMIDT, C. Die Verdauungssafte und der Stoffwechsel. p. 45, G. A. Reyher, Leipzig, 1852.

BLOOMFIELD, A. L. AND POLLAND, W. S. Gastric anacidity; its relation to disease. The Macmillan Co., New York, 1933.

CANNON, W. B. Bodily changes in pain, hunger, fear and rage. Appleton-Century-Crofts, Inc., New York and London, 1915.

CARLSON, A. J. The control of hunger in health and disease (psychic secretion in man). Chicago University Press, Chicago, 1916.

CARLSON, A. J. Secretion of gastric juice in health and disease. Physiol. Rev., 1923, **3**, 1.

CUSHING, H. Peptic ulcer and the interbrain (Fourth Balfour Lecture, University of Toronto). *In* The pituitary body, hypothalamus and parasympathetic nervous system. Charles C Thomas, Springfield, Ill., 1932.

GREENGARD, H. Hormones of the gastrointestinal tract. *In* The hormones, edited by G. Pincus and K. V. Thimann. Academic Press, New York, 1948.

GROSSMAN, M. I. Gastrointestinal hormones. Physiol. Rev., 1950, **30**, 33.

GROSSMAN, M. I. A critical analysis of various theories of the pathogenesis of peptic ulcer. *In* Peptic ulcer, p. 65, edited by David Sandweiss. W. B. Saunders Co., Philadelphia, 1951.

HOLLANDER, F. The mucous barrier in the stomach. *In* Peptic ulcer, p. 65, edited by David Sandweiss. W. B. Saunders Co., Philadelphia, 1951.

HOLLANDER, F. AND PENNER, A. History of gastric analysis. Am. J. Dig. Diseases, 1938, **5**, 739, 786. Also see 1939, **6**, 22 and Am. J. Med., 1952, **13**, 453.

IVY, A. C. The role of hormones in digestion. Physiol. Rev., 1930, **10**, 282. The gastrointestinal hormones. Tr. & Stud., Coll. Physicians, Philadelphia, 1944, **12**, 101.

IVY, A. C. AND GRAY, J. S. Enterogastrone. Cold Spring Harbor Symposia on Quantitative Biology, 1937, **5**, 405.

IVY, A. C. GROSSMAN, M. I. AND BACHRACH, W. H. Peptic ulcer. Blakiston Company, Philadelphia, 1950.

JAMES, A. H. The physiology of gastric digestion. Edward Arnold & Co., London, 1957.

KINSELLA, V. J. The mechanism of abdominal pain. Australasian Medical Publishing Co., Sydney, Australia, 1948.

MACHELLA, T. E. Gastric analysis procedures and other laboratory aids. *In* Peptic ulcer, p. 252, edited by David Sandweiss, W. B. Saunders Co., Philadelphia, 1951.

PAVY, 1923. Cited by Dragstedt and Vaughn, 1924.

RYLE, J. A. Gastric function in health and disease. Milford, London, 1926.

Series of papers by various authors on production of peptic ulcer. Arch. Surg., 1942, 44, 399–530.

WINKELSTEIN, A. Continuous intragastric drip therapy for peptic ulcer. *In* Peptic ulcer, p. 377. David Sandweiss, Editor, W. B. Saunders Co., Philadelphia, 1951.

WOLF, S. AND WOLFF, H. G. Human gastric function. Oxford University Press, 1943.

# 39

## PANCREAS, LIVER AND BILIARY SYSTEM

### Secretion of Pancreatic Juice

#### STRUCTURE OF THE PANCREAS

The pancreas is an elongated gland which extends from the duodenum obliquely upward behind the stomach, across the posterior abdominal wall to the spleen at the level of the first and second lumbar vertebrae. It develops from two outgrowths of the primitive gut, one arising from the ventral and the other from the dorsal gut wall immediately below the primitive stomach. As a result of the rotation of the gut and its mesenteries and the growth of the rudiments themselves, the two portions of the pancreas come into contact at the left of the duodenum and eventually fuse. The duct of the ventral pancreas joins the duct of the dorsal portion somewhere along the course of the latter, usually near its origin, and the two subsequently form a continuous channel which constitutes the major pancreatic duct (ductus pancreatus or duct of Wirsung). In keeping with the fact that the proximal portion of this duct was developed in conjunction with the liver bud, the duct of Wirsung in the adult enters the duodenum in close association with the common bile duct. That portion of the duct of the dorsal rudiment which lies between the duodenum and the point of anastomosis with the ventral duct is normally retarded in subsequent development and becomes the accessory duct (ductus pancreaticus accessorius or duct of Santorini).

For descriptive purposes the adult pancreas is divided into a head, body and tail. The most massive portion of the gland is the head; it is flattened dorsoventrally and lies within the concavity of the duodenum to which it is attached by numerous blood vessels, the pancreatic duct and loose connective tissue. The uncinate process is a hooklike medial projection from the lower part of the head. The body of the pancreas makes up the major portion of the remainder of the gland; it is somewhat prismatic in shape and presents an anterior, a posterior and an inferior surface. The tail is the pointed, tonguelike left end of the gland which lies in contact with the spleen.

When studied microscopically, the pancreas is seen to be made up chiefly of groups of cells forming acini which tend to be spherical or ovoid in general contour; in the closely packed tissue of the pancreas they are actually polygonal. Groups of acini form primary lobules, also polygonal in contour, which are imperfectly separated from other primary lobules by incomplete connective tissue septa. Numerous adjacent primary lobules form a secondary lobule; the secondary lobules are completely surrounded by connective tissue and can be dissected out as separate structures connected to the rest of the gland by ducts, nerve fibers, lymphatic vessels and blood vessels. The pancreatic tissue proper is composed of acinous cells, islet cells (described in chapter 48) and duct cells. The acinous cells, owing to the spherical shape of the acini, tend to be pyramidal with the truncated apex of the pyramid directed toward the lumen of the acinus; they are large cells with a well developed nucleus and abundant granular cytoplasm. The granules, called *zymogen granules*, vary in number and position in the cells depending on the state of activity of the gland but tend to be more abundant in the apical region of the cell which is adjacent to the lumen of the acinus.

The microscopic appearance of the pancreatic acinous cells changes considerably during functional activity. In the resting gland, i.e., the one that has not been stimulated to secrete for many hours, the cells are filled with granules that are large and closely packed and may displace the nucleus toward the base of the cell. When the pancreas is made to secrete, either by food or by drugs, the following changes can be observed: first, the entire cell is reduced in size; second, the granular, inner or apical zone is diminished in size more than the outer zone; the latter, though smaller, now occupies relatively more of the cell volume; the zymogen granules of the inner zone are smaller in size and fewer in number than in the resting cell, and those that remain are congregated near the apical border of the cell (R. Heidenhain, 1883). The changes in appearance of the acinous cell during secretion have been taken as indicating that the pancreas has been secreting enzymes. Secretion of pancreatic juice containing little or no enzymatic material causes correspondingly little change in the appearance of the acinous cell.

An interesting feature of the duct system of the pancreas is the manner in which the small or terminal intralobular ducts end in relation to the acinus. Cells, corresponding in structure to the cells of the terminal ducts, may be seen in microscopic sections within the acini. These are called centroacinar cells; most investigators have concluded that the terminal ducts extend into the lumen of the acini where they form a sort of lining.

## Pancreatic Juice

The pancreas secretes a colorless, odorless, alkaline fluid of low viscosity, tasting strongly of sodium bicarbonate. Some specimens have been described as having a faint straw color. Exceptional specimens having a high concentration of enzymes may be viscous and may even jell at low temperatures. Pure pancreatic juice collected from dogs without loss of carbon dioxide has a pH between 8 and 8.3 and an extreme range of specific gravity of 1.007 to 1.042, the usual values being between 1.010 and 1.018. The osmolar concentration of the juice is the same as that of the blood when the two are collected simultaneously from the same animal. When the osmolar concentration of the blood is altered experimentally the pancreatic juice shows a corresponding change.

The distinguishing chemical characteristic of the juice is its high bicarbonate content. This is in contrast to the strongly acid character of the gastric juice which is secreted at the same time. The fact that the pancreas secretes base while the stomach is secreting acid is a factor in maintaining the acid-base balance of the rest of the body. Likewise, the fact that the two secretions are mixed in the intestine helps to maintain the normal pH of the intestinal contents. The fact is now well established that the bicarbonate and chloride concentrations of pancreatic juice vary in a reciprocal manner so that the sum of the two expressed in milliequivalents is approximately constant, and nearly the same as the total base of the blood plasma. Also, that within physiological limits, the bicarbonate concentration increases and the chloride concentration decreases with increasing rates of secretion. This relationship holds over a wide range of secretory rates and is such that a straight line results when the logarithm of the bicarbonate concentration in m.eq. per liter is plotted against the *reciprocal* of the rate of secretion expressed as cubic centimeters of secretion per kilogram of body weight per minute; the slope indicates an inverse relation. The rate of increase in bicarbonate concentration with the rate of increase in the rate of secretion varies with different animals so that the rate of secretion cannot be estimated from the bicarbonate concentration of an unknown sample; however, it is possible to say that if the bicarbonate concentration is high the pancreatic juice was secreted at a rapid rate, or a rate that was rapid for that particular animal. The maximum bicarbonate concentration in juice collected from different dogs ranges between 135 and 148 m.eq. per liter and the maximum rate of secretion is about 0.1 cc. per kg. per minute, or about 1 cc. per minute for a 10-kg. dog; higher rates than this are occasionally seen. In addition to chloride and bicarbonate the pancreatic juice contains a small amount of phosphate, but less than that occurring in blood plasma.

The principal bases of pancreatic juice are sodium, potassium, and calcium. The concentrations of sodium and potassium are approximately equivalent to those of the blood plasma but the calcium concentration is only 3 or 4 mg. per cent as compared to about 10 mg. per cent for blood. The low calcium concentration compared to that of the blood is attributed to the fact that much of the blood calcium is combined with protein and is not in a diffusible state.

The protein content of pancreatic juice varies over a wide range but in an orderly manner with the conditions governing secretion. In 200 samples of dog's pancreatic juice collected under different conditions, the protein content in different samples varied between 0.1 per cent and 10 per cent. Concentrations found in human pancreatic juice collected through accidental or surgical fistulas are nearer the lower extreme, ranging from 0.1 to 0.3 per cent. The protein in the juice consists mainly of enzymes. Using electrophoresis, a method by which the proteins in a mixture can be separated by means of their different mobilities in an electrical field, it has been possible to determine that there are at least ten distinct proteins in pancreatic juice, with the possibility of still others that fail to separate out in the time during which the electrical field is maintained (Grossberg, Komarov, and Shay, 1952). This method of separating the proteins of pancreatic juice also separates the enzymatic activity; proteolytic activity is found in one component, lipolytic activity in another, and amylolytic activity in another, a fact which confirms the belief that the proteins dealt with in the electrophoretic procedure are the actual enzymes of the juice. It is interesting that when different methods were used to stimulate secretion of the juice the electrophoretic patterns differ, depending upon the method used; for example, a meat meal produces pancreatic juice having a different electrophoretic pattern and therefore a different protein composition from that secreted in response to stimulation by means of urocholine and secretin. This suggests that the relative concentration of the different enzymes in the juice can be made to vary by using different stimuli to cause secretion.

The enzymes of pancreatic juice are capable of digesting all three types of foodstuff, that is, the juice contains proteolytic, amylolytic and lipolytic enzymes. The proteolytic enzymes as they occur in the pancreatic tissue and freshly secreted pancreatic juice possess no proteolytic activity and are referred to in that state as zymogens. In the older literature the proteolytic activity was attributed to trypsin, the corresponding zymogen being trypsinogen. Kunitz and Northrup (1934) have shown that what was called trypsin or trypsinogen consists of at least two components, for one of which they retained the name *trypsin* and for the other they coined the name *chymotrypsin*. The zymogen of chymotrypsin is known as chymotrypsinogen. These several substances have been isolated and obtained in crystalline form and many of their properties determined by Kunitz and Northrup.

Trypsin and trypsinogen have a molecular weight of 34,000. As an enzyme trypsin hydrolyzes native protein, producing proteoses and peptides. It accelerates coagulation of the blood, in which it acts as a thrombokinase, but has only a feeble action in clotting milk. Its optimum pH for digestion of casein lies between pH 8 and 9. When pure, it is reversibly inactivated by heat in acid solution; it slowly decomposes in alkaline solution. Trypsinogen is indistinguishable on chemical analysis from trypsin, but has different solubilities and a different crystalline form; it exhibits no proteolytic activity. In solution it changes spontaneously to active trypsin but the change is accelerated by acid or by exposure to concentrated magnesium sulfate, calcium chloride, active trypsin or to certain activating enzymes called *kinases*. The effectiveness of trypsin

in the activation of trypsinogen is of great importance because such autocatalytic reactions progress with great rapidity once they are started and require only minute amounts of activating agents to set them going. Spontaneous activation of trypsinogen is suppressed in crude extracts, and doubtless also in living pancreas, by the presence of an inhibitor which inactivates small amounts of trypsin. The trypsinogen as secreted in the living animal is activated on contact with the intestinal mucosa by means of an enzyme in the mucosa called enterokinase. Enterokinase does not appear in the intestinal secretion in the absence of pancreatic juice but is present in intestinal mucosal extracts. A similar substance is present in pancreatic extracts. Kunitz has observed that certain common molds (penicillium) produce an enzyme capable of activating trypsinogen.

Chymotrypsinogen has a molecular weight of 25,000; it is converted to chymotrypsin by active trypsin only but indirect activation can be accomplished by enterokinase if trypsinogen is also present. If chymotrypsinogen is activated rapidly by fairly large amounts of trypsin, $\pi$-chymotrypsin is formed which then changes spontaneously to $\delta$-chymotrypsin, as a result of the $\pi$-chymotrypsin acting upon itself. If smaller amounts of trypsin are used the major products are $\alpha$-, $\beta$-, and $\gamma$-chymotrypsin which appear to have essentially the same molecular weight as chymotrypsinogen and $\pi$- and $\delta$-chymotrypsin. A sixth type, known as chymotrypsin (and chymotrypsinogen) $\beta$, has also been isolated. Alpha chymotrypsin is the active enzyme first crystallized by Kunitz and Northrup. The nature of the structural differences among the various chymotrypsins, other than in their crystal form, is unclear. The activity of chymotrypsin is comparable to that of trypsin but it has different specificities, for example, it coagulates milk but not blood. Chymotrypsin digests casein somewhat more rapidly than does trypsin but the digestion is carried much further by a mixture of the two enzymes than by either alone, a fact which indicates that the two enzymes attack different linkages in the protein molecule. Like trypsin, chymotrypsin is reversibly inactivated by boiling in acid solution. Its optimum activity occurs in the same pH range as that of trypsin, i.e., 8 to 9 for casein digestion.

The peptides resulting from protein digestion by trypsin and chymotrypsin are further digested by enzymes known as *peptidases*; most of these come from the intestinal mucosa but one has been identified and isolated from pancreatic juice, an enzyme known as carboxypeptidase which splits off the end amino acid containing a free carboxyl group from polypeptides. In fresh pancreas it occurs in an inactive form, procarboxypeptidase and, like chymotrypsinogen, it is activated by trypsin.

The ability of pancreatic juice to emulsify and hydrolyze fats is probably due to a single enzyme called *pancreatic lipase*. This enzyme is known principally through its activity and has not been isolated in a pure state or crystallized. Pancreatic lipase hydrolyzes fat only in the presence of bile salts or other substances with similar properties, for example, some of the synthetic detergents. Bile salts in high concentration inhibit the action of lipase as do salts of certain heavy metals, e.g., copper, iron and cobalt; it is also inhibited by the halogens, fluorine, iodine and bromine. The pH at which pancreatic lipase exhibits its optimum activity varies with the substrate, but is always on the alkaline side of neutrality.

The amylolytic activity of pancreatic juice is due to *pancreatic amylase* which may be one or two enzymes. The finding of amylolytic activity in two components of the juice which can be separated electrophoretically (Grossberg *et al.*, 1952) and the fact that different methods of measuring amylase activity give different results in the same sample of pancreatic juice (Waldron, 1951) indicates that there may be more than one enzyme involved in the digestion of carbohydrate by the pancreas and that these two enzymes have somewhat different activity. Pancreatic amylase is secreted in active form but becomes inactive if dialyzed against distilled water, owing to the removal of neutral salts which are thus proved to be essential for the activity of the enzyme; the most efficient activating ion is chloride. The optimum pH for activity of pancreatic amylase varies between 6.5 and 7.2 depending upon the kind and concentration of neutral salts present in the solution. The enzyme digests glycogen as well as starch. Under favorable conditions, the end product in both instances is maltose. The pancreatic juice is said also to contain maltase and sucrase and under certain conditions, lactase.

Pancreatic juice also contains ribonuclease and desoxyribonuclease which partially hydrolyze the corresponding nucleic acids into mononucleotides. The action of these enzymes has not been clearly characterized. The optimum pH for desoxyribonuclease is in the neighborhood of 7.

The importance of the pancreatic enzymes in digestion is evidenced by that fact that when pancreatic juice is excluded from the intestine by pancreatectomy or ligation of the ducts there is serious impairment of digestion and absorption of the various foodstuffs. This is most pronounced in the case of fat and protein, unabsorbed fat particularly appearing in large amounts in the stools; this condition is known as *steatorrhea*. The bicarbonate of the juice also serves to neutralize the gastric juice as it enters the intestine and to establish in the intestine a pH more favorable for intestinal digestion than would otherwise be the case.

### Methods of Collecting Pancreatic Juice

In order to obtain pancreatic juice for study it is necessary to make some kind of pancreatic fistula, that is, some sort of preparation through which the pancreatic juice, instead of flowing into the intestine as it does normally, is brought to the outside of the body where it may be collected. The first such fistula was described by Regner de Graaf in 1664. He cannulated the pancreatic duct of a dog with a quill from a wild duck which he selected "because that kind of bird hath longer and thinner (quills) than all others." The cannula was brought out through the abdominal wall and the pancreatic juice collected in a small vessel attached to its outer end. Of great historical interest is the permanent fistula devised by Pavlov in 1879 (see Pavlov, 1910). Pavlov cut out a rhomboid portion of the duodenal wall surrounding the opening of the major pancreatic duct and, after repairing the duodenum, transplanted the excised papilla, with the duct attached, into the skin of the abdominal wall. It is now customary to collect pancreatic juice from animals through a duodenal fistula which is provided with a metal or plastic tube that can be closed when the fistula is not in use (Thomas, 1951). The opening of the duct can be seen through the fistulous opening into the duodenum and a glass or metal cannula inserted into the duct. If the accessory duct is tied at the time the fistula is made the total secretion of the pancreas can be collected in this manner over a period of hours.

### Pancreatic Fistula

The digestive disturbances that follow ligation of the ducts or removal of the pancreas are also observed when the pancreatic juice is diverted from the intestine through a complete fistula. Such fistulas, however, give rise to other, more serious complications which tend to obscure the digestive disturbances. Within a few days after the fistula has been made the secretion becomes continuous and increases in amount, and its composition changes. The concentration of total solids falls to 1 or 2 per cent, chiefly owing to the almost complete absence of protein (Babkin, 1928). These changes are associated with changes in the microscopic appearance of the pancreas (Heidenhain, 1883); the acinous cells decrease in size and lose most of their granules. The animal loses weight rapidly, refuses to eat and dies.

In animals with complete fistulas Johnston and Ball (1930) found a decrease in chloride and an equivalent increase in the bicarbonate concentration of the pancreatic juice as drainage progressed. The increase in bicarbonate is not a constant finding since Heidenhain obtained some specimens of juice which did not effervesce on addition of acid and some samples collected by Johnston and Ball had a pH as low as 7.16. The total base of the juice remains normal or nearly so and because of this and the hypersecretion there is a substantial loss of base (Na, K, Ca) from the body which gives rise to changes in the blood that ultimately prove fatal.

The most important blood changes are lowered plasma volume (dehydration), decrease in chloride, decrease in bicarbonate and a decrease in total base (Elman and McCaughan, 1927; Gamble and McIver, 1928; Dragstedt *et al.*, 1930). The pH of the blood may increase or decrease, probably depending on the relative amounts of chloride and bicarbonate lost; excessive vomiting is common and this tends to increase the loss of chloride. Hypersecretion of the stomach has been observed in pancreatic fistula and this would add to the chloride loss when vomiting is present. It may also account for the hypersecretion of the pancreas when HCl from the stomach enters the intestine. In one group of animals studied by McCaughan (1929) the blood chemistry remained approximately normal; the animals, nevertheless, died within 5 to 8 days (the usual survival time) apparently because of dehydration. Changes in blood chemistry corresponding to those seen in experimental animals, but usually less severe, have been observed in human patients with pancreatic fistula (Miller and Wiper, 1944).

Administration of sodium chloride or sodium bicarbonate intravenously or by mouth prolongs the life of experimental animals with pancreatic fistula, sometimes indefinitely, but the ideal treatment is return of the secreted juice to the gastrointestinal tract. For animals with an incomplete fistula of the Pavlov type the administration of sodium bicarbonate and a diet that does not stimulate excessive secretion such as bread and milk may be all that is required.

A summary of the results observed in experimental pancreatic insufficiency is presented in tables 39.1 and 39.2.

### REGULATION OF PANCREATIC SECRETION

Claude Bernard believed that the pancreas secretes only when stimulated as, for example, during digestion. Heidenhain noted, however, that the secretion was continuous in herbivorous animals but he agreed with Bernard that in the dog and cat and other carnivora there was no secretion without stimulation. Proof has since been obtained that secretion is continuous in rabbits, white rats, white mice, guinea pigs and frogs. Baxter (1931) found that secretion in the rabbit continued even after removal of the small intestine and after decapitation. The idea that

TABLE 39.1

*Functional disturbances in experimental pancreatic insufficiency*

| Procedure | Functional Changes | | |
| --- | --- | --- | --- |
| | Absorption deficit | Duodenal ulcer | Fatty liver |
| Pancreatectomy | 100% of animals (severity variable) | Rare | 92% (Dragstedt) |
| Ligation of ducts | 100% of animals (severity variable) | 33% (Dragstedt) | 50% (Dragstedt) |
| Total fistula | 100% of animals (severity variable) | Limited by early death; otherwise probably 100% (Dragstedt) | None |
| Mann-Williamson operation | Some deficit (no exact data) | 90–100% | No data |

TABLE 39.2

*Blood changes in experimental pancreatic insufficiency*

| Procedure | Blood Changes | | | |
|---|---|---|---|---|
| | Enzymes | Salts and Water | Sugar | Fat |
| Pancreatectomy | No change | No change | Hyperglycemia | Hypolipemia |
| Ligation of ducts | Increase in blood amylase ("diastase") | No change | No change—hyperglycemia possible late effect | Hypolipemia in 50 per cent |
| Total fistula | No change | Decrease in total base, decrease in Cl, decrease in $HCO_3$ dehydration; pH variable. | No change | No change |

the pancreas of the fasting dog does not secrete unless stimulated by means of food or other external agents has had to be modified in the light of subsequent work. Boldyreff (1916) observed pancreatic secretion at intervals in fasting animals, associated with periods of secretory and motor activity in other organs of digestion which we now recognize as hunger periods. This periodic secretion was studied thoroughly by Scott and his coworkers (1940, 1941) and they found that although periodic secretion did occur it was associated with hunger activity of the stomach only about half the time. Continuous secretion is the rule in human patients with pancreatic fistulas and McClure (1937) states that pancreatic enzymes are always found in the intestinal contents collected by intubation of normal subjects.

Whether continuous or intermittent, the amount of secretion is always increased after meals. This occurs in response to specific stimuli associated either with the act of eating or the presence of food in the gastrointestinal tract. Proof that the act of eating serves as a stimulus to the pancreas was obtained in Pavlov's laboratory (later confirmed by Ivy, 1926) by means of sham feeding (ch. 37) that is, feeding a dog provided with an esophagostomy so that the food did not reach the stomach. In these circumstances the pancreas begins to secrete within one to one and a half minutes after feeding and continues for 12 to 20 minutes. The volume secreted is small but the concentration of enzymes is increased over the fasting secretion. The short latent period as well as direct experimental evidence has served to prove that the secretion is not due to gastric hydrochloric acid entering the duo-

denum (Tonkish, 1924). The response is abolished by cutting the vagus nerves. Food and food products in the stomach do not, apparently, have any direct stimulating effect on the pancreas; however, they become effective stimuli when the gastric contents enter the intestine.

All the major constituents of the gastric chyme influence the secretory activity of the pancreas in one way or another after they have entered the intestine; these include water, hydrochloric acid, products of protein digestion, fats, fatty acids, soaps and products of starch digestion. Each of these substances has a different effect on the pancreas, producing a characteristic type of pancreatic juice. Hydrochloric acid produces an abundant secretion of dilute alkaline fluid containing a minimum amount of enzymes. Fatty acids and soaps, although producing an abundant secretion, increase the concentration of enzymes, whereas the products of protein digestion when used in the absence of other stimuli produce only a small amount of secretion which is highly concentrated in enzymes; fats are said to act in a similar manner.

*Secretin and Pancreozymin*

The mechanism through which the various stimuli act on the pancreas to promote secretion has been under investigation for more than half a century. The discovery of secretin in 1902 by Bayliss and Starling was an event of great historical significance inasmuch as secretin was the first chemical substance known to be secreted into the blood and act as a stimulus to an organ at a distance from the site of its formation. Recognizing this fact, Bayliss and Starling coined the word *hormone* to characterize this and similar substances. Before the discovery of secretin it was known that acid in the intestine induced secretion of pancreatic juice in animals in which all the nerves to the pancreas and to the intestine had been severed. While workers in Pavlov's laboratory in St. Petersburg were busily searching for the unknown nervous pathways which, they supposed, conveyed impulses to the pancreas after all the known fibers had been cut, Bayliss and Starling in England did the simple experiment of making an acid extract of the mucous membrane of the intestine and injecting it into an animal. This caused the pancreas of the injected animal to secrete. The excitement in Starling's laboratory can well be imagined. A "chemical reflex" had been discovered, something hitherto unknown in physiology. They called the new substance *secretin*. The response in Pavlov's laboratory was less enthusiastic; the idea that something other than the nervous system could regulate body function was not in keeping with Pavlov's philosophy, nevertheless he ultimately accepted the fact with good grace.

Although it is probably true that the pancreatic response to Bayliss and Starling's extract was as much due to impurities as to the secretin that it contained, subsequent research has shown that such extracts do contain an active principle which, when highly purified, has a powerful secretory effect on the pancreas. The purest secretin available stimulates only the pancreas and liver; in both organs it causes a dilute, watery secretion and has little or no influence on the secretion of organic solids. Secretin is probably a polypeptide with a molecular weight of about 5,000. It has been obtained in a highly purified state by Hammarsten and his coworkers (1923, 1933) and by many others subsequently. Jorpes and Mutt (1956), of the Karolinska Institute in Stockholm have made a preparation of which 0.1 mg contains 70 "clinical units"[1] or an amount that will cause the human pancreas to secrete at a rapid rate for an hour or more. Since one clinical unit is equal to sixteen cat units, less than 0.0001 mg. of the preparation should cause detectable secretion in a cat. Greengard, Stein and Ivy have shown that secretin is destroyed by an enzyme found in the blood and urine, which they called *secretinase*.

[1] A clinical unit of secretin is equal to 1 dog unit (Ivy *et al.*, 1930) or 16 cat units (Wilander and Agren, 1932). A dog unit is the amount that will increase the rate of secretion in a 10- to 12-kg. dog by 10 drops in 10 minutes. A cat unit is the least amount that will cause detectable secretion in a cat.

The crude extract prepared by Bayliss and Starling caused the pancreas to secrete enzymes as well as water and bicarbonates. Since purified secretin seemed to stimulate only the output of water and bicarbonate a search was made by Harper and Raper (1943) for the material in the extracts which stimulated secretion of enzymes. They succeeded in separating a fraction which did not increase the volume of pancreatic juice but did greatly increase the enzyme concentration. This substance they called *pancreozymin*. Their observations were quickly confirmed by Greengard and others (1944).

It has long been known that hydrochloric acid in the intestine liberates secretin into the blood thus causing the pancreas to secrete. It was not known whether other pancreatic stimuli liberated secretin or pancreozymin or depended on some other mechanism for their effect. In 1951, Wang and Grossman succeeded in preparing a functioning, nerve-free transplant of the canine pancreas. They imbedded a portion of the pancreas in the tissue of the mammary gland leaving its nerve and blood supply intact for the time being. After it had established a new blood supply in its new location the original nerves and blood vessels were cut, leaving a piece of pancreas whose activity could be influenced only through chemical substances reaching it by way of the blood stream. It was found that the flow of pancreatic juice from this transplant was increased by all the common pancreatic stimuli including distilled water, hydrochloric acid, soaps, and peptones. The enzyme concentration was also increased by these same stimuli, thus proving that both secretin and pancreozymin are released by all the ordinary stimuli used to excite pancreatic secretion.

## The Secretory Nerves of the Pancreas

The pancreas receives an abundant nerve supply from both the vagi and splanchnic nerves. According to Richins (1945) who made his studies on cats by strictly morphological methods, the entire extrinsic nerve supply to the pancreas passes through the celiac plexus and reaches the gland by way of the nerve plexus surrounding the arteries, chiefly the superior pancreaticoduodenal artery. The vagus fibers end in the intrinsic ganglia of the pancreas, and from these the parasympathetic path is continued through postganglionic unmyelinated fibers to the acinous cells, islet cells and the smooth muscles of the ducts. The efferent splanchnic fibers destined to supply the pancreas, according to this author, all end in the celiac and associated ganglia and from there the sympathetic path is continued through unmyelinated, postganglionic fibers which are distributed solely to the pancreatic blood vessels. However, the presence of cholinergic secretory fibers in the splanchnic nerves of the cat, which do not synapse in the celiac ganglia, is indicated by the physiological studies of Babkin and others (1939). Myelinated visceral afferent fibers from the pancreas are also present in the splanchnic nerves.

Guillaumie (1934), who used physiological methods on dogs reached conclusions quite different from Richins regarding the course of the vagus fibers. Confirming, with few exceptions, the early observations of Popielski (1896), she concluded that a majority (80 per cent) of the vagus fibers to the pancreas course along the lesser curvature of the stomach, cross the pylorus, and after proceeding a certain distance in the duodenal wall, enter the pancreas by way of the nerve plexus which surrounds the major pancreatic duct. Incidentally, according to her findings, any method of collecting pancreatic juice in which the ducts are severed or separated from the intestine involves a partial denervation of the pancreas. The remaining 20 per cent of the vagus fibers, according to this author, traverse the hepatic plexus and join the pancreas in the region of the pylorus.

It is often incorrectly stated that the pancreas receives the greater part or all of its vagus nerve supply from the right vagus. This error arises from the tendency to overlook the fact that after the vagi merge in the esophageal plexus the right and left nerves can no longer be distinguished. Two or more trunks emerge from the esophageal plexus and the trunk that occupies the more posterior position at the level of the diaphragm, although referred to by some anatomists as the right vagus, contains fibers from both the right and left vagi as they occur in the neck. When stimulated in the neck, the right and left vagi are equally effective in modifying pancreatic function.

The intrinsic ganglia of the pancreas undoubtedly develop in association with the enteric nerve plexuses. It would be interesting to know whether they retain connections with this plexus and whether such connections have anything to do with the effects of intestinal stimuli on pancreatic secretion. In this relation it is interesting that, in addition to the rich plexus of nerve fibers surrounding the pancreatic ducts, there are many nerve fibers in the loose areolar tissue between the pancreas and duodenum.

The first clear demonstration of secretory nerves to the pancreas we owe to Pavlov (1910), who devised a unique method for demonstrating the function of the vagus nerves in unanesthetized animals. He exposed one vagus nerve under anesthesia in a dog with a pancreatic fistula and, after cutting it, brought the peripheral portion into the wound directly under the skin. The wound was closed with sutures and the animal allowed to recover. When the nerve was again exposed 4 to 8 days later, this time without anesthesia, stimulation of the peripheral portion caused an abundant secretion of pancreatic juice. Since stimulation of the freshly cut nerve or of the intact nerve with the animal under anesthesia usually failed to cause secretion, Pavlov concluded that the vagus nerve to the pancreas contained not only secretory but inhibitory fibers (which degenerate earlier than the secretory fibers). It has since been shown that the fibers believed to be inhibitory are those that cause contraction of the large ducts, thus preventing the flow of juice even though secretion occurs. Secretory fibers were demonstrated in the splanchnic nerves in Pavlov's laboratory using a similar method; this observation was subsequently confirmed by Babkin and his associates (1939).

The precise function of the secretory nerve fibers is still unknown. Experiments in which the vagus nerves have been cut have failed to give consistent results in either animal or human subjects; it is therefore not known at the present time whether the denervated pancreas responds to stimuli in the same way as the pancreas with a normal nerve supply. Since the amount of pancreatic juice secreted by the fasting animal, when the individual food products are placed in the intestine, is less than one would expect, compared to the volume of pancreatic juice secreted after a normal meal, one is led to suspect that in the fasting state the pancreas does not respond to stimuli to the same extent as the same gland does during digestion. It may be that a combination of stimuli is more effective than the response to individual stimuli would indicate when they are used separately, or it may be that some influence associated with the taking of food operates to increase the irritability of the pancreas to intestinal stimuli. That such may be the case is indicated by experiments of Gayet and Guillaumie and of Crider and Thomas (see Thomas, 1950, p. 109) in which it was shown that the action of the secretory nerves and the action of secretin on the pancreas are synergistic, each augmenting the effect of the other. If these observations should be confirmed by further study they would indicate at least one function of the secretory nerves. The only positively known function is the production of the initial reflex or cephalic phase of pancreatic secretion.

The fact that stimulation of the secretory nerves increases the output of enzymes, as do also various parasympathomimetic drugs such as urocholine, pilocarpine and physostigmine, suggests that they play a part along with pancreozymin in regulating the enzyme output of the pancreas. The parasympatholytic drugs such as atropine and the newer synthetics cause a much more profound depression of pancreatic secretion, including secretion of enzymes, than does section of the secretory nerves. This fact suggests that there are local cholinergic mechanisms involved in the process of stimulation of the pancreas that are not destroyed when the vagi are cut. The location, nature and function of such mechanisms, if they exist, are entirely unknown. The enteric plexuses and the intrinsic ganglia of the pancreas and their connections are possible mechanisms.

### *Adaptation of Pancreatic Enzyme Secretion to Diet*

The fact has already been mentioned that the total enzyme concentration of pancreatic juice is determined to a great extent by the type of stimulus used to provoke secretion. This mode of adaptation is an established fact, and its mechanism is well understood (see above under *secretin and pancreozymin*). Another type of adaptation, which involves changes in enzyme composition, is more controversial. Pavlov, as a result of certain errors in enzyme determinations in his laboratory, came to the conclusion that the relative concentration of the different enzyme of pancreatic juice was adapted to the nature of the food undergoing digestion; for example, according to his concept, a meal consisting largely of carbohydrate would call forth secretion of pancreatic juice containing a large amount of amylase, whereas a fat meal would call forth secretion of lipase, etc. Babkin, using more precise methods in the same laboratory, found that this was not true, but that the enzymes tended to be secreted in parallel concentration regardless of the nature of the immediate stimulus to secretion. This concept has been challenged recently, especially by Guth, Komarov and their coworkers (1958) who find that there may be considerable variation in the relative concentration of the different enzymes in different samples of pancreatic juice, even when taken on the same day from the same animal. Although the differences they found are statistically significant the fact remains that a large increase in enzyme concentration involves all the enzymes of the juice, although not necessarily all equally.

Efforts to determine whether the composition of the juice can be altered by a prolonged change in the diet have given confusing results. It has been established that a diet low in protein gives rise to considerable alteration in the enzyme composition of the juice (Grossman *et al.*, 1943), as does deficiency or *excess* of certain amino acids (Magee *et al.*, 1956, 1957, 1958); however, it is not clear that this represents an adaptation in any accepted sense of the word; rather it suggests that the pancreatic cells, which have the task of synthesizing the relatively enormous amounts of protein secreted in the pancreatic juice, are hampered in their work if they are not supplied with adequate and appropriate building material (Hokin, 1952). The pancreatic cells cannot make bricks without straw any more than could the Israelites of old.

### *The Mechanism of Pancreatic Secretion*

At this point the student should read again the introductory paragraphs of chapter 36.

As in the case of other digestive glands secretion of enzymes by the pancreas involves two distinct processes: (1) synthesis within the cell of the enzymes or their precursors and (2) discharge of enzymes from the secretory cells into the ducts. Synthesis is a continuous process formerly believed to be controlled only by the laws that govern chemical equilibriums in general. However, the recent work of Magee and his associates (1955, 1956, 1957, 1958) indicates that the nature of the dietary protein, and in particular its amino acid composition, has a profound effect on the total concentration of enzymes in the pancreas and on the relative concentration of different enzymes. For example, Magee and Anderson (1955) found that in animals fed a high protein diet (casein) the trypsin and lipase content of the resting pancreas was greater than in animals fed a low protein diet. Also daily administration of urocholine (a parasympathomimetic drug) or of DL-valine had an effect similar to casein. Since DL-valine is a powerful stimulant for release of pancreozymin and the parasympathomimetic drugs stimulate enzyme *secretion* these authors conclude that the stimuli for enzyme *secretion* (casein, urocholine, DL-valine) also stimulate enzyme synthesis. A similar interpretation could be given the earlier work of Grossman, Greengard and Ivy (1943) who reported changes in enzyme content of the pancreas with changes in diet.

Interesting light has been shed on the synthesis of enzymes, by the recent studies of L. E. Hokin (1951, 1952) and Mabel Hokin (1956) on pigeon and mouse pancreas *in vitro*. It was found that pigeon pancreas slices would synthesize amylase *in vitro* in glucose solutions, in serum, in amino acid solutions and in saline. Synthesis was most rapid in solutions of amino acids and least rapid in normal saline; it proceeded at an intermediate rate in serum. One can see here the effect of an increased concentration of reacting substances (amino acids) on synthesis of protein by the cells of the pancreas. Although pancreozymin and parasympathomimetic drugs caused discharge of amylase from the cells into the surrounding medium (secretion), the rate of synthesis of the enzymes was not materially affected. This is not in accord with the conclusions of Magee and his associates but does not invalidate their conclusions since the experimental conditions were different, particularly with regard to the time during which the stimulus could act. It was found that certain amino acids were essential for synthesis whereas others could be supplied from sources in the medium. The amino acids essential for maximum synthesis were tryptophane, arginine, threonine, valine, tyrosine, lysine, lucine, histidine, isoleucine, and phenylalanine. Similar results were obtained on mouse pancreas, except that there was no acceleration of synthesis on addition of amino acids if the animal had been fed before being killed for removal of the pancreas. However, if the animal had been starved for 24 hours, addition of amino acids to the medium increased the rate of synthesis by 25 per cent.

The synthesized material appears within the acinous cells as zymogen granules which accumulate in the resting gland until they come to occupy most of the available space within the cells (Heidenhain, 1883; Hirsch, 1939, 1957; Sluiter, 1944). Under the influence of appropriate stimuli the zymogen granules diminish in number and in size; at the same time enzymes appear in the secretion. The exact mechanism is not known but at some point the granules dissolve in the intracellular fluid and are discharged through the cell wall into the ducts. Stimuli such as HCl and secretin which produce a watery secretion with a low enzyme content have little effect on the granules whereas stimuli which call forth secretion rich in enzymes deplete the granules and, if they act over a long period of time, may leave the cells almost free of zymogen granules. According to the observations of Hokin and Hokin (1956) on pancreatic and salivary gland slices *in vitro*, effective stimuli for secretion of enzymes cause a remarkable increase in the rate of turnover of phosphorus and its incorporation into the ether soluble phospholipids. In the pancreas, secretin has no such effect although it does increase the uptake of oxygen by about 10 per cent. They conclude that "all active transport of proteins out of the cell involves the breakdown and resynthesis of the glycero-phosphate bonds in phospholipids." Since the cell membrane is believed to contain a higher concentration of phospholipids than other elements in the cell, one is tempted to speculate on whether or not this observation signifies that the transport of protein out of the cell involves the alternate breakdown and reconstitution of the cell membrane.

It has long been assumed that the inorganic constitutents of the juice are secreted by the same cells that produce the enzymes, namely the acinous cells. However, the fact that fluid secretion and enzyme secretion are separately regulated raises a theoretical objection to this view. All current theories of stimulation require that cells shall respond to a stimulus with a characteristic type of functional activity regardless of the nature of the stimulus. In the other digestive glands, about which we have more information, each component of the secretion that is independently regulated is formed by a different type of cell. We must also take account of the clinical observation that in certain types of pancreatic disease enzyme secretion may be depressed or absent whereas secretion of fluid and bicarbonate remains normal (Lagerlöf, 1939; Friedman and Snape, 1950). On the other hand, in glands injured by alloxan, fluid secretion may be subnormal whereas enzymes are secreted normally. This latter observation, reported by Grossman and Ivy (1946), contains a hint as to a possible solution of the problem. Histological examination of the glands which failed to respond normally to secretin showed no injury to the acinous cells but the cells of the intralobular ducts appeared abnormal; in particular they exhibited vacuolization. The intralobular duct cells are continuous with the centroacinar cells that line the alveoli and are identical with these cells in their cytological structure. It is possible that cells of this type secrete water and bicarbonate whereas the acinous cells secrete only enzymes.

*Tissue Damage by Pancreatic Enzymes*

Under certain conditions pancreatic enzymes may escape into the tissues surrounding the acini, or into the blood. In explanation of this we may assume that the enzymes, as they are being synthesized, appear first in solution in the cell protoplasm before being precipitated as zymogen granules. Some sort of equilibrium must exist between enzymes in solution and enzymes in the form of the more or less solid granules. We can only speculate on the concentration of dissolved enzymes that may be present at any time, but there is strong indirect evidence that the concentration is considerably increased by such stimuli as cause discharge of enzymes into the ducts. Simple diffusion of dissolved enzymes through the cell membrane of the acinous cells will explain the presence of enzymes in the minute quantities found in the blood in the normal fasting state. The rate of diffusion will vary with (1) the concentration gradient between the cells and the blood, (2) the hydrostatic pressure gradient between the interior and exterior of the cell and (3) the permeability of the cell membrane. The increases in enzyme concentration in the blood which are seen during active secretion in response to food, pancreozymin or parasympathomimetic drugs (Cherry and Crandall, 1932; Zucker *et al.*, 1932) are probably reflections of the increased concentration of enzymes within the cells. If such secretion is accompanied by closure of the ducts, as for example, by inflammatory edema or spasm due to morphine, the increase in hydrostatic pressure within the acini will accelerate the diffusion. Cell damage, from whatever cause, can further augment the diffusion by increasing the permeability of the cell membrane.

As a practical matter we see increases in concentration of pancreatic enzymes in the blood during digestion, after administration of certain drugs, notably morphine (Lagerlöf, 1945; Ryan *et al.*, 1949), in acute pancreatitis, in carcinoma of the pancreas, and in many other conditions associated with injury to the cells or obstruction of the ducts, provided only that the damage is not so severe as to destroy the ability of the cells to synthesize enzymes. In order for tissue digestion to occur it is necessary that the inactive proenzymes be activated. The mechanism of activation of extracellular pancreatic enzymes is obscure; probably tissue kinases that may be released from injured cells play a part in activating the proteolytic enzymes. It is commonly believed that reflux of bile (Bernard, 1856; Opie,

1910) into the pancreatic ducts may cause sufficient tissue damage to activate the proteolytic enzymes, whereas the bile itself serves to activate the lipase. In acute pancreatitis from whatever cause there is always the danger of extensive tissue destruction and fat necrosis brought about by activated pancreatic enzymes.

THE SECRETIN TEST FOR PANCREATIC FUNCTION. Since secretin in injectable form has become available for clinical use a test of pancreatic function using this material as a stimulus to promote secretion has been developed. The test was introduced by Ågren, Lagerlöf and Berglund (1936) and has since been used in North America by a number of investigators. To perform the test, a double lumen tube is passed through the patient's nose or mouth into the stomach and duodenum, one lumen opening into the stomach for draining gastric juice and the other into the duodenum for collecting the pancreatic and other duodenal secretions. It is necessary to drain the stomach in order to avoid false results caused by contamination of the pancreatic juice with gastric secretions. The gastric and duodenal contents are collected for a period of time to serve as a control and then a dose of 1 clinical unit of secretin per kg of body weight is injected slowly into a vein. Usually the patients are tested for hypersensitivity to the secretin preparation before it is injected. The duodenal contents are then collected in separate 10- or 20-minute samples for a period of time, usually 80 minutes. Volume, bicarbonate and enzyme determinations are made on the material collected from the duodenum. Enzyme determinations have not yielded much diagnostic information and the tendency at the present time is to omit them. The test gives useful information in pancreatic diseases associated with diminished secretion such as advanced chronic pancreatitis and cancer of the pancreas.

The secretin test also yields useful information regarding the functional state of the gall bladder. It will be recalled that although secretin increases the output of bile from the liver it does not cause the gall bladder to empty; consequently the bile secreted during a test is normally stored in the gall bladder and does not appear in large amounts in the duodenal contents. If the gall bladder has been removed, or it is so diseased as to be nonfunctional the secreted bile is poured into the duodenum and appears in all the samples collected. Three types of response are recognized: (1) no bile in any sample; this indicates obstruction in the biliary system, or if jaundice is absent, it may be considered normal; (2) some, but not all, samples are free of bile or contain only traces, the normal response; (3) all samples heavily colored with bile, indicates a nonfunctioning gall bladder.

## Secretion of Bile by the Liver

The liver forms a secretion which is also an excretion consisting of water, bile salts, bile pigments, inorganic salts and a mixture of lipid materials including fats, cholesterol and lecithin; see table 40.3. The formation of bile is accomplished by two types of cells, the *reticuloendothelial cells*, which help to line the liver sinusoids, and the *liver cells proper*. The sinusoids convey blood from the portal vein and hepatic artery to the hepatic vein. The reticuloendothelial cells, known in the liver as Kupffer cells, are not confined to the liver but occur also in the spleen and bone marrow where they likewise help to line vascular channels. Another name for the Kupffer cells is stellate cells, so called because the cells are frequently star-shaped when seen in the endothelial lining of the liver sinusoid. Similar cells occur free in the connective tissues, and elsewhere in the body and together comprise what is known as the reticuloendothelial system. In general these cells have a phagocytic function; their role in the production of bile will be considered later.

The other cells concerned in the secretion of bile, hepatic cells proper, make up the liver lobule and surround the biliary canaliculi. The liver cell has an unusually intimate relation to the blood and to the secretion that it forms. The lining of the liver sinusoids is said to be deficient in places allowing the blood to come into direct contact with the liver cells. On the other hand branching, intracellular canaliculi containing bile have been described as occurring in actively secreting cells. The liver cell thus forms a narrow wall between the blood stream on the one hand and the bile stream on the other and it is not surprising that bile sometimes escapes from, or through, the liver cells into the blood.

The steady flow of bile from the liver serves as an avenue for the secretion of certain substances important in digestion, and for the excretion of others. The most important secretory products of the liver are the bile acids which

appear in the bile as salts of sodium or potassium. There are a variety of bile acids to be found in the bile of different species of animals, all of which are formed by conjugation of an amino acid with cholic acid. The structural formula of cholic acid contains the tetracyclic carbon group characteristic of the sterols; this is shown below in skeleton form:

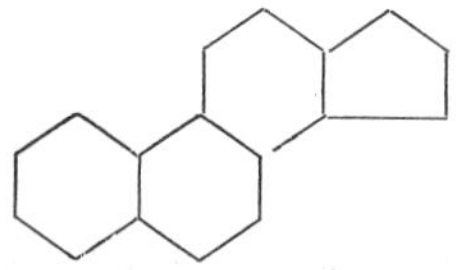

Cholic acid is therefore related to cholesterol, to the male and female sex hormones (ch. 60) and to corticosterone and other adrenal steroid fractions (ch. 58). It is highly probable that cholesterol is a precursor of cholic acid in normal metabolism. Block and his associates have demonstrated the production of cholic acid from cholesterol. The latter containing deuterium was fed to dogs; cholic acid containing the isotope was isolated from the urine.

### The Composition of the Bile

Table 39.3 gives the composition of human liver bile (parts in 1000), modified from Hammarsten. Liver bile has a pH of between 8.0 and 8.6. The reaction of human gall-bladder bile is neutral or slightly alkaline; that of the dog (or cat) is definitely acid—pH between 5.0 and 6.0. The chief biliary components are the *bile salts, bile pigments, cholesterol* and *lecithin*. These organic materials make up over 60 per cent of the total biliary solids. As a result of the absorption of water and inorganic salts gallbladder bile is several times more concentrated in organic solids than liver bile. The biliary constituents may vary independently of one another. The acids of human bile are glycocholic and taurocholic acids in which the cholic acid is conjugated with glycocoll, or with taurine. Taurine is related to cystine, a sulfur containing amino acid; glycine we are familar with as the simplest amino acid and one which can be synthesized by the body. The bile acids therefore all contain nitrogen and taurine contains sulfur in addition. The bile acids are presumed to be synthesized in the liver cells, but positive proof of their origin is not available.

Little can be said concerning the *site of origin* of the cholic acid; whether it is formed by the hepatic epithelium, or is merely brought preformed to the liver from other body tissues is not

### TABLE 39.3

| | |
|---|---|
| Water | 976.22 |
| Solids | 23.78 |
| Mucin and pigments | 5.00 |
| Bile salts | 9.00 |
| Fatty acids from soaps | 1.23 |
| Cholesterol | 0.63 |
| Lecithin ⎫ Fat ⎬ | 0.60 |
| Inorganic salts | 7.32 |

known. That some is formed in the body is indicated by the fact that the bile salts continue to be discharged from a biliary fistula during long periods of starvation. That it is derived also from the food appears from the observation that increased excretion follows the ingestion of protein material. Though the supplies of glycocoll and taurine within the body are apparently plentiful the supply of cholic acid is limited, for experiments in which taurine was fed alone caused no increase in the excretion of bile salts whereas cholic acid ingestion alone caused a rise in the excretion of taurocholic acid. It is possible to deplete the taurine stores by feeding cholic acid for several days to a dog with a biliary fistula. When cystine disulphoxide, cysteine, cysteinesulfinic acid or cysteic acid is then fed with cholic acid, an increase in the taurocholic acid of the bile follows (Virtue and Doster-Virtue). This result suggests that from such or similar compounds, taurine is produced in the body. That is, taurine under these circumstances is evidently supplied from body sources whereas cholic acid must be furnished in the diet. The quantity of cholic acid available apparently determines the level of bile acid production (Whipple).

So far as is known the liver is the only situation where the *conjugation* of taurine or of glycocoll with cholic acid, and the production of the respective bile acid can take place. The following observations suggest that their formation is a specific function of the liver. (1) When the function of the liver is depressed by injury, or by the establishment of an Eck fistula, the output of bile salts may be reduced by 50 per cent or more (Smyth and Whipple, 1924). (2) Bile acids appear in the blood of dogs when the common bile duct is ligated. On the other hand, no accumulation occurs in the blood after removal of the liver.

### The Circulation of the Bile Salts

After their passage into the intestine, the bile salts undergo reabsorption and are carried in the portal blood stream back to the liver for re-excretion. This portal-biliary circulation of the bile salts is intimately connected with the absorption of fat (p. 646). When bile salts are fed to an animal they can be recovered almost quantitatively from a biliary fistula. This indicates that in the intact animal the reabsorption of bile salts is almost complete (about 90 per cent). Under ordinary circumstances comparatively small amounts (about 10 per cent) of bile salts are formed afresh, i.e., their concentration in the bile is maintained largely as a result of their being circulated over and over again through the portal and biliary systems. Nevertheless, if the bile is prevented from entering the intestine by

draining it to the exterior through the fistula, its concentration in bile salts does not become materially reduced. Experiments by Berman and associates (1941) indicate that a homeostatic mechanism regulates synthesis of bile acids in such a way that the amount synthesized balances the amount lost. Thus, if an animal is fed an excess of bile acids, synthesis is depressed until the excess amount has been eliminated. On the other hand, if bile acids are drained away by removing bile from the body, synthesis of bile acids is increased.

*Test for bile salts. Pettenkoffer's test.* Five cubic centimeters of the fluid to be tested are mixed in a test tube with a few drops of a 10 per cent solution of cane sugar. One or two cubic centimeters of concentrated sulfuric acid are introduced beneath the surface of the mixture. The appearance of a red ring at the junction of the two liquids indicates the presence of bile salts; upon agitation the color diffuses through the solution. The color is due to the formation of cholalic acid from the bile acids and its combination with the furfural resulting from the decomposition of the cane sugar. A few drops of a 1 in 1000 aqueous solution of furfural itself may be employed (Mylin's modification) instead of the sugar solution.

Rowntree and associates have developed a method for the quantitative estimation of bile salts in blood based upon the Pettenkoffer reaction. The bile salts are extracted from the blood with alcohol and the test performed upon the extract. The color is compared in a colorimeter with that produced under similar conditions in a standard solution of pure glycocholic acid. The results are expressed in terms of glycocholic acid. Normal human blood contains from 2.5 to 6 mg. per cent of bile acids. In obstructive jaundice the value is increased, sometimes several fold.

Hay's test is based upon the property of the bile acids to lower surface tension (p. 646).

### The Bile Pigments

The biliary pigments are *bilirubin* and *biliverdin*. Bilirubin ($C_{33}H_{36}N_4O_6$) is the chief pigment in human bile and in the bile of the carnivora. Biliverdin ($C_{33}H_{36}N_4O_8$) is an oxidative derivative of bilirubin and is present only in small amounts in human bile but is the chief pigment of birds' bile. The pigments constitute from 15 to 20 per cent of the total solids in liver bile.

The readiness with which the bile pigments are oxidized and the color changes which they undergo in the process are the basis for Gmelin's test for bile in body fluids. If, for example, a fluid containing bile is passed through filter paper, and a drop of fuming nitric acid be then dropped upon the wet surface of the filter, the pigment is oxidized and a series of concentric rings of different colors appears—yellow, yellowish-red, violet and blue-green from within outwards. Besides biliverdin other derivatives of bilirubin are found in the body. *Urobilinogen* (cf. below and ch. 6) is a reduction product of bilirubin; upon oxidation it yields *urobilin*. *Bilicyanin* and *bilifuscin* are formed by the oxidation of biliverdin. The latter two pigments are not found in bile but may be present in gallstones.

*Origin of the bile pigments.* Bile pigments are derived from the free hemoglobin which results from the destruction of red cells in the body and, in smaller amounts, from other chromoproteins. The red cells have a life span of about 100 to 120 days. Those that perish are disposed of by the

The bilirubin is believed to be taken out of the blood and transferred into the bile through the activity of the liver cells. In the process the pigment is separated from the plasma globulin and, in the liver cells, is conjugated with glycuronic acid forming bilirubin glycuronide (Schmidt, 1956; Billing *et al.*, 1957). Since bilirubin is capable of combining with two molecules of glycuronic acid either the mono- or diglycuronide may be formed. The conjugation may take place also in the kidney but apparently does so only to a slight extent. The iron is stored in the liver, spleen and other tissues and with the globin is eventually utilized for synthesis of new hemoglobin. The chemical relationship between bilirubinglobin and the various bile pigment derivatives is shown schematically below.

Bilirubinglobin

reticuloendothelial cells distributed throughout the body. From these cells an average of about 8 grams of hemoglobin is released per day which yields about 280 mg of bile pigments. In order to produce bile pigment from hemoglobin the hemin portion must be separated from the protein (globin) portion of the hemoglobin molecule. There is then oxidative scission of the iron-porphyrin. This involves opening of the tetra-pyrrol ring at the $\alpha$ position and the "shelling out" of iron. The resulting iron-free pigment is probably biliverdin which is later reduced to bilirubin by the addition of one hydrogen atom. All these reactions are presumed to take place in the reticuloendothelial cells, but the order in which they occur is not known (Drabkin, 1951). In particular it is not known if the splitting of the hemin moiety on the protein portion of the molecule must take place before the porphyrin ring is open. In any case the bilirubin is not carried in the blood as such but as a bilirubin protein complex. The bilirubin probably combines with $\alpha_1$-globulin of the blood.

It is evident from the distribution of the reticuloendothelial system that bile pigments may be formed, not only in the liver, but also in the spleen and bone marrow and at various other places in the body. This was not generally recognized until the experiments of Whipple and Hooper (1913) and the more conclusive experiments of Mann and his associates (1924, 1925, 1926). The former attempted to isolate the liver from the general circulation whereas the latter removed the liver completely. In either case bile pigments continued to be formed and, since they could not be excreted through the liver, they accumulated in the blood and produced a condition analagous to jaundice. Mann and his associates also showed, by a spectroscopic method, that the blood of the splenic vein of a normal animal has a higher bilirubin concentration than that in the corresponding artery.

UROBILINOGEN, UROBILIN; THE CIRCULATION OF BILE PIGMENT. The bilirubin that enters the intestine undergoes reduction by bacteria to form *urobilinogen* (also called *stercobilinogen*). A part of this is excreted in the stools and, by exposure to air, is oxidized to *urobilin (stercobilin)*. The latter can be detected spectroscopically or by the green fluorescence which it gives with a solution of alcoholic zinc acetate. A certain proportion of the urobilinogen is reabsorbed into the portal circulation and passes to the liver where is is reconverted in part to bilirubin in the bile (fig. 39.1). It is then almost entirely re-excreted both as bilirubin and as urobilinogen. Any urobilinogen which may escape into the general circulation and be excreted by the kidney becomes oxidized to *urobilin* after the urine has been voided. Normally, however, no urobilin or mere traces (0.5 to 2 mg.) appears in the urine. Only traces are present in normal blood. Bilirubin itself does not appear normally in the urine, so the color of urine is due to neither of these pigments. That the urobilinogen normally present in bile merely represents reexcretion of this pigment after its absorption from the intestine was clearly shown by Elman and McMaster. When the entire output of bile was collected through a fistula (i.e., none was allowed to enter the intestine) there was complete disappearance of urobilinogen from the bile after the pigment already present in the intestine had been carried away in the feces. The fistula bile remained free from urobilinogen unless infection of the biliary tracts had occurred, under which circumstance bacterial action in these situations caused its formation. When a part of the bile was allowed to enter the intestine or bile was fed by mouth the derived pigment invariably appeared in the fistula bile.

Also, complete experimental obstruction of the common bile duct, since it prevented the reexcretion of the urobilinogen absorbed from the intestine, resulted in its accumulation in the blood and its excretion in the urine. These effects, however, can only occur for a short time after the duct has been obstructed, and are due to the absorption of pigment remaining in the intestine from the period prior to obstruction. After the pigment has been cleared from the intestine, the urine, although it may contain large amounts of bilirubin, is quite free from the derived pigment. Depression of the excretory function of the liver by such hepatic poisons as chloroform, carbon tetrachloride, phosphorus, etc., caused urobilinogen to appear in the urine; hepatic damage from other causes, e.g., infectious hepatitis is also associated with the urinary excretion of urobilinogen even though the injury is slight and there is no bilirubinuria. When bilirubin formation is increased by hemolytic agents urobilinogen

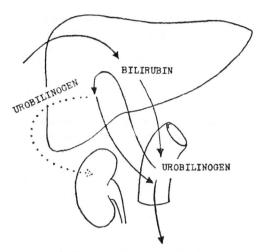

FIG. 39.1. Diagram illustrating the formation of urobilinogen from bilirubin in the intestine, its excretion in part in the feces and its absorption in part into the portal blood. Normally, the absorbed pigment except in negligible amounts is practically all re-excreted in the bile. The dotted lines indicate its passage into the blood, and its excretion by the kidney in cases of liver damage, excessive blood destruction or in the early stages of obstructive jaundice.

production is also increased; the liver even though its function is normal is unable to reexcrete the excess pigment absorbed from the intestine, and urobilin appears in the urine.

Urobilinogen is in rare instances formed in situations other than the intestinal tract and independently of bacterial action. Rabinowitch (1930), for example, has reported a case in which large quantities of urobilinogen were present in the urine. A sterile ovarian cyst containing an old blood clot and a high percentage of urobilinogen was revealed by operation. When the cyst was removed the urobilinogen disappeared from the urine.

*Lecithin and Cholesterol*

*Lecithin* is present in human liver bile to the extent of from 0.02 to 0.05 per cent. The *cholesterol* content is normally from 0.04 to 0.16 per cent. The cholesterol is present in the free state, i.e., not in the form of esters. The percentages of these materials in the bile of the gall-bladder is, as a result of the absorption of water and salts through the gall-bladder mucosa, much higher than the percentages in liver bile. The ratio of the concentration of cholesterol in bile to that of the bile salts is from 1:20 to 1:30. The ability of the bile to hold cholesterol in solution is in large degree dependent upon the bile salts. If the ratio falls to 1:13 precipitation of cholesterol occurs. Andrews and associates showed that if bile be dialyzed against water, bile salts are removed and the bile becomes turbid as a result of cholesterol precipitation. The importance of this observation in relation to gallstone formation is considered on page 651. The fatty acid concentration of the bile is of as great if not greater importance than the bile salt concentration in holding cholesterol in solution. Little is known concerning the origin and function of the biliary cholesterol. It may be derived from the stroma of disintegrated red cells or from nervous tissue, which of course contains it in large amounts. According to Gardner the cholesterol of the bile does not vary with changes in the total blood cholesterol, nor is its concentration raised by increasing the cholesterol content of the diet; it continues to be excreted upon a cholesterol-free diet. A biliary-portal circulation of cholesterol has been shown to occur, i.e., excretion in the bile, reabsorption from the intestine and re-excretion by the liver.

## Regulation of the Secretion of Bile

Bile is secreted continuously. This is consistent with the fact that bile is an excretion as well as a secretion. On a normal feeding schedule more bile is secreted during the daylight hours than during the night. This is due to the fact that more bile is secreted after meals than in the fasting state and meals are normally eaten in the daytime. If an animal is fed at regular intervals throughout the 24 hours as much bile is secreted at night as in the daytime. The stimulating effect of food on the volume output of bile is mainly due to its protein content. Kocour and Ivy (1937) studied a variety of foods for their effect on the output of bile and found that only meat and liver were consistently effective. Fat had some tendency to increase the output but was unreliable. Glucose given orally tended to decrease the output of bile provided the bile secreted was not returned to the intestine. When the secreted bile was returned to the intestine the glucose had no consistent effect on the output.

Before proceeding to discuss in detail the various agents that influence the flow of bile it is well to define some of the terms that will be used. A more extensive list of terms with definitions is given by Ivy (1944). A *cholagogue*, is any agent which increases the flow of bile into the intestine. The bile may come from the gall bladder so the word does not necessarily signify an increase in the secretion of bile by the liver. A *choleretic* is an agent which increases the output of bile from the liver without necessarily changing its concentration; thus a choleretic will usually increase the outputs of bile solids as well as the liquid portion of the bile. A *hydrocholeretic* causes an increase in the volume of bile without a corresponding increase in the output of bile solids.

The natural bile salts have a powerful choleretic action on the liver and no doubt a great part of the increase in the flow of bile after a meal is the result of the discharge of bile from the gall bladder which increases the amount of bile acids in the intestine and consequently in the portal blood. Certain oxidized bile acids, notably dehydrocholic acid, act as hydrocholeretics and are sometimes used in therapy to produce an abundant flow of dilute bile. The hydrochloric acid of the gastric juice when present in the intestine increases the volume flow of bile; this is probably a result of the release of secretin, or possibly a more specific hormone from the intestinal mucous membrane by the action of the acid.

Although the intravenous injection of various secretin preparations is followed by an increase in bile flow, there is some doubt as to whether the action is really due to secretin. Friedman and Snape (1945) found that the effect of an intestinal extract on the secretion of bile by the liver was not always proportional to its secretin content as judged by its effect on the pancreas. Some secretin preparations were effective choleretics but had little effect on the pancreas. Their experiments suggest that there may be a specific liver hormone (*hepatocrinin*) in intestinal extracts. Since foods also caused release of secretin from the intestine it may be that some part of the action of food, aside from the action of hydrochloric acid, may also be attributed to secretin or hepatocrinin as the case may be. At any rate the purest secretin available increases the secretion of bile by the liver although it does not contract the gall bladder. Studies by Grossman and his coworkers (1949) indicate that in the human, secretin acts as a hydrocholeretic.

Secretin causes only a moderate increase in bile flow and none at all if the liver is already secreting vigorously. The maximal rate of flow that can be induced by secretin is only about one-tenth the rate that can be attained by the administration of bile acids and this ratio cannot be increased by increasing the dose of secretin. The increase in the amount of bile formed is usually less than the increase in the amount of pancreatic juice secreted in response to a given dose of highly purified secretin and the latent period of the liver is longer than that of the pancreas (Friedman, 1950). These facts suggest that secretin is not a major factor in the regulation of bile secretion. On the other hand hepatocrinin, if it exists as a separate hormone, may be a major factor.

In addition to humoral and hormonal factors affecting the secretion of bile, the nervous system may take part in the regulation of bile flow. The secretion of bile is increased by stimulation of the vagus nerves, but the principal effect of the autonomic innervation on bile secretion appears to be inhibitory. Denervating the liver, insofar as this is possible, causes an increase in bile flow; distention of the colon or stimulation of any one of a number of visceral afferent nerves causes inhibition of the flow of bile from the liver. It is not known whether the inhibitory effect is due to direct inhibition of the liver cells or to alterations in hepatic blood flow.

### The Mechanism of Secretion of Bile by the Liver

In considering the mechanism of bile secretion it is convenient to divide the bile constituents into two classes (Brauer, 1958): Class A, which includes water, the inorganic salts, and other highly diffusable constituents and Class B, which includes the bile pigments, bile acids and certain foreign substances such as Bromsulphalein which may be used in liver function tests and appear in the bile. There is good evidence that water is secreted by the liver cells by an active process involving expenditure of energy. Pure mechanical filtration is ruled out by the fact that bile may be secreted under a pressure which is higher than the pressure of the blood in contact with the liver cells. As pointed out by Brauer, in order for a filtration process such as is utilized in the kidney to be effective it would be necessary that capillary pressure should exceed the maximum pressure of bile in the bile ducts by an amount at least equal to the colloid osmotic pressure of the blood; this condition is not attained in the liver. The flow of bile has been shown to be independent of blood flow or of blood pressure so long as the oxygen supply is adequate. Another bit of evidence is that cooling the liver greatly reduces the rate of flow of bile. For example, in the rat liver a 10°C. reduction in the perfusion temperature between 18° and 38°C. reduces bile flow by a factor of 4. Such a change in temperature should have little or no effect on a pure mechanical process. Ether anesthesia also reduces the flow of bile. The situation is not so clear with respect to the inorganic salts and it may be supposed that they are transferred along with the water. The evidence suggests that there is a free interchange of inorganic salts between the blood and the bile as the bile passes through the bile ducts; thus osmotic equilibrium is established between the blood and the bile.

It is interesting that if the concentration of salts in blood plasma is increased so as to make the blood hypertonic, vacuoles appear in the polygonal cells of the liver. This is taken as evidence that these cells are involved in secretion of water into the bile. That these hepatic cells secrete the water is further evidenced by the fact that in certain forms of toxic hepatitis in which only the polygonal cells are damaged, a sharp reduction in the volume of bile is one of the earliest signs (Brauer, 1958). Bile may be reabsorbed into the blood if the pressure of bile in the bile ducts is elevated above a certain critical level but at normal pressures reabsorption of bile is negligible.

That the organic constituents of the bile are actively secreted has never been questioned. They appear in such concentrations in the bile relative to their concentration in the blood that an active process is inevitable. The liver cells exhibit a certain maximum capacity for secreting various of the bile constituents comparable to the tubular maximum of the kidney tubules for certain of the constituents of the urine. For example, there is a maximum rate of secretion of Bromsulphalein into the bile beyond which an increase in the dose or in the rate of infusion into the blood no longer alters the secretion rate. Similar phenomena have been observed for sodium dehydrocholate, bilirubin, and certain dyes. That the same cells are involved in the secretion of different organic compounds is indicated by the fact that the secretion of some of these by the liver cells limits the rate of secretion of certain others; for example, if the liver is actively secreting Bromsulphalein its capacity to secrete bilirubin is limited, and if it is actively secreting bilirubin near its maximum capacity it is unable to secrete bile salts at their normal maximal rate. These facts indicate that there is competition within the individual liver cells among the various substances that are secreted into the bile.

It has been possible to observe in suitable preparations, the path taken by certain of the substances that are secreted into the bile. For example, fluorescein can be seen to appear first in the parenchymal cells of the liver, then to be secreted into the bile canaliculi and to be transported down the bile ducts. Similar observations are possible by different methods using radioactive isotopes. Thus it appears that all the constituents of the bile, both organic and inorganic are normally secreted by the liver cells and, with the possible exception of the inorganic salts, by a process which involves the expenditure of energy.

## THE FUNCTION OF BILE IN DIGESTION

Only the salts of the bile acids are useful in digestion. The other constituents of bile are present as excretory products (with the exception of the inorganic salts which probably reach the bile by diffusion and are neither secreted nor excreted). The bile salts in the intestine aid in digestion and absorption of fat largely because of their surface tension lowering properties and their ability to form chemical compounds with fatty acids, thus increasing their solubility. The ability of bile salts to reduce the surface tension of water aids in emulsification of fats and increases the activity of pancreatic lipase. Fats, being insoluble in water, present special difficulties to the digestive apparatus since digestion is a hydrolytic process and the digestive enzymes are dissolved in water. Special means are necessary in order to bring the fat particles into contact with lipase which is dispersed in the aqueous phase. This can be accomplished by any one of several wetting agents; bile being a natural detergent accomplishes this purpose in the living body.

The fatty acids that are liberated by hydrolysis of triglyceride fat form soluble soaps in an alkaline medium but the intestinal contents are usually not sufficiently alkaline to maintain any considerable quantity of fatty acids in solution in this way. After liberation from the glycerol molecule the free fatty acids are said to combine with bile salts (Verzar and McDougall). It is believed that these soluble compounds can penetrate the epithelial cells of the intestine and thus facilitate absorption of fatty acids. Absorption of fats will be discussed in greater detail in the next chapter.

The idea put forward by Mellanby that bile acts as a stimulus for release of secretin from the intestinal mucosa and in this way brings about secretion of pancreatic juice has been proved to be erroneous. In certain circumstances bile may facilitate the release of secretin into the blood but this is not an important part of the secretin mechanism (Thomas and Crider, 1943). Bile in the intestine has a tendency to stimulate peristalsis and is often credited with having a mild laxative action. This action would probably be manifest only in a condition in which there was a pathological deficiency of bile in the intestine.

## JAUNDICE

### *Definition and Classification*

When bile pigment is present in excessive amount in the blood (hyperbilirubinemia) it diffuses from the capillaries; the skin, mucous membranes and conjunctivas then become stained a pale yellow tint. But the pigment is not merely dissolved in the tissue fluids but appears to be bound in some way to the tissues. The discoloration is called *jaundice* or *icterus*. The bilirubin appears in the urine and sweat but does not pass into the saliva or milk, nor as a rule into the cerebrospinal fluid.[2] Jaundice may be due to the production of bile pigment in excess of the amount with which the excretory power of the liver can cope. Or, it may result from the failure of a damaged liver to excrete the bilirubin produced in normal amounts. Jaundice may therefore be divided into two main groups corresponding to the mode of its production. These are, the *hemolytic* and the *hepatic*, the former resulting from increased production of bile pigment from hemoglobin, and the latter from depressed or suppressed excretion of pigment by the liver. In the hepatic form the retention of pigment may be due to (a) obstruction of the bile passages or (b) damage of the liver cells by toxic agents or infections. Jaundice is also sometimes classified into obstructive and nonobstructive, the latter being subdivided into hemolytic, on the one hand, and toxic or infective on the other. These principal varieties of jaundice are tabulated below.

Hepatic { 1. Hemolytic jaundice } nonobstructive
{ 2. Toxic, or infective jaundice }
{ 3. Obstructive jaundice }

A third classification proposed by Rich has come into use based upon whether bile pigment has been taken up by the liver cells and then returned to the blood, or has been rejected by the cells (due to hepatic dysfunction or to an excess of pigment), and thus retained in the circulation. The *first* mentioned type is called *regurgitation jaundice*; it includes obstructive jaundice, and jaundice due to damage of liver cells, and, therefore of the walls of the biliary canaliculi which permits whole bile to "regurgitate" into the circulation.

In the *second* form, called *retention jaundice*, excessive amounts of bile pigment are produced (hemolytic jaundice) part of which is not taken

[2] Its appearance in the cerebrospinal fluid is not uncommon in children.

up by the hepatic parenchyma and is therefore retained in the circulation; or the function of the hepatic cells is so depressed that a large part of the circulating bilirubin, even though not produced in excess, fails to be excreted.

### Hemolytic (Retention) Jaundice

It has already been mentioned that a small amount of bile pigment (0.2 to 0.8 mg. per cent) is present in normal human serum and that any condition which increases red cell destruction also increases the formation of bile pigment. However, the functional reserve of the liver is so great that is is very doubtful whether overproduction of bile pigment ever taxes the excretory capacity of an undamaged liver to the limit. But when the hepatic reserve is reduced as a result of disease and hemolysis is excessive the normal balance between the production and the excretion of pigment cannot be maintained; retention occurs and the bilirubin concentration in the blood rises above the normal limits. *Hemolytic agents* of all sorts, such as the toxins of certain infections, septicemia, etc., and various chemical poisons may induce icterus (p. 77) of this type. It also occurs to some degree in such states as *pernicious anemia, malaria*, etc., in which blood destruction is a pronounced feature. It may be produced in animals by the injection of such hemolytic poisons as toluylenediamine and arseniuretted hydrogen. The disease known as *acholuric jaundice*, which tends to run in families and is associated with splenic enlargement and increases fragility of the red cells (p. 77), is of this type. Jaundice in the newborn, *icterus neonatorum, (benign)* frequently occurs as a slight transient staining of the skin and is most probably the result of the destruction of the red cells that are in excess at birth (p. 12). It is perfectly innocent and indeed may be considered physiological. It does not appear until a day or two after birth and lasts for five or six days.

### Obstructive (Regurgitation) Jaundice

Obstructive jaundice results from blockage of the hepatic or common bile duct by (a) a gallstone or parasites within its lumen, (b) compression of the duct by a tumor (e.g., in head of pancreas) or occlusion of its opening into the duodenum, (c) congenital obliteration of the ducts (a fatal form of icterus neonatorum).

In complete biliary obstruction the stools are clay-colored; urobilinogen (p. 642) is absent from the feces and urobilin from the urine. In this type of jaundice bile pigment is believed to pass into

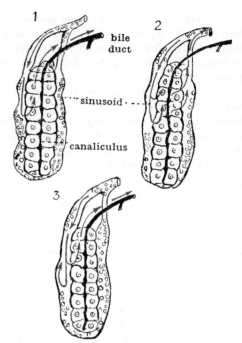

Fig. 39.2. Illustrating the course taken by bile pigment, (1) normally, (2) in jaundice due to obstruction or to liver damage (regurgitation jaundice) and (3) in hemolytic (retention) jaundice. In (2) bilirubinate is formed by the liver cells and is absorbed into the circulation; in (3) part of the bilirubin itself or of bilirubinglobin is retained in the blood.

the liver cells where globin is split off and the pigment combined with glycuronic acid to form bilirubin glycuronide. The latter after its discharge into the biliary canaliculi is returned—"regurgitated"—into the blood as a result of the rupture or, in parenchymatous liver disease, disintegration of the canalicular walls.

McMaster and Rous found, for example, that when obstructive jaundice was induced in dogs, the ducts, if occluded for long, became filled with a fluid free from pigment and bile salts—the so-called *"white bile"* (p. 656). According to these observers the colorless fluid is not bile but a simple seromucoid material secreted by the membrane lining the ducts.

The excretory mechanism of the liver has been shown by McMaster and Rous to possess a very large reserve since, in the dog, jaundice does not develop until from 90 to 95 per cent of the excretory ducts have been occluded.

### Toxic and Infective Jaundice—Liver Damage

Liver damage and consequent depression of the secretory functions of the liver may be produced by: (a) various *poisons*, e.g., arsphenamine, phosphorus, chloroform, etc., (b) *acute and chronic liver diseases*, e.g., infectious hepatitis, homologous serum jaundice (p. 42), acute yellow atrophy, cirrhosis, inflammation of the bile passages (catarrhal jaundice, suppurative cholangitis); (c) *toxins* of various pathogenic bacteria; (d) engorgement of the hepatic vessels as a result of *cardiac failure*. It has been pointed out by Meakins that in the latter condition the edema or ascitic fluid does not contain bilirubin and the skin over edematous regions is not stained. There is no explanation of this fact.

### The Features in Different Types of Jaundice Compared (See Table 39.4)

In obstructive jaundice and in jaundice resulting from liver damage, the staining of the skin, mucous membranes and urine with bilirubin tends to be much more pronounced than in the hemolytic type. Except for a short time after the duct has been obstructed urobilin is absent from the urine and urobilinogen from the feces (p. 642). The plasma alkaline phosphatase shows a pronounced increase in obstructive jaundice, a smaller rise in parenchymatous liver disease, but little or no change in the hemolytic type. In obstructive jaundice the effects, e.g., *bradycardia*, *itching of the skin (pruritus)* referable to the retention of biliary constituents other than pigment may be evident. The cardiac slowing has been attributed to the action of the bile salts, though proof is lacking. Since the bile acids are conjugated in the liver it is not to be expected that their concentration in the blood will be raised in a purely hemolytic type of jaundice; this is found to be the case. On this account the latter type is sometimes spoken of as "dissociated jaundice." Also in severe liver damage bile acids may be absent from the blood although the hyperbilirubinemia is pronounced. In other instances of relatively mild degrees of hepatic insufficiency a converse type of "dissociated jaundice," namely, increased concentration of bile acids in the blood without icterus, is sometimes seen.

The bleeding tendency in obstructive jaundice is a serious hazard should a patient be required to undergo a surgical operation. Only within recent years, as a result of the work of Roderick, of Quick and his associates, and of Dam and Glavind, has the cause of the prolonged coagulation time been discovered. It is due to prothrombin deficiency, which is the result in turn of a virtual lack of vitamin K (p. 913), for when bile is absent from the intestine the vitamin is not absorbed in adequate amounts. The oral administration of vitamin K with bile salts corrects the hemorrhagic tendency. Possibly an additional though minor factor in the lengthened coagulation time is the retention in the blood of certain organic sulfur-containing compounds (e.g., cysteine and taurine) possessing anticoagulant properties (Carr and Foote). Jaundice due to liver damage is also sometimes associated with a prolonged bleeding time and then appears to be due to the incapacity of the liver to manufacture adequate amounts of prothrombin even though there is no lack of vitamin K in the diet or any failure in its absorption. The cause of the pruritus in obstructive jaundice is unknown. Rowntree and associates found that though a high concentration of bile acids in the blood was frequently associated with pruritus this symptom may occur with a normal bile-acid concentration or be absent when the latter is high.

In obstructive jaundice, with complete stoppage of the bile flow, urobilinogen is absent from the urine and feces, but bilirubin excretion in the urine is pronounced, whereas, in hemolytic jaundice the reverse is true, urobilinogen is excreted in the urine and feces in excess, but little bilirubin appears in the urine (see table 40.4). In parenchymatous liver disease the albumin per globulin ratio is reduced and may be reversed due to an increase in the $\beta$- and $\gamma$-globulin fractions, the albumin concentration often being reduced as well. In the other types of jaundice the ratio shows little change from the normal although there may be some reduction in the total protein concentration. Certain observations relevant to the foregoing discussion are given in table 39.4.

### Jaundice Usually Due to a Combination of Causes

It should be pointed out that in any given case of jaundice two or all three causative factors may, and frequently do, coexist. Blood destruction alone, according to Rich, is not capable of producing jaundice except perhaps in rare instances when the hemolytic process is of extreme degree. In pernicious anemia, for example, there is an associated hepatic insufficiency and even in the ordinary icterus of the newborn the immaturity of hepatic function is claimed to be a factor; also, many hemolytic substances are liver poisons as well. In obstructive jaundice the liver cells suffer damage from pressure and the retention of bile salts probably induces a certain amount of hemolysis. Furthermore, in many inflammatory conditions of the liver or bile ducts an obstructive element (due to plugging of the intrahepatic ducts by the so-called bile-thrombi) exists in conjunction with the hepatic damage. In the jaundice of

TABLE 39.4

*Chief differences in the three types of jaundice*

| | Types of Jaundice | | |
| --- | --- | --- | --- |
| | Parenchymatous liver damage | Hemolytic | Obstructive (complete) |
| Serum bilirubin.............. | Moderate increase | Slight or moderate increase | Great increase |
| Urinary bilirubin.............. | Moderate increase | Little or no change | Great increase |
| Urobilinogen in urine......... | Great increase | Moderate increase | Absent |
| Biluribin and urobilinogen (stercobilin) in feces.........•..... | Moderate increase | Great increase | Absent |
| Albumin:globulin ratio......... | Greatly reduced or reversed | Little change | Little change |
| Van den Bergh test........... | Delayed direct or biphasic | Indirect | Direct |
| Plasma alkaline phosphatase... | Little change | Little change | Great increase |
| Thymol turbidity cephalin flocculation and galactose tolerance tests.................... | Positive | Negative | Negative |
| Jaundice...................... | Moderate or slight | Moderate or slight | Pronounced, with pruritus |

cardiac diseases the hepatic engorgement produces obstruction of the finer bile capillaries as well as injury to the liver cells through anoxia. The occurrence of infarcts in the lung is also a factor in some cases; bilirubin production is increased through the breakdown of red cells in the infarcted areas.

*Clinical Tests Employed in the Study of Jaundice*

*The van den Bergh reaction.* This test—a modification of Ehrlich's diazo reaction—is employed for the detection of bile pigment in blood serum. There are two main types of the reaction—the *direct* and the *indirect*. The direct reaction occurs without the addition of alcohol, which is essential for the indirect reaction.

The reagents used in the test are:

> *Solution A:*
> Sulphanilic acid............     0.1 gram
> Concentrated HCl.........     1.5 cc.
> Water up to..............   100    cc.
> *Solution B:*
> Sodium nitrite.............     0.5 gram
> Water....................   100    cc.

To perform the test 10 cc. of solution A and 0.3 cc. of solution B are freshly mixed. This mixture is used as the reagent in both forms of the test.

The *direct reaction* is that which follows the addition of 1 cc. of the reagent to 1 cc. of serum. It may occur in one of three forms, (a) *immediate* or *prompt*; a violet color due to the formation of

diazobilirubin develops in from 10 to 30 seconds. (b) *Delayed reaction*; no change appears until several minutes (5 to 15 or more) elapse, then a reddish color develops which gradually deepens to violet. (c) *Biphasic*; a red color appears promptly as in (a) but takes a variable but longer time than in (b) to change to violet.

The *indirect reaction* is carried out as follows. One cc. of serum is mixed with 2 cc. of 95 per cent alcohol. After shaking and centrifuging, to 1 cc. of the supernatant fluid, 0.25 cc. of the reagent mixture and 0.5 cc. of alcohol are added. A reddish-violet color develops almost immediately.

Normal bile and the serum in obstructive jaundice give the prompt direct reaction. Normal serum, the serum in hemolytic jaundice and the bilirubin formed in old blood extravasations into the connective tissues, serous cavities, etc., give the indirect reaction and occasionally a delayed direct reaction. The sera in types of jaundice due to liver damage, e.g., hepatitis gives a direct reaction (usually of the delayed or biphasic type) all sera which give the direct reaction also give the indirect but the reverse does not hold. The qualitative van den Bergh reaction as a means of distinguishing between the different types of jaundice is regarded today with less favor than formerly.

The indirect reaction used as the basis for the *quantitative* estimation of bilirubin in all types of sera is of much more value. The serum after the color reaction has developed is compared in a colorimeter with a standard solution made by dissolving 2.161 grams of anhydrous cobaltous sulfate in 100 cc. of distilled water. The color of this standard corresponds to that developed by 1 unit of bilirubin. A *unit* is defined by van den Bergh as 1 part of bilirubin in 200,000 parts of serum. Normal serum contains from 0.4 to 1.5 unit (i.e., bilirubin is present in a dilution of 1 part in from 500,000 to 100,000 parts of serum, or from 0.2 to 1.0 mg. per 100 cc.). In the quantitative estimation of bilirubin in sera showing the direct reaction the method has been rendered more accurate by the modification of Thannhauser and Anderson. This consists in first adding 0.5 cc. of the reagent to 1 cc. of the serum, and a minute or two later 2.5 cc. of alcohol and 1 cc. of a saturated solution of ammonium sulphate. By adding the diazoreagent before the alcohol the loss of bilirubin which results from its being carried down with the albuminous precipitate is avoided. When the alcohol is added later the diazobilirubin compound is not thrown down but remains in the supernatant fluid.

The quantitative van den Bergh reaction is of value in the detection of latent jaundice, i.e., a a hyperbilirubinemia which has not reached the level at which jaundice appears, and in recording the progress of a case of manifest jaundice.

The difference between the direct and indirect van den Bergh reactions is due to the difference in the state of bilirubin in hemolytic and obstructive jaundice. Bilirubin that has passed through the liver cell and has been conjugated with glycuronic acid is soluble in water and is able to react at once with the reagents used in the direct test without addition of alcohol. Consequently bilirubin that has been secreted and reabsorbed as in obstructive jaundice gives the direct test. Circulating bilirubin that has not passed through the liver cell is insoluble except as a compound with some blood protein. It has to be set free and made soluble by addition of alcohol to the reagent before it will give the test.

*The icteric index.* The bile pigment concentration may also be estimated by comparing the color of the serum with that of a standard solution. A sample of blood is allowed to clot; after centrifuging, 5 cc. of serum are pipetted off and the color of the sample compared in a colorimeter with a 1 in 10,000 solution of potassium bichromate. The colorimeter is set at 15 mm. for the standard solution. This number is divided by the number on the serum scale when the color of the serum and of the standard solution match. The result is called the *icteric index.* Thus if the reading of the serum scale is 3 the icteric index is 5. The test is invalidated by the presence in the serum of other coloring matter, e.g., carotenoids.

## Gallstones—Cholelithiasis

Gallstones are composed of constituents of the bile which have been thrown out of solution. Cholesterol is present in greater or less amounts in the commoner varieties of gallstone. Some stones may be composed almost entirely of this substance. In other types of stone, bile pigment or calcium is an important or the predominant constituent. Gallstones therefore differ considerably in size, color and inner structure according to the materials of which they are composed. They are classified according to their compositions into *"pure" cholesterol, cholesterol-pigment-calcium, "pure" bilirubin, bilirubin-calcium* and *calcium carbonate* stones. The latter are very rare in man but not uncommon in cattle. The "pure" cholesterol stone contains from 90 to 98 per cent of cholesterol, the remainder being made up of calcium, bile pigments, protein, etc. The "pure" pigment and the bilirubin-calcium stones, on the other hand, contain varying amounts of cholesterol. The cholesterol-pigment-calcium stone is the commonest variety. Stones of this type are usually multiple and, as a result of pressure of one stone against another, show numerous facets upon their surfaces. They contain about 80 per cent of cholesterol which is deposited in cream-colored layers alternately with darker bilirubin-calcium laminas. The great majority of stones are formed in the gall-bladder, but they may also form in the hepatic duct or even in the smaller ducts within the liver.

### THE FORMATION OF GALLSTONES

The mechanism of gallstone formation is not clearly understood but the following are recognized as being the most important factors to be considered: (a) *Injury, especially of an infective nature* to the gall-bladder wall, (b) *disturbance in cholesterol metabolism*, (c) *stasis* of the bile, and (d) *reaction of the bile.*

(a) INFECTION. Following the classical work of Naunyn, infection was looked upon as the main, if not the only, cause of gallstone formation. Naunyn maintained, and it is now current teaching, that the cholesterol of the bile was not dependent upon the cholesterol level of the blood and could not be altered by diet. He also claimed, however, that abnormalities of cholesterol metabolism played a minor role in the production of gallstones. The mucosa of the gall-bladder, he believed, normally secreted cholesterol and calcium and the secretory process was stimulated by any local inflammatory state. Experiments in which human cholesterol stones were shown to be dissolved after a time in the gall-bladder of the dog under sterile conditions, but not if infection were present, the production of gallstones by injections of microörganisms into the circulation after injury to the gall-bladder, and the frequent occurrence of cholelithiasis after infective conditions, notably typhoid fever, were all taken to indicate that infection was essential for the production of biliary calculi. The solvent action of the bile salts upon cholesterol was also held to support this view and to be against the suggestion that this biliary constituent could be thrown out of solution in the absence of infection. It was argued that the bile as it came from the liver could never have so high a concentration of cholesterol that simple deposition could result, but that the cholesterol must be produced in excessive amounts by an inflamed gall-bladder in order to be precipitated. Of the normal concentrating power of the gall-bladder little was then known (see p. 655).

Though not denying the importance of gall-bladder injury and the production of cholesterol from the inflamed mucosa in many cases of cholelithiases, Aschoff and others have insisted that these conditions are not essential to the formation of calculi, and that certain types, especially the solitary cholesterol stone (see below), can arise in sterile bile and in the absence of any diseased condition of the lining membrane. This view is now generally accepted. Much of the earlier work upon cholesterol metabolism to which Naunyn pinned his faith has been proved to be erroneous.

The multiple cholesterol-pigment-calcium stones are usually looked upon as typical infection stones. They are laminated on cross section and have usually a framework of coagulated protein. These stones are often very numerous, sometimes numbered by hundreds, and an examination of their structure indicates that they have all been formed at about the same time. According to Aschoff, the starting point of their formation is the deposition of pigment in the form of fine rosette-like structures upon which coatings of cholesterol, pigment and calcium are subsequently laid. The inflammatory exudate is rich in protein material derived from the blood, as well as in cholesterol and calcium. The protein, it is pointed out, carries an electric charge of opposite sign to that held by the cholesterol, pigment and inorganic constituents of the bile. It is believed that as a result of these physicochemical relations the deposition of cholesterol combined in varying degree with the other biliary constituents is effected.

(b) "METABOLIC." The typical "metabolic" calculus is the large single stone of almost pure cholesterol—the *cholesterol solitaire*. This type of stone, according to Aschoff, is formed quite independently of infection or injury of any sort and is due to the crystallization of cholesterol out of a bile surcharged with this material. The common mixed stones (cholesterol-pigment-calcium) are also composed predominantly of cholesterol and probably in many instances are metabolic rather than infective in origin. In certain conditions, e.g., pregnancy, in which gallstones are prone to develop, the blood cholesterol has been said to be higher than normal (hypercholesterolemia) and there is evidence of a disturbance in cholesterol metabolism. But as a matter of fact, hypercholesterolemia, according to Gardner, (Gardner and Gainsborough, 1930) is not common in pregnancy, the normal proportions of free cholesterol to cholesterol esters (cholesterol combined with fatty acids), however, are altered, the former being increased, the latter reduced. Abnormalities in cholesterol metabolism leading to such changes are probably of more importance in the production of gallstones than a rise in the total blood cholesterol. It has already been mentioned that a high blood cholesterol does not cause an increase in the cholesterol of the bile. Also, in certain forms of renal disease and in myxedema in which hypercholesterolemia exists there is little evidence that the latter leads to the production of gallstones; in other forms of renal disease the incidence of gallstones is higher than usual, yet hypercholesterolemia does not occur.

It has been mentioned that increasing the cholesterol of the diet does not raise the cholesterol concentration of the bile, so there is no logical reason, as pointed out by Gardner and Gainsborough for excluding cholesterol-rich materials from the diets of those subject to cholelithiasis. Indeed, a high fat diet, by stimulating gall-bladder contractions and so preventing undue concentration and stasis of bile, may exert a beneficial effect.

The ratio of cholesterol in bile to the bile salts is an important factor in the formation of gallstones. The cholesterol-bile acid ratio in normal bile is between 1:20 and 1:30. Since neither bile salts nor cholesterol are absorbed under normal circumstances from the gall-bladder this ratio holds for both liver and gall-bladder bile. According to Andrews, deposition of cholesterol occurs when the ratio falls to 1:13. He believes that infection, when it is a factor, plays its part in gallstone formation not so much through increasing cholesterol production as through reducing the bile salt concentration, for he claims that bile salts are absorbed through the inflamed gall-bladder mucosa. Dolkart and associates attach more importance to the concentration of fatty acids in the bile than to that of the bile salts in preventing the precipitation of cholesterol.

"Pure" pigment stones (they contain calcium and cholesterol as well) also occur apart from infection. They are small, and dark and, although usually occurring in the gall-bladder, may be found in the bile passages. Their origin is not clear, but since they often occur in conditions associated with an abnormally high bilirubin excretion, e.g., acholuric jaundice, they may be the result of the precipitation of bilirubin from a bile which contains excessive amounts of the pigment.

(c) STASIS OR SLOWING OF THE BILIARY FLOW within the bile passages may be responsible for the formation of small stones of pigment-calcium in these situations. When there is complete stasis, due to mechanical obstruction, the fluid in the larger bile passages contains none of the important biliary constituents. The so-called "white bile" fills the ducts and in consequence the formation of calculi is not possible (p. 651). Complete biliary stasis appears also to be a very minor factor in the production of stones in the gall-bladder.

(d) REACTION OF THE BILE. Until the work of Drury, Rous and McMaster this factor had received comparatively little attention. These observers caused gallstones composed, in varying proportions, of calcium carbonate, pigment and cholesterol to be formed in the bile of dogs which had their gall-bladders removed and their common ducts drained into a system of tubing. Encrustations of biliary constituents as well as more or less discrete calculi formed upon the walls of the tubing. These occurred under sterile conditions and in the absence of stasis. The deposits are claimed to result from the alkalinity of the liver bile. Normal bile of the dog as it flows along the bile passages was shown by Okada to be definitely alkaline whereas that of the gall-bladder was acid. Rous and his associates found the liver bile of dogs to have a pH of 8.20 or more, while after its stay in the gall-bladder its reaction became decidedly acid—pH 5.18 to 6.00. Bile from the human gall-bladder, though less alkaline than liver bile, has rarely a pH below 7.0. One of the functions of the normal gall-bladder (p. 656) therefore appears to be depression of the pH of liver bile. So long as this occurs in the usual manner the calcium carbonate of the bile remains in solution. In an alkaline bile, such as is collected from the common duct in the absence of the gall-bladder the calcium carbonate is thrown down, and with it the pigment and cholesterol constituents, to be deposited upon the walls of the delivery tubing. These observations suggest therefore that in any condition which interferes with gall-bladder function, e.g., infection, injury, or intermittent stasis, the usual acidification of the liver bile will not occur; calcium carbonate will then undergo spontaneous precipitation, and serve as a center or centers upon which the other biliary constituents become deposited.

*An Enumeration of Hepatic Functions*

Besides its secretory and excretory functions dealt with in this section the liver plays an important role in many other physiological processes. For the reader's convenience a list of these with page references is given below.

(a) Blood formation in the embryo (p. 99); storage of vitamin $B_{12}$ (p. 81).

(b) Fibrinogen production (p. 6).

(c) Prothrombin production (p. 114).

(d) Heparin production (p. 112).

(e) Iron and copper storage (pp. 72, 75).

(f) Blood volume regulation (ch. 20).

(g) Reticuloendothelial activity (Kupffer cells) (p. 102).

(h) Detoxication (p. 721).

(i) Protein metabolism, deamination (ch. 20), amino acid synthesis (ch. 45), urea (ch. 20), and uric acid (ch. 47).

(j) Carbohydrate metabolism (ch. 48).

(k) Fat metabolism (ch. 49).

(l) Heat production (ch. 52).

(m) Formation of vitamin A from carotene (ch. 53).

(n) Liberation of a depressor principle (p. 408).

The hepatic circulation is dealt with in chapter 26.

## LIVER FUNCTION TESTS

Several of the specific functions of the liver have been utilized as tests for an investigation of the functional capacity of the liver as a whole, i.e., as a means of detecting the presence of hepatic damage and, in some instances, of gauging the extent to which such damage has occurred, and to distinguish between different types of jaundice. Some of these tests will be very briefly described, the accounts being confined in the main to the general principles upon which the tests are based.

*Tests Based upon the Excretory Functions of the Liver*

The quantitative van den Bergh reaction has been described (p. 629). Since the excretion of bilirubin is an essential hepatic function a determination of the quantity of circulating bilirubin is a valuable means of estimating the extent of liver damage associated with jaundice, provided the hyperbilirubinemia is not the result of biliary obstruction or of blood destruction.

The estimation of the quantity of *urobilinogen* excreted in the urine has also been employed as a test of liver function. Increased blood destruction, as in pernicious anemia, quite apart from liver damage will also cause urobilinogenuria, but it is usually much less pronounced than that due to parenchymatous liver disease. Also, infection of the biliary passages may increase the urobilinogen output out of all proportion to the reduction of liver function.

Other tests based upon the excretory function of the liver are the *Bromsulphalein, bilirubin* and *rose bengal* tests. In each of these tests the respective material is injected intravenously and the rate of excretion estimated from the quantity retained in the serum after the lapse of a specified time; the concentration of the material in the serum is determined colorimetrically. These three substances are excreted almost entirely by the liver and no significant amounts are taken up by the reticuloendothelial cells. In normal persons less than 5 per cent of bromsulphalein (5 mg. per kg. of body weight injected) is retained after 45 minutes, or of bilirubin (1 mg. per kg. of body weight injected) is observed at the end of 4 hours. In the case of rose bengal (10 cc. of 1 per cent solution injected without regard to subject's weight) 50 per cent or more disappears from the serum within 8 minutes after the injection. These tests, like the van den Bergh test, will of course be of no value if obstruction of the bile ducts exists; obviously, whether damaged or not the liver cannot then excrete the injected substances. Colorimetric difficulties also render the dye tests inapplicable in the presence of hyperbilirubinemia from whatever cause. The bilirubin injection test is employed only in the absence of jaundice, for if the liver's power to excrete the endogenous bilirubin is depressed it is a foregone conclusion that it will show a corresponding incapacity to excrete the injected pigment. In the absence of jaundice, however, the bilirubin injection test is one of the most reliable means of estimating the degree of liver damage. Determination of the *serum alkaline phosphatase* level is one of the most sensitive tests of liver function (ch. 59).

## Tests Based upon the Metabolic Functions of the Liver

(a) THE GALACTOSE AND LEVULOSE (FRUCTOSE) TOLERANCE TESTS. In the *levulose tolerance* test the blood sugar curve is determined after the ingestion of from 40 to 50 grams of pure levulose dissolved in 250 cc. of water—the dose of sugar is varied according to the subject's weight. The test is performed in the morning, that is, after a 12-hour fast. The blood sugar level is first determined before the ingestion of the sugar and every half hour for 2 hours thereafter. The liver converts levulose to glycogen, the greater quantity of sugar so converted the less pronounced will be the rise in the blood sugar. In absence of hepatic disease the ingestion of 40 grams or so of the sugar causes a maximum rise of the blood sugar curve of 30 mg. per cent or less above the fasting level (when this is between 80 and 100 mg. per 100 cc.) within 1

hour; the curve returns to within 10 mg. per cent of the fasting level within 2 hours. Definite hepatic injury is indicated by a rise in the blood sugar of over 30 mg. per cent when the fasting level is between 80 and 100 mg. per cent, and a rise of 35 mg. per cent, and of 40 mg. per cent when the fasting levels are from 70 to 80 and from 60 to 70 mg. per cent, respectively. Failure of the curve to return to within 15 mg. per cent of the fasting level after 2 hours, regardless of the height of the curve is also definitely abnormal.

A similar test may be made using galactose. At the end of a 12-hour fast the blood sugar level is determined and 40 gm. of galactose given in 400 cc. of water. The blood galactose level is then estimated at half-hour intervals for 2 hours. Normally the maximum value is reached in 1 hour and does not rise to more than 63 mg. per 100 cc. and falls to 0 by the end of the 2 hours. Normally by the end of the fifth hour the total urinary excretion is less than 2.5 gm. Higher values than these in blood and urine are found in hepatic insufficiency. (Peters and Van Slyke, 1946.)

(b) Tests based upon the function of the liver to deaminate the amino acids with the production of urea or upon its detoxicating function have also been devised. Although in the dog hippuric acid is synthesized (from glycine and benzoic acid) only in the kidney, in the rabbit and in man this function is performed to an important extent by the liver as well. In carrying out this test benzoic acid (5.9 grams) is given orally, 1.77 gram of sodium benzoate (equivalent to 1.50 gr. benzoic acid) is given intravenously and the hippuric acid excretion is determined. Normally, at least 1 gram of hippuric acid is excreted within an hour and the quantity of hippuric acid excreted in the urine at hourly intervals for 4 hours thereafter is determined. If the liver possesses some reserve from 3 to 3.5 grams are excreted within this time. The determination of the *prothrombin time* (ch. 12) is also employed as a liver function test. In damage of the liver, the prothrombin time is prolonged.

## Tests Based upon the Protein Constitution of the Plasma

When damage to the hepatic parenchyma exists the albumin:globulin ratio of the plasma is reduced due to an absolute increase in the β- and γ-globulin fractions and usually, as well, to an absolute reduction in the albumin fraction. The tests to be described are based upon the rise in the globulin fractions and the reduction in albumin, for the latter fraction tends to protect the globulin from the action of the reagent and thus to inhibit the reaction. The higher the serum globulin and the lower the albumin the more pronounced will the reaction be. The tests to be described cannot be correlated specifically with any given liver function and are, therefore, largely empirical. The first test of this type to be introduced is known as the *Taka-Ara test,* after its originators. In the presence of an excess of globulin a reagent composed of sodium carbonate, mercuric chloride and acid fuchsin, when added to the abnormal serum, causes the precipitation of the mercuric chloride. A similar test is the *colloidal gold* test of Gray. But the most commonly used and the most satisfactory tests of this group are the *thymol turbidity* test of Maclagan, and the *cephalin-cholesterol flocculation test* of Hanger. In the former, 3 cc. of the thymol reagent[3] are added to 0.05 cc. of serum and the degree of turbidity measured after $\frac{1}{2}$ to 1 hour in a spectrophotometer at a wave length of 650 m$\mu$. The turbidity is believed to be due to the precipitation of a globulin-thymol-phospholipid complex. The cephalin-cholesterol flocculation test consists of adding an emulsion of cephalin (100 mg. from sheep's brain) and cholesterol (300 mg.) to the serum and allowing the mixture to stand for from 24 to 48 hours. Normal serum remains clear, whereas the serum from a patient with parenchymatous liver disease (inflammatory, or degenerative) shows flocculation.

Several investigators have studied the reliability of the different liver function tests by comparing the results obtained with the histological findings in biopsy samples of hepatic tissue. Sherlock obtains a cylinder of hepatic tissue by the use of a needle 1 mm. in caliber and provided with a trocar. The liver is punctured through the skin under local anesthesia. She finds the most useful and reliable tests were determinations of serum bilirubin, serum alkaline phosphatase and the albumin:globulin ratio. In experiments upon dogs in which the liver was damaged by carbon tetrachloride, Drill and Ivy found that the number of hepatic functions affected increased with the severity of the liver damage. The excretion of Bromsulphalein was the first to become depressed. Serum alkaline phosphatase showed a rise about the same time or slightly later. Next in order of sensitivity was the test for the prothrombin time; the galactose tolerance test was the least sensitive of the four tests employed. From these results Drill and Ivy suggest that the *association* of hepatic functions rather than their *dissociation* (i.e., the singling out of one or other function by liver damage) should receive emphasis.

It is to be remembered that the foregoing are purely functional tests and that a negative result does not necessarily indicate the absence of liver injury. On the contrary, liver disease may exist without its condition being revealed by any of these means. This is obvious from the observations of McMaster and Rous and of Mann and his associates upon the reserve function of the liver. The

first mentioned observers showed that in the dog 95 per cent of the excretory function could be abolished before jaundice appeared; Mann and his associates found that the liver tissue of the dog could be reduced by 80 per cent or more without a fall in urea production occurring.

## The Gall-Bladder and Bile Ducts

### ANATOMY

The human gall-bladder has a capacity of about 50 cc. Its wall is composed of a thin layer of muscle fibers and fibroelastic tissue, with a lining of mucous membrane. The muscle fibers are sparse and loosely interlaced with one another and with the strands of fibroelastic tissue. The mucosa is surmounted by a layer of columnar epithelium.

The *cystic duct* through which the bile enters and later leaves the viscus is tortuous, or S-shaped and shows spiral folds of mucosa—the *valves of Heister* —within its lumen. These so-called valves have not a valvelike action, for they offer little resistance to the passage of bile in either direction; nor do they seem to prevent a too rapid flow of bile as some have supposed. They develop late in phylogenetic history being associated apparently with the erect posture; they are found only in primates. The folds are formed in the embryo by the twisting or winding of the duct during development. Their function, as suggested by Keith and supported by Lichtenstein and Ivy, is to stiffen the wall of the duct and prevent its kinking.

The *common bile duct*, formed by the union of the hepatic and cystic ducts, passes very obliquely through the muscular wall of the duodenum and joins with the pancreatic duct to form the *ampulla of Vater* (fig. 39.3). The latter opens into the duodenum through an orifice situated at the summit of a small papilla about $3\frac{1}{2}$ inches below the pylorus. The ampulla of Vater is surrounded near its outlet into the duodenum by a ring of muscle fibers—the *sphincter of Oddi.* Boyden has studied the circular fibers surrounding the common bile duct at its duodenal end (i.e., the smooth muscle usually referred to as the sphincter of Oddi) and distinguishes three sets of fibers (a) *sphincter choledochus* (or *Boyden's sphincter*), fibers which surround the duct between its penetration of the duodenal wall and the point where it is joined by the pancreatic duct, (b) fibers encircling the pancreatic duct where it opens into the ampulla and (c) those which surround the ampulla itself. These latter are present in only about one-sixth of human subjects; when in spasm they may block the ampullary portion of the common bile duct and permit bile to pass into the pancreatic duct, or pancreatic juice to ascend the common bile duct. The mucosa of the common duct is devoid of the usual mucous glands, but contains special branched tabular glands lined with tall columnar

---

[3] This consists of: 1.38 grams barbitone; 1.03 grams sodium barbitone; 3 grams thymol; 500 ml. doubly distilled water.

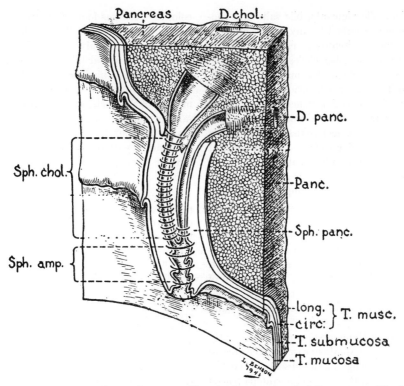

FIG. 39.3. Showing the smooth muscle surrounding the duodenal end of the common bile duct. (After Boyden, slightly modified.) D. chol., *common bile duct*; D. panc., *pancreatic duct*; Sph. chol., *sphincter choledochus (Boyden's sphincter)*; Sph. amp., *sphincter ampullae*; Sph. panc., *sphincter pancreaticus* surrounding the pancreatic duct; T. musc., T. submucosa and T. mucosa, *coats of the duodenal wall.*

cells. These glands furnish a thin fluid which dilutes the bile.

The gall-bladder, though it possesses important functions, is not indispensable since it can be removed with impunity. After such an operation, however, the larger bile ducts undergo dilation, which may in part compensate for the removal of the viscus. The gall-bladder is absent in some animals whose habits and digestive processes are not essentially different, apparently, from those of animals that possess one. It is absent in the horse, deer and rat but present in cattle, sheep, dogs, cats and mice. It is present in fish, amphibia, reptiles and birds, but is absent from orders lower than these.

*Contractions of the Gall-Bladder and Common Bile Duct*

The gall-bladder shows spontaneous *rhythmical contractions* which occur at the rate of from 2 to 6 per minute (in the dog), and also a *tonic contraction* which lasts for from 5 to 30 minutes or more. The rhythmical contractions (in the dog) are capable of producing a pressure change of from 250 to 300 mm. of water which is about the maximal pressure at which bile can be secreted by the

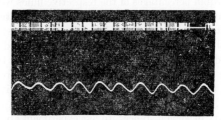

FIG. 39.4. Examples of normal gall-bladder contractions. Time marker, 1 second. (After Taylor and Wilson.)

liver (fig. 39.4). Rhythmical contractions of the common bile duct have also been demonstrated in animals.

THE FUNCTIONS OF THE GALL-BLADDER

*The Concentration and Storage of Bile—The Secretion of Mucus*

Gall-bladder bile may be some ten times more concentrated in total solids than bile collected from the hepatic duct. Water and inorganic salts are absorbed through the lymphatics and blood vessels of the gall-bladder wall. The composition of the absorbed fluid is virtually that of physiological saline. Bile pigments, bile salts and cholesterol are not absorbed to any appreciable degree under normal circumstances.

It is undecided whether cholesterol is excreted by the normal gall-bladder mucosa, although Elman and Taussig present evidence for such a process. In this connection it may be mentioned that a pronounced diffuse deposition of a cholesterol ester in the connective tissue of the human gall-bladder, amounting to from 35 to 60 per cent of its dry weight, is seen as a pathological condition. The tissue of the vesicle is stiff and greatly thickened as a result of its impregnation with lipid material. The disturbances leading to this condition, which is spoken of as *cholesterosis of the gall-bladder* or, from the appearance of the mucosa, as the *"strawberry gall-bladder,"* are unknown; the existence of this condition cannot, however, be used as evidence for the secretion of cholesterol by the gall-bladder mucosa under physiological conditions (see Elman and Graham.)

To the work of Hammarsten and more recently to that of Rous and McMaster we owe the greater part of our knowledge of the absorptive powers of the gall-bladder. By means of a cannula placed in the bile duct the latter observers collected the bile as it came from the liver and compared its composition with that in the gall-bladder. The bilirubin percentages of the respective fluids were used as a measure of the degree of concentration that had been effected in the bile during its stay in the gall-bladder. The bladder bile was found to be darker, thicker and more "syrupy" than the bile collected from the ducts. It contained from 3.1 to 10.8 times more bilirubin than the liver bile. Absorption occurred with remarkable rapidity in some instances. In one experiment about 50 cc. of bile which entered the gall-bladder was reduced to less than 5 cc. in about 22 hours. In experiments involving the drainage of the gall-bladder through a cannula inserted into its fundus it has been shown that the mere passage of bile through the organ causes a nearly fivefold concentration. Inflammation of the gall-bladder reduces or abolishes its concentrating power.

The gall-bladder mucosa also adds to the viscosity of the bile by the *secretion* of a thick mucinous material. Little or none of this material is furnished by the bile ducts. Nor were the latter observed to have any concentrating power but were found, on the contrary, to dilute the bile with a thin watery fluid.

When the ducts were obstructed by ligation and the gall-bladder tied off, after some days a clear colorless fluid was found to have collected within the ducts. This fluid—the so-called *"white bile"* —is not uncommonly seen during an operation upon an obstructed bile duct associated with a functionless gall-bladder. The "white bile" under these circumstances is furnished solely by the mucosa of the ducts. It contains no pigment, bile salts or cholesterol and bears almost no resemblance to bile. The secretion of the latter had been suppressed by the rise in pressure (to 300 mm. or so of water) within the ligated duct system.

If the gall-bladder is healthy and left in communication with the obstructed system the sequence of events is entirely different. Biliary stasis then causes thick *greenish bile* to collect in the ducts and bladder as a result of the latter's concentrating activity, and of the mucinous material which it secretes. After a lapse of weeks the imprisoned bile develops an almost tarry consistency. The functions of the ducts and of the bladder are therefore antagonistic, the former tending to dilute, the latter to concentrate the biliary fluid. The diluting effect is at first overbalanced by the concentrating action of the gall-bladder, and when this remains in communication with the duct system, the net result is marked thickening of the bile. There is, however, a tendency with time for the activity of the ducts to overcome that of the gall-bladder. The biliary constituents disappear and ultimately the contents of the system are entirely replaced by the thin simple secretion of the ducts and mucinous material from the bladder (hydrops) (Rous and McMaster).

Another type of "white bile" is sometimes produced. In dogs a clear colorless fluid is secreted by the liver cells when their true secretion is suppressed by some severe liver injury such as that induced by the administration of chloroform (Drury and Rous). "White bile" of this type is sometimes seen in the human subject as a result of hepatic disease.

*Other functions of the gall-bladder* subsidiary to its concentrating power are the *reduction in the alkalinity* of the bile and the *equalization of pressure* within the biliary duct system. Without the ability to absorb fluid and reduce the bulk of the bile its power to equalize pressure would be negligible. It is to be remembered that the amount of bile secreted in 24 hours is some twenty times or so greater than could be contained in the gall-bladder. The loss of its action in equalizing the pressure within the duct system is probably a factor leading to the dilation of the bile ducts, which so frequently follows removal of the gall-bladder (cholecystectomy). After this operation the flow of bile into the intestine is at first nearly continuous, but later the adaptation of the ducts permits intermittent discharge.

The importance of the gall-bladder in the control of pressure within the biliary ducts is apparent from the results of the experiments of Mann and Bollman. They found that after ligation of the common duct in dogs a rise in the bilirubin concentration of the blood did not occur until from 24 to 36 hours had elapsed, and jaundice did not appear for 2 days. If, on the other hand, the gall-bladder was removed at the time that the duct was ligated jaundice was fully developed within 24 hours due, presumably, to the rise in duct pressure, and the "regurgitation" of bile into the blood.

In dogs, cholecystectomy causes some impairment of liver function, as shown by the serum phosphatase test, for at least 70 days following the operation. In man, the excretion of Bromsulphalein is reduced for a short time after this operation, presumably until the ducts can function vicariously for the gall-bladder.

### The Filling and Evacuation of the Gall-Bladder

The bile as it leaves the liver flows into the hepatic duct and thence into the common bile duct. During fasting its entrance into the duodenum is blocked by the tonic contraction of the sphincter muscle (sphincter choledochus) at the duodenal end of the duct. As the bile accumulates within the duct its pressure rises, and reaching a height of from 50 to 70 mm. of water, forces it way along the cystic duct into the gall-bladder. During fasting therefore the viscus becomes gradually distended with retained bile.

The nature of the force by which the gall-bladder is evacuated has been a question of some debate. As the wall of the gall-bladder is relatively thin and its muscle fibers so sparse, it seemed unlikely that it could exert the pressure required to discharge its contents—especially since the gall-bladder is evacuated with considerable difficulty by manual compression. Intraabdominal pressure, "milking" action exerted by the duodenal movements, and simple leaking into the duodenum as a result of relaxation of the sphincter of Oddi have been variously suggested as possible factors. It has however been proved quite definitely as a result of evidence derived from several modes of investigation that the contractions of the gall-bladder itself, despite the apparent muscular weakness of its walls, are responsible for the expulsion of its contents. The times of emptying of the gall-bladder are related to gastric digestion. During fasting it remains

distended with bile although the sphincter guarding the common duct is relaxed, plainly indicating that the viscus is competent to retain the bile without the aid of the sphincter of Oddi. That changes in intra-abdominal pressure are not responsible for its emptying was shown by Mann and Higgins working with guinea pigs, whose gall-bladders can be readily mobilized.

The abdomen was opened under local anesthesia, the gall-bladder exposed and drawn outside the abdominal wound, which was then sutured around the cystic duct. The vesicle was observed to contract and expel its contents in response to food placed in the duodenum. It was also shown that in fish, which of course have no diaphragm and in which, apparently, the intrabdominal pressure remains constant, intermittent evacuations occurred. In dogs the influence of the sphincter was removed by suturing a catheter into the common duct; the abdomen was left open in order to minimize the effects of intraabdominal pressure. The gall-bladder remained distended; only during the digestion of a meal did it discharge its contents.

When the walls of the gall-bladder contract, bile is discharged along the cystic and common ducts into the duodenum. The sphincter or sphincters guarding the lower end of the common bile duct normally can withstand a pressure of 100 to 120 mm. of water but the pressure developed by the contractions of the gall-bladder in dogs was shown by Mann and his associates to amount to over 250 mm. $H_2O$. Moreover, it is probable that relaxation of the sphincter occurs as part of a coordinated mechanism when the bladder wall contracts, and that the passage of bile through the sphincter is not simply a matter of the latter "giving way" before the biliary pressure created by the gall-bladder contractions. The duodenal muscle surrounding the oblique intramural portion of the common bile duct is capable when contracted of offering a resistance of over 750 mm. of water. Since this is much higher than the pressure which contractions of the gall-bladder can exert, the flow of bile is completely blocked during contractions of the duodenal muscle but during the latter's relaxation the compression of the duct is relieved (fig. 39.5). Therefore, during the evacuation of the gall-bladder and active duodenal movements, the bile may be observed to enter the duodenum in squirts. This is not due to the "milking" action of the peristaltic movements of the bowel but is the result of the alternate blockage and release of the duct; the bowel movements are incapable

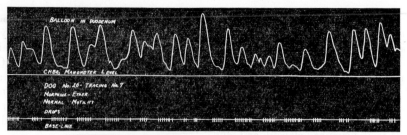

FIG. 39.5. This figure shows the relation between duodenal contractions and flow of bile (indicated in drops near bottom of figure) from the common duct into the duodenum (after Lueth).

of causing any flow of bile when the gall-bladder is not contracting.

The most effective stimulus for the discharge of bile is fatty food, particularly egg yolk, cream or olive oil. It appears that some degree of digestion of the fat must occur before evacuation results. The effect of fat upon the gall-bladder was shown definitely by Boyden. He found that during a period of fasting the gall-bladder in the cat was distended with bile, and its walls so stretched that they were reduced to about one-fifteenth of their thickness in the collapsed state. It emptied slowly after a meal, being collapsed, or nearly so, in from 1¾ to 2 hours. The effect of meat upon the discharge of bile is much less than that of fat. Pure protein, such as egg white, and carbohydrate food is almost without effect. These findings have been amply confirmed by several observers. Whitaker, for example, observed changes in the contour of the gall-bladder after filling it with iodized oil and examining it radioscopically. The human gall-bladder when rendered opaque to the X-rays by the administration of tetraiodophenolphthalein can also be seen to discharge its contents in response to a meal of fat. Its contractions during operations have also been observed frequently. The products of fat digestion, hydrochloric acid of a strength comparable to that in the chyme, or magnesium sulphate when placed in the duodenum, cause evacuation of the gall-bladder and relaxation of the sphincter of Oddi. Bile salts injected intravenously, on the other hand, cause relaxation of the gall-bladder. Liquid petrolatum introduced into the duodenum is without effect.

The emptying time of the gall-bladder is prolonged in duodenal ulcer, during pregnancy and in pernicious anemia (Boyden).

THE MECHANISMS CONTROLLING EVACUATION OF THE GALL-BLADDER. (a) *Nervous.* It has been mentioned that relaxation of the sphincter of Oddi probably occurs as the gall-bladder contracts. A coordinated action of this nature points to a nervous mechanism. The latter may depend upon intrinsic nervous plexuses in the walls of the biliary passages. The gall-bladder contractions initiated by the stimulus of a meal might be due similarly to short reflexes through the intrinsic plexuses of the stomach or duodenum and biliary tract. Nervous mechanisms are also indicated by the following observations. Electrical stimulation of the stomach and duodenum in animals is followed by contractions of the gall-bladder. Contractions are occasionally induced by psychic influences, e.g., the smell or taste of food. The gall-bladder also responds to experimental excitation of the vagus or sympathetic nerves. Experiments attempting to demonstrate the precise actions of the extrinsic nerves upon the gall-bladder movements have, however, given very conflicting evidence. Several observers have obtained weak motor effects from both vagal and sympathetic stimulation, a motor action of the latter is also indicated by the fact that adrenaline is excitatory.

The results of the experiments of Johnson and Boyden, however, seem clear cut. Section of the right vagus nerve of the cat retarded emptying of the gall-bladder, apparently, as a result of the interruption of motor fibers to the gall-bladder and of inhibitory fibers to the sphincter of Oddi. The left vagus was found to carry motor fibers to the gall-bladder, but apparently does not contain inhibitory fibers for the sphincter. Reflex effects upon the movements of the gall-bladder may be initiated from other abdominal viscera. Stimulation of the cecum, for example, causes inhibition of the movements. This reflex is abolished after section of the splanchnic nerves or excision of the celiac ganglion. In the cat, Boyden has demonstrated an inhibitory effect upon gall-bladder motility of electrical stimulation of the duodenum by means of tied-in electrodes. But in a similar human experiment (an electrode being passed into the duodenum through a Rehfuss tube) an inhibitory effect could not be demonstrated. From this and from the fact that the rate of gall-bladder emptying is little altered in subjects of double vagotomy, Boyden concludes that in man nervous control of the gall-bladder is of little importance as compared with hormonal control.

(b) *Hormonal.* Even in animals nervous mechanisms are not essential to gall-bladder activity; this is evident from the fact that the reaction to the introduction of fat into the duodenum occurs after all nervous connections between the biliary and gastrointestinal tracts, and between the former and the central nervous system have been severed. That gall-bladder contractions can occur under such circumstances suggests, of course, a hormonal or humoral mechanism. Boyden found that the blood of an animal taken at the height of digestion, when injected into a fasting animal causes the evacuation of bile; blood from a starved animal has no such effect.

Ivy obtained an acid extract from the mucosa of the upper part of the intestine which caused contraction of the gall-bladder when injected intravenously into animals. The injection of acid alone is without effect. Nor will fat or its derivatives excite contractions of the gall-bladder when administered intravenously. Acid and other substances which are excitatory when placed in the duodenum or fed therefore act apparently by causing the production or liberation of a hormone in or from the intestinal mucosa. The active principle is related to secretin but is quite distinct from this hormone, for it does not cause pancreatic secretion, and secretin does not cause gall-bladder contractions. In crossed circulation experiments the introduction of acid into the duodenum of one animal caused contractions of the gall-bladder of the other. Ivy and Oldberg named this hormone "*cholecystokinin.*" As little as 0.2 mg. of the solid material prepared from a potent extract causes definite contractions of the gall-bladder. It is free from histamine and other vasodilator substances. Its effect has been demonstrated upon man. The transfusion of blood from a human subject digesting egg yolk has been found to cause evacuation of the gall-bladder of the recipient. No effect was observed with blood from a fasting donor.

*The actions of drugs upon the motility of the gall-bladder.* Adrenaline, pitressin, histamine and mecholyl stimulate the smooth muscle of the gall-bladder, whereas morphine, ergotamine and atropine are inhibitory.

## CHOLECYSTOGRAPHY

Graham and Cole showed in 1924 that if the chlorine radical of a dye such as tetrachlorphe-

nolphthalein, which is excreted selectively by the liver, is replaced by iodine or bromine, the compound, after concentration in the gall-bladder, is opaque to the X-rays. Sodium tetraiodophenolphthalein or the corresponding bromine compound (sodium tetrabromphenolphthalein) is given intravenously or by mouth in a special coated capsule. After a fasting period of about 14 hours a radiogram is taken. The normal gall-bladder at this time shows a well defined shadow. The gall-bladder is then stimulated to contract by means of a meal containing egg yolk and cream, and a second radiogram taken 5 hours later, when the normal organ should be found practically empty. The depth of the shadow after dye administration depends directly upon the concentrating power of the gall-bladder. For this reason a diseased gall-bladder may throw only a faint shadow or none at all.

Gallstones, especially those of a high cholesterol content, which are relatively transparent to the X-rays, show up against the gall-bladder shadow. Gallstones containing more than 0.5 per cent of calcium are visible without the aid of an opaque dye.

### Affections of the Gall-Bladder and Bile Ducts

Among the common diseases of the gall-bladder are *inflammation (cholecystitis), gallstones (cholelithiasis)* and *new growths.* The factors involved in the formation of gallstones have been considered (p. 650).

In the absence of inflammation, stones in the gall-bladder give rise, as a rule, to no definite symptoms, but in their passage along the ducts severe pain—*biliary colic*—may be experienced as a result of the spasmodic contractions of the gall-bladder and consequent distension of the duct walls. Vomiting may occur as a reflex phenomenon. In the dog pain is produced when the gall-bladder is distended by a pressure of 540 mm. of water. This, of course, is a much higher pressure than the contractions of the gall-bladder can create. Pain is produced, however, by distending the *ducts* with a pressure of 270 mm. of water—just about the maximal pressure which the gall-bladder contractions can produce. The cause of the expulsion of the stone from the gall-bladder is not altogether clear. Although contractions of the gall-bladder have been observed to cause movements of stones within its cavity, and even to force a stone into the cystic duct, gall-bladder contractions do not in the majority of instances offer satisfactory explanation for the expulsion of the stone. According to some, inflammation and distension of the gall-bladder are important factors leading to the passage of the stone into the cystic duct.

BILIARY DYSKINESIA. It is now generally recognized that biliary colic may occur in the absence of stone, inflammation or of any anatomical abnormality, such as kinking of the cystic duct, which would hinder the expulsion of bile from gall-bladder. In such instances the colic has a functional origin, being due to the gall-bladder contracting against a sphincter of Oddi in a state of spasm. Normally as already mentioned the sphincter relaxes when the gall-bladder contracts. In biliary dyskenesia the nervous mechanisms upon which this reciprocal action depends are, apparently, disordered. It has also been claimed that a sphincterlike action may be exerted at the junction of the cystic duct with the gall-bladder and that spasm of this ring of muscle during contraction of the gall-bladder may give rise to biliary colic. Also, sudden distention with saline of the common bile duct of conscious patients causes pain resembling that of biliary colic. The pain is felt in the upper right quadrant of the abdomen and in the interscapular or the right scapular region. Nausea and vomiting may occur. The pain impulses travel by splanchnic fibers and enter the cord by the posterior nerve roots from the fourth to the ninth thoracic segments, inclusive.

Gall-bladder disease frequently gives rise to derangements of other organs, particularly of the stomach. Anacidity or hypoacidity and increased motility of the pyloric part of the stomach are commonly encountered. Ivy and Fishback (See Ivy, 1934) experimenting with dogs found that mild stimulation of the biliary tract inhibited gastric motility and lowered gastric tone. They suggest that in the human subject stimulation of this nature is conducive to gastric flatulence and belching. A sudden sharp distension of the bile duct caused pylorospasm and vomiting in their animals. According to some authorities dyspeptic symptoms in from 40 to 50 per cent of subjects are due to biliary tract disease. Cardiac irregularities may result through reflexes initiated from the gall-bladder or bile ducts.

## REFERENCES

Ågren, G., Lagerlöf, H. and Berglund, H. The secretin test of pancreatic function in the diagnosis of pancreatic disease. Acta med. scandinav., 1936, 90, 224.

Babkin, B. P., Hebb, C. O. and Sergeyeva, M. A. The parasympatheticlike effect of splanchnic nerve stimulation on pancreatic secretion. Quart. J. Exper. Physiol., 1939, 29, 217.

Barron, E. S. G. Bilirubinemia. Medicine, 1931, 10, 77.

Baxter, S. G. Continuous pancreatic secretion in the rabbit. Am. J. Physiol., 1931, 96, 343.

Bayliss, W. M. and Starling, E. H. The mechanism of pancreatic secretoin. J. Physiol., 1902, 28, 325.

Berman, A. L. Effect of alcohol on bile volume and constituents in biliary fistula dogs. Quart. J. Studies Alcohol, 1941, 1, 645.

Berman, A. L., Snapp, E., Ivy, A. C. and Atkinson, A. J. On the regulation or homeostasis of the cholic acid output in biliary-duodenal fistula dogs. Am. J. Physiol., 1941, 131, 776.

Billing, B. H., Cole, P. G. and Lathe, G. H. The secretion of bilirubin as a diglucuronide giving the direct van den Bergh reaction. Biochem. J., 1957, 65, 774.

Bloch, K., Berg, B. N. and Rittenberg, D. Biological conversion of cholesterol to cholic acid. J. Biol. Chem., 1943, 149, 511; 157, 601.

Boldyreff, W. N. Fonction périodique de l'organisme chez l'homme et les amimaux d'ordre supérieur. (Pancreas comme principal agent du processus de l'assimilation dans tout les corps). Quart. J. Exper. Physiol., 1916, 10, 175.

Boldyreff, W. N. The periodical activity of the organism and its physiological and clinical significance. Bull. Battle Creek San. and Hosp. Clinic, 1928, 23, 157.

Boyden, E. A. Analysis of reaction of human gall bladder to food. Anat. Rec., 1928, 40, 147.

Boyden, E. A. Sphincter of Oddi in man and certain representative mammals. Surgery, 1937, 1, 25; 1941, 9, 443; 1941, 10, 567.

Boyden, E. A. and Rigler, L. G. Cholecystographic and fluoroscopic study of reaction of human gall bladder to faradic stimulation of stomach and duodenum. Anat. Rec., 1934, 59, 427; 1940, 76, 485.

Brauer, R. W. Mechanisms of bile secretion. Gastroenterology, 1958, 34, 1021.

Carr, J. L. and Foote, F. S. Progressive obstructive jaundice; changes in certain elements of blood and their relation to coagulation. Arch. Surg., 1934, 29, 277.

Cherry, I. S. and Crandall, L. A., Jr. Specificity of pancreatic lipase; its appearance in the blood after pancreatic injury. Am. J. Physiol., 1932, 100, 266.

Dam, H. and Glavind, J. Vitamin K in human pathology. Lancet, 1938, 1, 720.

Dolkart, R. E., Jones, K. K. and Brown, C. F. G. Chemical factors concerned in formation of gallstones. Arch. Int. Med., 1938, 62, 618.

Dragstedt, L. R., Montgomery, M. L. and Matthews, W. B. Fatal effect of total loss of pancreatic juice. Proc. Soc. Exper. Biol. & Med., 1930, 28, 110.

Drill, V. A. and Ivy, A. C. Comparative value of Bromsulphalein, serum phosphatase, prothrombin time, and intravenous galactose tolerance tests in detecting hepatic damage produced by carbon tetrachloride. J. Clin. Invest., 1944, 23, 209.

Drury, D. R., Rous, P. J. and McMaster, P. D. Some causes of gallstone formation; relation of reaction of bile to experimental cholelithiasis. J. Exper. Med., 1924, 39, 403.

Drury, D. R. and Rous, P. Jaundice as an expression of physiological wastage of corpuscles. J. Exper. Med., 1925, 41, 601.

Elman, R. and Graham, E. A. Pathogenesis of "strawberry" gall bladder (cholesterosis of gall bladder). Arch. Surg., 1932, 24, 14.

Elman, R. and McCaughan, J. M. On the collection of the entire external secretion of the pancreas under sterile conditions and the fatal effect of total loss of pancreatic juice. J. Exper. Med., 1927, 45, 561.

ELMAN, R. AND McMASTER, P. D. Studies on urobilin physiology and pathology. I. The quantitative determination of urobilin. J. Exper. Med., 1925, 41, 503. II. Derivation of urobilin. J. Exper. Med., 1925, 41, 513. III. Absorption of pigments of biliary derivation from the intestine. J. Exper. Med., 1925, 41, 719. IV. Urobilin and the damaged liver. J. Exper. Med., 1925, 42, 99. V. The relation between urobilin and conditions involving increased red cell destruction. J. Exper. Med., 1925, 42, 619. VI. The relation of biliary infections to the genesis and excretion of urobilin. J. Exper. Med., 1926, 43, 73.

ELMAN, R. AND TAUSSIG, J. B. Increase in cholesterol content of gall-gladder bile following ligature of cystic duct. Proc. Soc. Exper. Biol. & Med., 1931, 28, 1066, 1068, 1070.

ELMAN, R. AND TAUSSIG, J. B. Cholesterol function of the gall-bladder. J. Exper. Med., 1931, 54, 775.

FRIEDMAN, M. H. F. AND SNAPE, W. J. Comparative effects of extracts of intestinal mucosa in stimulating the external secretion of pancreas and liver. Fed. Proc., 1945, 4, 21.

FRIEDMAN, M. H. F. Personal communication to the author. See Thomas, 1950, p. 96.

FRIEDMAN, M. H. F. AND SNAPE, W. J. Dissociation of secretion of pancreatic enzymes and bicarbonate in patients with chronic pancreatitis. Gastroenterology, 1950, 15, 296.

GAMBLE, J. L. AND McIVER, M. A. Body fluid changes due to continued loss of external secretion of the pancreas. J. Exper. Med., 1928, 48, 837, 849, 859.

GARDNER, J. A. AND GAINSBOROUGH, H. Blood cholesterol studies in biliary hepatic disease. Quart. J. Med., 1930, 23, 465.

GAYET, R. AND GUILLAUMIE M. Sur les modifications de l'excrétions pancréatique consécutives l'hyperglycémie des centres encéphalique. Compt. rend. soc. biol., 1930, 105, 373.

GREENGARD, H., GROSSMAN, M. I., WOOLLEY, J. R. AND IVY, A. C. Confirmation of presence of pancreozymin in duodenal mucosa. Science, 1944, 99, 350.

GREENGARD, H. AND IVY, A. C. The isolation of secretin. Am. J. Physiol., 1938, 124, 427.

GREENGARD, H., STEIN, I. F. AND IVY, A. C. Secretinase in blood serum. Am. J. Physiol., 1941, 133, 121. Modification of the pancreatic response to secretin by urine and urine concentrates. Am. J. Physiol., 1941, 134, 245.

GREENLEE, H. S., LONGHI, E. H., DELGADILLO GUERRERO, J., NELSON, T. S., EL-BEDRI, A. L. AND DRAGSTEDT, L. R. Inhibitory effect of pancreatic secretin on gastric secretion. Am. J. Physiol., 1957, 190, 396.

GROSSBERG, A. L., KOMAROV, S. A., AND SHAY, H. Distribution of proteins and enzymatic activities in electrophoretic components of canine pancreatic juice. Am. J. Physiol., 1952, 168, 269.

GROSSMAN, M. I., GREENGARD, H. AND IVY, A. C. The effect of dietary composition on pancreatic enzymes. Am. J. Physiol. 1943, 138, 676. See also Am. J. Physiol., 1944, 141, 38.

GROSSMAN, M. I. AND IVY, A. C. Effect of alloxan upon external secretion of the pancreas. Proc. Soc. Exper. Biol. & Med., 1946, 63, 62.

GROSSMAN, M. I., JANOWITZ, H. D., RALSTON, H. AND KIM, K. S. The effect of secretin on bile formation in man. Gastroenterology, 1949, 12, 133.

GUTH, P. H., KOMAROV, S. R., SHAY, H. AND STYLE, Z. C. Relationship between protein nitrogen, proteolytic, amylolytic and lipolytic enzymes in canine pancreatic juice obtained under various conditions of stimulation. Am. J. Physiol., 1956, 187, 207. See also Am. J. Physiol., 1958, 192, 1.

HAMMARSTEN, E., JROPES, E., AND ÅGREN, G. Versuche zur Reinigung von Sekretin. Biochem. Ztschr., 1933, 264, 272.

HAMMARSTEN, E., WILANDER, O., AND ÅGREN, G. Versuche zur Reinigung von Sekretin. Acta. med. scandinav., 1928, 68, 239.

HARPER, A. A. AND RAPER, H. S. Pancreozymin, a stimulant of the secretion of pancreatic enzymes in extracts of the small intestine. J. Physiol., 1943, 102, 115.

HIGGINS, G. M. AND MANN, F. C. Emptying of the gall bladder. Am. J. Physiol., 1926, 78, 339.

HIRSCH, G. C., JUNQUEIRA, L. C. V., ROTHSCHILD, H. A. AND DOHI, S. T. Die Pankreassaft-Sekretion bei der Ratte. I. Pflüger's Arch. ges. Physiol., 1957, 264, 78.

HOKIN, L. E. The synthesis and secretion of amylase by pigeon pancreas in vitro. Biochem. J., 1951, 48, 320.

HOKIN, L. E. Amino acid requirement of amylase synthesis by pigeon pancreas slices. Biochem. J., 1952, 50, 216.

HOKIN, L. E. AND HOKIN, MABEL, R. The actions of pancreozymin on pancreas slices and the role of phospholipids in enzyme secretion. J. Physiol., 1956, 132, 442.

HOKIN, MABEL, R. The formation of amylase by mouse pancreas in vitro. J. Biol. Chem., 1956, 319, 77.

HONG, S. S. AND MAGEE, D. F. Influence of dietary amino acids on pancreatic enzymes. Am. J. Physiol., 1957, 191, 71.

IVY, A. C. Contributions to the physiology of the pancreas. Ann. Clin. Med., 1926, 4, 798.

IVY, A. C. Applied physiology of the gastrointestinal innervation. Bull. New York Acad. Sc., 1934, 10, 643.

IVY, A. C. Cholecystagogues, choleretics and cholepoietics. Gastroenterology, 1944, 3, 54.

IVY, A. C., KLOSTER, G. AND LEUTH, H. C. Preparation of a secretin concentrate. Am. J. Physiol., 1930, 95, 35. (See also Greengard and Ivy, 1938.)

IVY, A. C. AND OLDBERG, E. Hormone mechanism for gall-bladder contraction and evacuation. Am. J. Physiol., 1928, 86, 599.

JOHNSON, F. E. AND BOYDEN, E. A. Effect of sectioning various autonomic nerves upon rate of emptying of biliary tract in cat. Surg. Gynec. and Obst., 1943, 76, 395.

JOHNSTON, C. G. AND BALL, E. G. Variations in

inorganic constituents of the pancreatic juice during constant drainage of the pancreatic ducts. J. Biol. Chem., 1930, **86**, 643.

JORPES, E. AND MUTT, V. Secretin, pancreozymin and cholecystotsinin; their physiology and future clinical usefulness. Nord. Med. 1956, **56**, 1511.

KARUSE, W. F. AND WHITAKER, L. R. Effects of different food substances upon emptying of the gall bladder. Am. J. Physiol., 1928, **87**, 172.

KOCOUR, E. J. AND IVY, A. C. The effect of certain foods on bile volume output recorded in the dog by a quantitative method. Am. J. Physiol., 1937, **122**, 325.

KUNITZ, M. AND NORTHRUP, J. H. Isolation, crystallization and general properties of a new proteolytic enzyme and its precursor. J. Gen. Physiol., 1934, **18**, 433. See also J. Gen. Physiol., **21**, 60; **22**, 429; **17**, 591; **19**, 991; and Science, **78**, 558; **80**, 190.

LAGERLÖF, H. The secretin test of pancreatic function. Quart. J. Med., 1939, **8**, 115.

LAGERLÖF, H. Normal esterases and pancreatic lipase in the blood (a second secretin test). Acta med. scandinav., 1945, **120**, 407.

LICHENSTEIN, M. E. AND IVY, A. C. Function of "valves" of Heister. Surgery, 1937, **1**, 38.

LEUTH, H. C. Studies on flow of bile into duodenum and existence of sphincter of Oddi. Am. J. Physiol., 1931, **99**, 237.

MAGEE, D. F. AND ANDERSON, E. G. Changes in pancreatic enzymes brought about by changes in the nature of the dietary protein. Am. J. Physiol., 1955, **181**, 79. See also Hong and Magee, 1957 and Wang, 1955. (Cited by above.)

MAGEE, D. F. AND HONG, S. S. Changes in pancreatic enzymes brought about by amino acid additions to the diet. Am. J. Physiol., 1956, **184**, 449.

MAGEE, D. F. AND WHITE, T. T. Effect of alteration in dietary protein levels on pancreatic enzymes in the rat. Am. J. Physiol., 1958, **193**, 21.

MANN, F. C. The effects of complete and partial removal of the liver. Medicine, 1927, **6**, 419.

MANN, F. C. AND ASSOCIATES. The formation of bile pigment after total removal of the liver. Am. J. Physiol., 1924, **69**, 393. The site of formation of bilirubin. Am. J. Physiol., 1925, **74**, 497. The formation of bile pigment from hemoglobin. Am. J. Physiol., 1926, **76**, 306. Spectrophotometric determination of bilirubin. Am. J. Physiol., 1926, **76**, 577. The liver as a site of bilirubin formation. Am. J. Physiol., 1926, **77**, 219. An experimental study of reduced hepatic function. Am. J. Physiol., 1926, **77**, 179. An evaluation of the relative amounts of bilirubin formed in the liver, spleen and bone marrow. Am. J. Physiol., 1926, **78**, 384. A method for making a satisfactory fistula at any level of the gastrointestinal tract. Ann. Surg., 1931, **93**, 794.

MANN, F. C. AND BOLLMAN, J. L. Relation of gallbladder to development of jaundice following obstruction of common bile duct. J. Lab. and Clin. Med., 1925, **10**, 540.

McCAUGHAN, J. M. Lethal factors in complete pancreatic drainage. Changes in chemistry of the blood. The mechanism of death. Proc. Staff Meet. Mayo Clin., 1929, **4**, 199.

McMASTER, P. D. AND ROUS, P. The biliary obstruction required to produce jaundice. J. Exper. Med., 1921, **33**, 731.

MEAKINS, J. C. Distribution of jaundice in circulatory failure. J. Clin. Invest., 1927, **4**, 135.

MILLER, J. M. AND WIPER, T. B. Physiologic observations on patients with external pancreatic fistulas. Ann. Surg., 1944, **120**, 852.

OKADA, S. On the reaction of bile. J. Physiol. 1915, **50**, 114.

POPIELSKI, L. Über secretorische Hemmungsnerven des Pankreas. Zentralbl. Physiol., 1896, **10**, 405.

QUICK, A. J., STANLEY-BROWN, L. M. AND BANCROFT, F. W. Study of coagulation defect in hemophilia and in jaundice. Am. J. M. Sc., 1935, **190**, 501.

RABINOWITCH, I. M. Arch. Int. Med., 1930, **46**, 1014.

RICH, A. R. Formation of bile pigment from hemoglobin in tissue cultures. Bull. Johns Hopkins Hosp., 1924, **35**, 415; also 1930, **47**, 338.

RICH, A. R. AND DUFF, G. L. Experimental and pathological studies on the pathogenesis of acute hemorrhagic pancreatitis. Bull. Johns Hopkins Hosp., 1936, **58**, 212.

RICHINS, C. A. The innervation of the pancreas. J. Comp. Neurol., 1945, **83**, 223.

RODERICK, L. M. Pathology of sweet clover disease in cattle. J. Am. Vet. M. A., 1929, **74**, 314.

ROUS, P. AND McMASTER, P. D. Concerning activity of the gall bladder. J. Exper. Med., 1921, **34**, 47.

ROUS, P. AND McMASTER, P. D. Physiological causes for the varied character of stasis bile. J. Exper. Med., 1921, **34**, 75.

ROWNTREE, L. G., GREENE, C. H. AND ALDRICH, M. Quantitative Pettenkofer values in blood with special reference to hepatic disease. J. Clin. Invest., 1927, **4**, 545.

RYAN, J. D., DOUBILET, H. AND MULHOLLAND, J. H. Observations on biliary-pancreatic dynamics in a normal human. Gastroenterology, 1949, **13**, 1.

SHERLOCK, S. P. V. Aspiration liver biopsy; technique and diagnostic applications. Lancet, 1945, **II**, 397. (Also J. Path. & Bact., 1946, **58**, 523.)

SCHMIDT, R. Direct reacting bilirubin, bilirubin glucuronide, in serum, bile, and urine. 1956, Science, **124**, 76.

SCOTT, V. B., COLLIGNON, U. J., BUGEL, H. J. AND JOHNSON, G. C. Relation of external pancreatic secretion to variations in blood sugar. Am. J. Physiol., 1941, **134**, 208.

SCOTT, V. B., GRAHAM, J. S. AND McCARTNEY, D. H. Exocrine pancreatic secretion in fasting dogs. Am. J. Digest. Dis., 1940, **7**, 533.

SCOTT, V. B., SCOTT, C. C. AND BUGEL, H. J. Relation of fasting external pancreatic secretion to hunger. Am. J. Physiol., 1940, **131**, 60.

SLUITER, J. W. Das Restitutionsproblem in der

Pankreaszelle. I. Die Bedeutung des Golgi-Apparates. Ztschr. Zellforsch., 1944, **33**, 187.

SMYTH, F. S. AND WHIPPLE, G. H. Bile pigment metabolism: etc. J. Biol. Chem., 1924, **59**, 623, 637 and 647. See also Whipple and Hooper, 1917.

SOFFER, L. J. Present day status of liver function tests. Medicine, 1935, **14**, 185.

THOMAS, J. E. AND CRIDER, J. O. The effect of bile in the intestine on the secretion of pancreatic juice. Am. J. Physiol., 1943, **138**, 548.

TONKISH, ANNA. Zur Physiologie des Pankreas. Pflüger's Arch. ges. Physiol., 1924, **206**, 525.

VIRTUE, R. W. AND DOSTER-VIRTUE, M. E. Continued studies on production of taurocholic acid in dog; cysteine, homocysteine, and thioglycolic acid. J. Biol. Chem., 1939, **127**, 431.

WAKIM, K. G. The physiology of the liver. Am. J. Med., 1954, **16**, 256.

WALDRON, J. M. Photometric determination of amylase in pancreatic juice. J. Lab. and Clin. Med., 1951, **38**, 148.

WANG, C. C. AND GROSSMAN, M. I. Physiological determination of release of secretin and pancreozymin from intestine of dogs with transplanted pancreas. Am. J. Physiol., 1951, **164**, 527.

WATSON, C. J. New England J. Med., 1942, **227**, 99; 1947, **237**, 225, 261; also Blood, 1946, **1**, 225, 261.

WHIPPLE, G. H. AND HOOPER, C. W. Hematogenous and obstructive icterus; experimental studies by means of the Eck fistula. J. Exper. Med., 1913, **17**, 593.

WHIPPLE, G. H. AND HOOPER, C. W. Icterus. A rapid change of hemoglobin to bile pigment in the circulation outside of the liver. J. Exper. Med., 1913, **17**, 612.

WHIPPLE, G. H. AND HOOPER, C. W. Bile pigment metabolism: etc. Am. J. Physiol., 1917, **42**, 544.

WHITAKER, L. R. The mechanism of the gall bladder. Am. J. Physiol., 1926, **78**, 411.

WILANDER, O. AND ÅGREN, G. Biochem. Ztschr., 1932, **250**, 489.

ZUCKER, T. F., NEWBURGER, P. G. AND BERG, B. N. The amylase of serum in relation to functional states of the pancreas. Am. J. Physiol., 1932, **102**, 209.

*Monographs and Reviews*

ASCHOFF, L. The origin of gall-stones. Hoeber, New York, 1924.

BABKIN, B. P. Die äussere Sekretion der Verdauungsdrüsen. 2nd Ed., Julius Springer, Berlin, 1928.

BABKIN, B. P. Secretory mechanism of the digestive glands. 2nd ed., Hoeber, New York, 1950.

BERNARD, CLAUDE. Leçons de Physiologie Experimentale, 1856, Vol. 2, p. 278. (Cited by Opie, 1910.)

DEGRAAF, REGNER (1664). English translation quoted by J. F Fulton, Selected readings in the history of physiology. Chas. C Thomas, Springfield, Ill., 1930.

DRABKIN, D. L. Metabolism of hemin chromoproteins. Physiol. Rev., 1951, **31**, 345.

FLOREY, H. W., WRIGHT, R. D. AND JENNINGS M. A. The secretions of the intestine. Physiol. Rev., 1941, **21**, 36.

GRAHAM, E. A. The clinical application of some recent knowledge of the biliary tract. Harvey Lectures, 1933–34, **29**, 176.

GRAHAM, E. A., COLE, W. H., COPHER, G. H. AND MOORE, S. Diseases of the gall-bladder and bile ducts. Lea and Febiger, Philadelphia, 1928.

GREENGARD, H. Hormones of the gastrointestinal tract; *in* The hormones. Ed. by G. Pincus and K. V. Thimann. Academic Press, N. Y., 1948.

GROSSMAN, M. I. Gastrointestinal hormones. Physiol. Rev., 1950, **30**, 33.

GROSSMAN, M. I. The physiology of secretin. Vitamins and Hormones, 1958, **16**, 179.

GUILLAUMIE, M. Recherches expérimentales sur le rôle du nerf vague dans le fonctionnement exocrine du pancréas. Brenner & Cie., Paris, 1934.

HEIDENHAIN, R. Hermann's Handbuch d. Physiol. Vol. V, part 1, F. C. W. Vogel. Leipzig 1883.

HIRSCH, G. C. Form-und Stoffwechsel der Golgi-Körper. Protoplasma-Monographie, 19. Bornträger, Berlin, 1939.

IVY, A. C. The role of hormones in digestion. Physiol. Rev., 1930, **10**, 282.

IVY, A. C. The physiology of the gall bladder. Physiol. Rev., 1934, **14**, 1.

MANN, F. C. The functions of the gall bladder. Physiol. Rev. 1924, **4**, 251.

MCCLURE, C. W. Functional activities of the pancreas and liver. Medical Authors Pub. Co., New York, 1937.

MACLEAN, H. Modern views on digestion and gastric disease. Constable, London, 1928.

MCNEE, J. W. Jaundice; a review of recent work. Quart. J. Med., 1923, **16**, 390.

MCNEE, J. W. Discussion on jaundice. Brit. M. J., 1924, **2**, 496.

OPIE, E. L. Disease of the pancreas. Its cause and nature, p. 140. Lippincott, Philadelphia, 1910.

PATEY, D. H. Modern views on the mechanism of gall-stone formation. Brit. M. J., 1933, **1**, 866.

PAVLOV, I. P. The work of the digestive glands. Translation by W. H. Thompson. 2nd ed. Lippincott, Philadelphia, 1910.

PETERS, J. P. AND VAN SLYKE, D. D. Quantitative clinical chemistry. Williams & Wilkins, Baltimore, 1946. Vol. 1, p. 347.

RICH, A. R., The formation of bile pigment. Physiol. Rev., 1925, **5**, 182.

ROLLESTON, H. D. AND MCNEE, J. W. Diseases of the liver, gall bladder and bile ducts. Macmillan, London, 1929.

SCHMIDT, C. L. A. The extra-hepatic functions of bile. Physiol. Rev., 1927, **7**, 129.

SOBOTKA, H. The chemistry of the bile acids and related substances. Chem. Rev., 1934, **15**, 311. The physiological chemistry of bile. The Williams & Wilkins Co., Baltimore, 1937.

STILL, E. U. Secretin. Physiol. Rev., 1931, **11**, 328.

THOMAS, J. E. The external secretion of the pancreas. Am. Lecture Series. Charles C Thomas, Springfield, Ill., 1950.

THOMAS, J. E. Methods for study of external secretory function of the pancreas. In method in medical research, Vol. IV, pp. 149–166; ed. by Maurice B. Visscher. Year Book Publishers, Inc., Chicago, Ill., 1951. Also see Gastroenterology, 1959, 36, 362.

VERZAR, F. AND McDOUGALL, E. J. Absorption from the intestine. Longmans, Green & Co., London, 1936.

WALDSCHMIDT-LEITZ, E. Enzyme actions and properties. Wiley, New York, 1929.

WHIPPLE, G. H. The origin and significance of the constituents of the bile. Physiol. Rev., 1922, 2, 40.

# 40

# SECRETION AND ABSORPTION IN THE INTESTINE

The food substances in the gastric chyme are far from being ready for absorption. The products of peptic digestion of protein are still relatively large molecules containing many amino acids. Starch digestion is incomplete and fat digestion has barely begun. In the intestine the enzymes of pancreatic juice carry the digestion of protein a step further but leave most of it still in the form of peptides which need further digestion before being absorbed. Starch and dextrins are reduced to maltose which is unabsorbed as such. Fat digestion is, presumably, accomplished by pancreatic lipase but even this may be aided by lipase from the intestine. Final preparation of food for absorption is accomplished by enzymes contained in the intestinal secretions.

## Secretions of the Small Intestine

### METHODS OF STUDY

The secretion of the intestine may be collected in anesthetized, operated animals by opening the abdomen and inserting a tube into the part of the intestine from which the secretion is to be collected. This method has the serious disadvantage that operative trauma and anesthetic drugs depress the secretory activity of the intestinal glands. The effects of anesthesia may be largely overcome by decerebrating or decapitating the animal under anesthesia and then allowing time for the anesthetic to be eliminated, as was done by Wright and his coworkers (1940). It is also advantageous to immerse the animal in physiological saline, which eliminates the irritant effects on the intestine of drying and exposure. The best results have been obtained by study of unanesthetized animals with surgically isolated loops of intestine. A loop is prepared by cutting through the intestine at two points, thus isolating a segment and re-establishing the continuity of the bowel by end to end anastomosis. To make a *Thiry (1864) loop* one end of the isolated segment is closed and the other end brought out through the abdominal wall to form a fistula. The preparation was modified in 1888 by Vella

who brought both ends of the loop out through the abdominal wall; such a preparation is known as a *Thiry-Vella loop*. These loops maintain their mesenteric connections and retain so much of their innervation as reaches them through the mesentery but are separated from the myenteric and submucous plexuses of the intestine above and below.

Intestinal loops without a nerve supply have been prepared by isolating a segment of intestine, as in the preparation of a Thiry loop, and implanting it under the skin of a mammary gland of a lactating female animal (Ivy *et al.*, 1927). The reason for choosing a lactating female is that the subcutaneous tissue in the vicinity of the mammary glands in such an animal has a very abundant blood supply. At first the mesenteric pedicle is left intact but after a time the local blood vessels grow into the intestine and provide it with a new blood supply. It is then possible to sever the mesenteric pedicle without causing degeneration of the intestinal loop. When this is done a portion of intestine is obtained which is entirely deprived of nervous influences; such a preparation is used to detect hormonal influences on secretion.

In man, and in animals with a simple intestinal fistula, it is possible to collect intestinal secretion by means of a multilumen intestinal tube (Miller and Abbott, 1934). Two of the lumens of the tube are used to inflate balloons; a third lumen having an opening between the balloons can be used to collect the secretion that accumulates in this area. In these as in all studies of intestinal secretion it is important to remember that mechanical stimulation, and especially distention of the intestine, is a profound stimulus to secretion; consequently, when the quantity of secretion is to be determined, or when quantitative differences in secretion obtained under different circumstances are sought, it is essential that mechanical stimulation of the mucosa be avoided. For example, a Thiry fistula into which a catheter has been inserted for collecting the secretion will produce a greater than normal amount of succus entericus.

## The Intestinal Glands

The mucous membrane of the small intestine is everywhere covered with minute projections (about 1 mm. in height and somewhat less in diameter) called intestinal villi. The villi are invested by a layer of columnar cells, of the type characteristic of the intestinal mucosa, set upon a basement membrane beneath which is a fine layer of a smooth muscle fibers continuous with the muscularis mucosae. In the center of each villus is a lymphatic vessel continuous with the lymph vessels of the mucous membrane. This lymphatic is somewhat enlarged into a small sinus lined with endothelium. In some of the larger villi there are several lymphatics. Between the epithelium and the central sinus is a network of blood vessels. Contraction of the smooth muscle of the villus causes a characteristic type of movement which will be described in chapter 41. Between the villi are the openings of the *intestinal glands,* or *crypts of Lieberkühn,* which are simple tubular glands. The crypts do not penetrate the muscularis mucosae. The epithelium covering the villi is of the same type as that lining the crypts and consists of a single layer of columnar cells with certain specialized cells interspersed among them. The free end of each columnar cell, next to the lumen of the intestine, is provided with a specialized cuticular border, resembling the brush border of certain renal tubular cells. Its appearance suggests that it either contains fine pores or is constituted of substances of varied chemical nature arranged in the form of columns. This border may play some essential role in absorption (Verzar and McDougall, 1936).

Here and there among the columnar cells are goblet cells that secrete mucus and specialized cells that stain with silver and are called *argentaffine* or *enterochromaffin cells.* Other cells with a large acidophile nucleus known as *Paneth cells* are also present. The argentaffine cells are of particular interest because they secrete serotonin or at least synthesize its precursor, 5-hydroxytryptophane (Erspamer and Asero, 1952). The functions of serotonin in the body are not known, but it has many powerful pharmacologic actions, among which are stimulation of gastrointestinal motility and inhibition of gastric secretion (Olson and Gray, 1958).

In the bottoms of the crypts many of the epithelial cells may be seen to be undergoing mitosis and at the tips of the villi one can see that cells are being shed into the lumen of the intestine (Leblond and Stevens, 1948). It seems reasonable then, to believe that there is going on in the intestinal mucous membrane a process of continuous replacement of the epithelial lining, new cells being produced in the bottoms of the crypts and the older cells continuously shed at the tips of the villi. The importance of this process will be more evident when we come to consider the mechanism of secretion of the intestinal enzymes.

In the first part of the duodenum, in addition to the regular intestinal glands, are special mucous glands known as *Brunner's glands.* These are similar in structure to the pyloric glands of the stomach. They are made up of long tubules frequently branched and often tortuous which penetrate the muscularis mucosae. Their ducts empty into the crypts of Lieberkühn. Brunner's glands are very numerous in the duodenum between the pylorus and the entrance of the bile and pancreatic ducts. Below this level they are seen less frequently and none are found beyond the duodeno-jejunal junction.

## Intestinal Secretion or Succus Entericus

The composition of the fluid secreted by the intestinal mucous membrane varies somewhat in different parts of the intestine. For example, in the duodenal area, due to the secretion of the mucous glands of Brunner, the secretion contains more mucus than is found elsewhere. In general the secretion of the small intestine is a thin, colorless, or slightly straw-colored fluid somewhat opalescent and containing flecks of mucus. On centrifuging and examining the sediment it can be seen that the cloudy appearance of the juice is partially due to mucus and partly to cellular debris, including some intact cells of the type characteristic of the intestinal mucous membrane (Florey *et al.,* 1941). When collected from the duodenum only, the juice has a more glairy appearance and a heavier consistency, and evidently contains a greater proportion of mucus. In chemical composition, the juice consists of water, inorganic salts, and organic material. The inorganic salts are those commonly present in body fluids, except that the bicarbonate concentration is higher than it is in blood or interstitial fluid. The alkalinity on titration is said to vary between 0.02 and 0.67 per cent sodium bicarbonate equivalent. Various estimates of the pH of the intestinal secretion have been given ranging from 6.3 to 9. The higher values undoubtedly are the result of loss of carbon dioxide from the juice. It is certainly an alkaline fluid and may probably have a true pH as high as 8.3.

Except in the duodenum the quantity of fluid secreted by the small intestine is never very great, a few cc. per hour being the usual amount that it is possible to obtain experimentally, even under conditions of stimulation. It is difficult to determine with accuracy the amount actually secreted because of the tremendous absorptive capacity of the intestine. Many times more than the amount that it is possible to collect may be secreted and reabsorbed during an observation period. That the mucosa is capable, under some circumstances, of passing enormous amounts of fluid into the lumen of the intestine is evident from the great water loss that occurs through the intestine in pathologic states such as cholera, diarrhea, or intestinal obstruction.

The organic matter of the juice consists of mucus, enzymes and cellular debris. The source of the enzymes is unknown but is assumed that they are produced by the columnar cells, although the argentaffine cells or the Paneth cells may be responsible for some of them. A really formidable array of enzymes have been reported as occurring in intestinal secretion. A pepsinlike protease, (from the duodenum only) an amylase, a lipase, at least two peptidases, sucrase (invertase), maltase, lactase, enterokinase, alkaline phosphatase, nucleophosphatases, and nucleosidases have been described.

*Protease.* A weak proteolytic enzyme with properties similar to pepsin was described as occurring in the duodenal secretion by investigators of the Pavlov school (Salaskin, 1902). The similarity of the Brunner's glands to the pyloric glands and the fact that the pyloric portion of the stomach secretes pepsin in small amounts made this observation seem plausible. However, Wright and his associates (1940) who made the most thorough study of intestinal secretion yet reported, could find no protease in duodenal secretion.

*Peptidases.* One of the major functions of intestinal digestion is final reduction of the products of peptic and tryptic digestion to amino acids; this is accomplished by intestinal peptidases. The presence of peptidases has been reported by all investigators who have studied the problem. The ones usually described are amino peptidase, which act on the peptide linkages of terminal amino acids possessing a free amino group; tripeptidases and dipeptidases which split tri- and dipeptides respectively into their constituent amino acids.

*Lipase.* Most investigators have reported finding a weak lipase action in intestinal secretion (Boldyreff, 1904, 1912).

*Disaccharidases.* The various disaccharidases, sucrase, lactase and maltase are present in succus entericus under all normal circumstances.

*Enterokinase.* Enterokinase, the enzyme which converts trypsinogen to trypsin (see under Pancreatic Secretion), is present in the intestinal secretion under normal circumstances. However, Savich (1904) stated that if pancreatic juice was excluded from the intestine, enterokinase gradually disappeared from the secretion as it did also from an intestinal loop in which the pancreatic juice did not circulate. Waldschmidt-Leitz and Harteneck (1925) likewise concluded that pancreatic juice was necessary for liberation of enterokinase from the epithelial cells. Florey, Wright and Jennings (1941) considered that the evidence in neither case was sufficient. The point is of considerable interest and merits further investigation.

The studies of Wright, Jennings, Florey and Lium in 1940, raised a question as to a source of the enzymes ordinarily found in intestinal secretion. They reported that when they took precautions to prevent injury to the mucous membrane while collecting the secretion, and then immediately centrifuged the collected secretion so as to remove cellular debris, only amylase and enterokinase were consistently present in the supernatant fluid. They consider that these enzymes, and possibly maltase, are secreted by the intestinal glands in the usual sense. The others, they believe, are intracellular enzymes which exist in the cells of the mucous membrane and appear in the juice only as a result of the shedding of these cells and their disintegration in the intestine. They point to the opinions of many physiologists that most of the digestion of peptides and disaccharides takes place in the epithelial cells while these substances are being absorbed. This is not, however, a necessary conclusion from the observed facts. The rapid rate of mitosis in the depths of the glands of Lieberkühn and the continuous shedding of epithelial cells from the tips of the villi may represent a special kind of holocrine (see chapter 36) secretory process by which endocellular enzymes are secreted into the intestinal juice, the secretory product being the entire epithelial cell with its contained enzymes. Under normal circumstances the presence of active trypsin in the intestinal contents would seem to insure the rapid disintegration of these cells and liberation of their contained enzymes into the intestinal secretion. In this connection it may be significant that entero-kinase is secreted directly and so insures that activation of trypsinogen does not depend on the disintegration of shed epithelial cells.

## REGULATION OF INTESTINAL SECRETION

### Control of Brunner's Gland Secretion

Secretion of Brunner's glands is controlled by nervous and humoral mechanisms which do not affect the other intestinal glands, or if they do so it is to only a slight extent. The secretion of Brunner's glands increases on stimulation of the vagus nerves or the administration of para-sympathomimetic drugs such as pilocarpine and physostigmine; it is not augmented by stimulation of the sympathetic nerves (Florey and Harding, 1934). The amount of secretion is increased after meals (Blickenstaff *et al.*, 1949), even in transplanted denervated pouches of the duodenum (Florey and Harding, 1935b). This proves that there is a humoral mechanism for regulating the secretion in addition to whatever nervous mechanism there may be. The nature of the humor has been the subject of some discussion and is still undetermined; Florey and Harding (1935a) were convinced that it is pancreatic secretin. They were led to this conclusion by the fact that practically all the stimuli which increase pancreatic secretion, including contact of hydrochloric acid with the duodenal mucous membrane, also increase the secretion of Brunner's glands. They also found that what they considered to be a highly purified secretin preparation stimulated duodenal secretion when given intravenously. Sonnenschein and his associates (1947) were unable to confirm the results with secretin. Using what they believed was a crystalline picrolonate of secretin they observed little effect on Brunner's glands, although crude secretin caused an abundant secretion. Grossman (1950) has suggested that there is a special hormone for these glands which he proposes to call *"duocrinin"*; however, writing in 1958, he still considers the subject to be *"subjudice."*

*Functions of the duodenal secretion.* Florey and Harding (1933) emphasized the protective function of the secretion of Brunner's glands and considered it an important factor in preventing duodenal ulceration. In addition it may assist in emulsification and suspension of fat and other food particles. Since, like other intestinal secretions, it contains enterokinase it helps to activate the trypsinogen of pancreatic juice. Duodenal

secretion is also said to contain "intrinsic factor" and therefore, probably assists in absorption of vitamin $B_{12}$. The various hormones known to be produced by the duodenal mucosa are probably not secreted into the lumen of the intestine except incidentally and in small quantities and are not functional in this situation.

### Control of Secretion of Succus Entericus

*Nervous regulation.* It was demonstrated in Pavlov's laboratory that stimulation of the vagus nerve in animals in which the spinal cord has been severed in the neck caused a moderate secretion of intestinal juice from the duodenum and also from the rest of the small intestine after a latent period of from 1 to $1\frac{1}{2}$ hours (Savich, 1917). Wright and his coworkers (1940) were able to obtain an increased secretion from the duodenum on stimulation of the vagus in decerebrated or decapitated animals, but were unable to obtain clear evidence that vagal stimulation caused secretion from the jejunum or ileum.

Stimulation of the sympathetic causes no secretion but cutting the nerves results in a marked increase in secretion. This *paralytic secretion* as it is called, is increased by physostigmine and inhibited by atropine; it is therefore considered to be dependent upon some cholinergic mechanism in the intestine. Parasympathomimetic drugs, in general, increase the paralytic secretion and sympathomimetic drugs tend to inhibit it. From these observations we can conclude that secretion is augmented by a cholinergic mechanism and that this mechanism is antagonized by the sympathetic. Whether this antagonism is direct or is caused by contraction of the blood vessels remain uncertain. One interpretation of the paralytic secretion is that section of the sympathetic nerves results in dilation of the blood vessels of the intestine and in this way greatly increases the blood flow. Such an increase in blood flow would provide a greater amount of fluid for secretion and, presumably, might produce the augmentation of secretion seen on section of the sympathetic nerves (Starling, 1906). Babkin (1950) has pointed out that cutting the sympathetic nerves to the small intestine increases its motility, which undoubtedly has a massaging effect on the mucous membrane; in view of the fact that one of the most effective stimuli for intestinal secretion is mechanical stimulation of the mucosa, this factor alone may be sufficient to account for the increased secretion.

*Humoral regulation.* The most effective stimulous for secretion of succus entericus is local, mechanical or chemical stimulation of the intestinal mucous membrane. Such stimuli are always present in the digesting intestine due to the presence of chyme and the food particles which it contains. Feeding is not very effective in increasing the rate of intestinal secretion from an isolated intestinal loop, provided the nerve supply is intact, but if the sympathetic nerves have been severed a noticeable increase in secretion takes place when the animal is fed. This indicates that some factor, either nervous or humoral, operates to increase the secretion during digestion. The early investigators were of the opinion that pancreatic secretin was an effective stimulus for intestinal secretion (Delenzenne and Frouin, 1904). This point of view was a result of experiments in which injections of secretin-containing preparations resulted in undoubted increases in secretion of intestinal juice. However, as more highly purified preparations of secretin became available the influence on intestinal secretion became less so that now it is doubtful whether secretin as such acts on the intestinal glands. On the other hand, intestinal extracts, from which secretin has been totally eliminated remain potent stimuli for intestinal secretion. This subject has been investigated most fully by Nasset and his coworkers (1938) who have prepared an extract of the intestinal mucous membrane which is free from secretin, from vasodilator material and from toxic substances, but has a powerful effect upon the secretion of the small intestine when given intravenously. Subcutaneous injection is less effective but in large doses produces some secretion. The material undoubtedly contains a hormone which augments the intestinal secretion; it is called *"enterocrinin."* The fact that a hormonal mechanism is involved in normal intestinal secretion has been amply demonstrated by Nasset and his coworkers (1935) by means of denervated loops of intestine; such loops secrete when acid and certain other substances are placed in the intact portions of the intestine, and also after meals.

*Regulation of enzyme secretion.* There is little published data on the control of secretion of organic compounds in the succus entericus. However Nasset (1956) is of the opinion that the parasympathetic nerves control the output of enzymes from the intestinal glands as they do the secretion of organic matter in saliva. He also suggests that crude enterocrinin may contain a specific hormone for the secretion of intestinal enzymes comparable to pancreozymin which promotes secretion of pancreatic enzymes.

### The Function of the Succus Entericus

Enzymatic digestion of food, in all its phases, is a hydrolytic process; an abundance of water to serve as one of the reacting substances is therefore essential. The succus entericus provides this water in the area in which the major part of digestion of food occurs. Water is also necessary to serve as a solvent and as a medium of suspension and transport for the solids which are either dissolved or suspended in the chyme. The enzymes, either in the secretion or in the cells, complete the digestion of protein and carbohydrate by reducing the peptides, resulting from peptic and tryptic digestion, to amino acids and the disaccharides, resulting from amylolytic digestion of starch to glucose. Other disaccharides that may be present in the food are likewise digested liberating their constituent monosaccharides. In fat digestion the succus entericus serves as a source of water and as a medium for suspension and emulsification of the fat particles; it also provides a certain amount of lipase.

### Secretion of the Colon

The mucosa of the mammalian cecum and colon is in many respects similar to that of the small intestine; crypts are present but there are no villi. As in the small intestine, the cells at the bottoms of the crypts exhibit numerous mitoses, suggesting the continuous replacement of shed epithelial cells. Goblet cells are more numerous than in the small intestine and the epithelial cells between the goblet cells differ among themselves but in the majority the protoplasm is clear and free from secretory granules. The secretion is scanty (Wright *et al.*, 1938) as is to be expected from the fact that a major function of the large intestine is absorption of water. The decrease in volume of intestinal contents that occurs in this area indicates that secretion does not keep pace with absorption. Actually, it is usually not possible to collect any secretion from a colonic fistula unless the mucous membrane is stimulated mechanically by insertion of a catheter or other instrument. Even with this stimulation only a few tenths of a cubic centimeter per hour can be collected. When anything can be collected it consists of watery fluid with clumps of white mucus; often it is viscous and opalescent. The reaction is alkaline due to sodium bicarbonate which may be present in concentrations as high as 80-90 m.eq. per liter, according to deBeer *et al.* (1935). Of the solids 0.63 percent is organic and the remainder is inorganic material.

The secretion of the cecum apparently contains enzymes corresponding to those found in the small intestine, with the exception of enterokinase which is not present. The secretion of enzymes becomes progressively less and ultimately disappears toward the distal colon. The large intestine has an extraordinary capacity to secrete mucus and under certain circumstances may secrete a surprisingly large amount of the material. As elsewhere in the intestine, mucus is secreted in response to strong local stimulation or irritation, hence, mucus is likely to be secreted in unusual amounts in the presence of bacterial infection or other causes of local irritation, such as irritant cathartics. The secretion is an active process involving utilization of oxygen; it is inhibited by perfusion of the intestine with cyanide.

### Nervous Control of Colonic Secretion

Florey (1930) and Wright *et al.* (1938) found that stimulation of the nervus erigens caused the colon to secrete a clear mucoid fluid; in contrast to the practical absence of spontaneous secretion, stimulation produced as much as 55 cc. in one 8-hour period from the distal half of the colon; the average rate was about 5 cc. per hour. Reflex secretion was observed on stimulation of the cut end of one nervus erigens, the other being intact; the reflex center was located in the lumbar spinal cord. Larson and Bargen (1933) observed secretion of mucus in an isolated segment of the colon at the time of defecation. It should be recalled that the nervus erigens supplies only the distal portion of the colon with parasympathetic fibers; the parasympathetic supply for the proximal colon comes from the vagi. Acetylcholine and pilocarpine increase colonic secretion whereas atropine inhibits it. Histamine has been reported to cause a slight increase in secretion. The secretion is reduced by anesthetics. Cutting the sympathetics does not produce paralytic secretion in the large intestine, but stimulation of the sympathetics diminishes the secretory response to stimulation of the nervus erigens.

The relationship of the secretory function of the colon to the autonomic nerves has a bearing upon the occurrence of certain diseases of the colon in which there is excessive secretion of mucus, for example, *mucous colitis*. This is a disease in which excessive amounts of mucus appear in the stools constituting, in some cases, tubular casts of the colon. This has often been considered a psychosomatic disease and has a close relationship to abnormal emotional states.

### The Intestinal Mucosa as an Excretory Organ

The feces contain small amounts of fat, even during prolonged starvation, indicating that some fat is eliminated by way of the intestine. Probably a great deal more fat is excreted into the intestine than escapes in the feces, the majority being reabsorbed (Sperry and Bloor, 1924). It has been claimed also that the colon excretes calcium, phosphorus, iron and various heavy metals. Although this is probably true, it is not likely that the intestine constitutes an important avenue of excretion for these substances once they have been absorbed.

Although probably not normally an important organ of excretion, the intestinal mucous membrane, by virtue of its permeability to numerous diffusable substances can be made to function as an organ of excretion. For example, if a double lumen tube is placed in the intestine with one opening high up and the other low down and fluid perfused through so that it enters at a high level and escapes through the tube after passing through the intestine, it will carry away diffusable substances from the blood. Use has been made of this mechanism in cases of renal failure in which nonprotein nitrogenous substances and other toxic waste products accummulate in the blood. Since any diffusable substance will tend to establish an equal concentration in the blood and the intestinal contents, any mechanism which continually replaces and removes the intestinal contents will remove these substances from the body; thus the intestine may be used an an "artificial kidney." One great difficulty with this procedure is that not only the toxic substances which it is desired to remove, but all the diffusable constituents of the blood are removed in this manner. It is necessary, therefore, that the fluid used for perfusion should approximate the composition of the blood plasma with respect to all normal diffusable constituents insofar as possible. The normal excretory function of the intestine, of course, has to do with the disposal of the residues remaining after completion of digestion and absorption in the small intestine. This is accomplished mainly in the large intestine where the water and salts of the intestinal contents are recovered and the solid residues formed into feces (see ch. 42).

### The Absorptive Function of the Intestine

The mucous lining of the small intestine is one of the most remarkable organs of the body. It secretes a variety of hormones which help to regulate gastric secretion and motility, the secretion of the pancreas and of the intestine itself, and the movements of the gall bladder and the intestinal villi. This endocrine activity, which is mainly concentrated in the upper intestine, has led Dr. E. S. Nasset to characterize the duodenum as the "hypophysis of the abdomen." The same tissue which secretes hormones into the blood forms an external secretion containing a variety of digestive enzymes, at least as numerous as those found in the pancreatic juice. During absorption the mucosal cells perform a variety of hydrolytic and synthetic operations upon the food substances passing through them, greatly modifying the character of the absorbed material. Even while producing their own secretions the epithelial cells are transferring water and dissolved substances from the lumen of the intestine into the interstitial fluid to be taken up by the blood. This absorptive activity is highly selective and frequently involves the expenditure of considerable energy. Probably nowhere, except possibly in the liver, is so great a variety of functions performed by a single tissue.

The ultimate aim of digestion is absorption. Only after the products of digestion have passed through the epithelial lining of the digestive tract and entered the blood stream are they able to serve their purpose of providing nourishment for the tissue cells of the body. Absorption of such materials takes place almost entirely from the small intestine. Although the stomach is capable of absorbing small amounts of water and certain food substances, notably glucose and some foreign substances such as alcohol, the absorption that occurs here is negligible, partly because the food is not digested sufficiently in the stomach to be readily absorbed, but mainly because the gastric mucous membrane is not adapted for absorption as is that of the small intestine. A possible exception is iron, which may be absorbed in significant quantities from the stomach. Although absorption of food occurs mainly in the small intestine, water and salts are absorbed in significant amounts from the large intestine.

The mucous lining of the small intestine is admirably adapted to its absorptive function. The structure of the epithelium has been described in connection with the discussion of intestinal secretion. The intestinal villi will be referred to in the chapter on movements of the alimentary canal. It has been estimated that the presence of the villi results in an increase of seven- or eight-fold in the surface area of the mucous membrane of the intestine.

*Methods for study of intestinal absorption.* The methods described in the section on intestinal secretion are also available for the study of absorption. In acute experiments one places the material, the absorption of which is to be studied, in an isolated loop of intestine and, after a measured time, removes it and observes the volumetric or chemical changes that have taken place. The Thiry or Thiry-Vella loop may be used in the same manner. In the case of substances that can be readily detected in the blood, the material can be placed in the intact intestine and its absorption estimated by the rate of its appearance in the circulating blood, or in the portal blood, or the intestinal lymph, if the experiment is of such a nature as to make these vessels available. In recent years it has been possible through the use of food materials tagged with radioactive isotopes to gain much information that could not have been obtained by means of the older methods.

The development of *in vitro* techniques for the study of excised segments of intestine have also greatly increased our knowledge in recent years. A variety of techniques for this purpose have been described by different authors; all depend upon maintaining the vitality of a portion of the intestine that has been removed from the body by keeping it in contact with oxygenated fluid of appropriate composition. The preparation can be so arranged that the fluid inside the intestine which is in contact with the absorbing surface can be kept separate from that on the outside in contact with the serosal surface and the changes in composition of the internal and external fluid used to measure the degree of absorption by the mucosa. Studies of this sort are done chiefly on smaller animals, such as rats, guinea pigs and hamsters since their relatively thin intestines are more easily maintained in a viable condition in an artificial medium.

### ABSORPTION OF WATER

Much that has been published on the absorption of water from the intestine is of little value because, until recently, it has been impossible to distinguish between the water that was secreted into the intestine and water that left the intestine by absorption. Changes observed in the volume of water in the intestine did not represent total absorption of water but merely the difference in the volume of water secreted into the intestine and that absorbed. Since there is reason to believe that water moves freely through the intestinal mucosa it is essential that we know how much water entered the intestine in a given time if we are to make an intelligent estimate of the amount leaving by way of absorption in the same time. It has been possible to get around this difficulty and to determine accurately the amount of water leaving the intestine by absorption in a unit of time by the use of heavy water. Water containing heavy hydrogen can be readily detected in the blood and also the amount remaining in the intestine can be accurately measured. Since, in a short period of time the water secreted into the intestine will be normal water, the change in heavy water content represents water actually absorbed. Or if, as in experiments on human subjects, it is not possible to determine the amount of water remaining in the intestine, the amount of heavy water appearing in the blood can be used as an estimate of the water absorbed.

Scholer and Code (1954) studied absorption of water from the human stomach and small intestine using heavy water as a tracer. They found that when 50 grams of water were given 2.5 per cent of this amount was absorbed per minute so long as it remained in the stomach. When the water was placed in the small intestine it was absorbed at about ten times that rate, 26.1 per cent of the dose being absorbed per minute. If the water remained in the stomach it required 34.2 minutes to absorb 67 per cent of the administered amount; whereas in the intestine, this percentage was absorbed in 3.7 minutes. In the intestine 95 per cent of the administered water was absorbed in ten minutes. In these experiments only absorption was measured and the net volume change was not observed; hence, no account was taken of the water that might have been secreted into the stomach or intestine during this same period of time. One interesting fact brought out in these studies is the extremely rapid absorption of water from the intestine. Another is that there is an appreciable absorption of water from the stomach. The statement often seen in the literature that water is not absorbed in appreciable amounts from the stomach is based on the net change in volume in which no account is taken of the concurrent secretion of fluid into the stomach. Considering net absorption only, that is the decrease in the volume of intestinal contents, it appears that water is absorbed more rapidly from the terminal ileum than from other parts of the small intestine. Most of what remains is absorbed from the large intestine.

The net absorption of fluids from the intestine in influenced by hydrostatic and osmotic pressures. Blickenstaff and others (1952) found that there was a significant difference in the rate of absorption of chloride and water at different levels of hydrostatic pressure. Between the extremes there was an optimal pressure at which absorption was most rapid. He also noted that water was absorbed more rapidly from dilute than from concentrated solutions. Absorption is accelerated by an increase in hydrostatic pressure, up to the point where the pressure begins to interfere with the blood supply to the intestinal mucous membrane. Nasset and Parry (1934) found that negative hydrostatic pressure tended to accelerate the net flow of fluid into the intestine whereas increasing the pressure favored net absorption provided the pressure exceeded 25 cm. of solution. Between 5 and 25 cm. there was no change. It has been suggested by Verzar and McDougall (1936) that absorption of water from the large intestine is largely dependent on the relatively high hydrostatic pressure said by them to be maintained in this organ. Other things being equal, it has been found that, within physiological limits, the rate of absorption of water is directly proportional to the hydrostatic pressure in the intestine. When considering net absorption only, the rate of absorption of water decreases with increasing osmotic pressure of the intestinal contents but this relationship is not linear. More water is absorbed from hypotonic than from isotonic solutions and more from isotonic than from hypertonic solutions.

### Absorption of Inorganic Salts

Of the inorganic salts that are presented to the intestine for absorption, the more important are sodium, potassium and calcium chlorides, and phosphate. Absorption of iron will be considered in chapter 8. The absorption of chlorides of sodium and potassium are always accompanied by absorption of water and the more rapidly the water is absorbed the more rapidly will the salts be absorbed. The salt concentration in the solution passing through the mucosa from the lumen of the intestine toward the blood is not necessarily the same as that of the intestinal contents. From an isotonic solution in the intestine the fluid absorbed tends to be hypertonic so that as absorption progresses the fluid in the intestine becomes hypotonic due to loss of salt (Visscher *et al.*, 1944). The salt concentration in the absorbed mixture is proportional to the concentration in the intestinal contents but due to the osmotic effect of concentrated salt solutions on the net movement of water, less salt may be absorbed from a concentrated than from a dilute solution. Rabinovitch (1927) found that the greatest percentage absorption of water was from salt solutions ranging in concentration from 0.4 to 0.6 per cent and that the absolute amount of salt absorbed increased with increasing concentration of salt up to 0.8 per cent. He noted also that water and chloride are absorbed more rapidly when potassium ions are present and that absorption was accelerated even more by calcium ions in the solution. An interesting paradox is that atropine, which inhibits most intestinal functions, accelerates net water and salt absorption. This is due to the inhibitory effect of atropine on intestinal secretion.

Calcium salts, including the phosphate, are absorbed more readily from the upper intestine than from the ileum. A problem in calcium absorption is the relative insolubility of the commonly occurring calcium salts, such as the phosphate, in alkaline and neutral solutions; consequently, calcium is absorbed better from an acid than from an alkaline medium; this fact may explain the better absorption of calcium from the relatively acid upper intestine. It has been noted that the phosphates enter the intestine chiefly as phosphoproteins or phospholipids which may not be readily digested in the upper intestine where the principal calcium absorption occurs; hence, calcium and the phosphates may be absorbed in different regions of the intestine, thus avoiding the formation of insoluble calcium phosphates. Nevertheless in the absence of normal hydrochloric acid secretion by the stomach, calcium absorption tends to be poor, so that achlorhydrics often suffer from a calcium deficiency.

Calcium is said to be absorbed more readily by individuals suffering from a calcium deficiency, indicating some control of calcium absorption by systemic factors. The presence of an excess of magnesium is said to interfere with calcium absorption as does phytic acid which occurs in cereal grains and which may be responsible for the tendency of these grains to produce rickets when fed exclusively or in excess. The administration of vitamin D accelerates absorption of calcium from the lower ileum but not from other parts of the intestinal tract. Vitamin D counteracts the effect of phytic acid so that when given in adequate amounts it offsets the tendency of cereal grains to cause rickets.

*The mechanism of water and salt absorption.* Considering the apparently free permeability of the intestinal mucous membrane to water and the simple inorganic salts it is tempting to try to explain the absorption of these substances on the basis of simple diffusion or osmosis. As we have seen, the physical and chemical laws are operative in the transfer of water through the intestinal mucosa, but as our knowledge has increased, it has become increasingly evident that these principles are inadequate to explain all the observed phenomena. Ingraham and Visscher (1936, 1938) showed that, in the presence of a sulfate solution, sodium chloride was absorbed against a concentration gradient; that is, its absorption went on until the concentration in the intestine fell far below that in the interstitial fluid and in the blood. Likewise the osmotic activity of the fluid in the intestine decreased in their experiments until it fell to as much as half an atmosphere below the osmotic pressure of the blood plasma, thus leaving no doubt that the absorption took place as the result of osmotic work by the intestinal epithelium. In a later study (1944) in which they used isotopic tracer techniques so that they could measure absorption and secretion separately and determine precisely the amount of water and salt absorbed, they were able to determine that the rate of movement of water from gut to blood (absorption) was often as much as 100 times as rapid as it would have been under the same circumstances if only the laws of diffusion and osmosis were operating. Likewise the amount of salt moved in either direction was often found to be at variance with the amount determined by calculation on the basis of the laws of diffusion and osmosis. Studies on isolated preparations have given results with a similar significance.

McHardy and Parsons (1957), studying intact animals, found that chloride was absorbed from solutions containing from 20 to 50 m.eq. per liter less than the blood plasma. Sodium was absorbed from isotonic solutions containing from 45 to 75 m.eq. per liter less sodium than the plasma. They noted a statistically linear relation between the total absorption of solutes and the absorption rate of water indicating an interrelationship between the absorption of these two types of products but they were unable to determine which was dependent on the other. In isolated preparations, Smyth and Taylor (1957) found that the transfer of water from the mucosal to the serosal side of excised rat small intestine was dependent upon the presence of glucose and oxygen in the medium and was affected by temperature. It was prevented by various metabolic inhibitors indicating that the transfer was an active metabolic process. Others have found that the transfer of a salt solution from the mucosal to the serosal side failed in the absence of oxygen.

It is necessary to conclude that the absorption of both water and salts, although influenced by physicochemical forces, is for the most part an active process dependent upon the metabolic activity of the mucosal cells of the intestine. Little is known of the chemical mechanisms involved but oxygen appears to be necessary. There remains the possibility that only one of the two substances, water and salt, is moved actively since the movement of either would necessitate the transfer of the other in order to maintain osmotic equilibrium; thus either water or salt may be absorbed actively and the other carried passively, but the evidence favors active transfer of salt. For example, in a salt restricted diet sodium practically disappears from the contents of the terminal ileum (Field *et al.*, 1955). This suggests a sodium conserving action of the upper intestine and strongly implies selective absorption of sodium.

### Absorption of Carbohydrates

Only the monosaccharides are readily absorbed by the intestinal mucous membrane. Some disaccharides may enter the blood by diffusion, but if they do they are promptly excreted and not metabolized. The intestinal epithelium is, in general, impermeable to the polysaccharides. The important monosaccharides are destrose, levulose and galactose. Dextrose occurs as the final product of starch digestion and as one of the two products of hydrolysis of sucrose and lactose. Levulose occurs as a product of sucrose digestion and also in certain natural products such as some fruits and in honey. Galactose is one of the constituents of lactose. Other simple sugars such as mannose and pentoses are quantitatively unimportant. The three simple sugars, galactose, dextrose and levulose are all actively absorbed from the small intestine, galactose more rapidly and levulose less rapidly than glucose.

The ability of the intestine to absorb glucose against a concentration gradient has been repeatedly demonstrated; that is to say that glucose can be absorbed when the concentration of glucose in the intestinal contents is lower than the concentration in the blood. In an excised preparation, glucose passes from the mucosal to the serosal side even when the concentration on the mucosal side of the preparation is lower than it is on the serosal side. Active absorption of glucose is prevented by phloridzin, a substance that inhibits the enzymes involved in phosphorylation; this suggests that the phosphorylation of glucose, which is known to occur in the mucosal cells, is essentially involved in the mechanism of active absorption. Glucose may still be absorbed in the presence of phloridzin but only if a favorable concentration gradient exists. Absorption in this case is by simple diffusion.

Phosphorylation of glucose is of interest as being probably typical of the mechanisms through which active absorption can occur. It is believed that the glucose molecule enters the mucosal cell by simple diffusion where it is promptly transformed into glucose-6-phosphate through the action of glucokinase plus adenosine triphosphate (ATP). Since glucose-6-phosphate is a different compound from glucose, its accumulation in the cell does not lower the concentration gradient from lumen to cell so that glucose continues to diffuse in to be phosphorylated. The glucose-6-phosphate is hydrolyzed as the sugar passes out of the cell and into the interstitial fluid from which it is transferred into the circulating blood as glucose. The process involves expenditure of energy which is obtained by oxidation of a certain percentage of the glucose; this appears as lactic acid which is also absorbed. Probably levulose and galactose are similarly phosphorylated on absorption. Some of the levulose is converted into glucose in the epithelial cells but the conversion occurs mainly in the liver as it does also with galactose. In addition to active absorption, since the intestinal mucosa is permeable to the simple sugars, some are absorbed by simple diffusion when a favorable concentration gradient exists. This is usually the case with galactose and levulose since these sugars are never present in the blood in any considerable concentration (Canterow and Shepartz, 1954).

The sugars are absorbed much more rapidly from the upper than from the lower small intestine. Fisher and Parsons (1949), have shown that there is a linear gradient in the intestine in its ability to absorb glucose from the intestinal contents. The rate of absorption is directly proportional to the distance of the segment in question from the ileocecal valve (see figure 40.1). Absorption of sugars is diminished in the presence of sodium chloride deficiency such as may occur in adrenal cortical insufficiency. This suggests that the neutral salts play a part in the active absorption of sugar, possibly by being secreted into the intestinal contents to make up for the osmotic loss when the sugar is taken away. Absorption of sugars is accelerated in hyperthyroidism and depressed in hypothyroidism and in the latter case administration of thyroxin improves absorption. Pantothenic acid, thyamine and pyridoxine, members of the B vitamin group, are essential for normal sugar absorption.

It is interesting to note that although the pentoses are more diffusible than the hexoses, the pentoses are absorbed at a much slower rate, proving again that the hexoses are actively absorbed. With most sugars, particularly those that are not actively absorbed, the rate of absorption increases with increasing concentration in the intestinal contents. With glucose and galactose however, this is true only up to about a 5 per cent concentration, which for these sugars is approximately isotonic with the blood. Further increase in concentration of these sugars fails to increase or decrease their rate of absorption. Furthermore, if glucose and galactose are given simultaneously each suppresses the absorption of the other (Cori, 1931) so that the total amount of sugar absorbed is not more than would be absorbed if only one of the sugars were present. These facts indicate that the mechanisms for active absorption can be saturated in a manner somewhat analogous to the tubular maximum for glucose in the renal tubules.

A certain amount of absorption of glucose and other simple sugars may take place in the large intestine but in the human this is relatively unimportant. Absorption of carbohydrates from the small intestine is usually so complete that by the time the intestinal contents reach the terminal ileum there is no sugar present. However, glucose solution may be injected into the large intestine in situations in which oral feeding is impractical. Such sugar is absorbed, although much more slowly than from the small intestine. In certain animals in which cellulose constitutes a considerable fraction of the diet, a major part of the digestion of carbohydrate may occur in the large intestine since it depends upon the action of bacteria and not upon digestive enzymes secreted by the animal. In such animals absorption of sugars from the large intestine may be a necessary mechanism.

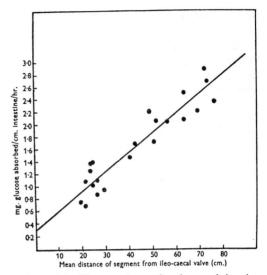

FIG. 40.1. Glucose absorption in surviving intestine. Relation between glucose disappearance from inner fluid and mean distance of segment from ileocecal valve in 1-hour experiments. From Fisher and Parsons, 1949. Courtesy of Cambridge University Press.

### PROTEIN ABSORPTION

Some absorption of native protein and of intermediate products of protein digestion may take place in the small intestine but by far the greater part of the protein in the food is reduced to amino acids before being absorbed. Protein absorption is, therefore, essentially amino acid absorption. All available evidence indicates that amino acids are readily absorbed throughout the entire length of the small intestine. They are taken up about as rapidly as they are produced by the action of digestive enzymes; consequently only small amounts of amino acids can be found at any time in the intestinal contents. Also, any excess in the blood due to absorption disappears rapidly so that it is difficult to trace the absorption of amino acids from the intestine by chemical means. Although all the amino acids are rapidly absorbed from the intestine, some are absorbed more rapidly than others. The following list is in the order of rapidity of absorption: glycine, alanine, cystine, glutamic acid, valine, methionine, leucine, tryptophane, isoleucine, norleucine, isovaline (Verzar and McDougall, 1936).

Wiseman (1953) has shown that the levorotatory, or naturally occurring forms of alanine, phenylalanine, isoleucine, valine, methionine and histidine are absorbed more rapidly than the dextrorotatory isomers and that the levo- forms could be transferred through the intestinal wall against a concentration gradient, whereas the dextro- forms tended to reach the same concentration on the two sides of the membrane (as did glutamic and aspartic acids). Eldsen and others (1950) have found that if a racemic mixture of amino acids is introduced into the intestine, the levorotatory isomers will be absorbed as much as six times more rapidly than the dextro-isomers. These facts—and the fact that there are differences in the rate of absorption of amino acids that are not related to their diffusibility—as well as the rapid disappearance of amino acids from the intestine, all point to the fact that there is an efficient mechanism for the active absorption of many of the amino acids and that their absorption does not depend upon diffusion and osmosis. This conclusion is further supported by the fact that amino acid absorption is inhibited by absence of oxygen and by several metabolic inhibitors such as dinitrophenol and desoxypyridoxine (Friedlander and Quastel, 1955). Phloridzin, which interferes with phosphorylation and prevents active absorption of glucose, does not interfere with active absorption of amino acids. Nevertheless amino acids are said to compete with sugars for the absorptive mechanisms; that is, sugars are absorbed more slowly from a sugar-amino acid mixture than from a pure sugar solution (Cori, 1931).

Considerable transamination of amino acids occurs in the mucosal cells, consequently, they are not necessarily delivered to the blood in the same form in which they are absorbed; for example, glutamic and aspartic acids may be converted to alanine during absorption. If the absorption rate is slow, practically all the glutamic and aspartic acids undergo such change; on the other hand, during rapid absorption there is relatively less transamination and considerable quantities of glutamic and aspartic acids appear in the blood (Neame and Wiseman, 1957). It has been suggested that in this way the intestinal mucosa modifies the amino acid mixture that is being absorbed from a particular meal, reducing the amount of amino acids that are in excess in the digesting mixture and increasing the amount of those that are in short supply so as to more nearly meet the needs of the organism for specific amino acids.

Since many of the intermediate products of protein digestion are soluble in water and some are diffusible, the question naturally arises as to whether some proteoses and peptones may be absorbed from the intestine without being reduced to amino acids. Peptone solutions certainly disappear from intestinal loops but this does not prove that the peptone was absorbed as such. It will be recalled that the peptidases of the intestinal secretion are believed by some to be intracellular enzymes which are not actually secreted but appear in the intestinal contents as a result of a breakdown of shed epithelial cells. It seems unlikely that peptides could get through the mucosal cells in any considerable quantity without being reduced to amino acids by the intracellular peptidases. The same reasoning does not apply to native protein which may have escaped digestion for one reason or another by the pepsin of gastric juice or the trypsin of pancreatic juice. Except for traces of pepsin in the Brunner's gland secretion, there are no proteases in the intestinal secretion or in the mucosal cells that are known to be able to attack native protein. It is not surprising, therefore, to find that egg albumin and milk protein can sometimes be demonstrated in the blood by immunological methods, after these proteins have been placed in the intestine. Absorption of native protein is not necessarily a result of a pathological condition of the intestinal mucosa, although the absorption may be greatly increased by an inflammatory condition. Gruskay and Cooke (1955) have found that after feeding 1 gram of crystalline egg albumin per kilogram of body weight to normal children, they could detect in the plasma of these children between 0.45 and 7.3 $\mu$g. of egg albumin per ml. of plasma. In children recovering from diarrhea the amount ranged from 4 to 53 $\mu$g. per ml. It seems likely that many cases of food allergy result from such absorption of native protein, either from a normal or from an inflamed intestine. Since the absorption is greater in inflammatory states it appears that some caution is indicated in the feeding of patients suffering from enteritis.

## ABSORPTION OF FAT

Fat absorption is a complicated process which, even now, is not fully understood. It is known that bile and pancreatic juice are essential for normal fat absorption, yet appreciable amounts of fat can be absorbed from the intestine in the absence of both. Elaborate mechanisms exist in the intestine for splitting triglycerides into fatty acids and glycerol, and yet the fat that appears in the lymphatics after absorption is nearly all triglyceride fat.

Efforts to explain fat absorption have been embodied in two main theories. The older, known as the *lipolytic theory*, was proposed by Pflüger in its original form and modified and supported by Verzar (Verzar and McDougall, 1936). According to this theory all fat is hydrolyzed in the intestine to fatty acids and glycerol by the action of pancreatic, gastric and intestinal lipases. Previous to hydrolysis the fat is emulsified by the action of bile and, after some hydrolysis has occurred, by soaps produced by the interaction of the liberated fatty acids with the alkali of the intestinal fluids. Since the upper intestine is usually acid and the ileum only slightly alkaline the fatty acids are insoluble in the intestine at the usual pH levels of the intestinal contents; they are made soluble through the formation of complexes with the bile acids, glycocholic and taurocholic acids chiefly. During absorption these complexes enter the mucosal cells where the bile acids are split off and, for the most part, returned to the intestinal lumen. The fatty acids are recombined with glycerol to form triglycerides which are then transferred to the lymphatics. Somewhere in the process, either during absorption into the epithelial cells or during synthesis into triglycerides, phosphorylation takes place, the function of which is not clear but which is assumed to be essential to the process. Verzar leans to the opinion that phosphorylation is essential to the resynthesis of triglycerides. According to this theory, although some fatty acid may be absorbed by way of the portal vein, the amount is negligible. No fat is absorbed directly as triglyceride.

Frazer (1946) has raised objections to the lipolytic hypothesis and presented one of his own which has come to be called the *partition hypothesis*. According to Frazer's view bile and soap are not adequate emulsifying agents under the conditions found in the intestine, chiefly due to the acid reaction in the duodenum. However, emulsions can be formed in an acid medium, if in addition to bile, mono- and diglycerides are added to the mixture. These agents are produced by the hydrolytic action of lipases in the intestine as steps in the process of hydrolysis of triglycerides. According to Frazer's view, the function of the lipases is mainly to form these compounds for the purpose of emulsifying the fat. Some free fatty acids are produced in the process and these are absorbed into the portal blood, after forming complexes with the bile acids as postulated by Verzar. According to Frazer, the important step in absorption is not lipolysis but emulsification and when the fat has been reduced to particles not exceeding 0.5 micron in diameter they enter the epithelial cells as triglycerides and are directly transferred to the lymphatics. The small fat particles are known as *chylomicrons* and

appear in the lymph and the blood as such. Each chylomicron has a coating consisting of lipoprotein and phospholipid and it may be that the phosphorylation is concerned with producing the necessary phospholipids for the formation of chylomicrons. Resynthesis of fat in the epithelial cells is not a necessary part of the process of absorption according to this theory.

Neither theory conforms to all the known facts but certain features of each are well substantiated. Resynthesis of fatty acids into triglycerides within the epithelial cells, as postulated by Verzar, has been abundantly confirmed by many investigators. For example, Bergström and others (1954) found that when free oleic acid labelled with carbon-14 was fed, 63 per cent of the fed acid was recovered in the lymph as neutral fat. When triolein was fed 65 per cent was recovered in the lymph. These authors also found that when fatty acids containing 10 or fewer carbon atoms were fed they were absorbed by way of the portal blood where they were transported mainly as free fatty acids. Longer chain fatty acids were synthesized in the epithelial cells into triglycerides and absorbed by way of the lymphatics. Kiyasu, Bloom and Chaikoff (1952) also found that short chain fatty acids were transported mainly by the portal pathway and long chain saturated fatty acids by way of the lymph. Therefore, a sort of partition does occur in the intestine, but not based on the degree of hydrolysis as proposed by Frazer.

Not all fat has to be reduced to free fatty acid and glycerol before it is absorbed. Reiser and his coworkers (1952) fed animals triglyceride in which both the glycerol and the fatty acid were labelled by means of appropriate isotopes. They found that only 25 to 45 per cent of the triglyceride was completely hydrolyzed. The remainder was hydrolyzed to monoglyceride and absorbed as such; resynthesis to triglyceride occurred in the mucosal cells. If monoglycerides and diglycerides are fed, only triglycerides are found in the intestinal lymph. It is interesting that the labeled glycerol was not utilized in the resynthesis but apparently took some other metabolic pathway. The mucosal cells, evidently, not only are capable of synthesizing glycerol for incorporation into triglycerides but actually do so preferentially even when glycerol is available from the hydrolytic products.

During digestion of fat there is synthesis as well as hydrolysis of glycerides in the intestinal lumen (Knoebel and Nasset, 1957); consequently the triglycerides that are absorbed may have an entirely different arrangement of the fatty acids within the fat molecules than that which is fed. However, some of this redistribution probably takes place during resynthesis in the epithelial cells (Bergström and Borgström,1956).

Although exclusion of bile from the intestine greatly reduces absorption of ordinary fat, if the fat is fed as an emulsion ligation of the bile duct makes no significant difference in the amount of fat absorbed (Coffee *et al.*, 1940). However, even with emulsified fat, removal of the pancreas seriously interferes with absorption (Wells *et al.*, 1955). These observations suggest that bile is concerned in the emulsification rather than the absorption of fat and raises a question as to the role of the bile salts in absorption of fatty acids. The results with pancreatectomy also suggest that hydrolysis of fat is more important than emulsification in determining total absorption. Studies of the excised intestine of the rat (Smyth and Taylor, 1957) and of the golden hamster (Johnston, 1958) show that fatty acids are absorbed or may be absorbed by the intestinal mucous membrane against a concentration gradient and that this activity is prevented or greatly reduced in the absence of oxygen. There is also suppression of absorption by dinitrophenol and in the absence of glucose, but phloridzin has little effect. These observations indicate that fatty acids are absorbed by an active process which involves oxidation but not necessarily phosphorylation (the effect of phloridzin is somewhat equivocal, see Jervis *et al.*, 1956).

It is commonly stated that fat absorption takes place most rapidly in the upper intestine, particularly in the duodenum and upper jejunum, but several recent studies have suggested that the ileum is the site of the major part of fat absorption; this may have something to do with the more alkaline reaction of this portion of the intestine. For example, Kremen and his coworkers (1954) found that in dogs the proximal 50 to 70 per cent of the small intestine could be removed with no apparent ill effects on food absorption, particularly fat absorption. However, if the distal 50 per cent were removed there was a profound interference with fat absorption associated with loss of weight; under these circumstances, from 80 to 90 per cent of the fat intake was lost in the feces Benson and others (1956), also found that in animals that were sacrificed after a fat meal, the mucosa of the third quarter of the intestine, as measured from the pylorus contained a greater amount of fat apparently in

processes of absorption than did any other portion of the intestine. However, fat is certainly absorbed from the upper intestine in appreciable quantities, as anyone who has opened the abdomen of an experimental animal that has recently eaten a fat meal will testify.

Fat absorption is seriously impaired following bilateral adrenalectomy, due to the absence of cortical hormones. The role of the cortical hormones in fat absorption has not been clarified but it has been suggested that they play a part in the synthesis of triglycerides in the mucosal cells (Verzar). Another suggestion is that the loss of salt which follows adrenal cortical insufficiency is responsible for the poor fat absorption. This idea receives some support from that fact that fat absorption is improved in adrenalectomized animals by administration of sodium chloride solutions in adequate quantities.

*Absorption of cholesterol.* Cholesterol absorption takes place only in the distal one-half of the intestine (Byers *et al.*, 1953). Absorption occurs only in the presence of bile and a source of fatty acid. Since the cholesterol that appears in the intestinal lymph is practically all in the form of cholesterol esters with fatty acids, the function of the fatty acid is probably to provide material for esterification. Absorption of cholesterol is also reduced in the absence of pancreatic juice. Optimal absorption of cholesterol occurs from a mixture of fatty acid, taurocholate and cholesterol in which the molar concentrations are in the ratios of 8, 4 and 1 respectively (Vahouny, 1958). Cholesterol continues to appear in the intestinal lymph for some time after it has disappeared from the intestinal contents. This suggests that there is a considerable accumulation of cholesterol in the mucosal cells during absorption.

## ABSORPTION OF VITAMINS

The water soluble vitamins are assumed to be freely absorbed by the intestinal mucosa, along with the other constituents of the foods in which they occur. It is generally believed that thiamin is less readily absorbed by older people than by young people in good health. This may be applicable also to some of the other vitamins and provides the basis for administration of vitamin supplements in the dietary of older people.

Absorption of the fat soluble vitamins, particularly vitamins D and K, takes place under the same conditions as the absorption of fat. In any disease or dietary deficiency in which fat absorption is inadequate the absorption of these vitamins is apt to be impaired. This is well demonstrated by the deficient absorption of vitamin K in obstructive jaundice. A deficiency of this vitamin causes inadequate prothrombin production by the liver and a tendency to hemorrhage, hence jaundiced patients are apt to bleed on the operating table. The situation is remedied by the parenteral administration of vitamin K over a period of time preoperatively until the prothrombin level is normal. Absorption of vitamin E is also said to be impaired in the absence of bile.

Absorption of vitamin $B_{12}$, which is essential for normal red cell production and perhaps for cell division in general, presents special problems. Although it is absorbed from the intestine, its absorption takes place only in the presence of a certain constituent of the gastric juice known, for want of a better name, as intrinsic factor. There may also be some intrinsic factor in duodenal secretion. This name comes down to us from the days when vitamin $B_{12}$ itself was unknown, (see ch. 9).

Vitamin A is absorbed chiefly in the form of esters of the vitamin A alcohol with fatty acids. The esters are hydrolyzed in the intestinal lumen but re-esterified in the epithelial cells. This mechanism parallels the one that is supposed to operate in the absorption of fat; it is not surprising therefore to find that the conditions that favor fat absorption also favor absorption of vitamin A. The presence of bile in the intestine apparently is necessary for the absorption of carotene, a precursor of vitamin A, but not for vitamin A itself. The absorption of the fat soluble vitamins is adversely effected by the presence in the intestine of unabsorbable oil, such as mineral oil; it is therefore necessary to pay particular attention to the supply of these vitamins if mineral oil is to be administered in any considerable quantity over a period of time.

## REFERENCES

ABBOTT, W. O. AND MILLER, T. G. Intubation studies of the human small intestine. J. A. M. A., 1936, 106, 16.

ÅGREN, G. Über die pharmakodynamischen Wirkungen und chemischen Eigenschaften des Secretins. Skandinav. Arch. Physiol., 1934, 70, 10.

BENSON, J. A., JR., CHANDLER, G. M., VANSTEENHUYSE, F. E. AND GAGNON, J. O. Studies concerning the site of fat absorption from the small intestine of the rat. Gastroenterology, 1956, 30, 53.

BERGSTRÖM, S., BLOMSTRAND, R. AND BORGSTRÖM, B. Route of absorption and distribution of oleic acid and triolein. Biochem. J., 1954, 58, 600. (See also Bergström and Borgström, Ann. Rev. Biochem., 1956, 25, 177.)

BLICKENSTAFF, D. D., GROSSMAN, M. I. AND IVY, A. C. Stimulating effect of fat and meat meals on duodenal secretion in the dog. Am. J. Physiol., 1949, 158, 122.

BLICKENSTAFF, D. D., BACHMAN, D. M., STEINBERG, M. E. AND YOUMANS, W. B. Intestinal absorption of sodium chloride solutions as influenced by intraluminal pressure and concentration. Am. J. Physiol., 1952, 168, 303.

BOLDYREFF, W. N. (1904), Diss. St. Petersburg. (Cited by Babkin, 1927.)

BOLDYREFF, W. N. (1912), Die Lipase des Darmsaftes und ihre Charakteristik. Hoppe Seyler's Ztschn. physiol. Chem., 50, 394. (Cited by Babkin, 1927.)

BYERS, S. O., FRIEDMAN, M. AND GUNNINGS, B. Observations concerning the production and excretion of cholesterol in mammals. XI. The intestinal site of excretion and absorption of cholesterol. Am. J. Physiol., 1953, 175, 375.

COFFEE, R. J., MANN, F. C. AND BOLLMAN, J. L. The effect of exclusion of bile on the absorption of foodstuffs. Am. J. Digest. Dis., 1940, 7, 144.

DEBEER, E. J., JOHNSTON, C. G. AND WILSON, D. W. Composition of intestinal secretions. J. Biol. Chem., 1935, 108, 113.

DELENZENNE, C. AND FROUIN, A. (1904). La sécrétion physiologique du suc intestinal. Action l'acide chlorhydrique sur le sécrétion duodenale. Comp. rend. Soc. biol., 56, 319. (Cited by Babkin, 1950; see also Ågren, 1934.)

ELDSEN, S. R., GIBSON, Q. H. AND WISEMAN, G. Selective absorption of amino acids from the small intestine of the rat. J. Physiol., 1950, 11, 56.

ERSPAMER, V. AND ASERO, B. Identification of enteramine, the specific hormone of the enterochromaffin system as 5-hydroxytryptamine. Nature, London, 1952, 169, 800.

FIELD, H., JR., SERVELL, L., DAILEY, R. E., TROUT, E. C. AND BOYD, R. S. Electrolyte changes in ileal contents and in feces during restrictions of dietary sodium with and without the administration of cation exchange resins. Circulation, 1955, 12, 625.

FISHER, R. B. AND PARSONS, D. S. Glucose absorption from surviving rat small intestine. J. Physiol., 1949, 110, 281.

FLOREY, H. Secretion of mucus by the colon. Brit. J. Exper. Path., 1930, 11, 348.

FLOREY, H. W. AND HARDING, H. E. The functions of Brunner's glands and the pyloric end of the stomach. J. Path. & Bact., 1933, 37, 431.

FLOREY, H. W. AND HARDING, H. E. Further observations on the secretion of Brunner's glands. J. Path. & Bact., 1934, 39, 255.

FLOREY, H. W. AND HARDING, H. E. The nature of the hormone controlling Brunner's glands. Quart. J. Exper. Physiol., 1935a, 25, 329.

FLOREY, H. W. AND HARDING, H. E. Humoral control of secretion of Brunner's glands. Proc. Roy. Soc., London, ser. B., 1935b, 117, 68.

FRIEDLANDER, L. AND QUASTEL, H. H. Absorption of amino acids from isolated surviving intestine. Arch. Biochem., 1955, 56, 424.

GRUSKAY, F. L. AND COOKE, R. E. The gastrointestinal absorption of native protein in normal infants and in infants recovering from diarrhea. Pediatrics, 1955, **16,** 763.

INGRAHAM, R. C. AND VISSCHER, M. B. The production of chloride-free solutions by the action of the intestinal epithelium. Am. J. Physiol., 1936, 114, **667.**

INGRAHAM, R. C. AND VISSCHER, R. B. Further studies on intestinal absorption with performance of osmotic work. Am. J. Physiol., 1938, **121,** 77. (See also Roepke and Visscher, 1939.)

IVY, A. C., FARRELL, J. I. AND LUETH, H. C. Contributions to the physiology of the pancreas. III. A hormone for external pancreatic secretion. Am. J. Physiol., 1927, **82,** 27. (See also Nassett *et al.*, 1935 and Florey and Harding, 1935 a & b.)

JERVIS, E. L., JOHNSON, F. R., SCHEFF, M. F. AND SMYTH, D. H. The effect of phlorhizin on intestinal absorption and intestinal phosphatase. J. Physiol., 1956, **134,** 675.

JOHNSTON, J. M. An in vitro study of fatty acid absorption. J. Physiol., 1958, **134,** 675.

KIYASU, J. Y., BLOOM, B. AND CHAIKOFF, I. L. The portal transport of absorbed fatty acid. J. Biol. Chem., 1952, **199,** 415.

KNOEBEL, L. K. AND NASSET, E. S. The digestion and absorption of fat in dog and man. J. Nutrition, 1957, **61,** 405.

KREMEN, A. J., LINNER, J. H. AND NELSON, C. H. An experimental evaluation of the nutritional importance of proximal and distal small intestine. Ann. Surg., 1954, **140,** 439.

KUTSCHER, F. AND SEEMAN, J. (1902). Hoppe Seyler's Ztschr. Physiol. Chem., **35,** 432. (Cited by Florey *et al.*, 1941.)

LARSON, L. M. AND BARGEN, J. A. Action of cathartics on isolated dog's colon. Arch. Surg. 1933, **27,** 1120.

LEBLOND, C. P. AND STEVENS, C. E. The constant renewal of the intestinal epithelium in the albino rat. Anat. Rec., 1948, **100,** 357.

McHARDY, G. J. R. AND PARSONS, D. S. The absorption of water and salt from the small intestine of the rat. Quart. J. Exper. Physiol., 1957, **42,** 33.

MILLER, T. G. AND ABBOTT, W. O. Intestinal intubation: a practical technique. Am. J. M. Sc., 1934, **187,** 595. (See also Abbott and Miller, 1936.)

NASSET, E. S., Enterocrinin, a hormone which excites the glands of the small intestine. Am. J. Physiol., 1938, **121,** 481. (See also Schiffrin and Nasset, 1939.)

NASSET, E. S. AND PARRY, A. A. Passage of fluid and certain dissolved substances through the intestinal mucosa as influenced by changes in hydrostatic pressure. Am. J. Physiol., 1934, **109,** 615.

NASSET, E. S., PIERCE, H. B. AND MURLIN, J. R. Proof of a humoral control of intestinal secretion. Am. J. Physiol., 1935, **111,** 145.

NEAME, K. D. AND WISEMAN, G. The transamination of glutamic and aspartic acids during absorption by the small intestine in the dog in vivo. J. Physiol., 1957, **135,** 442. (See also J. Physiol., **124,** 414.

OLSON, T. E. AND GRAY, S. J. Serotonin and gas-

troenterology. Am. J. Gastroenterol. 1958, **29,** 280.

RABINOVITCH, J. Factors influencing absorption of water and chlorides from the intestine. Am. J. Physiol., 1927, **82,** 279.

REISER, R., BRYSON, M. J., CARR, M. J. AND KNIKEN, K. A. The intestinal absorption of triglycerides. J. Biol. Chem., 1952, **194,** 131.

ROEPKE, R. R. AND VISSCHER, M. B. Osmotic relationships between blood plasma and intestinal fluid during absorption. Proc. Soc. Exper. Biol. & Med., 1939, **41,** 500.

SALASKIN, S. S. (1902). Über das Vorkommen des Peptons bzw. albumosenspaltenden Ferments (Erepsin von Conheim) in reinen Darmsaft vom Hunde. Hoppe Seyler's Ztschr. f. Physiol. Chem. **35,** 419. (Cited by Florey *et al.*, 1941; see also Kutscher and Seeman, 1902.)

SAVICH, V. V. (1904). The secretion of intestinal juice. Thesis, St. Petersburg. (Cited by Babkin, 1950.)

SAVICH, V. V. AND SOCHENSTVENSKY, N. A. (1917). L'influence du nerf vague sur la sécrétion de l'intestin. Comp. rend. Soc. biol., **80,** 508. (Cited by Babkin, 1927.)

SCHIFFRIN, M. J. AND NASSET, E. S. Response of jejunum and ileum to food and enterocrinin. Am. J. Physiol., 1939, **128,** 70.

SCHOLER, J. F. AND CODE, C. F. Rate of absorption of water from stomach and small bowel of human beings. Gastroenterology, 1954, **27,** 568.

SMYTH, D. H. AND TAYLOR, C. B. Transfer of water and solutes by an in vitro intestinal preparation. J. Physiol., 1957, **136,** 632.

SONNENSCHEIN, R. R., GROSSMAN, M. I. AND IVY, A. C., 1947: The humoral regulation of Brunner's glands. Acta med. scandinav., **28**(supp. 196): 296.

SPERRY, W. M. AND BLOOR, W. R. Fat excretion; quantitative relations of fecal lipoids. J. Biol. Chem., 1924, **60,** 261.

THIRY, L. (1864). Eine neue Methode den Dünndarm zu isoleiren. Sitzungsber. Akad. Wiss. Wien., Math.-Naturw. Kl., Vol. 1 (S. 77), p. 50. (Cited by Babkin, 1927.)

VAHOUNY, G. V. Quantitative effect of bile salt and fatty acid on cholesterol absorption. Am. J. Physiol., 1958, **193,** 41.

VELLA, L. (1888). Untersuch. Naturl. Mensch. Tiere. **13,** 40 and 432. (Cited by Florey *et al.*, 1941.)

VISSCHER, M. B., FETCHER, E. S., JR., CARR, C. W., GREGOR, H. P., BUSHEY, M. S. AND BARKER, D. E. Isotope tracer studies on movement of water and ions between intestinal lumen and blood. Am. J. Physiol., 1944, **142,** 550.

WALDSCHMIDT-LEITZ, E. AND HARTENECK, A. Zur Kenntnis der spontanen Activierung des Tryspins. Hoppe Seyler's Ztschr. Physiol. Chem., 1925, **149,** 221.

WISEMAN, G. Active sterochemically selective absorption of amino acids from rat small intestine. J. Physiol., 1951, **114,** 7. (See also J. Physiol. 1953, **120,** 63.)

WRIGHT, R. D., FLOREY, H. W. AND JENNINGS, M. A. The secretion of the colon of the cat. Quart. J. Exper. Physiol., 1938, **28,** 207.

WRIGHT, R. D., JENNINGS, M. A., FLOREY, H. W. AND LIUM, R. The influence of nerves and drugs on secretion by the small intestine and an investigation of the enzymes in intestinal juice. Quart. J. Exper. Physiol., 1940, **30, 73**.

*Monographs and Reviews*

BABKIN, B. P. Die Sekretorische Tatigkeit der Verdauungsdrüsen. Handbuch der normalen und pathologischen Physiologie, **3,** 689. Springer-Verlag, Berlin, 1927.

BABKIN, B. P. Secretory mechanism of the digestive glands. Paul B. Hoeber, New York, 1950.

BERGSTRÖM, S. AND BORGSTRÖM, B. Metabolism of lipids; under "Digestion and absorption." Annual Rev. Biochem., **25,** 177, 1956.

CANTAROW, A. AND SHEPARTZ, B. Biochemistry, p. 384, W. B. Saunders Company, Philadelphia, 1954.

CORI, C. F. Mammalian carbohydrate metabolism. Physiol. Rev., 1931, **11,** 143.

FLOREY, H. W., WRIGHT, R. D. AND JENNINGS, M. A. The secretions of the intestine. Physiol. Rev., 1941, **21,** 36.

FRAZER, A. C. The absorption of triglyceride fat from the intestine. Physiol. Rev., 1946, **26,** 103.

GRANICK, S., FERRITIN, its properties and significance for iron metabolism. Chem. Rev. 1946, **38,** 379.

GRANICK, S. Structure and physiological functions of ferritin. Physiol. Rev., 1951. **31,** 489.

GROSSMAN, M. I. Gastrointestinal hormones. Physiol. Rev., 1950, **30,** 33.

NASSET, E. S. *In* Bard's Medical physiology, 10th ed., p. 532, C. V. Mosby Co., St. Louis, 1956.

STARLING, E. H. Recent advances in the physiology of digestion. A. Constable Co., London, 1906. (Cited by Babkin, 1950.)

VERZAR, F. AND McDOUGALL, E. Absorption from the intestine. Longmans, Green & Co., London, New York, 1936.

# 41

## MOVEMENTS OF THE ALIMENTARY CANAL: MASTICATION, SWALLOWING, MOVEMENTS OF THE STOMACH

---

### Mastication

The first mechanical process to which the food is subjected in its progress through the alimentary tract is mastication, or chewing, which serves to break down the food particles into smaller masses, to enable the saliva to lubricate and moisten dry food and to distribute the salivary constituents throughout the food mass. The decrease in the size of the food particles is accomplished by the action of the teeth through the movements of the lower jaw. The moistening is accomplished by the addition of saliva to the food and lubrication is due to the mucus secreted by the salivary glands. Starch digestion in the mouth by the salivary amylase is unimportant but the presence of food in the mouth gives rise to stimuli which serve to initiate reflexes that are important in the later stages of digestion. This relationship has been discussed in connection with the reflex phase of gastric secretion (ch. 37).

The importance of mastication as a health measure has been the subject of considerable discussion, much of it speculative. Among the few efforts to obtain scientific information on the subject, are the experiments of Erik Becker (1927) who undertook to determine the completeness of digestion and absorption of protein, fat, carbohydrate and minerals in a patient by studying the losses in the stool of these various substances. He studied his patient during a period of time when her teeth were in very poor condition and not satisfactory for chewing, then again after her teeth had been removed and before she had been fitted with a prosthesis, and finally after she had been fitted with a good set of false teeth which enabled her to chew satisfactorily. There were no significant differences in the three sets of data. For example, when the patient had no teeth she lost 15.2 per cent of the ingested protein in her stool, 5.2 per cent of the ingested fat, 4.2 per cent of the ingested carbohydrate and 25.9 per cent of the ingested minerals. After

being fitted with false teeth, the corresponding figures were 16.0 per cent for protein, 5.4 per cent for fat, 5.2 per cent for carbohydrate and 25.9 per cent for minerals. The total calories lost were 6 per cent with no teeth and 6.7 per cent after being fitted with teeth. These experiments are open to the criticism that no observations had been made when the patient had a good set of natural teeth. These might have given better results.

### The Form and Structure of the Teeth

A tooth consists of a *crown*, a *neck* and a *root*. The crown is the part projecting beyond the gum; the root fits into the socket or *alveolus* of the jaw bone. The neck is the junction between crown and root, and, normally, lies just below the gum. Three kinds of tissue, *enamel*, *dentin* and *cementum*, compose the hard portion of the tooth. The cavity occupying the center is filled with a soft substance, called the *pulp*, composed of connective tissue fibers and a gelatinous matrix in which the nerves and blood vessels are embedded (fig. 41.1).

The enamel, which is of epithelial origin, is a white, translucent, and very hard material—the hardest in the body. It is composed of calcium salts (95 per cent) in the form of apatite crystals (ch. 59), with from 3 to 5 per cent of organic material. Its structure consists of thin prisms or rods running through its entire depth, perpendicular to and resting on the dentin; the prisms are cemented together by protein material or one containing protein. The dentin surrounds the pulp cavity except at the apex of the root where the nerves and vessels enter; it resembles bone chemically and structurally, but is harder, and contains numerous canaliculi—the *dentinal tubules*—which radiate from the pulp cavity. In the pulp lying against the dentine are large elongated cells with a radial and epitheliumlike arrangement; they are called *odontoblasts* and send fine processes (fibers of Tomes) into the overlying dentinal tubules. The cementum surrounds the root outside the dentin; it is a bony material, but (except in old age), lacks Haversion canals. It is penetrated by bundles of coarse fibers (Sharpey's fibers) derived from the *peridontal membrane*; this membrane lines the alveolus, for which it serves as periosteum, and acts as a close bond between the cementum and the bone. Bone cells are embedded in the cementum near the apex of the root. The viability of the cementum is dependent upon the integrity of the periodontal membrane; it undergoes necrosis when the latter is destroyed.

Like bone, tooth structure is in a continuous state of flux, minerals, calcium and phosphorus being continually removed and replaced.

### Dental Decay, or Dental Caries

Calcium salts, which constitute such a large proportion of dental tissue, are soluble in acid; an increase in the acidity of the saliva was thought, therefore, to favor decalcification of the teeth, and in this way prepare them for the inroads of microorganisms. But the saliva is normally slightly acid, and any significant increase in its acidity has not been demonstrated in caries (Geis).

Bacterial decomposition of carbohydrate food with the production of lactic acid, especially in regions where food is likely to collect, as in crevices between the teeth and at the margin between the tooth and gum, has long been recognized as an important element in tooth decay. Sugar, especially if highly refined, is undoubtedly potent in increasing susceptibility to the disease. Sugar has been shown to facilitate the penetration of the H-ion into the enamel.[1]

Another local factor which has been suggested as predisposing to caries is the mucin content of the saliva. A juice rich in mucin flows less freely and as a result of its high viscosity is less likely to penetrate into, and flush out the smaller crevices where microörganisms lurk and flourish upon food debris. Mucin may also encourage decay by forming a tenacious coating upon a sheltered surface of the tooth and thus serve to protect underlying bacteria from the action of the saliva.

The investigations of Pincus suggest that decalcification of the teeth by acid is of less importance than an attack upon the organic substance of the enamel by proteolytic bacteria. Such a process has been suggested earlier by Hines. Pincus claims that digestion of the protein material permits the enamel prisms to fall apart, and this occurs apparently without a preliminary production of acid. Sulfuric acid liberated by the hydrolysis of chondroitin sulfate, according to Pincus causes, secondarily, decalcification of the enamel. Atkinson and Matthews agree that the

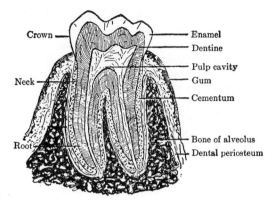

FIG. 41.1. Section through a molar tooth.

primary point of attack is upon the organic matrix of the enamel, but that decalcification of both enamel and dentine is produced by the liberation of aspartic and glutamic acids. They found some 18 amino acids present in normal dentine, including aspartic and glutamic acids. These two amino acids were found in the free state in carious dentine but not in healthy dentine. The well known brown discoloration of carious teeth is due to a melanin which is thought to be formed by the oxidation of tyrosine by proteolytic bacteria.

The researches of M. Mellanby on the teeth of dogs suggest that, in some cases at least, the structure of the teeth themselves—maldevelopment, or an inherently poor tooth structure—or dietary deficiencies (especially of vitamin D) may play a part in the occurrence of the disease. Contrary to the general belief, caries in wild animals is not so very uncommon. It starts, with few exceptions, in the dentine or cementum of the root, where this has become bare, and not in the enamel. The decay is most likely to occur in situations where food tends to pack and stagnate. In domestic animals and animals in captivity, caries is much commoner and the first signs of decay appear in the enamel, as in man. A survey of some 280 wild animals belonging to 60 different species was made by Sprawson, and the tooth enamel compared with that in human teeth. The structure of the animal enamel was found to be less dense, less fully calcified and, on the average, of poorer quality than that of human enamel, a finding which, taken in conjunction with the less common occurrence of caries in wild animals, suggests a dietary factor in the production of the disease in man.

The beneficial effects of small amounts of fluorine upon tooth structure has received no small amount of attention since Dean and his

---

[1] This action is analogous to the effect of sugar in favoring the penetration of toxins.

associates pointed out the low incidence of caries in districts where there was evidence of high concentrations (over 1 part per million) of fluorine in the drinking water. Excessively high concentrations of fluorine in the drinking water cause mottling of the enamel. Fluorine has also been shown to inhibit acid production by the *Lactobacillus acidophilus* and in a concentration of 0.5 to 1 part per million to be protective against dental caries. Another possible action of fluoride is to reduce the solubility of the enamel by acid. Stannous fluoride is more effective as a preventive than the sodium salt. From the dental examination of som 7,000 children in over 20 American cities it was found that the incidence of caries was inversely related to the concentration of fluorine in the drinking water. Mottling of the enamel does not occur in concentrations below 1 part in a million.

A curious condition, known as *dermeus*, occurring in domestic animals and man is seen in North Africa, and is attributed to a high concentration of calcium fluoride in the drinking water. It is characterized by dystrophy of the second dentition. Kilborn has also reported the endemic occurrence of a severe arthritis and spondylitis in a region of Southwest China which apparently is induced by the drinking of water rich in fluoride.

It is quite evident that the problem of dental caries is not a simple one. Several factors are involved in its production and much work must be done before the details of their actions are known and the relative value of each can be appraised. But from the point of view of prevention the most valuable measures are the curtailment of sugar in the diet and the addition of fluoride to the drinking water in those communities in which the latter has a low concentration of this element.

The movements of the lower jaw in chewing are accomplished by the muscles of mastication which include the masseter, the temporal muscles and the internal and external pterygoid muscles, all of which receive their nerve supply from the mandibular division of the trigeminal nerve. The buccinator muscle, which may also be considered a muscle of mastication, is supplied by the facial nerve. Through the action of the muscle of the jaw, the mandible may be moved in any one of several directions. Simple closing of the mouth as in biting or crushing food is accomplished by the combined action of the masseter, temporal and internal pterygoid muscles. Opening the mouth is accomplished by the action of the relatively weak digastric and myloid muscles

and aided by gravity. The grinding movements of the molar teeth are accomplished by a rotational movement of the jaw which results from contraction of the pterygoid muscles of one side. Contraction of the right pterygoid muscles, for example, causes protrusion of the right half of the mandible whereas the left half remains relatively stationary. This results in a rotational movement with the lower teeth on one side sliding over the upper teeth of the same side. The jaw is returned to a midposition and then rotated to the opposite side by contraction of the left pterygoid muscles. This kind of chewing is accomplished by the alternate contraction of the right and left pterygoid muscles. When all four pterygoid muscles contract, protrusion of the jaw results. Retraction of the jaw is accomplished by contraction of the posterior fibers of the temporal muscles and the geniohyoid muscles.

The force of the bite apparently is limited by the sensitivity of the peridental membrane and not necessarily by the power of the muscles of mastication. In the human the molars have been observed to exert a pressure in excess of 270 pounds (122+ kg.) (Black, 1895). The pressure exerted by the incisor teeth is necessarily less due to the lesser mechanical advantage in this location. According to Howell and Manly (1948) pressure exerted by the incisors ranges from 11 to 25 kg. These authors found a force of 29 to 90 kg. for the molars. A dog, when chewing bones, may exert a force as great as 165 kg. (Trisca, 1924).

Chewing may be carried on voluntarily but for the most part it is a reflex act. The dual nature of the nervous mechanism is indicated by the fact that chewing movements may be elicited by electrical stimulation of appropriate areas of the cerebral cortex (Ferrier, 1886; Magoun and others, 1933) as well as by sensory stimulation of the mouth in decerebrate animals (Sherrington, 1917; Bazett and Penfield, 1922). Magnus (1945) reports that there is a center in the medulla which mediates rhythmic movements of the jaw in response to stimulation of receptors in the mouth, but that this center is dominated by a thalamocortical center which is responsible for the finer regulation of the movements. Efficient chewing is accomplished only when the higher centers are functioning.

## Deglutition

Magendie (1838) described the act of swallowing as occurring in three stages which he described as follows: "For the better understanding of the subject we shall divide deglutition into three stages. In the first the aliments pass from the mouth into the pharynx; in the second they pass over the opening of the glottis and nasal fossae and arrive at the esophagus; in the third they pass through this canal into the stomach." It is convenient to refer to Magendie's first stage as the oral stage, the second stage as the pharyngeal stage and the third as the esophageal stage.

## THE FIRST OR ORAL STAGE OF SWALLOWING

During the first stage the food is moved by the action of the muscles of the cheeks and tongue into position on the dorsum of the tongue; the tongue is pressed against the roof of the mouth progressively from the front backward, causing the food to move backward toward the oral pharynx. In this situation the food mass is put under pressure, mainly by contraction of the mylohyoid muscle, and the act passes into the second stage.

According to Hegner (1936) who made his observations with a laryngoscope, the first phase may vary depending upon the circumstances at the time the food is swallowed. He distinguishes what he calls "pure swallowing" from "mastication swallowing." Food swallowed during mastication passes from the mouth into the pharynx with very little muscular effort and goes down the side on which it is being chewed. In pure swallowing, with conscious effort, it may pass down on both sides but usually also in this case, down the accustomed side; this is most often the right side. The lack of muscular effort in the first stage distinguishes mastication swallowing from pure swallowing.

## THE SECOND OR PHARYNGEAL STAGE OF SWALLOWING

Understanding of the second or pharyngeal stage of swallowing will be easier if we keep in mind the fact that the alimentary tract crosses the respiratory tract in the region of the pharynx so that the swallowing movements have to serve two quite different functions: one, to propel the food through the pharynx and into the esophagus, and the other, to protect the airway, both above and below, from the possible entrance of food particles. Although the propulsive and the protective mechanisms operate simultaneously, it is simpler to describe them separately.

Food is propelled from the mouth, through the pharynx, and into the esophagus by muscular movements which increase the pressure in the mouth and oral pharynx and decrease it in the upper end of the esophagus. Pressure in the oropharyngeal space is increased by contraction of the mylohyoid muscle which presses the tongue against the roof of the mouth. The intrinsic muscles of the tongue assist by making the tongue firm and insuring a proper distribution of the pressure, which increases progressively from the front backward. Although the pressure is rising in the mouth and oral pharynx, it is decreasing in the laryngeal pharynx and upper esophagus (Barclay, 1930). The cricopharyngeus muscle, which serves as a sphincter for the upper end of the esophagus, relaxes and at the same time the laryngeal assembly, including the hyoid bone, larynx and cricoid cartilage, moves forward and upward carrying the anterior wall of the esophagus with it. Since the posterior esophageal wall remains in contact with the prevertebral muscles the movement of the anterior wall tends to create a space between the walls and so lowers the pressure in the upper end of the esophagus.

When the bolus reaches the base of the tongue its movement is accelerated by a rapid downward and backward movement of the tongue, which takes place at the same time as the forward movement of the larynx mentioned above. As a result of the combined forces acting on it the bolus moves with such speed that it is often projected deep into the esophagus. In a remarkable study made with fluoroscopic motion picture technique, Rushmer and Hendron (1951) observed that a bolus approached the pharynx with a velocity of 9 feet per second. Passing through the pharynx it attained a velocity of 19½ feet, 24 feet and 28½ feet per second, in successive frames, then slowed to 12 feet per second and finally to 5 feet per second as it passed into the esophagus. These data were obtained with the subject in a horizontal position; in the erect position the bolus moved even faster. The pharyngeal muscles doubtless participate in the second stage in some way but their action is not essential. The relative importance of the oral and pharyngeal muscles in this stage is indicated by the fact that in the experiments of Kronecker and Meltzer (1883) denervation of the pharyngeal muscles in the dog caused little or no disturbance in swallowing, whereas the animal was unable to swallow after the mylohyoid muscle had been denervated.

The development of negative pressure in the upper esophagus during the second stage of swallowing has been denied by some investigators but has recently been confirmed by Code

## DEGLUTITION PRESSURES
## AT THE PHARYNGO—ESOPHAGEAL JUNCTION
### Recorded At High Speed (5 cm./second)

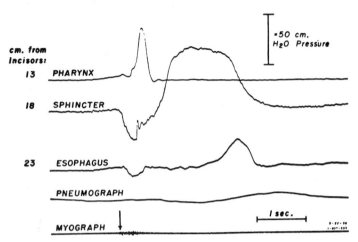

FIG. 41.2. Records of pressure changes in the pharynx, pharyngoesophageal junction (sphincter) and upper esophagus during the second stage of swallowing. The increase in pharngeal pressure and primary decrease in esophageal pressure are clearly shown. From Code *et al.*, 1958. Courtesy of Charles C Thomas Co., Springfield, Ill.

and his coworkers (1958) (see figure 41.2) in a careful study of the esophageal pressure by modern, highly accurate techniques. The negative pressure is of brief duration and is therefore easily missed; the entire second stage occupies less than 1 second (Kupferle, 1913).

We must now consider how the airway is protected while the food is passing the pharyngeal crossroads. It will be recalled that there are four possible outlets from the oral pharynx through which food may be expelled. These are: back into the mouth, up into the nasopharynx, forward into the larynx and downward into the esophagus. The swallowing reflex has to be so coordinated that the food takes only one of these possible paths, namely that into the esophagus. Return into the mouth is prevented by the position of the tongue against the roof of the mouth and the high pressure developed in this area. Passage into the nasopharynx is normally prevented by the combined action of the tensor veli palatini and the levator veli palatini muscles which together stiffen the soft palate and cause it to press against the posterior pharyngeal wall. It thus forms a protective partition between the oral pharynx and the nasopharynx. If these muscles are paralyzed or if there should be a defect in the soft palate, food enters the nasopharynx and swallowing becomes extremely difficult or impossible. An important factor in preventing entrance of food into the respiratory

tract during swallowing, is the inhibition of respiration which occurs during the second stage of swallowing (Magendie, 1838).

The exact mechanism by which the larynx is protected during the passage of the bolus has been the subject of much study and controversy. It seems clear from the various descriptions that are available that the laryngeal opening is closed during the act of swallowing by the approximation of both the true and the false vocal chords. In addition, the epiglottis serves to divert the oncoming bolus to one side or the other of the larynx. Only when liquid is being swallowed in considerable volume does the swallowed material cascade over the end of the epiglottis. In any case, it usually prevents the passing material from coming directly in contact with the upper surface of the larynx. The position of the epiglottis at the moment of the passage of the bolus has been the subject of considerable argument; however most observers agree that it is carried into a horizontal position by the backward movement of the tongue and the forward movement of the larynx. This same combination of movements results in the larynx being drawn up under the base of the tongue where it is completely out of the way of the oncoming bolus.

Many authors prefer to combine the first and second stages into a buccopharyngeal stage. The buccopharyngeal stage has been described by Pancoast, Pendergrass and Schaeffer (1940) as occurring in four phases; first, filling of the mouth and movement of the base of the tongue backward toward the postpharyngeal wall; second, as the bolus begins to move backward from the mouth, the base of the tongue comes against the postpharyngeal wall and the epiglottis goes backward and downward. Simultaneously the larynx rises and the arytenoid cartilages come in contact with the under surface of the epiglottis so that the tongue, epiglottis and arytenoids form a single homogenous X-ray shadow. The meeting of these three structures closes the air passage to the larynx. Third, the bolus enters the laryngeal pharynx and immediately passes down into the esophagus, and fourth, the structures return to the resting position.

The depth to which the bolus penetrates into the esophagus depends on the consistency of the material being swallowed and also on the position of the individual. In a horizontal position, if the food is solid, it usually comes to rest at about the level of the clavicle and is not immediately propelled into the thoracic esophagus until the third stage of swallowing begins. In the upright position even solid food may be projected into the thoracic esophagus. Liquids, on the other hand, are apt to be carried all the way to the cardia if the subject is in the upright position, and some may pass directly into the stomach (Meltzer, 1897).

### The Third or Esophageal Stage of Swallowing

A peristaltic wave appears in the upper end of the esophagus associated with each swallowing effort, regardless of whether the food is swallowed. This wave consists of a constriction of the esophagus caused by contraction of the esophageal muscle at the site of the wave, and relaxation beyond. The contraction and associated relaxation move together down the esophagus and eventually reach the cardia. The advancing wave of relaxation affects the cardiac sphincter, causing it to relax. Although the contraction phase caries the bolus ahead of it the relaxation phase facilitates its passage through the esophagus, especially in the region of the cardia; failure of the cardiac sphincter to relax can be a cause of difficult swallowing. If there is a succession of swallows, as for example, in drinking a glass of water, the relaxation phase of the second swallow inhibits peristalsis initiated by the first and so on throughout the series; a peristaltic wave follows only the last of the series (Meltzer, 1899). The type of peristalsis which is always associated

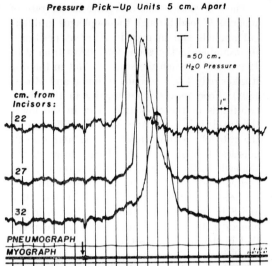

FIG. 41.3. Pressure changes caused by passage of a primary peristaltic wave over the midportion of the esophagus. The arrow on the myograph record indicates the moment of voluntary swallowing effort. From Code *et al.*, 1958. Courtesy of Charles C Thomas Co., Springfield, Ill.

with the act of swallowing, and does not require the presence of food for its appearance, is known as *primary esophageal peristalsis*. (Figure 41.3).

If for any reason the esophagus is not emptied, by the primary wave, contact of the food mass with the wall of the esophagus will initiate additional peristaltic waves; these comprise *secondary esophageal peristalsis*. They do not require the swallowing reflex for their initiation but occur whenever the esophagus contains a bolus; usually they continue until the esophagus is empty, or until the reflex responsible for their initiation is fatigued.

As will be explained later, if the vagus nerves are cut, swallowing immediately becomes impossible; however, in some animals in which the lower portion of the esophagus contains smooth muscle, as it does in the cat, monkey and human, some degree of peristalsis ultimately reappears in the smooth muscle portion. This enables the esophagus to empty itself of such material as has accumulated in the upper portion. This phenomenon was first observed and given the name of *tertiary esophageal peristalsis* by Cannon in 1907. This is the only type of esophageal peristalsis recognized physiologically as tertiary; however, in the clinic, "tertiary" peristalsis may mean any one of several types of abnormal movements seen in the lower third of the esophagus in elderly patients or in patients suffering from some form of neurosis.

There is considerable difference in the rate of progress of food through the esophagus in different animals and in man in different positions; for example, in the goose food takes from 9 to 12 seconds to reach the stomach, but in the dog it takes only 4 to 5 seconds (Cannon and Moser, 1898). Food moves more rapidly in the upper two-thirds of the esophagus than in the lower third; this is in accordance with the difference in the rate of contraction of striped and smooth muscles. In man food takes longer to reach the stomach in the horizontal position than in the vertical position; this difference is especially pronounced if liquids are swallowed. Hurst in 1907 and Schreiber in 1915 studied swallowing in the human in the inverted position. Hurst reported that in the inverted position, fluid could be seen steadily ascending the esophagus at about one-third the rate it travels in the normal position. Sometimes a little fluid could be seen flowing back from the stomach into the esophagus. Well chewed bread behaved like liquids. Cachets, however, moved very slowly. Schreiber noted that 30 seconds after a single swallow, with the subject standing on his head, the contrast medium was only at the level of the seventh cervical vertebra at the entrance of the esophagus. When a large amount was swallowed the esophagus filled and became distended but the liquid did not enter the stomach. Both sets of observations point to the fact that in the human, gravity is an important factor in the progress of foods through the esophagus. However, it is obvious that in animals such as the goose and the horse, which normally drink with the head down, peristalsis is capable of moving liquids against gravity.

Associated with the swallowing reflex there is cessation of activity and loss of tone in the entire gastric musculature but whether this is an extension of the relaxation phase of the esophageal peristalsis or the result of a separate reflex is not clear at the moment. This behavior of the stomach was described by Cannon and Lieb in 1910 and is known as *the receptive relaxation of the stomach*. The relaxation also commonly involves the first portion of the duodenum where (in the dog, at least) it persists for a considerable time after the last swallow (Thomas and Crider, 1935).

### THE SWALLOWING REFLEX

The first stage of swallowing, like chewing, may be initiated voluntarily but is normally a reflex action. A large part of the second stage and all of the third stage of swallowing are entirely involuntary. If one wishes to swallow when the mouth is free of food or foreign material, a little saliva is passed backwards by the tongue and thus serves as a mechanical stimulus for the initiation of the second and third phases of the act which are purely reflex. If the mouth is kept perfectly free of saliva deglutition becomes impossible.

Like chewing, swallowing may be produced by stimulation of appropriate areas of the cerebral cortex (Miller, 1919; Rioch and Brenner, 1938) or by stimulation of local receptors even in the decerebrate preparations (Ferrier, 1886; Bazett and Penfield, 1922). The receptors for initiation of the swallowing reflex are situated in the vicinity of the entrance to the oral pharynx in all animals but are distributed somewhat differently in different species.

The most sensitive areas for initiating swallowing in a rabbit is the membrane of the soft palate above the tonsils. Receptors are also located on the upper surface of the epiglottis and the posterior wall of the oral pharynx below the soft palate. In this animal, the soft palate is innervated by the second division of the trigeminal nerve, and the pharyngeal wall by the glossopharyngeal; the epiglottis is supplied by the superior laryngeal nerve. In the dog, the posterior pharyngeal wall, the dorsal surface and the base of the epiglottis, and the soft palate contain receptors for the swallowing reflex. Cutting the second division of the trigeminal nerve eliminates the reflex from the upper part of the pharynx and the soft palate. The posterior pharyngeal wall is innervated by the glossopharyngeal. The superior laryngeal contains afferent fibers for the swallowing reflex in the dog but is said not to be stimulated by food that takes the usual pathway (Kahn, 1903). In cats the distribution of receptors and afferent nerves is similar to that in the dog. In monkeys the upper part of the palatine arch, near the tonsils, is the most sensitive area. This region is innervated by the trigeminal nerve. Less sensitive areas are the soft palate and the postpharyngeal wall. Reflexes may also be obtained in the monkey from the false vocal chords and the base of the epiglottis (Kahn, 1903).

In the human the receptors for the swallowing reflex are distributed in a ringlike fashion around the entrance to the oral pharynx and are found in the mucous membrane covering the anterior and posterior pillars of the fauces, the tonsils, the soft palate, the base of the tongue and the posterior pharyngeal wall. According to Pommerenke (1928) the most sensitive areas in the human are in the vicinity of the anterior and posterior pillars of the fauces and the tonsils.

## THE SWALLOWING CENTER

INNERVATION OF THE MUSCLES OF DEGLUTITION. Coordination of the numerous somatic and visceral muscles involved in the act of swallowing is controlled by a group of neurons in the floor of the fourth ventricle known as the swallowing center, first described by Markwald in 1889. He found that destruction of the brain substance above and somewhat lateral to the alae cinereae of the medulla eliminates the swallowing reflex while leaving respiration intact. Destruction of the alae cinereae stops respiration but does not interfere with swallowing. Thus the swallowing center is closely associated with, although distinct from, the respiratory center. This fact is of considerable clinical interest because in diseases of the medulla as bulbar polio or brain tumor difficulty in swallowing often precedes respiratory failure and is therefore an ominous sign in such conditions.

The efferent nerve fibers involved in the act of swallowing are chiefly in the hypoglossal, glossopharyngeal and vagus nerves. The hypoglossal and glossopharyngeal nerves are chiefly concerned with the buccopharyngeal stage, the vagus, with the esophageal stage of swallowing. The vagus nerves supply the striped muscle of the esophagus with motor fibers, hence, one of the more serious consequences of cutting the vagi above the origin of the main esophageal branches is interference with swallowing. The striped muscle of the esophagus is permanently paralyzed after a high vagotomy (e.g., in the neck), but the smooth muscle of the lower third shows some degree of recovery; peristalsis in this portion may return and swallowing may again become possible (Cannon, 1907). In animals such as the dog and rabbit in which the entire esophagus is made up of striped muscle, high vagotomy results in permanent inability to swallow. Paralysis of the esophagus with the resultant accumulation of food and liquid in the esophagus and pharynx, associated with the loss of the sensory innervation of the larynx, results in the aspiration of food and liquids into the lungs; the animal either suffocates or dies of aspiration pneumonia. Aspiration pneumonia is the most common cause of death after a high vagotomy in dogs.

The fact that peristalsis, at least in the striped muscle portion of the esophagus, is coordinated outside of the esophagus itself, within the central nervous system, was demonstrated in experiments by Mosso in 1876. He made a transverse section through the esophagus of the dog and placed a small wooden ball in the part below the cut. The animal was then stimulated to swallow; one or two seconds after contraction of the pharyngeal muscles the peristaltic wave began to traverse the esophagus. The wave did not stop at the point of the incision but in due time appeared below and carried the ball into the stomach. These observations were later confirmed by Meltzer in 1899. Meltzer observed that if he used ether anesthesia he obtained results similar to those of Mosso. However, if the animal was narcotized with morphine alone the peristaltic wave did not progress beyond the transverse incision. Likewise it stopped at a longitudinal incision which permitted the contents of the esophagus to escape. Evidently under these circumstances, local reflexes initiated by the contact of food with the mucosa of the esophagus were essential to the normal progress of peristalsis. Meltzer concluded that peristalsis in the striped muscle portion of the esophagus is coordinated in the central nervous system, but is aided by local reflexes arising within the esophagus.

Consideration of the manner of ending of the motor nerves to the esophagus will aid us in understanding this situation. The striped muscle is directly innervated by the vagus nerves, the fibers ending on the muscle cells without the intervention of any local ganglion cells. In the smooth muscle portion, however, there is an extensive local plexus including nerve cells and their branches similar to the myenteric plexus in other parts of the gastrointestinal tract. In this part the vagus fibers do not go to muscle cells but end on nerve cells within the esophageal plexus. It is true that a less dense plexus extends into the striped muscle portion, but this is perhaps concerned with secretion of fluid by the esophageal mucous membrane rather than with contraction of the muscle. As we have already noticed, the local nerve plexus is capable of coordinating peristalsis in the smooth muscle portion of the esophagus, even in the absence of the extrinsic nerves.

### The Cardia

The muscular ring encircling the lower end of the esophagus is commonly known as the cardiac sphincter, although, as a matter of fact, in man the thickness of the muscle in this situation is scarcely greater than that in the rest of the tube. We have already seen that the cardia is held tonically contracted, but relaxes upon the approach of a peristaltic wave or may even remain relaxed during a series of swallows, as in drinking (p. 687).

Experiments upon animals suggest that the cardia is supplied with both motor and inhibitory fibers from the vagus; stimulation of this nerve, although followed in many cases by relaxation of the sphincter, at other times causes contraction. Although in some animals a tonic contraction of the cardiac sphincter follows section of the vagi, Hwang and his associates found that bilateral vagotomy in the dog in no instance caused increased tone of the sphincter, as would result had they an inhibitory function; but hypotonia was sometimes the result of this operation. However, the character of the response, inhibitory or excitatory, depends, apparently, upon the degree of tone, high or low respectively, exhibited by the sphincter at the moment of stimulation. Species differences may also be responsible for the variability of results. Observations upon cardiospasm (q.v.) suggest that in the human subject *the chief influence exerted by the vagal fibers is inhibitory*.

CARDIOSPASM. Cardiospasm is the term applied to a condition in which the sphincter does not relax properly during deglutition; difficulty in swallowing (dysphagia) results, the subject complaining that the food "sticks in his throat." X-ray examination frequently shows that the lower portion of the esophagus is dilated into a funnel-shaped or fusiform structure. The condition is usually one of incoordination between the muscle of the esophageal wall and the sphincter—*achalasia*—rather than one of actual spasm. Hurst showed that in most instances a tube weighted with mercury passed readily through the obstruction, and suggested the term achalasia in these cases in preference to cardiospasm. The mode of its production is not known for certain. In some instances it may be reflex in nature and due to the irritation of afferent fibers in the stomach, gall-bladder or other abdominal viscus. In two cases reported by Rake, from which tissue was obtained for histological examination, degeneration of Auerbach's plexus (which receives vagal fibers) was found. Degenerative changes in the ganglion cells of this plexus have been described by several investigators. The recent observations of Code and his coworkers (1958) led them to the conclusion that achalasia is associated with degeneration of Auerbach's plexus and is characterized by absence of peristalsis in the body of the esophagus. A remarkable finding in their cases was increased response of the esophageal muscle to Mecholyl—a choline compound that acts like acetylcholine.

The cardia is also innervated by the sympathetic, but there has been uncertainty again as to whether this nerve exerts an inhibitory or an excitatory action. As in the case of the vagus, both inhibitory and motor effects have been reported (Luckhardt) to result from its stimulation. In man the sympathetic has been thought to have a motor action. The fact mentioned earlier—that in some animals bilateral vagotomy causes spastic contraction of the cardia—would also suggest that the usual action of the sympathetic upon the sphincter is excitatory, were it not for the observations of Hwang and associates that sympathetic ganglionectomy is without any effect upon sphincter tone, whereas vagal section may be followed by hypotonia. Knight, in experiments upon cats, found that although vagal stimulation, in all instances, caused relaxation of the cardia, sympathetic stimulation invariably resulted in contraction.

Thus, as in the case of the vagus, the conflict of experimental results in respect to the sympathetic innervation of the cardia does not permit any clear cut statement to be made. The confusion is likely due to species differences. Observations in cases of cardiospasm (see below) have suggested a motor action of the sympathetic in man but Grimson and his associates have thrown doubt upon such a function as they could find no change in sphincter action after double supradiaphragmatic vagotomy.

The cardia relaxes much more readily to pressure applied to its esophageal aspect than to pressure from within the stomach. In animals, a pressure of 5 to 7 cm. of water on its upper surface is sufficient to cause relaxation, but a pressure of 25 cm. is required to be exerted from the stomach side. Alvarez found, however, that in the human subject the mere pressure of the stomach contents upon the cardia may cause it to relax. This fact was brought out by placing persons in the head-down position. The tonicity varies in degree in different individuals, and in some, simply bending over forces the cardia, and causes a reflux of fluid into the pharynx or mouth, as a result, no doubt, of the compression of the abdomen, and the consequent elevation of intragastric pressure. It is to be recalled in this regard that the pressure in the esophagus is, like that within the rest of the thorax generally, subatmospheric. In individuals in which the tone of the cardia is lessened, the "negative" pressure in the esophagus (together with any increase of pressure in the abdomen) will encourage the regurgitation of fluid from the stomach.

The tone of the cardia is inhibited by mild stimulation of the gastric mucosa, and by sensory impulses arising in the mouth and pharynx. Its tone increases as digestion proceeds. The factor responsible for the increased tone does not appear to be the acidity of the gastric contents; the hypertonicity apparently is a part of the general increase in tone that occurs in the fundic portion of the stomach with the progress of digestion.

The tone of the sphincter may be *increased* reflexly by abnormally strong stimulation of the stomach or of more remote regions of the alimentary tract. Afferent impulses arising from a diseased gall-bladder and other abdominal organs have been held responsible for abnormally hypertonic states of the cardia.

### ANTIPERISTALSIS IN THE ESOPHAGUS; HEARTBURN; BELCHING

According to Alvarez, reverse wavelets or ripples commencing at the cardia and passing upwards along the esophagus to the pharynx are not an uncommon occurrence in man; but true reverse peristalsis is not seen unless some obstruction exists. The reverse ripples in the esophagus are thought to be responsible for some of the symptoms of dyspepsia, e.g., the deposition of "fur" upon the back of the tongue, bad breath and regurgitation of fluids into the mouth. Evidence for the existence of reverse movements in the esophagus was obtained by Kast who found that lycopodium spores swallowed in a capsule were recoverable from the mouth washings next morning in over 50 per cent of a series of human subjects. The possibility of material from even the lower bowel reaching the mouth is strongly suggested by the fact that lycopodium spores introduced into the colon by enema have been recovered some hours later from washings of the stomach.

"HEARTBURN" is ascribed by Alvarez to the stimulation of the mucosa of the upper part of the esophagus by acid fluid regurgitated from the stomach. Payne and Poulton suggest that a tonic spasm of the esophagus set up by the acid stimulus is responsible for the sensation. Jones and Richardson produced it in normal persons by distension of the lower third of the esophagus. The introduction of acid, cold water or gastric contents into this part of the esophagus also caused the burning sensation. Spasm of the wall of the tube was observed at the level in contact with the material and reversed peristalsis above. It is generally agreed that the sensation does not originate within the stomach itself.

BELCHING. The tendency, after a meal, for small amounts of gas to be expelled from the stomach into the esophagus and mouth is experienced by most normal persons. It is brought about, most probably, by reverse waves originating in the cardiac region of the stomach and ascending the esophagus. The repeated belching of gas is, however, abnormal. The gas in these instances is not, as a rule, produced by digestive or fermentative processes in the stomach, but is simply air which has been previously swallowed (aerophagy); it has the composition of atmospheric air. The greater part of the swallowed air does not enter the stomach but is held in the lower part of the esophagus until a sufficient volume has collected to give the subject a certain satisfaction when it is belched. The condition is seen in the nervous type of subject or in one who has some gastric discomfort; he resorts to the air swallowing trick in an effort to gain relief. The intragastric pressure is not increased above the normal, apparently, in subjects who have the sensation of "gas on the stomach" and the pressure is not lowered after gas has been belched.

### Movements of the Stomach

Before attempting to describe the movements of the stomach it is desirable to define the anatomical terms that will be used (see figure 41.4). The stomach as a whole consists of a *fundus, body* and a *pyloric portion* (antrum). The fundus is that portion of the stomach which, in the human in the upright position, lies above a horizontal plane passing through the esophageal opening. The body of the stomach (corpus ventriculi) extends from the fundus to the *incisura angularis* on the lesser curvature and to a corresponding notch on the greater curvature. The incisura is a conspicuous notch on the lesser curvature which serves not only to separate the anatomical divisions of the stomach but also marks the position of a band of smooth muscle which has a higher degree of tonus than most of the remainder of the gastric muscle and causes a narrowing of the gastric lumen at this point. The pyloric portion (pars pylorica) extends from the incisura angularis in the lesser curvature and the corresponding notch on the greater curvature to the junction of the stomach with the duodenum. The pyloric portion differs from the remainder of the stomach in having much heavier musculature.

The cardia is simply the esophageal orifice,

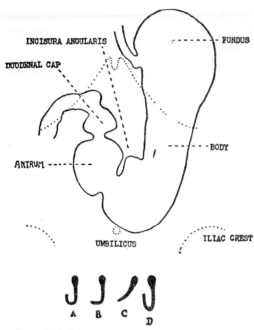

FIG. 41.4. Diagram showing the position and subdivisions of the stomach. A, B and C represent J, reversed L and steer horn types of stomach, respectively. D, stomach of the J-shaped type with the greater curvature lying well below the level of the umbilicus. Antrum is also known as the vestibule.

that is, the opening between the esophagus and the stomach. Properly speaking it refers to no anatomical structure; nevertheless the term is often used to refer to the entire region of the stomach surrounding the cardia and in that sense it includes the mucous membrane and muscle in the immediate vicinity of the orifice. The cardia is surrounded by a sphincter muscle known as the cardiac sphincter. This sphincter, although it appears thicker and heavier than the adjacent muscle when in the contracted state, is difficult to see in the dead stomach. The pylorus is the opening between the stomach and duodenum and, like the cardia, refers to no anatomical structure. However, the term is often used to designate the pyloric portion of the stomach. Likewise the pyloric sphincter is sometimes referred to as the pylorus. These usages are incorrect and often give rise to misunderstandings. The lumen of the pyloric portion may be divided into an antrum and a pyloric canal. The separation between these two portions is marked by a sulcus intermedius when this is present. The portion to the right of the sulcus is known as the pyloric canal and the portion to the left as the pyloric antrum; the antrum, too, is not a structure but a space; nevertheless, the entire pyloric

portion is often called the antrum in clinical literature.

### THE PERIODIC ACTIVITY OF THE EMPTY STOMACH

The smooth muscle of the stomach is seldom completely inactive, but its activity increases during gastric digestion and periodically when the stomach is empty. The activity of the empty stomach was first observed by Schirokich (1901) whose observations were extended by Tscheschkow (1902) and later by Boldyreff (1904) all working in Pavlov's laboratory in St. Petersburg. Boldyreff, in particular, noted periodic activity of other organs of digestion including the small intestine and pancreas. The contractions of the empty stomach were further studied by Cannon and Washburn at Harvard in 1912. These authors recognized the relation between the contractions and the sensation of hunger and proposed for them the name *hunger contractions*. Later, hunger contractions were studied and described in detail by Carlson (1916) and his coworkers at the University of Chicago.

Hunger contractions are peristaltic waves superimposed on contractions of the gastric smooth muscle as a whole. In contrast to digestive peristalsis, which is evident chiefly in the distal part of the corpus and pyloric portion of the stomach, the hunger waves travel the entire length of the stomach.

Carlson recognized three types of hunger contractions: Type I occurs when the tone of the stomach is feeble. It consists of single contractions superimposed on a low tone level. The tonus of the stomach does not rise between contractions and there is always an interval of time between the end of one contraction and the beginning of the next. Each contraction lasts for about 30 seconds and the interval between contractions is from $\frac{1}{2}$ second to 3 or 4 seconds. These contractions occur during a hunger period which lasts for from 15 to 30 minutes. The hunger periods are separated by rest periods lasting for from $\frac{1}{2}$ hour to 3 hours. Type II hunger contractions occur when the tonus of the stomach is strong. There is no intervening pause between the contractions each of which lasts for 20 to 30 seconds. The tonus of the stomach tends to rise as the contractions follow one another. Often toward the end of a series of contractions there is a period of incomplete tetanus of the stomach lasting for 1 to 5 minutes. This type of hunger contraction tends to be continuous in the sense that there are no rest periods between the hunger periods. Type III hunger contractions ap-

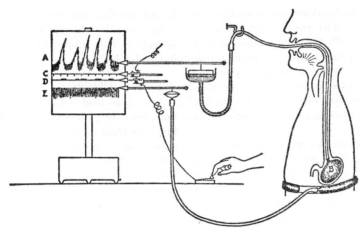

FIG. 41.5. Diagram showing the method used to record the gastric hunger contractions. A, kymograph record of the increase and decrease of volume of the gastric balloon B; C, time records in minutes; D, record of the subjective experience of hunger pangs; E, record of the pneumograph placed about the waist. (From Cannon.)

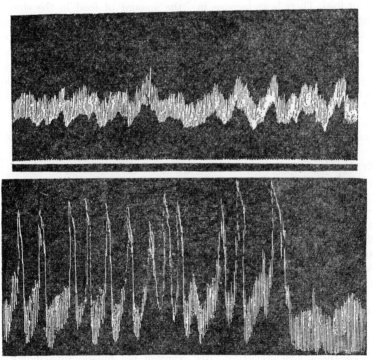

FIG. 41.6. Upper, tracing of the tonus rhythm of the stomach (man) 3 hours after a meal. Lower tracing from the stomach during the culmination of a period of vigorous gastric hunger contractions (From Carlson.)

pear when the tonus of the stomach is very high and tends to increase with the first contraction. The characteristic performance of the stomach is an incomplete tetanus which lasts for 1 to 10 minutes. Superimposed on the high tone level are individual contractions lasting from 12 to 15 seconds each.

Carlson noted that hunger contractions are apt to begin soon after the stomach has emptied. In the beginning they tend to be type I and the hunger periods at first are of short duration. As the fast continues the hunger periods become longer and the rest periods shorter and eventually the contractions become type II in character. Type III contractions are seen in animals after prolonged fasts; they rarely occur in humans. Hunger contractions are more vigorous in young than in older persons and the sensations associated with the contractions vary a great deal in different people. In some people they are definitely painful, whereas others are conscious merely of a vague feeling of emptiness which is exaggerated during the contraction phase but is apt to be more or less continuously present.

Associated with severe hunger contractions are certain systemic effects which are of interest in explaining the discomfort and inefficiency that is associated with severe hunger. There is for example, an increased excitability of the reflex centers of the central nervous system which can be demonstrated by studying the knee-jerk. At the same time there is general restlessness and increased movements in those animals that are governed by instinct; this doubtless has to do with the search for food. There is an increase in heart rate during the actual contractions and an increase in the salivary flow with each contraction. The latter is evident during strong contractions only. There is apt to be a feeling of weakness and a general indisposition to make any vigorous effort, mental or physical. Along with the sensation of emptiness, which is referred to the epigastrium, there is often headache. The headache of hunger is peculiar in that it is relieved at once on taking food; it is probably reflex in origin. Finally there is apt to be a sensation of nausea with severe hunger. As pointed out by Ivy and his associates in 1925, this latter effect is probably due to contractions of the duodenum. The duodenum and upper jejunum usually participate in hunger contractions.

Hunger contractions are inhibited by taking food. The presence of almost any substance in the stomach is sufficient to inhibit the contractions for a time; food in the mouth or in the intestine is also effective. Strangely enough, hunger contractions cease on the presentation of food even though the food is not eaten.

HUNGER CONTRACTIONS AND APPETITE. Although the sensation of hunger is associated with changes in the viscera which can be easily demonstrated by physical means, this is not true of appetite. Appetite is largely due to anticipation of the pleasure of eating; although it is frequently associated with hunger, it is not necessarily so. One may have his hunger completely satisfied and still have an appetite for palatable food. Likewise one may be hungry but because the food presented is distasteful, or the surroundings disagreeable, he may suffer from loss of appetite. Extreme hunger, may, of itself, reduce appetite through producing a sensation of nausea. This subject is discussed more fully in chapter 43.

## DIGESTIVE PERISTALSIS

As soon as food is taken the hunger contractions cease and, after a variable period of time, they are replaced by digestive peristalsis. The outstanding characteristic of this type of gastric peristalsis is the constancy of its rhythm. When the stomach contains food, peristaltic waves occur regularly at a frequency of about three per minute in the human, four per minute in the dog and about five per minute in the cat. Each wave begins as a slight circular constriction of some part of the body of the stomach or corpus ventriculi (Cannon, 1898, 1911b). The exact point of origin varies with conditions, one of which is the amount of food in the stomach. The contraction appears in the X-ray silhouette as a slight indentation on the greater and lesser curvatures which travels toward the pylorus, becoming deeper meanwhile, until it finally ends with a contraction of the pyloric sphincter (Wheelon and Thomas, 1920, 1921). Not all gastric waves reach the pylorus in this manner. Some appear to terminate at the incisura angularis (Hofmeister and Schutz, 1886) or they may end at some point on the pyloric portion, most frequently in the region of the pyloric canal. When this happens the portion of the stomach beyond the point of termination of the wave appears to contract concentrically, expelling its contents either into the duodenum or back into the proximal portion of the stomach.

The difference between waves that go all the way to the pylorus and those that appear to stop short may be explained by assuming that all waves progress peristaltically until they become deep enough to obliterate the gastric lumen. This would cause a sudden rise in pressure in the space beyond and might act as a stimulus causing the muscle surrounding this space to contract. It is probably significant that the antral muscle shows a greater tendency to contract in response to the stimulus of stretching, than do the other gastric muscles (Gellhorn and Budde, 1923).

A peristaltic wave takes one minute, more or less, to travel from its point of origin to the pylorus. Since there are three waves per minute, the stomach will usually be occupied by three waves at one time, or by four or more if the origin is near the fundus (figure 41.7). If the origin

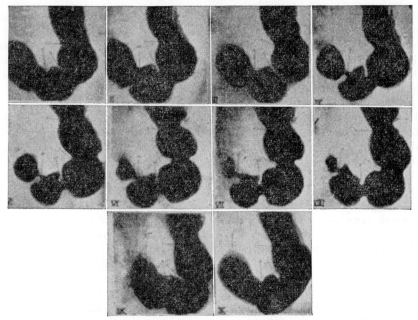

FIG. 41.7. Serial X-ray photographs of human stomach taken at 2-second intervals during digestion (From Cole.)

is low only one or two may be seen. Cole recognized this fact and spoke of one-, two-, three-, or four-cycle stomachs, depending on the number of waves that were visible at one time.

During digestion the body and fundus of the stomach, which serve the reservoir function primarily, behave quite differently from the pyloric portion which serves mainly the function of mechanical digestion and propulsion. The muscle of the body and fundus are relatively thin and participate to only a moderate extent in visible peristalsis. It is this portion of the stomach that undergoes the greatest changes in size and shape, accommodating itself through changes in tonus to the volume of its contents.

### THE TONUS OF THE STOMACH

*Tonus* is a word that has a variety of meanings and is difficult to define precisely; nevertheless, there are certain characteristics of smooth muscle for which no other name is available. Tonus, as applied to smooth muscle, refers to the relation between the length of the muscle and the tension which it maintains; thus, it may mean either the tension in the muscle when maintained at constant length, or the length which the muscle assumes under constant tension. This is another way of saying that a change in the tonus of a muscle constitutes a change in its elastic properties. In the digesting stomach, the length of the muscle fibers is determined largely

by the volume of the gastric contents. In these circumstances changes in tonus express themselves primarily in terms of tension and are indicated by the pressure within the stomach. If the stomach is empty, changes in tonus will express themselves largely by changes in the length of the muscle fibers and this becomes manifest through changes in the shape of the stomach. The shape of the human stomach is subject to wide variations. Some of the shapes which it may assume are illustrated in figure 42.4, a, b, c, d. The shape of the stomach is, of course, also influenced by the volume of its contents and by the posture. In the reclining position it tends to assume a more nearly transverse position, whereas in the upright position the midportion of the stomach has a tendency to descend, producing more of a J shape.

The tonus of the gastric muscle, in so far as it is inversely related to the average volume capacity of the stomach, must increase progressively as the stomach empties during digestion, otherwise the intragastric pressure would fall to a level too low to maintain emptying. Whether this necessary gain in tonus takes place by continuous gradual shortening of the fibers as postulated by Cannon (1911b), or in a stepwise manner as proposed by Cole (1911, 1917) is still uncertain. Cole described what he called "systole" and "diastole" of the stomach. These are contractions and relaxations, respectively, of the entire gastric musculature occurring approximately once every twenty seconds in man. During each systole the peristaltic waves increase in force as indicated by deeper indentations on the greater and lesser curvatures as seen in the X-ray silhouette. Decrease in the vigor of peristalsis is associated with the phase of diastole. If Cole's description is correct, the problem of gain in tone becomes merely a matter of a slightly lessened relaxation after each successive systole, the resulting decrease in volume corresponding to the volume of material expelled from the stomach.

The tonus of the gastric muscle and the peristaltic movements are closely related; anything that decreases gastric tonus depresses peristalsis and any increase in tone is apt to be associated with an increase in the vigor of the peristaltic waves. For example, if the vagus nerves are cut the stomach becomes hypotonic and propulsive peristaltic waves cease. After several weeks or months the tonus is partially restored and with it peristaltic activity. The apparent dependence of peristalsis on tonus suggested to Cannon (1911a) the thought that rhythmic peristalsis arises in muscle fibers that are under a certain optimal degree of tension, depending on the relationship between the volume of the gastric contents and the tonus of the muscle. Since systole and diastole of the stomach as described by Cole occur approximately once every twenty seconds, which is also the interval between peristaltic waves, it may be that each peristaltic wave is initiated by an increase in the tone of the entire gastric muscle.

As already pointed out, the tonus of the stomach increases progressively during a prolonged fast and eventually the stomach becomes tubular in shape. When food is taken the stomach begins to relax progressively with each swallow so that the intragastric pressure does not rise during the act of eating; this is the receptive relaxation of the stomach referred to earlier in this chapter. Once the stomach is filled, the tonus begins to recover and after it reaches a certain level digestive peristalsis makes its appearance.

## THE RELATION BETWEEN HUNGER CONTRACTIONS AND DIGESTIVE PERISTALSIS

Hunger contractions and digestive peristalsis have been described as though they were entirely separate and distinct types of activity. This is largely the result of their having been investigated by different authors under different experimental conditions. In the pyloric portion at least, one cannot distinguish between a hunger contraction and a peristaltic wave such as might occur during digestion. The contractions of the entire stomach that are seen during the hunger periods are very similar to the systoles and diastoles described by Cole (1911) as occurring when the stomach was filled with a barium mixture. It is not unlikely that such real differences as there are between hunger contractions and digestive peristalsis are due merely to the different conditions under which they occur, and that they really represent the operation of a single motor mechanism.

COORDINATION OF ANTRUM, SPHINCTER AND DUODENUM. The fact that there is a relationship between duodenal motility and the gastric peristaltic cycle was first noted by Joseph and Meltzer. In a study on rabbits they observed that "during each contraction of the pyloric part of the stomach, the duodenum stops its rhythmic activity and loses tone, only to resume both again as soon as the contraction of the stomach passes off." They remarked that the phenomenon resembles the relaxation of the stomach that occurs during the act of swallowing. Later Wheelon and Thomas (1922) and Thomas and Crider noted a similar relationship in dogs. As interpreted by Thomas and Crider (1935), a typical gastroduodenal cycle is as follows: as the gastric peristaltic wave approaches the pylorus, the tone and the rhythmic activity of the first part of the duodenum are progressively inhibited, reaching their lowest point just before the gastric wave reaches the pylorus. As the gastric wave ends in a contraction of the pyloric sphincter the duodenum resumes its tone and rhythmic activity. The contraction of the sphincter is therefore accompanied by a contraction of the duodenum. Since the rhythmic contractions of the pyloric sphincter coincide with contractions of the duodenal cap they are probably concerned primarily with control of regurgitation of duodenal contents into the stomach.

## THE GASTRODUODENAL PRESSURE CYCLE

Numerous efforts have been made to measure pressures in the stomach and intestine, but the methods used were so inadequate that the observations contributed little to an understanding of gastric function. About 1940, Brody, Werle, Meschan and Quigley devised methods for the precise determination of intraluminal pressures in the gastrointestinal tract. They utilized modern precision manometers connected to small open tubes or tubes ending in small, metal-shielded balloons. The open ends of the tubes or the end that was fitted with balloons was placed in the areas from which pressures were to be recorded. The experimental animals were unanesthetized dogs provided with appropriate fistulas. Ordinarily the receiving ends of the pressure tubes were placed just above and just below the pylorus, hence, intragastric pressures were recorded from the terminal antrum and duodenal pressures from the duodenal bulb. In some of their studies graphic methods were combined with X-ray and fluoroscopic observations. This method yielded, in addition to pressure measurements, significant information regarding gastric and duodenal motility, pyloric sphincter activity and the passage of contents through the pylorus. Brody and Quigley and their associates extended the study to human subjects.

When the stomach is at rest (peristalsis absent) or in the intervals between gastric peristaltic waves the antral and duodenal (bulbar) pressures are low, being slightly above or below atmospheric levels. These pressures are referred to as basal pressures. Basal pressure in the antrum is 1 to 2 cm of fluid above the basal pressure in the duodenum. Taking food increases basal pressure in both the antrum and the duodenum, but the pressure rise is greater in the antrum, hence the pressure difference between the antrum and the duodenum is increased. When a peristaltic wave approaches the pylorus the antral pressure increases, usually to between 15 and 30 cm. $H_2O$, followed by an increase in bulbar pressure. However, the bulbar pressure rises more rapidly than the antral pressure so that the two reach their peaks simultaneously, after which they both fall again to basal levels. This cycle is repeated, with only quantitative variations, with each gastric cycle. By other means it was established that contraction of the pyloric sphincter usually begins near the start of the rise in bulbar pressure but outlasts the increase in bulbar pressure.

In the fluoroscopic studies, passage of gastric contents through the pylorus could be seen to begin as the antral wave approached the pylorus but before the elevation in antral pressure could be detected. Evacuation continued through the early part of the rise in antral pressure but ceased sometime during the succeeding rise in bulbar pressure (and the sphincteric contraction). Consequently the time during which gastric contents could be seen passing into the duodenum could be divided into two distinct but continuous phases—one during which only basal pressures

served as a driving force and resistance at the pylorus was low (designated evacuation period "A") and another during which the antral pressure substantially exceeded the duodenal pressure and the pyloric resistance was rising (called evacuation period "B") (Quigley, 1943, 1944).

Figure 41.8 is an attempt to correlate the gastroduodenal pressure cycle with the motility cycle described in the preceding section. The antral pressure rise is seen to be related to the terminal phase of the antral contraction. The bulbar pressure rise is clearly a result of the contraction phase of the duodenal cycle. Both are closely related in time to the contraction of the sphincter muscle. By way of explanation let us assume that a strong antral wave is approaching the pylorus. Presumably it obliterates the gastric lumen at some point and would put pressure on the contents of the terminal antrum if they were not free to escape by way of the pylorus.

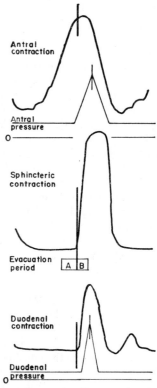

Fig. 41.8. Composite diagram showing the successive contractions of the pars pylorica ("antrum"), pyloric sphincter, and duodenum during a single gastric cycle and the associated intraluminal pressure changes. Evacuation periods A and B are also shown. The contraction curves are traced from a kymographic balloon water-manometer record. The pressure curves are approximate copies of the curves published by Quigley *et al.*, 1950. Vertical lines mark simultaneous points.

However, they do escape at first (evacuation period "A") hence no pressure rise is evidenced. Presently as the wave approaches the sphincter the contraction of that muscle begins, the pyloric lumen narrows, resistance increases and the trapped contents of the terminal antrum are put under pressure, recorded as the antral pressure rise. At first the pressure is sufficient to overcome the increasing resistance at the pylorus (evacuation period "B") but the rapidly contracting sphincter soon closes the pylorus and puts an end to this cycle of evacuation. It is not to be inferred that the stomach always empties in the manner described. Liquids have been observed to leave the stomach without any rhythmic changes in intragastric pressure or any evidence of gastric peristalsis (Thomas, 1957, Shay and Gershon-Cohen, 1934).

## GASTRIC FILLING AND EMPTYING

It is possible to determine how solid or semisolid food arranges itself within the stomach of an animal by marking successive portions of the food with dyes or pigments so that they can be identified later. After the stomach is filled the animal is killed and the stomach removed and frozen, or otherwise fixed, and sectioned. In this way it has been found that the first food eaten lies against the greater curvature in the body and fundus of the stomach. Successive layers lie progressively nearer the lesser curvature until the last portion eaten is near the upper end of the lesser curvature in the vicinity of the cardiac orifice. Liquids, on the other hand, tend to remain near the lesser curvature of the stomach and to flow toward the pylorus along a V-shaped groove formed by the muscle in this region. This is the so-called *magenstrasse* which is evident in some animals but less so in the human. In any case, if a large volume of liquid is swallowed it flows around the food mass and tends to be distributed over the entire interior of the stomach between the food mass and the stomach wall.

A relatively small part of the energy expended by the gastric muscle is utilized in propelling food from the stomach into the intestine through the pyloric orifice. The vigor of the gastric muscular contraction is such that if it were all utilized in propulsion the stomach would empty itself within a very few minutes. By far the greater part of the work is utilized in mechanical digestion, serving to macerate the food particles and break them up into small fragments. This work is done largely by the pyloric portion which in some ways resembles in function the gizzard

of birds. The powerful contractions of the pyloric muscle drive the food against the pylorus. All but the small part that escapes into the duodenum is forced back through a narrow orifice formed by the contraction wave, into the body of the stomach. It is this manipulation of the food mass which results in its being broken down and mechanically digested in the pyloric portion of the stomach.

The rate at which food leaves the stomach is determined by a variety of factors among which are the total volume of the gastric contents and the consistency, chemical composition, pH, and osmolar concentration of the food. Hunt and his coworkers (1951) have shown that for any individual and type of meal the amount evacuated in a unit of time is a function of the volume of the gastric contents. The effect of consistency on rate of emptying is best seen by comparing the emptying of liquids with the emptying of solids. Inert liquids, which neither stimulate the stomach chemically nor osmotically, leave the stomach rapidly. Water, for example, begins to leave the stomach almost as soon as it is swallowed. Solids, on the other hand, are not normally evacuated from the stomach until they are reduced to a fluid or semifluid consistency. Undigested solids are not normally allowed to pass the pyloric sphincter but are returned to the body of the stomach (Cannon, 1911b).

The influence of the chemical composition of the food on emptying is shown by the relative rate of emptying of the three major foodstuffs. Cannon (1904) showed that for meals of a given size, a meal consisting mainly of carbohydrate left the stomach more rapidly than one consisting mainly of protein or fat and that a protein meal left more rapidly than a fat meal. Fat, especially if eaten in large quantities, remains in the stomach for a very long time. It is not unusual to find food in a dog's stomach as long as 24 hours after a meal consisting largely of fat meat.

The osmolar concentration of the gastric contents has a profound effect upon the rate of gastric emptying. One of the earliest facts to be determined with respect to gastric emptying was that physiological saline leaves the stomach faster than salt solutions of either greater or lesser concentration. More recently Hunt (1956) has shown that in human subjects adding salt to water hastened emptying of the water from the stomach up to a concentration of about 100 m.eq. per liter. Above 150 m.eq. per liter the emptying was delayed. In this way he showed that making the gastric contents either hypertonic or hypotonic with respect to the blood caused a delay in emptying. This is an important factor in the slow emptying of sugar solutions although, as will be pointed out later, sugar slows gastric emptying in another way.

The effect of acid on gastric emptying has been the subject of considerable study and extensive speculation. The fact that strongly acid solutions leave the stomach slowly and that the rate of emptying of such solutions can be accelerated by neutralizing the acid is well known. For example, in some experiments by Crider and Thomas (1937) 300 cc. of physiological saline left the stomach of a dog in an average time of 17 minutes, whereas it took 42 minutes for the stomach to dispose of an equal amount of $N/20$ hydrochloric acid. However, it does not necessarily follow that hydrochloric acids plays an important part in regulating gastric emptying under ordinary circumstances. The acidity of the gastric and intestinal contents is usually not great enough during digestion to materially affect gastric emptying. For example, a pH of 3.0 in the duodenum is necessary in order to influence the rate of emptying of the stomach but the intestinal contents usually have a pH that is well above this level, pH values of 4.0 to 6.0 being most common. Nevertheless, the inhibitory effect of acid on gastric emptying has an important function in protecting the duodenal mucous membrane against excess acidity.

### Regulation of Gastric Emptying

At least two mechanisms are available for regulating the rate at which the gastric contents pass into the duodenum. One is the powerful sphincter muscle that surrounds the pyloric orifice at the junction of the stomach and duodenum. Strong contraction of the pyloric sphincter could, if maintained, effectively prevent the passage of the gastric contents through the pyloric orifice. The other mechanism has to do with the control of gastric motor activities. In the early days of physiology it was taken for granted that gastric emptying was controlled entirely by the pyloric sphincter. This was the result of reasoning from structure to function; there was no other apparent use for the powerful sphincter muscle so strategically situated between the stomach and duodenum. However, a closer scrutiny of the function of the pyloric portion of the stomach reveals the fact that a sphincter muscle is necessary at this point to enable the pyloric muscle to carry out its function of comminution and maceration of the food

mass. It is important, too, to have a sphincter to serve as a valve to prevent excessive regurgitation of duodenal contents into the stomach.

Another fact which has contributed to the concept of pyloric control of gastric emptying is the existence of a powerful pyloric reflex. This reflex is elicited by mechanical or chemical stimulation of the duodenum and results in contraction of the pyloric sphincter muscle. One of the stimuli which is capable of eliciting a pyloric reflex is relatively strong hydrochloric acid in the duodenum. This fact, along with other observations made in connection with his classical studies of gastric motility, led Cannon (1907) to propose his theory of the acid control of the pyloric sphincter. He assumed that the pylorus remains closed and thus prevents emptying of the stomach until the gastric contents become acid in reaction. As soon as the secretion of hydrochloric acid in the stomach is sufficient to acidify the gastric contents in the pyloric portion, the pylorus opens and allows some of the chyme to escape into the duodenum. The acid chyme in the duodenum then elicits a pyloric reflex and causes the pylorus to close and to remain closed until such time as the duodenal contents are neutralized. This attractive theory failed to take into account the facts that gastric emptying proceeds normally in persons who secrete no hydrochloric acid, that there is no failure of regulation of gastric emptying when the pyloric sphincter area has been removed surgically, and that the acidity of the duodenal contents necessary to close the pylorus is far in excess of that which normally occurs in the duodenum. Thomas et al. (1934) found that even when the pyloric sphincter does contract in response to duodenal irritation, the contraction is of brief duration and is followed by relaxation to below the previous tone level.

If the pyloric sphincter were to act as a regulator of gastric emptying, it would be necessary that the sphincter muscle and the muscle of the remainder of the stomach should be reciprocally innervated, that is, that the innervation would have to be so arranged that when the sphincter is contracting the stomach would relax, and vice versa. The true situation is quite the contrary; stimuli which cause contraction of the gastric muscle also increase the tone and activity of the pyloric sphincter, whereas those which cause relaxation of the sphincter also cause relaxation of the gastric musculature (Thomas and Wheelon, 1922).

It has been shown that the major factors

regulating gastric emptying are still effective even though the pyloric sphincter is mechanically prevented from contracting by placing an open tube in the pyloric orifice (Crider and Thomas, 1937). In these circumstances the differences in the rate of emptying of acid, saline, alcohol and olive oil are in no way modified by maintaining the pylorus in an open condition except that the emptying time for alcohol and fat are somewhat prolonged. This is evidently due to the fact that duodenal contents regurgitate freely into the stomach when these two substances are being emptied through an open pylorus.

THE ENTEROGASTRIC REFLEX. As soon as it became apparent that the characteristic response of the pyloric sphincter to acid in the duodenum was not contraction, although this sometimes occurs, but prolonged and persistent relaxation and that this is associated with loss of tonus and relaxation of the remainder of the gastric muscle, it was evident that the acid control of the pyloric sphincter could not be a major factor in the regulation of gastric emptying. A more adequate explanation was found in the diminution of gastric peristalsis and gastric tone with the consequent decrease in intragastric pressure which follows duodenal stimulation. So long as the pressure in the stomach is below that in the duodenum, emptying cannot occur. Further study revealed that not only acid but many other constituents of the gastric chyme such as products of protein digestion (Thomas and Crider, 1939), products of starch digestion (Quigley and Phelps, 1934), fats and fatty acids, when present in the duodenum, all cause inhibition of the gastric muscle. None of these substances, with the exception of hydrochloric acid, causes even momentary contraction of the pyloric sphincter. Mechanical distention of the intestine by means of saline also has a moderate inhibitory effect on gastric motility. However, this particular method of stimulation also causes sustained contraction of the pyloric sphincter; hence, the inhibitory effect on the gastric muscle is probably of little consequence in regulating emptying in response to mechanical stimulation. Thomas, Crider and Mogan (1934) found that the inhibitory effect of many chemical substances disappears after the vagus nerves have been cut. They concluded that the inhibitory effect of these substances is caused by a reflex involving the vagus nerves and proposed that it be designated the *enterogastric reflex*.

*Enterogastrone.* The inhibitory effect of fat on gastric motility has been known for many years and was recognized by Cannon who exempted the delayed emptying due to fat from his acid control theory. Fat exerts its effect in the absence of any available nerve supply (Farrell and Ivy, 1926). Kosaka and Lim (1930, 1933) and also Quigley, Zettleman and Ivy (1934) showed that fat inhibition is caused by a hormone which Lim (1933) called *enterogastrone*. This hormone is released from the intestinal mucous membrane by fat or fatty acids and by some other substances in the duodenum and, while circulating in the blood, it is carried to the stomach where it has an inhibitory effect on the gastric muscle. The fact that it also inhibits gastric secretion was mentioned in chapter 36. Quigley and Phelps (1934) were also able to demonstrate inhibition of the denervated stomach by carbohydrate substances when present in the intestine. It is assumed that carbohydrates also release enterogastrone or some closely related substance. In the experiments on vagotomized animals, Thomas and Crider (1934) noted that in dogs hydrochloric acid continued to exert some (although slight) influence on gastric motility after the vagus and splanchnic nerves were cut. They concluded that a hormonal as well as a nervous mechanism was probably involved in the action of hydrochloric acid. Schapiro and Woodward (1955) have found that acid in the intestine inhibits gastric motility in human subjects equally well whether or not the vagi are intact.

In summary, we can visualize the events following a meal approximately as follows: gastric emptying begins as soon as any part of the gastric contents become fluid enough to pass through the pylorus. Once started it proceeds rhythmically, a small amount being evacuated about every 20 seconds in man. Regulation of emptying begins as soon as the evacuated material has accumulated in the intestine to the point where any one of the numerous stimuli to the intestine associated with the chyme reaches threshold value. These stimuli are comprised in the chemical constituents of the chyme and to some extent in its volume. The chemical stimuli include the following, listed in the order of inhibitory potency in the concentrations usually encountered: fats, fatty acids, proteoses, peptones, amino acids, sugars and other products of starch digestion, and hydrogen ions; also effective are osmotically active substances and nonspecific irritants. The effect of these stimuli is to decrease the tone and peristaltic activity of the stomach, thus reducing the pressure gradient which develops with each gastric cycle and which is responsible for the passage of fluid through the pylorus. With the more powerful inhibitors, e.g., fat, the gradient may be reversed and duodenal contents will then regurgitate into the stomach. The inhibitory effect is exerted through a reflex involving the vagus nerves (*the enterogastric reflex*) or through a hormone (*enterogastrone*), released into the blood from the intestinal mucous membrane, or both. Products of protein digestion, acid and nonspecific irritants act mainly through the reflex mechanism; fats and carbohydrates act mainly through the hormone, enterogastrone. However, there may be a reflex element in the effect of the latter group and there is undoubtedly a hormonal component in the effect of hydrochloric acid. The pyloric sphincter plays a part by preventing regurgitation of the duodenal contents into the stomach; it also contracts rhythmically in such a way as apparently to limit the volume evacuated at each cycle but there is as yet no evidence that this function is utilized in regulating the over-all rate of gastric emptying.

### VOMITING

Vomiting is a reflex which serves to relieve the upper gastrointestinal tract of its contents. This may occur either because the contents are irritating, or because the organs themselves, or the nerves that supply them, are more irritable than normal; in either case there is an unusual degree of stimulation of some part of the tract. The most sensitive area is the first portion of the duodenum (Luckhardt, Phillips and Carlson, 1919) but adequate stimulation of other parts of the intestine or of the stomach, can induce the reflex. Even mild mechanical stimulation of the pharynx or fauces is effective in most people. Inflammation, or mechanical disturbances in the intestine such as appendicitis, obstruction, or strangulation, may induce violent emesis. Vomiting may be induced by abnormal stimulation of sensory receptors in organs outside the gastrointestinal tract, for example, the uterus, kidneys, heart or semicircular canals. Effective stimuli may also enter by way of the eyes, nose or mouth in the form of nauseating sights, odors or tastes; these give rise to what is called psychic vomiting. It is not unusual for a soldier to vomit on going into battle, or at some time during the battle experience; some people vomit at the sight of blood.

Vomiting that is induced by irritation of organs other than those of the gastrointestinal tract is sometimes referred to as "reflex" vomiting. This is an incorrect distinction however, since nearly all vomiting is reflex in origin. Even psychic vomiting is probably the result of conditioned reflexes.

Vomiting may be induced by certain types of motion as, for example, in seasickness, air sickness, carsickness, and the nausea and vomiting that some people experience when in a swing. This is probably the result of unusual stimulation of the equilibratory sense organs of the labyrinth.

### The Vomiting Center

The vomiting center lies in the dorsal part of the lateral reticular formation of the medulla oblongata close to (and to some extent including) the tractus solitaris. It lies in close relation to (but is quite distinct from) the respiratory centers. It is one of a constellation of visceral centers in this situation—salivatory nuclei, defecation and vasomotor centers, as well as the vestibular nuclei—a relationship consistent with the physiological reactions (salivation, vasomotor and respiratory, etc.) associated with the vomiting act. The *efferent* fibers are contained chiefly in the phrenics, the vagi and the sympathetics, but fibers are also conveyed by spinal nerves to the abdominal muscles and by cranial nerves to the muscles of the pharynx, palate, etc. The *afferent* impulses reach the center along a multitude of routes, the chief being the vagal and sympathetic fibers of the stomach and abdominal viscera.

"CENTRAL" VOMITING. Vomiting may occur as a result of direct stimulation of the vomiting center in the medulla. Certain substances such as *apomorphine, ipecac (or emetine), picrotoxine,* when administered intravenously cause vomiting through a specific action upon the center. These substances induce vomiting in animals when applied directly to the center. Typical vomiting efforts (retching) follow the injection of apomorphine after removal of the stomach and intestines. The experiments of Wang and Borison point to a chemoreceptor "trigger" mechanism in the ala cinerea which, through its connection with the vomiting center itself, induces vomiting when stimulated by these emetics. Copper sulfate was found by these investigators to act as an emetic both peripherally, through the gastrointestinal tract, and centrally; a lesion in the ala cinerea abolished the central action only.

Most important clinically is the central vomiting caused by traumatic stimulation of the center due to head injuries, increased intracranial pressure, brain tumor or meningeal irritation.

This type of vomiting is characterized by the great force with which the vomitus is ejected ("projectile vomiting"). There is also a minimum of nausea and a relative absence of participation of the voluntary muscles.

The persistence of pernicious *vomiting of pregnancy* is probably due to increased excitability of the center resulting from some metabolic disturbance. According to Harding the important factors in its production are carbohydrate starvation and dehydration with ketosis. Ordinary morning sickness is looked upon as a minor form of this condition, and differing from pernicious vomiting only in degree. As a result of the demands of the fetus, liver glycogen is low during pregnancy. After the fast of the night the reserves of carbohydrate are further reduced; a mild ketosis results which leads to nausea and vomiting. The distaste for food by hindering the replenishment of the carbohydrate stores aggrevates the ketosis. Thus morning sickness merges insensibly into the pernicious type of vomiting. A neurotic element is also frequently a potent influence in the development and persistence of the condition. The obvious corrective measures are, high carbohydrate feeding, the free administration of fluids, injections of glucose if necessary, mild sedatives, rest and quiet.

### The Vomiting Movements

Vomiting usually begins with nausea which is characterized by secretion of excessive quantities of saliva containing a large amount of mucus, in addition to certain well known disagreeable sensations. In the dog, in which it has been possible to analyze by graphic methods the sequence of events in vomiting, the first muscular movement to occur in a strong sustained contraction of the upper small intestine. Next, the pyloric sphincter contracts and then the pyloric portion of the stomach. These changes all take place during the period of nausea and result in emptying the contents of the upper jejunum, duodenum and pyloric portion of the stomach into the fundus and body of the stomach which are relaxed and dilated. After this has occurred the voluntary muscles come into play and at the same time the cardiac sphincter, esophagus and esophagopharyngeal sphincter relax. Following an inspiratory movement the glottis is closed and the abdominal muscles contract in a characteristic jerky manner (retching), compressing the stomach between the contracted diaphragm and the abdominal organs. The resulting pressure on the gastric contents causes their evacuation through the relaxed esophagus.

The precise sequence described above is probably not always followed and the mechanism may differ somewhat in different animals; for example, Cannon (1911b) gives the following graphic account of the act of vomiting in a cat as observed by means of X-rays.

The upper part of the stomach showed complete inhibition of its tone and appeared as a perfectly flaccid bag; the cardia relaxed. There then followed several deep peristaltic contractions which, commencing about the middle of the body of the organ, swept downward toward the incisura angularis where they came to a standstill forming a sharp ring of constriction. From this point a weaker wave continued to the pylorus. Finally, a very deep, strong contraction at the incisura appeared to almost divide the stomach in two, the upper part of the stomach and the cardia meanwhile remaining quite relaxed. A sharp contraction of the diaphragm and abdominal muscles then followed and ejected the gastric contents through the open cardia into the esophagus. The stomach played a more or less passive part in the process, its evacuation being effected by the strong compression to which it was subjected by the sharp descent of the diaphragm and the contraction of the abdominal muscles. Antiperistalsis was observed only once and then the wave did not proceed beyond the antrum. The deep contraction at the incisura offered an effectual barrier to the passage of stomach contents in a downward direction. Similar movements have been described in man.

Definite antiperistaltic waves in the stomach are rarely seen although violent churning movements may occur.[2] In certain types of vomiting, e.g., intestinal obstruction, or in persistent vomiting from other causes, antiperistalsis arises in the small intestine and sweeps material into the stomach or there may be a strong contraction of the duodenum which reverses the pressure gradient between the antrum and the duodenal bulb. Such movements of the duodenum occur

---

[2] In certain lower forms, however, e.g., the fish and the frog, which of course have no diaphragm, vomiting is carried out by the activity of the stomach alone, antiperistaltic waves carrying the food through the cardia. This more primitive type of vomiting, i.e., where reverse peristalsis and relaxation of the cardia are the prominent features, occurs normally in infants. The excess fluid of an oversized meal is regurgitated without the assistance, apparently, of the abominal muscles or diaphragm; position, and external pressure upon the abdomen following the meal sometimes, no doubt, also play a part.

sometime prior to the actual vomiting or at the same time; it accounts for the fact that a short time after the stomach has been thoroughly washed out, bile-stained fluid or fecal material may be vomited. According to Alvarez, reverse peristalsis starting in the upper bowel is itself a potent cause of nausea and vomiting.

Relaxation of the cardia is an essential part of the vomiting act, for the stomach is subject to strong compression during coughing, defecation, etc., yet the gastric contents are not as a rule forced into the esophagus. The tone of the cardia is probably actually increased at these times. It has been mentioned that division of the vagi in animals causes the cardia to enter into a spastic state. Hatcher and Weiss found that if after such a procedure a vomiting reflex was initiated, mucus was expelled from the esophagus and the usual muscular movements were called into play, with the exception of relaxation of the cardia. That is, the animal retched but material was not expelled from the stomach. It is well known that with some persons vomiting is difficult whereas in others little distress is experienced. Differences in the degree of tone of the cardia are probably responsible for these individual peculiarities (table 42.1).

During the ejection of the vomitus the esophagus is relaxed throughout; the glottis is closed and the respirations are inhibited, the larynx and hyoid bone are drawn upward and forward and are held rigidly in this position. The throat is thus enlarged to allow free exit for the stomach contents which are prevented from entering the nasopharynx by the elevation of the soft palate.

### ABNORMAL GASTRIC MOTILITY

Either hyper- or hypomotility of the stomach may be seen clinically. In the absence of specific diseases involving these conditions, such changes are most often psychogenic and result from acute or chronic emotional disturbances. Acute emotional upsets are usually associated with relaxation of the gastric muscle due to increased activity of the thoracolumbar sympathetic nerves and the adrenal medulla. Hypermotility is said to occur more frequently in prolonged or chronic emotional states involving resentment or prolonged anger. Hyperperistalsis is seen in pyloric obstruction; in this situation it is due in part to the absence of inhibitory reflexes from the duodenum (the enterogastric reflex) and probably also in part to continued stimulation by retained gastric contents. Excessive belching, heartburn (pyrosis), regurgitation of food, hiccuping and

### TABLE 41.1

| Drugs | Afferent Autonomic Fibers Acted upon | Organs Containing Susceptible Fibers |
|---|---|---|
| Mercuric chloride | Sympathetic and vagus | Stomach |
| Tartar emetic | Vagus | Stomach, duodenum and heart |
| Digitalis | Sympathetic and vagus | Heart |
| Pilocarpine | Sympathetic and vagus | Heart |

other types of gastric distress are probably traceable to some abnormality in the movements of the stomach but the relationships have not been well defined.

Hypotonus or general loss of tonus in the gastric muscle is likely to be associated with the deterioration of all body function seen in asthenic states. Hypertonus is supposed to be associated with a condition called *vagotonia*. Vagotonia, if it exists, is a form of hyperactivity of the parasympathetic innervation of the viscera but the condition has never been well defined clinically. Cardiospasm and pylorospasm are conditions in which these sphincter muscles are supposed to be in a state of sustained contraction. Doubtless such abnormalities occur but probably much less frequently than they are diagnosed. Cardiospasm for example, could be easily confused with loss of power in the esophageal muscle or absence of esophageal peristalsis; pylorospasm likewise is often diagnosed when the true condition is failure of the gastric peristaltic mechanism to develop adequate gastric pressures, e.g., following the operation of vagotomy. In such instances the pylorus is usually less contracted than normally, the appearance of a closed pylorus being due to failure of the gastric muscle to develop sufficient power to force the gastric contents past even a relaxed pyloric sphincter. True pylorospasm occurs as a congenital condition in infants who suffer from hypertrophy of the pyloric muscle. It is also seen in adults, associated with irritative lesions in the region of the pylorus, either of the duodenum or pyloric portion of the stomach.

### REFERENCES

ATKINSON, H. F. AND MATTHEWS, E., Brit. Dent. J., 1949, **86**, 167.
BARCLAY, A. E. The normal mechanism of swallowing. Brit. J. Radiol. 1930, 3 (new series), 534.

BAZETT, H. C. AND PENFIELD, W. G. A study of the Sherrington decerebrate animal in the chronic as well as the acute condition. Brain, 1922, **45**, 185.

BECKER, E. Zur Kenntnis der Bedeutung der zähne für die Ausnutzung des Nahrungsmittel im Verdauungsapparat bei normaler Sekretion der Magendrüsen. Skandinav. Arch. Physiol., 1927, **50**, 283.

BLACK, G. V. An investigation of the physical characters of the human teeth in relation to their diseases and to practical dental operations together with the physical characters of filling materials. II. The force exerted in the closing of the jaws. Dental Cosmos, 1895, **37**, 469.

BOLDYREFF, W. N. Die periodische Tätigkeit der Verdauungsapparates ausser der Verdauungszeit. Zentralbl. Physiol., 1904, **18**, 489.

BRODY, D. A., WERLE, J. M., MESCHAN, I. AND QUIGLEY, J. P. Intralumen pressures in the digestive tract, especially the pyloric region. Am. J. Physiol., 1940, **130**, 791. (See also Gastroenterology, 1947, **9**, 570; J. Lab. & Clin. Med., 1944, **29**, 863; Med. Physics, 1950, **2**, 280).

CANNON, W. B. The movements of the stomach studied by means of the roentgen rays. Am. J. Physiol., 1898, **1**, 359.

CANNON, W. B. Esophageal peristalsis after bilateral vagotomy. Am. J. Physiol., 1907, **19**, 436.

CANNON, W. B. The acid control of the pylorus. Am. J. Physiol., 1907, **20**, 283.

CANNON, W. B., The nature of gastric peristalsis. Am. J. Physiol., 1911a, **29**, 250.

CANNON, W. B., (1904). The passage of different foodstuffs from the stomach and through the small intestine. Am. J. Physiol., 1904, **12**, 387. (See also Cannon, 1911b.)

CANNON, W. B. AND LIEB, C. W. The receptive relaxation of the stomach. Am. J. Physiol., 1910, **27**, (proc.) xiii.

CANNON, W. B. AND MOSER, A. The movements of food in the esophagus. Am. J. Physiol., 1898, **1**, 435.

CANNON, W. B. AND WASHBURN, A. L. An explanation of hunger. Am. J. Physiol., 1912, **29**, 441.

COLE, L. G. Systole and diastole of the stomach. Arch. of the roentgen ray, 1911, **16**, 242.

COLE, L. G. Motor phenomena of the stomach, pylorus and cap observed roentgenographically. Am. J. Physiol., 1917, **42**, 618.

CRIDER, J. O. AND THOMAS, J. E. A study of gastric emptying with the pylorus open. Am. J. Digest. Dis. & Nutr., 1937, **4**, 295.

DEAN, H. T. AND ASSOCIATES, U. S. Pub. Health Rep., 1938, **53**, 1443; 1941, **56**, 365; **57**, 1155.

FARRELL, J. I. AND IVY, A. C. Studies on the motility of the transplanted gastric pouch. Am. J. Physiol., 1926, **76**, 227.

GEIS, W. J. AND ASSOCIATES. J. Allied Dent. Soc., 1914, **9**, 345.

GELLHORN, E. AND BUDDE, W. Beiträge zur Physiologie der Magenmuskulatur. Arch. ges. Physiol., 1923, **200**, 604.

GRIMSON, K. S., REEVES, R. T., TRENT, J. C. AND WILSON, A. D. Treatment of patients with achalasia by esophago-gastrostomy. Surgery, 1946, **20**, 94.

HARDING, V. J. Nausea and vomiting in pregnancy. Lancet, 1921, **II**, 327.

HARDING, V. J. AND WATSON, B. P. Carbohydrates in nausea and vomiting of pregnancy. Lancet, 1922, **II**, 649.

HEGNER, K. Untersuchungen über die Schluckstrasse. Arch. f. Ohren-, Nasen- u. Kehlkopfheilk. ver. Ztschr. Hals-, Nasen- u. Ohrenheilk., 1936, **140**, 387.

HATCHER, R. A. AND WEISS, S. Studies on vomiting. J. Pharmacol. & Exper. Therap., 1923, **22**, 139.

HOFMEISTER, F. AND SCHUTZ, E. Ueber die automatischen Bewegungen des Magens. Arch. exper. Path. u. Pharmakol., 1886, **20**, 1.

HOWELL, A. H. AND MANLY, R. S. An electronic strain gauge for measuring oral forces. J. Dent. Res., 1948, **27**, 705.

HUNT, J. N. Some properties of an alimentary osmoreceptor mechanism. J. Physiol., 1956, **132**, 267.

HUNT, J. N. AND SPURRELL, W. R., The pattern of emptying of the human stomach. J. Physiol., 1951, **113**, 157, 185.

HWANG, K., ESSEX, H. E. AND MANN, F. C. Study of certain problems resulting from vagotomy in dogs with special reference to emesis. Am. J. Physiol., 1947, **149**, 329.

JONES, C. M. AND RICHARDSON, W., Observations on the nature of "heartburn." J. Clin. Invest., 1926, **2**, 610 (proc.).

JOSEPH, D. R. AND MELTZER, S. J. Inhibition of the duodenum coincident with the movements of the pyloric part of the stomach. Am. J. Physiol., 1910, **27**, proc. 1910 xxxi.

KAHN, R. H. Studien über der Schluckreflex. I. Die sensible Innervation. Arch. f. Physiol. (Suppl. bd.), 386, 1903.

KAST, L. Rückläufige Strömung in der Speiseröhre als Euklärung der belegten Zunge. Berl. klin. Wchnschr., 1906, **43**, 947.

KNIGHT, G. C. The relation of the extrinsic nerves to the functional activity of the esophagus. Brit. J. Surg., 1934. **22**, 155 and 864.

KOSAKA, T. AND LIM, R. K. S. Demonstration of a humoral agent in fat inhibition of gastric secretion. Proc. Soc. Exper. Biol. & Med., 1930, **27**, 890.

KOSAKA, T. AND LIM, R. K. S. On the mechanism of the inhibition of gastric motility by fat. An inhibitory agent from the intestinal mucosa. Chinese J. Physiol., 1933, **7**, 5.

KRONEKER, H. AND MELTZER, S. J., 1883: Schluckmechanismus, seine Erregung und seine Hemmung. Arch. f. Physiol. (DuBois Raymond) Suppl. Bd. (1883) p. 328.

KUPFERLE, L. Schluckmechanismus nach Röntgen-kinematographische Anfnahmen. Arch. ges. Physiol., 1913, **152**, 579.

LIM, R. K. S. Observations on the mechanism of the inhibition of gastric function by fat. Quart. J. Exper. Physiol., 1933, **23**, 263.

LUCKHARDT, A. B., PHILLIPS, H. T. AND CARLSON, A. J., Contributions to the physiology of the stomach. II. The control of the pylorus. Am. J. Physiol., 1919, **50**, 57.

MAGNUS, W. O. C. Über die Zentren für Lecken

und Kawen. Monatschr. Psychiat. u. Neurol., 1945, **110**, 193.

MAGOUN, H. W., RANSON, S. W. AND FISHER, C. Corticifugal pathways for mastication, lapping and other motor functions in the cat. Arch. Neurol. & Psychiat., 1933, **30**, 292.

MARKWALD, M. Über die Ausbreitung der Erregung und Hemmung von Sckluckcentrum auf das Athemcentrum. Ztschr. Biol. New Series, 1889, **7**, 1.

MELTZER, S. J. A further experimental contribution to the knowledge of the mechanism of deglutition. J. Exper. Med., 1897, **2**, 453.

MELTZER, S. J. On the causes of the orderly progress of the peristaltic movements in the esophagus. Am. J. Physiol., 1899, **2**, 266.

MESCHAN, I. AND QUIGLEY, J. P. Spontaneous motility of the pyloric sphincter and adjacent regions of the gut in the unanesthetized dog. Am. J. Physiol., 1938, **121**, 350.

MILLER, F. R. The cortical paths for mastication and deglutition. J. Physiol., 1919, **53**, 473.

PAYNE, W. W. AND POULTON, E. P. Visceral pain in the upper alimentary tract. Quart. J. Med., 1923, **17**, 53.

PINCUS, P. Caries: Attack on enamel protein in an alkaline medium. Brit. Dent. J., 1937, **63**, 511.

POMMERENKE, W. T. A study of sensory areas eliciting the swallowing reflex. Am. J. Physiol., 1928, **84**, 36.

QUIGLEY, J. P. A modern explanation of the gastric emptying mechanism. Am. J. Digest. Dis., 1943, **10**, 418.

QUIGLEY, J. P. AND PHELPS, K. R. The mechanism of gastric motor inhibition from ingested carbohydrate. Am. J. Physiol., 1934. **109**, 133.

QUIGLEY, J. P., ZETTLEMAN, H. J., AND IVY, A. C. Analysis of factors involved in gastric motor inhibition by fats. Am. J. Physiol., 1934, **108**, 643.

RAKE, G. W. Pathology of achalasia of the cardia. Guy's Hosp. Rep., 1927, **77**, 141.

RIOCH, D. M. AND BRENNER, C. Experiments on the corpus striatum and rhinencephalon. J. Comp. Neurol., 1938, **68**, 491.

RUSHMER, R. F. AND HENDRON, J. A. The act of deglutition. A cinefluoroscopic study. J. Appl. Physiol., 1951, **3**, 622.

SCHAPIRO, H. AND WOODWARD, E. R. Inhibition of gastric motility by acid in the duodenum. J. Appl. Physiol., 1955, **8**, 121.

SCHIROKICH, P. O. Prot. d. XI Kong. russ. Naturforscher in Ärzte, 1901, **10**, 448. (Cited by B. P. Babkin, 1928.)

SCHREIBER, J. Über den bewegenden Einfluss der Schwerkraft beim Trinken in Awfrechten und Kopfstellung. Arch. Verdauungs-krankh. Stoffwechselpathol. u Diätetik, 1915, **21**, 1.

SHAY, H. AND GERSHON-COHEN, J. Experimental studies in gastric physiology in man. II. A study of pyloric control. The roles of acid and alkali. Surg. Gynec. & Obst., 1934, **58**, 935.

SHERRINGTON, C. S. Reflexes elicitable in the cat from the pinna, vibissae and jaws. J. Physiol., 1917, **51**, 404.

THOMAS, J. E., CRIDER, J. O. AND MOGAN, C. J. A study of reflexes involving the pyloric sphinc-

ter and antrum and their role in gastric evacuation. Am. J. Physiol., 1934, **108**, 683.

THOMAS, J. E. AND CRIDER, J. O. Rhythmic changes in duodenal motility associated with gastric peristalsis. Am. J. Physiol., 1935, **111**, 124.

THOMAS, J. E. AND CRIDER, J. O. Inhibition of gastric motility associated with the presence of products of protein hydrolysis in the upper small intestine. Am. J. Physiol., 1939, **126**, 28.

THOMAS, J. E. AND WHEELON, H. The nervous control of the pyloric sphincter. J. Lab. & Clin. Med., 1922, **7**, 375.

TRISKA, W. Experimentelle Studien über die Beisskraft. Arch. ges. Physiol., 1924, **204**, 660.

TSCHESCHKOW, A. N. (1902). Diss. St. Petersburg. (Cited by B. P. Babkin, 1928).

WANG, S. C. AND BORISON, H. L. Copper sulphate emesis: Study of afferent pathways from the gastrointestinal tract. Am. J. Physiol., 1951, **164**, 520; **166**, 712. Arch. Neurol. Psychiat., 1950. **63**, 928. Gastroenterology, 1952, **22**, 1.

WHEELON, H. AND THOMAS, J. E. Observations on the motility of the antrum and the relation of the rhythmic activity of the antrum to that of the pyloric sphincter. J. Lab. & Clin. Med., 1920. **6**, 124.

WHEELON, H. AND THOMAS, J. E. Rhythmicity of the pyloric sphincter. Am. J. Physiol., 1921, **54**, 460.

WHEELON, H. AND THOMAS, J. E. Observations on the motility of the duodenum and the relation of duodenal activity to that of the pars pylorica. Am. J. Physiol., 1922, **59**, 72.

*Monographs and Reviews*

ALVAREZ, W. C. The mechanics of the digestive tract. Paul B. Hoeber Inc., N. Y., 1928.

ALVAREZ, W. C. Nervous indigestion. Paul B. Hoeber Inc., New York, 1931.

ALVAREZ, W. C. An introduction to gastroenterology. 2nd ed., Paul B. Hoeber Inc., N. Y., 1940.

BABKIN, B. P. Die äussere Sekretion der Verdauungsdrüsen. Springer-Verlag, Berlin, 1928.

BARCLAY, A. E. The digestive tract. Cambridge University Press, 1933.

BORISON, H. L. AND WANG, S. C. The physiology and pharmacology of vomiting. Pharmacol. Rev., 1953, **5**, 193.

CANNON, W. B. The mechanical factors of digestion. Edward Arnold & Co. London, 1911b.

CARLSON, A. J. The control of hunger in health and disease. University of Chicago Press, Chicago, 1916.

CODE, C. F., CREAMER, B., SCHLEGEL, J. F. *et al.* An atlas of esophageal motility in health and disease. Charles C Thomas, Springfield, Ill., 1958.

EVANS, C. L. The physiology of plain muscle. Physiol. Rev., 1926, **6**, 358.

FERRIER, D. The functions of the brain. 2nd ed., p. 260. G. P. Putnam's Sons, N. Y., 1886.

GOTTLIEB, B. Dental caries; its etiology, pathology, clinical aspects and prophylaxis. Lea and Febiger, Philadelphia, 1947.

HATCHER, R. A. The mechanism of vomiting. Physiol. Rev., 1924, 4, 479.

HURST, A. F. The passage of food along the alimentary canal. Guy's Hosp. Rep., 61 (46 of third series), 389.

JONES, C. M. Digestive tract pain; diagnosis and treatment; experimental observations. The MacMillan Co., New York, 1938.

MAGENDIE, F. Precis elementaire de physiologie. Trans. by John Revere. (An elementary treatise on human physiology.) 5th ed., Harper and Bros., New York, 1838.

McSWINEY, B. A. Innervation of the stomach. Physiol. Rev., 1931, 11, 478.

MELLANBY, M. The influence of diet on the structure of the teeth. Physiol. Rev., 1928, 8, 545.

MOSSO. Moleschott's Untersuchungen, XI, 331, 1876 (Cited by Cannon and Moser, 1898.)

MURLIN, J. R. The emptying mechanism of the stomach. J. Nutrit., 1930, 2, 311.

NOBLE, R. L. Treatment of experimental motion sickness in humans. Canad. J. Res. Feb., 1946, p. 12. Motion sickness with special reference to air sickness. Practitioner, 1948, 160, 453.

PANCOAST, H. K., PENDERGRASS, E. P. AND SCHAEFFER, J. P., The head and neck in roentgen diagnosis, p. 797. Charles C Thomas, Springfield, Ill., 1940.

QUIGLEY, J. P. Medical Physics, p. 310. Year Book Publishers, Chicago, 1944.

THOMAS, J. E. Mechanics and regulation of gastric emptying. Physiol. Rev., 37, 453, 1957.

TOVERUD, G. AND ASSOCIATES. A survey of the literature of dental caries. Pub. 225, Nat. Res. Council, Nat. Acad. Sc., Washington, 1952.

TODD, W. T. Behavior patterns of the alimentary tract. The Williams & Wilkins Co., Baltimore, 1933.

TYLER, D. B. AND BARD, P. Physiol. Rev., 1940, 29, 281.

# 42

## MOVEMENTS OF THE ALIMENTARY CANAL—*Continued*

## SMALL AND LARGE INTESTINE. INNERVATION

### Movements of the Small Intestine

The major part of the smooth muscle of the small intestine is distributed in a thick circular layer and a much thinner longitudinal layer. The circular layer is responsible for most of the visible intestinal movements. The longitudinal layer undoubtedly participates in the movements but the relation of its activity to that of the circular muscle has been described differently by different authors and is therefore somewhat uncertain. The outstanding characteristic of the muscle is its rhythmicity which is manifest under appropriate conditions by alternate contractions and relaxations at a remarkably regular frequency.

#### RHYTHMIC SEGMENTING CONTRACTIONS

The more common type of rhythmic contractions occurs at regularly spaced intervals along a section of the intestine dividing it into short segments; also, they may occur singly, in pairs, or in a variety of other arrangements. The area involved in each segment may be less than one centimeter or it may be several centimeters long. In the cat Cannon (1902) saw a certain type of rhythmic contraction in which a section of intestine was divided into short segments by rings of contractions occurring at regularly spaced intervals. When the contracted areas relaxed, the relaxed areas between contracted, dividing each segment into halves. The two halves of adjacent segments joined together to form a new segment (Fig. 42.1). Cannon described these contractions as *segmenting contractions* and that is the name that is most commonly applied to them at the present time.

The rhythmic nature of this activity reminded Ludwig (1861) of a pendulum, hence he applied the name "pendulum" movements to these contractions. Ludwig used the pendulum as a symbol of rhythm only, but some authors have attempted to apply the simile in the sense of the to-and-fro motion of a pendulum. Swaying movements of the intestinal coils are to be seen at times as well as a to-and-fro motion of opaque masses within the intestine as is seen with a fluoroscope. Alvarez (1940) described them as follows: "in the rabbit, and to a certain extent in other animals and in man, a local mixing of the intestinal contents with digestive juices, similar to that produced by the segmenting contractions is brought about by sway or 'pendular' movements. A segment of bowel is pulled first in one direction and then in the other. The wall apparently being drawn over its contents like a stocking over a foot. My impression from watching these movements in men and women who have taken a barium meal is that, in man, activity is more like a short pendular movement than a rhythmic segmentation." However to identify these movements and these only as pendular movements is confusing, since the term as originally used and commonly applied is synonymous merely with rhythmic movement without regard to the effect of the activity on the intestinal coils or their content. If we exclude the swaying movements described by Alvarez, then the rhythmic segmenting contraction and pendular movements are one and the same thing.

The frequency of the rhythmic contractions varies with the species of animal and with the region of the intestine in which they occur. For example, in the rabbit the contractions occur at a frequency of about 20 per minute in the duodenum and about 10 per minute in the lower ileum. In the dog they occur at a frequency of about 18 per minute in the duodenum and 8 to 9 per minute in the lower ileum. The frequency in other parts of the intestine is intermediate between these extremes, becoming less frequent the greater the distance from the pylorus. The frequency is suprisingly constant in any one area and is not affected by stimulation of the extrinsic nerves or by neurotropic drugs. In excised material the frequency varies with the temperature.

The variation in frequency at different levels

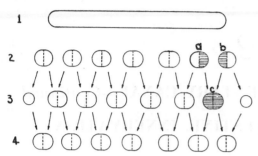

FIG. 42.1. Diagram representing the process of rhythmic segmentation. Lines 1, 2, 3, 4, indicate the sequence of appearances in a single loop. The dot lines represent the regions of division. The arrows show the relation of the particles (eg., a and b) to the segments they subsequently form (c). (After Cannon, 1911.)

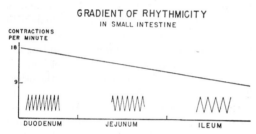

FIG. 42.2. Diagrammatic representation of the gradient of rhythmicity in the small intestine. The zig-zag lines are stylized representations of kymographic records of the contractions and relaxations of segments taken from the indicated levels of the intestine. The sloping line suggests a linear distribution of the gradient; however, there is no evidence that this is so.

of the intestine suggested to Alvarez and his pupils the idea that there is a gradient in the various physiological properties of the intestine, the activity being highest at the duodenal end and lowest at the ileal end of the small intestine. Among the properties for which a gradient has been established are rhythmicity, irritability, shortness of latent period, susceptibility to drugs, and certain others of less obvious importance (Alvarez and Hosoi, 1929). The most easily observed is the gradient of rhythmicity manifested by the variation in frequency of rhythmic contractions (fig. 42.2).

An interesting question with respect to the rhythmic contractions of the intestine is whether they originate in nervous or muscular tissue. All the available evidence indicates that the rhythmic contrations are *myogenic*. The problem has been studied by Magnus (1904), Gunn and Underhill (1914), Alvarez and Mahoney (1922) and numerous others. Using various methods of eliminating the influence of nerves upon the smooth muscle,

each of these groups of investigators was able to demonstrate rhythmic activity in denervated intestinal muscle. Probably the most complete denervation was accomplished by Gasser (1926) and van Esveld (1928) who made serial sections of their preparations and found a considerable number in which no nerve cells could be found. Such preparations, however, still respond to cholinergic and adrenergic drugs. When excised preparation of intestine are treated with high concentrations of nicotine (1 mg. per ml.) the response of the muscle to stimulation of the mesenteric nerves and also the response to the autonomic drugs disappears; the autonomic receptors are apparently paralyzed by the nicotine. The smooth muscle, however, continues to contract rhythmically (Kuntz and Thomas, 1923). It should not be inferred from this that the rhythmic activity is uninfluenced by the intrinsic or extrinsic nerves. Although the frequency of the contractions is apparently not subject to nervous control they can be made to increase or decrease in amplitude or to disappear altogether by stimulation of appropriate extrinsic nerves or by the application of drugs which mimic the action of the autonomic nerves.

Although the frequency of the rhythmic contractions is not influenced by ordinary nervous stimuli, it may be modified or perhaps the contraction may even be initiated by stimuli of another sort. In 1929 Douglas reported that the frequency of rhythmic contractions in the dog's jejunums changed from about 18 per minute to 12 per minute if the jejunum was cut off from the duodenum. This observation suggests that the rhythm of the pendular contraction is not determined locally but by conducted impulses which are initiated at a higher level and which are conducted along the intestine in an aboral direction as a wave of excitation. The electrical studies of Ambache (1947), Bozler (1949) and of Milton and Smith (1956) lend support to this view. These authors have described the electrical activity of the intestine as consisting of slow waves which are frequently, but not necessarily, associated with local muscular contractions, and rapid, spikelike waves which appear only when the muscle contracts. The slow waves have the same frequency as the rhythmic contractions, whether or not these are present, and (according to Milton and Smith) they are regularly conducted along the intestine in an aboral direction. It is interesting in this connection to recall that Bayliss and Starling (1899) saw shallow waves which travelled aborally over the intestine at regular intervals and which seemed to them to initiate the rhythmic contractions in an area subject to local stimulation. These waves could have been caused by the regularly conducted impulses described by Milton and Smith.

The function of the rhythmic contractions is evidently to agitate the intentinal contents. Such agitation facilitates several processes: it tends to increase the degree of subdivision of food particles, to mix the food with the intestinal secretions and other digestive fluids, and constantly to change the layers of fluid in contact with the mucosa, thus facilitating absorption. Changes in pressure brought about by these contractions may also be a factor in intestinal absorption.

## PERISTALSIS IN THE SMALL INTESTINE

Stimulation of the intestinal smooth muscle causes contractions which tend to travel from the stimulated point in both directions. However, under normal circumstances the progress of the contractions in an oral direction is quickly inhibited and the contractions disappear. The contractions which travel in an aboral direction tend to persist, so that the intestine may be said to be polarized in the sense that conducted contractions travel normally in only the aboral direction. Such aborally conducted contractions are commonly described as peristalsis. The term has been used to describe a variety of contractile phenomena which have only one thing in common, namely the direction of travel. The common conception of peristalsis as consisting of a wave of contraction progressing smoothly over otherwise relaxed intestine is erroneous. Usually the peristaltic movement is superimposed upon the rhythmic segmenting contractions in such a way that the two are present simultaneously. The peristaltic contraction makes itself manifest as a rise in the tone level of the intestinal muscle without any interruption in the rhythm of the segmenting contractions; indeed, these are usually increased in amplitude at the peak of the wave. This of course has the effect of narrowing the lumen of the intestine at the point at which the increase in tonus occurs and it may actually obliterate it. As this wave of contraction, or tonus, travels down the intestine it tends to sweep the contents forward, or toward the distal end of the intestine. In another type of propulsive movement rhythmic contractions, although retaining their rhythmic character, recur at successively more aboral levels and thus appear to travel along the intestine as a wave of peristalsis. Ordinarily, peristaltic waves appear in the small intestine at irregular intervals

and travel for varying distances (Bayliss and Starling); some travel only a few inches, others a few feet.

Under the influence of especially strong stimuli such as irritant cathartics, a peristaltic wave may sweep over the entire length of the small intestine without interruption, or several such waves may occur in succession. Peristaltic waves of this character were described by van Braam Houckgeest in 1872; he called them "rollbewegungen" but they are usually described in the modern literature as *rush waves* or as *peristaltic rush*, after the terminology proposed by Meltzer and Auer in 1907.

Whether the conditions that give rise to rhythmic contractions on the one hand or to peristaltic movements on the other, differ qualitatively or only quantitatively is not known. It is known that both mechanical and chemical stimuli are effective in promoting peristalsis, and that mild stimulation favors rhythmic activity. Doubtless not only the nature and strength of the stimuli, but also the irritability of the intestinal neuromuscular mechanism play a significant part in determining the nature and location of the activity. The latter may be influenced by local and central reflexes and by circulating hormones and metabolites, as well as by the previous history of the muscle (e.g., by refractoriness or fatigue following a period of activity).

THE LAW OF THE INTESTINE. The polarity of the intestine, that is the fact that peristaltic waves characteristically travel in one direction only, has been the subject of much interesting speculation but no satisfactory explanation has as yet been offered. Bayliss and Starling (1899, 1901) to whose classical studies we owe most of our basic knowledge of intestinal motility, observed that the response of the small intestine to local stimuli consists of a contraction of the smooth muscle above and relaxation below the stimulated area. "This," they said, "is the law of the intestine." Since the contraction wave and the preceding inhibition usually travel down the intestine in an aboral direction from the stimulated point, Bayliss and Starling thought that intestinal peristalsis might consist simply of a succession of responses to stimuli manifesting the law of the intestine. In their opinion, a particular mass might give rise to stimulation resulting in contraction above the stimulated point with relaxation below and this would cause the mass to move aborally; in its new position it would also act as a stimulus and again cause contraction of the muscle above and relaxation below, again being

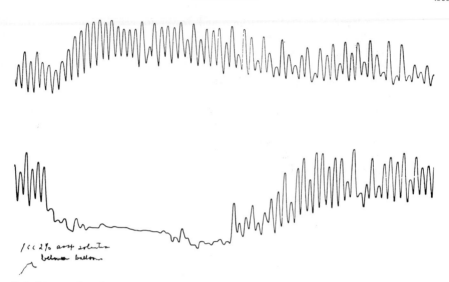

/ cc 2% soap solution

below balloon

FIG. 42.3. Myenteric reflex in a dog's duodenum. Water manometer records from two balloons 5 cm. apart in the lower duodenum. Upper record is from the upper balloon. A stimulus consisting of 2 cc. of 2 per cent soap solution in the intestine between the balloons caused contraction above (over the upper balloon) and relaxation below (over the lower balloon) the stimulated point. (Thomas.)

moved by this to a new, lower level. A succession of such responses could, according to them, constitute a peristaltic wave.

Cannon (1912) proposed that the reflex responsible for the law of the intestine be designated the myenteric reflex (fig. 42.3). The myenteric reflex disappears if the intestine is paralyzed by applying such drugs as nicotine or cocaine to the serosal surface. Presumably these drugs penetrate the longitudinal muscle layer and paralyze the underlying nervous mechanism. Under these circumstances the polarity of the intestine is also abolished and contractions initiated by local stimulation travel equally well in the oral and aboral directions. Evidently, both the myenteric reflex and the polarity of the intestine are dependent upon the integrity of the myenteric plexus. This does not, of course, prove that intestinal polarity is due to the myenteric reflex. In fact, most observers have failed to find evidence of the occurrence of a myenteric reflex in ordinary peristalsis in the intestine. Although the rollbewegungen or rush waves are usually preceded by a phase of inhibition, the inhibitory phase has been difficult to demonstrate in spontaneous peristalsis of the intestine.

THE GRADIENT THEORY. Alvarez (1940) has proposed that the polarity of the intestine is related to the gradients of irritability, conductivity, rhythmicity, etc., that are known to exist, but he has failed to define the precise mechanism through which such gradients establish polarity.

Some idea may be obtained from the study of the polarity of the heart muscle where forward conduction is known to be related to the gradients of irritability manifested by the several chambers of heart. In the heart the gradients are significant only to the extent that they enable certain chambers always to initiate activity because of their higher degree of rhythmicity. In this situation the impulse always arises at the most irritable point and because it has nowhere else to go it travels in the direction of the less irritable chambers. A similar situation could exist in the intestine but up to the present time no pacemaker has been demonstrated anatomically. However, the slow electrical waves mentioned in a preceding paragraph may arise in such a pacemaker, for which there is as yet only physiological evidence. If such is the case and if we may assume that in the intestine, as in the heart, each transmitted impulse is followed by a refractory phase, contraction waves travelling in an oral direction would be quickly extinguished by the refractoriness following the descending impulses. Aborally travelling contractions on the other hand would encounter no such difficulty (see fig. 42.4).

### THE INTESTINAL VILLI AND THE MUSCULARIS MUCOSAE

The absorbing surface of the small intestine is much greater than the serosal surface because of the superabundance of the mucosa which, under normal conditions, is thrown into circular folds

## POSSIBLE MECHANISM OF POLAR CONDUCTION

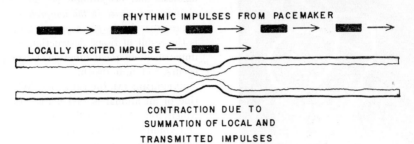

RHYTHMIC IMPULSES FROM PACEMAKER

LOCALLY EXCITED IMPULSE

CONTRACTION DUE TO
SUMMATION OF LOCAL AND
TRANSMITTED IMPULSES

FIG. 42.4. Mechanism of polar conduction in the intestine suggested by physiological evidence for a pacemaker mechanism in the upper intestine. The block rectangles represent excitatory impulses; those in the upper row presumably arose in the pacemaker and are being conducted analward. A local excitory process cannot be conducted oralward because of the refractive phase following each conducted impulse from the pacemaker. (Thomas, 1955.)

called *plicae circulares*. A still greater increase in surface is provided by the *intestinal villi*. These are titlike projections of the mucous membrane about 1 mm. in length which occur everywhere on the mucosal surface and macroscopically resemble the pile on a piece of velvet. Our interest in these structures at this point has to do with the activity of the *muscularis mucosae* which lies everywhere beneath the mucous membrane, following each fold and extending into each villus as a filament of smooth muscle fibers. In the fasting animal the villi are inactive and lie flat on the mucosal surface when first exposed for study. Covering them with a liquid such as a solution of sugar, salts, amino acids, weak alkalies or even with distilled water causes them to become active. In the fed animal activity of the villi can be observed without special stimulation. The activity is of two kinds: a lashing movement and a more or less rhythmical shortening and lengthening. It is generally believed that these movements accelerate the flow of blood and lymph and that they increase absorption, although King, Arnold and Church (1922) were unable to find evidence for any of these functions. More recent studies, especially those of von Kokas and von Ludany (1938) leave little doubt that efficient absorption of food stuffs from the intestine is dependent to some extent on the activity of the villi. The movements of the villi are partly under nervous control, being augmented by stimulation of the splanchnic but not the vagus nerves, and by sympathomimetric drugs. They are depressed by atropine and nicotine. Their activity is also increased by *villikinin*, one of the intestinal hormones.

No regular or consistent activity of the main sheet of muscle comprising the muscularis mucosae has been described, but it is believed to be active during digestion and to be in part responsible for the various mucosal patterns seen in roentgenograms of the small intestine. One function of the muscularis mucosae has to do with protecting the intestine from penetration from within by sharp objects. It does this by forming deep pits or grooves in the mucosa at the point of contact with any sharp foreign body in the intestinal contents. The contracted muscle gives these depressions a firm base which is difficult to penetrate (Exner, 1902; King and Arnold, 1922). Abnormal motility patterns in the small intestine are seen in some nervous and endocrine disturbances and in vitamin deficiency. Their significance when they occur is not always clear.

### PARALYTIC ILEUS

Although the small intestine usually shows some degree of activity in the intact animal, a dramatic and persistent quiet ensues when the abdomen is opened. It is rare to see activity in the exposed intestine unless stimulating drugs are given or special measures adopted such as cutting the splanchnic nerves, stimulation of the vagi or immersing the whole animal in warm physiological salt solutions. Abdominal surgery, particularly if it involves handling the intestine, is apt to be followed by a period of *ileus*, as the loss of motility is termed clinically. Peritoneal irritation from any cause, including bacterial peritonitis, may cause ileus. As a rule recovery is prompt following removal of the cause but if the condition persists for some time it tends to be self perpetuating, due to the paralytic effect of the gaseous distention that usually develops. When this occurs removal of the gas through an intestinal tube of the type described by Miller

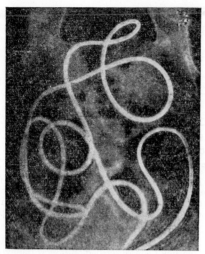

Fig. 42.5. X-ray photograph showing Miller-Abbott tube in the small intestine.

and Abbott (1934) may save the patient's life (see fig. 42.5).

The cause of postoperative ileus was investigated by Cannon and Murphy (1906) and found to be reflex inhibition of motility through reflexes from the irritated peritoneum in which the splanchnic nerves were an essential part of the reflex path. They found that cutting the splanchnic nerves prevented the ileus. There was one exception to this finding; if the intestine itself was subjected to severe trauma, ileus ensued even with the splanchnics cut. Apparently, in this instance, the local nerve plexus serves as a pathway for the inhibitory reflexes. It has since been shown that intestinal paresis from a variety of causes (e.g., peritonitis) is relieved by spinal anesthesia, which is neurologically equivalent to splanchnic section.

### Acute Intestinal Obstruction

Symptoms of intense severity result when the lumen of the small bowel is completely obstructed as a result of constriction by an adhesive band, kinking, twisting or pressure by new growth, intussusception, strangulation by a hernial ring, etc. The condition is ushered in by severe cramplike abdominal pain, vomiting and shock. If the condition is not relieved by operation, reverse peristalsis arises above the point of obstruction, intestinal contents passing into the stomach and the vomiting becomes fecal in character. Later the bowel above the obstruction loses its tone, becoming dilated and filled with intestinal secretions and gas. The loss of fluid in the vomitus and the drainage of large quantities of fluid into the

distended bowel leads to a *fall in blood chloride, alkalosis* and *dehydration* (p. 24). Other blood changes are a *rise in the nonprotein nitrogen* and an *increase in the fibrinogen content.* The former is the result of tissue destruction combined with impairment of renal function. Great prostration occurs, ending in death.

EXPERIMENTAL OBSTRUCTION. When the intestine of an animal is tied across, the symptoms which follow are chiefly weakness, prostration and vomiting. The animal shows little or no evidence that it is suffering pain. The higher in the intestinal tract the obstruction is made, the more severe are the symptoms, and the shorter is the duration of life after the operation. Following obstruction of the colon the animal may survive for some weeks, whereas after obstruction of the jejunum or duodenum it dies as a rule within five or six days. Reduction in blood volume (anhydremia); fall in blood chloride (see below); increased alkali reserve and nonprotein nitrogen of the blood, and a rise in the percentage of fibrinogen occur.

Paralytic ileus may be produced in dogs by the injection of a solution of iodine into the peritoneal cavity. It was shown by Markowitz and Campbell that the intestinal inhibition produced in this way could be abolished by spinal anesthesia which apparently blocked inhibitory impulses reaching the bowel through the splanchnic nerves (p. 723–725).

### A CONSIDERATION OF THE CAUSE OF DEATH IN MECHANICAL OBSTRUCTION

A number of theories have been advanced in recent years in attempts to given an explanation for the symptoms and death in acute mechanical obstruction of the bowel. We may, at the outset, dismiss the possibility that death is simply the result of blockage of the alimentary tract, and the prevention of the passage of food along its lumen. It was shown originally by Stone, Bernheim and Whipple that if a few inches of the bowel were excised, both ends of the segment closed and the continuity of the digestive tract then re-established by an anastomosis of the cut ends of the bowel, death occurred even more rapidly than if the bowel had been obstructed by ligation. The survival time after the closure of such an isolated segment or loop is rarely more than 3 or 4 days and may be only 24 hours.

### *Toxic Theories*

A *bacterial theory* in one or other of its modifications has had its adherents. The toxin of the

Welch bacillus has been suspected by some, but little support has been given by recent work to the belief that this or any other bacterial toxin is responsible for the symptoms. Others have thought that a toxic agent derived from the bacterial decomposition of protein within the intestinal lumen was the lethal agent. It is impossible to consider seriously any bacterial theory of intestinal obstruction, for such theories ignore the fact that the symptoms diminish in intensity, and the survival time is lengthened, the lower in the intestinal tract that the obstruction is produced. Bacterial growth, protein decomposition and histamine concentration on the other hand, are all greater in the lower than in the higher reaches of the intestinal tract.

### The Dechlorination and Dehydration Theory

It was first shown by Hartwell and Hoguet (1912) that obstructed animals which survived for some days showed marked dehydration. Vomiting, it was claimed, was responsible for the reduction in body water; the symptoms of obstruction and death were believed to be the direct consequence of the dehydrated state. They showed, and their observation was confirmed by Haden and Orr and others, that the life of an animal with an obstructed intestine could be prolonged by the subcutaneous or intravenous administration of saline.

That the loss of chloride in the vomitus may cause a profound fall in blood chloride, and dehydration is an established fact. Hastings, Murray and Murray found that in dogs, obstruction at the pylorus caused a reduction in the blood chloride to 50 per cent of the normal within a few days after the operation. Gamble and Ross confirmed this observation and made a more extended study of the changes in blood chemistry which follow pyloric obstruction. They consider that loss of chloride, by leading to a reduction in the electrolytes of the body, is the primary cause of the dehydration. They state that "a withdrawal of the electrolytes of the body fluids will be accompanied by a proportionate reduction in the volume of body water and that this change can only be repaired by replacing both the lost water and the lost electrolytes." These observers showed that the loss of chloride in the vomitus is repaired for a time by the retention of carbon dioxide and the consequent increase in bicarbonate. By this means the concentration of electrolytes is maintained. In other words, the sum of $(Cl^-)$ and $(HCO_3^-)$ remains constant for a time (30 hours or so) after the obstruction has been

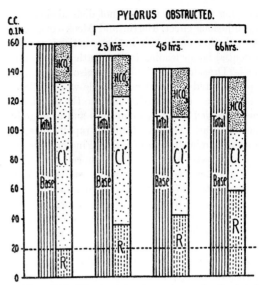

FIG. 42.6. Diagram to show change in the total content and distribution of electrolytes in the body fluids following pyloric obstruction. (After Gamble and Ross.)

established. A degree of alkalosis, however, results, which is countered by a loss of base (Na) in the urine; a reduction in $(Cl^-) + (HCO_3^-)$ occurs. The reduction in ionic concentration of body fluids resulting from the depletion of base, which unlike $Cl^-$ cannot be substituted for, is accompanied by a proportionate loss of water (fig. 42.6). The value of sodium chloride injections in prolonging life in obstructed animals depends chiefly upon the fact that the replenishment of the stores of sodium permits the retention of water. Chlorides such as $NH_4Cl$ or $KCl$ are without any beneficial effect, nor will water alone or a solution of glucose prolong life.

The reduction in the blood chloride is not necessarily the result of vomiting. The accumulation of secretions above the point of obstruction will just as surely cause chloride depletion and dehydration. In the rabbit for example, which cannot vomit, obstruction causes the characteristic blood changes. A most powerful stimulant to secretion is distension of the bowel wall; the dilated bowel in the later stages of obstruction thus becomes a receptacle for large quantities of fluid. In the case of the rabbit, fluid amounting to thirteen per cent or so of the body weight may be found in the stomach and bowel after death. The fatal effect of distension has been shown by Herrin and Meek. They distended a loop of bowel by means of a balloon and allowed the continuous secretion which resulted to drain to the exterior. The animals died in from 6 to 14 days. A loop of bowel opening to the exterior but not distended causes no injurious effect. Herrin and Meek concluded that the loss of chloride in the secretions was the essential factor leading to the death of their animals. Dragstedt and Ellis have also shown that the profound fall in blood chloride which follows the drainage of the gastric juice to the exterior is accompanied by grave symptoms and ultimately ends in death. The symptoms are rapidly relieved by the administration of saline. Fine and his associates have reported a pronounced reduction in the plasma volume of patients suffering from acute obstruction of the small intestine.

There is no doubt that chloride loss and dehydration are important factors in the *later* stages of obstruction. The administration of saline is one of the most valuable measures possessed by the clinician for combating the condition at this stage either before or following operation.

Nevertheless, although the blood changes at this time undoubtedly prejudice the animal's chance of survival, it is unlikely that they play the primary role in causing death. For one thing, correction of the blood chemistry, although it prolongs life, does not permit survival. Moreover, death frequently occurs before any significant change in the blood chlorides takes place, whereas on the other hand, the blood chlorides may be maintained at a level considerably lower than that usually seen in obstruction without the animal becoming ill. The following experiments[1] indicate a nervous element as the primary cause of the train of symptoms seen in acute obstruction. A balloon was placed in the lower duodenum and distended to a pressure of about 100 mm. Hg. A large sized rubber tube attached to one side of the balloon and extending into the bowel below prevented any actual obstruction. X-ray examination showed that a barium mixture moved freely beyond the distended region. These animals had symptoms indistinguishable from acute obstruction yet little fluid was lost by vomiting and the blood chlorides showed practically no change. On the other hand, otherwise normal animals who had had the blood chloride depleted by means of histamine injections (to stimulate gastric secretion) and apomorphine (to induce vomiting) remained in apparent good health even though the blood chloride had been maintained at a level 50 per cent below the normal for three weeks.

It is evident that in the balloon experiments just mentioned, distention of the bowel caused death in some way other than by chloride depletion. Another group of animals in which the bowel was distended by a balloon as described, but in which the segment of bowel had been first denervated survived for a much longer time than those in which a preliminary denervation had not been performed. This result indicates that afferent impulses arising from the distended segment of bowel are concerned in some way with the severe symptoms of obstruction. Herrin and Meek also observed that if a distended draining loop were denervated the animals survived indefinitely. They, however, offer an explanation of the benefit derived from denervation based upon the theory that dechlorination plays the essential role, namely, that when the vomiting and loss of appetite produced reflexly from the distended loop are abolished by nerve section, chloride loss is reduced and chloride ingestion increased. The importance of afferent impulses from the intestine in the production of the symptoms of obstruction therefore must be admitted; that they may cause death quite independently of dechlorination is undoubted. It is well known that many reflex effects upon the cardiovascular system and upon several important functions can be initiated from the gastrointestinal tract. The severe pain and collapse which result from the distention of other hollow viscera, e.g., the gall-bladder, stomach, kidney pelvis, etc., may also be recalled in this connection. Moreover, the severe symptoms and early death which result from the mere distention of the bowel by a balloon calls to mind the analogous clinical condition known as Richter's hernia. In this condition only a portion of the intestinal lumen is pinched off and isolated from the main passage. The bowel is not obstructed, yet all the symptoms of acute obstruction are present. It is quite conceivable that acute distention of the small isolated pocket by secretions and gas is responsible for the symptoms.

The importance of distention as a factor in acute obstruction of the intestine is now generally recognized and it has become the practice in suitable cases to decompress the bowel by suction-drainage through a tube passed from the mouth to the duodenum (Wagensteen and Paine) or, as in the method of Miller and Abbott, to insert a long slender tube through the nose into the stomach and allow it to be carried to the level of the obstruction. The tube has a double lumen and is provided at its tip with a small balloon which can be moderately inflated after it has entered the duodenum. The balloon serves as a stimulus to peristalsis which carries it and the tubing along the bowel to the point of obstruction (fig. 43.5).

[1] Taylor, Weld and Harrison.

## The Ileocolic Valve (Valvula Coli)

This structure permits the passage of the contents of the small intestine at intervals into the cecum, but when competent hinders the return of the material into the ileum. Its ability to do this depends, according to one view, not upon any mechanical valvelike device, but upon the contraction of the circular fibers of the gut which are thickened in this region to form a sphincter guard for the ileocecal orifice. But, although a sphincter-like thickening of the circular muscle fibers is found in this situation, most anatomists agree that the competency of the ileocolic valve is mainly, or at least partly due to a valvelike construction. The ileum enters the cecum obliquely and in doing so invaginates the cecal wall; this alone would tend toward a valvelike action. The valve proper is formed as follows. As the lower end of the ileum enters the cecum, the invaginated portion of the cecal wall forms two transverse folds or lips, one above the other on the cecal aspect of the ileocolic orifice. The lips fuse laterally to produce a fold on either side of the orifice (*the frenula coli*) which are continued around the interior of the cecum. As the cecum distends the frenula are stretched and pulling upon the lips from either side draw them firmly together. Thus the valve can withstand a high pressure in the cecum but yields to a low pressure from above. Materials introduced by enema may in some instances pass through the valve into the ileum. Such incompetence may permit the enema fluid to reach the duodenum. The ileocolic opening has been observed in man through a cecal fistula. It appears as an oval or round opening from 2 to 3 cm. in diameter situated in the center of a small papilla. When tightly closed the valve was found to offer considerable resistance to the passage of the finger. While digestion was in progress the papilla was observed to flush, its color altering from a pale pink to a vivid red. The orifice opened rhythmically at frequent intervals and allowed a jet of fluid to escape into the cecum. Emotional excitement or the swallowing of food increased the frequency of the ejections (*gastroileal reflex*). During fasting nothing passed through for long periods, but in from $\frac{1}{2}$ to 4 minutes after food was taken into the mouth, fluid appeared in gushes of about 15 cc. every half minute or so.

The functions of the ileocolic valve appear to be (a) to prevent the contents of the ileum from passing into the cecum before the digestive processes have been completed, (b) to serve as a barrier which prevents the bacteria-laden contents of the large bowel from contaminating the small intestine.

## Movements of the Large Intestine

The colon receives the mixed residues remaining after completion of intestinal digestion and absorption. These consist of undigested or undigestible food residues, whatever remains of the digestive secretions including considerable quantities of water, and the fluid that has been swallowed or secreted and has escaped absorption in the small intestine. The colon extracts the water from this mixture and forms the indigestible residues into fecal masses which are later evacuated. The motor activities are appropriate to these functions; they may be divided into two classes; first, those that appear to be designed primarily to facilitate absorption; second, those concerned principally with propulsion.

Movements of the first type have been studied principally in experimental animals, since the human colon does not lend itself readily to experimental study. Barcroft and Steggerda (1932) studied the exteriorized cecum and proximal portion of the colon in dogs. In their experiments, the organ to be studied was brought out through an incision in the skin and after healing had taken place observations were made without anesthesia. They observed what they called kneading movements, antiperistalsis and mass peristalsis. The kneading movements seemed to them to resemble segmenting contractions in the small intestine, except that they occurred at a slower rate and involved longer sections of the intestine; they appeared at intervals of about one-half minute. Antiperistaltic waves appeared when the colon became distended and followed each other at a frequency of 5 to 7 per minute. The "mass peristalsis" belongs to the second class of contractions and will be considered a little later.

Cannon (1902) studied the movements of the colon in cats by means of X-rays. He noted that the characteristic movement of the transverse and ascending portion was antiperistalsis. He described what he called mass contractions of the cecum and ascending colon which forced material into the transverse colon from which it was driven back by antiperistaltic waves. This is obviously a stirring and mixing function and is not concerned with the transport of material in the aboral direction.

Templeton and Lawson (1931) studied the movements of the colon in dogs, using multiple balloons and manometers. With these they were able to determine the extent of the contractions, if any, and whether they progressed and in what direction. They described three types of contractions which they designated as type I, type II and type III respectively. Type I movements were simple, rapid contractions and relaxations, frequently simultaneous over the three balloons but often confined to one balloon. These they considered to be stationary, rhythmic contractions. They are evidently analogous to the segmenting contractions in the small intestine. Type II are slower contractions on which type I movements were superimposed. Analysis indicated that these either swept analward, oralward, or remained stationary. They might start in one direction, become stationary, then move in the other direction. Antiperistaltic waves would be of this type but some were obviously peristaltic. Type II contractions are suggestive of the kneading movements described by Barcroft and Steggerda. Type III contractions were tone changes on which were superimposed type II contractions. They were apt to be in opposite phase in the proximal and distal colon, and to increase in one region while decreasing in the other. These movements would result in a to-and-fro motion of the intestinal contents and are suggestive of Cannon's alternate mass contractions and antiperistaltic movements. Elliot and Barclary-Smith (1904) observed antiperistalsis in the colon of the dog, cat, rabbit and rat.

Todd (1930) observed slow peristaltic movements in the cecum of human subjects when it was being filled with barium from the ileum. He described these as follows: "As the ileal coils

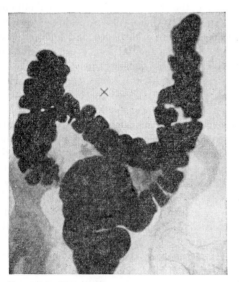

Fig. 42.7. X-ray photograph of normal large bowel completely filled. (After Barclay.)

empty themselves, slow peristalsis taking place meanwhile, the outlines become better defined and the cecal peristaltic movement is plainly seen. The shadow of the cecum becomes denser as more contents are poured into it and slow massive movements occur, involving its entire outline. How they can drive the contents onward is altogether obscure but the dense barium shadow does progress upward." He also observed a "concertina-like" action of the transverse colon, which he attributed to contractions and relaxations of the teniae.

In the rabbit and probably in other animals there are contractions of the haustra (which are the bulgings of the wall of the colon between the teniae). Alvarez (1940) describes these contractions as resembling "those of the jointed curtains of two roll top desks facing one another. First one top is pulled down and then the other."

To summarize this rather confusing mass of data, it appears that the colon agitates its contents by means of segmenting contractions similar to those seen in the small intestine, haustral contractions in which the colonic walls roll back and forth over the contents, kneading movements in which fairly large segments can contract while adjacent segments are relaxing to be followed by contraction and relaxation in reverse phase; and finally, by means of alternate peristalsis and antiperistalsis. It should be pointed out that these movements occur principally in the ascending and transverse colon where absorption of most of the water takes place. It is not to be inferred that each type of movement occurs in every species of animal. We can only be certain that they occur in those species in which they have been observed; for example, antiperistalsis has rarely been observed in the human colon. In spite of the variety of movements described, it is common to find no activity whatever on X-ray examination of the human colon. Templeton and Lawson observed that in spite of the presence of balloons in their animals, periods of activity in the colon alternated with periods of complete rest.

The second class of movement consists of those which propel the colonic contents analward and includes colonic peristalsis and mass movements. Peristalsis of the colon has been observed by a number of investigators, beginning with Bayliss and Starling in 1901. It does not differ materially from peristalsis in the small intestine, except perhaps in frequency of occurrence. It consists of a contraction wave preceded by relaxation (Auer and Kreuger, 1947) and its forward progress is dependent upon the integrity of the myenteric plexus. The movement proceeds with great power, particularly in the descending colon, due perhaps to the hard dry character of the material to be moved. Auer speaks of seeing a hemostat with which the intestine was clamped, twisted apart by a peristaltic movement in the descending colon of the cat. Peristalsis is relatively rare in the human colon except in association with mass movements or during the act of defecation (Todd, 1930).

Mass movements occur at relatively infrequent intervals and, generally, in the past, have been confused with peristalsis; however Code and his coworkers (1954) have pointed out that these movements, although their propulsive nature has not been questioned, are not true peristaltic waves since they involve simultaneous contractions of large segments of the colon. Holzknecht (1909) (Fig. 42.8) was the first to describe these contractions and they were later studied in detail by Hurst (1907) and by Hertz (Hurst) and Newton (1913). The latter authors noted that they occur usually after a meal or on any occasion when the stomach is being filled with food. They described the increase in colonic motor activity following a meal as the *gastrocolic reflex.* Hurst later observed that the terminal ileum also became hyperactive following meals and proposed to call this phenomenon "the *gastro-ileac*" reflex. Douglas and Mann (1940) found that the entire small intestine manifests increased motility under these circumstances and that the excitation is transmitted along the intestine, and not by way of the central nervous system. In any case, not only mass movements but all motor activities of the colon are increased at this time; for example, in the experiment of Barcroft and Steggerda, kneading movements and antiperistalsis were increased in dogs after feeding. Hurst remarked that the taking of food is the most powerful of all stimuli to the motor activity of the colon in man. He found that the feces advanced considerably after each meal, much more progress having been made in one patient for example, during the hours in which dinner was taken than in the previous four hours.

The mass movements of the colon serve to empty the contents of the proximal colon rapidly into the more distal portions. Frequently such movements are followed by a desire to defecate and it is assumed that on these occasions the movement has been vigorous enough to carry fecal masses into the rectum. Since normally a desire to defecate does not follow every mass movement of the colon it must be assumed that on some occasions the forward movement of the

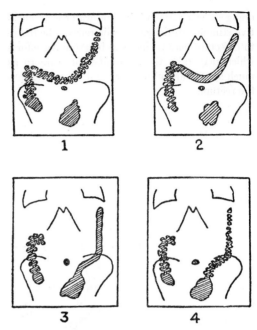

FIG. 42.8. Holzknecht's diagrams of the happenings during a mass movement of the large intestine. 1, distribution of the food before any change was noted; 2, the haustral segmentation in the transverse colon has disappeared; 3, the whole colon beyond the hepatic flexure passes on suddenly; 4, it is again a picture of "still life" a few seconds later and the haustral segmentation has returned. (After Barclay.)

colonic contents stops short of the rectum. People differ considerably with respect to their susceptibility to the gastrocolic or gastroileac reflex. Alvarez (1940) describes a patient in whom every mass movement resulted in defecation. He found that even the sight or smell or taste of food induced the gastrocolic reflex, so that in walking down the street it was necessary for him to avoid passing in front of restaurants if he wished to avoid trouble.

### Defecation

As pointed out by Hurst (1909) the rectum is normally empty. The fecal masses driven forward by the mass movements of the colon are stored, not in the rectum, but in the sigmoid or pelvic colon. Fecal matter does not collect elsewhere if defecation is regular; if, however, defecation is long deferred, the descending colon becomes filled when the pelvic colon can hold no more. The desire to defecate occurs when, as a result of a mass movement, some feces enter the rectum. While the usual stimulus is the taking of food, a glass of cold water or smoking a cigar may have the same effect. Many people find that a glass of cold orange juice or lemon juice and water is an effective stimulus to the gastrocolic reflex. The desire to defecate may be induced by straining efforts which may raise the abdominal pressure to as much as 200 mm. of mercury and force feces into the rectum.

The act of defecation is, in the adult, preceded by a voluntary effort consisting of assumption of an appropriate posture, voluntary relaxation of the external anal sphincter, and usually, compression of the abdominal contents by means of straining efforts. These movements in turn prob-

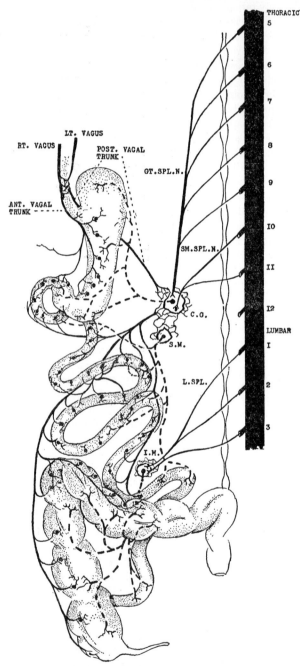

FIG. 42.9. Diagram of the innervation of the stomach, small intestine. and proximal part of the colon. GT.SPL.N., great splanchnic nerve; SM.SPL.N., small splanchnic nerve; L.SPL., least splanchnic nerve; C.G., celiac ganglion; S.M., superior mesenteric ganglion; I.M., inferior mesenteric ganglion. Continuous lines, vagal and sympathetic preganglionic fibers; broken lines, sympathetic postganglionic fibers; ganglion cells and postganglionic fibers of vagus in gastrointestinal wall.

ably give rise to stimuli which augment the visceral reflexes although these originate primarily in the distended rectum. As a result of these reflexes peristaltic waves appear in the entire colon (Hurst, 1909) and the internal anal sphincter relaxes. Peristalsis in the descending colon carries its contents into the pelvic colon which in turn transfers them into the rectum eventually to be evacuated by way of the anus; hence, the entire distal colon from the splenic flexure to the anus may be emptied at one time. A prominent mechanical feature of the final act of evacuation is contraction of the longitudinal muscle of the distal colon which is most pronounced in the rectum itself. The shortening of the distal colon tends to elevate the pelvic colon and obliterate the angle which it normally makes with the rectum. This straightening of the passage doubtless facilitates evacuation. Shortening of the rectum itself is an important factor in expelling the feces through the anal orifice.

The act of defecation provides another instance of a reflex that is under some degree of voluntary control. The voluntary regulation consists of the ability to inhibit the reflex under normal circumstances and to initiate it voluntarily provided the necessary visceral stimulus (recent distention of the rectum) is present. Reflex centers for defecation have been located in the hypothalamus, in the lower lumbar and upper sacral segments of the spinal cord, and in the ganglionic plexus of the gut. The intrinsic intestinal plexus of the lower colon is able to take over the function of controlling defecation even in animals in which the spinal cord has been destroyed. For this reason, in severe spinal injury, the defecation reflex suffers less than does, for example, the reflex of micturition.

THE COMPOSITION OF THE FECES. According to Cantarow and Schepartz (1954) adults on an average diet excrete from 75 to 170 grams of feces daily, about 25 to 30 per cent of which is made up of solids; the remainder is water. If the diet is rich in vegetables the quantity is greater, especially if the vegetables are eaten raw. Bacteria comprise about one-third of the dry weight of the feces under average conditions. The pH is 7.0 to 7.5. The feces contain those inorganic substances which are relatively insoluble at alkaline pH ranges such as calcium phosphate and oxalate, iron phosphate and similar compounds. The organic material is principally cellulose, protein and fats. About half the protein nitrogen of the feces is of bacterial origin; the remainder represents unabsorbed intestinal secretions and digestive fluids, mucus, and desquamated epithelial cells from the mucosa. Only a small amount is actual food residue. Enzymes are also present but in very small quantities: these are pancreatic amylase and trypsin, nucleases, maltase, sucrase, lipase and lysozyme. Fats comprise from 5 to 25 per cent of the feces under normal circumstances; they are greatly increased in conditions in which there is interference with pancreatic or biliary function. In total absence of pancreatic juice from the intestine as much as 90 per cent of the ingested fat may be excreted in the stools. Much of the fecal fat has undergone digestion as indicated by the following average composition of fecal lipids: neutral fat, 7.3 per cent of dry weight of feces; free fatty acids, 5.6 per cent; and soaps, 4.6 per cent.

The color of the feces is due chiefly to bile pigments, stercobilin (*urobilin*), produced by reduction of bilirubin by the intestinal bacteria. The characteristic odor is due largely to indole and skatole, but is contributed to also by hydrogen sulfide and other odoriferous substances.

GAS IN THE INTESTINE. A variable amount of gas is always to be found in the small and large intestine, principally the latter. This consists of the respiratory gases—oxygen and carbon dioxide, nitrogen, methane, hydrogen and small amounts of other gases including the rate atmospheric gases. The average composition according to Pogrund and Steggerda (1948) is as follows: carbon dioxide, 7.5 per cent; oxygen, 3.0 per cent; methane, hydrogen and other rare gases, 9.5 per cent; and nitrogen, 80 per cent. The source of the oxygen, nitrogen and carbon dioxide is swallowed air and diffusion from the blood. Bacterial fermentation and putrefaction of food residues in the intestine produce the methane and hydrogen. No matter what the composition of swallowed air may be it quickly comes into equilibrium with the venous blood with respect to oxygen and carbon dioxide, and more slowly with respect to nitrogen; hence, the relative constancy of composition of intestinal gas with respect to these gases. The amount of putrefactive gas is much more variable. It is the rapid expansion of these gases that gives rise to intestinal cramps on ascending to high altitudes in an unpressurized plane. Some of this gas is absorbed into the blood and some escapes from the rectum as flatus. The amount in the intestine can be reduced by giving the subject pure oxygen to breathe. This reduces the partial pressure of nitrogen in the blood and thus favors diffusion of nitrogen from the intestine toward the circulating blood. Since nitrogen diffuses very slowly it is necessary to continue the treatment over a long period of time in order to obtain any beneficial results. The same result could be obtained by using oxygen diluted with helium or other inert gas, as long as nitrogen is not present.

## ABNORMAL COLONIC MOTILITY—CONSTIPATION

Abnormal motor activity in the colon is one of the most common conditions for which the physician may be consulted. The causes may be local only or they may involve systemic disease. Psychic factors are important and it can be safely asserted that no other part of the gastrointestinal tract is so profoundly affected by emotional disturbances as is the large intestine. This statement is supported by lay observation as well as clinical experience and also by experimental observations on suitable human subjects. It has been possible to demonstrate changes in tone, motility, or vascularity of the large intestine in response to experimentally induced emotional reactions. For example, in three children, four, nine and ten years old, studied by Friedman and Snape (1946), changes in color and motility were observed during emotional excitement; mild, painful stimuli or even the suggestion of pain or discussion of unpleasant experiences caused blanching of the mucous membrane; the sight or smell of appetizing food caused reddening. During eating the mucous membrane was engorged, but returned to normal after the meal. These changes of course indicate constriction (blanching) or dilation (reddening) of the blood vessels. In two adults studied by Grace, Wolf and Wolff (1948), experimentally induced anger or feelings of guilt or resentment or of hostility caused hyperfunctioning of the colon; there was increased motor activity, increased blood flow, increased lysozyme production and increased secretion of mucus; acute fear caused pallor and relaxation. Increased motor activity and blood flow were also observed in these subjects while they were eating a meal. During psychometric examination subjects also showed hyperfunction of the colon.

The most frequent manifestation of malfunction of the large intestine is constipation. For a discussion of the various causes and the treatment of this condition, appropriate clinical texts should be consulted. It may be mentioned here that one of the most frequent causes of chronic constipation is neglect of the call to stool. The desire to defecate is experienced whenever the pressure within the rectum is increased. An increase in the volume of the contents of the rectum of from 15 to 25 cc has been shown to be sufficient to produce an urge. If the rectum is not emptied at such a time, the sensory mechanism becomes adapted to the pressure and the urge is no longer felt; it then requires a further increase in volume with a corresponding increase in pressure to produce a sensation. This will also pass if neglected and a still further increase in volume is required to arouse a sensation; finally the irritability of the rectum is so reduced that an urge is no longed induced. Usually the subject will then take a cathartic which further injures the sensory mechanism. Frequent repetition of this cycle results ultimately in dependence on cathartics. An important factor in the prevention or treatment of such a condition is the establishment of a conditioned reflex. Taking advantage of the gastrocolic reflex which follows a meal the subject selects a convenient time of day for going to stool, usually after breakfast. He then makes an effort to defecate at this time each day whether or not he gets the urge. In the beginning mild laxatives may be necessary to facilitate the establishment of the reflex but once it is thoroughly established they can be omitted. Such a conditioned reflex can become so firmly established that one feels the desire to defecate at a particular time of day whether or not a meal has been eaten.

Tryptophan　　　　　Indole propionic acid　　　　Ethylindole　　　　Skatole　　　　Indole

The formation of indican:

Indole      Indoxyl      Indoxyl sulfuric acid      Indican

Conversion of tyrosine to tyramine, cresol and phenol:

Tyrosine      *p*-Hydroxyphenyl propionic acid      *p*-Hydroxyphenyl acetic acid      Cresol

Tyramine      Methylamine      Cresol      Phenol

## Intestinal Intoxication

THE LARGE INTESTINE. Several substances, some intensely toxic in character, are formed in the large intestine as a result of the decomposition of protein by the normal bacterial flora (colon type of organism). Among such putrefactive products are histamine, phenol, cresol, indole, skatole, ethylamine, isoethylamine, tryamine, etc. Choline is also formed as a result of the decomposition of lecithin, and choline gives rise to traces of neurine. Some observers, impressed by the powerful actions of these substances when injected into animals, have suggested that their absorption into the general blood stream is responsible for many ills, and particularly for the well known symptoms of constipation. Metchnikoff (1907) arraigned the colon as the body's greatest enemy. Arbuthnot Lane, in more recent times (1918), inveighed against this cesspit and recommended its extirpation under certain circumstance. No reliable evidence can, however, be cited to connect any of the toxic products mentioned with the symptoms of disease. Many of them are produced only in mere traces, and even though some, such as indole, are produced in relatively large amounts (60 mg., according to Herter (1907), may be present in 100 grams of

feces) toxic doses are prevented from entering the systemic circulation by the barrier offered by the bowel wall and through the detoxicating action of the liver. Indole, for example, when given to the human subject by mouth in an amount (1 gram), which is more than would ever be present in the bowel at one time, produces no symptoms; 2 grams causes only some dizziness and slight headache, whereas large amounts may be introduced into the colon without ill effect. The slight absorption of indole and skatole under ordinary circumstances is indicated by the fact that although the feces contain considerable amounts of both these substances, the detoxicated product indican may be absent from the urine. On the other hand the ability of the liver to protect the body against these substances is shown by the observation that large amounts of indican are constantly present in the urine of certain individuals, showing that considerable quantities of the putrefactive products are absorbed, yet such persons enjoy good health.

Choline may be given by mouth with impunity; even when relatively large amounts (15 to 20 mg. per kg. in the cat) are given intravenously no toxic effects are produced. Since this substance is rapidly destroyed in the blood stream, large amounts may be injected slowly over a period of time without noticeable effect.

Histamine, another powerful depressor substance was found by Meakins and Harington in minute amounts in the cecum, but only insignificant amounts, they conclude, pass through the intestinal wall. Even after the introduction of a large dose into the *small* bowel only slight absorption was evident. Koessler and Hanke (1924) gave the amine by mouth in doses of 100 mg. to guinea pigs; there were no ill effects, and upon analysis of the intestinal contents 24 hours after the administration of this amount, less than 2 mg. were recovered. The chief protection against the toxic effects of histamine is apparently in the bowel wall itself. It has also been found by Weiss and associates that in the case of the human subject 20 mg. of histamine may be injected per hour without causing a depressor effect; 500 mg. given orally were inert.

According to Alvarez the symptoms of constipation—headache, furred tongue, foul breath, malaise, etc., are of reflex rather than of toxic origin. Afferent impulses set up from the wall of the overloaded rectum appear to be responsible. Distention of the rectum by inert material such as absorbent cotton has been shown to produce almost all the symptoms of constipation. In the dog, packing the rectum in this way causes a rise of some 10 mm. Hg in blood pressure which is maintained until the foreign material is removed.

The manifestations of constipation referable to the alimentary tract, namely, the loss of appetite, coated tongue and offensive breath are, according to Alvarez, probably due to small waves of contraction originating in the wall of the loaded bowel and travelling in a reverse direction over the small intestine, stomach and esophagus (p. 691). A strong argument against the symptoms of constipation being due to toxic absorption is the almost immediate relief which follows evacuation of the bowels—it would certainly take some time for the blood to be cleared of a poisonous material. Furthermore, in constipation the feces are relatively dry and hard, conditions much less, rather than more favorable to the absorption of putrefactive products. One should expect, indeed, that the latter would occur more readily during diarrhea. Apart from all the indirect evidence against a toxic element being concerned in constipation, is the positive fact that many subjects of the disorder, even though this is of a severe grade, do not excrete indican in the urine and, as mentioned above, other individuals who for some

unknown reason excrete large quantities remain free from symptoms.

There seems little doubt that toxic products of the bacterial flora of the large intestine are prevented from entering the systemic circulation in amounts that are pathologically significant.

THE SMALL INTESTINE. The immunity of the body to autointoxication applies only to the large intestine. The small intestine is not equipped in the same degree to resist the passage of toxic products into the blood stream. Normally, however, the bacterial flora of the small intestine are quite different from those of the large intestine. The microorganisms (e.g., *Bacillus bifidus*) in the former situation have a fermentative action not a putrefactive action. Through their action upon carbohydrate, organic acids—acetic, butyric and lactic—are produced. The acid reaction of the ileal contents is unfavorable to the growth of the proteolytic bacteria. As long as the supply of carbohydrate material is adequate the microorganisms of the acid-producing type flourish and any of the bacteria of the large intestine which may have invaded the small intestine are unable to gain a foothold. Under certain circumstances, however, especially in infants, this does occur. In young children, in whom the protective power of the small intestine is even less than that of adults, a severe type of toxemia results, characterized by vomiting, diarrhea, dehydration, acidosis, fever, emaciation and great prostration.

Some believe that guanidine is the toxic product concerned in certain types of intestinal intoxication in infants. In intestinal disorders associated with the extension into the small intestine of the flora of the large, measures are directed toward encouraging the normal acid-producing type of organism in gaining the upper hand. Carbohydrate is supplied, usually in the form of lactose, which passes farther down the intestinal tract than other sugars before it is absorbed. It has also been common practice to administer cultures of the fermentative type of organism, such as that of sour milk—*Bacillus bulgaricus* (so-called as the result of the writings of Metchnikoff (1907) who attributed the health and longevity of the Bulgarian peasant to his drinking large quantities of sour milk). Today cultures of *Bacillus acidophilus*, one of the normal inhabitants of the small intestine, are usually employed. Ordinary *antiseptics* given with the view of inhibiting bacterial growth exert no appreciable effect, although certain sulphonamides are valuable for their bacteriostatic action.

## Nervous and Hormonal Regulation of the Gastrointestinal Smooth Muscle

The gastrointestinal tract receives an abundant nerve supply *via* the autonomic nerves. In addition, it contains within its walls an elaborate plexus of interconnected ganglia. This is usually described as consisting of two plexuses, the *myenteric plexus* situated between the circular and longitudinal layers of the smooth muscle and the *submucous plexus* situated in the submucosa. Kuntz (1953) considers that this is an artificial division and that actually the plexuses function as a unit. Langley (1921) suggested that the enteric plexuses should be regarded as a separate subdivision of the autonomic nervous system and proposed that they be designated the "enteric nervous system." He wrote as follows: "This classification is, I think, advisable for the central connection of the enteric nerve cells is still uncertain and evidence has been obtained that they have automatic and reflex functions which other peripheral nerve cells do not possess. Functional evidence for reflex activity in the enteric nervous system has been available since the work of Bayliss and Starling." In 1922, Kuntz presented anatomical evidence of the existence of reflex arcs in the enteric plexuses. Understanding of the fact that the enteric plexuses constitute a complex and highly coordinated reflex mechanism is essential to an intelligent interpretation of the effects of the extrinsic nerves on intestinal smooth muscle.

### EXTRINSIC NERVES

The autonomic nerves are classified as sympathetic and parasympathetic but it is more in keeping with modern thought to consider them as cholinergic or adrenergic, depending upon whether they liberate acetylcholine or an adrenalinelike substance at their final terminations on the muscles. In this sense most parasympathetics are cholinergic and sympathetics are adrenergic, but there is considerable mixing since cholinergic fibers have been demonstrated in considerable abundance in the sympathetics.

The parasympathetic nerve supply to the gastrointestinal smooth muscle comes mainly from the vagus; however, the pelvic nerves supply the distal portion of the colon. The parasympathetic fibers, whether vagus or pelvic in origin, do not end directly on the smooth muscle cells but end by making synapses with cells in the enteric plexuses. Therefore, as pointed out by Carlson (1922), they stand in relation to these plexuses

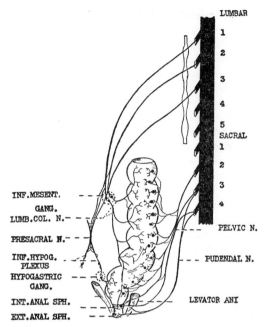

FIG. 42.10. Diagram of the innervation of the distal colon.

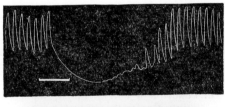

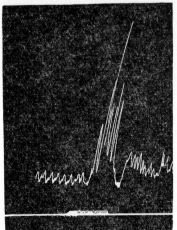

FIG. 42.11. Upper, shows the inhibitory effect of splanchnic stimulation upon the movements of the small intestine; the heavy white line indicates the time during which the stimulus was applied (after Starling). Lower, shows effect upon intestinal motility of stimulating vagus nerves. (After Thomas and Kuntz.)

as intercalated or internuncial fibers between reflex centers and not as ordinary motor nerve fibers. The function of such fibers in the central nervous system, and presumably in this situation also, is to increase or decrease the excitability of the reflex centers and not directly to initiate muscular activity.

The sympathetic supply to the stomach and small intestine is by way of the splanchnic nerves. The cecum, appendix and ascending and transverse colon are supplied by nerves which arise from the superior mesenteric plexus. These nerves include both vagus and sympathetic fibers. The descending colon and upper part of the rectum are supplied by nerves which arise from the inferior mesenteric plexus. This plexus is a derivative of the aortic plexus through which it also receives vagus fibers from the celiac plexus. The lower part of the rectum is supplied by sympathetic fibers which arise from the upper and lower divisions of the hypogastric plexus (Kuntz, 1953). The preganglionic sympathetic fibers end in the celiac, superior or inferior mesenteric, or aortic ganglia. The fibers that reach the intestine, therefore, are postganglionic. They probably have no functional relation to the enteric plexuses even though they traverse the enteric ganglia and are distributed along with the postganglionic enteric plexus fibers. Most of them are concerned with the vasomotor supply of the numerous blood vessels in the intestine but some go to the intestinal smooth muscle.

THE FUNCTION OF THE EXTRINSIC NERVES. The gastrointestinal tract is capable of carrying on its major functions after all the extrinsic nerves have been severed. This automaticity may be attributed partly to the local nervous mechanism and partly to the properties of the smooth muscle. Probably the essentially rhythmic functions, such as gastric peristalsis, segmentic contractions of the small and large intestine, and antiperistalsis in the colon are dependent upon the properties of the smooth muscle, whereas the more highly coordinated functions such as forward peristalsis in the small and large intestine are dependent upon the functional integrity of the myenteric plexus. Both the neurogenic and myogenic functions are regulated through central nervous system reflexes by way of the autonomic nerves.

The tone and peristaltic activity of the stomach is usually increased on stimulation of the vagus nerves. The statement that the vagus increases the activity of the muscle in the gastric wall while inhibiting the sphincters has been

proved to be an error; when motor effects are observed in the muscle of the pyloric portion, for example, the pyloric sphincter responds in the same sense; thus the idea of a reciprocal innervation of the sphincters and the other muscle of the stomach is not borne out by the experimental facts (Thomas and Wheelon, 1922). There may be somewhat more justification for such a concept in regard to the relation between the esophagus and cardiac sphincter but in order to demonstrate inhibition of the cardiac sphincter by vagus stimulation Langley found it necessary to first atropinize the animal so as to paralyze the motor fibers.

The effects on the stomach of stimulating the splanchnic nerves is usually described as inhibitory but it is far from being invariably so. In simply acute experiments on anesthetized animals increased motor activity is seen about as frequently as inhibition on stimulation of the splanchnic nerves; indeed only motor responses are seen unless care is taken to permit full recovery from the shock of the operation and to avoid undue handling of the viscera while making the preparation. The fact is, as Carlson and his associates (1922) pointed out, that motor responses are more likely to be obtained when the muscle is in a state of relaxation, whereas inhibitory effects occur when the muscle is in a state of high tonus or vigorous activity. This rule applies to both vagus and sympathetic stimulation; nevertheless with the muscle in a medium state of tonus, the vagi will more often produce excitatory effects and the splanchnics, inhibitory effects. The reason for the preponderance of sympathetic motor effects in recently anesthetized, operated animals is that the stomach, in such circumstances, is always in a state of very low tone.

In the small intestine the parasympathetic nerves are nearly always excitatory and the sympathetics nearly always inhibitory; however, the excitatory vagus effect, as mentioned previously, is usually preceded by a brief inhibition. In the upper portion of the small intestine motor effects from stimulation of the sympathetic nerves are by no means uncommon. The tonus rule holds here also; motor effects are more apt to be observed in the relaxed intestine.

In the large intestine, stimulation of the parasympathetic innervation is reported to cause mainly increased activity, whereas stimulation of the sympathetic nerves gives results that are even more confusing than those obtained in the stomach. Some investigators report only inhibitory effects, others report only motor effects whereas still others report inhibition of the walls of the viscera with contraction of the sphincters. There seems to be somewhat more basis for this last concept in the large intestine than in the case of the stomach. The sympathetic tends to cause retention of contents, for example in the rectum, through contraction of the internal anal sphincter and relaxation of the rectal walls; the parasympathetics tend to promote evacuation of contents by causing relaxation of the sphincters and contraction and propulsive motility in the walls. Here also muscle in high tonus tends to respond to nerve stimulation with relaxation, whereas muscle in low tonus tends to respond with contractions.

The effects of stimulating the autonomic nerves is confusing if one attempts to classify them simply as excitatory or inhibitory to the smooth muscle. It is much more understandable if we bear in mind the fact that at least the parasympathetic nerves serve merely to increase or decrease the excitability of the local reflex mechanism. Although it is true that stimulation of either vagus nerve generally increases the activity of the gastric and intestinal smooth muscle, inhibitory effects have been observed. Brief inhibition regularly precedes contraction in the small intestine following vagus stimulation (Bayliss and Starling, 1899); inhibitory effects are also seen occasionally in the stomach. The varying responses to parasympathetic stimulation may be interpreted as being due to the vagaries of the enteric reflex arcs which are subject to stimuli from many sources. The vagus impulses, being only one of these sources, could not be expected always to determine the response. The responses to sympathetic stimulation are undoubtedly influenced by changes in the blood supply brought about by the vasomotor fibers which always accompany the nerves to the intestinal smooth muscle, but mixed responses are obtained even in excised, bloodless preparations so we must assume the existence of fibers leading to both excitatory and inhibitory nerve endings.

### Visceral Reflexes

While studying the effects of electrical stimulation of autonomic nerves it is well to bear in mind the fact that nerves were not developed for the purpose of being artificially stimulated. Under normal circumstances the autonomic nerves serve only reflex functions and when aroused normally through their reflex connections they may produce effects quite different from those seen on electrical stimulation. Normal reflex stimulation is selective, exciting only those fibers which will promote the function subserved by the reflex, whereas ordinary electrical stimulation excites all the fibers without regard to their normal function.

Certain gastrointestinal reflexes involving the peripheral autonomic nerves have already been mentioned; among these are the receptive relaxation of the stomach, the enterogastric reflex, and the so-called gastrocolic reflex. These reflexes chiefly involve the parasympathetic nerves and are concerned with regulation of the normal functioning of the gastrointestinal smooth muscle. Other reflexes have been described which occur only under unusual circumstances and generally involve the functioning of the sympathetic nerve supply. One of these is the *intestino-intestinal inhibitory reflex*. This consists of reflex inhibition of the whole intestinal tract as a result of distention of some one segment. The stomach may also be inhibited but in this case we are dealing with a mechanism different from the enetrogastric reflex previously mentioned. The reflex is abolished or greatly diminished when the splanchnic nerves are cut, hence it involves discharge of impulses over the sympathetic nerves. It probably belongs in the category of responses to noxious stimuli which, generally throughout the body, tend to cause increased activity of the sympathetic nervous system and to inhibit gastrointestinal motility. Other examples of reflex responses to noxious stimuli are inhibition of the intestine due irritation of the peritonium, distention of the gallbladder and bile ducts, overfilling of the bladder, or forcible stretching of the anal sphincters. All of these stimuli produce inhibition of the gastrointestinal smooth muscle through activation of adrenergic mechanisms, mainly the sympathetic nerves.

### REFERENCES

ALVAREZ, W. C. The metabolic gradient underlying peristalsis. J. A. M. A., 1919, 73, 1483. (Also, series of papers by Alvarez and by Alvarez and Starkweather in Am. J. Physiol., from 1915, vol. 37 to 1919, vol. 50.)

ALVAREZ, W. C. AND HOSOI, K. A gradient of irritability in the small intestine. Am. J. Physiol., 1929, 89, 182, 187; 1918, 45, 342; 1918, 46, 186; 1918, 47, 293.

ALVAREZ, W. C. AND MAHONEY, L. J. The myogenic nature of the rhythmic contractions of the intestine. Am. J. Physiol., 1922, 59, 421.

AMBACHE, N. Electrical activity of isolated mammalian intestine. J. Physiol., 1947, 106, 139.

AUER, J. AND KREUGER, H. Experimental study of antiperistaltic and peristaltic motor and inhibitory phenomena. Am. J. Physiol., 1947, 148, 350.

BARCLAY, A. E. The normal stomach. Lancet, 1922, **2**, 261.

BARCROFT, J. AND STEGGERDA, F. R. Observations on the proximal portion of the exteriorized colon. J. Physiol., 1932, **76**, 460.

BAYLISS, W. M. AND STARLING, E. H. The movements and innervation of the small intestine. J. Physiol., 1899, **24**, 99.

BAYLISS, W. M. AND STARLING, E. H. The movements and innervation of the large intestine. J. Physiol., 1901, **26**, 107.

BOZLER, E. Reflex peristalsis of the intestine. Am. J. Physiol., 1949, **157**, 338; 1945, **144**, 693; 1942, **136**, 543, 553; 1939, 127, 301; 1938, 124, 502.

CANNON, W. B. The movements of the intestine studied by means of röntgen rays. Am. J. Physiol., 1902, **6**, 251.

CANNON, W. B. Peristalsis, segmentation and the myenteric reflex. Am. J. Physiol., 1912, **30**, 114.

CANNON, W. B. AND MURPHY, F. T. The movements of the stomach and intestines in some surgical conditions. Ann. Surg., 1906, **43**, 512.

CARLSON, A. J., BOYD, T. E. AND PEARCY, J. F. Studies on the visceral sensory nervous system. Arch. Int. Med., 1922, 30, 409. Am. J. Physiol., 61, 14.

CODE, C. F., WILKINSON, G. R. AND SAUER, W. G. Normal and some abnormal colonic motor patterns in man. Ann. New York Acad. Sc., 1954, **58**, 317.

DOUGLAS, D. M. The decrease in frequency of contraction of the jejunum after transplantation to the ileum. Am. J. Physiol., 1949, **110**, 66.

DOUGLAS, D. M. AND MANN, F. C. The gastro-ileac reflex: Further experimental observations. Am. J. Digest. Dis., 1940, **7**, 53.

DRAGSTEDT, L. R. AND ELLIS, J. C. The fatal effect of total loss of gastric juice. Am. J. Physiol., 1930, **93**, 407.

ELLIOTT T. R. AND BARCLAY-SMITH, E. Antiperistalsis and other muscular activities of the colon. J. Physiol., 1904, **31**, 272.

EXNER, A. Wie schützt sich der Verdauungstract von Verletzungen durch spitze Fremdkörper. Arch. ges. Physiol., 1902, **89**, 253.

FINE, J., HARWITZ, A. AND MARK, J. A clinical study of the plasma volume in acute intestinal obstruction. Ann. Surg., 1940, **112**, 546.

FRIEDMAN, M. H. F. AND SNAPE, W. J. Color changes in the mucosa of the colon of children as affected by food and psychic stimuli. Fed. Proc., 1946, 5 (**part** 1), 30.

GAMBLE, J. L. AND ROSS, S. G. The factors in the dehydration following pyloric obstruction. J. Clin. Invest., 1924, **1**, 403.

GASSER, H. S. Plexus-free preparations of the small intestine; a study of their rhythmicity and their response to drugs. J. Pharm. & Exper. Therap., 1926, **27**, 395.

GRACE, WM. J., WOLF, S. G. AND WOLFF, H. G. Influence of emotions and feeling states on the behavior of the human colon. Am. J. Physiol., 1948, **155**, 439.

GUNN, J. A. AND UNDERHILL, S. W. F. Experiments on surviving mammalian intestine. Quart. J. Physiol., 1914, **8**, 275.

HADEN, R. L. AND ORR, T. G. The effect of sodium chloride on the chemical changes in the blood of the dog after pyloric and intestine obstruction. J. Exper. Med., 1923, **38**, 55; also Arch. Surg., 1925, **11**, 859.

HARTWELL, J. A. AND HOUGET, J. P. Experimental intestinal obstruction in dogs with especial reference to the cause of death and the treatment by large amounts of normal saline solution. J. A. M. A., 1912, **59**, 82.

HASTINGS, A. B., MURRAY, C. D. AND MURRAY, H. A. JR. Certain chemical changes in the blood after pyloric obstruction in dogs. J. Biol. Chem., 1921, **46**, 223.

HERRIN R. C. AND MEEK, W. J. Distention as a factor in intestinal obstruction. Arch. Int. Med., 1933, **51**, 152.

HERTZ, A. F. AND NEWTON, A. The normal movements of the colon in man. J. Physiol., 1913, **47**, 54, 57.

HOLZKNECHT, G. Die normale Peristaltik des Kolon. München. med. Wchnschr. 1909, **56**: 3401.

HOUCKGEEST, v. B. Untersuchungungen über Peristaltik des Magens und Darmkanals. Arch. ges. Physiol., 1872, **6**, 266.

HURST, A. F. The passage of food along the alimentary canal. Guy's Hosp. Rep., 1907, **61**, 389.

KING, C. E. AND ARNOLD, L. The activities of the intestinal mucosal motor mechanism. Am. J. Physiol., 1922, **59**, 97.

KING, C. E., ARNOLD, L. AND CHURCH, J. G. The physiological role of the intestinal mucosal movements. Am. J. Physiol., 1922, **61**, 80.

KOESSLER, K. K. AND HANKE, M. T. The intestinal absorption and detoxication of histamine in the mammalin organism. J. Biol. Chem., 1924, **59**, 889.

VON KOKAS, E. AND VON LUDANY, G. Relation between villikinine and the absorption of glucose from the intestine. Quart. J. Exper. Physiol., 1938, **28**, 15. (See also Arch. ges. Physiol., 1933, **232**, 293.

KUNTZ, A. On the occurrence of reflex arcs in the myenteric and submucous plexuses Anat. Rec., 1922, **23**, 193.

KUNTZ, A. AND THOMAS, J. E. On the nature of the rhythmic contractions in the stomach and intestine. Proc. Soc. Exper. Biol. & Med. 1923, **20**, 256.

MAGNUS, R. Die Beziehungen des Darmnervensystems zur automatischen Darmbewegung. Arch. ges. Physiol., 1904, **102**, 349.

MARKOWITZ, J. AND CAMPBELL, W. R. The relief of experimental ileus by spinal anesthesia. Am. J. Physiol., 1927, **81**, 101.

MEAKINS, J. AND HARINGTON, C. R. The relation of histamine to intestinal intoxication. I. The presence of histamine in the human intestine. J. Pharmacol. & Exper. Therap., 1921, **18**, 455; 1922, **20**, 45.

MELTZER, S. J. AND AUER, J. Peristaltic rush. Am. J. Physiol., 1907, **20**, 259.

MILLER, T. G. AND ABBOTT, W. O. Intestinal intubation, a practical technique. Am. J. M. Sc., 1934, **187**, 595.

MILTON, G. W. AND SMITH, A. W. M. The pacemaking area of the duodenum. J. Physiol., 1956, **132**, 100. (See also Quart. J. Exper. Physiol., 1955, **40**, 79.)

POGRUND, R. S. AND STEGGERDA, F. R. Influence of gaseous transfer between the colon and bloodstream on percentage gas composition of intestinal flatus in man. Am. J. Physiol., 1948, **153**, 475.

TAYLOR, N. B., WELD, C. B. AND HARRISON, K. Experimental intestinal obstruction. Canad. M. A. J., 1933, **29**, 227.

TEMPLETON, R. D. AND LAWSON, H. Studies on the motor activity of the large intestine. I. Normal motility in the dog recorded by the tandem balloon method. Am. J. Physiol., 1931, **96**, 667.

THOMAS, J. E. The gradient theory versus the reflex theory of intestinal peristalsis. Am. J. Gastroenterology, 1955, **23**, 13.

THOMAS, J. E. AND WHEELON, H. The nervous control of the pyloric sphincter. J. Lab. & Clin. Med., 1922, **7**, 375.

VAN ESVELD, L. W. Verhalten von plexushaltigen und plexusfreien Darm-muskelpräparaten. Arch. exper. Path. u. Pharmakol., 1928, **134**, 347.

WEISS, S., ROBB, G. P. AND ELLIS, L. B. The systemic effects of histamine in man. Arch. Int. Med., 1932, **49**, 360.

WHIPPLE, G. H. AND ASSOCIATES. Bull. Johns Hopkins Hosp., 1912, **23**, 159. J. Exper. Med., 1913, **17**, 286, 307; 1914, **19**, 144; 1916, **23**, 123. Contributions to medical and biological research, dedicated to Sir William Osler. Hoeber, New York, 1919.

### Monographs and Reviews

ALVAREZ, W. C. Intestinal autointoxication. Physiol. Rev., 1924, **4**, 352.

ALVAREZ, W. C. An introduction to gastroenterology, 3rd ed. Hoeber, N. Y., 1940.

AMBROSE, A. M. AND SHERWIN, C. P. Detoxication mechanisms. Ann. Rev. Biochem., 1933, **2**, 377.

BARCLAY, A. E. The digestive tract. Cambridge University Press, London, 1933.

BAUMGARTNER, C. J. Survey of intestinal obstruction. Arch. Surg., 1947, **55**, 607.

CANTAROW, A. AND SCHEPARTZ, B. Biochemistry, p. 276. W. B. Saunders Co., Philadelphia, 1954.

CODE, C. F. AND ASSOCIATES. Motility of the alimentary canal in man. Am. J. Med., 1952, **13**, 75.

GARRY, R. C. The movements of the large intestine. Physiol. Rev., 1934, **14**, 103.

GASK, G. E. AND ROSS, J. P. The surgery of the sympathetic nervous system. William Wood, Baltimore, 1934.

HANDLER, P. AND PERLZWEIG, W. A. Detoxication mechanisms. Ann. Rev. Biochem., 1945, **16**, 617.

HERTER, C. A. Bacterial infections of the digestive tract. Macmillan, N. Y., 1907.

HURST, A. F. Constipation and allied intestinal disorders. H. Frowde, London, 1909.

KUNTZ, A. The Autonomic nervous system, 4th ed. Lea and Febiger, Philadelphia, 1953.

LANE, W. A. The operative treatment of chronic intestinal stasis. Ed. 4. Oxford University Press, London, 1918.

LANGLEY, J. N. The Autonomic nervous system. Cambridge University Press, London, 1921.

LUDWIG, C. Lehrbuch der Physiologie des Menschen, vol. 2, p. 615. Wintersche, Leipzig u. Heidelberg. 1861.

MAGGEE, H. E. The role of the small intestine in nutrition. Physiol. Rev., 1930, **10**, 473.

METCHNIKOFF, E. The prolongation of life; optimistic studies. The English translation. Ed. by Chalmers Mitchell, W. Hinemann, London, 1907.

THOMAS, J. E. Digestion and the nervous system. A review of the literature. Am. J. Digest. Dis., **6**, 201, 1943.

TODD, T. W. Behaviour patterns in alimentary canal. The Williams & Wilkins Co., Baltimore, 1930.

VAN LIERE, E. J. The effect of anoxia on the alimentary tract. Physiol. Rev., 1941, **21**, 307.

VERZAR, F. AND McDOUGALL, E. J. Absorption from the intestine. Longmans, Green & Co., London, 1936.

# *43*

# VISCERAL SENSATIONS

## True and Referred Pain

The abdominal and thoracic viscera are insensitive to the several types of stimuli which readily arouse sensations in the skin and more superficial tissues of the body. The effects of the different varieties of stimulus—*thermal, chemical, tactile* and *pain*—have been investigated by a large number of observers.

Sensations of pain cannot be elicited from the viscera by the *usual means*. The intestine or the liver, the stomach or the heart may be cut, burned or pinched without arousing any immediate sensation. In the second stage of a colostomy operation, for example, the colon can be opened without pain being experienced by the patient. Harvey remarked upon the absence of sensation in the exposed heart of Viscount Montgomery.[1]

The insensibility of the alimentary tract to ordinary forms of stimulation commences in the lower or middle third of the esophagus and extends as far as the commencement of the anal canal. How can these observations be reconciled with the well known fact that pain is one of the commonest manifestations of visceral disease?

The whole subject of pain arising in or referred from the viscera is still highly controversial. No final answer can be given. The most that can be attempted is a summary of some of the more significant experimental results and clinical observations, the opinions of those who have especially interested themselves in the subject.

Lennander considered that abdominal pain was always due to the stimulation of somatic nerve terminals in the parietal peritoneum or root of the mesentery; the bowel itself was supposed to be quite devoid of pain fibers. According to this view

[1] Harvey records, "I carried the young man to the King (Charles I) that His Majesty might with his own eyes behold this wonderful case; that, in a man alive and well, he might, without detriment to the individual, observe the movement of the heart, and with his proper hand even touch the ventricles as they contracted. And His Most Excellent Majesty, as well as myself, acknowledged that the heart was without the sense of touch; for the youth never knew when we touched his heart. . . ."

therefore, pain localized within the organ itself—*true visceral pain*—was an impossibility.

Ross's theory postulated that pain from the abdominal viscera was of two types: (a) *referred (somatic) pain*, and (b) *true visceral* or *splanchnic pain*, which was diffuse, poorly localized but felt in the viscus itself.

Mackenzie, as a result of his clinical observations, strongly supported Ross's idea of referred pain, but maintained that *all* visceral pain was of this nature, the viscera being quite insensitive to all forms of stimulation. In agreement with Lennander, he did not believe that the viscera contained pain fibers; true visceral pain, i.e., pain in the organ itself, was therefore never experienced.

### CONCEPTION OF REFERRED PAIN ACCORDING TO ROSS AND MACKENZIE

When a viscus is diseased, pain or tenderness is frequently felt in the tissues overlying it approximately (abdominal or chest wall) or in some part quite remote from it. For example, pain is felt in the neck or shoulder (fig. 43.1) in conditions affecting the diaphragm, between the scapulas in gastric disease, in the region of the umbilicus in appendicitis, in the testis in renal colic and in the sternal region, or down the left arm in angina pectoris (ch. 28). When traction is made upon a coronary artery of a dog, the animal whines and indicates the location of the pain by limping on the left forepaw. In dextrocardia anginal pain is felt in the right arm. Other examples are, the pain in the perineum and tip of the penis caused by a stone in the region of the neck of the bladder, and the pain in the groin due to a stone in the ureter.

It will be recalled (ch. 65) that a given spinal segment supplies a visceral area with autonomic nerve fibers (afferent and efferent) and also a well delineated area of the skin (dermatone) with somatic nerves. The two types of structure linked in this way through the afferent nerves and the central nervous system may be some distance apart (e.g., diaphragm and shoulder) or be more closely related (e.g., area of abdominal wall and

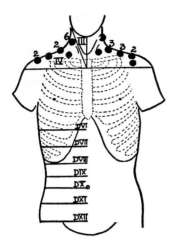

FIG. 43.1. Location of maximum points of referred neck pain from irritation of the diaphragm. The figures refer to the number of stimulations in each instance. They are all situated in the region supplied by the third and fourth spinal segments. (After Capps.)

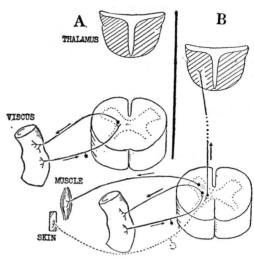

FIG. 43.2. Diagram to illustrate Mackenzie's theory of referred pain. A, representing normal conditions, a visceral reflex is shown. B, illustrates a visceromotor and a viscerosensory reflex. Impulses from a viscus are conceived as setting up an irritable focus in the cord which through the involvement of neighboring neurons increases the tone of muscles innervated by the same segment, and causes a discharge of impulses over the pathway for pain. The sensation is then projected in consciousness to the periphery, as indicated by the dotted line.

an underlying abdominal viscus). Mackenzie believed that afferent autonomic impulses arising in a diseased organ, although of themselves incapable of arousing any sensation, would upon entering the spinal cord set up an "irritable focus" with the result that cells accustomed to receive impulses from the corresponding somatic area were excited. Thus, the impulses from the viscera spread, or "irradiated," on to cells of the corresponding somatic center. New impulses originating in these cells travelled along the usual paths to higher perceptive centers (thalamus) which projected or referred the sensation to the somatic area, e.g., skin or muscle, from which it was accustomed to receive impulses. In this way, *spontaneous pain* in superficial structures remote from the diseased site was accounted for. Mackenzie spoke of these reactions as *viscerosensory "reflexes."* [2] *Tenderness* to touch, pressure or light pinching of the skin (hyperesthesia and hyperalgesia) was ascribed to the impulses, which ordinarily would be below the threshold for pain, arriving in the segment rendered hyperexcitable as a result of impulses received from the diseased organ. In the case of the abdominal viscera, Mackenzie claimed that the area of tenderness in the abdominal wall remained fixed, although the position of the diseased organ changed, thus indicating the referred nature of the pain. He explained the rigidity (hypertonus) of muscles overlying a diseased organ, the right rectus abdominis

[2] This is obviously a most unsuitable term for it is not a reflex in the ordinary accepted sense of that word.

in acute appendicitis, for example, upon a similar basis. Afferent impulses of normal intensity arising in the muscle proprioceptors upon arriving at the spinal centers, which had been rendered hyperexcitable by the receipt of abnormal visceral impulses, resulted in a reflex increase in tonus of the corresponding muscles. The referred motor reaction he spoke of as a *visceromotor reflex* (see fig. 43.2).

The conception of referred pain was supported by the work of Head, who mapped out the segmental distribution of the cutaneous nerves responsible for hyperalgesia in diseased states, and showed that they came from the same segments as received autonomic fibers from the diseased organ.

In table 43.1 are given the segmental areas to which pain is referred in disease of various viscera (Head).

### TRUE VISCERAL (SPLANCHNIC) PAIN

True visceral pain, although denied by Mackenzie, exists. The pains of dysmenorrhea or childbirth, for example, or the pain of intestinal colic, or of an overdistended bladder, or the substernal pain of coronary occlusion, although diffuse, seems to arise in the organ itself, even when referred as well, to a somatic structure, such

TABLE 43.1*

| Viscus | Spinal Segments |
|---|---|
| Lungs............. | 1–7 dorsal, mostly 2–5 dorsal |
| Heart............. | 3–5 cervical, 1–8 dorsal, predominantly on left side, sometimes bilateral |
| Esophagus....... | Mainly 5 dorsal, also 6, 7 and 8 dorsal |
| Breast........... | 4 and 5 dorsal |
| Stomach......... | 7, 8 and 9 dorsal, usually bilateral |
| Intestine........ | 9–12 dorsal, bilateral or on left side only |
| Liver............ | 8–10 dorsal on right side |
| Gall Bladder..... | Mostly 8 and 9 dorsal, also 5–7 |
| Kidney.......... | Mostly 10 dorsal, also 11 and 12 dorsal and 1 lumbar |
| Ureter........... | 11 and 12 dorsal and 1 lumbar |
| Testis........... | 10 dorsal |
| Epididymis...... | 11 and 12 dorsal |
| Bladder.......... | 11 and 12 dorsal and 1 lumbar, also 3 and 4 sacral |
| Prostate......... | 10 and 11 dorsal, also 1–3 and 5 sacral |
| Ovary........... | 10 dorsal |
| Fallopian tubes.. | 11 and 12 dorsal |
| Uterine cervix... | 11 and 12 dorsal and 1–4 sacral |
| Uterine body..... | 10 dorsal to 1 lumbar |

* From W. R. Brain, Diseases of the Nervous System, after Head.

as muscle or skin. Kinsella observed that, in conscious patients, pressure with the fingers upon an inflamed appendix caused pain centered in the viscus: a healthy appendix is insensitive. He and others have also shown that a chronic duodenal ulcer is also tender to direct contact. In transsection of the cord at the third thoracic vertebra in a patient (reported upon by Kinsella) in whom there was complete paralysis and anesthesia of the abdominal wall, intestinal pain was experienced, which obviously could not be caused by reference to somatic nerves. Impulses in such cases must reach the central nervous system along intact visceral afferents. They travel apparently by sympathetic fibers which enter the cord above the level of the transection. It is unlikely that they are transmitted by the vagus.

Pain in a normal viscus may also result from disease in a distant organ through a visceromotor reflex. Painful pylorospasm, for example, may accompany disease of the appendix. A distinction should be drawn between pain of this nature and referred pain.

## The Adequate Stimulus for True Visceral Pain

The existence of true visceral pain is not incompatible with the statement made above that the viscera are insensitive to the ordinary types of stimulus. From his investigations Hurst concluded that the only adequate stimulus for visceral pain fibers is tension. Distention of a hollow viscus, e.g., stomach, intestine, gallbladder, etc., gives rise to pain as a result of the stretch stimulus applied to the nerve terminals in its wall. The pain is roughly localized to the viscus itself, or referred. Under certain circumstances chemical substances produced in an ischemic organ, as in angina pectoris or intermittent claudication, may stimulate nerve fibers subserving pain.

Although the question is by no means settled, it appears that *contraction* of the muscular wall of a hollow viscus, such as the intestine, does not cause pain unless the movement of the bowel makes traction upon the mesentery. Pain arises, however, if the contraction causes distention of a neighboring portion of the wall as may result when the contraction wave approaches a mechanical obstruction, a length of bowel in spasm or a sphincter which fails to relax (*achalasia*). Poulton, for example, found that when a balloon was inserted into the lower part of the human esophagus, the approach of a peristaltic wave toward the obstruction caused pain, but during its passage over the esophageal wall in contact with the balloon no sensation was felt. Poulton ascribes the absence of pain during the passage of the contraction wave to the reduction in the diameter of the tube and the consequent release from stretch of the nerve endings lying between the muscle fibers. Pain was also relieved if the esophageal muscle relaxed to accommodate the balloon; that is, adjusted the length of its fibers to the distending force (see p. 695). As further evidence for the effectiveness of distention in causing pain, the following observations may be cited. In animals, when an intestinal loop exposed under local anesthesia is stimulated to powerful contraction, there is no evidence of pain, whereas even moderate distention of the loop (as by inflating it with a balloon) is manifestly painful. Distention of the gall-bladder of the cat is accompanied by reactions indicative of intense pain. Distention of the human appendix by the injection of fluids through an appendicostomy opening causes severe pain in the epigastrium or in the region of the umbilicus, and when the duodenum is distended by the injection of material through a duodenal tube, pain is felt on the

right side. The pain impulses undoubtedly reach
the central nervous system through the splanchnic nerves. Bentley and Smithwick distended the
duodenum of patients whose splanchnics had been
divided on one or on both sides. After unilateral
denervation, distention caused pain on the unoperated side only; no pain whatever was felt
after bilateral splanchnic section.

## MORLEY'S THEORY OF THE PARIETAL ORIGIN OF REFERRED ABDOMINAL PAIN

Morley contends that the referred pain of abdominal disease does *not involve visceral afferents* (as postulated by Mackenzie) but is due
to the stimulation of *somatic* pain fibers in the
parietal peritoneum or mesentery, the sensation
being referred to the superficial area innervated
from the same spinal segment. He expresses what
he terms the *law of referred pain* in the following
words. *Referred pain only arises from irritation of
nerves which are sensitive to those stimuli that produce pain when applied to the surface of the body,*
that is, by the stimulation of somatic sensory
nerves. He believes that the somatic innervation
of the peritoneum extends along the mesentery
to within a short distance of its attachment to
the bowel and does not terminate as has been
generally supposed near the root of the mesentery.[3] The mesentery or peritoneum is therefore
sensitive to tearing, cutting, etc., whereas the
organ itself which contains only visceral afferents is insensitive to these types of stimulus.
In support of his views Morley cites the pain in
the shoulder associated with irritation of the peritoneal covering of the diaphragm. He points out
that the diaphragm is innervated (through the
phrenic) chiefly by the fourth cervical spinal segment and to a less extent by the third and fifth.
None of these segments gives rise to autonomic
fibers but the third and fourth cervical nerves
furnish somatic afferent fibers to the shoulder
area in which the referred pain of diaphragmatic
disease is located. Morley explains muscular
rigidity in a similar manner—the radiation of
impulses over the motor nerves. He replaces

[3] Sheehan has made a study of the nerves of the
mesentery and finds the following types of fiber:
(a) Fibers ending in Pacinian corpuscles scattered
throughout the mesentery. These are afferent
sympathetic fibers which travel in the splanchnic
nerves. (b) Free nonmyelinated fibers. These are
afferent and efferent sympathetic fibers; their
terminals are distributed to the serous covering
of the bowel. They provide a medium for the transmission of true visceral pain. (c) Free myelinated
fibers derived presumably from somatic nerves.
These apparently do not extend as far as the serous
covering of the bowel itself.

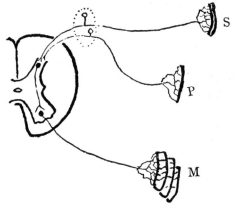

FIG. 43.3. Diagram to illustrate Morley's theory of peritoneocutaneous radiation and peritoneomuscular reflex; M, muscle; P, peritoneum; S,
skin. After Morley, redrawn.

Mackenzie's terms, viscerosensory and visceromotor reflexes by *peritoneocutaneous radiation*
and *peritoneomuscular reflex* respectively. Morley
also recognizes spontaneous, true (unreferred)
visceral pain, resulting from an adequate stimulus
—namely, tension. The pain and tenderness that
result from pressure upon an inflamed viscus (e.g.,
ulcer of the duodenum) through the abdominal
wall, and that seems to arise in the organ itself,
he ascribes, however, to the parietal peritoneum
being brought into contact with the roughened
surface of the lesion. As evidence that the sensation is not, in such instances, referred to the skin
from the diseased structure, but is due to the
stimulation of nerves in the parietal peritoneum
he states that (a) the area of tenderness shifted
with the movement of the viscus, and (b) direct
pressure upon the inflamed organ when exposed
by operation in a conscious patient (i.e., under
local anesthesia) did not give rise to any sensation
(see fig. 43.3).

Morley has made out a case for the production
of pain in some instances through a peritoneocutaneous reaction, and for pain and tenderness
upon pressure being the result of the stimulation
of somatic nerves in the parietal peritoneum.
But his views cannot be accepted in their entirety. Others have reported that a duodenal
ulcer is tender to direct touch, and there is no
doubt that referred pain can be brought about
through the mediation of either visceral or somatic nerves. Woollard and Carmichael, for example, have obtained evidence for the latter from
experiments upon the human testis which, since
it has migrated from the abdominal cavity and
is enveloped by peritoneum, may be looked upon
as an abdominal organ, in so far as the question

of referred pain is concerned. These observers found that after all the nerves to the testis had been blocked by means of novocaine, except the autonomic fibers passing along the spermatic artery, no sensation was felt within the organ when it was compressed; but pain, referred to the tenth dorsal segment—lower abdomen and back —was experienced. The observation of Bentley and Smithwick, mentioned above, point in the same direction.

## The Views of Lewis and Kelgren

Lewis and Kelgren postulate a common system of afferent nerves supplying deep somatic structures as well as the viscera. They maintain with good reason that since referred pain can follow the irritation of either visceral on somatic afferent nerves, there is no physiological justification for making a distinction between pain referred from a viscus and that referred from the parieties, nor between the motor reactions (e.g., muscular rigidity) resulting from stimulation in either situation. Although in the first instance visceral afferent fibers are stimulated, and in the second it is somatic sensory nerves, the impulses in either case enter the spinal cord by the posterior nerve roots, and the nerve fibers which transmit them have their cell stations in the posterior root ganglia, there is no indication that they do not follow identical paths in the central nervous system. Thus impulses from a viscus or a deep somatic structure cause a sensation which in either case is projected to a part remote from that stimulated but innervated by the same spinal segment. The pains whether referred from a viscus or from part of the soma, have common characteristics, being diffuse and poorly localized.

Lewis and Kellgren carried out experiments on a number of human subjects; their results are highly significant to the question of referred pain. Pain closely resembling in character the referred pain of visceral disease was induced by the injection of a small quantity (0.3 cc.) of hypertonic saline into an interspinous ligament at various spinous levels. Injection into the first lumbar interspinous ligament caused pain distributed in a manner strikingly similar to the pain of renal colic, namely, in the loin and in the inguinal and scrotal regions. The pain was accompanied by retraction of the testis. Injection into the ninth thoracic interspinous ligament caused pain in the back in the region of the first lumbar spine and over an area in front extending from the ninth costal cartilage on the affected side to the umbilicus. Rigidity of the abdominal muscles and deep tenderness were associated with the pain. Stimulation of the eighth

cervical ligament was followed by pain in the interscapular region, over the pectoralis major muscle and down the inner side of the elbow and forearm, together with a sensation of constriction in the upper part of the chest on the stimulated side. Several subjects of angina pectoris were chosen for experiment and were asked to compare the pain which they experienced in an attack with that caused by the stimulation of the seventh cervical or the first thoracic interspinous ligament. In all instances the patients described the experimentally induced pain as being identical in character with that caused by the disease, although it showed some minor differences in distribution.

Lewis and Kellgren also found that in cats mechanical stimulation (pinching) of the pancreas or of the mesentery in the duodenal loop caused motor reflexes from the abdominal muscles which resembled closely those caused by stimulation of the back muscles.

## An Explanation of Referred Pain on the Basis of Reflex Vasomotor Changes (Viscerosomatic Reflex) or the Liberation of a Chemical Substance at Somatic Nerve Endings

Pollock and Davis stimulated the peritoneal surface of the diaphragm in dogs. The animals showed every sign of suffering pain, which was abolished by any one of the following procedures. Section of the phrenic nerve; removal of the cervical sympathetic chains; severing the eighth cervical and the first, second and third thoracic anterior roots; transection of the cord at the seventh cervical segment; destroying the cord at the first and second dorsal segments; or section of the cervical posterior roots. Pollock and Davis conclude from these results that the pain impulses following stimulation of the diaphragm travel over the phrenic, enter the cord by the posterior cervical roots, descend the cord to the level of the eighth cervical and first, second and third thoracic segments. Connections are then made with cells in the lateral horn of gray matter (intermediolateral column) from where impulses pass by sympathetic preganglionic fibers to the cervical sympathetic chain, and then by postganglionic fibers "effectors in the skin, blood vessels, meninges and other structures, where by some vasomotor (?) or hormonal (?) process the sensory endings of the cerebrospinal system are stimulated and a sensory impulse travels over the ordinary cerebrospinal system, enters the spinal cord by the posterior roots and ascends to consciousness." The pain and cutaneous lesions of herpes zoster come to mind in this connection.

The diffuse character of deep pain in contrast to the accurate localization of cutaneous stimulation can be accounted for by (a) the existence of relatively few afferent fibers in deep structures, (b) the lack of experience and training in the localization of sensations from the viscera, since such are normally felt very infrequently, and (c) when impressions from the internal organs do occur their localization is not aided by sight as in the case of more superficial sensations. However, in experiments with intelligent subjects having some knowledge of anatomy, and in whom pain was evoked by inflating balloons inserted into hollow viscera, the subjects' sense of localization was much improved above the ordinary.

## The Sensibility of the Alimentary Tract to Tactile, Thermal and Chemical Stimulation

*Touch.* The sensation of touch disappears at the lower end of the pharynx. This was shown by Hurst by means of an esophageal tube with a slit on one side through which the mucosa of the esophagus could be stimulated. Carlson, by means of a test tube brush passed into the stomach, was unable to elicit the sensation of touch from the gastric mucosa. The rectum possesses no tactile sensibility but the anal canal is sensitive.

*Thermal sensibility.* The esophagus is sensitive to extremes of heat and cold. The sensations of temperature that are felt when hot or cold materials enter the stomach have been thought by some to originate in the lower end of the esophagus, by others to arise in the skin of the epigastrium, either through thermal conduction or by reflex changes in the cutaneous blood vessels. Carlson has shown, however, that the gastric mucosa is sensitive to extreme temperature changes, i.e., protopathic thermal sensibility (below 13°C. or above 45°C.). It is the lower end of the esophagus, however, which is responsible for the greater part of the thermal sensation that is experienced when excessively hot or cold materials are swallowed. This is due to the greater sensitivity of the esophageal mucosa, as well as to the fact that the material is retained for an appreciable length of time above the cardia. The colon is insensitive to temperature changes, but even comparatively slight differences in temperature can be detected in the anal canal.

*Chemicals,* with the exception of alcohol, cause no sensation whatever when introduced into the stomach or intestinal canal. The mucosa is completely insensitive to acids; the introduction into the healthy stomach of a solution of 0.5 per cent hydrochloric acid causes no pain or sensation of any kind. Alcohol stimulates the mucosa of the esophagus and stomach and causes a sensation of warmth. Peppermint and various condiments free from alcohol arouse no sensation. The pelvic colon and rectum show a similar sensitivity to alcohol but are insensitive to other chemicals. The anal canal is extremely sensitive especially to alcohol and glycerine. Both cause a burning sensation.

### Nausea

Nausea usually precedes the act of vomiting (p. 701) but may occur alone. On the other hand vomiting may occur without nausea, as in certain cerebral conditions. The sensation is felt in the back of the throat or pit of the stomach, and in its milder degrees is merely a "sinking" sensation in the epigastrium. It is frequently associated with vasomotor disturbances and sweating. Increased tension upon the walls of the stomach or duodenum is a potent cause of the sensation, and Poulton has shown that it is also induced by distention of the lower part of the esophagus. During the passage of a peristaltic wave which relieves the tension upon the nerve fibers in the esophageal walls the sensation is relieved. Barclay showed by radioscopy in the human subject that nauseous odors caused the lower border of the stomach to descend an inch or two evidently as a result of sudden relaxation of the abdominal muscles. This movement would tend to stretch the esophagus and gastric walls and so exert tension upon the nerve endings. The stimulus which induces nausea is, therefore, the same, apparently, as that which causes visceral pain, but of lower intensity. It is likely that the sensations experienced during changes in speed of an elevator are also the result of tension exerted upon the esophagus and gastric walls. This element is also probably a contributory factor in the production of seasickness, being brought into play by the pitch and roll of the ship.

The relief of nausea and vomiting by the application of counter irritants to the epigastrium or over the sternum is probably due to either a reflex change in the tone of the gastric walls or to the reflex initiation of peristaltic contractions. The tension upon the nerve endings in the latter instance is taken up by the muscle fibers. Poulton observed, for example, that the sensations caused by a balloon in the esophagus were relieved by vigorous friction of the skin over the sternum; contraction of the esophagus in some cases or adjustment of the postural tone of the esophageal wall in others were observed to accompany the disappearance of the sensation.

### Regulation of Food And Water Intake

The energy requirements of the body are met by the food that is consumed and absorbed. If an excess of food were consumed continually and there were no change in the energy expenditure there would be a consistent gain in weight. A shortage in the energy value of the food as-similated would result in a steady loss of weight. The fact that the average adult maintains a constant weight or gains or loses weight very slowly is sufficient evidence that a balance is usually maintained between the energy expended by the body and the energy content of the food that is assimilated. The precision of this adjustment can be appreciated when we realize that the addition of 500 mg. of dry food (less than one soda cracker) to each meal would cause an increase in weight over a 10-year-period of more than 10 pounds if there were no compensatory increase in energy expenditure. Of course some people do gain weight but it is believed that this is usually the result of some abnormality affecting the regulation of food intake.

The balance between food intake and energy output is maintained by regulating both the food intake and the output of energy. There is an immediate effect of the excess food through its specific dynamic action, which results in an increase in energy output. This however, is rarely sufficient to account for all the energy contained in the excess food eaten. If it were, there would never be a gain in weight. If an individual consumes a certain measured excess of food at each meal over a period of time he will gain weight steadily but the gain in weight will result in an increase in his basal metabolic rate which, if the excess food intake is not too great, will ultimately increase the metabolism to a point where the energy output will again equal the energy of the food, including the excess. In this way a new balance is established at a higher weight level. In addition, there is apparently another mechanism less well understood which, in some cases at least, balances the energy output against the food intake even when this is in excess. In experiments on dogs at the University of Illinois it was found that dogs that were maintaining a constant weight on the amount of food which they ate voluntarily could be given an excess over this amount through a gastric fistula amounting to 33 per cent of their voluntary food intake without either diminishing their voluntary food intake or causing a gain in weight (Share *et al.*, 1952). Evidently the animals had some means of metabolizing the excess food without increasing their total body mass. This suggests that there is some mechanism for adjusting the total body metabolism to the energy content of the food consumed, even though that is in excess of the need; however, we are here concerned with the other aspect

of the adjustment of food consumption to energy output, that is, the regulation of food intake.

There are several methods of demonstrating the fact that food intake is regulated in some manner so as to equal the energy requirements of the animal. Healthy animals when allowed all the food that they will eat will consume only as much as is necessary to meet their energy requirements and to maintain their weight, or their normal growth if they have not already attained their adult weight. If the caloric value of the food is increased, the amount consumed will be diminished so as to maintain a normal intake of food calories. If, on the other hand, the caloric value of the food is decreased by dilution with inert material ordinarily the animal will consume more food, up to the limit of its capacity, in order to maintain an adequate caloric intake. This mechanism may be tricked by human devices into permitting an excess food intake as in the experiments of Share and his coworkers, described above, but usually it works very well. Adjustment of food intake to energy expenditure is illustrated in figure 43.4.

## HUNGER AND APPETITE

Since eating is a voluntary act, regulation of food intake must be accomplished through conscious sensations which indicate either that food is needed or that enough food has been consumed. The sensations that cause food to be eaten are described as hunger and appetite. These terms have never been precisely defined in the scientific sense but in a general way we recognize that hunger is the sum of the sensations aroused by the physical need for food. Appetite on the other hand is a psychic or emotional desire to eat, and may or may not be associated with the need for food. Cessation of eating is also a voluntary act and is induced by a conscious sensation called satiety when a sufficiency of food has been eaten. The mechanisms of hunger and satiety are probably inborn and dependent on the inherent organization of the nervous system. Appetite, on the other hand, is acquired and is probably dependent upon pleasurable past experiences associated with eating. For example, an individual who is hungry will eat almost any wholesome food so long as it is reasonably palatable. When he has reached a state of satiety, however, he will eat only those foods which are particularly pleasing to him and with which he has had pleasant experiences in the past. Thus, because of hunger, one may eat a wholesome meal which is fully adequate for his needs and then because of ap-

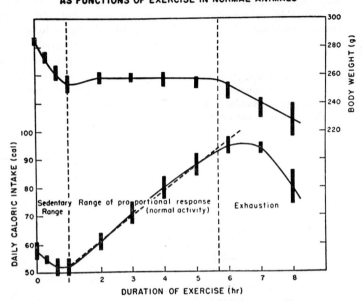

VOLUNTARY CALORIC INTAKE AND BODY WEIGHT
AS FUNCTIONS OF EXERCISE IN NORMAL ANIMALS

Fig. 43.4. Illustrating the effect of exercise of various durations on caloric intake and body weight of exercised rats. Three ranges can be distinguished: sedentary, normal activity and exhaustion. (From Mayer, 1955. Courtesy of New York Academy of Science.)

petite add to it a dessert which is entirely unnecessary so far as caloric requirements are concerned.

## THE NEURAL REGULATION OF FOOD INTAKE

It has long been known that persons suffering from tumors of the hypophysis have a tendency to become obese; the condition is known as Frölich's syndrome. In 1940 Hetherington and Ranson showed that a similar condition could be produced in animals by injury to the hypothalamus in the vicinity of the hypophysis. Later, Brobeck and others (1943), showed that the obesity was caused by injury to the ventromedial hypothalamic nucleus situated in the tuber cinerium. If this area is destroyed in rats, cats or monkeys, instead of being satisfied with an amount of food appropriate to its caloric requirements, the animal continues to eat as long as it is able to swallow food or as long as food is available, with the result that it becomes excessively obese. A little later, Anand and Brobeck (1951) found that injuries to the lateral hypothalamic nuclei just lateral to those involved in obesity would cause the animal to stop eating altogether. Animals with such injuries absolutely refused food even though they starved to death. If an animal with a medial hypothalamic injury and consequent hyperphagia (habitual overeating) was subjected to an injury to the lateral hypothala-

mus, such an animal not only recovered from its hyperphagia but refused absolutely to eat anything. From these observations it was concluded that the nuclei in the lateral area of the hypothalamus contain a "feeding center" and the medial hypothalamic nuclei contain a "satiety center." Since injury to the medial nuclei was effective only if the lateral nuclei were intact it was concluded that the medial satiety center acted by inhibiting the lateral feeding center.

It is interesting to note that the areas of the hypothalamus involved in the control of food intake have a much higher concentration of high energy phosphate compounds (adenosine triphosphate, creatine phosphate) in fasted animals than in animals recently fed; the increase in these compounds implies increased activity of these areas in hungry animals (Larsson, 1954). The medial hypothalamic areas, which are believed to inhibit the feeding centers in the lateral hypothalamus, exhibit increased electrical activity when drugs which reduce or abolish appetite, such as amphetamine, are given. It is believed that the increased electrical activity indicates stimulation of the medial nuclei and that these then inhibit the action of the feeding centers. It has been shown that electrical stimulation of the lateral hypothalamic nuclei by means of implanted electrodes produces hyperphagia (Brobeck *et al.*,

TABLE 43.2*

*Classification of feeding reflexes on a basis of initial sensory stimulus (left side) or behavior pattern induced (right side)*

| Sensory Basis | Behavior Basis |
|---|---|
| Visual reflexes | Reflexes of attention |
| Olfactory reflexes | Reflexes of approach |
| Auditory reflexes | Reflexes of examination |
| Tactile reflexes | Reflexes of incorporation |
| Gustatory reflexes | Reflexes of rejection |
| Enteroceptive reflexes | |

* From Brobeck, 1957.

1956) in rats, cats, mice, monkeys, goats and sheep. During period of stimulation the animals exhibit a compulsive desire to eat and if food is available will eat as much as it is possible for them to swallow (Larsson, 1954).

Brobeck (1957) has suggested that the areas of the hypothalamus that control food intake do so either by facilitating or inhibiting the reflex mechanisms involved in the acquisition and consumption of food; he calls these feeding reflexes. These he classifies in two ways: (a) according to the sensory mechanism arousing the reflex and (b) according to the nature of the response. The reflexes are listed in table 43.2. Probably the list could be extended if the mechanisms involved were better understood. The important point is that the hypothalamic centers do not control food intake directly but do so by making more or less responsive to stimuli the lower brain centers which control the reflexes governing the acquisition, consumption and assimilation of food.

### Peripheral Mechanisms

Consumption of food brings about consequences which induce satiety and stimulate the mechanisms that are inhibitory to the feeding reflexes; starvation, or the absence of food brings about consequences which excite hunger and stimulate the feeding centers. In spite of extensive study and even more widespread speculation the peripheral mechanisms which contribute to hunger and satiety are still not fully understood. Among the possible operating devices we can recognize gastrointestinal mechanisms and metabolic mechanisms. The gastrointestinal mechanisms are mainly of a physical nature whereas the metabolic mechanisms are chemical. The physical mechanisms are presumed to act through stimulation of sensory nerve endings, whereas, the chemical

mechanisms are supposed to act on some hypothetical sensory device within the central nervous system or connected with it through afferent nerves, although this is by no means certain.

Among the gastrointestinal stimuli which tend to increase food intake and to cause a sensation of hunger, are the so-called hunger contractions of the stomach and intestine (see Quigley, 1955). These have been described in detail in chapter 41. The fact that hunger contractions cause a sensation of hunger helps us little in the solution of our problem for we still do not know what causes the hunger contractions. Probably besides mere emptiness of the stomach and intestine they are excited by something in the metabolic category. Emptiness is not the whole answer because, although the stomach may be completely empty a few hours after a meal, hunger contractions become more intense and more distressing the longer the fast is continued. However, they cease at once when food is taken and before any metabolic changes have taken place, therefore, whatever their cause, they can be completely inhibited by the presence of food in the stomach and intestine.

It is known that hunger contractions can be induced, or made more intense if already present, by inducing a state of hypoglycemia through administration of insulin (Quigley et al., 1929, 1930). This brings about stimulation of medullary centers in which increased activity of the vagus centers is a prominent feature. If the vagus nerves are cut, insulin hypoglycemia does not stimulate hunger contractions (Quigley and Templeton, 1930); indeed it tends to inhibit them if they are already present. The hunger contractions induced by insulin evidently are due directly to an action of low blood sugar on the central nervous system. They can be inhibited by administration of glucose intravenously but the normally occurring changes in blood sugar level are in no way related to the presence or absence of gastric or intestinal hunger contractions (Quigley, 1955; Scott et al., 1938). Hyperglycemia may or may not inhibit hunger contractions; it obviously does not in diabetic subjects. In a majority of experiments on normal animals hyperglycemia induced by injecting glucose intravenously does not inhibit gastric hunger motility. It has been shown by Stunkard and Wolff (1956) that in those instances in which the hunger contractions were not inhibited by intravenous glucose that the injection of glucose did not cause a great rise in the arterial as compared to the venous glucose concentration. The arteriovenous glucose concentration difference is taken as an index of the rate of utilization of glucose by the tissues. On the other hand in those instances in which there was inhibition of hunger contractions there was an increase in arteriovenous glucose difference. Reference will be made to this fact a little later under the head of "Metabolic Factors."

Undoubtedly gastric hunger contractions contribute to the hunger state but they are by no means solely responsible for it. Enough human cases have been studied in which both splanchnic nerves were severed to establish the fact that this operation abolishes all sensation produced by contraction of the stomach during hunger. The contractions persist but they are no longer felt. However, individuals so operated upon do not experience any decrease in their desire for food and they have periods of hunger just as intense as before the splanchnic nerves were severed (Grossman and Stein, 1948). Cutting the vagus nerves abolishes the hunger contractions altogether for a time but by no means abolishes the sensation of hunger. On the contrary, as judged by the amount of food consumed, the hunger sensation is intensified by vagotomy (Volkmann, 1844). We may conclude that the hunger sensation arises not only in the stomach and intestine but elsewhere in the body also and that the gastrointestinal component is dispensable.

Sensations arising in the gastrointestinal tract which diminish or abolish food intake are somewhat better understood. The act of eating will in itself diminish hunger and appetite. For example, if an animal is prepared with an esophagostomy so that food that is eaten passes through the mouth and pharynx and upper esophagus but does not enter the stomach, the animal will eat more food than would a normal animal, but feeding ceases eventually. If an animal is given a measured amount of food before its regular mealtime it will reduce the amount of its voluntary food intake proportionately. If the prefeeding is carried out through a gastric fistula instead of by mouth the reduction in voluntary food intake is much less pronounced, indicating that the decrease in food intake was not all due to distention of the stomach but partly to the oropharyngeal stimulation of eating.

Distention of the stomach alone inhibits hunger and appetite. For example, if an animal is given a portion of its food a few minutes before regular feeding time through a gastric fistula and this practice is continued over a period of time, eventually the animal will come to reduce the size of its subsequent meal by an amount equal to an amount given through the gastric fistula, in other words the total size of the meal will be maintained constant (Janowitz and Hollander, 1955). This adjustment does not occur immediately and is never very precise, but it does show that gastric distention with food tends to reduce hunger and appetite. Similarly, if the stomach is partly filled with inert materials the size of the subsequent meal will be reduced. Inflation of a balloon in the stomach has the same effect (Janowitz and Grossman, 1949). That these effects are mechanical and not metabolic in nature is shown by the fact that if the artificial feeding, instead of being given immediately before the regular meal is given some 4 hours after and time allowed for it to be disposed of, the animal will eat a normal amount at the next regular meal, provided the artificial feeding was not too large. As much as one-third of the animal's regular food consumption can be given in this manner over a period of time without affecting his voluntary intake (Share *et al.*, 1952). The fact has already been referred to that animals so fed, although receiving 30 per cent or more in excess of their regular food intake do not necessarily gain weight. The effect of gastric distention on hunger and appetite is doubtless due to the presence in the stomach of stretch receptors (Paintal, 1954) situated in the muscular walls and connected to afferent fibers of the vagus nerves; section of the vagi does away with the effects of gastric distention on appetite. Indeed vagotomy produces a condition of hyperphagia comparable to that caused by lesions of the medial hypothalamic nuclei.

The effects of the gastrointestinal stimuli are largely confined to determining the size of an individual meal. They do not serve to regulate the over-all balance between energy intake as represented by the food and the energy output as represented by the total metabolism of the body. Presumably metabolic factors are responsible for this type of regulation but any discussion of such factors at the present time would be in the nature of speculation. We know certainly only that some metabolic consequences of the assimilation of food are not effective as regulatory factors. It has been shown, for example, that changes in blood sugar, at least those that are not associated with changes in arteriovenous glucose difference have no effect on voluntary food intake nor do they influence hunger contractions except those induced by insulin (Quigley and Hallaran, 1932). An increase in the amino acid concentration of the blood caused by intravenous injection of the amino acids has no effect upon voluntary food intake in dogs.

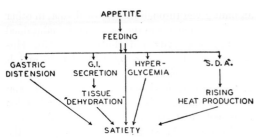

FIG. 43.5. Outline of mechanisms taking part in transition from appetite to satiety. (From Brobeck, 1957.)

However the slight increase in temperature which results from the presence of pyrogens in some intravenous solutions does definitely influence appetite, even though the rise in temperature is too small to be recognized clinically as a fever. This, and the fact that taking food causes a slight increase in temperature due to the specific dynamic action of the food has suggested to Brobeck (1957) the possibility that the increase in body temperature caused by the specific dynamic action of the food may be a factor limiting food intake (figure 43.5).

Mayer (1955) has suggested that food intake is controlled in some way through the metabolism of glucose, the so-called glucostatic hypothesis. Recognizing the fact that hunger and appetite are not related to changes in blood sugar level Mayer contends that they are governed by the utilization of carbohydrate food by the tissues. To quote from a recent article (1955) "According to the glucostatic theory the mechanism postulated for the short term regulation of energy intake rests on the concept that somewhere, possibly in the hypothalamic centers shown to be implicated in the regulation of food intake, perhaps peripherally as well, there are glucoreceptors sensitive to blood glucose in the measure that they can utilize it." In other words, when the tissues are rapidly utilizing glucose, thus establishing a high arteriovenous glucose difference, the glucoreceptors are stimulated and through their central connections suppress hunger and appetite and inhibit food intake. On the other hand, when glucose is not available for tissue utilization and the arteriovenous glucose difference tends toward zero, a state corresponding to tissue hunger exists and this is in some way sensed by the hypothalamic centers which then facilitate the feeding reflexes.

Another theory suggests that the total energy stores of the body are maintained at a certain predetermined level by the balance between hunger and satiety. Whatever the mechanism may be, it is evident that metabolic factors are important and quite possibly play a determining role in the regulation of the balance between food intake and energy output in the body.

### THIRST

The sensation of thirst is referred to the pharynx and is due to the stimulation of sensory nerve endings in this situation. Two theories have been advanced to explain the mechanism by which the sensation is aroused.

According to one view, thirst is due simply to the drying of the pharyngeal mucous membrane, the salivary glands being given a role in the regulation of the water balance of the body. When the water content of the body falls below a certain level salivary secretion is depressed, the consequent drying of the mucous membrane of the throat then elicits the characteristic sensation. If such a view is correct, drying of the pharyngeal mucosa from whatever cause should cause thirst. Cannon, who provided the principal support for this theory, found in studies upon himself that after abstinence from fluids for a time the depression of salivary secretion which resulted was definitely associated with thirst. Atropine, which inhibits salivary secretion, also produced the typical sensation, and thirst aroused by the deprivation of water was relieved by the application of cocaine to the mucosa. Pilocarpine or acid substances which stimulate the flow of saliva also relieve thirst. In dogs, however, atropine and pilocarpine are without effect upon the water intake.

According to the other view, thirst is a sensation resulting from changes in blood composition, probably due to a rise in its osmotic pressure, which stimulates the afferent nerve endings; or acts perhaps upon central nervous structures. Rowntree and his associates, for example, found that the thirst of diabetes insipidus was relieved neither by cocainization of the mucous membrane nor when salivation was induced by pilocarpine. The experiments of Gilman suggest that cellular dehydration rather than a rise in osmotic pressure is the prime factor in arousing thirst. Elevation of the osmotic pressure of the blood of dogs by the injection of a hypertonic salt solution, and the imbalance thus caused in the osmotic relationship between intra- and extracellular fluids, caused a much greater intake of water than an equivalent rise in osmotic pressure resulting from the administration of urea. After the injection of salt, sufficient water was drunk to quickly reduce the osmotic pressure of the blood, whereas after urea, to which the cells are readily permeable, and which, therefore, did not disturb the osmotic relationships, the water intake was but little increased and the osmotic pressure of the blood remained elevated. In support of the view that a lowered water content of the cells is the true thirst stimulus, Gilman cites an experiment in which anhydremia was induced by the withdrawal of large quantities of extracellular electrolytes (e.g., NaCl) without the withdrawal of water. In such anhydremic animals dehydration of the tissue cells does not occur, and although the oral mucous membranes are quite dry there is no evidence of thirst—water is refused.

That the two theories are not incompatible is indicated by the work of Holmes and Gregerson (1947) who found that in human subjects following the intravenous injection of 300 ml of 5 per cent sodium chloride, although there was an increase in plasma volume there was a considerable decrease in salivary secretion associated with the sensation of thirst. This proves that the decrease in salivary secretion leading to a sensation of thirst may be caused by an increase in the osmotic pressure of the blood, and suggests that tissue dehydration may induce the sensation of thirst through the reduction in the flow of saliva.

The neural mechanisms for the regulation of water intake are similar to those for regulation of food intake. Indeed they are closely associated and have not as yet been clearly separated. Certain types of injuries to the lateral hypothalamus induce not only a cessation of food intake but also cessation of water intake. The animals die of dehydration unless given water by stomach tube (Greer, 1955; Morrison and Mayer, 1957). Greer found that stimulation of the dorsomedial nucleus in the cat caused violent drinking activity, thus there are probably centers for the regulation of water intake in the hypothalamus comparable to the feeding centers but these have not been so precisely localized; apparently they are very near to the feeding centers. Like the intake of food, the intake of water is influenced by gastric distention. Animals made thirsty by intravenous injection of hypertonic salt solution will usually drink an amount of water over a short period of time approximately equal to the amount necessary to dilute the injected salt to an isotonic concentration. If the stomach is distended by means of a water filled balloon, the amount of water that is voluntarily drunk will be diminished and the replacement of the water deficit delayed. The vagi play a part in the regulation of water intake. Vagotomized animals not only eat more food

but also drink more water than normal animals. The food intake and the water intake are increased proportionately by vagotomy; they are decreased by sympathectomy (Towbin, 1955).

Excessive thirst also occurs in lesions of the anterior hypophysis, leading to diabetes insipidus. In this disease there is failure of production of the antidiuretic hormone of the anterior hypophysis resulting in an excessive loss of water through the kidneys. In this case thirst is probably secondary to dehydration.

## REFERENCES

ANAND, B. K. AND BROBECK, J. R. Localization of a feeding center in the hypothalamus of the rat. Proc. Soc. Exper. Biol. & Med., 1951, 77, 323; Yale J. Biol. & Med., 1951, 24, 122.

BENTLEY, F. H. AND SMITHWICK, R. H. Visceral pain produced by balloon distention of jejunum. Lancet, 1940, 2, 389.

BROBECK, J. R. Neural regulation of food intake. Ann. New York Acad. Sc., 1955, 63, 44.

BROBECK, J. R., LARSSON, S. AND REYES, E. A study of the electrical activity of the hypothalamic feeding mechanism. J. Physiol., 1956, 132, 358.

BROBECK, J. R., TEPPERMAN, J. AND LONG, C. N. H. Experimental hypothalamic hyperphagia in the albino rat. Yale J. Biol. & Med., 1943, 15, 831.

CANNON, W. B. Proc. Roy. Soc., London, ser. B., 1917, 90, 283.

CARLSON, A. J. AND HOELZEL, F. Alleged disappearance of hunger during starvation. Science, 1952, 115, 526.

GILMAN, A. Relation between blood osmotic pressure, fluid distribution and voluntary water intake. Am. J. Physiol., 1937, 120, 323.

GREER, M. A. Suggestive evidence of a primary drinking center in the hypothalamus. Proc. Soc. Exper. Biol. & Med., 1955, 89, 59.

GREGERSEN, M. L. AND CANNON, W. B. Studies on regulation of water intake; effect of extirpation of salivary glands on water intake of dogs while panting. Am. J. Physiol., 1932, 102, 336.

GROSSMAN, M. I. Integration of current views on the regulation of hunger and appetite. Ann. New York Acad. Sc., 1955 63, 76.

GROSSMAN, M. I. AND STEIN, I. F. Vagotomy and the hunger producing action of insulin in man. J. Appl. Physiol., 1948, 1, 263.

HEAD H. On disturbances of sensation with especial reference to the pain of visceral disease. Brain, 1893, 16, 15; 1894, 17, 339; 1896, 19, 150.

HEATHERINGTON, A. W. AND RANSON, S. W. Hypothalamic lesions and adiposity in the rat. Anat. Rec., 1940, 78, 149.

HOLLANDER, F. Introduction (to conference on hunger and appetite). Ann. New York Acad. Sc., 1955, 63, 3.

HOLMES, J. H. AND GREGERSON, M. I. Relation of salivary flow to the thirst produced in man by intravenous injection of salt solution. Am. J. Physiol., 1947, 151, 252.

JANOWITZ, H. D. AND GROSSMAN, M. I. Some factors affecting food intake of normal dogs and dogs with esophagostomy and gastric fistula. Am. J. Physiol., 1949, **159**, 143.

JANOWITZ, H. D. AND HOLLANDER, F. The time factor in the adjustment of food intake to varied caloric requirements in the dog. A study of precision of appetite regulation. Ann. New York Acad. Sc., 1955, **63**, 56.

LARSSON, S. On the hypothalamic organization of the nervous mechanism regulating food intake. Acta physiol. scandinav. (suppl.), 1954, **115**, 1.

LEWIS, T. AND KELLGREN, J. H. Observations relating to referred pain, viscero-motor reflexes and other phenomena. Clin. Sc., 1939, **4**, 47.

MAYER, J. Regulation of energy intake and body weight. The glucostatic theory and the lipostatic hypothesis. Ann. New York Acad. Sc., 1955, **63**, 15.

MAYER, J. The physiological basis of obesity and leanness. Nutrition Abstr. & Rev., 1955, **25**, 597 and 871.

MONTGOMERY, M. F. Role of salivary glands in the thirst mechanism. Am. J. Physiol., 1931, **96**, 221; **98**, 35.

MORRISON, S. D. AND MAYER, J. Adipsia and aphagia in rats after lateral subthalamic lesions. Am. J. Physiol., 1957, **191**, 248; **193**, 230.

PAINTAL, A. S. A study of gastric stretch receptors. J. Physiol., 1954, **126**, 255.

PAYNE, W. W. AND POULTON, E. P. Experiments on visceral sensation relation of pain to activity in human esophagus. J. Physiol., 1937, **63**, 217.

POLLOCK, L. J. AND DAVIS, L. Visceral and referred pain. Arch. Neurol. and Psychiat., 1935, **34**, 1041.

POULTON, E. P. Oliver-Sharpey lectures on experimental study of certain visceral sensations. Lancet, 1928, II, **12**, 1223; J. Physiol., 1927, **63**, 217.

QUIGLEY, J. P. The role of the digestive tract in regulating the ingestion of food. Ann. New York Acad. Sc., 1955, **63**, 6.

QUIGLEY, J. P. AND HALLARAN, W. R. The independence of spontaneous gastro-intestinal motility and blood sugar levels. Am. J. Physiol., 1932, **100**, 102.

QUIGLEY, J. P., JOHNSON, V. AND SOLOMON, E. I. Action of insulin on the motility of the gastro-intestinal tract. I. Action on the stomach of normal and fasting man. Am. J. Physiol., 1929, **90**, 89.

QUIGLEY, J. P. AND SOLOMON, E. I. Action of insulin on the motility of the gastrointestinal tract. V. a. Action on the human duodenum. b. Action on the colon of dogs. Am. J. Physiol., 1930, **91**, 488.

QUIGLEY, J. P. AND TEMPLETON, R. D. Action of insulin on motility of the gastrointestinal tract. IV. Action on the stomach following double vagotomy. Am. J. Physiol., 1930, **91**, 482.

ROSS, J., 1887–1888. On the segmental distribution of sensory disorders. Brain, **10**, 333.

ROWNTREE, S. J., WEIR, J. F. AND LARSON, E. E. Studies in diabetes insipidus, water balance and water intoxication. Arch. Int. Med., 1922, **29**, 306.

RYLE, J. A. Visceral pain and referred pain. Lancet, 1926, **1**, 895.

SCOTT, W. W., SCOTT, C. C. AND LUCKHARDT, A. B. Observations on the blood sugar level before, during and after hunger periods in humans. Am. J. Physiol., 1938, **123**, 243.

SHARE, I., MARTYNIUK, E. AND GROSSMAN, M. I. Effect of prolonged intragastric feeding on oral food intake in dogs. Am. J. Physiol., 1952, **169**, 229.

SHEEPAN, D. Afferent nerve supply of mesentery and its significance in causation of abdominal pain. J. Anat., 1933, **67**, 233.

STUNKARD, A. J. AND WOLFF, H. G. Studies on the physiology of hunger. I. The effect of intravenous administration of glucose on gastric hunger contractions in man. J. Clin. Invest., 1956, **35**, 954.

TOWBIN, E. J. Thirst and hunger behavior in normal dogs and the effects of vagotomy and sympathectomy. Am. J. Physiol., 1955, **182**, 377.

WOOLLARD, H. H. AND CARMICHAEL, E. A. Testis and referred pain. Brain, 1933, **56**, 293.

*Monographs and Reviews*

ADOLPH, E. F. AND ASSOCIATES. Man in the desert. Interscience Publishers, Inc., New York, 1947.

BROBECK, J. R. Neural basis of hunger, appetite and satiety. Gastroenterology, 1957, **32**, 169.

CANNON, W. B. Hunger and thirst. Murchison's handbook general experimental psychology. Clark Univ. Press, Worcester, Mass., 1934.

CARLSON, A. J. The control of hunger in health and disease. Chicago University Press, Chicago, 1916.

HURST, A. F. The sensibility of the alimentary canal. Frowde, London, 1911.

JANOWITZ, H. D. Hunger and appetite. Am. J. Med., 1958, **25**, 327.

KINSELLA, V. J. The mechanism of abdominal pain. Australasian Medical Publishing Co., Sydney, Australia, 1948.

LENNANDER, K. G. Observations on the sensibility of the abdominal cavity. Bale, London, 1903. (Quoted by Morley)

LEWIS, SIR T. Pain. The Macmillan Co., New York, 1942.

MACKENZIE, J. Symptoms and their interpretations. Shaw & Sons, Ltd., London, 1920.

MAYER, J. Genetic, traumatic and environmental factors in etiology of obesity. Physiol. Rev., 1953, **33**, 472.

MORLEY, J. Abdominal pain. E. & S. Livingstone, Ltd., Edinburgh, 1931.

RYLE, J. A. Gastric functions in health and disease. Milford, London, 1926.

VOLKMANN, A. W. Wagner's Handwörterbuch der Physiologie, 1844, **ii**, 585. (See also Holinger, Kelley and Ivy. Proc. Soc. Exper. Biol. & Med., 1932, **29**, 884.)

# 44

## COMPOSITION AND ENERGY CONTENT OF FOODS: GENERAL METABOLISM

### General Outline of the Function and Composition of Foods

Nutrition deals with the needs of the organism for sustenance. Nutrition concerns a complex aspect of living things (both plants and animals) that consists of the taking in and assimilation through chemical changes (metabolism) of material, whereby tissue is built up and energy liberated. There are three successive stages in the process, known as absorption, assimilation and excretion. In all animals, and certain plants, a stage known as digestion precedes the three stages named. In the more highly developed animals, digestion is preceded by mastication and deglutition, and excretion is effected by four routes, the processes being referred to as expiration, perspiration, urination and defecation. The essential feature in nutrition is the *intake* of the raw materials needed for the maintenance of life, but it overlaps victualling, food preparation and metabolism. The modern science of nutrition deals mainly with the requirements of the body, both in kind and amount, and the choice of foods to meet these needs.

The three chief functions of food are (1) to supply energy, (2) to form (or maintain) body tissue, and (3) to preserve a suitable internal environment so that the enzymes bringing about the metabolic reactions and the hormones regulating the processes may function properly.

Chemical methods for the analysis of foodstuffs, as they developed over the years, revealed that natural foods contain (besides water and the ash constituents) cellulose, lignins, galactosans, pentosans, starches, sugars, fats, waxes, sterols, carotenoids and other pigments, proteins, purines, pyrimidines, acids (such as oxalic, lactic, tartaric, citric, malic, benzoic, salicylic, quinic, and uric) and many other minor components, such as tannins, alkaloids and simpler bases, glucosides, and essential oils. Magendie (1783–1855) first tested the effects (in dogs) of feeding gelatin, sugar and butter alone and noted that animals cannot survive for long on such individual foodstuffs. Prout (1785–1850) in his notable book *Chemistry, Meteorology, and the Function of Digestion* (1834) developed the modern view that of the many components of natural foods, three kinds are essential in the diet, each possessing characteristic nutritive properties. Prout referred to them as the albuminous group (gelatin, cooked egg-white, cooked flesh being examples), the saccharine group (sugars and starches) and the oleaginous group; these are known today, of course, as the proteins, carbohydrates and the fats.

For many years (about 1860 to 1910) interest was focussed on the energy content of foods and the energy requirement of the body. The nitrogen (protein) requirement continued to receive much attention. Although chemists recognized that the methods for the analysis of foods were only approximate, and that carbohydrates were usually estimated by difference, so that the values always added to 100 per cent, the conclusion had been reached that minerals, proteins, carbohydrates and fats were the only nutrients required by man and animals. There seemed to be no room in the make-up of foods for any other ingredient of nutritive importance.

Besides the seven principal ash components (calcium, magnesium, sodium, potassium, phosphorus, sulfur and chlorine) at least seven other minerals, the so-called "trace elements" are to-day known to be essential for animals and man: iron, copper, manganese, zinc, cobalt, iodine and fluorine. The possible essentiality of aluminum, silicon, arsenic, boron, selenium and other elements has been suggested but not established.

## Energy Content of Foodstuffs

There have been many tabulations showing the average chemical composition and energy values of the edible portion of common food materials. The values in these tables are based upon a number of assumptions that are commonly made by food chemists. A brief review of the techniques used and errors involved will illustrate the uncertainties inherent in many tabulations. In spite of these limitations, certain valuable generalizations about the nutritive worth of the commoner food materials have been reached.

The energy value of foods is measured in kilogram-calories or large Calories (spelled with a capital C). This is the amount of heat required to raise the temperature of a kilogram of water 1° (from 15 to 16°C.). The potential energy of a foodstuff can be estimated in three ways: (1) It may be determined *directly* by measuring the amount of heat generated when a weighed sample of the material is burned in a *bomb calorimeter* (see. p. 751). (2) *Indirect calorimetry* involves measurement of the oxygen required to burn completely a sample of the foodstuff in the *oxy-calorimeter* (see p. 753) and calculation of the energy content from the oxygen used. (3) As will be shown later, an approximation to the number of calories that a foodstuff will provide may be *calculated* from the chemical estimates of protein, fat and carbohydrate in it. "Physiological corrections" are then applied to allow for incomplete combustion and losses in the urine and feces.

Antoine Laurent Lavoisier (1743–1794), the founder of modern chemistry, first used the thermometer and balance in the study of metabolism.[1]

His careful experiments and clear deductions explained the nature of oxidation, of combustion and of respiration and showed their similarities. He recognized that fuels and foods are composed of carbon, hydrogen and oxygen. Lavoisier showed that oxidation of these organic substances to carbon dioxide and water led to the production of characteristic amounts of heat.[2] Simultaneously, in Britain, Crawford was making similar experiments on "animal heat" and combustion.

In 1842, half a century later, the English physicist, James Prestcott Joule (1818–1889) determined the mechanical equivalent of heat.[3] In the same year, the German physician-physicist, Julius Robert von Mayer (1814–1878) published his revolutionary theory of heat together with his views on the conservation of energy. Mayer stated that the sum total of the energy in the universe remains constant but that any one form (mechanical, potential, thermal, chemical, electrical) may be converted into another. Several years later (1845) another German scientist, von Helmholtz (1821–1894) extended the application of the Law of Conservation of Energy and formulated it mathematically. It is interesting to know that at the time the contributions of both men were rejected by the leading German scientific journal!

Through the work of Voit, Pettenkofer and Rubner the Law of Conservation of Energy was shown to hold true in the animal body. Rubner established the heat value of carbohydrates, fat and protein when burned outside the body in a calorimeter (for operational details see p. 751).

ship the Munich School became the outstanding centre of research in nutrition and metabolism (about 1860–1910). The conversion of carbohydrate to fat, and of part of the food protein to carbohydrate was demonstrated at Munich. Voit taught Rubner (1854–1932), Atwater (1844–1907), E. P. Cathcart (1877–1954) of Glasgow University, Graham Lusk (1866–1932) of Cornell University Medical College, New York, and others who were the authorities 30 to 50 years ago. They in turn taught and inspired many of the present leaders in nutrition.

[1] Graham Lusk has given an account of the scientific descent of the leading chemists who have devoted their lives to the nutritional aspects of physiology. Berthollet (1748–1822), who established the composition of ammonia and of hydrogen sulfide, and who showed (in 1786) that nitrogen is a constant constituent of animal tissues, (a colleague of Lavoisier and instructor of Napoleon I in chemistry), bequeathed his sword to his favorite student, Gay-Lussac, originator of volumetric methods and formulator of the gas laws. Gay-Lussac (1778–1850) was the teacher of Liebig (1803–1873), the father of modern methods of organic analysis. Liebig, author of the first chemical text to deal extensively with agricultural matters and the composition of foods, tissues and excreta (*Animal Chemistry*, 1846) taught Carl von Voit (1831–1908). Under Voit's energetic leader-

[2] Lavoisier believed that the heat was produced through the oxidation of carbon and hydrogen in the *lungs*. Not until some years later was it shown that heat production was the result of the combustion of foodstuffs in the various tissues of the body.

[3] The unit of work, the erg = a force of 1 dyne acting through 1 cm. The joule is $10^7$ ergs. The mechanical equivalent of heat is the quantity of energy which, when transformed into heat, is equivalent to unit quantity of heat: 1 calorie = 4.18 joules = 4.18 × $10^7$ ergs.

## TABLE 44.1

*Energy content (by bomb calorimetry) of some fuels, foods and metabolic products*

(Kilocalories per gram)

| | | | | | |
|---|---|---|---|---|---|
| Hydrogen | 34.2 | Ethanol | 7.13 | Castor oil | 8.85 |
| Carbon | | Glycerol | 4.32 | Cod liver oil | 9.40 |
| charcoal | 8.09 | Arabinose | 3.74 | Citric acid | 2.47 |
| diamond | 7.87 | Glucose | 3.73 | Malic acid | 2.42 |
| graphite | 7.85 | Fructose | 3.76 | Glycine | 3.14 |
| Methane ($CH_4$) | 13.2 | Galactose | 3.73 | Alanine | 4.35 |
| Ethane ($C_2H_6$) | 12.3 | Sucrose | 3.95 | Leucine | 6.55 |
| Ethylene ($C_2H_4$) | 11.8 | Lactose | 3.96 | Casein | 5.85 |
| Acetylene ($C_2H_2$) | 12.0 | Starch | 4.12 | Gelatin | 5.30 |
| Benzene ($C_6H_6$) | 10.0 | Acetaldehyde | 6.34 | Albumin | 5.80 |
| Petroleum | 10.3 | Acetic acid ($C_2$) | 3.49 | Dried muscle | 5.40 |
| Coal gas | 10.7 | $n$-Butyric acid ($C_4$) | 5.96 | Edestin | 5.64 |
| Anthracite coal | 7.0–8.7 | Palmitic acid ($C_{16}$) | 9.36 | Gliadin | 5.74 |
| Wood | | Stearic acid ($C_{18}$) | 9.54 | Legumin | 5.62 |
| Pine | 4.4 | Oleic acid ($C_{18}$) | 9.41 | Uric acid | 2.74 |
| Beech | 4.2 | Butter fat | 9.30 | Urea | 2.53 |
| Oak | 4.0 | Cottonseed oil | 9.40 | Creatinine | 4.98 |
| Methanol | 5.33 | Linseed oil | 9.41 | | |

He then fed the three types of foodstuffs separately to a dog in a calorimeter. Carbohydrate and fat produced the same amount of heat, within the limit of experimental error, whether combustion occurred within the body or outside it. The physiological heat value of protein, however, was found to be distinctly less than the bomb value. Carbohydrates and fats, after absorption, are fully oxidized to carbon dioxide and water in the body as well as in the bomb, but this is not so for protein. In the bomb calorimeter, proteins are burned completely to carbon dioxide, water and sulfuric acid; part of the nitrogen is converted to oxides of nitrogen and part occurs as free nitrogen. The body excretes in the urine urea and other nitrogenous compounds. These carry out some of the carbon, hydrogen and nitrogen before they are fully oxidized and thus some of the potential energy of the protein is lost. Only about three-quarters of the calories obtained from protein in the bomb are physiologically available because of the less complete oxidation in the body.

The caloric values (bomb) of different carbohydrates, fats and proteins are not identical, as may be seen in table 44.1. Animal proteins are often said to liberate slightly less energy per gram than do plant proteins but this is an unsafe generalization (*cf.* table 44.1).

Rubner found the heats of combustion (Calories per gram) for glucose, lactose, sucrose and starch to be 3.69, 3.88, 3.96 and 4.12, respectively. He suggested 4.1 as the factor for the mixture of sugars plus starch in a mixed diet. Rubner adopted 9.3 as the mean factor for fat and 4.1 for the physiologically available energy from proteins. Atwater and Bryant proposed 4.0, 8.9 and 4.0, respectively. For practical purposes the simple factors 4, 9 and 4 are adequate.

UNCERTAINTIES IN ENERGY VALUES OF FOODS ESTIMATES FROM COMPOSITION. The main reasons for uncertainty about the correct energy value to assign to natural foodstuffs are (1) the difficulty of choosing a representative sample, (2) difficulties connected with accurate chemical analyses, (3) inconstancy of the moisture content of the samples, and (4) the difficulty of choosing appropriate factors (a) for conversion of nitrogen to protein and (b) for the energy available to the body from different foodstuffs. This latter point includes the uncertainties introduced by variations in digestibility. Each type of foodstuff raises special problems. These will be dealt with separately.[4]

CARBOHYDRATE. In the early days of food chemistry (and often today) carbohydrate was determined by difference, i.e., 100 − (moisture + ash + protein (N × 6.25) + fat). All the errors in the previous determinations, plus the undetermined matters in the food, are thus included with the carbohydrates. Only in recent years

[4] Specific dynamic action of foodstuffs, which will be discussed in the following section, is concerned with alterations in the basal metabolic rate induced by ingestion of foodstuffs and not with the intrinsic potential energy of the foods.

have efforts been made to determine individual carbohydrates.

The energy content of individual carbohydrates varies from 3.7 to almost 4.2 (table 44.1). The physiological availability varies from almost 100 per cent to zero. The energy of celluloses, although somewhat available to ruminants, is unavailable in man. Substances such as galactans, pentosans and hemicelluloses are poorly (if at all) utilized by man. The edible portions of most foods do not contain excessive amounts of indigestible carbohydrate but it is erroneous to conclude that all of the "carbohydrate" (as determined by difference) provides energy. Estimates of "crude fiber" are not given in older food tables. Sometimes no mention is made of whether a correction has been applied for indigestible carbohydrate. In a few cases, e.g., soyabean flour, only about 40 per cent of the carbohydrate is utilized by rats, and this probably represents the digestibility of these carbohydrates in man. The "average availability" figure of 97 per cent may be too high for mixed foods but is probably correct for mixed sugars and starches.

Organic acids occur in many foods, especially fruits; oxalic, malic and citric are the most widely found. Oxalic and tartaric are not utilized; malic and citric are completely oxidized in the body, giving 2.42 and 2.47 Calories per gram, respectively. In a few cases a large percentage of the total calories comes from acids, e.g., in lemon juice 62, grapefruit and squash 12, oranges and tomatoes 6, pineapple and cucumber 4, cabbage and carrot 2 to 3.

In general, the value 4.0 Calories per gram of carbohydrate is essentially correct if adjustment for crude fiber has been made. When pure sugars are added to a ration, their exact values can, of course, be used although it is questionable whether one gains much in precision thereby. The reason for this pessimistic statement is that recent careful studies have shown that indigestible residues can interefere with the absorption of carbohydrates that would be completely utilized if fed separately. Thus other materials in the ration can play unpredictable roles in altering availability.

FATS. The fat content of foods is usually determined by extraction of the dried and powdered material with ether. Evaporation of the solvent leaves the "crude fat" which is conventionally weighed as such. It is sometimes grossly contaminated with nonlipid materials that have been taken out by the ether, e.g., pepper-corns contain 6.5 per cent of ether-soluble matter but only about 2 per cent ot glycerides; ground ginger contains 3.3 per cent of "crude fat," only one-eighth of which is glyceride. For this reason the saponification procedure (Liebermann, 1898) and estimation of fatty acids has sometimes been used as a control. More often ether extraction gives low values, in some cases much too low: fat values found by ether extraction (Soxhlet) and by Liebermann's method on Horlick's malted milk are 1.2 and 8.6 grams per 100 gram, respectively; corresponding data for Kellogg's All-Bran are 1.0 and 4.5, for Grape-Nuts 0.4 and 3.0 and for whole wheat flour 0.6 and 2.1, respectively.

The energy value of most edible oils and fats lies in the range 9.2 to 9.4 Calories per gram. The availability in the 3 adult male subjects studied by Atwater and Bryant (1900) varied from 90 to 95 per cent, but it is unsafe to accept their mean value of 92 as being of universal applicability.

The main difficulty in deciding about energy values from dietary fat data in food tables concerns the decision as to what constitutes a representative sample of the food, especially of meat cuts. Because fat has a controlling influence on the energy content, small differences between the character of the sample eaten and that analyzed may introduce gross errors in the computation. One large lean steak (200-gram portion, raw weight) of the following percentage composition: water 71, ash 1, protein 20 and fat 8 may be estimated to supply about 300 Calories; another steak of equal weight analyzing water 65, ash 1, protein 18 and fat 16 would supply more than 100 extra Calories (about 430), whereas a similar portion of a moderately fatty sirloin steak (28 to 32 per cent fat) would provide nearly 800 Calories if all the fat were consumed. Much is rendered out, however, some or all of which is left in the pan.

PROTEINS. Proteins differ in many ways from the other two foodstuffs. Proteins typically contain (besides carbon, hydrogen and oxygen) nitrogen, almost always sulfur and sometimes phosphorus. Heterogeneous substances varying in nitrogen content from about 12 per cent (in tendomucoid) to about 19 per cent (in silk fibroin), in molecular weight from about 12,000 to about 60,000,000 and in digestibility from 0 to 100 per cent are covered by the same name. Their nutritional value, which can be determined only by biological testing, varies just as greatly. Casein (15.8 per cent N) and egg albumin (15.5 per cent N) are high quality proteins, being well supplied with essential amino acids and readily digested. Zein and gelatin contain more nitrogen (16.1 and 18.0 per cent, respectively) but are incomplete,

TABLE 44.2

*Composition and energy content of common foodstuffs*

| Foodstuff | Usual Serving | Food Energy | Composition of Foods, 100 Grams Edible Portion | | | | | | | |
|---|---|---|---|---|---|---|---|---|---|---|
| | | | Water | Protein | Fat | Carbohydrate | | Ash | Calcium | Phosphorus |
| | | | | | | Total | Fiber | | | |
| | *gm.* | *Calories per 100 gm.* | *%* | *gm.* | *gm.* | *gm.* | *gm.* | *gm.* | *mg.* | *mg.* |
| Bread | | | | | | | | | | |
| White[a]............... | 50[b] | 275 | 34.7 | 8.5 | 3.2 | 51.8 | 0.2 | 1.8 | 79 | 92 |
| Toasted............. | 39[b] | 313 | 25.5 | 9.7 | 3.7 | 59.0 | 0.2 | 2.1 | 90 | 105 |
| Wholewheat......... | 50[b] | 240 | 36.6 | 9.3 | 2.6 | 49.0 | 1.5 | 2.5 | 96 | 263 |
| Rye[c]............... | 50[b] | 244 | 35.3 | 9.1 | 1.2 | 52.4 | 0.4 | 2.0 | 72 | 147 |
| Doughnut[d].......... | 50 | 425 | 18.7 | 6.6 | 21.0 | 52.7 | 0.2 | 1.0 | 73 | 286 |
| Candy | | | | | | | | | | |
| Fondant.............. | 25 | 352 | 8.0 | 0 | 0 | 91.0 | 0 | 1.0 | 0 | 0 |
| Fudge (plain)........ | 25 | 411 | 5.0 | 1.7 | 11.3 | 81.3 | 0.3 | 0.7 | 48 | 67 |
| Hard................ | 25 | 383 | 1.0 | 0 | 0 | 99.0 | 0 | 0 | 0 | 0 |
| Peanut brittle....... | 25 | 441 | 2.0 | 8.3 | 15.5 | 72.8 | 0.8 | 1.3 | 38 | 124 |
| Ginger root.......... | 25 | 340 | 12.0 | 0.3 | 0.2 | 87.1 | 0.7 | 0.4 | | |
| Candied peel......... | 25 | 315 | 17.7 | 0.3 | 0.3 | 80.4 | 1.9 | 1.3 | | |
| Cereals | | | | | | | | | | |
| Barley (pearled)...... | | 349 | 11.1 | 8.2 | 1.0 | 78.8 | 0.5 | 0.9 | 16 | 189 |
| Cassava............. | | 345 | | 1.6 | | 84.6 | | | | |
| Corn meal (whole bolted)............. | | 362 | 12.0 | 9.0 | 3.4 | 74.5 | 1.0 | 1.1 | 6 | (178)[e] |
| Corn (degermed and cooked)............. | 200 | 50 | 87.7 | 1.1 | 0.2 | 10.7 | 0.1 | 0.3 | 1 | 14 |
| Millet[f]............... | | 350 | 9–13 | 7–13 | 2.2± | 73.0 | 2.0± | 1–3 | | |
| Oatmeal (dry)........ | | 390 | 8.3 | 14.2 | 7.4 | 68.2 | 1.2 | 1.9 | 53 | 405 |
| Oatmeal (cooked)..... | 200 | 63 | 84.8 | 2.3 | 1.2 | 11.0 | 0.2 | 0.7 | 9 | 67 |
| Rice (brown, raw).... | | 360 | 12.0 | 7.5 | 1.7 | 77.7 | 0.6 | 1.1 | 39 | 303 |
| Rice (milled, cooked). | 160 | 119 | 70.5 | 2.5 | 0.1 | 26.2 | 0.1 | 0.7 | 8 | 45 |
| Rye flour (light)...... | | 356 | 11.0 | 9.4 | 1.0 | 77.9 | 0.4 | 0.7 | 22 | 185 |
| Rye flour (dark)...... | | 318 | 11.0 | 16.3 | 2.6 | 68.1 | 2.4 | 2.0 | 54 | (536)[e] |
| Wheat flour (whole, from hard wheats).. | | 333 | 12.0 | 13.3 | 2.0 | 71.0 | 2.3 | 1.7 | 41 | 372 |
| Wheat flour (80% extraction)........... | | 365 | 12.0 | 12.0 | 1.3 | 74.1 | 0.5 | 0.65 | 24 | 191 |
| Wheat germ.......... | 25 | 361 | 11.0 | 25.2 | 10.0 | 49.5 | 2.5 | 4.3 | 84 | 1096 |
| Tapioca (dry)........ | | 360 | 12.6 | 0.6 | 0.2 | 86.4 | 0.1 | 0.2 | 12 | 12 |
| Dairy products | | | | | | | | | | |
| Butter............... | 14[g] | 716 | 15.5 | 0.6 | 81 | 0.4 | 0 | 2.5 | 20 | 16 |
| Cheese (cheddar)..... | 30 | 398 | 37.0 | 25.0 | 32.2 | 2.1 | 0 | 3.7 | 725 | 495 |
| Cheese (cottage, from skim milk)......... | 60 | 95 | 76.5 | 19.5 | 0.5 | 2.0 | 0 | 1.5 | 96 | 189 |

Most of the data are from U.S.D.A. Handbook No. 8 (1950), but the data for cassava are from U.S.D.A. 34.

[a] Four per cent nonfat milk solids.

[b] Two slices. Slices vary considerably in weight depending on the freshness: one slice fresh bread weighs about 23 to 28 grams.

[c] American rye bread (⅓ rye flour, ⅔ wheat flour).

[d] Cake type batter.

[e] Estimated value.

[f] Data for husked millet from Winton and Winton, 1932. It is a staple cereal in Central Africa, Southern China, in India and parts of Europe.

[g] Two patties.

TABLE 44.2—*Continued*

| Foodstuff | Usual Serving | Food Energy | Composition of Foods 100 Grams Edible Portion | | | | | | | |
|---|---|---|---|---|---|---|---|---|---|---|
| | | | Water | Protein | Fat | Carbohydrate | | Ash | Calcium | Phosphorus |
| | | | | | | Total | Fiber | | | |
| | *gm.* | *Calories per 100 gm.* | *%* | *gm.* | *gm.* | *gm.* | *gm.* | *gm.* | *mg.* | *mg.* |
| **Dairy Products—** *Continued* | | | | | | | | | | |
| Ice cream (plain)..... | 80[h] | 207 | 62.1 | 4.0 | 12.5 | 20.6 | 0 | 0.8 | 123 | 99 |
| Milk (cow, whole).... | 250 | 68 | 87.0 | 3.5 | 3.9 | 4.9 | 0 | 0.7 | 118 | 93 |
| Milk (cow, skim)..... | 250 | 36 | 90.5 | 3.5 | 0.1 | 5.1 | 0 | 0.8 | 123 | 97 |
| Milk (dried, skim).... | 10 | 362 | 3.5 | 35.6 | 1.0 | 52.0 | 0 | 7.9 | 1300 | 1030 |
| **Eggs (hen)** | | | | | | | | | | |
| Fresh (whole)........ | 50 | 162 | 74.0 | 12.8 | 11.5 | 0.7 | 0 | 1.0 | 54 | 210 |
| Fresh (white)........ | | 50 | 87.8 | 10.8 | 0 | 0.8 | 0 | 0.6 | 6 | 17 |
| Fresh (yolk)......... | | 361 | 49.4 | 16.3 | 31.9 | 0.7 | 0 | 1.7 | 147 | 586 |
| Fresh (dried, whole).. | 5 | 592 | 5.0 | 46.8 | 42.0 | 2.5 | 0 | 3.6 | 190 | 767 |
| **Fish** | | | | | | | | | | |
| Cod (raw)........... | 150[i] | 74 | 82.6 | 16.5 | 0.4 | 0 | 0 | 1.2 | 10 | 194 |
| Halibut (raw)....... | | 126 | 75.4 | 18.6 | 5.2 | 0 | 0 | 1.0 | 13 | 211 |
| Halibut (broiled)..... | 120 | 182 | 64.2 | 26.2 | 7.8 | 0 | 0 | 1.9 | 14 | 267 |
| Salmon (broiled)...... | 120 | 170 | 64.5 | 28.0 | 5.6 | 0.2 | 0 | 1.7 | | |
| Salmon (canned, sockeye)............... | 90 | 173 | 67.2 | 20.2 | 9.6 | 0 | 0 | 3.0 | 259 | 344 |
| **Shell fish** | | | | | | | | | | |
| Crab (canned)........ | 90 | 104 | 77.2 | 16.9 | 2.9 | 1.3 | | 1.7 | 45 | 182 |
| Scallops (raw muscle). | 140[i] | 78 | 80.3 | 14.8 | 0.1 | 3.4 | 0 | 1.4 | 26 | 208 |
| **Fowl** | | | | | | | | | | |
| Chicken (raw, total edible)............. | 150[i] | 200 | 66.0 | 20.2 | 12.6 | 0 | 0 | 1.0 | 14 | 200 |
| Turkey (raw)........ | 150[i] | 268 | 58.3 | 20.1 | 20.2 | 0 | 0 | 1.0 | 23 | 320 |
| **Fruits (raw)** | | | | | | | | | | |
| Apple................ | 150 | 58 | 84.1 | 0.3 | 0.4 | 14.9 | 1.0 | 0.3 | 6 | 10 |
| Avocado............. | 100 | 245 | 65.4 | 1.7 | 26.4 | 5.1 | 1.8 | 1.4 | 10 | 38 |
| Banana.............. | 120 | 88 | 74.8 | 1.2 | 0.2 | 23.0 | 0.6 | 0.8 | 8 | 28 |
| Cherries............. | 150 | 61 | 83.0 | 1.1 | 0.5 | 14.8 | 0.3 | 0.6 | 18 | 20 |
| Orange.............. | 150 | 45 | 87.2 | 0.9 | 0.2 | 11.2 | 0.6 | 0.5 | 33 | 23 |
| Peach............... | 120 | 46 | 86.9 | 0.5 | 0.1 | 12.0 | 0.6 | 0.5 | 8 | 22 |
| Raspberries (red)..... | 90 | 57 | 84.1 | 1.2 | 0.4 | 13.8 | 4.7 | 0.5 | 40 | 37 |
| **Meat** | | | | | | | | | | |
| Bacon (raw)......... | | 630 | 20.0 | 9.1 | 65.0 | 1.1 | 0 | 4.3 | 13 | 108 |
| Bacon (fried)........ | 20 | 607 | 13.0 | 25.0 | 55.0 | 1.0 | 0 | 6.0 | 25 | 255 |
| Beef (rib roast, cooked)............ | 100 | 319 | 51.0 | 24.0 | 24.0 | 0 | 0 | 1.2 | 10 | 185 |
| Beef (liver, fried)..... | 90 | 208 | 57.2 | 23.6 | 7.7 | 9.7 | 0 | 1.8 | 8 | 480 |
| Lamb (leg roast, cooked)............ | 100 | 274 | 56.0 | 24.0 | 19.0 | 0 | 0 | 1.1 | 10 | 257 |
| Pork (boiled ham).... | 100 | 302 | 47.8 | 22.8 | 22.7 | 0 | 0 | 6.7 | 9 | 92 |
| **Nuts** | | | | | | | | | | |
| Almonds............. | 20 | 600 | 4.7 | 18.6 | 54.1 | 19.6 | 2.7 | 3.0 | 254 | 475 |
| Brazil............... | 30 | 640 | 5.3 | 14.4 | 65.9 | 11.0 | 2.1 | 3.4 | 186 | 693 |
| Peanuts (roasted)..... | 30 | 560 | 2.6 | 26.9 | 44.2 | 23.6 | 2.4 | 2.7 | 74 | 393 |
| Walnuts............. | 30 | 650 | 3.3 | 15.0 | 64.4 | 15.6 | 2.1 | 1.7 | 83 | 380 |

[h] Based on factory product containing 5 lb. of ice cream to the U. S. gallon.

[i] Weight after cooking will be less.

TABLE 44.2—*Continued*

| Foodstuff | Usual Serving | Food Energy | Composition of Foods 100 Grams Edible Portion | | | | | | | |
|---|---|---|---|---|---|---|---|---|---|---|
| | | | Water | Protein | Fat | Carbohydrate | | Ash | Calcium | Phosphorus |
| | | | | | | Total | Fiber | | | |
| | *gm.* | *Calories per 100 gm.* | *%* | *gm.* | *gm.* | *gm.* | *gm.* | *gm.* | *mg.* | *mg.* |
| Vegetables | | | | | | | | | | |
| Beans (green, cooked). | 100 | 22 | 92.5 | 1.4 | 0.2 | 4.7 | 0.5 | 1.2 | 36 | 23 |
| Beans (red kidney, cooked) . . . . . . . . . . . | 200 | 90 | 76.0 | 5.7 | 0.4 | 16.4 | 0.9 | 1.5 | 40 | 124 |
| Beets (red, cooked) . . . | 150 | 41 | 88.3 | 1.0 | 0.1 | 9.8 | 0.8 | 0.8 | 21 | 31 |
| Cabbage (raw) . . . . . . . | 100 | 24 | 92.4 | 1.4 | 0.2 | 5.3 | 1.0 | 0.8 | 46 | 31 |
| Carrots (raw) . . . . . . . . | 100 | 42 | 88.2 | 1.2 | 0.3 | 9.3 | 1.1 | 1.0 | 39 | 37 |
| Corn (sweet, cooked). | 150 | 85 | 75.5 | 2.7 | 0.7 | 20.2 | | 0.9 | 5 | 52 |
| Kale (raw) . . . . . . . . . . | 50 | 40 | 86.6 | 3.9 | 0.6 | 7.2 | 1.2 | 1.7 | 225 | 62 |
| Potatoes (peeled, boiled) . . . . . . . . . . . | 140 | 83 | 77.8 | 2.0 | 0.1 | 19.1 | 0.4 | 1.0 | 11 | 56 |
| Potatoes (French fried) . . . . . . . . . . . . . | 80 | 393 | 19.6 | 5.4 | 19.1 | 52.0 | 1.1 | 3.9 | 30 | 152 |
| Sweet potatoes (boiled) . . . . . . . . . . . | 160 | 123 | 68.5 | 1.8 | 0.7 | 27.9 | 1.0 | 1.1 | 30 | 49 |
| Tomatoes (raw) . . . . . . | 150 | 20 | 94.1 | 1.0 | 0.3 | 4.0 | 0.6 | 0.6 | 11 | 27 |
| Turnips (cooked) . . . . . | 150 | 27 | 92.3 | 0.8 | 0.2 | 6.0 | 1.2 | 0.7 | 40 | 34 |

lacking certain essential amino acids, and although they are readily digested have low sustenance value when fed by themselves. Thus knowledge of protein *content* is of limited value in assessing foods until some biological tests have established the nutritional usefulness of the protein. Proteins that are useless for supporting growth may still be utilized (oxidized) to supply energy. It is wrong to think of proteins only as fuel, but it is equally wrong to think that they are not oxidizable if not used efficiently by the body for other purposes. Many proteins contain about 16 per cent of nitrogen. Food chemists therefore adopted the convention of using the factor 6.25 (i.e., 100:16) to convert *nitrogen found* in food to *protein content*. This factor has been used in preparing most food tables, although Rubner used 6.45 and Plimmer (1921) used 5.68 for nitrogen in plant products, 6.38 for dairy products and 6.25 for meats.

Use of the factor 6.25 is based on two assumptions. The first is that all proteins contain 16 per cent of nitrogen, but this is far from true. The second assumption, that all the nitrogen in food is present as protein, is also untrue. The amount of nitrogen present in simpler natural bases (choline, betaine, stachydrine, trimethylamine, creatine, etc.), purines, pyrimidines and other nitrogenous

compounds is usually small, but in a few cases it is far from negligible.

For flesh, the factor 6.25 is reasonably correct. For milk proteins a factor of 6.38 is appropriate. The factor 5.83 is more correct for calculating the protein content of barley, oats, rye and whole wheat. For refined wheat flour the factor $5.70 \times N$ is recommended. The factor believed most appropriate for rice proteins is 5.95, for soyabeans is 5.71, peanuts and Brazil nuts 5.46, almonds 5.18, and other nuts and oil seeds 5.30. The factor 6.25 may still be applied to the nitrogen in foods where specific information is not available.

Besides uncertainty as to the actual *protein content* of foods, it must be remembered that different purified proteins on combustion release different amounts of energy. Further, there is considerable difference between proteins in their digestibility. Attempts to evaluate the *biological availability* of the energy of food proteins require two corrections (1) for loss in unabsorbed protein and (2) for further loss (from the portion digested and absorbed) in the urine of some potential energy in incompletely oxidized compounds such as urea.

Rubner determined the heat of combustion of urea and found it to be 2.52 Calories per gram or 5.4 Calories per gram of urea-nitrogen. He pointed out that the urine contains also creati-

TABLE 44.3

*Ash content of the edible portion of some common foods*

(from Sherman)

| | In 100 Grams Fresh Substance | | | | | | |
|---|---|---|---|---|---|---|---|
| | Iron | Calcium | Magnesium | Sodium | Potassium | Phosphorus | Chlorine |
| | mg. | mg. | mg. | mg. | mg. | mg. | mg. |
| Beefsteak, lean. | 3.0 | 11 | 22 | 65 | 333 | 204 | 76 |
| Liver. . . . . . . . . | 12.0 | 8 | 22 | 91 | 296 | 373 | 101 |
| Eggs. . . . . . . . . . | 2.7 | 54 | 13 | 137 | 138 | 210 | 120 |
| Milk, whole. . . . | 0.1 | 118 | 12 | 51 | 143 | 93 | 106 |
| Cornmeal. . . . . . | 2.7 | 16 | 86 | | 349 | 174 | |
| Oatmeal . . . . . . . | 5.0 | 53 | 145 | 2 | 431 | 405 | 49 |
| Rice, polished. . | 0.8 | 9 | 28 | 4 | 92 | 92 | 6 |
| Wheat flour. . . . | 1.3 | 16 | 37 | 2 | 128 | 100 | 49 |
| Wheat, entire grain. . . . . . . . | 5.7 | 54 | 147 | 12 | 430 | 374 | 49 |
| Beans, lima, dried . . . . . . . . | 7.5 | 68 | 181 | | 1727 | 381 | 31 |
| Beans, string, fresh. . . . . . . . | 1.1 | 65 | 27 | 3 | 251 | 44 | 33 |
| Cabbage. . . . . . . | 0.5 | 46 | 12 | 5 | 294 | 31 | 39 |
| Corn, sweet. . . . | 5.0 | 9 | 38 | 1 | | 120 | 14 |
| Peas, dried. . . . . | 5.2 | 72 | 140 | 35 | 979 | 388 | 44 |
| Potatoes. . . . . . . | 0.7 | 11 | 27 | 5 | 496 | 56 | 35 |
| Spinach. . . . . . . . | 3.0 | 81 | 52 | 84 | 502 | 49 | 65 |
| Turnips. . . . . . . . | 0.5 | 55 | 15 | 5 | 253 | 41 | 31 |
| Apples. . . . . . . . . | 0.3 | 6 | 6 | 2 | 111 | 11 | 4 |
| Raisins. . . . . . . . | 3.3 | 60 | 27 | 31 | 803 | 110 | 24 |

nine, uric acid and other nitrogenous end-products capable of further oxidation. Attempts to estimate the physiologically available calories per gram of protein ingested were complicated by the finding that the heats of combustion of the organic substances excreted in the urine did not have a constant caloric value per gram of nitrogen. For example, the urine passed by a man eating a meat diet at one time and a potato diet at another gave 7.69 and 7.85 Calories per gram N, respectively, whereas the urine of a baby living on breast milk gave 12.1 Calories per gram N. Rubner also analyzed the feces of the man who acted as his experimental subject. The loss of energy in the nitrogenous substance amounted to 6.9 per cent of that of the ingested protein. Adding this value to that of 16.3 per cent lost in the urine he obtained a total calorie loss of about 23 per cent. Rubner therefore deducted 23 per cent from the bomb value for the heat of combustion of proteins.

A summary of our current knowledge of the composition and energy content of certain foodstuffs that are widely used is given in table 44.2. Most of the data were taken from Agriculture Handbook No. 8 (Composition of Foods), issued by the U. S. Department of Agriculture (1950). The mineral content of certain foods is given in table 44.3.

## Main Food Groups

*1. Meats, fish, poultry, eggs.* Protein-rich foods, also rich sources of certain vitamins of the B group. Eggs sometimes classed separately because of richness in vitamin A.

*2. Legumes (dried peas and beans) and nuts.* Protein-rich, but less costly; the proteins of these foods are of somewhat lower quality and vitamins in these products are less abundant.

*3. Milk and milk products (other than butter).* Economical sources of proteins of high quality, rich in calcium and riboflavin.

*4. Grain products.* Inexpensive sources of energy and of protein, although the latter are present in smaller amounts than in meats and milk products. If not too highly processed, good sources of iron and vitamins of the B group.

*5. Green and yellow vegetables.* Sources of vitamin A, minerals and certain other vitamins.

*6. Tomatoes and citrus fruits.* Rich sources of vitamin C.

*7. Other vegetables and fruits.* Sources of vitamins and minerals.

## General Metabolism

The word metabolism has a broad meaning. It is the term employed to describe the chemical changes that occur within the tissues. The integration of these reactions leads (1) to growth, (2) to the production of the heat required to maintain body temperature, and (3) to supply the energy for other vital processes. It is convenient for teaching purposes to consider *energy metabolism,* which is concerned with the gross energy changes (heat production, muscular activity and energy for maintenance of vital functions), separately from *intermediary metabolism* which is concerned with specific chemical reactions occurring in the body. This customary differentiation is, however, not a real one since energy changes are essential components of chemical reactions. Many metabolic reactions, especially those concerned with the breakdown of large molecules into simpler units, release energy; other reactions, especially those involving synthesis, absorb energy. The assimilative processes involved in the formation of new tissue are referred to as *anabolism*; the reactions concerned with tissue breakdown are referred to as *catabolism*.

Energy is required to maintain the body temperature, to support the automatic muscular movements of the heart, respiratory organs and gut and for the synthetic reactions that occur in the tissues (formation of protein, hormones and other complex metabolites). These activities, called *basal metabolism*, in an adult require about 500 Calories during an average 8-hour period of sleep or rest in bed. A similar energy expenditure continues during the waking hours (another 1000 Calories) giving a total basal expenditure of about 1500 Calories. A portion must be added for nonlabor activities (feeding, clothing, washing and amusing oneself); the energy required for these will vary considerably but probably averages about 500 Calories. The quota for the day's work varies from as low as 600 Calories (more frequently 800) for a sedentary student or clerk to possibly as much as 3600 Calories in a miner, woodcutter or athlete. Thus the total daily expenditure of energy of an average sedentary person weighing about 65 kg. would be about $1500 + 500 + 800 = 2800$ Calories. Total daily expenditures above 4400 Calories are uncommon.

Energy metabolism may be studied from several aspects: (a) the energy content (caloric value) of foods; (b) direct calorimetry; (c) the significance of the respiratory quotient (R.Q.), i.e., volume of carbon dioxide expired divided by the volume of oxygen consumed in the same period of time ($CO_2/O_2$); (d) indirect calorimetry; (e) basal metabolism; (f) energy cost (caloric requirement) of various types of activity; (g) the specific dynamic action (S.D.A.) of foods, i.e., the increased production of heat by the body as a result of a stimulus to metabolic activity caused by taking food.

## HISTORICAL SURVEY

The first gas to be mentioned in the history of chemistry is one of great physiological importance, carbon dioxide. Van Helmont (1577–1644) corked up limestone with acid in a bottle and found that the pressure created by the substance being formed burst the bottle. He coined the word *gas*, derived from the Greek word *chaos*, to describe the wild motion of the particles responsible for the bursting force so generated. He called the product *gas sylvestre*. Joseph Black rediscovered

and investigated carbon dioxide in 1754 and called it *fixed air*, Van Helmont's name *gas* having not yet been generally accepted.

In 1669 John Mayow (1641–1679) put a large glass globe over a mouse on a platform in a shallow dish of water. A perceptible contraction of the air occurred slowly and caused the level of the water to rise in the globe. A burning candle produced the same effect. A mouse introduced into a vessel with a burning lamp lived only about half as long as a mouse in the same vessel without a lamp. From these observations Mayow concluded that air is composed of two gases, one concerned in combustion and respiration (which he called *nitro-aerial spirit*, because it was apparently the same substance that is "fixed" in saltpeter, i.e., niter, and freed from it by heat), and a second gas incapable of supporting either combustion or respiration. Joseph Priestley (1733–1804) discovered several new gases (at that time called "airs") and established the existence of different airs, each with definite properties. In 1772 he made oxygen by heating niter (potassium nitrate) strongly, and observed that a mouse lived twice as long in the "new air" as in the same volume of common air. Priestley breathed the new air himself and fancied his "breast felt peculiarly light and easy for some time afterwards"; he therefore recommended its use in medicine! Priestley wrote, "Who can tell but that, in time, this pure air may become a fashionable article in luxury. Hitherto only two mice and myself have had the privilege of breathing it." Today it is a common privilege.

A generation later Crawford placed a guinea pig in a water calorimeter and demonstrated a parallelism between the oxygen consumed and the heat generated by the animal. Approximately the same quantity of heat was produced by the animal as when the same amount of oxygen was used to burn carbon outside the body.

A few years later two French scientists, the chemist, Lavoisier (1743–1794), and the physicist, Laplace (1749–1827), performed a similar experiment but measured the carbon dioxide produced rather than the oxygen used. They placed a guinea pig in a closed chamber and showed that the same product of oxidation of carbon is formed in the body and eliminated from the lungs as is produced by the burning of a candle. They determined the quantity of carbon dioxide eliminated by the animal in a 10-hour period and found that it was the same (12.1 grams) as that produced when 3.3 grams of pure carbon were burned in air. The guinea pig was next placed in a closed space surrounded by ice (fig. 44.1) and the heat given out by the animal's body was calculated from the quantity of ice that was melted. A comparable amount of heat was generated when 3.3 grams of carbon were burned in the ice calorimeter. Lavoisier and Laplace concluded that the heat generated by the animal was

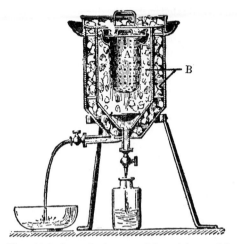

Fig. 44.1. Ice calorimeter of Lavoisier and Laplace. (After Luciani.) A, chamber for animal; B, two concentric chambers filled with ice.

produced by the combustion of 3.3 grams of the body's carbon. With this demonstration that animal heat is the result of the oxidation of carbon in the body, and establishment of a *parallelism between the amount of heat generated* in the animal's body *and the quantity of carbon dioxide eliminated*, the science of metabolism was begun.

Lavoisier believed that the oxidation of carbon and hydrogen occurs in the lungs. Heat production is now known to result from combustion of foodstuffs in the various tissues of the body.

J. von Liebig (1803–1873) established that it is not *carbon* and hydrogen that are burned by the tissues, but *carbohydrate* and *fat*. Liebig (1842) believed that oxygen is used in the metabolic combustion of these two foodstuffs but he thought that the breakdown of protein is of a different nature, being caused by muscular work. This belief, although unsupported by any experimental evidence, was generally accepted until Carl von Voit (1831–1908) showed conclusively in 1860 by experiments on dogs and man that the metabolism of protein is not affected by muscular work.

Metabolic balance studies originated with J. B. Boussingault (1802–1887). He compared the carbon, hydrogen, nitrogen and oxygen ingested by a dairy cow in its feed with the amounts of these elements excreted in the milk, urine and feces. The portions unaccounted for were considered to have been used in respiration. Bidder and Carl Schmidt (1852) measured the protein intake and nitrogen excretion of adult dogs and cats and found that nearly all of the ingested nitrogen was eliminated in the urine and feces. Their findings were doubted until Voit (1857) measured the protein intake and nitrogen output of a dog for 58 days and recovered 99.7 per cent of the nitrogen in the excreta.

Regnault and Reiset in 1849 devised the first closed circuit apparatus for respiration experiments (to be described later) and in it measured the metabolism of poultry, swine, sheep and calves. They showed that the respiratory quotient (volume of carbon dioxide expired divided by the volume of oxygen consumed in the same time-period) is controlled by the nature of the foodstuffs being oxidized and does not depend on the species of animal used in the experiment. Pettenkoffer (1818–1901) constructed the first respiration chamber in which a man could live without discomfort for several days. He and Voit conducted many studies in it and established the fundamentals of energy metabolism. This aspect of metabolism received exhaustive study in the closing years of the last century by Rubner and his colleagues in Germany. Atwater, (1844–1907), the outstanding American authority in this field, spent some time with Rubner; later, with the physicist, Rosa, he constructed the first human respiration calorimeter to be made on this side of the Atlantic and with F. G. Benedict and others perfected the study of energy metabolism.

### Energy Content of Substances

As explained in the previous section, the *physiologically* available energy of the three major foodstuffs is generally taken as 9, 4 and 4 Calories per gram for fat, carbohydrate and protein, respectively.

The potential energy of a chemical compound or foodstuff is determined by measuring the amount of heat generated when the material is burned. The *bomb calorimeter* (fig. 44.2) employed for this purpose consists of a small, strong, platinum-lined steel vessel immersed in a can containing a known weight of water. This in turn is enclosed in an insulating outer container. A known weight of the dried foodstuff is placed in the bomb which is then filled with pure oxygen under pressure. The bomb is immersed in the water and the mixture is ignited electrically. A thermometer graduated in very small units, capable of being read to the nearest 0.001°C., is used. The amount of heat produced is calculated from the rise in temperature of the water, with appropriate corrections being made for the "water equivalent" of the bomb and calorimeter parts. The rise in temperature multiplied by the sum of the weight of the water (in kilograms) plus the "water equivalent" of the apparatus divided by the dry weight of the substance (in grams) gives in Calories the heat value of the material per gram.

Thermal equivalents. The heat production per liter of oxygen consumed varies from compound to compound (table 44.4) but the variation within groups of related compounds (e.g., carbohydrates) is smaller than between different groups of compounds (e.g., carbohydrates, fats and proteins). The thermal equivalent of the foodstuff is the number of calories liberated per liter of oxygen consumed or of carbon dioxide eliminated. The thermal equivalent of $CO_2$ varies much more than does that of $O_2$ (table 44.4). It is more usual, therefore, to estimate heat production from oxygen consumption rather than from carbon dioxide output. The thermal equivalent of oxygen when carbohydrate (mainly starch) is being burned is generally given as 5.04 and the corresponding value for fat is about 4.68. The thermal equivalent for protein varies; it has been given by Loewy as 4.683 and by Benedict and Fox as 4.60. For practical purposes an average value of about 4.5 Calories per liter of oxygen may be used for protein.

OXYCALORIMETER. Another type of apparatus used to determine the energy value of foodstuffs is the *oxycalorimeter* (fig. 44.3) devised by F. G. Benedict. Although less accurate than the bomb method, this procedure is useful for determining the energy value of actual meals. The sample is burned in a combustion chamber connected to a gas holder containing oxygen. The carbon dioxide is absorbed, permitting measurement of the *volume of oxygen used*. From the thermal equivalent of a liter of oxygen when used to burn the three primary foodstuffs (table 44.5), a value may be calculated for the heat available from the particular sample of food. This is an adaptation of the method of *indirect calorimetry* used in the clinic (see p. 760).

Since the Calories liberated per liter of oxygen used in the combustion of foodstuffs in the oxycalorimeter vary only between 4.5 and 5.0, the use of a mean figure of 4.8 will result in values with an error no greater than 5 per cent of the true (bomb) value. If the foodstuff is predominantly of one type, choice of a more appropriate factor (e.g., 5.0 for a starchy food, or 4.5 for a protein-rich one) gives a value very close to the true one.

In the body the caloric value of oxygen varies similarly between 4.5 and 5.0, depending upon the type and proportion of foodstuffs being oxidized. Because the respiratory quotient gives an indication of this ratio, it will be discussed next.

### The Respiratory Quotient

The ratio, vol. $CO_2$ expired : vol. $O_2$ used, is called the respiratory quotient or, briefly, the R.Q. Different relative amounts of carbon, hy-

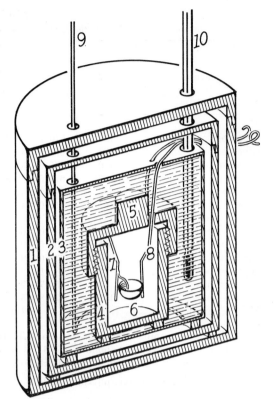

FIG. 44.2. The bomb calorimeter consists of three vessels (1, 2, 3) one inside the other. The outer vessels (1 and 2) are usually of a plastic composition and serve merely to provide insulating dead air-spaces. The innermost vessel (3) is of highly polished metal and contains a known weight of water in which the bomb (4) is immersed while the foodstuff is being burned. The top (5) of the bomb screws off to permit a known weight of dried foodstuff to be placed in the crucible (6). The top is replaced and through a valve oxygen under pressure of about 300 pounds per square inch is introduced. The foodstuff is ignited by means of electrical leads (7, 8). The water is mixed (stirrer, 9) and its rise in temperature is measured by the thermometer (10).

drogen and oxygen are contained in the molecules of carbohydrates, fats and proteins. Therefore, different characteristic amounts of oxygen are required to oxidize the constituent carbon and hydrogen to carbon dioxide and water. In the case of proteins, part of the sulfur may be oxidized to sulfate, thus using up slightly more oxygen without any concomitant production of $CO_2$.

CARBOHYDRATE. The complete oxidation of glucose may be represented by the equation

$$C_6H_{12}O_6 + 6O_2 \longrightarrow 6CO_2 + 6H_2O \ldots\ldots(+\ 673.0 \text{ Calories})$$

| | | | |
|---|---|---|---|
| 1 mol. | 6 mol. | 6 mol. | 6 mol. |
| 180 gm. | 192 gm. | 264 gm. | 108 gm. |
| 6 × 22.4 liters (at S.T.P.) | | 6 × 22.4 liters (at S.T.P.) | |

## TABLE 44.4

*Data required to calculate the R.Q. and thermal equivalents of typical food components*

| Substance | Mol. Wt. | Calories per G.M.W. | Calories per gm. | O₂ Used | CO₂ Formed | R.Q. | Thermal Equivalents Calories per liter O₂ | Thermal Equivalents Calories per liter CO₂ |
|---|---|---|---|---|---|---|---|---|
| | | | | *l./gm.* | *l./gm.* | | | |
| Galactose............. | 180 | 670.7 | 3.73 | 0.746 | 0.746 | 1.00 | 4.99 | 4.99 |
| Glucose............... | 180 | 673.0 | 3.74 | 0.746 | 0.746 | 1.00 | 5.01 | 5.01 |
| Fructose.............. | 180 | 675.6 | 3.75 | 0.746 | 0.746 | 1.00 | 5.03 | 5.03 |
| Starch................ | (162) | 677.5 | 4.18 | 0.829 | 0.829 | 1.00 | 5.04 | 5.04 |
| Sucrose............... | 342 | 1349.6 | 3.95 | 0.787 | 0.787 | 1.00 | 5.02 | 5.02 |
| Fucose[a] ............. | 164 | 712.0 | 4.34 | 0.888 | 0.819 | 0.92 | 4.89 | 5.30 |
| Desoxyribose.......... | 134 | | | 0.914 | 0.837 | 0.92 | | |
| Tributyrin............ | 302 | 1941.0 | 6.43 | 1.372 | 1.112 | 0.81 | 4.69 | 5.78 |
| Tristearin............ | 891 | 8503.0 | 9.54 | 2.048 | 1.433 | 0.70 | 4.66 | 6.65 |
| Triolein.............. | 885 | 8339.0 | 9.43 | 2.025 | 1.443 | 0.71 | 4.66 | 6.53 |
| Glycine (bomb)........ | 75 | 234.5 | 3.12 | 0.672 | 0.597 | 0.88 | 4.64 | 5.23 |
| Glycine (physiol.)...... | 75 | 158.7 | 2.12 | 0.448 | 0.448 | 1.00 | 4.73 | 4.73 |
| Leucine (physiol.)[b] ..... | 131 | 779.8 | 5.95 | 1.282 | 0.940 | 0.73 | 4.64 | 6.33 |
| Muscle protein[c]........ | | | 4.23 | 0.981[d] | 0.774[e] | 0.79 | 4.32 | 5.43 |

[a] Fucose is an example of a desoxyhexose, $C_6H_{12}O_5$ .

[b] Leucine—energy content (bomb)—855.6 Cal./mole.

" —physiological oxidation: $2 C_6H_{13}O_2N + 15 O_2 = CO(NH_2)_2 + 11 CO_2 + 11 H_2O$.

" —energy content (physiol.)/mole $= \dfrac{(2 \times 855.6) - 151.6}{2} = \dfrac{1559.6}{2} = 779.8$.

[c] Physiological value, calculated according to Loewy (as modified in text).

[d] It is customary to determine urinary N as a measure of protein metabolism. As shown in table 44.6, 1.00 gram of urinary N in the case of this particular protein arose from the catabolism of $100/16.28 = 6.14$ grams protein requiring $6.14 \times 0.981 = 6.02$ liters of $O_2$ (STP) for its metabolism.

[e] Similarly $CO_2$ produced per gram of urinary N $= 6.14 \times 0.774 = 4.75$ liters (STP).

Since 1 gram molecular weight of any gas occupies 1 gram molecular volume (22.4 liters at standard temperature and pressure (S.T.P.)) it will be apparent that 180 grams of glucose require 134.4 liters of $O_2$ and that 1.00 gram would, therefore, require 0.746 liter, or approximately 0.75 liter. Similarly it may be calculated that 0.75 liter of $CO_2$ would be produced. Thus the R.Q. is 0.75/0.75 = 1.00. One may use the ratios of the number of Gram Molecular Volumes (G.M.V.) directly, as a chemist would do, R.Q. = 6/6 = 1.00.

For starches, the equation would be

$$(C_6H_{10}O_5)_n + 6n\ O_2 \rightarrow$$

$$6n\ CO_2 + 5n\ H_2O \dots (+677.5 \text{ Calories})$$

$$R.Q. = \frac{6n\ G.M.V.\ CO_2}{6n\ G.M.V.\ O_2} = 1.00$$

FAT. The fats, being more highly reduced compounds than the carbohydrates, have a higher energy content. Because of their lower oxygen content, they require more oxygen per gram for their combustion. Equations for the complete oxidation of several fats are as follows:

$$2 C_3H_5O_3 (OC_4H_7)_3 + 37 O_2 \rightarrow$$
tributyrin (302)

$$30 CO_2 + 26 H_2O \dots (+1941.1 \text{ Calories})$$

$$2 C_3H_5O_3 (OC_{18}H_{35})_3 + 163 O_2 \rightarrow 114 CO_2 + 110 H_2O$$
tristearin (891)

$$C_3H_5O_3 (OC_{18}H_{33})_3 + 80 O_2 \rightarrow 57 CO_2 + 52 H_2O$$
triolein (885)

tributyrin R.Q. =   30/37   = 0.881

tristearin R.Q. = 114/163 = 0.699

triolein R.Q. =   57/80   = 0.713

The mixed fats of the food, when burned in the body, are generally taken to have an R.Q. of 0.71.

PROTEIN. Amino acids are not oxidized completely in the body, as mentioned earlier. Approximate values for $O_2$ consumed and $CO_2$ produced may be calculated as follows. Assuming complete oxidation, glycine would react thus:

$$4 CH_2 (NH_2) COOH + 9 O_2 \rightarrow 8 CO_2 \\ + 10 H_2O + 2 N_2 .. (+ 4 \times 234.5 \text{ Calories}) \quad (1)$$

Such a reaction does not occur in the body, however; 40 per cent of this substance is excreted as urea. Assuming excretion of all the nitrogen of glycine in the form of urea, the equation for the partial oxidation would be

$$4 \, CH_2 \, (NH_2) \, COOH + 6 \, O_2 \rightarrow \\ 2 \, CO \, (NH_2)_2 + 6CO_2 + 6H_2O \quad (2)$$

One mole of urea, on combustion, liberates 151.6 Calories.

$$2 \, CO \, (NH_2)_2 + 3 \, O_2 \rightarrow 2CO_2 + \\ 4 \, H_2O + 2 \, N_2 \,.. (+ \, 2 \times 151.6 \text{ Calories}) \quad (3)$$

This energy does not become available to the organism because the urea is not oxidized in the body. Therefore the energy liberated in the physiological (partial) oxidation of glycine shown in the second equation is $(938.0 - 303.2) = 634.8$ Calories per 4 moles of glycine, or 158.7 Calories per mole (2.12 Calories per gram). Because of its relatively large oxygen content, glycine is an atypical amino acid. Corresponding calculations for leucine give the data shown in table 44.4.

A typical meat protein (according to Loewy) analyzed as shown in table 44.6, and the constituents contained in the urine and feces per 100 grams of ingested protein are shown in the third column.

The carbon and hydrogen unaccounted for in the excreta were presumably completely oxidized

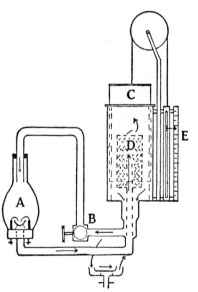

FIG. 44.3. Diagram of oxycalorimeter for determining energy values of foods, etc. (A) Combustion chamber, crucible and electrical connections. (B) Rotary blower. (C) Spirometer bell with oxygen in water seal. (D) Soda lime container. (E) Scale in millimeters for measuring the oxygen used. (F) Mouthpiece with valves for B.M.R. estimation (enlarged). Principle of the Benedict-Roth apparatus for determining B.M.R. is seen by replacing A and B by F. (After Cruickshank, E. & S. Livingstone, Ltd., Edinburgh.)

## TABLE 44.5

*"Metabolic constants" of fat, protein and carbohydrate*

| | Potential Energy | | Oxygen Required[a] | CO2 Produced[a] | R.Q. | Thermal Equivalent of O2 |
|---|---|---|---|---|---|---|
| | Bomb Calorimetry | Physiologically available | | | | |
| | *Cal./ gm.* | *Cal./ gm.* | *l./gm.[a]* | *l./gm.[a]* | | *Cal./l.[a]* |
| Fat....... | 9.3 | 9.0 | 1.94[b] | 1.39 | 0.71 | 4.74 |
| Protein... | 5.4 | 4.0 | 0.97 | 0.78 | 0.80 | 4.46 |
| Carbohydrate... | 4.1 | 4.0 | 0.83 | 0.83 | 1.00 | 5.05 |

[a] Gas measured at S.T.P.

[b] Depends on the fatty acid. For short-chain fatty acids this value is greater, e.g., for tributyrin 2.41.

## TABLE 44.6

*Data used in calculation of R.Q. for oxidation of protein*

(After Loewy)

All values are expressed in grams per 100 grams meat protein

| Constituent | Constituent Ingested | Excreted in Urine and Feces | Portion Not Excreted |
|---|---|---|---|
| C | 52.38 | 10.88 | 41.50 |
| H | 7.27 | 2.87 | 4.40 |
| O | 22.68 | 15.00 | 7.68 |
| N | 16.65 | 16.65[a] | |
| S | 1.02[b] | 1.02[c] | |

[a] The bulk of this nitrogen (16.28 grams) was in the urine. Therefore 1.00 gram urinary N represents 6.14 grams meat protein.

[b] Present as sulfide (methionine) and disulfide (cystine).

[c] Present mainly as ethereal sulfate.

because none of the nitrogen was retained and therefore probably *all the protein was completely burned in the body.* The 7.68 grams of oxygen not excreted may be assumed to have oxidized an equivalent amount of hydrogen ($2/16 \times 7.68 = 0.96$ grams) to form what is sometimes called "intramolecular water," i.e., $H_2O$ formed from H and O in the parent molecule. This would leave $4.40 - 0.96 = 3.44$ grams hydrogen and 41.50 grams carbon to be oxidized.

41.50 grams C require 110.6 grams $O_2$ and produce 152.2 grams $CO_2$

3.44 grams H require 27.5 grams $O_2$

Total $CO_2$ produced: 152.2 grams $\equiv$ 77.4 liters at S.T.P.

Total $O_2$ required: 138.1 grams $\equiv$ 96.7 liters at S.T.P.

Loewy's estimated R.Q. for this protein = 77.4/ 96.7 = 0.80.

Loewy made no allowance for oxygen used in the oxidation of sulfur. The chemistry of cystine was not well understood at that time and methionine was unknown, but it is odd that the conversion of organic sulfur to $SO_3$ was not considered. For simplicity we may use $H_2S$ for writing the equation because the sulfur atoms of methionine and of cysteine are both at the same oxidation level as that in $H_2S$.

$$H_2S + 2\ O_2 \rightarrow SO_3 + H_2O$$

32 grams S require 64 grams $O_2$ ($\equiv$ 44.8 liters at S.T.P.)

1.02 grams S require 2.04 grams $O_2$ ($\equiv$ 1.43 liters)

$\therefore$ Total $O_2$ used for this protein = 138.1 + 2.04 = 140.14 grams $\equiv$ 96.7 + 1.4 = 98.1 liters. Revised estimate for R.Q. of this protein:

$$77.4/98.1 = 0.79$$

The portion used for the oxidation of protein sulfur is small, probably always less than 1.5 per cent of the total oxygen requirement for protein; for practical purposes it may be neglected. Different proteins have different R.Q.'s, as do different fats and carbohydrates, but the values remain close to the commonly used figure of 0.80.

Because alcohol sometimes provides energy for man it may be of interest to note that the R.Q. of ethanol is 0.67.

The value of the respiratory quotient is taken as an indication of the *type* of food being metabolized. It gives no quantitative estimation of the metabolism. An R.Q. around unity is taken to indicate that the material being used is chiefly carbohydrate; one around 0.70 indicates that it is mainly fat.[5]

On an ordinary mixed diet the R.Q. is about 0.85 and in the postabsorptive state (p. 764) about 0.82. In the formation of fat from carbohydrate, as in the fattening of farm animals, an oxygen-rich substance is being converted into one poor in oxygen. Oxygen is "liberated" in the conversion and less, in consequence, is taken in from the outside for general oxidative processes. The R.Q. may therefore rise above unity (up to 1.4). A very low quotient, as is seen in the hibernating animals, is supposed by some to indicate the reverse process, i.e., the conversion of fat to carbohydrate. In the hibernating marmot the R.Q. is between 0.6 and 0.7.

## CALORIMETRIC MEASUREMENTS IN ANIMALS AND MAN

An animal's energy is derived from the food, which is to the body what fuel is to a furnace or machine.[6] We have seen that the law of conservation of energy holds true for the animal body: in a healthy animal which is maintaining a constant weight the intake and output of energy are equal. The food undergoes combustion in the tissues, its carbon being oxidized to carbon dioxide, its hydrogen to water and its potential energy being converted into other forms of energy (mechanical, electrical, chemical and thermal). In a growing animal or in an animal during fattening the energy of the food is in part stored as newly formed tissue.

In the resting body all the energy liberated from the food ultimately appears as heat. It was for this reason that a heat unit was chosen as the most convenient one for measuring and expressing the energy exchanges of the body. This unit, the *large calorie* (Calorie or Cal.) is 1000 times the *small calorie* (calorie or cal.) used in physical measurements.

Calorimetry in man and animals involves two main types of procedure: (a) *direct*, the same in principle as that described above for the bomb calorimeter, and (b) *indirect*, in which the heat production is calculated from the respiratory exchanges. The latter is commonly used, the former rarely.

DIRECT CALORIMETRY. Respiration calorimeters permit measurement of the gaseous exchange and simultaneous heat production. The apparatus (fig. 44.4) designed by Atwater and Rosa (1897) was of such technical perfection that when a known quantity of alcohol was burned in it the resulting carbon dioxide was recovered with an accuracy of 99.8 per cent and the heat to 99.9 per cent of the theoretical value.

The elaborate nature of the apparatus required for this method precludes its use, especially for

---

[5] Cathcart and Markowitz point out, however, that probably too much reliance has been placed upon the value of the R.Q. as an unequivocal criterion of the type of foodstuff undergoing metabolism. The R.Q. in a given instance is undoubtedly a resultant of several different metabolic processes, syntheses and interconversions as well as combustion.

[6] It may be well to remember that the analogy between *fuel for machines* and *food for men* (or animals) must not be pushed too far. Nutrition involves more than chemistry and physics. The available energy of a single foodstuff cannot be estimated without considering the adequacy of other factors in the diet, the effect of other factors on absorption (availability) and the level at which the nutrient is being fed.

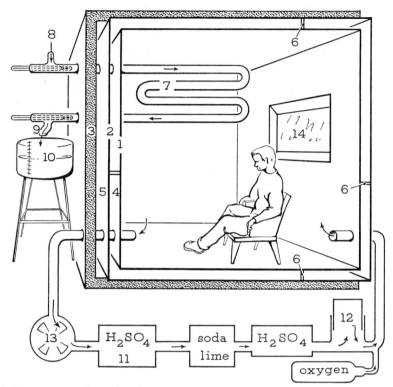

Fig. 44.4. The Atwater-Rosa-Benedict respiration calorimeter has two functional parts, one for measuring the heat production of the subject, the other for measuring the gaseous exchange. An air-tight copper box or small room (1), which is essentially a constant temperature, water-cooled calorimeter, is surrounded by a second copper box (2) and the whole is insulated by an outer layer of cork (3). This construction results in two insulating dead air-spaces (4, 5). Rosa placed thermocouples (6) in series between the two copper walls on the tops, sides and bottom to detect differences in temperature. When the inner and outer copper walls have the same temperature there can be no heat exchange between them. If the temperature of the outer wall increases it is quickly restored to that of the inner wall by a cooling current of water run through pipes (not shown) between the outer copper wall and the insulating wall. A fall in temperature of the outer wall is corrected by electrical warming of this interspace. The heat produced by the subject would cause the temperature of the chamber to rise unless the heat could be removed in some way. This is accomplished by allowing a current of cold water to flow through the copper tubes (7, suspended from the ceiling) at such a rate as to maintain a constant temperature in the chamber. Thermometers on the water intake (8) and outlet (9) give the temperature change; the volume of water which has passed through the cooling system is collected in a vessel (10) and weighed. The weight of water (in kilograms) multiplied by the temperature change in degrees Centigrade gives heat lost by radiation and conduction. To this must be added the latent heat present in the water vapor of the insensible perspiration and exhaled air (about one-quarter of the total heat produced by a man). The amount of this water is determined by weighing the first sulfuric acid absorber (11) before and after the experiment. The heat so carried out is calculated, knowing the latent heat of vaporization of water at 20°C. to be 0.585 Calories per gram.

The same apparatus can be used to determine the gaseous exchange of the subject. In principle, the procedure is as follows: air from the chamber is passed through the first sulfuric acid absorber to remove the water vapor, then through a moist soda lime absorber to remove carbon dioxide. A second sulfuric absorber takes up the moisture liberated from the soda lime. The gain in weight of the last pair of absorbers equals the carbon dioxide produced by the subject. The oxygen used is determined by adding sufficient oxygen to a spirometer (12) to maintain a constant pressure in the system and by weighing the oxygen cylinder before and after the experiment. The circulation of the air in the system is maintained by a fan (13). A window (14) permits observation of the subject. Thermometers (not shown) record the temperature of the room and of the subject.

the human subject, in any ordinary laboratory or clinic. There are indeed only a very few in existence.

The calorimeter consists of an insulated chamber large enough to accommodate an animal or a man. The heat conducted and radiated from the body is absorbed by water circulating in coils of copper pipes. The temperature of this water as it enters and leaves the chamber being known, and also its quantity, the heat production in Calories can be determined. To this must be added the energy carried out by the water vapor given off by the lungs and skin. This amounts to about one-quarter of the total heat production. (Further details about the apparatus and the calculations are given in the legend, fig. 44.4.) A calorimeter of this type is usually combined with apparatus for determining the heat production by indirect calorimetry as described below, the instrument being then referred to as a respiration calorimeter.

INDIRECT CALORIMETRY. The heat production of the body during a given period can be estimated using the thermal equivalents if one knows the quantity of oxygen consumed or of carbon dioxide produced during that time. As mentioned above, the estimate is more reliable when based upon oxygen consumption. Even so, the

### TABLE 44.7
(After Zuntz and Schumberg, modified by Lusk*)

| Nonprotein Respiratory Quotient | Calories per Liter $O_2$ | Calories Derived from | |
|---|---|---|---|
| | | Carbohydrate | Fat |
| | | *per cent* | *per cent* |
| 0.707 | 4.686 | 0 | 100 |
| 0.71 | 4.690 | 1.10 | 98.9 |
| 0.72 | 4.702 | 4.76 | 95.2 |
| 0.73 | 4.714 | 8.40 | 91.6 |
| 0.74 | 4.727 | 12.0 | 88.0 |
| 0.75 | 4.739 | 15.6 | 84.4 |
| 0.76 | 4.751 | 19.2 | 80.8 |
| 0.77 | 4.764 | 22.8 | 77.2 |
| 0.78 | 4.776 | 26.3 | 73.7 |
| 0.79 | 4.788 | 29.9 | 70.1 |
| 0.80 | 4.801 | 33.4 | 66.6 |
| 0.81 | 4.813 | 36.9 | 63.1 |
| 0.82 | 4.825 | 40.3 | 59.7 |
| 0.83 | 4.838 | 43.8 | 56.2 |
| 0.84 | 4.850 | 47.2 | 52.8 |
| 0.85 | 4.862 | 50.7 | 49.3 |
| 0.86 | 4.875 | 54.1 | 45.9 |
| 0.87 | 4.887 | 57.5 | 42.5 |
| 0.88 | 4.899 | 60.8 | 39.2 |
| 0.89 | 4.911 | 64.2 | 35.8 |
| 0.90 | 4.924 | 67.5 | 32.5 |
| 0.91 | 4.936 | 70.8 | 29.2 |
| 0.92 | 4.948 | 74.1 | 25.9 |
| 0.93 | 4.961 | 77.4 | 22.6 |
| 0.94 | 4.973 | 80.7 | 19.3 |
| 0.95 | 4.985 | 84.0 | 16.0 |
| 0.96 | 4.998 | 87.2 | 12.8 |
| 0.97 | 5.010 | 90.4 | 9.58 |
| 0.98 | 5.022 | 93.6 | 6.37 |
| 0.99 | 5.035 | 96.8 | 3.18 |
| 1.00 | 5.047 | 100.0 | 0 |

* This table has been further modified by Cathcart and Cuthbertson, see J. Physiol., 1931, **72**, 349.

food mixture undergoing combustion, as indicated by the R.Q., must be taken into account. The heat or caloric values (thermal equivalent) of a liter of oxygen at different respiratory quotients is given in table 44.7 compiled by Zuntz and Schumberg (as modified by Lusk).

In table 44.7 the percentages of fat and carbohydrate undergoing combustion have been calculated for respiratory quotients ranging from 0.707 to 1.00. These so-called *nonprotein respiratory quotients* were obtained by determining the total oxygen consumption and carbon dioxide produced and then subtracting the volumes of these gases exchanged in the catabolism of protein. The quantity of protein undergoing catabolism is obtained from the urinary nitrogen, each gram of the latter being considered, by convention, equivalent to 6.25 grams of protein. In *precise* experiments upon heat production, the calories produced from the catabolism of protein as well as those derived from fat and carbohydrate would require to be determined. For example, a subject may be found to produce per hour 13.50 liters of carbon dioxide, consume 16.00 liters of oxygen and excrete 0.50 gram of nitrogen in the urine. According to Loewy's data, each gram of urinary nitrogen represents the production of 4.75 liters of carbon dioxide and the consumption of 6.02 liters of oxygen (table 44.4, footnote).

Therefore:

$CO_2$ produced by the subject in the catabolism of protein is $0.50 \times 4.75 = 2.38$ liters

$O_2$ consumed in the catabolism of protein is $0.50 \times 6.02 = 3.01$ liters

Then:

non-protein $CO_2$ production is $13.50 - 2.38 = 11.12$ liters

non-protein $O_2$ consumption is $16.00 - 3.01 = 12.99$ liters

the nonprotein respiratory quotient is

$$11.12/12.99 = 0.86$$

It will be seen from table 44.7 that at this R.Q. the caloric equivalent of a liter of oxygen is 4.875. The heat produced by the combustion of non-protein materials is therefore, $12.99 \times 4.875 = 63.3$ Calories of which 54.1 per cent is derived from carbohydrate and 45.9 per cent from fat.

The heat production due to protein is $3.01 \times 4.50 = 13.5$ Calories. As will be shown in the section on *Energy Balance* this may be estimated in another way: the caloric equivalent of each gram of urinary N is 26.4, so the heat production due to protein may also be obtained approximately by multiplying the figure for the urinary nitrogen (0.50) by 26.4 = 13.2. The average value may be taken as 13.4 Calories.

The total heat production per hour is therefore 63.3 + 13.4 = 76.7 Calories. Of this 34.2 Calories or 45 per cent are derived from carbohydrate, 29.1 Calories or 38 per cent from fat and 17 per cent from protein.

In ordinary determinations of the basal metabolic rate (p. 765) urinary nitrogen is not measured and the foregoing calculations are not undertaken; only a slight error is involved if the R.Q. is assumed to be 0.82 and the heat production taken directly from table 44.7.

THE ISODYNAMIC LAW. It was demonstrated by Rubner that just as the production of heat by a stove may be maintained at a constant level by burning different types of fuel, so in the generation of animal heat the different foodstuffs may replace one another in the diet in accordance with their heat producing values. The amounts shown of the following substances are isodynamic:

| | | |
|---|---|---|
| 100 grams of fat × 9 | = | 900 Calories |
| 225 grams of starch × 4 | = | 900 Calories |
| 225 grams of protein × 4 | = | 900 Calories |
| 128 grams of ethanol × 7 | = | 900 Calories |

HEAT PRODUCTION IN RELATION TO SURFACE AREA. The heat produced by an individual at rest is proportional to the surface area of his body. Thus a fasting adult man and a starving dog, although the surface area of each and the *total* heat production were widely different, were shown by Rubner to give out in 24 hours closely similar amounts of heat *per square meter of body surface*, namely, 1134 and 1112 Calories respectively. A small animal, e.g., a mouse, therefore, since its surface area is greater in proportion to its mass, and since it generates the same amount of heat per unit of body surface, must obviously generate more heat per unit of body weight than a larger animal. The heat is produced in the tissues (muscles, liver, etc.); consequently these, in the case of the smaller animal, must be the seat of a much more active metabolism (see table 44.8).

The shape of an object controls its surface area per unit weight. A sphere has the least surface area per unit of mass. The area of a cube is also relatively small; that of a thin sheet reaches the maximum. A few examples will illustrate the variation. A *sphere* (of material with density = 1) weighing 1000 gm. would have a radius of 6.20

### TABLE 44.8

*Showing relation of heat production per kilogram and per square meter of body surface in animals of different sizes*

| | Weight | Calories | |
|---|---|---|---|
| | | Per kilogram | Per square meter surface |
| | *kg.* | | |
| Ox | 391 | 19.1 | 1567 |
| Pig | 128.0 | 19.1 | 1078 |
| Man | 64.3 | 32.1 | 1042 |
| Dog | 15.2 | 51.5 | 1039 |
| Goose* | 3.5 | 66.7 | 967 |
| Fowl* | 2.0 | 71.0 | 947 |
| Mouse | 0.018 | 654.0 | 1188 |

* The relatively low figures for the heat production of birds shown in the last column is due to their bodies containing a high proportion of osseous tissue which has an extremely low metabolism.

cm. and a surface area of 484 sq. cm. A *cube* of the same weight would have an area of 600 sq. cm. An *elongated cylinder* (31.9 cm. by 6.32 cm. in diameter) would have a surface area of 694 sq. cm.; the same amount of material in the form of a *squat cylinder* (20 cm. diameter by 3.18 cm.) would have an area of 828. A rectangular block of the same weight (5 by 10 by 20 cm.) would have an area of 700 sq. cm.; a thick sheet (0.2 by 10 by 500) would have 10,204 and a thin sheet (0.01 by 200 by 500) would have approximately 200,000 sq. cm. Elliptical bodies with cylindrical appendages have a surface area per unit of weight intermediate between that of a sphere and an elongated cylinder.

PHYSIOLOGICAL CONDITIONS WHICH STIMULATE METABOLISM. The heat production of the body is increased by (a) muscular work, (b) food, (c) a fall in environmental temperature, or (d) a rise in body temperature (fever). These influences will be considered later.

### *Indirect Calorimetry: Determination of the Heat Production from the Respiratory Exchanges*

The results of indirect calorimetry agree within less than 1 per cent with those obtained by the direct method. Two forms of apparatus—the *closed-circuit* and the *open-circuit* or *air-current* types—are employed for indirect calorimetry. In the *closed-circuit* method the subject rebreathes the air contained in a closed system; the carbon dioxide eliminated by the subject is re-

## TABLE 44.9

*Table for reduction to 0°C. and 760 mm. Hg and dry of 1 liter of air saturated with humidity, from 10° to 25°C., and 740 to 780 mm. (29.13 inches to 30.71 inches) of mercury*

(Intermediate values may be obtained by interpolation)

| Temperature | Barometer | | | | | | | | | | | | | | | | | | | | | Temperature |
|---|---|---|---|---|---|---|---|---|---|---|---|---|---|---|---|---|---|---|---|---|---|---|
| | 29.13 740 | 29.21 742 | 29.29 744 | 29.37 746 | 29.45 748 | 29.53 750 | 29.60 752 | 29.68 754 | 29.76 756 | 29.84 758 | 29.92 760 | 30.00 762 | 30.08 764 | 30.16 766 | 30.24 768 | 30.31 770 | 30.39 772 | 30.47 774 | 30.55 776 | 30.63 778 | 30.71 780 | |
| 10 | 927.7 | 930.2 | 932.6 | 935.1 | 937.6 | 940.4 | 942.9 | 945.4 | 947.9 | 950.5 | 953.0 | 955.6 | 958.0 | 960.6 | 963.1 | 965.7 | 968.3 | 970.8 | 973.3 | 975.9 | 978.4 | 10 |
| 11 | 923.6 | 926.1 | 928.5 | 931.0 | 933.5 | 936.3 | 938.8 | 941.3 | 943.8 | 946.4 | 948.9 | 951.5 | 953.9 | 956.5 | 959.0 | 961.6 | 964.1 | 966.6 | 969.1 | 971.6 | 974.2 | 11 |
| 12 | 919.5 | 921.8 | 924.2 | 926.7 | 929.3 | 931.8 | 934.3 | 936.8 | 939.4 | 942.0 | 944.4 | 947.0 | 949.4 | 951.9 | 954.4 | 957.0 | 959.5 | 962.0 | 964.5 | 967.1 | 969.6 | 12 |
| 13 | 915.4 | 918.0 | 920.4 | 922.9 | 925.4 | 928.0 | 930.4 | 932.9 | 935.5 | 938.1 | 940.5 | 943.1 | 945.5 | 948.1 | 950.6 | 953.1 | 955.6 | 958.1 | 960.6 | 963.2 | 965.7 | 13 |
| 14 | 911.3 | 913.9 | 916.3 | 918.8 | 921.3 | 923.8 | 926.2 | 928.8 | 931.3 | 933.9 | 936.2 | 938.9 | 941.3 | 943.8 | 946.3 | 948.8 | 951.3 | 953.8 | 956.3 | 958.8 | 961.3 | 14 |
| 15 | 907.1 | 909.7 | 912.1 | 914.6 | 917.1 | 919.6 | 922.0 | 924.5 | 927.1 | 929.7 | 932.0 | 934.6 | 937.0 | 939.5 | 942.0 | 944.4 | 947.0 | 949.6 | 952.0 | 954.5 | 957.0 | 15 |
| 16 | 902.9 | 905.5 | 907.9 | 910.4 | 912.9 | 915.4 | 917.8 | 920.3 | 922.8 | 925.4 | 927.8 | 930.4 | 932.8 | 935.2 | 937.7 | 940.1 | 942.6 | 945.2 | 947.6 | 950.1 | 952.6 | 16 |
| 17 | 898.7 | 901.3 | 903.7 | 906.2 | 908.7 | 911.1 | 913.5 | 916.0 | 918.5 | 921.1 | 923.5 | 926.0 | 928.5 | 930.9 | 933.4 | 935.8 | 938.3 | 940.9 | 943.3 | 945.8 | 948.3 | 17 |
| 18 | 894.5 | 897.1 | 899.5 | 902.0 | 904.5 | 906.8 | 909.2 | 911.8 | 914.2 | 916.8 | 919.2 | 921.7 | 924.2 | 926.6 | 929.1 | 931.5 | 933.9 | 936.5 | 938.9 | 941.4 | 943.9 | 18 |
| 19 | 890.2 | 892.7 | 895.1 | 897.6 | 900.1 | 902.5 | 904.9 | 907.4 | 909.9 | 912.5 | 914.8 | 917.2 | 919.7 | 922.2 | 924.7 | 927.1 | 929.5 | 932.0 | 934.4 | 936.9 | 939.4 | 19 |
| 20 | 885.9 | 888.4 | 890.8 | 893.3 | 895.8 | 898.1 | 900.5 | 902.9 | 905.3 | 907.7 | 910.4 | 912.8 | 915.2 | 917.7 | 920.2 | 922.6 | 925.0 | 927.5 | 930.3 | 932.5 | 935.0 | 20 |
| 21 | 881.8 | 884.3 | 886.7 | 889.2 | 891.7 | 894.0 | 896.4 | 898.9 | 901.3 | 903.9 | 906.2 | 908.6 | 911.1 | 913.5 | 916.0 | 918.4 | 920.8 | 923.3 | 925.7 | 928.2 | 930.7 | 21 |
| 22 | 877.1 | 879.5 | 881.9 | 884.4 | 886.9 | 889.0 | 891.4 | 894.1 | 896.6 | 899.2 | 901.4 | 903.8 | 906.3 | 908.7 | 911.2 | 913.6 | 916.0 | 918.4 | 920.9 | 923.4 | 926.0 | 22 |
| 23 | 872.6 | 875.0 | 877.4 | 879.9 | 882.4 | 884.7 | 887.1 | 889.5 | 892.0 | 894.6 | 896.9 | 899.2 | 901.7 | 904.1 | 906.6 | 909.0 | 911.4 | 913.8 | 916.3 | 918.8 | 921.3 | 23 |
| 24 | 868.1 | 870.6 | 873.0 | 875.5 | 878.0 | 880.1 | 882.5 | 885.0 | 887.5 | 890.1 | 892.3 | 894.6 | 897.1 | 899.5 | 902.0 | 904.4 | 906.8 | 909.2 | 911.6 | 914.0 | 916.5 | 24 |
| 25 | 863.5 | 865.9 | 868.3 | 870.8 | 873.3 | 875.7 | 878.1 | 880.5 | 882.9 | 885.5 | 887.9 | 890.1 | 892.6 | 895.0 | 897.4 | 899.8 | 902.1 | 904.5 | 906.9 | 909.3 | 911.7 | 25 |

TABLE 44.10

*Volumes of oxygen in inspired air corresponding to 100 volumes of expired air with different percentages of nitrogen*

| Percentage Nitrogen in Expired Air | Volumes of Oxygen in Inspired Air | Percentage Nitrogen in Expired Air | Volumes of Oxygen in Inspired Air |
|---|---|---|---|
| 78.5 | 20.80 | 79.6 | 21.09 |
| 78.6 | 20.83 | 79.7 | 21.12 |
| 78.7 | 20.85 | 79.8 | 21.14 |
| 78.8 | 20.88 | 79.9 | 21.17 |
| 78.9 | 20.91 | 80.0 | 21.20 |
| 79.0 | 20.93 | 80.1 | 21.22 |
| 79.1 | 20.96 | 80.2 | 21.25 |
| 79.2 | 20.99 | 80.3 | 21.28 |
| 79.3 | 21.01 | 80.4 | 21.30 |
| 79.4 | 21.04 | 80.5 | 21.33 |
| 79.5 | 21.07 | | |

moved by soda-lime and weighed; a measured volume of oxygen is supplied to replenish that which has been absorbed. In the *open-circuit* type, the subject inspires room air and expires into some form of container: the entire volume of expired air is measured and a sample analyzed for its carbon dioxide and oxygen percentages. Among the closed-circuit types of apparatus are those of Regnault and Reiset, and of Benedict and associates. The Douglas bag and Tissot methods are of the open-circuit type. In Haldane's method for small animals, although it is of the open-circuit or air-current type, the carbon dioxide is absorbed and weighed.

CLOSED-CIRCUIT METHODS. In the Regnault-Reiset type of apparatus, the air is circulated through a closed system of which a chamber, large enough to accommodate the subject, forms a part. Only a few institutions on this continent, such as the Russell Sage Institute in New York and the Nutrition Laboratory at Washington, possess an apparatus of this type (Atwater-Rosa) suitable for metabolic studies upon man. It is usually combined with an apparatus of the direct type. The construction of a closed circuit type of apparatus for laboratory animals is not, however, such a difficult matter (fig. 44.5). The air in the system is rebreathed repeatedly, carbon dioxide and water vapor being removed and oxygen supplied to replace that consumed. The quantity of carbon dioxide eliminated by the animal is given by the difference between the weights of the soda-lime container at the beginning and end of the experiment. Oxygen is run into the system from a cylinder and meas-

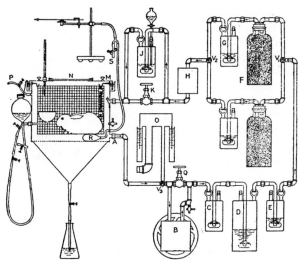

FIG. 44.5. Schematic outline of respiration apparatus for small animals. The air leaves the chamber at A and after passing through the rotary blower B, which keeps the ventilating current in motion, is forced through the glass vessel C, which serves as a safety trap. The air then passes through the bottles D and E containing sulphuric acid to remove the moisture. The air, now water-free, but containing the $CO_2$ produced by the animal and lacking the $O_2$ which the animal has consumed, passes into the 2-way valve $V_1$, where it may be deflected into the bottle F containing soda lime for the absorption of $CO_2$. The moisture gained from the soda lime is absorbed by sulphuric acid in bottle G. The air then passes through a second 2-way tap $V_2$ to H containing dry sodium bicarbonate which removes the traces of acid vapor taken up by the air in passing through bottle G. J is a glass vessel containing water which supplies sufficient moisture to the air for the comfort of the animal. K is a by-pass valve. The chamber is constructed of copper and has a cover with a water seal M. N is a glass plate through which the animal can be observed. O is a spirometer attached to the system on the intake side of the rotary blower B. (From F. G. Benedict.)

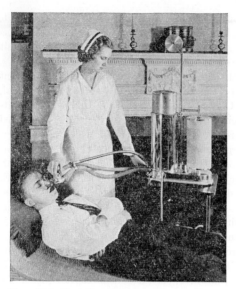

FIG. 44.6. Benedict-Roth apparatus (courtesy of Warren E. Collins, Inc., Boston).

ured by means of a gas meter or by weighing the cylinder at the beginning and end of the experiment. The air in the chamber is analyzed at the end of the observation in order to ensure that no change in its composition has occurred.

In other closed-circuit methods, such as the one described below, the subject is not enclosed within a chamber; he simply breathes in and out of the apparatus through a connecting tube.

*Clinical types of closed-circuit apparatus.* In the earlier clinical types the subject was connected by means of a mouthpiece and flexible tubing to the closed system and both carbon dioxide elimination and oxygen usage were determined. In the type most commonly used today—the Benedict-Roth apparatus (figs. 44.6 and 44.7)—the heat production is calculated from the oxygen consumption alone. In order to purify the air the carbon dioxide is absorbed by soda-lime but the amount of this gas eliminated is not measured. In determining the basal metabolism (p. 764) the subject lies upon a couch and breathes in and out of the instrument through a mouthpiece and two wide-bore tubes (inspiratory and expiratory) provided with valves. The nose is clipped. The main part of the instrument consists of a bell-type spirometer. This is a hollow double-walled cylindrical vessel. In the narrow space between the two walls fits a second inverted hollow cylindrical vessel or bell. The bell is counterpoised so that it rides easily up or down in the annular space between the two walls. This space contains water which acts as a seal.

At the commencement of the experiment, sufficient oxygen is admitted from an oxygen cylinder to raise a pointer on the spirometer bell to the zero mark upon an adjoined scale which has been calibrated to oxygen volumes. The breathing of the subject through the inspiratory and expiratory tubes keeps the air circulating freely through the system. As oxygen is consumed the spirometer falls and from the difference in the levels of the pointer at the beginning and end of the experiment the oxygen usage is calculated. The volume of oxygen used, dry and reduced to standard temperature and pressure (see p. 457) is then calculated. The heat production is found by reference to the table of respiratory quotients given on page 756.

The R.Q. of the subject is not determined. The average R.Q. in the postabsorptive state (see p. 764) (0.82) is assumed. It will be seen from table 44.7 that at this R.Q. the caloric equivalent of 1 liter of oxygen is 4.825.

OPEN-CIRCUIT OR AIR-CURRENT METHODS. In the *Haldane type* of calorimeter (which is suitable only for small animals, mice, rats or rabbits)

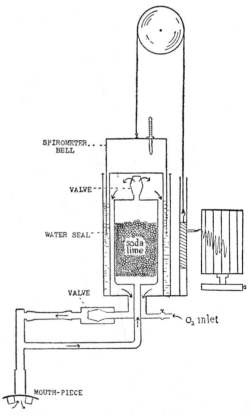

FIG. 44.7. Sectional view of Benedict-Roth closed-circuit respiration apparatus.

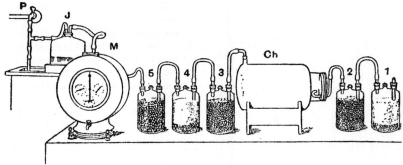

FIG. 44.8. Haldane's respiration apparatus. 1 and 4, soda lime; 2, 3 and 5, pumice stone soaked in sulphuric acid; Ch, animal chamber; M, meter. J is an inverted bell-jar standing in a trough of water, it serves to prevent sudden excess of negative pressure and to indicate the pressure actually employed. P, pump. (After Haldane.)

a current of air is drawn through the system (fig. 44.8). Carbon dioxide and water are removed from the air before it enters the chamber and again after its exit therefrom. The carbon dioxide absorber on the outgoing current of air is weighed at the commencement and end of the experiment as in the Regnault-Reiset method, in order to obtain the quantity of carbon dioxide eliminated. The system with the exception of the first pair of absorbers and including the animal is then weighed. Since only oxygen has entered this part of the system (the air being $CO_2$-free and dry) the gain in weight during the experiment gives the quantity of oxygen consumed by the animal.

*The Douglas bag and Tissot methods (gasometric methods).* In these methods the subject inspires *atmospheric* air and expires into a bag (Douglas method) or into a large bell-type spirometer (Tissot method). At the end of the experiment the total volume of expired air is measured and samples are analyzed for carbon dioxide and oxygen (figs. 44.9 and 44.10).

*Gas analysis.* The sample of expired air is drawn into the graduated burette of a Haldane gas analysis apparatus, saturated with water vapor and its volume measured (fig. 44.11). It

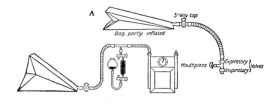

FIG. 44.9. Showing A, Douglas bag and tubing; B, Douglas bag with sampling bulb attached and gas meter for measuring the total volume of expired air (after Douglas and Priestley); C, subject equipped with Douglas bag apparatus during running or other types of muscular exercise. (After Hill.)

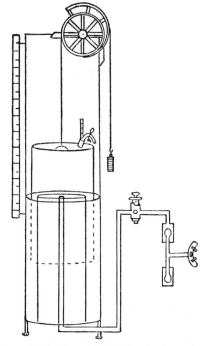

FIG. 44.10. Diagram of Tissot spirometer

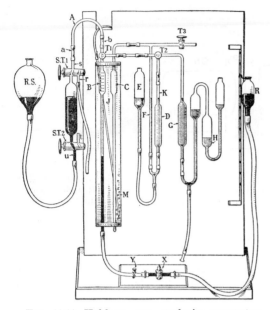

FIG. 44.11. Haldane gas analysis apparatus (small pattern) showing a gas sampler in position. A, glass tube connected to gas sampler; B, gas burette; C, control tube; D, caustic soda absorption pipette; E, caustic soda reservoir; F, caustic pressure tube; G, pyrogallol absorption pipette; H, caustic soda seal; J, waterjacket; M, aeration tube; R, mercury reservoir; X, one-way tap to control movements of mercury; Y, screw clip for fine adjustments of pressure in K after the tap X has been closed; R.S., mercury reservoir for gas sampler; S.T.1 and S.T.2, taps of gas sampler with double ports; r and t, side tubes by means of which, when S.T.1 or S.T.2 are placed in position, the "dead spaces" of these taps and of the tube A can be filled with mercury; a, rubber connection, any air bubble in A may be expelled here as described in text; F, pressure tube for control; K, pressure tube for burette. Note T3 is usually a three-way tap, placed at the junction of the vertical and horizontal tubes. (From Lamb, *An Introduction to Human Experimental Physiology*.)

is then passed back and forth through the bulb containing potassium hydroxide solution which absorbs the carbon dioxide. It is then measured again. The difference between the two measurements gives the volume of carbon dioxide in the sample. Next, the oxygen is removed by passing the sample through a solution of potassium pyrogallate. The sample is measured a third time and the shrinkage in volume as shown by the difference between the second and third readings gives the quantity of oxygen absorbed. From the data so obtained the percentages of carbon dioxide and oxygen in the sample of air are calculated.

*Calculation of results* The following illustrates the steps in an actual metabolism experiment, using the Douglas or Tissot method.

Period of observation 10 minutes, barometer 751.5 mm. Hg.

Volume of expired air as determined by passing the expired air, collected in a bag, through a meter (Douglas method) or as indicated by spirometer (Tissot method) = 70 liters.

Temperature of expired air (in meter or spirometer) 20°C.

The volume of the gases must be reduced to standard conditions, namely, to 760 mm. Hg pressure and to 273° absolute temperature (i.e., to 0°C.), and dry (i.e., the pressure of water vapor must be deducted from the barometer reading). The pressure of water vapor at 20°C. is 17.5 mm. So the corrected reading is;—

$$751.5 - 17.5 = 734.0 \text{ mm.}$$

The volume of the expired air at standard temperature and pressure (S.T.P.) and dry is therefore

$$70 \times \frac{734}{760} \times \frac{273}{273 + 20}$$

or

$70 \times 0.8993 = 62.95$ liters during the period of observation (10 minutes) or 6295 cc. per minute. In practice these detailed calculations are avoided by reference to table 44.9 which gives the required factor by which the observed volume is multiplied in order to reduce it to standard conditions and dry.

Result of gas analyses:

| Expired air | Inspired air |
|---|---|
| $CO_2 = 3.50$ per cent | $CO_2 = 0.04$ per cent |
| $O_2 = 16.90$ per cent | $O_2 = 20.93$ per cent |
| $N_2 = 79.60$ per cent | $N_2 = 79.03$ per cent |

Since the $O_2$ percentages in expired and inspired airs are 16.90 and 20.93 respectively it might be thought that $20.93 - 16.90$ would give the percentage of $O_2$ absorbed. It will be noticed, however, that the percentage of $N_2$ is higher in the expired than in the inspired air. Nitrogen is inert insofar as respiration is concerned, being neither produced nor retained in the body, i.e., its absolute amount is not altered. Therefore, its greater proportion in the expired air can only mean that the volume of the inspired air (which of course was not measured) must have been greater than that of the *dry* expired air. So then, the volume of $O_2$ inspired must also have been greater than appeared from the analysis of the expired air. The cause of the discrepancy is that part of the absorbed oxygen has combined with hydrogen and in other ways, and so has not appeared as $CO_2$. The extent to which the $O_2$ in the inspired air exceeds that shown by the analysis of the expired air is proportional to the increased percentage of $N_2$ in the latter. Instead of the inspired air having contained 20.93

volumes of $O_2$ for every 100 volumes of air expired, it must have contained

$$20.93 \times \frac{79.60}{79.03}, \text{ or } 0.265 \text{ (a constant factor)} \times 79.60$$

$$= 21.09 \text{ volumes.}$$

Therefore the $O_2$ absorption is

$$\frac{21.09 - 16.90}{100} \times 6295 = 264 \text{ c.c. per minute.}$$

The calculation is abbreviated by the use of table 44.10.

The quantity of $CO_2$ produced may be calculated without correction since its percentage in the inspired air is negligible. Hence:

$$\frac{3.50 - 0.04}{100} \times 6295 = 218 \text{ c.c. per minute.}$$

The respiratory quotient is therefore

$$\frac{\text{Vol. } CO_2 \text{ expired} = 218}{\text{Vol. } O_2 \text{ consumed} = 264} = 0.82$$

The caloric values of $O_2$ and $CO_2$ are given in, or can be calculated from table 44.7, p. 756. The heat production may be calculated from either of these values. For example, when the R.Q. is 0.82 the caloric value of 1000 cc. of $O_2$ is 4.825. Therefore, 264 cc. of $O_2$ represents a heat production of $4.825 \times (264/1000) = 1.27$ Cal. per minute or 76.20 Cal. per hour.

### The Energy Balance

Rubner placed a full-grown dog in a calorimeter in which the heat production could be measured directly. He fed the animal measured amounts of food for which the actual heat values had been calculated. The heat generated by the animal during the experiment, which extended in most cases over several days, when added to the heat equivalent of the excreta was found to agree, within about 1 per cent, with the calculated heat value of the ingested food. In other words, the energy intake and output balanced and the application to the body of the law of the conservation of energy was demonstrated (see table 44.11). Corresponding results were obtained by Atwater for man.

Rubner also demonstrated that the heat production of an animal as *calculated from the respiratory exchanges* (indirect calorimetry) agrees within 1 per cent with that *measured by direct calorimetry* a brilliant confirmation of the conclusion arrived at by Lavoisier 100 years earlier.

TABLE 44.11*

*Comparison of heat actually produced from metabolism of food with that calculated.*

| Food | Number of Days | Heat Calculated | Heat Directly Determined | Difference in Percentage |
|---|---|---|---|---|
| | | *Cal.* | *Cal.* | |
| Starvation | 5 | 1296.3 | 1305.2 | +0.68 |
| | 2 | 1091.2 | 1056.6 | −3.17 |
| Fat | 5 | 1510.1 | 1495.3 | −0.97 |
| Meat and fat | 8 | 2492.4 | 2488.0 | −0.17 |
| | 12 | 3985.4 | 3958.4 | −0.68 |
| Meat | 6 | 2249.8 | 2276.9 | +1.20 |
| | 7 | 4780.8 | 4769.3 | −0.23 |

* From Rubner. (Ztschr. Biol., **30**, 73, 1894.)

Rubner fed 100 grams dried muscle powder (5.5 grams ash) with the following results:

| *Material balance* | C | H | O | N |
|---|---|---|---|---|
| Content in protein fed (grams) | 50.50 | 7.60 | 20.97 | 15.40 |
| Excreted in urine | 9.63 | 2.52 | 10.90 | 15.16 |
| Excreted in feces | 1.67 | 0.25 | 0.54 | 0.24 |
| Total in urine and feces | 11.30 | 2.77 | 11.44 | 15.40 |
| Balance for respiration | 39.20 | 4.83 | 9.53 | |

*Energy balance*

| In 100 grams muscle powder (bomb) | 534.50 Calories |
|---|---|
| Lost in excreta { urine | 112.94 Calories |
| { feces | 16.83 |
| Total lost | 129.77 |
| Fuel value to body | 404.73 Calories |

(Energy lost per gram urine-N

$$= 112.9/15.16 = 7.45 \text{ Calories})$$

N in muscle protein

$$= 15.40 \times 100/94.5 = 16.3 \text{ per cent.}$$

Since the urinary N arises from the N in dietary protein it is obvious that 1 gram urinary N represents $100/16.3 = 6.14$ grams dietary protein absorbed by the body. Energy loss per gram urine − N ($\equiv 6.14$ grams protein) $\equiv 7.45$ Calories.

$\therefore$ Energy loss in urine per gram *protein* $\equiv 1.21$ Calories. Rubner even made corrections for the heat of imbibition of the protein and heat of solution of urea (2.69 and 1.99 Calories, respectively) to give a value of 400.05 as the number of Calories available from 100 grams of dried meat solids (94.5 grams of muscle protein). The physiologically available energy per gram of muscle protein is thus $400/94.5 = 4.23$ Calories.

It is sometimes useful to be able to estimate the energy obtained from dietary protein using the so-called calorie equivalent of each gram of urinary nitrogen. In Rubner's experiment 15.16 grams of urinary N were excreted when 400 Calories were liberated from the ingested protein. Thus each gram of urinary N corresponds to about 26.4 Calories retained by the body.

Atwater and his colleagues in America analyzed urines from 46 persons and measured the heat of combustion of the organic residue. For every gram of *nitrogen in the urine* they found unoxidized material sufficient to yield 7.9 Calories. This value is close to Rubner's estimate of 7.5. It represents about 1.25 Calories per gram of protein absorbed, *if the person is in nitrogen equilibrium.*

Although nitrogen in the urine can only arise from protein that has been absorbed, some writers have erroneously applied the correction to the protein *eaten!* Obviously, if digestibility is low or if the person or animal under study is retaining nitrogen for growth or losing nitrogen as a result of a wasting disease, different values would be obtained per gram of protein ingested. The use of the factor 1.25 Calories per gram of protein for the loss in the urine is hallowed by convention although it is based on work done over 50 years ago with diets (the details of which are unknown today) fed to adult men. The effects of individual foodstuffs on males and females at different stages of growth should be determined, since the available energy doubtless varies considerably with age.

## The Basal Metabolic Rate (B.M.R.)

This is the term applied to the heat production of a subject who though awake is as nearly as possible at complete *muscular* and *mental rest*, and is in the *postabsorptive* state (i.e., from 12 to 14 hours after a light meal when, it is assumed, the digestive processes are quiescent). The room temperature should be 20°C. For example, the prospective subject of a basal rate determination is directed to refrain from undue muscular exertion or fatiguing effort of any kind for 24 hours previously. A light meal with the minimum amount of protein is taken not later than 7 o'clock the night before the test which is undertaken at about 9 o'clock in the morning. For a period of 30 minutes or so before, as well as during the test the subject should be lying down comfortably in a room with subdued lighting.

The apparatus most commonly employed for the determination of the basal metabolic rate in the clinic is the instrument of Benedict and Roth (p. 760). Tissot's method or the bag method of Douglas is also sometimes used.

### Basal Metabolic Rate Standards

We have seen that the metabolism is proportional to the body's surface area rather than to its weight (p. 757). Of two men of the same weight, one tall and lean and the other short and stout, the former will have a greater heat production. It is possible that this explains, in part at least, why a man of thin build often eats more than a stouter man of about the same weight. Since normal adults do not differ very greatly in size and shape, it may be stated as an approximation that the heat production of the human body is one Calorie per kilogram per hour. But for the reasons just given it is much more accurate to express the basal metabolism in terms of body surface. Thus, the average basal rate of normal men between the ages of 25 and 50 years is from 40 to 37 Calories per square meter of body surface per hour. This value is constant for all normal men whether they are tall, short, thin or stout, large or small. Knowing a subject's height and weight his surface area can be determined at a glance from the chart (fig. 44.12), or from table 44.12; or it may be calculated from the height-weight formula.[7] The average surface area for adults in Canada and the United States is about 1.6 square meters for women and 1.8 for men; the total basal heat production of the majority of normal adults ranges from 1400 to 1800 Calories per day.

The heat production per square meter of body surface is arrived at by dividing the value for the total heat production per hour of the subject, as determined by one or other of the methods already described, by the figure for the surface area. For example, a man 175 cm. tall weighing 75 kg. has a surface area of 1.91 sq. meters. His total heat production is, say, 76.20 Calories per hour. His heat production per square meter per hour is therefore

$$76.20/1.91 = 39.8 \text{ Calories}$$

[7] The formula introduced by Meeh and modified by Du Bois and Du Bois is as follows:
$$A = W^{0.425} \times H^{0.725} \times 71.84 \text{ (a constant)},$$
where $A$ = surface area in square centimeters, $W$ = weight in kilogram, and $H$ = height in centimeters.

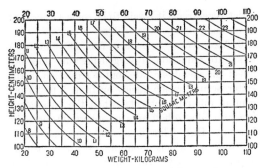

Fig. 44.12. Chart for determining surface area in man in square meters. (After Du Bois.) Example weight 60 kilograms, height 170 cm. = 1.70 sq. m.

Having obtained this figure it is customary to express the B.M.R. as normal or as a percentage above (+) or below (−) the normal. Thus, in the foregoing example the rate would be said to be normal. If it were 30 Calories per square meter per hour it would be expressed as −25 per cent and if 50 Calories as +25 per cent. The age and sex must also be considered since 39.8 Calories per square meter though normal for a full-grown man of 25 years or so would be above normal for a woman of the same age and below normal for a child (see below).

Tanner has pointed out that more recent studies of "per-surface area" and "per kilo of body weight" ratios, so widely used in physiology (e.g., for expressing B.M.R.'s, oxygen consumption, cardiac output, glomerular filtration rate, drug dosage, etc.) are theoretically fallacious, being a special case of the condition known to statisticians as the spurious correlation of indices. Although the values often have practical utility, extrapolations based on these ratios have led to the invention of new (nonexistent) clinical syndromes.

### Conditions Which Influence the Basal Metabolic Rate

#### A. *Physiological*

1. AGE AND SEX. The heat production per square meter of body surface diminishes progressively from infancy to old age being about 50 Cal. per square meter per hour at the age of ten or twelve and about 32 Cal. at 90 years. The metabolism of the new-born is much lower (25 Cal.) than that of infants a few weeks older. Premature infants have a lower rate than those born at full term. Females have a metabolic rate a little lower than that of males in the same age group. The relationship of heat production to age and sex is given in table 44.13.

2. RACE AND CLIMATE. Cramer and Lusk were both of the opinion that climate does not influence metabolism. In spite of suggestions by several workers that the B.M.R. of Eskimos is elevated and that that of persons in the tropics is lower than normal, more carefully controlled studies have shown that other explanations usually account for the findings. Seasonal fluc-

TABLE 44.12

(Relation of height and weight to surface area after Du Bois)

| Height in centi-meters | Weight in Kilograms | | | | | | | | | | | | | | | | |
|---|---|---|---|---|---|---|---|---|---|---|---|---|---|---|---|---|---|
| | 25 | 30 | 35 | 40 | 45 | 50 | 55 | 60 | 65 | 70 | 75 | 80 | 85 | 90 | 95 | 100 | 105 |
| 200 | | | | | | | 1.84 | 1.91 | 1.97 | 2.03 | 2.09 | 2.15 | 2.21 | 2.26 | 2.31 | 2.36 | 2.41 |
| 195 | | | | | | 1.73 | 1.80 | 1.87 | 1.93 | 1.99 | 2.05 | 2.11 | 2.17 | 2.22 | 2.27 | 2.32 | 2.37 |
| 190 | | | 1.56 | 1.63 | 1.70 | 1.77 | 1.84 | 1.90 | 1.96 | 2.02 | 2.08 | 2.13 | 2.18 | 2.23 | 2.28 | 2.33 | |
| 185 | | | 1.53 | 1.60 | 1.67 | 1.74 | 1.80 | 1.86 | 1.92 | 1.98 | 2.04 | 2.09 | 2.14 | 2.19 | 2.24 | 2.29 | |
| 180 | | | 1.49 | 1.57 | 1.64 | 1.71 | 1.77 | 1.83 | 1.89 | 1.95 | 2.00 | 2.05 | 2.10 | 2.15 | 2.20 | 2.25 | |
| 175 | 1.19 | 1.28 | 1.36 | 1.46 | 1.53 | | 1.67 | 1.73 | 1.79 | 1.85 | 1.91 | 1.96 | 2.01 | 2.06 | 2.11 | 2.16 | 2.21 |
| 170 | 1.17 | 1.26 | 1.34 | 1.43 | 1.50 | 1.57 | 1.63 | 1.69 | 1.75 | 1.81 | 1.86 | 1.91 | 1.96 | 2.01 | 2.06 | 2.11 | |
| 165 | 1.14 | 1.23 | 1.31 | 1.40 | 1.47 | 1.54 | 1.60 | 1.66 | 1.72 | 1.78 | 1.83 | 1.88 | 1.93 | 1.98 | 2.03 | 2.07 | |
| 160 | 1.12 | 1.21 | 1.29 | 1.37 | 1.44 | 1.50 | 1.56 | 1.62 | 1.68 | 1.73 | 1.78 | 1.83 | 1.88 | 1.93 | 1.98 | | |
| 155 | 1.09 | 1.18 | 1.26 | 1.33 | 1.40 | 1.46 | 1.52 | 1.58 | 1.64 | 1.69 | 1.74 | 1.79 | 1.84 | 1.89 | | | |
| 150 | 1.06 | 1.15 | 1.23 | 1.30 | 1.36 | 1.42 | 1.48 | 1.54 | 1.60 | 1.65 | 1.70 | 1.75 | 1.80 | | | | |
| 145 | 1.03 | 1.12 | 1.20 | 1.27 | 1.33 | 1.39 | 1.45 | 1.51 | 1.56 | 1.61 | 1.66 | 1.71 | | | | | |
| 140 | 1.00 | 1.09 | 1.17 | 1.24 | 1.30 | 1.36 | 1.42 | 1.47 | 1.52 | 1.57 | | | | | | | |
| 135 | 0.97 | 1.06 | 1.14 | 1.20 | 1.26 | 1.32 | 1.38 | 1.43 | 1.48 | | | | | | | | |
| 130 | 0.95 | 1.04 | 1.11 | 1.17 | 1.23 | 1.29 | 1.35 | 1.40 | | | | | | | | | |
| 125 | 0.93 | 1.01 | 1.08 | 1.14 | 1.20 | 1.26 | 1.31 | 1.36 | | | | | | | | | |
| 120 | 0.91 | 0.98 | 1.04 | 1.10 | 1.16 | 1.22 | 1.27 | | | | | | | | | | |

TABLE 44.13

*Basal and total metabolic rates of males and females*

From Cruickshank compiled from Boothby and associates

| Age | B.M.R. Calories per sq. Meter per Hour | | Total Basal Metabolism in Calories per 24 Hours | | Total Calories per Day | |
|---|---|---|---|---|---|---|
| | Males | Females | Males | Females | Males | Females |
| Birth | 30 | 30 | 288 | 288 | 440 | 440 |
| 1 | 55 | 52 | 660 | 624 | 1000 | 1000 |
| 2 | 57 | 53 | 780 | 725 | 1200 | 1200 |
| 3 | 55 | 52 | 845 | 798 | — | — |
| 5 | 53 | 52 | 915 | 886 | 1600 | 1600 |
| 8 | 51.8 | 47.0 | 1143 | 993 | 2000 | 2000 |
| 11 | 47.2 | 45.2 | 1268 | 1193 | 2500 | 2500 |
| 12 | 46.8 | 43.3 | 1347 | 1267 | — | — |
| 13 | 46.5 | 42.0 | 1428 | 1330 | — | — |
| 14 | 46.4 | 41.5 | 1537 | 1391 | 3200 | 2800 |
| 15 | 46.0 | 40.0 | 1667 | 1420 | — | — |
| 16 | 45.7 | 38.8 | 1764 | 1434 | 3500 | 2600 |
| 18 | 43.2 | 37.5 | 1783 | 1440 | 3800 | 2500 |
| 20 | 41.6 | 36.3 | 1756 | 1437 | 3500 | 2400 |
| 25 | 40.3 | 36.0 | 1760 | 1442 | 3000 | 2400 |
| 40 | 38.0 | 35.0 | 1641 | 1344 | 3000 | 2400 |

tuations do occur which have contributed to the difficulty of drawing conclusions.

3. HABITS. Owing to the greater development of their muscular tissues athletes and laborers have in general a higher B.M.R. than persons leading a sedentary life.

4. PREGNANCY. The basal metabolic rate of the pregnant woman shows little change until the sixth or seventh month when the fetus causes an appreciable increase in the weight of the mother. The metabolism of the mother from this time to term is the sum of her own metabolism in the nonpregnant state and that of the fetus. It was found by Murlin and Carpenter, for example, that the metabolism of the new-born infant and the postpartum metabolism of the mother added together practically equaled the metabolism of the pregnant state near the end of term. Boothby and Sandiford estimated the surface area of the fetus throughout gestation and concluded that the excess heat production of the pregnant state was derived from the fetus and the increased mass of the maternal structures, the energy production per unit of mass of the maternal organism remaining constant. Normal pregnancy, then, exerts little or no *specific* effect upon the basal metabolic rate.

5. DIET. The nature of the diet seems to have little influence upon the B.M.R., although in strict vegetarians it is said to be some 11 per cent lower than that of meat eaters.

6. VARIATIONS IN BAROMETRIC PRESSURES. A moderate reduction in oxygen pressure does not affect the metabolic rate, but a reduction in the latter occurs, which varies by from 5 to 25 per cent in different subjects, when the barometric pressure falls to half an atmosphere ($O_2$ pressure 75 mm. Hg). This is around the barometric pressure at which mountain sickness usually appears (ch. 33). Breathing excessively high tensions of oxygen does not raise the B.M.R. above the normal level. That is, the oxygen consumption cannot be raised simply by increasing the oxygen supply.

7. CHEMICAL SUBSTANCES. Caffeine, adrenaline, thyroid extract or thyroxine, benzedrine, and dinitrophenol, raise the basal metabolic rate. Smoking a cigarette, especially if the smoke is inhaled, increases the metabolism of most subjects, the average increase being around 9 per cent.

### B. Pathological

1. The B.M.R. is below normal in the following conditions:
Starvation and undernutrition (ch. 50).
Obesity due to pituitary or hypothalamic disorders (chs. 50 and 56).
Hypothyroidism (myxedema, ch. 57).
Addison's disease
Lipoid nephrosis
2. Conditions with a high B.M.R.:
Hyperthyroidism (exophthalmic goiter, ch. 57).
Fever (ch. 52). The basal rate is raised about 7 per cent for each degree (Fahrenheit) rise in temperature.
Diabetes insipidus (ch. 56).
Cardio-renal disease with dyspnea (+25 to +50 per cent).
Leukemia (+21 to +80 per cent).
Polycythemia (+10 to +40 per cent).

INFLUENCES WHICH RAISE THE METABOLISM
OF A NORMAL INDIVIDUAL ABOVE
THE BASAL LEVEL

We have already seen that the basal metabolism is defined as the heat production of a subject as nearly as possible at complete physical and mental rest, some hours after food and with the room temperature at about 20°C. These three factors—muscular exercise, the ingestion of food and environmental temperature—have a powerfully stimulating influence upon metabolism.

*Muscular and mental effort.* Even light muscular exertion, e.g., sitting, standing, dressing and

TABLE 44.14

*Extra Calories of metabolism per hour attributable to occupation*

(After Harrop)

| | Extra Calories per Hour |
|---|---|
| Occupations of men:..................... | |
| Tailor............................... | 44 |
| Bookbinder......................... | 81 |
| Shoemaker......................... | 90 |
| Metal worker, filing and hammering. | 141 |
| Painter of furniture................. | 145 |
| Carpenter making a table........... | 164 |
| Stonemason chiselling a tombstone.. | 300 |
| Man sawing wood.................... | 378 |
| Occupations of women: | |
| Seamstress, needlework.............. | 6 |
| Typist, 50 words per minute......... | 24 |
| Seamstress, using sewing machine... | 57 |
| Bookbinder......................... | 63 |
| Housemaid (moderate work)......... | 81 |
| Laundress (moderate work)......... | 124 |
| Housemaid (hard work)............. | 157 |
| Laundress (hard work)............. | 214 |

undressing, sewing, etc., raises the metabolism by from 25 to 60 per cent above the basal level. Moderate exercise, such as walking, swimming, housework, light carpentry, etc., raises it from 100 to 200 per cent, and very hard work may increase it from 10 to 15 times over the basal level. Henderson and Haggard found that in three members of the Yale University boat crew, the total heat production during rest amounted to 1.65, 1.42 and 2.4 Calories per minute respectively. The corresponding values during strenuous exercise on a rowing machine were 18.90, 21.83 and 29.37 Calories per minute. The extra energy expenditure caused by various occupations is shown in table 44.14. Mental effort, on the other hand, causes an almost negligible increase in metabolism. Benedict, for instance, after a series of experiments in which intense mental effort was expended in solving mathematical problems found an increase of only 3 or 4 per cent. He states, "The cloistered scholar at his books may be surprised to learn that the extra Calories needed for one hour of intense mental effort would be completely met by the eating of one oyster cracker or one-half of a salted peanut." The *basal* oxygen consumption of the brain however, is high (p. 1134), amounting to about 10 per cent of that of the entire body. *Strong emotion* may raise the metabolism from 5 to 10 per cent above the basal level.

During *sleep*, when the muscles are more completely relaxed than is possible during the waking day the metabolism falls below the basal level. The reduction amounts to from 10 to 13 per cent. (Strictly speaking, the metabolism during restful sleep, since it is the physiological minimum, *is* the true basal level.) If sleep is disturbed and associated with muscular activity the metabolism may be as high as or even higher than the "resting level" conventionally referred to as the basal level.

The influence of *food* and of *environmental temperature* (pp. 787 and 891) upon metabolism are dealt with elsewhere.

## REFERENCES

BLOCK, R. J., AND BOLLING, D. The amino acid composition of proteins and foods, ed. 2. Charles C Thomas, Springfield, Ill., 1951.

JACOBS, M. B. The chemical analysis of foods and food products, ed. 2. Van Nostrand Co., Inc., New York, 1951.

McCANCE, R. A., AND WIDDOWSON, E. M. The chemical composition of foods, ed. 2. Medical Research Council, London, Special Report Series, No. 235, 1946.

WATT, B. K., AND MERRILL, A. L. Composition of foods: raw, processed and prepared. United States Dept. Agriculture, Agriculture Handbook, No. 8, 1950.

WINTON, A. L., AND WINTON, K. B. The structure and composition of foods, Vol. I. John Wylie and Sons, Inc., New York, 1932.

Energy-yielding components of food and computation of calorie values. Food and Agricultural Organization Report, Washington, 1947.

Food composition tables: F.A.O. Nutritional studies. No. 3, Washington, 1949.

Food composition tables: Minerals and vitamins. F.A.O., No. 11, Rome, 1954.

Maize and maize diets: a nutritional survey. F.A.O. Nutritional studies, No. 9, Rome, 1953.

Symposium on the assessment of the energy value of human and animal foods. Proc. Nutrition Soc., 14, 130–160, 1955.

Tables of food values recommended for use in Canada. Nutrition Div., Dept. Health and Welfare, Ottawa, 1951.

### GENERAL METABOLISM

LUSK, G. The elements of the science of nutrition. W. B. Saunders Co., Philadelphia, 1928.

McCOLLUM, E. V., ORENT-KEILES, E., AND DAY, H. G. The newer knowledge of nutrition, ed. 5. The Macmillan Co., New York, 1940.

McHENRY, E. W. Basic nutrition. Lippincott Co., Montreal, 1957.

McLESTER, J. S., AND DARBY, W. J. Nutrition and diet in health and disease, ed. 7. W. B. Saunders Co., Philadelphia, 1959.

PETERS, J. P., AND VAN SLYKE, D. D. Quantitative clinical chemistry, ed. 2. Vol. I, The Williams and Wilkins Co., Baltimore, 1946.

SHERMAN, H. C. Chemistry of food and nutrition, ed. 8. The Macmillan Co., New York, 1952.

ENERGY METABOLISM

ATWATER, W. O., AND BENEDICT, F. G. Carnegie Inst. Washington, Pub. No. 42, 1905.
BENEDICT, F. G., AND COLLINS, W. E. Boston. Med. Surg. J., **183,** 449, 1920.
CATHCART, E. P. AND MARKOWITZ, J. J. Physiol., **63,** 309, 1927.
DOUGLAS, C. G. J. Physiol., **42,** xvii, 1911.
HALDANE, J. J. Physiol., **13,** 419, 1892.

*Monographs and Reviews*

BOOTHBY, W. M. Basal metabolism. Physiol. Rev., **4,** 69, 1924.

DU BOIS, E. F. Basal metabolism in health and disease, ed. 3. Lea & Febiger, Philadelphia, 1936.
KROGH, A. The respiratory exchange of animals and man. Longmans, Green & Co., London, 1916.
PETT, L. B. A Canadian table of average weights. Canad. M. A. J., **72,** 12, 1955.
RICHARDSON, H. B. The respiratory quotient. Physiol. Rev., **9,** 61, 1929.
SWIFT, R. W., AND FRENCH, C. E. Energy metabolism and nutrition. Scarecrow Press, New Brunswick, N. J., 1954.
TANNER, J. M. Fallacy of per-weight and per-surface area standards and their relation to spurious correlation. J. Applied Physiol., **2,** 1, 1949.
Symposium on energy expenditure in man. Proc. Nutrition Soc., **15,** 72–93, 1956.

# *45*

# PROTEIN METABOLISM

## General Description and Classification of Proteins

Protein is a fundamental component of protoplasm and consequently forms a proportion of all living tissues—animal or vegetable; it is the predominant solid component of some tissues, e.g., muscle. It differs from the other foodstuffs—carbohydrates and fats—in containing (in addition to carbon, hydrogen and oxygen) nitrogen, sulfur and sometimes phosphorus. The molecules of certain proteins contain a prosthetic group, e.g., hemoglobin, glycoproteins, lecithoproteins, nucleoproteins, etc.

A classification and brief description of the various types of protein are given in table 45.1.

## The Protein Molecule

The protein molecule is constructed of a number of units linked together. These units or "building stones" are called *amino acids*. They are separated when the protein molecule is hydrolyzed by boiling with acid or alkali, or by the action of the digestive enzymes (proteases). Some 25 different amino acids have been definitely identified as constituents of the protein molecule (see table 45.2). Some proteins contain nearly all of these in varying proportions; in others such as gelatin there are only 14 or 15 different kinds, some *essential* amino acids being missing, whereas such simple proteins as the protamines, sturine and salmine, contain only 3 and 4, respectively. The single amino acids have molecular weights ranging from 75 for glycine to over 200 for tyrosine and nearly 800 for thyroxine. The molecular weights of those proteins composed of large aggregations of amino acids are correspondingly great and extend over a very wide range. The molecular weight of egg albumin, for example, is 45,000, that of hemocyanin, over 6,000,000, and of tobacco mosaic virus, 40,000,000. Some basic proteins, protamines and histones, on the other hand, have molecular weights of about 2000 only.

Protein molecules also vary in shape. Studies of protein structure by means of X-ray diffraction photographs reveal that the molecules of some proteins, such as keratin, collagen and myosin—the so-called *fibrous proteins*—have an elongated fiberlike form, resulting, it is believed, from the extended arrangement of the polypeptide linkages of which the molecule is constructed (see below). When stretched such molecules become elongated still further but return to their previous length when released from the stretching force. The changes in length are described as being due to folding and unfolding of the polypeptide chains in a concertinalike fashion. Other proteins—the *globular proteins*—such as egg albumin and the serum proteins, are composed of molecules which are folded or arranged into a lattice pattern to form a compact structure of a more or less globular shape. Unfolding and the assumption of a permanent extended form is associated with denaturation. Proteins of approximately the same molecular weight may differ considerably in their molecular structure and for this reason may show differences in such physical properties as elasticity, osmotic pressure or viscosity. The fundamental structure of all proteins is believed by Astbury to be fibrous, but the intermolecular arrangement of the polypeptide chains varies widely between different types and in the same protein under different conditions. Thus a variety of patterns is produced.

The average elementary composition of the molecule of a protein such as albumin or globulin is as follows: C, 54 per cent; H, 7 per cent; N, 16 per cent; S, 1 per cent; O, 22 per cent.

## THE AMINO ACIDS

The amino acids may be regarded as derivatives of the saturated fatty acid series in which the *alpha* hydrogen atom has been replaced by an amino ($NH_2$) group; in the case of proline and hydroxyproline, the substitution is by an imino

(NH) group. The simplest amino acid is amino-acetic (glycine or glycocoll)

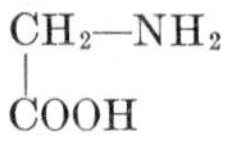

$$CH_2-NH_2$$
$$|$$
$$COOH$$

and the structure of the other amino acids, with the exception of proline and oxyproline, may be represented by the following type formula.

$$R.CH-NH_2$$
$$|$$
$$COOH$$

Amino acids therefore contain a basic (NH₂) group and an acid (COOH) group. R represents a chemical group which varies greatly in size and structure. In the synthesis of the protein molecule chains of amino acids are formed by the linkage of the basic group of one amino acid with the acid group of another and the liberation of a molecule of water. Thus

$$CH_3 \cdot CHNH_2CO[OH \ H]HN \cdot CH_2 \cdot COOH \rightleftharpoons CH_3 \cdot CHNH_2 \cdot CO-HN \cdot CH_2 \cdot COOH + H_2O$$

Alanine          Glycine                              Alanylglycine

The junction, CO-NH, whereby amino acids become grouped together, is called the *peptide linkage*. The reverse process, namely, the separation of amino acids from one another is also effected at this link in the chain, a molecule of water first being taken up. This process is called *hydrolysis*.

Upon hydrolysis by heating with acid the ring is broken, and in the case of glycine anhydride the dipeptide glycyl-glycine is formed.

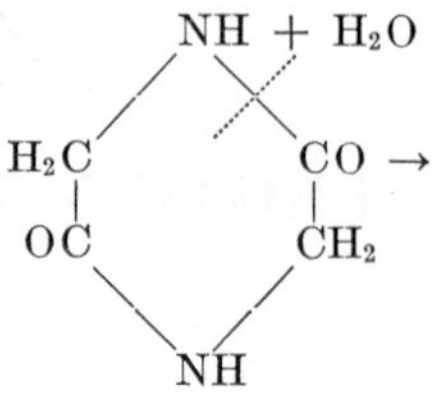

Diketopiperazine
(glycine anhydride)

$$CH_2-CO-NH-CH_2-COOH$$
$$|$$
$$NH_2$$

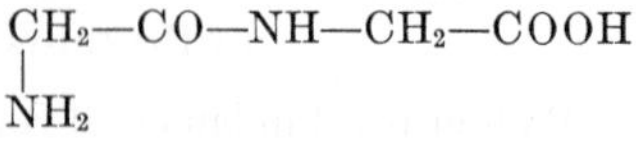

Glycyl-glycine

*Terminal* amino acids of peptide chains always have a free polar group. At one end a carboxyl group is found (e.g., in the glycine moiety of alanylglycine or of glutathione), at the other end an amino group (in the alanine moiety of alanylglycine, in the glutamic acid portion of glutathione). Diamino or dicarboxylic amino acids will also contribute further free amino or acid groups (as in the free carboxyl of the glutamyl radical of glutathione). By virtue of these it can act either

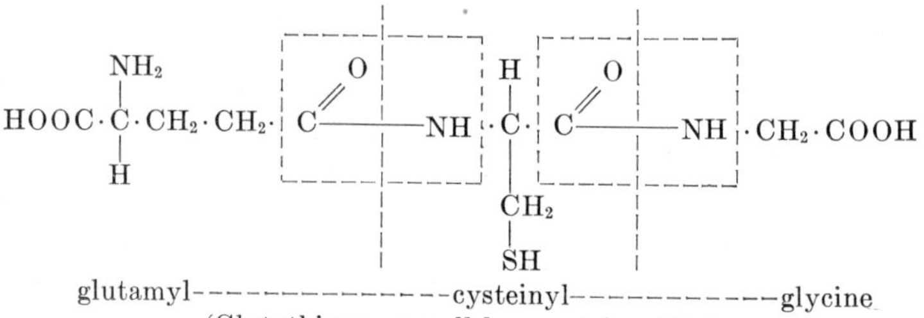

glutamyl- - - - - - - - - - - - - - - - - cysteinyl- - - - - - - - - -glycine
(Glutathione—a well known tripeptide)

Besides the chainlike combination of the amino acids in the protein molecule, a smaller proportion are believed to be united to form closed-ring compounds—*diketopiperazines (amino acid anhydrides)*. The amino acids undergo dehydration and unite by their free amino and carboxyl groups to form the diketopiperazine ring. In the example shown below two glycine molecules join to produce glycine anhydride.

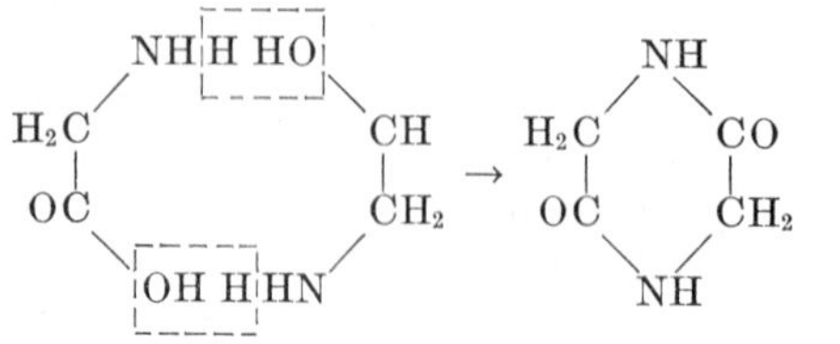

Glycine   Glycine          Diketopiperazine
(glycine anhydride)

as a weak base or as a weak acid. In acid solution it acts as a base yielding cations to form protein chloride, sulfate, etc. When a current passes through the solution the amino acid cation migrates to the cathode or positive pole.[1] In alkaline solution it behaves as an acid, forming anions to produce a proteinate of sodium, potassium etc., In an electric field the amino acid anion migrates to the anode. On account of these opposite reactions, depending upon the acidity or alkalinity of the solution, amino acids and the proteins which they compose are called *amphoteric electrolytes* or *ampholytes* (Gk. *amphō*, both). At a certain hydrogen ion concentration, which varies rather widely

[1] This migration in an electric field of cation and anions to the respective poles is called *electrophoresis* or *iontophoresis*.

TABLE 45.1

| Class of Protein | Characteristics | Examples |
|---|---|---|
| *A. Simple proteins* | | |
| (1) Albumins | Soluble in water and coagulable by heat. Present in both animal and plant tissues | *Serum albumin, egg albumin, lactalbumin* and various vegetable albumins such as *leucosin* (in wheat, rye and barley), *legumelin* in lentils, soy beans, beans and peas and *phaselin* in kidney beans |
| (2) Globulins | Soluble in dilute saline solutions; insoluble in water. Animal globulins are coagulated by heat. Vegetable globulins imperfectly or not coagulated by heat | *Serum globulin, fibrinogen* (and *fibrin*) *vitellin* of egg yolk and vegetable globulins such as *excelsin* (Brazil nuts), *edestin* (hemp), *phaseolin* (kidney beans), *legumin* (peas and lentils) and *tuberin* (potatoes). A number of other vegetable globulins have been isolated and named |
| (3) Glutelins | Found only in plants. Insoluble in water, saline or alcohol, but soluble in very dilute alkali | *Glutenin* of wheat, *oryzenin* of rice and *glutelin* of maize |
| (4) Prolamines or gliadins | Found in cereals (except rice). Soluble in 70 to 90 per cent alcohol; insoluble in water. They contain a large proportion of proline and compounds giving rise to ammonia-nitrogen | *Gliadin* of wheat, *hordein* of barley and *zein* of maize |
| (5) Albuminoids or scleroproteins | Especially resistant to the usual reagents. They enter into the construction of protective and connective tissues, e.g., skin, tendons, ligments and bones | *Keratin* of hair, skin, bone, feathers, tortoise shell and eggshell, *elastin*, *collagen*, *ossein* and *gelatin* of tendons, ligaments, bone, etc. |
| (6) Histones | Soluble in water and precipitated by ammonia solution and by alkaloids. They contain a large percentage of diamino acids (p. 774) | *Globin* of hemoglobin, *thymus histone*; *scombron* and *gadus histone* in spermatozoa of mackerel and codfish respectively |
| (7) Protamines | Found in combination with nucleic acid in heads of fish spermatozoa. Constructed predominantly of diamino acids | *Salmine* and *sturine* in spermatozoa of salmon and sturgeon respectively |

*B. Conjugated proteins.* Proteins whose molecule is combined with another nonprotein group

| Class of Protein | Characteristics | Examples |
|---|---|---|
| (1) Nucleoproteins | Nucleic acid in combination with a protein belonging usually to the class of histones or protamines. Found in cell nuclei | See ch. 47 |
| (2) Chromoproteins | Protein in combination with a pigment (e. g., hematin) containing iron, copper or other metal | Hemoglobin, hemocyanin, etc. |
| (3) Glycoproteins | Proteins other than nucleoproteins in combination with a carbohydrate group | *Mucin* in salivary gastric and intestinal secretions; *ovomucoid* of egg white and *chondromucoid* of cartilage |
| (4) Lipoproteins | Proteins in combination with lipid | Present in plasma, milk, cell nuclei |
| (5) Phosphoproteins | Proteins other than nucleoproteins and lecithoproteins in combination with a phosphorus-containing group | *Caseinogen* (and casein), *vitellin* of egg yolk |

TABLE 45.1—*Continued*

| Class of Protein | Characteristics | Examples |
|---|---|---|

*C. Derivatives of proteins—derived proteins.* These are produced by the action of acids, alkalis or proteolytic enzymes upon certain of the proteins listed above

| Class of Protein | Characteristics | Examples |
|---|---|---|
| (*a*) *Primary deriva- tives* | | |
|   (*1*) *Proteans* | Insoluble products formed in the early stage of the action upon proteins of water, dilute acids and enzymes | |
|   (*2*) *Metaproteins* | Formed in a later stage of the action of acid or alkali | *Acid* metaprotein, *alkali* metaprotein |
|   (*3*) *Coagulated proteins* | Formed by the action of heat or of alcohol upon solutions of proteins | |
| (*b*) *Secondary de- rivatives* | | |
|   (*1*) *Proteoses* | Formed by the action of pepsin or trypsin upon proteins. They are soluble in water from which they are precipitated by saturation with ammonium sulfate. They are incoagulable by heat | *Albumose* from albumen, *globulose* from globulin, *caseose* from casein |
|   (*2*) *Peptones* | These represent a further stage in action of proteolytic enzymes. They are soluble in water but are not precipitated from an aqueous solution by ammonium sulfate. They are not coagulated by heat | |
|   (*3*) *Peptides, di- peptides, tripep- tides* and *poly- peptides* | Products formed in the final stages of proteolytic digestion | Glycyl-alanine, leucyl-glutamic acid, etc. |

between different proteins, the amino acids are electrically neutral and protein behaves neither as an acid nor as a base. In an electric field no migration either to anode or cathode occurs. The pH at which this occurs is known as the "*isoelectric point*" though the effect rather than being restricted to a point extends over a pH range which with some proteins is considerable. *Isoelectric zone* is therefore a better term (table 45.3). Within the isoelectric zone the solubility of the protein is least; here it is readily precipitated by alcohol, neutral salts and other reagents. Some proteins are quite insoluble at the isoelectric point and precipitate spontaneously. According to the classical conception the electrical neutrality of protein at the isoelectric point was due to ionization of the amino acids being at a minimum or absent, as represented below in formula I. This view has

given place to the *Zwitterion theory*, which more readily explains the experimental findings.

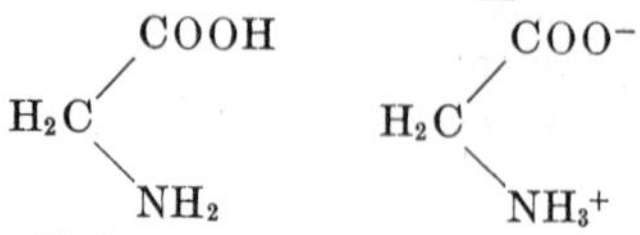

*The "Zwitterion" theory.* This postulates that the amino acids at the isoelectric point carry equal numbers of positive and negative charges and this accounts for their electrical neutrality. They are called "*zwitterions*" (Ger. *Zwitter*, hemaphrodite) or *dipolar ions* (see formula II above). Much experimental support has been gained for this theory since it was first proposed.

The behavior of an amino acid (glycine) in acid and in alkaline solution according to the two conceptions is illustrated below (on p. 773). It will be seen that the end result on either side of the isoelectric point is the same according to either view. According, however, to the *Zwitter hypothesis* the ampholyte molecule gives off, at the isoelectric point, *equal numbers* of basic and acid ions, thus leaving ions—the so-called zwitterions— holding equal numbers of negative and positive charges (formula II). Many proteins, e.g., metaproteins, casein, etc., are almost insoluble at the isoelectric point—*isoelectric precipitation*.

Isoelectric glycine

$$\underset{\text{Unionized}}{\overset{\text{I}}{\underset{H_2C}{\overset{COOH}{\diagup}}\diagdown NH_2}} \qquad \underset{\text{``Zwitterion''}}{\overset{\text{II}}{\underset{H_2C}{\overset{COO^-}{\diagup}}\diagdown NH_3^+}}$$

Isoelectric
glycine

$$
\begin{array}{ll}
\text{In acid}\\
\text{solution}
\end{array}
\begin{cases}
\text{Classical view} & \text{H}_2\text{C} \diagdown^{\text{COOH}}_{\text{NH}_2} \xrightarrow{\text{HCl}} \\
\\
\text{"Zwitterion" theory} & \text{H}_2\text{C} \diagdown^{\text{COO}^-}_{\text{NH}_3^+} \xrightarrow{\text{HCl}}
\end{cases}
$$

Protein
hydrochloride

$$\text{H}_2\text{C} \diagdown^{\text{COOH}}_{\text{NH}_3^+} + \text{Cl}^-$$

Isoelectric
glycine

$$
\begin{array}{ll}
\text{In}\\
\text{alkaline}\\
\text{solution}
\end{array}
\begin{cases}
\text{Classical view} & \text{H}_2\text{C} \diagdown^{\text{COOH}}_{\text{NH}_2} \xrightarrow{\text{NaOH}} \\
\\
\text{"Zwitterion" theory} & \text{H}_2\text{C} \diagdown^{\text{COO}^-}_{\text{NH}_3^+} \xrightarrow{\text{NaOH}}
\end{cases}
$$

Sodium
proteinate

$$\text{H}_2\text{C} \diagdown^{\text{COO}^- + \text{Na}^+}_{\text{NH}_2}$$

## The Absorption of Protein

Under ordinary circumstances only negligible amounts of unchanged protein, or even such of its derivatives as proteoses, peptones and polypeptides, are absorbed into the blood from the alimentary tract. Generally speaking the protein molecule must first be hydrolyzed into its constituent amino acids. These are absorbed from the small intestine but not from the stomach to any significant extent. They enter the circulation mainly through the portal blood; much smaller amounts pass into the lymph (chyle) and hence into the thoracic duct.

Small quantities of certain proteins, e.g., raw egg white and blood serum are sometimes absorbed from the intestine into the blood stream. They are excreted in the urine to a large extent unchanged. Such absorption which occurs more readily in young animals and children, should be regarded as a defect rather than as a physiological process. Nevertheless, experiments have shown that small quantities of protein introduced parenterally may be utilized by the tissues, and may even be capable of maintaining nitrogen equilibrium. It is, however, only for a short period and to a very limited extent that the body can utilize injected protein, for proteins are species specific and after a number of injections immunity is established to the foreign protein; an antibody known as a *precipitin* is formed which causes its precipitation. Furthermore, if a subsequent injection is given two weeks or so after a single injection or after the last of a series of such injections, a most serious toxic state—*anaphylaxis*—may ensue and

prove fatal. In the human subject such anaphylactic (or anaphylactoid) reactions may follow the second injection of a foreign protein, e.g., diptheria antitoxin (horse serum) or antitetanic serum. Skin rashes such as urticaria, erythema, eczema, giant edema, etc., or pain and swelling of the joints may occur. Collapse and death occasionally result. The sensitivity of some persons to certain proteins is also sometimes responsible for dietary idiosyncrasies. Certain foods such as shellfish, milk, strawberries, celery, etc., when ingested by persons sensitive to the proteins contained in these substances, result in cutaneous eruptions and sometimes localized edema. Minute amounts of the protein apparently enter the blood stream in an unchanged or partially digested state. Asthma, hay fever and other allergic conditions have been traced to foreign proteins (pollen, cat or horse hair, feathers, etc.) entering the body through the respiratory passages.

Homologous plasma protein, on the contrary, does not cause these effects and Whipple and his associates found that dogs could be maintained in nitrogen equilibrium (p. 785) by the intravenous injection of plasma from other dogs as the sole source of protein.

A suitable assortment of amino acids, such as an hydrolysate of casein supplemented by cystine and tryptophane, injected intravenously, is capable of maintaining an animal in nitrogenous equilibrium. Animal gelatin or isinglass (fish gelatin) which differs from complete proteins in being nonantigenic, might be used for this purpose if supplemented by the missing amino acids.

## The Fate of Amino Acids after Absorption

DEAMINATION. This term means the removal of amino groups from the amino acids. Less than 20 per cent of the amino acids absorbed into the portal blood pass through the liver unchanged into the general circulation. A very small proportion of these are excreted intact in the urine, some are deaminated by the kidney and the

### TABLE 45.2

*Classification of the amino acids*

#### I. ALIPHATIC AMINO ACIDS

##### A. *Monoamino-monocarboxylic acids*

(1) Glycine (or glycocoll) $C_2H_5NO_2$, or amino-acetic acid

$$\begin{array}{c} CH_2-NH_2 \\ | \\ COOH \end{array}$$

(2) Alanine, $C_3H_7NO_2$, or $\alpha$-amino-propionic acid

$$\begin{array}{c} CH_3 \cdot CH-NH_2 \\ | \\ COOH \end{array}$$

(3) Serine, $C_3H_7NO_3$, or $\alpha$-amino-$\beta$-hydroxy propionic acid

$$\begin{array}{cc} CH_2 \cdot & CH-NH_2 \\ | & | \\ OH & COOH \end{array}$$

(4) Threonine, $C_4H_9NO_3$, or $\alpha$-amino-$\beta$-hydroxy-$n$-butyric acid

$$\begin{array}{cc} CH_3CH \cdot & CH-NH_2 \\ | & | \\ OH & COOH \end{array}$$

(5) Valine, $C_5H_{11}NO_2$, or $\alpha$-amino-isovaleric acid

$$\begin{array}{c} CH_3 \\ \diagdown \\ CH \cdot CH-NH_2 \\ \diagup \qquad | \\ CH_3 \qquad COOH \end{array}$$

(6) Norleucine, $C_6H_{13}NO_2$, or $\alpha$-amino-$n$-caproic acid

$$\begin{array}{c} CH_3 \cdot CH_2 \cdot CH_2 \cdot CH_2 \cdot CH-NH_2 \\ | \\ COOH \end{array}$$

(7) Leucine, $C_6H_{13}NO_2$, or $\alpha$-amino-isocaproic acid

$$\begin{array}{c} CH_3 \\ \diagdown \\ CH \cdot CH_2 \cdot CH-NH_2 \\ \diagup \qquad\qquad | \\ CH_3 \qquad\qquad COOH \end{array}$$

(8) Isoleucine, $C_6H_{13}NO_2$, or $\alpha$-amino-$\beta$-ethyl-$\beta$-methyl-propionic acid

$$\begin{array}{c} CH_3 \\ \diagdown \\ CH \cdot CH-NH_2 \\ \diagup \qquad | \\ CH_3 \cdot CH_3 \qquad COOH \end{array}$$

##### *Sulfur-containing monoamino-monocarboxylic acids*

(9) Cystine, $C_6H_{12}N_2S_2O_4$, (or dicysteine) or di-($\beta$-thio-$\alpha$-amino-propionic) acid

$$\begin{array}{cc} CH_2-S-S-CH_2 \\ | \qquad\qquad | \\ CH-NH_2 \quad CH-NH_2 \\ | \qquad\qquad | \\ COOH \qquad COOH \end{array}$$

(10) Methionine, $C_5H_{11}SNO_2$, or $\alpha$-amino-$\gamma$-methyl-thiol-$n$-butyric acid

$$\begin{array}{c} CH_3 \cdot S \cdot CH_2 \cdot CH_2 \cdot CH-NH_2 \\ | \\ COOH \end{array}$$

##### B. *Monoamino-dicarboxylic acids*

(11) Aspartic acid, $C_4H_7NO_4$, or $\alpha$-amino-succinic acid

$$\begin{array}{c} COOH \cdot CH_2 \cdot CH-NH_2 \\ | \\ COOH \end{array}$$

(12) Glutamic acid, $C_5H_9NO_4$, or $\alpha$-amino-glutaric acid

$$\begin{array}{c} COOH \cdot CH_2CH_2CH-NH_2 \\ | \\ COOH \end{array}$$

(13) Hydroxyglutamic acid, $C_5H_9NO_5$, or $\alpha$-amino-$\beta$-hydroxy-glutaric acid

$$\begin{array}{c} COOH \cdot CH_2CHOH \cdot CH-NH_2 \\ | \\ COOH \end{array}$$

##### C. *Diamino-monocarboxylic acids*

(14) Arginine, $C_6H_{14}N_4O_2$, or $\alpha$-amino-$\delta$-guanidine-$n$-valeric acid

$$\begin{array}{c} NH_2 \\ | \\ HN=C-NH \cdot CH_2 \cdot CH_2 \cdot CH_2 \cdot CH-NH_2 \\ | \\ COOH \end{array}$$

(15) Lysine, $C_6H_{14}N_2O_2$, or $\alpha$-$\epsilon$-diamino-caproic acid

$$\begin{array}{c} NH_2 \\ | \\ CH_2 \cdot CH_2 \cdot CH_2 \cdot CH_2 \cdot CH-NH_2 \\ | \\ COOH \end{array}$$

TABLE 45.2—Continued

## II. Aromatic Amino Acids

(16) Phenylalanine, $C_9H_{11}NO_2$, or $\alpha$-amino-$\beta$-phenyl-propionic acid

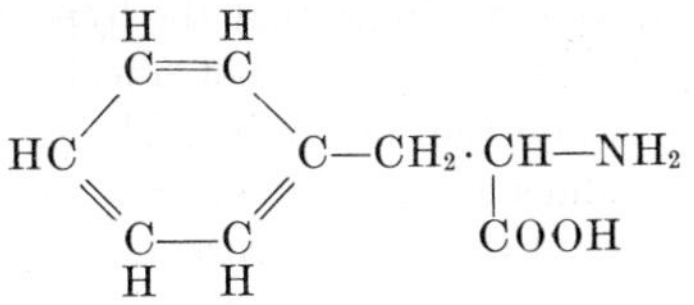

$$
\begin{array}{c}
\text{H} \quad \text{H} \\
\text{C}=\text{C} \\
\text{HC} \qquad \text{C}-\text{CH}_2\cdot\text{CH}-\text{NH}_2 \\
\text{C}-\text{C} \qquad\qquad \text{COOH} \\
\text{H} \quad \text{H}
\end{array}
$$

(17) Tyrosine, $C_9H_{11}NO_3$, or $\alpha$-amino-$\beta$-parahydroxy-phenyl-propionic acid

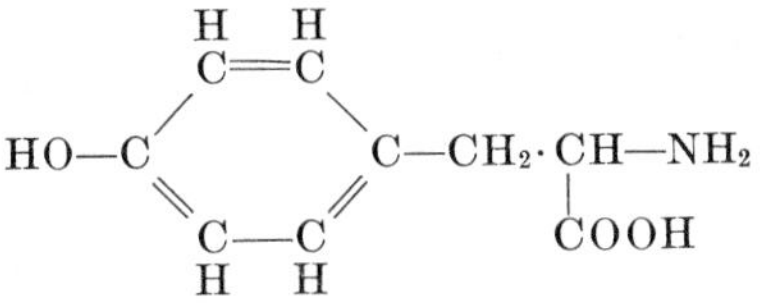

$$
\begin{array}{c}
\text{H} \quad \text{H} \\
\text{C}=\text{C} \\
\text{HO}-\text{C} \qquad \text{C}-\text{CH}_2\cdot\text{CH}-\text{NH}_2 \\
\text{C}-\text{C} \qquad\qquad \text{COOH} \\
\text{H} \quad \text{H}
\end{array}
$$

## III. Heterocyclic Amino Acids

(18) Tryptophane, $C_{11}H_{12}N_2O_2$, or $\alpha$-amino-$\beta$-indole-propionic acid

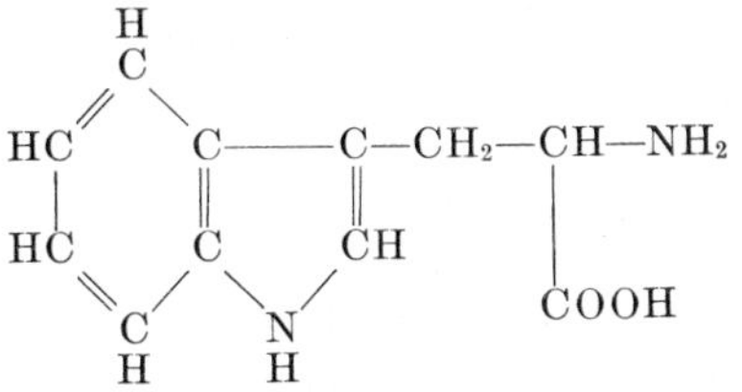

$$
\begin{array}{c}
\text{H} \\
\text{C} \\
\text{HC} \quad \text{C}\text{---}\text{C}-\text{CH}_2-\text{CH}-\text{NH}_2 \\
\text{HC} \quad \text{C} \quad \text{CH} \\
\text{C} \quad \text{N} \qquad \text{COOH} \\
\text{H} \quad \text{H}
\end{array}
$$

Indole nucleus

(19) Histidine, $C_6H_9N_3O_2$, or $\alpha$-amino-$\beta$-imidazol-propionic acid

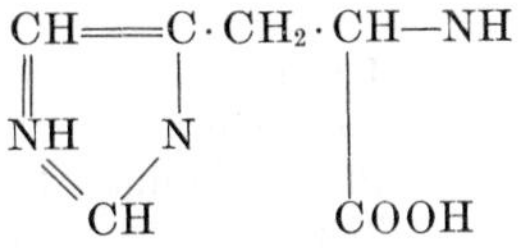

$$
\begin{array}{c}
\text{CH}=\text{C}\cdot\text{CH}_2\cdot\text{CH}-\text{NH} \\
\text{NH} \quad \text{N} \\
\text{CH} \qquad\qquad \text{COOH}
\end{array}
$$

Imidazole ring

(20) Proline, $C_5H_9NO_2$, or pyrrolidine-$\alpha$-carboxylic acid

$$
\begin{array}{c}
\text{CH}_2\text{---}\text{CH}_2 \\
\text{CH}_2 \quad \text{CH}-\text{COOH} \\
\text{NH}
\end{array}
$$

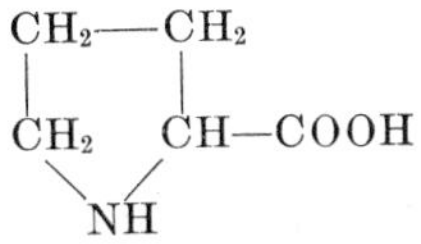

Pyrrole nucleus

(21) Hydroxyproline (oxyproline), $C_5H_9NO_3$, or $\gamma$-hydroxy-pyrrolidine-$\alpha$-carboxylic acid

$$
\begin{array}{c}
\text{HO}-\text{CH}\text{---}\text{CH}_2 \\
\text{CH}_2 \quad \text{CH}-\text{COOH} \\
\text{NH}
\end{array}
$$

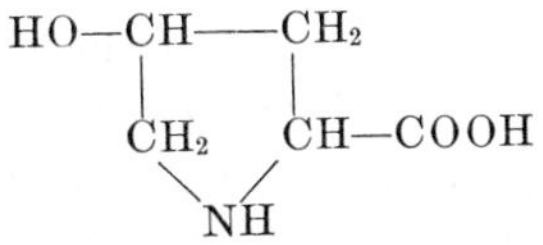

*Thyroxine* (ch. 58), 3-5-*diiodotyrosine* or iodogorgoic acid, *citrulline* (*α-amino-δ-carbamido-n-valeric acid*) and *ornithine* (*α,δ-diamino-valeric acid*), and several others, would have to be added to complete the list of naturally occurring amino acids.

nitrogen excreted as ammonia; others are utilized without alteration by the tissues. The greater part of the amino acids reaching the liver are there retained and deaminated. The ammonia which is split off combines with carbon dioxide to form urea as described on page 780. The deaminated remainder, i.e., the keto acid residue of the amino acid molecule may either undergo oxidation, and thus furnish energy to the body, or be transformed into glucose. The glucose may be burned or be stored as glycogen, or again it may be transformed into fat. Not all amino acids, however, are sugar or glycogen formers. Those which play the chief role in this respect are *glycine, alanine, aspartic, glutamic* and *hydroxyglutamic acids, serine, cystine, hydroxyproline* and *proline*. With the exception of *hydroxyproline* and *proline* these are all straight chain amino acids with less than six carbon atoms. *Arginine, valine,* and *threonine* form sugar to a limited extent,

TABLE 45.3

*Approximate isoelectric points of some amino acids*

| Amino Acid | Approximate Isoelectric Points, pH |
|---|---|
| Glycine | 6.1 |
| Alanine | 6.1 |
| Valine | 6.0 |
| Leucine | 6.0 |
| Glutamic acid | 3.2 |
| Aspartic acid | 3.0 |
| Arginine | 10.5 |
| Lysine | 9.6 |
| Histidine | 7.4 |
| Phenylalanine | 5.4 |
| Tyrosine | 5.4 |

whereas, *leucine, isoleucine, lysine, methionine, tryptophane, histidine, tyrosine* and *phenylalanine* are not glycogenic (see table 45.4). The quantity of amino acids present in 100 grams of protein is

TABLE 45.4

*Classification of amino acids according to their glycogenic or ketogenic properties*

| Glycogenic | Ketogenic | Neither Glycogenic nor Ketogenic |
|---|---|---|
| Glycine | Leucine | Norleucine |
| Alanine | Isoleucine | Methionine |
| Serine | Phenylalanine | Lysine |
| Threonine | Tyrosine | Tryptophane |
| Cysteine | | Histidine |
| Aspartic acid | | |
| Valine | | |
| Glutamic acid | | |
| Arginine | | |
| Ornithine | | |
| Proline | | |
| Hydroxyproline | | |

sufficient to form some 58 grams of glucose.[2] A depancreatized or phloridzinized dog, for instance, or the subject of severe diabetes, although upon a carbohydrate-free diet, continues to excrete large quantities of glucose. Also, the normal animal during prolonged starvation maintains its blood sugar at practically the normal level, which suggests that body protein is undergoing conversion to glucose. When protein is fed after a

[2] Since different proteins contain varying amounts of sugar-forming amino acids, this is an average figure. It was arrived at by calculation from the proportion of glucose (dextrose) to nitrogen in the urine—the so-called G:N (or D:N) ratio—in phloridzinized dogs fed exclusively upon protein or during a period of starvation. Lusk found the G:N ratio under such circumstances to be 3.65:1. The nitrogen of the urine is derived, of course, almost entirely from protein. The urinary glucose of an animal under the influence of phloridzin and whose glycogen stores have been exhausted is also assumed to be derived exclusively from protein. Now each gram of urinary nitrogen represents catabolism of 6.25 grams of protein. Therefore with a G:N ratio of 3.65:1 every 3.65 grams of glucose excreted indicates the conversion of 6.25 grams of protein. Thus,

$$(3.65/6.25) \times 100 = 58 \text{ per cent}$$

In diabetic (depancreatized) animals during starvation or upon a protein diet the G:N ratios obtained by different observers vary widely. Minkowiski's figure of 2.8:1 is most usually quoted (this would indicate the conversion of 45 per cent of protein to sugar). Macleod and his associates, however, have obtained ratios in depancreatized dogs after the withdrawal of insulin as high as 6:1 in some experiments, and less than 2:1 in others. The ratio did not show a constant value, either in different animals or in the same animal at different times. They have seriously questioned the reliability of the G:N ratio as an index of the extent of the protein to glucose conversion, and consider that protein is not the only source of the urinary glucose.

period of starvation, glycogen accumulates in the liver. There is also evidence that the conversion of protein to glucose occurs even in a normal animal upon a mixed diet. The conversion process probably occurs almost entirely in the liver. Mann and Magath found that the hypoglycemia following hepatectomy was not affected by the intravenous injection of glycine. The conversion process is influenced by the anterior lobe of the hypophysis and the adrenal cortex.

Although deamination is a function of the kidney and other tissues as well, its main site is the liver. In the dog it appears to be carried on exclusively by hepatic tissue. Mann and his colleagues found no evidence in dogs of extrahepatic deamination. The injection of amino acids into the blood stream of a normal dog caused a rapid rise in the amino acid concentration of the blood and increased amino acid excretion in the urine. The level in the blood returned to normal in about two hours. *About 25 per cent of the injected amino acid nitrogen appeared in the urine as urea.* After hepatectomy, the urea concentration of the solid tissues, blood and urine fell, whereas the concentration of amino acids rose; amino acids injected into the blood stream were *completely recovered* unchanged, about a third from the urine and the remainder from the muscles. There was no sign of deamination or of urea synthesis.

Deamination is generally believed to be an oxidative process brought about by various enzymes in liver, kidney, and to some extent in other tissues. Oxidation of the *a*-carbon atom, i.e., the carbon atom to which the $NH_2$ group is attached, first occurs with the production of an *α-imino acid*. This involves the transference of two hydrogen atoms to a hydrogen acceptor through the action of *d-amino-oxidase*, *glycine oxidase*, or of *l-glutamic dehydrogenase*:

$$\underset{\alpha\text{-amino-acid}}{\overset{R}{\underset{|}{\overset{|}{\text{CHNH}_2}}} \atop \text{COOH}} \rightarrow \underset{\alpha\text{-imino-acid}}{\overset{R}{\underset{|}{\overset{|}{\text{C=NH}}}} \atop \text{COOH}} + 2H \xrightarrow[\text{acceptor}]{\text{to hydrogen}}$$

The imino acid then undergoes spontaneous hydrolysis to form an *α-keto acid*:

$$\underset{\alpha\text{-imino acid}}{\overset{R}{\underset{|}{\overset{|}{\text{C=NH}}}} \atop \text{COOH}} + H_2O \rightarrow \underset{\alpha\text{-keto acid}}{\overset{R}{\underset{|}{\overset{|}{\text{CO}}}} \atop \text{COOH}} + NH_3$$

TRANSAMINATION. An important reaction occurring in the metabolism of protein is the interconversion of amino acids by transference of the amino group from an $\alpha$-amino acid to an $\alpha$-keto acid. The change is catalyzed by an enzyme *transaminase*.

The reaction is reversible and occurs according to the equation:

$$R^1 \cdot CH(NH_2) \cdot COOH + R^2 \cdot CO \cdot COOH \leftrightarrows$$
$$R^1 \cdot CO \cdot COOH + R^2 CH(NH_2) COOH.$$

Transamination was first suggested as a possibility by Needham and later demonstrated in pigeon breast muscle by Braunstein and Kritzmann. They found that when *l*-glutamic acid and pyruvic acid were incubated with chopped liver or muscle $\alpha$-ketoglutaric acid and alanine were produced, the amino group of the glutamic acid being transferred to pyruvic acid:

| COOH | | COOH | |
|------|------|------|------|
| CH₂ | CH₃ | CH₂ | CH₃ |
| CH₂ | CO | CH₂ | CH·NH₂ |
| CH·NH₂ | COOH | C=O | COOH |
| COOH | | COOH | |
| l-glutamic acid | pyruvic acid | α-ketoglutaric acid (sometimes incorrectly called α-ketoglutamic acid) | alanine |

According to these investigators the majority of the amino acids (lysine is an exception) can take part in transamination reactions, their $NH_2$ groups being transferred to other amino acids or to various keto acids. Glutamic acid is especially active in this respect. Transamination occurs not only in liver and muscle but has been demonstrated in a number of other tissues and appears to be a function of tissues in general. Krebs observed that glycolysis in brain and retina was inhibited by glutamic acid, an effect which has since been shown to be due to the conversion of pyruvic acid to alanine through the transference of amino groups from the glutamic acid. Since transamination is a rapid process and concerned chiefly with those compounds, which play key roles in intermediary metabolism, Cohen suggests that it represents a "shuttle" mechanism in tissue respiration "whereby certain key protein and carbohydrate intermediates are rapidly interconverted." The demonstration of transamination affords further evidence for the highly dynamic character of protein metabolism. Amino groups are being continually exchanged between nitrogenous and non-nitrogenous compounds, and

amino acids thereby synthesized. When an amino acid into which isotopic nitrogen ($N^{15}$) has been incorporated is fed and the tissues of the animal are analyzed a large number of amino acids are found to contain the isotope. Even ammonium citrate containing $N^{15}$ fed to rats upon a low protein diet, is utilized for amino acid synthesis. Aspartic acid, histidine, arginine, glutamic acid and proline, isolated from the animals' bodies, were found to contain the isotope.

TRANSMETHYLATION. Although it has long been known that certain compounds when fed are excreted by the kidney in methylated form, e.g., pyridine as N-methyl pyridine, the mechanism involved in the transference of the methyl group from one compound to another has been discovered comparatively recently by du Vigneaud and his associates. Homocystine can be converted in the body to methionine by the addition of a methyl group. The methyl group is furnished by choline or betaine. An animal fed upon a diet lacking in methionine, but containing homocystine fails to grow; growth is resumed upon the addition of choline or betaine; the essential amino acid methionine being thus formed. The transference of the methyl groups from methionine or choline to glycocyamine with the formation of creatine is described on page 782. Methionine, choline and betaine are, therefore, spoken of as transmethylating agents. The conversion of nicotinic acid to trigonelline may be another example of transmethylation, although it may be due, in part, to direct methylation. The methyl group is not improbably derived from methionine.

*Transamidation.* This is the transference of an amidine group $NH_2$ as from arginine to glycine

$$\overset{|}{C} = NH$$

to form glycocyamine (p. 783).

## The Synthesis of Amino Acids

That the body tissues, given the necessary amino acids, can link them together and so synthesize protein is, of course, unquestioned. The extent to which the amino acids themselves can be synthesized has been a more difficult question to decide. That synthesis of amino acids does occur is clearly indicated by the fact that only a limited number (10) of amino acids found in animal tissue are essential constituents of the diet. Undoubtedly the body is able to synthesize glycine—the simplest amino acid. For example, milk proteins contain no more than 0.1 to 0.3 per cent of glycine, yet from 100 grams of the former the suckling animal can build up 78 grams of tissue protein containing 2.5 grams of glycine (Magnus-Levy). Also, the liver and kidney detoxicate benzoic acid by combining it with glycine to form hippuric acid which is excreted in the urine. When large quantities of benzoic acid are fed, the glycine in the excreted hippuric acid is greater in amount than that which could have been supplied preformed from body tissue. Analogous experiments with the detoxication of phenylacetic acid to phenylacetyl glutamine indicate that glutamic acid can also be synthesized. The mode by which synthesis of the amino acids takes place is obscure. The formation of amino acids by the transference of amino groups to non-nitrogenous compounds, e.g., pyruvic acid formed in the breakdown of carbohydrate, or even the utilization of ammonia, fed in the form of ammonium salts, has been mentioned. The ammonia probably unites with a keto acid to form an aminated hydroxy acid which by reduction yields an amino acid.

$$R \cdot CH_2CO \cdot COOH + NH_3 \rightarrow$$
keto acid

$$R \cdot CH_2COHNH_2COOH \rightarrow$$
hydroxyamino-acid

$$R \cdot CH_2CHNH_2 \cdot COOH + H_2O$$
amino acid

Embden found that alanine was formed by the surviving liver perfused with blood to which the ammonium salt of pyruvic acid had been added. Phenylalanine and tyrosine were also formed when the liver was perfused with the ammonium salts of the corresponding keto acids. Even the addition of ammonium chloride to the fluid perfusing a glycogen-rich liver resulted in the production of alanine. The latter also followed perfusion with ammonium lactate. Furthermore, it was shown by Knoop that when $\gamma$-phenyl-$\alpha$-keto-butyric acid was administered to dogs the corresponding amino acid appeared in the urine, whereas the experiments of Cox and Rose and of Sherwin and their associates indicate that histidine, an essential amino acid, can be formed in the body when imidazole pyruvic acid or imidazole lactic acid is fed. The synthesis of arginine has also been demonstrated by Rose and his colleagues.

To sum up: it is established that glycine can be synthesized from precursors already present in the body. The same may also be said for glutamic and aspartic acids alanine and arginine. The perfusion experiments just mentioned suggest that alanine may be synthesized from the derivatives of carbohydrate metabolism plus the ammonia which would otherwise be excreted as urea. Other more complex amino acids, e.g., tryptophane, histidine, and proline, etc. (p. 775) contain special groupings which cannot be formed in the body. They are therefore essential constituents of the diet (ch. 46). If, however, the special groups are supplied, as in the form of the keto acid or hydroxy acid, the corresponding amino acid can in some instances be formed.

## Protein Synthesis

The synthesis of protein from free amino acids requires energy; the latter is derived from the oxidation of carbohydrate and fat. The energy liberated during oxidative catabolism is not contributed directly to the reactions involved in protein formation but is first used to synthesize adenosine-triphosphate (ATP) which acts as an intermediate source of energy (see Carbohydrate Metabolism). Thus, in conditions such as diabetes mellitus, where carbohydrate and fat utilization are severely impaired, peptide synthesis is also impaired. Protein formation is also reduced by substances such as dinitrophenol, which interfere with ATP synthesis and allow the energy liberated from oxidative reactions to be dissipated as heat.

The mechanisms responsible for the formation of peptide bonds and the factors which guide the selection of amino acids so that they may be linked together in the specific sequence that characterizes a particular protein, are not thoroughly understood. An increasing amount of data supports the view, originally proposed by Borsook, that there are three steps involved in the formation of a protein molecule. The *first step* consists of activation of the carboxyl group of an amino acid. The results of recent investigations indicate that this is achieved in the following manner:

1. Enzyme + ATP → enzyme − P + ADP

2. Enzyme − P + amino acid → enzyme − amino acid + P

It is pertinent that, through this reaction, it is always the carboxyl group that is activated and the activation occurs at the expense of ATP. It is believed that in the second step the activated amino acids are transported to a template or mold which aligns them in the specific sequence characteristic of the protein to be synthesized. In the *third step* the activated carboxyl groups combine with the amino groups of the adjacent molecules to form peptide bonds. The newly formed molecule then peels off the template. According to this concept, the whole protein molecule is formed through the simultaneous condensation of the activated amino acids; the formation of polypeptides of intermediate sizes is not involved in the process. If this is true, it accounts for the fact that protein synthesis cannot occur unless all of the essential amino acids are available simultaneously. The template upon which protein is formed appears to be ribonucleic acid (RNA) for it has been shown that inhibition of RNA synthesis is invariably followed by an inhibition of protein synthesis. Similarly, a stimulation of protein synthesis is always associated with an increased synthesis of RNA.

### The Classical as Opposed to the Modern View of Protein Metabolism

The classical view of protein metabolism was proposed originally by Folin. He believed that the creatinine and neutral sulfur excreted in urine were derived from the wear and tear of the body tissues and the amounts of these substances in the urine were taken as indices of endogenous protein metabolism. The urea, on the other hand, was believed to be derived solely from the catabolism of dietary or exogenous protein. Since creatinine represents a very small amount of the total urinary nitrogen and remains constant in amount, it was concluded that the tissue proteins were relatively inert and that only minute amounts of the dietary amino acids were needed to replace the protein lost from body tissues. This concept was challenged in 1935 by Borsook and Keighley who, on the basis of much indirect evidence, suggested that endogenous protein metabolism was a very active process and that a large proportion of the dietary amino acids were utilized by various tissues. Direct substantiation of this concept was obtained by Schoenheimer and his associates through the use of isotopically labelled compounds. Schoenheimer fed rats leucine and glycine labelled with $N^{15}$. If, as Folin believed, the body proteins were inert, nearly all of the label from the amino acids should have been recovered from the urine. However, only a fraction of the isotopic nitrogen was found in the urine whereas the remainder was found incorporated into the body tissues. It appears, therefore, that the body proteins are in a constant state of turnover, they are continually being broken down and replaced by new protein synthesized from dietary amino acids. Subsequent work indicates that the replacement of protein is

rapid in plasma, liver, kidney and intestinal tract, and comparatively slow in hemoglobin, muscle and skin.

The rapid turnover of amino acids in various tissues has been considered by some to be due to the degradation and resynthesis of the intracellular proteins. Cohn and Monod have expressed reservations concerning this belief. They point out that what has been interpreted as evidence of intracellular turnover of protein may represent a turnover of whole cells, that is to say, the rate at which cells, not just the protein within them, are destroyed and replaced. It appears then that protein turnover may be due to both intracellular degradation and resynthesis and to replacement of whole cells.

### Protein Storage—Labile Protein

In the latter half of the 19th century Voit observed that when dogs were starved, or fed a diet free of protein the nitrogen excretion fell rapidly for 5 or 6 days and then became relatively constant. The larger amounts of nitrogen excreted during the first few days were believed by Rubner to arise from unorganized storage protein that was utilized to fill a metabolic need for nitrogen during times of protein deprivation. Research during the intervening years has failed to reveal a depot or special form of protein that functions exclusively as a reserve supply. However, the body tissues, particularly those of liver thymus, prostate, seminal vesicles, alimentary tract, pancreas, spleen and kidneys, do contain labile proteins that can be drawn upon when the need arises. These organs lose their labile protein rapidly. This process seems to account for the rapid fall and subsequent stabilization of urinary nitrogen excretion that occurs during the first few days of starvation. Some of the protein mobilized is utilized for the synthesis of other body proteins. This phenomenon is well illustrated by the experimental findings of Madden and Whipple. When severe hypo-proteinemia was produced by repeated plasmapheresis, a normal dog resynthesized 40 to 60 per cent of its plasma proteins while fasting. This, however, is not the only function of the protein. A large proportion is converted into carbohydrate, which is subsequently used to provide the energy required for vital processes. It appears then that the body tissues, particularly those of the viscera, do contain labile proteins, the supply of which, however, is quickly exhausted. The temporary loss of this protein does no permanent damage to the organ involved; there is no reason to believe that it differs chemically or functionally from the proteins that normally constitute the donor cell.

## The End Products of Protein— Metabolism, Urea

The great proportion of the nitrogen released by the catabolism of the amino acids appears in the urine of man, mammals, amphibia and elasmobranch fish as urea. In birds and reptiles, on the other hand, the chief end product of protein breakdown is *uric acid*. In man and other mammals the latter is derived from the metabolism of the purines (ch. 47). Urea is formed directly (i.e., without preliminary deamination), from *arginine*, which is hydrolyzed by the action of an enzyme—*arginase*—into *urea* and *ornithine*. Arginase is present in the liver of mammals but not in that of birds and reptiles. The reaction may be represented thus

This important mechanism has been thought

$$HN=\overset{\displaystyle NH_2}{\underset{\displaystyle NH\cdot(CH_2)_3\cdot CHNH_2\cdot COOH}{C}} + H_2O \rightarrow O=\overset{\displaystyle NH_2}{\underset{\displaystyle NH_2}{C}} + NH_2\cdot(CH_2)_3\cdot CHNH_2\cdot COOH$$

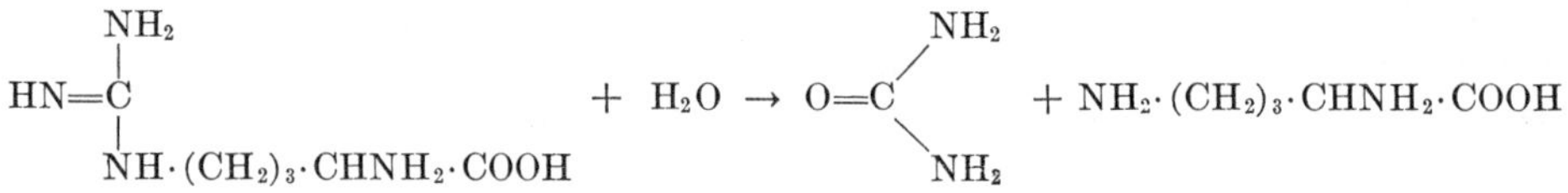

Arginine                         Urea           Ornithine

to account for the greater proportion of the urea formed in the body. When ornithine was incubated with slices of liver in the presence of ammonia and carbonic acid, large amounts of urea were formed. It is supposed that the ornithine combines with the ammonia and carbonic acid to form arginine which in turn is hydrolyzed by arginase into urea and ornithine. Thus arginine serves as an intermediary in the production of urea from the ammonia supplied by other amino acids. The ornithine liberated by the decomposition of arginine is used over again. Ornithine thus acts after the manner of a catalyst to facilitate urea production.

According to Krebs and Henseleit, the formation of arginine from ornithine occurs in two steps. (1) The formation of the amino acid *citrulline* by the addition of a molecule each of ammonia and carbon dioxide to ornithine.

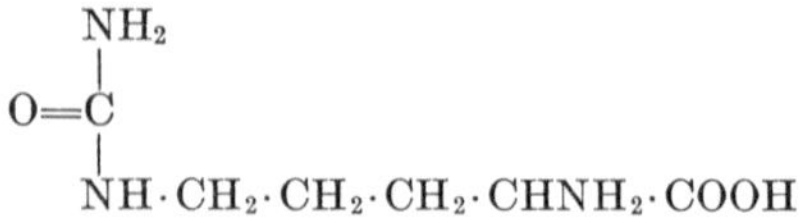

$$O=\overset{\displaystyle NH_2}{\underset{\displaystyle NH\cdot CH_2\cdot CH_2\cdot CH_2\cdot CHNH_2\cdot COOH}{C}}$$

Citrulline

(2) The addition of a second molecule of ammonia to citrulline with the production of arginine. Therefore, the production of urea from ammonia and carbonic acid may be represented thus:

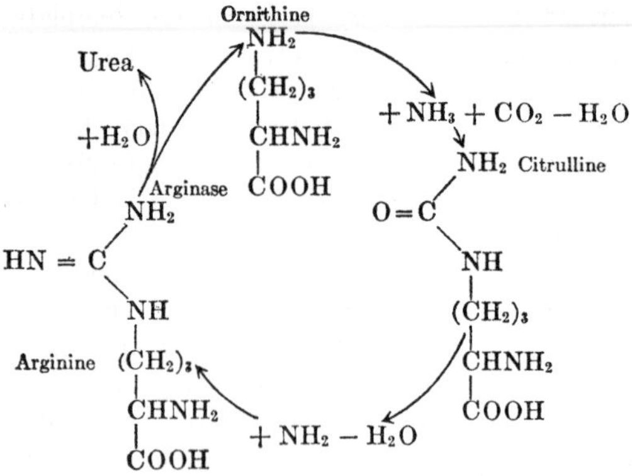

The ornithine cycle

Although the ornithine cycle is probably not the only mechanism involved in the production of urea, it is generally considered to be the major one. Some of its details have been clarified by the work of several investigators (Cohen and Hayano, Borsook and Dubnoff, and Ratner and associates). Cohen and Hayano reported that for the production of arginine from citrulline glutamic acid rather than ammonia appeared to be the nitrogen donor, and that Mg ions, adenosinetriphosphate (ATP) and oxygen were required for the reaction. The transfer of the $NH_2$ group it has been suggested, is effected by transamination and the simultaneous loss of two H atoms (transamination). The citrulline-arginine conversion occurred only in the presence of oxygen. Glutamate also acts as an acceptor of $CO_2$ and $NH_3$ in the synthesis of citrulline from ornithine, in the first stage of the ornithine cycle. Aspartic acid is, however, according to the researches of Ratner and her colleagues, the specific nitrogen donor in the conversion of citrulline to arginine, which occurs anaerobically in the presence of Mg ions and ATP. Fumaric acid is also formed in this reaction, but undergoes oxidation to oxalacetic acid. Through this latter reaction the tricarboxylic and ornithine cycles are interlocked. The following scheme is given by Ratner.

Urea is decomposed into $NH_3$ and $CO_2$ by the action of urease. This enzyme is found in leguminous plants, especially in soy bean, and in relatively high concentration in the gastric mucosa (ch. 38). Urease is employed in the deter-

SUCCINATE — FUMARATE

α- KETOGLUTARATE

~ATP~

MALATE

OXALOACETATE

ISOCITRATE

·ACETYL

CITRATE

GLUTAMATE — OXALOACETATE

$NH_3$

α- KETOGLUTARATE — ASPARTATE

CITRULLINE — ATP

ARGININO SUCCINATE

Carbamyl phosphate

2 ATP
Acetyl glutamate

ORNITHINE

FUMARATE

$CO_2 + NH_4$

UREA — ARGININE

mination of urea (from ammonia evolved) in urine and in other body fluids and in tissues.

THE EXCRETION OF UREA AND ITS DISTRIBUTION IN THE BODY. On an ordinary mixed diet from 80 to 90 per cent of the urinary nitrogen is urea-nitrogen. The absolute amount of urea-nitrogen excreted daily is usually from 9 to 13 grams (20 to 30 grams of urea). Minimal amounts are also excreted in the sweat (ch. 52), salivary, intestinal and mammary secretions. The urea-nitrogen varies with the protein content of the diet. Upon a low protein diet the output may be as low as 2 grams and on a diet rich in protein it may be over 25 grams. The value of urea-nitrogen is therefore taken as an index of the magnitude of the catabolism of food protein (exogenous metabolism, see table, p. 784).

The blood contains from 8 to 15 mg. of urea-nitrogen (18 to 35 mg. urea) per 100 cc. Urea is readily diffusible and is found in about the same concentration in the various tissues and other fluids, e.g., lymph, bile, cerebrospinal fluid and pancreatic juice, as in blood. The kidney, however, is an exception since it contains some 150 to 200 mg. of urea per 100 grams of tissue. We have already seen that the urinary ammonia is formed from glutamine and amino acids in the kidney and not from urea (ch. 34).

THE SITE OF UREA PRODUCTION. It has long been known that the liver is an important site of urea formation. Perfusion of the liver with amino acids or their addition to sliced liver tissue leads to the production of urea. Urea is very widely

distributed throughout nature, being a constituent of the body fluids of the lowest forms of animal life. It is also found in plants. For this reason its formation in animals might be thought to be a function common to all tissues. But the experiments of Mann and his associates in hepatectomized dogs, points to the liver as being the main if not the sole site of urea production. After complete removal of the liver the formation of urea ceased, so that its concentration in the blood and urine fell progressively. If the kidneys as well as the liver were excised there was no accumulation of urea in the blood although the amino acid concentration rose. Also, after the injection of glycine or alanine into the hepatectomized animal, in contrast to the result obtained in the normal animal, the concentration of the injected amino acid rose in the blood and urine, and there was no evidence of urea production. That these results in dogs apply to man is indicated by the observation of Rabinowitch. He has reported that in a case of extensive damage to kidneys and liver (acute yellow atrophy) the excretion of urine was almost suppressed yet the blood was urea-free. The appearance of leucine and tyrosine in the urine which occurs in acute yellow atrophy of the liver may also be ascribed to the failure of deamination of these amino acids. Nevertheless, although the liver undoubtedly plays the predominant role in the production of urea, certain other tissues may under certain circumstances share to some degree in its formation. Graham and associates found, for example, that the active mammary gland produces not inconsiderable amounts.

### Creatine and Creatinine

*Creatine* ($C_4H_9N_3O_2$) (methyl guanido-acetic acid or methyl-glycocyamine)

$$HN=C \begin{cases} NH_2 \\ N(CH_3) \cdot CH_2 \cdot COOH \end{cases}$$

may be looked upon as a derivative of glycine, of guanidine or of guanido-acetic acid. It is also related to arginine. It is readily converted by acid *in vitro* to creatinine.

*Creatinine*, $C_4H_7N_3O$ (methyl glycocyamidine) is the anhydride of creatine. Its molecular constitution is shown by the following formula:

$$HN=C \begin{cases} NH \text{———} C=O \\ N(CH_3) \cdot CH_2 \end{cases}$$

*Distribution of creatine and creatinine.* There are about 120 grams of *creatine* contained in the adult human body. Of this 98 per cent is contained in the muscles and 1.5 per cent in the nervous system. The remaining 0.5 per cent is distributed throughout the other organs of the body; of these, the testes contain it in highest concentration. The skeletal and cardiac muscles and the gravid uterus are a great deal richer in creatine than the smooth muscle of the gastrointestinal tract and elsewhere. About 80 per cent of the creatine in muscle is combined with phosphoric acid as *phosphocreatine* (ch. 51). Of the striated muscles, the rapidly contracting, pale type contain more than the slowly contracting red variety (p. 1165). In the muscle of invertebrates creatine is replaced by arginine.

*Creatinine* is present in muscle in much smaller amounts. One hundred grams of skeletal muscle, for example, contain 300 to 500 mg. of creatine and only 10 mg. of creatinine. The creatine of whole blood amounts to from 3.5 to 5.0 mg. and the creatinine to about 2.5 mg. per 100 cc. By far the greater part, if not all, of the creatine is contained in the corpuscles. The creatinine is about equally distributed between cells and plasma.

*Excretion of creatine and creatinine.* Creatine is normally absent from the urine of men, but is present in the urine of male and female children up to the age of puberty and frequently in the urine of women. The significance of these sex differences is not evident. In nonpregnant women the *creatinuria* is intermittent but is not related to menstruation. During pregnancy creatine is present continuously in the urine. This may be related to high creatine content of the uterus. For two or three weeks after childbirth the quantity excreted is even higher than during pregnancy. Reduction in the muscular mass of the uterus (involution) may account in part for the high output during the puerperium, but that uterine involution is not the chief cause is shown by the fact that it occurs although Caesarian section and removal of the uterus have been performed. Creatine also appears in the urine of either sex under the following conditions; *high protein diet, starvation, carbohydrate deprivation, diabetes, wasting diseases* and *fevers, exophthalmic goiter* and in certain *muscular dystrophies.* The creatinuria in all of these conditions except the last is probably due to an increase in the normal catabolism of muscular tissue, the liberation of creatine occurring more rapidly than its conversion to creatinine. Protein food, for example, has a stimulating effect upon metabolism (p. 787), whereas in wasting diseases,

fevers, etc., tissue breakdown is accelerated. Carbohydrate deprivation probably acts indirectly in that its sparing effect upon protein catabolism is absent. In the muscular dystrophies, e.g., *myasthenia gravis, progressive muscular atrophy, amyotonia congenita, anterior poliomyelitis,* etc., the urinary creatine is probably derived from the degenerating muscle fibers; the muscles also appear to be defective in their power to store creatine. The creatinuria of normal children has received no satisfactory explanation; it is said to be due to an increased production of creatine, induced in some way by the growth impulse, and also probably to a low capacity for creatine storage of the undeveloped muscles. Another possibility is that children have a relatively low power to convert creatine to creatinine (Hunter).

*The origin of creatine and creatinine.* Creatinine is undoubtedly derived from creatine but there has been much uncertainty concerning the latter's origin. One or other of the substances to which its chemical formula suggests a relationship, e.g., guanidine, glycine or arginine, has been considered as a possible precursor. The opportunity afforded by the creatinuria of muscular dystrophies has been taken advantage of by Brand and his colleagues in the investigation of this question. Various amino acids and other guanido compounds were fed to patients suffering from such disorders; ingested glycine, or gelatin which is rich in this amino acid, causes a pronounced rise (40 per cent) in the creatine excretion of these patients but not of normal persons. The proportion of ingested creatine which is retained is also much less than the normal (*creatine tolerance test*). Arginine and glycocyamine (guanidoacetic acid) were also effective. Feeding benzoic acid, which drew upon the body's glycine store for detoxication purposes (p. 721) caused a decrease in the creatine excretion. The importance of glycine in creatine synthesis is emphasized by the observation of Almquist and Mecchi that glycine, which is an indispensable amino acid for chicks, can be replaced in the diet of this species by creatine. These results pointed to arginine, guanidoacetic acid, and especially glycine as precursors of creatine.

The subject of creatine synthesis has been clarified recently through a number of experiments in which isotopes were used as markers to identify the particular substance under investigation after it had been absorbed. The administration of isotopic glycine (i.e., heavy nitrogen, $N^{15}$, incorporated in the glycine molecule) was shown by Bloch and Schoenheimer to give rise to creatine with a high concentration of the nitrogen isotope. Of all the other amino acids investigated by this method, arginine alone was found to be a primary precursor of creatine. The isotope $N^{15}$ was incorporated into the amidine part ($NH_2$—C=NH) of the arginine molecule. When the isotopic arginine was fed, the creatine isolated from the tissues of the animal was found to contain the isotope in this part of its molecule. The researches of du Vigneaud, and of Borsook and Dubnoff, show clearly that the methyl group of creatine is furnished by methionine. The former worker prepared methionine in which the three hydrogen atoms of the S-methyl group were present as the isotope $H^2$ (deuterium). When this was fed and the creatine of the animals' bodies determined, the isotope concentration indicated that nearly 70 per cent of the methyl groups of the creatine molecule had been derived from methionine. Borsook and Dubnoff incubated liver slices with guanidoacetic acid (glycocyamine) which they found was slowly converted to creatine, the conversion being hastened by the addition of methionine. Glycocyamine is apparently an intermediary in the synthesis of creatine in the body; when the isotopic form of this compound is fed isotopic creatine is formed. The conclusions to be drawn from these experiments are that arginine, glycine and methionine enter into the synthesis of creatine but that other amino acids do not serve as precursors. The first reaction, it appears, is between the amidine part of arginine and glycine with the formation of glycocyamine. The guanidoacetic acid then undergoes methylation by the transference of the methyl group from methionine. Thus:

Glycine     Amidine group of arginine

$NH_2$            $NH_2$

$CH_2COOH$ + —C=NH →

Glycocyamine                    Creatine

$NH_2$                          $NH_2$

C—NH              + $CH_3$ →   C=NH

NH                 from         $NCH_3$

$CH_2COOH$         methionine   → $CH_2COOH$

The site of creatine production is not known definitely but it is probably in the muscles. These also in all probability are the site of creatine-creatinine transformation (by dehydration). Mann and Magath found that removal of the liver was without effect upon creatinine production. The creatine which gives rise to urinary creatinine is derived very largely from the phosphocreatine of muscle.

Creatine is not, as was held by some authorities in the past, simply a waste product of protein metabolism like urea. If, for example, a large dose of creatine is fed the greater part or the whole is retained in the body.[3] Creatinine, on the other hand is purely a waste product. Up to 80 per cent or more of an amount fed can be recovered unchanged in the urine. The investigations of recent years into the chemistry of muscular contraction have revealed the essential importance of creatine (as phosphocreatine) in the contractile process (ch. 51).

## CREATININE EXCRETION AS AN INDEX OF MUSCLE METABOLISM

The daily output of creatinine in the urine is constant for the individual, amounting to from 1.5 to 2.0 grams for men and from 0.8 to 1.5 grams for women. This corresponds to about 2 per cent of the creatine of the body. Unlike the excretion of urea, which is derived largely from exogenous sources, the creatinine output is practically independent of the protein level of the food. This is evident from table 45.5. The creatinine excretion is therefore considered to be an index of the magnitude of the metabolism of the tissues and especially of muscle. The daily output of creatinine is extraordinarily constant for the individual; it is not influenced by ordinary exercise or by the urine volume. The creatinine coefficient—

$$\frac{\text{milligrams creatinine[4] excreted per day}}{\text{body weight in kilograms}}$$

is from 20 to 26 for the majority of normal men and from 14 to 22 for women. Its value depends upon the muscular development of the individual; the sex variation being due presumably to the different relative amounts of fatty and muscular tissues of male and female bodies. Athletic women for this reason have a coefficient as high as or higher than a man of obese build and poor muscular development.

[3] In the experiments of Benedict and Osterberg over half a gram of creatine hydrate was fed daily to dogs for a period of several weeks. In the first week none of the administered creatin was excreted, either as such or as creatinine. During subsequent weeks when the "creatine reservoirs" had apparently become filled a large part was excreted unchanged. A rise in the creatinine output also occurred, indicating the transformation of creatine to creatinine. Nevertheless, of some 33 grams of creatine administered over the entire period of 70 days about 20 grams were retained. Retention of ingested creatine is also demonstrable in man.

[4] Or creatine + creatinine, when creatinuria exists.

TABLE 45.5

*Effect of dietary protein on composition of urine*
(After Folin)

| | Nitrogen-Rich Diet | Nitrogen-Poor Diet |
|---|---|---|
| Volume of urine.. | 1170 cc. | 385 cc. |
| Total nitrogen.... | 16.8 grams | 3.60 grams |
| Urea nitrogen.... | 14.70 grams = 87.5% | 2.20 grams = 61.7% |
| Ammonia nitrogen | 0.49 gram = 0.3% | 0.42 gram = 11.3% |
| Uric acid nitrogen | 0.18 gram = 1.1% | 0.09 gram = 2.5% |
| Creatinine nitrogen........... | 0.58 gram = 3.6% | 0.60 gram = 17.2% |
| Undetermined nitrogen......... | 0.85 gram = 4.9% | 0.27 gram = 7.3% |
| Total sulfur....... | 3.64 grams | 0.76 gram |
| Inorganic $SO_3$.... | 3.27 grams = 90.0% | 0.46 gram = 60.5% |
| Ethereal $SO_3$..... | 0.19 gram = 5.2% | 0.10 gram = 13.2% |
| Neutral S........ | 0.18 gram = 4.8% | 0.20 gram = 26.3% |

### THE METABOLISM OF SULFUR

Sulfur enters the body mainly as a constituent of the amino acids *cystine* and *methionine*. Food also contains inorganic sulfates, small amounts of sulfur in the form of sulfolipids (sulfatides) in certain glycoproteins (mucoitin-sulfuric acid and chondroitin-sulfuric acid) and in organic sulfides, isothiocyanates, and sulfonium compounds. Sulfur in inorganic form cannot be used in the construction of body protein. Practically speaking, the body is dependent for its sulfur supplies upon the two sulfur-containing amino acids mentioned above.

### THE DISTRIBUTION OF SULFUR IN THE BODY

Sulfur is contained in the ordinary tissue proteins; in hair, horn, feathers, etc.; in mucin, as mucoitin-sulfuric acid and chondroitin-sulfuric acid; in certain glycoproteins of tendons, vitreous humor, cornea and connective tissues; in glutathione and insulin; in the taurocholic acid of bile; as solfocyanate in saliva; in ergothionine, a compound found in red corpuscles; in certain pigments (melanins, urochrome), and in nervous tissue as sulfolipoids. Inorganic sulfates are contained in the body fluids generally.

*The loss of sulfur from the body* occurs in the shedding of hair, nails, etc., in the bile, saliva and gastrointestinal secretions. The great bulk of the sulfur loss, however, occurs through the kidneys.

*The history of sulfur in the body.* The sulfur liberated in the catabolism of dietary protein is largely converted to inorganic sulfates. A part of the inorganic sulfate derived from this and other sources becomes conjugated in the liver with substances produced in the intestine by the bacterial decomposition of protein to form *ethereal sulfates*. The latter are excreted in the urine. The products of bacterial action, among which are phenol derived from phenylalanine and tyrosine, and indole and skatole from tryptophane, possess toxic properties. Their excretion as ethereal sulfates constitutes a detoxicating mechanism. When the detoxicating function of the liver is depressed as a result of hepatic disease, some of these toxic substances are excreted by the kidney in abnormal amounts in the free state.

*Urinary sulfur.* The total urinary sulfur is made up of the following:

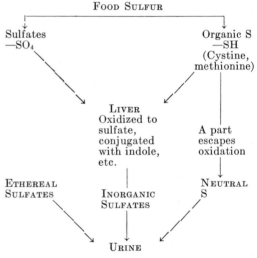

(1) Inorganic sulfur (85 to 90 per cent). Compounds of sulfuric acid with Na, K, Ca and $NH_3$.

(2) Ethereal sulfate sulfur (6 to 8 per cent), e.g., potassium and sodium salts of indoxyl sulfuric acid (p. 721). The former is known as indican.

(3) Neutral sulfur (4 to 6 per cent) e.g., sulfur-containing amino acids, urochrome, thiosulfates, thiocyanates, taurocholic and oxyproteic acids.

The quantities of inorganic and ethereal sulfates in the urine vary with the protein level of the diet, and run more or less parallel with the nitrogen excretion; the neutral sulfur is influenced to a less degree. For this reason the two former partitions of the urinary sulfur were considered by Folin to represent food (exogenous) sulfur while the neutral sulfur was taken to be derived mainly from body protein (endogenous sulfur). On a diet of meat or during prolonged starvation the ratio of sulfur to nitrogen in the urine is about 1 to 14, i.e., for every gram of sulfur there are approximately 14 grams of nitrogen. This is approximately the S:N ratio found in muscular tissue. A graphic summary of sulfur metabolism is shown above.

As a result of the excessive production and absorption of putrefactive products the excretion of ethereal sulfates is increased in acute intestinal obstruction. They are also increased in carcinoma of the liver. Chronic constipation, however, exerts little or no influence upon the excretion of these substances).

The excretion of neutral sulfur is increased in the rare metabolic anomaly known as *cystinuria* and in cases of *melanotic sarcoma*, when an abnormal sulfur-containing pigment appears in the urine.

*The nonprotein sulfur of blood.* The sulfur of blood, other than that present as a constituent of protein, amounts to from 3 to 5 mg. per 100 cc. The concentrations of the three forms are given in table 45.6.

### AMMONIA (SEE PAGE 565)

### NITROGEN BALANCES

The difference between the nitrogen taken in the food and that excreted in the feces and urine is spoken of as the nitrogen balance (that lost in the hair, sweat, saliva, etc., is negligible). On an ordinary diet, the amounts of nitrogen excreted daily in the feces and urine, respectively, average 1.5 and 13 grams. The nitrogen of the feces is in part unabsorbed nitrogen of the food and in part nitrogen excreted through the intestinal wall. When the intake and output are equal, the body

### TABLE 45.6
*Concentrations of different forms of sulfur in whole blood and serum*
(After Denis)

|  | Whole Blood | Serum |
|---|---|---|
|  | *per 100 cc. mg.* | *per 100 cc. mg.* |
| Inorganic sulfur............ | 0.1–1.1 | 0.5–1.1 |
| Ethereal sulfate sulfur....... | 0.1–1.0 | 0.1–1.0 |
| Neutral sulfur.... .......... | 2.2–4.5 | 1.7–3.5 |

The inorganic sulfur of blood is elevated in *renal insufficiency, intestinal obstruction* and *leukemia.*

### TABLE 45.7
*Example of adjustment of nitrogen balance to increased intake*

| Day | Nitrogen in Food | Nitrogen in Feces | Nitrogen "Absorbed" | Nitrogen in Urine | Nitrogen Balance |
|---|---|---|---|---|---|
|  | *grams* | *grams* | *grams* | *grams* | *grams* |
| 1 | 14.40 | 0.70 | 13.70 | 13.60 | +0.10 |
| 2 | 14.40 | 0.70 | 13.70 | 13.80 | −0.10 |
| 3 | 14.40 | 0.70 | 13.70 | 13.60 | +0.10 |
| 4 | 20.96 | 0.82 | 20.14 | 16.80 | +3.34 |
| 5 | 20.96 | 0.82 | 20.14 | 18.20 | +1.94 |
| 6 | 20.96 | 0.82 | 20.14 | 19.50 | +0.64 |
| 7 | 20.96 | 0.82 | 20.14 | 20.00 | +0.14 |

* Modified from H. C. Sherman, "Chemistry of Food and Nutrition," 4th edition.

is said to be in *nitrogen equilibrium*. When the intake exceeds the output the body is in *positive nitrogen balance*—nitrogen is being retained. If the reverse is the case, i.e., the output exceeds the intake, the balance is said to be *negative*—the body is losing nitrogen. When the nitrogen of the food is increased a greater quantity for a time thereafter is retained, but the body soon becomes adjusted to the higher intake and gradually a balance is re-established (table 45.7).

The healthy adult requires protein to replace the inevitable loss of tissue protein. When given a sufficient amount of protein to repair this so-called "wear and tear" his output and intake of nitrogen will balance, i.e., he will be in nitrogen equilibrium. If his diet contains protein in excess of this amount the nitrogen not employed for repair is excreted and nitrogen equilibrium maintained. In starvation or on a low protein intake, or on a diet which lacks certain essential amino acids, the individual continues to excrete nitrogen derived from the dissolution of his own protoplasma, and so goes into negative balance. In children, in adults recovering from wasting diseases or undergoing muscular training, and in pregnant women, the body, if the protein intake is liberal, does not excrete as much nitrogen as it received. Nitrogen is retained for the manufacture of new tissue. The daily excretion of nitrogen of a man of average weight upon a nitrogen-free diet amounts to from 0.75 to 3 grams. It might be thought that nitrogen equilibrium could be re-established by simply feeding this quantity of protein nitrogen. It is found however that a considerably larger quantity is necessary. Part of the reason for this is that the amino acids are required by the body in different proportions from those present in the food protein. In order that the body shall obtain a sufficient quantity of suitable amino acids for the replacement of its own protoplasm and for the manufacture of various secretions and other essential materials, a relatively large assortment must be available from which it can choose. Those not required are discarded. For this reason, equilibrium can be established upon a smaller quantity of animal protein, such as beef muscle which contains amino acids more nearly in the same proportions as those in human body protein, rather than upon vegetable proteins. The wastage of nitrogen is less in the former instance. If the only protein in the food is one entirely lacking in certain essential amino acids (lysine, threonine, etc.) the loss of nitrogen resulting from the breakdown of such amino acids in the body's protoplasm cannot be replaced. A negative balance results no matter how much of the inferior protein has been fed (see ch. 46).

The quantity of protein required to establish nitrogen equilibrium depends very greatly upon the content of the diet in the other two food principles—fats and carbohydrates. It is impossible, for example, to establish nitrogen equilibrium in man upon an exclusively protein diet; the excretion of nitrogen always exceeds the intake even though the individual ingests protein to his full capacity. The reason for this is that man cannot consume and digest sufficient amounts of protein to satisfy his energy requirements. Under such circumstances he draws upon his stores of carbohydrates and fats, but after these have been exhausted the protein elements of his tissues are disrupted. The non-nitrogenous portions of the amino acid molecules are burned to make up the calorie deficiency, and, as a consequence, quantities of nitrogen derived from food and body protein are excreted. It has been calculated that the human subject would have to consume, daily, some 8 pounds of meat—practically an impossible feat for a civilized man—in order to furnish the necessary energy and maintain the body in nitrogen equilibrium. On the contrary, a carnivorous animal such as the dog which possesses a large capacity for the digestion of protein food[5] thrives

upon a diet composed entirely of lean meat. The Eskimos are also capable—according to Krogh—of consuming relatively enormous quantities of meat. On a mixed diet, as we shall see immediately, nitrogen equilibrium can be established on a very low protein intake.

## PROTEIN SPARERS

Carbohydrates and fats are called *protein sparers* since their presence in the diet relieves tissue protein of the necessity of furnishing energy. The protection of body protein by carbohydrate has been shown clearly by numerous experiments. The following experiment performed by Lusk upon himself may be cited in illustration of this important principle. After a period during which a mixed diet had been fed and a small positive nitrogen balance established, 350 grams of carbohydrate were withdrawn from the diet. The nitrogen excretion increased from 19.84 to 27.00 grams daily, the balance becoming negative. Also, the nitrogen excretion in the urine in starvation is nearly three times greater than that upon a diet, nitrogen-free, but of adequate energy value (i.e., one composed exclusively of fat and carbohydrate). The nonprotein food has reduced the breakdown of tissue protein.

The nitrogen excretion on such a protein-sparing diet is therefore an index of the inevitable disintegration of body protoplasm which occurs under ordinary physiological conditions. For this reason it was called, by Rubner, the "wear and tear" quota of protein metabolism (see p. 779). One of the lowest values reported for nitrogen excretion is that of Boothby and Sandiford, namely, 1.74 grams daily (0.024 gram per kg. of body weight).

Carbohydrate exerts a specific sparing action quite apart from the fact that it furnishes energy and so relieves protein of the necessity of performing this duty, for the sparing effect exhibited by a given quantity of carbohydrate cannot be brought about by an amount of fat possessing double the caloric value. Carbohydrate when fed alone has a marked sparing action, whereas fat alone has little or no protein-sparing effect and a positive nitrogen balance cannot be established in man on a diet composed entirely of fat and protein. Nor will fat by itself, when given after a period of fasting, reduce the nitrogen excretion below that during the fast. Indeed, it actually increases the output of nitrogen. A diet whose calories, up to 50 per cent or more, are derived from fat and the remainder from carbohydrate has, however, as

[5] The daily energy requirement of man is, say, 3000 Calories. Eight pounds of meat (3600 grams approximately) which is 20 per cent protein, has a caloric value of $(20/100) \times 3600 \times 4.1 = 2900$. The energy expenditure of an average-sized dog, on the other hand, is around 600 Calories. It can consume in less than a minute 2 pounds (900 grams) of meat, yielding more than 700 Calories.

great a protein-sparing action as one whose calories are derived from carbohydrate alone. Lactic and pyruvic acids, products of carbohydrate metabolism, are also protein-sparers to some extent. The sparing effect of carbohydrates can be demonstrated in the well nourished animal as well as during starvation. When dogs in nitrogen equilibrium are given extra glucose, nitrogen is retained but the balance is re-established when the administration of glucose is stopped (Larson and Chaikoff).

The difference between the sparing actions of fat and carbohydrate is not easily explained. According to one view (Landergren) the specific sparing effect of carbohydrate depends upon the fact that glucose is vitally essential to the body and must be constantly supplied whatever the cost. If it is not available from outside sources or from the glycogen stores, tissue protein is broken down to yield materials from which it may be synthesized.

Another more probable explanation of the peculiar sparing action of carbohydrate is, that it is used in the synthesis of the amino acids which are incorporated into body proteins. According to this view the nitrogen resulting from the breakdown of tissue protein during fasting (or from tissue and food protein when the diet consists exclusively of protein and fat) is largely or entirely excreted. If, on the other hand, certain intermediary products of carbohydrate metabolism are available, e.g., pyruvic acid, etc., it is possible for amino acids to be resynthesized. That is, nitrogen which would otherwise be wasted is retained.

### THE SPECIFIC DYNAMIC ACTION OF FOOD

When a subject in the basal state ingests food, an increase is observed in the rate of heat production. This increase above the BMR due to ingestion of food is known as the specific dynamic action (SDA) or the calorigenic effect of food. The amount of extra heat produced and the length of time during which the heat production is above basal depends upon the kind and amount of food ingested. The heat production commences to rise within an hour after the food has been eaten, attains a maximum in about the third hour and is maintained above the basal level for several hours. The greatest specific dynamic action is exerted by protein food. When protein is fed alone to a fasting animal, in an amount possessing a heat value equivalent to the animal's estimated basal metabolism, the heat production is raised 30 per cent or more above the basal level. Carbo-

hydrate causes a rise of about 6 per cent and fat of 4 per cent. That is to say, when a quantity of protein, carbohydrate or fat possessing an energy value of 100 Calories is fed separately to an animal whose basal metabolism is 100 Calories daily, its actual heat production will be 130, 106 or 104 Calories, respectively. The extra heat is generated by the combustion of body substance, so if loss of weight is to be prevented such an animal must be supplied with slightly more than 130 Calories if his diet is protein; or if carbohydrates and fats are also consumed extra allowances must be made for the amounts of these substances which have been included.

To take a theoretical case in illustration; if a man with a basal metabolism of 1500 Calories were kept on a 1500-Calorie diet, his body weight would decline until the total heat production (basal + SDA) would just equal the energy value of the food; from there on, the body weight, and total metabolism would remain steady at the new levels. But if the energy value of the food were again reduced to the point where it just balanced the basal metabolism (no allowance being made for SDA) a further weight loss and diminution in basal metabolism would occur, and should the adjustment of food to basal heat production be carried out repeatedly, the body tissues would be gradually consumed, as long as the subject survived, in order to furnish the extra heat caused by SDA. In planning a diet, therefore, an extra caloric allowance must be made for the SDA of the food itself (ch. 55).

The extra heat resulting from protein food cannot be employed for the production of mechanical or other forms of energy. It is waste heat and is simply added to heat produced by the muscular exertion. A diet very rich in protein is therefore unsuited to heavy muscular work. The SDA of protein is an important factor, however, in the regulation of body temperature (p. 52). With fat and carbohydrate the case is different, for the extra heat is harnessed in the performance of work. When exercise is undertaken upon either of these substances the heat due to their specific dynamic action is almost abolished, the extra energy being incorporated in the energy exchanges of the exercise (table 45.8).

When new tissue is being formed, i.e., when the nitrogen balance is positive, protein does not exert its usual specific dynamic action. Nor does it occur in a fever, such as typhoid, when there is great destruction of tissue protein. The ingested food then merely replaces or spares the tissue protein.

TABLE 45.8

*The results of an experiment of Rapport's which illustrates the utilization of the "waste heat" of the specific dynamic action of fat and glucose in exercise*

Heat production at rest and in exercise and recovery

| | Rest-ing (per hour) | Devia-tion from (A) | Excess in Ex-ercise and Re-covery (per kg. of Work)* | Devia-tion from (A) |
|---|---|---|---|---|
| | calo-ries | per cent | calories | per cent |
| A. In the postabsorp-tive state........ | 12.7 | | 2.40 | |
| B. After ingestion of fat............. | 15.2 | +19.7 | 2.54 | + 5.8 |
| C. After ingestion of glucose.......... | 15.4 | +21.3 | 0.38 | −0.8 |
| D. After ingestion of meat: | | | | |
| 100 grams......... | 16.2 | +27.6 | 3.38 | +40.8 |
| 200 grams..... .... | 17.8 | +40.1 | 3.48 | +45.0 |

* Based on ½-hour period after beginning of exercise.

## The Cause of the Specific Dynamic Action

Several explanations for the phenomenon have been offered. It is certainly not due to digestive processes, i.e., to the contractions of smooth muscle of the alimentary canal or to the work entailed in the secretion of the digestive juices. This is proved by the following facts. Bones given to a dog, or agar agar, saline cathartics, water or meat extracts (which stimulate powerfully the gastric secretion) given to man, have no effect upon the heat production. Also, as already mentioned protein has no SDA when new tissue is being laid down. On the other hand, the injection of certain amino acids into the blood stream is followed by a specific dynamic effect.

The cause of the SDA is still imperfectly understood. It is generally accepted that the extra heat produced by protein food is associated with the metabolism of the amino acids. They exert in some way a stimulating effect upon the tissue cells, raising their heat production to a high level, i.e., the oxidation of the cells' own fuel material is increased; the rate of other metabolic processes within the cells is raised. The extra heat is not due to the amino acids themselves being utilized as fuel nor to a stimulating action upon the tissue cells of these materials in the unchanged state. It is in the intermediary reactions of the amino acids

that the specific dynamic action of protein should be sought—e.g., in the deamination process. Borsook and Winegarden conclude from their studies that the SDA of protein results from the metabolism (deamination and urea production) and the excretion of nitrogen; an increased excretion of nitrogen accompanies the greater heat production. According to Borsook an increase of from 7 to 10 Calories of extra heat are produced for each gram of extra nitrogen excreted. The remainder of the extra heat produced is a more variable and usually a larger fraction of the total; it is attributed to the metabolism of the carbon part of the protein molecule. There is a considerable body of evidence for the view that the deamination of the amino acids with the formation of urea contributes very considerably to the specific dynamic action of protein. Lundsgaard found, for example, that although the administration of sodium acetate or sodium lactate was followed by only a slight increase in heat production, ammonium acetate or ammonium lactate caused a pronounced rise; even ammonium chloride caused a well marked increase in heat production.

The reactions responsible for the SDA of protein are apparently situated in the liver and not in the tissue cells generally, since Wilhelmj, Bollman and Mann were unable to obtain any effect in hepatectomized dogs following the injection of amino acids. Dock also found that after the administration of casein to rats the oxygen consumption of the hindquarters (muscular tissue) was 8 per cent greater than in the corresponding tissues of a control group, whereas the oxygen consumption of the abdominal viscera was 141 per cent greater.

The specific dynamic action of carbohydrate is thought to represent the energy liberated in excess of that required for the conversion of glucose to glycogen. After a fast which depletes the glycogen stores, ingested glucose is oxidized in negligible amounts, yet it causes a pronounced specific dynamic action (Dann and Chambers).

The specific dynamic action of fat is ascribed to the increased concentration of fat in the tissue fluids and, as a consequence, to its more rapid oxidation ("plethora theory" of Lusk).

The glands of internal secretion appear to have no direct influence upon the SDA of protein; the usual effect has been observed in a cretin with a basal metabolic rate 20 per cent below normal and it is not altered in hyperthyroidism. Thyroidectomy in animals is said, however, to reduce the SDA of carbohydrate and fat. Cushing and Fulton found the SDA of protein within the normal range in a number of cases of pituitary disease (hypopituitarism and acromegaly). Gaebler found it of normal value in hypophysectomized animals. In undernutrition the SDA of all foods is increased. It is, according to some observers, diminished in simple obesity (ch. 50).

The SDA of carbohydrate and protein or of carbohydrate and fat is less than the sum of the values of each when fed separately. There is only a slight discrepancy, however, between the values for protein and fat, fed together or separately.

## REFERENCES

ALMQUIST, H. J. AND MECCHI, E. J. Biol. Chem., 1940, **135**, 355.

BACH, S. J. Biol. Rev., 1945, **20**, 158.

BENEDICT, S. R., AND OSTERBERG, E. J. Biol. Chem., 1923, **56**, 229.

BLOCH, K. AND SCHOENHEIMER, R. J. Biol. Chem., 1940, **133**, 633.

BOLLMAN, J. L., MANN, F. C. AND MAGATH, T. B. Am. J. Physiol., 1924, **69**, 371; 1926, **78**, 258; 1930, **92**, 92.

BOOTHBY, W. M. Arch. Int. Med., 1934, **53**, 39.

BORSOOK, H. AND DUBNOFF, J. W. J. Biol. Chem., 1940, **132**, 559.

BORSOOK, H. AND KEIGHLEY, G. L. Proc. Roy. Soc., London, ser. B, 1935, **118**, 488.

BORSOOK, H. AND WINEGARDEN, H. M. Proc. Nat. Acad. Sc., 1931, **17**, 31. Ibid., p. 75.

BORSOOK, H. AND DUBNOFF, J. W. J. Biol. Chem., 1941, **141**, 717.

BORSOOK, H. AND DUBNOFF, J. W. J. Biol. Chem., 1947, **169**, 247.

BRAND, E. AND ASSOCIATES. Am. J. Physiol., 1929, **90**, 296 (Proc.). J. Biol. Chem., 1930, **87**, ix; 1932, **92**, lix. J. A. M. A., 1933, **101**, 1047.

BRAUNSTEIN, A. E. AND KRITZMANN, M. G. Enzymologia, 1937, **2**, 129.

CHAMBERS, W. H. AND LUSK, G. J. Biol. Chem., 1930, **85**, 611.

COHEN, P. P. Fed. Proc., 1942, **1**, 273.

COHEN, P. P. AND HAYANO, M. J. Biol. Chem., 1948, **166**, 239, 251; 1948, **172**, 405.

COHN, M., Enzymes: Units of biological structure and function. Edited by O. H. Gaebler. Academic Press, Inc., New York, 1956.

COX, G. J. AND ROSE, W. C. J. Biol. Chem., 1926, **68**, 781.

CUSHING, H. AND FULTON, M. N. Arch. Int. Med., 1932, **50**, 649.

DANN, M. AND CHAMBERS, W. H. J. Biol. Chem., 1930, **89**, 675.

DENIS, W. AND ASSOCIATES. J. Biol. Chem., 1921, **49**, 311. Arch. Int. Med., 1928, **41**, 385.

DOCK, W. Am. J. Physiol., 1931, **97**, 117.

DU VIGNEAUD, V. AND ASSOCIATES. J. Biol. Chem., 1939, **131**, 57.

EMBDEN, G. AND SCHMITZ, E. Biochem Ztschr., 1910, **29**, 423.

Enzymes: Units of biological structure and function. Edited by O. H. Gaebler, Academic Press, Inc., New York, 1956.

FOLIN, O. Am. J. Physiol., 1905, **13**, 45, 66, 117.

GAEBLER, O. H. J. Biol. Chem., 1929, **81**, 41.

GORNALL, A. G. AND HUNTER, A. Biochem. J., 1941, **35**, 650.

GRAHAM, W. R., HOUCHIN, O. B. AND TURNER, C. W. J. Biol. Chem., 1937, **120**, 29.

HANDLER, P., Brookhaven Symposia in biol., 1952, **5**, 99.

HOLT, J. E. AND ASSOCIATES. Bull. Johns Hopkins Hosp., 1944, **74**, 308.

HOUSSAY, B. A. AND BIASOTTI, A. J. Physiol., 1932, **77**, 81. Endocrinology, 1931, **15**, 511.

JONES, M. E., SPECTOR, L., AND LIPMANN, F. J. Am. Chem. Soc., 1955, **77**, 819.

KNOOP, F. Ztschr. physiol. Chem., 1910, **67**, 489; 1925, **146**, 267.

KREBS, H. A. Biochem. J., 1935, **29**, 1951.

KREBS, H. A. AND HENSELEIT, K. Ztschr. physiol. Chem., 1932, **210**, 33.

LARSON, P. S. AND CHAIKOFF, I. L. J. Nutrition, 1937, **13**, 287.

LEUTHARDT, F. Ztschr. physiol. Chem., 1938, **252**, 238.

LUNDSGAARD, E. Skandinav. Arch. Physiol., 1931, **62**, 223. Ibid., p. 243.

MACLEOD, J. J. R. The fuel of life. Princeton University Press, Princeton, N. J., 1928.

MANN, F. C. AND ASSOCIATES. Am. J. Physiol., 1928, **87**, 497.

MARSHALL, R. O., HALL, L. M., AND COHEN, P. P. Biochem. et biophys. Acta, 1955, **17**, 279.

MARTIN, G. J. Proc. Soc. Exper. Biol. & Med., 1944, **55**, 182.

NEEDHAM, D. M. Biochem. J., 1930, **24**, 208.

RABINOWITCH, I. M. J. Biol. Chem., 1929, **83**, 333.

RAPPORT, D. AND BEARD, H. H. J. Biol. Chem., 1927, **73**, 299.

RATNER, S. Fed. Proc., 1949, **8**, 603.

RATNER, S., AND PETRACK, B. J. Biol. Chem., 1953, **200**, 175.

REICHARD, P. AND HANSHOFF, G. Acta. Chem. Scand., 1956, **10**, 548.

ROSE, W. C. AND BUNNEY, W. E. J. Biol. Chem., 128, **76**, 521.

ROSE, W. C. AND SCULL, C. W. J. Biol. Chem., 1930, **89**, 109.

SADOU, D. P. Missouri Agric. Exper. Station, Res. Bull., 1947, **108**, 1.

SCHOENHEIMER, R. AND ASSOCIATES. J. Biol. Chem., 1942, **144**, 541.

SHERWIN, C. P. AND HARROW, B. J. Biol. Chem., 1926, **70**, 683.

TROWELL, O. A. J. Physiol., 1941, **100**, 432.

DU VIGNEAUD, V. Harvey Lectures, 1942—1943; Biol. Symposia, 1941, **5**, 234.

WALKER, M. B. Lancet, 1934, **1**, 1200; 1935, **1**, 448.

### Monographs and Reviews

BEARD, H. H. Ann. Rev. Biochem., 1941, **10**, 246.

BORSOOK, H. Biol. Rev., 1936, **11**, 147.

BORSOOK, H. Chemical pathways of metabolism. Edited by D. Greenberg. Academic Press, Inc., New York, 1954, **2**, 211.

CATHCART, E. P. The physiology of protein metabolism. Longmans Green & Co., London, 1921.

DAKIN, H. D. Oxidations and reductions in the animal body. Longmanns Green & Co., London, 1922.

DU VIGNEAUD, V. AND DYER. Ann. Rev. Biochem. 1936, **5**, 159.

HUNTER, A. Physiol. Rev., 1922, **2**, 586. Creatine and creatinine. Longmans, Green & Co., London, 1928.

KOTAKI, Y. Ann. Rev. Biochem., 1934, **3**, 193.

LEWIS, H. B. Physiol. Rev., 1924, 4, 394.

LUSK, G. The elements of the science of nutrition. W. B. Saunders Company, Philadelphia, 1906.

LUSK, G. Medicine, 1922, 1, 311. J. Nutrition, 1930, 3, 519.

MANN, F. C. Medicine, 1927, 6, 419.

MITCHELL, H. H. AND HAMILTON, T. S. The biochemistry of the amino acids. Chemical Catalog Co., New York, 1929.

OSBORNE, F. B. The vegetable proteins. Longmans, Green & Co., London, 1924.

PETERS, J. P. AND VAN SLYKE, D. D. Quantitative clinical chemistry. Vol. I. The Williams & Wilkins Co., Baltimore, 1931.

PLIMMER, R. H. A. The chemical constitution of the proteins. Longmans, Green & Co., London, 1917.

RAPPORT, D. Physiol. Rev., 1930, 10, 349.

RATNER, S. Urea synthesis and metabolism of arginine and citrulline. Advances in Enzymol., 1954, 15, 319.

SCHOENHEIMER, R. AND RITTENBERG, D. Physiol. Rev., 1940, 20, 218.

SHERMAN, H. C. The chemistry of food and nutrition. Macmillan, New York, 1933.

J. Cell. & Comp. Physiol. 1956. Suppl. 1.

Symposium on amino acid metabolism. Edited by D. McElroy and B Glass. Johns Hopkins Press, Baltimore, 1955.

WILHELMJ, C. M. Physiol. Rev., 1935, 15, 202.

# 46

## PROTEIN METABOLISM—*Continued*

**The Nutritional Value of Various Proteins**

Two factors must be considered in determining the nutritional value of a given protein: (a) its digestibility, i.e., the amount absorbed, and (b) its suitability for the construction of tissue protein.

1. THE DIGESTIBILITY OF PROTEINS. Although by far the greater part of the nitrogen arising from the catabolism of amino acids within the body is excreted in the urine, a small fraction is eliminated through the secretions of the digestive glands and intestinal mucosa. This, the so-called *metabolic nitrogen*, is estimated from the nitrogen of the feces upon a nitrogen-free diet. In a man it amounts to from 0.5 to 1.5 gram daily, varying in amount with the bulk (roughage) of the diet. In order, therefore, to determine the proportion of a given protein which has undergone digestion and absorption, the total nitrogen content of the ingested protein is determined (each 6.25 grams of protein equals 1 gram of nitrogen), and from this value the nitrogen of the feces less that for the metabolic nitrogen is subtracted. Thus—

food N − (feces N − metabolic N) = absorbed N.

The digestibility of the particular protein is then expressed as a percentage of the food nitrogen which has been absorbed. This percentage value is referred to as the *coefficient of digestibility*. For example, if the food contains, let us say, 10 grams of nitrogen and it is found that 9.5 grams have been absorbed the digestibility is 95 per cent. Digestibility in the sense just defined is quite different from the popular meaning of the term which refers rather to the subjective sensations accompanying digestion.

Proteins of animal origin have the highest digestibility which runs from 95 to 100 per cent. That is, the wastage in digestion is 5 per cent or less. The digestibility of the proteins of nuts and fruits is low, that of the proteins of legumes and of potatoes is around 80 per cent (see table 46.1). The digestibility of wheat proteins is from 90 to 100 per cent thus approaching that for animal proteins.

2. THE SUITABILITY OF A GIVEN PROTEIN FOR THE SYNTHESIS OF BODY PROTEIN. This depends upon the amino acid constitution of the protein. It is obvious that the greater the proportion of amino acids in the dietary protein which can serve for the construction of tissue protein, the greater will be its potential nutritive value. In other words, the more closely the amino acid assortment in the food protein resembles that in body protein the less of the former need be furnished. A smaller proportion of the amino acids will then be discarded, their nitrogen eventually being excreted in the urine, i.e., less of the food protein will be wasted.

*Methods employed for estimating the nutritive values of proteins.* Osborne and Mendel, employing rats, added a known amount of the protein to be tested to a diet free from all other proteins, but adequate in other respects (i.e., one possessing the necessary energy value, minerals, and the vitamins then known). They expressed the nutritive value of the protein as the weight, in grams, gained by the animals per gram of protein fed, in the case of young rats (value for growth), or in the case of adult rats, the smallest quantity of the fed protein in grams, per gram of rat per week, necessary to maintain a constant body weight (value for maintenance). McCollum and associates also employed rats, feeding a basal diet of first class quality in all respects except that it lacked protein. The lack was made good by adding the protein to be tested, and the percentage of protein required to be added to the food mixture in order to promote normal nutrition gave an index of its nutritive value. The general state of nutrition of the animals, as indicated by rate of growth, fertility, care of young and longevity, was noted over a period corresponding to two-thirds or more of their life span. On this basis, proteins were classed as "excellent" "good" or "poor." An excellent or first class protein is one which "will support nearly optimum nutrition over periods approximating two-thirds or more of the normal life

## TABLE 46.1

*Protein values of foods for maintenance and growth:*
*Level of protein feeding, 8 to 10 per cent*

(After Mitchell and Hamilton)

| Food | Water Content[a] | Protein Content[a] on Fresh Basis | Quality of Protein Digestibility | Quality of Protein Biological value | Metabolic Protein in Feces[b] on Fresh Food Basis | Protein Value of Food on Fresh Basis |
|---|---|---|---|---|---|---|
| | *per cent* | *per cent* | *per cent* | *per cent* | *per cent* | *per cent* |
| Whole egg[c] . . | 73.2 | 13.2 | 100 | 94 | 0.4 | 12.0 |
| Milk . . . . . . . . | 87.0 | 3.3 | 100 | 85 | 0.2 | 2.6 |
| Egg white[c] . . | 86.2 | 12.3 | 100 | 83 | 0.2 | 10.0 |
| Beef liver . . . | 71.2 | 20.4 | 90 | 77 | 0.4 | 14.9 |
| Beef kidney . | 76.7 | 16.6 | 99 | 77 | 0.3 | 12.3 |
| Beef heart . . . | 62.6 | 16.0 | 100 | 74 | 0.5 | 11.3 |
| Beef round . . | 70.0 | 21.3 | 96 | 69 | 0.4 | 13.7 |
| Pork ham . . . | 60.0 | 25.0 | 100 | 74 | 0.6 | 17.9 |
| Veal[d] . . . . . . . . | 73.4 | 20.7 | 100 | 62 | 0.4 | 12.4 |
| Rolled oats . . | 7.7 | 16.7 | 90 | 65 | 1.3 | 9.8 |
| Whole wheat . | 11.4 | 13.8 | 91 | 67 | 1.3 | 7.1 |
| White flour . . | 12.8 | 10.8 | 100 | 52 | 1.3 | 4.3 |
| Whole corn . . | 10.3 | 7.5 | 95 | 60 | 1.3 | 3.0 |
| Potato . . . . . . | 78.3 | 3.2 | 78 | 67 | 0.3 | 0.8 |
| Navy beans[c] . | 12.6 | 22.5 | 76 | 38 | 1.3 | 4.2 |

[a] Average analyses taken, as far as possible, from Bulletin 28 (revised), Office of Experiment Stations, U. S. Dept. of Agriculture.

[b] The metabolic nitrogen in the feces is assumed to equal 0.23 gram per 100 grams of dry matter of food. See Bulletin National Research Council, 1926, xi, part 1, no. 55, p. 23.

[c] Cooked.

[d] The cut tested was not recorded. It proved to be very fibrous. Analysis for shoulder cut assumed.

span of the rat when fed in amount corresponding to 9 per cent in the food mixture." Nine per cent is therefore the critical level for a protein of the highest nutritive value. Inferior proteins must be fed at higher levels. The relative values of several food proteins are shown below in descending order.

> Fish muscle, beef muscle
> Beef liver and kidney
> Egg (whole)
> Milk
> Soya bean
> Oats (rolled)
> Wheat (whole)

The determination of the minimal quantities of different proteins required for the maintenance of nitrogenous equilibrium in adult animals or of a positive balance (storage of nitrogen) in growing animals is also used as a means of arriving at the nutritional values of proteins.

The nutritive value of a particular protein, based upon the nitrogen metabolism following the feeding of known amounts, is employed by Mitchell. In this method, the value of the protein for repair (maintenance) or building of new tissue (growth) is given as a percentage of its *adsorbed* nitrogen which is not lost in the urine, i.e., the percentage retained in the body. This is called its *biological value*. The animal is placed upon a basal diet complete in so far as nonprotein factors are concerned. In order that none of the protein shall be burned for energy purposes, its level in the diet is kept low, i.e., there should be no excess over that required for growth or maintenance. The following example from Mitchell will serve for illustration.

A rat receiving a diet containing about 4 per cent of protein, ingested daily 56.9 mg. of nitrogen and excreted 27.6 mg. of nitrogen in the feces. Of the latter 21.7 mg. constituted metabolic nitrogen (p. 791). The unabsorbed nitrogen was therefore only $(27.6 - 21.7 =) 5.9$ mg., and the absorbed nitrogen $(56.9 - 5.9 =) 51.0$ mg. The daily urinary nitrogen was 48.6 mg. Of this, 37.7 was derived from the body tissues (estimated from urinary nitrogen on a nitrogen-free diet (p. 785). The total urinary nitrogen less this value for the endogenous nitrogen must represent the quantity of absorbed nitrogen which was excreted, that is, $(48.6 - 37.7 =) 10.9$ mg. is the quantity of absorbed nitrogen which had been wasted in metabolism. The absorbed nitrogen, as just stated, amounted to 51.0. So, $(51.0 - 10.9 =) 40.1$ mg. were retained in the body. The biological value of the dietary protein was therefore $((40.1/51.1) \times 100 =) 79$ per cent.

In order to know the value of a food as a source of protein the "biological value" must be considered as well as the quantity present (nitrogen $\times 6.25$). A food may contain a first class protein in small amounts or a poor protein in larger amounts. In some foods the protein is both poor in quality and low in amount whereas in others both the quantity and quality of the protein are high. The *protein value* of a food must take both these factors into account.

The values of individual amino acids were tested by Osborne and Mendel by feeding purified proteins known to be deficient in their amino acid constituents. The weights of the animals on the deficient protein were observed for periods before and after the missing amino acid had been added to the diet. Rose's method consists in feeding a mixture of purified amino acids such as are found in casein. The effect upon growth was then determined after one or other amino acid had been omitted from the mixture.

The value of a protein in nutrition depends entirely upon its amino acid constitution. Block and Mitchell have shown a very close correlation between the biological value of a protein and its amino acid content. Thus, by the hydrolysis of a protein and determining the percentages of the various amino groups of which it is composed, a very accurate appraisal of its nutritive value can be made. Although animal proteins are usually superior to those of plant origin, no generalization can be made in this respect. It is a matter of the amino acids of which the protein, animal or vegetable, is made up. In table 46.2 the amino acid percentages in the proteins of liver and of soy bean are compared.

## THE ESSENTIAL IMPORTANCE OF CERTAIN AMINO ACIDS FOR GROWTH AND MAINTENANCE

In 1907 Willcock and Hopkins found that when young mice were fed upon a diet which contained zein (a protein of maize) as its sole protein, growth was arrested and the animals died in about 17 days. Zein is almost completely free from tryptophane. Yet, the addition of this amino acid to the diet was not capable of promoting growth, and the survival period of the animals was extended to only 33 days. The addition of tyrosine was without effect since zein already contains this amino acid in adequate amounts. It was shown by Osborne and Mendel that when lysine, which is also absent from this protein was added to the zein diet together with tryptophane, the animals grew normally and remained in good health (fig. 46.1). Lysine added alone was of no more benefit than tryptophane alone. *Gelatin*, like zein, is an incomplete protein. It lacks tyrosine and tryptophane and is very deficient in cystine. A diet which contains gelatin as its sole protein will not permit growth nor even maintain nitrogen equilibrium in an adult animal. When, however, the lacking amino acids are added to the gelatin diet its defects are corrected.

*Casein.* Casein is deficient in glycine and has a low cystine content. However, when, casein is fed in sufficient quantity—about 18 per cent of the diet—or if cystine is added, normal growth results (fig. 46.2).

*Edestin* (a protein in hemp seed) is relatively poor in lysine as is also *gliadin* (of wheat) whereas *phaseolin* (of navy bean) is deficient in cystine and tryptophane. If these, or other incomplete proteins, are supplemented by adding to the diet the amino acids in which they are deficient, growth is supported. Also when the amino acid deficiency is not too great, growth can be promoted by increasing the percentage of the incomplete protein in the diet (see table 46.3).

An essential or indispensable amino acid has been defined by Rose as one that cannot be synthesized by the animal organism out of the materials ordinarily available, at a speed commensurate with the demands for normal growth and which must therefore be supplied in the diet.

Of the 25 amino acids which have been identified as constituting protein material, 10 are indispensable for normal growth. They are as follows.

| | |
|---|---|
| Arginine | Methionine |
| Histidine | Phenylalanine |
| Isoleucine | Threonine |
| Leucine | Tryptophane |
| Lysine | Valine |

Experiments, in which it was shown that casein when constituting the sole protein of the diet would not support growth unless fed in relatively large amounts or in smaller amounts and supplemented by *cystine*, led to the belief that this amino acid was indispensable. The mistake was evidently the result of confusion with the other sulfur-containing amino acid, *methionine*. The failure of growth on the low casein diet was due to this protein's inadequate methionine content, but this could be made good by the addition of

### TABLE 46.2
(From data of Block and Mitchell)

*Approximate amino acid content of liver and of soy bean compared*

(Calculated to 16.0 grams of nitrogen)

| Amino Acid | Liver | Soy Bean |
|---|---|---|
| | grams | grams |
| Arginine.................. | 6.6 | 7.1 |
| Histidine................. | 3.1 | 2.3 |
| Lysine.................... | 6.7 | 5.8 |
| Tyrosine................. | 4.6 | 4.1 |
| Tryptophane............. | 1.4 | 1.2 |
| Phenylalanine............ | 6.1 | 5.7 |
| Cystine.................. | 1.4 | 1.9 |
| Methionine............... | 3.2 | 2.0 |
| Threonine................ | 4.8 | 4.0 |
| Leucine.................. | 8.4 | 6.6 |
| Isoleucine............... | 5.6 | 4.7 |
| Valine................... | 6.2 | 4.2 |

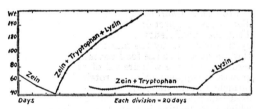

FIG. 46.1 Shows the indispensability of lysine for growth. (After Mendel.)

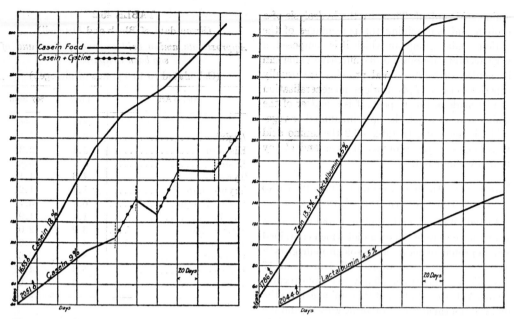

FIG. 4.6.2. *Chart on left* shows satisfactory growth of rat when 18 per cent of casein was present in the diet as the sole protein. With a smaller amount of casein—9 per cent—much less rapid growth ensued. That the insufficiency of the smaller amount of casein is essentially due to its relative deficiency in cystine is shown by the marked accelerating influence upon growth brought about by the addition of this amino acid to the food containing 9 per cent of casein and the prompt retardation of growth which resulted from the withdrawal of cystine from the diet. *Chart on right* shows the favorable effect upon growth of supplementing a protein (zein), incapable of maintaining animals when it is the sole protein furnished in the diet, with a more "perfect" protein (lactalbumin). The proportion of the lactalbumin used—4.5 per cent—was of itself insufficient for full growth. It evidently furnished the amino acid groups which were lacking in zein. (After Mendel.)

cystine. In other words, cystine can substitute *in part* for methionine; cystine itself is not essential, for it can be *completely* replaced in the diet by methionine[1] which can be converted to cystine in the body. Proof of the derivation of cystine from methionine was obtained by Tarver and Schmidt who fed animals methionine containing the radio-active isotope of sulfur ($S^{35}$) and later isolated isotopic cystine from their tissues. Cystine is a constituent of plasma protein and unless it or methionine is furnished in adequate amounts in the diet hypoproteinemia results. Cystine is also an essential component of keratin, the protein of hair, feathers, nails, horn, etc. *Arginine* (p. 774) can be synthesized in the body but not in adequate amounts for normal growth; it is therefore an essential constituent of the diet of young animals. *Tyrosine* can be formed from phenylalanine.

[1] To make this point clear we may use an illustration the case of a typesetter who has lost a number of dies for, say, the letter A. He can continue to set type so long as his supply of A letters lasts, but when this is exhausted his work must cease though there is still a large number of other letters. His typesetting is limited by his supply of A letters.

In rats deprived of *valine* grave nutritional defects develop which have been the subject of studies of Epstein and Rose. The animals become very sensitive to touch and show severe muscular incoordination, (e.g., staggering gait and circus movements) together with loss of appetite, emaciation and eventually death.

The amino acid requirements for building new tissue (growth) are more exacting than those for repair (maintenance), i.e., for the maintenance of nitrogen equilibrium in the adult and the prevention of a loss of weight. Some amino acids which are essential for the growing animal can be dispensed with in the adult. Arginine, for example, is not required in the diet of the adult dog, and in the adult rat nitrogen equilibrium can be maintained upon a diet lacking in this amino acid, but, as just mentioned, it is not synthesized rapidly enough to promote maximal growth. Even of the amino acids essential for maintenance the level in the diet need not be as high for maintenance as for growth. Adult man can be maintained in nitrogen equilibrium upon eight amino acids, histidine being dispensable.

TABLE 46.3[a]

*The amino acid content of a number of proteins, grams per cent*

| Amino Acid | Gelatin | Casein | Lactal-bumin | Egg Albumin | Gliadin | Zein | Edistin |
|---|---|---|---|---|---|---|---|
| Glycine | 25.5 | 0.4 | 0.4 | 0.0 | 0.0 | 0.0 | 3.8 |
| Alanine | 8.7 | 1.8 | 2.4 | 2.2 | 2.0 | 9.8 | 3.6 |
| Valine | 0.0 | 7.9 | 3.3 | 2.5 | 3.3 | 1.9 | |
| Leucine-isoleucine | 7.1 | 9.7 | 14.0 | 10.7 | 6.6 | 25.0 | 20.9 |
| Aspartic acid | 3.4 | 4.1 | 9.3 | 6.2 | 0.8 | 1.8 | 10.2 |
| Glutamic acid | 5.8 | 21.8 | 12.9 | 13.3 | 43.7 | 31.3 | 19.2 |
| Hydroxyglutamic acid | 0.0 | 10.5 | 10.0 | | 2.4 | 2.5 | |
| Serine | 0.4 | 0.5 | 1.8 | | 0.1 | 1.0 | 0.3 |
| Proline | 9.5 | 8.0 | 3.8 | 3.6 | 13.2 | 9.0 | 4.1 |
| Hydroxyproline | 14.1 | 0.2 | | | | 0.0 | 2.0 |
| Phenylalanine | 1.4 | 3.9 | 1.2 | 5.1 | 2.3 | 7.6 | 3.1 |
| Tyrosine | 0.01 | 6.5 | 1.9 | 4.0 | 3.1 | 5.9 | 4.5 |
| Cystine | 0.17 | 0.3 | 4.0 | 0.9 | 2.4 | 0.8 | 1.0 |
| Arginine | 9.1 | 5.2 | 3.0 | 6.0 | 3.2 | 1.8 | 15.8 |
| Histidine | 0.9 | 2.6 | 1.5 | 2.3 | 2.1 | 1.2 | 2.1 |
| Lysine | 5.9 | 7.6 | 8.4 | 3.8 | 0.6 | 0.0 | 2.2 |
| Tryptophane | 0.0 | 2.2 | 2.7 | 1.3 | 0.8 | 0.17 | 1.5 |
| Total | 92.4 | 94.8 | 81.9 | 63.2 | 91.8 | 103.4 | 96.6 |

[a] Modified from Mitchell and Hamilton, "The Biochemistry of the Amino Acids," Am. Chem. Soc. Monograph Series No. 48, p. 191.

The utilization of a protein deficient in one or other amino acid is limited by that deficiency. For example, if edestin, which is poor in lysine, is the sole protein of the diet, the other amino acids of which it is composed are utilized only in certain proportions limited by the lysine content. A large part of the remainder is discarded. Similarly the utilization of casein is limited by its cystine plus methionine content. Now if lysine is added to the diet of which edestin is the sole protein, or cystine or methionine is added to the casein diet, the other amino acids in these proteins can be utilized and built into body tissue. Lysine is essential for maintenance as well as for growth, but for the former, relatively small quantities are required. Gliadin (of wheat), which contains less than 1 per cent lysine, is inadequate for growth even though fed in large quantities but is suitable as the sole source of protein in an adult. Zein, on the other hand, which is entirely lacking in lysine and contains little tryptophane is inadequate for either growth or maintenance. Serum albumin is deficient in tryptophane and isoleucine; it will not promote growth in young rats and will scarcely maintain body weight. The proteins of several common foods are given in table 46.4.

Most of the work relating to the indispensability of the various amino acids has been carried out upon rats. The amino acid requirements of adult man have been investigated by Holt and his colleagues and by Rose and his coworkers. Their results, in general, accord with those of animal experiments. Methionine, as the sole source of sulfur-containing amino acids, was found to be capable of maintaining nitrogen equilibrium. The nitrogen balance could not be maintained upon a diet completely lacking in *lysine*, whereas *histidine* and *arginine* proved to be dispensable. Others have found, however, that while nitrogen equilibrium can be maintained in men on a diet lacking in histidine, loss of weight occurred. *Tryptophane* was found to be indispensable, the subjects developing negative nitrogen balances within a few days after having been placed upon a diet lacking in this amino acid; nor could nitrogen equilibrium be maintained when *valine, threonine, leucine, isoleucine* or *phenylalanine* was lacking from the diet. *Lysine* and *methionine* were also found to be indispensable, but as mentioned above, adults can be maintained in nitrogen equilibrium in the absence of histidine.

Rose and his collaborators using synthetic diets have attempted to determine quantitatively the amino acid requirements of man. The diets used supplied from 6.7 to 7.1 grams of nitrogen per day and contained in addition to essential amino

TABLE 46.4[a]

*Character of proteins in some common foods*

| Food Materials | Chief Kinds of Protein Present | Complete or Incomplete |
|---|---|---|
| Almonds... | Excelsin | Complete |
| Cheese... | Casein | Complete (low in cystine) |
| | Lactalbumin | Complete |
| Corn..... | Glutelin | Complete |
| | Zein | Incomplete (lacks lysine and tryptophane, low in cystine) |
| Eggs..... | Ovalbumin | Complete |
| | Ovovitellin | Complete |
| Gelatin.... | Gelatin | Incomplete (lacks tryptophane and tyrosine; only a trace of cystine, high in lysine) |
| Lean meat | Albumin | Complete |
| | Myosin | Complete |
| Milk..... | Casein | Complete (low in cystine) |
| | Lactalbumin | Complete |
| Navy beans | Phaseolin | Incomplete (low in cystine) |
| Peas...... | Legumin | Incomplete (low in cystine) |
| Soy beans | Glycinin | Complete |
| | Legumelin | Incomplete |
| Wheat.... | Gliadin | Incomplete (lacks lysine) |
| | Glutenin | Complete |

[a] From M. S. Rose, *Foundations of Nutrition.*

TABLE 46.5

*Amino acid requirements of adult man*

| Amino Acid | Range of Requirements Observed | Proposed Tentative Minimum | "Safe Intake" |
|---|---|---|---|
| | *grams per day* | *grams per day* | *grams per day* |
| L-Isoleucine | 0.65–0.70 | 0.70 | 1.40 |
| L-Leucine | 0.50–1.10 | 1.10 | 2.20 |
| L-Lysine | 0.40–0.80 | 0.80 | 1.60 |
| DL-Methionine[a] | 0.80–1.10 | 1.10 | 2.20 |
| L-Phenylalanine[b] | 0.80–1.10 | 1.10 | 2.20 |
| L-Threonine | 0.30–0.50 | 0.50 | 1.00 |
| L-Tryptophan | 0.15–0.25 | 0.25 | 0.50 |
| L-Valine | 0.40–0.80 | 0.80 | 1.60 |

[a] L-Cystine may replace up to 80 to 89 per cent of the minimal methionine needs. D-Methionine is fully as active as L-methionine.

[b] L-Tyrosine may replace up to 70 to 75 per cent of the minimal phenylalanine requirement.

acids, glycine and urea. The latter two compounds served as a source of nitrogen for the synthesis of the dispensable amino acids. The amount of a given amino acid in the diet was decreased until the nitrogen balance of the subject became negative. The diet was then supplemented with the amino acid until nitrogen equilibrium was reestablished. The amino acid requirements of man determined by Rose in this manner are shown in table 46.5.

It seems that, generally speaking, the several amino acids which have been found indispensable for rats are also essential dietary constituents for other mammals, including man. There are, however, certain minor species differences, the growing mouse, for example, can dispense with arginine in the diet, since, apparently, it can synthesize this amino acid in greater amounts than can the rat. *Glycine* which is required especially for the manufacture of collagenous tissue and of protoporphyrin (ch. 6) can be synthesized by the body and, therefore, is not an essential constituent of the diet in mammals. It is indispensable, however, for the growth of chicks, although it can be replaced in this species by creatine. The chick, also unlike the rat, has no ability to synthesize arginine. The essential or nonessential nature of a particular amino acid, as well as the species differences, may possibly depend upon bacterial synthesis in the intestine; the bacterial synthesis of amino acids and even of protein is known to occur in the intestinal tract of ruminants. It has been found by Martin, for example, that rats fed a diet containing all the essential amino acids and the known vitamins fail to grow if succinylsulfazole, a bacteriostatic drug, is added to the food.

The most suitable proteins for growth are those of animal origin and especially those which nature has provided for the nourishment of the growing animal, namely,

*lactalbumin* (of milk)    *ovovitellin* (of hen's egg)
*ovalbumin* (of hen's egg)

These support growth when given at a level of about 9 or 10 per cent in the diet. Next in order of their biological value come,

    *proteins of meat*     *glutelin* (maize)
    *glutenin* (wheat)     *glycinin* (soy bean)
    *casein* (milk)

These support growth if given in sufficiently high concentration in the diet. Casein, for instance, is required to be given at a level of 18 per cent for growth and 10 to 12 per cent for maintenance. A comparison of the value for growth of several proteins, when given in the same percentage in the diet, is shown in figure 46.3.

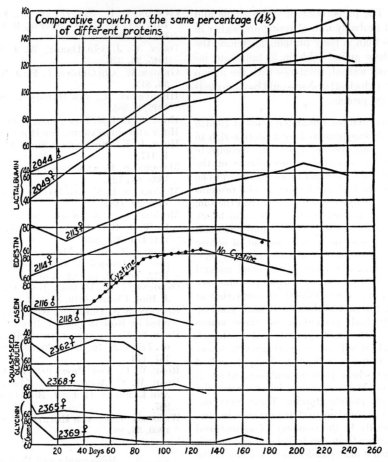

Fig. 46.3. Comparison of growth on diets containing approximately the same percentage (4.5 per cent) of different proteins, namely, lactalbumin, edestin, casein, globulin (squash seed) and glycinin (soy bean). (After Lusk.)

The following vegetable proteins are incapable of supporting growth but are suitable for maintenance:

    *gliadin* (wheat or rye)
    *legumin* (pea)
    *legumelin* (soy bean)
    *phaseolin* (kidney bean)
    *hordein* (barley)

The following are incomplete proteins and are unsuitable for either growth or maintenance:

    *zein*
    *gelatin*

The biological values of the protein mixtures in the various foods are shown in table 46.1, p. 792, from which it is seen that the values are in descending order as follows: eggs, milk, meats, whole wheat and potato, rolled oats, corn, white flour and beans. The nutritional value of ordinary meat varies largely with the cut—a tough fibrous meat, i.e., one with a high proportion of collagen and elastin has a low coefficient of digestibility and a

low biological value. The biological value of some samples of very fibrous beef, for instance, may be little higher than that of white flour.

### THE SUPPLEMENTARY RELATIONS AMONG PROTEINS

It does not necessarily follow that because a certain protein is inadequate for growth or even for maintenance that it is worthless in nutrition. It is evident from what has been said in the preceding paragraphs that an incomplete protein can be utilized if its shortcomings in one or more of the essential amino acids are made good by the addition to the diet of some other protein, rich in the elements which the first one lacked. Zein, for instance, fed in any quantity, is inadequate for either growth or maintenance. Lactalbumin at a level of less than 8 or 9 per cent is incapable of promoting normal growth. Yet normal growth and nutrition are supported by a diet containing 13.5 per cent zein and 4.5 per cent lactalbumin (fig. 46.2). The proportions of tryptophane and cystine and probably also of lysine are higher in lactalbumin than in body protein. Therefore, the excess of these amino acids in lactalbumin, instead of being wasted, combines with the amino acids of zein (which otherwise would be discarded) to form tissue protein.

In a similar manner the amino acids of gelatin are utilized if supplemented by a protein rich in tryptophane and cystine. Even two incomplete proteins, if one contains an abundance of the amino acids which the other lacks supplement one another. So, the biological value of two proteins given together may be much greater than the sum of their values when fed alone. Proteins which lack the same amino acid (e.g., casein and phaesolin which are deficient in cystine) cannot of course supplement one another. The supplementary relations of proteins is evident in the chief natural foods: these all contain two or more proteins (see table 46.4). For example, in milk, the deficiency of casein in cystine and methionine is made good by the reltively high percentage of these amino acids in the other milk proteins. Also, though gliadin of wheat will not support growth, wheat itself will. The lysine-poor gliadin is supplemented by the other wheat protein, glutenin, which is rich in lysine. Maize contains, besides zein, the supplementary protein glutelin. These facts, obviously, are of fundamental importance in dietetics, especially in the economy of agricultural feeding. Cheaper foods can be fed and good nutrition promoted if due consideration be given to the supplementary relations of their contained proteins. Gelatin rich in lysine improves the nutritional value of wheat and oats, both relatively poor in this amino acid. There is also a pronounced supplementary relation between the proteins of milk and those of oats and wheat.

## REFERENCES

BLOCK, R. J. AND MITCHELL, H. H. Nutrition Abstr. & Rev., 1946, 16, 249.

BOOTHBY, W. M., SANDIFORD, I., SANDIFORD, K. AND SLOSSE, J. Trans. A. Am. Physicians, 1925, 40, 195.

CANNON, P. R., STEFFEE, C. H., FRAZIER, L. J., ROWLEY, D. A., AND STEPTO, R. C.: Fed. Proc., 1947, 6, 390.

DANN, W. J. AND DARBY, W. J. Physiol. Rev., 1945, 25, 326.

GEIGER, E., AND GEIGER, L. E.: J. Nutrition, 1948, 36, 813.

HENDERSON, R., AND HARRIS, R. S.: Fed. Proc., 1949, 8, 385.

HOLT, L. E. Fed. Proc., 1942, 1, 117.

HOLT AND COLLEAGUES. See HOLT AND NAJJAR.

HOLT, L. E. AND NAJJAR, V. A. Fed. Proc., 1942, 1, 117.

MADDEN, S. C. AND ASSOCIATES. J. Exper. Med., 1939, 69, 721.

McCOLLUM, E. V. AND DAVIS, M. J. Biol. Chem., 1915, 20, 415.

McCOLLUM, E. V., SIMMONDS, N. AND PARSONS, H. T. J. Biol. Chem., 1919, 37, 155; 1921, 47, 111, 175, 207, 235.

OSBORNE, T. B. AND MENDEL, L. B. Series of papers in Journal of Biological Chemistry from 1912, Vol. 12, to 1920, Vol. 41.

OSBORNE, T. B., MENDEL, L. B. AND FERRY, E. L. J. Biol. Chem., 1919, 37, 223.

EPSTEIN, S. S. AND ROSE, W. C. Unpublished data cited by Rose in Physiol. Rev., 1938, 118, 109.

ROSE, W. C. AND ASSOCIATES. J. Biol. Chem., 1924, 61, 747; 1928, 76, 521; 1930, 89, 109; 1931, 94, 155, 167, 173.

ROSE, W. C.: Fed. Proc., 1949, 8, 546.

ROSE, W. C., WIXOM, R. L., LOCKHART, H. B., AND LAMBERT, G. F.: J. Biol. Chem., 1955, 217, 987.

WILLCOCK, E. G. AND HOPKINS, F. G. J. Physiol., 1906, 35, 88.

### Monographs and Reviews

McCOLLUM, E. V. AND SIMMONDS, N. The newer knowledge of nutrition. The Macmillan Company, New York, 1925.

MENDEL, L. B. Harvey Lectures, 1914–1915, 10, 101.

MENDEL, L. B. Nutrition: the chemistry of life. Yale University Press, 1923.

MITCHELL, H. H. Physiol. Rev., 1924, 4, 424.

MITCHELL, H. H. AND HAMILTON, T. S. The biochemistry of the amino acids. Chemical Catalog Co., New York, 1929.

ROSE, W. C. Harvey Lectures, 1934–1935, 30, 49. Physiol. Rev., 1938, 18, 109.

# 47

# THE METABOLISM OF THE PURINE
# AND PYRIMIDINE BASES

One class of conjugated proteins—the *nucleo-proteins* (p. 771)—are compounds of simple basic proteins, *protamines* and *histones*, with *nucleic acid*. The protein is in saltlike combination with the acid but appears to be present in excess. When a nucleoprotein is hydrolyzed the protein is split off leaving nucleic acid. Cell nuclei contain nucleoprotein in relatively high concentration, and it was from pus cells obtained from used bandages of surgical wards, and from the heads of salmon sperm, that this conjugated protein was originally isolated by Miescher.

The nucleic acids are composed of (a) phosphoric acid, (b) a pentose and (c) a nitrogenous group—a purine or a pyrimidine. A mononucleotide, the fundamental unit of the complex nucleic acid molecule may therefore be represented thus:

*phosphoric acid—pentose—purine*
*or pyrimidine base.*

The pentose part of the mononucleotide may be either 2-*d*-desoxyribose or *d*-ribose and the resulting compounds are referred to respectively as desoxyribonucleic acid (DNA) and ribonucleic acid (RNA). Early investigations revealed that the thymus gland is a rich source of DNA and it was thought that this nucleic acid was found only in animal tissues whereas the RNA isolated from yeast was present only in plants. However, this belief was erroneous for it has been amply demonstrated that DNA and RNA are normal constituents of both plant and animal cells.

It was originally believed that each nucleic acid molecule contained four bases which were present in equimolecular amounts. In view of this Levene proposed that four mononucleotides, each containing a different nitrogenous base, were linked together to form a tetranucleotide. The tetranucleotides were considered to be the subunits of long chain polymers that constitute the nucleic acid molecules. The tetranucleotide theory had to be abandoned when more accurate techniques showed that the different bases contained

in a nucleic acid molecule were not necessarily present in equimolecular amounts. The four pyrimidine bases commonly found in the nucleic acids are cytosine which is present in both DNA and RNA, 5-methyl cytosine and thymine which appear to be found only in DNA, and uracil which is found only in RNA.

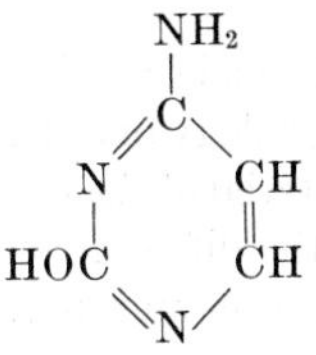

Cytosine

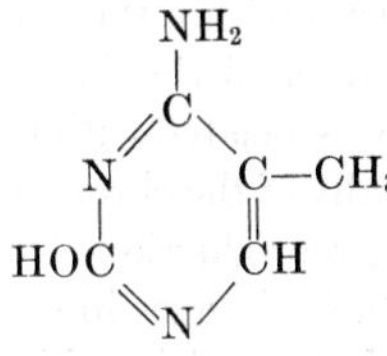

5-Methyl cytosine

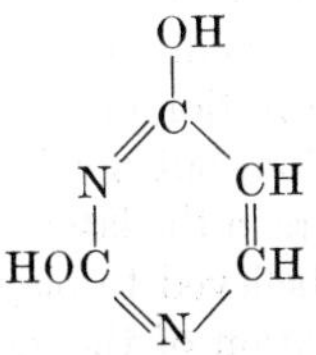

Uracil

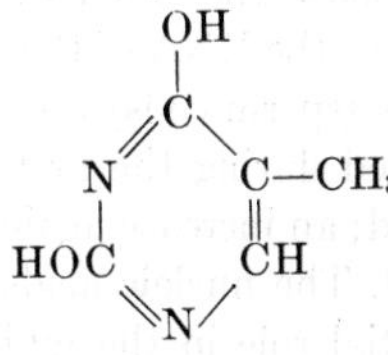

Thymine

The purine bases, adenine and guanine, are present in both the DNA and RNA.

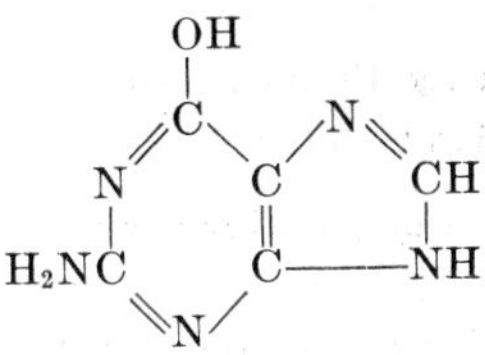

Guanine

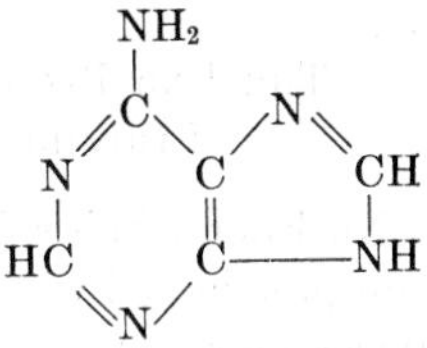

Adenine

Estimations of the molecular weight of nucleic acids by various methods have produced results that vary over a wide range. Values of 10,000 to 23,000 have been postulated for the molecular weight of RNA whereas figures for DNA lie between 500,000 and 3,000,000. Upon hydrolysis nucleic acid is split into its constituent nucleotides. The purine nucleotides are termed *adenylic acid* and *guanylic acid*, respectively. The further action of hydrolytic agents splits off phosphoric acid from the nucleotides. The residue (sugar + purine or pyrimidine) is then called a *nucleoside*. The adenine-containing nucleoside is known as *adenosine*; the one containing guanine is called *guanosine*.

### The Nucleic Acid Distribution in the Cells

The chief nucleic acid of animal cells is desoxyribonucleic acid (DNA); smaller amounts of ribonucleic acid (RNA) are also present, largely in the nucleolus. DNA is found mainly in the chromosomes together with small amounts of RNA. The protein with which the nucleic acid is combined is usually a histone, but is a protamine in sperm cells. The cytoplasm of the cells also contains both nucleic acids but RNA predominates: it appears from the ribonuclease test[1] that the RNA is contained mainly in inclusion bodies (e.g., mitochondria) within the cytoplasm.

There is little doubt that nucleic acids are closely associated with the physiology of cells, and especially of the chromatin material of the nucleus during reproduction. During the different phases of mitosis changes in concentration and distribution of the nucleic acids of the cells occur. In the metaphase the DNA of the chromatin increases whereas the RNA of the cytoplasm diminishes. In miosis (sperm cells) the concentration of DNA is doubled during the first division, but not in the second; an increase again occurs in the later spermatid. The nucleic acids are believed to play an essential role in the multiplication of the genes. A number of pathogenic viruses have been shown to be complex nucleoproteins. Staphylococcus bacteriophage also is most probably a nucleoprotein.

### The End Products of Purine and Pyrimidine Metabolism

Nucleoprotein is split by the digestive enzymes into protein and nucleic acid. Specific tissue enzymes known as *desoxyribonuclease* and *ribonuclease* break the respective nucleic acid molecules into smaller groups of nucleotides—*oligonucleotides* and *tetranucleotides*. These enzymes are present in pancreas and other animal tissues, in yeast,

and in certain bacteria (see streptodornase, ch. 12). The further changes which the molecule undergoes in the tissues are not clear, but nucleotidases and nucleosidases which break off phosphoric acid and sugar groups respectively have been described.

Uric acid (first isolated by Steele in 1776 from urinary calculi). This urinary constituent is the end product of purine metabolism in man (see scheme below), higher apes, birds and reptiles.[2] *Adenine* is deaminated by a specific tissue enzyme, *adenase* to form *hypoxanthine*. Hypoxanthine is then oxidized by the enzyme, *hypoxanthine oxidase*, to *xanthine* which in turn is oxidized, by means of *xanthine oxidase*, to uric acid. The other purine, *guanine*, is converted by the deaminative action of *guanase* to xanthine and by further oxidation to *uric acid*.[3] In mammals other than the primates, and in insects excepting the *Diptera*, from 80 to 98 per cent of the uric acid is oxidized further by an enzyme *uricase*, to *allantoin* and carbon dioxide.[4,5] These animals would appear to possess an advantage over man, since allantoin is some 250 times more soluble than is uric acid. The conversion of uric acid to allantoin occurs in the liver (dog). Mann and his associates, for example, have shown that after hepatectomy uric acid accumulates in the blood, and when uric acid is injected, from 70 to 100 per cent can be recovered from the urine unchanged. This is in marked contrast to the behavior of the normal dog which excretes 98 to 100 per cent as allantoin. Extracts of dogs' liver are rich in uricase.

In some classes of ureotelic animals (most fishes and amphibia) further degradation of uric acid occurs, allantoin being converted to allantoic acid (catalyzed by allantoicase), and then to urea. In

---

[1] This test depends upon the fact that basophilic granules in the cytoplasm are stained red by pyronine, a basic dye, but fail to do so after incubation with an aqueous solution of ribonuclease. A specific test (Feulgen's) for DNA in cell nuclei consists in treating the tissue with HCl and then immersing it in fuchsin-sulfurous acid reagent (Schill's reagent); in the presence of DNA a purple color appears. By means of these two tests DNA and RNA can be distinguished.

[2] In birds and reptiles uric acid is the end product of protein metabolism as well as of purine metabolism. Arginase is absent from the liver of these forms. According to Benedict, from 60 to 70 per cent of the urinary nitrogen of these species is in the form of uric acid. Thus, the end product of nitrogen metabolism differs according to the animal class. Those animals, birds and reptiles in which the main end product is uric acid, are called *uricotelic* (Gk. *telos*, end), whereas, mammals which excrete nitrogen mainly as urea, are termed *ureotelic*.

[3] The production of uric acid may follow another course, namely, conversion of the nucleoside adenosine or guanosine, by deamination, to hypoxanthosine or xanthosine, which is then split into its pentose and purine groups, hypoxanthine or xanthine, respectively (see plan on p. 801).

[4] The spotted coach dog (Dalmatian) oddly enough is an exception: like man and unlike other canine breeds it excretes uric acid.

[5] Guanine is the end product of purine metabolism in the spider.

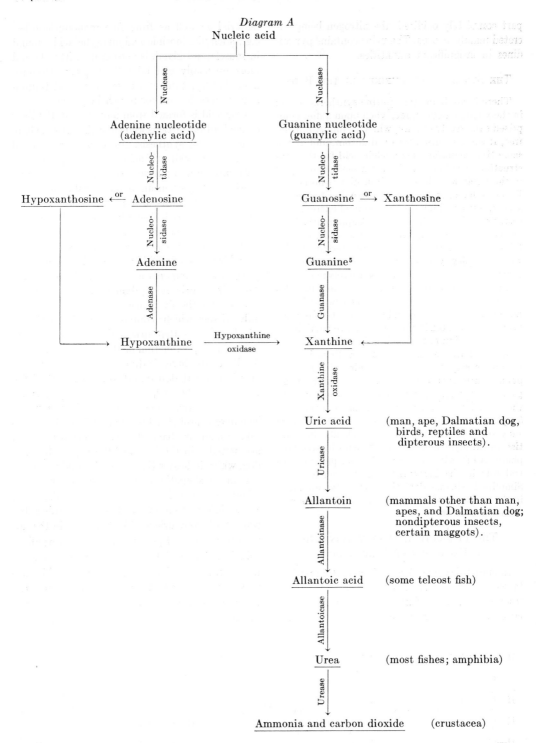

Diagram A
Nucleic acid

Nuclease
Nuclease

Adenine nucleotide
(adenylic acid)
Guanine nucleotide
(guanylic acid)

Nucleo-
tidase
Nucleo-
tidase

Hypoxanthosine ←⁻ᵒʳ⁻ Adenosine          Guanosine ⁻ᵒʳ⁻→ Xanthosine

Nucleo-
sidase
Nucleo-
sidase

Adenine                                  Guanine[5]

Adenase
Guanase

Hypoxanthine ⟶ Hypoxanthine oxidase ⟶ Xanthine ←

Xanthine
oxidase

Uric acid            (man, ape, Dalmatian dog,
                      birds, reptiles and
                      dipterous insects).

Uricase

Allantoin            (mammals other than man,
                      apes, and Dalmatian dog;
                      nondipterous insects,
                      certain maggots).

Allantoinase

Allantoic acid       (some teleost fish)

Allantoicase

Urea                 (most fishes; amphibia)

Urease

Ammonia and carbon dioxide        (crustacea)

crustacea, the latter is finally broken down to ammonia and carbon dioxide.

The stages through which uric acid or allantoin is derived from nucleic acid are shown in the scheme on page 805.

The chemical changes involved in the conversion of guanine and adenine to uric acid or allantoin are indicated in the formulae.

Little is known concerning the fate of the pyrimidines in man. In animals they are for the most part completely oxidized, the nitrogen being excreted mainly as urea. The urine contains pyrimidines in insignificant quantities.

### The Synthesis of Purines in the Body

There is no doubt that purine synthesis occurs in the young mammal, for, when upon a diet comprised exclusively of milk, which is almost purine-free, it excretes uric acid or allantoin, and at the same time manufactures nucleic acid for the construction of cell nuclei. That synthesis also occurs in the adult was shown by Benedict, who kept a Dalmatian dog under a purine-free diet for nearly a year, during which time the animal excreted 100 grams of uric acid. This had not apparently been derived from body tissue since the animal maintained a constant weight. In more recent studies with isotopically labelled nitrogen ($N^{15}$), purine synthesis has been proved conclusively; after the administration of amino acids or ammonium salts containing $N^{15}$ the isotope has been found in the nucleic acids of the animal's tissues. Glycine has been demonstrated in the same way, to participate in the formation of the purine ring.

Much of the recent success in delineating the metabolic sequences through which simple compounds are incorporated into the more complex purines and pyrimidines has been due to the isolation by Kornberg and his associates of 5 - phosphoribosylpyrophosphate (PRPP). This substance which is formed enzymically in body tissues through the reaction of adenosine-triphosphate (ATP) with ribose phosphate, plays a central role in the biosynthesis of the nucleotides. Simplified schemes depicting the metabolic steps in the synthesis of some mononucleotides are presented below.

### The Production, Destruction and Excretion of Uric Acid

In man, uric acid is formed in part from purines taken in the food (*exogenous uric acid*) and in part from body purines (*endogenous uric acid*). The latter are derived from the breakdown of nuclear material as well as from free mononucleotides, e.g., adenylic, inosinic and guanylic acids, found in muscle and glandular structures. Muscle and more especially glandular tissues, e.g., thymus, liver, kidney, pancreas, testes, etc., and leguminous vegetables are foods rich in purines.

Uric acid is formed from ammonia in the liver of the bird but little is known of the intermediate stages of the synthesis. As already mentioned (footnote, p. 800) uric acid is the end product of both protein and purine metabolism in birds and most reptiles; when ammonium salts containing $N^{15}$ are fed to birds, uric acid labelled with the isotope is excreted. According to Krebs and his associates hypoxanthine is first produced. Just as in the dog no urea is formed after hepatectomy, so in birds, no uric acid is produced after removal of the liver; ammonia accumulates in the blood. The site of uric acid production in man is unknown, but the liver, according to Jones, is the only tissue which contains xanthine oxidase, which suggests that uric acid production is, in part at least, a function of the human liver. The results of the investigations of Folin and associates indicate that from 30 to 70 per cent of the uric acid produced by the human subject is destroyed, the remainder appearing in the urine. The liver is probably the site of uric acid destruction in man. We have already seen that uric acid accumulates in the blood of the hepatectomized dog, which indicates that uric acid production occurs in extrahepatic tissues and that the uric acid allantoin conversion is a function of the liver. Little information is available concerning the process whereby uric acid is destroyed in the human body; its end products are unknown; allantoin is not one of them however, since human urine contains insignificant amounts of this substance, and what little is present is simply that taken preformed in the food. Uric acid is excreted in the urine as the urates of sodium, potassium

*Diagram B*

α-5-phosphoribosyl-pyrophosphate (PRPP)     Ribosamine phosphate     Glycinamide ribotide

*Diagram B—cont.*

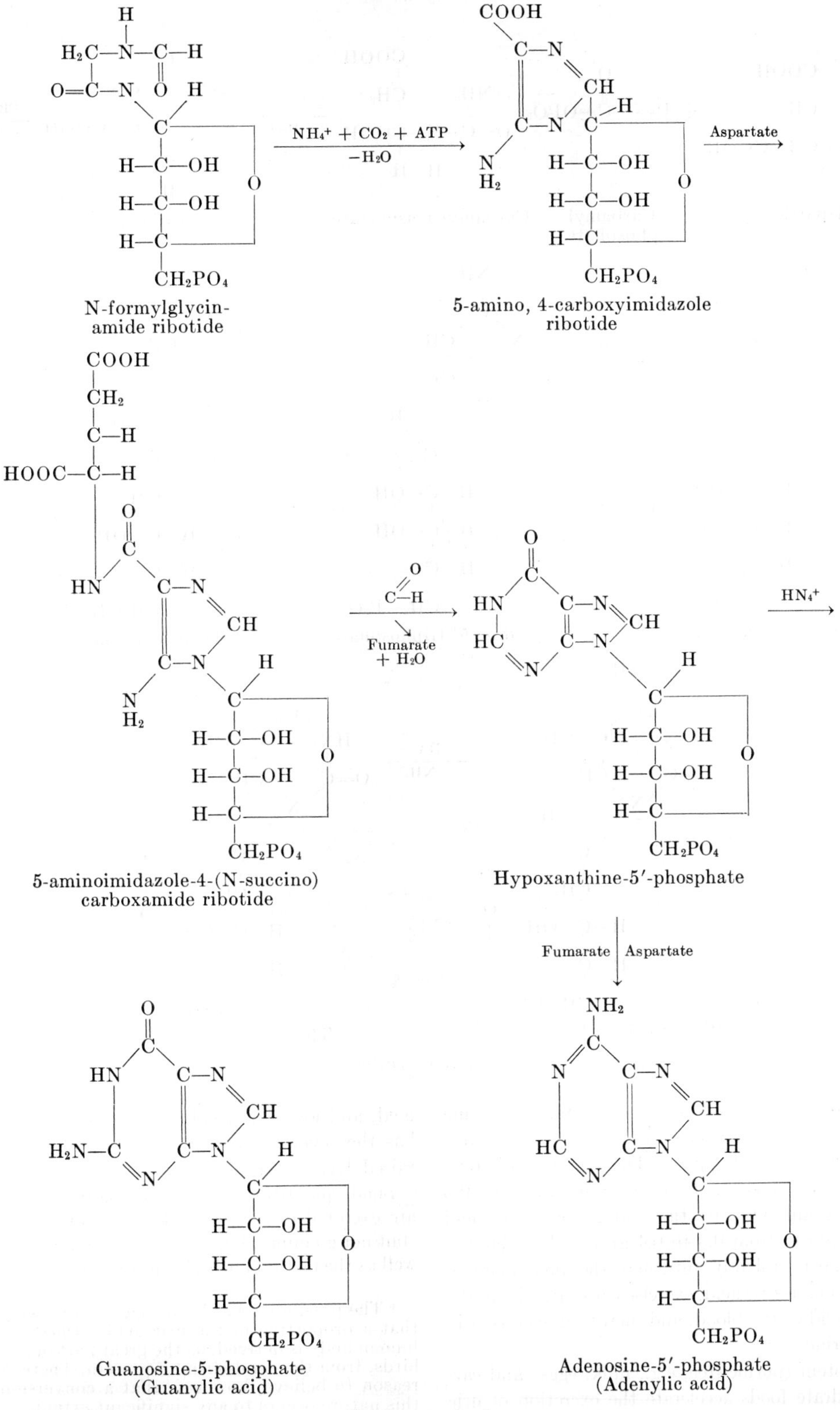

N-formylglycin-
amide ribotide

$NH_4^+ + CO_2 + ATP$
$-H_2O$

5-amino, 4-carboxyimidazole
ribotide

Aspartate

5-aminoimidazole-4-(N-succino)
carboxamide ribotide

Fumarate
+ $H_2O$

Hypoxanthine-5′-phosphate

$HN_4^+$

Fumarate | Aspartate

Guanosine-5-phosphate
(Guanylic acid)

Adenosine-5′-phosphate
(Adenylic acid)

Purine synthesis

*Diagram C*

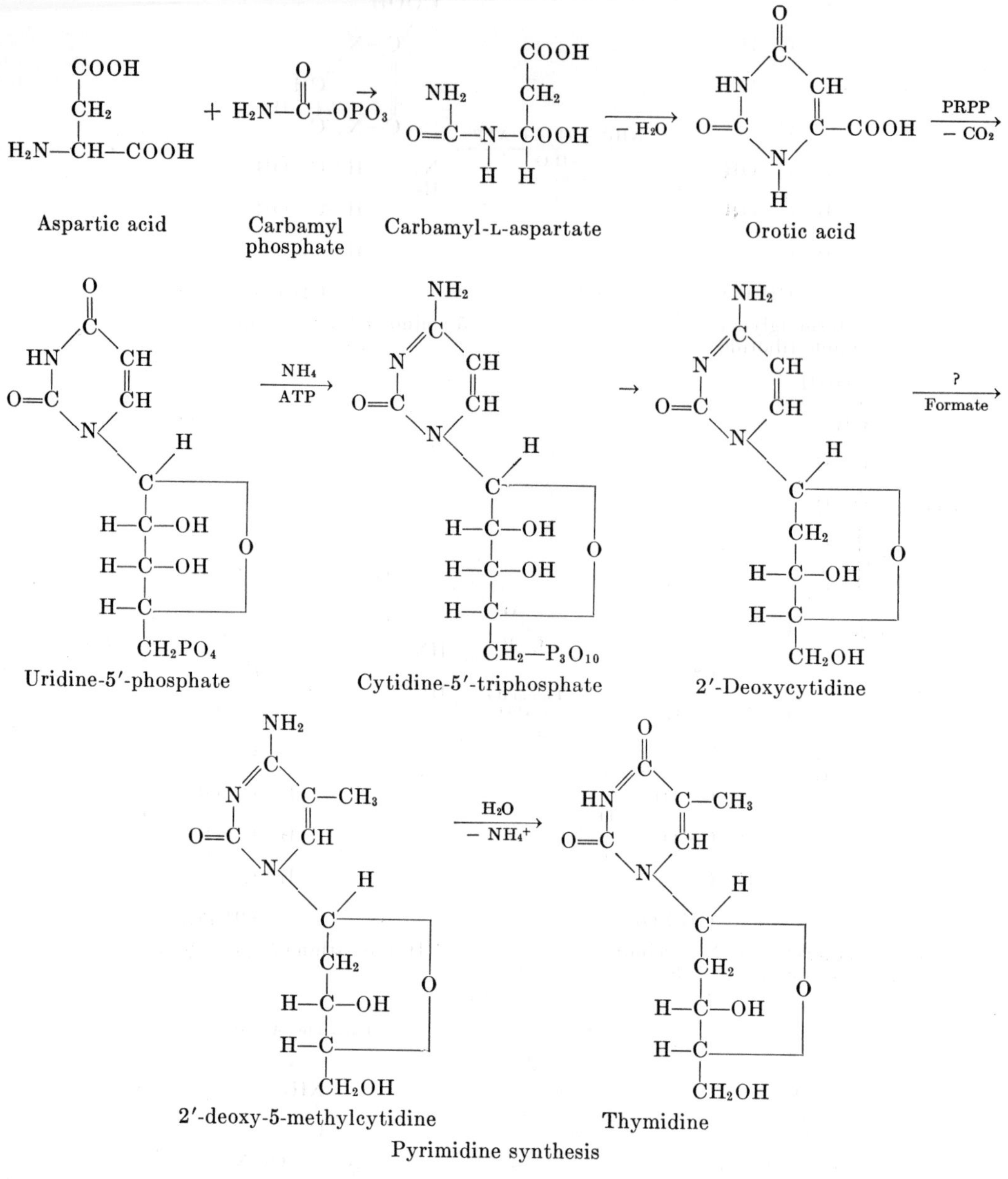

$$
\begin{array}{l}
\text{COOH} \\
\text{CH}_2 \\
\text{H}_2\text{N—CH—COOH}
\end{array}
\quad + \quad
\text{H}_2\text{N—C(=O)—OPO}_3
\quad \rightarrow
$$

Aspartic acid      Carbamyl phosphate

Carbamyl-L-aspartate

$\xrightarrow{-\text{H}_2\text{O}}$ Orotic acid $\xrightarrow[-\text{CO}_2]{\text{PRPP}}$

Uridine-5'-phosphate $\xrightarrow[\text{ATP}]{\text{NH}_4}$ Cytidine-5'-triphosphate $\rightarrow$ 2'-Deoxycytidine $\xrightarrow[\text{Formate}]{?}$

2'-deoxy-5-methylcytidine $\xrightarrow[-\text{NH}_4^+]{\text{H}_2\text{O}}$ Thymidine

Pyrimidine synthesis

and ammonium, and in the free state. After urine has been voided a crystalline deposit of urates and free uric acid appears. The average daily output of uric acid, on an ordinary diet, is from 0.5 to 1 gram. Of this the endogenous uric acid amounts to from 0.3 to 0.4 gram. Muscular tissue most probably furnishes the precursors of endogenous uric acid, exercise causing a rise in the uric acid of the blood, and increased excretion in the urine.

Protein (purine-free, e.g., milk, eggs) and carbohydrate foods accelerate the excretion of uric acid, and lower its level in the blood.[6] Food fat has the reverse effect—reduced excretion and a raised level in the blood.

Small quantities (15 to 45 mg. daily) of purines are excreted in the urine. These include adenine (but not guanine), hypoxanthine and xanthine, as well as the methyl purines contained in beverages.

[6] The possibility has been suggested in the past that a proportion of the uric acid formed in the human body is derived, as the great part of it is in birds, from the catabolism of protein. There is no reason to believe, however, that a conversion of this nature occurs to any significant extent.

*Diagram D*

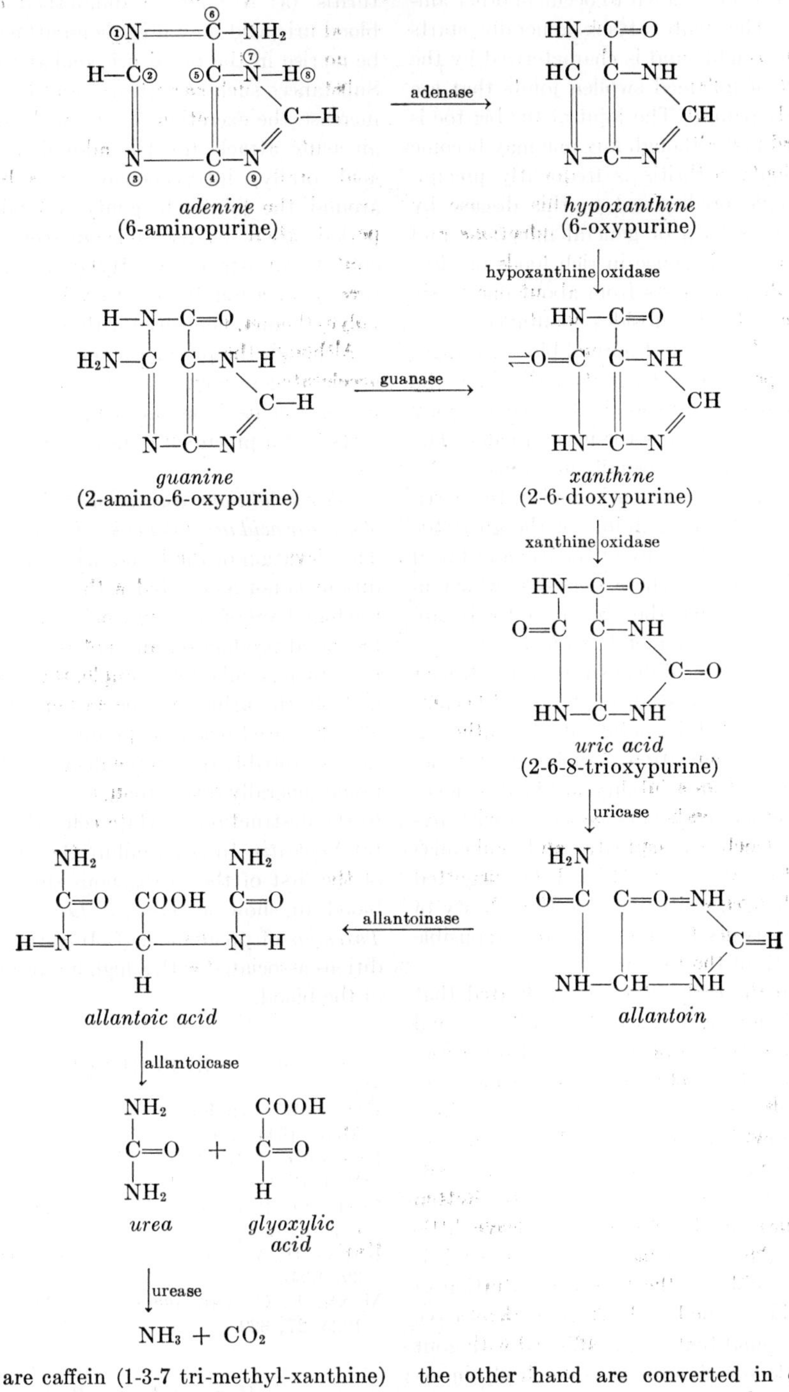

$$\overset{\textcircled{6}}{\text{N}}=\text{C}-\text{NH}_2$$
$$\text{H}-\text{C}_\textcircled{2} \quad \textcircled{5}\text{C}-\overset{\textcircled{7}}{\text{N}}-\text{H}\textcircled{8}$$
$$\text{C}-\text{H}$$
$$\underset{\textcircled{3}}{\text{N}}-\underset{\textcircled{4}}{\text{C}}-\underset{\textcircled{9}}{\text{N}}$$

*adenine*
(6-aminopurine)

→ adenase →

$$\text{HN}-\text{C}=\text{O}$$
$$\text{HC} \quad \text{C}-\text{NH}$$
$$\text{CH}$$
$$\text{N}-\text{C}-\text{N}$$

*hypoxanthine*
(6-oxypurine)

↓ hypoxanthine oxidase

$$\text{H}-\text{N}-\text{C}=\text{O}$$
$$\text{H}_2\text{N}-\text{C} \quad \text{C}-\text{N}-\text{H}$$
$$\text{C}-\text{H}$$
$$\text{N}-\text{C}-\text{N}$$

*guanine*
(2-amino-6-oxypurine)

→ guanase →

$$\text{HN}-\text{C}=\text{O}$$
$$\rightleftharpoons\text{O}=\text{C} \quad \text{C}-\text{NH}$$
$$\text{CH}$$
$$\text{HN}-\text{C}-\text{N}$$

*xanthine*
(2-6-dioxypurine)

↓ xanthine oxidase

$$\text{HN}-\text{C}=\text{O}$$
$$\text{O}=\text{C} \quad \text{C}-\text{NH}$$
$$\text{C}=\text{O}$$
$$\text{HN}-\text{C}-\text{NH}$$

*uric acid*
(2-6-8-trioxypurine)

↓ uricase

$$\text{H}_2\text{N}$$
$$\text{O}=\text{C} \quad \text{C}=\text{O}=\text{NH}$$
$$\text{C}=\text{H}$$
$$\text{NH}-\text{CH}-\text{NH}$$

*allantoin*

← allantoinase ←

$$\text{NH}_2 \qquad\qquad \text{NH}_2$$
$$\text{C}=\text{O} \quad \text{COOH} \quad \text{C}=\text{O}$$
$$\text{H}=\text{N}-\text{C}-\text{N}-\text{H}$$
$$\text{H}$$

*allantoic acid*

↓ allantoicase

$$\text{NH}_2 \qquad\qquad \text{COOH}$$
$$\text{C}=\text{O} \quad + \quad \text{C}=\text{O}$$
$$\text{NH}_2 \qquad\qquad \text{H}$$

*urea*      *glyoxylic acid*

↓ urease

$$\text{NH}_3 + \text{CO}_2$$

The latter are caffein (1-3-7 tri-methyl-xanthine) of coffee, *theophylline* (1-3-di-methyl-xanthine) of tea and *theobromine* (3-7 di-methyl-xanthine) of cocoa. The methyl purines undergo partial de-methylation in the body and are excreted as mono- and dimethyl purines. It appears that theobromine is excreted entirely in this form and is not converted to uric acid. Caffeine and theophylline on the other hand are converted in considerable amounts to uric acid and excreted as such. This is an important point to bear in mind when considering dietary restrictions for gouty subjects.

## Gout

Gout is a disease which predominantly afflicts the human male. Its incidence is very low in women and it is not known to occur in other animal species. The acute attack generally starts suddenly (overnight) and is characterized by the development of inflamed swollen joints that are excruciatingly painful. The joint of the big toe is often affected first although any one may become involved. Gouty arthritis is frequently precipitated in people predisposed to this disease by traumas such as local or general infections and may follow overindulgence in rich foods or alcohol. The acute stage lasts from about one to six weeks and eventually subsides spontaneously.

The uric acid content of normal blood averages about 3 mg. per 100 cc. In gouty individuals the blood uric acid concentration is elevated and may reach levels 10 to 20 times the normal value. The hyperuricemia of gout is usually accompanied by the presence of deposits of uric acid in the cartilaginous tissue about the joints of the great toe and fingers and in the helix of the ear and tarsal plates of the eyelids. These deposits, which in some areas may reach the size of golfballs, are called *tophi* and are completely painless.

The cause of uric acid deposition in the tissues is obscure. It is not a result of the blood becoming saturated with this metabolite for although the uric acid concentration may be greatly elevated the limit of its solubility in blood is never reached. In other conditions associated with hyperuricemia (such as nephritis and leukemia) tophi do not usually occur. It has been suggested that local changes which increase the affinity of cartilaginous tissues for uric acid are responsible for the growth of the tophus.

Reports in the early literature indicated that the hyperuricemia of gout was the result of a renal defect in the excretion of uric acid. However, in numerous recent investigations, where more refined methods have been used to assess kidney function, no evidence has been obtained of any abnormality in urate excretion in victims of gout. The result of investigation carried out by Stetten and colleagues and by Wyngaarden leave little doubt that the *overproduction* of uric acid is largely responsible for the high concentration of this metabolite in the blood. These workers have consistently found that people afflicted with gout incorporate two to five times as much glycine-1-$C^{14}$ into uric acid as do normal individuals.

The factors responsible for the production of acute inflammation in gout are unknown. The following observations serve as convincing evidence that the high blood level of uric acid is not directly responsible for the attack of gouty ar-

thritis. (a) Although a diminished excretion of blood uric acid may precede an attack there may be no rise in the blood uric acid at this time. (b) Substances such as cortisone and benemid which increase the excretion of uric acid fail to relieve an acute attack. (c) The administration of uric acid orally, intravenously or subcutaneously around the joints, to gouty individuals during periods when the disease is quiescent, fails to precipitate an attack. (d) Hyperuricemia may be present in a number of other diseases (leukemia, polycythemia, nephritis) with no signs of gout.

Although the production of uric acid is greatly accelerated in gout the substance itself does not produce acute inflammation. This strongly suggests that a precursor of uric acid is the offending agent.

*Other conditions associated with a high level of blood uric acid are:* (a) *Leukemia and polycythemia.* The elevation of the blood uric acid in these conditions is not associated with symptoms of gout; the high level of blood uric acid is evidently due to increased production and not to failure in excretion. In leukemia, for example, the amount passed daily in the urine may be as much as 12 grams. The increased uric acid production in this condition is probably due to the disintegration of body tissue generally rather than, as has been supposed, to the destruction of white cells. (b) *Pneumonia.* (c) *Nephritis.* In renal failure the uric acid is one of the first of the nitrogenous substances of the blood to show a rise. (d) *Lead poisoning.* (e) *Toxemias* of pregnancy. (f) In certain other conditions associated with a high nonprotein nitrogen of the blood.

## REFERENCES

BAUER, W. AND KLEMPERER, F. New England J. Med., 1944, **231**, 681.

BENEDICT, S. R., DAVIS, A. R. AND NEWTONE, E. B. J. Biol. Chem., 1922, **54**, 595.

FOLIN, O., BERGLUND, H. AND DERICK, C. J. Biol. Chem., 1924, **60**, 361.

KREBS, H. A. AND ASSOCIATES. Biochem. J., 1936, **30**, 1380.

MANN, F. C. AND ASSOCIATES. Am. J. Physiol., 1925, **27**, 629.

*Monographs and Reviews*

BENEDICT, S. R. Uric acid in its relations to metabolism. Harvey Lectures, 1915–1916, **11**, 346.

CARTER, C. E., Ann. Rev. Biochem., 1956, **25**, 123.

DAKIN, H. D. Oxidations and reductions in the animal body. Longmans, London, 1912. Physiological oxidations. Physiol. Rev., 1921, **1**. 394.

DAVIDSON, J. N. The Biochemistry of the Nucleic Acids. Methuen, London, 1950.

GARROD, A. E. Inborn errors of metabolism. Frowde, London, 1923.

GREENSTEIN, J. P. Advances in Protein Chem. 1944, 1, 209.

HEPPEL, L. A. Ann. Rev. Biochem., 1958, 27, 613.

JONES, W. Nucleic acids; their chemical properties and physiological conduct. Longmans, London, 1920.

LEVENE, P. A. AND BASS, L. W. Nucleic acids. Chemical Catalog Co., New York, 1931.

LORING, H. G. Proc. Fed. Am. Soc. Exper. Biol., 1947, 6, 487.

PETERS, J. P. AND VAN SLYKE, D. D. Quantitative Clinical Chemistry, Vol. I. The Williams & Wilkins Co., Baltimore, 1932.

ROSE, W. C. Physiol. Rev., 1923, 3, 544. Metabolism, 1957, 6, 193.

# 48

# CARBOHYDRATE METABOLISM

Without doubt the carbohydrate substance most important in metabolism is glucose. All organisms seem to be able to utilize glucose. Glucose, sometimes called dextrose because its solution rotates the plane of polarized light in a dextro-rotatory direction and often written $d$-glucose, dissolves in water to give an equilibrium mixture of $\alpha$- and $\beta$-glucose, approximately two-thirds of the glucose being of the $\alpha$-form. The formulae of these two isomers are written:

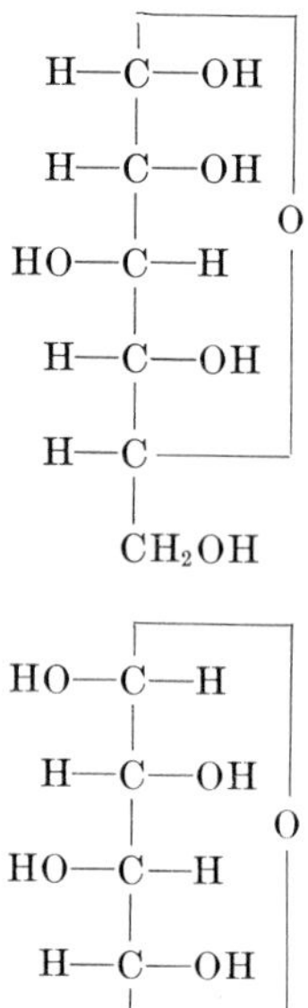

H—C—OH

H—C—OH

HO—C—H    O    $\alpha$-Glucose

H—C—OH

         $[\alpha]_D = +110°$

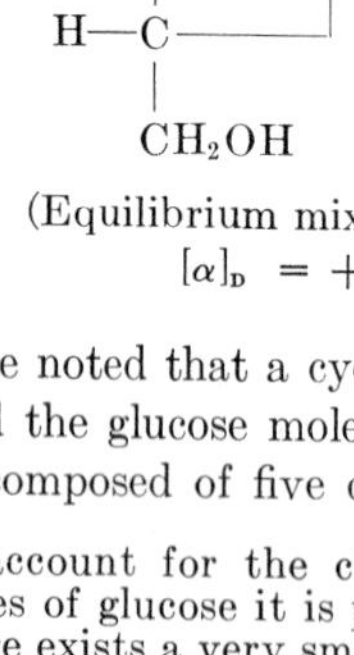

H—C

CH$_2$OH

HO—C—H

H—C—OH

HO—C—H    O    $\beta$-Glucose

H—C—OH

         $[\alpha]_D = +17.5°$

H—C

CH$_2$OH

(Equilibrium mixture)

$[\alpha]_D = +52.5°$

It will be noted that a cyclic structure has been accorded the glucose molecule.[1] In this case the ring is composed of five carbon atoms and one

[1] To account for the characteristic reducing properties of glucose it is presumed that in solution there exists a very small amount of the open chain aldehydic form in equilibrium with the cyclic forms.

oxygen atom, sometimes referred to as an amylene oxidic ring. $\alpha$ and $\beta$ isomers of glucose may also possess a ring composed of four carbon atoms and one oxygen atom. This is the so-called $\gamma$-glucose. Such a ring is a butylene oxidic ring. These forms of glucose are very reactive, that is, unstable. They have not been isolated. It may be pointed out, as an example of their reactivity, that they reduce Fehling's solution in the cold. Because of this marked reactivity it has been postulated that such compounds must be the first intermediaries in glucose metabolism. But there is no conclusive evidence for such a change, and all theories of glucose metabolism involving the formation of a "reactive" form of glucose have very little factual basis. Glycogen, or animal starch, is a polysaccharide composed of glucose units and so is written $(C_6H_{10}O_5)_x$ [according to Haworth, $x = 12$. In liver glycogen formed from galactose $x$ may equal 18 (Bell)]. Glycogen is widely distributed in the animal body, but the bulk occurs in the muscles and the liver. Glycogen may be isolated from tissue by hot water extraction, or more readily and completely by hot alkali. It is worthy of note that whereas polysaccharides are very stable in alkaline solution, monosaccharides (glucose, fructose, galactose, etc.) are unstable. The reverse behavior is exhibited in acid solution. The glycogens, as Cori has shown, are a series of branched polysaccharides differing mainly in the degree of branching and the length of the so-called inner and outer chains. Step-wise degradation by the action of phosphorylase and amylo-1,6-glucosidase and synthesis by phosphorylase and the branching enzyme of liver and muscle has revealed the structure.

Glucose occurs in the body in combination with other substances; such as salts of glucose phosphoric acids, and in the lactating animal in combination with galactose as lactose. The latter sugar (glucose-$\beta$-galactoside) may be obtained in two distinct crystalline forms, referred to as $\alpha$- and $\beta$-lactose, respectively.

Glucose unit

$$HO-C-H$$
$$H-C-OH$$
$$O$$
$$HO-C-H$$
Galactose unit
$$H-C———O———C-H$$
$$H-C———————H-C-OH$$
$$O$$
$$CH_2OH \quad HO-C-H$$
$$HO-C-H$$
$$H-C$$
$$CH_2OH$$

Lactose

The slight difference in chemical configuration between glucose and galactose should be noted. Carbohydrates occur as substituent groupings in certain proteins. Such proteins may be extracted from tissues paying due regard to their solubility properties. From such extracted proteins there have been isolated glucose (from glycoproteins) glucosamine, mannose (from certain blood proteins) and various pentoses, that is 5 carbon sugars possessing the general formula ($C_5H_{10}O_5$) in nucleic acid which is combined with certain proteins to give the so-called nucleoproteins (ch. 47). It may be pointed out that pentoses also occur in combined form as nucleotides, and that very rarely cases of human pentosuria are encountered.

Carbohydrates also occur linked with fatty substances. Thus the cerebrosides contain within their molecule galactose units. The galactose is present in the normal or amylene oxidic ring form. Cerebrosides may be extracted with the usual fat solvents. The galactose may be split off from such extracted substances by acid hydrolysis. Glucose may also be present in cerebrosides (p. 843).

## Methods of Estimation

*Glucose.* The simple sugars have four properties which permit their identification and estimation: (1) their ability to reduce the salts of heavy metals in alkaline solution, (2) their optical activity, (3) fermentation by yeast and by various microörganisms, (4) oxidation by specific enzymes (glucose oxidase). The methods depending on the reduction of the salts of heavy metals have been of great value in physiological work but since other compounds present in the body also possess this property it is necessary to prove that the reduction is due to glucose. This is accomplished by utilizing the third or fourth property mentioned above, i.e., by fermenting the glucose with yeast or with certain microörganisms or oxidizing with a specific enzyme such as that derived from *Penicilliun notatum.* The optical activity of the carbohydrates is an invaluable property when they are present in solutions uncontaminated by various other optically active substances which are present in physiological fluids.

*Glycogen.* Glycogen is very resistant to alkaline hydroloysis, but, as Claude Bernard discovered, readily yields reducing sugar on acid hydrolysis. Pflüger boiled glycogen for several weeks in strong alkali without destroying it. Advantage is taken of this property to free glycogen of contaminating substances. After alkaline hydrolysis of the tissue the glycogen is precipitated from solution by alcohol. This material is then broken down by acid hydrolysis to glucose, which is stable in acid solution. The sugar is then estimated as described above and the amount of glycogen calculated from the result. The histochemists using the most effective "vital" staining procedures will probably soon be able to tell us the approximate amount of particulate glycogen in the living cell and perhaps also of the soluble form which is, of course, one step nearer the metabolic pathway.

*Lactic acid.* In muscle, glycogen is broken down to lactic acid during muscular exercise and in the recovery from exercise part of it is resynthesized to glycogen. The lactic acid is estimated by oxidation to acetaldehyde and the latter is determined by distilling it into sodium bisulphite with which it forms a double-compound. Residual unbound bisulphite is titrated with iodine.

APPROXIMATE DISTRIBUTION OF CARBOHYDRATES

|  | Liver per cent | Muscle per cent | Blood per cent |
|---|---|---|---|
| Glucose.... | 0.06–0.15 | 0.02–0.04 | 0.08–0.11 |
| Glycogen... | 0.2–10.0 | 0.2–1.8 | trace |
| Lactic acid. | 0.01 | 0.01 | 0.01 |

Human liver is about 3 per cent, muscle 50 per cent and blood 7 per cent of body weight (Brody and Kibler). Glucose and lactic acid are found in the other soft tissues and some of these contain small amounts of glycogen. The glycogen content of kidney and of heart muscle has been extensively studied under various physiological and pathological conditions.

## Absorption of Sugar

The monosaccharides formed during digestion are rapidly absorbed from the small intestine. In the rat, galactose disappears from the intestine most rapidly, glucose a little more slowly and fructose much more so. There is, therefore, a selective action of the intestinal cells in the absorption of sugars (Cori). Evidence is accumulating that the absorption of sugar may proceed against a concentration gradient, i.e., when the concentration is lower in the lumen of the small intestine than in the blood. There is an increase in the amount of esterified phosphate in the intestinal mucosa during the absorption of both glucose and fructose but this phosphorylation may be related to metabolism rather than to absorption. It has, however, been suggested by Lundsgaard that the relatively high level of esterified phosphate in the intestinal mucosa during the absorption of fructose may be due to slow dephosphorylation and thus account for the well known delay in the rate of absorption of this sugar.

The slow absorption of glucose from the small intestine after hypophysectomy or adrenalectomy may be a part of the picture of inanition rather than a result of the loss of a specific adrenal phosphorylating factor, as has been suggested. The fact that the administration of sodium salts restores the rate of glucose absorption in adrenalectomized animals (Deuel) is in favor of the non-specific effect.

Glucose is not absorbed in appreciable amounts from the stomach until high concentrations are reached, and only slowly from the large bowel.

## The Fate of Ingested or Injected Glucose

There is good evidence that no other monosaccharide is as effective in the liverless animal as glucose. This finding suggests, and there is indeed good evidence, that the other monosaccharides are normally changed to glucose in the liver. Fructose is a better glycogen former than glucose but galactose is much inferior in this respect. When glucose is absorbed or is injected some of it can be accounted for by the increase in liver glycogen; some is converted to muscle glycogen. The concentration of glucose in the soft tissues is temporarily raised. The use of isotopes has revealed a rapid and extensive conversion of glucose to fat (Stetten) and a more delayed increase in oxidation (Wick and Drury). Various intermediates in glucose metabolism may be converted to amino acids by transamination reactions and the amino acids subsequently converted into protein (p. 777). These processes, but not the precise time relationships have been well established.

## The Formation of Glucose in the Body

Glucose is apparently formed in large amounts only in the liver. When this organ is removed (Mann and Magath) hypoglycemia soon appears and sugar must be provided if the animal is to survive more than a few hours. Sugar is made from protein in the liver and evidence obtained on phloridzinized animals indicates that some of the amino acids, glycine, alanine, cystine, aspartic and glutamic acids may yield glucose in the theoretical amounts (Lusk). It is well established that plants form sugar from fat. There are a certain number of reports of respiratory quotients below 0.7 which disturb those who believe in the unitarian significance of the quotient, but this ratio should not be used as a weapon against itself. It has been established that an appreciable amount of sugar is formed in the kidney (Bergman and Drury; Reinecke), but this appears to be a small fraction of that supplied by the liver.

### *The Common Metabolic Path*

The recent discovery of the nature of the active "2-carbon" fragment, which has long been postulated as being an important intermediate in the metabolism of fatty acids, indicates pathways by which the conversion of carbohydrate to fat (or the reverse change) occurs. The labile acetyl groups found in acetyl-coenzyme A which arise in the oxidation of pyruvate or from the oxidation of fatty acids, appear to be identical. It is not surprising, therefore, in view of this common pathway in the metabolism of carbohydrate and fat to note that the old controversy as to whether or not conversion of fatty acid into glycogen can occur has been settled in the affirmative by the use of isotopes. The small amount of isotopes incorporated into glycogen agree, however, with the view that fat is not quantitatively an important precursor of glycogen or glucose. Since certain amino acids form sugar, it is becoming increasingly clear that the various metabolic materials share a common pathway and that acetyl-coenzyme A provides a link which joins them (see Fat Metabolism).

## Formation and Breakdown of Glycogen and the Oxidation of Sugar

Great advances in our knowledge of the most fundamental aspects of carbohydrate metabolism have been made in recent years. Most of the steps in the formation and breakdown of glycogen and the oxidation of sugar have been revealed by the work of Harden, Young, Embden, Meyerhof, Warburg, Cori, Lohmann, Peters and numerous other investigators. Many of the individual steps are not observed in the intact cell since the intermediate products which have been identified *in vitro* do not accumulate. There are, for example, at least twelve enzymatic reactions involved in the anaerobic conversions of glycogen to lactic acid. Practically all of these have been shown to be reversible but since the final product of one reaction is immediately removed by the following step the process proceeds in one direction. The phosphorylation of glycogen and of glucose has been proved to be the introduction to a long series of changes by which these products are transformed through various phosphate esters to pyruvic or lactic acid. Glycogen after phosphorylation breaks down to glucose-1-phosphate. This (Cori ester) is converted to glucose-6-phosphate which is also the first step in the oxidation of glucose.

The work of Cori and Cori in which the enzyme phosphorylase, which catalyzes the reversible reaction glycogen (or starch) + inorganic phosphate ⇌ glucose-1-phosphate, was isolated and purified, is of great interest. This enzyme is widely distributed in animal tissues and is responsible for the first stage in the breakdown of glycogen. It also affects the synthesis of a polysaccharide indistinguishable from glycogen. Some glycogen must be present to "prime" this latter reaction and adenylic acid is an essential constituent of the mixture for activity in either direction. It is now well established that this transfer of phosphate groups is of paramount importance in the mechanism by which cells derive energy from the breakdown of food materials. Muscle glycogen breaks down to $CO_2$ and $H_2O$ under physiological conditions. The steps from glycogen to pyruvic acid can occur anaerobically but from pyruvic acid on, an adequate oxygen supply is necessary. When there is a relative lack of oxygen lactic acid is formed. Pyruvic and lactic acids are interconvertible in the body. This lactic acid may diffuse out into the blood stream. It may be used directly by other peripheral tissues or may be converted to glycogen in the liver.

This part of the cycle is apparently not brought into play under ordinary circumstances but may be involved in muscular exercise or under conditions of anoxia.

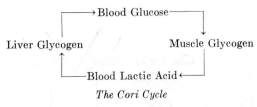

*The Cori Cycle*

Glycogen-containing tissues, with the exception of the liver, exhibit the same pattern of breakdown of this polysaccharide as has been described in muscle. In the liver, glycogen does not normally break down to $CO_2$ and $H_2O$ or to lactic acid but to dextrose. This is probably due to the fact that the liver contains a very active phosphatase which converts the glucose-1-phosphate and the glucose-6-phosphate to glucose and thus removes these esters from the medium.

Under certain conditions, *in vitro*, glyceric aldehyde phosphate and dihydroxyacetone phosphate can be isolated from the breakdown products of muscle glycogen. In the diabetic dog these substances, and also pyruvic acid, form "extra sugar," but so does methyl glyoxal which is not a part of the accepted schemes.

### The Regulation of Blood Sugar

The blood sugar level represents the resultant of oxidation, storage and excretion on the one hand and formation and absorption on the other. This may be represented graphically (fig. 48.1).

The relative constancy of the blood sugar which is an equilibrium mixture of $\alpha$- and $\beta$-glucose in the normal fasting animal is made more remarkable by the fact that the production, storage, and utilization of sugar are affected by a great number of chemical and nervous factors.

When sugar is not being absorbed from the intestinal tract it must be made in the liver or kidney from non-carbohydrate sources or liberated by the breakdown of glycogen. The liver glycogen is the emergency supply which is available while the process of gluconeogenesis is gathering speed. In the average man approximately 100 grams of glycogen are present in the liver and this would only supply the demands for sugar for some five hours if the gluconeogenesis were to cease. The rate of glycogen breakdown is affected by adrenaline which is liberated in emergencies (see also glucagon) and the rate of gluconeogenesis by the internal secretions of the anterior pituitary gland, the adrenal cortex, the thyroid and the pancreas, as will be discussed later. An important part of this homeostatic mechanism for the regulation of blood sugar appears to be the level of

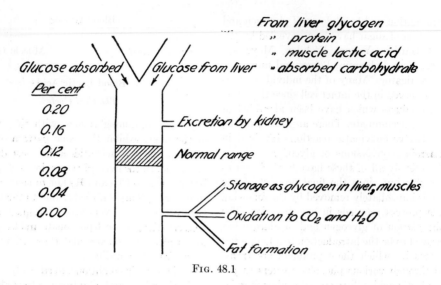

From liver glycogen
        " protein
        " muscle lactic acid
        - absorbed carbohydrate

Glucose absorbed    Glucose from liver

Per cent

0.20

0.16     Excretion by kidney

0.12     Normal range

0.08

0.04     Storage as glycogen in liver, muscles

0.00     Oxidation to $CO_2$ and $H_2O$

                 Fat formation

Fig. 48.1

blood sugar itself (Soskin and Levine). Under experimental conditions in which variation in the rate of secretion of insulin is impossible, i.e., in the depancreatized dog given insulin at a constant rate, indirect evidence indicates that the administration of dextrose decreases the rate of output of sugar by the liver. In the intact animal the pancreatic mechanism is also involved. The insulin content of the blood may determine at what level of blood sugar gluconeogenesis in the liver will be

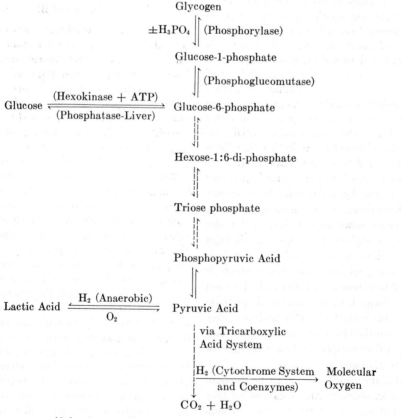

Glycogen

$\pm H_3PO_4$ ‖ (Phosphorylase)

Glucose-1-phosphate

‖ (Phosphoglucomutase)

Glucose $\xrightarrow[\text{(Phosphatase-Liver)}]{\text{(Hexokinase + ATP)}}$ Glucose-6-phosphate

Hexose-1:6-di-phosphate

Triose phosphate

Phosphopyruvic Acid

Lactic Acid $\xrightarrow[\text{O}_2]{\text{H}_2 \text{ (Anaerobic)}}$ Pyruvic Acid

       via Tricarboxylic
       Acid System

       $H_2$ (Cytochrome System    Molecular
           and Coenzymes)       Oxygen

      $CO_2 + H_2O$

(Other intermediate steps in this process shown in ch. 51)

inhibited. In the absence of insulin only extremely high levels of blood sugar exert a protein-sparing action.

### Hyperglycemia

An increase in the blood sugar beyond the normal range constitutes a hyperglycemia. This may be a protective phenomenon. With the exception of insulin a rise in blood sugar provides the greatest single stimulus for the formation of glycogen and the utilization of glucose.

Prolonged hyperglycemia may be present when either or both of the following processes are operating: (1) diminished utilization of glucose, (2) overproduction and discharge of sugar from the liver. Disturbances in endocrine function are the main causes and the mechanism of these changes will be discussed later.

Transient hyperglycemia may be due to either physiological or pathological processes. Alimentary hyperglycemia is a physiological process and its height depends on the amount and nature of the carbohydrate in the meal. Adrenaline hyperglycemia is a part of the physiological response to an emergency. Nerve impulses acting on the liver, changes in hydrogen-ion concentration of liver cells due to asphyxia or other causes, may produce a transient rise in blood sugar. Toxic products of infection acting on the liver to increase gluconeogenesis or on tissues in general to diminish utilization of sugar may produce a hyperglycemia of short or long duration. The role of glucagon will be discussed later.

### Glucosuria

The occurrence of glucose in the urine is the result of hyperglycemia except when the renal threshold to glucose is lowered (phloridzin diabetes in animals, renal diabetes in man). The following list of the methods of causing experimental glucosuria is slightly modified from Ingle.

1. Pancreatic (insulin) insufficiency
   Pancreatectomy—Von Mering and Minkowski.
   Alloxan—Dunn, Sheehan and McLetchie.
   Subtotal pancreatectomy and high caloric intake—Allen.
   Withdrawal of insulin following its prolonged injection in the force-fed normal rat—Ingle and associates.
2. Hormonal
   Crude anterior pituitary extract or purified growth hormone—Houssay and Biasotti; Evans; Young; Campbell; Anderson.
   Adrenal C-11-oxygenated steroids—Long, Katzin and Fry; Ingle.
   Estrogens—Dolin, Joseph and Gaunt; Ingle.
   Thyroid—Houssay.
   Glucagon—Cavallero; Ingle; Salter, Davidson and Best.
3. Dietary
   Starvation and subsequent feeding—Lehmann.
   Overfeeding—Hofmeister.
   Sudden shift from high fat to high carbohydrate diet.
4. Glycogenolysis
   Piqûre—Bernard.
   Emotion—Cannon, Shohl and Wright.
   Epinephrine, drugs, toxins, trauma.
   Glucagon—transient hyperglycemia partly by glycogenolysis and partly by gluconeogenesis.
5. Renal
   Phloridzin—Von Mering.

### Pancreatic Diabetes

#### Removal of the Pancreas

When the pancreas is completely removed from a dog or cat, a characteristic syndrome rapidly develops (Mering and Minkowski, 1889). When a diet including the known essentials is provided, the animals may live indefinitely if adequate amounts of insulin are administered. The animals recover rapidly from the operation and appear normal, but the diabetic state quickly supervenes when insulin is discontinued. The sugar content of the blood begins to rise within a very short time, depending on the size of the last dose of insulin, and increases from the normal level of 0.08 to 0.11 per cent to 0.20 to 0.40 or higher within 24 hours. The urine gives a positive Benedict's qualitative test for sugar when the blood sugar rises above approximately 0.16 per cent. This point, the so-called renal threshold, is the level of blood sugar above which large amounts of sugar are excreted in the urine. In some animals the "threshold" rises when the diabetic state is allowed to persist. (There is some glucose in normal urine and small amounts of other sugars.) The excretion of nitrogen is increased and this may be taken to indicate protein breakdown or decreased protein formation. The ratio of glucose to nitrogen excreted in phloridzin poisoning is

3.6:1 but this ratio is not observed in depancreatized dogs and indeed that obtained is so variable that little significance can be attached to it. The ratio is low in animals on a high protein diet and there is evidence that the addition of fat may increase it somewhat. It is established that glycerol may be converted to sugar. In the fasting diabetic the blood sugar and sugar excretion are maintained at high levels. The sugar is apparently formed from body protein in the liver since the blood sugar of the diabetic falls rapidly after hepatectomy. The amino acid contents of the blood and urine are increased. The loss of protein contributes to the decrease in body weight.

The disturbed metabolism of fat in the depancreatized animal is indicated by the accumulation of the ketone bodies in the blood and by the excretion of excessive amounts in the urine. The ketosis in a fat dog is greater than in a lean, but this species is characterized by its efficiency in metabolizing fats, without ketosis. The loss of body fat is rapid but the ketosis may be so severe, even in this species, that the animal dies in coma before the fat reserves are depleted.

$\beta$-Hydroxy-butyric and acetoacetic acids and others derived from tissue breakdown appropriate base and thus when the available reserve of base is depleted may produce an acidosis. In acidosis the respiratory center is stimulated and "air hunger" and coma are produced. The mechanism of coma production in diabetes is not completely known. Some observers believe that acetoacetic acid is particularly toxic. This acid is oxidized in the bladder and lungs to form acetone, which is excreted in the urine and expired air.

The neutral fat content of the blood increases, due probably to the increased rate of mobilization of depôt fat, and there is also a rise in cholesterol esters and the phospholipid.

While there is proof that the depancreatized dog can still burn sugar—all the criteria of sugar combustion in the normal have been satisfied—it is not permissible to conclude that there is no interference with this process. The rapid sugar utilization in the hepatectomized diabetic animal and the production of a diabetic condition by the administration of cortisone, which apparently acts, in part, by stimulating the liver to produce more glucose, tend, however, to emphasize overproduction rather than underutilization. On the other hand the anterior pituitary and the adrenal cortex contain substances which inhibit the utilization of glucose. The evidence now indicates that both overproduction of sugar from protein and

diminished utilization play a part in the creation of the diabetic state. Calculations of these rates of production and utilization of glucose based on the rate of disappearance of ingested $C^{14}$-glucose in diabetic animals have indicated that underutilization is a more prominent feature than overproduction (Weinhouse; de Bodo; Wrenshall).

The respiratory quotient of the depancreatized animal not receiving insulin assumes the low level 0.69 to 0.73 and is not usually raised when sugar is given. Under certain conditions, in animals which have received a high protein diet and insulin, for a time the quotient may be higher (Soskin). The characteristic low quotient may indicate combustion of fat but if any process, such as conversion of fat to sugar which gives a very low quotient, should be taking place the ratio might indicate the resultant between sugar combustion, fat combustion, and the conversion. In brief, since more than one interpretation of a quotient is possible great caution must be observed in drawing conclusions with regard to its significance. When the liver is removed from a depancreatized dog the quotient rises, indicating either that relatively more sugar is being burned or that conversions giving a low quotient are taking place to a smaller extent.

The glycogen content of the muscles of a depancreatized animal may be reduced below the normal level, but appreciable amounts remain. There is no diminution of heart muscle glycogen and indeed convincing evidence of an increase has been obtained. Liver glycogen falls to very low levels. A slight increase in both muscle and liver glycogen can be produced by giving large amounts of sugar without exogenous insulin. This might be due to small amounts of residual insulin which would now appear to persist, under certain conditions, for rather long periods.

Whereas the glucose utilization of the normal heart is low, that of the diabetic animal is even less when the blood sugar concentrations are the same. Lactate, however, is used almost as well by the diabetic as by the normal heart (Lovatt Evans). These findings eliminate the necessity of supposing that the diabetic heart depends for its energy *entirely* on protein and fat. The rate of usage of glucose but not of lactate by the diabetic heart is increased when insulin is supplied.

The excretion of phosphorus is increased in the depancreatized animal. The administration of sugar or adrenaline does not cause the prompt fall in the inorganic phosphate of the blood which is observed in normal animals. These substances, therefore, produce their effects by raising blood sugar which in turn calls forth insulin. Adrenaline and insulin thus affect blood inorganic phosphate similarly, but insulin is effective in the absence of the adrenal glands, i.e., the action is in both cases due to the pancreatic hormone.

The diabetic animal is very susceptible to infections but it is not established that this is due to the raised sugar content of the tissues. Some diabetic patients have a decreased ability to form antibodies. This defect appears to be more closely related to hypoproteinemia than to hyperglycemia. Pathological conditions are observed with considerable frequency in the eyes of diabetic animals. Many of these abnormalities including cataracts may be eliminated in the diabetic dog by adequate treatment with diet and insulin. The liver rapidly undergoes extensive fatty degeneration and there may be an accumulation of large amounts of neutral fat.

Although there is considerable variation in the length of life of the depancreatized dog or cat, most individuals fed on a mixed diet do not live for more than two or three weeks without insulin. Under certain conditions dogs may survive for seven weeks. It is now established, however, that when the anterior pituitary is also removed the animal (dog) may live for nine months, at least,

and exhibit only a mild form of diabetes. Severe diabetes produced under these conditions by administration of the diabetogenic substances of the anterior pituitary is alleviated by insulin.

### The Antidiabetic Hormone—Insulin

The name *insuline* was suggested by de Meyer in 1909 for the hypothetical internal secretion of the pancreas the search for which had been stimulated by von Mering's and Minkowski's findings (1889). While other workers, among whom Hédon, Zuelzer, and Scott may be mentioned, obtained very suggestive results, which in some cases were probably due to the presence of insulin, Banting and Best working in Macleod's laboratory (1922) were the first to obtain a preparation containing the antidiabetic hormone in a form which consistently alleviated all signs of diabetes in completely depancreatized dogs (fig. 48.2).

#### SOURCE OF INSULIN

Small amounts of insulin are presumably present in tissues other than the pancreas but methods are not yet available for their quantitative estimation. Blood provides an exception to this generalization and this subject is discussed on page 818. In the mammalian organism the pan-

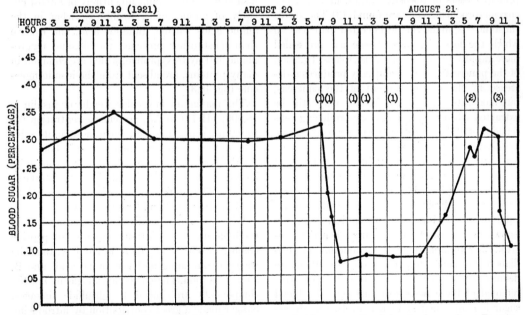

FIG. 48.2. Effect of insulin on the blood sugar curve of a depancreatized dog (redrawn from Banting and Best). (1) Injection of extract of degenerated pancreas; (2) extract after incubation with pancreatic juice; (3) extract incubated without pancreatic juice. Blood sugars by Myers-Bailey modification of Lewis-Benedict method.

creas appears to be the only organ to manufacture insulin or to store it in more than minute amounts.

The islet cells of the pancreas are of four types —$\alpha$, $\beta$, $\gamma$ and $\delta$. The $\alpha$- and $\beta$-types contain granules. The $\gamma$ are non-granular. The $\delta$-cells have been seen only in human pancreas (Bloom) and are not well defined. In dog pancreas the number of cells per islet varies greatly, as do the relative numbers of the various types of cells. One study gives the average number per islet as 30 and the average ratio of $\alpha$- to $\beta$-cells as 20:75. The islet volume may be about one one-hundredth of the pancreas. The $\beta$-cells occupy the periphery of the islets and are smaller than the others. It is these cells which are considered to be producers of the antidiabetic hormone; indeed, the granules of these cells may consist, in part, of this substance. Epithelial cells of the small ducts are considered to be the "mother cells" of the islet and acinar cells. New islet cells may, therefore, be produced from them. The reader is referred to recent papers by Lazarow in "Diabetes" and other journals.

The main points of evidence which indicate that the hormone is produced in the islet cells are as follows: (1) Histologically, the islets are glandular structures, the obvious outlet for the secretion of which is through the blood stream. (2) There are relatively large amounts of the hormone in the principal islets of teleosteal fishes, in which few enzyme-producing cells are found. (3) The active substance is found in degenerated pancreas in which the loss of acinous tissue has proceeded more rapidly than that of the islet cells. Ligation of the pancreatic ducts eventually produces a decrease in the insulin content of the pancreas, but moderate amounts of insulin may still be extracted when very few enzyme-producing cells remain. (4) When most of the pancreas, approximately nine-tenths, is removed from a dog, characteristic lesions (glycogen infiltration) are found in the $\beta$-cells of the remnant. These changes can be accelerated by a high carbohydrate diet, and prevented or eliminated by administration of insulin or by fasting. (5) The clinical condition known as hyperinsulinism occurs when the pancreas liberates abnormally large amounts of antidiabetic hormone. In many of the cases there are definite tumors of the islet cells. After operative removal of these masses of islet cells the blood sugar is maintained at higher levels. (6) Metastases in other tissues arising from carcinoma of the islet cells have been shown to contain insulin. (7) The injection of anterior pituitary extracts

leads to destructive changes in the islet cells, chiefly in the $\beta$-cells, while there is little or no effect on the $\alpha$-cells. (8) Alloxan and other chemical substances destroy the cells of the islands of Langerhans, leaving the other cells essentially intact. The pancreases from a number of dogs treated with diabetogenic materials have been assayed for their insulin content, and the values obtained were roughly proportional to the concentration of granules in the $\beta$-cells as determined by histological studies of these tissues. Good agreement between the amount of extractable insulin and the size and number of granules in the $\beta$-cells of human pancreas has also been obtained (Hartroft and Wrenshall).

## CHEMISTRY OF INSULIN

Insulin was first isolated in crystalline form by J. J. Abel in 1926. In 1934, D. A. Scott showed that it could be readily crystallized as the zinc salt and that Abel's crystals contained zinc. Nickel, calcium and cobalt also aid in effecting crystallization of insulin preparations. There is about 0.5 per cent of metal in the crystals. The "salts" of the insulin protein may appear in various forms—the zinc compound usually as twin platelike rhombohedra. Chemical analysis by Brand and by the Cambridge workers under the leadership of A. C. Chibnall indicates that the insulin molecule is built up entirely or almost entirely of amino acids. Insulin is richer in the amino acids leucine, glutamic acid, and cystine than most other proteins; methionine, tryptophane and hydroxyproline, which are common in many proteins, are absent from the insulin molecule (fig. 48.3).

The maximum molecular weight of insulin is 48,000; pH 7.0 to 7.5; protein concentration 0.4 to 0.9 per cent. However, when more dilute solutions of the hormone are used below pH 4 or above 7.5 the insulin molecule dissociates into subunits having a molecular weight of about 12.000 (Gutfreund). The single insulin molecule has a weight of 5733 (Harfenist and Craig; Sanger).

When insulin is oxidized with performic acid the molecule is split into its separate polypeptide chains. Two fractions can be isolated: A, an acidic fraction containing no basic amino acids and B, a basic fraction. These two physiologically *inactive* components are joined by disulfide linkages. Sanger made a great contribution by introducing the use of partial hydrolysis of dinitrophenyl derivatives of the fractions to determine the sequence of the amino acid components. He had available the invaluable tool of paper chromatography of Martin and Synge and the newer knowledge of the chemical linkages attached by specific enzyme systems, such as pepsin, trypsin and chymotrypsin. The exact sequence of all the amino acids in the two chains of insulin is now known but we are still far removed from the knowledge of how the chains are formed and joined together in the beta cells of the islets (fig. 48.4).

When a dilute acidic solution of insulin containing a small amount of salt is heated, a flocculant precipitate forms. In experiments in which slightly different conditions were used, Waugh has shown that the insulin can be modified to yield fibrils. The rate of fibril formation increases with increasing hydrogen ion, salt and protein concentration, and with temperature. In fibril formation two reactions are involved. First the formation of active centers, and second the elongation of these into fibrils. These fibrils have little or no antidiabetic activity but can be converted into active insulin, as can the so-called heat precipitate of insulin, by changing the reaction to the alkaline side. Seeding an insulin solution with fibrils may bring about a complete conversion of the active insulin into inactive fibrils.

Slightly acidified insulin has been kept for long periods, but in dilute alkali insulin is relatively unstable. Various attempts have been made to ascertain if there is in the molecule a specific grouping of certain of the amino acids which is really responsible for its hormonal activity. It may be concluded that the physiological activity of

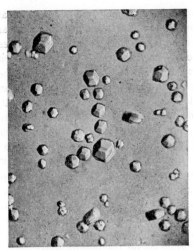

Zinc Insulin Crystals

N-amylamine Insulin Crystals
(Kindness of Dr. D. A. Scott)
Fig. 48.3

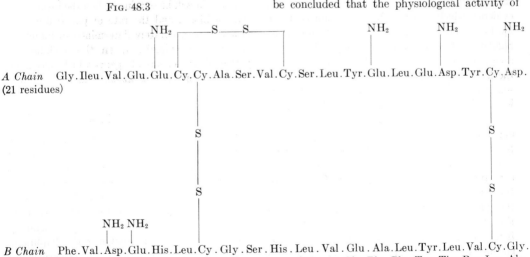

Fig. 48.4. The structure of beef insulin. (Sanger, F., Thompson, E. O. P. and Kitai, R., Biochem. J., **59,** 509, 1955.)

insulin may be slightly and sometimes reversibly decreased by certain minor chemical changes in the molecule, whereas appreciable chemical alteration gives a considerable diminution or complete absence of activity. Other changes have been suggested, such as the action of sulfhydryl groupings, as in glutathione, which may reduce the cystine disulfide linkage, a change which is known to be accompanied by inactivation.

### STANDARDIZATION OF INSULIN

Zinc insulin crystals from all sources so far examined (man, cattle, hog, sheep, bison, fish) have the same potency. The fourth international standard, a preparation of zinc insulin crystals, contains 24 units per mg. There are two well established methods of assaying the potency of an insulin preparation. The lowering of blood sugar in fasting rabbits and the production of convulsions in fasting mice are both satisfactory effects of insulin for the comparison of unknown and standard products. This new international yardstick of insulin is free of glucagon.

### LIBERATION OF INSULIN

The arrangement of the capillary loops about the islet cells and the reported scarcity of lymph channels provide morphological evidence in favor of the capillary blood stream as the pathway by which insulin reaches the systemic circulation. It is important to remember that insulin passes first to the liver, but there is no proof that this tissue takes advantage of this favorable arrangement.

Although there are many pieces of experimental evidence which support the conclusion that the level of blood sugar is an important factor in the regulation of insulin liberation, the possibility that a decrease in the rate of discharge of sugar from the liver may also be produced when the blood sugar is raised, is frequently overlooked. This latter effect is apparently produced by a direct action on liver cells. The injection of small amounts of glucose into the artery supplying a pancreas grafted into the neck of a depancreatized dog or into the pancreatic artery in a decerebrate cat causes a prompt lowering of blood sugar. In this latter case the effect was not obtained when the splenic or portal vein was used. The production of hyperglycemia, glycogen infiltration of the beta cells of the islets and permanent diabetes by the intraperitoneal administration of glucose (Lukens and Dohan) strongly suggests an overstimulation of pancreatic islets by the raised blood sugar level. Anderson and Long have demonstrated an output of insulin from perfused rat pancreas when dextrose was added to the perfusion fluid and Lukens and his group have obtained similar results in the dog. The results of experiments with denervated pancreatic grafts indicate that the nervous control is not essential. The nerve impulses which affect the islet cells are apparently conducted in part, at least, by the vagus. Vagus fibers have been traced to the islet cells and nonmedullated branches are said to pierce them. The results of stimulating the vagus *appeared* to be clear cut and the pathway was traced by one group of investigators to the hypothalamic region, but other workers have as yet been unable to confirm these findings. There may, of course, be a constant liberation of a small amount of insulin.

Information on the factors controlling the secretion of insulin has accumulated very slowly. The finding of Houssay, Foglia and their collaborators that two or three pancreases from normal dogs, when introduced in series into the carotid-jugular circulation of a depancreatized dog, produce no more effect than one pancreas, is strongly indicative of a chemical control of insulin liberation. These workers have studied the rate of liberation of insulin from the pancreas of hypophysectomized dogs, and of dogs made transiently or permanently diabetic by anterior pituitary extracts. The findings in general conform to those obtained by studying the insulin content of pancreas in relation to the state of carbohydrate metabolism of the animal (p. 825). Neither of these methods yields information as valuable as that which will be obtained when the insulin content of blood, and the rate of pancreatic blood flow can be accurately determined in intact unanesthetized animals. When this technique is perfected, the effects of agents which may affect the level of plasma insulin can be carefully studied.

### INSULIN IN BLOOD

As a result of the work of Gellhorn, Anderson, Bornstein, Groen, Tuerkischer and Wertheimer, and their collaborators, methods for estimating the amount of insulin in blood are now available. These depend on the blood sugar response of hypophysectomized, adrenalectomized, alloxan-diabetic rats or mice or on the increase in sugar uptake of segments of isolated rat's diaphragm. While few laboratories have the necessary procedures readily available some interesting results have been obtained. The value for normal human blood was approximately $4 \times 10^{-6}$ mg. per cc., i.e., $\frac{1}{250}$ µg. per cc. Some insulin can be detected in the blood of most maturity-onset diabetics but none in the blood of growth-onset, i.e., childhood, diabetics (Lawrence and Bornstein). These findings are in accord with Wrenshall's reports on extractable insulin from the pancreas in these two groups of diabetics.

In recent years as a result of the work of Randle and of Vallance-Owen, who use the rat diaphragm technique, and of Renold and his colleagues, who use the epididymal fat pad of the rat, this field has become much more active. Plasma insulin is low in cases of hypopituitarism, high in acromegalics and in hyperinsulinism. The administration of dextrose, of somatotropin and possibly of the hypoglycemic sulfonamides increases plasma insulin.

## GENERAL EFFECTS OF INSULIN ON THE DIABETIC ORGANISM

It is well established that insulin restores to the depancreatized animal its ability to utilize sugars and fats in a normal manner. The excessive breakdown of protein is prevented. The ketosis rapidly disappears. Glycogen is deposited in large amounts in the liver. Muscle glycogen may be increased. The respiratory quotient rises when sugar is made available, or in fact when insulin alone is administered. Animals recover their ability to deal with infective agents. In brief, a well-treated depancreatized animal is difficult to distinguish from a normal one. There has been the difficulty, of course, that in the animal without a pancreas relatively large amounts of insulin are made available (by subcutaneous or intravenous injection) while in the intact animal small or large amounts are presumably liberated from the pancreas as the need arises. Adult depancreatized dogs on an adequate diet including the enzymes of the external secretion of pancreas have been maintained in good condition for more than six years (Macleod; Hédon; Bliss; Fisher; Wrenshall).

## THE MECHANISM OF ACTION OF INSULIN

In both the diabetic and the normal animal the level of blood sugar is lowered by the administration of insulin. The sugar is not used in the blood itself but its rate of passage out into the tissues is accelerated.

GLYCOGEN STORAGE. Small amounts of glycogen may be deposited in the muscles and liver of the depancreatized dog when no insulin is given but the administration of insulin produces a dramatic increase in the rate of deposition in both these tissues. Stetten's work using deuterium as a tracer, indicates that the diabetic organism makes its liver glycogen from three carbon compounds (lactic acid) while the normal or insulin treated animal uses largely the six carbon compound (dextrose). In the normal animal one of the most clear cut effects of insulin is the increase in the rate of glycogen deposition in the muscle. It is obvious that insulin also promotes glycogen storage in the liver of the normal animal and this situation should not be confused with the results of adding more insulin to an already normal supply. In the normal adult animal there may be an actual loss of glycogen from the liver when extra insulin is administered. This may be due to the accelerated glycogen deposition in muscle, a process which has a high priority in the disposition of sugar, to the presence of glucagon in the insulin used, or to the increased rate at which fat is formed and sugar oxidized. These latter processes would decrease the amount of sugar available for storage as glycogen in the liver. The liver slice is not a good preparation for the study of glycogen formation.

The action of insulin can be well demonstrated in eviscerated and in isolated perfused preparations such as the hind limbs of the cat or dog. Dextrose must be supplied. Very great use has been made of the finding by Gemmill in 1940 that the rat diaphragm *in vitro* takes up more sugar and forms more glycogen when insulin is added. As little as 0.1 unit of insulin per kilo will double the diaphragmatic glycogen in the fasting adreno-demedullated rat. Nelson (1944) demonstrated the inhibiting effect of a prior *injection* of anterior pituitary extract. The isolated rat diaphragm does not respond to insulin with an increased use of oxygen but the skeletal muscle from the same species does.

There is an increase in the glycogen of heart after removal of insulin from the body (Cruickshank). The renal tubules exhibit a deposition in the diabetic state which may be related to the increase in sugar which they are attempting to reabsorb. The beta cells in the islands of the pancreas show glycogen infiltration (Duff and Toreson) in the diabetic organism. This used to be termed hydropic degeneration.

ON FAT METABOLISM. In the depancreatized animal insulin decreases the lipemia and cholesterolemia and prevents the deposition of the large amounts of excess fat which accumulate in the liver in the untreated animal. The level of the ketone bodies in the blood is restored to normal.

The fact that insulin increases the formation of fat has been obvious ever since the first emaciated dog or diabetic patient demonstrated a fine pad of adipose tissue, made as a result of treatment with the hormone. This effect was not perceptible in short term experiments without the aid of tracers and the disappearance of sugar was usually attributed to oxidation or perhaps in part to decreased gluconeogenesis. Using the technique of isotopic tracers, Stetten has calculated that in the well nourished rat only about 3 per cent of the glucose ingested each day is converted to glycogen, while 30 per cent is used to make fatty acids. In the absence of insulin the diabetic animal exhibits a much lower level of lipogenesis, as well as of glycogenesis.

In 1948 Bloch and Kramer were the first to demonstrate an *in vitro* effect of insulin on fat formation. Liver slices incubated in the presence of pyruvate and labelled acetate showed incorporation of the label into fatty acids and this process was enhanced by prior administration of insulin. This work has been strongly supported and extended by Gurin with Brady and Lukens and by Chaikoff and his group. Thus we learn that insulin has widespread effects on fat formation and mobilization. It promotes lipogenesis from glucose and acetate in the liver and in many extrahepatic tissues. It prevents the loss of depot fat and the accumulation of fatty deposits in the liver. It suppresses ketosis by inhibiting the formation of ketone bodies. It is probable that these different effects of insulin are closely interrelated and that they are all linked with its action on the oxidation of glucose, i.e., lipogenesis is dependent on glycolysis. The effect of insulin on the unesterified fatty acids of the blood plasma is discussed under fat metabolism (ch. 49).

ON PROTEIN METABOLISM. The early work on insulin in Toronto demonstrated that insulin reduced the elevated nitrogen excretion characteristic of the diabetic state. In 1926 Janney and Shapiro noted a fall in blood urea and nonprotein nitrogen of normal human subjects given insulin and other investigators found a fall in blood amino acids in animals and man. In a classical study Mirsky showed that insulin decreased the rate of protein catabolism in the nephrectomized dog. Chaikoff and Forker in extension of F. N. Allan's original findings established a linear relation between insulin dose and nitrogen retention in depancreatized dogs. The evidence obtained by Forker, by Lotspeich, and by Sinex, MacMullen and Hastings indicates that insulin encourages the incorporation of labelled amino acids into protein. Krahl has reported the incorporation of $C^{14}$ labelled glycine into glutathione and into protein in liver slices. This process is greatly reduced in diabetes but is restored to normal by insulin. The evidence suggests that insulin stimulates peptide synthesis rather than inhibiting breakdown. Sinex and associates, Krahl, and Manchester and Young have provided evidence that the incorporation of amino acids into the protein of isolated rat diaphragm is augmented by insulin in the absence of added carbohydrate. These findings suggest that this action of insulin is largely independent of a stimulation of carbohydrate metabolism. It may be produced by either or both of two mechanisms, (1) increasing intracellular protein synthesis, or (2) accelerating the transfer of amino acids across the cell membrane.

The literature records that Mirsky, Young, Gaebler, Lotspeich, Frame and Russell, and Lukens in distinct investigations have agreed that the presence of insulin is essential for the protein anabolic effect of the pituitary growth hormone, somatotropin. There is now direct evidence that an increased secretion of insulin occurs in response to somatotropin in several species of normal animals. Somatotropin has little anabolic effects in the complete absence of insulin and recent work has shown that insulin can stimulate growth, i.e., nitrogen retention, bone growth, fat formation, etc., in the complete absence of somatotropin (Salter and Best). Normal growth undoubtedly requires the coordinated action of somatotropin, insulin and the other hormones.

ON OXIDATION OF SUGAR. The interpretation of most of the early work on this subject was confused by the lack of a suitably labelled dextrose. In 1949 Villee and Hastings found that insulin increased the oxidation of glucose as judged by the rate of appearance of the carbon label in the $CO_2$ formed by the isolated rat diaphragm. Similar results have been secured by Sacks and Sinex who found that insulin increased the turnover of isotopic phosphorus in various phosphorus compounds, the deposition of $C^{14}$-labelled glucose as glycogen, and the oxidation of glucose. Feller, Chaikoff and associates, using $C^{14}$-glucose have established that the rate of utilization was reduced to half the normal value in dogs by removal of insulin and restored completely by giving the hormone. Using $C^{14}$-labelled glucose in eviscerated rabbits Wick, Drury, Bancroft, and MacKay were able to distinguish between the glucose oxidized and the total amount which disappeared. When insulin was given there was a delayed, but large, increase in the labelled carbon of the expired air and therefore in the amount of glucose oxidized. The rest of the labelled carbon was found in glycogen, fatty acids, proteins, and in nonglucose water-soluble compounds.

ON CELL PERMEABILITY. The suggestion that a key point in the action of insulin may be on the permeability of muscle cells to glucose has been revived and strongly supported by Levine and Goldstein. This view has been supported by Drury and Wick who interpret their evidence to indicate that insulin is not an oxidative catalyst and by Mirsky, who finds that entry into cells does not depend on the molecular configuration of the sugar as previous authors had suggested. Park, Bornstein, Post and Johnson have found an increase in the intracellular content of glucose after insulin administration and this finding favors an action on the cell membrane rather than one on intracellular enzymes. These authors and Randle and Smith have noted an increased glucose uptake of isolated rat diaphragm by procedures which inhibit oxidative phosphorylation. Insulin does not inhibit oxidative phosphorylation (Stadie). Randle and Smith suggest that insulin may promote glucose uptake by diaphragm by preventing access to the process regulating glucose entry of some substance generated during oxidative phosphorylation. Shaw and Stadie have suggested that glucose may be utilized partly at the cell surface and partly within the cell.

THE COMBINATION OF INSULIN WITH TISSUES. Stadie and his colleagues have obtained evidence to support their working hypothesis that insulin and other hormones must form a rather firm chemical compound with the intact cells on which they act. Isolated rat diaphragm dipped for a few seconds in a solution of insulin fixes insulin which reveals itself by increased utilization of sugar by the tissue. Diabetic tissue has a decreased ability to bind insulin. Growth hormone and cortisone inhibit this combination of insulin with muscle cells. Insulin injected into the living animal and much much higher concentrations in the fluid bathing the diaphragm *in vitro* lead to the binding of about the same effective amounts of insulin. Mammary and adipose tissue also bind insulin.

INSULIN AS A GROWTH HORMONE. The various anabolic effects of insulin show that it possesses some of the characteristics of a growth hormone. True growth, including lengthening of the epiphyseal discs, can be elicited in completely hy-pophysectomized animals by giving gradually increasing amounts of slow acting insulin (Salter and Best). While it had been known that young hypophysectomized animals may grow for a time after removal of the pituitary (Selye and Collip), and while it had been suggested that growth hormone liberates insulin (Young), proof that hypophysectomized rats, which had in some cases not grown for months, could be made to resume growth by insulin had not been previously secured. When hypophysectomized rats are force-fed (Scow) or made hyperphagic by hypothalamic puncture (Kennedy) endogenous insulin is presumably liberated and this may be an essential factor for the growth and nitrogen retention observed. Under these circumstances the effect of exogenous insulin may not be demonstrable, i.e., an optimal concentration of insulin may already be present.

ON PHOSPHATE AND POTASSIUM. Insulin produces a dramatic fall in the inorganic phosphate of blood plasma (Harrop). Ingestion of glucose or injection of adrenaline has the same effect but not in the absence of the pancreas. Levine, Loube and Weisberg (1949) have shown that the intravenous administration of fructose to untreated depancreatized dogs consistently produces a fall in blood inorganic phosphate. The change in phosphate is apparently a consequence of the rapid entry of hexoses into cells. Insulin is necessary for the entry of glucose but not of fructose. After insulin there may be a rise in the hexose monophosphate of muscle. This is an indirect effect apparently due to adrenaline liberation and a stimulation by it of phosphorylase action on glycogen and the formation of the first breakdown product, glucose-1-phosphate. Insulin does not significantly change the amount of adenosine triphosphate (ATP), phosphocreatine, or inorganic phosphate in muscle. There may be a rise in the ATP fraction of liver. The rate of turnover or regeneration of these phosphate compounds is increased by insulin and this is probably an index of the increased rate of phosphorylation of sugar which is, as we have seen, an indispensable preliminary step in its metabolism. The free energy for this change is made available by the conversion of ATP to adenosine diphosphate (ADP) plus a high energy phosphate grouping. This phosphorylation of glucose then permits glucose to make available the free energy which it possesses. New molecules of ATP are provided as a result of subsequent steps in the anaerobic breakdown of glucose.

Bornstein and Park in Cori's laboratory have found that serum from alloxan-diabetic rats inhibits the uptake of glucose *in vitro* by the diaphragm of normal fasted rats. Removal of either the adrenals or pituitary from the diabetic rat eliminates this inhibitory effect of its serum, and the injection of both growth hormone and cortisone restores the effect. These findings, therefore, suggest that the insulin-reversible inhibitor of glucose uptake is formed as the product of joint pituitary and adrenal activity. Studies will undoubtedly soon be made on the sera of diabetic patients.

Various changes in the concentration of the metallic constituents of the blood have been reported after insulin injection. These, and particularly that in the concentration of potassium, suggest a fundamental relationship between electrolyte and carbohydrate metabolism. The decrease in blood sugar produced by insulin is accompanied by a simultaneous fall in potassium.

It is now well established that the administration of insulin lowers the insulin content of the pancreas in fasting or fed animals. Furthermore it protects the islet cells against the degenerative changes which occur after the removal of a large part of the pancreas. Similarly the degenerative changes in the islets and the loss of insulin content produced by the administration of the diabetogenic substance of the anterior pituitary gland are prevented if insulin is supplied. If, after the diabetic state has been produced in partially depancreatized cats by administration of diabetogenic preparations, insulin is given in adequate amounts, the diabetes may disappear. Thus insulin under these experimental conditions can both prevent and cure diabetes (Haist, Campbell and Best; Lukens and Dohan).

## INTERFERENCE WITH THE ACTION OF INSULIN

*Other hormones.* There are five internal secretions the action of which may be considered to be antagonistic to that of insulin. There is no evidence of any chemical interaction of these hormones with the antidiabetic substance.

*Enzymes.* Insulin is destroyed by pepsin-HCl and by the activated proteolytic pancreatic enzyme, chymotrypsin. Crystalline trypsin does not destroy insulin. I. A. Mirsky and his colleagues have shown that the liver and to a lesser extent other tissues contain a factor which is capable of inactivating insulin and a second one which inhibits this action. These factors are referred to as insulinase and insulinase-inhibitor. Their physio-

logical significance is not established but their presence suggests the possibility that an increased rate of destruction of insulin as well as a decreased formation must be considered.

*Reaction of tissues.* Since insulin acts on the cells of the liver and muscles, factors which influence these tissues, acidosis for example, may modify insulin action. Furthermore, since the liver is so largely responsible for the regulation of blood sugar, influences affecting this organ may cause a change in sugar content quite apart from the action of insulin. A change in the acid-base equilibrium of the body toward the acid side renders injected insulin less effective, a change toward the alkaline makes insulin more effective.

*Products of infection.* The toxic products elaborated by many microörganisms may interfere with the action of insulin. There is experimental evidence (1) that the insulin content of pancreas is decreased in certain severe infections but this does not necessarily indicate a decreased rate of liberation of the hormone, (2) that the suprarenal and thyroid glands are stimulated to release more of their internal secretions,[2] (3) that the synthesis of glycogen from lactic acid in the liver is inhibited and (4) it now appears that normally liver glycogen is changed to glucose by glucose-6-phosphatase. Amylase, which splits glycogen to dextrins, maltose and finally to glucose, does not have access to the liver cells. When certain toxins are administered, however, amylase activity can be demonstrated and this abnormal route of glycogen breakdown provides another mechanism by which the products of infection make the organism resistant to the action of insulin. Insulin has no effect on the activity of amylase. Certain toxins may act on one or more of these mechanisms but investigation of this field is still in the preliminary stages.

*Anesthetics.* All anesthetics interfere somewhat with the action of insulin. More or less asphyxia is produced by all general anesthetics. In asphyxia (1) adrenaline is liberated and (2) acid products tend to accumulate. Chloralose and amytal cause the least disturbance of carbohydrate metabolism.

## INSULIN REQUIREMENT AND ADMINISTRATION

Interesting studies have been made of the insulin requirements of depancreatized dogs under different conditions. Thus the blood sugar has

---

[2] The first effects of the products of infection may be to excite liver tissue to increased gluconeogenesis and discharge of glucose. Later the liver cells may be damaged so that less glucose is produced.

been kept at a normal level by simultaneous and continuous intravenous injection of insulin and dextrose solutions. The insulin required was between 0.06 and 0.4 units per kg. per hour, while the corresponding requirement of dextrose was 0.2 and 0.6 gm. per kg. per hour. The higher values for insulin and dextrose were those required by unanesthetized dogs; the others by anesthetized dogs. In another study the amount of insulin necessary to keep the blood sugar at a normal value in depancreatized dogs under basal conditions was between 0.005 and 0.035 units per kg. per hour, with an average value of 0.017 units per kg. per hour. The duration of action of insulin is not proportional to the size of the dose injected but is a simple function of the logarithm of the dose; i.e., insulin is inactivated in the body at a rate proportional to the amount in the body at the time. Thus if 1 unit lasts four hours, 10 units would last eight hours. It is established that the completely depancreatized human subject may require less insulin than many "spontaneous" diabetics. Similarly, the alloxan-diabetic dog may require more insulin than the depancreatized. There are three obvious possibilities to be advanced in explanation. (1) The absorption of food is reduced by removal of the pancreas. Comparisons should be made on the same levels of nutrition. (2) The $\alpha$-cells of the pancreas elaborate an antagonist of insulin, glucagon. (3) The alloxan or the *meta*-pituitary diabetic may and frequently does have some pancreatic insulin available. This may be liberated more physiologically than exogenous insulin and thus help to maintain the organism in a condition which creates a demand for more insulin.

Insulin may be administered effectively by the subcutaneous or intravenous route. Some absorption may be obtained by inunction or by application to the sublingual or other mucous surfaces. Rectal administration is ineffective. Studies continue to be made on the problem of the oral administration of insulin. Efforts have been made to combine it with various materials, dyes, phenolic substances, tannic acid, etc. which might protect the protein molecule from destruction by the intestinal enzymes. The difficulties involved are obvious, and it is therefore not surprising that, while some success has attended these efforts in the laboratory, no satisfactory application to the treatment of diabetic patients has yet been made.

### MODIFIED INSULIN

One of the most obvious difficulties in the use of regular insulin in clinical diabetes is its transient and sometimes too violent action. This difficulty has been much more frequently encountered since the highly purified preparations of insulin have been made available. The cruder products were absorbed more slowly. While a great many attemps have been made to slow and prolong the action of insulin, the first important success has been obtained by Hagedorn, Jensen, Krarup and Wodstrup. These investigators have shown that a compound of insulin with any one of several protamines exerts a slower and more prolonged anti-diabetic effect than regular insulin. This has been shown by microscopic observation (Beecher and Krogh) to be due to the much slower absorption of the insulin combined with protamine than is the case with the regular preparations of this substance.

Completely depancreatized dogs may be maintained sugar free, while receiving a very liberal diet, on one dose of protamine insulin daily without the development of any hypoglycemic reactions (Kerr and Best).

Scott and Fisher demonstrated that protamine insulin is greatly improved by the addition of a small amount of zinc. The resulting product, protamine zinc insulin, exerts a more prolonged hypoglycemic action and forms a much more stable suspension than protamine insulin.

Various other forms of modified insulin have been prepared and tested clinically. Histone insulin and globin insulin are examples. Protamine zinc insulin has been prepared in crystalline form (Hagedorn) and free insulin is stable when added to this compound. Zinc insulin preparations, without protamine, exerting a prolonged action, have recently been made available by Hallas-Møller and associates.

### Hypoglycemia

Under certain exceptional circumstances hypoglycemia may be produced by excessive utilization of glucose (prolonged very violent muscular exercise) but interference with the formation of sugar in the liver is largely responsible for most types. The three main factors which diminish sugar production may be classified as follows: (1) abnormality of liver cells, (2) the inhibiting action of insulin on gluconeogenesis in the liver, and (3) the decreased hepatic gluconeogenesis resulting from diminished output of the anterior pituitary, thyroid, or cortical and medullary adrenal secretions. Under the first heading a great variety of experimental and clinical conditions may be listed —for example—phosphorus or hydrazine poison-

TABLE 48.1

*Spontaneous hypoglycemia or dysinsulinism*

| Hyperinsulinism:* (Hyperactivity or Tumor of Islands of Langerhans) | Interference with Gluconeogenesis in Liver | Hypofunction of Anterior Pituitary Adrenals or Thyroid |
|---|---|---|
| *In experimental animals:* Hypertrophy after duct ligation? Hypertrophy after anterior pituitary extracts? No tumors carefully studied | *In experimental animals:* Hepatectomy Interference with arterial blood flow Poisoning: Phosphorus Chloroform Hydrazine Synthalin, etc. Deposition of fat | *In experimental animals:* Removal of pituitary (anterior lobe) Removal of adrenals Removal of thyroid Hypoglycemia (or increased susceptibility to insulin) |
| *Clinical observations:* Cases of hyperplasia and hypertrophy Cases of tumor | *Clinical observations:* Hepatitis Carcinomata Yellow fever Acute yellow atrophy Poisoning: Phosphorus Carbon tetrachloride Benzol Chloroform Synthalin, etc. Surgical interference with blood flow | *Clinical observations:* Hypoglycemia in so-called pituitary cachexia or Simmond's disease Hypoglycemia in Addison's disease (some cases) Increased susceptibility to insulin after thyroidectomy |

There may also be excessive utilization of sugar by muscles—dogs in tread mill, marathon runners, etc.

* The term "hyperinsulinism" was introduced by Seale Harris in 1924 to describe cases exhibiting signs of hypoglycemia. The first report of a tumor of the islet cells which in this case had secondary growths in the liver was made by Wilder, Allan, Power and Robertson in 1927. Many cases of tumor have now been studied. A histological section from the first tumor successfully removed is shown in fig. 48.5.

ing, yellow fever, acute yellow atrophy, and the bacterial infections. When the normal liver is completely removed, profound hypoglycemia occurs promptly. Approximately 80 per cent of the normal liver must be removed before hypoglycemia is produced. Under the second heading we may consider *hyperinsulinism.* This term should be reserved for conditions in which it is established that there is liberation of excessive amounts of insulin from the pancreas. This has been the case in numerous instances in which the removal of a tumor of islet cells has corrected the hypoglycemia. Correction of the condition by removal of a large part of the pancreas does not prove that the cause was liberation of abnormal amounts of insulin since decreasing the amount of insulin may merely compensate for the first abnormality. The relative importance of the three glands of internal secretion listed under the third heading may vary in different species. Removal of the thyroid increases the sensitivity of an animal to insulin and the same is true of the adrenal medulla, but hypoglycemia is not produced. When the anterior pituitary is extirpated, however, there may be profound hypoglycemia and this finding suggests that diminished secretion of the diabetogenic substance may be an important factor in certain clinical cases in which the liver and pancreas appear perfectly normal. In some species removal of the whole adrenal gland causes hypoglycemia and this is, at least partially, corrected by the administration of cortical extract. Clinically certain cases of Simmond's disease (diminished anterior pituitary secretion) and of Addison's disease (involvement of adrenal cortex) may exhibit hypoglycemia. (See table 48.1 and fig. 48.5).

## SIGNS AND SYMPTOMS

The signs of hypoglycemia were first adequately described by Mann and his collaborators. The low blood sugars were produced in dogs by removal of the liver. The description of this condition enabled the Toronto investigators to recognize that the effects of large doses of insulin were the same as those due to hypoglycemia produced by other means. The signs and symptoms vary in the different species. The first signs in the rabbit are hyperexcitability and desire for food. The excitability becomes greater, and mild and then severe convulsions are exhibited. The head is retracted and the hind limbs extended in the intervals between convulsive seizures. Coma is frequent. The animals may exhibit rigor mortis immediately after death. The signs in dogs are quite similar. Mice, in some instances, may become comatose without exhibiting convulsions. Cold blooded animals do not show any signs until many hours or even days after insulin injections.[3] The signs and symptoms in man have been extensively studied in the laboratory and clinic. The initial symptoms may be hunger or a feeling of nervousness—a sense of impending danger. A little later there may be profuse perspiration, alternate pallor and flushing of the face, vertigo and diplopia. The blood sugar at this stage is 0.06 to 0.04 per cent but the level varies greatly in different individuals. Most hypoglycemic reactions proceed no further than this. In very severe cases there may be delirium, convulsions, and death. The true blood sugar may decrease until only nonsugar-reducing power remains.

Sakel's insulin-shock treatment for schizophrenia has focussed attention on the metabolism of brain and the effects of prolonged hypoglycemia. Brain tissue utilizes carbohydrate almost exclusively. Hypoglycemia interferes with the supply and produces much the same condition as $O_2$ deficiency. The electrical activity of the cerebral cortex is depressed in hypoglycemia and restored to normal by the administration of glucose. The reduction in the oxidative metabolism of brain is undoubtedly responsible for this and other changes.

Cerebral damage, which may be permanent, has been observed in both animals and man as a result of prolonged hypoglycemia.

### ALLEVIATION OF HYPOGLYCEMIA

The intravenous administration of glucose is the most effective method of alleviating hypoglycemia. The prompt recovery of almost moribund animals provides one of physiology's most fascinating demonstrations. Mannose is almost as useful as glucose, and fructose also occupies a preferential position. Galactose and maltose have a slight but transient effect. Sucrose,[4] lactose and pentoses are not effective. Glycogen and glycerol have been shown to exert some beneficial action. The effect of these substances in hypoglycemia is probably largely dependent on the rapidity with which they are transformed into glucose in the

[3] Similar prolonged delay may be observed in mammals after injection of huge doses of insulin.
[4] Carbohydrates which form glucose are, of course, effective. The above statement refers to the results of intravenous injections.

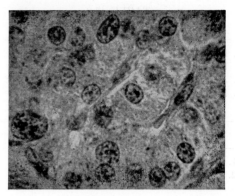

Fig. 48.5. Photomicrograph of adenoma of pancreatic islets associated with clinical hypoglycemia. This tumor illustrated was the first to be surgically removed. Hematoxylin and eosin stain × 1000. From Howland, G., Campbell, W. R., Maltby, E. J., and Robinson, W. L., J.A.M.A., *93:* 674–79, 1929.

liver. Fructose may be converted slowly to glucose in muscle but there is a possibility that it may be burned directly (Griffiths and Waters). It is generally assumed that the only sugar directly oxidized in the muscle, where a large part of the total oxygen use takes place, is *d*-glucose. The usefulness of the other carbohydrates would therefore depend on the ease of their conversion into this sugar. Adrenaline and pituitrin may be used to alleviate hypoglycemia but glucose is much more efficacious and safe. Liberation of adrenaline is, however, one of the physiological mechanisms by which hypoglycemia is corrected. Intense anger, such as that which might well be experienced by a diabetic whose hypoglycemia was mistaken for alcoholic intoxication (Duncan) may correct hypoglycemia through liberation of adrenaline.

### The Insulin Content of the Pancreas under Different Conditions

The insulin content of the pancreas has been determined in various animal species. The insulin is extracted from minced pancreases with an acid aqueous alcohol solution. Certain contaminating material is removed and the active material is precipitated. This is then redissolved and estimated by the mouse method of assay. In the dog the insulin content of the free splenic end of the pancreas is greatest, that of the attached duodenal portion has an intermediate value, while that of the free duodenal end is lowest, the values being about 4, 3, and 2 units per gram, respectively. In

TABLE 48.2

*Factors depressing islet growth*

1. Restriction of caloric intake.
   Restriction of carbohydrate intake.
2. Administration of large amounts of insulin.
3. Removal of the pituitary gland.

*Factors increasing islet growth*

| | Intact | Hypox |
|---|---|---|
| 1. High carbohydrate intake. | | |
| 2. Continuous injection of glucose. | | |
| 3. Injections of anterior pituitary extract............... | + | + |
| 4. Injections of growth hormone preparations.............. | + | + |
| 5. Injections of ACTH......... | + | + |
| 6. Injections of cortisone...... | + | + |
| 7. Thyroid administration...... | + | + |
| 8. Estradiol benzoate.......... | + | † |
| 9. Diethylstilbestrol.......... | + | † |
| 10. Progesterone................. | + | † |
| 11. Testosterone................ | * | † |

From R. E. Haist.
* Not significant.
† Not done.

partially depancreatized dogs, provided sufficient pancreas is left to prevent the onset of diabetes, the insulin content does not differ from that of the corresponding part in a normal dog, nor are any degenerative changes in the $\beta$-cells noted. If diabetes supervenes, hydropic degeneration of these cells is observed, and the insulin content of the remnant of pancreas falls to extremely low values. The daily injection into dogs of diabetogenic extracts from the anterior lobe of the pituitary gland produces a prompt and profound decrease in the insulin content of the pancreas (in seven days to 0.2 units per gram). If the injections are stopped at this stage, the insulin content is restored to normal within four days. If the administration is continued the insulin is reduced to negligible amounts. No recovery will occur when this point is reached. Simultaneous administration of insulin prevents or greatly modifies the fall in the insulin stores. This fact strongly suggests that the $\beta$-cells are permanently damaged by the extract through overwork and that the simultaneous administration of insulin relieves the cells of some of this excessive demand for the hormone.

Starvation (seven days) or a diet rich in fat produces a decrease in the insulin content of the rat's pancreas to about half the normal value, which is about $2\frac{1}{2}$ units per rat. These animals have their insulin stores speedily restored to normal (in six days) when they are returned to a balanced diet; carbohydrate alone effects a partial restoration. Daily injection of insulin into rats causes an even more marked decrease in the insulin content of the pancreas than does starvation (Haist and Best). Massive doses of insulin over prolonged periods may produce atrophic changes in the pancreatic islets of partially depancreatized dogs which survive the treatment (Mirsky).

The injection of anterior pituitary extracts in certain strains of rats increases the islet volume and the insulin content of pancreas (Young, Richardson and Marks). In other strains there is no increase in insulin content.

The factors which affect the volume (growth) of the $\beta$-cells of the pancreas are given in table 48.2.

Subcutaneous estrogen transplants or the administration of stilbestrol produce an increase in the insulin content of rat's pancreas. This effect is not observed in the absence of the pituitary (Griffiths, Marks and Young; Funk). Stilbestrol may exert a diabetogenic effect in force-fed normal and partially depancreatized rats, and under these conditions Ingle has been able to demonstrate diabetogenic effects of all the estrogens. Under more physiological conditions Houssay, Foglia, Martinez and their colleagues have demonstrated that the estrogenic substances decrease the incidence of diabetes in partially depancreatized rats—presumably by stimulation of the $\beta$-cells in the pancreatic remnant.

The effect of age on the insulin content of the pancreas has been studied in the cow. In fetal calves under 5 months the concentration was 34 units per gram; in calves 6 to 8 weeks old, 10 units per gram; in heifers 2 years old, 5 units per gram; in cows over 9 years, 2 units per gram. Pregnant cows 7 years old and older showed no change from the normal insulin content of about 2 units per gram (Scott and Fisher). In Wistar rats the total insulin content of the pancreas increases with age.

Pancreases obtained from nondiabetic persons at autopsy have an average insulin content of about 2 units per gram. This is probably somewhat lower than the true value. Pancreatic tissue from diabetic persons shows wide variations. The pancreas from diabetic children contains very little insulin. Pancreas from diabetic adults contains on the average some 40 per cent of the normal amount of insulin (Wrenshall). The insulin content of a tumor of islet tissue surgically removed from a patient suffering from hyperinsulinism may be as high as 214 units per gram.

It is, of course, apparent that these "insulin contents" indicate the balance between the rate of production of the hormone in the islets and the rate of liberation. There is good reason to believe that under certain conditions the rate of liberation is proportional to the content. Under other circumstances this is probably not true, but the rate of liberation of insulin can at present only be inferred from data which are susceptible of various interpretations. The conclusion has been drawn from some of these results, combined with histological studies, that the islet cells are "rested" after administration of insulin, by starvation and by a high fat diet and that less insulin is excreted by the pancreas than under normal conditions. Partial pancreatectomy, sufficiently extensive to result in diabetes, or administration of diabetogenic extracts causes (1) marked stimulation of the islets and (2) subsequent degenerative changes and loss of insulin.[5]

## The Use of Insulin in Nondiabetic Conditions

Favorable results have been claimed for the use of insulin in a very great variety of nondiabetic conditions. It has been used in pernicious anemia, in acute infectious diseases, in eclampsia, in pernicious vomiting of pregnancy, and in hepatitis—to mention only a few. While it is conceivable that insulin might be of slight benefit in some of these conditions, it would appear that equally satisfactory results can be secured by the administration of glucose alone. It is a clinical fact that the administration of glucose produces favorable results in a variety of hepatic abnormalities. A high glycogen content appears to protect the liver cells from damage and inhibition of gluconeogenesis produced by both insulin and glucose may also play a role.

Insulin can now be considered, however, an established adjuvant in the treatment of certain cases in which lack of appetite prevents the ingestion of adequate amounts of food. The physiological basis for this use of insulin in these nondiabetic individuals rests very largely upon the increase in hunger and appetite which may be caused by the administration of sufficient material to produce a definite but not too marked hypoglycemia. In 1924 Bulatao and Carlson reported that production of hypoglycemia in experimental

animals by the subcutaneous injection of insulin was uniformly accompanied by hypertonus and hypermotility of the stomach. The gastric tonicity and motility increase as the hypoglycemia deepens until complete tetanus is reached, which persists until the dog exhibits hypoglycemic convulsions or until sugar is given. The effect of sugar is immediate, but if a large dose of insulin has been given the hyperactivity of the stomach returns as soon as the blood sugar falls again. The first record of the increase in gastric peristalsis in the human individual after insulin administration was that of Dickson and Wilson, 1924. One hour and ten minutes after the administration of insulin the tone, depth and rate of peristalsis and rate of emptying of the stomach were definitely increased. This condition persisted for two hours, when the blood sugar was found to be 70 mg. per 100 cc. Glucose was then given, and while the acute symptoms were definitely relieved the hunger persisted. Subsequently Quigley, Johnson and Solomon studied the effect of insulin on the gastric movements of four human subjects. They found that doses of from 12 to 20 units of insulin definitely increased the gastric activity. The first definite augmentation was observed about an hour after the injection and persisted for at least five hours. There was prolonged duration of the hunger period, and this was considered to be the most characteristic effect of insulin. The increased peristalsis produced by insulin is not inhibited by such procedures as smoking, unpleasant emotions, body discomfort, or the presence of moderate amounts of noncarbohydrate food in the stomach. The increased movement was inhibited by atropine. The immediate relief of the excess peristalsis when appropriate amounts of glucose were given was confirmed. More recently Grossman and Stein have shown that the sensations of hunger induced by insulin, with the exception of the epigastric pangs of distress associated with individual gastric contractions, continue to occur after complete vagotomy in man.

It is known that insulin does not exert its effect on gastric motility and secretion after section of the vagus nerves. This means that either insulin acts centrally by stimulating the vagus, or that the continued elaboration of acetylcholine, which we now know is an essential part of the mechanism by which the vagus exerts its action, provides a foundation upon which the peripheral effects of insulin may be superimposed.

Insulin augments also, to some extent, peristaltic movement in the duodenum and in the colon,

---

[5] For references to work on insulin content of pancreas, see Haist, 1944 and Wrenshall, 1952.

but the effect is not as marked as in the case of the stomach. It will be remembered that one of the early symptoms observed in experimental animals and also in human subjects after the administration of insulin is an increase in hunger. In animals an attempt to consume material of little nutritive value which under ordinary conditions they would not attempt to eat is often observed. It would appear, therefore, that the clinician is able to take advantage of this situation by providing nutritious food for his hungry patient. The increase in weight observed in both animals and patients when appropriate doses of insulin are given for prolonged periods is due to increased deposition of fat, and to a lesser extent to increased deposition of carbohydrate and protein. The increase in weight is not attributable to unphysiological retention of water.

## Influence of Other Endocrine Glands on Carbohydrate Metabolism

### THE ADRENALS

The glucosuria produced by adrenaline was first noted by Blum. The intravenous route of administration gives the greatest rise of blood sugar but subcutaneous, intramuscular or intraperitoneal injections are effective. The immediate rise in the sugar of the blood is due to breakdown of liver glycogen to glucose. There may be a considerable decrease in the amount of liver glycogen. Adrenaline also mobilizes muscle glycogen (Cori) but here the immediate product is lactic acid and not glucose. A part of the lactic acid is carried by the blood to the liver where it is converted to glycogen, which in turn furnishes the blood with glucose. Muscle glycogen is therefore available indirectly to replenish blood glucose. When lactic acid from the muscles has been changed in appreciable amounts to glycogen in the liver the amount of substance in this organ may be increased over the normal level. Adrenaline therefore in moderate dosage, first causes a decrease and then an increase in liver glycogen. Very large doses over prolonged periods may lower both muscle and liver glycogen. The nervous control of adrenaline secretion will be discussed in chapter 58, and the manner in which thoracic autonomic impulses may affect blood sugar through its liberation will be appreciated. Adrenaline does not accelerate sugar formation from other substances in the liver. Diabetes has not been produced by the continued administration of adrenaline.

Insulin and adrenaline are not chemical antagonists but possess opposing physiological actions. Adrenaline accelerates the breakdown of both liver and muscle glycogen but the lactic acid made from muscle glycogen may result in an actual increase in the liver. Insulin promotes the formation of glycogen in both organs, but the increase in muscle glycogen may be at the expense of sugar, which would have formed liver glycogen. These are excellent examples of the manner in which the action of a hormone may be obscured by other effects. When the blood sugar is lowered to about 0.06 per cent by insulin an increased rate of liberation of adrenaline may be detected (Cannon; Houssay). Adrenaline has also been reported to increase the rate of liberation of insulin from the pancreas.

Adrenaline is one of the steps in the mechanisms by which liberation of adrenocorticotropic hormone (ACTH) is released in animals (Vogt; Long and Fry) but it has not been possible to demonstrate this effect in man. Thus a substance released in emergency causes a prompt hyperglycemia and may at the same time set in motion other changes (liberation of ACTH) which stimulate gluconeogenesis and thus provide for the continuation of the blood sugar rise. On the other hand, a meal high in carbohydrate given to fasted rats causes a reduction in the cholesterol content of adrenal cortex (liberation of cortical hormone) which is coincident with a rise in liver glycogen (Abelin). This and related studies are perhaps the beginning of a more complete understanding of the physiological coordination of medullary and cortical activities. There is some evidence that a mechanism even more rapid than one which could be mediated by adrenaline may play a role in ACTH liberation.

THE ADRENAL CORTEX AND CARBOHYDRATE METABOLISM. After double adrenalectomy in some species (cat and rat) the carbohydrate reserves of the liver and muscles are depleted and there may be definite hypoglycemia (Britton and Silvette). These workers showed that the hypoglycemic condition may be corrected when the cortical hormone and glucose are provided but not when the latter alone is given. They reported that the administration of extracts of the cortex elevated the carbohydrate stores of adrenalectomized animals well beyond the normal limits. Insulin and glucose do not increase glycogen deposition in the adrenalectomized animal unless cortical extract is supplied (Britton) but it is possible that this effect might occur if the animals were supplied with a diet adequately low in potassium and high in sodium. Long and his collaborators have greatly extended the earlier experiments of Britton and

Silvette and find rather remarkable increases in liver glycogen in fasted or fed normal animals when extracts of the adrenal cortex are administered. Muscle glycogen was not affected by the cortical material in these experiments but may be increased when adequate amounts of sugar are supplied.

After Houssay's demonstration that removal of the pituitary gland attenuates the severe diabetes resulting from total pancreatectomy in the toad and dog, Long and Lukens showed that a very similar change could be produced by adrenalectomy in the depancreatized cat or dog. It has been shown by Lukens and Dohan that the diabetes of adrenalectomized depancreatized animals and also that of hypophysectomized depancreatized animals can be increased in severity by the injection of cortical extracts.

Long, Katzin and Fry have shown that the rat, partially depancreatized by the method of Shapiro and Pincus, is an excellent preparation for the demonstration of the role of the adrenal cortex in carbohydrate metabolism. Adrenalectomy attenuates the diabetes which may be observed in these animals. The grafting of cortical tissue may restore the glucosuria to the extent which has been observed before adrenalectomy.

The relative diabetogenic potency of various adrenal steroids has been studied by Long and his collaborators, by Kendall and by Ingle and Thorn. In 1941 Ingle demonstrated adrenal steroid diabetes in normal rats which were forced to ingest a diet rich in carbohydrate but of normal caloric value. This adrenal diabetes was highly resistant to insulin. Corticosterone, 17-hydroxycorticosterone and 17-hydroxy-11-dehydrocorticosterone have all been shown to produce hyperglycemia and glucosuria in the normal rat. Ingle, Li and Evans have induced these signs of diabetes in normal force-fed rats by the administration of pure adrenocorticotropic hormone. The hypertrophy of the adrenal cortex was very marked in these animals. The production of a decreased carbohydrate tolerance in human subjects by ACTH (Browne) and of a state of metabolism similar in many respects to clinical diabetes by administering more highly purified adrenocorticotropic hormone (Conn, Louis and Johnston) are landmarks in the clinical extension of laboratory findings. The diabetes in human subjects which persisted for as long as the injections were continued (10 days) was resistant to insulin. (See also Alloxan Diabetes, p. 836.)

It has been shown by Long and his collaborators and by Ingle and other workers that the mechanism through which these adrenal extracts produce glucosuria is in part by stimulating gluconeogenesis from protein, but as the increase in nitrogen excretion is insufficient to account for the extent of the glucosuria, interference with glucose oxidation has also been postulated.

Some but not all of the abnormalities of carbohydrate metabolism in adrenalectomized animals are apparently due to the disturbance in sodium and potassium metabolism. Thus the delayed absorption of sugar and fat and the failure to store glycogen from glucose can be favorably affected by appropriate salt treatment. On the other hand the sharp fall in carbohydrate levels in fasting adrenalectomized animals and the amelioration of diabetes in partially depancreatized rats by adrenalectomy are not corrected by feeding salt but are by the administration of suitable cortical material.

While it has been shown that the pituitary preparations may exert a diabetogenic action in the absence of the adrenal a part of the pituitary effect is undoubtedly exerted through the adrenal cortex. The recent work of de Bodo has demonstrated that the sensitivity of the hypophysectomized dog to insulin is considerably greater than that of the adrenalectomized dog.

Many of these findings which have been obtained on experimental animals have been confirmed by Thorn and his colleagues in studies on patients with Addison's disease.

### THE PITUITARY AND CARBOHYDRATE METABOLISM

It has been appreciated for many years that abnormalities in carbohydrate metabolism may be associated with acromegaly of long standing or with the presence of various pituitary tumors. In 1908 Borchardt found that an extract of the posterior pituitary raised the blood sugar. In 1911 Cushing observed that "pituitary deficiency" may be accompanied by an increased carbohydrate tolerance. When insulin became available Burn demonstrated an antagonism between "pituitrin" and insulin, and several workers (Olmsted; Geiling; Houssay) showed that animals were more sensitive to insulin after removal of the pituitary body.

It appeared for a time that both the oxytocic and pressor principles of the posterior lobe produced hyperglycemia and thus interfered with the action of insulin. The work of Ellsworth and others indicates that the oxytocin is probably the more important factor from this viewpoint but it is doubtful, from the dosage necessary to produce the effect, whether this is of physiological significance. Griffiths has reported that posterior lobe extract, i.e., the vasoconstrictor principle, interferes with the absorption of insulin. The action of subcutaneously administered insulin is inhibited but when the intravenous route is used this effect is not observed.

Interest has been focussed on the anterior lobe of the pituitary by the brilliant researches of Houssay and his collaborators and of other investigators. The main points established in Houssay's laboratory are as follows: (a) Removal of the anterior lobe of the pituitary increases the sensitivity to insulin of the normal animal and diminishes the intensity of diabetes in the depancreatized animal. (b) Injections of preparations from the anterior pituitary into normal or hypophysectomized animals diminish their sensitivity to insulin and increase the severity of the diabetic state in hypophysectomized - depancreatized (Houssay) animals. (c) The administration of a suitable extract of the anterior pituitary can induce a diabetic condition. This point was independently established by the reports of Evans and his colleagues and of Baumann and Marine.

The effects of pancreatectomy and hypophysectomy are contrasted in the following summary, and the condition of the animal from which the pancreas and the pituitary have both been removed is briefly described.

| *Pancreatectomy (Dog)* | *Hypophysectomy (Dog)* |
|---|---|
| Hyperglycemia | Low blood sugar, hypo- |
| Polyuria | glycemic convulsions |
| Glycosuria | during fasting |
| Ketonuria | |
| Azoturia | |
| Insulin necessary for survival | Greatly increased sensitivity to insulin |
| Metabolic rate normal or slightly raised | Low metabolic rate |
| Decreased ability to utilize carbohydrate | Carbohydrate furnishes increased proportion of fuel |
| Decreased ability to form glycogen fat and protein | Rapid disappearance of liver and muscle glycogen due to utilization of carbohydrate and decreased gluconeogenesis.[6] |

### Pancreatectomy and Hypophysectomy

Animals survive without insulin. Polyuria, glucosuria, ketonuria, azoturia slight or absent.

[6] For direct evidence of this effect see Crandall and Cherry.

Administered carbohydrate partially or completely retained, i.e., carbohydrate utilization much better than in depancreatized dog. Metabolic rate low. Glycogen deposition.

PERMANENT DIABETES. The anterior pituitary gland contains a number of substances which affect carbohydrate metabolism in a variety of ways. These will now be considered briefly. Evans, Meyer, Simpson and Reichert in 1932 demonstrated the production of a prolonged diabetes in normal intact animals by anterior pituitary extract, F. G. Young, 1938, was however, the first to produce a permanent diabetes comparable in intensity to that resulting from complete pancreatectomy, by injection of extracts of the anterior lobe of the pituitary. He has found, in a very large number of dogs, that he is able consistently to produce a permanent state of diabetes by the daily injection, either intraperitoneally or subcutaneously, of a preparation of anterior lobe material. The permanent state of diabetes may be produced after as few as eleven daily injections but more are usually required. The diabetogenic activity, that is, the active material which will produce permanent diabetes in dogs, is associated with the globulin and pseudoglobulin fraction of the pituitary extract. Young's work was confirmed by Campbell and Best and by Dohan and Lukens and many others. Degenerative lesions of the islet cells of the pancreas were first noted in these permanently diabetic animals by Richardson and Young. Signs of proliferative changes in the islet cells in the early stages of the injections were found by these workers and by Ham and Haist who also observed proliferative changes in the acinar and duct cells of the pancreas (fig. 48.6). The diabetogenic extract produced proliferative changes in various other glandular tissues in the body. Campbell, Haist and Best noted that the diabetic state produced by the pituitary extract was not intensified by complete removal of the pancreas and secondly, that the insulin content of pancreas was reduced to a negligible quantity. This latter point has been discussed elsewhere.

It would appear that the main effect of the substance or substances which produced the permanent diabetes is exerted upon the Islands of Langerhans. These cells are apparently first stimulated and then destroyed by the repeated injections of the active material.

The permanent diabetes produced by the above procedures differs from that caused by pancreatectomy, in that the animals may live for long periods without the administration of insulin. In some

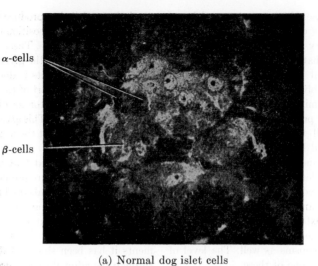

α-cells

β-cells

(a) Normal dog islet cells

β-cells with
  glycogen-
  containing
  vacuoles

acinar
  cells

(b) Islet from dog made diabetic with extract of anterior pituitary gland.

FIG. 48.6

cases, however, insulin is required. Starvation or a diet very rich in fat causes a marked diminution in the intensity of diabetes in the permanently diabetic animal.

The production of permanent diabetes by the diabetogenic substance of the anterior pituitary can be prevented by the simultaneous administration of large doses of insulin (Haist, Campbell and Best). The islet cells are protected from profound degenerative changes, the insulin content of the pancreas remains at a moderately high level, and the state of permanent diabetes is not induced. Lukens and Dohan have shown that permanent diabetes produced in partially depancreatized cats by administration of the diabetogenic substance of the anterior pituitary gland can be cured by the use of insulin, by a reduction in the caloric value of the diet or by an increase in its fat content. Recovery from early diabetes has followed a reduction in the diet only when the diabetes was very mild but treatment with insulin produced recovery at this stage regardless of the severity of the disease. If treatment were delayed until after the Islets of Langerhans had become atrophic, no recovery was possible.

It is to be noted that in the prevention and cure of this experimental diabetes, the level of the blood sugar is probably one of the most important factors which determines the direction in which the islet lesions will progress. This interpretation is supported by all the results which Young; Haist, Campbell and Best; and Lukens and Dohan have obtained and is in line with the earlier studies of F. M. Allen, Copp and Barclay, and others. The rise of blood sugar in itself would not, however, constitute an adequate stimulus for the production of the extensive changes in the islet cells. The diabetogenic factor must operate through other mechanisms as well. The level of blood insulin may be one of these.

Highly purified growth hormone has been shown to be diabetogenic, i.e., to produce permanent diabetes in cats (Cotes, Reid and Young, 1949) and in dogs (Campbell, Davidson, Snair and Lei, 1950). It would appear that this is the main diabetogenic component of anterior pituitary extracts but the cortical hormone liberated by ACTH and the thyroid product by the thyroid stimulating hormone must also play their part, as described elsewhere. Growth hormone stimulates growth in young dogs and does not produce diabetes until the animals have matured (Young). If a part of the rat's pancreas is removed, but not enough to cause diabetes, this condition may be produced by large doses of growth hormone, thyroxin or cortisone (Houssay). The rat is very resistant to these diabetogenic influences, perhaps in part because of its ability to make more insulin when needed. In the intact rat, however, on a high carbohydrate diet, growth hormone and ACTH (given together) regularly produce hyperglycemia and glucosuria (Engel).

THE GLYCOTROPIC OR ANTI-INSULIN ACTION OF ANTERIOR LOBE EXTRACTS. It was first demonstrated by Houssay and Potick and adequately confirmed by many later investigators that treatment with anterior lobe extract can induce in either normal or hypophysectomized animals an insensitivity to the action of insulin.

Bennett observed hyperglycemia and increased liver glycogen values upon prolonged administration of the adrenotropic hormone. Jensen and Grattan, and Ingle have shown that the adrenotropic substance as well as extracts of the adrenal cortex, and crystalline corticosterone produce a definite glycotropic effect. The adrenocortico-

tropic factor failed to produce this anti-insulin effect or to promote deposition of liver glycogen in adrenalectomized mice. These findings, therefore, strongly suggest that the glycotropic effect of anterior pituitary extracts is due to the adrenocorticotropic factor. A part of the anti-insulin action may be due to the storage of large amounts of glycogen in the liver. This glycogen is presumably available to counteract the hypoglycemic effect of insulin.

It is well established that hypophysectomized animals are unable to preserve their glycogen stores as normal animals do during fasting. It has been found by Russell and Bennett that this function can be restored, under certain conditions, by anterior pituitary extracts. In subsequent experiments it has been shown that this action is not through the adrenal since muscle glycogen can be maintained at a normal level in the absence of both adrenal glands in the fasting animal. In fed animals, however, adrenalcortical activity is required to maintain muscle glycogen. It has recently been shown by Russell and Wilhelmi (1950) that purified growth hormone is able to prevent loss of glycogen from skeletal muscle and from diaphragm and to restore heart glycogen to the normal fasting level in hypophysectomized rats. It is unnecessary, therefore, to postulate a separate glycogen-sparing factor.

THE PANCREOTROPIC ACTION OF ANTERIOR PITUITARY EXTRACTS. In 1933 Anselmino, Herold and Hoffmann reported that frequent injections of anterior lobe extracts in rats produce in a few days an increase in the size and number of the Islets of Langerhans. Richardson and Young were not able to confirm the findings under the conditions defined by the German investigators. They were, however, able to show that the daily treatment of rats with crude anterior pituitary lobe extract for a period of two weeks doubled the amount of islet tissue in the pancreas. More recently Marks and Young showed that the insulin content of rat pancreas was greatly increased under these conditions. (See Insulin Content of Pancreas.)

It will thus be apparent that the anterior pituitary gland affects metabolic processes by a variety of mechanisms. The permanent diabetes produced by growth hormone is due to destruction of the $\beta$-cells of the pancreas, but growth hormone inhibits the peripheral utilization of carbohydrate. It raises the blood sugar and intensifies the diabetes of completely depancreatized animals. It inhibits the "binding" of insulin by muscle and other tissues. ACTH, by liberating adrenal cortical steroids greatly increases gluconeogenesis and probably also inhibits peripheral utilization of glucose. Cortisone under certain conditions also stimulates the islets and thus may modify the diabetic state. The action of growth hormone or cortisone in decreasing peripheral utilization of sugar raises the blood sugar and this is undoubtedly part of the mechanism by which the $\beta$-cells are stimulated and destroyed.

The anterior pituitary gland also affects carbohydrate metabolism through the thyrotropic and probably also the gonadotropic hormones. Removal of the adrenal cortex, thyroid or gonads produces histological changes in the anterior pituitary indicative of overactivity, i.e., of attempts to stimulate the missing target organs.

Inhibition of the anterior pituitary effect on carbohydrate metabolism by the use of X-rays or by injection of estrogenic substances can be demonstrated in animals and in man, but little of practical clinical value can be expected from these procedures.

## The Thyroid and Carbohydrate Metabolism

The aggravation of diabetes in man by hyperthyroidism and its amelioration by removal of the thyroid establishes a link between this gland and carbohydrate metabolism. It is surprising that very little influence on the diabetes of depancreatized animals can be demonstrated by thyroidectomy. This may be due in part to incomplete removal of thyroid tissue. When very extensive atrophy of the thyroid is produced by hypophysectomy in dogs, the blood sugar and a normal level of urinary nitrogen can be maintained for long periods during fasting if thyroxin is supplied. Without it hypoglycemia may soon terminate the experiment. Thus it appears that the thyroid may play a role in the effect of the anterior pituitary on carbohydrate metabolism. The slight effect of thyroxin administration on the intensity of pancreatic diabetes in some animals still requires explanation but Houssay, Foglia and their colleagues have shown that in thyroidectomized rats 95 per cent of the pancreas can be removed without causing glucosuria. The administration of thyroid preparations to such animals may result in the development of permanent diabetes (metathyroid diabetes). In some partially depancreatized dogs permanent diabetes could also be induced by large doses of thyroid material.

The administration of thyroid substance or of thyroxin to normal animals has no immediate effect on blood sugar but a loss of liver glycogen may be demonstrated within six hours. There is also apparently a rise in the protein content of liver due perhaps to mobilization from peripheral tissues. Increased gluconeogenesis from protein can be readily demonstrated when thyroid substance is fed. An increase in the d-amino-acid oxidase activity of liver has been reported.

In clinical hyperthyroidism a mild hyperglycemia and glucosuria may be present. A comparable condition may be produced in animals by administration of thyroid material. At this stage liver glycogen is easily mobilizable (the actual amount present may be less than normal) and adrenaline elicits more hypoglycemia and insulin less hypoglycemia than normally.

When thyroid feeding is continued there is a profound decrease in liver, muscle and heart glycogen. In this second stage the animals are resistant to adrenaline and extremely susceptible to insulin. They may exhibit spontaneous hypoglycemia or develop it as a secondary result of a small injection of dextrose. This latter effect may be due to the liberation of insulin the action of which is not buffered by liver glycogen.

Thus the effect of the thyroid on carbohydrate metabolism is the resultant of several actions: (1) increased oxidation of carbohydrate in tissues generally, (2) the increased rate of hepatic gluconeogenesis, and (3) destruction of islet tissue in partially depancreatized animals.

## Glucagon

Kimball and Murlin were the first to suggest that the initial transient rise in blood sugar in normal animals which received the solution of crude insulin intravenously was due to a separate substance. They introduced the name "glucagon" which was adopted by Bürger (1929) who, with his colleagues, has been responsible for most of the early studies of the properties of this material. Bürger demonstrated that glucagon could be separated from insulin and that the hyperglycemia was accompanied by a fall in liver glycogen. Adrenalectomy did not eliminate this effect. Shipley and Humel (1945) showed that crude insulin preparations accelerated glycogen breakdown in liver slices. Sutherland and Cori (1948) obtained evidence that this glycogenolysis was due to glucagon and that this substance activated the phosphorylase system. Staub, Sinn and Behrens (1953) have now obtained glucagon in crystalline form as a polypeptide differing significantly from insulin in amino acid content. Bromer, Sinn, Staub and Behrens have shown that glucagon is a single polypeptide chain containing 29 amino acid residues. There are many converging paths of evidence which suggest that this substance is made in the α-cells of the pancreas and perhaps also in similar cells of the fundic mucosa of the stomach. Sutherland and de Duve obtained glucagon activity from these two sources only. Makman, Makman and Sutherland have now reported the presence of a glucagonlike material in the blood of man and dog.

It has been found more recently that glucagon in addition to stimulating hepatic glycogenolysis produces many other metabolic changes in animals and human subjects. It greatly increases the catabolism of amino acids as indicated by the fall in their concentration in blood and the rise in urea production. The deaminated residues of the amino acids are presumably synthesized into glucose. Thus the hepatic glycogenolysis and gluconeogenesis may both contribute to the hyperglycemic action of glucagon. The overproduction of glucose under experimental conditions can be of sufficient magnitude to produce a diabeticlike state in many animal species including man. The characteristic hyperglycemia, glucosuria, and excessive nitrogen excretion persists only as long as the glucagon is administered. A permanent diabetes has not yet been produced. The significance of glucagon, if any, in the pathogenesis of human diabetes remains obscure (Izzo, 1957; Elrick, 1958). In man glucagon stimulates ketone body production and reduces creatinuria (Ezrin, Salter and Best, 1958).

The metabolic rate of rats treated with glucagon may show a 50 per cent rise within an hour. Glucagon also affects certain aspects of gastrointestinal function. It has been reported to decrease gastric motility and acidity and the flow of pancreatic juice (Stunkard et al. 1955; Robinson et al. 1957; Necheles et al. 1957).

All of the effects of glucagon noted above have been observed only under conditions of experimental or chemical investigation. The doses used may be far in excess of what may prove to be physiological amounts.

## The Nervous Regulation of Carbohydrate Metabolism

As is the case with many other aspects of carbohydrate metabolism, Claude Bernard paved the way for the investigation of the influence of the nervous system. Bernard (1855) punctured the floor of the fourth ventricle in unanesthetized animals and observed that the piqûre produced a prolonged glucosuria. (The blood sugar of a rabbit may rise to 0.40 per cent within an hour and the effect may persist for several days or longer.)

It has been appreciated for some time that lesions in the hypothalamic region may cause glucosuria and the relation of these lesions to pituitary secretion has been in doubt. While lesions in this region might interfere with the absorption of the pituitary hormones or more likely, stimulate or destroy the nerve fibers going to the gland, it has been established that stimulation of the thoracic autonomic center in the hypothalamus may produce hyperglycemia. This gave rise to the idea that lesions lower in the brain stem might act by irritating the fiber tracts from the thoracic autonomic center but the situation is apparently not so simple. Donhoffer and Macleod attribute special significance to the pons and there may be various centers, the impulses from which affect the level of blood sugar by more or less indirect paths.

In a paper, with an excellent review of previous work, Anderson, Rioch and Haymaker (1952) showed that in dogs and rats a prolonged (20 to 30 days) decrease in glucose tolerance was produced by transection of the brain whether at the pontine, midbrain or hypothalamic level. In animals in which decortication was performed and in those in which the brain stem was hemisected there was no change in glucose tolerance. These findings provide evidence for a homeostatic control of blood sugar level by centers in the brain stem.

It will be appreciated that lesions of the brain involving (1) the pathways which carry glycogenolytic impulses to the liver or (2) the tracts which supply the adrenals, pancreas or pituitary, may cause serious disturbances of carbohydrate metabolism by interfering with these normal mechanisms. The work of Anderson and associates does not suggest that failure of glycogen formation or that increased secretion of adrenal corticoids provides an important part of the answer to this problem. It is apparent that the field demands much further exploration with the light of modern endocrinology and neurophysiology focussed on it.

## Glucose Tolerance Curves

When glucose is administered by mouth to a normal animal the blood sugar begins to rise within two or three minutes. This indicates that the sugar solution passes rapidly through the stomach to the duodenum. If large amounts of sugar are provided there may be considerable loss in the urine, i.e., *alimentary hyperglycemia* and *glucosuria*. After the usual meal, however, the hyperglycemia is not sufficient to produce glucosuria. When moderate amounts of sugar are given the rise in blood sugar is transient and the return to the normal level rapid. This phenomenon is extensively used to test carbohydrate tolerance. The factors which determine the shape of the curve when from 50 to 100 grams of sugar are given by mouth are: (1) The rapidity of absorption, (2) the extent of the storage and utilization of glucose by the tissues, and (3) the rate of discharge of sugar from the liver. The first factor may, of course, be eliminated by injecting the sugar intravenously.[7] The reaction of the tissues and of the liver to injected sugar may be direct or indirect. When more sugar is presented to the tissues more is utilized even though the insulin available remains constant. When the blood sugar rises the liver may discharge less sugar (Soskin, Allweiss and Cohn). The hyperglycemia may affect the liver and other tissues indirectly by increasing the insulin output and perhaps by other endocrine adjustments. The insulin liberated increases storage of glucose and fat and may decrease gluconeogenesis. An abnormal curve may indicate inability of the liver or pancreas, or of both to perform their normal functions. It might be due in part or completely to defective oxidation and storage in the muscles. It must be emphasized that an abnormal glucose tolerance curve *does not* necessarily indicate a deficiency of available insulin.

### UNDERNUTRITION AND CARBOHYDRATE METABOLISM

In 1873 Lehmann and in 1877 Claude Bernard noted a glucosuria in fasting animals after the administration of carbohydrate, and in 1890, Hofmeister, who made the first quantitative studies, named the condition "hunger diabetes." Utilization of carbohydrates is at a maximum in animals which have been fed on diets rich in these substances. After periods of fasting or of fat feeding, there is a definite impairment of glucose utilization which may easily be detected by the results

of a glucose tolerance test. The feeding of an exclusively fat diet produces effects on glucose utilization indistinguishable from those of complete starvation. Proteins exert an effect intermediate between that of sugar and fat, i.e., some impairment of glucose utilization is produced by an exclusively protein diet. Diets adequate in other respects but providing a low caloric intake cause little disturbance in carbohydrate utilization. The administration to animals or human subjects exhibiting hunger diabetes of a diet containing glucose causes a prompt improvement in carbohydrate tolerance.

The mechanisms of production and alleviation of the defect in carbohydrate utilization produced by fasting are not as yet completely elucidated. It would appear from the recent findings of Chambers, Cori and others that oxidation of glucose in the tissues is interfered with to a much greater extent than is glycogen formation. It has been established that the administration of insulin effects a partial restoration of carbohydrate utilization (Cori and Cori; Dann and Chambers). This finding suggests that insulin liberation may be depressed in hunger diabetes. Himsworth feels that a change in sensitivity to insulin is involved rather than a diminution of pancreatic output. On the other hand, the observation by Haist, Ridout and Best shows that the insulin content of the pancreas of rats may be reduced to nearly half the normal value by starvation or by fat feeding. This finding in conjunction with others supports the view that insulin liberation may be decreased. The evidence, which has been well reviewed by Chambers, does not indicate that the complete explanation of hunger diabetes will be found in the abnormal response of any one organ or tissue. This conception is supported by Ingle's report that insulin alone does not rapidly restore the carbohydrate tolerance of fasted animals to normal and by the finding that at least one important enzyme system (phosphorylase) is increased in activity during starvation (Lundbaek and Goranson). The lipogenic ability of the liver is reduced to the diabetic level by fasting.

GLYCOGEN DISEASE. A clinical condition characterized by the enlargement of one or more organs resulting from the accumulation of glycogen has attracted the attention of research workers. The disease usually bears the name of von Gierke who published an autopsy report on a case in 1929. Van Creveld, in the previous year, had concluded that the hepatomegaly which he observed in a young boy was probably due to excessive glycogen deposition. The glycogen deposits may be in

---

[7] Normal dogs may be given 0.85 gram of glucose per kg. per hour for long periods (Woodyatt) without producing glucosuria. This is approximately the same value as the maximum rate at which glucose is absorbed from the intestinal tract.

the liver, kidney, heart or in other tissues. The disease is characterized by hypoglycemia and ketosis in the fasting condition, by an abnormal effect of adrenaline which causes only a slight rise in blood sugar and lactic acid but a large increase in ketosis, and by an increased sensitivity to insulin. The glucose tolerance test gives a prolonged hyperglycemia without glucosuria. The glycogen content of the blood is increased and van Creveld noted a resistance of this material to glycogenolysis. The glycogen in liver and kidney does not disappear at a normal rate after removal from the body and an interference with the glycogenolytic process is therefore indicated.

It would appear probable, as van Creveld has suggested, that glycogen disease is a continuation in childhood of a fetal condition in so far as certain aspects of carbohydrate metabolism are concerned There are large deposits of liver glycogen in the fetus and this material is resistant to the action of adrenaline. It is well established that in some species the fetal pancreas, at or near term, contains very high concentrations of insulin. Hyperinsulinism may produce excessive deposits of glycogen in well fed animals and ketosis under fasting condition. It has been suggested that the secretion of the anterior pituitary gland makes liver glycogen more resistant to breakdown. But all these observations must be considered in the light of the findings by Cori and associates that the structure of glycogen from the liver of these cases is sometimes definitely abnormal and that the abnormalities in response to enzymes differ from case to case. There may, therefore, be many different types of glycogen disease.

ALLOXAN DIABETES. This type of experimental diabetes was first produced by Dunn, Sheehan and McLetchie (1943) who showed that alloxan has a selective necrosing action on the Islets of Langerhans. In 1937 Jacobs had noted the effect of alloxan in rabbits—an initial hyperglycemia and a subsequent hypoglycemia. No histological studies were made and Jacobs postulated an insulinlike action of alloxan. It has now been shown that the hypoglycemia is due to liver damage or liberation of excess insulin from damaged islets or to both. The diabetic state is caused by a failure of islet cells to produce insulin. The diabetic action of alloxan has been demonstrated in the rabbit, rat, cat, monkey and dog. An unsuccessful attempt has been made to destroy the abnormally active islet cells in advanced cases of hyperinsulinism in man by the administration of alloxan. Lesions in the liver and kidney, less marked than those produced in the islets, are seen in some species after the injection of this chemical.

There is, as yet, no evidence that alloxan has any physiological significance. A substance resembling it was reported, many years ago, in the urine and intestinal mucus in certain pathological conditions in man.

Griffiths has produced hyperglycemia and glycosuria but not permanent diabetes with uric acid which is chemically related to alloxan. To secure this effect the glutathione level of blood was depleted by a diet deficient in cystine and methionine and feeding large amounts of ascorbic acid. Lazarow in 1945 was the first to show that glutathione injected just before the diabetogenic dose of alloxan protected the rats. While many other substances, such as dehydroascorbic acid, exert this effect, glutathione as a normal constitutent of cells is of particular physiological interest. Glutathione reacts with alloxan to reduce it to dialuric acid which is not diabetogenic. Leech and Bailey found an extensive fall in blood glutathione after alloxan, and previous investigators had shown similar changes in other tissues. The injection of various pituitary preparations has been found to lower the glutathione content of tissues. Cohn found in his studies of transient diabetes in man produced by injecting ACTH that there is a direct correlation between the blood glutathione level and the diabetogenic effect, i.e., the higher the blood glutathione, the less the effect. In animals injected glutathione consistently potentiates steroid diabetes by some unknown mechanism. The protective effect against diabetes may be attributed to the removal of diabetogenic compounds from the blood or $\beta$-cells. It has been suggested (Hédon, Lazarow) that factors which increase insulin production may exhaust the supply of sulfhydryl groups by appropriating the cysteine for the insulin molecule and thus decrease the available glutathione and in this way make the $\beta$-cells particularly susceptible to alloxan or naturally occurring damaging factors.

THE ORAL HYPOGLYCEMIC AGENTS. In 1918, Watanabe noted that guanidin poisoning was accompanied by hypoglycemia. In 1926, Frank, Nothman and Wagner found a derivative of guanidin which produced a lowering of blood sugar, and which they felt was not as toxic as guanidin. This material was synthalin, a decamethylene guanidin. Very soon, however, clinicians noted disturbing side reactions, primarily in the gastrointestinal tract, and in 1929 Karr reported fatty degeneration and necrosis of the livers of patients receiving this material. The use of synthalin was followed by that of a great variety of oral preparations: Glukhorment, Anticoman, etc. These were various mixtures of guanidin derivatives. Eventually they all proved to be dangerously toxic for human use. In 1942, Janbon and co-workers accidentally observed that a new sulfonamide, para-aminobenzene-sulfamidoisopropyl-thiodiazol, a drug that was originally synthesized by von Kemmel and Kimmig, produced severe hypoglycemia in patients who had been treated for typhoid fever. Loubatières investigated the mode of action of this drug in animal experiments and suggested that it stimulated the Islands of Langerhans. Clinical application of this substance was not made, however, until December 1955, and in the meantime a group of German workers carried out experimental and clinical studies with another sulfonamide, $N_1$-sulfanilyl-$N_2$-N-butyl-carbamide (BZ-55). This drug soon became widely used for oral treatment of obese elderly diabetics. Prolonged experiments in animals, however, revealed disturbing bleeding tendencies (Sirek et al., 1957) as well as hepatic damage (Schambye, 1957). A few accidents in human patients were also reported and the drug was withdrawn from the market in North America. Almost at the same time another sulfonylurea derivative was made available, the N-(4-methyl-benzene-sulfonyl)-N-butyl-urea (D860 or tolbutamide). This substance has now been widely used in the obese elderly type of diabetics, and the incidence of disturbing side effects in man has remained negligible. Liver damage is produced in dogs by doses of the drug which are well tolerated by man.

In addition to these derivatives of sulfonylureas, which do not act in the absence of the pancreas or in cases of juvenile diabetes, derivatives of guanide have also been tried. Phenyldiguanide (DBI) has been reported to be effective in certains cases of juvenile diabetes. But the incidence of side effects is high although liver and kidney function tests have not as yet revealed any damage.

Various new sulfonylurea derivatives are now in the stage of experimental or clinical trial.

## REFERENCES

ABEL, J. J., GEILING, E. M. K., ROUILLER, C. A., BELL, F. K. AND WINTERSTEINER, O. J. Pharmacol. & Exper. Therap., 1927, **31**, 65.

ALLEN, F. M., J. Metabolic Res., 1922, **1**, 75.

ANDERSON, E., RIOCH, O. M. AND HAYMAKER, W. Acta Neuroveg., 1952, **5**, 1–2.

BANTING, F. G. AND BEST, C. H. J. Lab. & Clin. Med., 1922, **7**, 251.

BERGMAN, H. AND DRURY, D. R. Am. J. Physiol., 1938, **124**, 279.

BERNARD, C. Compt. rend. Soc. biol., 1849, **1**, 14.

BLUM, F. Deutsches Arch. klin. Med., 1901, **71**, 146.

BORNSTEIN, J. Diabetes, 1953, **2**, 23.

BRITTON, S. W. AND SILVETTE, H. Am. J. Physiol., 1932, **100**, 693.

BROMER, W. W., SINN, L. Y., STAUB, A. AND BEHRENS, O. K. Diabetes, 1957, **6**, 234.

BÜRGER, M. Ztschr. ges. inn. Med., 1947, **2**, 311.

CAMPBELL, J. AND BEST, C. H. Lancet, 1938, **1**, 1444.

CANNON, W. B., SHOHL, A. T. AND WRIGHT, W. S. Am. J. Physiol. 1911, **29**, 280.

CAVALLERO, C. AND MALANDRA, B. Acta Endocrinol., 1953, **13**, 79.

CONN, J. W., LOUIS, L. H. AND JOHNSTON, M. W. Proc. Am. Diabetes, A., 1948, **8**, 213.

CORI, G. T. AND CORI, C. F. J. Biol. Chem., 1927, **72**, 615.

CRANDALL, L. A. AND CHERRY, I. S. Am. J. Physiol., 1939, **125**, 658.

CRANDALL, L. A. AND LIPSCOMB, A. Am. J. Physiol., 1947, **148**, 312.

DE MAYER, J. Arch. Fisiol., 1909, **7**, 96.

DOHAN, F. C. AND LUKENS, F. D. W. Am. J. Physiol., 1939, **125**, 188.

DONHOFFER, C. AND MACLEOD, J. J. R. Proc. Roy. Soc., ser. B, 1932, **110**, 125.

DUNN, J. S., SHEEHAN, H. L. AND MCLETCHIE, N. G. B. Lancet, 1943, **1**, 484.

ELRICK, H., RACHIELE, F. J. AND HLAD, C. J. Diabetes, 1958, **7**, 129.

EVANS, H. M., MEYER, K., SIMPSON, M. E. AND REICHERT, F. L. Proc. Soc. Exper. Biol. Med., 1932, **29**, 857.

EZRIN, C., SALTER, J. M., OGRYZLO, M. A. AND BEST, C. H. Canad. M. A. J., 1958, **78**, 96.

GELLHORN, E., FELDMAN, J. AND ALLEN, A. Endocrinology, 1941, **29**, 137.

GEMMILL, C. L. Bull. Johns Hopkins Hosp., 1941, **68**, 329.

GRIFFITHS, J. P. AND WATERS, E. T. Am. J. Physiol., 1936, **117**, 134.

GRIFFITHS, M. J. Biol. Chem., 1948, **172**, 853.

GROSSMAN, M. I. AND STEIN, I. F. J. Applied Physiol., 1948, **1**, 263.

HAGEDORN, H. C., JENSEN, B. N., KRARUP, N. B. AND WODSTRUP, I. J. A. M. A., 1936, **106**, 177.

HAIST, R. E., CAMPBELL, J. AND BEST, C. H. New England J. Med., 1940, **223**, 607.

HALLAS-MØLLER, K., JERSILD, M., PETERSEN, K AND SCHLICHTKRULL, J. J. A. M. A., 1952, **150**, 1667.

HAM, A. W. AND HAIST, R. E. Am. J. Pathol., 1941, **17**, 787.

HARFENIST, E. J. AND CRAIG, L. C. J. Am. Chem. Soc., 1952, 74, 3087.

HARTROFT, W. S. AND WRENSHALL, G. A. Diabetes, 1955, 4, 1.

HÉDON, E. J. Physiol., Path. gen., 1927, **25**, 1.

HIMSWORTH, H. P. Clinical Sc., 1935, **2**, 67.

HOFMEISTER, F. Arch. exper. Path. u. Pharmakol., 1889, **25**, 240.

HOUSSAY, B. A. Endocrinology, 1944, **35**, 158.

HOUSSAY, B. A. AND BIASOTTI, A. Rev. Soc. argent. biol., 1930, **6**, 8.

HOUSSAY, B. A., FOGLIA, V. G., SMYTH, F. S., RIETTI, C. T. AND HOUSSAY, A. B. J. Exper. Med., 1942, **75**, 547.

HOUSSAY, B. A. AND POTICK, D. Compt. rend. Soc. biol., 1929, **101**, 940.

INGLE, D. J., BEARY, D. F. AND PURMALIS, A. Proc. Soc. Exper. Biol. Med., 1954, **85**, 432.

IZZO, J. L., RONCONE, A. AND PALIANI, M. A. Fed. Proc. 1957, **16**, 200.

JACOBS, H. R. Proc. Soc. Exper. Biol. Med., 1937, **37**, 407.

JENSEN, H. AND GRATTAN, J. F. Am. J. Physiol., 1940, **128**, 270.

KENNEDY, G. C. AND PARROT, D. M. V. J. Endocrinol., 1958, **17**, 161.

KRAHL, M. E. Ann. New York Acad. Sc., 1951, **54**, 694.

LAZAROW, A. Diabetes, 1952, **1**, 171.

LEHMANN, W. L. Arch. exper. Path. u. Pharmakol., 1874, **2**, 463.

LONG, C. N. H., KATZIN, B., AND FRY, E. G. Endocrinology, 1940, **26**, 309.

LONG, C. N. H. AND LUKENS, F. D. W. J. Exper. Med., 1936, **63**, 465.

LUKENS, F. D. W. AND DOHAN, F. C., Endocrinology, 1938, **22**, 51.

LUKENS, F. D. W. AND DOHAN, F. C. Endocrinology, 1942, **30**, 175.

LUNDBAEK, K. AND GORANSON, E. S. Nature, 1948, **162**, 1002.

MAKMAN, M. H., MAKMAN, R. S. AND SUTHERLAND, E. W. J. Biol. Chem., 1958, **233**, 894.

MANN, F. C. AND MAGATH, T. B. Arch. Int. Med., 1922, **30**, 73.

VON MERING, J. Verhandl. Congresses inn. Med., 1887, **6**, 349.

VON MERING, J. AND MINKOWSKI, O. Arch. exper. Path. u. Pharmakol., 1889, **26**, 371.

MIRSKY, I. A. AND BROH-KAHN, R. H. Arch. Biochem., 1949, **20**, 1.

NECHELES, H. Am. J. Physiol., 1957, **191**, 595.

OTTAWAY, J. H. AND SMITH, R. H. Quoted by F. G. Young, Lancet, 1948, **2**, 955.

RANDLE, P. J. Lancet, 1954, **1**, 441, 809.

RANDLE, P. J. AND YOUNG, F. G. J. Endocrinol., 1956, **13**, 335.

REINECKE, R. M. Am. J. Physiol., 1943, **140**, 276.

RICHARDSON, K. C. AND YOUNG, F. G. J. Physiol., 1937, **91**, 352.

RICHARDSON, K. C. AND YOUNG, F. G. Lancet, 1938, **1**, 1098.

ROBINSON, R. M., HARRIS, K., HLAD, C. J. AND EISEMAN, B. Proc. Soc. Exper. Biol. Med., 1957, **96**, 518.

SALTER, J. M., DAVIDSON, I. W. F. AND BEST, C. H. Diabetes, 1957, **6**, 248.

SANGER, F., Bull. Soc. chim. biol., 1955, **37**, 23. SANGER, F. AND TUPPY, H. Biochem. J., 1951, **49**, 463. SANGER, F. AND THOMPSON, E. O. P. Ibid., 1953, **53**, 353.

SCOTT, D. A. Biochem. J., 1934, **28**, 1592.

SCOTT, D. A. AND FISHER, A. M. J. Pharmacol. & Exper. Therap., 1936, **58**, 781.

SOSKIN, S., ALLWEISS, M. D. AND COHN, D. J., Am. J. Physiol., 1934, **109**, 155.

STETTEN, DEW. Bull. New York, Acad. Med., 1953, **29**, 446.

STUNKARD, A. J., VAN ITALLIE, T. B. AND REISS, B. B. Proc. Soc. Exper. Biol. Med., 1955, **89**, 258.

SUTHERLAND, E. W. AND CORI, C. F. J. Biol. Chem., 1948, **172**, 737.

TUERKISCHER, E. AND WERTHEIMER, E. Biochem. J., 1948, **42**, 603.

VALLANCE-OWEN, J. AND HURLOCK, B. Lancet, 1954, **1**, 68.

WAGNER, E. M. AND SCOW, R. O. Endocrinology, 1957, **61**, 419.

WICK, A. N., DRURY, D. R., BANCROFT, R. W. AND MACKAY, E. M. J. Biol. Chem., 1951, **188**, 241.

WILDER, R. M. Diabetes, 1952, **1**, 183.

WILDER, R. M., ALLAN, F. N., POWER, M. H. AND ROBERTSON, H. E. J. A. M. A., 1927, **89**, 348.

WINEGRAD, A. I. AND RENOLD, A. E. J. Biol. Chem., 1958, **233**, 267, 273.

YOUNG, F. G. Lancet, 1936, **1**, 237; 297. Ibid., 1937, **2**, 372.

### Monographs and Reviews

CHAMBERS, W. H. Physiol. Rev., 1938, **18**, 248.

CORI, C. F. Biol. Symposia, 1941, **5**, 131.

CREVELD, S. VAN. Medicine, 1939, **18**, 1.

HAIST, R. E. Physiol. Rev., 1944, **24**, 409.

HAWORTH, W. N. The constitution of sugars. Edward Arnold & Co., London, 1929.

HORECKER, B. L. AND HIATT, H. H. New England J. Med., 1958, **258**, 177, 225.

Hormonal factors in carbohydrate metabolism. Ciba Foundation Colloquia Endocrinol., **6**, 1953, for articles on enzymes and hormones in carbohydrate metabolism by G. and C. F. Cori, F. Dickens, C. DeDuve, C. N. H. Long, F. D. W. Lukens, A. E. Wilhelmi, F. G. Young, and others.

HOUSSAY, B. A. AND BIASOTTI, A. The hypophysis, carbohydrate metabolism and diabetes. Endocrinology, 1931, **15**, 511.

JENSEN, H. F. Insulin: its chemistry and physiology. Oxford University Press, London, 1938.

LUSK, G. The elements of the science of nutrition. W. B. Saunders Co., Philadelphia, 1928.

XIX International Physiological Congress. Symposium on Insulin, 1953. Recent Prog. hormone Res.: Proc. Laurentian Hormone Conference, 1953, **8**, for articles on insulin and growth hormone by F. G. Young and R. C. deBodo.

SAKEL, M. Neue Behandlungsmethode der Schizophrenie. Perles, Wien, 1935.

STADIE, W. C. Recent advances in insulin research. Diabetes, 1956, **5**, 263.

STETTEN DE WITT, JR., (Ed.). Symposium on disorders of carbohydrate metabolism. Am. J. Medicine, 1959, **26**, 659.

Third International Standard for Insulin. Miles, A. A., Mussett, M. V. and Perry, W. L. M. Bull. World Health Org., 1952, **7**, 445.

Fourth International Standard for Insulin. D. R. Bangham and M. V. Mussett, Bull. World Health Org., 1959, **20**, 1209.

# 49

## FAT METABOLISM

### Classification of the Fats and Fatty Substances Occurring in the Body

When a tissue is thoroughly extracted with a mixture of ether and alcohol almost all of the fatty substances are removed.

The amount of fatty acids combined in the cerebrosides and phospholipids may be determined by taking advantage of the insolubility of these materials in acetone to which some magnesium chloride has been added. The fatty acids may then be liberated and estimated by one of a variety of procedures. An estimate of the amount of the phosphorus-containing substances can be obtained by determining the phosphorus content of the extract, and similarly with those containing carbohydrate by estimating the sugar. The free cholesterol is removed by precipitation with digitonin and estimated gravimetrically or by colorimetric means. In another sample of the extract the bound cholesterol is liberated by saponification as with sodium ethylate and the total cholesterol determined. The difference between the free and the total is the amount of cholesterol combined with fatty acid and this can be calculated from the known combining weight of fatty acids with cholesterol. The result is an estimate of the amount of cholesterol ester. The difference between the total fatty acid content and the sum of the amounts combined with carbohydrate, phosphoric acid and cholesterol, gives us an estimate of the amount combined with glycerol. The fatty materials or lipids may therefore be classified as follows·

(1) *Fats.* Esters of fatty acids and glycerol.

(2) *Lipoids.*[1]

   (a) *Phospholipids* (phosphatides). Fatty substances containing fatty acids, phosphoric acid and some of the following constituents; glycerol, inositol, choline, eth-

anolamine, serine and sphingosine. Examples are—lecithin, cephalin and sphingomyelin.

   (b) *Cerebrosides* (glycolipids). Combinations of fatty acid, sugar and sphingosine (phrenosin, kerasin, etc.).

   (c) *Waxes.* Esters of fatty acids and certain alcohols (but *not* glycerol), (cholesterol esters, beeswax, etc.).

(3) *Sterols.* Hydrogenated phenanthrene derivatives (free cholesterol, ergosterol, etc.).

(4) *Hydrocarbons* (squalene, carotene, etc.).

### THE TRIGLYCERIDES

CHEMICAL STRUCTURE. In the members of the first group, the fats, one molecule of glycerol is combined with three of fatty acid: oleic acid $C_{18}H_{34}O_2$, stearic acid $C_{18}H_{36}O_2$, and palmitic acid $C_{16}H_{32}O_2$, are the three which account for the bulk of the fatty acids of the neutral fat fraction of body tissues. The latter two are saturated, while oleic acid has a double bond in the middle of its fatty acid chain. This renders it less stable and more easily oxidized. Oleic acid is liquid at low temperatures while stearic and palmitic are solid even at body temperature. It is now thought that the glycerides are usually mixed, i.e., they contain two or more different fatty acids in their molecule. Fatty acids more unsaturated than oleic (linoleic and arachidonic) are also found in the triglycerides. The naturally occurring fatty acids in tissues usually have 12 to 20 carbon atoms and one terminal carboxyl group.

The neutral fats obtained from animal tissues contain fatty acids which have an even number of carbon atoms. The characteristic fatty acids in the depot fat vary with different animals. Hilditch and Lovern have shown that certain fatty acid mixtures are characteristic of marine animals, others of fresh water fish and others of land animals. The fat of the fish, for example, contains large quantities of higher unsaturated fatty acids $C_{20}$ and $C_{22}$, but in the depots of ox and pig these are almost absent.

---

[1] The phospholipids, cerebrosides and waxes which resemble fats may be termed lipoids or fat-like substances. The sterols and hydrocarbons while associated with fats are chemically quite distinct.

## TABLE 49.1

*Distribution of tissue lipids*

Column (1) (after Campbell and Lucas) gives the distribution of the total lipids of the mouse in the various tissues.

Column (2) shows the distribution of adipose tissue in the rat (after Mendel) as per cent of total adipose tissue.

| | (1) | | (2) |
|---|---|---|---|
| Carcass............. | 34 | Subcutaneous.... | 50 |
| Adipose tissues..... | 32 | Genital.......... | 20 |
| Skin................ | 18 | Perirenal........ | 12 |
| Liver............... | 5 | Mesenteric...... | 10 |
| Intestine and spleen. | 3 | Inter-muscular.. | 5 |
| Genital organs...... | 3 | Omental......... | 3 |
| Kidneys and adre- | | | |
| nals.............. | 2 | | |
| Brain............... | 2 | | |
| Lungs and thymus.. | 1 | | |

DISTRIBUTION. It is evident from gross inspection of tissues that reserve fat is laid down in large quantities subcutaneously, in the omentum, the mesentery, retroperitoneally, and at other sites. Reserve fat is also contained in the interstitial tissues of most other organs. Exceptions include the brain and the cornea (see table 49.1). The distribution of fat is largely independent of the type of diet but the amount and kind of fat deposited are influenced by the food intake and the type of diet.

PHYSIOLOGY. The main function of the glycerides is undoubtedly to provide a source of energy. Fat not only furnishes more energy per gram (9.3 Calories) than carbohydrate and protein but it is the only food material stored in the dry state. The total fat content of a well-nourished animal may be between 10 and 12 per cent and under unusual conditions much higher. A very large proportion of the total energy store of the body is in the form of fat.

While animals grow normally when diets containing only very small amounts of fat are provided, several investigators have reported that growth is seriously retarded on a diet free of fat (McAmis, Anderson and Mendel). Palmitic, stearic and oleic acids are not essential but Burr and Burr have provided evidence that certain of the unsaturated fatty acids are necessary. Growth is favorably affected by linoleic, linolenic and arachidonic acids and the development of skin lesions (similar to acrodynia) is prevented. These acids should be considered separately in dietary studies since there are definite differences in the magnitude of their effects on growth and on the skin lesions. There is an interesting interrelationship of the actions of the unsaturated fatty acids and those of pyridoxine, pantothenic acid and other accessory food factors (see also p. 945).

In some species, of course, the layers of fat in the subcutaneous spaces serve as an insulating mechanism against extreme cold. Thus in cold climates the fat deposited just under the skin contains a relatively large amount of oleic acid. It is therefore more liquid than the material which is found in the less superficial subcutaneous reserves. Henriques and Hanson have pointed out that since the temperature of the outermost subcutaneous fat is appreciably lower than that of the deeper parts, the body requires a less congealable type of fat at this place. In a somewhat similar investigation of fat in different parts of the body Anderson and Mendel could find no difference in saturation of the fat from the superficial subcutaneous region and that of deeper and warmer parts of the body. These latter workers used animals which are not normally subjected to extremely low temperatures.

Recovery from the depot fat of a particular *dietary* fatty acid has been repeatedly demonstrated. This deposition is, however, limited to the higher fatty acids (above $C_{10}$). Interconversion of the fatty acids within the body is well established. Schoenheimer and Rittenberg have shown that the length of the carbon chain of fatty acids can be increased or decreased by two carbon atoms at a time and further that desaturation or hydrogenation of unsaturated acids can take place in the body. While one double bond can be formed the body appears unable to introduce more than one. Thus the highly unsaturated fatty acids such as linoleic and linolenic are not found in fat which has been synthesized in the body. They must be provided in the food.

### Conversion of Carbohydrate And Protein to Fat

The formation of body fat from carbohydrate of the diet was established by the classical work of Liebig (1852) and Lawes and Gilbert (1853). The rate at which the fatty acids are formed has now been studied by the use of isotopes. These studies have shown that conversion of carbohydrate to fat proceeds continuously and does not occur only (as was formerly believed) when there is excessive intake of carbohydrate.

The formation of carbohydrate from protein is

well established. It has been assumed that this newly formed carbohydrate is available for fat synthesis and good evidence for this assumption has been secured by Longenecker and by Hoagland and Snider. On an almost exclusively protein diet the fat formed was similar in composition to that synthesized from dietary carbohydrate.

Many of these recent additions to our knowledge establish the fact that the fat depots are not essentially inert storehouses of energy as was previously thought, but are centers of continuous metabolic activity. Glycogen and fat formation take place in adipose tissue and there is a brisk uptake of dextrose the rate of which is controlled, in part, by the presence of insulin.

### THE PHOSPHOLIPIDS

CHEMICAL STRUCTURE. The phospholipids probably occur mainly in combination with tissue proteins. They are divided into the monoaminophospholipids in which the ratio of nitrogen to phosphorus is 1:1 and the diaminophospholipids in which the ratio of nitrogen to phosphorus is 2:1. The identified monoaminophospholipids are lecithin (phosphatidyl choline), phosphatidylethanolamine and phosphatidylserine. These two latter compounds with some inositol-containing substances and uncharacterized basic materials have been referred to as the "cephalin" complex.

Lecithin and the members of the cephalin complex are composed of glycerol and fatty acids as are the triglycerides, but one fatty acid may be considered to be replaced by the phosphoric acid-nitrogenous base complex. There may be one saturated and one unsaturated fatty acid but in some cases two saturated or two unsaturated fatty acids occur. Oleic and either palmitic or stearic acids are commonly found but more highly unsaturated fatty acids such as linoleic and linolenic have been identified. In recent years pure synthetic lecithins identical in every respect with the natural substances have been made by Baer and his associates. Their work indicates that the naturally-occurring lecithins are of the alpha type. Sphingomyelin is a diaminophospholipid and contains two bases, choline and sphingosine, and one fatty acid radical but no glycerol. Different sphingomyelins containing respectively, stearic, lignoceric and nervonic acids have been found.

DISTRIBUTION. The phospholipids are widely distributed in the body and it is thought that all cells contain one or more of these compounds.

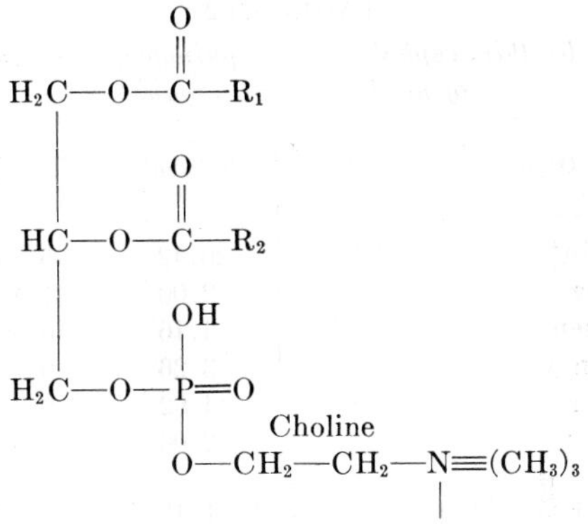

$$
\begin{array}{c}
O \\
\| \\
H_2C\!-\!O\!-\!C\!-\!R_1 \\
| \\
\quad\quad O \\
\quad\quad \| \\
HC\!-\!O\!-\!C\!-\!R_2 \\
| \\
\quad\quad OH \\
| \\
H_2C\!-\!O\!-\!P\!=\!O \\
| \quad\quad \text{Choline} \\
O\!-\!CH_2\!-\!CH_2\!-\!N\!\equiv\!(CH_3)_3 \\
\text{Lecithin} \quad OH
\end{array}
$$

$$
\begin{array}{c}
O \\
\| \\
H_2C\!-\!O\!-\!C\!-\!R_1 \\
| \\
\quad\quad O \\
\quad\quad \| \\
HC\!-\!O\!-\!C\!-\!R_2 \\
| \\
\quad\quad OH \\
| \\
H_2C\!-\!O\!-\!P\!=\!O \\
| \quad\quad \text{Ethanolamine} \\
O\!-\!CH_2\!-\!CH_2\!-\!NH_2 \\
\text{(or serine)}
\end{array}
$$

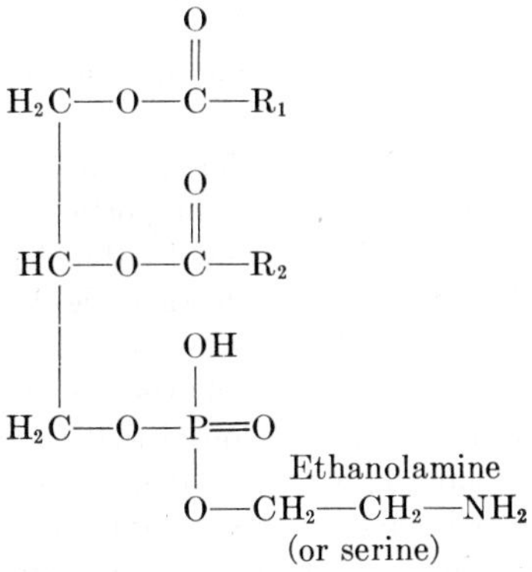

Phosphatidyl ethanolamine

$$
\begin{array}{c}
CH_3 \\
| \\
(CH_2)_{12} \\
| \\
CH \\
\| \\
CH \\
| \\
H\!-\!C\!-\!OH^* \quad O \\
| \quad\quad\quad \| \\
H\!-\!C\!-\!NH\!-\!C\!-\!R \\
| \\
\quad\quad O\!-\!CH_2CH_2N\!\!\diagup^{\displaystyle CH_3}_{\displaystyle\diagdown CH_3} \\
H\!-\!C\!-\!O\!-\!P \\
| \quad\quad OH \\
H \quad O \quad\quad OH
\end{array}
$$

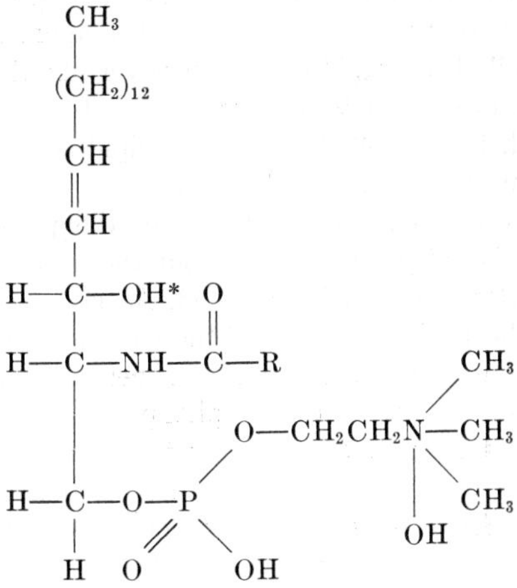

Sphingomyelin

\* May be esterified with fatty acid.

Sphingomyelin is present in much larger amounts in the brain and nerve tissues than elsewhere and is usually associated with the cerebrosides.

The "cephalin" content of the brain is considerably higher than the lecithin concentration. In the liver and spleen they occur in almost equal

TABLE 49.2

*The lecithin, cephalin, and sphingomyelin content of normal human organs\**

| Organ | Lecithin† | Cephalin† | Sphingo-myelin† |
|---|---|---|---|
| Brain‡....... | 4.81 | 20.42 | 5.66 |
| Lung........ | 3.85 | 2.00 | 1.45 |
| Spleen....... | 3.54 | 4.16 | 0.86 |
| Kidney...... | 5.10 | 3.26 | 0.72 |
| Liver........ | 4.81 | 4.62 | 0.38 |
| Heart........ | 4.47 | 2.06 | 0.34 |

\* From Thannhauser et al. (J. Biol. Chem., **129,** 717, 1939).

† The values representing mg. per 100 mg. of dried organ.

‡ Including both white and grey matter.

amounts while in the kidney, heart and lung, lecithin predominates in a proportion of about two to one. "Cephalin" and lecithin have been isolated from the gastric mucosa of pigs but sphingomyelin could not be demonstrated.

The evidence of the French workers Mayer and Schaeffer, and Terroine showed that the amount of phospholipid in a particular organ in a given species remains relatively constant under a variety of conditions including extreme starvation. As a result, they have called this fraction the "élément constant". This evidence strongly suggests that the lipids are structural components of the cell. Their rapid rate of turnover like that of many other structural elements has been established. In table 49.2 the phospholipid content of various human tissues is given.

PHYSIOLOGY. The exact role of the phospholipids is not yet understood but their metabolic importance is widely accepted. As noted above the phospholipid content of the various tissues is much more constant than that of neutral fat. Significant variations in phospholipids may, however, be induced by changing the nature of the diet or by alterations in the hormonal balance.

Insulin decreases the plasma phospholipid. Repeated injections of thyroid substance increase the amount in liver while removal of the thyroid causes a decrease. With the onset of pregnancy in the human subject the plasma phospholipids show a rise which continues to term (the other lipids also increase). The work of Aten and Hevesy indicates that milk phospholipids are synthesized in the mammary gland.

Bloor has suggested that the phospholipid content of a tissue may be considered an index of the extent and variety of its physiological functions. Thus, the phospholipid content is increased with physiological activity and decreased when the cells become less active. A secreting salivary gland of the dog (Caminade, Mayer and Vallée) has a higher phospholipid content than the resting one on the other side. The development of the corpus luteum is accompanied by a very significant increase in its phospholipid content (Bloor, Okey and Corner). When the body temperature of rabbits and dogs was greatly reduced by immersion in very cold water, Mayer and Schaeffer found a decrease in the phospholipid content of the liver and a compensatory rise when the animal had recovered from the experience. The phospholipid content of rapidly growing malignant tumor cells is higher than in normal tissue or in benign tumors of the same tissue.

The metabolic function of the phospholipids is most readily studied experimentally. The injection or feeding of synthetic compounds containing labelled atoms such as deuterium or radioactive tritium in place of hydrogen, heavy carbon $C^{13}$, radioactive carbon $C^{14}$, heavy nitrogen $N^{15}$, and radioactive phosphorus $P^{32}$ has made it possible to study the synthesis of the phospholipids. Schoenheimer, Bloch, Rittenberg, Hevesy, Artom, Chaikoff, Stetten and many others have used these techniques to increase our knowledge of phospholipid metabolism. Sinclair used elaidic acid, the unnatural trans-isomer of oleic acid, as a labelled compound in similar studies. The assumption that the body is unable to distinguish between the cis- and trans-isomer may not be justified. Indeed, recent reports of studies with compounds doubly or trebly labelled have shown that sometimes the different tracers have given different answers. Caution is necessary in the interpretation of data obtained with isotopes.

These methods have shown that the turnover of phospholipids is most rapid in the mucosa of the small intestine during fat absorption, somewhat slower in the liver and much slower in the muscles and kidneys. In the brain the incorporation into phospholipids of $P^{32}$ (given as inorganic phosphate) is a slow process. The correspondingly slow loss of $P^{32}$ from the brain confirms the sluggish turnover of phospholipids in nervous tissue. The limited data on the turnover rates of sphingomyelins in liver and muscle indicate that they are of about the same order of magnitude as that of lecithin although the latter always has the fastest regeneration rate.

A close relationship between liver and plasma

in regard to phospholipids has been established. Chaikoff and his associates have shown that virtually all the plasma phospholipids are derived from the liver. This was demonstrated by administering phosphate labelled with $P^{32}$ and palmitic acid labelled with $C^{14}$ to normal and hepatectomized dogs. Only traces of isotope were recovered from the plasma of hepatectomized dogs although other tissues (kidney, intestine, etc.) were able to synthesize phospholipids at the same rate as in the control dogs. The liver appears also to be the tissue principally concerned in the utilization of plasma phospholipids since their concentration changes but slowly in the absence of the liver. The incorporation of administered $P^{32}$ into phospholipids of the corpuscles is a much slower process than into those of the plasma.

## THE CEREBROSIDES (GLYCOLIPIDS)

In cerebrosides the base sphingosine is combined with a sugar (galactose or glucose) and a fatty acid. Thus the cerebrosides differ from one another in the nature of their fatty acids or carbohydrate. They can be distinguished from the phospholipids by the absence of phosphorus. The only individual cerebrosides that have been isolated in a pure condition contain galactose; they differ in their fatty acid component: kerasin contains a characteristic saturated acid (lignoceric, $C_{24}H_{48}O_2$); phrenosin (also called cerebron) contains the corresponding $\alpha$ hydroxy acid (cerebronic, $C_{24}H_{48}O_3$); nervone contains the corresponding $\Delta_{15}$ unsaturated acid (nervonic, $C_{24} \cdot H_{46}O_2$); hydroxynervone contains the corresponding unsaturated $\alpha$ hydroxy acid (hydroxynervonic, $C_{24}H_{46}O_3$). They are found particularly in nervous tissue; only minute amounts occur elsewhere in the normal body.

## CHOLESTEROL

*Chemical nature.* Cholesterol is found associated with the fats but chemically it is not related to them. Cholesterol, a white waxy solid, is the principal sterol found in animal organisms. The sterols are crystalline saturated or unsaturated complex alcohols derived from cyclopentanoperhydrophenanthrene. They occur both free and combined as esters or glycosides. Very minor changes in their structure sometimes produce extraordinary differences in physiological activity. The term steroid is applied to a group of closely related compounds containing the same complex nucleus. These substances include the sex hormones, bile acids, cardiac glycosides, toad poisons and vitamin D. Cholesterol has been known since the eighteenth century as the chief component of human gall stones. It is an unsaturated secondary alcohol. Most of the cholesterol occurs in the body as the so-called free form (the unesterified alcohol) which is precipitable by digitonin. A much smaller portion is present as the ester of long chain fatty acids (the so-called bound cholesterol). Recent studies indicate that both forms of cholesterol are present in some loose combination with protein. These complex materials of very high molecular weight, referred to as lipoproteins, have been studied by Chargaff, Gofman and others.

DISTRIBUTION. Cholesterol is found in all cells and fluids of the body. The free and bound forms are not equally distributed. The free cholesterol content of any particular tissue is characteristic and normally remains relatively constant; the esters, on the contrary, vary considerably in amount with changes in dietary, hormonal and other factors. The brain and suprarenals have the richest supply of cholesterol. In the former it is found mainly in the free form and in the latter about 90 per cent as ester. In bile it occurs only in the free state. In the corpuscles of human blood cholesterol exists chiefly in the free state while in the plasma more than half is present as the ester. In most other tissues the ester makes up a small fraction of the total. Table 49.3 shows the average total cholesterol content of normal tissues of rabbit and man.

ABSORPTION, TRANSPORT AND EXCRETION OF CHOLESTEROL. Crystalline cholesterol administered orally is absorbed in only small amounts unless some fatty material is also present in the intestine. Bile and pancreatic juice are said to aid in its absorption. Colloidal or amorphous cholesterol may be absorbed in the absence of dietary fat. Combination with the bile acids increases the solubility of cholesterol in intestinal fluids. The experiments of Mueller in 1915 on the absorption of cholesterol have been confirmed and extended by the tracer studies of Chaikoff and his associates using cholesterol labelled with $C^{14}$ at carbon atom 4. When free cholesterol is fed a portion is esterified and about half appears in the chyle in the bound form; on the other hand when cholesteryl esters are fed some hydrolysis occurs and again about half appears in the lymph in the free form. Thus, the processes of esterification or of hydrolysis (either before, during or after absorption) lead to essentially the same pro-

TABLE 49.3

*Total cholesterol content of normal tissues
(per cent of fresh tissue)*

|  | Rabbit* | Man† |
|---|---|---|
| Adrenals | 7.3 | 4.74 |
| Brain | 1.8 | 1.93 |
| Skin |  | 0.93 |
| Kidney | 0.44 | 0.33 |
| Spleen | 0.38 | 0.36 |
| Lung | 0.38 |  |
| Liver | 0.29 | 0.32 |
| Adipose tissue (subcut.) |  | 0.24 |
| Hair |  | 0.17 |
| Blood (whole) | 0.08 | 0.17 |
| Plasma | 0.06 | 0.23 |
| Corpuscles | 0.12 | 0.12 |
| Heart |  | 0.14 |
| Muscle | 0.06 | 0.07 |

The tissues of a man weighing 70 kg. may be calculated to contain slightly over 100 grams of total cholesterol: about 30 grams in adipose tissue, 25 grams in brain, 20 grams in muscle, slightly over 5 grams in whole blood, 5 grams in liver; because of their small size adrenals account for only about 0.5 gram.

  * After Chamberlain.
  † After Cook.

portions of free to bound cholesterol in the lymph. The exact site of this esterification whether in the lumen or intestinal wall is at present undecided. The increased cholesterol of the blood during fat absorption is probably due in large part to absorption of cholesterol contained in the pancreatic and intestinal juices and the bile. The increase in cholesterol ester has been taken to indicate that the sterol may play a part in the transport of fatty acids. It is very interesting that closely related sterols (phytosterol, coprosterol) are absorbed only in very small amounts (Schoenheimer and Sperry). The blood contains an enzyme which will split the esters and presumably, under other conditions, will cause synthesis (Shope; Sperry and Schoenheimer). Part of the absorbed free cholesterol, but not the ester, is excreted in the bile and part is changed to coprosterol by hydrogenation and eliminated in the feces. Some unchanged cholesterol is also excreted. The cholesterol plus coprosterol in the feces is usually greater than the cholesterol content of the diet. Some of the biliary cholesterol is reabsorbed in the small intestine. Gardner and Gainsborough state that cholesterol can be found in normal urine and that the amount is increased by cholesterol

feeding and in certain diseases. Under these circumstances cholesterol deposits may be found in the kidney tubules.

THE PHYSIOLOGY OF CHOLESTEROL. Synthesis and degradation of cholesterol go on simultaneously in the animal body. Herbivorous animals do not get any cholesterol in their food yet their tissues contain essentially the same levels of cholesterol as do those of omnivores and carnivores. Synthesis of cholesterol has been shown to occur in many tissues (adrenal, kidney, testis, ovary, small intestine, skin, etc.) but the liver is the most important site. Plasma cholesterol comes chiefly from the liver. The "two-carbon fragment", now identified as acetyl coenzyme A, has been recognized for some years as a metabolic intermediate in the synthesis of cholesterol in the body. Attempts have been made to measure the rate of synthesis of cholesterol by feeding acetate labelled with deuterium or $C^{14}$. The time required to synthesize an amount of cholesterol equal to the amount present in the body is called the regeneration time. Schoenheimer and Rittenberg suggested the term "regeneration" to denote replacement by *synthesized* molecules, since "turnover" implies only replacement without regard to source. Turnover could, for example, be applied to the replacement of tissue cholesterol by labelled *dietary* cholesterol. The regeneration time can be shown mathematically to be 1.44 × the "half-life regeneration time" as determined by standard techniques.

Rittenberg and Schoenheimer found the regeneration time for total body cholesterol in the mouse to be about 25 to 30 days. The regeneration time of cholesterol in the liver has been estimated to be about 4 to 5 days in the rabbit (Popjak) and in the rat about 9 days (Bloch). Regeneration in the carcass is very much slower, about 48 days being required in the rat. The regeneration time for plasma cholesterol has been found to be about 12 days in both man and dog. The rate of synthesis of plasma cholesterol in normal man appears to be about 500 to 600 mg. per day (Rittenberg). The nature and caloric value of the diet affect the rate of synthesis of cholesterol; during fasting the process is much retarded. The amount synthesized per day in man is probably about ten times the average daily intake. An increase in the dietary intake decreases the amount formed in the body.

Hormonal factors also affect the metabolism of cholesterol. A single injection of an anterior pituitary extract containing the adrenocorticotrophic hormone (ACTH) causes a definite fall in adrenal cholesterol within a few hours (Sayers, Long). When the thyroid is overactive, the concentration of cholesterol in the blood is decreased; drugs such as thiouracil, which depress the activity of the thyroid, increase the level of blood cholesterol. In human subjects estrogens depress serum cholesterol. Cyclic variations of serum cholesterol have been described in women during both the menses and pregnancy. On the other hand, there is no convincing evidence for a primary effect of androgens or progesterone upon cholesterol metabolism.

Bloch has demonstrated with the aid of deuterium the conversion of cholesterol to pregnanediol. It appears that cholesterol may also act as a precursor of other steroid hormones.

Ever since Overton's work in 1899, the lipoid nature of the cell membrane has aroused interest. The hydrophilic nature of the lecithins, the hydrophobic nature of cholesterol and the peculiar intermediate properties of the cholesteryl esters have been invoked to explain the phenomena at membranes. While there are many examples of the physicochemical antagonism of cholesterol and lecithin, little exact information is available as to the physiological role of the cholesterol moiety of the lipoproteins in cell membranes.

## The Absorption of Fat

(See also p. 676)

Since the fats and their hydrolytic products, the fatty acids, are very sparingly soluble in water, the explanation of their absorption presents special difficulties. The exact mechanism is still unsolved. There are two main schools of thought concerning the processes involved. One group champions Pflüger's lipolytic theory, the other Frazer's partition hypothesis. Nearly 200 years ago Hewson (1774) observed that the milky fluid seen in the lacteals following a meal leaves a grease spot when dried on paper. Under the microscope the milky fluid was seen to contain numerous tiny particles for which Gage in 1920 proposed the name chylomicron. In 1856 Claude Bernard had demonstrated that a fine emulsification of fat occurs in the intestine and showed that this depends upon the presence of bile and pancreatic lipase. Bernard also noted that lipemia was present in the systemic circulation following ingestion of a fat-rich meal. Further study of this phenomenon was made by Munk and Rosenstein in 1891, utilizing a patient with a lymphatic fistula of the leg.

The mode of transfer of the neutral fat from the epithelial cells to the central lacteals remains a matter for conjecture. The leukocytes have been credited with this function but most of the evidence is against their playing such a role. During fat absorption the central lacteals show rhythmical contractions which evidently serve to pump the chyle contained within them into the lymphatics tributary to the thoracic duct. Thus the absorbed fat is constantly propelled along the lymphatic channels of the mesentery.

According to the classical lipolytic theory, fat is emulsified and split completely to fatty acids and glycerol before absorption. The fatty acids, rendered water-soluble by complex formation with bile salts, are believed to enter the epithelial cells of the intestinal villi where they are combined with glycerophosphoric acid or phosphatidic acid to form phospholipids and finally reappear as neutral fat. This is carried largely in the lymph, by way of the lacteals, to the thoracic duct where it enters the systemic circulation.

The partition theory suggests that it is not necessary for all the fats to be completely hydrolyzed. Frazer believes that free fatty acids are absorbed by the blood and pass to the liver by way of the portal vein, while glycerides (tri-, di- or mono-), with particle size below 0.5 $\mu$ are absorbed through the intestinal mucosa directly into the lymph. Thus absorption of fat is partitioned between portal blood and lymph according to the degree of hydrolysis.

Recently studies have been made with free fatty acids and triglycerides labelled with $C^{14}$. When these compounds were given by stomach tube to rats, over 90 per cent of the absorbed fatty acids were recovered from the thoracic duct lymph in both cases. Such findings are *not* consistent with the original partition theory. The main tenet of this theory, i.e., that complete hydrolysis of glycerides is not necessary, is however now well established. By feeding synthetic glycerides labelled with $C^{14}$ in the glycerol part of the molecule, it has been conclusively shown that hydrolysis of long chain glycerides in the intestine is neither rapid nor complete. Other studies indicate that in some cases a large proportion of dietary fat is absorbed in the form of glyceride. Small amounts of monoglyceride, formed in the intestinal lumen by the hydrolytic action of lipases, can exert a powerful emulsifying effect, thus enabling the bulk of the dietary glycerides to be dispersed to particles of extremely fine size. These particles, as noted above, can be directly absorbed.

Fat is not only transported as chylomicrons which are largely triglycerides but as phospholipids and cholesterol esters, and in lipoproteins. The relative importance of these vehicles and of the nonesterified fatty acids in plasma is a subject for further research.

### The Elimination of Fat from the Body

There is no fat or phospholipid in the urine under normal conditions but the latter may appear in disease. There are only traces of fat in the secretion of the skin.

The fat content of the feces is normally between 6 and 12 per cent of the fat which is absorbed but as Sperry has pointed out this bears

TABLE 49.4

*Lipid components of plasma in the fasting state (mean values in mg. per 100 ml.) After Boyd.*

|  | Man | Rat | Rabbit | Cockerel |
|---|---|---|---|---|
| Total lipid............ | 530 | 230 | 243 | 520 |
| Total fatty acid...... | 316 | 152 | 169 | 361 |
| Neutral fat.......... | 142 | 85 | 105 | 225 |
| Phospholipid......... | 165 | 83 | 78 | 155 |
| Total cholesterol..... | 152 | 52 | 45 | 100 |
|   Free cholesterol.... | 46 | 21 | 22 | 34 |
|   Cholesteryl esters*.. | 178 | 52 | 39 | 111 |

\* Bound cholesterol $\times$ 1.68.

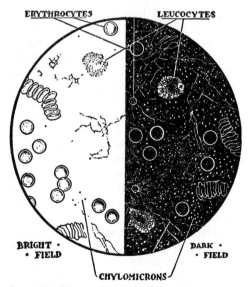

FIG. 49.1. Shows chylomicrons. (After Gage.)

no relation to the food fat. In dogs, even after five weeks or more on a fat-free diet, there are considerable amounts of fat in the feces. Some 60 per cent of this is neutral fat and 40 per cent fatty acids. A large part of this lipid excretion is derived from bacteria and cellular debris.

When the bile duct is ligated, large, light colored stools are usually observed as this procedure interferes greatly with fat absorption. Digestion is nearly complete, however, as is shown by the fact that the fat is excreted chiefly as fatty acids. Fatty stools are found also when the pancreatic ducts are tied although the absorption of fat is by no means completely prevented. When pancreatic lipase is excluded in this way the excreted fat contains more glyceride and less fatty acid.

### Blood Fat

Blood transports not only the fatty materials absorbed from the intestines but also lipids resulting from intermediary metabolism. The amount of lipid material found in the plasma of animals in the postabsorptive state (i.e., at least 12 hours after the last meal) does not vary greatly under normal conditions. Table 49.4 gives typical values for the lipid components in the plasma of several species. If, however, a sample of blood is withdrawn 3 to 6 hours after the ingestion of a large amount of fat, such as olive oil or thick cream, a distinct milkiness of the plasma will usually be observed. The milkiness is due to the presence of the tiny microscopic fat particles called chylomicrons (fig. 49.1). This is a physiological occurrence which is often associated with the postprandial hyperlipemia following a fatty meal. The extent to which the amount of fat in the blood has increased is sometimes studied by counting these particles under a dark field microscope. Erroneous impressions may be obtained by this method, however, since an increased amount of heparin in the blood, and possibly other factors, can minimize or prevent the appearance of this milkiness in plasma which, by chemical methods, can be demonstrated to contain abnormally large amounts of fatty material. Thus, great variations in the degree of milkiness may be observed in a single individual under apparently identical experimental conditions. Part of the discrepancy can be explained in other ways, since the amount of fat present in the blood at any given instant depends on the balance between the rate of absorption and the rate at which it is being utilized or deposited in adipose tissue. It is obvious, therefore, that the degree of alimentary lipemia is not a consistently reliable index of the rate at which fat is being absorbed. The postprandial increase in blood lipids is due chiefly to neutral fat; smaller increases in cholesteryl esters and phospholipid are often observed. Besides the transient alimentary hyperlipemia there are the so-called retention and transportation hyperlipemias. As stated above, the cholesterol and phospholipids found in plasma originate chiefly in the liver. The plasma phospholipids consist chiefly of the choline-containing types (lecithin and sphingomyelin). The larger proportion of the lipid components of the plasma appear to be in combination with proteins.

The mechanism of production of the interesting lipemia which follows hemorrhage in certain species requires further study.

## Fat Transport

The long held belief that phospholipids are particularly active in fat metabolism and transport, seems now to be disproved. Pihl and Bloch, for example, using acetate labelled with $C^{14}$, have shown that the rate of regeneration of neutral fat is faster than that of phospholipid, from which they concluded that phospholipids are not obligatory intermediates in the synthesis of neutral fat. Their data on plasma lipids suggest that it is unlikely that phospholipids are a major vehicle for fat transport. Indeed, the data suggest that neutral fat may represent the most important means of lipid transport in the plasma.

It was thought, until recently, that all the fatty acids of the blood and tissues were present in bound forms, as esters. It is now known that small amounts of non-esterified fatty acids occur in plasma, loosely bound to protein, particularly albumin. This unesterified or nonesterified fraction of the plasma lipids (UFA or NEFA) consists chiefly of oleic, linoleic, palmitic and stearic acids. As Gordon and Dole and their colleagues have shown, NEFA arise from the fat of adipose and other tissues, including plasma lipoproteins. An enzyme "lipoprotein lipase," isolated by Korn from heart and adipose tissue, catalyzes the release of fatty acids from lipoprotein in the presence of albumin or other acceptor protein for the fatty acids. Heparin is part of this enzyme complex, which has the same properties as the "clearing factor" of plasma.

Labeled NEFA are very rapidly removed from the blood by the liver, muscle and other organs, and are either incorporated into the lipids of the tissues or oxidized to carbon dioxide. Little uptake by adipose cells occurs. The half-life of NEFA in the blood is very brief (a matter of minutes), indicating that they have great metabolic activity. Calculations indicate that they account for most of the lipid utilized.

In the fasting condition the NEFA are somewhat elevated and are diminished by the ingestion of glucose. Thus their release from the depots appears to be influenced by demands for energy and the availability of other nutrients. In normal individuals given insulin the changes in NEFA parallel those of the blood glucose. In diabetic acidosis the NEFA levels are very high, but may be rapidly lowered by the administration of insulin and glucose. Thus insulin appears to regulate, in part, the release of NEFA from the lipid depots. During lipid mobilization produced by growth hormone in fasting animals, on the other hand, the NEFA rise, indicating increased production.

A relatively unexplored possibility is that the calorie-rich lipids in blood may be used to supply energy to areas of higher metabolic activity. To explain the large amounts of lipids found in plasma was not easy in view of the well known insolubility of neutral fats and free cholesterol in water. It was first suggested that incorporation of fatty acids into phospholipids and cholesteryl esters would account for the findings. The more recent discovery that these latter substances and neutral fats occur in the plasma largely in combination with protein, may provide a hypothesis to account for the transport of energy-rich compounds in the form of lipids. It is conceivable that the lipoproteins may transport water-soluble lipids in the plasma by some mechanism similar to that in which hemoglobin transports oxygen (Turner).

### Lipid Mobilization

Mobilization of lipid at elevated rates from the body depots occurs during fasting, after the administration of certain anterior pituitary gland extracts or hormones to fasting animals, when there is deficiency of insulin. A characteristic pattern of changes can be recognized during lipid mobilization, although there are considerable differences in degree from species to species. During the first phase of fasting the carbohydrate reserves are rapidly depleted. In the second phase fat accounts for about four-fifths of the total energy utilized in man, and protein the remainder. Large amounts of lipid accumulate in the liver of the mouse, guinea pig and rabbit, but not in that of the rat, while the lipid of the reserves is being depleted. In primates, including man, ketonaemia and ketonuria occur and the non-esterified fatty acids (NEFA) of the serum increase. Incubation of liver tissue from fasting animals *in vitro* reveals that the production of acetoacetate is increased and the synthesis of fatty acids is decreased; while the production of NEFA by incubated adipose tissue is increased.

Certain fractions of the anterior pituitary gland intensify the mobilization of lipid in fasting animals (Best and Campbell). This activity is possessed by the growth, adrenocorticotrophic and thyroid-stimulating hormones, and the possibility of a more specific factor is not yet excluded. Treatment with these factors causes (a) over-all increased utilization of fat in the body with depletion of fat reserves, (b) rapid and massive deposition of fat in the liver and, to a lesser extent, in the kidney, (c) increased retention of nitrogen and glycogen in the liver, (d) ketonaemia and ketonuria, (e) increase in NEFA of the serum. The protein and glycogen-sparing effects on the liver may be due to the increased utilization of lipid. A fat-mobilizing fraction, termed "adipokinin" by Weil and Stetten, occurs in the urine of fasting animals and has been obtained also in the urine of fasting man. This material is possibly of pituitary origin. The liver tissue of the pituitary-treated rats produces acetoacetate and utilizes oxygen, *in vitro*, at greatly increased rates. These effects are due, apparently, to increased concentration of substrate (lipid) and to the stimulation of oxidative activity in the liver tissue.

Lipid mobilization by anterior pituitary administration is inhibited by adrenalectomy. However, the adrenocorticotrophic hormone can induce mobilization in the absence of the adrenals (Engel). The adrenal cortical hormones do not induce mobilization, but sensitize the tissues to the adipokinetic factors. Seifter finds that the administration of cortisone to normal (but not to hypophysectomized) animals causes the appearance in the serum of a dialysable substance that elicits fat mobilization when injected into test animals. This factor appears to come from the posterior pituitary gland. Thyroidectomy causes inhibition and loss of response to adipokinetic factors, and thyroid treatment restores the response (Best and Campbell).

Deficiency of insulin, as in depancreatized dogs, rapidly induces (a) wastage of body tissues, with depletion of carbohydrate, fat and protein re-

serves, (b) rapid and massive accumulation of fat in the liver, with increase in the size and friability of the organ (lipid accumulates also, but to a lesser extent, in the kidney and heart), (c) ketonaemia and ketonuria, (d) increase in the NEFA of the blood serum, and (e) inhibition of synthesis of fat. The conclusion is inescapable that these changes are associated with increased utilization of lipid and mobilization of lipid, with deposition of lipid from the depots in liver and kidney. The administration of insulin prevents or reverses all these alterations. It is well known that all these effects of insulin deficiency and of insulin treatment can be recognized in diabetes mellitus. Insulin added to the medium bathing adipose tissue *in vitro* increases the uptake of labelled glucose, the production of carbon dioxide and the synthesis of fatty acids (Renold) and also decreases the output of NEFA (Gordon and Cherkes).

The pituitary gland may be involved in producing these effects of insulin deficiency. The ketosis and the accumulation of fat in the liver of the depancreatized dog are diminished or abolished by hypophysectomy. Diabetes induced in dogs by the administration of growth hormone for four or five days is accompanied by massive accumulation of fat in the liver, with enlargement and increased friability. Lipid also accumulates in the kidney and the heart, while in the blood the lipids, the NEFA and the ketone bodies, rise.

### The Liver and Fat Metabolism

Recent tracer studies have confirmed the importance of the liver in the metabolism of fat. As mentioned earlier, the liver is the main site of formation of plasma phospholipids and of plasma cholesterol. The liver is the major organ for the synthesis of fatty acids from carbohydrate (although this process has been shown to occur in other tissues, e.g., adipose tissue, kidney, muscle, gastrointestinal mucosa and lung) and it is the principal site for the oxidation of the higher fatty acids. Some of the earlier observations which linked the liver with fat metabolism are as follows: (1) The fatty acids combined as liver phospholipids and glycerides are more unsaturated than the fatty acids found in other tissues. (2) The rate of phospholipid turnover in the liver is more rapid than in any other tissue, with the possible exception of the intestinal mucosa during fat absorption. (3) The liver is the principal site of formation of the ketone bodies which are well-known metabolic intermediates in the metabolism of fat.

(1) The fact that the fatty acids in the liver are more unsaturated than those in other tissues was interpreted by Leathes and Meyer-Wedell as evidence for desaturation of fatty acids (formation of double bonds) in the liver; Raper suggested that the liver cells may selectively retain the more unsaturated fatty acids. Using fatty acids labelled with deuterium Schoenheimer and Rittenberg were able to supply direct evidence for the desaturation of stearic acid to oleic acid; they also showed that degradation of stearic acid to palmitic acid (with two less carbon atoms) occurs in the body. The lipids of the body were shown to be constantly undergoing synthesis, interconversion and degradation and the rate at which these processes occur was found to be much greater in the liver than in other organs. More recent studies using fatty acids and glycerides labelled with $C^{14}$ have emphasized the important role of the liver in the utilization of fat. Experiments on hepatectomized and eviscerated animals have revealed the possible importance of lipids as sources of energy in extrahepatic tissue.

(2) The rate of phospholipid turnover in the liver has been studied by giving radioactive inorganic phosphate ($P^{32}$), fatty acids labelled with $C^{14}$ and choline labelled with heavy nitrogen ($N^{15}$). All these experiments have shown that the liver phospholipids are regenerated rapidly. More recent studies indicate that the several parts of the molecule (choline, P and fatty acids) are turning over at about the same rate.

(3) It has been well established that the liver is by far the most important site for the production of ketone bodies (see below).

The liver normally contains about 6 per cent of total lipids. Variations within the range from 5 to 7 per cent are considered normal; about 50 per cent of this lipid material consists of phospholipids, about 3 per cent of free cholesterol, about 1 per cent of cholesteryl esters and the remainder (45 to 55 per cent) consists principally of glycerides.

The amount of fat which is present in the liver at any time depends on the following factors:

1. The rate at which fat is brought to the liver by the blood.
2. The rate at which the liver is able to take up fat from the blood.
3. The rate at which the liver can deal with fat,
    (a) by direct oxidation in the liver cells,
    (b) by passing it on in the same or in a slightly changed form to other parts of the body.

4. The rate of synthesis of fat in the liver from other materials.

There is an increase in the fat of the liver within a few hours after the ingestion of a meal containing large amounts of fat. Under these conditions the ingested fatty acids appear in the liver lipids thus altering their composition. Under certain conditions the liver may become intensely fatty when no fat is fed; here the fatty acids are derived from the depot fat or from ingested carbohydrate or protein. When "ear-marked" fats are deposited in the tissues and then some poison such as phosphorus or chloroform is administered, the excess of liver fat contains the fatty acids which were present in the depot fat.

FATTY LIVERS. Under a variety of conditions neutral fat or cholesteryl esters may accumulate in the liver to a very much greater extent than in other tissues. In experimental animals fatty livers have been produced containing over 50 per cent of total lipids but this is an extreme situation and values between 20 and 40 per cent are more frequently encountered. These fatty livers are much larger and paler than normal livers; the greater part of the increase in weight of the liver is due to accumulation of glycerides and water. Phospholipids and free cholesterol remain remarkably constant; cholesteryl esters increase significantly whenever glycerides increase.

Some conditions which result in an excessive deposition of fat in the liver are as follows:

1. Starvation—the fatty liver of starvation is clearly seen in some species of animals. It disappears when the fat reserves are exhausted.

2. Injection in fasting animals of a fraction obtained from the anterior pituitary gland—purified growth hormone ACTH and TSH are active and the possibility remains that a more specific unidentified factor is operating.

3. Insufficiency of insulin.

4. Dietary deficiency—diets deficient in choline or its precursors, diets rich in fat or containing excessive amounts of cholesterol, diets deficient in protein.

5. Environmental changes—reduced atmospheric pressure (e.g., at high altitudes or elevated temperatures.

6. Poisons—phosphorus, chloroform and other chlorinated compounds, benzol, ketene, phloridzin, or bacterial toxins.

7. Clinical conditions in which one or more of the above situations are present, e.g., kwashiorkor (world-wide malignant undernutrition), diabetes

mellitus, pernicious anemia, yellow fever, pregnancy.

THE LIPOTROPIC FACTORS. Choline and its dietary precursors, betaine and methionine, are in the rations of animals so as to prevent the accumulation of excessive amounts of fat in the liver (fig. 49.2). Choline, a quaternary ammonium base:

$$(CH_3)_3N—CH_2 \cdot CH_2OH,$$
$$|$$
$$OH$$

occurs widely distributed in nature although it is rarely found in the free condition in more than traces. It was first isolated (from bile) by Strecker in 1849 and has long been known as a constituent of lecithin and sphingomyelin. Lean meats (muscle) contain about 100 mg. choline per 100 grams of fresh meat. Kidney contains 200 to 300 mg., brain 350 to 450 mg., liver from 450 to 600 mg., fish muscle 50 to 80 mg., whole eggs 350 to 700 mg.; egg yolk about 1400 to 1700 mg., whole wheat 50 to 100 mg., wheat germ 350 to 400 mg., oats, barley, rye, corn and rice contain about 60 to 100 mg., yeast (brewer's dried) 240 to 360 mg. per 100 g. Vegetables as a group are low in choline and fruits are very low. Edible fats as obtained commercially are almost free from choline.

The other naturally occurring substances which possess lipotropic activity are betaine (the internally neutralized acid formed by oxidizing the primary alcohol group of choline), methionine and β-propiothetin. They have been shown to possess labile methyl groups and it is believed that they possess lipotropic activity by acting as precursors of choline. Vitamin $B_{12}$ and folic acid, which are important in hematopoiesis, are also able under some conditions to produce a lipotropic effect. The relations between these two substances in lipotropic phenomena are not yet clearly understood but vitamin $B_{12}$ appears to be concerned in the biosynthesis of labile methyl groups and folic acid in transmethylation reactions or in the synthesis of some other part of the choline molecule. Inositol exerts a limited lipotropic effect in fat-free diets but this effect is minimized when any fat is in the food. The crude pancreatic extract which has been referred to as "lipocaic" was at one time thought to possess some unique lipotropic influence since it was believed to be free from choline. While it may contain only traces of free choline its content of bound choline sometimes makes it one of the richest known sources of this base. Methionine and vitamin $B_{12}$ are also present in this extract and if proteolytic enzymes are present they may make methionine available from the dietary protein.

In 1924 Allan, Bowie, Macleod and Robinson in Toronto, and Fisher in Chicago, noted that large fatty livers developed in depancreatized dogs maintained for a long time with insulin. Inclusion of raw beef pancreas in the diet prevented this fatty change. Hershey and Soskin noted a similar protective effect with crude egg lecithin. In 1932 Best, Hershey and Huntsman found that they could produce fatty livers in rats by dietary means in about three weeks as contrasted with a period of more than six months required in the depancreatized dog. With this more rapid method of investigation they quickly identified choline as the active constituent in the lecithin molecule. Betaine was found to exert a similar effect. It was soon discovered that casein and certain other proteins possess lipotropic activity. This activity of protein was largely accounted for in 1937 when Tucker and Eckstein discovered the lipotropic property of methionine. It exerts a lipotropic effect by transferring its methyl group to ethanolamine, thus effecting the biosynthesis of choline (du Vigneaud). When choline, betaine or methionine labelled in the methyl group with deuterium were fed singly to rats, the choline of tissue phospholipids, the methionine of tissue proteins and urinary creatinine were all found to contain labelled methyl groups. The enzymatic process involved is known as transmethylation and the particular groups concerned are said to be labile methyl groups. Not all methyl groups are labile; a distinction must be made between the processes of *de*methylation and *trans*methylation since *de*methylation does not necessarily give rise to a labile methyl group (e.g., sarcosine).

The original view that the animal body is unable to synthesize methyl groups had to be modified when it was found that rats could survive and grow slowly under certain dietary conditions on rations devoid of any preformed methyl groups (Bennett, Medes and Toennies). Later, the importance of vitamin $B_{12}$ and of folic acid in the biosynthesis of methyl groups and in the metabolism of the "one carbon fragment" became apparent.

A labile methyl group is not necessary for lipotropic action. Tracer studies have indicated that the methyl groups of choline are not labile and *only become so after oxidation* to betaine. It had been recognized previously that arsenocholine

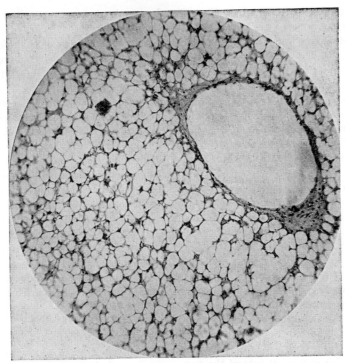

FIG. 49.2 Section from liver of depancreatized dog fed a diet low in choline. Ether-soluble material over 60 per cent of wet weight. ×200. (From Best, Huntsman and Young.)

(Welch), triethylcholine (Channon, McArthur), and sulfocholine (du Vigneaud) which contain *no labile methyl groups* exert a lipotropic effect. When fed, they are incorporated into liver phospholipids as the intact molecule. These observations suggest that the lipotropic action of choline is exerted by the intact molecule and not by virtue of its methyl groups. Dietary components with labile methyl groups exert their lipotropic effect by favoring biosynthesis of choline.

The physiological test for a labile methyl group is to feed the compound containing the methyl group to a rat being fed a synthetic diet complete in every sense except that methionine is replaced by homocystine. If growth occurs, which can only happen when methionine is formed, transfer (or synthesis) of methyl groups must have taken place.

When the lipotropic factors[2] are not available

in the diet large amounts of fat accumulate in the liver. In young animals hemorrhagic lesions are seen in the kidneys and other tissues (Griffith and Wade), and these may produce death. The antilipotropic factor cholesterol aggravates the liver and kidney changes while choline, betaine and methionine prevent their development. When young rats are subjected for only five days to a diet deficient in choline and its precursors and are then returned to a full normal diet a malignant hypertension of renal origin develops, four or five months later, in a considerable proportion of the animals (Hartroft and Best).

In the depancreatized dog, choline has been shown to be one of the active components of beef pancreas which as previously stated prevents the development of fatty livers. The protein of pancreas through its methionine content will pre-

[2] The term lipotropic was originally used to describe the action of choline which prevented the deposition of, or accelerated the rate of removal of fat from the liver. It now has a somewhat broader meaning and is used to describe the action of choline and its precursors methionine and betaine on fat deposition in liver and kidney. Only those effects of methionine and betaine which are exerted through formation of choline are included in the term "lipotropic." Substances such as cholesterol which cause a deposition of liver fat are referred to as antilipotropic and hypothetical diets free of lipotropic factors may be described as alipotropic. Cystine, under certain dietary conditions increases the deposition of liver fat and the incidence of hemorrhagic kidneys. This is apparently related to an improvement in the diet; the resulting increased food intake stimulates growth and creates an additional need for the lipotropic factors.

sumably also exert a lipotropic effect. Furthermore, the pancreatic enzymes will help to liberate choline and methionine from the phospholipids and protein of the diet. There are thus three pathways by which the minced pancreas, the study of which initiated these investigations, may have contributed the lipotropic agents.

The mechanism by which choline exerts its lipotropic action is unknown. There is a little evidence suggesting that complex esters of choline may act as coenzymes in the metabolism of the lipids.

CIRRHOSIS. Prolonged exposure to certain toxic chemical or infectious agents or dietary deficiencies which cause fatty livers can lead eventually to an excessive production of fibrous connective tissue. The shrunken, distorted liver which results is usually of a peculiar orange to brownish color. It is this aspect which Laennec featured in the name *cirrhosis. Kwashiorkor* is a pandemic form of cirrhosis found among severely undernourished infants and children in many parts of the world. It appears to be related to diets in which the protein is both low in quantity and poor in quality. No significant role of the lipotropic factors has, as yet, been detected. Some forms of experimental cirrhosis are attributable to deficiency of the lipotropes. The first lesions of this type, preventable by administration of the lipotropic agents, were noted by Maclean and Best in 1934. In depancreatized and later in normal dogs Chaikoff produced cirrhosis by prolonged feeding of diets which permitted fat to accumulate in the liver. Later the lesion was studied in rats by György and Goldblatt, Blumberg and McCollum, by Daft, Sebrell and Lillie, by Hartroft and by others. Experimental *dietary* cirrhosis begins by condensation of fibrous stroma supporting centrolobular cells which have been distended by excessive fat to their bursting points. The ruptured cells atrophy and disappear leaving a scar formed by their stromal remnants. By repetition and extension of the process these scars eventually spread through the rest of the liver including some areas around large portal veins. It can be prevented or, in its early stages, cured in animals by the addition of choline or its precursors to the diet.

*Alcoholic cirrhosis* is probably often of dietary rather than of toxic origin. The excessive consumption of alcohol supplies sufficient calories so that the patient feels no need for other foods which would provide the necessary proteins, vitamins and minerals. The toxic effect of alcohol in very large doses, on various tissues cannot be doubted.

The acute effects of chloroform poisoning on the liver in protein-depleted dogs are diminished or prevented by the administration of methionine (Miller and Whipple).

Methionine, cystine or $\alpha$-tocopherol protect rats against a massive necrosis of the liver which appears when these substances are in large part removed from the diet. These protective effects of methionine are not exerted through its lipotropic action. Schwarz has recently established the importance of selenium as a protective agent against necrosis of dietary origin.

FAT AND GLYCOGEN IN LIVER. While it is true that very small amounts of glycogen are present in very fatty livers and that the fat content is low when large amounts of glycogen are found, it can also be shown that moderate amounts of glycogen can accumulate in moderately fatty livers.

## Intermediary Metabolism of Fat

During the oxidation of fat to carbon dioxide and water a number of intermediary substances are formed. It has been known for a long time that three substances are produced during the oxidation of fatty acids, namely, acetoacetic acid, $\beta$-hydroxybutyric acid and acetone. These are collectively known as the ketone bodies. The discovery of coenzyme A by Lipmann in 1945 and the identification of "active acetate" as acetyl coenzyme A by Lynen and his colleagues (1951) are achievements of historic importance. We shall attempt to correlate these recent studies with the previously known facts.

Under ordinary conditions the ketone bodies are present in the blood in very small amounts (about 1 to 3 mg. of total ketones per 100 ml. blood) and only about 0.3 gram are excreted daily. Ketosis (increased amounts of ketones in blood and urine) may occur when increased amounts of fat are metabolized, for example when the diet is rich in fat, or during fasting when the fat reserves of the body are being rapidly utilized. Certain clinical conditions in which ketosis occurs are: diabetes mellitus, fevers, the postoperative state, toxemias of pregnancy, hyperthyroidism, glycogen disease. Ketosis is seen experimentally in pancreatic or phlorhizin diabetes, after administration of certain hormones (growth hormone, adrenocorticotrophic, adrenocortical and, in fasting animals, insulin). The amino acids leucine, isoleucine, phenylalanine, tyrosine and hydroxyproline, produce an increased excretion of ketone bodies in diabetic animals. Other amino acids may give rise to glucose in the body. It has been estimated that protein predominantly forms glucose rather than ketones. Ketones may be produced through the oxidation of pyruvate by liver slices *in vitro* but in the intact animal the effect of pyruvate appears to be antiketogenic. In general, it may be taken that the precursors of the ketone bodies are the fatty acids.

### INTERCONVERSION AND EXCRETION OF THE KETONE BODIES

Acetoacetic acid is the ketone body that is produced first by the tissue cells. Acetone arises by decarboxylation of this acid—a spontaneous reaction that does not necessarily require the enzymatic activity of the tissue cells. The acetoacetic acid may be reduced by the tissues to β-hydroxybutyric acid. The reaction is reversible. In ketosis the greater part of the total ketones occurs as the hydroxy acid. Since β-hydroxybutyric acid is weaker than acetoacetic acid this conversion tends to reduce the unfavorable effects of accumulation of fixed acid.

All three ketone bodies are excreted in the urine. Acetone may also be excreted in the expired air, giving a characteristic odor to the breath of the individual with ketosis. In the days before insulin the diabetic ward could be thus detected at a distance.

### SITES OF ORIGIN OF THE KETONE BODIES

It is generally accepted that the liver is by far the most important site of production of ketone bodies. The perfused liver produces abundant quantities of ketones while little comes from other organs such as kidneys, lung and skeletal muscle (Embden; Snapper, Grünbaum and Neuberg). Himwich and his associates found that liver consistently added ketones, while striated muscle, heart and the organs drained by the portal vein only occasionally added small amounts of ketones,

and sometimes removed them from the blood. It has been observed repeatedly that liver slices may add ketones to the medium and produce relatively large amounts from added fatty acids while other tissues are very much less active. The rate of utilization of acetoacetate by liver tissue is practically nil, i.e., acetoacetate appears to be an end-product of fatty acid oxidation by the liver. In contrast, acetoacetate and β-hydroxybutyrate are readily utilized by muscle and other extrahepatic tissues.

### THE MODE OF FORMATION OF KETONES

The higher fatty acids that occur in the body contain an even number of carbon atoms in a straight-chain arrangement. This is not the place to describe the contributions of Knoop, Raper, Schoenheimer and Rittenberg, and many others, all of which pointed to a fundamental two-carbon unit concerned in the metabolism of fatty acids. Two of these units were assumed by MacKay and associates to condense to form acetoacetic acid. Support for this assumption was provided by Weinhouse, Medes and Floyd by labelling octanoic acid with isotopic carbon in the carboxyl group. The acetoacetate formed when this was incubated with liver slices was found to contain the isotope distributed almost equally between the carbonyl and the carboxyl carbon atoms. This could only have resulted from the condensation of pairs of molecules, each containing two carbon atoms (acetyl groups) arising by β-oxidation of the fatty acid. These experiments establish the principle of beta-oxidation and of condensation of "acetate" molecules in the formation of acetoacetate. Subsequent studies have shown that when carboxyl-labelled fatty acids are utilized to form acetoacetate the ratio of the label in the carbonyl:label in the carboxyl carbon varies in a regular manner with chain length, rising from about 0.3 for butyrate to 0.8 for octanoate and to 1.0 for higher fatty acids. The reasons for this

$$CH_3COCH_3 + CO_2 \rightarrow \text{Expired air}$$
$$\text{acetone}$$

Fatty acids $\xrightarrow[\text{Enzymes}]{\text{Liver}}$ "Active acetate" $\rightarrow CH_3COCH_2COOH \rightarrow$ Urine
acetoacetic acid
$$CH_3CHOHCH_2COOH$$

Oxidation in extrahepatic tissues to ← β-hydroxybutyric acid
$$CO_2 + H_2O$$

Scheme showing the metabolism and routes of excretion of the ketone bodies.

inequality have been explained by Lynen and by Mahler.

### The Role of the Coenzyme of Acetylation (CoA) in Fatty Acid Metabolism

While studying "active acetate", Lipmann investigated the acetylation of aromatic amines such as sulfanilamide by tissues and tissue enzymes and discovered that a heat-stable co-factor, the coenzyme of acetylation (CoA) is required.

Coenzyme A has been isolated from liver, which is a rich source, and also from yeast and other microorganisms. It is a dinucleotide consisting of 2-thiol-ethylamine (I) and pantothenic acid (II) linked by a pyrophosphate bridge (III) to adenosine (IV) which has a phosphoryl radical at position 3 of its ribose moiety.

Observations in several laboratories suggested that "active acetate" might be an acetylated derivative of this coenzyme (Lipmann, Stadtman, Ochoa). The brilliant studies of Lynen and his colleagues led to the isolation from yeast of a substance able to acetylate without the intervention of ATP. This substance proved to be identical with "active acetate". Chemical investigations showed it to be acetyl-coenzyme A, in which the labile acetyl group (i.e., the "active two-carbon unit") is linked to the sulfur atom. To emphasize the presence and importance of sulfur in this high-energy bond the abbreviated

formula is often written Ac-SCoA instead of Ac-CoA.

The substrates involved in the enzymic degradation or synthesis of the fats are not the free fatty acids but the activated conjugates with CoA. Coenzyme A acts as an acceptor of the two-carbon units (acetyl groups) formed in the $\beta$-oxidation of the fatty acids. The coenzyme combines also with many other organic acids, fatty and otherwise, e.g., propionic, butyric, $\beta$-hydroxy-butyric, acetoacetic, crotonic, succinic, etc. Thus it may be described as an acyl $\left( R{-}C\begin{smallmatrix} \diagup O \\ \diagdown \end{smallmatrix} \right)$ acceptor. The sulfur linkage whereby the acyl groups are united to coenzyme A is a new type of high-energy bond. Acetyl-SCoA may be regarded as analogous in some respects to a mixed acid anhydride and in others to an ester. In spite of the high energy of the thiol-ester bond, these compounds are relatively stable in neutral aqueous solutions at room temperature, a property which fits them for utilization in cellular metabolism. The bond is split and the energy is released in tissues by the activity of specific enzymes. In tissues (e.g., liver, heart, yeast) these fatty acid oxidizing enzymes are bound to the mitochondria of the cells. Ways have been devised to prepare them in soluble form and to separate those involved at each step. The *in vitro* studies were thus made possible.

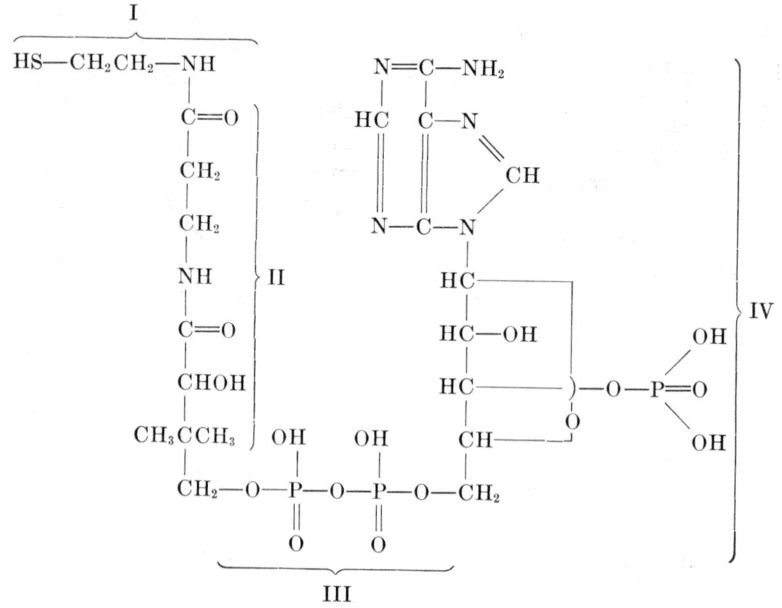

I

HS—CH₂CH₂—NH
|
C=O
|
CH₂
|
CH₂
|
NH   } II
|
C=O
|
CHOH
|
CH₃CCH₃  } OH   OH
|
CH₂—O—P—O—P—O—CH₂
‖   ‖
O   O

N=C—NH₂
|
HC   C—N
‖   ‖   \\
|   |    CH
N—C—N  ⁄
|
HC
|
HC—OH
|
HC
|
CH

) —O—P=O
O
OH
⁄
OH
\\
OH  } IV

III

Coenzyme A

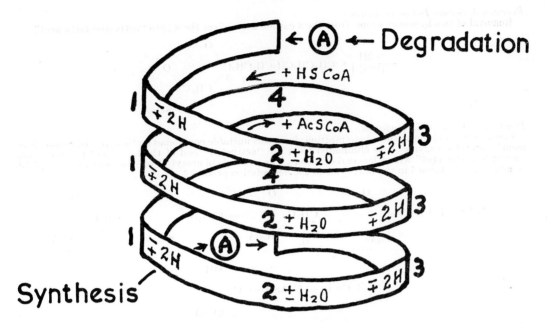

FIG. 49.3. Helical scheme to represent the oxidative degradation and synthesis of fatty acids. (Bruno Rosenfeld and C. C. Lucas. With acknowledgement of Lynen's suggestion.)

Each complete cycle involves four reactions. In *oxidative degradation* these are (1) dehydrogenation, (2) hydration, (3) a second dehydrogenation, and (4) thiolytic degradation, i.e., elimination of 2 carbon atoms as acetyl coenzyme A following addition of coenzyme A. *The synthetic reactions* occur in the reverse order and in the opposite direction: (1) addition of an active 2-carbon unit (acetyl coenzyme A), (2) hydrogenation, (3) dehydration, and (4) a second hydrogenation. Before the oxidation or synthesis can take place, the fatty acid must be activated (Reaction A) by condensation with coenzyme A. These steps are explained more fully on following pages.

OXIDATIVE DEGRADATION (after Mahler)
*Reaction A. Activation Reaction:*

$$\text{Fatty acid} + \text{coenzyme A} \xrightarrow{\text{ATP}} \text{"Activated fatty acid"}$$

e.g.

$$CH_3CH_2CH_2CH_2CH_2CH_2CH_2C\!\!\begin{array}{c}O\\\diagup\\\diagdown\\OH\end{array} + HSCoA \rightarrow C_7H_{15}C\!\!\begin{array}{c}O\\\diagup\\\diagdown\\SCoA\end{array} + H_2O$$

*Reaction 1. Dehydrogenation:*
Enzymatic removal of two hydrogen atoms gives $\alpha\beta$ unsaturated "activated fatty acid"

$$C_7H_{15}C\!\!\begin{array}{c}O\\\diagup\\\diagdown\\SCoA\end{array} \xrightarrow[\text{(FAD)*}]{-2H} CH_3CH_2CH_2CH_2CH_2CH=CHC\!\!\begin{array}{c}O\\\diagup\\\diagdown\\SCoA\end{array}$$
$$\qquad\qquad\qquad\qquad\qquad\qquad\qquad\gamma\quad\beta\qquad\alpha$$

*Reaction 2. Hydration:*
Addition of water at the double bond gives $\beta$-hydroxy "activated fatty acid"

$$CH_3CH_2CH_2CH_2CH_2CH\!\overset{HO|H}{=\!=\!=}\!CHC\!\!\begin{array}{c}O\\\diagup\\\diagdown\\SCoA\end{array} \xrightarrow[\text{(hydrase)}]{+H_2O} CH_3CH_2CH_2CH_2CH_2CHOHCH_2C\!\!\begin{array}{c}O\\\diagup\\\diagdown\\SCoA\end{array}$$
$$\qquad\qquad\qquad\qquad\qquad\qquad\qquad\qquad\qquad\qquad\qquad\gamma\quad\beta\ \alpha$$

* FAD represents an enzyme derived from flavin-adenine-dinucleotide.

*Reaction 3. Second Dehydrogenation:*
Removal of two hydrogen atoms from the $\beta$-carbon atom gives the $\beta$-keto "activated fatty acid"

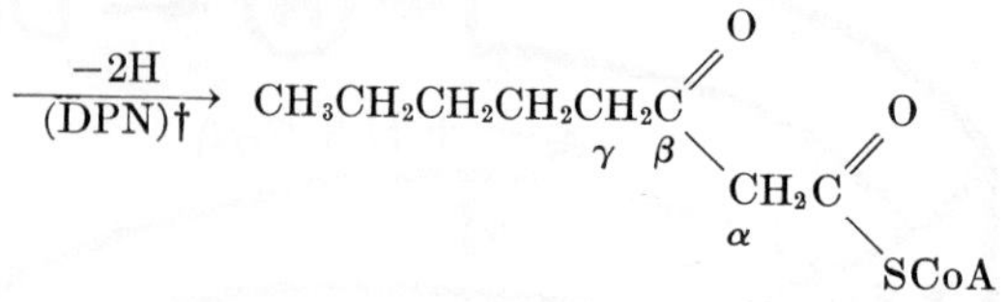

$$\xrightarrow[\text{(DPN)}\dagger]{-2\text{H}} \quad \text{CH}_3\text{CH}_2\text{CH}_2\text{CH}_2\text{CH}_2\overset{\gamma\ \ \beta}{\text{C}}\diagup^{\text{O}}\diagdown_{\text{CH}_2\text{C}}\overset{\alpha}{\phantom{C}}\diagup^{\text{O}}\diagdown_{\text{SCoA}}$$

*Reaction 4. Thiolytic Degradation:*
Coenzyme A adds on at the $\beta$-keto position; from this unstable compound an "active two-carbon fragment" (acetyl coenzyme A) is eliminated from the "activated" end of the fatty acid to give a new "activated fatty acid" with 2 less carbon atoms. The molecule of acetyl-SCoA thus formed is available to add on at Reaction 4 in the next cycle of the degradation process.‡

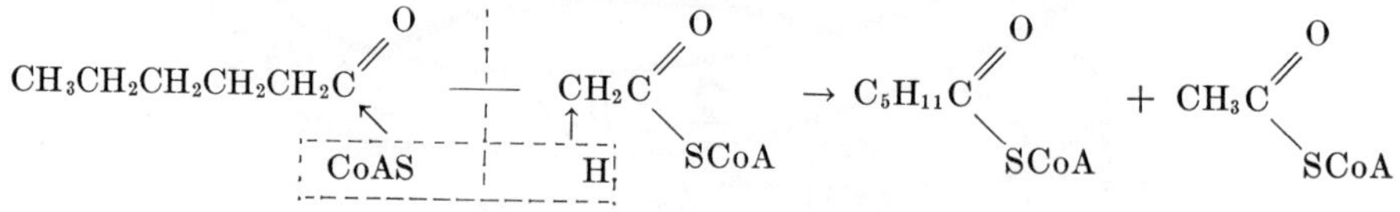

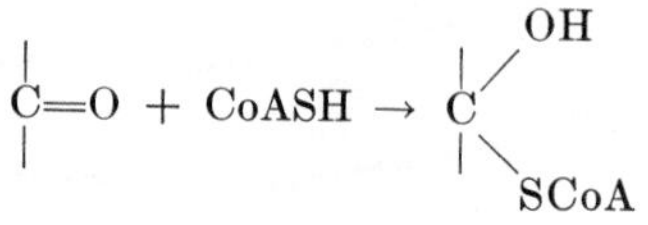

$$\text{CH}_3\text{CH}_2\text{CH}_2\text{CH}_2\text{CH}_2\text{C}\diagup^{\text{O}} \quad \cdots \quad \text{CH}_2\text{C}\diagup^{\text{O}}\diagdown_{\text{SCoA}} \quad \rightarrow \quad \text{C}_5\text{H}_{11}\text{C}\diagup^{\text{O}}\diagdown_{\text{SCoA}} \quad + \quad \text{CH}_3\text{C}\diagup^{\text{O}}\diagdown_{\text{SCoA}}$$

$$\text{CoAS} \qquad \text{H}$$

$$\overset{|}{\underset{|}{\text{C}}}{=}\text{O} + \text{CoASH} \rightarrow \text{C}\diagup^{\text{OH}}\diagdown_{\text{SCoA}}$$

then rearrangement occurs with splitting as shown.

SYNTHESIS

*Reaction A. Activation Reaction:*

$$\text{Fatty acid} + \text{coenzyme A} \rightarrow \xrightarrow{\text{ATP}} \text{"Activated fatty acid"}$$

e.g.

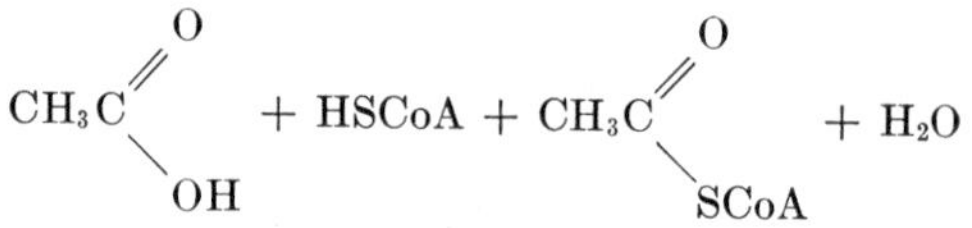

$$\text{CH}_3\text{C}\diagup^{\text{O}}\diagdown_{\text{OH}} \quad + \text{HSCoA} + \text{CH}_3\text{C}\diagup^{\text{O}}\diagdown_{\text{SCoA}} \quad + \text{H}_2\text{O}$$

*Step 1 (Reverse of Reaction 4). Thio-condensation:*
The "activated fatty acid" condenses with an "active two-carbon fragment" (= "active acetate" = acetyl coenzyme A) to give the activated $\beta$-keto acid with 2 more carbon atoms; one molecule of coenzyme A is released to effect this condensation.

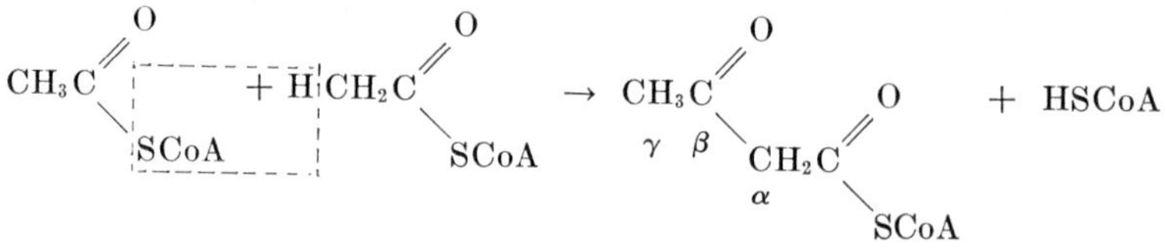

$$\text{CH}_3\text{C}\diagup^{\text{O}}\diagdown_{\text{SCoA}} \quad + \text{H}\,\text{CH}_2\text{C}\diagup^{\text{O}}\diagdown_{\text{SCoA}} \quad \rightarrow \quad \text{CH}_3\text{C}\overset{\gamma\ \ \beta}{\phantom{C}}\diagup^{\text{O}}\diagdown_{\text{CH}_2\text{C}}\overset{\alpha}{\phantom{C}}\diagup^{\text{O}}\diagdown_{\text{SCoA}} \quad + \text{HSCoA}$$

*Step 2 (Reverse of Reaction 3). Hydrogenation:*
Addition of 2 hydrogen atoms to the $\beta$-keto activated acid gives the $\beta$-hydroxy activated acid.

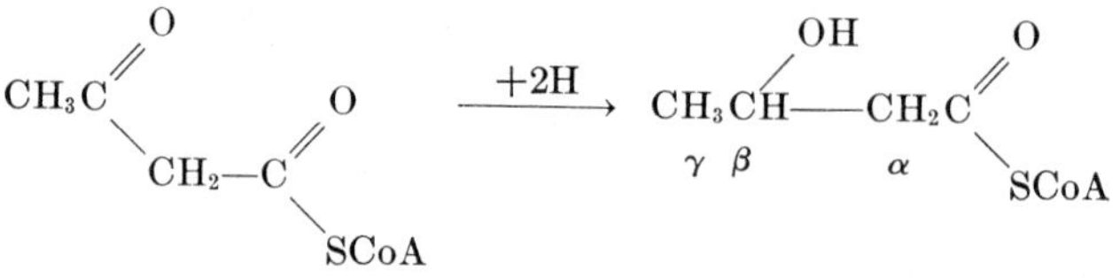

$$\text{CH}_3\text{C}\diagup^{\text{O}}\diagdown_{\text{CH}_2{-}\text{C}}\diagup^{\text{O}}\diagdown_{\text{SCoA}} \quad \xrightarrow{+2\text{H}} \quad \text{CH}_3\overset{\text{OH}}{\text{CH}}{-}\overset{\gamma\ \ \beta}{\phantom{C}}\overset{\alpha}{\text{CH}_2}\text{C}\diagup^{\text{O}}\diagdown_{\text{SCoA}}$$

---

† DPN represents diphosphopyridine dinucleotide.
‡ The coenzyme A does not add on as shown in the simplified scheme above. Most likely it first adds on to the carbonyl group.

*Step 3 (Reverse of Reaction 2). Dehydration:*
Removal of water gives the $\alpha\beta$ unsaturated activated acid.

$$\underset{\substack{| \\ H}}{CH_3C}\overset{\overbrace{OH}}{\underset{\substack{| \\ SCoA}}{CHl_2}} {-}\overset{O}{\underset{}{C}} \xrightarrow{-H_2O} \underset{\gamma \quad \beta \quad \alpha}{CH_3CH{=}CHC}\overset{O}{\underset{SCoA}{}}$$

*Step 4 (Reverse of Reaction 1). Second Hydrogenation:*
Addition of 2 hydrogen atoms to the unsaturated acid finally gives an activated (saturated) fatty acid with 2 more carbon atoms than the acid which entered the cycle.

$$\rightarrow \quad CH_3CH_2CH_2C\overset{O}{\underset{SCoA}{}}$$

Energy is required for the first step in the metabolism of the fatty acids, i.e., for the formation of the "activated fatty acid" (CoA Thiol-ester, Reaction A). This energy is provided by a concomitant oxidation of a member of the citric acid cycle. This is the so-called "sparking reaction" that initiates the oxidation of the fatty acid. Once the degradation has been "primed" it proceeds without further addition of energy, two carbon atoms being spit off (as acetyl-SCoA) until the acid has been entirely broken down to 2-carbon units. The "active acetate" so formed either enters the citric acid cycle, to be burned to $CO_2$ and water, or is used in biosynthetic processes. Fatty acid catabolism produces energy, their anabolism requires energy. In both cases the free energy is provided by "active acetate", or more specifically by the bond energy in the acetyl-SCoA linkage.

From a comparison of the turnover number of the individual enzymes, it has been concluded that the $\beta$-ketoacyl derivatives, e.g., acetoacetyl-S-CoA, may be expected to occur at a much higher steady state concentration than any other intermediate in the whole enzymatic sequence. Liver, in contrast to kidney and heart, contains a very active deacylase enzyme catalysing the reaction:[3]

acetoacetyl-S-CoA $\rightleftharpoons$ acetoacetate + HS-CoA

and a very weak transfer enzyme catalyzing the

reaction:

Acetoacetate + succinyl-S-CoA $\rightleftharpoons$

　　　　　acetoacetyl-S-CoA + succinate

Thus we are able to explain why liver tissue gives rise to the formation of acetoacetate as distinct from kidney, heart and muscle tissue (relatively good sources of the transfer enzyme) by which fatty acids are conducted to the catabolic cycle and thus via oxalacetate and citrate to $CO_2$ and $H_2O$.

If processes similar to these enzymatic reactions occur in the living organism, active acetate would become available to the cells of the liver and other tissues by oxidations of fatty acids, amino acids and carbohydrates. The active acetate would be utilized by several alternative routes (fig. 49.4). The relative rates of utilization through these various pathways must be determined by the inherent characteristics of the cells, and by chemical, hormonal and nervous influences.

### Ketosis

As mentioned above certain experimental and clinical conditions are characterized by the accumulation of ketone bodies in the blood. Ketosis, in experimental animals, can be attributed largely to increased rate of production rather than diminished utilization of ketones. The ketosis is apparently due to the increased proportion of fatty acids being used by the organism. These are presented to the liver in excessive amounts, causing an accumulation of fat. In both experimental and clinical experience it has been found that when ketosis occurs there is a relative lack of carbohydrate available for use by the liver cells. The administration of carbohydrate produces an antiketogenic effect as do the intermediates of

[3] An alternative mode of formation of acetoacetate by the liver has been shown by Lynen and his colleagues. Condensation of acetyl-SCoA with acetoacetyl-SCoA yields CoASH and $\beta$-hydroxy-$\beta$-methylglutaryl-SCoA. Cleavage of this compound yields acetyl-SCOA and free acetoacetate. The $\beta$-hydroxy-$\beta$-methylglutaryl-SCoA is also utilized in the formation of cholesterol. It is interesting that acetoacetate and cholesterol, which are both produced in increased amounts by the liver of the diabetic organism, should have this common precursor.

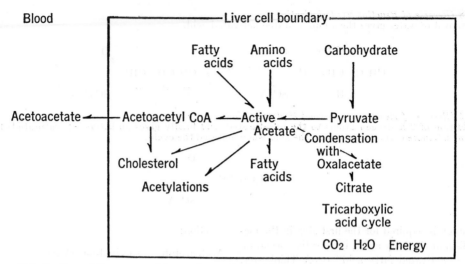

Fig. 49.4. Outline of the routes of formation and of utilization of active acetate (acetyl coenzyme A) by liver cells.

carbohydrate oxidation *in vitro.* Leninger has shown that addition of oxalacetate or succinate to the medium in which liver slices were oxidizing fatty acids decreased the rate of production of acetoacetate and increased that of citrate and other components of the Krebs' cycle. Acetoacetate is an alternative but not an obligatory product of the oxidation of fatty acids by the liver.

There are indications that kidney and other organs may produce acetoacetate, but only in small amounts (Medes, Floyd, and Weinhouse). The enzymatic constitution of kidney and heart provides an explanation for the difference between the ketogenic activity of these tissues and that of liver. The ketone bodies are rapidly utilized by extrahepatic tissues. The rate of utilization is not influenced by the amount of carbohydrate or of insulin present.

Drury and Wick (1953) using $C^{14}$ glucose, have studied the relative rates of oxidation of glucose and $\beta$-hydroxybutyrate and of glucose and acetate. Insulin increases the oxidation of glucose but not that of the other compounds in eviscerated rabbits. When insulin activity is maximal the administration of hydroxybutyrate or acetate causes a sharp decline in glucose oxidation but has no effect on the rate of its disappearance from the blood. These findings indicate that the cells burn acetate preferentially under these conditions and glucose is displaced from the oxidative sites.

### Effects of Ketosis

Ketone bodies in small or moderate amounts provide a source of energy for tissues when the supply of carbohydrate is restricted or its utiliza-

tion is impaired. Acetoacetic and $\beta$-hydroxybutyric acids formed in liver cells are nonvolatile and moderately strong acids which must be neutralized by base as soon as they enter the blood stream. In severe ketosis, i.e., when the rate of formation greatly exceeds that of utilization, there may be a dangerous disturbance in acid-base equilibrium. These acids are excreted by the kidney and tend to carry base out of the body with them. The kidney attempts to minimize this loss of base by holding it back and thus produces a highly acid urine. A further process to conserve fixed base (K, Na, etc.) is by increasing the formation of ammonia in the kidney. The urine volume is usually high in ketosis. The excretion of these organic acids represents a loss of potential energy. Thus ketosis results in a loss of base, water, nitrogen and energy and leads to acidosis and dehydration.

### The Metabolism of Adipose Tissue

Metabolic changes in the adipose tissue itself had, until recently, only infrequently been studied. Wertheimer and his colleagues have reported that the adipose tissues of well fed or fasted rats contain little or no glycogen. If, however, after fasting the animals are fed a diet rich in sugars glycogen appears in the adipose tissue. It is not yet established that the glycogen is a step on the road to fat synthesis. The so-called "brown fat" present in the rat and some other mammals is said to be more active in glycogen synthesis than white adipose tissue. Mirsky found that adipose tissue brei contains enzymes which can both synthesize glycogen from glucose-1-

phosphate and promote the reverse reaction. The enzyme amylase is also present in adipose tissue. In adipose tissue *in vivo*, insulin promotes the formation of glycogen (Wertheimer and Shapiro, 1948), of fat (Chernick and Chaikoff, 1951; Wick, Drury et al., 1951) and the uptake and oxidation of dextrose (Winegrad and Renold, 1958).

## Abnormalities of Fat Metabolism

The problems of starvation and obesity (ch. 50), abnormalities of fat metabolism associated with endocrine disturbances (p. 865), and the conditions in which there is an excessive deposition of fat in the liver are discussed elsewhere. A profound disturbance of phospholipid metabolism occurs in Niemann-Pick's disease, a condition which is seen in infancy and in early childhood and is invariably fatal. The spleen and liver are enormously enlarged and contain very large amounts of phospholipids. The cholesterol content of these tissues is also increased but not to nearly the same degree. The blood phospholipid is also definitely raised. Histologically there is a great hypertrophy of the reticuloendothelial system. Very little is known about this disease but it has been suggested that there is some interference with the activity of the enzymes which are responsible for various stages of fat metabolism in the tissues.

In the rare clinical condition involving a disorder of lipid metabolism, Tay-Sachs disease, there is an abnormally high proportion of cerebrosides in the brain. Liver, normally, contains little or no cerebrosides but in Gaucher's disease the cerebroside content of both liver and spleen is high. The physiological significance of the cerebrosides is not known.

*Retention hyperlipemia* appears to be caused by the sluggish removal of fat from the blood stream. The mechanism underlying the disorder is not clear. Its clinical designation is "idiopathic hyperlipemia." The neutral fat may be increased from 20 to 100 times the normal concentration, and total cholesterol may be about double the normal value. It sometimes occurs as an inherited disorder. This retention type of hyperlipemia does not respond to insulin but does to a diet low in fat. The diabetic (transportation) type of lipemia does respond to insulin. The effect of insulin on the experimental lipemia following hemorrhage or that produced by protamine and decreased by heparin has not been adequately studied.

In 1893 Hand described a condition in children which was characterized at autopsy by yellow nodules in the cranial bones and in other situations. Since it will become increasingly difficult to add more names when further cases are described it may be expedient to call the syndrome Hand's disease (Hand-Schuller-Christian, etc.). While these nodules show a predilection for the tissues of the head, i.e., cranial bones, orbit, tuber cinereum, they have been noted in most portions of the skeleton (Chester and Kugel). The signs and symptoms depend on the areas affected. Diabetes insipidus and exophthalmos are common disturbances, i.e., due to lesions near the pituitary gland and in the orbit. Rowland believes that the condition is due to an osseous form of xanthomatosis. These xanthomatous nodules contain large amounts of cholesterol and cholesterol esters, which together may account for a large proportion of their total fat. There is no alteration in the fat content of the unaffected parts of the body. The etiology of the disease is unknown. The generalized xanthomatosis, which is sometimes seen in diabetes mellitus, may disappear when the blood fats are reduced to normal values by appropriate treatment of the diabetic condition.

A great deal of attention is being paid at the present time to the metabolism of fat in tumor tissue but no review will be attempted here. The important part played by cholesterol in the formation of gall-stones has been dealt with (p. 651).

*Familial hypercholesterolemia* is an inherited condition in which there is an abnormally high total serum cholesterol with a normal proportion of free and bound cholesterol. There is frequently an increase in plasma phospholipids. The disease is inherited as an incomplete dominant. The increase in blood cholesterol is not due to dietary intake but to increased production or diminished utilization within the body. There are many reports which indicate that the condition is characterized by a raised incidence of vascular disease.

### ATHEROSCLEROSIS

There is now considerable statistical evidence that prolonged hypercholesterolemia and atherosclerosis are associated in some way. The characteristic, but by no means the earliest, lesion of an atherosclerotic artery is the cholesterol-rich plaque (containing up to 70 per cent of cholesterol). It is probable that this cholesterol comes from the blood, but this is not proven. The cholesterol in the blood is not present in simple solution, but is carried as lipoprotein complexes, the so-called "giant molecules" ($S_f$ 10–20) of Gofman. While the total serum cholesterol values, or the concentration of the "giant" lipoprotein molecules afford a significant differentiation between *groups* of men who are clinically healthy and *groups* of men who have (or may develop) coronary heart disease, the forecasting efficiency of the values for *individual* diagnosis or prognosis is very low. Ancel Keys and others have shown convincingly that the serum cholesterol level is not readily altered even by large changes in the cholesterol content of the diet. There is, however, a relationship between total serum cholesterol and the total fat content of the diet. Excessive intake of fat or of calories in any form rather than of cholesterol or that indefinite process called "ageing *per se*" may be concerned in the causation of degenerative vascular disease.

Serum cholesterol levels can be reduced, in man, through control of the diet in three ways (a) by reducing excess calorie intake, (b) by reducing the intake of animal fats (Keys), and (c) by increasing the intake of vegetable oils (Kinsell, Sinclair, and others). These oils are rich in unsaturated fatty acids. Beveridge and others have shown that certain steroid fractions from these oils, containing for example sistosterol, also reduce cholesterol levels in man. The relative efficacies of the unsaturated fatty acids, the mechanism of action of which is unknown, and of the steroids, which decrease the absorption of cholesterol and may have other effects, is still unsettled.

Fat metabolism is undoubtedly concerned in the production of atherosclerosis but in the search for the initial causative factor protein which is associated with all fat fractions in blood may be equally important. Abnormalities in the metabolism of the cells of the vessel wall or in their permeability are also obvious possibilities. All of these factors and their integration are being actively investigated.

Diets rich in fat given to dogs in which kidney damage had been produced may result in cardiovascular lesions (McCormick and Holman, 1949). In rats aortic sclerosis may be produced by diets rich in fat when kidneys have been injured by drugs (Lehr and Churg, 1952). Rations extremely low in choline and its precursors may produce severe kidney and cardiovascular lesions in young rats fed diets rich in certain synthetic or natural fats (Stetten; Wilgram and Hartroft). There is a possibility that deficiency of Vitamin E may be important in the production of some of these experimental lesions. The bearing of these experimental findings on human atherosclerosis remains unsettled. The arguments implicating dietary cholesterol as a causative factor in human atherosclerosis have been well presented by Katz,

Stamler and Pick (1958) and discussed by Keys (1956).

## REFERENCES

ALLAN, F. N., BOWIE, D. J., MacLEOD, J. J. R. AND ROBINSON, W. L. Brit. J. Exper. Path., 1924, **5**, 75.

ANDERSON, W. E. AND MENDEL, L. B. J. Biol. Chem., 1928, **76**, 729.

BENNETT, M. A., MEDES, G. AND TOENNIES, G. Growth, 1944, **8**, 59.

BEST, C. H. AND CAMPBELL, J. J. Physiol., 1936, **86**, 190.

BEST, C. H., HERSHEY, J. M. AND HUNTSMAN, M. E. J. Physiol., 1932, **75**, 56.

BLUMBERG, H. AND McCOLLUM, E. V. Science, 1941, **93**, 598.

BOYD, E. M. J. Biol. Chem., 1942, **143**, 131.

BREUSCH, F. L. Science, 1943, **97**, 490.

BUCHANAN, J. M., SAKAMI, W., GURIN, S. AND WILSON, D. W. J. Biol. Chem., 1945, **159**, 695.

CHAIKOFF, I. L., ENTENMAN, C. AND MONTGOMERY, M. L. J. Biol. Chem., 1947, **168**, 177.

DAFT, F. S., SEBRELL, W. H. AND LILLIE, R. D. Proc. Soc. Exper. Biol. Med., 1942, **50**, 1.

DU VIGNEAUD, V., CHANDLER, J. P., MOYER, A. W. AND KEPPEL, D. M. J. Biol. Chem., 1939, **131**, 57.

EMBDEN, G. AND KALBERLAH, F. Beitr. Chem. Physiol. Path., 1906, **8**, 121.

ENTENMAN, C., CHAIKOFF, I. L. AND ZILVERSMIT, D. B. J. Biol. Chem., 1946, **166**, 15.

FISHER, N. F. Am. J. Physiol., 1924, **67**, 634.

GOLDMAN, D. S., CHAIKOFF, I. L., REINHARDT, W. O., ENTENMAN, C. AND DAUBEN, W. G. J. Biol. Chem., 1950, **184**, 727.

GYÖRGY, P. AND GOLDBLATT, H. J. Exper. Med., 1942, **75**, 355.

HARTROFT, W. S. AND BEST, C. H. Brit. Med. J., 1949, **1**, 423.

HARTROFT, W. S. AND RIDOUT, J. H. Am. J. Path., 1951, **27**, 951.

HENRIQUES, V. AND HANSEN, C. Skandinav. Arch. Physiol., 1901, **11**, 151.

HERSHEY, J. M. AND SOSKIN, S. Am. J. Physiol., 1931, **98**, 74.

HURTLEY, W. H. Quart. J. Med., 1916, **9**, 301.

JOWETT, M. AND QUASTEL, J. H. Biochem. J., 1935 **29**, 2181.

KEYS, A., ANDERSON, J. T., MICKELSEN, O., ADELSON, S. F. AND FIDANZA, F. J. Nutrition, 1956, **59**, 39.

KNOOP, F. Beitr. Chem. Physiol. Path., 1905, **6**, 150.

LEACH, E. H. J. Physiol., 1938, **93**, 1.

LYNEN, F. Fed. Proc., 1953, **12**, 683.

McAMIS, A. J., ANDERSON, W. E. AND MENDEL, L. B. J. Biol. Chem., 1929, **82**, 247.

McARTHUR, C. S., LUCAS, C. C. AND BEST, C. H. Biochem. J., 1947, **41**, 612.

MacKAY, E. M. J. Clin. Endocrinol., 1943, **3**, 101.

MAHLER, H. R. Fed. Proc., 1953, **12**, 694.

MEDES, G. Acta Med. Skandinav., 1947, Suppl. **196**, 646.

MILLER, L. L. AND WHIPPLE, G. H. J. Exper. Med., 1942, **76**, 421.

STETTEN, DeW., JR. J. Biol. Chem., 1941, **140**, 143.

TUCKER, H. F. AND ECKSTEIN, H. C. J. Biol. Chem., 1937, **121**, 479.

VERZÁR, F. AND VON KÚTHY, A. Biochem. Ztschr., 1931, **230**, 451.

WEINHOUSE, S., MEDES, G., AND FLOYD, N. F. J. Biol. Chem., 1944, **155**, 143.

WEINMAN, E. O., CHAIKOFF, I. L., ENTENMAN, C. AND DAUBEN, W. G. J. Biol. Chem., 1950, **187**, 643.

WELCH, A. D. AND LANDAU, R. L. J. Biol. Chem. 1942, **144**, 581.

### Monographs and Reviews

ARTOM, C. Am. J. Clin. Nutrition, 1958, **6**, 221.

BLOCH, K. Circulation, 1950, **1**, 214.

BLOCH, K. Ann. Rev. Biochem., 1952, **21**, 273.

BLOOR, W. R. Biochemistry of the fatty acids. Reinhold Publ. Corp., New York, 1943.

BURR, G. O. Fed. Proc., 1942, **1**, 224.

CAMPBELL, J. AND BEST, C. H. Metabolism, 1956, **5**, 95.

DEUEL, H. J. JR. The lipids: biochemistry digestion, transport and storage, vol. II. Interscience Publishers, New York and London, 1955.

DORFMAN, R. I. AND UNGAR, F. Metabolism of steroid hormones. Burgess Publ. Co., Minneapolis, Minn., 1953.

DRILL, V. A. Pharmacol. Rev., 1952, **4**, 1.

DU VIGNEAUD, V. A trail of research in sulfur chemistry and metabolism and related fields. Cornell University Press, Ithaca, N. Y., 1952.

FRAZER, A. C. Ann. Rev. Biochem., 1952, **21**, 245.

FREDRICKSON, D. S. AND GORDON, R. S., JR Physiol. Rev., 1958, **38**, 585.

GRIFFITH, W. H. Am. J. Clin. Nutrition, 1958, **6**, 263.

GURIN, S. AND BRADY, R. O Recent Prog. Hormone Res., 1953, **8**, 571.

HOLMAN, R. T. Nutrition Rev., 1958, **16**, 33.

KATZ, L. N., STAMLER, J. AND PICK, R. Nutrition and atherosclerosis. Lea and Febiger, Philadelphia, 1958.

KENNEDY, E. P. Ann. Rev. Biochem., 1957, **26**, 119.

LEATHES, J. B. AND RAPER, H. S. The fats. Longmans, Green & Co., London, 1925.

LIPMANN, F. Bacteriol. Rev., 1953, **17**, 1.

LONG, C. N. H. Recent Progr. Hormone Res., 1947, **1**, 99.

OLSON, R. E. Ann. Rev. Biochem., 1959, **28**, 467.

PORTMAN, O. W. AND STARE, F. J. Physiol. Rev., 1959, **39**, 407.

ROBERTSON, J. S. Physiol. Rev., 1957, **37**, 133.

SCHOENHEIMER, R. The dynamic state of body constituents. Harvard University Press, Cambridge, 1942.

SHAPIRO, B. AND WERTHEIMER, E. Metabolism, 1956, **5**, 79.

Symposium on nutritional factors and liver diseases, ed. by R. W. Miner. Ann. New York Acad. Sc., 1954, **57**, 615.

Symposium on metabolism of lipids, ed. by G. Popják. Brit. Med. Bull., 1958, **14**, 197.

Symposium on the influence of hormones on lipid metabolism in relation to atherosclerosis, ed. by A. Dury. Ann. New York Acad. Sc., 1959, **72**, 789.

# 50

# THE METABOLISM IN STARVATION, SEMISTARVATION AND OBESITY

## Starvation

An animal deprived of food derives energy first from the combustion of its own carbohydrate stores (glycogen). Next, the fat reserves mainly are drawn upon and finally, after these have been exhausted, tissue protein is broken down, the fatty acid part of the molecule is burned while the nitrogen is excreted in the urine mainly as urea. The metabolism of several professional fasters has been investigated. Among the most famous of these are Succi, whose metabolism was studied by Luciani and others, Cette, investigated by Munk and Zuntz, Levanzin by Benedict and Beauté by Cathcart. One of the longest of such fasts upon record is that of Merlatte of Paris which lasted for 50 days. A dog has been starved for 117 days. By the end of this time it had lost 63 per cent of its weight, but was fairly active. Succi on the 40th day of his fast had lost about 25 per cent of his weight. The length of time a man could survive would depend largely upon his physical condition (fat stores, etc.) at the commencement of the fast, but it would probably not exceed 9 or 10 weeks in any event. Terence MacSwiney, Mayor of Cork, after his arrest during the Irish troubles in 1920, went upon a hunger strike which lasted 74 days; it was terminated by his death in coma.

During starvation the loss of weight is not distributed evenly throughout the body, some organs and tissues losing a much greater proportion of their weight than others (fig. 50.1). During the first few days the subcutaneous tissues and other fat depots bear the brunt of the effect of the fast. Large quantities of extracellular water are also lost at this time. Later, dissolution of muscular tissue occurs, as indicated by the N:S ratio of the urine (about 14:1). The water lost during this period is derived mainly from intracellular sources. Later, dissolution of protoplasmic structure occurs. The central nervous system, even in prolonged starvation, loses only about 5 per cent of its weight (as estimated from normal standards), whereas the muscles lose about 35 per cent or more. The weight losses of muscular tissue, liver, gastrointestinal tract and spleen run approximately parallel with that of the body as a whole. The muscle fibers are reduced in size, and many are destroyed. Contrary to general belief, the percentile weight loss of the heart is only a little less than that of the skeletal muscles. The kidney loses only 20 per cent or less of its weight, and the gonads, adrenals and thyroid only from 2 to 8 per cent. Some of the small weight losses reported, e.g., of the central nervous system, may be due to the replacement of solid substance by fluid (see fig. 50.1).[1]

NITROGEN EXCRETION. *The total output of nitrogen* in the urine falls for the first day or two of the fast when the body is subsisting chiefly upon its carbohydrate supplies. The length of this period varies, of course, with the size of the carbohydrate stores at the commencement of the fast. A steady rise in nitrogen excretion follows, and usually reaches a maximum about the third or fourth day, but from then on it shows a progressive decline and may reach a value of less than 6 grams per day. The nitrogen excreted during the earlier part of the fast is apparently derived largely from the mobilization of "reserve protein" (p. 779). The *urea nitrogen* excretion at first rises, then falls; its percentage of the total nitrogen excretion also diminishes. The *ammonia* excretion rises. The *creatinine* output shows a steady decline but this is largely compensated for by the appearance of creatine (p. 781) so that the creatinine + creatine excretion remains fairly constant. As a result of some experiments of Voit many years ago, it is very often stated that a pro-

[1] There does not appear to be any definite level of emaciation, that is, of weight loss of the body as a whole as a percentage of the normal body weight, at which death is inevitable. Recoveries with judicious feeding and transfusions of plasma have been recorded after losses of body weight up to 50 or even 60 per cent of the normal weight.

nounced rise in nitrogen excretion occurs shortly before death from starvation, which is attributed to an accelerated breakdown of tissue protein. But this so-called *premortal rise* in nitrogen excretion is a very inconstant phenomenon, and of very doubtful significance, for death very often occurs in starved animals in its absence. The total quantity of body protein catabolized may be determined by calculation from the total nitrogen excretion on the assumption that tissue protein contains 16 per cent of nitrogen and that practically all the nitrogen derived from the breakdown of body protein appears in the urine. That is, each gram of urinary nitrogen represents the deamination of 6.25 grams of protein, so the quantity of protein broken down is calculated by multiplying the figure for the nitrogen excretion by 6.25. On this basis the average daily loss of body protein of an average sized man during starvation is about 50 grams or about 0.4 per cent of the total amount in his body. For a few days following the termination of a prolonged fast the nitrogen excretion shows a pronounced fall—nitrogen is retained for the reconstruction of tissue protein.[2]

MINERAL METABOLISM. The urinary excretion of *phosphorus* and *sulfur* shows an initial rise, and then a gradual decline, thus showing a curve which roughly parallels that of the total nitrogen excretion. Toward the latter part of the fast the N:P and N:S ratios are around 5.3:1 and 14:1 respectively. The excretion of P in relation to N is greater than one would expect were it all derived from the soft tissues; the same is true for Ca, which indicates that the skeleton contributes to the quantities of these minerals in the urine. The calcium excretion above that which the soft tissues can account for is much greater (10 times) than that of phosphorus, from which it is deduced that calcium carbonate rather than calcium phosphate is liberated from the bones. The ratio of N to S is a little higher than that of the bulk of the soft tissues, which suggests that the sulfur-con-

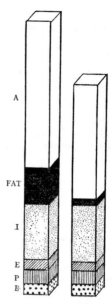

FIG. 50.1. The weights of the major compartments of the body of young men in normal nutrition, on left; after 24 weeks of semi-starvation, on right; A, active tissue (total body weight less the other indicated compartments); B, bone mineral; E, erythrocytes; I, interstitial fluid, (thiocyanate space less plasma volume), from Keys and associates, the Biology of Human Starvation, University of Minnesota Press, redrawn and modified.

taining amino-acids are conserved or excreted in only minimal amounts.

The urinary excretion of *chloride, sodium, potassium* and *magnesium* is reduced from the beginning of the fast. This is to be expected since the intake of minerals is restricted to that provided by the water which is drunk. The concentrations of these minerals in the blood shows little change, but the sodium bicarbonate is reduced when ketosis supervenes.

KETOSIS. The increase in urinary ammonia (p. 563) is a result of the production of excessive amounts of acid metabolites, especially β-hydroxybutyric and acetoacetic acids. The latter are formed as a result of the carbohydrate deprivation, and the consequent excess combustion of fat. Succi toward the end of his fast excreted, daily, from 7 to 13 grams of acetone bodies. In a fasting female subject reported by Folin and Denis the acidosis was extreme, some 18 grams of β-hydroxybutyric acid being excreted upon the fourth day of the fast. Fasting ketosis is much more pronounced in women than in men. This sex difference is not related to the usually greater adipose tissue of females, for a very lean woman excretes larger amounts of ketone bodies than

[2] The loss of protein varies widely among different organs and tissues. Addis and his colleagues found that in rats fasted for 7 days the several tissues contributed to the total protein loss in the following proportions, muscles and skin 62 per cent, liver 16 per cent, alimentary tract, spleen and pancreas 14 per cent, blood 6 per cent, kidneys 1 per cent, heart 0.5 per cent and the remaining organs 0.5 per cent. Or put in percentages of the protein contents of individual normal organs; the brain loses about 4 per cent of its protein; the muscles, skin and bones about 8 per cent; the heart 18 per cent; the kidneys 20 per cent; the gastrointestinal tract 28 per cent; and the liver 40 per cent.

TABLE 50.1

*Subject L. Height, 170.7 cm. Only distilled water was taken during this fast*

(Abridged, after Benedict)

| | Day of Fasting | | | |
| --- | --- | --- | --- | --- |
| | 1st | 11th | 21st | 31st |
| Body weight, kg | 59.60 | 53.88 | 50.49 | 47.39 |
| Rectal temperature at 7 a.m. | | 36.54 | 36.04 | 35.96 |
| Pulse-rate, morning, awake | 74 | 61 | 59 | 60 |
| Urine: | | | | |
|   Total solids, grams | 43.51 | 42.05 | 31.88 | 27.07 |
|   Total N | 7.10 | 10.25 | 7.93 | 6.94 |
|   Urea N | 5.68 | 7.66 | 5.54 | 4.84 |
|   Ammonia N | 0.41 | 1.58 | 1.57 | 1.24 |
|   Uric acid N | 0.112 | 0.116 | 0.112 | 0.122 |
|   Creatinine + Creatine N | 0.48 | 0.49 | 0.38 | 0.32 |
|   Chlorine | 3.77 | 0.36 | 0.18 | 0.13 |
|   $P_2O_5$ | 1.66 | 1.95 | 1.60 | 1.32 |
|   $N:P_2O_5$ ratio | 4.28 | 5.26 | 4.96 | 5.26 |
|   S | 0.46 | 0.62 | 0.51 | 0.49 |
|   N:S ratio | 15.4 | 16.5 | 15.5 | 14.2 |
|   $\beta$-oxybutyric acid | | 1.4 | 5.0 | 4.5 |
|   Ca | 0.217 | 0.220 | 0.237 | 0.138 |
|   Mg | 0.046 | 0.072 | 0.053 | 0.052 |
|   K | 1.630 | 1.006 | 0.644 | 0.606 |
|   Na | 2.070 | 0.100 | 0.066 | 0.053 |
| Loss of flesh calculated from N loss | 213 | 308 | 238 | 208 |
| R.Q., night | 0.78 | 0.72 | 0.73 | 0.72 |
| Calories, indirect, 24 hours' complete rest | 1441 | 1193 | 1032 | 1072* |
| Calories per square meter (DuBois), 24 hours | 843 | 732 | 653 | 701† |

\* Previous day = 1025.

† Previous day = 661.

does a man of overweight. Nor, generally speaking, is ketosis (p. 875) during fasting greater in an overweight person than in one of normal weight.

CARBOHYDRATE METABOLISM. Even in the later stages of the fast glycogen is found in the liver, and the blood sugar is little depressed. Sugar is apparently synthesized from protein. In the earlier stages there may be a temporary hypoglycemia.

The *basal metabolic* rate, the *body temperature*, *pulse rate* and the *blood pressure* all show a progressive fall throughout the fasting period. See table 50.1.

### Semistarvation, Undernutrition[3]

If a diet possessing a caloric value considerably below the energy requirements of the individual is

[3] Comprehensive reports of studies on undernutrition have been published within recent years,

persisted in, as during famine, war blockade, extreme poverty, disease (e.g., stricture of the esophagus or pylorus) or improper feeding of infants, serious nutritional effects result. It must also be remembered that just as an intake of calories over the output will cause obesity so an energy expenditure in excess of the caloric intake will result in a loss of weight. Consequently a man who performs heavy work upon a diet which is adequate only for a sedentary worker will suffer from undernutrition. The economic or other conditions which lead to extreme reductions in the total caloric value of the diet obviously must also cause, as a rule, a reduction in the intake of vitamins, essential minerals and first class proteins. As a consequence, the incidence of specific de-

e.g., *Malnutrition and Starvation in the Western Netherlands*; Netherlands Government 1944–1945; and the two volume monograph by Ancel Keys and his associates, *The Biology of Human Starvation*, Univ. of Minnesota Press, 1950.

ficiency disorders, e.g., stunting, xerophthalmia, rickets, osteomalacia, scurvy, etc., is also high when the caloric value of the diet is markedly lowered. These special aspects of undernutrition are dealt with in other chapters.

The most pronounced instances of undernutrition and emaciation are met with most commonly in anorexia nervosa, pituitary cachexia, the later stages of malignant disease, and in prolonged and severe infections.

The following is a summary of the main effects of severe undernutrition.

(1) Reduction in body weight—emaciation. The body attempts to make up the caloric deficiency by burning its own tissues. The loss of weight is due chiefly to loss of fat, but also in severe instances to a loss of protein. The nitrogen balance is negative. In children growth is retarded. The positive nitrogen balance is smaller than normal, it may even be negative. In the less severe grades of undernutrition in children the growth impulse continues to cause an increase in height of the skeleton but the muscles and the breadth of the body are poorly developed.

(2) Reduction in basal metabolic rate. The total basal metabolism, i.e., the heat production as related to surface area, is, as one would expect owing to the reduction in the mass of active tissue, diminished in semistarvation, but the metabolism per unit (kilogram) of body weight is reduced as well. The total metabolism is diminished by nearly 40 per cent, and the heat production per unit of body weight by nearly 20 per cent. The cause of the reduction per kilogram has not been fully explained, but it can be accounted for in part by the decline in cardiac work (by about 50 per cent), the lowered tone of the skeletal muscles, and the subnormal body temperature, which would tend to slow the rate of all chemical reactions in the tissues. The subject is abnormally sensitive to cold, due to the fact that the skin vessels are constricted in an attempt to reduce the dissipation of heat through radiation and convection (ch. 52). The skin temperature upon which our thermal sensations depend is therefore lowered. The specific dynamic response to food may be increased.

(3) The subject is readily fatigued, and shows a lack of a zest for physical exertion. Work is performed with the same expenditure of energy as normally, so, though energy is economized in the carrying on of the vital processes as shown by the reduced B.M.R. and cold skin, no economy is effected in the execution of muscular work.

(4) The loss of internal fat which normally serves to support the organs—stomach, kidneys, uterus, etc.—against the effect of gravity, results in their displacement (visceroptosis). The lost body fat is partially replaced by water.

(5) Susceptibility to infections: "Fever and plague dog the footsteps of famine." This is an old adage, but with the exception of tuberculosis (in which resistance is definitely lowered) and certain specific effects of vitamin deficiences there is really little evidence that undernutrition increases the susceptibility to infection.

It is natural to suppose that the production of $\gamma$-globulin which is so closely associated with immune bodies would be depressed by undernutrition, especially if involving severe protein deficiency. The investigations of Cannon and his colleagues have gone far to show that this, indeed, does occur. In the Minnesota experiment the concentration of $\gamma$-globulin in the plasma of the subjects was moderately reduced, but this was not accompanied by any apparent increase in susceptibility to infections; the semistarved subjects of the experiment had slightly fewer colds over a comparable period than the controls. On the other hand, there is a considerable body of evidence to support the conception that undernutrition actually reduces the susceptibility to certain infections. It has been reported, for example, by McCay that underfed rats were surprisingly free from the usual laboratory infections; others have concluded from their experiments and observations of naturally occurring disease, that well nourished animals are more susceptible to infection than are undernourished ones. When a severe infection is established, however, the undernourished animal is at a disadvantage, and is more likely to succumb.

It is recognized that some noninfectious conditions such as hypertension, neoplastic diseases, and diabetes are benefited by undernutrition. In animals, very severe undernutrition definitely inhibits tumor growth, but whether less severe caloric deficiency has such an effect in man is uncertain. The evidence for the incidence of hypertension being reduced is mainly statistical.

(6) Edema not uncommonly (see ch. 4).

(7) Psychological changes. Mental apathy, moral deterioration, depression, tendency toward introversion and other changes in personality, and lowered intellectual capacity are common effects. "The brain is in some sort of custody of the stomach and relief of malnutrition gives relief of mental dullness" (Roger Bacon). An unresponsive, complaining and uncooperative attitude in semistarved persons of Western Europe receiving relief after World War II was very frequently observed. Drummond remarked upon this and stated that it disappeared completely when the food intake was raised above 1500 to 1800 Calories per day.

## Obesity

Some forms of obesity are quite definitely due to a hypothalamic lesion or to a disorder of an endocrine organ, pituitary (ch. 56), adrenal cortex (ch. 58), thyroid or gonads; they will not concern us here. Such origins of obesity are rare and associated with other manifestations of hypothalamic or endocrine dysfunction. Ordinary obesity—the so-called *simple obesity*—is very common and afflicts persons showing no other abnormality.

In many cases of simple obesity there appears to be a genetic element, a conclusion borne out by statistical studies. In surveys of a large number of obese persons, one or both parents were obese, whereas the incidence of obesity in persons both of whose parents are of normal weight is only about 10 per cent. The hereditary obesity of a strain of yellow mice is well known. A Mendelian dominant gene carries the characters for yellowness and obesity; nonyellow mice of the same litter are not obese. The basal metabolic rate of the obese animals is said to be reduced and the body temperature subnormal; an hereditary hypothalamic origin of the obesity has been suggested. Another form of obesity in mice which is accompanied by hyperglycemia has been described. The food consumption of these animals is much greater than nonobese controls. An inherent tendency to fatness seems to be illustrated by the common observation that of two persons who appear to eat about the same amount of food, and exercise to the same extent, one may remain thin or of normal weight while the other grows fat. Furthermore, the "spare" person may have a large appetite and remain underweight while the obese may diet himself and still be fat. In order to explain such cases it has been suggested that they are due to an inherited endocrine characteristic. Yet if this were so, some evidence of it should be forthcoming from metabolic studies. On the contrary, the basal metabolic rate per unit of body surface of the subject of the common or simple type of obesity is within normal limits—that is, his energy expenditure at rest is not less than the normal. Nor is work performed more economically than usual by the obese; the reverse is probably true on account of the greater amount of inert adipose tissue.[4] His greater storage of energy cannot therefore be explained upon this basis. It has been claimed that the specific dynamic action of food (p. 787) is reduced in cases of simple obesity; and it has

been suggested that such a reduction, by conserving energy, may play a causative role. The smaller specific dynamic action which has been observed could, however, account for no more than a 3 per cent reduction in the total daily metabolism, and is quite inadequate as an explanation. An almost inappreciable increase in the caloric intake or a slightly reduced bodily activity would produce a much greater effect upon the energy exchange. For example, 10 grams of extra fat daily in the diet (e.g., a teaspoonful of butter) yielding 90 Calories, or 23 grams of sugar (about 2 teaspoonsful) would increase the caloric intake of a person of ordinary activity by 3 per cent or so, while a slow walk of a mile would increase the metabolism to a corresponding extent.

Other possibilities have been explored, namely, that the obese person may absorb his food more efficiently, that there exists an inborn peculiarity of the tissue cells, whereby they accumulate fat in excess, or that they release the fat less freely into the circulation for use as fuel. None of these factors has been found to play a significant part.

It is probable that a hereditary or constitutional factor, in the great majority of instances of ordinary obesity, is more apparent than real, and that a careful investigation of these cases with respect to food intake and muscular activity would reveal a positive energy balance. It is therefore likely that, when obesity shows a familial tendency, the inclination of members of the same family to follow similar habits with respect to diet and exercise, rather than that some inherited endocrine peculiarity, is responsible. Or again, traits which lead to obesity—overindulgence of the appetite, or a distaste for muscular exertion may be inherited. Also, the obese person often, though not a "big eater," indulges in highly concentrated food.

The possibility of a hypothalamic or an endocrine element in the development of obesity is very difficult to prove or disprove. From what is known of the role played by the hypothalamus and the endocrines in the control of food intake and in fat metabolism, it is tempting to look in this direction for an explanation of obesity. Obesity might conceivably be due to some hypothalamic or endocrine idiosyncrasy. There is experimental evidence that the hypothalamus exerts an influence upon the hunger sensation (ch. 43), but endocrine effects are more often exerted upon the *distribution* of fat rather than upon the total body weight. There is no *substantial evidence that obesity is due to any other cause than overindulgence*

---

[4] Newburgh states that obese persons as compared with the normal produce more heat in the basal state, and expend more energy for the performance of a given amount of work. Their total metabolism measured over 24-hour periods is also considerably greater than the normal.

*in food in relation to the body's energy requirements.*
It must be remembered that the law of the conservation of energy holds for the animal body (ch. 44). Energy taken in the food is either expended or stored as fat and carbohydrate, and to some extent as protein. Whatever the primary cause may be, whether hypothalamic or endocrine disease, or whether it is due simply to overeating, obesity is the result of an energy intake in excess of the energy output. Theoretically, an energy balance could be struck by increasing the exercise of an obese subject. But increasing the energy output by exercise is much less effective than dietary restriction; physical exertion increases the appetite and the subject finds it difficult to resist satisfying it.

The basic problem in obesity is the cause of the increased appetite. Many psychological aspects of this question are obvious but they will not be discussed here. Endocrine factors have been considered elsewhere. Mayer and his colleagues have suggested a general distinction between "regulatory" obesities where the primary impairment is one of the central mechanisms regulating food intake (psychological disturbances, hypothalamic injury and "metabolic" obesities where the primary lesion leading to overeating is in tissues other than the regulating centers, i.e., pancreatic or sex gland disturbances). The prolonged effects of one type of lesion may induce the other.

THE "COST" OF OBESITY. (See table 50.2.) (1) Owing to the increased weight, muscular exertion places a greater load upon the heart and circulatory system. The incidence of arterial hypertension is relatively high in persons who are overweight. (2) Dissipation of heat by conduction and radiation (ch. 52) is reduced through the heat-insulating effect of the mantle of subcutaneous fat. Sweating is in consequence more profuse. (3) Diabetes is more common in the obese than in persons of normal weight. Joslin refers to diabetes as "the fat man's folly," and to obesity as "the open door to diabetes." Reducing the weight of an obese diabetic has been found to diminish the sugar excretion by as much as 75 per cent. (4) Persons who are grossly obese are said to be less resistant to infections and poorer surgical risks than those of normal weight. (5) The incidence of gallstones is relatively high in the obese according to Baumann; 88 per cent of persons with gallstones are overweight. (6) *Life expectancy.* Insurance statistics show that overweight after the age of 35 years is associated with a death rate much higher than that of lean persons or of those

TABLE 50.2*

*Influence of overweight on mortality in persons aged 45 to 50 years*

| Pounds Overweight | Increase in Death Rate over Average |
|:---:|:---:|
| 10 | 8 |
| 20 | 18 |
| 30 | 28 |
| 40 | 45 |
| 50 | 56 |
| 60 | 67 |
| 70 | 81 |
| 90 | 116 |

* After Newburgh.

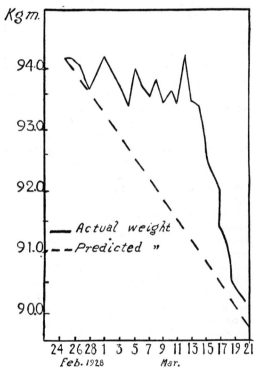

FIG. 50.2. Showing the delay in the loss of weight on a reducing diet owing to the retention of the water. (After Newburgh, modified.) This subject lost as much weight in 6 days as it was predicted would be lost in about three weeks as a result of the destruction of body tissue and without water retention.

of normal weight, a fact which has been pithily expressed in the phrase, "the longer the belt the shorter the life."

GENERAL PRINCIPLES IN THE TREATMENT OF OBESITY. The basis of treatment should be, as already indicated, (a) reduction in the caloric intake and (b) increase in the energy expenditure through moderate exercise. The dietary restrictions should not be extreme and should be made gradually. The extent to which the caloric intake should be reduced will depend upon the degree of obesity and the amount of exercise prescribed, but it should never be pushed to the point where the protein of the subject's tissues is drawn upon for energy purposes; nitrogen equilibrium should be maintained. Above all things a properly balanced diet should be devised and an adequate supply of vitamins and minerals provided. When the obesity is pronounced (body weight 25 per cent or more above normal), weight reduction is brought about by placing the subject upon a diet possessing a caloric value 40 or even 60 per cent below his energy requirement; he is thus forced to consume his own fat. The caloric value of human adipose tissue is about 3500 Calories per pound.[5] The total requirement of the average obese subject is around 2500 Calories per day. A reduction in the energy intake by 40 per cent of the requirement, that is, to 1500 Calories, will therefore entail a weight loss of nearly a third of a pound per day. The subject is kept upon the restricted diet until the desired weight has been reached; his caloric intake is then adjusted to his requirement (see ch. 55).

The failure of an overweight person to lose weight after having been placed upon a "reducing" diet has been a mystifying observation which appeared to refute the conclusion that obesity is due simply to a balance of energy intake over energy output. But the original weight is maintained for only two or three weeks, and is due to the retention of water which replaces the tissue broken down for energy purposes. At the end of this period water excretion increases above the normal and the weight falls rapidly (Fig. 50.2).

In planning a weight-reducing diet, it is toward the restriction of the more concentrated forms of food that attention is particularly directed. It will be recalled that the caloric value of fat is more than twice that of carbohydrate. Also fatty foods, since they contain little or no water, are more concentrated than starchy materials. Lard, dripping, olive oil, etc., are 100 per cent fat, whereas the protein and carbohydrate of white bread amount together to only about 60 per cent of its fresh weight. Ordinary fats and oils should therefore be restricted. Emphasis should again be placed on the provision of essential food factors commonly contained in foods which are denied to the obese subject. Sugar in the form of sweetening for beverages, in jams, honey or chocolates is a highly concentrated food. By curtailing its consumption a large reduction in

the caloric value of the diet can be effected without the disadvantages attending the reduction of some of the other foods. Bulky foods, e.g., green vegetables and salads of low caloric value but satisfying to the appetite may be substituted. Undue restriction of the water intake is sometimes practiced but this measure appears to be of no benefit and may be a detriment to health. Alcohol has a high caloric value and is therefore, except in minimal amounts, excluded from the diet. *Thyroid extract* is sometimes employed to raise the metabolic rate and so reduce the obesity. The hormone is clearly indicated as a means of raising a low metabolic rate to normal, otherwise its use is not to be advocated except in exceptional cases and only when the subject's basal metabolic rate can be followed by frequent determinations. *Dinitrophenol* is another agent which raises the metabolic rate and has been employed in the treatment of obesity. It is a dangerous drug unless given under the strictest supervision. Cataract has been reported following its use; liver injury may also result.

While the above well established facts should continue to be the basis of the treatment of obesity some new ones are struggling for acceptance. The work of Kekwick and his colleagues indicates that some aspects of metabolism in the obese differ from that of those who are not overweight. Alteration in the composition as distinct from the total caloric value of a diet may induce changes in the energy output of the obese individual. In some obese cases the rate of weight loss was greatest when fat provided 90 per cent and least when carbohydrate supplied 90 per cent of the caloric value. A striking resistance to ketosis was found in the obese. The treatment of obesity is in a "dynamic state."

## REFERENCES

### Monographs and Reviews

BENEDICT, F. G. A study of prolonged fasting. Carnegie Inst., Washington, Pub. 203, 1915.

BERRYMAN, G. H. Metabolism, 1954, **3**, 544.

CANNON, P. R. Sc. Monthly 1943, **56**, 5. Food and the War. *In* Medicine and the War, ed. by W. H. Taliaferro, pp. 23–39. University of Chicago Press, Chicago, 1944.

CONN, J. W. Physiol. Rev., 1944, **24**, 31.

GOLDNER, M. G. (ed.) Metabolism, 1957, **6**, 404.

KEYS, A., BROZEK, J., HENSCHEL, A., MICKELSEN, O. AND TAYLOR, H. L. The biology of human starvation, vols. I and II. University of Minnesota Press, Minneapolis, 1950.

LUSK, G. Physiol. Rev., 1921, **1**, 523.

MAYER, J. Physiological and nutritional aspects of obesity. Borden's Rev. Nutrition Res., 1958, **19**, 35.

NEWBURGH, L. H. Physiol. Rev., 1944, **24**, 18.

TEPPERMAN, J. Perspectives Biol. Med., 1958, **1**, 293.

[5] Pure human fat has a caloric value of approximately 9.5 Cal. per gram. 3500 Cal. per pound here given is the value after allowance has been made for connective tissue and water content.

# 51

# METABOLISM IN MUSCULAR ACTIVITY

*The Structure of Skeletal Muscle*

A typical skeletal muscle such as the gastrocnemius or biceps is composed of large numbers of elongated cells, usually referred to as muscle fibers. The fibers are bound together into bundles or fasciculi of different sizes which are grouped again into larger masses to form the whole muscle. A connective tissue sheath of reticulated fibers, called the *perimysium*, encloses each fasciculus and separates it from its neighbors. The connective tissue sheath enveloping the whole muscle is called the *epimysium*. The muscle fibers of different muscles range in length from 1 mm., in a minute muscle such as the stapedius, to about 4 cm. in a long muscle such as the sartorius. The cells traverse the entire length of the shorter fasciculi but in the longer muscles they are joined together by tapering ends the tips of which are applied side to side, to form elongated chains. This is the commonest arrangement, but in some muscles designed for maximum contractile force with a minimum of shortening the fibers are disposed in parallel instead of in series or they may run diagonally to a central tendon. The muscle fibers also vary widely in diameter, which measures about 10 microns in the small muscles to 100 microns in the larger.

The body of the cell contains a limited and variable amount of material which corresponds to the cytoplasm of other cells, and is called the *sarcoplasm*. The latter surrounds large numbers of fine threads packed closely together and running from end to end of the cell. These are the *myofibrils*; they have a diameter of from 1 to 2 $\mu$. Under the high power of the microscope they appear as a faint pattern of parallel lines. At the insertion of the muscle they become continuous with the fibrils in the tendon. This longitudinal striation is also seen in smooth muscle. But the most striking and characteristic microscopical appearance of skeletal muscle fibers is their *cross-striation* or *stripes*. These are alternating light and dark bands which run across the width of the fiber. When the myofibrils are separated by microdissection, the cross-striations are seen to be a feature of the fibrils themselves; the cross stripes of the whole fiber are the result of the accurate alignment of the dark and light bands from fibril to fibril across the breadth of the cell. The dark and light sections of the fibers are known as the A (or Q) and I (or J) bands, respectively. The A band in the relaxed fibers is from 3 to 6 $\mu$ long, and is a little broader than the I band. It stains deeply with the usual stains while the I band remains pale; but even in unstained sections of muscle the A band is dark compared with the adjacent I band. When the fresh muscle fiber is viewed by polarized light, the A band appears bright and the I band dark. This is due to the former being doubly refractive (DR). The I band has a single refractive index. On account of its birefringent property the A band is also known as the *anisotropic* band or disc, while the I band is termed *isotropic*. Both the A and the I bands are bisected by narrow cross lines. The line in the A band is bright and known as the H line (or Henson's line); that in the I band is called the Z line, Dobie's line or Krause's membrane. The Z line is not confined to the myofibrils but in teased specimens can be seen to pass through the sarcoplasm between them, and appears to be of a membranous nature. It extends to the sarcolemma to which it becomes attached. The Z line is probably of importance in the linkage between the changes in electrical potential across the sarcolemma which accompany excitation and the contraction of the myofibrils. Local depolarizations which cause no effect elsewhere may bring about a local contraction of a single sarcomere if they occur opposite a Z line.

Each muscle cell contains several hundred nuclei which in vertebrate skeletal muscle are situated, for the most part, superficially just beneath the sarcolemma. The latter is a delicate, transparent, but tough membrane which envelops the entire cell. It is composed of interlacing collagenous fibrils embedded in a clear matrix of colloidal material. The fibrils are continuous with those in the endomysium. Lying in intimate association with the myofibrils are the *sarcosomes* or *muscle mitochondria*. These particles contain the very active repiratory enzymes of the cell and are the principal sites of synthesis of the phosphate anhydrides which are believed to provide the immediate source of energy for contraction.

When as a result of growth or athletic training the muscles enlarge and become more powerful, they do so not by increasing the number of their

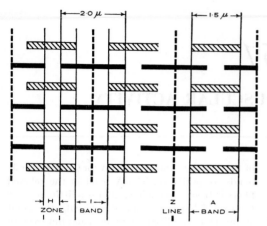

FIG. 51.1. Schematic representation of the ultrastructure of muscle as revealed by the electron microscope. The dimensions shown are those which remain constant when a fiber is stretched while the width of the H-zone and the distance between adjacent Z-lines are both increased. (After H. E. Huxley and A. F. Huxley.)

constituent fibers but by an increase in size of the individual fibers. The fibers are also larger in persons who are well nourished as compared with those in states of malnutrition. The difference in size of the fibers in the two instances is due to the amounts of sarcoplasm which they contain.

The foregoing is a description of the muscle fibers as seen under as high a magnification as is possible with the ordinary microscope. But, when observed with the electronmicroscope, it is found that the myofibrils are themselves made up of still finer longitudinal filaments. These filaments, which are the ultimate contractile structures, are composed of two proteins (see below) and have a diameter ranging from 50 to 100 Ångström units (1 Å = $10^{-8}$ cm.).

Recent electronmicroscopic studies by H. E. Huxley have shown that two types of filament exist in the myofibril. The thicker ones have a diameter of about 100 Å and are found in the A band extending from one end to the other of this region. On the other hand, the thinner filaments are seen not only in the I bands, where they occur alone, but also in the A bands where they interdigitate with the thicker filaments in an orderly fashion, each thick filament being surrounded by an array of six thin filaments. It has been shown by differential extraction and subsequent examination in the electronmicroscope that the thick filaments are composed of myosin, and similar evidence suggests that the other important structural protein, actin, must be localized in the thin filaments.

This new picture of muscle ultrastructure is complemented by recent observations of A. F. Huxley using the interference microscope. With

this instrument it was possible to show, in contradistinction to older views, that when an isolated muscle fiber is stimulated to contract, the length of the A bands remains constant (1.5 $\mu$). This dimension is also unchanged on stretching, when it is observed that the Z lines separate while the H band increases in width. These observations strongly suggest that the interdigitating filaments seen in the electronmicroscope are able to slide past each other, and that muscular contraction is brought about by just such a sliding motion.

### The Chemical Constitution of Muscle

Muscle is composed mainly of protein (18 to 20 per cent). The remainder of its substance is made up of various minerals and a large number of organic compounds some of which are found exclusively in muscular tissue. The chief electrolyte is potassium which is present in a concentration of about 400 mg. per 100 grams. *Magnesium, calcium* and *sodium* are found in much smaller amounts. Muscle contains a great variety of substances generally grouped under the heading of nitrogenous extractives, such as *creatine, phosphocreatine, alanylhistidine, adenosinetriphosphate, creatinine, purine bases, carnosine, anserine* (bird and fish muscle).

Muscle contains between 0.5 and 1.5 per cent of glycogen, from 0.02 to 0.04 per cent of glucose and about 0.01 per cent of lactic acid. Phospholipids (1.0 per cent), cholesterol (0.07 to 0.18 per cent), vitamins, enzymes and a host of other organic materials are present, many of which will be mentioned later.

Reference has already been made to the chief proteins of the myofibrils, myosin and actin. Myosin has a molecular weight of about 500,000 while that of actin is about 80,000. Under certain conditions actin and myosin may be extracted from the muscle fiber as a complex which is known as actomyosin, containing three parts of myosin to one of actin. A third protein of the myofibril, tropomyosin, is present only to the extent of about 5 per cent, but this is probably the best characterized of the fibrillar proteins, its molecular weight being between 52,000 and 55,000. The oxygen-holding pigment *myoglobin* (ch. 6) in red muscle is about 1 per cent and is free in the cytoplasm of the myofibril. The sarcoplasm also contains the soluble enzymes of the glycolytic sequence while the "insoluble" enzymes of the respiratory sequence (cytochromes, flavoproteins) are present in the sarcosomes.

### The Chemical Physiology of Muscular Contraction

The mechanical response of an isolated muscle to stimulation is not *accompanied* by an increased consumption óf oxygen; extra oxygen is not consumed until after contraction and relaxation are over. So, there are two phases in the contraction cycle, an *anaerobic (anoxidative) phase* and an *aerobic (oxidative)* or *recovery* phase, during which the muscle is restored to its previous state. If the muscle be stimulated repeatedly in an atmosphere of nitrogen it contracts forcibly at first, but soon becomes fatigued, since it cannot obtain the oxygen necessary for its recuperation between the individual contractions. Lactic acid accumulates and the muscle enters into rigor. If, at the onset of fatigue, oxygen is readmitted, the lactic acid disappears, and the muscle recovers its original power to contract. The lactic acid concentration at which complete fatigue of skeletal muscle ensues (lactic acid maximum) is from 0.3 to 0.6 per cent. The lactic acid is derived from the breakdown of glycogen (ch. 48). As the lactic acid concentration rises the carbohydrate stores diminish. Yet, the onset of fatigue is not due to the exhaustion of the glycogen stores, for the muscle fails to contract before the latter have disappeared. It may be that the high acidity inhibits the enzymes through whose action glycogen breakdown is brought about. Inorganic phosphate also accumulates in a muscle contracting in the absence of oxygen. The phosphate production rises rapidly during the earlier contractions, soon reaches a maximum and then ceases.

That a muscle can contract anaerobically has been known for many years. It has also long been known that lactic acid and $CO_2$ are produced by a muscle contracting in nitrogen. Spallanzani over 150 years ago observed that snails placed in nitrogen evolved $CO_2$. In spite of these earlier observations it was thought, nevertheless, that a muscle derived its energy from oxidative processes—for how otherwise was the $CO_2$ produced? In order to explain the phenomenon it was supposed (Hermann, Pflüger) that an oxygen store was contained in some giant molecule (termed "inogen" by Hermann) within the muscle substance itself. So "intramolecular" oxygen was spoken of as the hidden oxygen reserve from which the muscle drew for its anaerobic contraction. Lactic acid also, it was thought, was derived from the breakdown of this hypothetical molecule. This theory was disproved by the classical experiments of Fletcher and Hopkins in 1907. These observers showed that the $CO_2$ which appeared during the anaerobic contraction was not the result of oxidation but was *preëxisting* $CO_2$—i.e., simply $CO_2$ which had been liberated by the action of lactic acid upon sodium bicarbonate in the muscle fluids. They showed that the oxidative processes occurred after the contraction was over, that lactic acid then disappeared and

$CO_2$ was formed. It was erroneously supposed at this time, that the lactic acid which disappeared had been *completely* oxidized to $CO_2$ and water. That glycogen was the lactic acid precursor was indicated by the fact that the appearance of lactic acid in muscle fatigued in nitrogen was proportional to the glycogen loss. Also, an R.Q. of around unity, found later by Meyerhof, for the recovery phase of isolated muscle, indicated that its fuel was carbohydrate.

Meyerhof also showed that when oxygen was admitted to a fatigued frog's muscle, the amount of gas consumed was only one-fifth of that expected if the disappearance of the lactic acid were due to its oxidation to $CO_2$ and water. The heat produced during the oxidative phase was also much less than it should be, were all the lactic acid burned. It was found, further, that glycogen *increased* in the fatigued muscle recovering in oxygen.

Embden had previously shown the importance of phosphate in the activity of muscle. Increased excretion of phosphate in the urine occurs as a result of muscular exercise, and Embden found that when muscle juice was incubated with a solution of bicarbonate, lactic acid and free phosphoric acid appeared in nearly equimolecular amounts. He suggested that the *immediate* precursor of lactic acid was a hexose-phosphate. This he termed *lactacidogen*. A hexose-phosphate had been shown by Harden and Young to be formed as an intermediary in the fermentation of sugar by yeast. When Embden added this ester to muscle juice an increased formation of lactic and phosphoric acids occurred. He also claimed to have demonstrated an increased production of phosphoric acid in a muscle during its contraction. The phosphoric acid as well as the lactic acid was believed to be derived from the breakdown of *lactacidogen* (i.e., hexose-phosphate).

## The Chemical Changes Occurring in Muscle Contracting in the Absence of Oxygen; Phosphorylation, Glycogenolysis and Glycolysis

### (See also chapters 32 and 48)

Muscle does not depend upon immediate oxidative processes to liberate the energy necessary for its contraction. It will continue to contract for some time in the complete absence of oxygen. The energy stored in glycogen is thus liberated anaerobically. But for the recovery of the muscle, that is, for the reaccumulation of its energy stores, oxygen is required. The chemical changes involved in the entire contractile process are thus divided into two phases, the *anaerobic* or *contraction phase* and the *aerobic, oxidative* or *recovery phase*. The muscle is comparable to a machine, such as a submarine engine which runs when submerged upon stored energy supplied in electric batteries. The batteries are recharged when the submarine comes to the surface. Expressed in another way, the muscle when it contracts runs up an oxygen debt (p. 879) which it pays when the contraction is over.

Evidence for the anaerobic chemical changes about to be outlined has been obtained very largely from studies of the enzyme systems in aqueous extracts of muscle and in yeast juice during alcoholic fermentation.

One of the first steps in the liberation of energy for contraction is the breakdown of glycogen stored in the muscle fiber. The glycogen reacts with inorganic phosphate and splits off glucose-1-phosphate (Cori ester) molecules in stepwise fashion. This reaction is catalyzed by phosphorylase. It is known that phosphorylase of muscle can exist in an active (*a*) and an inactive form (*b*), although the activation process is quite different from that of liver phosphorylase (see p. 811). It is possible that there is a production of phosphorylase *a* from phosphorylase *b* during muscular activity thus making the glycogen stores of muscle available for metabolic processes. Muscle phosphorylase contains pyridoxal phosphate as a tightly bound cofactor (see table 51.1). The cleavage of the glycogen molecule occurs successively at the 1:4 C—O—C linkages between the glucose units. In the separation of the latter, an H atom of the phosphate group becomes attached to the 4 carbon atom, while the 1 carbon atom of the adjacent glucose unit holds the —O—$PO_3H_2$ group. The uptake of phosphate and its cleavage into glucose phosphate units has been aptly called *phosphorolysis* by Parnas, since, obviously, it is analogous to hydrolysis in which water (H·OH) instead of phosphate is taken up, the H atom and OH atoms becoming attached, respectively, to the adjacent groups of the larger molecule (protein, disaccharides, poly-saccharides, etc.) when they separate (see table 51.1).

The glucose-1-phosphate formed in the phosphorylytic reaction undergoes an intramolecular transference of its phosphate group to the 6 carbon atom, being thus converted to *glucose-6-phosphate* (Robison ester). This reaction is catalyzed by the enzyme *phosphoglucomutase*. The glucose-6-phosphate, through the action of *phosphohexose isomerase*, gives rise to fructose-6-phosphate (Neuberg ester), which then receives a phosphate group from adenosine triphosphate (ATP), to form fructose-1-6-diphosphate and adenosine diphosphate (ADP).

The fructose-1-6-diphosphate is acted upon by *aldolase* and split into the triosephosphates, *dihydroxyacetone phosphate* and *3-phosphoglyceraldehyde* (Fischer-Baer ester). The 3-phosphoglyceraldehyde reacts with inorganic phosphorus, and in the presence of *triosephosphate dehydrogenase* and DPN (diphosphopyridine nucleotide or Coenzyme 1) is converted to *1,3-diphosphoglyceric acid*. DPN accepts $H_2$ and is reduced to $DPNH_2$. As rapidly as dihydroxyacetone phosphate is produced it is transformed to 3-glyceraldehyde phosphate (called the "reactive form" of the sugar) which in the presence of triosephosphate dehydrogenase is rapidly removed. The reaction is thus "drawn to the right."

The 1,3-diphosphoglyceric acid undergoes dephosphorylation to form *3-phosphoglyceric acid*, the released phosphate group converting ADP to ATP. By intramolecular transfer of the phosphate group 3-phosphoglyceric acid is converted to *2-phosphoglyceric acid*, the reaction being catalyzed by *phosphoglyceric mutase*. 2-Phosphoglyceric acid is converted by dehydration to *phospho-enolpyruvic acid* through the action of *enolase*.

The phospho-enolpyruvic acid reacts with ADP to form *pyruvic acid* and ATP. This reaction is catalyzed by a *transphosphorylase* in the presence of magnesium and potassium ions.

Pyruvic acid in the absence of oxygen is reduced to *lactic acid* by the reduced coenzyme ($DPNH_2$) in the presence of *lactic dehydrogenase*, the coenzyme being restored to the oxidized form (DPN).

Under aerobic conditions the reduced coenzyme is not oxidized by pyruvic acid, as shown in the last reaction, but by molecular oxygen through the combined action of a specific flavoprotein and the cytochrome system (ch. 32). The result is that with an adequate supply of oxygen no lactic acid is formed, and of that produced anaerobically one-fifth is oxidized through pyruvic to carbon dioxide and water, and the remainder resynthesized to glycogen. In the intact animal synthesis occurs in the liver.[1] The oxidation of lactic acid to pyruvic acid is brought about through the action of lactic dehydrogenase in the presence of DPN. In the presence of oxygen the pyruvic acid is oxidized in a series of steps called the *tricarboxylic acid cycle*. Although there is not

[1] According to Meyerhof resynthesis of glycogen from lactic acid occurs in the isolated frog muscle, but this probably does not occur in intact mammalian muscle.

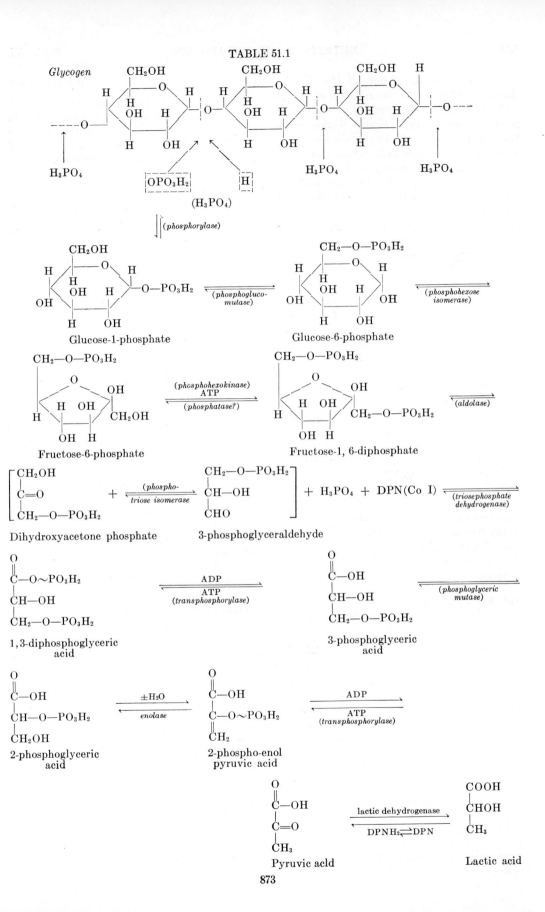

TABLE 51.1

873

unanimity as to the details of the chemical changes involved in the dissimilation of pyruvic acid, the researches of a number of workers, especially Szent Györgyi, Krebs, Werkman and Wood and Evans and Slotin, permit the scheme to be drawn as in table 51.2, p. 875. Thus oxalo-acetic acid and acetylcoenzyme A undergo condensation to form citric acid. The citric acid loses a molecule of water and is converted to *cis*aconitic acid; this then regains a molecule of water to produce *iso*citric acid which is oxidized to oxalo-succinic acid. The latter is decarboxylated to yield $\alpha$-ketoglutaric acid which is oxidized to succinic acid, carbon dioxide and water. The succinic acid is oxidized through fumaric and malic acids to oxaloacetic acid. With the regeneration of oxaloacetic acid the cycle repeats. At each turn of the cycle an acetyl group derived from pyruvate is oxidized; each molecule of pyruvic acid, therefore, yields two molecules of water and three molecules of carbon dioxide, while a molecule of oxaloacetic is reformed. A single molecule of oxaloacetic acid can be used in this way repeatedly in the oxidation of acetyl groups to carbon dioxide and water; it, therefore, acts in the manner of a catalyst.

The energy which the anaerobic production of lactic acid from glycogen yields for the performance of work is only a small fraction of that which results from the oxidation of lactic acid. For each gram molecule of lactic acid produced the free energy amounts to about 23,000 calories, whereas some 325,000 calories are liberated by the oxidation of a corresponding amount of lactic acid to carbon dioxide and water.

### THE ROLE PLAYED BY PHOSPHATE ANHYDRIDES (CREATINE PHOSPHATE AND THE ADENYLIC ACID SYSTEM)

In 1927 Eggleton and Eggleton obtained a creatine-phosphorus compound from muscle which they named *phosphagen*. About the same time Fisk and Subbarow isolated the same substance and called it *phosphocreatine*; it is also known as *creatine phosphate*, or briefly CP. It has the following formula.

$$NH=C \begin{cases} NH{\sim}PO(OH)_2 \\ \\ N(CH_3){\cdot}CH_2{\cdot}COOH \end{cases}$$

*Phosphoarginine* is the corresponding phosphagen in invertebrate muscle. In the muscles of some species both compounds are present.

### CONTRACTION WITHOUT LACTIC ACID PRODUCTION

An experiment of Lundsgaard (1929) revealed the essential importance of phosphocreatine in the contractile process. He found that after the injection of sodium iodoacetate into the dorsal lymph sac of a frog, violent contractions of the muscles occurred followed by rigor. When a muscle of the poisoned animal was isolated and stimulated electrically in nitrogen, it responded, but *no lactic acid was produced*. After about 100 contractions, it became fatigued. This is much sooner than the onset of fatigue in normal muscle, and, unlike the latter, the poisoned muscle became slightly *alkaline* in reaction. About 0.5 mg. of lactic acid per gram of tissue is formed in a normal muscle after a similar number of contractions.

Upon analysis the poisoned muscle shows a loss of glycogen, and of phosphocreatine, and an increased content of hexose-phosphate. The lactic acid and phosphocreatine-phosphorus values of normal and poisoned muscles after 150 contractions each are shown in the following table (after Lundsgaard).

| | | Lactic acid mg. per cent | Phosphagen phosphorus mg. per cent |
|---|---|---|---|
| Normal | Resting | 25 | 61 |
| | Working | 84 | 40 |
| Poisoned | Resting | 16 | 57 |
| | Working | 15 | 0 |

It was concluded that the disappearance of CP was not due to its being used up more rapidly, but to its failure to be resynthesized. The energy for resynthesis was presumably derived from glycogen—lactic acid breakdown (glycolysis). Iodoacetate reacts with sulphydryl groups of triose-phosphate dehydrogenase which are essential to its action. This inhibition arrests glycolysis at the stage where 3-phosphoglyceric aldehyde is converted to 1,3-phosphoglyceric acid. Thus, iodoacetate inactivates the glycolytic system which is essential for the resynthesis of phosphocreatine.

Such observations led to the concept that the energy for contraction is derived from the breakdown of phosphocreatine, the role of carbohydrate dissimilation being to provide the energy for the resynthesis of this compound. However, in 1934, Lohmann showed that dialyzed muscle extracts are incapable of hydrolyzing CP, and that its breakdown occurs in a series of two reactions, the first of which, known as the Lohmann reaction after its discoverer, may be written as follows:

CP + adenosine diphosphate (ADP) $\rightarrow$ C +

### TABLE 51.2

*The citric acid cycle in relation to the metabolism of carbohydrate and fatty acids*

(Kindness of Professor A. M. Wynne)

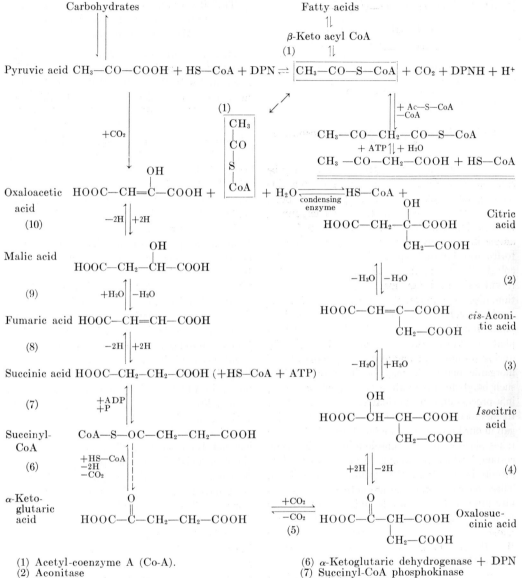

(1) Acetyl-coenzyme A (Co-A).
(2) Aconitase
(3) Aconitase
(4) Isocitric dehydrogenase + TPN
(5) Oxalosuccinic decarboxylase

(6) $\alpha$-Ketoglutaric dehydrogenase + DPN
(7) Succinyl-CoA phosphokinase
(8) Succinic dehydrogenase
(9) Fumarase
(10) Malic dehydrogenase + DPN

adenosine triphosphate (ATP), the latter compound being broken down by adenosine triphosphatase to form ADP and inorganic phosphate. This work suggested that the breakdown of ATP must precede that of CP and that this reaction is closer to the primary processes of contraction. The nucleotide ATP (also called adenylpyrophos-phate) is a compound of adenine, D-ribose, and three molecules of orthophosphate. Both CP and ATP posses energy-rich phosphate bonds, indicated by the symbol $\sim$ in their formulas. The free energy of hydrolysis of such a bond is about 10,000 calories per gram molecule of phosphate liberated.

N=C—NH
CH C—N
CH H H H H
N—C—N—C C C C—CH₂O—
OH OH
—O—

OH OH OH
P—O∼P—O∼P—OH
O O O

Adenosine triphosphate [Adenyl-pyrophosphoric acid ATP]

The terminal phosphate group of ATP may be split off by the action of the enzyme adenosine triphosphatase (ATPase) or the phosphate bond energy may be transferred to other compounds; ADP is formed. Phosphate is given up for example in the conversion of fructose-6-phosphate to fructose-1:6-diphosphate in the course of glycolysis. There are three main pathways for the resynthesis of ATP in muscle, the Lohmann reaction, discussed above, glycolysis, and respiration. In the glycolytic sequence, the energy-rich phosphate bonds are generated at the triosephosphate dehydrogenase and enolase levels, while during respiration as many as three molecules of inorganic phosphate may be incorporated into such bonds for every atom of oxygen consumed, in a process known as oxidative phosphorylation, the detailed mechanism of which remains a major gap in our knowledge of metabolism. This process takes place within the muscle mitochondria (sarcosomes) which lie among the myofibrils, while glycolysis occurs in the "soluble" sarcoplasm. These recovery processes are activated very rapidly after a muscle twitch, indeed Millikan has found that the disoxygenation of myoglobin commences within 0.2 sec. of stimulation indicating that the respiratory system has been activated in that time.

The resynthesis of phosphagen is effected by a reversal of the Lohmann reaction, i.e., ATP yields phosphorus to creatine, CP and ADP being formed. The equilibrium of this reaction is, however, markedly in favor of creatine and adenosine triphosphate. Phosphocreatine can, therefore, function as a reserve of phosphate bond energy which will bring about a rapid resynthesis of ATP, even in the iodoacetate poisoned muscle although the normal resynthesis of energy-rich bonds, which is a concomitant of carbohydrate break-

down, cannot take place in the presence of the inhibitor and after a series of contractions the supply of CP will be exhausted.

## THE RELATIONSHIP BETWEEN ADENOSINE TRIPHOSPHATE BREAKDOWN AND MUSCULAR CONTRACTION

There are many experimental facts which suggest that the breakdown of ATP is in some way associated with the contraction of muscle. Three main pieces of evidence have led to this belief that the ATP/ADP system is the immediate source of energy for contraction. Firstly, the work of Lundsgaard and Lohmann, considered above, leads clearly to the idea that contraction may occur at the expense of phosphate bond energy, with the breakdown of ATP preceding that of phosphocreatine and therefore being more intimately related to the contraction process.

Secondly, it was discovered by Engelhardt and Lyubunova that myosin, the chief protein of muscle and long recognized as an element of the contractile apparatus, possessed ATPase activity. This identity or, at least, close relationship of myosin with ATPase appears to bring the breakdown of ATP into intimate association with the mechanical effects, i.e., with the actual contraction of muscle. Myosin has been obtained by Szent Györgyi in the form of minute needle shaped crystals. Upon repeated recrystallization no loss in ATPase activity, but rather an increase, occurs. From this fact and the following observations, myosin and ATPase are generally assumed to be identical, although absolute proof has not been secured. They are at least very closely associated. (a) Crude preparations of myosin contain several other enzymes, but these can be removed completely by successive precipitations. (b) The thermolability of myosin and of ATPase are closely similar, the protein undergoing denaturation, and enzyme activity is abolished at about the same temperature, which is relatively quite low. (c) Electrophoretic studies show that myosin possesses a high degree of homogenicity, the large rapidly moving fraction which constitutes over 90 per cent of the protein of the preparation has been found to have double the ATPase activity of the smaller slowly moving fraction which possesses a low protein content.

Only one phosphate group is split from ATP by myosin. ADP is not attacked. It shows a high degree of specificity in this regard. Inosinetriphosphate and inorganic triphosphate are split in a similar manner. Calcium ions activate

ATPase, whereas magnesium, copper and silver are inhibitory; the enzyme activity is unaffected by cyanide.

The third line of evidence relating ATP to contraction, and perhaps the most dramatic, is that certain preparations can be made from muscle which undergo mechanical deformation on the addition of ATP. Thin strips of rabbit psoas muscle may be extracted with 50 per cent (volume per volume) aqueous glycerol at $-10°C.$ for several days. During this extraction, the soluble proteins of the muscle fiber are leached out but the myofibrils retain their structure and orientation. When adenosine triphosphate in low concentration is added to such a preparation it will shorten by as much as 70 to 75 per cent and may exert tensions which compare well with those exerted by living muscle. Even simpler systems will display contractile properties; the proteins actin and myosin form a complex called actomyosin which may be precipitated in threadlike form. Such threads will shorten in the presence of ATP.

These findings provide strong circumstantial evidence for the view that ATP breakdown is intimately associated with the contraction process. However, the attempt to provide experimental evidence of a direct nature, i.e., a demonstration of the dephosphorylation of ATP during contraction by a living muscle has so far failed. The expected breakdown of ATP would be of the order of 0.25 $\mu$mole per gram muscle per twitch, but the values found are considerably lower than this estimate. Indeed it appears that at least one twitch and possibly a short tetanic contraction (1 to 2 sec.) may take place without any significant breakdown of either ATP or creatine phosphate. There is, however, some evidence in favor of a liberation of inorganic phosphate under these circumstances which may provide the key to a resolution of this apparent discrepancy, since it may mean that some presently unknown phosphate compound is breaking down and either bringing about a very rapid rephosphorylation of ADP or is itself providing the immediate energy for contraction.

Whatever may issue from this controversy, a fundamental problem will remain, namely, how is the energy of hydrolytic reaction, if such it be, linked to the physical changes in the muscle—the shortening and thickening which we call contraction. An earlier view of the molecular basis of contraction regarded it as a reflection on the macroscopic scale of a folding of the polypeptide chains of myosin but the newer knowledge of the ultra-structure of the myofibril (p. 869) suggests that contraction represents a change of intermolecular orientation rather than of intramolecular configuration, a suggestion which is confirmed by recent studies of X-ray diffraction by muscle. The nature of the forces which bring about the sliding motion of the two types of filament relative to one another is unknown but it may be assumed that this structural interaction is related to the biochemical interaction between actin and myosin. A scheme has recently been proposed by A. F. Huxley in which active side groups on the myosin filament react with sites on adjacent actin filaments, *the rates of association and dissociation depending on the relative position of the filaments.* The reaction is blocked by ATP (or some other high-energy phosphate compound) and the splitting of ATP would bring about activation of the contraction mechanism. This model is remarkably successful in providing an exact relationship between parameters having the form of the rate constants of a cycle of chemical reactions and the over-all mechanical and thermodynamic constants of muscle. This and other schemes suggest that the resting state of muscle will be characterized by a low ATPase activity and that the electrical changes in the sarcolemma which initiate the contraction process must bring about a rapid activation of ATPase. This may conceivably be effected by an alteration in the free concentration of $Mg^{++}$, $Ca^{++}$ or other changes in the ionic environment of the active site of the myofibrillar ATPase but the detailed nature of these steps remains a central problem of muscle physiology.

## HEAT PRODUCTION IN MUSCLE

Our present knowledge of the relationships between the activity of muscle and the energy set free is very largely due to A. V. Hill. During muscular activity, energy is liberated in two forms, as mechanical work and as heat. The heat production associated with a muscle twitch occurs in two stages, a very rapid outburst of heat which occurs during the twitch itself and a slow, prolonged production of heat following the contraction. This latter is called the *recovery heat* (to be sharply distinguished from the so-called heat of relaxation) and is identical in time course with the extra oxygen consumption which follows activity. Both then reflect the increased metabolism which restores the energy supplies of the muscle (ATP, phosphocreatine, etc.) to their resting levels. It is of interest that the recovery heat is about equal to the total energy set free during

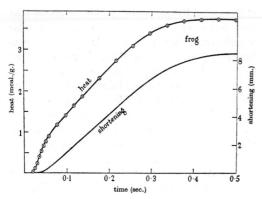

F_IG. 51.2. A comparison of the kinetics of shortening and heat production during an isotonic twitch (frog sartorius). The liberation of the heat of activation precedes shortening and is succeeded by a phase in which the curves are approximately parallel and heat production is proportional to shortening. (From Hill, Proc. Roy. Soc., **136B**, 242, 1949, by kind permission of the author and of the Royal Society.)

contraction. During recovery, the chemical changes which are associated with this initial liberation of energy are reversed and since an equivalent amount of energy is wasted as heat, the efficiency of the recovery process is about 50 per cent.

The initial energy itself may be divided into three forms. Firstly, the *heat of activation* (A) which is associated with the process whereby the muscle passes from the resting to the active state, e.g., the hydrolysis of phosphate anhydrides. In frog muscle at 0°C. this heat production commences about 10 msec. after electrical stimulus; at 38°C. the latent period of the activation heat would be much shorter. At about 20 msec. after shock shortening commences and a second phase of heat liberation is associated with this process, and indeed this *heat of shortening* is directly proportional to the amount of shortening, i.e., heat of shortening $= ax$ where $x$ is the shortening in cm. and $a$ is a constant, having the dimensions of a force if the heat is expressed in mechanical units. These two processes of heat liberation may be clearly observed in figure 51.2. The magnitudes of these effects are also indicated here, $A + ax = 3$ mcal. per gram muscle, $A$ is about one-half of $ax$, for maximum values of $x$.

The third form of energy liberation is performance of work. In an isotonic contraction under load $P$, this will be equal to $Px$. If the muscle is allowed to relax under load, an amount of heat equal to this work will appear; this may be conceived as having its molecular basis in the return of contractile and elastic elements in the fiber to their resting orientation. It is however of prime theoretical importance that *there is no true heat of relaxation*, i.e., if a muscle is allowed to relax under zero tension (a condition which may only be attained under ingenious experimental conditions) no measurable heat appears. It is therefore highly improbable that there are any chemical changes such as ATP breakdown associated to the relaxation process.

The total initial energy of a twitch $E$ may therefore be written,

$$E = A + (P + a)x$$

In a tetanic contraction, activation heat is produced in response to each of the series of shocks and is summated. It is then referred to as the maintenance heat and is proportional to the duration of the contraction ($t$)

$$E = kt + (Px + a)x$$

Since the work done is $Px$, it will be seen that during contraction the efficiency of the muscular machine,

$$\frac{\text{work performed}}{\text{energy expenditure}} = \frac{Px}{kt + (P + a)x}$$

In order to relate the efficiency to velocity of contraction, the numerator and denominator are divided by $t$. Thus, allowing $v$ to stand for the speed of shortening ($x/t$) we obtain

$$\text{efficiency} = \frac{Pv}{k + (P + a)v}$$

The efficiency of the muscular machine is, therefore, a function of the speed of contraction, itself a function of the load. The maximal efficiency is reached at about a fifth of the maximal speed of shortening, i.e., under zero load, and is equal to about 40 per cent, though when the heat of recovery is added to the total initial energy (to which it is approximately equal; see above) the efficiency falls to 20 per cent.

It has been shown by Hill that the sum of the rate of work and the rate of production of shortening heat (i.e., the rate of energy liberation in excess of the heat of activation) is linearly related to the tension, in the following manner

$$(P + a)v = b(P_0 - P)$$

where $P_0$ is the isometric tension and $b$ is a constant. On rearrangement, this becomes

$$(P + a)(v + b) = \text{constant}.$$

This equation relates the velocity of shortening in an isometric contraction to load, and is of considerable importance, since it is possible to derive the constants $a$ and $b$ quite independently from thermal data or by purely mechanical measurements, with very good agreement. The physical basis for this very simple and fundamental relationship is unknown although it is one of the very noteworthy features of the model proposed by A. F. Huxley that it does in fact yield a mathematical formulation which is consonant with Hill's equation.

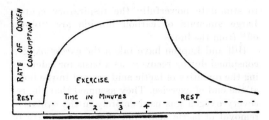

FIG. 51.3. Illustrating the increase in $O_2$ consumption above the resting level following exercise—"oxygen debt." (From Hill, *Muscular Movement in Man.*)

### MUSCULAR CONTRACTION IN THE INTACT ANIMAL

#### *Oxygen Debt*

We have seen that an isolated muscle is able to contract when stimulated in an atmosphere of nitrogen but its recovery phase is postponed until oxygen is re-admitted. During strenuous exercise the muscles of the intact animal behave similarly. While working strenuously, the circulatory and respiratory systems are incapable of supplying adequate amounts of oxygen for the removal (by oxidation and resynthesis to glycogen) of the large quantities of lactic acid produced. Complete recovery must be postponed until the exercise is over, when the accumulated lactic acid is gradually removed. The muscles of the intact animal during strenuous exertion are comparable, therefore, to the isolated muscle contracting anaerobically. It was shown by A. V. Hill and his associates that an athlete during great muscular effort such as sprinting cannot possibly inhale more than a fraction of the oxygen required. That is, the body works its muscles but does not furnish them with the total oxygen required for the work until some time after this has been completed—it "goes into debt for oxygen" paying up during the recovery period (see fig. 51.3). In a 100-yard sprint, for example, the oxygen requirement may be over 6 liters. It is obviously impossible to deliver this amount to the muscle in the few seconds in which the race is run. The maximum consumption possible is not more than 4 liters of oxygen per minute. Furthermore, a sprinter can dash 100 yards with the breath held. The great value of the anaerobic phase of muscular contraction is thus revealed. Through the ability of the muscles to contract when deprived of oxygen and to replenish their stores of energy during the phase of oxidative recovery, they are enabled to perform for short periods an amount of work which otherwise would be impossible, that is, were they as in the

case of a motor engine, dependent entirely upon a contemporaneous oxygen supply.

The oxygen debt is determined by measuring the oxygen used during the period of recovery, i.e., from the termination of the exercise to the time when the oxygen consumption has returned to normal, and subtracting from it the quantity of oxygen used during a corresponding resting period. The length of the recovery period may be 80 minutes or more. In very severe exertion the oxygen debt amounts to over 10 liters (or about 0.3 cc. per gram of muscle tissue). The maximum recorded in man is over 18 liters. During less strenuous exercise the discrepancy between lactic acid production and lactic acid removal is less pronounced, and the oxygen debt is correspondingly smaller. In light exercise the lactic acid is removed during the work—the body "pays as it goes"—and no oxygen debt is incurred. This is called the *steady state*. In other words, anaerobic and aerobic processes are balanced. The average man cannot maintain the steady state unless the oxygen requirement of the work does not exceed about 2 liters per minute. After severe exercise the normal level of lactic acid in the blood may not be reached until an hour or more after the exercise has ceased.

#### *Lactic Acid Production during Exercise*

The lactic acid produced in a short bout of strenuous exercise may amount to as much as 3 grams per second, and its concentration in the blood rise as high as 0.2 per cent. The lactic acid, though buffered by the muscle protein thus

$$H^+ + L^- + K^+ + P^- \rightarrow K^+ + L^- + HP$$

| lactic acid | potassium proteinate | potassium lactate | acid proteinate undissociated |
|---|---|---|---|

and to a less extent by phosphates and bicarbonates, causes a sufficient change in blood reaction to stimulate powerfully the respiratory center. Large amounts of carbon dioxide are "blown off" from the lungs.

Hill and Lupton have taken the excess oxygen consumed during recovery as a basis for calculating the quantity of lactic acid present in the body at the end of exercise. They assumed that the recovery oxygen was used entirely in the oxidative removal of lactic acid, and that the quantity of lactic acid removed by oxidation was, as in the case of isolated muscle, only about one-fifth of the total quantity which disappeared. Thus;

$$C_3H_6O_3 + 3O_2 \rightarrow 3CO_2 + 3H_2O.$$

That is, for every 3 molecules of oxygen consumed during recovery 1 molecule of lactic acid has been oxidized, and for every molecule of lactic acid oxidized 4 have disappeared through synthesis to glycogen. Three gram molecules of oxygen consumed therefore represent the disappearance of 5 gram molecules ($90 \times 5 =$) 450 grams of lactic acid. Or, 1 gram molecule (22.4 liters) of oxygen represents the disappearance of $\frac{5}{3}$ gram molecules (150 grams) of lactic acid. Each liter of oxygen consumed during recovery would therefore indicate the disappearance of ($150/22.4 =$) 7 grams, approximately, of lactic acid.

Nonmuscular tissues, liver, heart, brain and muscles not actually engaged in the exercise, share in the removal of any lactic acid carried to them in the general circulation. Barr and Himwich showed this in animal experiments. From the results of their experiments upon rabbit muscle with intact nerve and blood supply, Sacks and Sacks conclude that, contrary to what is believed to occur in isolated frog muscle, lactic acid is not resynthesized to glycogen in the mammalian muscle during recovery, but diffuses into the circulation to be mainly converted in the liver to glycogen. A smaller part is oxidized by brain, heart and probably by other tissues as well. If produced in large amounts, as in strenuous exercise, an appreciable amount finds its way into the urine.

### The Fuel of Exercise

We have seen that in the case of isolated frog muscle the respiratory quotient is around unity, which indicates that the ultimate source of the energy for the contractile process is mainly, if not entirely, carbohydrate. That is, the energy required to restore the muscle to its pre-contraction state is derived from the oxidation of this food material. Though the glycogen of the isolated muscle is reduced by activity, no diminution of its fat content has been demonstrated. It has also been shown that if an isolated muscle be stimu-

lated while suspended in Ringer's solution so that the lactic acid as it forms may diffuse away, fatigue sets in only when the glycogen stores have been exhausted (see p. 871). If glucose be added to the Ringer's, something like 10,000 twitches can be evoked and a total tension of 6 tons per square centimeter of cross-section of the muscle developed. It cannot, however, be concluded from experiments upon the isolated frog muscle, which for one thing is poorly supplied with oxygen, that the muscles of the intact mammal can use only carbohydrate fuel. Himwich and Rose, for example, by determinations of $CO_2$ and of $O_2$ of venous and arterial bloods of intact muscles obtained an average respiration quotient (R.Q.) of only 0.80. Attempts to decide the question for the intact body have been made by determinations of the respiratory quotient of the *excess metabolism of exercise* in man. The results are, however, difficult to interpret and no definite conclusion can be drawn from them.

The excess metabolism of exercise is determined from the oxygen consumed (or of the $CO_2$ eliminated) during the work and recovery periods less the amount of oxygen used (or $CO_2$ eliminated) during a corresponding period preceding the exercise. The ratio between the excess quantities of the two respiratory gases will, of course, be the R.Q. of the excess gaseous exchange. But certain precautions must be taken in order to obtain the true R.Q., i.e., the R.Q. of the oxidative processes, for as already mentioned a large proportion of the $CO_2$ which is eliminated following exercise is not oxidative in origin but is simply gas which has been liberated from chemical combination (p. 871). The period of increased $CO_2$ elimination and high R.Q. immediately following the exercise is followed by one in which the output of the gas is reduced and the R.Q. is well below the normal level of 0.85—$CO_2$ is being retained to replenish the bicarbonate stores (fig. 51.4). During a period of sufficient length, therefore, one effect (retention) will just balance the other (blowing off) and the quantity of $CO_2$ eliminated during this time in excess of the output during a pre-exercise period will be the extra quantity actually produced by oxidative processes. This value is used in calculating the R.Q. of the excess metabolism resulting from the exercise.

In experiments on man involving short periods of strenuous exercise, the R.Q. of the excess metabolism has been found by several observers to rise above that of the resting period and to reach or exceed unity. Best, Furusawa and Ridout ob-

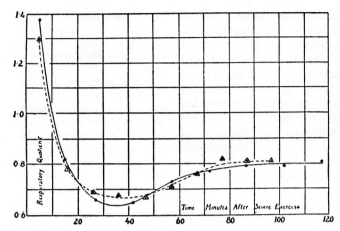

Fig. 51.4. Curve of the R.Q. of the excess metabolism caused by muscular exercise. (From Hill, *Muscular Movement in Man.*)

tained a R.Q. of between 1.18 and 1.68 for very arduous exercise. For less strenuous work the R.Q. was around unity and for mild exercise it was considerably lower—little above that for the rest period. The degree of exercise required to raise the quotient to unity varied in different subjects. The very high quotients (above unity) which these observers obtained have since been observed by others, but Gemmill, in more rigidly controlled experiments in which the subject was kept under basal conditions for a period of several hours preceding the exercise, obtained an average R.Q. for the excess metabolism of a little less than unity. Determinations of the oxygen consumption and carbon dioxide elimination were made over a recovery (post-exercise) period of 3 hours.

The. R.Q. of the excess metabolism has also been determined by a number of workers upon diets high, respectively, in fat or carbohydrate. Benedict and Cathcart, for example, found an R.Q. of 0.90 on a carbohydrate-rich diet and one of 0.82 (indicating the utilization of fat) on the fat-rich diet. They concluded that the fuel of exercise was not exclusively carbohydrate but depended largely upon the previous diet. Krogh and Lindhard decided that the food material oxidized during work was the same as that during rest, and that in either case the relative quantities of fat and carbohydrate oxidized varied with their proportions in the diet. Work, however, was performed less economically (by 10 per cent) upon fat than upon carbohydrate. Others have observed an increase in efficiency upon high carbohydrate diets, though, as a rule, the increase was not as great as that found by Krogh and Lindhard.

Carpenter and Fox carried out two comparable groups of experiments. In one group 50 grams of glucose were given just prior to the commencement of the exercise. In the other group the subjects were fasting. The R.Q. of the excess metabolism of those which had received the glucose was considerably higher than those of the other group.

Anderson and Lusk obtained in a starving dog working a treadmill respiratory quotients suggestive of the combustion of fat, namely, from 0.71 to 0.73. Also in prolonged severe exercise in man Talbot and associates observed a fall in the R.Q. following an earlier rise.

Other lines of approach have yielded more important evidence for carbohydrate being the main fuel, though not necessarily the only one, used in muscular work. Other food-stuffs, especially fat can serve under certain circumstances, the proportion of each which undergoes oxidation varying with the amount available and the severity of the exercise. In *short periods of light exercise* it is probable that the energy is derived from the oxidation of materials of the same nature as those which furnish energy during rest. These are small molecules of carbohydrate, fat and protein material already present in the circulation (Carpenter). Such materials are soon exhausted, however, by heavier work, when the glycogen reserves are drawn upon. There is general agreement that in *strenuous exercise* the fuel used by the muscles is mainly if not entirely carbohydrate. If the exercise is long continued, as in a marathon race, hypoglycemia results. The administration of glucose at the commencement of the race prevents the fall in blood sugar and exerts a definitely beneficial effect upon the athlete's performance. The production of large quantities of lactic acid in strenuous muscular exercise also points to carbohydrate material as the source of energy. In short but strenuous bouts of work a rise in blood sugar up to a concentration of nearly 200 mg. per cent has been observed. The mechanism governing this mobilization of the carbohydrate reserves has not been definitely determined. It does not appear to have an emotional basis (liberation of adrenaline or stimulation of the sympathetic). Gemmill suggests that the high blood lactate stimulates the production of glucose by the liver.

In prolonged and exhausting exercise the carbohydrate stores become depleted. Fat and, to some extent, protein are then utilized to drive the muscular machine. Both these materials are used indirectly, i.e., after their conversion to carbohydrate.[2] As the carbohydrate stores are used up physical exhaustion ensues. Dogs can be worked for 17 hours or so before they are completely fatigued if fed carbohydrate, but become exhausted in less than 5 hours if worked without food (Dill and associates). The fatigued animals are capable of further work if then given carbohydrate.

The use of protein as fuel has been a subject of controversy for a number of years. It has been common teaching that this food material, except in minimal quantities when fat and carbohydrate are unavailable is not a source of energy for muscular work, but served merely to repair tissue "wear and tear." This conclusion was arrived at chiefly from studies of the nitrogen excretion. Ordinary exercise, for example, does not increase appreciably the output of nitrogen in the urine nor does it increase the non-protein nitrogen of the blood. More strenuous work causes a slight rise in the blood nonprotein nitrogen and a moderate increase in the urinary nitrogen in man and in animals. In work experiments upon fasting dogs it has been calculated that at the most not more than 7 per cent of the energy required for the exercise could have been derived from protein; the great part of the energy had apparently been ob-

tained from the combustion of fat. In prolonged starvation after exhaustion of the stores of carbohydrate and fat, protein (carbon part of the amino acids) must then, serve as the sole source of energy.

It has been pointed out by Cathcart, however, that the nitrogen excretion during short periods of exercise may not be a true criterion of protein metabolism since the nitrogen released in the breakdown of protein may be utilized in synthetic processes and consequently not appear in the urine. Or, muscle protein may be catabolized and its nitrogen excreted, yet if, as is quite possible, an equivalent amount of nitrogen derived from the food were diverted to the muscles to replace that which had been lost, the total nitrogen excretion would remain unchanged. This observer also considers that, in the long run, muscular work exerts a very definite influence upon protein metabolism and cites the familiar observation that persons engaged in heavy muscular work demand a diet rich in protein, particularly meat. It has also been shown by several investigators that a retention of nitrogen occurs during a period of training—apparently for the manufacture of muscular tissue.

Such views are in harmony with modern conceptions of protein metabolism (p. 779). Since catabolism and synthesis may go hand in hand the total quantity of nitrogen excreted gives no indication of the interchanges which are taking place between food and tissue nitrogen. It is scarcely reasonable to assume that after deamination the nonprotein portions of the amino acids can not serve as a source of oxidative energy. A carnivorous animal, for example, can subsist upon a diet composed almost exclusively of protein. Canzanelli and Rapport also draw attention to the irrelevancy of the nitrogen excretion and insist that it can give no information respecting the nonnitrogenous part of the catabolized protein. From a study of the respiratory quotient of the excess metabolism of exercise performed by a dog on a high protein diet, they conclude that oxidative energy for muscular exercise can be supplied quite as readily by protein as by carbohydrate or fat.

The question whether or not *alcohol* can furnish energy for muscular work has been investigated repeatedly. The results obtained by different workers are not entirely in agreement. Some have reported that muscular exercise hastened the disappearance of alcohol from the blood, presumably by increasing combustion (see Mellanby). On the other hand, Carpenter and his associates in a recent careful study did not find that work exerted such an effect. They conclude that alcohol disappears from the human body at a uniform rate whether the subject is at rest or performing muscular exercise. Nor did muscular work alter the concentration of alcohol in the expired air (i.e.,

[2] This statement may have to be modified in the light of recent experiments by K. L. Zierler and I. B. Fritz. It now seems clear from the results of the former author (J. Clin. Invest., **35,** 671, 1956) that the oxygen uptake of the resting human forearm is greatly in excess of that suggested by the arteriovenous difference in glucose concentration. That some of this discrepancy may be accounted for by the oxidation of fatty acids is suggested by the experiments of Fritz and his collaborators (Am. J. Physiol., **194,** 379, 1958) who show that $C^{14}$-labeled fatty acids are oxidized by isolated skeletal muscle and that the rate of oxidation is increased on faradic stimulation. The quantitative aspects of the role of nonesterified fatty acids as fuel for muscular exercise remain to be examined.

the amount eliminated per liter of $CO_2$ remained unchanged), in the urine or in the blood.

## REFERENCES

*Monographs and Reviews*

Physiology of voluntary muscle. Brit. M. Bull., 1956, **12,** 161.

BUCHTAL, F., SVENSMARK, O. AND ROSENFALCK, P. Mechanical and chemical events in muscle contraction. Physiol. Rev., 1956, **36,** 503.

HILL, A. V. Muscular Movement in Man. McGraw-Hill Book Co., New York, 1927.

HUXLEY, A. F. Muscle structure and theories of contraction. Progr. biophysics, 1957, **7,** 255.

MOMMAERTS, W. F. H. M. Muscular Contraction. Interscience Publishers, Inc., New York, 1950.

PERRY, S. V. Relation between chemical and contractile function and structure of the skeletal muscle cell. Physiol. Rev., 1956, **36,** 1.

SZENT-GYÖRGI, A. Chemistry of Muscular Contraction, 2nd. Ed. Academic Press, Inc., New York, 1951.

# 52

# THE BODY TEMPERATURE

The normal body temperature, recorded from the mouth, is usually given as 98.6°F. (37.0°C.). The rectal temperature averages 6/10 of a degree F. higher than this and the axillary temperature at least 1 degree F. lower. No absolute figure can be given, for there is a wide variation between individuals. The oral temperatures of a large group of normal persons range from 96.6° to 100.0°F. (35.8° to 37.8°C.), the average being around 98.4°F. (36.9°C.). Ivy, in a study of nearly 300 medical students, obtained a mean oral temperature of 98.1°F. (36.7°C). Variations in the body temperature also occur in the same individual throughout the day—a difference of 2.0 or even 3.0°F. occurring between the maximum in the late afternoon or early evening, and the minimum between 3 and 5 o'clock in the morning. In night workers the times of the maximal and minimal temperatures may be reversed. The temperature of the internal organs is higher by several degrees than the temperature of the skin. The temperature of the liver, for example, is about 100°F. (37.8°C.), whereas that of the skin covered with clothes is from 85° to 93°F. (29.5° to 33.9°C.). The temperature of the bare skin varies widely, of course, with the environmental temperature. The influence of the latter upon the temperature of the covered skin will depend upon the heat-insulating properties of the clothing, air movement (breeze, wind), atmospheric moisture, etc. Strenuous muscular exercise causes a temporary rise in body temperature of 1.0° to 4.0°F. or more; a temperature of over 104°F. (40.0°C.) during exercise has been reported (L. Hill).

The heat-regulating mechanisms are not fully developed at birth. The body temperature of the newborn child, although in general the same as that of the adult, tends to be irregular and unstable. Spontaneous variations of from 1 to 2°F. are common during the first year. Excitement or other strong emotion, even in older children, may raise the temperature by as much as 2°F.

## The Regulation of Body Temperature

The almost unchanging body temperature of warm-blooded animals, living under a variety of environmental conditions, indicates a remarkably efficient thermostatic control and regulating system. The temperature of a warm-blooded (homoiothermic) animal remains practically unchanged although the surrounding temperature may vary between 0°F. or less and 100°F. or upwards. On the contrary, the body temperature of a cold-blooded (poikilothermic) animal such as the frog, turtle, etc., is practically that of its environment (fig. 52.1).

Heat is continuously being produced within the body by metabolic activity, the rate of heat production being minimal during sleep and increased by muscular activity. In order to maintain a constant temperature, the rate of heat loss must be adjusted to equal the rate of heat production. This process is complicated by the varying environmental temperatures. A high ambient temperature reduces the rate of heat loss. A low temperature may increase the rate of heat loss to such an extent that metabolism must be increased by means of shivering to maintain the balance. With environmental temperatures in excess of the body temperature, or if heat is being produced rapidly by muscular activity, the evaporation of sweat is necessary to dispose of the excess heat. Shivering and sweating are "emergency" measures. Throughout the range of moderate temperatures the rate of heat loss can be regulated by varying the rate of blood flow through the skin. Heat is produced mainly in the deeper structures (muscles and viscera), which are insulated from the environment by subcutaneous fat and skin. The heat is transported by the blood which is warmed in the deep central structures and cooled at the body surface. Although the temperature of the skin may vary widely, the central or "core" temperature is maintained homeostatically within a very narrow range. The body absorbs heat radiated from surrounding objects with temperatures higher than its own, and from direct or reflected sunshine, a stove or an open fire. Heat is also gained by the ingestion of hot food. Heat production is the result of chemical reactions and was therefore called the "chemical" regulation of body temperature by Rubner. Heat loss is dependent upon physical (and physiological) factors—"physical" regulation. These terms are redundant and an oversimplification, since the chemical and physical cannot be separated.

Under basal conditions, when no external work is being done, all the metabolic energy ultimately appears as heat. If this heat were not lost to the body, the body temperature would rise. The basal metabolic rate usually produces heat amounting to about one calorie per kilogram of body weight per hour. Since the body is composed chiefly of water, it has a specific heat of a little less than one, so the body temperature would rise about 1°C. per hour if no heat were lost.

With strenuous physical exertion more than three-quarters of the increased metabolism appears as heat within the body; the remainder appears as external work. Fever increases the metabolic rate; the average increase being 13 per cent to each degree C. rise (7.2 per cent per degree F.). This change in metabolism corresponds to a temperature coefficient ($Q_{10}$) of between 2.0 and 3.0. The temperature coefficients of the various metabolic reactions are not, however, identical, consequently, a rise in temperature causes a disturbance in the metabolic pattern of the body. The resulting disorganization of function in the brain is made evident by the delirium induced by high fever and the mental confusion accompanying hypothermia.

The body's heat-regulating mechanism is supposed to be in abeyance below an internal temperature of 75°F., because the activity of the underlying nervous structures is suppressed. The body then gains or loses heat like an inanimate object. The lower lethal temperature for the human is about 79.5°F. (26°C.), although lower temperatures have been induced with survival during therapeutic hypothermia. Death is due to cardiac failure. The upper lethal limit is not clearly defined; cases are recorded to have recovered after attaining a rectal temperature of 110.8°F. (43.5° C.). Probably the average upper limit is about 110°F. (43°C.) (See DuBois).

## Heat Loss

Although the body temperature is in excess of the ambient temperature in temperate climates, the constant production of heat by metabolism necessitates a constant dissipation of heat. It is only under exceptional circumstances that in such climates the excess heat of the environment must be counteracted in addition to the normal metabolic heat. In cold weather where more heat is lost than can be balanced by that of the resting

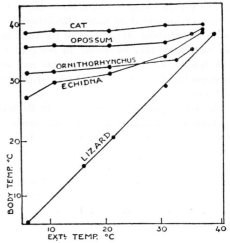

FIG. 52.1. Variation of body temperature of different types of animals by sojourn for two hours in an environment of 5° to 35°C. (After Martin.)

metabolism extra heat is produced by increased muscular activity—increased tension of muscles, shivering, "goose flesh," and shaking. Throughout the range of moderate temperatures, i.e., within the comfort zone, neither shivering nor sweating occurs even while the body is at rest. Heat is lost from the body mainly at the skin surface, although some is lost through the respiratory passages where air comes in contact with the body.

Heat is lost from the body through: (a) radiation, conduction and convection from the skin; (b) warming and humidifying inspired air; (c) evaporation of sweat and insensible perspiration; (d) urine and feces.

Of these various routes only (a) and (c) are directly under physiological control. The temperature of the skin determines the rate of heat loss from the body surface. The heat lost in warming and moistening the inspired air, and the rate of evaporation through the skin (insensible perspiration) will depend upon the temperature and humidity of the ambient air. It is only indirectly, by creating a "local climate" by means of clothing or air conditioned dwellings, that these avenues of heat loss can be regulated.

Under the ordinary conditions of every day life over 95 per cent of the total heat loss occurs through (a), (b) and (c). The heat lost in raising the temperature of the inspired air to body temperature (c) will, of course, vary with the air temperature, but at ordinary room temperatures it does not amount to more than 2 or 3 per cent of the total. Air is a very poor conductor, so in terrestrial animals conduction plays a very minor role except under special circumstances, as when the body is in contact with a cool object, cold ground or immersed in water. Radiation is responsible for about 50 per cent of the total heat loss and convection for about 15 per cent (see table below). The heat lost in the urine and feces accounts for only 2 per cent, or less, of the total heat loss.

The total quantity of heat lost in 24 hours must, of course, just equal the amount produced; otherwise the body temperature would rise or fall. The heat production of an average man doing light work is about 3000 Calories. The proportions of this which are dissipated through the various channels at ordinary room temperature are given in the following table, in approximate figures.

| | Calories | Per cent |
|---|---|---|
| (a) Radiation, convection and conduction............... | 1950 | 65 |
| (b) Evaporation of water from skin and lungs, and liberation of $CO_2$............... | 900 | 30 |
| (c) Warming inspired air........ | 90 | 3 |
| (d) Urine and feces (i.e., heat of these excreta over that of the food and water)........ | 60 | 2 |
| Total daily heat loss............. | 3000 | 100 |

### RADIATION AND CONVECTION AND THEIR VARIATION BY PHYSIOLOGICAL FACTORS

The rate of cooling of any warm object varies with the temperature of the air and of colder objects in contact with or near it. When a large temperature difference exists between the two, the warm object loses heat rapidly through radiation, convection and conduction. The rate of heat loss, however, becomes gradually less as the temperature of the object approaches that of the environment. The dead human body behaves in a manner similar to that of any inanimate object, taking from 10 to 20 hours on an average to reach the temperature of its surroundings. In the living body, on the other hand, factors operate to encourage or minimize heat loss, respectively, when the environmental temperature is high or low, or corresponding changes in the body's heat production occur.

The factors involved in heat conservation or heat loss are dependent to a large extent upon reactions of the autonomic nervous system. The following are the principal adjustments which take place in the blood-vascular system. (a) *Redistribution of blood.* The subcutaneous tissue acts as an insulating layer. The insulating quality of this layer can be altered by varying the blood flow through it. By the redistribution of blood the temperature of the skin may be adjusted to any temperature from about 15°C. (59°F.) up to the central body temperature. At a room (ambient) temperature of 34°C. (93°F.) the quantity of blood circulating through the skin may, according to DuBois, amount to 12 per cent of the cardiac output. Scott, Bazett and Mackie found that the blood flow through the fingers would increase from 1 cc. per minute per 100 grams of tissue in a cool environment to 80 or 90 cc. per minute upon exposure to heat. These changes may be initiated in one or all of four ways, a change in temperature of the blood supplying the nervous centers; reflexly through centers in the brain and cord in response to changes in skin temperature (stimulation of hot or cold spots, p. 1139); through local axon reflexes, and finally through responses of the vessels to direct stimulation by changes in external temperature. (b) *Variations in blood volume* (see p. 28). A rise in temperature causes an increase in blood volume; the blood is diluted by fluid drawn into the circulation from the tissues, chiefly the skin, muscles and liver. Blood is expelled from the spleen (p. 67). It has been found that an unacclimatized man is capable of increasing the total circulating blood volume by about 10 per cent in 2 or 4 hours on exposure to heat of sufficient severity to cause a diffuse cutaneous vasodilatation. The increased blood volume is chiefly in the plasma although additional cells may be added from the spleen. The initial increase of the blood is brought about by dilution with water drawn from the other cells, so that the hematocrit drops a little and the plasma protein concentration decreases. Associated with the decreased osmotic pressure of the plasma protein a mild edema of the ankles is frequently observed in unacclimatized persons suddenly exposed to heat. The body can manufacture the proteins rapidly so that after two or three days exposure to heat the blood osmotic pressure has been restored and the edema will disappear. At low temperatures the blood volume is reduced, the blood becoming more concentrated as shown by an increase in the percentage of blood solids. The sudden return to a cool environment causes a rapid decrease of blood volume associated with a marked diuresis. This is frequently seen in moving from the tropical plains in India to the temperate hill stations (Powell, personal comment). (c) *Increased circulation rate.* The increased cardiac output ensures a rapid blood flow through the dilated cutaneous vessels.

As already stated, half of the total heat loss is brought about through radiation. The human skin (of whatever color) within the range of the infrared to which it is usually exposed, is an almost perfect "black body radiator." That is to say, it radiates nearly all infrared rays[1] (up to 1 or 2 per cent) or absorbs to the same extent such rays as fall upon it (Hardy and Muschenheim).

The skin and the subcutaneous tissues when the vessels are constricted are a little more efficient as insulating material than a layer of cork of the same thickness (DuBois). The subcutaneous layer varies considerably in thickness in different persons and is thicker in women than in men. This accounts for the greater ability of women than of men to withstand cold.

The radiating surface of the standing human body[2] is only about 85 per cent of the total surface area, for apposed surfaces, e.g., axillae, inner surfaces of the thighs and upper arms, do not lose heat to the environment by radiation. It is for this reason that one huddles in the cold and spreads out one's limbs in the heat. Adolph has shown that the nude man, sitting in the sun, absorbs on an average 143 Calories per hour by radiation this is reduced by clothing. Molnar *et al.* found that clothing by reflecting radiation can diminish the absorption of heat from the sun and sky by about 60 Calories per hour. On the other hand, clothing will reduce heat loss by radiation since the external surface of the clothing has a lower temperature than the skin and consequently radiates less heat. The main factor influencing heat loss through radiation is the temperature of surrounding objects relative to that of the skin. The body, for example, radiates heat to a block of ice but absorbs heat from a hot stove or radiator. It should be remembered that the air intervening between the body and the source of heat is not heated by radiant energy, but only by convection. Another factor, though a very minor one, is the humidity of the atmosphere. Air with a high water vapor content is more opaque to radiant heat than dry air. Heat lost through radiation is therefore slightly reduced when the relative humidity is high.

CONVECTION. The rate of movement of warm air from the neighborhood of a heated object varies, of course, with the temperature of the atmosphere. The clothed body has a layer of warm moist air in contact with the skin which tends to become trapped in this situation and in the spaces of the clothing. In the absence of a temperature difference between it and the external air or of some movement to cause mixing, this air will remain practically stagnant and little or no heat is lost through convection. However, when the atmosphere is cooler, convection currents are set up which mix the air lying against the skin with fresh air. Convection is essentially dependent upon the relative densities of air at different temperatures, the warmer and lighter air rising, the cooler air falling. Dry air is denser than air possessing a high content of water vapor. One would expect therefore that changes in the humidity of the atmosphere should alter the heat lost by convection, but as a matter of fact, the relative humidity of the external air has little effect upon heat loss through convection. Probably the most important factor influencing heat loss by convection is air movement, the loss increasing with the square of the wind velocity up to 60 miles per hour; a wind velocity beyond this exerts little or no further effect.

### EVAPORATION OF WATER

It is obvious that the nearer the temperature of the environment comes to that of the blood the smaller will be the amount of heat which can be lost by radiation and convection. At an air temperature of about 98.6°F. (37°C.) heat loss by these means must cease. At higher air temperatures than this the body, would actually gain heat if no other means of cooling were available. Large quantities of heat are lost to the body through the secretion and evaporation of sweat and the exhalation of water vapor, expired air being 95 per cent saturated with moisture. Its temperature can for this reason, be maintained constant when the atmosphere (dry) has a temperature about 150°F. (65°C.) above that of the blood. The heat absorbed in the evaporation of 1 cc. of water amounts to 0.58 Calorie. Even at ordinary room temperatures, when there is no obvious perspiration, the heat lost through evaporation from the lungs and skin amounts to about 17 Calories per hour. About two-thirds of this is from insensible perspiration through the skin, the remainder from the lungs. Newburgh and his associates have found that people, living in a cool environment performing only the routines of life, lost heat by the insensible evaporation of water from the skin and lungs, equivalent to about 24 per cent of the metabolic rate; the absolute amount depending upon the metabolic rate. At higher temperatures the increase in the proportion of heat lost by evaporation of water

[1] The wave length of the infrared rays emitted by skin at usual temperature (34°C.) is 9440 m$\mu$.
[2] This has been called the *profile area.*

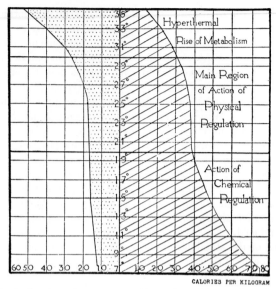

CALORIES PER KILOGRAM

Fig. 52.2. Rubner's chart showing the manner of heat loss in the dog at different room temperatures. Stippled area, heat loss in calories through evaporation of water; cross-hatched area, heat loss in calories through radiation and convection. The distance between opposite points on the curved boundary lines represents the total heat production at a particular temperature. (Redrawn and slightly modified from Lusk.)

as compared with that lost by radiation and convection is shown in figure 52.2. It will be seen that evaporation plays little part in heat regulation until the air temperature reaches between 28° and 30°C. (82° to 84.5°F.), the heat loss by this means remaining nearly constant below this level but increasing rapidly above it. At a temperature above 35°C. evaporation accounts for all or nearly all the heat lost.

It is to be remembered that evaporation from the body surface occurs quite independently of sweat secretion, for the skin is not entirely impervious to water; fluid extravasated from the cutaneous capillaries seeps into the epidermis. There is a continuous diffusion through the epidermis from the moist deep layers to the dry skin surface. The evaporation of this water that diffuses through the skin has been called insensible perspiration. The speed by which water diffuses through the skin is determined by the diffusion gradient and is greatest in dry atmospheres when the water vapor pressure of the air is low and the skin dries rapidly. It has been shown in persons in whom sweat glands were absent from birth that some 18 grams of water per square meter of body surface may be lost hourly by evaporation. This is about the same as that of a normal man under ordinary conditions, and represents a total daily heat loss of about 450 Calories for a body of average size (surface area 1.8 square meters), which is not far from the normal. At high temperatures, or even during mild exercise, however,

a person without sweat glands is at a great disadvantage; his body temperature is likely to rise.

The respirations are increased by a rise in air temperature or by a greater heat production; the heat loss through warming the inspired air and the vaporization of water from the lungs, and the liberation of $CO_2$, is thereby increased. Hyperpnea (panting) is the chief means possessed by the dog (in which functioning sweat glands are largely confined to the footpads) for increasing the vaporization of water and combating a rise in body temperature.

The rate of evaporation of water is influenced inversely by the degree to which the atmosphere is already saturated with moisture, i.e., by its relative humidity.[3] Sweat which is not evaporated but simply drips from the skin, of course does not increase heat loss. For this reason the sweating mechanism for the elimination of heat is badly crippled when the relative humidity is high.[4] We

[3] It is dependent essentially upon the difference in the vapor pressure at the skin and of the surrounding air.

[4] The relative humidity is defined as the ratio of the weight of water vapor contained in a given volume of air to the weight which the same volume of air would contain when saturated. The quantity of water vapor which air can hold when saturated increases with the temperature. The relative humidity is expressed as a percentage. Thus, if a sample of air at a certain temperature contains 20 per cent of the water vapor which it is possible for it to contain at that temperature, it is 20 per cent saturated, and so has a relative humidity of 20 per cent.

are all familiar with the insufferable heat of a hot humid day, and the comparative comfort when the air is simply hot and dry. A man can maintain a normal temperature in an atmosphere of from 240° to 260°F. (a temperature that will grill a beefsteak) provided the air is perfectly dry; his ability to sweat profusely is sustained by large draughts of water, and evaporation is facilitated by stripping the greater part of the body's surface. On the other hand, a damp atmosphere with a temperature of 120°F. causes the body temperature to rise rapidly, and cannot be endured for more than a few minutes. Evaporation and consequently heat loss by this means is greatly hastened by air movement. The layer of air nearly saturated with water vapor lying next the skin is thus replaced by drier air.

### SWEATING

Sweat is a weak solution of sodium chloride in water together with urea and small quantities of potassium and lactic acid. It has a specific gravity of from 1.002 to 1.003. Its pH as reported by different observers varies from 4.2 to 7.5. The percentage of sodium chloride varies between 0.2 and 0.5. Muscular exercise increases the salt concentration, which is also higher in sweat secreted by clothed than by naked skin. The quantity of nonprotein nitrogen ordinarily excreted in the sweat, per day, is according to Benedict, 0.071 gram; on the other hand, if the sweating is copious from 0.5 to 1.0 gram may be eliminated per hour. The actual concentration of nitrogen in the sweat falls, however, when sweating becomes profuse, whereas the concentrations of sodium chloride and potassium rise. However, when acclimatization has been established the percentage of salt diminishes. About 3 grams of salt daily are required after acclimatization to maintain the salt balance. Nevertheless, even after acclimatization, if strenuous work is performed for a long period in a high temperature, and large quantities of water are drunk, depletion of the body's supplies of chloride and a lowered concentration of this element in blood and tissue fluids occurs, producing severe cramps in the muscles of the limbs and abdominal wall (heat or stoker's cramps; see p. 894).

THE CONTROL OF SWEAT SECRETION. The sweat glands, which number over two and a half million in a man living in temperate climates, are cholinergic yet under the control of the sympathetic nervous system. These glands are, however, anomalous in their responses to sympathetic and parasympathetic drugs, in that they are stimu-lated by muscarine, pilocarpine and acetylcholine, and inhibited by atropine (p. 1399). According to Coon and Rothman, the action of acetylcholine is twofold—stimulation of the glands directly through a muscarinelike action and through the initiation of axon reflexes (nicotinelike action). In man and most animals, they are not excited by adrenaline nor paralyzed by ergotoxine. The usual stimulus to sweat secretion is a rise in blood temperature which exerts its effect in two ways—directly upon the nervous centers, which is of more importance, and reflexly by stimulation of heat receptors in the skin. The sweat response to a rise in temperature is abolished by sectioning the nerves to a part and is therefore not due to direct stimulation of the glands. That a rise in temperature of the centers alone will induce the secretion of sweat has been shown by heating the hypothalamus in the cat (whose sweat glands are confined to the paw pads); sweating then occurs although the paws themselves remain cold. The centers may also be stimulated in man by the injection of pituitrin into the lateral ventricle. In the initial stages of muscular exercise sweating is apparently initiated by the discharge of impulses from the motor cortex. It occurs before there is any change in rectal temperature. Later on, the effect of a rise in body temperature comes into play. In a man (indoor clothing) at rest, visible sweating usually commences at an air temperature between 27° and 32°C. (80 and 90°F.). Sweating may be induced by the experimental stimulation of regions of the diencephalon (hypothalamus, p. 1227). Spinal centers for segmental control of sweating exist, for peripheral sweating occurs in quadraplegic patients who have complete transverse cervical cord lesions. Such patients have lost temperature control to a large extent, for neither adequate sweating, shivering nor changes in cutaneous blood flow can occur for the regulation of body temperature. Destruction of the sympathetic nerve supply to a part completely abolishes the sweating response to a rise in temperature. The sweat glands, however, still respond to pilocarpine and acetylcholine. The former drug, which has been employed in the past for the purpose of demarcating areas deprived of their sympathetic supply, is of no diagnostic value, for it acts peripherally, i.e., directly upon the gland cells. Sweating is not dependent upon the circulation for it occurs after occlusion of the vessels and can even be induced by stimulation of the nerves in an amputated limb. Although usually associated with cutaneous vasodilation it may occur with constricted vessels—"cold sweat." This is usually the result of psychic influences, e.g., nervousness, fear, fatigue or mental work. The sweating occurs most noticeably in these instances on the forehead, the palms of the hands, and the soles of the feet, which do not, as a rule give a pronounced response to heat. In many persons, reflex sweating, confined to the face and neck, is induced by eating spicy or appetizing food (gustatory sweating), or sometimes sweating over a remote part, e.g., the knee, occurs. Faradic stimulation of the human skin over the forearm induces local sweating due apparently to direct stimulation of the glands, for it occurs after section and degeneration of the nerve supply.

The few observations that have been made upon the secretion pressure of sweat indicate that it is high, 250 mm. of mercury or more. Sweat is therefore a true secretion and not simply a filtrate. The secretion rate may be enormous, amounting to a liter or more per hour, and may be increased some 80 times over the normal by immersing the body in a bath at 108°F. At ordinary room temperatures the sweat evaporates as quickly as formed, so that there is no apparent secretion.

## HEAT PRODUCTION

The several factors which stimulate the chemical processes of the body and so increase the heat production have been dealt with in chapter 44. An account of the manner in which chemical and physical factors interact to maintain a constant body temperature remains to be given.

A low environmental temperature is a potent influence in stimulating heat production. At air temperatures below about 28°C. (82.4°F.) the body (nude) loses heat rapidly. Within the temperature range between 28° and 31°C. (87.8°F.), the naked male body is able quite easily to maintain the balance between heat loss and heat production. There is neither sweating nor shivering and a male subject feels comfortable. This range of temperature is therefore called the "comfort zone." For reasons given below the comfort zone is broader (27° to 33°C. or 80.6°F. to 91.4°F.) for women. The external temperature (about 23°C. or 73.4°F.) below which heat production must be increased in order to maintain a normal body temperature is sometimes called the "critical temperature."

Below the critical temperature heat loss by radiation and convection increases progressively with falling air temperature, but heat loss by vaporization shows little change. The naked body at a temperature below the comfort level (28°C. or 82.4°F.) loses more heat than it can produce in

the basal state, and at about 23°C. (73.4°F.) shivering occurs. Heat production is thus increased in an effort to raise the body temperature to the normal level. In the human, heat production is not increased until the onset of shivering and in nude men under basal conditions the metabolism remains constant within the range of air temperature from 35° to 23°C. (96° to 73.4°F.). It has been shown by Hardy and DuBois that this is not true for women. They show a reduced heat production of from 14 to 20 per cent at temperatures between 30° and 32°C. (86° and 89°F.). Also, owing to the greater insulation afforded by the thicker layer of subcutaneous fat the heat loss of the female body in a cold environment is some 10 per cent less than that of men. Thus women have the more efficient thermoregulating mechanism, being better able to maintain the heat balance at lower temperatures without shivering, and also to be more comfortable at higher temperatures.

The critical temperature and the temperature of comfort will vary of course with the amount and nature of the clothing. The cooling effect of water by conduction is some 20 times greater than that of air—a cold bath at 4°C. (40°F.) increasing the heat production some 5 times above the basal level.[5] Few men can survive for long in very cold water, below 4°C. (approximately 40°F.) which is about the winter temperature of the sea in temperate latitudes. Heat production becomes depressed after immersion for 20 minutes or so, and the body temperature falls. In an experiment in Germany during the last war, one man survived a temperature of 5.5°C. (42°F.) for three hours. His body temperature was then 25.2°C. (77.3°F.).

It will be seen from figure 52.3 that heat loss increases both above and below the critical temperature. At the lower temperatures heat is lost mainly by radiation and convection, at the higher temperatures mainly by vaporization. It will also be noticed that at the lower temperatures the skin temperatures follow a straight line, but that the curve commences to flatten out at around 30°C. (87°F.). This is attributed to dilation of the cutaneous vessels and the flooding of the skin with blood.

The muscular tissues (particularly of the extremities) and the liver, wherein numerous chemical reactions are carried out, are the main sources of the body's heat. The rise in metabolism which

---

[5] In cold-blooded animals the metabolism as measured by the carbon dioxide output falls with the environmental temperature.

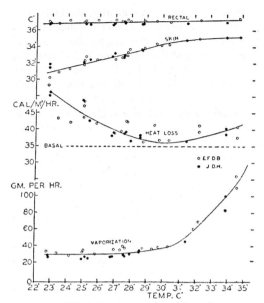

FIG. 52.3. Showing effect of a rising air temperature on rectal and skin temperatures, heat loss, and vaporization. (Modified from DuBois.)

results from a fall in atmospheric temperature is effected through an increase in activity of the skeletal muscles and in some instances by fine involuntary contractions, e.g., shivering and chattering of the teeth and increased muscular tension. By these means the heat production may be increased approximately three times over the resting level. Contractions of the smooth muscle of the skin, giving rise to "goose flesh" also contribute heat. In some mammals and in birds, the contraction of the cutaneous muscles also curtails heat loss through ruffling of the hair or feathers. In man, too, the smooth muscle of the skin may, when stimulated by cold, cause erection of the fine hair on the body surface; the effect however is rudimentary and without value. After the skeletal muscles are paralyzed by curare, an animal loses the power to maintain a normal body temperature in a cold environment. Its ability to dissipate heat is, however, intact so that it can resist high air temperatures. Isolation of the muscles from control by section of the cord in the lower cervical region (C6) also abolishes the extra heat production. This operation divides as well the vasoconstrictor nerves which travel through the cervical cord to the sympathetic outflow in the thoracic region. A redistribution of blood is not possible, and the body temperature will fall if the animal is exposed to a low air temperature. The rise in body temperature in strenuous muscular effort is apparently due, not to any failure of the heat-dissipating mechanisms, but because heat is produced more rapidly than it can be dissipated.

Food, especially protein through its specific dynamic action, is an important factor in the regulation of body temperature. At high environmental temperatures the specific dynamic action of food increases the heat production and adds an extra burden upon the heat loss mechanisms. For this reason a low protein diet is more suitable in hot weather. At very low atmospheric temperatures, on the contrary, the specific dynamic effect of food is almost completely masked, since it simply replaces the environmental effect (cold) upon heat production. That is to say, the neuromuscular mechanisms called into play to increase heat production at low temperature are less necessary since the food itself raises the level of metabolism. Protein food in cold climates is therefore a valuable aid to the regulation of body temperature.

The effect of protein ingestion upon the heat production of a dog at different temperatures is shown in table 52.1 (Lusk).

STORAGE OF HEAT. The body has a large specific heat (about 0.85), so that a rise in the temperature of a 70-kg. man of 1°C. may increase the stored heat by about 60 Calories, or 2 per cent of the average daily heat production. A considerable storage of heat may occur in strenuous muscular exercise (140 Calories or so in a 100-yard sprint), and, until the heat-dissipating mechanisms become fully effective, the body temperature may rise 2°C. or more. A rise in rectal temperature may also occur in a robust person after a cold plunge. The cold water causes, through vasoconstriction, diminished heat dissipation and through involuntary muscular action increased heat production. The body temperature may rise for a few minutes. After the first effect of the plunge the vessels are released from spasm, the stored heat is eliminated, the surface of the body glows

TABLE 52.1

| Atmospheric Temperature | Heat Production in Calories per Kilogram of Body Weight | | |
| --- | --- | --- | --- |
| | Starved | 550 grams of meat fed | Increase |
| °C | | | |
| 4.2 | 128 | 133 | 4 |
| 14.5 | 101 | 111 | 9 |
| 22.1 | 71 | 101 | 43 |
| 30.7 | 62 | 117 | 89 |

and a feeling of comfortable warmth is experienced. This constitutes the "healthy reaction" of a cold shower. A comparable drop in rectal temperature has been observed on suddenly passing from a temperate to a hot environment, or on entering a hot bath.

### Heat Regulating Centers

Section of the neuraxis through the midbrain at the level of the superior colliculi, or at any level posterior to this and anterior to the lower cervical cord, renders an animal poikilothermic (fig. 52.4). Section of the cord in the upper thoracic region, i.e., above the level of the outflow of the greater part of the sympathetic fibers causes a gross disturbance in the temperature regulation. The muscles of the head, neck and forelimbs remain in communication with the brain, so that shivering in these parts will prevent a fall in body temperature. On the other hand, the hypothalamus has lost control over the temperature regulation of $\frac{2}{3}$ of the skin surface; and no sweat is produced for temperature regulation below the segmental

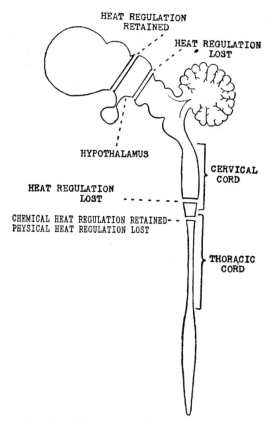

FIG. 52.4. Diagram to illustrate the nervous control of the heat-regulating mechanisms. (Modified from Martin.)

level of the lesion. Consequently, the body temperature tends to rise in warm environments, and may fall in cool environments, for the excess heat from shivering of the arms may be lost from the lower parts of the body. The effect of section through the brain stem indicates that the main center or centers controlling heat regulation must lie anterior to the superior colliculi. Removal of the cerebral cortex, thalamus or corpus striatum does not destroy the controlling mechanisms so long as the hypothalamus remains intact. Destruction of this region alone, however, was found by Keller and Hare to abolish the ability to maintain a normal body temperature upon exposure to cold. The heat-dissipating mechanisms remained intact and were, in fact, released from restraint by the hypothalamic lesion, as evidenced by pronounced panting, vasodilation, and sweating of the toe pads (of cats).

The thermoregulatory centers have been located more precisely by Ranson and his associates. From the results of their experiments upon cats and monkeys they place the centers controlling heat loss (sweating and panting) in the preoptic and supraoptic regions between the anterior commissure and the optic chiasma. Heating this area causes sweating and panting or rapid breathing and a fall in body temperature. Destructive lesions in this location are followed by hyperthermia when the animal is exposed to a degree of heat that would cause little effect upon the body temperature of a normal animal. Sweating or panting does not occur though the temperature rises to over 41°C (106°F.). Such lesions have little effect upon the animal's ability to resist cold. The centers controlling heat production and heat conservation, i.e., the mechanism whereby an animal is enabled to maintain a normal body temperature when exposed to cold, is situated, according to these investigators, in the caudal part of the lateral hypothalamus; it appears to be identical with the sympathetic center. The existence of a center for shivering (heat production) in the hypothalamus is suggested by the fact that under certain circumstances shivering in animals is accompanied by some of the manifestations of "sham rage" (Barcroft and Izquierdo). That the posterior part of the hypothalamus contains the main shivering center is indicated by the experimental results of Kellar and his associates and of Ranson and his colleagues who found that, in cats, shivering was abolished by a destructive lesion in this location. The efferent pathway for shivering is unknown, but an observation upon a patient in whom both spinothalamic tracts had been sectioned and who did not shiver when the legs were immersed in cold water, suggests that the impulses descend the cord by these paths. The impulses are not transmitted by sympathetic nerves, since shivering occurs in sympathectomized parts. Shivering is reduced or abolished by certain drugs, especially calcium chloride and aminopyrine which most probably act upon the shivering center.

From observations of patients with intracranial lesions involving the base of the brain, it seems most likely that in man the centers are situated as described by Ranson and his associates for animals. Lesions in the supraoptic region are sometimes associated with hyperthermia; hypothermia, on the other hand, may accompany lesions involving the posterior part of the hypothalamus.

The main heat-regulating centers are apparently influenced in two ways—reflexly from the skin and by the temperature of the blood flowing through them.

The posterior hypothalamic center apparently exerts its controlling influence upon temperature through the transmission of sympathetic impulses to the cutaneous vessels, sweat glands and pilomotor muscles; removal of the sympathetic renders an animal unduly susceptible to cold (ch. 71).

### The Endocrines in Thermoregulation

The thyroid and adrenals also play their roles, probably important ones, in the regulation of body temperature. The calorigenic effects of the secretions of these glands are well known (ch. 57 and 58). Cannon observed that exposure to cold caused an increase in the rate of the denervated heart. It has also been reported that the serum taken from an animal exposed to cold raises the metabolism of a second animal into which it has been injected. If the first animal has been thyroidectomized, the effect upon the metabolism of the second is not observed. The adrenal secretion exerts a calorigenic effect which is immediate and of short duration. Its liberation follows short periods of exposure to cold. But owing to the delayed action of the thyroid hormone, and the persistence of its effects, it does not seem possible that the thyroid could play any part in increasing heat production unless the cold stimulus were continued over a long period. Rats exposed over a period of weeks to low temperatures (7.8° to 12.2°C. or 46° to 52°F.) shows thyroid hyperplasia and a rise in metabolic rate of as much as 16 per cent which was not reached,

however, until the lapse of from 2 to 4 weeks. Thyroidectomized rats, on the contrary, show little rise in metabolic rate under the same conditions. The experiments of Uotila point to the pituitary as being responsible (influenced through the hypothalamus) for the thyroid response to cold, for hypophysectomy causes thyroid atrophy as usual, though the animals are exposed to a low temperature for long periods. It may be mentioned in this connection that the temperature tends to be subnormal in supradrenalectomized or thyroidectomized animals, in Addison's disease, and in cretinism.

## Disturbances of Heat Regulation (Other Than Fever)

Since the body temperature represents the balance struck between heat production and heat loss, an alteration in the value of one of these factors in relation to the other obviously will be followed by a change in body temperature.

Temporary rises in temperature may occur in health as a result of hot baths, which prevent heat loss through convection, radiation and the evaporation of sweat, as well as by actually adding heat to the body; or during violent muscular exercise which increases heat production. Since the metabolic rate can be increased easily and rapidly to several times the basal level, a fall in the temperature of a normal person is much more difficult to produce than a rise.

The heat regulating mechanisms are depressed by anesthetics, hypnosis and by general bodily fatigue. During sleep the heat regulating mechanisms continue to function though somewhat sluggishly. The body temperature falls a little, reaching a minimum between 3 and 5 a.m.

There are four separate syndromes which result from exposure to excessive heat. These are: *Heat exhaustion, dehydration exhaustion, heat cramps* and *heat stroke.* Although each of these syndromes is encountered in a pure form, there is frequently an overlap of the syndromes and difficulty in distinguishing between them.

Heat exhaustion. Upon sudden exposure to a high temperature there is a dilation of the peripheral vessels greatly increasing the vascular space. The heart rate and cardiac output increase and the blood pressure may fall a little. If, in addition, physical work is performed, the heart may not be able to maintain the blood pressure and the condition known as "heat exhaustion" ensues. The patient is confused, fatigued to exhaustion and feels hot. The skin is moist and sweating may be profuse. The pulse is rapid, the blood pressure low. The patient feels extremely uncomfortable and may be mildly dyspneic. The symptoms are indicative of cardiac insufficiency. The patient may collapse and loose consciousness. He is very uncomfortable and dyspneic lying flat, and is more comfortable with his head and shoulders propped up (orthopnoea). The condition responds rapidly to rest and fluids by mouth.

DEHYDRATION EXHAUSTION. Although heat exhaustion may occur any time after exposure to heat, it usually occurs when unusual physical demands are made upon an unacclimatized subject. Dehydration exhaustion, however, occurs after longer exposure to heat, if the fluid loss is not replaced. In a hot environment with extensive sweating the blood volume is reduced, this reduction in the blood volume associated with the larger vascular space again produces cardiac insufficiency and exhaustion to collapse. As dehydration progresses the heart rate rises and exertion becomes progressively more difficult. Ultimately even standing becomes an intolerable strain. This exhaustion occurs when the body has lost about 5 per cent of its weight. The patient may suddenly collapse unconscious with an extremely rapid heart rate. General discomfort and extreme fatigue are the main symptoms, just before collapse. Dehydration exhaustion responds to rest, restoration of body fluids and cooling of the body. Again, orthopnoea may be a prominent feature. Water may be administered by mouth or intravenously. The intravenous fluid provides a rapid recovery, but fluid by mouth is satisfactory. Death from dehydration exhaustion occurs suddenly with little warning, and may be proceeded for some hours by extensive edema of the legs, indicating the cardiac origin of the syndrome (see Rawicz).

HEAT CRAMPS. If the sodium chloride content of the body is decreased, as will occur with sweating and a low salt intake, exertion will induce severe painful muscle contractures. After exertion these painful cramps will continue until the salt balance is restored. The administration of sodium chloride, either by mouth or parenterally, will rapidly cure the cramps. In order to maintain the salt balance under desert conditions, 2 grams of salt should be provided for each hour of exercise and ½ gram for each hour of rest. This averages about 24 grams per day.

HEAT STROKE. This is a rare condition compared with heat exhaustion. It is characterized by a rising temperature with a dry skin. The patient, apparently well, may suddenly become unconscious. The rectal temperature is high 41° to 43°C. (106° to 110°F.). There appears to be a complete breakdown of the heat regulating mechanisms. Unless the temperature is promptly reduced, there may be permanent damage to the nervous system. Heat stroke often terminates in death. The pathogenesis of heat stroke is obscure, its onset usually occurs with exertion, which may be quite mild. It is probable that heat stroke requires an intercurrent infection, the toxins from which disturb the heat regulating centre in the hypothalamus.

SUN STROKE is a term applied to those cases of heat stroke that occur during exposure to tropical sun. Powerful sunshine itself, however, will not cause sunstroke provided heat dissipation is adequate to keep pace with heat production, i.e., when the air is dry and cool and strenuous exercise is not undertaken.

The frequent occurrence of heat exhaustion and heat stroke among British troops serving in the tropics during the nineteenth century was probably due to lack of understanding of the mechanisms of heat regulation, and the use of quite unsuitable uniforms. The use of toupees and spinal pads is quite unnecessary if proper clothing and adequate water are provided.

## Fever—Pyrexia

There are 5 types of fever. (1) *Infectious fever*, e.g., sepsis, typhoid, pneumonia, etc. (2) *Surgical fever* which arises after an extensive aseptic operation and is apparently due to toxic substances liberated by the injured tissues. (3) *Neurogenic fever* from injuries to nervous centers, especially lesions in the neighborhood of the third ventricle, internal capsule, medulla or upper part of spinal cord. (4) *Fever of dehydration* due to a reduction of blood water (anhydremia, p. 25). This is particularly likely to occur in young children. (5) *Fever produced by drugs and other chemical substances*.

Body temperatures as high as 45°C. (113°F.) have occasionally been reported, but survival with a hyperpyrexia above 44.5°C. (112°F.) is rare. In the great majority (over 95 per cent) of fevers, from whatever cause, the temperature does not exceed 41°C. (106°F.). Temperatures higher than 41.6°C. (107°F.) become harmful or dangerous from the high temperature itself. The infrequency of temperatures above 41°C. (106°F.) suggests that some safety thermostatic mechanism comes into operation around this level.

Intravenous injections of concentrated solutions of glucose or salt induce fever by causing anhydremia (p. 25). Drastic cathartics, by drawing water from the blood into the bowel, may cause fever in a similar manner. Caffeine and cocaine in large doses induce fever by increasing muscular activity (greater heat production) and by causing blood concentration (reduced heat loss). Hemoglobin solutions when injected into the blood stream exert a pyretic action; the hemolysis resulting from the intravenous injection of distilled water acts similarly. The manner in which the fever is produced is unknown. β-Tetrahydronaphthylamine injected subcutaneously raises the temperature by its action upon the central and peripheral sympathetic mechanisms, causing cutaneous vasoconstriction and consequently a greater conservation of heat. It also, through its action upon the muscles, causes increased heat production. The adrenal medulla is also probably stimulated by this drug and the outpouring of adrenaline may be an added factor in the temperature rise. Ergotoxine causes a rise in temperature in some animals (cat), presumably through a direct action upon the heat centers. Dinitrophenol, a drug sometimes used in the treatment of obesity, and injections of foreign protein also raise the body temperature. Dinitrophenol acts by stimulating oxidative processes in the tissues. Adrenaline and thyroxine in large doses may also, through their stimulating effect upon the metabolism, cause a rise in temperature.

### INFECTIOUS FEVERS

At the onset of an acute infectious fever the heat regulating center brings into action the mechanisms to conserve heat. It is as if the "thermostat" had been set to a higher level. This is brought about by the action of the bacterial toxins on the heat regulating centers in the hypothalamus. There is a redistribution of the blood flow, with constriction of the skin vessels, producing a cold, pale or slightly cyanotic skin. This reduces the heat loss by radiation and conduction. Since the normal comfortable feeling of warmth depends upon stimuli from temperature sensory endings in the skin and subcutaneous tissues, there is a feeling of cold. This is known as a *chill*. If this heat conserved by the redistribution of the blood flow does not raise the internal temperature fast enough, shivering and the other reactions of a normal person exposed to severe cold, occur. Such violent shivering at the onset of a fever is known as a *rigor*. The involuntary contractions produce heat, which with the constricted skin vessels causes a rapid rise in the internal temperature. The chills and rigors occur as the body temperature rises. When the "new setting of the thermostat" has been reached, and the fever is at its height, an unstable state occurs. Usually the skin is flushed, hot and dry but sweating or chills may supervene rapidly. At the elevated body temperature the *basal metabolism* is elevated 7 per cent for every °F. rise (p. 766). The effect of fever on the basal metabolic rate is shown in figure 52.5.

DuBois, in an experiment upon a normal man and a malarial fever patient, demonstrated the reduced heat elimination which occurs during the chill. The normal subject imitated as closely as possible for a period of 34 minutes the shivering of the patient and thereby increased his heat production by nearly 200 per cent. Most of the extra heat was eliminated as it was produced, the body temperature showing only a slight rise. In the malarial patient, on the contrary, in whom the heat production during the chill was increased to about the same degree, all the extra heat was retained. The heat retention caused a rise of 2°C. in body temperature. After the chill the heat elimination rose and the temperature fell.

The "continued" fever, which usually follows the initial chill of an infectious disease, or which develops in other instances without this preliminary, is due essentially to the raised threshold for heat loss. There is, of course, increased heat production but this is mainly secondary—the velocity of the oxidative processes of the tissues being increased by the rise in temperature induced by the diminished heat elimination. That the latter, rather than increased heat production, is the principal factor in the elevated temperature is indicated by the fact that in fever a temperature of 104°F. (40°C.) is accompanied by an increased heat production of only about 35 per cent, whereas in health the heat production must be increased several fold (as in muscular exercise) in order to raise the body temperature even transiently to this extent. Also, the metabolism may be raised 40 per cent or so in an animal by protein feeding (see specific dynamic action, p. 787) without the occurrence of a temperature rise. Furthermore, the increased metabolism in ordinary fevers occurs simultaneously with the temperature rise. If the latter were the result rather than the cause of the former, it should be possible to demonstrate by indirect calorimetry a period of increased

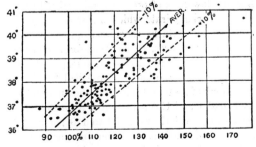

FIG. 52.5. Relationship between basal metabolism and body temperature in fever. Results in six different fevers grouped in one chart. The continued line shows the average metabolism, the interrupted lines the metabolism 10 per cent above and 10 per cent below the average respectively. (After DuBois.)

metabolism preceding the rise in temperature; this, however, does not occur.

When the infection has been overcome, the "thermostat" setting is returned to normal. This may occur rapidly as in malaria or the resolution by *crisis* in pneumonia, or gradually as in the resolution by *lysis*. In either case the body must dissipate the excess heat. The skin is flushed, warm and moist. In the crisis there will be profuse sweating. When the temperature regains its proper level, the normal heat regulating mechanisms again come into play.

### Special Metabolism in Fever

*Water and salt.* At the onset of a high fever there occurs a retention of chloride which apparently is deposited in the tissues, the chloride concentration of the blood being normal or below normal. The urinary chlorides in most fevers are greatly reduced. During the course of the fever there is a pronounced reduction in urine volume. The vaporization of water from the skin is increased owing to the high temperature, and from the lungs for the same reason, but to a more important extent, as a result of the more rapid breathing.

At the termination of the fever the retained water and chloride are eliminated by diuresis and sweating. Chloride retention is especially pronounced in pneumonia.

*Protein.* The excretion of nitrogen in the urine is greatly increased in most infectious fevers. This is furnished by body protein, the protein minimum, i.e., the "wear and tear" quota of protein metabolism (p. 786), being much higher than normal. In very severe infections from 300 to 400 grams of body protein may be destroyed daily. It has been found impossible to maintain the fever patient in nitrogen equilibrium (p. 785) by giving liberal allowances of protein combined with supplies of carbohydrate which under ordinary circumstances would be considered quite adequate for energy purposes. It has, therefore, been held that the toxins of the disease were responsible for the protein destruction, the so-called "toxic destruction" of protein. It has been shown, however, by Schaffer and Coleman that if a diet be given possessing a caloric value 50 to 110 per cent in excess of the patient's requirements, as actually determined by calorimetry, and containing a liberal supply of protein (160 to 200 grams), nitrogen equilibrum can be established. The high protein catabolism which has been observed in fever patients on the usual diet is therefore thought to have been due in large measure to the fact that

the caloric intake was far below the requirements, which owing to the higher metabolism in fever are considerably greater than has been supposed. In other words, a fever patient upon a diet which has been considered adequate in the past is actually in a half-starved state, and is, in consequence, forced to consume his own tissues.

Nevertheless, even on a high caloric diet composed of carbohydrate and a small quantity of fat, the nitrogen excretion still remains well above that of a normal person. Moreover, a protein allowance equivalent to that of a healthy man, together with carbohydrate somewhat more than sufficient to cover the calculated caloric requirements of the febrile state, will not maintain nitrogen equilibrium. As just mentioned, the caloric allowance must in some instances be double the heat production of the patient. It therefore appears that the toxic process itself must be responsible in part for the increase in protein metabolism. Creatinine, uric acid, purine bases and phosphates also appear in the urine in increased amounts—further evidence of a destruction of body protein. The manner in which the "toxic" effect is produced is not known. It does not seem to be due merely to the high temperature, for raising the temperature of a normal person to 40°C. (104°F.) by immersion in a hot bath does not increase the nitrogen excretion significantly. In fevers with much destruction of body protein the specific dynamic action of food is absent.

It must be apparent from the foregoing remarks that in order to reduce the waste of body tissue in fever a liberal diet should be given, provided such is not contraindicated by some special feature of the disease. The old adage "feed a fever" holds true. Since the very high protein diet required for the establishment of nitrogen equilibrium in the fever patient has its disadvantages, one must usually be satisfied with reducing the waste of body protein rather than aiming to abolish it. Special attention, therefore, is directed toward furnishing an abundance of protein-sparing food (p. 786), namely carbohydrate, and thus avoiding excessive quantities of protein. The more abundant diet causes a negligible increase in heat production and no elevation of the temperature.

*Fats and carbohydrates.* The metabolism of body fat or carbohydrate shows no definite abnormality in fever. In patients upon a low food intake body fat and glycogen are utilized as fuel. Acidosis results from the excess combustion of fat only if the available carbohydrate is inadequate in amount.

## THE ACTION OF ANTIPYRETIC DRUGS
### (FEVER-REDUCING)

A list of chemical substances which are capable of inducing a rise in body temperature has been given on page 766. Other drugs, e.g., antipyrine, acetylsalicilic acid (aspirin), salicylates, quinine, etc., although they exert little effect upon the normal temperature, lower the temperature in fever by increasing heat elimination. According to Barbour they bring about this effect through drawing water from the tissues into the vessels and thus increasing the volume of fluid in the body's heat-radiating system. They seem to exert little effect upon heat production. The effect upon the blood volume is possibly brought about indirectly. All these substances raise the blood sugar; the greater sugar concentration may then through osmotic forces attract water into the vascular system.

Morphine and general anesthesia depress cerebral activity, including the regulation of body temperature. During some stages of anesthesia sweating may occur which further disorganizes the regulation of body temperature. The anesthetic reduces metabolic activity, hence less heat is produced. The temperature of an anesthetized patient is liable to shift, either up or down, depending upon the room temperature, and the coverings. Under the drapes in an operating room body temperature frequently rises, but if left uncovered in a cool room the temperature will fall.

Alcohol causes cutaneous vasodilation. This hastens heat loss, for the skin is warm and often moist. The warm skin gives a sensation of warmth, hence the belief that alcohol will warm a person who is suffering from cold. In fact, it increases heat loss and may cause a lowering of body temperature.

THE VALUE OF FEVER. Fever is frequently the herald of serious disease; nevertheless, unless of high degree and on this account endangers the functions of vital tissues, it should not be looked upon as a reaction detrimental in itself. On the contrary, there is every indication that its occurrence is an important aid to the body in its combat with the disease. It is well known, for example, that in infections that overwhelm the patient the fever reaction is depressed. But the role played by fever in the defensive process is unknown. It has been suggested that antibodies can be elaborated in adequate amounts only at higher temperatures.

In support of the belief that moderate fever is not injurious in itself but is actually beneficial the following observations upon animals may be cited. (a) The body temperature of rabbits has been maintained by the application of external heat at a level of over 40.5°C. (105°F.) for weeks at a time without ill effects. (b) In animals infected with certain microorganisms the disease runs a milder course when the temperature is is raised (to 40°C. or 104°F.) artificially. High temperature is thought to be favorable for the elaboration of antibodies. (c) It has been reported that with moderate overheating the formation of various antibodies is increased, but at higher temperatures the process, apparently, is depressed. (d) The immunity of fowl to the ordinary pyogenic infections is ascribed to their higher body temperature which is inimical to the growth of pus-forming bacteria. (e) Fevers induced artificially by means of foreign proteins or injections of malarial blood are used as therapeutic agents in arthritis and in chronic nervous disease due to the pathogen of syphilis (Treponema pallidum). Short wave diathermy has been employed with success in the treatment of certain infections—the high temperature produced in the tissue exerting a lethal action upon the microorganisms. (f) In the past it has been common practice to reduce fever (above 40°C. to 104°F.) by cold bathing, but it was found that the patients did not do well and the practice, except in an extremely high fever which is dangerous in itself, has been abandoned.

REFRIGERATION—HYPOTHERMIA. The lowering of the body temperature occurs when the rate of cooling exceeds the rate of the heat production. This can occur with inadequate clothing in freezing weather, but will occur much more rapidly in water. As the temperature of the tissues fall, their metabolic rate falls, the oxygen needs are reduced and the circulation can be interrupted for a much longer time without damage. For these reasons hypothermia is induced artificially to protect the brain during operations on the heart and great vessels, or upon intracranial vessels. The patient is given a sedative, and a drug such as chlorpromazine to inhibit shivering. Under minimal anesthesia the patient is placed in ice water. The rectal temperature will fall to 30°C. (86°F) in 1½ to 2 hours. Respiratory and heart rates fall; the blood pressure is reduced a little to about 90/70. Urine production is decreased.

## REFERENCES

BARBOUR, H. G. AND PRINCE, A. L. J. Pharmacol. & Exper. Therap., 1914, 6, 1.

BARCROFT, J. AND IZQUIERDE, J. J. J. Physiol., 1931, 71, 364.

BURTON, A. C. Proc. Fed. Am. Soc. Exp. Biol., 1946, 5, 344.

COON, J. M. AND ROTHMAN, S. J. Pharmacol. & Exper. Therap., 1941, 73, 1.

DuBois, E. F. J.A.M.A., 1921, 77, 352.

HARDY, J. D. AND DuBois, E. F. Nat. Acad. Sci., 1940, 26, 389.

HARDY, J. D. AND MUSCHENHEIM, C. J. Clin. Invest., 1934, 13, 817; 1936, 15, 1.

KELLER, A. D. J. Neurophysiol., 1938, 1, 543.

KELLER, A. D. AND HARE, W. K. Proc. Soc. Exper. Biol. & Med., 1931, 29, 1067. Ibid., p. 1069.

KUNO, Y. Lancet, 1930, 2, 912.

MARTIN, C. Lancet 1930, 2, 561, 617, 673.

MOLNAR, G. W., TOWBIN, E. J., GOSSELIN, R. E., BROWN, A. A. H. AND ADOLPH, E. J. Am. J. Hyg. 1946, 44, 411.

NEWBURGH, L. H., JOHNSTON, M. W., LASHMET, F. H. AND SHELDON, J. M. J. Nutrition, 1937, 13, 203.

RANSON, S. W. and associates. J. Neurophysiol., 1939, 2, 61.

RAWICZ, S. The long walk. Constable, London, 1956, p. 165.

SCOTT, J. C., BAZETT, H. C. AND MACKIE, G. C. Am. J. Physiol., 1940, 129, 102.

SHAFFER, F. A. AND SWIFT, R. W. J. Nutrition, 1932, 5, 227.

SWIFT, R. W. J. Nutrition, 1932, 5, 227.

*Monographs and Reviews*

ADOLPH, E. F. Am. J. Physiol., 1938, 123, 486.

BARBOUR, H. G. Physiol. Rev., 1921, 1, 295.

BAZETT, H. C. Physiol. Rev., 1927, 7, 531.

DEIGHTON, T. Physiol. Rev., 1933, 13, 427.

COLEMAN, W. Arch. Int. Med., 1909, 4, 538. J.A. M.A., 190, 53, 1145. Ibid., 1912, 59, 363.

DILL, D. B., EDWARDS, H. T., BAUER, P. S. AND Levenson, E. J. Arbeitsphysiologie, 1931, 4, 508.

DuBOIS, E. Basal metabolism in health and disease. Lea & Febiger, Philadelphia, 1936. p. 432. Metabolism in fever and certain infections. In Barker's Endocrinology and Metabolism, 1922, 4, 95. Heat loss from human body. Bull. New York Acad. Med., 1939, 15, 143; Fever and the regulation of body temperature. Charles C Thomas, Springfield, Ill., 1948.

HILL, L. AND CAMPBELL, A. Health and Environment. Arnold, London. 1925.

KUNO, Y. The physiology of human perspiration. Churchill, Lond., 1934.

LUSK, G. The elements of the science of nutrition. Saunders, Philadelphia, 1906.

RANSON, S. W. A. Res. Nerv. & Ment. Dis., Proc., 1940, 20, 342.

SUNDSTROEM, E. S. Physiol. Rev., 1927, 7, 320.

# 53

# THE VITAMINS

The increasing understanding of metabolic processes has revealed that some of the enzymes catalyzing vital reactions need, as cofactors, minute traces of organic compounds. These cannot be made by the body and, therefore, must be supplied in the food. These compounds, now known as vitamins, posed nutritionists and biochemists with many a complex riddle. The student is referred to textbooks of biochemistry for details of the structure and properties of the vitamins. The present discussion will review their discovery, occurrence and principal functions.

Vitamins have been defined briefly as organic compounds required in minute amounts for normal health. Expanding knowledge of the metabolic roles of the vitamins makes it increasingly difficult to formulate a definition that is concise and yet complete. They occur in natural foods (either as the vitamin itself, or as a precursor) and are neither oxidized to supply energy nor used to build tissue structures.

Some 20-odd growth factors for animals have now been identified, but only about 15 (or fewer) seem to be required by man. For historical reasons they are usually classified and referred to as fat-soluble vitamins (A, D, E and K) and water-soluble ones (B complex and C). More than a dozen components have now been isolated and identified in the water-soluble group: thiamine, riboflavin, nicotinamide, pyridoxine, pantothenic acid, para-amino benzoic acid, choline, inositol, biotin, lipoic acid, folic acid, folinic acid and cyanocobalamin; ascorbic acid (vitamin C) and certain flavanoids (vitamin P) are in this same category.

Sir Frederick Gowland Hopkins (1861–1947) of Cambridge University in England is generally credited with the first experimental proof that accessory food factors are necessary to supplement the five well known dietary essentials: water, minerals, protein, carbohydrate and fat. Many years earlier several clinical and experimental studies had pointed clearly in the same direction but the publication in 1912 of Hopkins' findings aroused a world-wide interest in this new field. At about the same time Stepp in Germany was reaching similar conclusions.

### Historical Review. Development of the Vitamin Concept

A brief review of the discovery of the vitamins will serve to acquaint the student with the nature and seriousness of deficiency disease that were in former times the mysterious cause of millions of deaths. It will also show how the vitamin concept had its origins.

Scurvy. Scurvy is said to have afflicted the Crusaders. During the 1400's and 1500's it was apparently one of the more prevalent diseases in Europe. It attacked with particular virulence the inmates of besieged garrisons and sailors on long voyages. Vasco da Gama reported the death by scurvy of 100 sailors out of the crew of 160 men, and Jacques Cartier, obliged to winter in Canada in 1535, lost one-quarter of his men and the remainder were severely ill with the disease. Strangely enough, in view of its prevalence in Europe, Cartier wrote that " . . . the disease was wholly unknown to us." From the Indians, Cartier learned the curative value of a decoction of the leaves and bark of twigs of the "annedda" tree, apparently the cedar, arbor vitae.

Admiral Sir Richard Hawkins mentioned in 1593 that within his own personal experience 10,000 seamen had died of scurvy, and he reported that the juice of oranges and lemons was able to cure the disease. As early as 1601 the ships of the East India Company had adopted the regular use of oranges and lemons to prevent scurvy, apparently upon the recommendation of the English privateer, Sir James Lancaster.

In 1720 a physician to the Austrian army, Kramer by name, had written of scurvy and reported that a supply of green vegetables, or of oranges, lemons or limes could cure this dreadful disease without other help. Captain Lind of the British navy wrote a celebrated *Treastise on Scurvy* in 1753 in which he reported experiments on sailors which proved beyond doubt that "salads, summer fruits, etc." would prevent the disease and that the severest cases could be so cured within six days.

Beriberi. Three other diseases, beriberi, pellagra and rickets, are now known to be of dietary origin. The patient suffering from *beriberi* first notices numbness in his legs. Later pain develops in the calf muscles. Exhaustion, emaciation and paralysis, with increased heart rate and enlarged right heart, lead to death from heart failure. One of the most characteristic features, clinically, is peripheral neuritis. Nearly 80 years ago, Admiral Takaki, Director-General of the Medical Service of the Japanese navy, had convinced himself that beriberi, which sometimes crippled up to 50 per cent of the sailors on long voyages, was due to some fault in the diet. He arranged in 1882 to have the usual diet (largely of polished rice) on a Japanese training ship augmented with meat, fish and other protein-rich items. The improvement in the health of the sailors was so dramatic that the diet throughout the Japanese navy was similarly enriched and beriberi vanished. But in other parts of the world thousands continued to die from the disease which was still commonly believed to be due to poor sanitation, to contaminated rice or to a microbe.

In 1890 Eijkman (1858–1930), a medical investigator in the Dutch East Indies, accidentally made an observation which led him to discover an analogous disease in chickens. Birds fed milled (polished) rice developed polyneuritis and other signs resembling those of patients with beriberi. If they were fed unmilled rice, or if the bran was restored to their ration, the birds recovered. Eijkman soon showed that the curative principle could be extracted from the bran with water or alcohol and that it was dialyzable.

Eijkman thought that he had discovered a pharmacological antidote against the "toxin" or "microbe" in polished rice, but his colleague, Grijns, suggested in 1901 that beriberi was caused by a *lack* of some substance essential to the metabolism of the nervous system.

THE "VITAMINE" CONCEPT. Attempts to isolate the protective or curative principle from rice bran followed the adoption of Grijn's deficiency theory. Dr. Casimir Funk, of the Lister Institute in London, was among those who were more successful in their efforts to isolate Eijkman's anti-beriberi substance. When he thought he had it in pure form, Funk proposed for the substance a name which has since become famous. At the suggestion of Dr. Max Nierenstein the term *vitamine* was applied because the compound, he thought, was an *amine* that appeared to be essential to life.

Funk was also the originator of the "vitamine theory." He suggested in 1912 that there were four different vitamines: his antiberiberi vitamine, an antiscurvy vitamine, and probably also antirickets and antipellagra vitamines. Funk was led to this conclusion by a careful study of the pertinent medical and experimental literature. Some clinical observations pointing in this direction have already been described. Several other medical and earlier experimental studies will now be mentioned.

In 1888 Lunin, a student with Professor Bunge at Basle, had reported that mice could not survive on synthetic diets composed of purified proteins, fats and carbohydrates, plus mineral salts and water. Thus Lunin provided proof over 70 years ago that the known components of natural foods are unable to support life, and he drew the logical conclusion that natural foodstuffs (such as milk) must contain small quantities of unknown substances indispensable for normal nutrition. In the next 20 years many other workers confirmed the inability of the known dietary components to support growth.

In 1905 a Dutch physiologist, Pekelharing, published the results of experiments actually done some years earlier which showed that a very small amount of whole milk added to an artificial food mixture (i.e., made from purified chemicals) was able to transform the mixture to a nutritious food. Pekelharing wrote " . . . there is still an unknown substance in milk, which, even in very small quantities, is of paramount importance to nutrition." Similar experiments by Hopkins, published in English in 1912, and Funk's vitamine theory published in the same year, finally drew the attention of physiologists and chemists throughout the world to new fields of knowledge—clinically, to a group of affections that came to be recognized as *deficiency diseases*, and chemically, to a class of substances of great potency that would prevent and cure such diseases.

ARE GROWTH FACTORS AND "VITAMINES" THE SAME? For a period there was confusion as to whether only one or more than one factor was needed for growth, and whether the growth factor(s) were the same as the vitamine(s) that cured beriberi and scurvy. In 1915 E. V. McCollum and Margaret Davis showed that there are two *growth* factors at least: *fat-soluble A* found in butter and in egg-yolk but not in all fats (e.g., lard and olive oil lack it); *water-soluble B* found in the watery part of milk, in watery or alcoholic extracts of egg-yolk, in whole wheat or whole rice, but not in polished rice. It was soon found that the water-soluble B growth factor could cure polyneuritis in birds, indicating the presence of Funk's antiberiberi vitamine in the water-soluble B factor. Some workers were therefore tempted to assume that the growth factors and Funk's curative vitamines are one and the same.

Over the years, as one after another of the protective compounds was isolated from foodstuffs, and its chemical nature established, it was found that many were not amines. McCollum and Kennedy (1916) had pointed out that the word vitamine connoted a vital function, but that such a property had not been demonstrated for the growth factors. They, therefore, rejected Funk's term and proposed fat-soluble A and water-soluble B. However, the terminology was cumbersome, and Funk's designation had much popular appeal. In 1920 J. C. Drummond (1891–1952) proposed that the final *e* be dropped to avoid the indication of amine character and that these interesting substances (until fully characterized chemically) be provisionally called vitamin A, B, C, etc.

After McCollum and Davis proved that for the satisfactory growth of rats at least two different factors are required, the question arose as to how many growth factors there were and whether these were really the same as Funk's vitamines.

A few years earlier, Holst and Frölich in Norway, while trying to induce beriberi by feeding purified diets to guinea pigs, had produced instead a condition which they recognized as scurvy. Further work showed, as Funk had suggested, that the specific substance capable of curing scurvy differed from fat-soluble A and water-soluble B. Hence it was called vitamin C.

RICKETS. The number of recognized accessory food factors increased to four when the studies of Sir Edward Mellanby (1884–1956) in England and of McCollum and of Sherman and their associates in the United States showed that so-called fat-soluble A was not a unit substance but a complex of at least two factors. Mellanby was seeking the cause and cure of *rickets*, a bone disease known for at least 300 years to afflict especially children living in crowded industrial cities in the northern temperate zone (see also p. 910). Across the Channel A. Trousseau, in 1865, had described cod-liver oil as the perfect cure for rickets. Almost 30 years earlier another Frenchman, Jules Guerin, convinced that rickets is caused by faulty diet, had proved his point by producing the disease experimentally in puppies. In France and the Baltic countries the virtues of cod-liver oil were quickly recognized. But in England and many other countries rickets continued to deform and cripple thousands of children each year because medical teaching favored lack of lime salts, infection, hypothyroidism or confinement and lack of exercise as causes. The situation was very confused when in 1890 an English physician, T. A. Palm, made a thorough study of a widely held belief that exposure to sunlight prevents rickets and could even cure the disease in children. His data showed that rickets is common in cloudy regions and rather rare wherever sunshine is abundant. In 1919 Huldschinsky, in Berlin, had the idea of using artificial sunlight (ultraviolet rays) and was successful in curing rickets by so-called actinotherapy. Mellanby at Cambridge (1919, 1921) showed that cod-liver oil and other animal fats (e.g., butter and fat of egg yolk) that were known to contain the fat-soluble A of McCollum and Davis protected puppies against rickets. This observation provided experimental proof that a dietary factor is con-

cerned in rickets, and Mellanby at first assumed that it was fat-soluble A. In 1921 McCollum and associates showed that certain foods (e.g., carrots and green vegetables) failed to prevent rickets although they are rich in vitamin A activity. Further, it was soon found, both in Britain and the United States that the treatment of cod-liver oil with a stream of hot air to destroy vitamin A did not eliminate the rickets-preventing effect. The two factors must therefore differ. Since 1923 the antirachitic factor has been called vitamin D.

In 1924 two Americans, Hess, a physician, and Steenbock, a biochemist, independently made a surprising discovery; rickets could be prevented by irradiating the food of the animal with ultraviolet light just as well as by treating the animal itself. The solution to this puzzle proved to be, of course, that in both cases an inert precursor was converted by the ultraviolet light to the biologically active substance, vitamin D.

PELLAGRA. Meanwhile, evidence had been accumulating that water-soluble B was not a single factor but probably a complex mixture. Beriberi is practically unknown in Europe and America but in parts of the United States, in Egypt, Italy, Rumania and other countries where Indian corn (maize) is eaten, largely to the exclusion of other foods, another disease, *pellagra*, was very common. Between 1910 and 1930 pellagra, sometimes called the corn-eaters' disease, was extremely prevalent in the southern regions of the United States. The skin in this disease becomes bronzed and thickened, especially where exposed to sunlight, the tongue is swollen and glossy and mental troubles develop, which progress to dementia in the last stages. It was referred to as the disease of the "three D's"—*dermatitis, diarrhea* and *dementia*, and although at first its cause was unknown, it came in time to be associated with the use of a diet known as the "three M's"—*maize-meal, molasses* and *meat* (salt pork). Dr. Joseph Goldberger (1874–1929) was put in charge of a study of pellagra sponsored by the United States Public Health Service to determine whether it was caused by an infective agent, a chemical toxin, an amino acid deficiency or lack of a pellagra-preventing factor (the P-P factor). Goldberger's associates eliminated the possibility of an infective agent and showed that most foods rich in 'vitamin B' would prevent and cure pellagra. Lack of a suitable experimental animal delayed progress until it was found that dogs fed a certain purified diet developed a sore mouth, called "black tongue," resembling the oral lesions so characteristic of human pellagra. In 1926 Smith and Hendrick showed that the water-soluble growth factor B, (which seemed to be the same as the beriberi-preventing substance of Funk), contained two different substances, one destroyed by heat, and one heat-stable. The latter was soon found to cure pellagra.

TABLE 53.1
*The vitamins*

| Original Name | Currently Accepted Name | Alternative and Obsolete Names | Effect of Deficiency* | Human Daily Requirement† |
|---|---|---|---|---|
| Fat soluble A | Vitamin $A_1$ | Axerophthol, Biosterol, Ophthalamin, Anti-infective vitamin | Keratinization of epithelial structures; night blindness | 5000 IU |
| | Vitamin $A_2$ (Carotene) | (Provitamin A) | | (7500 IU) |
| Vitamin D | Vitamin $D_2$ | Calciferol, irradiated ergosterol, ergocalciferol | Rickets, osteomalacia | (400 IU) |
| | Vitamin $D_3$ | Cholecalciferol, activated 7-dehydrocholesterol Antirachitic vitamin | | |
| | Vitamin E | Alpha-tocopherol, fertility vitamin, anti-sterility vitamin | Sterility, muscular dystrophy | Unknown |
| | Vitamin K | Methylnaphthoquinone, menadione, antihemorrhagic factor, prothrombin factor | Bleeding | Unknown |
| | Lipoic acid | Thioctic acid, pyruvate oxidation factor, protogen | Growth failure (microorganisms) | Unknown |
| Water soluble B | Thiamine | Vitamin $B_1$ Aneurin Oryzamin Torulin | Beriberi; polyneuritis | 1.8 mg. |
| $B_2$ or G (later found to be a mixture of vitamins) | Riboflavin | Vitamin $B_2$ Vitamin G, lactoflavin Ovoflavin | Loss of appetite and weight; unspecific lesions; corneal vascularization; (cheilosis, dermatitis) | 1.8 mg. |
| | Nicotinic acid Nicotinamide | Niacin (USA) Niacinamide (USA), PP factor | Pellagra | 1.8 mg. |
| Vitamin $B_6$ | Vitamin $B_6$ Three active related compounds { | Pyridoxine Pyridoxal Pyridoxamine Adermin, yeast eluate factor | Dermatitis in rats; microcytic anemia in dogs; convulsions in infants (?) | 2.0 mg. (?) |
| | Pantothenic acid | Antidermatitis factor, liver filtrate factor | Dermatitis in chicks; spastic gait in pigs | Unknown |
| | Biotin | Bios II, Bios IIB, vitamin H, factor W, coenzyme R. | Dermatitis; gastrointestinal symptoms, lassitude | Unknown 300 µg. (?) |
| | p-Aminobenzoic acid | Anti-gray hair factor, bacterial growth factor P, PABA or PAB | Graying of hair | Unknown |
| | Folic acid | Pteroylglutamic acid (PGA), vitamin M, factor U, vitamin Bc | Macrocytic anemia | 0.5 mg. |
| | Folinic acid | Citrovorum factor (CF), Leucovorin | | |

TABLE 53.1—*continued*

| Original Name | Currently Accepted Name | Alternative and Obsolete Names | Effect of Deficiency* | Human Daily Requirement† |
|---|---|---|---|---|
| | Vitamin $B_{12}$ | Cyanocobalamin, animal protein factor (APF) | Macrocytic anemia | 1.2 $\mu$g. |
| | Choline | | Fatty livers, (cirrhosis) | Unknown |
| | Inositol | Inosite, meso-inositol, muscle sugar | Alopecia | Unknown |
| | Lipothiamide | (see lipoic acid) | | |
| Vitamin C | Ascorbic acid | Hexuronic acid, antiskorbutin | Scurvy | 75 mg. |

* Only the main effects can be shown here. See text for further details and for species concerned.

† The concept of *exact* nutrient requirements suggested by a single figure in a table is misleading. Great variation is encountered for a number of reasons: (1) biological variation, (2) effects of age, sex and environmental factors, (3) effects of dietary composition, e.g. the nicotinic acid requirement is influenced by the tryptophane content of the diet.

Goldberger called it the P-P factor but many Americans referred to it as vitamin G, in honor of Goldberger. The antineuritic factor they continued to call vitamin B. In Britain the antineuritic factor was referred to as vitamin $B_1$ and the antipellagra factor as vitamin $B_2$. The latter term became internationally accepted. Later the $B_2$ fraction was shown to consist of a number of vitamins.

This historical introduction would not be complete without mention being made of other accessory food factors that have subsequently been discovered as the techniques of preparing "purified diets" have been perfected. The isolation of vitamins A, $B_1$, $B_2$, C and D in pure form, their chemical identification and eventual availability in crystalline form made possible the recognition of other growth factors: choline, nicotinic acid, pyridoxine, pantothenic acid, biotin, inositol, folic acid, folinic acid, vitamin $B_{12}$, lipoic acid, vitamin E, vitamin K and other substances required specifically by certain organisms (see table 53.1).

It should be emphasized that not all organisms, not even all mammals, have the same nutritional requirements. Man, monkeys and guinea pigs require vitamin C; but rats, dogs and many other species are able to manufacture this vitamin. These varying nutritional requirements of different species have led to a great deal of confusion in past experimental studies. Now that the situation is recognized much fruitless work can be avoided by finding which species are suitable for a particular study and using only appropriate test organisms. In the confused period (1930–1940) during which fractionation of the vitamin B complex was being conducted in many laboratories, other vitamins were described whose existence has never been established. Some of the accepted vitamins have not yet been shown to be essential for man, and in some cases they are so ubiquitous that a deficiency is unlikely to arise. Choline, inositol, *p*-amino-benzoic acid, lipoic acid and possibly biotin, belong in this category.

## Fat-Soluble Vitamins

### VITAMIN A

In 1914 Osborne and Mendel noted that some fats (butter and egg yolk fat) when added to a purified diet caused good growth while other fats (lard and oil of almonds) did not. The eyes of rats fed these latter fats for long periods became red and sore and eventually purulent. The condition was quickly cured by butter fat and cod-liver oil. In 1915 McCollum and Davis announced similar findings and proposed the term "fat-soluble A." By 1919 Steenbock had shown that carotene iso-

lated from carrots is active (although xanthophyll is not) and had suggested that the vitamin A activity of foods is related to the yellow pigments they contain. It was puzzling to find that fractions rich in vitamin A from animal sources were often practically colorless. Today, we understand the reasons for what was then a baffling mystery.

### *Chemistry and Occurrence*

Vitamin A can be isolated only from animal tissues, but vitamin A *activity* is found in plants as well. This is due to the occurrence in many yellow-colored and green plant tissues of one or

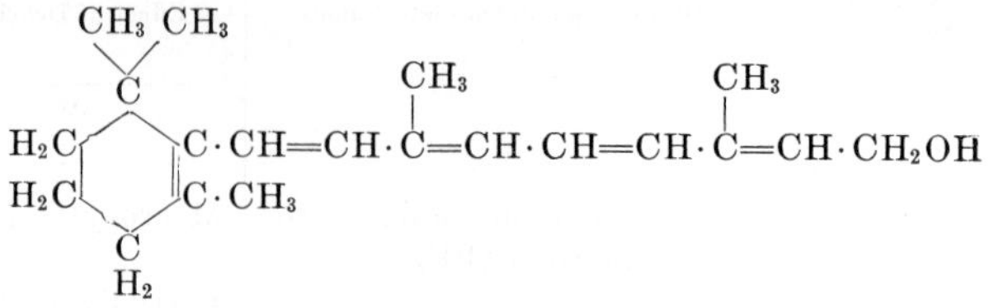

and egg yolk. Vitamin A in the blood plasma is mainly free, that in the liver is mainly present as

Vitamin A₁

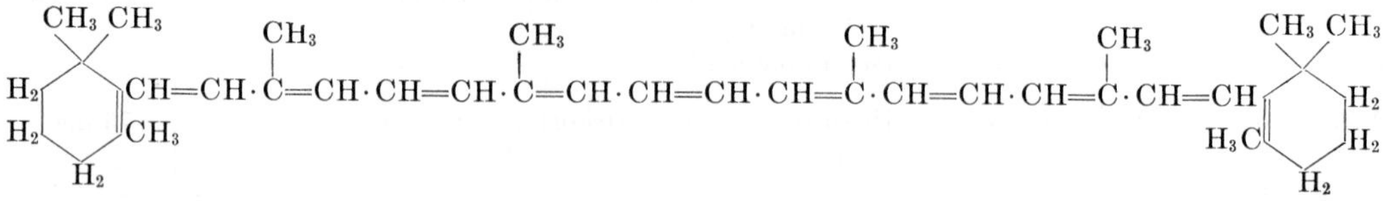

β-Carotene

more precursors called provitamins, the most important of which is β-carotene, an orange-yellow-colored hydrocarbon, $C_{40}H_{56}$. Vitamin A₁ (generally called vitamin A) is an unsaturated alcohol, $C_{20}H_{29}OH$.

Attention is drawn to the presence of 5 double bonds, one in the ring, because *cis-trans* isomerism can, and does, occur around the double bonds in the side-chain. Vitamin A is all *trans*-isomer. In many species of animals it is formed in the body (probably in the intestinal tract) by an imperfectly understood hydrolytic and oxidative scission of the provitamins. Some animals (the carnivores) are apparently unable to effect this cleavage and must therefore obtain vitamin A from the flesh of their prey.

The actual vitamin itself is found in animal tissues, especially the liver, and in butter, cream

TABLE 53.2

*Comparison of vitamin A and carotene*

| Vitamin A ($C_{20}H_{30}O$) | β-Carotene ($C_{40}H_{56}$) |
|---|---|
| Stored by animals (conversion of carotene in some animals). | Synthesized by plants |
| Almost colorless | Reddish-yellow |
| Absorption band at 325 to 328 mμ | No absorption band at 326 mμ |
| Vivid blue color with antimony trichloride (maximal absorption at 620 mμ) | Greenish blue color with antimony trichloride (maximal absorption at 590 mμ) |
| Vitamin A₂ plus SbCl₃ gives maximal absorption at 696 mμ. | |

esters. The richest and most important natural sources are the oils from the livers of salt-water fish (cod and especially halibut). A number of isomers are known. Vitamin A₂, possessing one more double bond in the ring, is found in the liver oils of fresh-water fish. Its biopotency is about 30 to 40 per cent of that of the all *trans* vitamin A₁. All natural samples of vitamin A₁ and even synthetic vitamin A₁ have been found to contain a stereoisomer, neovitamin A, in which the configuration around the $C_{7-8}$ double bond is believed to be *cis*. It constitues from 30 to 55 per cent of most commercial samples of vitamin A. Its potency is about 85 per cent of the all *trans* vitamin A. Synthetic vitamin A is on the market in the U.S.A. at a remarkably low price—in 1958 at about 25 cents per million units.

CAROTENE. In Canada and the United States carotene is the principal nutritional source (and also the cheapest) of vitamin A. There are several slightly different forms of carotene. β-Carotene is by far the most important; in many kinds of plants it is the only carotene present in appreciable amount. Other carotenes and cryptoxanthin, which may be present in minor quantities, also can function as provitamin A. The other carotenes display, on a weight basis, only one-half or less of the vitamin A activity of β-carotene. This was formerly explained by the symmetrical nature of the β-carotene molecule. Oxidative-hydrolytic cleavage at the central double bond theoretically could give rise to 2 molecules of vitamin A; other carotenes with the characteristic ring (an essential part of the vitamin A molecule) on only one end of the hydrocarbon chain could give rise to only one such structure per molecule. Recent more careful biological assays indicate that $\beta$-carotene itself appears to give rise to only one molecule of vitamin A. The reason for the lesser activity of the other carotenes must be in the lower efficiency of their biological conversion.

Carotene *injections* are relatively ineffective in correcting vitamin A deficiency. Large amounts of the injected carotene may be stored in the liver *while deficiency of vitamin A is present.* When carotene is given orally, vitamin A appears in the liver. These and other observations have led to the belief that the conversion of carotene to vitamin A occurs in the intestinal mucosa during absorption. There are great differences in the extent to which this change occurs. Some animals have white body fat (e.g., sheep, goats, pigs and rats) because carotenoids are almost completely absent from their tissues. In these species the conversion is virtually complete. In humans, however, and in hens, cattle and many other animals, considerable amounts of carotenoid pigments are absorbed without conversion to vitamin A. Dairy cattle convert part of the carotene of the fodder (alfalfa is a particularly rich source) into colorless vitamin A. The latter, as well as unchanged carotene, is secreted in the milk. It is thus evident that a pale-colored milk may have a vitamin A content equal to or higher than one that is more richly colored by carotene.

Clinical and experimental observations have shown a relationship between the activity of the thyroid gland and the availability of dietary sources of vitamin A. The earlier belief that thyroxine favored the conversion of carotene to vitamin A has been modified as the data are more consistent with a stimulating effect of the thyroid hormone (and an inhibitory effect of thiouracil, a drug which depresses thyroid activity) on the intestinal absorption of carotene.

### Effects of Deficiency

Deficiency of vitamin A may be caused by (a) inadequate amounts in the diet, (b) defective absorption, (c) inadequate conversion of the provitamin (carotene) to vitamin A, or to a combination of these. Absorption of the vitamin, and especially of carotene, is favored by the simultaneous uptake of fat. This relationship is of importance when the diet consists largely of vegetables, for these provide carotene but often in a medium low in fat. Absorption of vitamin A or its precursor is impaired in diseases (such as sprue and celiac disease) where fat absorption is defective. The chief function of vitamin A ap-

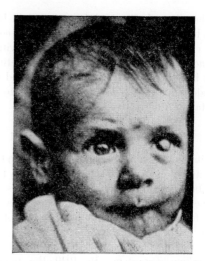

Fig. 53.1. Illustrates a baby which had suffered from an attack of ophthalmia of dietary origin, and was cured by administration of fat-soluble A as butter and cod-liver oil. The disease had, however, progressed so far that the sight of the left eye was destroyed and the right eye damaged. (After Bloch, from McCollum and Simmonds, *The Newer Knowledge of Nutrition.*)

pears to be the maintenance of epithelial tissues, but the method by which it operates has not yet been discovered.

Lack of vitamin A causes (1) failure of growth in the young (2) severe damage to the rods and cones of the retina, resulting in night blindness,[1] (3) redness and drying of the eye (xerophthalmia) with consequent softening or destruction of the cornea (keratomalacia), (4) drying and altered structure (xerosis and metaplasia) of epithelial tissues, such as papular eruptions and drying of the skin due to changes in hair follicles, atrophy of sebaceous and sweat glands, (5) secondary infections[2] due to the epithelial abnormalities, (6) swelling of the gums (gingival hypertrophy), (7) overgrowth of bones, especially those of the cranium and vertebral column which may compress or pinch off nerves in their passage through the foramina, (8) stones in the kidney (renal calculi), (9) degeneration of nervous tissue, (10) failure in reproductive function.

[1] Vitamin A deficiency is not the only cause of night blindness. Even when deficiency of vitamin A is the cause there is no proof that defects in regeneration of rhodopsin account fully for the night blindness. Degenerative changes may have occurred in the visual receptors or optical neurons.

[2] The former term, "anti-infective vitamin," is inappropriate and even misleading. Vitamin A does not improve immunological responses nor has it been beneficial in the treatment of infections. By its action in *maintaining* the epithelial tissues, infection is resisted.

The effect of vitamin A in curing night blindness has been explained in part by the discovery of a close chemical relationship between vitamin A and two compounds, rhodopsin and retinene, that have been isolated from dark-adapted eyes. Rhodopsin, (ch. 72) is a protein conjugate with a vitamin A derivative.

### Units and Requirement of Vitamin A

Vitamin A activity is usually expressed in terms of international units (IU). The unit has had a constant magnitude but it has been expressed or defined in different ways. The original standard of reference for vitamin A activity, adopted in 1931, was 1 μg. of crystalline (mixed) carotenes. This was replaced in 1934 by 0.6 μg. of pure, crystalline β-carotene. In 1949 the reference standard became 0.344 μg. of pure vitamin A acetate (equivalent to 0.300 μg. of vitamin A alcohol). For vegetable products, the carotene standard of 1934 has been retained.

TABLE 53.3

*Vitamin A activity of various
fresh liver oils and foods*

| | International Units Vitamin A* | |
|---|---|---|
| | per gram | per serving |
| Fish liver oils | | |
| Cod........................... | 2,000 | |
| Halibut...................... | 87,000 | |
| Ling cod..................... | 175,000 | |
| Sword fish................... | 250,000 | |
| Liver, beef (cooked, 2 oz.)........ | | 30,000 |
| Carrots (cooked, 1 cup)........... | | 18,000 |
| Squash (winter, cooked, 1 cup).... | | 12,700 |
| Sweet potatoes (baked, one medium)....................... | | 11,400 |
| Kale (1 cup)..................... | | 9,200 |
| Tomato (cooked, 1 cup)........... | | 2,500 |
| Egg (boiled, one medium)......... | | 550 |
| Milk (cow, whole, 1 cup).......... | | 390 |
| Butter (1 pattie, 7 grams).\....... | | 230 |
| Margarine (1 pattie, 7 grams)..... | | 230 |

\* The values shown are average. The variation is often considerable, sometimes up to fourfold (and in the case of the fish oils even more) depending upon the season of collection, etc. Both vitamin A and carotene are susceptible to oxidative breakdown, especially when heated. Losses during food processing (dehydration and canning) are minimized when the latter are conducted in a vacuum.

The careful biological comparisons upon which these standards are based have shown that one $C_{40}$ molecule of carotene gives rise to but one *biologically available* $C_{20}$ molecule of vitamin A. A number of factors (e.g., differential absorption, efficiency of conversion) affect the comparison.

The vitamin A requirements of certain species of animals are fairly well established but in man the picture is complicated by dietary variability (i.e., intake of other vitamins) in different regions, differences in activity, etc. Actual data on human requirements are meager. The Food and Nutrition Board of the National Research Council (U.S.A.) recommends (1958) a minimal intake of 5000 IU (from mixed sources) per day for a 70-kg. man. An ordinary mixed diet in North America provides about one-third of the total vitamin A activity as preformed vitamin and two-thirds in the form of carotene. Because carotene is often less efficiently absorbed than is vitamin A, it is usual to recommend higher unitage when vegetable sources provide the bulk of the dietary supply of vitamin A activity than when the principal sources are liver, milk, butter, cod-liver oil or pharmaceutical concentrates of vitamin A. A study at Sheffield under the auspices of the British Medical Research Council led to the recommendation of 2500 units of vitamin A as such, or an intake of 7500 units per day for adults, when carotene was the only source. In 1950 the Canadian Council on Nutrition reviewed the available data, decided that vitamin A requirements are proportional to body weight and recommended 72 units (43 μg.) of carotene per kg. of body weight (i.e., 5000 units for a man weighing 70-kg.) or one-fourth of this amount if preformed vitamin A is taken.

Although the evidence for an increased requirement during pregnancy and lactation is questionable, it is customary to recommend during the third trimester of pregnancy 6000 units of vitamin A per day and 8000 units per day during lactation.

SOURCES OF VITAMIN A. As mentioned earlier, vitamin A occurs only in the animal kingdom, but several provitamins (principally β-carotene) occur in vegetables and fruits. Vitamin A activity is most reliably assayed biologically, but this method of assay is time-consuming and costly. Values found by chemical or physical methods, especially for carotene, may give quite an erroneous impression of the vitamin available, because inefficient absorption and conversion may limit the amounts reaching the tissues (see table 53.3).

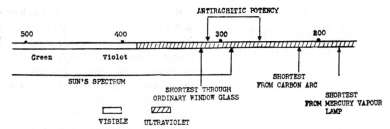

Fig. 53.2. Scheme of wave lengths of spectrum, showing the range of those possessing antirachitic properties. Figures refer to millimicrons. The hatched area indicates the ultraviolet part of the spectrum. (Redrawn and modified from Blunt and Cowan.)

HYPERVITAMINOSIS A (TOXICITY). Vitamin A given in excessive amounts causes toxic reactions. Adults who ingested 300 to 500 grams of polar bear liver became severely ill. Headache, vomiting, diarrhea and giddiness appeared promptly. About a week later desquamation of the skin and some loss of hair occurred. The intake may have been about seven million IU since the vitamin A content of polar bear liver may be as high as 18000 IU per gram. Numerous instances of poisoning have been described in infants and children given excessive dosage of vitamin A in the form of fish liver oil concentrates. Scaly dermatitis, patchy loss of hair, fissured lips, skeletal pain, irritability and anorexia were common to all these patients. The insidious onset of the symptoms and prompt response to cessation of overdosage are characteristic. Permanent sequelae are unusual. More cases of vitamin A overdosage than of deficiency have been reported in the medical journals in recent years. The condition has been studied in a human volunteer. Nothing is known of the biological properties of vitamin A that will account for these reactions.

## VITAMIN D

The curative value of cod liver oil in the treatment of rickets had been noted as early as 1782. Largely due to the efforts of Huldschinsky in Berlin and of Harriet Chick in Britain and in Vienna the curative effect of sunlight (and artificial sunlight, produced by mercury vapor lamps) on rickets was established (1919). The discovery by Hess and by Steenbock in the United States (1924) that irradiation of some foods generates protective substances led to reconciliation of the cod-liver oil and the actinotherapy schools of thought. It is now known that animals and man, under the influence of ultraviolet light (from the sun or elsewhere), can manufacture the antirachitic vitamin from steroid secretions on the surface of the skin (fig. 53.2). Ready-made vitamin D is obtained from certain foods, particularly dairy products.

CHEMISTRY. The term "vitamin D" refers to several chemically related compounds (steroids) that possess the property of preventing or curing rickets. They differ in the potency with which they are effective in different species. The provitamins of the D group are sterols whose molecules undergo slight rearrangement of structure under the influence of ultraviolet light. The naturally occurring antirachitic vitamin, now called $D_3$, arises upon irradiation by the sun of 7-dehydrocholesterol which is present in the oily secretions of the skin. Animals may lick it off the fur, but in man absorption is through the skin. The plant sterol, ergosterol, when irradiated, gives rise to vitamin $D_2$. The synthetic product is known as *calciferol* or *viosterol*. In both cases the complex ring system of the sterol nucleus is broken by opening of the B-ring between carbon

Ergosterol ($C_{28}H_{43}OH$)

Calciferol—Vitamin $D_2$
(viosterol)

7-Dehydrocholesterol

Activated 7-dehydrocholesterol—Vitamin D$_3$

atoms 9 and 10. The products, no longer sterols in the strict sense, are referred to as steroids. Toxic by-products are formed by other rearrangements during artificial irradiation of sterols and these must be removed, or conditions must be arranged to minimize their formation. Ergosterol and vitamin D$_2$ have similar structural formulas to those of vitamin D$_3$ and its provitamin, but with a double bond between carbon atoms 22 and 23 of the side chain and an extra methyl group on C-24. Vitamins D$_2$ and D$_3$ have equal antirachitic potency in the rat and in man, but in chicks the synthetic product (D$_2$, calciferol, made from ergosterol) is much less active. There is no vitamin D$_1$.

Vitamin D is soluble in fats and fat solvents. It is considerably more stable to oxidation than is vitamin A.

### Effects of Deficiency

When vitamin D is inadequate, the calcification of bone is defective. The resulting clinical condition is called rickets in children or osteomalacia in adults (figs. 53.3 and 53.4). In rickets the intestinal absorption of calcium is reduced; the renal clearance of phosphate is usually elevated. Aminoaciduria occurs as a result of a lowered renal threshold rather than to an increased concentration of amino acids in the blood.

Early signs of vitamin D inadequacy are an increased elimination of phosphate in the urine (elevated renal clearance), a fall in the concentration of inorganic phosphate in the plasma, and an elevation of alkaline phosphatase activity in the blood (reflecting increased osteoblastic activity in the bones). In vitamin D deficiency formation of cartilage continues but no longer in an orderly way; bone formation becomes irregular and calcification may stop entirely.

DEFECTIVE CALCIFICATION OF THE GROWING BONE AND COMPENSATORY HYPERTROPHY OF THE EPIPHYSEAL CARTILAGES ARE CHARACTERISTIC PATHOLOGICAL CHANGES. The band of cartilage at the end of growing long bones may become up to ten times wider than normal, leading to the typical X-ray picture (fig. 53.5). The cartilage expands at the ends of the long bones, especially the distal end of the radius; enlargement of the costochondral junctions leads to a series of small swellings on the thorax commonly referred to as a *rachitic rosary* (beading of ribs). Defective ossification causes the typical deformities (knock knees, bow legs, spinal curvature (*scoliosis*), malformations of the chest and pelvis, and soft, depressible areas in the parietal bones (*craniotabes*).

Animal experiments have confirmed clinical experience that the effects of a diet lacking vitamin D are greatly altered by the composition of the ration: the ratio of calcium to phosphorus is important. Some animals (e.g., rats) do not develop rickets unless this ratio is grossly abnormal. In children (and puppies) the disease develops when vitamin D is inadequate, even without serious disturbance in this ratio. Imbalance increases the susceptibility. Experience suggests that the ideal ratio of Ca:P in the diet is about 1:1, and that the calcium intake of children 3 to 13 years of age should be about 1 gram per day. In man, dietary ratios of Ca:P within the limits 2:1 to 1:2 appear to give optimal utilization of both elements.

Increasing the proportion of cereal in the diet, especially of oatmeal, has been found to have an aggravating effect on the tendency to develop rickets. Much of the phosphorus in cereals is present as *phytin* (the calcium magnesium salt of the hexaphosphoric ester of inositol), which is very poorly absorbed; phytin combines with dietary calcium in the intestine and renders it unavailable. The customary use of milk with porridge provides extra calcium needed under these conditions.

Vitamin D favors the absorption of calcium from the intestine; the coincident improvement

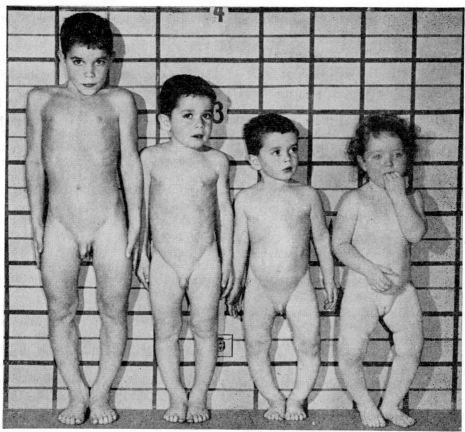

FIG. 53.3. Late effects of rickets in a family with hereditary refractoriness to vitamin D (three brothers and a first cousin). (Kindness of Dr. D. Fraser and the Hospital for Sick Children, Toronto, Canada.)

FIG. 53.4. A rickety dog. The animal was brought up on a diet deficient in the anti-rachitic vitamin D. (After E. Mellanby.)

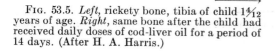

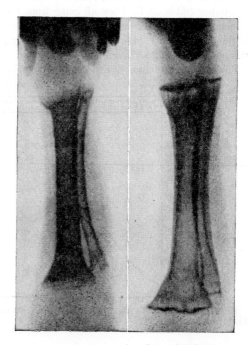

FIG. 53.5. *Left*, rickety bone, tibia of child 1$\frac{4}{12}$ years of age. *Right*, same bone after the child had received daily doses of cod-liver oil for a period of 14 days. (After H. A. Harris.)

TABLE 53.4

*Vitamin D in common foods*

| Food | I.U. per 100 Grams |
|------|--------------------|
| Cow's milk (raw)...... | 0.3 to 4 |
| Butter............... | 8 to 100 |
| Margarine (vitamins added)............... | 200 to 300 |
| Egg yolk............. | 150 to 500 |
| Liver (ox)........... | 40 to 50 |
| Herring (fresh)........ | 800 |
| Cod liver oil.......... | 2000 to 30,000 |
| Halibut liver oil....... | 20,000 to 400,000 |
| Tuna liver oil......... | 2,000,000 to 6,000,000 |

in tubular reabsorption of phosphate by the kidney may be a secondary effect of the improvement in calcium metabolism. Vitamin D, at least in excessive dosage, mobilizes calcium from the bones; it is possible therefore, that it may have the same action in physiological concentrations. The parathyroid hormone also affects calcium metabolism; this is discussed elsewhere.

Vitamin D is also concerned in the development and maturation of normal teeth. In the absence of vitamin D the structure of the teeth is defective and predisposes to the development of dental caries. Vitamin D can prevent or arrest dental caries, not by a direct action, but indirectly, by maintaining or improving the quality of these structures.

SOURCES. Foods containing vitamin D are few in number (table 53.4). They all come from the animal kingdom. Fish come first, notably the flesh of those fish that contain much body oil, e.g., salmon, herring and sardine.

The vitamin D content of dairy products varies greatly depending upon the diet of the cows and hens and on their exposure to sunlight. Natural milk has very little of this vitamin. Today milk is often fortified with vitamin D either by direct addition of the vitamin or by irradiation of the milk. There is some evidence that vitamin D supplied in milk is more readily absorbed, or at least has greater protective effect, than when supplied as an oily concentrate. Different fish liver oils vary tremendously in vitamin D content; oils from different species of tuna contain on the average from 38,000 to 45,000 IU per gram, halibut 1200, cod 100, dog fish 3, sturgeon 0. In any one species, there is considerable seasonal variation in the liver oils. Fish liver oils (especially cod, halibut, tunny), while not natural articles of diet, are important commercial sources of natural vitamin D, i.e., $D_3$. Because of the relative stability of vitamin D, losses during preparation and storage of foods are usually small.

It is an unfortunate fact that most natural foods are low in vitamin D content. Man should, therefore, endeavor to obtain as much sunlight as possible, so that by the natural irradiation of the sterols in or on the skin an adequate supply of vitamin D may be maintained. In northern regions the short days and low angle of the sun during winter months may not provide enough ultraviolet light to form adequate vitamin D for a rapidly growing child (fig. 53.6). If sunlight is filtered through smoke and dust, its effectiveness is reduced still further, and in industrial areas the antirachitic effect may be almost obliterated. This explains the former high incidence of rickets in large cities where industry was concentrated. Cod or other fish liver oils or commercial concentrates of vitamin D may be taken with ad-

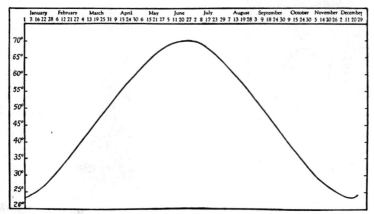

FIG. 53.6. Maximum daily altitude of the sun throughout the year at the latitude of Toronto. (From Tisdall and Brown.)

vantage especially by children during winter months.

STANDARDS AND REQUIREMENTS. The present international standard for vitamin D, adopted by the World Health Organization in 1949, is pure vitamin $D_3$. The international unit is defined as the vitamin D activity of 0.025 $\mu$g. of the standard.

The dietary requirement depends upon the amount of exposure to sunlight. Adults in a sunny climate may not need any vitamin D in their food. Pediatricians recommend that infants be started on supplementary vitamin D about 2 weeks after birth. Cod-liver oil, oleum percomorphum or vitamin D concentrates containing 400 to 500 units in a few drops are commonly used. Some workers suggest doses of 1000 to 3000 units per day to allow for defective absorption. However, the minimal toxic overdose does not appear to be far from the optimum curative dose. L. J. Harris in Great Britain gives the daily *preventive* dose as 500 to 1500 IU, the curative dose as 1000 to 3000 and the toxic overdose as anything over 10,000 IU. Where more sunshine is encountered, these values would be somewhat lower. *American and Canadian authorities suggest that children may require up to 400 IU per day.* The same intake (400 IU) is recommended during the last trimester of pregnancy and for nursing mothers during lactation.

HYPERVITAMINOSIS D (TOXICITY). Excessive intake of vitamin D in experimental animals or in man is deleterious. The first signs of toxicity are digestive disorders (vomiting and diarrhea) with

soluble substance for normal reproduction. Mattill and Conklin observed that rats reared on a diet of whole milk are usually sterile. Evans and Bishop found that addition of wheat germ, alfalfa or lettuce to a diet of casein, starch and lard (containing cod liver oil and other known vitamins) corrected its sterility-inducing effects. The active principle was referred to as the fertility vitamin or antisterility factor until Sure (1924) suggested that it be called vitamin E. Parallelism was noted between vitamin E activity and antioxidant (antirancidity) properties, suggesting a significant relationship. However, as fractionation progressed, the biological and antioxidant activities did not always have the same ratio to each other in different concentrates.

CHEMISTRY. A material possessing the characteristic biological activity was isolated in 1936 from the unsaponifiable fraction of wheat germ oil; it proved to be a mixture of three closely related compounds. A fourth member with similar characteristics was later found and recently (1955) two more have been recognized. All are viscous oils. Vitamin E activity resides to varying degrees in each of them, and all exhibit antioxidant properties, also to varying degrees, thus explaining the earlier discrepancies and confusion. The compounds are known collectively as tocopherols (from *tokos*: childbirth, *perhos*: to bear, and the chemical suffix-*ol*, signifying an alcohol). The most active of these, biologically, is $\alpha$-tocopherol, $C_{29}H_{50}O_2$ :

Vitamin E, $\alpha$-Tocopherol ($C_{29}H_{50}O_2$)

loss of appetite and considerable loss of weight. Kidney damage finally results in death. Excessive doses of vitamin D cause hypercalcemia and calcification of the joints and soft tissues, especially the kidneys, large and medium sized arteries, heart, lungs, bronchi, pancreas and parathyroid gland. What has been described as early retention of calcium followed by decalcification of the skeleton may represent a translocation of the mineral to abnormal sites.

## VITAMIN E (TOCOPHEROL)

During the early 1920's several groups of investigators became aware that rats required a fat-

The $\beta$- and $\gamma$-tocopherols ($C_{28}H_{48}O_2$) each contain one less methyl group and $\delta$-tocopherol ($C_{27}H_{46}O_2$) has still one less. These differences in methylation of the tocol nucleus affect profoundly the biological activity and other properties. The reported preponderance of the $\alpha$-form in American wheat germ oils and of the $\beta$-isomer in European wheat oils is interesting but unexplained.

RELATIVE POTENCY OF THE VITAMERS (VITAMIN ISOMERS). The physiological activity of the $\alpha$, $\beta$, $\gamma$ and $\delta$-isomers, by rat assay, varies considerably. The relative potencies have been reported to be approximately 100:40:8 (or less): 1, respectively; some workers believe the $\beta$ and $\gamma$ isomers to be

α-Tocopherol
(5, 7, 8-trimethyltocol)

β-Tocopherol
(5, 8-dimethyltocol)

γ-Tocopherol
(7, 8-dimethyltocol)

δ-Tocopherol
(8-methyltocol)

more nearly equal in biological activity. For the cure of muscular dystrophy in rabbits the potencies of natural α, β and γ-tocopherols are in the ratio of 100:30:20. The biopotency of the esters is equal to that of the free alcohols, or even slightly greater, because the esters are not auto-oxidizable.

Wheat germ oil (containing mainly α- and β-tocopherols), cottonseed oil (α- and γ-forms in about equal amounts), corn oil (largely γ-tocopherol) and soybean oil (α, γ- and δ-forms) are the main sources of the natural tocopherols. These oils contain from 0.1 to 0.3 per cent of total tocopherols. Today much of the vitamin E available commercially is not the natural d-α-tocopherol, but a synthetic dl-α-tocopheryl acetate.

By definition, synthetic α-tocopheryl acetate has been assigned a biological potency of 1000 IU per gram. Pure d-α-tocopheryl acetate has the highest potency of any vitamin E product, with 1,360 IU per gram. Other products have the following activity, d-α-tocopherol 920 IU, dl-α tocopherol 680 IU per gram.

### Effects of Deficiency

The relatively large amounts of vitamin E found stored in all tissues examined (from animals and man) suggest that it possesses an important metabolic role. However, no characteristic biochemical disturbances attributable to lack of vitamin E are known. One property of probable significance is the antioxidative effect of the tocopherols. It has been shown that the vitamin A requirement is partly dependent on the vitamin E content of the diet. The sparing effect of the natural vitamin E on vitamin A is not shared by the synthetic ester, dl-α-tocopheryl acetate, and hence it appears to be concerned with the anti-oxidant properties of the free tocopherols.

Deprivation of vitamin E in the rat leads to changes in the reproductive organs. In the female a mild deficiency may disturb the estrous cycle, a further deficiency leads to resorption of the fetuses about eight or ten days after normal conception. Prolonged deficiency in the female leads

to loss of ability to conceive. Restoration of vitamin E to the ration permits pregnancies to proceed normally once more, i.e., in females the changes are reversible. In the male rat, prolonged deficiency of vitamin E leads to atrophy of the testes and to irreversible changes in the germinal epithelium, with complete sterility.

A common finding in rats, guinea pigs and rabbits is the development of degenerative changes in the muscles, leading to actual paralysis (nutritional muscular dystrophy). Both sexes and all age groups appear equally susceptible to this effect of vitamin E deficiency.

A characteristic pigment, called *ceroid*, probably formed by autoxidation of unsaturated lipids, is often found in the muscles, sex glands and liver cells of rats fed E-deficient diets.

*Necrosis* and *fibrosis* of the *heart muscle* have also been reported in experimental animals kept for long periods on rations deficient in vitamin E. In chicks, vitamin E deficiency leads to *embryonic mortality* (due to disintegration of blood vessels), to the appearance of large patches of subcutaneous edema on the breast, abdomen, neck and legs (*exudative diathesis*), and a nutritional *encephalomalacia* characterized by motor incoordination, head retraction, stupor and death.

Experiments in rats and rabbits have shown that animals given adequate vitamin E survived hypoxia (reduced atmospheric pressure) much better than E-deficient ones. They also survived exposure to a high oxygen tension (98 per cent oxygen at 5 atmospheres pressure) much better. They way in which vitamin E protects against changes in oxygen tension is not known.

Although man apparently requires vitamin E, much less is known about the role of this vitamin in human nutrition. Beneficial results have been reported from its use in habitual abortion, muscular dystrophies, peripheral vascular disorders (indolent ulcers, early gangrene of the extremities, thrombophlebitis), heart diseases and the menopause. These claims have been denied or minimized by other clinical investigators. Many contend that it has never been established that the conditions seen in humans (superficially resembling those observed in animals) are due to lack of vitamin E. The literature is decidedly controversial. The high dosage levels of vitamin E often advocated in clinical medicine seem unreasonable. On the basis of animal studies of storage and utilization of fat-soluble vitamins, including E, the possibility seems remote that adults ever suffer from avitaminosis E. Moore (1956) has pointed out that in man the concentration, by weight, of vitamin E in the plasma normally exceeds by about thirty-fold that of vitamin A.

In early life the stores of vitamin E may be much less, but even in the case of infants some of the evidence for a beneficial therapeutic effect of vitamin E is unconvincing. There is evidence, however, that the sensitivity to hemolysis of the red cells of newborn and premature infants can be reduced by giving tocopherol.

SOURCES. Vitamins E occur so ubiquitously. being found in essentially every article of diet, that consumption of a normal mixed ration provides enough to keep the body stores well supplied. Unmilled cereals, vegetable oils and eggs are the richest sources. The average daily intake of $d$-$\alpha$-tocopherol by an adult man has been estimated to be 14 to 19 mg. Part of this is oxidized in the intestine to quinones and part is excreted in the feces. Possibly only one-third of the intake, or about 5 to 7 mg. per day, are actually absorbed. Nothing definite is known about the human requirement.

Vitamin E is stored in all tissues. Adipose tissue is the major storage site. Hypervitaminosis E has been studied in several species but no toxic effects have been observed even when massive doses have been administered over a prolonged period.

### VITAMIN K

#### (See also ch. 12)

Between 1929 and 1935 several reports appeared of a hemorrhagic condition in chickens raised on purified diets consisting of cereals plus yeast. The disease, due to defective blood clotting, was seemingly of dietary origin. In 1935 Dam proposed the name vitamin K (*Koagulation*) for the protective nutritional factor which his experiments, confirmed by Almquist and Stokstad, had shown to be present in the fat-soluble fraction of green leaves. There was no direct relationship of coagulation factor with the chlorophyll, carotene or xanthophyll content of the leaves. When the activity was shown to be in the nonsaponifiable nonsterol fraction it was obviously different from any previously known fat-soluble vitamin. In 1939, two groups

accomplished the isolation, Dam and Karrer and their colleagues from alfalfa, Doisy and his associates from both alfalfa and fishmeal. The fishmeal product proved to have 10 more carbon atoms in a longer side chain and was called vitamin $K_2$ to distinguish it from the alfalfa product, $C_{31}H_{46}O_2$, which was called $K_1$.

CHEMISTRY. A number of compounds possessing vitamin K activity are known, all being derivatives of 2-methyl-1,4-naphthoquinone, i.e., all active compounds appear to possess the general formula:

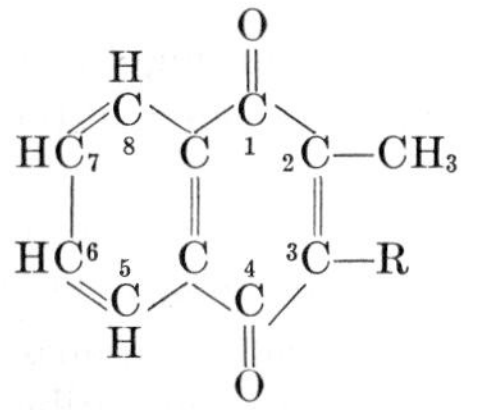

Synthetic 2-methyl-1,4-naphthoquinone, (R=H) sometimes called *menadione* and sometimes vitamin $K_3$, is readily prepared in pure, crystalline form, and apparently possesses all the physiological properties of the natural vitamin. Natural

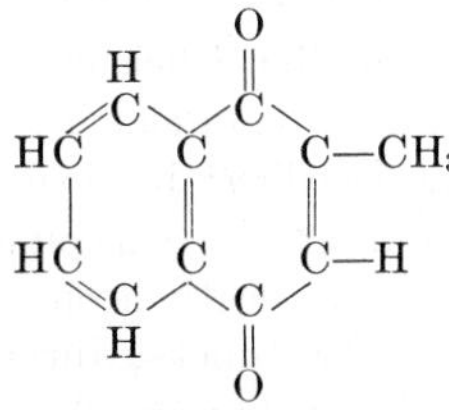

Menadione
(Vitamin $K_3$).

vitamin $K_1$ differs from menadione by having at position 3 a phytyl side chain $C_{20}$, with 1 double bond) and vitamin $K_2$ has a difarnesol substituent ($C_{30}$, with 6 double bonds).

The structure of vitamin K was elucidated fairly rapidly, after its isolation, because of similarities in chemical and physical properties to *phthiocol*. This substance had been isolated from tubercle bacilli six years earlier by Anderson and his colleagues, and its structure proven by synthesis to be 2-methyl-3-hydroxy-1,4-naphthoquinone:

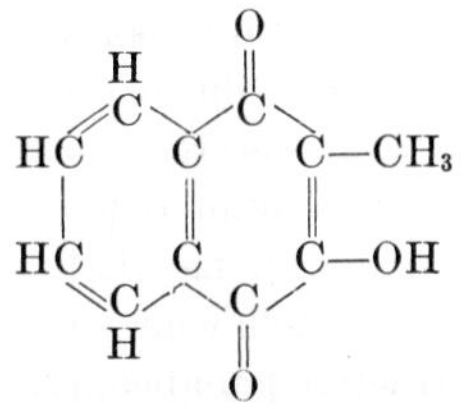

Phthiocol

When phthiocol was tested in vitamin K-deficient chicks it proved to be active and was thus the first form of vitamin K to be identified.

$$HC_7 \quad \overset{8}{C} \quad \overset{O}{\underset{1}{C}} \quad \overset{2}{C}-CH_3$$

Vitamin $K_1$ (2-methyl-3-phytyl-1, 4-naphthoquinone) $C_{31}H_{46}O_2$

It had been noted during the isolation that fishmeal improved as a source of the factor when putrefaction set in. Many bacteria, including those in the flora of the human and animal intestine, have since been shown able to synthesize vitamin $K_2$. Treatment of animals or patients with sulfonamides or certain antibiotics reduces, and may even abolish intestinal synthesis of vitamin $K_2$. Natural sources of vitamin $K_1$ include green-leaf vegetables (e.g., kale, cabbage, spinach) and tomatoes.

### Effects of Deficiency

In chicks, where the deficiency was first observed, the prolongation of clotting time may result in internal bleeding; in severely deficient birds even minor injury (such as pulling out a pin feather) may cause death from hemorrhage. Other poultry (geese, ducks, turkeys) develop the deficiency as readily as chickens, but in mammals it is much more difficult to produce. Later it appeared that this difference is due to a constant supply of vitamin $K_2$ being manufactured by bacteria in the intestine.

In vitamin K deficiency the disturbance in blood coagulation is caused by reduction of prothrombin and factor VII in the blood. Because prothrombin and factor VII are made mainly in the liver, their levels in the plasma may be dangerously low in patients with liver damage, in spite of an adequate intake of vitamin K in the diet.

Vitamin K cannot *substitute* for prothrombin; but it is necessary for the formation of prothrombin in the liver. It is also important to point out that vitamin K is of no value in other hemorrhagic conditions not due to lowered prothrombin levels (e.g., hemophilia). Vitamin K is of clinical value especially in four conditions: (1) to control bleeding that may occur following operations in patients with obstructive jaundice; (2) in the hemorrhagic diathesis of new-born infants; (3) in conditioned vitamin K deficiency due to failure of absorption from (or production in) the intestine; (4) to counteract overdosage with synthetic anti-coagulants such as Dicumarol, cyclocumarol, phenylindanedione, and accidental poisoning with Warfarin (a coumarin-type rat poison).

Vitamin K being fat-soluble, is absorbed from the gut, like other lipids and fat-soluble vitamins, only in the presence of bile salts. The water soluble analogs, however, do not require bile for their absorption.

In obstructive jaundice, bile salts being excluded from the intestine, vitamin K, either of dietary origin or produced by intestinal bacteria, is not absorbed in adequate amount. This would explain the prolonged prothrombin-time and tendency to bleeding in these patients. The bleeding sometimes seen in new-born infants may be due to failure of placental transfer of vitamin K, to inadequate intake of the vitamin by the mother, to delay in the development of the intestinal flora to make vitamin K, or to a combination of these defects.

Disturbances in blood coagulation due to lowered prothrombin (except those caused by liver disease) are promptly corrected (3 to 6 hours) orally or by injections of vitamin $K_1$ (oily emulsion) or the synthetic analogs of vitamin K. The usual therapeutic dose is 1 to 5 mg. per day. Other forms that have been used clinically include phytylmenadione oxide, menadione sodium bisulfite and Synkavite (2-methyl-1,4-naphtho-*hydroquinone* diphosphoric ester). Regardless of the route of administration a lag of several hours occurs before any change in the clotting response is perceptible.

Synthetic phytylmenadione, i.e., vitamin $K_1$, is commercially available but expensive. The weight of evidence is that the natural vitamin or synthetic $K_1$ is more effective than menadione in correcting the effects of overdosage with anticoagulant dicoumarins. It has been suggested that the effect of dicoumarol is an example of reversible inhibition by an antimetabolite. Woolley doubts that it acts this way since the dicoumarol-vitamin

K antagonism differs in several ways from the characteristic competition between analogs. Whatever the process by which it acts, dicoumarol(3,3'-methylene-bis-(4-hydroxycoumarin)), when administered by mouth to man or animals causes a marked lowering of the plasma prothrombin level with consequent lengthening of the clotting time. It is used clinically to control thrombus formation (see ch. 12).

TOXICITY OF VITAMIN K. Before dicoumarol came into clinical use, vitamin K and its analogues were given in small doses of a few milligrams per day. Larger doses, of several hundred milligrams per day, are now given to counteract overdosage with synthetic dicoumarins used as anticoagulants. Patients given 150 to 600 mg. daily of water-soluble synthetic vitamin K analogues intravenously have complained of nausea and of more severe reactions. Some deaths of infants have been attributed to overdosage with a water-soluble analogue. The naturally occurring phytyl compound is not toxic when fed or injected in relatively massive amounts.

Sublethal doses of menadione derivatives (but not of phytyl-menadione) have induced anemia in rats, rabbits and dogs. Occasionally polycythemia has been observed in the same animals. In the mouse, the LD$_{50}$ of menadione (orally) has been reported as 500, 620, 800 and 840 mg. per kg., by different workers; in rabbits it is 250 mg. per kg.

LIPOIC ACID. Lipoic acid, formerly known as protogen and as pyruvate oxidation factor, is a fat-soluble material which is an essential growth factor for certain bacteria and protozoa. It was isolated in 1951 from yeast and liver. Five different forms, with differing activities, have been described: a bound form, a water-soluble complex, and three fat-soluble varieties. All are derivatives of an acid containing eight carbon atoms and two sulfur atoms. Because of this it is also known as thioctic acid:

$$HOOC \cdot CH_2 \cdot CH_2 \cdot CH_2 \cdot CH_2 \cdot CH \cdot CH_2 \cdot CH_2$$
$$\underset{S \text{———} S}{\big| \qquad\qquad \big|}$$

Lipoic acid or its amide appears to function as a further cofactor sometimes necessary, along with thiamine pyrophosphoric ester (TPP), in the decarboxylation reactions (involving pyruvic and ketoglutaric acids) discussed briefly under *thiamine* and more fully under *carbohydrate metabolism*. The active agent, lipothiamide pyrophosphoric ester, is referred to briefly as LTPP.

# 54

# THE VITAMINS (*Continued*)

## Water-Soluble Vitamins

### VITAMIN B COMPLEX

Lack of vitamin B leads to loss of appetite with consequent loss of weight (fig. 54.1). Early fractionation studies of "growth factors" in aqueous extracts of yeast, liver and other animal and plant tissues revealed that an antineuritic substance (vitamin $B_1$ = aneurin = thiamine) could be separated from a pellagra-preventing (P-P) factor. Later, other growth factors were found in various fractions. Different names were applied in different laboratories so that a study of the literature of several decades ago may prove baffling to modern readers. Twelve substances are grouped together because of their close association in tissues and because for a long time their separation proved most difficult: *thiamine, riboflavin, nicotinic acid, pyridoxine, pantothenic acid, biotin, para-aminobenzoic acid, folic acid, folinic acid, cyanocobalamin, choline,* and *inositol.* All have been isolated in pure form, and most of them have been synthesized in the laboratory.

### THIAMINE

ISOLATION, IDENTIFICATION AND SYNTHESIS. The contributions of Takaki, Eijkman, Grijns, Hopkins and Funk have already been mentioned. McCollum and Davis (1915) had found that young rats grew poorly on a purified diet containing dextrin as the carbohydrate, but that growth improved when lactose was used. The growth-stim-

_____

[1] Growth promotion was less, due to loss of Funk's factor, but the factor remaining, designated $B_2$, (now known as riboflavin) stimulated growth considerably.

[2] Papers of fundamental importance appeared from other laboratories within a few days of each other, as has frequently happened with studies of other vitamins. Assignment of priority is difficult. Todd and Bergel in England, Windaus in Germany, and Makino and Imai in Japan made important contributions. Andersag and Westphal of the I.G. Farbenindustrie may have been the first to accomplish the synthesis but the company policy with respect to patent protection delayed publication of their work until 1937.

ulating principle was destroyed by heating the lactose, and it could be leached away from the milk-sugar with alcohol. The substance responsible for growth-stimulation was called "water-soluble B" by McCollum. Yeast was soon found to be an excellent source of this factor. In 1920 Emmett and Luros provided evidence for the dual nature of water-soluble B when they found that autoclaved yeast no longer contained Funk's antiberiberi substance but that it still promoted the growth of rats fed certain purified diets.[1] In 1926 the heat-sensitive antiberiberi-substance, vitamin $B_1$ (in those days often called the antineuritic factor) was isolated in Holland by Jansen and Donath. They proposed the name *aneurin.* The synthesis was accomplished in 1936 by R. R. Williams and his colleagues in the United States.[2] The presence of a sulfur atom and primary amino group led Williams to propose the name *thiamine,* which is now the term in general use.

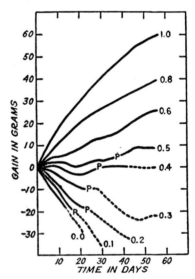

FIG. 54.1. Average weight gain curves of rats on vitamin B-free diet plus daily supplement of ground whole wheat of 0.1, 0.2, 0.3, 0.4, 0.5, 0.6, 0.8 and 1.0 grams. Negative controls (marked 0.0) received basal diet only. P, point where, on the average, chronic symptoms of polyneuritis appeared. Lines broken from the points at which some individuals died. (After Chase, from Sherman and Smith, *The Vitamins.*)

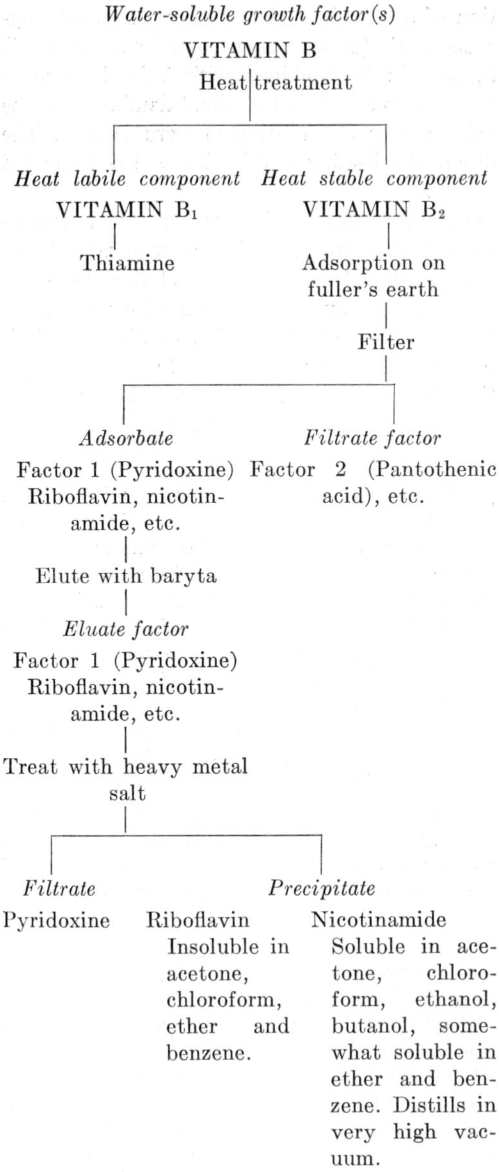

*Water-soluble growth factor(s)*

**VITAMIN B**

Heat treatment

*Heat labile component*     *Heat stable component*
**VITAMIN B₁**           **VITAMIN B₂**

Thiamine            Adsorption on
fuller's earth

Filter

*Adsorbate*         *Filtrate factor*
Factor 1 (Pyridoxine)   Factor 2 (Pantothenic
Riboflavin, nicotin-       acid), etc.
amide, etc.

Elute with baryta

*Eluate factor*
Factor 1 (Pyridoxine)
Riboflavin, nicotin-
amide, etc.

Treat with heavy metal
salt

*Filtrate*           *Precipitate*
Pyridoxine    Riboflavin     Nicotinamide
            Insoluble in    Soluble in ace-
            acetone,      tone, chloro-
            chloroform,    form, ethanol,
            ether and     butanol, some-
            benzene.      what soluble in
                         ether and ben-
                         zene. Distills in
                         very high vac-
                         uum.

CHEMISTRY OF THIAMINE (VITAMIN B₁). Thiamine contains two ring systems, the pyrimidine and thiazole, joined by a methylene bridge. It possesses a strongly basic quaternary nitrogen

atom and hence forms chlorides and other salts that dissolve in water and ionize freely; it also possesses a primary amino nitrogen which can form salts such as the hydrochloride. Sulphates, nitrates, picrates and other salts have been prepared. The naturally occurring vitamin is thiamine chloride hydrochloride although it is commonly referred to merely as thiamine. Today it is produced synthetically on a large scale and is available commercially at surprisingly low cost.

Thiamine is readily soluble in water and rather insoluble in most organic solvents. Its aqueous solution is strongly acid, due to the hydrochloric acid dissociated from the amino group. In acid solution (including acid foods) thiamine is reasonably stable even when heated, but is unstable on the alkaline side. At pH 3.5 boiling causes little destruction. At higher temperatures (autoclaving at 120°, for example) thiamine (in yeast) is stable for short periods, but after 2 to 3 hours most of it is destroyed. Riboflavin (vitamin B₂) is much more stable under these conditions. Near neutrality (pH 5 to 7) thiamine is much less stable to heat, and in alkaline foods it is rapidly destroyed by heating. Farrer measured the percentage loss on boiling thiamine at 100° for 1 hour in solutions of pH 3, 4, 5, 6, 7, 8 and 9 as 16, 20, 40, 53, 68, 100 and 100, respectively. Later he found that the buffer used was important: phosphate confers considerable protection and pyrophosphate even more. Storage on the alkaline side even at room temperature should be avoided. Thiamine is readily destroyed by an enzyme found in certain foods as well as by atmospheric oxygen. *Thiaminase* has been found in some raw fish (herring, carp), raw clams, shrimps and mussels and in certain plants (bracken ferns). Its occurrence was discovered following a study of the paralyses and convulsions seen in foxes and in cats fed rations containing large amounts of raw fish.

Thiamine is believed to act in the metabolic systems of the body as the ester, thiamine pyrophosphate (TPP). This molecule, known as *cocarboxylase*, is the coenzyme or prosthetic group of the enzyme decarboxylase which decarboxylates α-keto acids, especially pyruvic, in the body. Subsequent studies have shown that

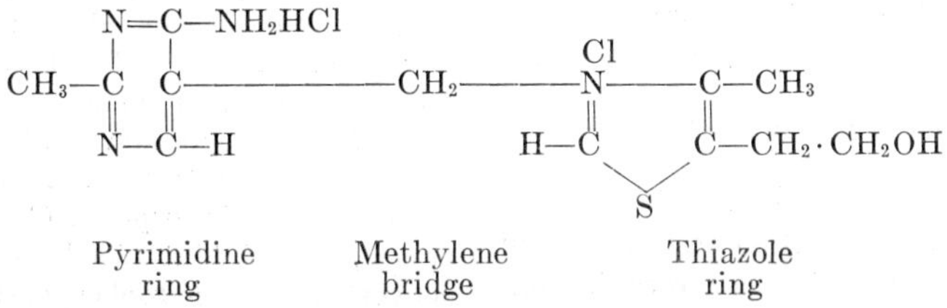

$$
\begin{array}{ccc}
\text{N=C—NH}_2\text{HCl} & & \text{Cl} \\
\text{CH}_3\text{—C} \quad \text{C————CH}_2\text{———N———C—CH}_3 & & \\
\text{N—C—H} & & \text{H—C} \quad \text{C—CH}_2\cdot\text{CH}_2\text{OH} \\
& & \text{S}
\end{array}
$$

Pyrimidine      Methylene      Thiazole
ring            bridge          ring

Thiamine (Vitamin B₁)
$(C_{12}H_{18}N_4OSCl_2)$

most, if not all, vitamins act as coenzymes to facilitate some essential step in intermediate metabolism.

## Thiamine Deficiency

The effects of thiamine deficiency have already been mentioned–beriberi in humans, and polyneuritis in chickens, pigeons, rats, mice, dogs and other species. Two types of beriberi are seen in Japan, Southern China, India, the Philippine islands, Dutch East Indies and other places where the staple is polished rice: (1) the wet type, with edema, (2) the dry type, without edema. Multiple peripheral neuritis and muscular atrophy are characteristic in both. Weakening of the muscles accounts for the cardiovascular and gastrointestinal defects (enlarged right heart, peripheral vasodilatation, indigestion, gastric atony, severe constipation). Anorexia (loss of appetite) leads to loss of weight and general debility; tenderness of the feet and legs, lameness, ataxia, paralysis, inflammation of the ocular nerve and heart failure are usual sequelae.

In experimental animals the first signs of thiamine deficiency are loss of appetite, arrested growth, reduced motility of the gastrointestinal tract, and marked slowing of the heart. An extreme degree of bradycardia is seen in rats fed rations deficient in vitamin $B_1$. In man the opposite effect is produced, i.e., tachycardia.

Thiamine is necessary for the utilization of pyruvic acid, i.e., for the final stages of carbohydrate metabolism. The debility and tissue degeneration in thiamine deficiency are probably due to decreased ability to use carbohydrate. The central nervous system derives its energy mainly from carbohydrate, and this doubtless explains the lesions in the central and peripheral nerves.

## Function of Thiamine

R. A. Peters at Oxford noted that lactic and pyruvic acids accumulated in the brains of thiamine-deficient pigeons and described the principal effect of vitamin $B_1$ deficiency as a "biochemical lesion" in which carbohydrate metabolism is impaired by the failure to convert

$$CH_3CO \cdot COOH + \tfrac{1}{2}O_2 \rightarrow CH_3 \cdot COOH + CO_2 \quad (1)$$

pyruvate to acetate. The original view that a simple oxidative decarboxylation occurs has had to be modified. A series of decarboxylating enzymes, all with thiamine pyrophosphate (TPP) as coenzyme, are concerned with the decarboxyla-

tion of $\alpha$-ketonic acids. More recent work suggests that (under some conditions, at least) lipoic acid is combined with TPP to form a more complex cofactor (lipothiamide) for the oxidation or dismutation of pyruvic acid. The discoveries leading to this view will be indicated briefly.

In 1929 Evans and Lepkovsky had demonstrated that the vitamin $B_1$ requirement decreases when the fat content of the diet is increased. Although this effect has been described as a thiamine-sparing action of dietary fat, it now appears more accurate to say that the thiamine requirement increases as the proportion of dietary carbohydrate increases.

In 1936 Platt and Lu showed that the blood of patients with beriberi contained pyruvic acid and other ketone bodies and that these increased on exertion. Seven years earlier Kinnersley and Peters had found more lactic acid in the brains of pigeons lacking vitamin $B_1$ than in normal brains, and in 1934 Westenbrink had claimed that either lactic acid or pyruvic acid was the toxic metabolite responsible for at least some of the conditions seen in vitamin $B_1$ deficiency.

In a paper of fundamental significance Peters (1936) reported that the brains of pigeons deficient in vitamin $B_1$ had a much lower oxygen uptake (measured on slices in Ringer phosphate solution) than did normal brains, when glucose was supplied as energy source. The same result was obtained when sodium pyruvate or lactate was provided as substrate. Addition of vitamin $B_1$ raised the oxygen uptake to normal in all three cases. The reaction proved to be not only highly specific for vitamin $B_1$ but extremely sensitive. Peters described it as the *catatorulin effect* and used it as the basis of a method for determining thiamine. The simultaneous accumulation of lactic acid was puzzling until Sherman and Elvehjem showed that the accumulating pyruvic acid inhibits the enzyme lactic dehydrogenase. Thiamine facilitates removal of pyruvate and permits the normal metabolism of lactic acid.

Actually, as was suggested earlier, thiamine itself is not the catalyst. Westenbrink and Pollak observed a ten-minute delay, after adding thiamine to a polyneuritic brain preparation, before oxygen uptake began. About the same time Lohmann and Schuster isolated from yeast the pyrophosphoric ester of thiamine, and Weil-Malherbe showed that the vitamin could be transformed into this ester (i.e., into cocarboxylase) by the action of adenosine triphosphate (ATP). Lipmann suggested, in 1937, that added thiamine must first be converted to the pyrophosphoric ester which then acts as the coenzyme (cocarboxylase) of a system catalyzing the liberation of $CO_2$ from pyruvic acid. Neither thiamine nor its monophosphoric ester has any coenzyme activity.

UNITS AND REQUIREMENTS. The International Unit of vitamin B₁ adopted by the Health Organization of the League of Nations was 3 μg., i.e., 3 one-millionths of a gram, of thiamine chloride hydrochloride. Today values are almost invariably given in μg. or mg.

Estimates of human requirements for thiamine are usually expressed in relation to the total daily calorie intake, values ranging from 0.17 to 1.0 mg. per 1000 Cal. having been advocated. In 1953, after consideration of the available data the United States Food and Nutrition Board recommended that the minimum requirement for adults be 0.23 mg. for each 1000 Cal. This value may be compared with those found in a dietary survey by E. G. Young among Canadian families on rather low incomes: 0.20 mg. for men, 0.19 mg. for women and 0.22 mg. per 1000 Calories for children. No evidence of thiamine deficiency could be detected clinically in this group. It is interesting to recall that many years ago Williams and Spies (1938) had suggested a thiamine intake of 0.18 mg. per 1000 Cal. when fat provided 40 per cent of the total calorie intake, and an increase to 0.3 mg. per 1000 Cal. when the diet was essentially free from fat. The Canadian Council on Nutrition, with this effect of fat in mind, recommends 0.3 mg. per 1000 Cal. since fats are costly items in the diet, and persons on low incomes will not consume as much fat as their more affluent countrymen.

Some workers in England, the United States and elsewhere are not satisfied that this dosage (0.75 mg. per 2500 Cal.) is adequate. The latest recommendation of the United States Food and Nutrition Board is 0.5 mg. per 1000 Cal. (up to 3000 Cal.) and 0.2 mg. for each 1000 Cal. above 3000. They recommend that the *total per day should not fall below 1 mg.* regardless of the calorie intake. No single figure can ever be given as the ideal value because the requirement varies with the composition of the diet as well as with the individual. A constant supply is necessary because the body is unable to store thiamine to any great extent.

These recommendations are generous and are possibly somewhat above the average requirement. They are easily met by the thiamine content of the foodstuffs commonly used in Canada and the United States, and a slight excess can do no harm. On the other hand, there is no evidence that an intake of thiamine in excess of the requirement affords any extra benefits.

TOXICITY. Tremendous doses of thiamine can be lethal. The acute fatal doses (mg. per kg.) by the *intravenous* route for mouse, rat, rabbit and dog were found to be 125, 250, 300 and 350 mg., respectively. The lethal dose by *subcutaneous* injection was about six times as great and *orally* about *forty* times these values. The toxic signs

observed in dogs were: marked but transitory vasodilation with consequent fall in blood pressure, bradycardia and death (due to respiratory arrest). In man, sensitivity to excessive dosage with thiamine (especially when injected) has been observed: nervousness, tremors, tachycardia, sweating, herpes zoster and even anaphylactic shock.

Mills has suggested (1941) that because parenteral injection of even moderate doses of thiamine may sometimes lead to anaphylactic reactions this route should never be used. Untoward reactions to oral administration of reasonable doses are virtually unknown.

SOURCES. Thiamine is widely distributed in natural foods of both plant and animal origin. Until man attempted to improve upon nature by refining his food, beriberi was apparently unknown. Plants synthesize thiamine which is found in roots, stems, leaves, flowers, fruits and seeds, e.g., average values (μg. per 100 gram edible portion) in beets 200, carrots 180, turnips 65, onions 120, asparagus 160, watercress 180, lettuce 270 and cauliflower 120 to 330. Peas and beans are rich sources, as are whole cereal grains. Nuts are also good sources of thiamine.

There tends to be more thiamine in the mature dry seed than in other parts of the plant. *Unmilled* cereal grains are richer in thiamine than the highest recommended dietary allowance (i.e., 0.5 mg. per 1000 Cal.) since whole wheat averages better than 1.0 mg. per 1000 Cal. Whole rice and rye may average somewhat lower than this but whole oats may sometimes contain more thiamine per 1000 Cal. than does wheat. The bulk of the thiamine in cereal grains resides in the germ which is removed in conventional milling processes. The refined white wheat flour, polished rice or corn meal (hominy) will keep much better in storage than the unmilled grains, but the unfortunate penalty paid for this "improvement" is that the bulk of the thiamine has been eliminated. In some regions, thiamine (synthetic) is now added to the milled products, with or without other nutrients. Such fortification of white flour and polished rice is technically and legally referred to as *enrichment*.

Dried yeast is the richest of all known sources, containing from 1800 to 36,000 μg. (usually about 10,000 μg.) per 100 grams. Among foods of animal origin lean pork is the richest source of thiamine (500 to 1500 μg. per 100 grams); other meats contain much less (e.g., beef 80 to 300 μg.). Ox liver contains 350 to 450 μg. per 100 grams. Milk contains relatively little thiamine, eggs somewhat more. Oatmeal is a good and cheap source, one serving supplying more thiamine than 2 cups of milk or 5 average boiled eggs. To illustrate that it is relatively easy for Americans and Canadians to obtain a liberal supply of thiamine the following tabulation (after McHenry) shows the thiamine contribution made by average servings of a few foods commonly used in North America:

| | |
|---|---|
| 1 orange | 0.12 mg. |
| 1 serving oatmeal | 0.22 mg. |
| 3 cups milk | 0.27 mg. |
| 4 slices enriched bread | 0.24 mg. |
| 1 serving roast beef | 0.05 mg. |
| 1 boiled potato | 0.14 mg. |
| 1 serving carrots | 0.04 mg. |
| 1 serving cabbage | 0.06 mg. |
| Total | 1.14 mg. |

## RIBOFLAVIN

As early as 1917 Emmett and McKim noted that two growth factors exist in the water-soluble extract of rice polishings, one (later called vitamin $B_1$) that cures rat polyneuritis and another, more heat stable, that produces weight gains under specific dietary conditions (see Fractionation scheme on p. 917). Emmett and Luros (1920) found the same two factors in yeast. The dual nature of water-soluble B was also shown by Smith and Hendrick (1926).

Goldberger and Lillie (1926), in the course of their study of pellagra, produced a deficiency disease in rats characterized by ocular changes (conjunctivitis, corneal vascularization and eventually corneal opacity), and bilaterally symmetrical loss of hair. The factor that prevented these lesions was heat stable and was called the "P-P" (pellagra preventive) factor by Goldberger although his admirers called it vitamin G and in Britain it was called vitamin $B_2$. Meanwhile, other workers, using different dietary conditions were reporting different lesions (including a dermatitis, so-called "rat pellagra") cured by a heat stable factor. Finally it became clear that several different factors, all more stable to heat than vitamin $B_1$, were involved. The discovery that canine black-tongue could be induced by diets similar to those producing rat pellagra seemed an indication of progress, but in due course, it appeared that neither lesion was caused by lack of vitamin $B_2$. Birch, György and Harris (1935) differentiated the anti-black-tongue and P-P factor from vitamin $B_2$ (riboflavin) and the dermatitis factor (vitamin $B_6$). In 1936 Dann reported that riboflavin did not cure human pellagra, and in 1937 Sebrell and his colleagues confirmed that it did not cure canine black-tongue. It was thus obvious by 1937, that vitamin $B_2$ (riboflavin) had no direct connection with pellagra although its absence from the ration may complicate the pellagrous condition. Thus the term vitamin $B_2$, *initially intended to designate the factor that cures pellagra*, came in the end to be applied to riboflavin, the rat growth factor that is responsible also for preventing characteristic ocular lesions.

CHEMISTRY. Elucidation of the chemical nature of vitamin $B_2$ was rather rapid because at the time (1925–1933) a number of workers were studying fluorescent pigments isolated from sources as varied as egg yolk, dandelion flowers, grass, milk, liver, kidney, muscle and retinae. Names indicating the source were applied (*ovoflavin* to the substance from eggs, *verdoflavin* from grass, *lactoflavin* from milk, etc.), but subsequently many of these substances proved to be identical. Kuhn, György and Wagner-Jauregg (1933) isolated from egg white an orange-yellow compound with an intense yellowish-green fluorescence which, at doses of 100 $\mu$g. per day, stimulated the growth of rats on a purified diet. A similar growth-promoting fluorescent substance was isolated from whey (Booher, 1933). Kuhn suggested that these pigments might be related to the "yellow enzyme" isolated from yeast by Warburg and Christian in the preceding year. This yellow respiratory ferment was separated by Theorell (1934, 1935) into a protein fraction and a small molecule (the pigment, flavin), neither of which alone possessed enzymic activity. The identity of this flavin with the yellow pigments from various sources was soon shown and its structure was established by synthesis (accomplished almost simultaneously by two groups in 1935—Kuhn and his colleagues at Heidelberg and Karrer and co-workers in Switzerland). When the yellow compound, $C_{17}H_{20}N_4O_6$, was shown to contain the pentose sugar, ribose, attached to a dimethyl derivative of isoalloxazine, the name *riboflavin* was suggested.

Riboflavin ($C_{12}H_{20}N_4O_6$)

Riboflavin crystallizes from dilute acetic acid, alcohol or pyridine in fine orange-yellow needles. It is only slightly soluble in water (about 12 mg. per 100 ml. at 25°) and is insoluble in ether, chloroform and benzene. Compounds such as urea, propylene glycol and sodium desoxycholate increase the solubility of riboflavin in water. It is relatively stable under ordinary cooking conditions but it is less stable to bright sunlight than many other vitamins.

The enzymes containing riboflavin are called flavoproteins. These enzymes accept hydrogen atoms from specific substrates, thus oxidizing them; the hydrogen is then passed on to other molecules. Alternate reduction and oxidation of the enzyme accomplishes oxidation of one and then reduction of a different component of the metabolic cycle.

The first of these prosthetic groups to be identified was the "riboflavin mononucleotide" of Warburg and Christian's "yellow enzyme" (which Theorell had split by dialysis into the protein carrier (apoenzyme) and the yellow coenzyme). The nature of the latter was established by Kuhn and Rudy (1936) as riboflavin-5'-phosphoric acid. It is the coenzyme for three different systems: Warburg's yellow enzyme, for *cytochrome c reductase* and for L-amino acid oxidase. A second active form of riboflavin (coenzyme) is riboflavin adenine dinucleotide, in which a complex of adenine-ribose-phosphoric acid is attached to the riboflavin phosphate to give a large complex molecule with a central pyrophosphate linkage. This compound acts as coenzyme for many systems, including xanthine oxidase, fumaric hydrogenase, the Schardinger enzyme aldehyde oxidase, glycine oxidase, D-amino acid oxidase, diaphorase, histaminase and other diamino-oxidases, etc.

### Riboflavin Deficiency

The role of riboflavin in human nutrition is still somewhat controversial. As in animal studies, the lesions affect the eyes and skin. In rats, failure of growth is followed by dermatitis, loss of hair, cataract, some nerve degeneration and reproductive defects (cessation of estrous cycles, atrophy of testes). The early studies in man were complicated by the presence (unsuspected, of course) of other dietary deficiencies. One of the earliest reports of artificial riboflavin deficiency in man (Sebrell and Butler, 1938) revealed (1) fissures developing in the lips and at the corners of the mouth (cheilosis), (2) a sore tongue (inflamed and smooth) simulating the glossitis of pernicious anemia, (3) a seborrheic dermatitis affecting especially the face (ears, nose, forehead). (4) Sydenstricker has described a vascularization of the cornea due to lack of riboflavin (fig. 54.2). The cornea does not normally contain blood vessels, but when the diet lacks sufficient riboflavin for prolonged periods, capillary loops extend into the cornea, the eye becomes itchy, light sensitive (photophobia), vision is poor in dim light, and in time the corneal vascularization may lead to severe interstitial keratitis. These

observations have been confirmed in a number of clinical centers and in several species of animals. Other workers have failed to induce corneal vascularization in subjects kept for some months on a diet very low in riboflavin. Several factors (some not yet understood) may be concerned. Corneal changes of this nature, when present, are not specific signs of riboflavin deficiency. Some patients with such lesions have responded to supplements of riboflavin; many have not. Whereas the cheilosis and glossitis often respond to riboflavin alone, sometimes nicotinic acid and other members of the vitamin B complex are required to effect improvement.

The absence of more profound and specific effects of riboflavin deficiency in man is curious because riboflavin is in the prosthetic group of so many enzyme systems catalyzing important transformations.

RIBOFLAVIN REQUIREMENT. There is no International Unit for riboflavin. The quantities of this (and of most other vitamins available in crystalline form) are now stated on a weight basis.

The riboflavin requirement of man, like that of most of the vitamins, is not known, although there is general agreement that the minimal intake for maintenance of health lies between 0.5 and 3 mg. per day. A common method of expression is to relate it to the energy intake. This is done because riboflavin is concerned in the oxidative processes going on in practically all cells and its loss and replacement quota might reasonably be expected to be proportional to the energy production. Several lengthy clinical studies indicate that about 0.3 mg. per 1000 Cal. of food are adequate. The Canadian Council

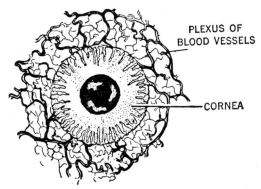

FIG. 54.2. Showing engorgement of the limbic plexus and vascularization of the cornea in riboflavin deficiency. Note the loops of vessels of the limbic plexus penetrating more than half way to the pupil. White areas are corneal opacities.

on Nutrition (1950) recommend 0.5 mg. riboflavin per 1000 Cal. For an average man consuming food to give 3000 Cal. per day this would be 1.5 mg. riboflavin.

The United States Food and Nutrition Board (1953) decided that the riboflavin requirement is *not* related to energy intake or muscular activity. They recommend that the riboflavin allowance be calculated in terms of the recommended protein intake, (although the evidence relating riboflavin need to protein metabolism is sketchy). They recommend 0.025 mg. of riboflavin for each gram of protein eaten; thus an average adult man getting 65 grams of protein per day would need 1.6 mg. per day, essentially the same value as recommended by the Canadian Council.

SOURCES OF RIBOFLAVIN. All cells seem to require riboflavin. It is one of the most widely distributed vitamins. The richest known edible sources are some highly pigmented crustaceans (dorsal muscles of some crabs contain from 2.4 to above 20 mg. per 100 grams). Other good sources are liver (0.1 to 4.4 mg. per 100 grams), kidney, heart, muscle (meat, fish, fowl), egg white, milk and growing leafy vegetables.

Cow's milk usually contains between 0.1 and 0.15 mg. per 100 ml. and pasteurization (143 to 145° for 30 minutes) has a negligible effect. Irradiation of milk to increase its content of vitamin D does not reduce the riboflavin content but prolonged exposure to sunlight does. Milk is the chief source of dietary riboflavin (3 cups per day provide about 1.2 mg.). Cheese, eggs, meats and vegetables in the diet usually fail to satisfy the riboflavin requirement: unless some milk is consumed a deficiency may occur.

Riboflavin can now be produced more cheaply by fermentation than by chemical synthesis. Exceptional yields are obtained from the molds *Eremothecium ashbyii* or *Asbya gossypii*, in submerged culture with continuous aeration and agitation; yields up to 600 mg. per liter in 4 days have been reported from commercial producers.

TOXICITY. The low solubility in water may be responsible for the low toxicity of riboflavin. Oral doses of 2 grams per kg. to dogs and 10 grams per kilo to rats produced no signs of toxicity. Mice given 5000 times the therapeutic dose, intraperitoneally, suffered no ill effects. In rats the $LD_{50}$[3] for riboflavin (intraperitoneally) is 560 mg. per kg. Death occurred in 2 to 5 days due to kidney concretions; cytological changes

[3] This means 50 per cent of the lethal dose (LD).

were also noted in the pituitary, adrenals, pancreas and heart.

## NICOTINAMIDE AND NICOTINIC ACID (P-P FACTOR)

Nicotinic acid and its amide have similar physiological activities, but it is in the form of nicotinamide that the vitamin is found in its natural, active combinations. Both compounds prevent pellagra. Nicotinamide functions as an essential unit of several different coenzymes that act as prosthetic groups for a variety of enzymes. Coenzyme I (also known as cozymase, codehydrogenase, and diphosphopyridine nucleotide, DPN) contains, besides nicotinamide, one molecule of adenine, two molecules of ribose and two molecules of phosphoric acid. Coenzyme II, previously known as the coferment of Warburg's yellow enzyme is a triphosphoric ester, the third phosphate group being attached to carbon atom 2 of the ribose joined to adenine; it is now more commonly referred to as triphosphopyridine nucleotide or TPN.

CHEMISTRY AND FUNCTION OF NICOTINAMIDE. Nicotinic acid was first obtained by Huber in 1867, by the oxidation of the alkaloid nicotine. Its presence in biological material was first shown almost simultaneously by Suzuki and associates (1912) who obtained it from rice bran during attempts to isolate the antiberiberi substance and by Funk (1911, 1913) who identified it as a component of his "vitamin" fraction from yeast. Both observed its inability to cure beriberi and set it aside as of no interest. Neither suspected that they had in hand the cure for another equally devastating deficiency disease but that 25 years would elapse before this was realized. In 1926 Vickery again isolated it from yeast and commented that "it has so far not been found in any other materials than rice polishings and yeast." Its nutritional importance remained unknown.

Nicotinic acid, $C_6H_5O_2N$, is a white crystalline substance that is only moderately soluble in water (about 1 per cent) but which is readily soluble upon the addition of alkali or acid, due to salt formation with the carboxyl group or

Nicotinic acid
(Niacin)
Pyridine-3-carboxylic acid

Nicotinic acid amide
(Nicotinic amide, nicotinamide, niacinamide).

basic nitrogen atom, respectively. The amide is more soluble in water. It is stable to heat in neutral solution but is converted to nicotinic acid by acid or alkali.

In the United States nicotinic acid is known as *niacin*. This name was coined to make the distinction between the vitamin and the alkaloid (nicotine) clear to the public lest they get the mistaken idea that "enriched" foods are being poisoned by the addition of the tobacco alkaloid. The terms niacin and niacinamide are official in the United States. In the present discussion the universally accepted names will be used.

Nicotinic acid, its ethyl ester, nicotinic acid *N*-methyl amide, β-picoline and several related compounds display vitamin activity, presumably being readily converted to nicotinamide in the animal body.

In 1934 Warburg and Christian found nicotinamide in coenzyme II, which they showed accomplishes hydrogen transport in cells, and a year later von Euler and his colleagues found it in coenzyme I, which is necessary for the fermentation of carbohydrate. Thus by an unusual inversion of the ordinary sequence of events in the vitamin field, the biological significance of nicotinamide was understood before its specific nutritional importance was realized. It was not until 1937 that Smith and others demonstrated its therapeutic value in pellagra.

The prosthetic groups containing nicotinamide (coenzyme I or DPN and coenzyme II or TPN) are unique in that they appear to be loosely bound to the protein part of the enzyme system, i.e., they are mobile coenzymes. About 40 reactions are known to be catalyzed by either one or both of these coenzymes. For example, DPN is specific for 3-phosphoglyceraldehyde dehydrogenase, TPN is specific for isocitric dehydrogenase, yet either can function with glutamic dehydrogenase. DPN occurs in all animal and plant cells in which carbohydrates are metabolized. It effects the conversion of glucose to gluconic acid, of α-glycerophosphoric acid into phosphoglyceric acid, and of ethanol into acetaldehyde. It also effects the dismutation of aldehyde into alcohol and acid, of β-hydroxybutyric acid into acetoacetic, of lactic acid into pyruvic acid and of malic into oxaloacetic acid. The list of reactions catalyzed by DPN in the presence of specific apoenzymes, i.e., different protein carriers, could be greatly extended. A different list, with some common items, could be made for metabolic reactions catalyzed by TPN.

## Nicotinamide Deficiency

Deficiency of nicotinamide in man leads to serious consequences. Lack of it has led to the most serious of the deficiency diseases encoun-

tered in North America—*pellagra*. Between 1907 and 1937 the disease was endemic in the southern United States. The name is of Italian origin (*pelle agra* means rough skin). The disease is known to have occurred in Spain before it was first described by an Italian physician in 1771. In the past century pellagra was endemic in parts of Egypt, Rumania and France. The skin, especially the areas exposed to sunlight (face, neck, hands, sometimes the feet) becomes bronzed, resembling sunburn, and later thickened. The tongue is swollen, glossy and "beefy." The disease follows a terrible and inevitable course from mild psychic disturbances through dementia to death.

That pellagra is undoubtedly of dietary origin was made clear by Goldberger and his associates in 1915. The consumption of maize was recognized to be a prominent feature, but some workers suspected the presence of a toxic principle or bacterium in the corn. In view of the relationship between dietary tryptophan and nicotinic acid, established in the early 1950's, it is interesting to recall that Goldberger suspected that an *amino acid deficiency* as well as a vitamin deficiency was involved in the etiology of pellagra.

Liver and a commercial extract of liver proved to be strongly curative and fractionation studies were initiated in a number of laboratories. The use of experimental animals in the search for the curative agent for pellagra led to bewildering and often contradictory results that were difficult to interpret. As mentioned earlier, canine black-tongue is readily produced when young dogs are maintained on the Goldberger diet; a dermatitis produced in rats by a similar maize diet was called "rat pellagra" and later a dermatitis of dietary origin in chickens was called "chick pellagra." In the end it turned out that the work with rats and chicks was irrelevant to the disease in man. The lesions in both species were cured by extracts of autoclaved yeast and of liver that cured black-tongue in dogs and pellagra in man, but the appellation "pellagra" was unfortunate and unwarranted in both cases. In 1934 György showed that these dermal lesions of rats are prevented by vitamin B$_6$ (pyridoxine), and five years later Jukes showed that the chick lesions are cured by pantothenic acid.

Eventually it became clear that the foodstuffs and liver fractions that cured black-tongue in dogs also cured pellagra in man. About this time Knight, in London, and others found that nicotinamide is a growth factor for bacteria. In

1937 Elvehjem, Madden, Strong and Woolley isolated nicotinamide from a fraction of liver extract with marked antiblack-tongue activity and showed that it, and nicotinic acid, were highly curative. The beneficial effect of nicotinic acid in pellagrous patients was soon established, and a new era dawned in the treatment of pellagra.

NICOTINIC ACID-TRYPTOPHAN RELATIONSHIP. A new aspect of the puzzling pellagra problem was exposed when Krehl and his colleagues in Elvehjem's group found, in 1945, that extra tryptophan could substitute for nicotinic acid in purified diets of rats: addition of either 1 mg. nicotinic acid or 50 mg. L-tryptophan per 100 grams of diet restored growth to the normal rate. This discovery was an outstanding event in nutritional research for, as a rule, vitamins of the B complex cannot be formed by the tissues of higher animals. Later work showed that nicotinic acid can be synthesized from tryptophan with variable efficiency in many species (rat, pig, dog, horse, chick, turkey, and others) provided that other B vitamins (pyridoxine, riboflavin and thiamine) are adequate. This discovery explained several curious paradoxes: (1) although wheat and rice are essentially as low in nicotinamide content as is maize, pellagra is far more prevalent among maize eaters (maize is much lower in tryptophan content); (2) milk and milk products are among the most valuable pellagra-preventing foodstuffs and yet they are known to be low in nicotinamide (the milk proteins are, however, very good sources of tryptophan). The reason for the special susceptibility of maize eaters to develop pellagra was at last understood, and also why rats (with good synthetic powers) failed to develop lesions and even thrived on diets that were deficient for monkeys and pigs.

REQUIREMENTS AND SOURCES. Since dietary tryptophan can to some extent supply the tissues with nicotinamide, and since many other factors are now known to affect the requirement, exact information on the human requirements is not available. In 1941 the Food and Nutrition Board of the National Research Council (United States) estimated the nicotinic acid requirement of adults to vary from 23 mg. per day for a very active man to 12 mg. for a sedentary woman. Current recommendations are somewhat lower, 12 to 18 mg. for man, 10 to 15 mg. for women. The Canadian recommendations for adults range from 5 to 16 mg. nicotinic acid per day.

Both nicotinamide itself and nicotinic acid may be present in foods. Animal tissues usually contain a larger proportion in the form of the amide, plant tissues often have more present as nicotinic acid. For practical purposes the ratios in which they occur are unimportant as they possess equal biological activity. Fish and meat are good sources; kidneys are richer than corresponding muscle, and liver is richer still. The richest edible and readily available source is yeast. Baker's yeast contains 7 to 12 mg. and dried brewers' yeast from 30 to 90 mg. per 100 grams. Nuts are richer than legumes, and these, in turn, contain more nicotinic acid than do most vegetables and cereals. Fruits are poor sources.

Nicotinic acid tablets (50 mg.) are sold by pharmaceutical suppliers. The acid has a marked pharmacological effect, a pronounced but transient vasodilator action. An oral dose of about 20 mg. causes flushing and tingling of the skin, fall of blood pressure and dizziness that may be alarming to patients not warned to expect these effects. Nicotinamide does not have this action. Both compounds are relatively nontoxic, the ratio of therapeutic dose to toxic dose being at least 1:1000. The toxicity of nicotinic acid is lower than that of nicotinamide, the $LD_{50}$[3] for rats being 4 to 7 grams per kg. and 1.5 to 1.7 per kg., respectively. As much as 5.4 grams of nicotinic acid per day has been given orally to man without harmful effect.

## PYRIDOXINE (VITAMIN $B_6$) AND ITS AMINE AND ALDEHYDE

In the previous section it was mentioned that when rats were fed a purified died deficient in vitamin $B_2$ they developed a dermatitis which Goldberger believed to be analogous to that seen in pellagrins. It was thought that cure of this condition in rats could be used as a test for the P-P factor. In Britain, where the lesion was called rat acrodynia, Birch, György and Harris (1935) found that it was cured not by nicotinic acid (the P-P factor) or vitamin $B_2$ (riboflavin) but by a factor to which György assigned the name vitamin $B_6$. György's substance was adsorbed from yeast extract onto charcoal, from which it could be eluted. It was found to be adsorbed also onto fuller's earth from which it could be eluted with baryta solution. Hence, it came to be called the *eluate factor*, or Factor 1. Meanwhile, in the United States a "chick dermatitis" factor was being investigated. Because it was not adsorbed on fuller's earth, the chick factor came to be called the *filtrate factor* or Factor 2. The use of different sources (yeast, liver, rice bran), of different adsorbents and of different test animals led to considerable confusion during this period. The fractionation scheme (p. 917) indicates the prominent characteristics that assisted in the fractionation and influenced interim naming of the components of the vitamin B complex.

In 1938 the isolation of vitamin $B_6$ in crystalline form was announced from five laboratories: (1) György and (2) Kuhn and Wendt, obtained it from yeast, (3) Lepkovsky, (4) Keresztesy and Stevens and (5) Ichiba and Michi isolated pyridoxine from rice bran extract; later a sixth laboratory reported a different method of isolation from rice bran (Matukawa, 1940). It is interesting to note that some years earlier, in 1932, Ohdake had isolated from rice polishings a nitrogenous compound with the same empirical formula, $C_8H_{11}O_3N \cdot HCl$. No biological activity was attributed to it, and only later was it shown by Wiardi (1938) to be identical with vitamin $B_6$.

CHEMISTRY. The constitution of vitamin $B_6$ was established in 1938 by Kuhn and Wendt in Germany, who proposed the name "adermin." An independent synthesis by Harris and Folkers in the United States in 1939 confirmed the structure. György and Eckardt (1939) proposed the name "pyridoxine" which is now the one generally accepted.

In 1942 Snell and his associates studied the growth-promoting effects of pyridoxine on different microorganisms. Marked discrepancies were found when three different assay procedures (chemical, animal and microbiological) were used to measure the vitamin $B_6$ potencies of extracts of tissues. Out of these studies came the finding of two new substances closely related to pyridoxine, one in which the —$CH_2OH$ on carbon 4 is oxidized to an aldehyde, the other in which the same —$CH_2OH$ group is altered to —$CH_2$-$NH_2$. These compounds are now called pyridoxal and pyridoxamine, respectively. All three have essentially equal growth effects in rats. However, in the case of some lactic acid bacteria, the aldehyde and amine have a growth-promoting activity several thousand times that of pyridoxine.

Pyridoxine (2-methyl-3-hydroxy-4, 5-di-[hydroxymethyl] pyridine ($C_8H_{11}O_3N$))

Transaminases, racemases and several other types of enzymes concerned with amino acid metabolism appear to contain pyridoxal phosphate as coenzyme.

In mammals, pyridoxine and pyridoxamine are converted to pyridoxal. Foods contain varying proportions of the three compounds. Since all three have equal growth-promoting effects in rats, the activity is usually expressed as "milligrams of vitamin $B_6$."

### Pyridoxine Deficiency

Effects of pyridoxine deficiency have been seen in all species of animals studied, but these signs vary considerably. Rats lose their appetite, fail to maintain their weight, sometimes develop a typical dermatitis with swelling and edema (acrodynia); after prolonged deficiency loss of muscle tone develops and convulsions occur. In dogs a microcytic hypochromic anemia is regarded as a characteristic feature of vitamin $B_6$ deficiency. Turkeys develop hyperexcitability and convulsions without anemia, ducklings develop anemia without convulsions or paralysis. Chicks exhibit various convulsive movements; pigs, like rats, may have epileptiform fits, and they develop a microcytic anemia.

Observations *in vitro* have tended to implicate vitamin $B_6$ in protein metabolism, but systematic attempts to explore this in animals have given ambiguous results. One observation that should be mentioned is the similarity in the dermatitis produced in rats by essential fatty acid deficiency and vitamin $B_6$ deficiency. Witten and Holman suggest that vitamin $B_6$ is concerned in the conversion of linoleic and linolenic acids to arachidonic acid, which they regard as the essential fatty acid.

In man the effects of pyridoxine deficiency are less definite. Attempts to produce vitamin $B_6$ deficiency in human subjects have not been very successful. After a subject had been fed for a 55-day test-period on a diet devoid of vitamin $B_6$, Hawkins and Barsky found no marked alterations in the blood picture or biochemical findings. Nitrogen equilibrium was maintained indicating

*Pyridoxal*          *Pyridoxamine*          *Pyridoxalphosphate*

Pyridoxal is the biologically active compound. Its phosphoric ester is the coenzyme concerned in the decarboxylation of certain amino acids.

no serious abnormality in protein metabolism. The test period may have been too short to bring on the deficiency state. Holt and associates fed a diet deficient in vitamin $B_6$ to two infants: one developed convulsions, the other hypochromic anemia. These limited observations made little impression and were practically overlooked. Then in 1951 an epidemic of convulsions among babies fed a commercial liquid formula occurred in the United States. A dry powder preparation made from the same formula in the same plant did not induce convulsions. The cause was traced to excessive destruction of vitamin $B_6$ in the sterilization of the liquid preparation. Addition of extra pyridoxine to the liquid formula eliminated the trouble.

Vilter and his associates produced vitamin $B_6$ deficiency in patients by giving a pyridoxine analogue, desoxypyridoxine, which appears to have antivitamin effects. Some of the patients developed skin lesions and various other effects were noted that could be cured by giving pyridoxine. It is now generally accepted that vitamin $B_6$ is essential for man.

For the most part, the therapeutic use of vitamin $B_6$ has been empirical. It has been of no value in the treatment of the anemias. Muscular weakness has not responded and various types of nervous disorders and convulsive seizures have not been cured. The nausea and vomiting of pregnancy as well as that following X-ray treatments were claimed to respond to 10 to 20 mg. doses three or four times daily, but there have been more failures than successes; where benefit was noted it may have been largely psychogenic. Pyridoxine has been reported to be of value in cheilosis and post-adolescent *acne vulgaris*.

### Requirements, Sources and Toxicity

The pyridoxine requirements of man are not known. A figure of 1.5 to 2 mg. per day has been suggested, based on animal studies, but it is only a guess. The vitamin occurs in the tissues of plants and animals, often combined in protein complexes.

The richest natural sources of pyridoxine are those foods known to be good sources of the other members of the B complex; yeast, rice polishings, meats, liver, egg yolk, whole grains and germs of various cereal grains. Celery, lettuce and green peppers are excellent vegetable sources. No natural antagonist is known. The synthetic antagonist, desoxypyridoxine, is phosphorylated in the body, and as phosphoric ester competes with pyridoxine phosphate for the apoenzyme.

Pyridoxine has very low toxicity, doses up to

1 gram per kg. being tolerated without obvious effect by rats, rabbits and dogs. In rats the $LD_{50}$ orally is 5.5 grams per kg., by subcutaneous injection 3.7 grams per kg. and intravenously 657 mg. per kg. Tonic convulsions precede death in mice and rats. Daily doses larger than 1 gram per kg. in rats, rabbits and dogs caused impaired coordination within two or three days, progressing to severe tonic convulsions and death in the stage of paralysis (Unna, 1940).

### PANTOTHENIC ACID

In 1901 the Belgian scientist, Wildiers, recognized that yeast requires, for optimal growth, a special factor in addition to the known nutrients. He called it *bios* and attempted to isolate it. Professor Lash Miller in Toronto with G. H. W. Lucas and others, separated bios into several components—bios I (later identified by Eastcott as meso-inositol) and bios II. The latter was soon shown to be a mixture. The component called bios IIa (later found to be pantothenic acid) was shown by Miller to contain $\beta$-alanine, which in itself is sufficient for some yeasts.

In 1938 R. J. Williams and associates isolated from liver an acidic substance that had a marked effect on the growth of yeast. Because it is found widely distributed in plant and animal tissues Williams suggested the name pantothenic acid (meaning from everywhere). In the same year Woolley and others in Elvehjem's laboratory isolated the chick pellagra factor (filtrate factor) and believed it to be identical with pantothenic acid. Within a few months this was confirmed by Jukes, and about a year later Williams and Major at the Merck laboratories established the structure by synthesis.

### CHEMISTRY

$$HO \cdot CH_2 \cdot \overset{\overset{\displaystyle CH_3}{|}}{\underset{\underset{\displaystyle CH_3}{|}}{C}} \cdot \overset{\overset{\displaystyle OH}{/}}{CH} \cdot CO \cdot NH \; CH_2 \cdot CH_2 \cdot COOH$$

Pantothenic Acid

This condensation product between pantoic acid ($\alpha,\gamma$-dihydroxy-$\beta,\beta$-dimethylbutyric acid) and $\beta$-alanine is a yellow, viscous oil, soluble in water, and labile to acid, alkali and heat. The sodium and calcium salts, which are soluble in water and crystalline, are considerably more stable.

ACETYL-COENZYME A (ACETYL-COA). A specific functional role for pantothenic acid was soon discovered. In 1942 a stimulatory effect of pantothenic acid upon pyruvic oxidation had been observed in *Proteus morgani*. Then in 1946 Lipmann, while studying the acetylation of sulfanilamide by liver, found that a new coenzyme was involved which could not be replaced by any of the coenzymes known at the time. Also in 1946, Feldberg and Mann in England and Nachmansohn and Behrman in the United States found that a new stable cofactor is necessary for the acetylation of choline. These and other observations on acetylating systems led to the isolation of a new cofactor, called coenzyme A (A for acetylation), and to the finding of pantothenic acid in it. The presence of 1 mole of adenosine, 3 moles of phosphoric acid and 1 atom of sulfur per mole of pantothenic acid was soon shown, and the following structure was finally established by Hoagland and Novelli (1954):

$$
\begin{array}{c}
\text{phosphate} \\
|
\end{array}
$$

adenine—ribose—phosphate
$$
|
$$
phosphate
$$
|
$$
pantothenic acid
$$
|
$$
thioethanolamine
$$
(-NH \cdot CH_2 \cdot CH_2SH)
$$
Coenzyme A

Coenzyme A acts as an acetyl carrier. It is shown elsewhere that carbohydrate (via pyruvate) and fat (via acetoacetate) give rise in the body to a metabolically active fragment containing two carbon atoms. The work of Lynen and Reichert in Germany, and of many others, culminated in proof that the "active two-carbon fragment" or "active acetate" is attached to the —SH group.

### Pantothenic Acid Deficiency

All species of animals tested (e.g., rat, mouse, dog, fox, monkey, pig, chick and others) require pantothenic acid. The effects of deficiency vary considerably from species to species. Deficiency of this vitamin in the rat results in failure of growth, achromotrichia (graying of the hair) in black or brown strains, adrenal necrosis, hemorrhagic lesions, "bloody whiskers" (porphyrin-caked), "spectacled eyes" (circumocular loss of hair) and a sticky exudate on the lids, dermatitis, a spastic gait, and, sporadically in some animals, anemia and leucopenia. In chicks, dermatitis (mouth and eyelids chiefly, feet slightly), poor feathering, poor growth with weight loss are seen, followed by incoordination, paralysis and death. Turkeys, ducks and pigeons react similarly to lack of pantothenic acid. In dogs, irritability develops and sudden prostration occurs; respiration and heart beat become rapid and convulsions lead to death.

In man, until recently, no definite pathological lesions due to deficiency of pantothenic acid had been described. Perhaps the abundance of pantothenic acid in most foodstuffs accounts for this. There is no evidence to support extravagant claims that graying or loss of hair in man is due to lack of pantothenic acid. One condition has come to light, "burning feet syndrome," that may be due to lack of pantothenic acid. This syndrome was observed in prisoner-of-war camps in Japan and Burma and is common in parts of India. It does not respond to thiamine, riboflavin or nicotinic acid, singly or together. Gopalan has reported striking improvement following daily injections of 20 to 40 mg. calcium pantothenate.

REQUIREMENTS, SOURCES AND TOXICITY. No data on human requirements for pantothenic acid are available. The average intake on different dietary regimens has been estimated. Average (American) diets probably provide between 3 and 12 mg. daily, with a mean value about 9 mg. The highest excretion on normal diets was 5.3 mg. per 24 hours. Liver, kidney, egg yolk and fresh vegetables are the best dietary sources of pantothenic acid. Yeast and royal jelly are also good sources. Milk, meat, grains, fruits and nuts are fair to good; corn and rice are relatively poor sources.

The pantothenic acid in foods is reasonably stable for periods of storage, up to one year, under proper conditions, e.g., eggs and meat in cold storage, cereal grains, intact or ground, at room temperature. Usual cooking procedures and dehydration do not cause appreciable loss, but holding products at high temperatures for long periods (100 to 150° for 2 to 6 days) destroys much of their pantothenic acid.

Little is known concerning the pharmacology of pantothenic acid. Its toxicity is very low. The $LD_{50}$, orally, for mice is 10 grams per kg. of body weight, but rats given the same dosage survive without showing any signs of toxicity. Monkeys weighing 4 to 5 kg., fed 1.0 gram daily over a period of 6 months, showed no abnormality. Doses of 100 mg. have been given to man, intravenously, without toxic reactions; doses of from 10 to 20 grams given orally occasionally produced diarrhea, and, in a few patients, edema.

### BIOTIN

The essentiality of biotin for man seems proven but whether it ever poses a problem in practical human nutrition is questionable. Biotin deficiency has been produced experimentally in human volunteers. Several spontaneous occurrences have been reported, but because biotin occurs so widely distributed in Nature (in wheat and most other seeds, in animal organs, in yeast, etc.) endemic deficiency is unknown.

The complex nature of Wildier's bios was suggested in 1922 by Fulmer and Nelson. By 1924 Lash Miller, in Toronto had separated bios into three fractions, all of which were essential for *Saccharomyces cerevisiae*. The identities of bios I and of bios IIa (thought to be β-alanine but later found to be pantothenic acid) have already been mentioned. The third factor, bios IIb, later given the name biotin, proved to be identical with vitamin H, a factor that cures the strange condition known as 'egg white injury'.

Skin lesions, loss of hair, progressive emaciation, nervous manifestations and death followed the feeding of diets containing a large proportion of raw or commercially dried egg white (Bateman, 1916; confirmed by others). Two women workers have contributed much to this field. M. A. Boas-Fixsen in 1927 observed that liver and yeast contain a "protective factor X," and that *cooked* egg white is not toxic. In 1933 Helen T. Parsons and E. Kelly reported that small supplements of liver, yeast or egg yolk to the diet neutralized the toxic effect of the uncooked egg white. The toxicity of raw egg white can be eliminated by digestion with pepsin or with hydrochloric acid as well as by adequate treatment with heat. Attempts to isolate vitamin H (a name chosen by György for this vitamin because of its ability to alleviate the peculiar skin lesions; H for *Haut* = skin, in German) from liver and yeast progressed slowly because the animal assays were laborious and not very sensitive. Identification of biotin (the potent growth factor for yeast, isolated from egg yolk by Kögl and Tönnis) with the curative factor (vitamin H) was made by György, Melville, Burk and duVigneaud in 1940. Its structure was published by du Vigneaud in 1942, and its synthesis was accomplished in 1943 by Harris and his colleagues.

CHEMISTRY, SOURCES AND REQUIREMENTS. Biotin, $C_{10}H_{16}O_3N_2S$, is an acid, sparingly soluble in cold water and dilute acids, but freely soluble in hot water and in dilute alkali. It is practically insoluble in organic solvents.

Biotin ($C_{10}H_{16}O_3N_2S$)

A number of homologues (compounds with side-chains of different length) and analogues (with oxygen replacing sulfur) have been prepared, some of which can substitute for biotin and some of which are inhibitory. Oxybiotin can cure biotin deficiency in rats and chicks, but larger doses than of biotin are required. Desthiobiotin stimulates the growth of yeast (*Saccharomyces cerevisiae*) in a biotin-free medium; in contrast, it acts as an antimetabolite with *Lactobacillus casei*, blocking the utilization of biotin. The most potent inhibitors are biotin sulfone and dl-homobiotin (with five methylene groups ($CH_2$) in the side chain).

Biotin occurs in natural products mainly in bound forms. One of these, biocytin, is a peptide with L-lysine. Biocytin, like biotin, is water-soluble and dialyzable, yet tissue biotin is not dialyzable until after treatment with acid (pH 3) or dilute sodium hydroxide. The binding is perhaps a peptide linkage since pepsin frees biotin. For the physiologist and nutritionist one of the most interesting bound forms of biotin is its combination with *avidin*, a special protein component of egg white. Avidin, so named because of its avidity for biotin, by forming an insoluble compound with biotin is responsible for the toxic effect known as "egg white injury." Avidin is denatured by heat and thereby inactivated. Biotin bound to avidin is not released by treatment with acid or the combined action of trypsin, pancreatin and papain. Biotin bound to avidin passes through the alimentary tract unchanged. Avidin has been found only in egg white (eggs of hens, turkeys, geese and ducks) and in the egg jelly of frogs. It appears to be a secretion from the mucosa of the oviduct.

The attempts to isolate biotin-containing coenzymes have not been successful although a number of enzymatic processes have been discovered in which biotin appears to play a part directly or indirectly. There is some evidence that biotin-coenzymes are concerned in decarboxylation and in carbon dioxide fixation as well as in the deamination of aspartic acid, serine and threonine.

The biotin requirement of many microorganisms is known, but that of man and higher animals is less certain. An intake of 150 to 300 μg. per day has been suggested for man. Such figures can at best be called a guess. Balance studies in man have shown a urinary excretion greater than the intake in some cases, and the fecal output is often greatly in excess of the intake. This suggests that in man synthesis by intestinal bacteria may provide more biotin than does the food.

## *p*-Aminobenzoic Acid (PABA)

In 1935 a new red dye with spectacular properties was described by Domagk. It could kill hemolytic streptococci in mice although it lacked this property *in vitro*. Tréfouël and his associates in France studied a series of related azo dyes and noted that all the ones displaying this property possess a sulfonamide group in the para position to the nitrogen linkage. Following this lead, para-aminobenzene-sulfonamide was tested and found to be highly active both *in vivo* and *in vitro*. Discovery of the potent antibacterial activity of sulfanilamide was not only a milestone in medicine, causing a tremendous new interest in chemotherapy, but led to a new concept in metabolism, viz. of antimetabolites. Woods (1940) fractionated an antisulfanilamide fraction of yeast extract and obtained a material (with many of the properties of PABA) that neutralized the antibacterial action of sulfanilamide. When he tested PABA and found that it did, indeed, nullify the antistreptococcal activity of sulfanilamide he suggested that the action of the latter was the result of its competing with PABA for an enzyme controlling metabolic reactions, essential for bacterial growth. Later Rubbo and Gillespie (1940) isolated pure PABA from yeast and showed that 1 mole of PABA could antagonize 23,000 moles of sulfanilamide. Fildes (1940) expressed Wood's theory in more general terms by suggesting that PABA is an *essential metabolite*, although not necessarily a growth factor, for organisms inhibited by sulfanilamide. Ansbacher (1941) believed that PABA is a vitamin necessary for the growth of chicks and that it acts as an anti-gray hair factor in the rat. There is no evidence to support the claim that PABA prevents or cures the graying of human hair. The modern view is that PABA should not be considered a vitamin since its essentiality is confined to microorganisms; it is not required in the diet of animals.

### Chemistry

$$\text{HCl} \cdot \text{H}_2\text{N}\!\!-\!\!\langle\text{C}_6\text{H}_4\rangle\!\!-\!\!\overset{\text{NH}_2 \cdot \text{HCl}}{\text{N}}\!\!=\!\!\text{N}\!\!-\!\!\langle\text{C}_6\text{H}_4\rangle\!\!-\!\!\text{SO}_2\text{NH}_2$$

Prontosil

$$\text{H}_2\text{N}\!\!-\!\!\langle\text{C}_6\text{H}_4\rangle\!\!-\!\!\text{COOH} \qquad \text{H}_2\text{N}\!\!-\!\!\langle\text{C}_6\text{H}_4\rangle\!\!-\!\!\text{SO}_2\text{NH}_2$$

*p*-aminobenzoic acid          Sulfanilamide

PABA is a white, crystalline solid that is readily soluble in alcohol and ether and slightly soluble in water. It occurs widely distributed throughout the plant and animal kingdom. It is found both free and in combined forms. One of the better known conjugates is folic acid. Thus the view expressed by Fildes, that PABA is an essential *metabolite*, even though it may not be a *dietary* essential, has been substantiated.

PABA is relatively nontoxic in either single doses or on prolonged administration. The acute $LD_{50}$ for mice, rats and dogs (oral administration) is about 3, 6 and 1 to 2 grams per kg., respectively. Large doses (20 to 30 grams per day) have been administered to patients with louse-borne rickettsial diseases (typhus and Rocky Mountain spotted fever) without serious pathological changes being caused by the drug.

## Folic Acid (Pteroylglutamic Acid, PGA)

### (See also ch. 9)

Five different fields of work merged in the discovery of folic acid. Some groups were fractionating liver extracts in the search for a cure for pernicious anemia, others were looking for vitamin M (needed by monkeys) and still others were trying to isolate vitamin Bc, a factor needed to prevent hyperchromic macrocytic anemia in chicks. Meanwhile microbiologists had found that certain bacteria, e.g., *Lactobacillus casei* ε and *Streptococcus fecalis* R (formerly called *S. lactis* R) would not grow on a mixture of salts, sugars, amino acids and known vitamins, but that addition of extracts of leaves, liver or yeast would initiate growth. Thus one of these latter groups of workers was searching for the *L. casei factor* and another for the *S. lactis* R *factor*. A feature common to the isolation of all these agents (i.e., the several factors comprising the folic acid complex) is that all are adsorbed on charcoal and eluted, more or less quantitatively, by dilute ammonia. Hence the term *norit eluate factor* was also applied to the material, before it was isolated and identified.

The isolation of an active agent from spinach, and its wide-spread occurrence in green leaves, led to the name folic acid (Mitchell, Snell and Williams, 1941, 1944) from *folium*, a leaf.

Concentrates from different sources displayed variable potency when tested in different species. For a short period the nature and relationships of these several closely related growth factors were uncertain.

"*Fermentation L. casei factor*" was found to contain *three* glutamic acid residues and "*yeast vitamin Bc conjugate*" contains *seven* such residues.

Pteroylglutamic acid produces partial and sometimes even complete remission of pernicious anemia, and certain other macrocytic anemias, in man. Although folic acid promotes regeneration of red blood cells it is unable to control the degener-

pteridine derivative        p-aminobenzoic acid

pteroyl—        glutamic acid

"Liver *L. casei* factor" = pteroylglutamic acid = folic acid.

ation of the spinal cord that occurs in pernicious anemia. In some cases treatment with folic acid hastens the degeneration. Thus early hopes that folic acid would prove to be the antipernicious anemia factor of liver were dashed.

Meanwhile the nutritional requirements of *Leuconostoc citrovorum* were being studied by Sauberlich and Baumann (1948) and isolation of another unknown factor, the so-called *citrovorum factor* (CF), also referred to as *leucovorin*, was attempted. A relationship to pteroyl-glutamic acid was soon discovered. The structure of this new growth factor, now referred to as *folinic acid*, is:

to be essential in man when the proper test has been made.

## Function of Folic Acid

The primary biochemical role of folic acid appears to be concerned with the incorporation of a one-carbon unit into a variety of essential metabolites: purines, pyrimidines and certain amino acids. The labile one-carbon unit has been referred to as "active formate" or "active formaldehyde." Formate precursors include the methyl groups of choline, methionine, sarcosine and dimethylglycine, the beta carbon of serine,

Folinic acid
(5-formyl-5,6,7,8 tetrahydropteroyl-glutamic acid)

It is probable that in many biochemical systems, folic acid is not active as such, but that it must be converted to folinic acid which is (or is closely related to) the citrovorum factor (CF) which seems to be the functional form of the compound or is closely related to a more labile intermediate (transformylating coenzyme).

## Effects of Deficiency

The pteroylglutamates are necessary for monkeys, chicks, turkeys, dogs, foxes, mink, guinea-pigs and for rats treated with sulfa drugs (see ch. 9). An experimental deficiency of folic acid has not been produced in man so it is not possible to state with assurance that man requires it. On the other hand, the proven value of folic acid in sprue and the pernicious anemia of pregnancy, and in megaloblastic anemia in infants, nutritional macrocytic anemia and related megalo-

blastic anemias, makes it likely that it will prove the methylene carbon of glycine, and histidine and acetone. Active formate or active formaldehyde appear to be compounds with tetrahydrofolic acid that aid in the transfer of one-carbon units, i.e., that act as transformylating coenzymes.

Although folic acid and vitamin $B_{12}$ have been shown to play a role in lipotropic phenomena, the details of the picture are obscure. The lipotropic effect is clear cut in rats fed certain diets; on other diets these vitamins may produce no alteration in liver fat or they may even exert an antilipotropic effect. Neither folic acid nor vitamin $B_{12}$ is necessary for *transmethylation*. Folic acid is needed for transformylation reactions and vitamin $B_{12}$ seems to be concerned in the reduction of formate via formaldehyde to biologically labile methyl.

The folic acid antagonists *aminopterin (4-amino-pteroylglutamic acid)* and *A-methopterin (4-amino-10-methyl-pteroylglutamic acid)* inhibit the incorporation of radioactive carbon from formate into the nucleic acid purines. These and other folic acid antagonists have been used therapeutically in attempts to control leukemia in man. Remissions have been induced that are more frequent and of longer duration than those common to the natural course of the disease, but no cures have been reported.

SOURCES AND TOXICITY. Substances with folic acid activity, as measured by microbiological assay, are widely distributed in nature. Most of the activity is present in 'bound forms' (conjugates). Liver has the highest activity; vegetables and many fruits are rich sources; nuts, dried beans and peas are good sources. Folic acid is synthesized by intestinal bacteria. The extent to which this occurs affects the dietary requirement.

Pteroylglutamic acid has very low acute and chronic toxicity.

## VITAMIN B$_{12}$: CYANOCOBALAMIN

### *Animal Protein Factor (APF)*

Several papers appeared during the period 1934 to 1946 indicating that an active substance, different from other known dietary factors, improved the hatchability of hen's eggs and increased the growth rate and survival time of chicks fed cereal rations free from animal protein. Because the factor (or a related substance) was found in products as diverse as liver, animal flesh, fish meals, condensed fish solubles, chicken droppings and cow-dung, but not in plant materials, it was called the "animal protein factor," or APF. In 1946 Cary and associates described a new factor, X, necessary for the growth of rats. It occurred in crude casein but could be leached out by suitable treatment. Factor X appeared to be the same as, or closely related to, the animal protein factor.

In 1948, Mary Shorb reported that a certain bacterium, *Lactobacillus lactis* Dorner, could be used to test for and assay the rat growth vitamin, APF. Later work of Shorb, Folkers and others suggested that this new factor, which they named vitamin B$_{12}$, was identical with the long-sought for antipernicious anemia principle. The final stages of the isolation of vitamin B$_{12}$ were greatly accelerated by using this bacterial assay method, which in a few hours gave answers that by animal tests had taken weeks, and months by the tedious and costly clinical tests.

CHEMISTRY. Vitamin B$_{12}$ is a red crystalline substance (mol. wt. about 1350) which contains a metal-porphyrin nucleus similar to that of heme or chlorophyll, but with cobalt (4.5 per cent) as the metal. It has the most complex structure of any vitamin known. The base dimethylbenzimidazole (which also occurs in riboflavin) was identified fairly early; later it was shown to be linked to ribose phosphate; a 2-aminopropanol unit, later shown to be Dg-1-amino-2-propanol, and a cyanide ion were also identified. The short name cobalamin was proposed for the active material.

A search for other and possibly richer sources of vitamin B$_{12}$ led to the discovery that it occurs in many animal products but that plant materials show no measurable activity. It now seems that neither animals nor higher plants can make vitamin B$_{12}$. Certain nonphotosynthetic organisms serve as the primary source. It was from the fermentation broth of a strain of *Streptomyces griseus* that the workers in the United States isolated crystalline vitamin B$_{12}$.

Fermentation broths from other organisms provided several closely related compounds with equal activity in the treatment of pernicious anemia. They are related coordination compounds of cobalt in which the CN$^-$ ion is replaced by a hydroxyl group or water molecule. The three compounds are, therefore, called cyanocobalamin (B$_{12}$), hydroxocobalamin (B$_{12}$b) and aquacobalamin, respectively. Analogous compounds are known in which "unnatural" nucleotide bases have been introduced by biosynthetic means, or in which halogens, thiocyanate or nitrite ions have replaced the cyanide ion.

Seven years were required to elucidate the arrangement of the recognized fragments in the antipernicious anemia vitamin. It is of great scientific interest that a new "tool" was used with outstanding success in solving this problem.

The structure of the formidably large and complex vitamin B$_{12}$ molecule was deduced largely from crystallographic evidence supplied by X-ray reflections (Hodgkin *et al.*). Using automatic computers, a series of calculations of successive degrees of approximation to the correct electron density distribution provided a solution to the chemical structure of the nucleotide-free hexacarboxylic acid (C$_{46}$H$_{60}$O$_{13}$N$_6$CoCl$\cdot$2H$_2$O) that was obtained from vitamin B$_{12}$ by alkaline hydrolysis. Elucidation of the structure of such a molecule from X-ray data represents a great triumph for crystallography. This information, in conjunction with the chemical evidence accumulated during the seven years, enabled Todd and Smith and their associates to propose the formula C$_{63}$H$_{90}$O$_{14}$N$_{14}$PCo and the probable structure:

VITAMIN B₁₂
(Taken from Nature **176**, 329, 1955.)

OCCURRENCE. Accurate figures for the occurrence of vitamin B₁₂ were not easily obtained; microbiological assays, animal tests and clinical trials frequently gave inconsistent data. Many values in the earlier literature are therefore suspect. Plant materials show no measurable activity, animal tissues and secretions usually show some, but extremely variable, potency. Extracts of human livers and of livers of 26 species of mammals and 3 species of fish were active in pernicious anemia. Estimates of the amount of vitamin B₁₂ in various foodstuffs (μg. per 100 grams) are: mammalian muscle (horsemeat, beef, pork, mutton) 1 to 5; different organs showed considerable variability (beef kidney and liver 15 to 20); egg yolk, 1 to 3; milk, traces; cheese, milk powder and crude casein, 1 to 3. Concentrates of cobalt-containing pigments from cow-dung and from certain mould cultures are inactive in pernicious anemia but become active after digestion with gastric mucosa or pancreatic enzymes.

### Effects of Deficiency

The greatest interest in vitamin B₁₂ concerns its effectiveness in the treatment of pernicious anemia. Doses as small as 1 to 3 μg. per day cure both the hematological and neurological defects. Vitamin B₁₂ is more effective in patients by in-jection than by mouth. Oral doses 30 to 60 times the effective parenteral dose may cause a slow response in some patients. Vitamin B₁₂ has other physiological effects besides the stimulation of hematopoiesis. It promotes the growth of animals fed diets low in the animal protein factor, i.e., consisting mainly of protein from plant sources. There appears to be a relationship between B₁₂ and thyroid activity but this needs further study.

In vitamin B₁₂ deficiency, rats develop enlarged kidneys and elevated blood urea levels. Deficient chicks also show an elevated blood NPN. A nutritional edema preventable by vitamin B₁₂ (and also by choline) has been described in dogs and rats. Vitamin B₁₂, in conjunction with folic acid, is concerned in the metabolism of the one-carbon fragment, including the biosynthesis of methyl groups. This vitamin is not involved in transmethylation reactions but it does seem to be concerned in the reduction of active formate (5-formyltetrahydrofolic acid) to active formaldehyde (5-hydroxymethyl-tetrahydrofolic acid) with ultimate formation of a biologically labile methyl group.

### INOSITOL

Inositol has been known since 1850 when Scherer isolated it from muscle and called it "muscle sugar." It was shown by Maquenne in 1887 to be a hexahydroxycyclohexane. In 1928 Edna V. Eastcott first demonstrated its biological importance when she showed mesoinositol to be the growth factor for yeast called bios I. Although inositol is essential for the growth of yeasts and some other microorganisms, its role in mammalian nutrition is less clear.

In 1940 D. W. Woolley found inositol to be an essential dietary factor for a mammal—attempts to rear mice on a purified diet lacking it, results in failure to grow and loss of hair. Production of alopecia in mice and rats fed diets lacking inositol has been confirmed by a number of workers. Inositol improves the growth rate of chicks, guinea-pigs and hamsters.

Inositol plays some role in fat metabolism although the mechanism is not known. In fat-free diets lacking choline it exerts a small but clear-cut lipotropic effect. It exerts a definite supplementary lipotropic action in diets containing choline. The presence of fat in the diet tends to block the lipotropic action of inositol. This fact and its inability to protect weanling rats from developing hemorrhagic kidney lesions when fed hypolipotropic diets shows that it is not a lipotropic agent in the usually accepted sense. Many text books have misinterpreted the data on the lipotropism of inositol (see Best *et al.*, 1950, 1951). The so-called "lipotropic effect of inositol under conditions where choline is ineffective" is really a synergistic lipotropic effect of inositol in a ration already containing much more than a maximally effective dose of choline in the basal diet. More choline obviously could have no further effect. The failure to appreciate that the basal diet contained so much choline led to the erroneous belief that inositol possesses some unique lipotropic properties.

CHEMISTRY. Inositol, $C_6H_{12}O_6$, is a hexahydroxycyclohexane:

(A)                 (B)

Formula A attempts to show the spatial arrangement of the hydrogen atoms and hydroxyl groups with respect to the plane in which the carbon atoms of the ring lie. Formula B is an abbreviated but very useful representation in which the short vertical lines represent the position of the hydroxyl groups. As the formula suggests, nine stereoisomers are possible. The isomer which is most frequently encountered in nature, and which is important in the nutrition of animals and some bacteria, was originally called "muscle sugar," but because it is optically inactive it has also been called *i*-inositol or *meso*-inositol. These names are inappropriate because there are six other optically inactive isomers. Lardy has suggested that these chemically incorrect and confusing terms be replaced by *myo*-inositol.

Inositol is present in combined forms in yeast and other microorganisms, in heart muscle, thyroid, kidney, spleen and testes.

REQUIREMENT AND SOURCES. No lesion due to lack of inositol is known in man and no role can be assigned to it in human nutrition or metabolism. No estimate can be made of the human requirement. Williams has estimated that the average mixed diet (2500 Cal.) provides about 1 gram of inositol.

Inositol occurs in leaves and seeds. It is found combined with phosphoric acid in esters (mono-, tri- and hexaphosphoric). The latter ester (phytic acid) occurs in cereals as a mixed calcium-mag-

nesium salt called *phytin*. This compound immobilizes calcium in a nonavailable form and is the compound responsible for the rachitogenic effect of oatmeal. Inositol has been found in the phosphatides isolated from soya beans, brain and livers.

### Choline and the Lipotropic Agents

Choline and the dietary components that serve as precursors are known as lipotropic agents (see ch. 49).

The word *lipotropic* was coined to describe *dietary* factors that prevent the accumulation of fat in the livers of experimental animals fed high-fat, low-protein diets. Later it was shown that no fat whatever in the food is needed to produce fatty livers, provided that the ration is made relatively low in lipotropic agents. The nutritional importance of choline was not discovered until 1932. Some workers doubt whether choline should be included with the other B vitamins. The amount required is large (5 to 30 mg. per day for a rat) compared with that of other recognized members of the B group whose requirement is often measured in micrograms; furthermore, choline is used for structural purposes in nervous tissue.

In 1924 Allan *et al.* and Fisher noted independently that depancreatized dogs maintained with insulin developed large, fatty livers. Feeding raw pancreas prevented this. Several years later Hershey showed that commercial egg yolk lecithin also prevented the development of these fatty livers. In 1932 Best, Hershey and Huntsman identified choline as the protective agent. Betaine was soon found to possess similar activity.

The nature of the protein used in the preparation of rations low in lipotropic action, affects the amount of fat deposited in the liver. The variable lipotropic effect of protein seemed to be explained when methionine was found to possess lipotropic properties. Choline, betaine and methionine are the three lipotropic agents found in common foodstuffs. Sulfur analogues of betaine

Choline                 Betaine

$$CH_3 \cdot S \cdot CH_2CH_2CH{-}COOH$$
$$\underset{\textstyle NH_2}{|}$$

Methionine

occur in small amounts in some plants. These so-called *thetins* are strongly lipotropic, but their distribution is limited; and probably they play a negligible lipotropic role in normal diets.

Dietary choline is necessary for normal growth and continued health in species as varied as rats, mice, dogs, rabbits, chicks, turkeys, trout, cockroaches, and mosquito larvae. Fatty livers due to lack of choline have been observed in rats, mice, dogs, rabbits, hamsters, guinea-pigs, calves, pigs, monkeys and ducklings. (It should be kept in mind that fatty livers may develop from other causes, such as infections, toxic chemicals, hepatic anoxia or other deficiencies that interfere with hepatic function. Choline cannot prevent damage occurring from these conditions.) A prolonged lack of choline leads to the appearance of fibrotic changes in the liver, with the eventual development of cirrhosis. Choline deficiency leads to a number of other abnormalities. Bradycardia has been observed in choline deficient rats. Sure has shown that it is needed for normal lactation in the rat. Weanling rats, calves and pigs develop a hemorrhagic renal lesion that is often fatal, and rabbits develop a nonhemorrhagic renal lesion preventable by choline. Muscular weakness has been noted in rats and pigs, and muscular dystrophy in rabbits fed choline deficient rations. Baby chicks, turkey poults and ducklings fail to grow on diets poor in choline and develop perosis (a paralyzing slipped-tendon disease). Many other defects due to choline deficiency have been described but cannot be listed here.

Besides the well known accumulation of glycerides and concomitant increase of cholesteryl esters in the liver, several other biochemical changes are caused by lack of choline. The turnover of hepatic phospholipids is decreased in choline deficiency. The prompt increase in the turnover of liver phospholipid-P caused by feeding or injecting choline is nonspecific, however, for a similar effect may be produced by methionine, cystine or ethanolamine. Plasma phospholipids of rats are decreased in choline deficiency and there is a marked reduction in the low-density lipoprotein fraction of the serum. As the liver damage in rats and dogs progresses to cirrhosis, with prolonged choline deficiency, the concentration of cholesteryl esters in the blood serum falls to very low levels.

## Ascorbic Acid (Vitamin C)

As recounted earlier, scurvy in man has been known for centuries and the protective value of fresh vegetables and fruits (especially lemons and limes) was discovered, forgotten and rediscovered several times. When Holst and Frölich in 1907 found that guinea-pigs develop an analogous scorbutic state, progress in the isolation of the cura-

tive principle became possible. Zilva and associates in Britain, Szent-Györgyi (1928) in Hungary and Waugh and King (1932) in the United States made the major contributions to the isolation of the "hexuronic acid" with unusual reducing properties which was soon identified with vitamin C. The configuration was established in 1933 in Haworth's laboratory in England and within a few months the synthesis was achieved almost simultaneously by Reichstein and associates in Switzerland and by Haworth's group.

CHEMISTRY. Ascorbic acid, $C_6H_8O_6$, is an enediol of the lactone of L-gulonic acid:

Ascorbic acid    Dehydroascorbic acid

Vitamin C is a moderately strong acid (pK = 4.21) which is stable in the crystalline state but in solution is readily oxidized by atmospheric oxygen. The product of this reaction, dehydroascorbic acid, is also produced quantitatively when iodine or the dye 2,6-dichlorophenolindophenol acts upon vitamin C. These reagents are used for its determination. The dehydro compound is readily reduced to reform ascorbic acid. This property of easily reversible oxidation and reduction is bound up with its apparent function in the tissue, namely, transport of hydrogen.

Vitamin C is one of the few vitamins that occurs in nature as a single active compound, *viz.* L-ascorbic acid and its reversibly oxidized form (*cf.* vitamins $A_1$ and $A_2$, the several active carotenoid pigments, the several forms of vitamins D, E, K, etc.). Vitamin C has not been found in any coenzyme complex, nor has any "combined form" been isolated. It is one of the few water-soluble vitamins for which no acceptable microbiological method of assay has been found. Some fruits and vegetables, notably bananas and cauliflower, contain *ascorbic oxidase*, an enzyme which can cause rapid oxidative loss of vitamin C when the foodstuff is cut or crushed during preparation for the table.

Little was known until recently about the precursors of vitamin C, but now evidence points to the sequence of changes: D-glucose →

D-glucurono-γ-lactone → L-gulono-γ-lactone → L-ascorbic acid. D-Galactose can also function as precursor by a corresponding series of changes via D-galacturonic acid and L-galactono-γ-lactone. The change from the D- to the L-series at the second step is remarkable, and it is thought that the few species requiring vitamin C do so because they lack the enzyme needed for this change.

### *Ascorbic Acid Deficiency*

All species of animals studied have shown a need for ascorbic acid in their *metabolism*, but most species have the ability to meet this requirement by biosynthesis from carbohydrate precursors. The quinea-pig and primates (including man) are the only animals known to require vitamin C in the diet. Early studies were complicated by the failure to realize that this dietary peculiarity is limited to a few species. Once it was recognized that the guinea-pig is highly susceptible to lack of vitamin C, and that the resulting lesions are similar to those seen in man, experimental studies enabled the sequence of changes due to vitamin C deficiency to be elucidated.

An outstanding feature of vitamin C deficiency is the failure to deposit intercellular cement substances (collagen, osteoid and dentine). This explains the petechial hemorrhages and ecchymoses (related to fragility of the tissues), the pains in bones and joints, the weakened bones and badly formed teeth (in children) and loosened teeth in adults with scurvy. There is no correlation, however, between the intake of vitamin C and the incidence of human caries. Although the final lesions can be attributed to an impairment in the functioning of the formative cells, the underlying biochemical defect is still not known. The well known liability to infection, in both quinea-pigs and man, during vitamin C-deficiency suggests that the lowered resistance to infection may be due to impairment in the disease-resisting mechanisms.

Ascorbic acid has been shown, both *in vivo* and *in vitro*, to promote the oxidation of tyrosine and phenylalanine. Because other substances, without antiscorbutic activity, can also stimulate tyrosine oxidation, it is doubtful whether this interesting property of ascorbic acid accounts for its prevention of scurvy.

The finding that ascorbic acid is needed by the system concerned with the conversion of folic acid to *citrovorum factor* (folinic acid) may lead to a better understanding of the unclear relationship between scurvy and anemia.

REQUIREMENT. Improvements in food handling (collection, transportation, storage and processing) have largely eliminated scurvy. It is still occasionally seen, however, on this continent, in Britain and elsewhere among both infants and adults.

The amount of vitamin C needed to prevent scurvy, known as the "minimum protective dose," appears to be in the region of 10 mg. per day, as established by a carefully controlled experiment on adult volunteers at Sheffield, England (1948). However, the amount needed for abundant good health is not known. The uncertainty has led to considerable controversy. The Accessory Food Factors Subcommittee of the British Medical Research Council concluded that there is no evidence that intakes exceeding 30 mg. per day confer any extra benefit. Others contend that such evidence does exist. The Food and Nutrition Board of the National Research Council, United States (1953) recommends (but without sound experimental data to support the values) daily intakes of 75 mg. for adults, with 100 to 150 mg. during pregnancy and lactation. They suggest that children up to 12 years of age should get 30 to 75 mg. daily.

Harris and his colleagues in Britain attempted to assess the nutritional status of patients with respect to vitamin C by doing so-called loading or saturation tests which were supposed to reveal the extent of the reserves. Persons whose diets have been rich in vitamin C presumably have their tissues saturated with the vitamin; those with lower intakes are presumably in a lower state of saturation. In partial support of this concept, a lower urinary excretion of ascorbic acid is usually observed with lower intakes of vitamin C. This resting level of excretion did not provide a reliable measure of nutritional status, however. A better assessment was obtained by administering a large test dose of the pure vitamin each day, for a period, and measuring the excretion during each 24 hours.

If the previous diet had been adequate with respect to vitamin C, the tissues did appear to be relatively saturated with it because most of the extra vitamin C in the loading dose was excreted promptly in the urine. The number of days required to reach a high level of excretion was found to be related to the previous intake; with higher intakes (75 mg. or more per day) the peak followed the first dose; an intake of 30

TABLE 54.1

*Typical vitamin content of some common foods*

| Food | A | Thiamine | Riboflavin | Nicotinic Acid | Ascorbic Acid |
|---|---|---|---|---|---|
| | IU/100 grams | mg. per 100 grams | | | |
| Cereals | | | | | |
| Corn, maize, meal bolted.. | 440 | 0.30 | 0.08 | 1.9 | 0 |
| Rice | | | | | |
| Brown, raw.. | 0 | 0.32 | 0.05 | 4.6 | 0 |
| White, milled..... | 0 | 0.07 | 0.03 | 1.6 | 0 |
| Wheat, whole.. | 0 | 0.55 | 0.12 | 4.3 | 0 |
| Flour (80%).. | 0 | 0.26 | 0.07 | 2.0 | 0 |
| Germ........ | 0 | 2.05 | 0.80 | 4.6 | 0 |
| Dairy products | | | | | |
| Butter......... | 3,300 | trace | 0.01 | 0.1 | 0 |
| Cheese, cheddar.......... | 1,400 | 0.02 | 0.42 | trace | 0 |
| Eggs, whole.... | 1,140 | 0.10 | 0.29 | 0.1 | 0 |
| Milk, cow, whole........ | 160 | 0.04 | 0.17 | 0.1 | 1 |
| Fish, flesh | | | | | |
| Cod, raw..... | 0 | 0.06 | 0.09 | 2.2 | 2 |
| Halibut, raw. | 440 | 0.07 | 0.06 | 9.2 | |
| Salmon, sockeye, canned..... | 230 | 0.04 | 0.16 | 7.3 | 0 |
| Fruit | | | | | |
| Apples......... | 90 | 0.04 | 0.03 | 0.2 | 5 |
| Apricots....... | 2,790 | 0.03 | 0.05 | 0.8 | 7 |
| Bananas....... | 430 | 0.04 | 0.05 | 0.7 | 10 |
| Orange juice... | 190 | 0.08 | 0.03 | 0.2 | 49 |
| Peaches........ | 880 | 0.02 | 0.05 | 0.9 | 8 |
| Plums......... | 350 | 0.06 | 0.04 | 0.5 | 5 |
| Fowl | | | | | |
| Chicken........ | 0 | 0.08 | 0.16 | 10.2 | 0 |
| Meat | | | | | |
| Beef, lean...... | 0 | 0.08 | 0.17 | 4.7 | 0 |
| Kidney...... | 1,150 | 0.37 | 2.55 | 6.4 | 13 |
| Liver........ | 43,900 | 0.26 | 3.33 | 13.7 | 31 |
| Pork, medium.. | 0 | 0.58 | 0.14 | 3.1 | 0 |
| Kidney...... | 130 | 0.58 | 1.74 | 9.8 | 13 |
| Liver........ | 14,200 | 0.40 | 2.98 | 16.7 | 23 |
| Nuts | | | | | |
| Almonds....... | 0 | 0.25 | 0.67 | 4.6 | trace |
| Peanuts, roasted...... | 0 | 0.30 | 0.13 | 16.2 | 0 |
| Vegetables | | | | | |
| Beans, dried... | 0 | 0.67 | 0.23 | 2.2 | 2 |
| Cabbage....... | 80 | 0.06 | 0.05 | 0.3 | 50 |
| Carrots........ | 12,000 | 0.06 | 0.06 | 0.5 | |
| Kale.......... | 7,540 | 0.10 | 0.26 | 2.0 | 115 |
| Potatoes....... | 20 | 0.11 | 0.04 | 1.2 | 17 |
| Spinach........ | 9,420 | 0.11 | 0.20 | 0.6 | 59 |
| Tomatoes...... | 1,100 | 0.06 | 0.04 | 0.5 | 23 |

TABLE 54.1—*Continued*

| Food | A | Thiamine | Riboflavin | Nicotinic Acid | Ascorbic Acid |
|---|---|---|---|---|---|
| | IU/100 grams | mg. per 100 grams | | | |
| Yeast, compressed Baker's........ | 0 | 0.45 | 2.07 | 28.2 | 0 |

Values for pyridoxine, pantothenic acid, biotin and folic acid are not given, as many data now in the literature are known to be unreliable.

Taken from United States Department of Agriculture Handbook No. 8, 1950.

mg. per day led to peak excretion after 1 or 2 days; patients ill with scurvy required dosing for 7 to 10 days to reach peak excretion values.

Similar loading or saturation tests have subsequently been used in studying the nutritional status of patients with respect to other vitamins. The significance of the findings has not always been clear. There is controversy over the value of some loading tests.

Attempts have been made to measure the vitamin C status of patients by determining the amount of ascorbic acid in their blood. In human blood plasma, ascorbic acid is normally found in the range 0.7 to 1.2 mg. per 100 ml.; values between 0.4 and 0.7 are believed to indicate a mild deficiency and below 0.4 mg. per 100 ml. a severe deficiency. There is some evidence that the ascorbic acid content of the white cells may have greater diagnostic value than that of the plasma.

DISTRIBUTION. Some fruits and vegetables are rich sources of vitamin C (currants, strawberries, citrus fruits, kale, parsley, spinach, tomatoes, cress and green peppers) while others provide a negligible amount (apples, cherries, pears, plums, lettuce, radish, celery, beets). Germinating grains and pulses contain vitamin C. Cow's milk has very little, 0 to 2 mg. per 100 ml. (calves do not need it). Human milk contains about 6 mg. per 100 ml. Foods devoid of ascorbic acid include yeast, eggs, meat, fish, nuts, cereals, bread, dried peas, beans and corn (maize).

SOME OTHER ACCESSORY FACTORS. In 1936 Szent-Györgyi and his colleagues noted that guinea pigs raised on scorbutic diets did not get as much protection from pure ascorbic acid as they did from an equivalent amount of vitamin C provided in natural food sources, such as citrus fruits and peppers. The difference was attributed to a new agent which Szent-Györgyi called vitamin P because it occurs in paprika and lemon peel and was believed to be concerned with capillary permeability and fragility. Other workers have been unable to confirm the role of vitamin P in capillary fragility but it does appear to improve utilization and/or storage of vitamin C. A number of pure compounds possess vitamin P activity. These are flavone glucosides: *rutin* (from tobacco and buckwheat), *hespiridin* and *eriodictin* (from lemon peel) and *esculin* (from horse chestnuts). The pure flavone glucosides are much less active than crude concentrates. Thus neither can properly be called vitamin P.

Joint stiffness has been observed in guinea pigs fed diets rich in milk (Wulzen and Bahrs). The condition has been confirmed in several laboratories. Extensive calcification of the joints, body wall and cavity occurs, and profound changes have been noted in the skull and teeth. Difficulties in assaying the protective principle have interfered with its isolation and identification. A number of steroids possess some antistiffness potency. The subject is still in an unsatisfactory state.

As an outgrowth of studies on rheumatic fever (Coburn, 1945, 1954), it was found that an active fraction from egg yolk will inhibit experimental anaphylactic arthritis in guinea pigs. Certain other lipid-rich materials were found to possess anti-inflammatory activity, e.g., peanut (arachis) oil and soybean lecithin. The active principle has been isolated from the latter source and identified as *N*-(2-hydroxyethyl)-palmitamide.

### ANTIMETABOLITES AND ANTIVITAMINS

It has long been known that when a small alteration occurs in the molecular structure of a metabolite, some (and often all) of its activity is lost. In some cases the new compound may actually antagonize the biological action of the metabolite; it is then called an antimetabolite. About fifty years ago chemists found that enzyme action is often inhibited by substances whose molecular structure resembles that of the substrate. Innumerable examples have since come to light.[4] Kinetic studies have indicated that these effects are due to combination of the unnatural substance with the enzyme to form a

more stable compound, thus blocking normal functioning of the enzyme. In some cases the union is so firm that the combination is classed as irreversible; in such a case the reaction is essentially a complete blocking, or poisoning, of the enzyme. In others, a large excess of the natural substrate can displace the unnatural substance from its union with the enzyme. This latter situation is spoken of as *competitive inhibition*. Antivitamins are compounds (antimetabolites) that antagonize the action of vitamins; they often function as competitive inhibitors of vital processes.

Antivitamin action was probably first observed in 1938 by Woolley, Strong, Madden and Elvehjem. Dogs suffering from nicotinic acid deficiency were given two analogous compounds, pyridine-3-sulfonic acid (II) and 3-acetylpyridine (III), to see whether these structures retained any protective properties. Surprisingly, the condition of the dogs was made worse.

About two years later Woods showed that PABA neutralizes the antibacterial action of sulfanilamide, and he suggested that this effect is due to competitive inhibition of some essential metabolic reaction. Fildes (1940) suggested that a series of useful new chemotherapeutic agents might be produced by synthesizing compounds closely resembling vitamins or essential metabolites, but with some small structural change. Within a few months McIlwain showed that pyridine-3-sulfonic acid (II) does inhibit several bacteria that require nicotinic acid, and that growth was resumed when a large excess of nicotinic acid was added to the medium. Since that time a large number of "antivitamins" that work in bacterial cultures have been found. Only a few of these have been shown to exert their effects in animals. A few of these have powerful chemotherapeutic effects and are used in medical practice, e.g., *p*-aminosalicylic acid in tuberculosis, pyrimethamine in malaria and A-methopterin in leukemia.

Several better known examples of antivitamins will be mentioned. Pyrithiamine (thiamine with the thiazole ring replaced by pyridine), produces a characteristic thiamine deficiency in mice. Oxythiamine (in which the amino group of the pyrimidine ring is replaced by hydroxyl) also causes death, but without the signs of polyneuritis produced by the pyridine compound. Oxythiamine prevents the *formation* of cocarboxylase; its diphosphate prevents *utilization* of this coenzyme.

---

[4] Malonic acid, for example, is a competitive inhibitor of succinic dehydrogenase.

    Malonic acid         Succinic acid

Powerful antiriboflavin activity in mice is displayed by an analog in which the pyrimidine ring is replaced by a 2:4-dinitrobenzene ring. Desoxypyridoxine (in which the $-CH_2OH$ group on position 4 is replaced by $CH_3$) produces signs of pyridoxine deficiency in chicks, rats and man. Recent evidence suggests that the analogue is inactive until it is phosphorylated in the body; the resulting ester combines with the apoenzyme and prevents the normal union of pyridoxal phosphate with the protein(s) to form the amino acid decarboxylase(s). Methoxypyridoxine (in which the same $-CH_2OH$ group is changed to $-CH_2OCH_3$) is an antivitamin in chicks, but rats and mice are able to convert it to pyridoxine.

The antituberculosis drug, *isoniazid*, causes signs of pyridoxal deficiency in man, but not by competitive inhibition; the vitamin aldehyde reacts with the drug to form the inert isonicotinyl hydrazone of pyridoxal.

Pantoyltaurine, in which the carboxyl group of pantothenic acid is replaced by a sulfonic acid $(SO_3H)$ group, displays competitive inhibition of the vitamin in a number of bacteria but is not inhibitory in animals. Although pyridine-3-sulfonic acid inhibits growth of some bacteria it does not produce nicotinamide deficiency in vertebrates. However, 3-acetylpyridine does compete in vertebrates, and either nicotinic acid or its amide can reverse the inhibition, but it is not an antivitamin for bacteria. A large number of antagonists of folic acid have been described; two of the more potent are 4-amino-pteroylglutamic acid, commonly called aminopterin and A-methopterin (4-amino-$N^{10}$-methylpteroylglutamic acid). From the observation that substances containing the 2:4-diaminopyrimidine nucleus are antagonists of folic acid in certain microorganisms, but possess low toxicity for mammals, has come a powerful antimalarial drug, pyrimethamine = Daraprim. A whole family of hydroxycoumarins substituted in the 3-position display antivitamin K properties. Even salicyclic acid has anticoagulant action that is reversible by vitamin K.

The combination of avidin with biotin to form an inactive compound and the interference of phytin (in cereals) with the absorption of calcium, which indirectly affects the requirement for vitamin D, are examples of vitamin anagonists that do not act as competitive inhibitors.

An enzyme, thiaminase, occurs in several species of fresh and salt water fish and other marine creatures. When these lake- or sea-foods are fed raw to foxes or other animals a form of paralysis (Chastek) develops that can be cured by giving extra thiamine.

Antagonists of amino acids, purines, pyrimidines, of hormones and of other metabolites are known but cannot be discussed here. An interesting compound which blocks the citric acid cycle is fluoroacetic acid. It is accepted by cells as if it were acetic acid and appears to cause no damage until it becomes fluorocitric acid. Here it competes with citric acid and quickly causes death of the cell. Some plants, by concentrating fluorides from the soil (when an excess is present) become toxic to cattle; the seeds of ratsbane contain a poisonous fluorinated fatty acid which exerts its lethal effect in this way. Many of the insecticides and herbicides now available act by competitive inhibition of some vital function of the insect or plant being controlled. Woolley has published a book on antimetabolites and Albert has recently reviewed the subject.

## REFERENCES

AXELROD, A. E. AND PRUZANSKY, J. Vitamins & Hormones, 1955, **13**, 1.

BEST, C. H , LUCAS, C. C. AND RIDOUT, J. H. Brit. M. Bull., 1956, **12**, 9.

COWARD, K. H. Biological Standardization of the vitamins. Ed. 2, Baillière, Tindall & Cox, London, 1947.

DAY, P. L. Vitamins & Hormones, 1944, **2**, 71.

EDDY, W. H. AND DALLDORF, G. The avitaminoses. Williams & Wilkins, Baltimore, 1944.

FOLLIS, R. H. JR. The pathology of nutritional diseases. Charles C Thomas, Springfield, Ill., 1948.

GOODHART, R. S. Vitamin therapy today. Medical Clinics of North America. W. B. Saunders Company, Philadelphia, 1956, **40**, No. 5.

GYÖRGY, P. Vitamin methods. Ed. 2, Academic Press, Inc. New York, 1951.

HARRIS, L. J. Vitamins in theory and practice. Ed. 4, Cambridge University Press, 1955.

KON, S. K. AND PORTER, J. W. G. Vitamins & Hormones, 1954, **12**, 53.

MAPSON, L. W. Brit. M. Bull., 1956, **12**, 73.

MCCOLLUM, E. V. Nutrition Rev., 1956, **14**, 257.

MICKELSEN, O. Vitamins & Hormones, 1956, **14**, 1.

MELLANBY, E. Nutrition and disease. The interaction of clinical and experimental work. Oliver & Boyd, Edinburgh, 1934.

PETT, L. B. Vitamins & Hormones, 1955, **13**, 214.

ROSENBERG, H. R. Chemistry and physiology of the vitamins. Interscience, New York, 1945.

SEBRELL, W. H. Harvey Lectures, 1943–44, **39**, 288.

SPIES, T. D. J. A. M. A., 1958, **167**, 675.

YOUNG, E. G. Canad. Bull. on Nutrition 1953, **3**, No. 1.

Bulletin. Canad. Council on Nutrition 1950, **2**, No. 1.

Recommended Dietary Allowances. Nat. Acad. Sci., Nat. Res. Co. Washington, 1953, No. 302; 1958, No. 589.

Recent Research on Vitamins. Brit. M. Bull. 1956, **12**, 1.

### Vitamin A

HOPKINS, F. G. J. Physiol. 1912, **44**, 425.

MCCOLLUM, E. V. AND DAVIS, M. J. Biol. Chem. 1913, **15**, 167. Ibid., 1914, **19**, 245.

OSBORNE, T. B. AND MENDEL, L. B.   J. Biol. Chem.
1913, **15**, 311. Ibid., 1913–14, **16**, 423.
STEENBOCK, H. Science, 1919, **50**, 352.

### Monographs and Reviews

COLLINS, F. D. Biol. Reviews of the Cambridge
Phil. Soc. 1954, **29**, 453.
DOWLING, J. E. AND WALD, G. Proc. Nat. Acad.
Sc. 1958, **44**, 648.
HARRIS, R. S., INHOFFEN, H. H., MASON, K. E.,
MATTSON, F. H., MILAS, N. A., POMMER, H.,
WALD, G. AND WOLBACH, S. B. The Vitamins.
Vol. I. Ch. 1, 1954.
JEGHERS, H. AND MARRARO, H. Amer. J. Clin.
Nutrition, 1958, **6**, 335.
LOWE, J. S. AND MORTON, R. A. Vitamins & Hor-
mones, 1956, **14**, 97.
NIEMAN, C. AND OBLINK, H. J. K. Vitamins &
Hormones, 1954, **12**, 691.
RUBIN, S. H. AND DE RITTER, E. Vitamins & Hor-
mones, 1954, **12**, 102.
RUSHTON, W. A. H., CAMPBELL, F. W., HAGINS,
W. A, AND BRINDLEY, G. S. Optica Acta, 1954, **1**,
183.
Symposium on vitamin A. Brit. J. Nutrition 1951,
**5**, 94.

### Vitamin D

HESS, A. F. AND WEINSTOCK, M.   J. Biol. Chem.
1924, **62**, 301.
HULDSCHINSKY, K. Deutsche med. Wchnschr.
1919, **45**, 712.
MELLANBY, E. Brit. Med. Res. Council, Spec. Rep.
No. 161, 1921. Ibid., No. 93, 1925.
STEENBOCK, H. AND BLACK, A.   J. Biol. Chem.
1924, **61**, 405.

### Monographs and Reviews

BILLS, C. E. Physiol. Rev., 1935, **15**, 1.
BILLS, C. E., HARRIS, R. S., JONES, J. J., KANOF,
A. AND KRAMER, B. The Vitamins. Vol. II, Ch.
6, 1954.
FRASER, D. AND SALTER, R. B. Pediat. Clin. North
America, 1958.
IRVING, J. T. Vitamins & Hormones, 1957, **15**, 292.
LAURENS, H. Physiol. Rev., 1928, **8**, 1.
MELLANBY, E. Physiol. Rev., 1928, **8**, 545.
NICOLAYSEN, R. AND EEG-LARSEN, N. Vitamins &
Hormones, 1953, **11**, 29.

### Vitamin E

EVANS, H. M. AND BISHOP, K. S. Science, 1922,
**55**, 650.
MATTILL, H. A. AND CONKLIN, R. E.   J. Biol. Chem.
1920, **44**, 137.
SURE, B.   J. Biol. Chem. 1924, **58**, 693.

### Monographs and Reviews

HARRIS, P. L., HARRIS, R. S., MASON, K. E. AND
MATTILL, H. A. The Vitamins. Vol. III, Ch. 17,
1954.
HICKMAN, K. C. D. AND HARRIS, P. L. Advances in
Enzymology, 1946, **6**, 469.
MOORE, T. Vitamin E. Brit. M. Bull. 1956, **12**, 44.
Biological Antioxidants. First to Fifth Confer-
ence. Josiah Macy, Jr., Foundation, New York,
1946–1950.

### Vitamin K

ALMQUIST, H. J., HARRIS, R. S. AND OWEN, C. A.
JR. The Vitamins, Vol. II, Ch. 9, 1954.
ALMQUIST, H. J. AND STOKSTAD, E. L. R.   J. Biol.
Chem., 1935, **111**, 105.
BUTT, H. R. AND SNELL, A. M. Vitamin K. Saun-
ders, Philadelphia, 1941.
DAM, H. Biochem. J., 1935, **29**, 1273; Vitamins
& Hormones, 1948, **6**, 28.

### Lipoic Acid

REED, L. J. Physiol. Rev. 1953, **33**, 544.

### Thiamine

ELVEHJEM, C. A.   J. A. M. A., 1948, **138**, 960.
EMMETT, A. D. AND LUROS, G. O.   J. Biol. Chem.,
1920, **43**, 625.
EVANS, H. M. AND LEPKOVSKY, S.   J. Biol. Chem.,
1929, **83**, 269.
FARRER, K. T. H. Biochem. J., 1947, **41**, 167.
MCCOLLUM, E. V. AND DAVIS, M. J. Biol. Chem.,
1915, **20**, 641. Ibid, 1915, **23**, 231.
PLATT, B. S. AND LU, G. D. Biochem. J., 1939, **33**,
1525.

### Monographs and Reviews

HARRIS, R. S., JANSEN, B. C. P., SEBRELL, W. H.,
JR., UNNA, K. R. AND WUEST, H. M. The Vita-
mins. Vol. III, Ch. 16, 1954.
REED, L. J. Physiol. Rev., 1953, **33**, 544.

### Riboflavin

EMMETT, A. D. AND MCKIM, L. H.   J. Biol. Chem.,
1917, **32**, 409.
SEBRELL, W. H. AND BUTLER, R. E.   U. S. Pub.
Health Rep., 1938, **53**, 2282. Ibid., 1939, **54**, 2121.
SYDENSTRICKER, V. P. Am. J. Pub. Health, 1941,
**31**, 344.

### Monographs and Reviews

BRO-RASMUSSEN, F. Nutrition Abstr. & Rev.,
1958, **28**, 1, 369.
GYÖRGY, P. Nutrition Rev., 1954, **12**, 97.
HARRIS, R. S., HEGSTED, D. M., HORWITT, M. K.,
SNELL, E. E. AND WAGNER-JAUREGG, T. The Vita-
mins. Vol. III, Ch. 15, 1954.
SNELL, E. E. Physiol. Rev. 1953, **33**, 509.

### Nicotinic Acid

ELVEHJEM, C. A., MADDEN, R. J., STRONG, F. M.
AND WOOLLEY, D. W.   J. Am. Chem. Soc., 1937,
**59**, 1767.
GOLDBERGER, J., WARING, C. H. AND WILLETS,
D. G. United States Pub. Health Rep., 1915,
**30**, 3117, and subsequent articles by Goldberger
and his associates up to 1927.
KREHL, W. A., TEPLEY, L. J., SARMA, P. S. AND
ELVEHJEM, C. A. Science, 1945, **101**, 489.

### Monographs and Reviews

HARRIS, R. S., HUNDLEY, J. M. AND SNELL, E. E.
The Vitamins. Vol. II, Ch. 10, 1954.
SYDENSTRICKER, V. P. Amer. J. Clin. Nutrition,
1958, **6**, 409.

## Pyridoxine

BIRCH, T. W., GYÖRGY, P. AND HARRIS, L. J. Biochem. J., 1935, **29**, 2830.

GYÖRGY, P. Amer. J. Clin. Nutrition, 1954, **2**, 44.

WITTEN, P. W. AND HOLMAN, R. T. Arch. Biochem. 1952, **41**, 266.

### Monographs and Reviews

GYÖRGY, P., HARRIS, R. S., KEEVIL, C. E. JR., KERESZTESY, J. C., SHERMAN, H., SNELL, E. E., UMBREIT, W. W. AND UNNA, K. R. The Vitamins, Vol. III, Ch. 14, 1954.

SNELL, E. E. Vitamins & Hormones, 1958, **16**, 78.

WAYNE, L., WILL, J. J., FRIEDMAN, B. I., BECKER, L. S. AND VILTER, R. W. A. M. A. Arch. Int. Med., 1958, **101**, 143.

## Pantothenic Acid

EASTCOTT, E. V. J. Phys. Chem., 1928, **32**, 1094.

FELDBERG, W. AND MANN, T. J. Physiol., 1946, **104**, 411.

HOAGLAND, M. B. AND NOVELLI, G. D. J. Biol. Chem., 1954, **207**, 767.

LUCAS, G. H. W. J. Phys. Chem., 1924, **28**, 1180.

WILDIERS, E. La Cellulé, 1901, **18**, 313.

### Monographs and Reviews

BRIGGS, G. M., DAFT, F. S., HARRIS, R. S., LEPKOVSKY, S., LIPMANN, F., RALLI, E. AND SNELL, E. E. The Vitamins, Vol. II, Ch. 11, 1954.

LIPMANN, F. Advances in Enzymology, 1946, **6**, 231.

NOVELLI, G. D. Physiol. Rev. 1953, **33**, 525.

## Biotin

BATEMAN, W. G. J. Biol. Chem., 1916, **26**, 263.

BOAS, M. A. Biochem. J., 1927, **21**, 712.

GYÖRGY, P., MELVILLE, D. B., BURK, D. AND DU VIGNEAUD, V. Science, 1940, **91**, 243.

KÖGL, F. AND TÖNNIS, B. Z. Physiol. Chem., 1936, **242**, 43.

PARSONS, H. T. AND KELLY, E. J. Biol. Chem., 1933, **100**, 645.

### Monographs and Reviews

GYÖRGY, P., HARRIS, R. S. AND SNELL, E. E. The Vitamins, Vol. I. Ch. 4, 1954.

HERTZ, R. Physiol. Rev., 1946, **26**, 479.

LICHSTEIN, H. C. Vitamins & Hormones, 1951, **9**, 27.

## p-Aminobenzoic Acid

ANSBACHER, S. Science, 1941, **93**, 164.

FILDES, P. Lancet, 1940, **238**, 955.

RUBBO, S. D. AND GILLESPIE, J. M. Nature, 1940, **146**, 838.

WOODS, D. D. Brit. J. Exper. Path., 1940, **21**, 74.

YEOMANS, A., SNYDER, J. C., MURRAY, E. S., ZARAFONETIS, C. J. D. AND ECKE, R. S. J. A. M. A. 1944, **126**, 349.

### Monographs and Reviews

HARRIS, R. S., SCOTT, C. C., TAVORMINA, P. A., WRIGHT, L. D. AND WUEST, H. M. The Vitamins, Vol. III, Ch. 12, 1954.

## Folic Acid

BROCKMAN, J. A. JR., et al., J. Am. Chem. Soc., 1950, **72**, 4325.

MITCHELL, H. K., SNELL, E. E. AND WILLIAMS, R. J. J. Am. Chem. Soc. 1941, **63**, 2284; Ibid., 1944, **66**, 271.

### Monographs and Reviews

BETHELL, F. H., HARRIS, R. S. AND STOKSTAD, E. L. R. in The Vitamins, Vol. III, Ch. 13, 1954.

DARBY, W. J. Vitamins & Hormones, 1947, **5**, 119.

PETERING, H. G. Physiol. Rev., 1952, **32**, 197.

TRUFANOV, A. V. Am. J. Clin. Nutrition, 1959, **7**, 302.

WELCH, A. D. Nutrition Rev., 1957, **15**, 33.

## Vitamin B₁₂ (Cyanocobalamin)

BONNETT, R., CANNON, J. R., JOHNSON, A. W., SUTHERLAND, I. AND TODD, A. R. Nature, 1955, **176**, 328.

HODGKIN, D. C., PICKWORTH, J. ROBERTSON, J. H., TRUEBLOOD, K. N., PRO'SEN, R. J. AND WHITE, J. G. Nature, 1955, **176**, 325.

MINOT, G. R. AND MURPHY, W. P. J. A. M. A., 1926, **87**, 470; Ibid., 1927, **89**, 759.

RICKES, E. L., BRINK, N. G., KONIUSZY, F. R., RUBIN, M. AND BIRD, H. R. J. Biol. Chem., 1946, **163**, 387.

SHORB, M. S. Science, 1948, **107**, 397.

### Monographs and Reviews

BETHELL, F. H., FOLKERS, K. E., HARRIS, R. S., JUKES, T. H., WILLIAMS, W. L. AND WOLF, D. E. The Vitamins, Vol. I, Ch. 3, 1954.

UNGLEY, C. C. Vitamins & Hormones, 1955, **13**, 139.

## Inositol

BEST, C. H., LUCAS, C. C., PATTERSON, J. M. AND RIDOUT, J. H. Biochem. J., 1951, **48**, 448. Ibid., 1951, **48**, 452.

(Note: In this article an unfortunate transposition of Figs. 1 and 3 was not detected in the galley proof. The curves over the caption "Fig. 3" on p. 456 represent data with fat-free diets and should be located on p. 454; the curves over caption Fig. 1 are from rats fed diets with 12% fat and should be on p. 456).

EASTCOTT, E. V. J. Phys. Chem. 1928, **32**, 1094.

GAVIN, G. AND McHENRY, E. W. J. Biol. Chem., 1941, **39**, 485.

GAVIN, G., PATTERSON, J. M. AND McHENRY, E. W. J. Biol. Chem., 1943, **148**, 275.

WOOLLEY, D. W. J. Biol. Chem., 1940, **136**, 113. Ibid., 1941, **139**, 29.

### Monographs and Reviews

CHARGAFF, E., CUNHA, T. J., HARRIS, R. S., LARDY, H. A., LIVERMORE, A. H., MILHORAT, A. T., SNELL, E. E. AND WEIDLEIN, E. R. JR. The Vitamins, Vol. II, Ch. 8, 1954.

## Choline

BEST, C. H., HERSHEY, J. M. AND HUNTSMAN, M. E. Am. J. Physiol., 1932, **101**. 7P.

CHANNON, H. J. AND WILKINSON, H. Biochem. J., 1935, **29**, 350.

HERSHEY, J. M. Am. J. Physiol., 1930, **93**, 657P.

TUCKER, H. F. AND ECKSTEIN, H. C. J. Biol. Chem., 1937, **121**, 479.

*Monographs and Reviews*

BEST, C. H. Proc. Roy. Soc., London. ser. B., 1956, **145**, 151.

BEST, C. H., GRIFFITH, W. H., HARRIS, R. S., HARTROFT, W. S., LUCAS, C. C. AND NYC, J. F. The Vitamins, Vol. II, Ch. 5, 1954.

DU VIGNEAUD, V. A trail of research. Cornell University Press, Ithaca, N. Y. 1952.

LUCAS, C. C. Am. J. Clin. Nutrition, 1958, **6**, 504.

OLSEN, R. A. Am. J. Clin. Nutrition, 1958, **6**, 197.

*Ascorbic Acid*

HOLST, A. AND FRÖLICH, T. J. Hyg., 1907, **7**, 634.

SZENT-GYÖRGYI, A. AND HAWORTH, W. N. Nature, 1933, **131**, 24.

WAUGH, W. A. AND KING, C. G. J. Biol. Chem., 1932, **97**, 325.

UHL, E. Am. J. Clin. Nutrition, 1958, **6**, 146.

*Monographs and Reviews*

HARRIS, R. S., MAPSON, L. W., OLLIVER, M., REID, M. E., SMITH, F. AND VILTER, R. W. The Vitamins, Vol. II, Ch. 2, 1954

JACQUES CARTIER et "La grosse maladie", reprinted for XIX International Physiol. Congress, Montreal, Canada, 1953.

LIND, J. Treatise on Scurvy. London, 1757. Quoted from Med. Res. Coun. London. Sp. Report, No. 167, 1932.

*Accessory Food Factors*

BENTSAITH, A., RUSZNYÁK, ST. AND SZENT-GYÖRGYI, A. Nature, 1936, **138**, 798.

COBURN, A. F. Am. J. Dis. Children, 1945, **70**, 339.

COBURN, A. F., GRAHAM, C. E. AND HANINGER, J. J. Exper. Med., 1954, **100**, 425.

KUEHL, F. A., JACOB, T. A., GANLEY, O. H., ORMOND, R. E. AND MEISINGER, M. A. P. J. Am. Chem. Soc., 1957, **79**, 5577.

*Monographs and Reviews*

CHELDELIN, V. B. The Vitamins, Vol. III, Ch. 18, 1954.

*Antimetabolites and Antivitamins*
*Monographs and Reviews*

ALBERT, A. Brit. M. Bull., 1956, **12**, 67.

WOOLLEY, D. W. Physiol. Rev., 1947, **27**, 308.

WOOLLEY, D. W. A study of antimetabolites. Chapman & Hall, London, 1952.

# 55

# DIETARY REQUIREMENTS

In planning a diet the following requirements must be taken into account:
1. The total caloric value.
2. The proportions of the different foodstuffs—carbohydrate, fats, and protein.
3. The mineral constituents.
4. The vitamin content.

In order that the body shall not be forced to consume its own tissues for fuel, the caloric value of the ingested food for 24 hours must balance the energy (work plus heat) output by the individual during the same period. The basal metabolic rate is obtained by direct determination (ch. 44) or by calculation from the subject's height and weight. The average extra caloric allowances for different grades of muscular activity are given in table 55.3 (p. 947).

## Sample Calculation of Caloric Requirement

The approximate basal metabolism of an average size man (20 to 40 years of age) may be calculated as follows: the energy output per square meter is 40 Calories per hour (p. 764); the average surface area of 1.8 square meters corresponds to 72 Calories per hour. While the subject is asleep (8 hours) the metabolism is about 90 per cent of this value; during this period about 520 Calories are required. The basal requirement for 16 waking hours (16 × 72) is about another 1150 Calories. The hourly work increment of those in sedentary occupations varies from 20 Calories for writing to 45 for tailoring while in the more strenuous occupations it varies from 180 (heavy carpentry) to 380

|  | Estimated daily Calorie requirement | |
|  | Clerk | Miner |
|---|---|---|
| Metabolism of sleep (8 hours) | 520 | 520 |
| Basal metabolism (16 hours) | 1150 | 1150 |
| Nonwork allowance (8 hours) | 400 | 400 |
| Work allowance (8 hours) | 300 | 3040 |
| Subtotal | 2370 | 5110 |
| 10 per cent for specific dynamic action | 240 | 510 |
| Total | 2610 | 5620 |

(mining, lumbering) or more. To the total so estimated, 10 per cent is added to cover the increased metabolism (specific dynamic action) due to the food itself.

For more precise calculation of the caloric requirements, other factors must be taken into account, e.g., the body weight and the temperature at which the work is performed. An allowance, or a deduction of 3 per cent is made, respectively, for each 10 degrees F. rise or fall from the average temperature (70°F.). Thus, if the total metabolism as calculated above is 5620 Calories, but the temperature is 60°F., the diet is planned for a total energy expenditure of (5620 + 170) = 5790 Calories. In performing certain types of work, such as walking, ascending stairs, or any work which entails lifting the body or its heavier parts, the energy expenditure is more nearly proportional to the body weight raised to the power 0.7, than to the surface area.

## The Relation of Age and Sex to the Caloric Requirement

Women have a somewhat lower basal metabolic rate than men, and, generally speaking, they expend less energy in muscular work; their food requirement is proportionately less, approximately 83 per cent of a man's or about 2000 to 3000 Calories per day. The calorie intake should be about 20 per cent greater during the latter part of pregnancy, and about 30 per cent greater during lactation than at ordinary times.

Children require, weight-for-weight, a greater food allowance than the average adult for three reasons: (a) Their basal metabolic rate is considerably higher, especially at the younger ages. (b) A proportion of the food material is utilized for building body tissue. (c) Children, as a rule, expend more energy in muscular activity than the average adult. For example, a boy of 16 years of age, of average physique and taking an active part in games, requires a daily energy intake equal to that of a man—from 3000 to 4000 Calories or from 50 to 70 Calories per kilogram of body weight per day (average adult requirement, 46 Calories per kilogram).

942

During the first 3 months of life the dietary requirement is about 120 Calories per kilogram. From 4 to 9 months the requirement falls to about 110, and during the ages 10 to 12 months it is about 100 Calories per kilogram. Since a child 1 year of age usually weighs about 9 to 11 kg., its dietary energy requirement is about 900 to 1100 Calories. Data for other age groups are shown in table 55.1.

### The Protein Allowance

A great deal of controversy has centered around the question of the protein requirement of the adult. Chittenden, some years ago, made a study of the subject in a series of experiments upon himself and groups of students, soldiers, and athletes. He showed that nitrogen equilibrium could be maintained upon a total daily intake of 25 grams or less of first-class protein.[1] Upon an ordinary mixed diet containing proteins of varying biological values, nitrogen equilibrium was established on an allowance of between 40 and 50 grams for a man of average weight (70 kg.). This is from 0.6 to 0.7 grams of protein per kilogram. Chittenden claimed that the larger protein intake recommended by previous observers, (e.g., 120 grams by Voit) was unnecessary, if not actually deleterious to health. It was contended that the renal work entailed in the excretion of large quantities of nitrogen was conducive to kidney disease. Many other ills were ascribed to the excessive consumption of protein. He also reduced the total energy intake to around 2000 Calories and stated that the more liberal diets were dictated by appetite rather than by physiological necessity. His subjects, he claimed, could carry out their usual activities just as well upon such a diet and enjoyed better health than they had previously upon their customary fare.

Since nitrogen equilibrium can be established upon a protein intake of around 40 grams per day, it *would* seem unnecessary to give more. The excess amount must obviously be catabolized to furnish energy, which can be furnished more economically by non-nitrogenous food[2] or be simply stored as carbohydrate or fat. The weak point in this argument is, as many critics of the low pro-

[1] The daily urinary excretion of N on a nitrogen-free diet but of adequate calorie value is around 3 grams. This represents the catabolism of 18.75 grams (3 × 6.25) of tissue protein.

[2] Calories furnished by protein are by far the most expensive. It has been calculated that 1,000,-000 Calories derived from cane sugar require for their production 0.15 acre, as compared with 17 acres necessary to produce the same amount of energy as represented by beef protein.

#### TABLE 55.1

*Effect of age and sex on estimated calorie requirements*

(Recommended daily allowances—F.A.O., 1957)*

| Age group | Calories per Day | | |
|---|---|---|---|
| | Male and Females | Males | Females |
| *years* | | | |
| 1 | 1150 | | |
| 2 | 1300 | | |
| 3 | 1450 | | |
| 4 to 6 | 1700 | | |
| 7 to 9 | 2100 | | |
| 10 to 12 | 2500 | | |
| 13 to 15 | | 3100 | 2600 |
| 16 to 19 | | 3600 | 2400 |
| 20 to 30 | | 3200 | 2300 |
| 31 to 40 | | 3100 | 2250 |
| 41 to 50 | | 3000 | 2150 |
| 51 to 60 | | 2800 | 2000 |
| 61 to 70 | | 2550 | 1800 |
| Over 70 | | 2200 | 1600 |

* Allowances are estimated for individuals engaged in moderate physical activity. They are excessive for those in sedentary occupations and low for laborers.

tein dietary have pointed out, that the ability of the body to adapt itself for a few months to a restricted protein intake is not proof that such constitutes the physiological optimum. It has also been pointed out that custom has dictated for persons in temperate climates a higher protein intake than Chittenden's standard. The daily protein intake per person in the United States is between 90 and 120 grams. Even the diets of the Japanese and of the hardier races of India, according to McCay, contain a greater quantity of protein than that recommended by Chittenden. Tribes in India who are accustomed to diets with the higher protein content are healthier and of better physique than those subsisting upon a more restricted protein intake. The value of a generous protein allowance is also illustrated by the report of Orr and Gilks concerning two African tribes who, though living side by side, eat quite different diets. The members of the meat-eating Masai tribe are some 5 inches taller and 50 pounds heavier than the vegetarian Akikuyu, and their muscular power is about 50 per cent greater. The Masai are comparatively free from disease, whereas bone deformities, dental caries, anemia, pulmonary diseases and tropical ulcer are prevalent among the Akikuyu. Arthritis, however, was found to be much more common among the Masai.

Protein probably plays an important part which is not revealed by short-term experiments based upon the study of nitrogen balances. There are indications that physical fitness and resistance to disease are associated with the higher protein intakes. There is little evidence, on the other hand, that a high consumption of protein causes renal or other diseases. Thomas records that the Greenland Eskimos are almost exclusively carnivorous, consuming enormous quantities of meat (and up to 300 grams of fat per day); yet renal and cardiovascular disease is not common among them. The Arctic explorers Stefanson and Anderson showed no ill-effects, either upon blood pressure or renal function, after living for 12 months upon a diet composed entirely of meat (reported by Lieb). The effect of a high protein diet upon established renal disease is another matter.

It now appears than the true protein requirement for the average man lies about midway between the two extremes of Chittenden and the older observers. A generous allowance is from 70 to 100 grams (somewhat more than 1 gram per kilogram of body weight) and about 15 per cent less than this for women.

Because of the large differences in the nutritive value of individual proteins any quantitative statement on protein requirement must be related specific proteins or types of protein. Milk, eggs, and meat have long been regarded as of excellent quality, and their superior value for human beings has been confirmed by research on infants and adults. The F.A.O. Committee on Protein Requirement (1957) decided to express requirements in terms of a *reference protein* which they defined as of "high nutritive value," citing the proteins of milk, eggs, and meat as examples. Later, from a study of human requirements for individual essential amino acids, a provisional *amino acid pattern* was put forward. Whereas neither milk nor egg proteins correspond precisely in composition with this "ideal" pattern, they are similar. It is assumed that a hypothetical protein containing amino acids in these ratios would be of high biological value, falling into the category of a reference protein.

The F.A.O. Committee, emphasizing the provisional nature of their recommendations, tentatively suggested 0.35 gram per kilogram of body weight as the average *minimum* requirement of adults for *high quality protein*. The requirement is greater in children and increases to a maximum in infancy. Unfortunately, the data are least reliable in this highly critical period of maximum rate of growth. Possibly it is as high as 2.3 grams per kilogram for suckling infants during the first few weeks, falling to about 1.5 by 6 months, to 1.0 gram per kilogram at about 3 years of age, and levels off between 0.6 and 0.7 grams per kilogram of body weight from 6 to 11 years. Just before puberty, a short-lived but acute spurt in growth occurs (in girls at 10 to 14 years, in boys at 13 to 16 years of age) during which the requirement for high quality protein is temporarily increased, being not lower than 0.8 gram per kilogram. Following this period the requirement falls slowly to the adult value of 0.35 gram per kilogram of body weight.

During pregnancy an additional 10 grams of high quality protein should be added per day to the value calculated using the adult factor (0.35), and during lactation the recommended daily increment is 30 grams. In many pathological states and during convalescence the protein requirement is increased, but it is impossible to give data of general applicability. Extremely heavy work (lumbering, mining, harvesting, and the like, without mechanical aids) causes an increase in muscle mass and a substantial increase in protein requirement.

The emphasis today is being placed on the dietary supply of essential amino acids and total utilizable nitrogen rather than on the protein content of a foodstuff or ration. Knowledge of the average requirement of human infants, children, and adults, for each of the essential amino acids is still fragmentary but is becoming increasingly available largely from the laboratories of W. C. Rose, Ruth M. Leverton, L. E. Holt, Jr., H. H. Mitchell, Marian E. Swendseid, and M. S. Dunn, and their associates. Many others have made important contributions. Only eight amino acids appear to be essential in the diet to maintain nitrogen equilibrium in adults. Histidine is essential for the growing child. Tentative values are shown in table 55.2. Whereas the adequacy of the essential amino acids determines the nutritional quality of a protein, the pattern of the nonessential amino acids is important for several reasons: (a) tyrosine can spare phenylalanine, (b) cystine can spare methionine, and (c) unless an ample supply of nonessential amino acids (or other forms of utilizable nitrogen) is provided, the need for essential amino acids will be increased because they will be used to make nonessential amino acids that are inadequately supplied by the ration.

It must be remembered that if one diet is higher

TABLE 55.2

*Suggested average minimal requirements for essential amino acids*

(milligrams per kilogram body weight)

| | Isoleucine | Leucine | Lysine | Phenylalanine | Sulfur-containing Acids | | | Threonine | Tryptophan | Valine |
|---|---|---|---|---|---|---|---|---|---|---|
| | | | | | Methionine | Cystine | Total | | | |
| Infants | 90 | ? | 90 | 90* | 85 | 0 | 85 | 60 | 30 | 85 |
| | | | | | 65 | Present | — | | | |
| Men | 10.4 | 9.9 | 8.8 | 4.3* | 1.5 | 11.6 | 13.1 | 6.5 | 2.9 | 8.8 |
| | | | | 13.3† | 13.2 | 0 | 13.2 | | | |
| Women | 5.2 | 7.1 | 3.3 | 3.1* | 4.7 | 0.5 | 5.2 | 3.5 | 2.1 | 9.2 |
| | | | | | 3.8 | 2.2 | 6.0 | | | |
| | | | | | 3.4 | 3.4 | 6.8 | | | |
| | | | | | 3.0 | 4.2 | 7.2 | | | |

\* Tyrosine present.            (Taken from F.A.O. Bulletin, No. 16, 1957.)

† Tyrosine absent.

in protein content than another, it is not necessarily superior, since the biological value depends upon the completeness of the essential amino acids provided. In very few countries is it possible for the bulk of the population to live principally on foodstuffs containing high quality proteins. In many regions wheat, rye or millet, rice, potatoes, maize, pulses, or cassava provide the major proportion of the food eaten. None of these supplies all of the essential amino acids in proper ratio or in adequate amount. As was pointed out by Osborne and Mendel many years ago, certain combinations of these vegetable proteins may supplement each other with marked improvement of nutritive properties. For example, the maize protein (which is very poor in tryptophane and lysine), the navy bean protein (deficient in methionine and tryptophane) and sesame seed protein (deficient in lysine and valine) when combined in the ratio 40:30:30 offer a product that is much improved nutritionally.

### The Indispensability of Fat

Since body fat can be derived from carbohydrate food, it might be thought that dietary fat could be dispensed with. However, this does not seem to be so. Fats provide fat-soluble vitamins and certain fatty acids (linoleic, linolenic, and arachidonic) that are essential for health which cannot be synthesized (at least not at an adequate rate) by the body. If purified fat-soluble vitamins and essential fatty acids are made available, there is no evidence that fats (glycerides) are essential components of the diet.

Although glycerides may not be dietary essentials, they increase palatability of the food and

decrease the bulk necessary to provide adequate calories.

The essential fatty acids are provided principally by plant oils, lard, egg-yolk fat, and butterfat. Highly unsaturated fatty acids are abundant in fish-liver oils, but they are of different structure from the animal oils and their value as essential fatty acids is doubtful.

In 1929, Mendel and his colleagues noted that the growth of rats on a fat-deficient ration is poor, and in the same year, Burr and Burr described a new deficiency disease (in rats) caused by the elimination of all fat from the diet. After about 3 months a scaly condition of the skin developed; later the tail became inflamed and swollen, and eventually the tip became necrotic. The feet also became swollen and sore. The hair fell out about the face, throat, and back, and sores often appeared on the body. Kidney lesions led to death. Later, Burr and his associates showed that very small amounts of either linoleic acid ($C_{18}H_{32}O_2$ with two double bonds) or linolenic ($C_{18}H_{30}O_2$ with three) produced beneficial effects in rats. More recently certain other polyunsaturated fatty acids (e.g., arachidonic, $C_{20}H_{32}O_2$, with four double bonds) have been found to possess similar activity, although the several members are not entirely equivalent in protective effect. Some restore growth and cure skin lesions, others only restore growth. Linoleic acid is the only *vegetable* acid that meets all the requirements of the animal for essential fatty acids. Arachidonic acid (found only in animal lipids) also restores growth and cures the skin defects. It appears to be from 2 to 6 times as effective as linoleic acid, depending on the methods of making the comparison. Probably arachidonic acid is the functional compound and linoleic and linolenic acids are dietary precursors. It has been suggested that conversion (in the animal) of some of the dietary linoleic acid of plant origin to arachidonic acid explains the disappearance of all the signs of deficiency. Linolenic acid, in contrast, is converted principally to a six double-bonded acid which is unable to cure the skin lesions but which does stimulate growth and fat synthesis. The wide-spread occurrence in vegetable oils of glycerides containing linoleic acid (soybean oil 50 to 60 per cent, cottonseed oil 40 to 48 per cent, and corn oil 34 to 42 per cent,) and the presence in animal fats of arachidonic acid (lard 0.4 per cent, and butterfat, a trace) makes it unlikely that deficiency of essential fatty acids will occur in man or animals eating a good variety of natural foods.

No data are available to indicate the magnitude of the human requirement for linoleic or arachidonic acids. Some workers even doubt whether the essential fatty acids are of importance in human nutrition.

There is some evidence, however, that certain eczematous conditions in the human subject are due to fatty acid deficiency. These subjects show a low content of unsaturated fatty acids in the blood lipids. Babies kept for several months upon a diet very low in fat often developed a generalized eczema which was corrected when the fat of the diet was restored. During the period of low fat feeding, the iodine number of the serum lipids of these infants was depressed. (See Burr and associates.) Fat pork, beans, and peas (vegetables relatively rich in fat) are prominent items in the diet of Canadian lumbermen and construction workers. The daily energy expenditure of some of the former workers may run to 8000 Calories. Another advantage of fat is its superior "staying power." Its digestion and absorption are extended over a much longer period than those of carbohydrates. Hunger, "emptiness," and fatigue are experienced much sooner upon a diet high in carbohydrate than upon one containing a liberal allowance of fat. The actual efficiency of fat as a fuel for muscular work as shown by Krogh and Lindhard (p. 881) and by Murlin and Marsh is from 10 to 12 per cent less than that of carbohydrate. It is often recommended that children be given a larger proportion of fat in the diet (30 to 35 per cent of the calorie intake) than is suggested for adults, 20 to 25 per cent. Actually, very little, if any, information is available on the fat *requirement* of man. It appears that fat and carbohydrate can replace each other, within wide limits, as a source of energy.

Much has been written on the comparative nutritive value of different fats. Better growth of rats was reported when diets containing butterfat were fed than when corn, cottonseed, coconut, or soybean oils were used. Later it appeared that this superiority depended upon the nature of the carbohydrate in the diet. The subject has been controversial; if there are any differences they are small.

Discovery of a statistical correlation between the concentration of cholesterol esters in the blood serum and the incidence of cardiovascular disease, led to the proposal that the incidence of atherosclerosis in adults is connected with the cholesterol content of the diet. More carefully controlled studies on patients, human volunteers, and animals revealed that dietary cholesterol has only a limited effect on the level of cholesterol esters in the serum. Epidemiological and experimental studies showed that the *fat* content of the diet is the dominant factor. Some workers believe that animal fats (especially butter) are more deleterious than vegetable oils. The effects of diet on the walls of the blood vessels and on blood-clotting are currently being studied with great vigor. A number of dietary factors appear to be involved in the enigma of atherosclerosis—the kind and amount of fat, cholesterol, protein, sulfur-containing amino acids, carbohydrate, choline, pyridoxine and possibly other vitamins, and magnesium; exercise (or lack of it) and energy balance are possibly contributing factors. Much experimental work is still necessary before proper dietary advice can be given on this subject. The preferential use of vegetable oils in cooking has been recommended. The data currently available do not warrant any drastic alteration in menus, such as *complete* elimination of eggs, bacon, and butter, as advised by some clinicians. Reduction of the intake of animal fat to minimal amounts providing palatability and variety may be desirable.

*Mineral Constituents (See pp. 72, 1005, and 1055)*

The minimal daily requirements of calcium, phosphorus and iron for the average adult (70 kg. in weight) are:

| | |
|---|---|
| Calcium | 0.8 gram |
| Phosphorus | 1.2 gram |
| Iron | 15–20 mg. |

In childhood and in pregnancy (especially in the later months) and in lactation the calcium requirement is higher than that given above. For

## TABLE 55.3

*Recommended dietary allowances (revised 1958)\**

(Food and Nutrition Board, National Research Council of the U. S. A.)

| | Calories | Protein | Calcium | Iron | Vitamin A† | Thia-min (B₁) | Ribo-flavin | Niacin (Nicoti-nic Acid) | Ascorbic Acid | Vitamin D |
|---|---|---|---|---|---|---|---|---|---|---|
| | | grams | grams | mg. | I.U. | mg.‡ | mg. | mg. | mg.‡ | I.U. |
| **Man (70 kg.)** | | | | | | | | | | |
| Sedentary | 2500 | 70 | 0.8 | 10 | 5000 | 1.3 | 1.8 | 18 | 75 | — |
| Moderately active | 3200 | 70 | 0.8 | 10 | 5000 | 1.6 | 1.8 | 21 | 75 | § |
| Very active | 4500 | 70 | 0.8 | 10 | 5000 | 2.3 | 1.8 | 30 | 75 | — |
| **Woman (58 kg.)** | | | | | | | | | | |
| Sedentary | 2100 | 58 | 0.8 | 12 | 5000 | 1.1 | 1.5 | 15 | 70 | — |
| Moderately active | 2500 | 58 | 0.8 | 12 | 5000 | 1.3 | 1.5 | 17 | 70 | § |
| Very active | 3000 | 58 | 0.8 | 12 | 5000 | 1.5 | 1.5 | 20 | 70 | — |
| Pregnancy (latter half) | (+300) | (+20) | 1.5 | 15 | 6000 | 1.4 | 2.0 | (+3) | 100 | 400 to 800 |
| Lactation | (+1000) | (+40) | 2.0 | 15 | 8000 | 1.6 | 2.5 | (+2) | 150 | 400 to 800 |
| **Children up to 12 years** | | | | | | | | | | |
| Under 1¶ | 100 per kg. | 3 to 4 per kg. | 1.0 | 6 | 1500 | 0.4 | 0.6 | 7 | 30 | 400 to 800 |
| 1 to 3‖ | 1300 | 40 | 1.0 | 7 | 2000 | 0.7 | 1.0 | 8 | 35 | § |
| 4 to 6 | 1700 | 50 | 1.0 | 8 | 2500 | 0.9 | 1.3 | 11 | 50 | — |
| 7 to 9 | 2100 | 60 | 1.0 | 10 | 3500 | 1.1 | 1.5 | 14 | 60 | — |
| 10 to 12 | 2500 | 70 | 1.2 | 12 | 4500 | 1.3 | 1.8 | 17 | 75 | — |
| **Children over 12 years** | | | | | | | | | | |
| Girls 13 to 15 | 2800 | 80 | 1.3 | 15 | 5000 | 1.4 | 2.0 | 17 | 80 | § |
| Girls 16 to 20 | 2400 | 75 | 1.3 | 15 | 5000 | 1.2 | 1.9 | 16 | 80 | — |
| Boys 13 to 15 | 3100 | 85 | 1.4 | 15 | 5000 | 1.6 | 2.1 | 21 | 90 | § |
| Boys 16 to 20 | 3600 | 100 | 1.4 | 15 | 5000 | 1.8 | 2.5 | 25 | 100 | — |

\* Tentative goal toward which to aim in planning practical dietaries; can be met by a good diet of natural food. Such a diet will also provide other minerals and vitamins, the requirements for which are less well known.

† Requirements may be less if provided as vitamin A; greater if provided chiefly as the provitamin carotene.

‡ 1 mg. of thiamin equals 333 I.U.; 1 mg. of ascorbic acid equals 20 I.U.

§ Vitamin D is undoubtedly necessary for older children and adults. When not available from sunshine, it should be provided, probably up to the minimum amounts recommended for infants.

¶ Needs of infants increase from month to month. The amounts given are for approximately 6 to 8 months. The amounts of protein and calcium needed are less if derived from human milk.

‖ Allowances are based on needs for the middle year in each group (as 2, 5, 8, etc.) and for moderate activity.

*Further Recommendations.*

The requirement for *iodine* is small; probably about 0.002 to 0.004 mg. a day for each kilogram of body weight (about 0.15 to 0.30 mg. daily for the adult). This need is easily met by the regular use of iodized salt; its use is especially important in adolescence and pregnancy.

The requirement for *copper* for adults is in the neighborhood of 1.0 to 2.0 mg. a day. Infants and children require approximately 0.05 mg. per kilogram of body weight. The requirement for copper is approximately one-tenth of that for iron.

Fatty foods, because of their high energy content, are preferred by men performing heavy work, especially in cold climates. Not only do fats provide 9 Calories per gram, as compared with 4 for carbohydrates and protein, but fat-rich foodstuffs are much lower in water content than are carbohydrate-rich foods (e.g., butter contains only 15 per cent water, bread contains 35 to 40 per cent). Thus, on a bulk or weight basis, fatty foods are up to four times as rich in energy as those low in fat.

infants and children up to 12 years the minimum is placed at 1.0 to 1.2 grams per day, and from 13 to 20 years at 1.4 for boys or from 1.3 to 1.0 for girls. In the later months of pregnancy, when from 20 to 30 grams of the mineral are being deposited in the fetus, daily allowance should be at least 1.5 grams; 2 grams should be the daily allowance during lactation. The best source of calcium for the growing child is milk, which contains about 1.3 grams per quart. Other dairy products, e.g., cheese and ice cream, are excellent sources of calcium. Cereals also are rich in calcium though much of it is not absorbed and retained; meat contains insignificant amounts of this element (see table 55.3) (p. 947).

It is unnecessary, as a rule, to pay attention to the phosphorus content of the diet provided that the protein and calcium of the diet are adequate, for protein is relatively rich in phosphorus, and the latter is associated with calcium in milk, eggs, cereals, legumes, and several other foods.

The daily requirement of children for iron is, on a weight basis, higher than for adults; milk-fed infants, therefore, tend to develop anemia (ch. 9) after the fourth month or so unless given iron in inorganic form because milk is very poor in this element. Egg yolk, meat, liver and kidney, fruits, and nuts are the main sources of iron.

TABLE 55.4

*Per capita consumption of some major foods (United States, 1949)*

| | Lb. per year |
|---|---|
| Dairy products (excluding butter) | 429 |
| Fats (including butter) | 65 |
| Eggs | 46 |
| Meats, poultry, fish | 159 |
| Potatoes (and sweet potatoes) | 116 |
| Grain products | 173 |
| Dry peas, beans and nuts | 16 |
| Citrus fruits and tomatoes | 98 |
| Leafy green and yellow vegetables | 111 |
| Other vegetables and fruits | 235 |
| Sugars and syrups | 106 |

These foods provided average amounts of certain nutrients per day, estimated to be as follows:

| | |
|---|---|
| Energy | 3250 Calories |
| Protein | 94 grams |
| Fat | 141 grams |
| Carbohydrate | 403 grams |
| Calcium | 1.05 grams |
| Vitamin A | 8500 I.U. |

The basic elements, sodium, potassium, and magnesium, are derived chiefly from cereals, fruits, and vegetables. Sodium chloride is also added during cooking and at the table. The average daily intake is from 10 to 12 grams. Many preparations of table salt are also sources of iodine, since it has become the custom of the manufacturer to add minute quantities of potassium iodide to his product. The daily iodine requirement of adults is from 100 to 150 $\mu$g. Other elements (trace elements), e.g., copper, cobalt (for erythropoiesis), fluorine (for tooth and bone structure), zinc (for the action of carbonic anhydrase and insulin), and manganese (for erythropoiesis and the action of phosphatase) are essential, but are present naturally in the diet in adequate amounts.

The dietary allowances recommended by the food and nutrition board of the National Research Council, Washington, are given in table 55.3.

## THE PROPER PROPORTION OF THE THREE FOODSTUFFS IN AN ADULT DIET

From data given in table 55.4 one may calculate the proportions of the different nutrients consumed by the average American citizen to be as follows:

| | Grams | Calories | Per cent of total Calories |
|---|---|---|---|
| Protein | 94 | 376 | 12 |
| Fat | 141 | 1269 | 39 |
| Carbohydrate | 403 | 1612 | 49 |
| Total | | 3257 | |

There is no evidence that these calorie-ratios (approximately 10:40:50) are *proper*. According to many authorities both the protein and fat intakes are greater than necessary. Stare and his associates, at the Harvard School of Public Health, found the protein requirement (for a 70 kg. man) to be met by 30 to 40 grams of mixed proteins (50 per cent from white bread), a range of values consistent with that found by Bricker, Mitchell, and Kinsman. Increasing the fat content of the diet can influence protein utilization, when both are fed at low levels, and there is other evidence that the nature of the nonprotein calories may affect the utilization of protein, i.e., different carbohydrates *are not strictly interchangeable*.

The daily dietary allowances recommended by the Food and Nutrition Board of the National Research Council (U. S. A., 1958) call for 1 gram of average mixed protein per kilogram of body weight (i.e., 70 grams for the average man or 58 grams for the average woman). These values appear to be generous. This figure will be used in the following calculation.

Data given in *Recommended Daily Dietary Allowances* (1948) support the recommendations of the British Medical Association Committee on Nutrition that 20 to 25 per cent of the calories should be provided as fat, with slightly larger proportions for very active persons (laborers, children, and adolescents). These proposals would result in calorie ratios of approximately 10:20: 70, as indicated below:

|  | Grams | Calories | Per cent of total Calories |
|---|---|---|---|
| Protein | 70 | 280 | 9 |
| Fat | 67 | 600 | 20 |
| Carbohydrate | 530 | 2120 | 71 |
| Total | | 3000 | |

Present knowledge does not permit us to state with exactness the optimal amount of fat compatible with health, nor the *proper* proportions in which the three major foodstuffs should be consumed. Balanced nutrition should supply sufficient calories (mainly as carbohydrate and fat) but should avoid excess; it should provide minerals, vitamins, essential amino acids, and utilizable nitrogen in adequate amounts and in proper ratios to calorie intake and to each other.

## REFERENCES

BAYLISS, W. M. The physiology of food and economy in diet. Longmans, Green & Co., Ltd., London, 1917.

BURR, G. O. Fed. Proc., 1942, **1**, 224.

BURTON, B. T. Fed. Proc., 1959, **18,** Suppl. 3, Part II, 1.

CHITTENDEN, R. H. Physiological economy in nutrition. Frederick A. Stokes Co., New York, 1907.

HEGSTED, D. M., TRULSON, M. F. AND STARE, F. J. Physiol. Rev., 1954, **34,** 221.

ROSE, M. S. Foundations of nutrition, 4th ed. The MacMillan Co., New York, 1945.

ROSE, W. C., Fed. Proc., 1949, **8,** 546.

SWANSON, P. P. Fed. Proc., 1951, **10,** 660.

An appraisal of Canadian nutriture. Canadian Bulletin on Nutrition, Vol. 3, No. 1, 1953.

A dietary standard for Canada. Canadian Bulletin on Nutrition, Vol. 3, No. 2, 1953.

Calorie requirements. F.A.O. Nutritional Studies, No. 15, Rome, 1957.

Present knowledge in nutrition, 2nd ed. The Nutrition Foundation, Inc., New York, 1956.

Protein requirement. F.A.O. Nutritional Studies, No. 16, Rome, 1957.

Recommended dietary allowances, Publication No. 589, National Academy of Sciences, National Research Council, Washington, 1958.

Supplement for 1949 to Consumption of food in the United States, Miscellaneous Publication No. 691. Department of Agriculture, Washington, 1950.

Symposium on nutrition. Proceedings of the Borden Centennial, New York, April, 1958.

# SECTION SEVEN
## *The Ductless Glands or Endocrines*

### (The Endocrine Function of the Pancreas is Dealt With in Chapter 48)

---

### Introduction

EVOLUTION. Two methods are used by the organism for transmitting messages from one organ to another. First, the nervous system forms an interconnecting mechanism by means of which rapid communication between different regions is established. And second, chemical substances called *hormones* are liberated into the blood from particular glands, and carried humorally to exert specific effects on distant structures. These latter act more slowly, and may have a more prolonged effect, than those messages sent by the nervous system. They are also of more ancient lineage, for it has been found that plants, in which no nervous system exists, use various hormones (auxins and others) to influence budding, growth, flowering, and possibly other functions. In the last 20 years much work has been devoted to the study of hormones in the invertebrates. Endocrine systems have been described in worms, crustaceans, insects, mollusks, and tunicates. Particular attention has been paid to the mechanisms controlling color changes in crustaceans and growth, differentiation, and moulting in insects. It is of special interest that in many of these forms the brain seems to play a dominant role as an organ of internal secretion. The process of elaboration of a hormone by the nervous system has received the term *neurosecretion*. Such a process in higher forms is discussed more fully below. The homology between higher invertebrate and lower invertebrate glands is, in many cases, uncertain.

HISTORY. The science of endocrinology began with the observations of Berthold in 1849, that removal of the testes in cocks resulted in changes in the birds so that they approached the build and behavior of the hen, and that these changes could be avoided by grafting the testes to the gut. The evidence was very strong then that the testes liberated some substance into the blood stream that was responsible for the masculine features and behavior of the normal cock. Claude

Bernard is usually regarded as the originator of present views regarding internal secretion, though his discovery that the liver liberates glucose into the blood cannot now be included as an endocrine phenomenon. It was from clinical studies that modern views of endocrinology first became clarified. Semon (1883) suggested, and Horsley (1888) showed, that myxedema and cretinism were due to failure of thyroid secretion, and Murray (1891) reported the benefit accruing to a case of myxedema from administration of thyroid extract. Later clinical studies suggested that various disease states might result from over secretion of endocrine glands (Greenfield, 1893, Graves' disease; Tamburini, 1894, and Benda, 1900, acromegaly). The physiological evidence on endocrine organs may be said to date from the classical studies of Oliver and Schäfer (1894) on the pressor principle of the adrenal medulla, Oliver and Schäfer (1895) and Dale (1909) on the pressor and oxytocic actions of posterior pituitary extracts, and Marshall and Jolly (1907, 1908) on the activity of ovarian transplants. Bayliss and Starling (1904) first established that a chemical substance could be secreted by one organ (in their case, secretin from the intestinal mucosa) and carried by the blood stream to exert a specific effect on distant structures. They also proposed the term '*hormone*' (from ὁρμάω—I arouse to activity). Great impetus was given to the subject by the studies of H. M. Evans and his group on the effects of hypophysectomy and replacement therapy in the rat (P. E. Smith, 1927), on the estrous cycle and vaginal smear technique in the rat (Long and Evans, 1922), on vitamin E and its relation to reproductive phenomena (Evans and Scott, 1922), and on the purification of various anterior pituitary hormones.

STRUCTURE. In the vertebrates the following organs are now well established as endocrine glands: anterior pituitary (adenohypophysis), posterior pituitary (neurohypophysis), ovary, testis, thyroid, adrenal cortex, adrenal medulla, parathyroids, islets of Langerhans in the pancreas, and various parts of the intestinal mucosa.[1] All these organs have certain anatomical features in common. *First*, they are typical glands (except the neurohypophysis which belongs to a special class of neurosecretory organs) in that they are composed of masses of secretory cells arranged usually in columns or clumps. These cells may occasionally, as in the case of the thyroid, be arranged in alveoli or acini with their secretory product stored in the lumen. More commonly, however, the hormones or their parent substances are stored as granules in the cells. *Second*, although glandular in nature, no ducts are present. *Third*, since the blood stream functions as a "duct" and carries off the secretory products, they are all richly vascularized. And *fourth*, the passage of the hormones into the vascular stream is facilitated by the replacement of thick collagenous connective tissue fibers by fine reticular fibers, and by the nature of the blood vessels which are thin-walled sinusoids.

CHEMISTRY. The hormones fall into several chemical groups. The pituitary hormones are proteins or polypeptides; the gonadal and adrenocortical hormones are steroids; whereas the thyroid and adrenomedullary hormones are composed of simpler and smaller molecules. These compounds seem to be surprisingly uniform in their nature and biological activity throughout the vertebrates. Extracts of sheep thyroid, for example, are active in amphibia, and pituitaries from amphibians, reptiles, and mammals accelerate sexual development in fish. However, it may be mentioned that anterior pituitary interstitial cell stimulating hormone from sheep has a lower molecular weight than the same hormone obtained from swine; that the vasopressor hormone extracted from beef and swine material has a slightly different amino acid constitution, and that growth hormone obtained from subprimate forms does not appear to be active in man.

THE HORMONES AND THEIR FUNCTIONS. In order to study the endocrine glands in detail, it is advantageous to have a general picture of the system as a whole first.

The pituitary gland or hypophysis is connected to the base of the brain by the pituitary stalk. The *anterior pituitary gland* is usually thought to secrete six hormones. The names of these, their

<hr>

[1] It is possible that the pineal and thymus are endocrine glands, but little is known as to their function at the present time.

synonyms, and abbreviations (their site of action being given in parentheses) are as follows:

Anterior pituitary hormones
  A. Gonadotrophic hormones
    1. Follicle stimulating hormone, FSH (ovary and testis)
    2. Luteinizing hormone, LH, or interstial cell stimulating hormone, ICSH (ovary and testis)
    3. Luteotrophic hormone, LTH, or prolactin, or lactogenic hormone (ovary (in some species) and mammary glands)
  B. Thyrotrophic hormone, TSH (thyroid)
  C. Adrenocorticotrophic hormone, ACTH (adrenal cortex)
  D. Growth hormone, or somatotrophic hormone, STH (body tissues (stimulates growth))

From this outline it may be seen that the anterior pituitary has a wide field of action. In addition to exerting a major influence over body growth (growth hormone) and over milk secretion in mammary tissue (lactogenic hormone), its hormones are largely, if not solely, responsible for maintaining and regulating the functions of the thyroid, adrenal cortex, ovary, and testes. In the absence of the anterior pituitary these latter four glands undergo atrophy and a great diminution in activity.

The *thyroid gland* secretes thyroxine and small amounts of tri-iodothyronine; hormones which are responsible for maintaining oxidative processes in bodily tissues in general. The *adrenal cortex*, like the thyroid, has no specific target organ upon which its hormones act, but by means of steroidal compounds it exerts a major influence over carbohydrate, protein, and electrolyte metabolism. The gonads also secrete steroidal hormones, estrogens and progesterone in the case of the *ovary*, and androgens in the case of the *testes*. They act both upon tissues in general (as may be seen from the changes produced under their influence at puberty), and upon specific target organs such as the breast, uterus, vagina, seminal vesicles, prostate, and penis.

The *posterior pituitary gland* secretes one or two hormones. Two physiologically active polypeptides have been extracted from the gland and obtained in a highly purified state. They have also been synthesized. The *antidiuretic* or vasopressor hormone exerts a regulating action on the volume of urine, and amount of chloride, excreted by the kidney. In large doses this hormone has a pressor action, increases intestinal motility, and raises the blood sugar. The *oxytocic hormone* causes contraction of uterine muscle and of mammary tissue. It thus aids in the expulsion of the fetus from the uterus and of milk from the breast. The *adrenal medulla*, a gland in several ways comparable with the posterior pituitary, secretes adrenaline and noradrenaline in amounts which vary in proportion in different species and probably in different individuals within a species. These two hormones are secreted during times of emergency or stress. Under conditions of fright, rage, pain, and similar states, the adrenal medulla is activated. In general it may be said that its hormones tend to reinforce the action of the sympathetic nervous system and exert widespread effects, such as increasing the general blood pressure, dilating the vessels of skeletal and cardiac muscle, and raising the blood sugar, which equip the animal as a more efficient machine for "fight or flight."

The *parathyroid glands* secrete a hormone, often referred to as *parathormone*, which has an important influence over calcium and phosphorus metabolism.

REGULATION OF ENDOCRINE ACTIVITY—THE NEUROENDOCRINE HIERARCHY AND THE FEED-

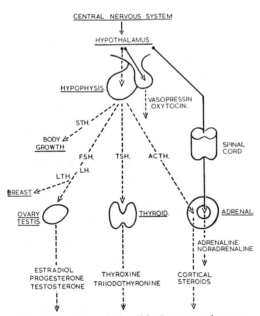

FIG. 56.1. The relationship between the nervous system and endocrine system. ——, nerve pathway; – – –, vascular pathway. Note that two glands, the adrenal medulla and neurohypophysis are regulated by a direct nerve supply whereas the activity of the other glands is controlled by humoral or hormonal agents carried in the blood stream.

BACK MECHANISM. The adjustment of endocrine function to meet the varying needs of an organism in an unstable environment is clearly a matter of some importance, but it is only in the last few years that data has become available on this subject.

A few of the glands may be dealt with briefly at this point. The regulation of insulin secretion by the islet tissue of the pancreas is dealt with elsewhere (ch. 48). Little is known regarding the control of parathyroid function. It appears unlikely that the parathyroids are under the control of either a secretomotor innervation or of a trophic hormone from the pituitary. Available evidence indicates that their activity is directly affected by the blood concentration of calcium.

Figure 56.1 depicts various relationships involved in the control of the major part of the endocrine system. The function of two of the glands is dependent upon, and regulated by, a direct secretomotor nerve supply. The neurohypophysis is controlled by the supraopticohypophysial tract from the hypothalamus. This same part of the diencephalon also regulates adrenomedullary activity by means of nervous pathways descending in the brain stem and spinal cord, with outflows to the gland through the sympathetic chain and splanchnic nerves. It is of interest that the posterior pituitary and adrenal medulla are among the most rapidly reacting endocrine glands and that they are under the direct control of the nervous system with its wellknown high speed of response.

There can be little doubt that various parts of the central nervous system (such as the reticular formation of the brain stem, the temporal lobes and amygdaloid nuclei, the frontal lobes, and other regions), acting through the hypothalamus, influence the secretory activity of the anterior pituitary which in turn controls the ovary, testis, thyroid, and adrenal cortex. The hypothalamohypophysial unit may, in general terms, be looked upon as a bottle-neck between the two great systems; the nervous and the endocrine. The neuroendocrine hierarchy, central nervous system, and hypothalamus → anterior pituitary → target glands, may be analyzed in terms of three "levels of activity."

1. Intrinsic or autonomic activity of the target glands. This is revealed in the hypophysectomized animal. In the absence of the pituitary the gonads show no sign of endocrine function, but the thyroid and adrenal cortex still secrete, though at a very low rate.

2. Intrinsic activity of the anterior pituitary.

If the pituitary gland is disconnected from the hypothalamus, by section of the pituitary stalk and insertion of a plate between the cut ends, or by transplantation of the gland to a distant site in the body, it also shows some low level intrinsic activity. As far as can be seen with present tests, secretion of FSH and LH ceases, though LTH, TSH, and ACTH are still released into the blood at low rates. Thus, in the pituitary stalk-sectioned animal the ovaries appear totally inactive (except that any corpora lutea present at the time of operation may be maintained) whereas the thyroid and adrenal cortex show some function. The level of function in these latter two glands is greater than that seen in the hypophysectomized animal, since to the autonomous function of the target glands is added the autonomous release of TSH and ACTH by the anterior pituitary.

3. Normal activity. The full activity of the anterior pituitary-target gland system is only seen when the central nervous system maintains and regulates anterior pituitary function through intact connections between the hypothalamus and adenohypophysis. The connections concerned are the hypophysial portal vessels of the pituitary stalk.

The hypothalamus, then, occupies a key position in regard to the endocrine system. Not only does it regulate the activity of the adrenal medulla and neurohypophysis through direct nerve supplies to these glands, but through its influence over the anterior pituitary it also regulates the activities of the ovary, testis, thyroid, and adrenal cortex. The effects exerted by the central nervous system over these endocrine organs may be summarized as follows:

1. It maintains their function at a normal level. In the absence of neural control, the activity of some glands ceases entirely (posterior pituitary gland) and in the others falls to low levels.

2. It is responsible for maintaining rhythmic activity, such as that of the ovary during normal sexual cycles.

3. It acts as an intermediary between the varying external environment and the endocrine system. Environmental stimuli, acting through the central nervous sytem, evoke changes in endocrine activity appropriate to the situation.

4. It possibly acts as part of the central mechanism involved in the "feed-back" action of the target gland hormones. The anterior pituitary and its target glands act in reciprocity. For example, if the blood concentration of thyroid hormone is increased, then by some central action the rate of secretion of TSH is reduced so that thyroid activity and the blood level of thyroid hormone is also reduced. If the blood concentration of thyroid hormone falls, the reverse situation is brought about.

Similar reactions occur with changes in the blood concentration of gonadal or adrenal cortical hormones. It is uncertain whether alterations in the blood level of the target gland hormones elicit these changes in pituitary activity by exerting a direct action on anterior pituitary cells, or whether the hypothalamus is sensitive to changes in blood concentration of these hormones and in turn regulates anterior pituitary activity appropriately. This feed-back mechanism whereby the anterior pituitary and its target glands form a self-balancing system, probably acts to stabilize endocrine activity under basal resting conditions, rather than to regulate activity under conditions calling for increased or decreased function. This phenomenon becomes a matter of practical importance in considering transplantation of endocrine glands. Halsted, many years ago, pointed out that most endocrine transplants take more readily if a state of deficiency in the host exists for the particular gland concerned. This statement has been verified many times and has become known as *Halsted's Principle of Deficiency*. As an example of this principle, it may be said that ovarian transplants survive better in an ovariectomized animal than in a normal animal. This is probably because the ovariectomized animal has a higher level of circulating gonadotrophic hormone than has the normal.

In summary, then, it may be said that the main factor maintaining endocrine activity at a normal level and concerned with regulating this activity under varying environmental conditions, is the influence exerted by the central nervous system. The feed-back mechanism probably operates as a stabilizing system whereby endocrine function is maintained at a preset level under constant conditions.

THE NATURE OF HORMONES AND THEIR TRANSPORT. The term *hormone* refers essentially to a chemical messenger in the blood stream. In the case of some glands the hormone has been identified in the venous blood from the gland or in the general systemic circulation, but in other cases data as to the nature of the hormone has been surmised from studies on material extractable from the gland itself. This latter approach may be fallacious. For example, it is known that the thyroid stores thyroglobulin, and that this substance is degraded before the hormone itself is liberated into the blood. Therefore, material extractable from a gland may represent a precursor of the hormone rather than the hormone itself. However, in the case of some glands, such as the anterior pituitary, the only information available is derived from studies of glandular extracts. Six purified and pharmacologically active extracts have been obtained from adenohypophysial tissue, and although it is convenient and customary to speak of these pituitary principles as separate hormones, there is no means of knowing whether the active materials obtained by rather drastic methods of extraction are actually secreted as separate entities by the living gland. It may be that the extraction products of the anterior lobe represent, as Riddle suggests, "hormone fragments" or as Collip expresses it, "chemically dissected" parts which represent prosthetic groups split off from a smaller number of larger hormone molecules. The only unequivocal test is the identification of the hormones, individually and separately, in pituitary venous blood. The position is further complicated by the fact that some hormones, such as thyroxine, become bound to plasma proteins during transport in the blood, and by the possibility, not yet established, that a hormone may need to be chemically changed in the tissues before it is able to exert its characteristic action.

CELLULAR ACTION AND EXCRETION OF HORMONES. It is not possible at the present time to state the precise nature of hormone action at a cellular level. Two general views are that hormones act at cell surfaces or boundaries to affect cellular excitability or metabolism, or that they form part of an enzyme system within the cell. It is too early to make a definite statement but studies such as those of Csapo, on the relationship between estrogens and the actomyosin content of uterine muscle and his finding that progesterone alters the balance of extracellular and intracellular sodium and potassium as well as the excitability of uterine muscle, may point the way to further elucidation of this difficult problem. For detailed discussions of this topic the reviews of Hechter (1955) and Levine (1957) may be consulted.

The rate of inactivation or excretion of some hormones is very rapid. For example, ACTH is quickly lost from the blood (in seconds-minutes), as are the posterior pituitary and adrenomedullary hormones. Some information is available as to the tissues which inactivate and/or excrete certain of these substances. Thyrotrophic hormone appears to be inactivated by thyroid and lymphatic tissue. Estrogens are conjugated in the liver and excreted to some extent in the bile. Thyroxine is also partly excreted in the bile and feces. Many hormones appear to be partially degraded and excreted in the urine (some anterior pituitary and placental hormones, ovarian and adrenal cortical steroids).

HORMONES AND BEHAVIOR. Attention has been drawn above to the regulating effects the central nervous system exerts on endocrine function. The reciprocal picture also exists. It is clear that various hormones act on the central nervous system to determine the behavioral response of the organism to environmental stimuli. A simple example may be taken from the field of reproductive physiology. A female cat with a low blood concentration of estrogen reacts to the attentions of a male cat with signs of displeasure (spitting, striking with the forepaws) and avoidance, whereas a female cat with a high blood concentration of estrogen reacts with a complicated but stereotyped pattern of courtship and mating activities. In the clinical field, a striking difference in mental state is seen in the extreme nervousness and irritability of patients suffering from hyperthyroidism (Graves' disease) as compared with the mental apathy and sluggishness of cases of hypothyroidism (myxedema). Although it seems almost certain that these behavioral changes are brought about by a direct action of the hormones on the central nervous system, very little information is available as to what regions of the nervous system are affected by the different hormones, or indeed to what extent the hormones are able to cross the "blood-brain barrier."

METHODS OF STUDY. Studies on an endocrine organ fall into two groups; those necessary to demonstrate that a particular organ is a gland of internal secretion, and those dealing in detail with its regulation, hormones, and mode of action.

To establish that an organ is an endocrine gland, several or all of the following criteria should be fulfilled:

1. A typical syndrome is induced by its destruction by disease or experimental removal. The initial observations have, in many cases, been made on the human. Attention was first drawn to endocrine deficiencies resulting from castration, tubercular destruction of the adrenal glands, and removal of the thyroid, from observations on man.

2. Substitution therapy. The deficiency state induced by removal or destruction of the gland should be reparable by administration of suitable extracts of the gland or by grafting the removed gland into a distant site in the body. The preparation of a suitable extract may present many difficulties. In the case of the thyroid gland it was early shown that a simple glycerine extract of the sheep's gland was curative in cases of myxedema.

However, the thyroid offered favorable circumstances for this demonstration in that it stores large quantities of active material which is effective when administered by mouth. Such is not the case for the other glands, for which delicate methods of chemical extraction may have to be developed before a suitable extract is obtained. The repair of a deficiency state by transplantation of an endocrine gland to a distant site in the body is a classical procedure in endocrine studies, and demonstrates that the organ concerned produces its effects by secretion into the blood stream, and also that its activity is dependent on some humoral agent carried in the general circulation. There is no evidence that the neurohypophysis or adrenal medulla has ever been transplanted and shown normal function. This is due to the fact that these glands are dependent on a nerve supply for normal function, and cannot be taken as evidence related to their mode of action. In transplantation studies attention must be paid to the source of the material. Tissue removed from and transplanted back into the same animal (*autotransplant*) has the best chance of 'taking' and remaining viable. Tissue removed from a donor animal and transplanted into a closely related member of the same species (*homotransplant*) often 'takes,' remains viable for a few weeks, and then undergoes lymphocytic infiltration and absorption. Tissue removed from a donor animal and grafted into a recipient of another species (*heterotransplant*) is usually absorbed within a few days. For this reason, it is unlikely that endocrine transplantation will ever form a useful therapeutic procedure. The beneficial results occasionally claimed following the transplantation of animal material into human cases may in part be due to absorption of hormone stored in the transplanted material or to the psychological effects of the procedure.

3. Administration of large doses of a glandular extract should produce signs of overdosage and a state that is often comparable to disease states, in which a secreting tumor of an endocrine gland results in the discharge of excessive amounts of hormone into the circulation. For example, excessive dosage with thyroid or adrenocortical hormones in the human produces states similar in many ways to Graves' disease and Cushing's syndrome, respectively.

After an organ has become established as a gland of internal secretion the following major points require investigation:

1. The factors regulating the activity of the gland. A change in the external environmental conditions exerts a powerful influence on the activity of many endocrine glands. Thus, the gonads of many seasonal breeding forms are activated by increased periods of illumination; a fall in environmental temperature leads to increased function of the thyroid gland; stresses and conditions of emergency excite adrenal cortical and medullary activity, and so on. The physiological mechanisms by which such factors influence endocrine function still require further investigation. In order to study these factors it is advantageous to have a simple and quick measure of glandular activity. From the point of view of the organism as a whole, the most exact definition of such activity is, the amount of hormone secreted into the blood in unit time. In order to obtain this estimate it is necessary to know the rate of blood flow through the gland and the hormone content of the arterial blood entering, and the venous blood leaving, the organ. Ideally, it is desirable to be able to make such observations in the unanesthetized animal. At the present time this is barely possible, so that indirect measures of glandular activity are generally used, such as observing the effect the hormone exerts on some process or target organ (e.g., vaginal epithelium in the case of the ovarian hormones, basal metabolic rate for the thyroid hormones), or observing the concentration of the hormone in the general systemic circulation, or the rate of excretion of the hormone or its degradation products in the urine.

2. The analysis of the biochemical processes occurring in the gland. Simple substances (glucose, amino acids, inorganic salts) are extracted by the gland from the blood, converted into more complex compounds (steroids, polypeptides) and secreted back into the blood. A rudimentary knowledge of the chemical changes involved has been obtained in some cases. Radioactive iodine has been a valuable tool in analyzing such processes in the thyroid, and the use of the arti-

ficially perfused gland with blood containing $C^{14}$-labeled substrates has aided materially in work on the adrenal cortex. In the case of other glands, such as the anterior and posterior pituitary, very little data exist. Such information may be of much practical use. In cases of hyperthyroidism it is possible to administer antithyroid compounds which block the organic binding of iodine by the gland and so prevent the secretion of excessive amounts of hormone.

3. The carriage and fate of hormones in the blood. Knowledge as to the carriage of hormones in the blood (i.e., whether as a complex with plasma proteins), the metabolic changes undergone in the tissues, and the processes of inactivation and excretion of the hormones are largely dependent on the development of reliable assay methods for the hormones in body fluids.

4. The mechanism of action of the hormones at an organ, cellular and organelle level. As mentioned above, very little knowledge has so far been obtained on this topic.

# 56

## THE PITUITARY GLAND OR HYPOPHYSIS CEREBRI

### Origin and Structure

The average weight of the human hypophysis is about 0.5 gram. It is slightly heavier in females, especially in those who have borne children, than in males. Its average dimensions are 10 mm. (sagittal) by 13 mm. (transverse) by 6 mm. (vertical). It lies within the small cavity formed by the *sella turcica* of the sphenoid bone which is closed above by a thin membrane, *diaphragma sellae*, except where it is pierced by the pituitary stalk. The stalk connects the pituitary gland below to the hypothalamus of the brain above.

The pituitary body consists of an anterior and posterior part readily separable along a natural line of cleavage, which represents the original, embryonic cavity of Rathke's pouch (see below). Until recently the two parts of the pituitary were generally referred to as the *anterior* and *posterior lobes*, and the stalk as the *infundibulum*. Though these terms are still used somewhat loosely, it is preferred, for more precise description of the hypophysis, to employ a nomenclature based upon the origins of its different parts. The pituitary has a dual origin in the embryo—from the ectoderm in the roof of the primitive mouth (stomodeum) just in front of the buccopharyngeal membrane as well as from the base of the brain. In the early embryo a pouch extends from the stomodeum to meet a corresponding hollow diverticulum prolonged downward from the floor of the third ventricle. The evagination from the primitive mouth is called *Rathke's pouch*. Through pressure upon its posterior wall by the downgrowth of nervous tissue, this wall of Rathke's pouch is approximated to the anterior wall and the cavity reduced to a cleft or (in the human) to a row of vesicles. The original stalklike connection of Rathke's pouch with the stomodeum, known as the *craniopharyngeal canal*, also becomes largely obliterated, though a remnant may remain as a "pharyngeal pituitary" (embedded in the mucosa on the dorsal wall of the pharynx) and other fragments may in later life give rise to tumors situated in the anterior wall of the sella turcica. The original cavity of the neural element of the pituitary disappears completely in man, so that the pituitary stalk becomes solid, though in some adult animals, such as the cat, this cavity persists and communicates with the third ventricle. It should be mentioned that bilateral diverticula of Rathke's pouch, the *lateral lobes*, climb upward to surround the upper end of the stalk and give rise to the pars tuberalis.

The part of the pituitary which originates from Rathke's pouch has a glandular structure and is, therefore, called the *adenohypophysis*. The portion developed from the brain is known as the *neurohypophysis*. Each division of the hypophysis is subdivided into three parts. Thus, the neurohypophysis consists of the expanded distal portion, the *infundibular process* or *neural lobe*, the nervous part of the stalk known as the *infundibular stem* or *neural stalk*, and the expanded upper end of the stalk, which is the *median eminence* of the tuber cinereum. It is important to realize that all three parts of the neurohypophysis are glandular and may liberate hormone into the blood stream. The tissue of the neural stalk and median eminence constitutes about 13 per cent of the total neurohypophysial tissue. The adenohypophysis consists of the *pars tuberalis* (a thin strip of tissue surrounding the median eminence and the upper part of the neural stalk), the *pars intermedia* (that portion posterior to the cleft and in contact with the neural lobe), and the *pars distalis* or anterior lobe (the major secretory part of the gland lying anterior to the cleft). The development and different parts of the gland are summarized in figure 56.2 and table 56.1.

The neural stalk, together with its sheath, the pars tuberalis, is known as the *hypophysial* or *pituitary stalk*.[2]

The *pars distalis* is richly vascular, showing numerous blood sinuses between cords of cells. The cells fall into two main groups; (a) *chromophobe* or *reserve* cells which possess no granules, stain lightly, and apparently do not secrete, and (b) chromophil cells which contain large numbers of granules which stain readily (they are believed to elaborate the secretions of the anterior lobe). On a basis of the character of the granules, the chromophil cells are grouped again into two varieties (a) *acidophil* (or $\alpha$) cells, which stain more readily with acid dyes, and (b) *basophil* (or $\beta$) cells, which have a greater affinity for basic

---

[2] The spelling "hypophysial" is correct. The alternative "hypophyseal" became current as the result of a misprint in one of Dr. Harvey Cushing's monographs.

stains. The three types of cells (chromophobe and the two types of chromophil cell) are scattered indiscriminately throughout the pars distalis. The proportions found in man by Rasmussen, were around 50 per cent chromophobes, 35 per cent acidophils, and 15 per cent basophils. It now appears that the chromophobes represent mother cells and, by development, give rise to either acid-

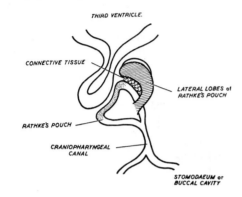

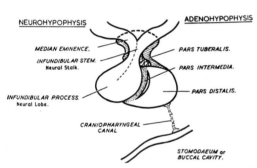

FIG. 56.2. The embryological development of the different parts of the pituitary. The neurohypophysis consists of three parts, the median eminence, infundibular stem, and infundibular process; and the adenohypophysis also of three parts, the pars tuberalis, pars intermedia, and pars distalis. In some forms (such as the whale and elephant) a thick connective tissue septum extends upward between the infundibular process and pars intermedia, to merge with the connective tissue wedge illustrated in the diagram. However, in all forms the pars tuberalis encircles the median eminence and forms the bed of a vascular path linking the median eminence and the pars distalis.

ophils or basophils. Catchpole (1947) first stained glycoproteins in anterior pituitary basophil cells, using the periodic acid-Schiff method (PAS). Since then two subdivisions of the basophils have been distinguished in the rat gland by the use of special stains. Halmi refers to these as $\beta$ and $\delta$ cells, whereas Purves and Griesbach, who used the PAS method, termed them *gonadotrophs* and *thyrotrophs* on the ground that they believe them to secrete gonadotrophic and thyrotrophic hormones, respectively. Dawson and Friedgood have described two classes of acidophils on the basis of a special azocarmine stain. The ordinary acidophil cell stains orange, whereas the *"carmine cell,"* which they believe to secrete luteinizing hormone, stains a bright red. It is of interest that the gonadotrophs, thyrotrophs, and carmine cells have their own distinctive distribution in the pars distalis. Under special physiological conditions variations of the above cell types become discernible. After castration certain basophils undergo enlargement and vacuolization, with displacement of the nucleus to one side of the cell. They thus have the appearance of a signet ring, and are termed "signet ring" or "castration cells." Other cell types described are "thyroidectomy cells" and "pregnancy cells." The *pars intermedia* is the least vascular part of the pituitary. In some forms (cat, rabbit) it forms a well marked, thick layer, but in the human it consists of only a few cells. It is common to find cysts of various sizes, containing a hyaline or colloid material, in the region of the pars intermedia. The *pars tuberalis* resembles the pars distalis in being constituted of cords of cells separated by blood sinuses. The cells, however, are nongranular.

The three parts of the neurohypophysis—the median eminence, infundibular stem, and process—are composed of similar tissue, which is different from that of the hypothalamus proper in vital staining properties, vascular supply, and cytology. Naked-eye inspection of the region would lead one to draw the line of demarcation between the neurohypophysis and hypothalamus at the level of the infundibular stem, whereas it is in reality at a considerably higher level. This fact has important implications when considering various ex-

TABLE 56.1

| Origin | Primary Division | Subdivisions |
|---|---|---|
| From primitive buccal cavity | Adenohypophysis | 1. Pars distalis (anterior lobe)<br>2. Pars tuberalis<br>3. Pars intermedia }(Posterior lobe) |
| From floor of third ventricle | Neurohypophysis | 1. Infundibular process, neural lobe<br>2. Infundibular stem }Neural stalk<br>3. Median eminence |

perimental findings concerning the neurohypophysis. The tissues of the neurohypophysis consist of (a) a profusion of unmyelinated nerve fibers, (b) fusiform cells with several processes and containing granules of a brown pigment in their cytoplasm (the *pituicytes* of Bucy), and (c) numerous blood vessels, neurological cells, mast cells, and hyaline bodies. The hyaline bodies are of historic interest, in that Herring (1908) put forward the view that the active material in the posterior lobe is derived from basophil cells of the pars intermedia migrating posteriorly into the neurohypophysis, and becoming transformed into hyaline masses. These hyaline masses, he supposed, were traveling up the pituitary stalk to be liberated into the cerebrospinal fluid in the third ventricle and there to exert their action on the nerve centers in the hypothalamus. This view was current for many years and had the support of such authorities as Harvey Cushing. However, it now seems clear that the neurohypophysis passes its secretion directly into the blood stream.

The extent to which the adenohypophysis makes contact with the neural lobe varies considerably. It may almost entirely surround the latter (cat), or in some forms (elephant, cetacea, armadillo) is separated from the neural lobe by a connective tissue septum. However, in all forms examined the pars tuberalis establishes contact with the neural stalk.

THE BLOOD SUPPLY OF THE HYPOPHYSIS (fig. 56.3). The vascular territory of the neural lobe is separated from that of the median eminence and adenohypophysis. It is supplied by posterior or inferior hypophysial arteries and drains by short veins into the surrounding venous sinuses.

The blood supply of the pars distalis may be compared with that of the liver in that it possesses a systemic arterial supply, a portal supply, and a venous drainage. The *venous drainage* is similar to that of the neural lobe in that it passes by short wide veins into adjacent venous sinuses. The *arterial supply* varies in different forms. The rabbit pituitary is supplied by a branch of one internal carotid, usually the left, arising and penetrating the gland at a level below the diaphragma sellae. However, Daniel and coworkers claim that the pars distalis of the human, and some other forms, lacks a direct arterial supply. The *portal supply* of the pars distalis was first described by Popa and Fielding (1930) in the human, and their anatomical findings confirmed by Wislocki and others in many lower forms. The general arrangement of the system is as follows. Small arterial twigs from the circle of Willis supply a vascular plexus situated in the pars tuberalis, which in turn supplies a multitude of capillary loops or tufts situated in the nervous tissue of the median eminence and infundibular stem. These capillaries are known as the *primary plexus of the hypophysial portal vessels*.

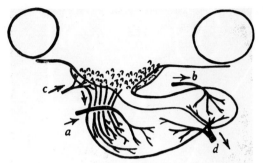

FIG. 56.3. Diagram of a sagittal section through the pituitary gland (below) and hypothalamus (above) of a rabbit, showing the blood supply of the gland. The anterior and posterior hypophysial arteries (*a* and *b*) are derived from the internal carotid arteries. The arterial twigs (*c*) to the pars tuberalis and the primary plexus of the portal vessels in the median eminence are derived from the internal carotid and posterior communicating arteries. The venous drainage (*d*) passes to surrounding venous sinuses in the dura mater or in the basisphenoid bone. In many forms the arterial supply to the pars distalis (*a*) is reduced or appears to be absent. In these cases the portal vessels may form the sole blood supply to the anterior pituitary gland. (From Harris.)

They drain by means of large vascular trunks which pass down the pituitary stalk to distribute their blood into the sinusoids of the pars distalis. These vessels, therefore, start as capillaries in the median eminence and end as sinusoids in the pars distalis (fig. 56.4). Since the median eminence is part of the neurohypophysis, the entire extent of the portal vessels is contained within the hypophysis and they should be referred to as the *hypophysial portal vessels* and not as the hypothalamo-hypophysial portal vessels. When it became apparent that these vessels might form an important part of the functional link between the central nervous system and the pars distalis of the pituitary, and be involved in some neurohumoral mechanism whereby the nervous system controls anterior pituitary activity, they were reinvestigated in detail and the following significant points established: (a) They are present in all the major classes of vertebrates (Green, 1951), (b) the direction of blood flow in these portal vessels is from the median eminence down to the pituitary (this was observed by microscopic examination of the vessels in living amphibians, rats, mice, and dogs), and (c) after cutting the pituitary stalk they have marked powers of regeneration, so that investigations on the effects of pituitary stalk section must be carried out on animals in which a plate or some impervious barrier is placed between the stalk ends.

THE NERVE SUPPLY OF THE HYPOPHYSIS (fig. 56.5). The *adenohypophysis* receives a very scanty innervation, if any at all. From time to time it has been suggested that the pars distalis might be

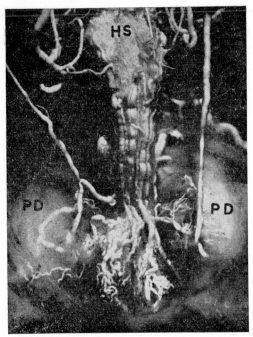

FIG. 56.4. Photograph of anterior aspect of pituitary stalk of man. The blood vessels have been injected with neoprene latex. Note the prominent trunks of the portal vessels. These vessels start as capillaries in the median eminence (*HS*) of the tuber cinereum and neural stalk and carry blood downward into the sinusoids of the anterior lobe (*PD*). (From Xuereb, Prichard, and Daniel.)

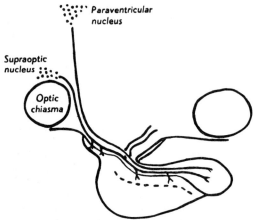

FIG. 56.5. Diagram of a sagittal section through the pituitary gland showing the large nerve tract, derived from the supraoptic and paraventricular nuclei and other nuclei of the hypothalamus, which innervates the neurohypophysis. A few nerve fibers penetrate into the pars intermedia. (From Harris.)

innervated from one or more of three sources: (a) by nerve fibers from the hypothalamo-hypophysial tract in the pituitary stalk, (b) by the carotid sympathetic plexus, and (c) by a parasympathetic

innervation derived from the greater superficial petrosal nerves. However, the most careful histological studies (Rasmussen, 1938; Green, 1951) have failed to reveal any innervation of the secretory cells. The scanty nerve fibers seen in the anterior lobe are (as seems to be the case with some other endocrine glands, such as the thyroid and adrenal cortex) in all probability vasomotor in nature. Such a view is supported by recent studies with the electron microscope.

The *neurohypophysis* is richly innervated by the *hypothalamo-hypophysial* tract from the hypothalamus. These fibers originate in the supraoptic and paraventricular nuclei in the hypothalamus and probably from other, as yet undetermined, nuclei. The number of fibers in this tract has been estimated at 10,000 (rat), 50,000 (dog, monkey), and 100,000 (man). They are fine unmyelinated fibers; they may be stained with one of the silver impregnation methods or with the Gomori chrome-alum haematoxylin method. Their origin has been determined by microanatomical studies and by the fact that the supraoptic and paraventricular nuclei undergo retrograde degeneration, and lose some 90 per cent of their cells, if the nerve tract is cut above the median eminence. Their termination is in close proximity to blood vessels in all three parts of the neurohypophysis. This has been clearly established by such studies as those of Bodian (1951) on the neurohypophysis of the opossum. In this animal a more orderly architecture prevails in the neural lobe than in most other animals. In recent years great interest has centered around the neurosecretory potentialities of this nerve tract (see below).

## The Physiology of the Adenohypophysis

The adenohypophysis is the master gland of the endocrine system. Many different types of effects have been identified with this part of the pituitary. Most of these actions can be produced by one of the six purified extracts that have been obtained from anterior lobe tissue. These extracts are, by common usage, referred to as hormones and are known as (a) the *growth* or *somatotrophic* hormone, (STH), (b) the *thyrotrophic* or *thyroid-stimulating* hormone (TSH), (c) the *adrenocorticotrophic* hormone (ACTH), (d) and (e) the *gonadotrophic* hormones (*follicle-stimulating* hormone (FSH), and *luteinizing* hormone (LH)), and (f) *prolactin* or *lactogenic* hormone (in some species also gonadotrophic, and known as *luteotrophic* hormone (LTH)).[3]

[3] The Third International Conference on the Standardization of Hormones has recommended that the suffix *-tropic* in the adjective qualifying the hormones of the anterior pituitary be replaced by *-trophic* (see Collip), and that the termination *-trophin* be used in forming the name of the hor-

*The effects of hypophysectomy.* The results of early work on hypophysectomy were complicated by the fact that the operation involved a trans-temporal intracranial approach to the gland, with the risk of concurrent damage to the hypothalamus. It was at first thought that removal of the pituitary was fatal within a few days. The development of the parapharyngeal operation by P. E. Smith, in which hypothalamic injury is avoided, showed that hypophysectomized animals may survive for long periods, though their life span is ultimately shortened. In this operation the gland is removed through a trephine hole in the base of the skull. The diaphragma sellae remains intact, and the infundibular stem and median eminence (of the neurohypophysis) and the pars tuberalis (of the adenohypophysis) are left *in situ*. These remnants may be sufficient to prevent signs of neurohypophysial deficiency (see below) but important abnormalities result from the loss of anterior lobe hormones. These are (a) arrested growth, (b) atrophy of the gonads and, indirectly, of the accessory organs of sex, (c) suppression of milk secretion and involution of the mammary glands, (d) atrophy of the thyroid and adrenal cortex, (e) lowered metabolic rate, (f) a tendency to hypoglycemia, and an increased sensitivity to insulin and reduction in liver and muscle glycogen, and (g) depression of spontaneous activity, and diminished resistance to infections and shock. With the advent of hypophysectomy as a therapeutic procedure for mammary carcinoma and other conditions, many of these effects have been observed in the human, though the position here is usually complicated by the necessary replacement therapy with thyroxine and cortisone.

It may be mentioned that in some fish and in amphibia the loss of the pars intermedia hormone (intermedin) results in a silvery, albino appearance. This is due to contraction of the melanophores of the skin. No deficit due to loss of this hormone is known in mammals.

*The Growth or Somatotrophic Hormone (STH)*

The first indication that the pituitary gland exerted an effect on body growth came from the observations that human cases of acromegaly and gigantism commonly have pituitary tumors, and that hypophysectomized dogs (Crowe, Cushing, and Homans, 1910), tadpoles (Smith, 1916; Allen, 1916), and rats (Smith, 1930) show reduced body growth. In 1921, Evans and Long showed that injection of an extract of ox pituitary resulted in gigantism in rats.

Purified preparations of growth hormone have been prepared from both ox and pig pituitary tissue. Such preparations have been reported free from other active contaminants and to behave as a homogeneous substance to various physicochemical tests. The data indicates that the material is a protein, with a molecular weight of 45,000 to 50,000. It is comparatively insoluble in water and has an isoelectric point at pH 6.85. It is destroyed by pepsin and trypsin. It is not active when given by mouth. After injection it remains in the circulation some 9 hours.

The source of growth hormone appears to be the acidophil cells of the anterior pituitary. The evidence is that acromegaly and gigantism in man are associated with oversecreting tumors (adenomata) of this cell type, and that pituitaries of dwarf mice are lacking in acidophils.

The loss of growth hormone resulting from hypophysectomy results in two main deficits in the organism—a reduction in the rate of body growth (fig. 56.6) and disturbances in metabolism, especially of proteins and carbohydrates. Growth does not always cease in the hypophysectomized animal, but may continue at a greatly reduced rate, perhaps 50 per cent of the normal. The fact that in the absence of the pituitary, mitotic figures appear in the mammary glands of parturient rats, and that hypertrophy of the remaining kidney follows unilateral nephrectomy, also demonstrates that STH is not the sole factor controlling growth. Growth of the hypophysectomized animal is favored, at least transiently, by the provision of a nutritious diet, by insulin adminis-

Fig. 56.6. Hypophysectomized puppy (right) and litter mate control (left) 3 months after removal of the hypophysis when 3 weeks old. (From Dandy and Rickert.)

mone (e.g., thyrotrophin). The suffix -tropic is from the Greek *trepein* to turn, and in this sense has been used in such terms as heliotropic, geotropic, etc. The suffix -trophic is derived from the Greek word *trophein*, to nourish or nurture and is, therefore, more appropriate as an ending for those pituitary hormones which affect the development and growth of other endocrines. The -tropic ending is also accepted usage.

tration, or by androgen therapy. Further, hypophysectomy affects the growth of some tissues more than others. Thus rats hypophysectomized at 6 days of age die at about 75 days, since growth of the skull fails to keep pace with that of the brain. Removal of the pituitary results in a striking increase in sensitivity to insulin. In some animals, such as rabbits, this results in a certain mortality from hypoglycemia during the first few days after operation. If placed on a restricted diet, hypophysectomized rats show a greater loss of body weight and a greater loss of body protein, but less of fat, than the controls. The deposition of protein is clearly an essential part of growth processes. The fasted hypophysectomized animal rapidly develops hypoglycemia and shows abnormally low liver and muscle glycogen stores.

The effect of anterior pituitary extracts on growth was first demonstrated by Evans and Long. These workers found that an alkaline or saline extract of the gland when given daily by intraperitoneal injection (but not by mouth) extended the growth period beyond the normal limit. Some of these animals finally attained a size larger, by 100 per cent or more, than that of their untreated litter mates (fig. 56.7). The effect was usually greater in the female. Similar results have been obtained in dogs. Gigantism, acromegaly (p. 989), and splanchnomegaly have been produced in bulldogs by Putnam, Benedict, and Teel. Airedales, Boston terriers, and dachshunds have been shown by others to respond to such an extract (fig. 56.6). Administration of growth hormone to adult rats produces more uniform body growth than in adult dogs. This is because the epiphysial cartilages of rats do not fuse so that the limbs retain the potentiality of growth in length (cf. the effect of acidophil adenomata in the immature and adult human). The width of the epiphysial cartilage is reduced after hypophysectomy. Growth hormone exerts a specific stimulating effect upon such a cartilage. The cartilage cells become enlarged, active osteoblasts appear, the whole plate becomes thicker, and a zone of newly formed bony trabeculae develops. Studies with radioactive calcium show that the rate of deposition of calcium in the cartilage is accelerated by STH. As might be expected, the stimulus to growth is accompanied by an increase in the body stores of protein and a positive nitrogen balance. The extra nitrogen stored under the influence of growth hormone is deposited as protein, mainly in the muscles. Some muscles of the rat have shown an increase of nitrogen content of as much as 60 per cent under these conditions. These changes are initiated quickly. Within a few hours after administration of STH to a fasted animal, the concentration of free amino acids in the blood and tissues decreases. That this is due to protein anabolism is shown by the simultaneous decrease in urea formation and excretion.

The anterior pituitary gland is related to carbohydrate metabolism in many ways. Houssay first showed that dogs made diabetic by pancreatectomy showed a marked amelioration of the diabetes if subjected to hypophysectomy. Such a preparation, known as the *Houssay dog*, may live for long periods without insulin. They are, however, in a state of unstable equilibrium and easily become diabetic or hypoglycemic if subjected to adverse conditions. These observations show the antagonistic influences the pituitary and pancreatic secretions exert over carbohydrate metabolism. This fact was again emphasized by the classical work of Young, who showed that administration of anterior pituitary extracts to adult dogs and cats for periods of several weeks might result in a permanent state of diabetes mellitus. Such animals show severe damage of the pancreatic islet tissue. This early study, performed with crude pituitary extracts, raised several questions; is the diabetogenic activity a property of a known pituitary hormone or not? and, why are immature dogs and cats, as well as adult animals of some other species such as the rat, resistant to the diabetogenic activity of pituitary extracts? With the advent of purified extracts it became clear that diabetogenic effects are associated with the growth hormone. Diabetogenic action can be demonstrated even with the most highly purified

Fig. 56.7. Litter mate female dachshunds 11½ months old. HY-26 injected with growth hormone for 35 weeks; HY-27 control. (From Evans and associates.)

preparation and is apparently a property of the growth hormone molecule itself. In reply to the second question, it has been suggested that the variability of the diabetogenic activity of STH in the young as opposed to the adult dog, and in different species, is due to variation in the capacity of the pancreas to secrete insulin. Administration of growth hormone results in certain metabolic effects which elicit increased secretion of insulin. If the pancreatic response is adequate then protein deposition and growth ensues. In the adult dog and cat, however, the pancreatic response fails, "exhaustion atrophy" of the islet tissue occurs, and a state of diabetes supervenes. In this context it may be noted that rats, which are resistant to the diabetogenic action of pituitary extracts, may respond to such extracts in the fasting states with a hypoglycemia; hypertrophy of pancreatic tissue may also occur. Administration of ACTH or adrenal cortical steroids results, in some respects, in effects similar to those induced by growth hormone. Thus adrenal cortical hormones increase gluconeogenesis and reduce the rate of glucose oxidation. If given to the fasting hypophysectomized animal the danger of hypoglycemia is reduced. Further, the effect of adrenalectomy on the carbohydrate metabolism of pancreatectomized animals may be very similar to that of hypophysectomy. Thus, in considering the overall relationship of the endocrine glands to carbohydrate metabolism, the pituitary gland, through its secretion of STH and ACTH, exerts opposing actions to those of insulin. ACTH acts through the intermediation of the adrenal cortex, although STH acts directly and not through the intermediation of other glands.

In the early days when only crude anterior pituitary extracts were available, a number of actions of these extracts were ascribed to specific "factors." These, and their actions, may be enumerated as follows: (a) *Hyperglycemic factor*, causes an immediate increase in blood sugar; (b) *hypoglycemic* or *pancreatrophic factor*, decreases blood sugar from stimulation of the islet tissue of the pancreas; (c) *glycotropic factor*, inhibits the action of small doses of insulin; (d) *glycostatic factor*, maintains the muscle glycogen of fasting, hypophysectomized animals; (e) *ketogenic factor*, increases the ketosis of a fasting state; and (f) *fat-mobilizing factor*, increases liver fat and the metabolism of fat, at the expense of depot fats. It is probable, though, that these actions are not due to "factors" separate from the usually accredited pituitary hormones, but may be attributed to the actions of either STH or ACTH, or both.

Until recently, growth hormone preparations derived from ox or pig tissue were disappointing in their effects on the primate. It now seems very likely that this hormone is species specific, since extracts of primate origin have been found capable of causing marked nitrogen retention and the typical changes in carbohydrate metabolism in primates, whereas bovine and porcine preparations are inert in this regard. The effect of primate growth hormone on growth has recently been demonstrated by Knobil and his colleagues, using the histological changes in the costochondral junction of hypophysectomized monkeys as a test object. Treatment of a pituitary dwarf with somatotrophin prepared from human glands has been found to result in increased body growth (Raben).

The bioassay of pituitary growth hormone is best performed on the hypophysectomized rat. The ability of the hormone to increase the body weight, or to increase the width of the tibial epiphysial cartilage, may be utilized. The tibial cartilage assay is a specific and sensitive test, and may detect as little as 5 $\mu$g. of an active extract.

The factors controlling secretion of STH are unknown. It is, indeed, debatable as to how actively this hormone is secreted in adult life. Young (1945) has suggested that growth hormone is secreted during conditions of starvation. This view is based on the fact that the metabolic pattern of an adult animal consuming a normal ration of food, but given anterior pituitary extract, is similar to that of a starving animal. The fragmentary data available suggests that secretion of STH is under hypothalamic control, since transplantation of the pituitary to a site remote from the sella turcica leads to marked retardation of body growth, and since hypothalamic lesions may be followed by signs of interference with carbohydrate metabolism which may be rectified by administration of growth hormone.

### The Thyrotrophic Hormone, Thyrotrophin, Thyroid Stimulating Hormone (TSH)

A functional relationship between the pituitary gland and thyroid was suspected during the last century after it had been found that thyroidectomy results in histological changes in the pars distalis. The effect of hypophysectomy in preventing metamorphosis of the tadpole was ascribed by Adler (1914) to the associated atrophy of the thyroid. Smith showed clearly that replacement therapy (pituitary implants) would repair the atrophic thyroid gland of the hypophysectomized rat. An acid extract of the anterior pituitary was then prepared (Loeb and Bassett; Aron) which was found to have thyroid stimulating properties on injection.

The cells of origin of TSH in the anterior pituitary are basophilic, and stain with the periodic acid-Schiff technique. They are centrally situated in the pars distalis of the rat and are angular and polyhedral in shape.

Several procedures are available for obtaining TSH in a highly purified state, though it has not yet been established that the preparations are entirely free from other pituitary hormones or that they are chemically homogenous. The data indicates that TSH is a protein or polypeptide with a molecular weight of about 10,000, and that the molecule probably contains a carbohydrate moiety. It is inactivated by proteolytic enzymes and must be administered by injection.

The thyrotrophic hormone exerts a powerful controlling influence over the activity of the thyroid gland, and has also been implicated as having a direct action in the development of exophthalmos in certain pathological states. The thyroid gland extracts iodide ions from the blood stream, combines these organically, and stores its hormonal activity as a protein known as thyro-

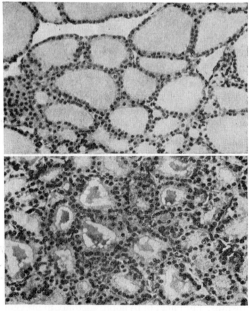

FIG. 56.8. Photomicrographs of sections through the thyroid gland of a normal dog (above) and a dog which had received seven daily injections of anterior pituitary extract containing thyrotrophin (below). (From Ham.)

globulin. From this protein, thyroxine and triiodothyronine are liberated into the blood stream to stimulate the metabolism of nearly every tissue in the body. Hypophysectomy does not abolish thyroid function completely, but greatly reduces it. In man, hypophysectomy results, within some weeks, in a condition of thyroid deficiency known as myxedema. The thyroidal changes resulting from removal of the pituitary may be summarized as follows: (a) Reduction in size, weight, and vascularization, (b) histological changes, notably a reduction in the height of the epithelial cells of the acini, and an increased amount of acinar colloid, (fig. 56.8) and (c) a reduction in all the chemical processes of iodine metabolism in the gland. The uptake of iodide ions from the blood, conveniently measured as a thyroid:serum (T:S) ratio (ch. 57) may be reduced in the rat from values of about a 100 to about 2. The organic binding of iodine in the gland and the liberation of iodine containing hormones from the gland are also markedly depressed by hypophysectomy. These changes are all reversible by the administration of an exogenous TSH extract. Not only may the state and function of the gland of the hypophysectomized animal be returned to normal, but injection of excessive doses of TSH result in a hyperplastic thyroid and signs of hyperthyroidism. The gland enlarges and becomes hypervascular. The acinar cells show hypertrophy and hyperplasia with a reversal in the polarity of the mitochondria and Golgi apparatus. The colloid undergoes a peripheral vacuolization, a change in its staining properties so that it appears basophilic instead of eosinophilic and becomes reduced in amount as the stored hormone is liberated into the blood in increased amounts. As the blood concentration of thyroid hormones rises, signs of thyrotoxicosis ensue. An increased metabolic rate, sweating, nervousness, tremor, and cardiac irregularities have been reported in the human. The above changes do not occur simultaneously after administration of TSH. Within half an hour of TSH injection there is, in the experimental animal, an increase of proteolytic enzyme in the follicles and an increased release of thyroidal hormone as detected by examination of thyroid vein blood. Some 8 hours or so later an increase in the rate of uptake of iodine from the blood occurs. The different time relationships of these processes are shown in figure 56.9. The enlargement of the gland and the signs of hyperthyroidism take longer to develop.

Thyrotrophic hormone acts directly on the thyroid gland and probably on intraorbital tissues. Patients with a diffuse enlargement of the thyroid gland and signs of thyrotoxicosis often show exophthalmos. This protrusion of the eyes is characterized by edema and a lymphocytic and fatty infiltration with fibrosis of the retrobulbar tissues. A similar state of the eyes has been produced in normal and thyroidectomized guinea pigs by injection of extracts rich in TSH, and on these grounds it has been suggested that in Graves' disease both the thyroidal disturbance and the exophthalmos are due to direct actions of TSH. Since in these cases blockage of thyroid activity by thyroid-inhibiting drugs, or thyroidectomy (procedures which increase TSH secretion in the normal animal) are often followed by an increase in the severity of the exophthalmos, and since administration of large doses of adrenal corticoids or pituitary stalk section (procedures which decrease the secretion of TSH in the normal animal) have been reported to decrease or abolish the exophthalmos, indirect support for this view is forthcoming. However, McCullagh, who has critically examined the evidence, points out that thyroidectomy or myxedema in previously normal subjects does not lead to the development of exophthalmos. A possible explanation of the pituitary relationship to exophthalmos comes from the work of Dobyns and his collaborators. It has previously been found that a marked exophthalmic state developed in Fundulus, the common Atlantic "minnow," following administration of small amounts of anterior pituitary extract. Using this animal as a test for exophthalmic producing substance (EPS), Dobyns found it possible to separate TSH and EPS in pituitary extracts by means of their different solubilities in trichloracetic acid. TSH was obtained free from EPS, although the EPS fraction still contained some TSH activity. The evidence is suggestive then that an exophthalmos producing principle is often, though not always, liberated in association with TSH. Another observation which may help to explain the increase in the exophthalmos seen after thyroidectomy is that thyroid tissue slices *in vitro* have been found to inactivate both the thyroid-stimulating and exophthalmic-producing actions of TSH extracts.

Species differences exist in the quantity of TSH stored in the pituitary gland and in the sensitivity of the thyroid gland to a given dose of TSH. The anterior pituitary content of thyrotrophic hormone of several forms has been given, in ascending order, as follows: guinea pig, chick, cat, rabbit, man, ox, sheep, pig, dog, mouse, and rat. The guinea pig and chick thus have a low TSH con-

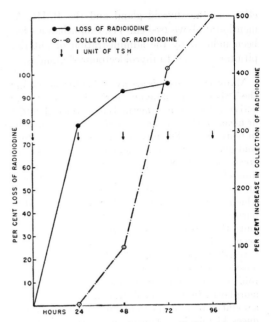

FIG. 56.9. Showing the percentile loss of radioiodine from and the delayed increase in radioiodine in the thyroid under influence of TSH. (From Rawson.)

tent in their anterior pituitaries and also less active thyroids than the other forms. They are, therefore, animals of choice for assay of TSH preparations. On the other hand, the rat, which normally has a more active thyroid, is less sensitive to administration of TSH.

A refractory state to the action of TSH develops after repeated administration of thyrotrophic extracts. This state has been shown by Collip and Anderson to be due to the formation of some inhibiting substance (antihormone; see p. 979) which they have found in the serum of the treated animals. Friedgood also found that though guinea pigs responded at first to an extract of the anterior lobe of the pituitary by thyroid hyperplasia and a rise in the basal metabolic rate, the animals later became refractory. The responsive period was followed by one during which the BMR fell to normal or to a subnormal level (though the injections were continued); the thyroid hyperplasia, however, persisted. Eventually the thyroid returned to its normal size and histological appearance, in spite of the uninterrupted administration of the extract. Slight prominence of the eyeballs appeared toward the end of the responsive phase, but the most pronounced exophthalmos occurred during the refractory phase. The production of the effect on the eyes appeared from this study also, to be independent of the effect on the thyroid gland and the BMR. As mentioned above (see ch. 44), exophthalmos has been induced by the administration of anterior pituitary extract to thyroidectomized animals.

Many *assay methods* are available for measuring the TSH content of materials rich in thyrotrophic activity. Few of these methods however will detect or measure the amounts of TSH normally present in body fluids. The increase in weight of the thyroid gland in immature male guinea pigs, the increase in mean cell height of the thyroidal epithelium of few-day-old chicks, the increase in uptake of $I^{131}$ by the thyroid glands of young rats (in which thyroidal activity has been depressed below normal by previous feeding with iodinated casein) and other criteria of thyrotrophic activity have been utilized as a basis for assay methods. The "stasis tadpole" method of D'Angelo is among the most sensitive. The starved tadpole develops thyroid atrophy and a consequent arrest of metamorphosis. Injection of TSH, in about 1:100th the amount detectable in the young guinea pig, produces histological changes in the thyroid gland. Other, recently published methods for which high degrees of sensitivity are claimed involve the release of radioactive hormone from the thyroid gland of the guinea pig or mouse, and the $I^{131}$ turnover in the guinea pig thyroid cultured *in vitro*. An assay method that would accurately determine TSH levels in body fluids would be of great value in the study of the factors determining the rate of TSH release in the normal animal and would throw light on the etiology and changes occurring in hypo- and hyperthyroid states in man. It should be emphasized that the thyrotrophic activity of any given sample is best expressed in terms of the recently established (1955) International Unit (I.U.). The International Unit is approximately equal to the pre-existing national (USP) Unit and is defined as the activity of 13.5 mg. of an international standard powdered preparation.

TSH is rapidly inactivated and excreted from the body. Using the stasis tadpole technique D'Angelo calculated that only 3 per cent of an injected dose was present in the blood of a rat at the end of 1 hour, and 1 per cent at 5 hours. The fate of the hormone is uncertain. Since it disappears from the blood of thyroidectomized animals more slowly than intact animals, and since *in vitro* tests show that thyroid (and lymphatic and thymic) tissue inactivates thyrotrophin, it is possible that it is inactivated by its own target gland.

The regulation of the release of TSH from the anterior pituitary gland is influenced by two chief factors, (a) the blood concentration of thyroid hormone, and (b) nervous influences from the hypothalamus. As described earlier, the blood concentration of hormones from the pituitary target glands determines, within limits, the rate of secretion of the appropriate pituitary trophic hormone. Thus a rise in concentration of thyroid hormone in the blood depresses the secretion of TSH, and a fall in concentration increases TSH release. This homeostatic or feed-back mechanism may be illustrated in several ways. A fall in level of thyroid hormone in the blood may be brought about by administration of a goitrogenic drug (which blocks the synthesis of thyroid hormone in the gland). Under these conditions the thyroid becomes depleted of colloid, shows hypertrophy and goiter formation, and all the signs of thyrotrophic activation. Such does not occur if the drug is administered to the hypophysectomized animal, or to an animal receiving large doses of thyroxine. Dempsey and Astwood (1943) used these observations to study the rate of release of thyroid hormone at various environmental temperatures. Thiouracil-treated rats were exposed to temperatures of 1°, 25°, and 35°C., and the least amount of thyroxine to maintain a normal thyroid histology was estimated. It was found that the daily dose required was 9.5 $\mu g.$ at 1°, 5.2 $\mu g.$ at 25°, and 1.7 $\mu g.$ at 35°C. These experiments demonstrate the amount of exogenous thyroxine required to maintain the pituitary-thyroid equilibrium under varying environmental conditions. The decreased secretion of TSH which follows a rise in blood level of thyroid hormone is shown by the thyroidal inhibition which follows administration of thyroxine to the normal animal. This has been clearly observed in the rabbit, in which the rate of release of radioactive hormone from the thyroid was studied. It was found that the release of thyroid hormone was inhibited within 2 hours by injection of thyroxine, and that a dose of about 15 $\mu g.$ per day was required to suppress thyroid function. This amount of thyroxine then appears to be the equivalent of the daily secretion of the thyroid in this species.

The hypothalamus regulates the pituitary secretion of thyrotrophic hormone through a mechanism involving the hypophysial portal vessels of the pituitary stalk. If the pituitary stalk is cut, or if the pituitary gland is transplanted to a distant site in the body, the activity of the thyroid is decreased, and various environmental influences which previously modified thyroid function are now without effect. The hypothalamus appears to exert a tonic influence in maintaining the basal level of thyrotrophic secretion and, by means of nervous reflexes, to modify TSH release in accord with the requirements of the environment. Thus, stress stimuli of an emotional or nervous type which normally inhibit TSH release, and the stimulus of a cold environment which normally excites TSH release, no longer do so after the pituitary is disconnected from the central nervous system. The influence of the hypothalamus on TSH secretion or thyroid activity has recently been investigated with regard to the effects produced by localized hypothalamic lesions and electrical stimulation. It has been found that lesions in the anterior hypothalamus, in the region of the supraopticohypophysial tract result in reduced thyroid function, whereas stimulation of approximately the same site results in an increase in thyroid activity. Since the supraopticohypophysial tract is known to regulate the release of posterior pituitary hormones, it has been suggested that the regulation of TSH secretion by the hypothalamus is mediated through the release of these hormones into the pituitary portal vessels, which supply the pars distalis.

Two questions arise from the above discussion. First, whether the feed-back effects of thyroid hormone act through the intermediation of the hypothalamus, and second, whether feed-back or neural influences take priority in the normal animal. The evidence relating to the former problem is indeterminate. The effect of the blood level of thyroxine in regulating TSH output is still apparent in the pituitary stalk-cut, or pituitary transplanted animal. However hypothalamic lesions decrease the sensitivity of the animal to the goitrogenic action of propylthiouracil (Greer), or to the effects of hemithyroidectomy (Reichlin). It may be that the feed-back system operates at both a hypothalamic and pituitary level and that in the normal animal the hypothalamus forms the more sensitive receptor mechanism. The answer to the second question is more certain. Presently available evidence indicates that the feed-back system acts to stabilize thyroid function at a particular level and that the nervous system superimposes its action on this baseline. Thus, as Brown-Grant has shown, emotional stress in the rabbit is associated with a decrease in thyroid activity *at the same time* as there occurs a fall in thyroid hormone in the blood. Conversely Harris and Woods have found that electrical stimulation of the hypothalamus results in a marked and maintained increase in thyroid activity in spite of a rise of blood concentration of thyroid hormone.

## The Adrenocorticotrophic Hormone (ACTH), Corticotrophin

Since the early work of Smith, it has become firmly established that the adrenal cortex is under the control of a hormone secreted by the anterior pituitary gland. Smith found that atrophy of the adrenal cortex occurred in the hypophysectomized rat and that repair took place under the influence of pituitary implants.

It is uncertain which cells of the anterior pituitary secrete ACTH. The observations of Cushing that a certain clinical entity characterized by adrenal cortical hypertrophy and overactivity was associated with a "basophil" adenoma of the pituitary led many workers to cite a basophil origin of this hormone. Recent studies of the human gland have indicated that under acute conditions of stress, in which it is known that ACTH is secreted in increased amounts, a basophil degranulation occurs with recovery under chronic conditions. However, other studies on the cytology of the rat pituitary, under a wide variety of experimental conditions, have not succeeded in establishing a correlation between ACTH secretion and any particular cell type.

Collip and his colleagues (1933) were the first to prepare an extract from the anterior pituitary which acted specifically upon the adrenal cortex. This extract was highly effective in restoring to normal the atrophied adrenal cortex of hypophysectomized animals. A protein with high corticotrophic activity was isolated by Li and his associates in 1942, and by Sayers and his colleagues in

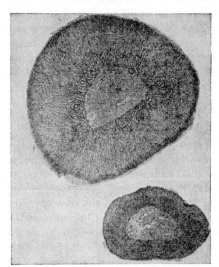

Fig. 56.10. Showing adrenal atrophy following hypophysectomy. Normal gland (above) and gland of hypophysectomized animal (below). (From P. Smith.)

1943. These extracts were found to have a molecular weight of around 20,000. The technique of Astwood and his colleagues, who employed oxycellulose to adsorb and purify adrenocorticotrophin, enables a polypeptide of a molecular weight of about 4000 to be extracted from these original preparations. This polypeptide retains all the physiological activity and is about 100 times as active as the starting protein extract. The amino acid components of ACTH are being elucidated and a proposed structure for one of the highly purified extracts ($\beta$-corticotrophin) has been proposed. ACTH is fairly resistant to pepsin but destroyed by trypsin. It is almost inactive when given by mouth. The most effective route of administration is by slow intravenous infusion. If injected subcutaneously or intramuscularly the effect of a given dose is increased if the extract is mixed with a diluent that slows absorption, such as beeswax and oil or gelatin.

The physiological activities of ACTH may be divided into those indirect functions which are dependent on stimulation of the target gland, and those direct activities which possibly occur in the absence of the adrenal cortex.

*Adrenal activities.* Hypophysectomy results in adrenal cortical atrophy, although the different zones of the cortex atrophy to different degrees. Greep and Deane emphasize that the zona glomerulosa of the rat remains well developed after hypophysectomy, and other workers have reported somewhat similar findings in the dog. Greep correlates this fact with the relatively intact electrolyte metabolism found in the hypophysectomized, but not adrenalectomized, animal and suggests that the zona glomerulosa is responsible for secreting aldosterone (see p. 1036) and that this function is largely free from pituitary control. It has recently been shown by *in vitro* methods that the outer zone of the adrenal cortex synthesizes aldosterone at a higher rate than other parts. The zona fasciculata shows marked thinning after hypophysectomy, loses much of its lipoid material and develops a characteristic sudanophobic zone. These changes are all reversible by administration of ACTH. The injection of ACTH into the hypophysectomized or normal animal, or the exposure of the normal animal to stressful or noxious stimuli (known to evoke ACTH discharge from the pituitary) results in the reverse changes. Thus administration of ACTH induces (a) increased size of the adrenal which may be detectable within a few hours, (b) a depletion of the ascorbic acid content of the

adrenal within 15 to 30 minutes (the exact physiological significance of this response is unknown, but it forms the basis of the most widely used assay method for ACTH), (c) a fall in concentration of adrenal cholesterol and stainable lipoid (it is now known that cholesterol is a precursor of the adrenal steroids, so that the fall in adrenal cholesterol presumably reflects increased hormonal synthesis), and (d) an increased release of adrenal steroids as detected by assay of adrenal vein blood (this is a rapid response, occurring within a few minutes, and is associated with an increased blood flow through the gland). In general, it may be said that the adrenal cortex secretes three groups of steroids; glucocorticoids, mineralocorticoids, and androgenic steroids. It is of interest that administration of ACTH may affect the type of glucocorticoid secreted in a particular species. Thus the rabbit, which normally secretes corticosterone, releases predominantly hydrocortisone after chronic treatment with corticotrophin. There has been much discussion as to the control the pituitary exerts over aldosterone secretion. It seems established that aldosterone release is less dependent on pituitary adrenocorticotrophin than is the release of the glucocorticoids. Aldosterone output is reduced, but not to such a marked degree as that of the glucocorticoids by hypophysectomy in the dog or cat, and the effect of administration of ACTH on aldosterone secretion is reported as inconstant or small in comparison with the effect on glucocorticoid secretion. Little is known about the regulation of secretion of adrenal androgens. 17-ketosteroids have been found in the adrenal vein blood of the dog and man, but their physiological role is uncertain. In certain pathological states of virilism in young girls, the androgenic secretion of the adrenal cortex seems to be maintained by pituitary ACTH, since Wilkins has found that administration of cortisone (which inhibits ACTH release through the feed-back mechanism) may control the disease.

The quantitative aspects of ACTH control of glucocorticoid secretion has been studied most carefully in the dog. Hypophysectomy lowers the amount of 17-hydroxycorticosterone (F) in adrenal vein blood, whereas injection of a large intravenous dose of ACTH (20 to 40 units), or surgical trauma, raises the 17-hydroxycorticosterone secretion from a resting figure of about 7 $\mu$g. per kilogram per hour to about 50 $\mu$g. per kilogram per hour. It should be pointed out that under certain conditions the adrenal cortex is relatively resistant to the action of ACTH. The atrophic adrenal consequent to hypophysectomy, a hypo-pituitary state or to chronic blockade of ACTH release by cortisone, is insensitive to ACTH and may require several days of corticotrophin administration before normal sensitivity is regained. States of adrenal cortical deficiency may be encountered clinically if cortisone therapy is stopped too suddenly.

Certain extra-adrenal activities of ACTH have been described from time to time. It is now known that many of these were due to impurities in the extracts used. However, it appears likely that ACTH does have melanophore-stimulating actions as an intrinsic property of its molecule. This may be due to the fact that a certain amino acid sequence in the polypeptide chains is common to both $\beta$-corticotrophin and melanophore-stimulating hormone (MSH). The present known preparations of ACTH also seem to possess fat-mobilizing (adipokinetic) activity and ketogenic activity.

The physiological actions observed after administration of ACTH are very largely those mediated by the adrenal cortex, and chapter 58 may be consulted for an account of these. Minor differences in the effects observed after ACTH or hydrocortisone administration in the human have been reported. ACTH therapy is said to be followed by a greater degree of salt and water retention, and by a greater incidence of virilizing manifestations. These effects may be due to the stimulation of secretion of aldosterone and androgenic steroids, as well as of 17-hydroxycorticosterone, by ACTH.

The *assay* of ACTH is dependent on biological methods. These may be divided into those employing intact or hypophysectomized animals, although *in vitro* procedures have been newly proposed. It is probably inadvisable to rely upon methods using intact animals in view of the ease in which endogenous ACTH can be discharged by such trivial stress stimuli as those associated with handling or with injection. However, the use of animals in which the release of ACTH has been blocked with DOCA has been proposed as an alternative to hypophysectomy (Buttle and Hodges). The more important methods include: (a) *Ascorbic acid depletion test* (Sayers' test) in which the left adrenals of male rats (120 to 180 grams) are removed 24 hours after hypophysectomy. The hormone preparation is then given intravenously and the right adrenal removed 1 hour later. Both adrenals are analyzed for ascorbic acid and the response is calculated as the difference in ascorbic acid between the right and left glands. As little as 0.2 milliunits of the international standard can be detected by this method. (b) The *repair test:* in this case the quantity of ACTH required in a 4-day period to restore the normal histological appearance of the adrenal cortex of 28-day-old female rats hypophysectomized 14 days previously is determined. (c) The *maintenance test:* a unit of ACTH as defined by this test is the amount required over a period of 15 days to maintain the preoperative weight of hypophysectomized 40-day-old male rats. (d) *Corticosteroid release:* hypophysectomized dogs are maintained on ACTH until about 16 hours before the assay. For the assay the adrenal vein is cannulated, samples of adrenal vein blood are collected at intervals and the corticosteroid content determined by the Porter-Silber reaction. The effect of ACTH preparations may then be directly compared with a standard by means of the increase in corticosteroid output induced (Nelson and Hume). (e) *Release of corticosteroids in vitro:* rat adrenal glands are cut into pieces and the fragments incubated with ACTH preparations in a Warburg apparatus. The steroids released are extracted from the medium and assayed by chemical means. It has been suggested that since the results obtained by the adrenal weight method and the Sayers' method do not give parallel findings for some pituitary extracts that there are two corticotrophins, an "adrenal weight factor" and an "adrenal ascorbic acid depletion factor." The different results obtained by the two methods are perhaps more easily explained by the different routes of administration of the extracts used in the two assays. Amounts of ACTH should be expressed quantitatively in terms of the international standard. The International Unit is the activity of 1 mg. of the international standard powder (La-1-A).

The *inactivation* of ACTH occurs very rapidly in the body. It is not excreted in the urine though appreciable amounts of an administered dose may be recovered from kidney tissue. The half-life of the hormone in the blood of the rat is about 1 minute.

*The regulation of the secretion of ACTH* by the anterior pituitary has been intensively investigated since it became realized that release of the hormone at increased rates was one of the organism's defense reactions to stress or trauma, and that ACTH given in large pharmacological doses was of use in rheumatoid arthritis, in other so-called collagen diseases, and in various allergic disorders. As with most other pituitary trophic hormones the secretion of ACTH appears to be controlled by two main factors, the feed-back of its target gland hormones (the adrenal steroids) and by an influence from the central nervous system *via* the hypothalamus. In the following discussion two points should be borne in mind. First, the adrenal cortex of the *hypophysectomized* animal still secretes sufficient steroids to maintain life under optimal conditions, and second, the pituitary gland removed from the influence of the central nervous system still secretes basal amounts of ACTH. Thus both the adrenal cortex and anterior pituitary possess some autonomous secretory activity and it is against this background that the factors regulating ACTH secretion have to be studied. It was at one time claimed that the feed-back mechanism of the adrenal cortical hormones was sufficient to regulate the output of ACTH under resting conditions and also under conditions of stress (starvation, cold exposure, infection, tissue damage, emotional excitement, etc.) in which corticotrophin secretion is greatly increased. It was argued that stressful stimuli increased the tissue utilization of adrenal cortical hormones, that the blood concentration of these hormones was thereby decreased, and that *via* the feed-back action the liberation of ACTH was augmented, leading to increased adrenal cortical activity. There can be no doubt that an increased blood level of adrenal steroids tends to suppress ACTH release and *vice versa*. Arguments against this view are: the lack of evidence that noxious influences do in fact increase the tissue utilization of adrenal corticoids, and that if this mechanism holds true then it would seem impossible for the organism to maintain an increased blood concentration of adrenal steroids for any length of time. That this hypothesis does not represent the whole story was shown most convincingly by Sydnor and Sayers (1954). These workers developed a method for assaying the blood level of ACTH in rats. It was found that adrenalectomized rats had a higher level than that of normal rats (which was undetectable by the method) and that stress stimuli (ether anaesthesia, scalding, bleeding) had a rapid and dramatic effect in increasing the blood ACTH concentration in both normal and adrenalectomized animals. It is clear that the stress stimuli could not have affected ACTH secretion by a feed-back action in the adrenalectomized rats. It is likely that the servo mechanism acts rather as a stabilizing system to maintain a constancy of adrenal cortical function at any set level. The most potent influence in maintaining the normal rate of ACTH secretion, and in increasing this rate under conditions of stress, appears to be derived from the hypothalamus. Reasons for this statement are as follows: (a) Separation of the pituitary from the hypothalamus by section of the pituitary stalk and the placement of a plate between the stalk ends, or by pituitary transplantation, results in adrenal cortical atrophy (though the ultimate size of the gland is somewhat greater than that of the hypophysectomized animal), (b) hypothalamic lesions have been found to result in a diminution of ACTH concentration in systemic blood, a diminution of 17-hydroxycorticosteroids in adrenal vein blood, a loss of the compensatory hypertrophy which follows unilateral adrenalectomy, and abolition of the adrenal cortical response to stress stimuli, (c) administration of morphine has been found to blockade the ACTH release evoked by such stress stimuli as injection of histamine or unilateral adrenalectomy (it seems likely that morphine exerts this effect by an action on the nervous system), and (d) electrical stimulation of the hypothalamus results in increased corticoids in adrenal vein blood and in signs of increased adrenal cortical activity (lymphopenia, eosinopenia, decreased adrenal ascorbic acid, and histological changes in the sudanophilic material of the adrenal cortex). The pathway by which the hypothalamus affects the activity of the pars distalis is a vascular one: the portal vessels of the pituitary stalk. The exact mechanism is unknown although evidence is accumulating that it involves the transmission of a humoral agent from the tuber cinereum to the anterior pituitary.

One corollary to the above discussion should be added. Stressful stimuli which involve tissue damage or metabolic disturbance still evoke ACTH discharge even when the pituitary gland is separated from the nervous system. On these grounds, Fortier originally divided stresses into two types: neural (emotional excitement, uncomfortable noise, pain, fright), acting on the anterior pituitary solely through the nervous system, and systemic (involving surgical trauma and changes in the composition of the circulating systemic blood), which can act directly on anterior pituitary cells without the mediation of the nervous system. In the intact animal the neural component probably plays a part in the response to both types of stimuli. As pointed out by Fortier, and later by Sayers, this distinction may involve not a difference of modality, but one of intensity, of the stresses used in the original experiments. Thus, a pituitary stalk cut animal may liberate enough "humoral transmitter" from the tuber cinereum, in response to a severe stress, to be carried around the general circulation to affect corticotrophin release by the pituitary gland.

*Gonadotrophic Hormones, Gonadotrophins (Follicle-Stimulating Hormone, FSH; Luteinizing Hormone, LH, or Interstitial-Cell Stimulating Hormone, ICSH)*

Several observations in the past have pointed to extraovarian factors as regulators of ovarian activity. After removal of one ovary the same number of follicles develop in the remaining ovary as in the original pair (law of follicular constancy). The fact that ovaries from immature animals grafted into the adult, or ovaries from

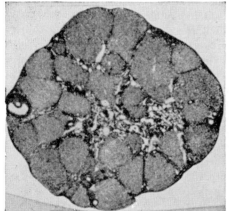

FIG. 56.11. Ovary of adult mouse injected with alkaline extract of anterior lobe of pituitary. Large numbers of corpora lutea are present, and few follicles. (From Parkes, *The Internal Secretions of the Ovary*, by permission of Longmans, Green & Co.)

adult animals grafted into the immature, behave according to the age of the recipient host, indicated that ovarian function was controlled humorally by some substance external to the ovary itself. This hypothetical substance was termed "generative ferment" by Heape, and "X substance" by other early workers. The gradual atrophy and suppression of sex functions which occurs with diseases of the anterior pituitary in man (acromegaly, Frohlich's syndrome) and the atrophy of the gonads after hypophysectomy in animals, indicated the pituitary as the source of this substance. A firm basis for this belief was established by the following observations: (a) Evans and his associates found that a crude saline extract of the anterior lobe caused luteinization of ovarian follicles (fig. 56.11), (b) Smith and Engle observed that when *fresh* mammalian anterior lobe tissue was implanted daily into immature female rats or mice, estrus was precipitated and ovulation followed. The ovaries and uterus showed enlargement to about 5 to 10 times normal size (fig. 56.12), the ovaries discharged an excessive number of ova (superovulation) and the solid vaginal canal (typical of the immature rat or mouse) developed a lumen. In immature male animals, the testes, seminal vesicles, and penis were stimulated to increased growth. Further, the gonadal atrophy which followed hypophysectomy was prevented by anterior lobe implants, (c) Ascheim and Zondek first found that injec-

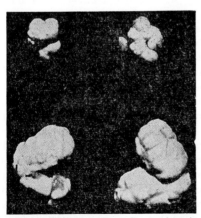

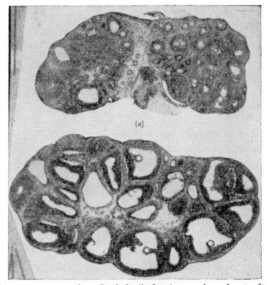

FIG. 56.12. Showing effect of anterior pituitary upon ovaries. On left (below), ovaries of rat after 12 implantations of fresh rat pituitary gland; (above) ovaries of litter mate control rat. (From Collip.) On right (below), follicular maturation induced in immature rat on 29th day by eight daily implantations of fresh pituitary gland; (above) ovary of litter mate control. (From Smith and Engle.)

tion of the blood or urine of pregnant women into immature rats caused follicular development, ovulation, and luteinization. They termed this substance Prolan. It has since been found that Prolan originates in the chorion of the placenta (*human chorionic gonadotrophin*, HCG) and not in the pituitary and that its action is mainly luteinizing, and (d) the discovery that the urine of menopausal women, or of castrated men and women, contains a substance which stimulates the ovary. This substance is probably of pituitary origin and its main action is follicle-stimulating. It is now generally held that the pituitary secretes two, if not three, gonadotrophic hormones. The first is concerned with ripening of the ovarian follicles (FSH) or spermatogenesis, the second with ovulation, luteinization, and maintenance of the interstitial tissue of the gonads (LH or ICSH), and possibly a third that maintains luteal activity (*prolactin* or *luteotrophic hormone*, LTH).

A detailed account of the reproductive processes may be found in chapter 60. A summary of the events occurring during a sexual cycle is given in figure 56.13. As a basis for future discussion it may be said that at the beginning of a sexual cycle, when the ovary and the uterus are in a resting phase, the pituitary liberates FSH. Under the influence of this hormone, follicles ripen in the ovary and estrogen secretion occurs. This in turn produces development of the uterus and other parts of the reproductive tract. At about the 14th day of the cycle in the human, release of LH

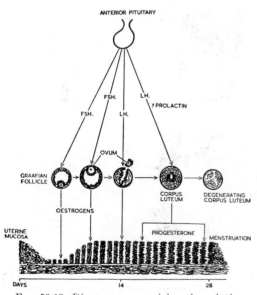

FIG. 56.13. Diagram summarizing the relationships of the anterior pituitary, ovary, and endometrium through the menstrual cycle.

occurs and under the continued action of LH and FSH, a ripe follicle ruptures, and a corpus luteum develops. This in turn secretes progesterone which results in secretory activity of the endometrium and characteristic changes in uterine muscle reactivity. In some forms luteal secretion is dependent upon prolactin release from the pituitary but this has not been established for primates. Thus the changes typical of the first, follicular, half of the sex cycle are regulated by FSH release from the pituitary and of the second, luteal, half of the cycle by LH and possibly LTH release.

The origin of the gonadotrophic hormones in the anterior pituitary lies in the basophil cells. Both FSH and LH are glycoproteins and their cells of origin, therefore, stain with the trichrome periodic acid-Schiff procedure. The basophil cells of the rat pituitary may be divided into a group placed centrally in the pars distalis (concerned with TSH secretion), a group located on the lower surface of the gland and another situated peripherally on the upper surface adjacent to the pars intermedia. There is general agreement that these latter groups are composed of cells concerned with gonadotrophin secretion, and there are indications that those on the lower surface release LH and the peripherally placed cells are associated with FSH.

The chemical separation of pituitary extracts into two gonadotrophic fractions was first accomplished by Fevold, Hisaw, and Leonard in 1931. Since then several methods have been developed for obtaining either FSH or LH in a highly purified form. It is perhaps doubtful whether either fraction has been obtained completely pure. It is also debatable whether the pituitary secretes one hormone with multiple gonadotrophic activities or two hormones with actions comparable to those of the present chemical extracts. FSH is a glycoprotein, rich in carbohydrate. Its hormonal activity is destroyed by ptyalin and takadiastase, so that its activity may be dependent on the integrity of the carbohydrate fraction of the molecule. It is not destroyed by trypsin, however, a fact which has been utilized in one method to separate it from LH. Purified preparations have been obtained from both sheep and swine pituitary tissue. It is of interest that the preparation derived from these two sources behave alike biologically but may differ chemically. LH is also a glycoprotein but its biological activity is not destroyed by ptyalin. It has likewise been prepared in a purified state from sheep and swine pituitaries; the material obtained from the two sources showing different physicochemical and immunological properties. For example, pig LH has a molecular weight of about 100,000 and sheep LH about 40,000.

The physiological properties of FSH and LH extracts are best investigated in hypophysectomized animals using biologically pure preparations. This is even more important in the study of gonadotrophins than for the other pituitary hormones since the presence of small amounts of other endogenous or exogenous gonadotrophins in the circulation may alter the effects observed both quantitatively and qualitatively. The gonads of hypophysectomized animals show pronounced loss of size and weight. Primordial follicles are still present in the ovaries but do not develop to the stage of antra formation. No ovulation occurs and no corpora lutea are formed. In animals such as the rat, in which interstitial tissue is present in the ovary, this tissue shows obvious degenerative changes. The cells become smaller with dense pyknotic nuclei. Hormonal activity on the part of the ovary also ceases, as shown by the atrophy of the accessory reproductive organs (fig. 56.14). On administration of FSH preparations to such an hypophysectomized animal, follicles enlarge and ripen and a marked increase occurs in ovarian weight. Such administration, however, does not result in ovulation or corpora lutea formation, nor repair of the interstitial tissue or hormone secretion by the ovary. The reproductive tract, therefore, remains atrophic. Administration of purified LH to the hypophysectomized rat repairs the interstitial tissue of the ovary. Follicular growth does not occur and no sign of estrogen secretion is apparent in the uterus and vagina. If FSH and LH are administered together then follicular ripening, ovulation, and corpus luteum formation occurs. The optimum dosage of these hormones for ovulation is about (FSH:LH) 10:1. FSH and LH given together also result in estrogen secretion and development of the genital tract. However, the corpora lutea do not become functional and secretory in the rat unless prolactin (luteotrophic hormone) is also present. The synergism which exists between the action of FSH and LH when given together is clearly seen when the effect upon ovarian weight is studied. FSH given alone increases the weight of the ovary in the hypophysectomized rat; LH alone has little effect. FSH and LH given together result in a much greater increment in ovarian weight than would be expected from a simple summation of responses. This is known as the *augmentation effect* and must be allowed for when considering assay

procedures for these hormones. In the hypophysectomized male rat, purified FSH results in development of the testicular tubules and spermatogenesis, but has no effect on the interstitial or Leydig cells. On the other hand, purified LH results in development of the interstitial cells and secretion of androgen. The androgenic activity in turn results in development of the seminiferous tubules and spermatogenesis, and also development of the accessory organs such as the seminal vesicles and ventral prostate. The stimulation of gametogenesis by LH in the male, through the androgenic secretion elicited, seems to have no equivalent in the female. It is, however, well established that androgens stimulate the seminiferous tubules directly both in the rat and probably in the human.

Evidence has accumulated that administration of the gonadotrophins results in a reduction of ovarian and testicular cholesterol. It is likely that the cholesterol in these glands is a precursor of estrogens and androgens, and the condition may be compared with that existing in the adrenal cortex.

It is probable that FSH and LH exert the same effects in man as those described above for the rat. However, the therapeutic uses of gonadotrophic hormones have limited value and their actions in the human are ill-understood.

Substances with gonadotrophic activity may be extracted from blood and urine in various normal and pathological states. These gonadotrophic substances may be of pituitary or placental origin, but all appear to be glycoproteins.

*1. Menopause or castration urinary gonadotrophin (CU).* This substance was first found in the blood or urine of menopausal women, and later in the urine of both sexes after castration. It is probably of pituitary origin. Cessation of

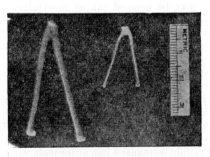

Fig. 56.14. Effect of hypophysectomy upon the uterus. On right, uterus of normal rat; on left, that of an hypophysectomized rat. (From van Dyke, *The Physiology and Pharmacology of the Pituitary Body*, by permission of the University of Chicago Press.)

function, or removal, of the gonads results in release of the pituitary from the feed-back of gonadal hormones and an increased secretion of pituitary gonadotrophins. In support of this view is the fact that extracts of the pituitary of the castrate animal have similar physiological effects to CU, in that they are very largely folliclestimulating in nature.

2. *Human chorionic gonadotrophin (HCG)*. In 1927, Ascheim and Zondek reported the presence of a gonadotrophic substance in the blood and urine of pregnant women. On injection of an extract of HCG into an immature mouse or rat, follicular development, ovulation, and luteinization occurs in the ovaries. However on injection into an hypophysectomized rat no follicular development occurs. Its actions are explainable on the grounds that HCG stimulates the animal's own pituitary to secrete FSH, while possessing LH-like activity itself (for further information see ch. 60).

3. *Pregnant mare serum gonadotrophin (PMS)*. Cole and Hart (1930) first observed the presence of a powerful gonadotrophic substance in the blood of pregnant mares. On injection into hypophysectomized animals it exerts a predominantly follicle-stimulating effect. Unlike the other gonadotrophic substances it persists in the blood stream, after a single injection, for many days (see also ch. 60).

The *bioassay* of gonadotrophins is usually performed with reference to their follicle-stimulating or interstitial cell-stimulating activity. The augmentation effect must be borne in mind and may be circumvented when assaying FSH either by eliminating the action of LH (by using hypophysectomized animals and purified preparations of FSH), or by deliberately adding to the extract to be assayed amounts of an LH substance which produces maximum augmentation. Thus FSH activity may be assayed (a) by ascertaining the amount of material necessary to re-establish follicular growth in the *hypophysectomized* animal, or (b) by finding the least amount of the preparation that will double the ovarian weight of the *normal* immature animal when administered in combination with a substance having LH activity. LH activity, on the other hand, may be measured more satisfactorily, since a test is available for LH which is independent of the augmentation effect. The increase in weight of the ventral prostate of the hypophysectomized immature male rat gives an index of the amount of LH activity in an injected extract.

The *inactivation* of pituitary gonadotrophic hormones in the blood stream proceeds more slowly than do some other anterior pituitary hormones, such as ACTH and TSH. Significant amounts of gonadotrophin may be detectable in the blood some 24 hours after administration of an extract. The measurement of the normal levels of gonadotrophic hormone in the blood is of questionable accuracy throughout the major part of the menstrual cycle. At the midpoint of the cycle, however, at about the time of ovulation, a rise of blood gonadotrophic activity undoubtedly occurs. There is evidence from *in vitro* studies that ovarian tissue inactivates gonadotrophin. Small amounts of these hormones are also excreted in the urine.

*The regulation of anterior pituitary secretion of gonadotrophins* has been studied in detail. Research in this field preceded investigation of the control of other anterior pituitary hormones since changes in gonadotrophin secretion could be easily inferred from study of the sexual cycles, and since in particular forms specific changes in the environment were found to be associated with alterations in the sexual rhythm. Thus growth of follicles and induction of estrus during periods of sexual quiescence, indicative of increased secretion of FSH, may be induced in birds (Rowan, 1926), ferrets (Bissonnette, 1932), and other forms by exposure to extra hours of daily illumination. Similarly, ovulation and the formation of corpora lutea, indicative of LH release, does not occur spontaneously in many birds, rabbits, cats, ferrets, and some other mammals, but requires the triggering stimulus of mating for its initiation. It is likely that these are examples of a general pattern of nervous control of the secretion of gonadotrophic hormones. A similar conclusion regarding a nervous influence may be drawn from clinical observations. The fear of pregnancy in unmarried girls, the change of occupation from day to night work, and emotional upsets of many types, such as those induced by aerial bombardment in World War II or by incarceration in a concentration camp, have all been found to be associated with loss of menstrual cycles.

The first clear-cut experimental data that gonadotrophin secretion from the anterior pituitary is dependent upon the nervous system came from experiments in which the pituitary stalk had been cut and a plate placed between the hypothalamus and pituitary, and others in which the hypophysis had been transplanted to a distant site in the body. It is now generally agreed that these procedures result in ovarian atrophy and cessation of hormonal secretion by the ovary. The reproductive tract thus undergoes atrophy. On the other hand, it has been found by Harris and Jacobsohn that if the pituitary gland is removed from the sella turcica, and anterior pituitary tissue placed not in a distant site but directly under the hypothalamus, the hypophysial portal vessels between the tuber cinereum and pars distalis regrow and normal reproductive functions are regained. Everett and Nikitovitch-Winer have even found that if the pituitary gland of a female rat is transplanted under the kidney capsule a period of sexual quiescence and atrophy occurs, but if this same transplanted pituitary tissue is then replaced under the hypothalamus, apparently normal reproductive functions return. In these latter animals the portal vessels were again found to have reconnected the tuber cinereum and anterior pituitary tissue. For these and other reasons given below, it may be said that the hypothalamus maintains and regulates the secretion of gonadotrophins.

In order to analyze the hypothalamic mechanisms involved in more detail, experiments have been conducted in which localized lesions and stimulation have been made in the hypothalamus. Lesions of the hypothalamus have been found to result in (a) cessation of sexual cycles and atrophy of the reproductive organs (median eminence lesions), (b) abolition of sexual cycles with the intervention of prolonged periods of follicular development in the ovary and a state of constant estrus (lesions in the anterior, paraventricular region of the hypothalamus), (c) the induction of a state of sexual activity and development at a time of year when seasonally breeding animals (ferrets) would normally show atrophic organs and sexual quiescence (anterior hypothalamic lesions), and (d) the precocious development of puberty in immature animals (anterior hypothalamic lesions). This last observation is of clinical interest in that young boys and girls afflicted with hypothalamic tumors, especially those of congenital origin known as hamartomata, may show full development of physical and psychic sexual function when only a few years of age. It seems likely that FSH secretion is regulated by a predominantly inhibiting influence of the hypothalamus over the anterior pituitary, and that if this influence is removed by a hypothalamic lesion then signs of a release effect on FSH secretion are observed. It is noteworthy that no records are available of an increase in FSH release following electrical stimulation of the hypothalamus.

Stimulation of the hypothalamus has, however, been shown to evoke release of LH and ovulation in the rabbit. As mentioned above, this species does not ovulate spontaneously but normally requires the sensory stimuli, associated with the act of mating, to excite various nervous reflex paths and, thus, in turn LH secretion and follicular rupture. Adapting Sherrington's term for spinal reflexes to neuroendocrine reflexes, it may be said that the hypothalamus and pituitary stalk form the "final common path" for the latter. Thus, it seems likely that the electrical stimuli which result in ovulation when applied to the posterior tuber cinereum and median eminence are activating the terminal parts of the reflex paths which normally underlie the ovulation response. The mechanism involved in the cyclical release of LH in spontaneously ovulating forms also seems to involve the hypothalamus, since hypothalamic lesions have been found to block ovulation and to result in a state of continuous estrus in rats, and since such drugs as barbiturates, well known for their action on the central nervous system, may also block ovulation in these animals. Recent data also implicate other areas of the brain, such as the reticular activating system and amygdaloid nuclei, as participating in the control of LH release. It is likely that these areas act through their projections to the hypothalamus.

The timing of puberty, and the endocrine changes associated with it, also seem to be under central nervous control. In the early days of this century it was believed that an "ageing process" in ovarian tissue might determine the time of puberty. However, this is clearly not the case since ovaries from immature animals transplanted into ovariectomized adults, behave as adult organs. Also, pituitary tissue from newborn rats, transplanted under the hypothalamus of hypophysectomized adults, has also been found capable of maintaining normal adult function. Therefore, it may be said that puberty is not dependent on a maturation process in ovarian or anterior pituitary tissue. When these data are combined with those indicating that hypothalamic lesions, both in the human and the experimental animal, may be associated with *pubertas praecox* it is clear that the central nervous system is in some way related to pubertal development. One hypothesis, that at the moment harmonizes with the experimental data, is that the gonads from birth to puberty secrete gonadal hormones at a low rate, but at a rate sufficient to exert a restraining influence on anterior pituitary activity. This influence may be exerted through the hypothalamus, and in this case would be abolished by a lesion in this structure.

A problem in some ways allied with that of puberty concerns the sexual differentiation of the mechanisms regulating gonadotrophic secretion. The secretion of gonadotrophic hormones occurs in a cyclical fashion in the adult female, but in a more constant manner in the adult male. This may be illustrated by the fact that ovaries transplanted into castrated males show constant follicular development but absence of ovulation and corpus luteum formation. Pfeiffer in 1936, made an extensive study of the effects of gonadal transplants in immature rats on their subsequent sexual function. He concluded that the immature gonads secrete hormone at a sufficient rate between birth and puberty to impose a sexual differentiation upon the maturing pituitary gland, and that the pattern of gonadotrophic release in adult life is dependent upon this sexual maturation of the pituitary. His data indicated that basically the mechanism concerned is cyclic in function and that this is converted in the developing male animal to one that is acyclic. It is now clear, however, that the anterior pituitary gland remains functionally plastic. This can be seen most easily from the fact that pituitary tissue obtained from a male rat can, if transplanted under the hypothalamus of an hypophysectomized female rat, maintain female sexual cycles and pregnancy. Thus pituitary tissue itself retains a male and female bipotentiality. It is likely that the sexual differentiation, observed by Pfeiffer, concerns not the tissue of the adenohypophysis but some neural mechanism in the hypothalamus responsible for regulating gonadotrophin release in the adult animal.

The feed-back of gonadal hormones then seems to be concerned in the changes attendant upon puberty and the sexual differentiation of the mechanism concerned with gonadotrophin secretion. It is an important factor controlling gonadotrophin release in the normal adult. Administration of estrogens to the normal female results in atrophy of the ovaries through inhibition of gonadotrophin secretion. Removal of an ovary results in hypertrophy of the remaining gland. Therefore, it is very probable that a similar feedback effect of target gland hormone occurs in the case of the ovary as for the thyroid and adrenal cortex. Moore and Price (1932) first expressed the view that the cyclical nature of sexual cycles was due to a self-regulating reciprocity between the pituitary and the gonads, based on the feed-back action. Later evidence tends to the view that the

gonadal hormones exert their effects on anterior pituitary secretion *via* the intermediation of the hypothalamus. In this case the gonadal hormones would exert an effect on some receptor mechanism in the central nervous system which would adjust pituitary activity accordingly. Such a view would be more in keeping with the finding that an anterior hypothalamic lesion may convert a female rat or guinea pig, showing normal cycles, to one in a state of constant estrus, and it would also explain the findings of Flerkó that small fragments of ovary transplanted into the hypothalamus near the paraventricular nuclei, but not in other regions, result in a diminution of uterine weights.

### Prolactin, Lactogenic Hormone, or Luteotrophic Hormone (LTH)

In 1928, Stricker and Grueter reported that injection of pituitary extract into a pseudopregnant rabbit before or after ovariectomy resulted in lactation. Within the next few years several groups of workers reported the isolation of a pituitary extract with lactogenic activity. Hypophysectomy prevents the onset of lactation, or results in abrupt cessation of an existing lactation. However, injection of a suitable anterior pituitary extract into hypophysectomized animals produces lactation. In 1931, Riddle and Braucher found that pituitary extracts caused development of the crop glands in pigeons. These glands consist of circumscribed areas of mucosa in the dorsal part of the crop, and are responsible for secreting "crop milk" which is regurgitated by either parent and utilized to feed the young. Riddle and his colleagues later showed that the crop gland effect in pigeons is probably due to the same hormones which cause lactation in mammals and suggested the term *prolactin*.

The cellular site of origin of prolactin is thought to be some type of acidophile cell in the anterior pituitary. The evidence for this is indirect, and is based on observations that the peripheral zone of the anterior lobe of the ox pituitary contains more prolactin and more acidophils than the central region, and that during the incubation period in pigeons, or lactation in mammals, the main cytological changes in the pituitary concern the $\alpha$ cells of the pars distalis.

Prolactin is a protein with a molecular weight of 25,000 to 30,000. A pure and potent preparation was first obtained by Lyons, and a crystalline preparation by White. Subsequent studies have shown that the extracts behave as pure proteins to physicochemical tests and that they are free from other pituitary hormones. The purified protein retains lactogenic, crop sac stimulating, and luteotrophic activity. To be effective it must be administered by injection.

The physiological activities of prolactin are exerted upon the mammary gland, the pigeon crop sac and, in certain species, the corpus luteum. The effects produced by prolactin on the mammary gland form a difficult subject of study. Species differences and the simultaneous actions of other hormones on the gland must be carefully considered. This subject is dealt with in chapter 60, and it will, therefore, suffice to say here that the initiation of lactation (lactogenesis) and its maintenance are probably due to a complex of pituitary hormones centering around prolactin as an essential element. Lyons and coworkers recently stated " . . . in the Long-Evans rat, at least 5 of the 6 well-identified anterior pituitary hormones play important parts in mammogenesis and lactogenesis." The effect of prolactin on the crop sac of the male or female pigeon, on the other hand, is a specific and direct action of the lactogenic hormone. It thus forms a more suitable reaction in many ways for assay purposes. The stimulating effect prolactin exerts on the secretory activity of the corpus luteum of the rat was observed in 1941, and led to the synonym luteotrophic hormone (LTH) for prolactin. It would seem established now, that FSH and LH are responsible for ovulation and the *formation* of the corpus luteum during the normal estrous cycle in the rat. This corpus luteum, however, does not necessarily become functionally active and secrete progesterone. If sterile or fertile coitus occurs during estrus, this in some way triggers the release of LTH from the pituitary and so results in a functionally active luteal phase and an associated period of pseudopregnancy or pregnancy. However, since the original observations, little evidence has accumulated that prolactin exerts a luteotrophic action in other species, such as the rabbit, monkey, or man. Recent work, however, indicates that prolactin has a definite effect in prolonging the active life of the corpus luteum in the sheep.

*The assay* of prolactin may be performed using the crop gland or mammary response. The increase in weight of the pigeon crop after intramuscular injection of the hormone, or histological changes in the crop mucosa after intradermal injection of the hormone immediately over the crop gland, are both used. It has been suggested that the increased uptake of radioactive phosphorus by the crop sac under the influence of prolactin may form the basis of a sensitive and objective assay method. In mammals the formation of milk in the mammary tissue of the estrogen-progesterone treated or pseudopregnant rabbit, following either systemic administration or injection into a lactiferous duct, may be employed. An international standard of prolactin is available. One I.U. is the activity contained in 0.1 mg. of the standard preparation.

Little is known regarding the *inactivation and excretion* of prolactin in the body. Some *in vitro* studies have indicated that prolactin is inactivated by the tissues of the mammary gland, ovary, and pigeon crop gland, that is by tissues of its three target organs.

*Factors regulating the secretion* of prolactin have been studied by observing the effect of different procedures on the activity of the mammary gland, or the corpora lutea of the rat. These indirect methods of assessing prolactin are necessary since the techniques for measuring prolactin in body fluids are not sensitive or accurate enough to allow direct measurement. In chapter 60 it is pointed out that there is suggestive evidence that the sensory stimuli associated with the act of suckling stimulate by various reflexes the pituitary secretion of prolactin, and, therefore, play an important part in maintaining milk secretion in the breast. Similar evidence relating to prolactin secretion is that the suckling may induce the development of functional luteal tissue in the rat. As mentioned above, corpora lutea are formed, but do not function, during the normal estrous cycle in this animal. If mating occurs, however, prolactin release is stimulated by reflex action, the corpora lutea become functional and the next extrus is delayed for the period of pregnancy or pseudopregnancy. During the period of pseudopregnancy, trauma to the endometrium results in the formation of a tumorlike mass in the uterus known as a deciduoma. Deciduoma formation only occurs in an endometrium under the influence of progesterone. Activation of corpora lutea with the development of a pseudopregnancy may be stimulated in the rat not only by sterile coitus but by experimental procedures such as glass rod stimulation of the vagina, electrical stimulation of the uterine cervix, or massive electrical stimuli passed through the head. The stimulus of suckling produces a similar response. Selye and coworkers showed that the regular estrous cycles of rats and mice could be interrupted by supplying them with relays of litters obtained from other animals. Prolonged suckling in these animals resulted in pseudopregnancy and lactational development of the mammary gland. It seems clear that in this condition, known as suckling pseudopregnancy, the stimulus of suckling has evoked prolactin release. Coitus and suckling then are physiological stimuli which act by nervous reflex paths and the hypophysial portal vessels, to excite prolactin secretion. The effect of disconnecting the anterior pituitary from the hypothalamus, on prolactin release, is difficult to understand. Everett has shown that autotransplantation of the pituitary to the kidney region of rats may even result in signs of augmented LTH release. One possible explanation is that the hypothalamus normally regulates LTH secretion by a tonic inhibitory process. The effect of a feed-back action of estrogens on prolactin secretion is discussed in chapter 60, when a possible relationship between estrogen concentration in the blood and lactogenesis is considered.

### THE CONTROL OF THE SECRETION OF THE ADENOHYPOPHYSIS

In discussing the individual hormones above, it has been emphasized that the secretory activity of the anterior pituitary is regulated by the following:

1. A feed-back of target gland hormones. It is uncertain whether this effect is due to a direct action on anterior pituitary cells or to an action on the nervous system which in turn modifies pituitary function. This mechanism serves as a homeostatic mechanism to maintain a *constant* level of hormones in the blood.

2. The central nervous system, acting through the hypothalamus and hypophysial portal vessels of the pituitary stalk. The hypothalamus acts to maintain anterior pituitary function at a *normal* level and to vary this level according to external stimuli and the needs of the organism. The liberation of gonadotrophic hormone by sexual excitement in the rabbit (p. 968) or by extra illumination in birds and many mammals; the release of adrenocorticotrophic hormone under states of emotional stress (p. 974), and the secretion of thyrotrophic hormone upon exposure to cold, are outstanding examples of the relationship between the anterior pituitary and the nervous system. It is most probable that peripheral sensory stimuli activate nervous reflex paths which eventually converge into the hypothalamus. However, very few, if any, nerve fibers pass from the hypothalamus to the anterior pituitary. What then is the functional link between the hypothalamus and adenohypophysis? The vascular supply to the pars distalis (p. 957) offers the basis for an explanation. The hypophysial portal vessels connect the tuber cinereum of the hypothalamus with the anterior pituitary gland, and the evidence is now convincing that these vessels mediate, in some way, the influence the nervous system exerts over the activity of the pars distalis.

### The Functional Significance of the Hypophysial Portal Vessels

1. All vertebrates possess a system of vessels passing from the median eminence to the anterior lobe of the pituitary. From amphibians to man, these vessels are truly portal, in that they start as capillaries in, or in contact with, the median eminence, form vascular trunks which run down the pituitary stalk, and break up into the sinusoids of the anterior pituitary.

2. The direction of blood flow in these vessels is *from* the median eminence *to* the anterior pituitary.

3. The effects of pituitary stalk section are conditioned by the subsequent state of the portal vessels. If these vessels regenerate across the site of the cut, normal anterior pituitary function may be regained. If regeneration of the vessels is prevented by the placement of a plate between the stalk ends, then anterior pituitary function remains greatly reduced.

4. The effects of pituitary transplantation vary with the anatomical site of the transplant. If the pituitary gland is removed from the sella turcica and placed in the subarachnoid space below the hypothalamus, the tissue may become revascularized by an outgrowth of portal vessels from the tuber cinereum and normal anterior pituitary function regained. If the transplant is placed in a distant site in the body (muscle, anterior chamber of the eye, kidney), then only fragments of normal anterior pituitary function are observed. However, if the tissue is transplanted a second time in the same animal, and placed in contact with the tuber cinereum, then normal anterior pituitary function may be regained.

5. Electrical stimulation of various sites in the hypothalamus has been found effective in causing discharge of luteinizing hormone, adrenocorticotrophic hormone, and thyrotrophic hormone from the anterior pituitary. On the other hand, if the electrode is placed directly in the adenohypophysis, similar electrical stimuli are ineffective in evoking hormonal release. This finding is compatible with the view that the activity of the gland is normally controlled by a humoral mechanism and not by a direct secretomotor nerve supply.

There can be no reasonable doubt that the functional activity of the adenohypophysis is dependent on its hypophysial portal blood supply. In some way these vessels transmit the influence the nervous system exerts over the activity of the gland. The mechanism involved is not yet clear. The most probable view is that various hypothalamic nerve tracts liberate some humoral substance(s) into the capillaries of the portal vessels in the median eminence, and that the humoral substance(s) is carried by these vessels to the pars distalis where it excites or inhibits the glandular cells. This idea of a neurohumoral mechanism regulating anterior pituitary activity finds indirect support from the present concepts regarding posterior pituitary function. It is now generally held that the posterior pituitary hormones are formed in the cells of the supraoptic and paraventricular hypothalamic nuclei (neurosecretion), are transported down the nerve fibers of the supraopticohypophysial tract in the pituitary stalk and liberated from the nerve terminals into the blood vessels of the neural lobe of the pituitary (see p. 960). Such a mechanism is very closely analogous with that suggested for anterior pituitary control. Both suppose the formation of hormonal substances by hypothalamic neurones, and both suppose the liberation of these substances into blood vessels of the neurohypophysis, either into the primary plexus of the portal vessels in the median eminence, or into the capillaries of the infundibular process. It is of interest that the blood vessels of both these parts of the neurohypophysis have similar permeability properties (as judged by the diffusion of vital dyes and radioactive substance), which are different from those of the hypothalamic blood vessels. It should be mentioned here that the neurosecretory concept is, of course, not new. The existence of secretory neurones in the nervous system of invertebrates (insects, mollusks, worms, etc.) has been well established.

The isolation, purification, and identification of a hormonal transmitter agent associated with the portal vessels has not been achieved. Markee and his colleagues suggested that an adrenergic agent was involved in the regulation of gonadotrophic secretion, on the grounds that injection of adrenaline into the anterior pituitary resulted in ovulation in rabbits and that the normal postcoital ovulation could be blocked in this animal by adrenolytic drugs. In view of the clinical importance of the adrenocorticotrophic hormone much interest has centered on the nature of a humoral transmitter underlying the release of this hormone. Saffran and his colleagues in Montreal, and Guillemin and coworkers, have incubated anterior pituitary tissue *in vitro* and obtained evidence that some substance extractable from the neurohypophysis is active in releasing ACTH from such tissue. The work of these and other investigators suggests there is a relationship between neurosecretory material, the antidiuretic hormone of the neurohypophysis, and the mechanism regulating the release of ACTH from the pars distalis. The antidiuretic hormone has also been implicated, by Martini, as a humoral agent regulating the release of thyrotrophic and growth hormones. It is impossible at the present time though to draw any definite conclusions regarding the nature of a transmitter agent. The present data could be explained on the view that a polypeptide(s) is liberated from nerve terminals in the median eminence into the portal vessels. Just as vasopressin and oxytocin have a similar molecular configuration and overlapping activities, so might the postulated polypeptide have part of its molecular configuration in common with the posterior pituitary hormones and thus have a qualitatively similar effect on anterior pituitary cells.

ANTIHORMONES AND PROHORMONES. Collip and his colleagues demonstrated that certain hormones when injected cause the formation of a substance in the serum of the treated animal which exerts a specific antagonism to, and may completely abolish the effect of, the injected hormone. They thought that the inhibitory principle was not an antibody in the ordinary sense, i.e., an immune body developed to some constituent of the hormone acting as antigen, but was rather in the nature of an *antihormone*. A substance of this character was first obtained by Collip and Anderson in 1934, in the course of experiments with the thyrotrophic principle of the anterior pituitary. Rats after repeated injections of the thyrotrophic hormone became refractory, and subsequently failed to respond to large doses. They were still responsive, however, to the thyroid hormone. It was found that the serum of these refractory animals was capable of preventing the effect of the thyrotrophic hormone upon nonrefractory animals. To give another example of this antagonism, hypophysectomized rats treated with purified growth hormone failed to respond to it after a period of 5 or 6 weeks. The serum of such animals neutralized the effect of the growth hormone upon other untreated hypophysectomized rats. Besides antithyrotrophic and antigrowth principles, inhibitory substances have been shown to exist for the ketogenic, lactogenic, and gonadotrophic principles of the anterior pituitary, respectively, as well as for the anterior-pituitarylike principle (HCG, ch. 60), but not for the adrenotrophic, or for insulin, or the sex hormones.

Collip suggested that the inhibitory principles or antihormones were present in the blood of normal animals, each serving to "oppose" or "buffer" the action of the corresponding hormone and that a given endocrine effect occurring naturally in the body was dependent upon the ratio existing between the hormone and antihormone concentrations.

Collip's observations have been confirmed repeatedly by other experimenters. But there has been a difference of opinion as to the nature of the inhibitory substances. The problem is one of extraordinary complexity for experimental investigation. From several later observations, however, e.g., that rats do not develop antihormones to implantation of anterior lobe tissue of their own species, and antigonadotrophic substances are not formed in the blood of women injected with human chorionic gonadotrophin, it is most probable that the effect of these so-called antihormones represents a form of antigen-antibody reaction due to contaminating foreign (antigenic) protein.

Augmentation of the action of the hormone after repeated injections has also been observed. The augmenting substance which develops in the serum of an injected animal is called a prohormone. The augmenting action may precede the antagonizing or antihormone effect.

### The Physiology of the Neurohypophysis

An active extract of the pituitary was first obtained in 1894, by Oliver and Schäfer who described its effect in raising the blood pressure. Howell, 3 years later, showed that the posterior lobe alone contained the pressor principle. The extract has been used in medicine for many years under such commercial names as *Pituitrin, Infundin, Infundibulin*, etc., or as the official solutions of the British and United States pharmacopoeias (B.P. and U.S.P.).[4] Much of our knowledge regarding the pharmacological actions of posterior pituitary principles has been derived from work using crude *whole extract* of the posterior pituitary. The single extract may be fractionated into *two extracts* which contain in a nearly pure form the vasopressor or antidiuretic hormone and the oxytocic hormone (marketed as *Pitressin* and *Pitocin*,

[4] The official solution of U.S.P. (XIII) *Posterior Pituitary Injection* is an aqueous solution of the principles of the posterior lobe of the pituitary of "healthy domesticated animals used as food by man." It has a specific activity (oxytocic, antidiuretic, or pressor) of 10 posterior pituitary units per cubic centimeter. A *Posterior Pituitary Unit* (B.P., U.S.P., or International) is the potency of 0.5 mg. of the Posterior Pituitary Reference Standard.

respectively, see p. 984). *Pitressin* and *Pitocin* have largely replaced *Pituitrin* in clinical use, and even more highly purified or synthetic compounds are being used for research purposes. However, an account of the actions of the whole posterior lobe extract will first be given.

### THE ACTIONS OF WHOLE POSTERIOR PITUITARY EXTRACT

These fall into 8 main groups.

1. CIRCULATORY. The blood pressure is raised, the systemic arterioles and capillaries both undergoing constriction. Marked pallor of the skin results. An initial depressor effect, or a pressor succeeded by a depressor effect, may precede the main rise in blood pressure. Repeated injections invoke smaller and smaller pressor responses (tachyphylaxis) and may even result only in a depression of the blood pressure (inversion effect). This depressor effect is cardiac in origin as indicated below. Posterior lobe extract causes constriction of the coronary and pulmonary vessels but dilates the cerebral and renal vessels. The dilator effect upon the two last mentioned sets of vessels is a passive one being caused by the rise in systemic blood pressure. The heart is slowed by posterior lobe extracts if the vagus nerves are intact, the effect being a reflex result of the blood pressure rise, but increased cardiac rate occurs if the nerves have first been cut. Some dilatation of the heart and weakening of its beat occur in the dog, rabbit and, with large doses, in the cat. The coronary constriction and the weakening effect upon the cardiac muscle cause a reduced cardiac output and a fall in pressure in the pulmonary artery (dog and rabbit). These experimental results indicate that commercial extracts are of no value *clinically* as a means of strengthening the action of a failing heart but may actually exert a deleterious effect. The fall in blood pressure which follows repeated injections of posterior pituitary extract (inversion effect) is due, according to Melville and Stehl, to the weakening of the heart and is not of vascular origin. The portal venous pressure is reduced by posterior pituitary extract, as a result of constriction of the splanchnic vessels.

2. RESPIRATORY EFFECTS, e.g., increased rate of breathing, alternating at times with periods of apnea, are produced by the extract, but they are secondary to the effects on the circulation.

3. PLAIN MUSCLE, in general, is stimulated by whole posterior lobe extract. This action differs from the smooth muscle stimulating action of adrenaline in that it does not parallel the action of the sympathetic nerves; smooth muscle, re-

ceiving motor innervation from the parasympathetic, is excited as well. The muscular walls of the *intestine, gall-bladder, ureter* and *urinary bladder* (detrusor and trigone) are excited. Peristalsis in the human small intestine and to a less extent in the colon, is stimulated, but the tone is unaffected. Sometimes the smooth muscle of the bronchioles is stimulated, but this is due to contamination of the extract with histamine and is not specific.

4. UTERINE. The stimulating effect of posterior pituitary extract upon the isolated virgin guinea pig's uterus was demonstrated by Dale in 1909, and termed the *oxytocic effect*. It is used as a means of assaying the potency of pituitary extracts. Some highly purified preparations exert an oxytocic effect in a dilution of 1 part in 2,000,-000,000. The effect of these extracts upon the uterine muscle is antagonized by the hormone of the corpus luteum (see p. 1088). The oxytocic effect varies with the species, and, as a consequence of the interplay of other hormones, especially of the luteal hormone, with the phases of the sexual cycle (e.g., period of estrus, pregnant or nonpregnant state of the uterus). An interrelation between the actions of adrenaline and posterior pituitary extract is indicated by the fact that if the nonpregnant uterus of the cat is first treated with pituitary extract, adrenaline causes contraction instead of the usual relaxation (p. 1026). The human uterus is most sensitive at the end of pregnancy, and the extract is used as an obstetric aid to produce uterine contraction after the expulsion of the placenta and so to prevent or check postpartum hemorrhage.

5. MAMMARY. Lactation consists of two main processes. First, milk formation or secretion which is intimately related to the anterior pituitary gland (p. 977), and second, a process known as milk ejection, which is controlled by the posterior pituitary gland. Ott and Scott in 1910, first showed that injection of posterior pituitary extract increased the amount of milk obtainable from the cannulated udder of the goat. This action of the extract, causing an active expression of the milk present in the lactating breast or udder, has been confirmed in many species including man. Much discussion centered at one time around the question of the contractile element concerned. In many forms plain muscle exists only around the larger ducts in the mammary gland, and it was difficult to understand how milk contained in the alveoli could be expressed. The histological studies of Richardson have now established that a specialized contractile tissue,

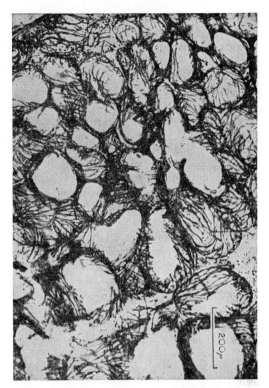

FIG. 56.15. Section of part of a lobule of the mammary gland of a goat, fixed in the distended state, showing the myoepithelial cells stained with silver. (From Richardson.)

composed of *myoepithelial cells* (see fig. 56.15), is extensively distributed around the alveoli and ducts of the mammary gland, and there can now be little doubt that this is the effector element stimulated by posterior pituitary extract. In order to demonstrate the action of posterior pituitary extracts on the mammary gland it is necessary to cannulate the nipple or teat (to overcome the sphincter action of this structure). Very small doses of extracts (of the order of 0.001 unit) are then effective in exciting milk ejection.

6. KIDNEY (Antidiuretic hormone, ADH). The action of posterior pituitary extracts upon renal function was discovered by Magnus and Schäfer in 1901, but they described only a *diuretic* effect. The diuresis, however, is of brief duration and may be preceded by anuria due to ureteral spasm; this early diuretic action is due to the rise in general blood pressure, and the passive dilatation, thereby, of the afferent glomerular vessels. The important and specific renal effect is, however, an increase in the reabsorption of water and, as a consequence, a reduction in urinary flow. In anesthetized animals the specific antidiuretic action is absent; diuresis due to the vascular factors

is the outstanding effect. Posterior lobe extract postpones for several hours the diuresis induced in normal animals by water drinking, and reduces the polyuria of diabetes insipidus. Associated with the antidiuretic effect is an increase in the percentage of sodium and chloride in the urine and, as a result of a reduction in the tubular reabsorption of these electrolytes, an increase in their total excretion (see also ch. 34).

The antidiuretic principle is an essential factor in the maintenance of the water balance of the body, being secreted when the need for water conservation arises. For example, the quantity of the hormone in the urine, which reflects presumably its concentration in the blood stream, is increased in dehydrated states but decreased in hydremia (Gilman and Goodman). In man, it is through a more active tubular reabsorption rather than by a reduction in the filtration rate through the glomerulus that the kidney plays its part in conserving water.

It is only in mammals and birds that posterior pituitary extract exerts any effect upon tubular reabsorption. And, as compared with mammals, the antidiuretic action of the extract in birds is feeble. Only these two classes secrete a hypertonic urine, and their nephrons alone possess a thin segment of Henle's loop. It is thought, therefore, that this part of the renal tubules is the site of action of the antidiuretic hormone (see also ch. 34). However, the hormone is not without effect upon the water exchange of amphibia and reptiles. Frogs, for example, immersed in water increase their body weight if injected with posterior pituitary extract (*Brunn effect*) as a result of the uptake of water through the skin; they also lose water readily in a dry environment if treated with the extract. This effect[5] is due to a principle in pituitary extracts other than ADH; it is closely associated with the oxytocic principle but does not seem to be identical with the latter. It is called the *water balance principle* and can be prepared from the pituitaries of mammals as well as from those of amphibians.

7. METABOLIC EFFECTS. Reduced tolerance for sugar, diminution in hepatic glycogen, hyperglycemia, glycosuria, and a fall in the basal metabolic rate follow the injection of posterior lobe extract. The effect of insulin is antagonized. That is to say, the pancreatic hormone produces less

effect upon the blood sugar and a greater amount is required to produce hypoglycemic convulsions if its administration has been preceded by an injection of posterior pituitary extract. This extract also causes an increase in liver fat. The effects on carbohydrate and fat metabolism are probably nonspecific, and, therefore, do not represent physiological actions.

8. MELANOPHORE-EXPANDING (-DISPERSING) PROPERTY. The skins of many cold-blooded animals contain peculiar cells with branching processes and mobile pigment granules whose movement toward the periphery of the cell or toward the center is under hormonal influence. Such cells have been given the general name of *chromophores*. Those containing black pigment (melanin) are known as *melanophores*, and those with red or yellow pigment are called *erythrophores* or *xanthophores*, respectively.

Hogben and Winton showed that posterior pituitary extracts caused the pigment granules in the melanophores of the frog to become dispersed throughout the bodies and branching processes of these cells. This results in darkening of the skin. Thus, the injection of a small dose of posterior pituitary extract into a frog causes its skin to become almost coal black as a result of the melanophore reaction. On the other hand, after hypophysectomy, owing to the disappearance of the pituitary hormone from the circulation, the pigment granules gather near the center of the cells and the skin becomes pale. Hypophysectomized tadpoles have, instead of the usual dark brown or green color, a silvery appearance. The changes in color which certain amphibia, reptiles, and fish undergo in order to blend into the color of their surroundings is largely due to variations in the concentrations of the pituitary hormone in the blood or to the balance between the concentrations of the melanophore-expanding principle and adrenaline. Blinding a frog deprives it of its adaptive power.[6] Nervous impulses arising in the

---

[5] It is not seen in fish or reptiles, but in the latter the extract exerts a renal effect, but one different from that induced in mammals, namely, a reduction of the filtration rate.

[6] The phenomenon of light influencing structure and function through the mediation of a retinohypophysial mechanism is not peculiar to cold-blooded animals. The work of a number of experimenters indicates that the well-known association of the seasonal periods with morphological changes (e.g., color and texture of hair or plumage) and with the sexual cycles of certain mammals and birds as well as with the migration of birds, is due, in part at least, to light acting upon the *anterior* pituitary through the medium of retinal impulses. Rowan, for example, was able to induce sexual activity in crows and canaries at any desired time of the year by varying the periods of their exposure to artificial light; it is also well known that the

retina are believed, therefore, to govern the liberation of the melanophore expanding principle. The *production* of melanin in the skin of the frog is said to be stimulated by this principle.

In most animals, the melanophore-expanding principle is elaborated by the pars intermedia.[7] Cultures of tissue from the pars intermedia alone yield this principle, whereas, cultures of the neural part of the pituitary or of the anterior lobe do not. Nevertheless, the principle finds its way into the neural part of the pituitary and unpurified extracts of the latter always contain it as a contamination. But it is possible to prepare it free from antidiuretic, pressor, and oxytocic effects. Moreover, the melanophore dispersing action of extracts from different parts of the posterior lobe does not run parallel with the pressor, oxytocic and antidiuretic properties. These factors argue for the melanophore effect being due to a separate and distinct hormone. Zondek has given the name *intermedin* or the *chromatophorotropic hormone* to this principle. It has been suggested that the melanophore-expanding principle also causes the migration of the melanin granules in the pigment layer of the retina (ch. 73) and is, therefore, a factor in dark adaptation of the eyes of higher vertebrates, but the experimental evidence in respect to such a function is conflicting. Nor is there any definite evidence that any relationship exists between this hormone and the occurrence of retinitis pigmentosa. It is natural that it should also be suspected of playing a role in cutaneous pigmentation in the human subject but few observations have been reported which

might connect this principle with either normal or abnormal pigmentation in man. It has, indeed, been suggested that intermedin and adrenocorticotrophic hormone are one and the same substance. This hypothesis would explain the occurrence of pigmentation in Addison's disease, when the atrophic adrenal cortex allows increased release of ACTH. However, melanophore-expanding activity and adrenocorticotrophic activity have been largely separated into different fractions of pituitary extracts. The interesting suggestion has been made that the amino acid sequence of the polypeptide molecules of these hormones partially overlap, thus affording a possible explanation of the melanophore-dispersing activity of ACTH.

### *Fractionation of the Posterior Lobe Extract. Oxytocin and Vasopressin*

Considerable quantitites of histamine may be present in commercial pituitary extracts which have not been carefully purified; indeed it was believed for a time by some (Abel and associates) that the plain muscle stimulating and depressor effects were due simply to histamine. Abel also maintained that the other effects (pressor and antidiuretic) were due to a single hormone. The work of Dudley, and especially of Kamm and his associates has shown that the specific effects are not due to histamine, and that there are at least two distinct active principles in a posterior lobe extract. From the crude extract Kamm and his associates have isolated two relatively pure fractions, one containing mainly vasopressin (the vasopressor or antidiuretic hormone) and the other mainly oxytocin (oxytocic hormone). They are marketed commercially as *Pitocin* and *Pitressin*. These are white amorphous powders freely soluble in water. However, van Dyke and colleagues obtained a noncrystalline material of protein nature from posterior lobe extracts which, from electrophoretic, ultracentrifuge, and solubility studies, seems to be a pure substance free from contaminating material. It possesses oxytocic and pressor activities in the same ratios as in the crude extracts. A significant advance was made by du Vigneaud and his team. Taking advantage of such modern techniques as countercurrent distribution between immiscible solvents, chromatographic separation on paper, or starch columns, they obtained highly purified preparations of vasopressin and oxytocin from beef material and were able to establish the structural formulas of these compounds. These are as follows:

---

domestic fowl will lay regularly in winter if its period of exposure to light is lengthened by artificial means. Cognate experiments have been carried out upon mammals; ferrets, hedgehogs, and racoons. The seasonal onset of estrus in the ferret has been shown to be conditioned by the length of the day; and optic nerve section or hypophysectomy abolishes the phenonenon. The sexual cycles are abolished, of course, by hypophysectomy (lack of gonadotrophic hormone) but their periodicity in relation to the length of exposure to light is lost after optic nerve section alone. The extreme sensitivity to light of the pigeon with respect to the time of egg laying is extraordinary. The pigeon lays a pair of eggs in the morning, the second of the pair being laid, with the regularity of clock-work, half an hour after the first. Lengthening or shortening the period of exposure to light alters the duration of the interval between the laying of the first and second eggs of the pair.

[7] In those species such as the chicken, porpoise and whale which do not possess a pars intermedia, the melanophore-dispersing principle is found in extracts of the anterior lobe; none is present in the posterior lobe.

*Structure of oxytocin and vasopressin (ox)*

Cys[8].Tyr.Ileu.Glu($NH_2$).Asp($NH_2$).Cys.Pro.Leu.Gly($NH_2$)

Oxytocin

Cys[8].Tyr.Phe.Glu($NH_2$).Asp($NH_2$).Cys.Pro.Arg.Gly($NH_2$)

Vasopressin

Each hormone contains eight amino acids, six of which (aspartic acid, cystine, glutamic acid, glycine, proline, and tyrosine) are common to the two. The isoleucine and leucine in oxytocin are replaced by phenyl alanine and arginine. It is of interest that in hog vasopressin lysine replaces the arginine of beef vasopressin. The molecular weight of oxytocin is 1007 and of beef vasopressin is 1084. Both these compounds have been synthesized by du Vigneaud and his group and the synthetic compounds have been found to be identical with the natural products in biological and chemical tests.

The preparation of highly purified and synthetic oxytocin and vasopressin has made possible the analysis of the physiological activities of whole posterior pituitary extract, described above, in terms of these two compounds. It seems clear that oxytocin is responsible for the action of pituitary extracts on uterine muscle and in the mammary gland, whereas vasopressin acts on the blood pressure and water excretion by the kidney. There are no good grounds for believing that the pressor and antidiuretic activities are due to two different substances. It is of interest that vasopressin has some slight oxytocic activity (uterine-stimulating and milk-ejecting activities) and oxytocin has slight pressor and antidiuretic actions. This is so even with the highly purified preparations and appears to be due to the similarity of molecular structure of these hormones.

Although the term oxytocic *hormone* and vasopressor *hormone* are applied to these two pituitary fractions, it is not yet certain that these compounds are hormones in the sense that they are secreted individually and separately into the blood stream. The possibility cannot be ruled out that they are secreted as part of a larger protein molecule which constitutes a single hormone with multiple activities. The evidence in support of this latter view is that physiological stimuli which evoke secretion of vasopressin or antidiuretic hormone (injection of hypertonic saline) also seem to excite release of oxytocic hormone, and stimuli

evoking release of oxytocic hormone (suckling) also result in an antidiuresis. However, if both hormonal activities are secreted together, then they are liberated in ratios different from those observed in standard whole posterior pituitary extract. Electrical stimulation of the nerve supply to the neurohypophysis, injection of hypertonic saline, and suckling, have all been found to result in the release of 1 part antidiuretic activity to about 50 parts of oxytocic activity, as compared with standard extracts.

## THE CONTROL OF, AND THE FUNCTIONS OF, THE NEURAL LOBE

The functional activity of the neurohypophysis is entirely dependent on its nerve supply from the hypothalamus. This innervation is described above (see p. 959); it consists of a large number of unmyelinated fibers (100,000 in man) arising from the supraoptic and paraventricular hypothalamic nuclei, and possibly other nuclear groups. These fibers converge to the pituitary stalk and end in all three parts of the neurohypophysis; the median eminence, the infundibular stem, and the infundibular process. This latter point is of much significance when earlier studies are considered, for section of the pituitary stalk clearly does not denervate the whole neurohypophysis. The upper end of the stalk and the median eminence of the tuber cinereum, which constitute about 13 per cent of total neurohypophysial tissue, remain intact and innervated. The statement that neurohypophysial function is dependent on its nerve supply is based on the facts that, first, a lesion placed in the supraopticohypophysial tract in the hypothalamus results in loss of posterior pituitary activity, atrophy of all three parts of the gland, loss of extractable activity from the gland, and disappearance of neurones from the supraoptic and paraventricular nuclei. Second, electrical stimulation of the supraopticohypophysial tract results in rapid discharge of posterior pituitary hormone as shown by an increase in uterine activity, milk ejection, antidiuresis, increase in intestinal peristalsis, possibly

---

[8] Position of free amino group.

a slight increase in blood pressure, and an increased excretion of antidiuretic material in the urine.

The physiological actions of the neurohypophysis are suggested by the responses excited by injection of small doses of posterior pituitary extract; they are confirmed as potential activities of the gland when similar responses are observed to follow electrical stimulation of the supraopticohypophysial tract; they are established as physiological functions if they are abolished by denervation, or removal, of the entire neurohypophysis, and they occur after physiological stimuli such as suckling.

1. ANTIDIURETIC ACTION. Very small doses of posterior pituitary extract, or purified vasopressin, are effective in inhibiting a water diuresis. In the rabbit, about 0.1 to 1 milliunit is sufficient in this respect. Electrical stimulation of the supraopticohypophysial tract in the conscious animal, by the remote control method, is also effective in inhibiting a water diuresis. The magnitude of the antidiuretic response varies with the strength and duration of the stimulus and can be very closely matched, in both the effect on water and chloride excretion, by injection of an appropriate dose of vasopressin.

It has long been known that a lesion in the floor of the third ventricle may be followed by the clinical condition of *diabetes insipidus*, in which large volumes of hypotonic urine are excreted each day (see p. 992). Ranson and his colleagues were able to produce a similar picture in cats and monkeys, by placing bilateral electrolytic lesions in the supraopticohypophysial tract in the hypothalamus. Their cats developed a permanent polyuria of 300 to 500 ml. of urine per day (normal urine output for the cat is about 100 ml. per day), which could be reduced to normal levels by replacement therapy with posterior pituitary extracts. After killing these animals they found that the greater number of nerve fibers in the neural lobe of the pituitary had disappeared, that the neurohypophysis was shrunken and hypercellular, and that extracts of these atrophic glands possessed greatly diminished pressor, antidiuretic, and oxytocic activity, though the melanophore activity was normal. This latter observation may be correlated with the normal pars intermedia found in these animals. Previous to this study it had been found by other workers that pituitary stalk section in the monkey did not lead to diabetes insipidus, though it did in the dog. On these grounds it was argued that denervation of the neural lobe was not essential to the onset of dia-

betes. However, Fisher and coworkers in a later study showed that stab wounds placed in the median eminence of the monkey resulted in a marked polyuria, and suggested that pituitary stalk section in this form left intact sufficient neurohypophysial tissue in the still innervated median eminence to prevent the onset of diabetes. It may be pointed out that animals deprived of the pars distalis, as well as the neurohypophysis, develop only a slight polyuria if any at all. The paris distalis exerts a general diuretic effect which is necessary for the development of a marked polyuria. This may be observed in human patients with an expanding lesion in the sella turcica. Destruction of the neurohypophysis results in diabetes insipidus, but further development of the lesion may destroy the pars distalis with amelioration of the diabetes.

The reflex release of antidiuretic hormone in response to physiological stimuli has been studied particularly by Verney and coworkers. Emotional excitement and the osmotic pressure of the blood are prominent factors in this category. Emotional stress produced in a variety of ways (exercise, loud noise, pain) was found to be associated with an antidiuresis of the same type as that following injection of posterior pituitary extract. Prior removal of the posterior lobe of the pituitary or section of the supraopticohypophysial tracts reduced the response to about 5 per cent of its previous magnitude. In early work, Verney formed the view that the diuresis which follows the drinking of water was due to inhibition of the posterior pituitary gland. If this inhibition was mediated by a reduced osmotic pressure of the blood, then injection or slow infusion of *hypertonic* sodium chloride, especially into the arterial supply of the hypothalamo-hypophysial region, would be expected to cause discharge of antidiuretic hormone. Such was found to be the case. For example, injection of 20 cc. of 0.343 M NaCl in 25 seconds into the carotid artery produced a marked inhibitory response on the course of a water diuresis. A similar injection made intravenously had little effect, and the response to the carotid injection was markedly reduced by previous removal of the neural lobe. It is likely that the sensitive osmoreceptors lie in or near to the supraoptic nuclei in the hypothalamus. By slow infusions of hypertonic solutions into the carotid artery, Verney showed that changes of only 1 per cent in the osmotic pressure of the blood are effective in exciting release of about 1 microunit per second of antidiuretic substance. Such changes in osmotic pressure are within the range of the falls reported in water diuresis in man. The dog has been found to liberate about 1 to 5 milliunits of antidiuretic hormone per hour, and under the influence of an emotional stimulus discharges 5 to 10 milliunits of hormone. For further information see the review by Verney (1947).

2. PRESSOR ACTION. Much larger doses of vasopressin are required to elicit a pressor than an antidiuretic response. Electrical stimulation of the supraopticohypophysial tract in the conscious animal excites a slight increase in blood pressure of the same type as that following injection of vasopressin. However, the fact that hemorrhage and fainting appear to stimulate secretion of the vasopressor hormone supports the view that this hormone plays a physiological role in maintaining the blood pressure.

3. ACTION ON INTESTINAL PERISTALSIS. Again, large doses of vasopressor hormone are required to elicit an observable increase in intestinal peristalsis. However, electrical stimulation of the nerve supply to the neurohypophysis evokes a clear increase in peristalsis in the colon of the conscious rabbit. Although posterior pituitary extracts have long been used in man for the treatment of paralytic ileus, there is little evidence in the human that the posterior pituitary normally plays a physiological role in regulating intestinal motility. In this respect, Cushing's observation that patients with tumors that have destroyed the neurohypophysis are " . . . notably victimized by chronic constipation," is of interest.

4. HYPERGLYCEMIC ACTION. Both vasopressin and oxytocin cause hyperglycemia, but which one will have the greater effect depends largely on the species. In rabbits vasopressin has the greater hyperglycemic action, whereas in dogs oxytocin is more effective. The dose necessary to induce this effect is very large. No equivalent hyperglycemic action has been obtained by electrical stimulation of the neurohypophysis. It is unlikely that the posterior pituitary plays a physiological role in regulating the blood sugar.

5. OXYTOCIC ACTION ON THE UTERUS. The discovery of the oxytocic (swift birth) action of posterior pituitary extracts led, as it was bound to do, to the theory that the elaboration and discharge of a principle by the pituitary constituted an important factor in the birth mechanism. Such a view received tacit acceptance until it was found that many forms, including mice, rats, rabbits, guinea pigs, and others, delivered their young after hypophysectomy. However, Fisher and coworkers noted that six out of seven cats, suffering from diabetes insipidus consequent to hypo-

thalamic lesions, had serious difficulty in parturition. They suggested that the reports of successful delivery after hypophysectomy might be due to the fact that neurohypophysial tissue in the pituitary stalk and median eminence had been left intact by the operation. A further study by Fisher and his colleagues showed that slightly less than one-third of a number of guinea pigs, in which the neurohypophysis had been completely denervated by hypothalamic lesions, could undergo normal parturition. Similar, somewhat discordant, findings have been reported for human patients with diabetes insipidus. It seems then that in the absence of neurohypophysial function other factors may compensate and result in apparently normal parturition in a proportion of cases.

Electrical stimulation of the neurohypophysis or its nerve supply has been found to result in increased uterine contractions in postpartum and estrous rabbits. Haterius and Ferguson showed that electrical stimulation of the pituitary stalk in anesthetized rabbits, 2 to 8 hours after delivery, resulted in increased uterine activity. Ferguson later showed that this response was still obtained even if all the tissues of the neck were crushed except the carotid arteries, jugular veins, and a flap of skin. In a more recent study by Harris it was found that electrical stimulation of the supraopticohypophysial tract in the conscious, estrous rabbit evoked increased uterine activity. The magnitude of the response varied with the intensity and duration of the stimulus. The pattern of the uterine response could be matched more nearly by intravenous injection of an oxytocic extract than by an injection of whole posterior pituitary extract. Maximal stimulation was found to be equivalent to the injection of 200 to 500 milliunits of the oxytocic fraction. Cross (1958) has recently found that labor may be induced in anesthetized rabbits at term by injection of 50 to 200 milliunits of oxytocin or by electrical stimulation of the supraopticohypophysial tract. From his experiments Cross concludes that the secretion of oxytocin may well play a part in initiating labor and may be secreted during the course of labor under the influence of nervous reflexes initiated by distension of the uterine cervix, as first suggested by Ferguson. The studies of Caldeyro-Barcia and coworkers on the reactivity of the human uterus to synthetic oxytocin infused intravenously, lend indirect support to the views that the oxytocic hormone forms part of the mechanism controlling uterine activity during normal labor. Also in favor of this view is the observation of Gunther who noted milk ejection from the nipple of a woman during parturition. The mammary expulsion of milk coincided with the labor pains, and afforded sound evidence of an increased concentration of oxytocin in the blood at these times.

The suggestion has been made that oxytocic hormone is released by a nervous reflex excited by the act of mating, and that the resultant increase in uterine motility normally plays a part in the transport of seminal fluid up the female reproductive tract. Data relating to this view may be summarized as follows.

1. The ascent of spermatozoa in the genital tract of many forms (rat, rabbit, guinea-pig, dog, sheep, and cow) occurs too rapidly to be accounted for in terms of sperm motility.

2. An increase in uterine activity has been found to follow mating or mechanical stimulation of the external genitalia or cervix of the uterus.

3. Evidence that oxytocin is released by the act of mating, or by manipulation of the vulva or cervix uteri is afforded by the milk ejection that has been observed to follow these stimuli.

4. Fitzpatrick and Hughes have observed an increase in oxytocic activity in jugular vein blood of cows consequent to manipulation of the uterus or cervix.

The evidence is suggestive that the oxytocic hormone normally plays a role in seminal transport, but further work involving assays of oxytocin before and after coitus and investigations of any disabilities in sperm transport in animals after disturbance or denervation of the neurohypophysis are required.

6. MILK EJECTING ACTION. As with the oxytocic effect on the uterus, milk ejection may be produced in the lactating mammary gland by administration of very small doses of oxytocin that seem within a physiological range. As recounted above, there has long been evidence that the transfer of milk from mother to suckling young involves an active squeezing out of milk from the mammary tissue by the maternal organism. Petersen was the first to suggest that reflex stimulation of posterior pituitary secretion was involved in the process. Definitive evidence that this is so came from experiments in sheep, goats, and rabbits in which it was demonstrated that electrical stimulation of the supraopticohypophysial tract results in milk ejection. Conversely, it was found that following denervation of the neurohypophysis by the placement of hypothalamic lesions in lactating rabbits, the young obtained only a small fraction of the normal quantity of milk. However, if the mother

animal was injected with oxytocin just prior to suckling, the milk obtained by her young approximated the normal amount. From this and other evidence there can be no doubt that the sensory stimuli associated with suckling, and probably conditioned stimuli as well, reflexly excite the neurohypophysis to discharge oxytocic hormone. This hormone in turn causes contraction of the specialized myoepithelial tissue in the mammary gland, so that a positive ejection of milk occurs.

There is much evidence that a similar mechanism occurs in the human. It is well known that embarrassment, worry, or fright at the time of nursing may inhibit the flow of milk to the baby. This inhibition may, however, be overcome by injection of oxytocin. Haeger and Jacobsohn have observed striking increases in milk yield to follow injection of oxytocin into women with poor lactational performance but with engorged and painful mammae. It is of interest that after a single injection of oxytocin lactation proceeded normally, without the need of further injections, in the majority of cases.

In summary it may be said that posterior pituitary hormones play a physiological role in regulating the excretion of water by the kidney, and the ejection of milk from the lactating mammary gland. In all probability the oxytocic activity is of importance in parturition, and may also be concerned with the transport of seminal fluid in the female reproductive tract. It is possible that neurohypophysial secretion is one of the factors regulating intestinal motility and in maintaining a falling blood pressure. The hypoglycemic action of posterior pituitary extracts is of pharmacological interest only.

The melanophore-expanding principle (present in posterior pituitary extracts but a secretion of the pars intermedia of the pituitary) plays an important role in lower forms (fishes, amphibians) in regulating the expansion of melanophores and erythrophores in response to retinal-nervous reflexes.

### Assay of Posterior Pituitary Hormone

Assays of posterior pituitary hormones are performed with regard to their antidiuretic, vasopressor, or oxytocic activity. Since the vasopressor and oxytocic hormones have overlapping activities, no assay method is entirely specific, though suitable corrections may be made for the overlapping activity. For further details see the review by van Dyke and coworkers (1955).

1. *Antidiuretic assays.* The unknown and standard extract are administered to rats or dogs during a water diuresis, and the antidiuretic response

measured. Probably the method of choice involves the use of the trained dog, given water by stomach tube, and the extracts by intravenous injection. This is a specific and sensitive method, and will detect 0.25 milliunit of antidiuretic hormone.

2. *Vasopressor assays.* In the past assay of the pressor potency of pituitary hormone has frequently been performed on the dog or cat, but the anesthetized rat now seems the method of choice. The extracts are injected intravenously; about 4 milliunits of vasopressin produces a definite pressor response.

3. *Oxytocic activity.* The classical method involving the use of the isolated guinea pig uterus *in vitro* is suitable for assay of material of high potency. The depressor action of oxytocin on the blood pressure of the fowl has been widely used as the basis of an assay method but is relatively insensitive. Probably the most sensitive and reliable method is that devised by van Dyke and his colleagues in which the milk ejection response of a cannulated teat duct of an anesthetized rabbit is employed. The threshold dose is of the order 2 to 3 milliunits in this preparation.

The results of all assays should be expressed in terms of the international standard. One international unit is the antidiuretic, pressor or oxytocic activity present in 0.5 mg. of the international standard preparation.

THE FORMATION AND FATE OF NEUROHYPOPHYSIAL HORMONES. The fact that the neurohypophysis lacks glandular cells has long posed the problem as to the cellular site of formation of the hormones. For a long time it was believed that the cells of the pars intermedia migrated posteriorly into the neurohypophysis and liberated posterior pituitary hormones. That this is not so is shown by the facts that such forms, such as the porpoise and whale, in which the neural lobe is separated from all parts of the adenohypophysis by a thick connective tissue septum, show the usual activities of neural lobe extracts (except melanophore-expanding activity), and also that animals with an atrophic neurohypophysis due to an hypothalamic lesion show a loss of extractable activity although the pars intermedia appears normal. It was then suggested that certain rather specialized cells in the neurohypophysis (pituicytes of Bucy; or the parenchymatous glandular cells of Gersh) secreted neurohypophysial hormones. However, the data regarding the secretory nature of these cells were controversial, and the evidence that material rich in posterior pituitary activity could be extracted from the hypothalamus was difficult to explain since such cells do not exist in this region.

An attractive view, which has received wide acceptance in the last 10 years, holds that the hypothalamo-neurohypophysial unit acts as a *neurosecretory mechanism.* E. and B. Scharrer have for many years investigated the possibility that neurons in the central nervous system secrete hormone into the blood stream. There was formerly more evidence to uphold this thesis in invertebrates than vertebrates, but in 1949, Bargmann demonstrated that the cells in the paraventricular and supraoptic nuclei, and their nerve fibers sweeping through the basal hypothalamus, pituitary stalk, and neural lobe, may be selectively stained by the Gomori-chrome-alum hematoxylin method. Striking histological pictures have been obtained in many forms in which cell groups and nerve tracts are deeply stained in contrast to surrounding neural structures. The general view is that the stainable material seen in these neurons is either neurohypophysial hormone or some carrier material closely linked with the hormone, and that it is found in the cell bodies in the hypothalamic nuclei and transported down the axons to be liberated into the blood vessels in three parts of the neurohypophysis. There are no reasons to doubt that these neurons function also as do other nerve cells, and that the rate of discharge of hormone from the nerve terminals into the vascular system is regulated by nervous impulses in the same nerve fibers. It is unlikely that the hormone can be discharged from any part of the neuron except the nerve terminals existing in the neurohypophysis, since lesions in the nerve tract above the median eminence uniformly result in diabetes insipidus and since the permeability properties of the blood vessels of the neurohypophysis are so markedly different from those of the hypothalamus proper. The evidence relating the stainable material to hormonal activity has been mainly concerned with the antidiuretic function. In different forms, and in the same form under different conditions of dehydration or exposure to stress, there is a correlation between the amount of stainable material and the content of vasopressor hormone. The relationship with oxytocin is less clear, since it has been established that there is very little oxytocic activity in extracts of hypothalamic tissue. It is possible that oxytocic hormone is formed during the transport of neurosecretory material into the neural lobe itself. The neurosecretory view of the origin of posterior pituitary hormones affords an obvious explanation for the lack of secretory cells in the neurohypophysis and for the presence of hormonally active material in hypothalamic extracts.

Although at one time it was thought that the hormones of the posterior pituitary passed up the pituitary stalk and into the third ventricle, it is now believed that they are secreted into the capillaries of the gland and into the venous system directly. The form in which the hormones are transported in the blood is unknown, but it is possible that they are secreted as polypeptides and become linked to the plasma protein. The hormonal activities of injected extracts disappear from the blood stream within a few minutes, and evidence exists that a major part of this inactivation occurs in the liver and kidneys (Heller, 1957). A further portion (about 25 per cent) of the activity of administered hormone, or of the hormone discharged from the neurohypophysis by electrical stimulation, appears in the urine; it is impossible to say though, whether this represents the unchanged hormone or a biologically active metabolite.

### Disorders of the Pituitary in Man

Derangements of pituitary function may take the form of overactivity or of deficiency. In the former case tumors composed of functioning endocrine tissue are frequently the cause of the disorder; in the latter, atrophy or degeneration of the specific secreting cells, either primarily or as the result of mechanical pressure by tumors, may be responsible. A pituitary tumor of the anterior lobe may be composed of any of the cellular elements of the gland; *chromophobe, acidophil, or basophil* adenomas. Squamous-celled growths (craniopharyngeomas) may also arise from epithelial rests (remnants of Rathke's pouch) near the root of the infundibular stalk. As a result of the confined position of the pituitary within the sella turcica the entire gland is likely to suffer from pressure effects when one of its parts becomes enlarged. For this reason and on account of the proximity of other important structures, e.g., hypothalamus and optic chiasma, and the proclivity of tumors to invade or press upon neighboring structures, the manifestations of a pituitary tumor are not always referable simply to the part of the pituitary originally involved. Any function (growth, sex, water elimination, or the metabolism of carbohydrate or fat) presided over by the pituitary-hypothalamic mechanism may, therefore, be disturbed by a lesion in this region. Nevertheless, the site wherein the tumor arises and the nature of the cells of which it is composed do very often determine the predominant features of the condition, and certain fairly well defined groups of symptoms (syndromes) are rec-

ognized. To these may or may not be added symptoms referable to pressure upon, or to irritation or destruction of, nearby nervous structures.

The following is a short classification of pituitary diseases.

I. Anterior lobe
  A. Overactivity
    1. Acromegaly
    2. Giantism
    3. Pituitary basophilism (Cushing's disease)
  B. Deficiency
    1. Dwarfism
    2. Pituitary cachexia (Simmond's disease)
    3. Acromicria
II. Posterior lobe deficiency or hypothalamic lesion
  A. Diabetes insipidus
III. Anterior lobe deficiency together with posterior lobe deficiency or hypothalmic lesion
  A. Dystrophia adiposo-genitalis (Frohlich)
    1. Infantile or juvenile type
    2. Adolescent or adult type

#### ACROMEGALY

This condition was first described by Pierre Marie in 1885. It is due to the excessive elaboration of the growth hormone during adult life, i.e., after the usual age of full skeletal growth (fig. 56.16). An adenomatous tumor of the anterior lobe composed of acidophil cells is responsible for the hypersecretion. The characteristic features of the condition are: (a) Overgrowth of the bones of the hands, feet, and face. Of the latter, the mandible, nasal bones, and supraorbital ridges are especially involved (fig. 56.17). The feet and hands are greatly increased in size, the latter being usually broadened and the fingers thickened; under the X-rays, the terminal phalanges appear tufted, thus resembling a wheat sheaf in shape. Bowing of the spine (kyphosis) is common. The soft tissues of the nose, lips, forehead, and scalp are thickened, the latter being thrown into folds or wrinkles (bulldog scalp). There is a general overgrowth of body hair. (b) Atrophy of the gonads and suppression of the sexual function (amenorrhea in women, impotence in men). (c) Moderate increase in the urinary excretion of 17-ketosteroids and corticoids with reduced excretion of gonadotrophins. In the earlier stages, however, there may be evidence of increased sexual function. (d) Enlargement of the viscera (splanchnomegaly). The tongue, lungs, thymus, heart, liver, and spleen are greatly enlarged. The thyroid, parathyroids, and adrenals may show hypertrophy or adenomatous growth. Hyperthyroidism may be present in the early stages. (e) Glycosuria and hyperglycemia are common, and a condition indistinguishable from diabetes of pancreatic origin may be present. The metabolic rate may be raised from 10 to 70 per cent; the specific dynamic action of protein is not altered (p. 787).

### GIANTISM

Giantism is due to a pituitary lesion of a similar nature to that responsible for acromegaly, but the condition arises in preadult life, i.e., before ossification is complete (fig. 56.18). A general overgrowth of the skeleton results and the production of persons of enormous stature, 7 or 8 feet or more in height. The limbs are usually disproportionately long. The viscera are not enlarged

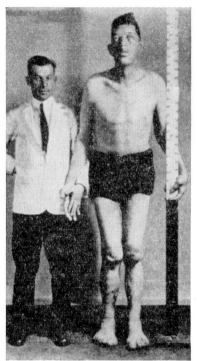

FIG. 56.16. Acromegaly, together with enlarged stature—acromegalic giantism. (From Cushing and Davidoff.)

FIG. 56.18. Giantism

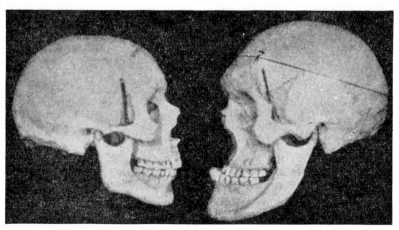

FIG. 56.17. Skulls of a normal person (left) and of an acromegalic (right). (From Cushing and Davidoff).

out of proportion to the frame unless, as is sometimes the case, the giantism is accompanied by
the characteristic features of acromegaly, as may
occur after adolescence.

### CUSHING'S DISEASE: CUSHING'S SYNDROME

This is a rare disease. Its main features are: (a)
Obesity of the trunk (especially of the abdomen),
face, and buttocks, but not of the limbs; these
latter show some wasting (fig. 56.19). The fattening of face leads to rounding of the facial contours
which obscures the bony structure, producing the
so-called "moon face." There is, thus, a redistribution of body fat, which is mobilized from the
limbs and deposited in the regions mentioned.
The fatty deposits are frequently tense, tender,
and painful. Purplish striae, due to distension, are
present over the lower abdomen. (b) Polycythemia with cyanosis of the face, hands, and feet,
pigmentation of the skin, and excessive growth
of hair. Women may grow a mustache or a beard.
(c) Loss of mineral from the bones, leading to
osteoporosis, softening or brittleness. The softening often involves the dorsal vertebrae, and causes
kyphosis, which with the deposition of fat in the
interscapular region gives the appearance known
as "buffalo neck." (d) Systolic hypertension. (e)
Suppression of sexual functions. (f) Hyperglycemia and glycosuria and in some cases increased
urinary excretion of nitrogen. (g) Atrophy of
testes or ovaries, and hypertrophy of the adrenal
cortex with signs of hypersecretion of its hormones. (h) Increased urinary excretion of 11-
oxycorticosteroids, and often of 17-ketosteroids;
high uric acid:creatinine ratio. (i) Eosinopenia,
lymphopenia, low blood potassium, and retention
of sodium chloride with increase of body fluids
and a tendency to edema.

The disease as originally described by Harvey
Cushing (1932) was associated with a basophil
adenoma of the adenohypophysis.[9] It has since
been found that the syndrome may arise either
as a result of a pituitary tumor (excess ACTH
production and stimulation of the adrenal cortex)
or from primary hyperplasia or tumor of the
adrenal cortex. The manifestations, it will have

---

[9] Susman found, however, that in the postmortem examination of a large number of pituitaries,
small basophil adenomas were present in 3.1 per
cent, though no sign of basophilism was observed
during life. Crook also states that a basophil
adenoma or a general increase in basophil cells is
an inconstant finding in Cushing's syndrome, but
that hyaline degeneration of these cells (with or
without adenoma) is invariable.

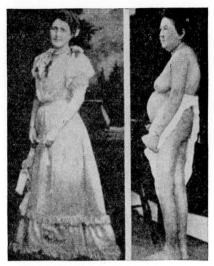

FIG. 56.19. On left, at 20 years of age; on right,
5 years later at height of the disease. (From Cushing and Turney.)

been observed, are in either case referable for the
most part to excessive adrenocortical secretion.
Sometimes Cushing's *disease* is restricted to cases
associated with a pituitary tumor, and Cushing's
*syndrome* applied to the condition due to primary
adrenal tumor or hyperplasia.

### DWARFISM

The arrested skeletal development which results from deficiency of the growth hormone of
the anterior pituitary is spoken of as the *Lorain*
type of infantilism (fig. 56.20). These dwarfs are
usually, though not invariably, undeveloped sex-
ually. They do not show deformity or, as a rule,
mental inferiority, and are generally not unat-
tractive in appearance. Sometimes, however, they
are wizened and except for their diminutive stature
appear older than their years (progeria). The
condition may then be considered the counterpart
of Simmond's disease, but commencing before
puberty. The anterior lobe dwarf at adult age
may be no more than 3 or 4 feet high. During
infancy and childhood, the ossification centers,
as observed by radioscopy, appear normal and
dentition is not delayed. The relative proportions
of the different parts of the skeleton are not far
from normal though they tend toward those characteristic of childhood; the head being large relative to the body. Some encouraging results have
been reported from the treatment of this type of
dwarfism with anterior pituitary extracts of primate origin.

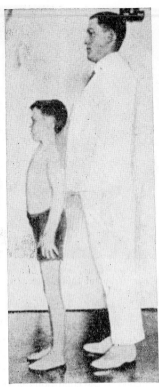

Fig. 56.20. Infantilism due to anterior lobar deficiency. Age 21 years. Man on right is 5 feet 7 inches tall. (From Lisser.)

## Pituitary Cachexia (Simmond's Disease)

This rare disease was first described by Simmonds of Hamburg. It is due to atrophy or degeneration of the anterior lobe. The main features of this disease form a picture which may best be described as that of a premature and rapidly developing senile decay (fig. 56.21). They are largely referable to severe depression of activity of the adrenal cortex and other target organs, e.g., gonads and thyroid, as a result of deficiency of the trophic hormones of the pituitary.

The characteristics of the disease are as follows: (a) *General appearance* (loss of axillary and pubic hair, hair of the head prematurely gray and sparse, loss of teeth, skin of face wrinkled and dry, often great emaciation, smallness of hands and feet, and shrunken appearance of the facial features); (b) *anemia;* (c) *low metabolic rate* and *hypoglycemia;* (d) *amenorrhea or impotence;* (e) *mental deterioration, muscular weakness, death in coma;* (f) *atrophy of the gonads* and a general smallness of the internal organs (*splanchnomicria*); (g) *reduced urinary excretion of gonadotrophins, 11-oxycorticoids and 17-ketosteroids, and depression of*

*protein bound iodine of the blood;* and (h) *acute adrenal insufficiency may occur.*

The disease most commonly follows childbirth in which there has been severe hemorrhage with peripheral circulatory collapse. It is likely that the hypophysial portal blood supply in some way becomes obstructed, thus accounting for the necrosis and fibrosis found on postmortem examination of the pituitary. Milder manifestations of the disease developing after childbirth have been described by Sheehan, which are now referred to as *Sheehan's syndrome.*

## Diabetes Insipidus (see also p. 985 and ch. 34)

Diabetes insipidus is a condition in which large quantities of urine of very low specific gravity, 1.002 to 1.006, and low chloride content are excreted. In an ordinary case the daily output of urine is 4 or 5 liters, but daily amounts several times these figures have been reported. A corresponding increase in the fluid intake occurs and thirst is often intense. The condition frequently accompanies tumors of the pituitary or hypothalamic region, and is essentially due to lack of posterior pituitary hormone through damage to the hypothalamo-neurohypophysial unit. As described above (p. 985), Fisher, Ingram, and Ranson were able to duplicate this state experimentally and showed that either damage to the neurohypophysis, or denervation of the neurohypophysis by means of a hypothalamic lesion, were equally effective in evoking this condition.

It will be recalled (ch. 34) that only about 15 per cent of the glomerular filtrate is reabsorbed by the nephron distal to the proximal convoluted

Fig. 56.21. Pituitary cachexia. On left, patient aged 42 years; on right, the same woman at the age of 34 years. (From Zondek, *Diseases of the Endocrine Glands,* by permission of Edward Arnold & Co., London.)

tubule ("facultative" reabsorption) and upon this fraction alone is the action of the antidiuretic hormone exerted; the reabsorption of water by the proximal tubule ("obligative" reabsorption) is not altered. Therefore, a limit is set to the increase in urine output even though ADH be completely absent. If, say, the glomerular filtrate amounts to 180 liters daily, at least 150 liters must be reabsorbed under all circumstances, leaving less than 30 liters as the maximum amount of urine which could be produced.

The failure of total hypophysectomy to produce diabetes insipidus is due to the loss of the anterior pituitary gland. This was first pointed out by von Hann from his findings at human autopsies, and confirmed by the experimental work of Richter. It seems that the anterior lobe, through its general metabolic effects, exerts a diuretic influence, and that in the absence of this action posterior pituitary deficiency is not revealed by the development of polyuria.

In diabetes insipidus the ingestion of large quantities of water of a temperature below that of the body necessitates readjustments in the heat regulating mechanisms. Vasoconstriction of the skin vessels occurs; the extremities are often cold and may be cyanotic, and the subject is very sensitive to cold. The vasoconstriction is apparently a compensatory measure for heat conservation. Shivering and a rise in the metabolic rate may also result; the food intake is then, as a consequence, increased.

Administration of posterior pituitary extract is the only available means for the control of diabetes insipidus and, as mentioned below, this is not successful in some cases. The whole extract (or the vasopressin fraction) may be given by injection or by means of pledgets of absorbent cotton soaked in the solution and inserted into the nose. The polyuria of nephritis is not influenced by this medication. Water intoxication may occur in diabetes insipidus if posterior pituitary extract is administered and the patient is requested to maintain the usual fluid intake. The urea clearances are normal as a rule.

The fundamental mechanisms concerned in the polyuria of diabetes insipidus appear to be allied in nature to those underlying the diuresis of water drinking in normal persons. But the thirst and the consequent excessive ingestion of water experienced by subjects of diabetes insipidus is not primary, as in the water diuresis of normal persons, but is secondary to the polyuria and the resulting tendency toward dehydration: the deprivation of water carried to the limit of endurance does not prevent the excretion of large quantities of water.

The results of Richter's work upon rats, in which diabetes insipidus was produced by partial hypophysectomy or a stab wound in the floor of the third ventricle, indicate that in the experimental condition polyuria is also primary. He states that polyuria preceded polydipsia and that animals deprived of water continued to excrete large quantities of urine.

About 10 per cent of cases, classed as diabetes insipidus, do not respond to postpituitary preparations, or do so very poorly. Such cases are congenital or show a familial tendency, and are thought to be due to an inherent defect of the renal tubules with respect to the renal absorption of water—a persistence, it would seem, of the infantile incapacity of the tubules to concentrate the urine.

Polyuria, simulating in some ways diabetes insipidus, occurs in *chronic nephritis* (ch. 35) and in *psychogenic polydipsia*. The polyuria in chronic nephritis is not corrected by pituitary extracts and in polydipsia thirst is *primary*; the urine volume is reduced and the specific gravity of the urine is raised by rigid deprivation of water; the polyuria is simply a normal diuretic response to water drinking.

### DYSTROPHIA ADIPOSO-GENITALIS

Dystrophia adiposo-genitalis, as its name suggests, is a condition in which obesity, sexual infantilism, and dwarfing (if the condition occurs during the growing period) are the essential features. It is due to a lesion of the anterior lobe of the pituitary, which accounts for the sexual immaturity and dwarfing, and of the hypothalamus. The experiments of Smith with hypophysectomized rats, and of other investigators, point to injury of the hypothalamus as being chiefly responsible for the obesity. Marked obesity is also a feature of certain hypothalamic disorders in man unassociated apparently with any disease of the pituitary itself. Dystrophia adiposo-genitalis appears in two forms according to the age at which it develops; the *infantile* or *prepubertal* and the *adolescent* or *adult*.

THE INFANTILE OR PREPUBERTAL TYPE, FRÖLICH'S SYNDROME (fig. 56.22). This type may occur in children of any age before puberty. It may be the result of an inherent defect of the pituitary, of atrophy of the secretory cells by pressure (e.g., by tumors), injury (e.g., a penetrating wound), or of some infectious disease. Polyuria and a high sugar tolerance are frequent accompaniments of

FIG. 56.22. Male aged 8 years. Hypopituitarism following whooping cough, with characteristic growth and sex defects and obesity; Fröhlich's syndrome. (From Gardiner-Hill.)

FIG. 56.23. Extreme case of obesity, due to pituitary or hypothalamic disease. (From Timme).

the disease. The subjects are lethargic or somnolent and often of subnormal intelligence. They usually have voracious appetites and especially a craving for sweets. The "fat boy" of *Pickwick Papers* was undoubtedly an example of this condition. The younger the age of the child at which the disease commences the greater, obviously, will be the degree of stunting. When the dwarfing is of high grade, this combined with the obesity

makes a very striking picture. These subjects are human counterparts of Smith's rats in which the pituitary was destroyed (and the hypothalamus presumably injured) by chromic acid injections. Since obesity and an *apparent* sexual infantilism may occur in normal adolescent boys, the diagnosis of Frohlich's syndrome in such cases should be applied only to those patients with proven hypothalamic damage.

THE ADOLESCENT OR ADULT TYPE. Male subjects of this condition are often effeminate in disposition and appearance. The excess fat has a feminine distribution, the adiposity being noticeable chiefly in the mammary region, buttocks, thighs, and over the mons veneris. The hair over the pubis and in the axillae is sparse or absent; the skin of the face and the body is smooth, soft, and hairless; the hips are broad. In female subjects the obesity is often extreme, a weight of 300 pounds being not very unusual (fig. 56.23). In both sexes the feet and hands are small and "pretty," the finger tips being slender and tapering with narrow pointed terminal phalanges. The extremities thus give a picture the reverse of that seen in acromegaly. The basal metabolic rate is often subnormal and sugar tolerance increased. Diabetes insipidus is a common, and narcolepsy (p. 1231) an occasional, accompaniment.

## REFERENCES

ALLEN, B. M. Anat. Rec., 1916, 11, 486.
ASCHNER, B. Arch. ges. Physiol., 1912, 146, 1.
BAILEY, P. AND BREMER, F. Arch. Int. Med., 1921, 28, 773.
BAYLISS, W. M. AND STARLING, E. H. Proc. Roy. Soc. London, Series B, 1904, 73, 310.
BERTHOLD, A. A. Arch. Anat. Physiol. Berlin, 1849, 42.
BEST, C. H. AND CAMPBELL, J. J. Physiol., 1936, 86, 190.
BEST, C. H. AND CAMPBELL, J. Lancet, 1938, 1, 1444.
BISSONETTE, T. H. Proc. A. Res. Nerv. & Ment. Dis., 1936, 17, 361.
BISSONETTE, T. H. Wilson Bull., 1937, 49, 241.
BISSONETTE, T. H. Endocrinology, 1938, 22, 92.
BLACK, P. T., COLLIP, J. B. AND THOMSON, D. L. J. Physiol., 1934, 82, 385.
BLOUNT, R. F. Proc. Nat. Acad. Sc., 1930, 16, 222.
BODIAN, D. Bull. Johns Hopkins Hosp., 1951, 33, 354.
BURN, J. H. AND LING, H. W. Quart. J. Pharm. & Pharmacol., 1933, 6, 31.
BURN, J. P. J. Physiol., 1923, 57, 318.
COLLIP, J. B. Proc. Soc. Exper. Biol. & Med., 1933, 30, 544.
COLLIP, J. B. Tr. Am. A. Study Goiter, 1937.
COLLIP, J. B. Endocrinology, 1938, 23, 718.
COLLIP, J. B. Endocrinology, 1939, 25, 318.
COLLIP, J. B. AND ANDERSON, E. M. Lancet, 1934, 1, 76.

COLLIP, J. B. AND ASSOCIATES. Lancet, 1933, **2**, 347.

CROOKE, A. C.  J. Path. & Bact., 1935, **41**, 339.

CROSS, B. A. J. Endocrinol., 1958, **16**, 261.

CUSHING, H. AND DAVIDOFF, L. M. Rockefeller Institute for Medical Research, New York, Monograph No. 22, 1927.

CUSHING, H. AND GOETSCH, E. Am. J. Physiol., 1910, **27**, 60.

DALE, H. H. Biochem. J., 1909, **4**, 427.

DANDY, W. E. AND REICHERT, F. L. Bull. Johns Hopkins Hosp., 1938, **62**, 122.

D'ANGELO, S. A. AND TRAUM, R. E. Ann. New York Acad. Sc., 1958, **72**, 239.

DOBYNS, B. M. AND STEELMAN, S. L. Endocrinology, 1953, **52**, 705.

DUDLEY, H. W. J. Pharmacol. & Exper. Therap., 1919, **14**, 295.

VAN DYKE, H. B. AND ASSOCIATES. J. Pharmacol. & Exper. Therap., 1942, **74**, 190.

EVANS, H. M. AND LONG, J. A. Anat. Rec., 1921, **21**, 62 (Proc.).

EVANS, H. M., MEYER, K. AND SIMPSON, M. E. Mem. Univ. California, 1933, **11**, 1.

FERGUSON, J. K. W. Am. J. Physiol., 1939, **126**, 489.

FISHER, C., INGRAM, W. R. AND RANSON, S. W. Arch. Neurol. & Psychiat., 1935, **34**, 124.

FISHER, C., INGRAM, W. R. AND RANSON, S. W. Anat. Rec., 1935, **63**, 29.

FISHER, C., INGRAM, W. R. AND RANSON, S. W. Arch. Int. Med., 1936, **57**, 1067.

FRIEDGOOD, H. B. Bull. Johns Hopkins Hosp., 1934, **54**, 48.

GEILING, E. M. K. AND DeLAWDER, A. M. Bull. Johns Hopkins Hosp., 1932, **51**, 1.

GEILING, E. M. K. AND DeLAWDER, A. M. Bull. Johns Hopkins Hosp., 1932, **51**, 335.

GEILING, E. M. K. AND OLDHAM, F. K. Tr. Am. A. Physicians, 1937, **52**, 132.

GILMAN, A. AND GOODMAN, L. J. Physiol., 1937, **90**, 113.

GRATTAN, J. F. AND JENSEN, H. J. J. Biol. Chem., 1940, **135**, 551.

GREEN, J. D. Am. J. Anat., 1951, **88**, 225.

HALMI, N. S. Endocrinology, 1950, **47**, 289.

HALMI, N. S. Endocrinology, 1952, **50**, 140.

HAM, A. W. AND HAIST, R. E. Am. J. Path., 1941, **17**, 787.

VON HANN, F. Frankfurt. Ztschr. Path., 1918, **21**, 337.

HARRIS, G. W. Physiol. Rev., 1948, **28**, 139.

HARRIS, G. W. J. Physiol., 1950, **111**, 347.

HARRIS, G. W. Ciba Foundation Colloquia on Endocrinology, 1952, **4**, 106.

HARRIS, G. W. AND JACOBSOHN, D. Proc. Roy. Soc. London, Series B, 1952, **139**, 263.

HELLER, H. Biol. Rev., 1945, **20**, 147.

HERRING, P. T. Quart. J. Exper. Physiol., 1908, **1**, 121.

HIMSWORTH, H. P. AND SCOTT, D. B. M. J. Physiol., 1938, **91**, 447.

HOGBEN, L. T. AND WINTON, F. R. Proc. Roy. Soc. London, Series B, 1922, **93**, 318.

HOUSSAY, B. A. AND ASSOCIATES. Compt. rend. Soc. biol., 1922, **86**, 115.

HOUSSAY, B. A. AND ASSOCIATES. Endocrinology, 1931, **15**, 511.

HOUSSAY, B. A. AND ASSOCIATES. J. Physiol., 1932, **77**, 81.

HOUSSAY, B. A. AND ASSOCIATES. Compt. rend. Soc. biol., 1932, **111**, 479.

HOUSSAY. B. A. AND ASSOCIATES. Compt. rend. Soc. biol., 1933, **112**, 497.

HOWELL, W. H. J. Exper. Med., 1898, **3**, 245.

INGRAM, W. R. AND FISHER, C. Anat. Rec., 1936, **66**, 271.

INGRAM, W. R. AND FISHER, C. Endocrinology, 1936, **20**, 762.

KAMM, O. AND ASSOCIATES. J. Am. Chem. Soc., 1928, **50**, 573 (I and II).

LI, C. H. AND ASSOCIATES. Science, 1942, **96**, 450

LI, C. H. AND ASSOCIATES. J. Biol. Chem., 1943, **149**, 413.

LI, C. H. AND ASSOCIATES. Harvey Lectures, 1951.

LOEB, L. AND BASSETT, P. B. Proc. Soc. Exper. Biol. & Med., 1929, **26**, 860.

MAGNUS, R. AND SCHÄFER, E. A. J. Physiol., 1901, **27**, ix.

MARIE, P. Brain, 1889, **12**, 59.

MARKS, H. P. J. Physiol., 1936, **87**, 15P.

MARSHALL, F. H. A. AND JOLLY, W. A. Tr. Roy. Soc. Edinburgh, 1907, **45**, 589.

MARSHALL, F. H. A. AND JOLLY, W. A. Quart. J. Exper. Physiol., 1908, **1**, 115.

NIKITOVITCH-WINER, M. AND EVERETT, J. W. Endocrinology, 1958, **63**, 916.

OLIVER, G. AND SCHÄFER, E. A. J. Physiol., 1895, **18**, 277.

PFEIFFER, C. A. Am. J. Anat., 1936, **58**, 195.

POPA, G. T. AND FIELDING, U. J. Anat., 1930, **65**, 88.

POPA, G. T. AND FIELDING, U.  J. Anat., 1933, **67**, 227.

PURVES, H. D. AND GRIESBACH, W. E. Endocrinology, 1951, **49**, 244, 427, 652.

PUTNAM, T. J., BENEDICT, E. B. AND TEEL, H. M. Am. J. Physiol., 1928, **84**, 157.

PUTNAM, T. J., BENEDICT, E. B. AND TEEL, H. M. Arch. Surg., 1929, **18**, 1708.

RASMUSSEN, A. Am. J. Path., 1929, **5**, 263.

RASMUSSEN, A. Am. J. Path., 1933, **9**, 459.

RAWSON, R. W. Ann. New York Acad. Sc., 1949, **50**, 279.

REID, E. J. Endocrinol., 1952, **8**, 50.

RICHARDSON, K. C. Proc. Roy. Soc. London, Series B, 1949, **136**, 30.

RICHARDSON, K. C. AND YOUNG, F. G. J. Physiol., 1937, **91**, 352.

RICHTER, C. P. Brain, 1930, **53**, 76.

RICHTER, C. P. Am. J. Physiol., 1934, **110**, 124.

RICHTER, C. P. Am. J. Physiol., 1935, **112**, 481.

RIDDLE, O. Ohio J. Sc., 1937, **37**, 446.

RIOCH, D. M., WISLOCKI, G. B. AND O'LEARY, J. L. Res. Publ. A. Nerv. & Ment. Dis., 1940, **20**, 3.

ROWAN, W. M. Nature, 1925, **115**, 494.

ROWAN, W. M. Nature, 1927, **119**, 351.

ROWLANDS, I. W. AND PARKES, A. S. J. Physiol., 1936, **88**, 305.

SHIPLEY, R. A. AND LONG, C. N. H. Biochem. J., 1938, **32**, 2242.

SIMMONDS, M. Deutsche med. Wchnschr., 1914, **40**, 322.

SMITH, P. E. Science, 1916, **44**, 280.
SMITH, P. E. J. A. M. A., 1927, **88**, 158.
SMITH, P. E. Am. J. Anat., 1930, **45**, 205.
SYDNOR, K. L. Endocrinology, 1955, **56**, 204.
SYDNOR, K. L. AND SAYERS, G. Endocrinology, 1954, **55**, 621.
DU VIGNEAUD, V. AND ASSOCIATES. J. Am. Chem. Soc., 1953, **75**, 4879, 4880.
WILKINS, L., BONGIOVANNI, A. M., CLAYTON, G. W., GRUMBACH, M. M. AND VAN WYCK, J. Ciba Foundation Colloquia on Endocrinology, 1955, **8**, 460.
XUEREB, G. P., PRICHARD, M. M. L. AND DANIEL, P. M. Quart. J. Exper. Physiol., 1954, **39**, 219.
YOUNG, F. G. Lancet, 1937, **2**, 372.
YOUNG, F. G. Proc. Roy. Soc. Med., 1938, **31**, 1305.
YOUNG, F. G. Biochem. J., 1945, **39**, 515.
ZONDEK, B. J. A. M. A., 1935, **104**, 537.

*Monographs and Reviews*

ABRAMOWITZ, A. A. AND ASSOCIATES. Endocrinology, 1944, **34**, 103.
BARGMANN, W. AND SCHARRER, E. Am. Scientist, 1951, **39**, 255.
BURN, J. H., AND DALE, H. H. Medical Research Council, London, Special Report No. 69, 1922.
CUSHING, H. The pituitary body and its disorders. Lippincott, Philadelphia, 1912.
CUSHING, H. Papers relating to the pituitary body, hypothalamus and parasympathetic nervous system. Charles C Thomas, Springfield, Ill., 1932.
CUSHING, H. Harvey Lectures, 1932–1933, **28**, 90.
VAN DYKE, H. B. The physiology and pharmacology of the pituitary body, Vols. I, II. University of Chicago Press, Chicago, 1936, 1939.
VAN DYKE, H. B. Bull. New York Acad. Med., 1953, **29**, 24.
VAN DYKE, H. B., ADAMSONS, K. AND ENGEL, S. L. Recent Progr. Hormone Res., 1955, **11**, 1.
EINHORN, J. Acta radiol., 1958, Suppl. 160.
EVANS, H. M., MEYER, K. AND SIMPSON, M. E. Mem. Univ. California, 1933, **11**.
FARRELL, G. Physiol. Rev., 1958, **38**, 709.
FITZPATRICK, R. J. *In* The neurohypophysis, edited by H. Heller. Butterworth Scientific Publications, London, 1957.

FISHER, C., INGRAM, W. R. AND RANSON, S. W. Diabetes insipidus. Edwards Brothers, Ann Arbor, Mich., 1938.
GEILING, E. M. K. Physiol. Rev., 1926, **6**, 62.
GEILING, E. M. K. Harvey Lectures, 1941–1942, **37**, 269.
GREER, M. A. Recent Progr. Hormone Res., 1957, **13**, 67.
HAM, A. W. Histology, 2nd ed. Pitman Medical Publishing Co., London, 1953.
HANSTRÖM, B. *In* The neurohypophysis, edited by H. Heller. Butterworth Scientific Publications, London, 1957.
HARRIS, G. W. Neural control of the pituitary gland. Edward Arnold, London, 1955.
HARRIS, G. W. Proc. Roy. Soc. London, Series B, 1958, **149**, 336.
HECHTER, O. Vitamins & Hormones, 1955, **13**, 245.
HELLER, H. *In* The neurohypophysis, edited by H. Heller. Butterworth Scientific Publications, 1957.
HOUSSAY, B. A. New England J. Med., 1936, **214**.
HOUSSAY, B. A. Endocrinology, 1942, **30**, 884.
LEVINE, R. *In* Survey of biological progress, Vol. III, edited by B. Glass. Academic Press, New York, 1957.
PINCUS, G. AND THIMANN, K. V. (editors). The hormones, Vols. I, II, III. Academic Press, New York, 1948, 1950, 1955 (various reviews).
RAWLES, R. E. Physiol. Rev., 1948, **28**, 383.
ROLLESTON, H. D. The endocrine organs in health and disease. Oxford, London, 1936.
SAYERS, G. AND BROWN, R. W. *In* Glandular physiology and therapy, 5th ed. Lippincott, Philadelphia, 1954.
SAYERS, G., REDGATE, E. S. AND ROYCE, P. C. Ann. Rev. Physiol., 1958, **20**, 243.
SCHARRER, E. AND SCHARRER, B. Recent Progr. Hormone Res., 1954, **10**, 183.
SEVERINGHAUS, A. Res. Publ. A. Res. Nerv. & Ment. Dis., 1936, **17**.
SEVERINGHAUS, A. E. Physiol. Rev., 1937, **17**, 556.
VERNEY, E. B. Proc. Roy. Soc. London, Series B, 1947, **135**, 25.
WHITE, A. Physiol. Rev., 1946, **26**, 574.
YOUNG, F. G. Recent Progr. Hormone Res., 1953, **8**, 471.

See also references in chapter 57.

# 57

# THE THYROID GLAND

---

## Development, Histology, Blood, and Nerve Supply

Very early in its evolutionary history the thyroid had a digestive function, a function lost long since but which its ontogeny recalls. The gland is developed from a single median outgrowth of hypoblast derived from the ventral wall of the primitive pharynx at the level of the first visceral cleft. This extends downward. Its lower end bifurcates and enlarges to form the isthmus and lateral lobes of the thyroid. Its upper end gives rise to the foramen cecum of the tongue. The intervening portion, *the thyroglossal duct*, normally disappears but sometimes persists and may give origin to accessory thyroids or to the so-called thyroglossal cysts.

The *thyroid tissue* is composed of cuboidal epithelial cells arranged in a single layer around spaces roughly circular or ovoid in shape and fairly uniform in size. These spaces, variously known as *follicles, vesicles, acini,* or *alveoli,* contain a homogenous gelatinous material, *the colloid substance,* which is the stored secretion of the gland. Connective tissue fibers support the alveolar walls and form septa which divide the gland into smaller masses. The cells lining the alveoli contain numerous mitochondria and a well defined Golgi apparatus. Studies with the electron microscope have shown that the inner (luminal) end of these cells possess cilia and a brush border. These are characteristic features of cells engaged in absorption or secretion. When the gland becomes active the Golgi apparatus hypertrophies and droplets of colloid appear in its proximity. Other histological changes typical of increased activity in the thyroid are, increase in the cell height of the epithelium, increase in mitotic figures, decrease in amount of colloid in the follicles with a tendency to become basophilic rather than acidophilic in staining properties, and an increase in vascularity. The maximal normal weight of the human thyroid is, according to Marine, from 20 to 35 grams or around 0.4 gram per kilogram of body weight. The thyroid tissue of the early fetus consists of masses of epithelial cells showing little or no arrangement into acini. The latter appear about the fourth month but are small and contain little colloid. Functional activity first appears in the fetal gland at about this time.

The *blood supply* comes from the superior and inferior thyroid arteries, chiefly the former. The blood flow is profuse, the blood passing with little resistance from the arterial to the venous side through a wide capillary bed. The flow amounts to from 3.5 to 6 cc. per gram of tissue per minute, or about 5 liters per hour for the whole gland. The gland is richly supplied with *lymphatics* which drain lymph spaces surrounding the vesicles.

The *nerve supply* of the thyroid is derived from the vagus and the sympathetic nerves. The sympathetic fibers leave the spinal cord between the second and fifth thoracic segments and pass to cell stations in the superior and middle cervical ganglia, where they are relayed to the gland through the superior laryngeal nerves and along the blood vessels. It is probable that the thyroid nerves are purely vasomotor in function and influence the activity of the gland indirectly, namely, by altering its blood supply. Control of thyroid activity is exerted mainly, if not exclusively, by the thyrotrophic hormone of the pituitary (p. 963).

## An Outline of Thyroid Function

Some of the first experiments on the thyroid were performed in 1856 by Schiff, who found that in dogs death followed its removal; from the symptoms preceding death it is now apparent that this was due to removal of the parathyroids (ch. 59). As in the case of some other ductless glands, clinical observations gave the first hint concerning the functions of the thyroid. Hilton Fagg in 1871, reported a case of *cretinism* (p. 1000) and ascribed it to absence or atrophy of the thyroid. Three years later, Gull described the condition which today is known as *myxedema* or *Gull's disease,* but called it the *cretinoid state in adult life.* Horsley, some years later, removed the gland from monkeys and produced conditions resembling human cretinism and myxedema. Later experiments upon other species have established the fact that the thyroid secretion is absolutely necessary for the *normal growth* and *development* of young animals, and for maintaining the *normal level of metabolism* of animals of all ages. Magnus-Levy, in 1895, demonstrated that thyroid deficiency was associated with a greatly reduced metabolism and that treatment with desiccated thyroid restored the metabolic rate to the normal level or above. Complete thyroidectomy reduces the basal metabolic rate by from 40 to 45 per cent in about 8 weeks after the operation. Thyroidectomy in lambs, young rabbits, goats, or calves has been shown to cause retarded skeletal growth and arrested sexual development (fig. 57.1). Apathy, lack of vigor, thickening of the skin, and a striking reduction in basal metabolism result in both young and full-grown animals. In young cattle, increase in bulk but not in height is a notable feature; the animals appearing short-legged and of a broad, stocky build. Other effects of thyroid removal in the young are: delay in the ossification of the epiphyses of the long bones, poor growth of hair, failure in thymic involution, and subnormal intelligence. The administration of thyroid extract to young animals shortly after thyroidectomy prevents these otherwise inevitable results. In full-grown animals the effects of thyroid removal can be corrected by thyroid administration at any time after operation.

The effects produced upon lower orders by thyroid removal and by thyroid feeding are even

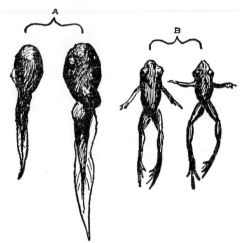

Fig. 57.2. The effect of removal of the thyroids upon the development of tadpoles. *A,* Thyroidless tadpoles; *B,* normal frogs of the same age as *A.* (From Allen, redrawn.)

more striking. Gudernatsch removed the thyroids from tadpoles, keeping a number of young animals of the same hatching as controls. The thyroidectomized larvae grew somewhat larger in size but did not metamorphose; the controls developed into frogs within the usual time (fig. 57.2). Metamorphoses of the thyroidless creatures could be induced to proceed at the normal rate by thyroid feeding.[1] Also, the time required for the normal larvae to metamorphose completely could be shortened (from 104 to 20 days) by feeding thyroid tissue. Swingle has shown that inorganic iodine alone will produce similar effects (p. 1005). The effect of the thyroid hormone upon the axolotl is extraordinary. This animal is allied to the frog, but is purely aquatic in its habits. It has, in its *adult* form, a finned tail, gills, and four short limbs, resembling somewhat an enormous tadpole which has undergone partial metamorphosis. Thyroid feeding causes the axolotl to lose its fin and gills, develop air breathing organs, and forsake the aquatic life for which Nature had designed it (see also ch. 57).

In growing birds (chicks) and mammals, a stimulating effect of the thyroid hormone on growth has been demonstrated. Acceleration of growth has also been observed in a twin child suffering from hyperthyroidism.

It is now known that the function of the thyroid gland is to extract iodide ions from the blood, combine them with a protein (thyroglobulin)

Fig. 57.1. Triplet kids. Center animal normal; right- and left-hand animals thyroidectomized at 20 days of age. Photograph taken 13 weeks after operation. (From Sutherland Simpson.)

[1] This effect has been made use of to assay the potency of thyroid preparations or to determine the activity of a particular thyroid gland (Gudernatsch test).

stored in the colloid of the alveoli, and to liberate thyroxine and allied compounds from this protein for secretion into the blood. The study of these reactions has been greatly aided by the use of radioactive iodine. The isotope most generally used is $I^{131}$ (half-life, 8 days). Injection of a tracer dose of $I^{131}$ adds such a minute amount of iodine to the circulation that for all practical purposes the iodine metabolism remains unchanged but, together with such techniques as paper chromatography, it allows quick and accurate analysis of the different iodine-containing compounds in the gland or body fluid. Unlike the other endocrine glands, the thyroid stores large amounts of hormone. It has been calculated that the human gland stores a 3 months' supply of thyroxine. Knowledge of the function of the thyroid in man has been derived largely from studies of clinical cases of hypothyroidism and hyperthyroidism, and for this reason a description of these states precedes the account of experimental studies of thyroid physiology.

## Goiter

Many abnormal thyroid states are accompanied by a visible swelling in the neck due to enlargement of the gland. Goiter is a generic term which may be applied to almost any noninflammatory and nonmalignant enlargement of the thyroid gland. The following is a short classification:

A. *Simple goiters. These are unaccompanied by constitutional features.* They are subdivided upon a histological basis into three groups
  1. Colloid (diffuse)
  2. Parenchymatous (diffuse)
  3. Adenomatous (nodular)
B. *Goiters associated with a deficiency of the thyroid hormone* (hypothyroidism)
  1. Cretinism
  2. Myxedema
C. *Goiters associated with an excess of the thyroid hormone* (hyperthyroidism)
  1. Exophthalmic goiter
  2. Toxic adenoma

### Diffuse Colloid Goiter

The alveoli are large, distended with colloid and lined by low cuboidal or flattened epithelial cells. There is no hypertrophy or hyperplasia of the latter (figs. 57.3 and 57.4). The iodine content per gram of gland tissue is low but as a rule the total quantity in the enlarged gland is not far from normal. Colloid goiter may become converted into, or result from, the following type (see also pp. 1007).

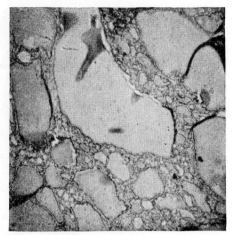

FIG. 57.3. Photomicrograph of a human sample of colloid goiter.

### Diffuse Parenchymatous Goiter

Hypertrophy and multiplication of the cells lining the alveoli, with great reduction in the amount of colloid material are characteristic features of this type. The alveolar cavities are of various sizes and shapes and often almost obliterated by infoldings of their walls. The epithelial cells are high columnar instead of the normal cuboidal type. The iodine content of the gland is low, usually much less than 0.1 per cent of its dried substance. Exhaustion of the gland and atrophy of its secretory elements with an increase in fibrous tissue may result, or, as mentioned above, the goiter may change to the colloid type, especially after iodine administration (fig. 57.4). Partial thyroidectomy in animals, as first shown by Halsted, results in regeneration of the thyroid remnant to produce the foregoing histological picture of diffuse parenchymatous hypertrophy. This observer also showed that removal of the thyroid from pregnant bitches led to parenchymatous goiter in the puppies.

### Adenomatous Goiter

As a result of the formation of isolated tumor-like masses of thyroid tissue (adenomata) the glandular enlargement is asymmetrical or nodular. The minute structure of the adenoma may resemble a section of colloid or parenchymatous goiter, or it may undergo cystic changes. Again, the alveoli may be unusually small, contain little colloid, and resemble fetal thyroid tissue (fetal adenoma). The iodine content of the nodule may be normal or high while that of the rest of the gland, which may also show diffuse colloid or parenchymatous changes, is usually low.

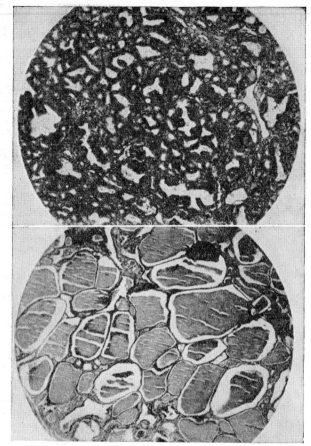

Fig. 57.4. Upper photograph, microscopical appearance of the gland in exophthalmic goiter showing hypertrophy and hyperplasia (parenchymatous goiter) before the administration of iodine. Lower photograph, appearance after involution had occurred from iodine administration (colloid goiter). (From Rienhoff.)

The simple enlargement of the thyroid which sometimes occurs at puberty or during pregnancy may be either of the colloid or parenchymatous type. A certain degree of thyroid enlargement at these times is physiological. The enlargements seen in goiter districts (endemic goiter) or occurring sporadically may show the features of any of the three types. Either of the first two forms may end in exhaustion atrophy (p. 1007).

## Hypothyroid States

### CRETINISM

A cretin is a type of dwarf for which deficiency or absence of the thyroid secretion in infancy or early childhood is responsible (fig. 57.5). Among the typical features of the condition are: (a) retarded and abnormal skeletal growth, (b) arrested sexual development, (c) mental deficiency varying in degree but often amounting to complete idiocy (deaf-mutism is common), (d) the facial features are coarse and appear bloated, the skin is dry, thick, pasty, and often deeply wrinkled; the nose is broad and its bridge depressed; the tongue is enlarged and appears between the thickened and usually parted lips, (e) the supraclavicular fossae are filled with pads of fat, (f) closure of the anterior fontanelle which normally occurs before the 20th month is postponed for several years; the epiphyses of the long bones fail to ossify at the usual time, and (g) the basal metabolic rate is depressed by from 20 to 40 per cent below the normal.

Endemic cretinism is much less common today. In the past it was seen most frequently in districts where goiter was prevalent (in the valleys of the Alps, Pyrenees, Himalayas, etc.) and was usually the result of atrophy and degeneration of the secretory epithelium of a goitrous gland. Some of the worst cases of cretinism appear, however, in

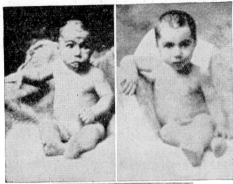

FIG. 57.5. Upper photograph (left), cretinism in an infant; (right) same child after treatment with thyroid extract. (From J. Huxley.) Lower photograph, a cretin aged 10 years. (From McCarrison after Thomson.)

infants, either in these districts or elsewhere, who are not goitrous. The condition is then due to (a) prenatal or early postnatal atrophy of the thyroid, (b) to its congenital absence, or (c) to its destruction by some inflammatory condition. A large percentage of the goiterless cretins in a goiter district are the result of hypothyroidism in one or both of the parents.

Although the majority of cretins are apathetic and sluggish, a very few are highly excitable, the *nervous cretinism of McCarrison.*

### MYXEDEMA (GULL'S DISEASE)

Myxedema is the result of thyroid deficiency in adults or older children and corresponds to the cretinism of infants and younger children. It follows atrophy or destruction of the thyroid from whatever cause, or may result from an operation in which too much of the gland has been removed (*operative myxedema* or *cachexia strumipriva*). The chief characteristics are (a) low metabolic rate (−20 to −40), (b) a thick puffy appearance of the skin; the hair is dry, brittle, and sparse; the facial features sometimes give the subject a mongoloid look (fig. 57.6), (c) apathy, lethargy, slow cerebration, though general intelligence is retained, (d) increased body fat and hypercholesterolemia, (e) greater susceptibility to cold, and (f) cardiac dilatation and low voltage electrocardiograms. The edemalike appearance of the skin was thought by Ord, who suggested the term myxedema, to be due to the accumulation of mucin in the subcutaneous tissues. The thickening of the skin is not due to a true edema, nor is it

FIG. 57.6. Left, myxedema; right, same subject after 3 months treatment with thyroid extract. (From Murray.)

the result of the accumulation of mucin but, according to Boothby, to the deposit of a semifluid albuminous substance containing over 13 per cent of protein.

### Hyperthyroid States, Thyrotoxicosis

#### Exophthalmic Goiter (Graves', Parry's, or Basedow's Disease)

In Graves' disease there is nothing in the histological appearance of the thyroid to distinguish it, with certainty, from a simple goiter. The gland usually shows a picture typical of parenchymatous goiter, i.e., hypertrophy and hyperplasia (p. 999); its iodine content is low. The blood iodine is elevated. After iodine administration the gland tends to assume the histological appearance of colloid goiter (fig. 57.4 and p. 1006). The blood supply of the gland is greatly increased, the rush of blood through the superior thyroid arteries often producing a loud bruit or a distinct thrill. In addition to the thyroid enlargement the chief features of the fully developed condition are:

1. Accelerated pulse (100 to 160 per minute) and increased circulation rate (50 per cent or more above normal), cardiac dilation and hypertrophy, myocardial failure, auricular fibrillation in 20 per cent of cases, flushing of the skin, and normal or low diastolic pressure with high systolic pressure (i.e., high pulse pressure).
2. Nervous excitability.
3. A fine involuntary tremor.
4. General muscular weakness.
5. Protrusion of the eyeballs (exophthalmos) and other ocular signs, e.g., widening of the pal-

pebral fissure (Dalrimple's sign) due to retraction of the upper lid; infrequent winking (Stellwag's sign); weakness in convergence of the eyes (Moebius); tremor of the closed lids (Rosenbach); lid lag (von Graefe), i.e., failure of the lid to follow the eye smoothly upon looking down; absence of wrinkling of the forehead when eyes are rotated upward (Joffroy); and difficulty in eversion of upper lid (Gifford). There is frequently edema of the conjunctiva (chemosis) and upper lid, and palsies of ocular muscles may occur (fig. 57.7).

6. Metabolic rate increased to varying degrees up to 80 per cent above normal. As a result of the increased activity of the heat-dissipating mechanisms the skin is hot and moist. Increased tolerance to cold and lowered tolerance to a high environmental temperature.
7. Dissipation of the fat stores; wasting.
8. Nitrogen and calcium excretion are increased (rarefaction of the skeleton may be demonstrated by X-rays in many cases).
9. Disturbance of carbohydrate metabolism is common, as evidenced by hyperglycemia, glycosuria, and reduced sugar tolerance. Hepatic glycogen stores are reduced.
10. The thymus is enlarged in 80 per cent of cases, and hyperplasia of lymphoid tissue in general is found.
11. Subjects of hyperthyroidism are especially susceptible to oxygen deficiency. Work is performed less economically and dyspnea occurs upon exertion (ch. 33).
12. Thyroid crises. During the course of exophthalmic goiter intense exacerbation of the symptoms may occur, accompanied by nausea, vomiting, diarrhea, dehydration, high temperature, a great increase in heart rate, erythema, extreme nervousness, thrashing about in bed, muscular weakness, and sometimes delirium or coma. Treatment of this condition with cortisone has been successful.

#### A Discussion of the Pathogenesis of Some of the Features Listed Above

The tachycardia is not dependent upon nervous connections but appears to be due to a direct and persistent effect of the hormone upon the cardiac muscle. The excised heart of an animal given thyroxine (p. 1015) in excess, beats at the increased rate when perfused, or transplanted to the body of another animal. Also, fragments of heart muscle of a 2-day-old chick embryo pulsate at a more rapid rate when thyroxine is added to the nutrient fluid. The high pulse pressure seen in hyperthyroidism is due to the general vasodilation combined with an increased stroke volume. The increased circulation rate is chiefly the result of the higher metabolic rate.

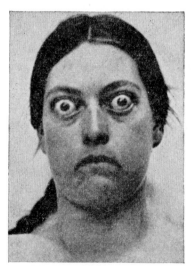

Fig. 57.7. Typical case of exophthalmic goiter showing characteristic facies. (From Crile.)

*Cardiac failure and thyrotoxic disease.* The association of cardiac failure with hyperthyroidism has led to the idea that the thyrotoxicosis is a cause of myocardial disease. But organic disease of the heart is not as common in Graves' disease as has been generally supposed. When cardiac failure does occur it is in the great majority of instances due to disease of the heart which had existed, though often without symptoms, before the development of thyrotoxicosis. The greater cardiac work (increased cardiac output) resulting from the higher metabolism, it is believed, by encroaching on cardiac reserve, merely reveals a hidden cardiac condition or aggravates a pre-existing manifest heart lesion.

*Exophthalmos.* The pathogenesis of exophthalmos in Graves' disease has been a puzzling question for years. Exophthalmos refers to a forward displacement of the eyeball in the bony orbit, and must be distinguished clinically from simple retraction of the upper lid which results in the same staring or frightened expression. The existence, and degree of, exophthalmos is established with special instruments (e.g., Hertel's exophthalmometer) which measure the distance at which the most forward point in the cornea lies anterior to the outer bony margin (external canthus) of the orbit. The distance in normal persons ranges from 14 to 16 mm.; whereas in Graves' disease it may be over 25 mm. Two questions are posed by exophthalmos; (a) what are the general factors responsible for producing the changes in the orbit in Graves' disease? and (b) what are the pathological changes in the orbit which result in protrusion of the eyeball?

There is sufficient evidence to state quite confidently that *exophthalmos is not an effect of the thyroid hormone itself.* Exophthalmos cannot be produced in animals by large and repeated doses of thyroid hormone, nor can it be induced in man by this means.[2] Furthermore, severe thyrotoxicosis may be present in the absence of exophthalmos (see toxic adenoma, p. 1004). Conversely, efficient treatment of a thyrotoxic state (by thyroidectomy or administration of goitrogenic drugs) may result in alleviation of all signs of the disease except that the exophthalmos fails to improve or becomes worse in about 40 per cent of cases, and becomes extremely severe in about 1

per cent. Administration of thyroid hormone to these cases occasionally induces an amelioration of the exophthalmos. Although repeated doses of thyroid hormone do not evoke exophthalmos, administration of thyrotrophic hormone readily induces this state in normal animals (guinea pigs) or thyroidectomized animals, and even to a greater degree in the latter. Whether this effect is due to the thyrotrophic hormone itself, or to an exophthalmos-producing substance (EPS) closely associated with it, has been discussed above (p. 965). Dobyns and Wilson have produced exophthalmos in the fish Fundulus by injection of sera from patients with progressive exophthalmos (see also ch. 56). The relationship of pituitary secretion to the exophthalmos of Graves' disease is also implied by the recent findings that hypophysectomy, or section of the pituitary stalk, may be beneficial in otherwise intractable and progressive cases.

The mechanism causing the actual proptosis or forward displacement of the eye must now be considered. One of the earliest theories was based on the contractile power of *Mueller's orbital muscle* situated at the back of the orbit or of the smooth muscle in the *fascia bulbi.* The tone of these muscles was thought to be increased as a result of the thyroid hormone having sensitized them to the action of circulating adrenaline. This view cannot be accepted, however, since (a) thyroid hormone does not induce exophthalmos, (b) Mueller's muscle in the human is a mere vestige and incapable of contraction powerful enough to produce this effect, and (c) the exophthalmos does not disappear after death as it would do if it were solely due to increased muscle tone. It is more likely that exophthalmos, both that induced experimentally by injection of thyrotrophin and that seen clinically in the human, is due to an increased bulk of the retro-ocular tissues. Smelser found in animals an increased bulk of the extrinsic ocular muscles and retro-ocular fat, due mainly to accumulation of fluid. The dorsal lacrimal gland (Harderian gland), which is not present in man, was enlarged. Pochin and others, in postmortem studies on the human, have found an increased bulk of periocular tissues; this was due largely to an increase of fat and mucopolysaccharides, and to an edema not associated with an excess of water in the tissues. The extraocular muscles were found to be swollen, edematous, and infiltrated with fat and lymphocytes. The lacrymal gland was enlarged. Although the above changes occur predominantly in the muscle of the

---

[2] Prolonged treatment with the thyroid hormone, as for obesity, may set up a thyrotoxic state, and exophthalmos sometimes develops as part of the syndrome. The exophthalmos, however, is not due to a direct effect of the administered hormone, but has the same pathogenesis as that of spontaneously developed Graves' disease.

eye they also occur, to a minor extent, in skeletal muscles.

In summary, the suspicion is very strong that a principle derived from the hypophysis is responsible for the increased volume of the orbital tissues, and thus for the exophthalmos occurring in Graves' disease.

*Malignant exophthalmos* is a very severe, and intractable form of exophthalmos, accompanied by ocular palsies. Brain prefers to call this condition *exophthalmic ophthalmoplegia*. The exophthalmos and weakness of the ocular muscles may be unilateral. The signs and symptoms of thyrotoxicosis are often mild, or, as after thyroidectomy, absent; in some cases, this severe form of exophthalmos occurs without evidence at any time of thyroid involvement. Proptosis of the eyeball is extreme, and drying of the corneal surface, ulceration or optic nerve injury is likely to result. The muscular weakness has been thought to be due to a coincident myasthenia gravis (which is not uncommonly associated with thyrotoxicosis), but its failure to be influenced by prostigmine disproves this supposition. It is probably due to stretching, and to infiltration and eventual fibrosis, of the muscles themselves.

*Retraction of the upper eyelid* is produced in a manner quite different from that which causes exophthalmos, being often present when the latter is absent. It is thought to be due either to increased tone of Mueller's *palpebral* muscle, which in conjunction with the levator palpebrae superioris elevates the upper lid, or to lessened opposition of striped muscle antagonists (orbicularis oculi) weakened by the action of excess thyroid hormone. The increased tone of Mueller's palpebral muscle is attributed to the action of the thyroid hormone in sensitizing this smooth muscle to adrenaline. Such action of the thyroid hormone upon sympathetically innervated structures is well known. Another example is the dilation of the pupil which occurs in hyperthyroid patients, but not in normal persons, when adrenaline is instilled into the conjunctival sac (Loewi's sign). The other lid signs are apparently due to a disorder of those muscles which constitute the lid-closure mechanism and are thus probably due to excess thyroid hormone and not to the thyrotrophic principle.

*The general muscular weakness* seen in thyrotoxicosis is of two types. One type is an associated but independent muscular dystrophy which has become aggravated by the thyrotoxicosis. In the other category the weakness of the muscles is the direct effect of the thyrotoxicosis; in this type

there is, as a rule, little muscular wasting. In both forms there is a defect in creatine-creatinine metabolism (p. 781); in the second, but not in the first, thyroidectomy, or the administration of iodine or of thiouracil abolishes the creatinuria.

## Toxic Adenoma

A simple adenomatous goiter (p. 1000) may undergo increased functional activity and produce the features of pure hyperthyroidism, i.e., those produced by the administration of thyroid extract in excessive amounts. The association of a benign secreting tumor (an adenoma), with signs of increased glandular function, may be seen not only in the thyroid but also in the case of the anterior pituitary (acidophile adenoma causing giantism or acromegaly), the adrenal cortex (Cushing's syndrome), the parathyroids (hyperparathyroidism), or the pancreatic islet tissue (hyperinsulinism).

Although many intermediate states of hyperthyroidism are seen clinically which show features of both Graves' disease and toxic adenoma, it is believed by most authorities that the two extreme conditions may be distinct. Graves' disease commonly occurs in young girls, the whole thyroid gland becomes diffusely enlarged and hyperactive, and exophthalmos is a prominent feature. Toxic adenomatous or nodular goiter on the other hand, often has its onset in elderly patients, the adenoma itself may be the only actively functioning part of the gland (the rest of the gland is often atrophic), eye complications are very rare, and the dominant signs are cardiac disturbances.

It may be mentioned here that hyperthyroidism can be, though rarely is, due to malignant tumors, carcinomata, of the thyroid. Secondary metastases in bone may maintain a hyperthyroid state even after complete thyroidectomy.

## Etiology of Hyperthyroid States

The etiology of adenomatous toxic goiter is akin to the etiology of any benign tumor formation, though why some adenomata remain nonsecretory and are termed 'simple' whereas others become functionally active and give rise to thyrotoxicosis, is unknown. The typical case of toxic nodular goiter is, then, explicable in terms of a small localized tumor or tumors in the thyroid gland which are autonomously secreting excess thyroid hormone. The raised concentration of thyroid hormone in the blood inhibits thyrotrophin secretion so that the remaining areas of the thyroid are inactive and atrophic. The absence of exophthalmos may also be explained on the grounds that the pituitary is not hyper-active in this condition.

The etiology of Graves' disease is unknown, but there is suggestive evidence that the immediate cause of the hyperthyroidism is a rise in the blood level of thyrotrophic hormone. The sudden diffuse enlargement of the thyroid which occurs, implies that some external stimulus has impinged upon the gland. This stimulus is unlikely to be nervous in type, since the thyroid appears to lack a secretomotor nerve supply. Of the blood-borne stimuli the most likely would appear to be an increased concentration of TSH. Direct data on this point were, until recently, absent since assay methods for measuring the blood concentration of TSH lacked the necessary sensitivity. In the last 10 years, however, improved methods have been used and several different groups of workers have found an increased blood level of TSH in some cases of Graves' disease. This is not a constant finding in all cases, and curiously seems to be related more to the degree of exophthalmos present than the hyperthyroidism. Recent work suggests that the thyrotrophic hormone found in some of these cases may have an abnormal action on the thyroid. It has been pointed out that a raised blood concentration of TSH in the presence of an increased concentration of thyroid hormone implies an extrathyroid defect in the feed-back mechanism. It should be mentioned that some authorities do not agree that the hyperthyroidism of Graves' disease is to be explained as a disorder of the anterior pituitary. Werner points out, for example, that patients with active toxic diffuse goiter are uniformly responsive to the administration of thyrotrophin, which would not be expected if a large excess of endogenous TSH were already present and maximally stimulating the gland.

A striking feature in the history of patients with Graves' disease is the frequency with which an emotional shock is reported preceding the onset of the condition. Studies have been made of the type of individual and type of emotional disturbance involved. It has been found that hyperthyroidism tends to develop in individuals who are highly dependent on their personal relationships with maternal or protective figures, and that it develops when this relationship is seriously threatened. It has been proposed that such psychological trauma might activate the hypothalamo-anterior pituitary mechanism, since it has been shown that lesions placed in the anterior hypothalamus of animals result in decreased secretion of thyrotrophin and decreased

thyroid activity, and that electrical stimulation of the same hypothalamic region results in increased thyroid activity in rabbits. Another factor which has been considered in respect to Graves' disease concerns the activity of the adrenal cortex. Marine pointed out that thyrotoxicosis in the human is often associated with signs of adrenal cortical underactivity (lymphoid hyperplasia and a large thymus) and a small adrenal cortex. It has since been observed that Graves' disease occurs more frequently in patients suffering from Addison's disease than in normal persons, may follow X-ray damage to the adrenals, and is associated with a low or normal level of urinary adrenal steroids. The surprising feature is that the urinary excretion of adrenal steroids in Graves' disease is not greatly increased since the emotional and physical state of these patients would appear to be a strong stimulus to adrenal cortical activity.

From the above discussion it may be tentatively proposed that emotional trauma, in the presence of a relative adrenal cortical deficiency, evokes increased discharge of thyrotrophin, thyroidal overactivity, and, thus, the condition of Graves' disease. Such a view does not exclude nutritional, genetic, or other factors from playing a role. The available data are at the moment inadequate to draw any definite conclusion.

## Iodine Metabolism

NATURAL OCCURRENCE OF IODINE. Since iodine forms an essential part of the thyroid hormone, it may be readily appreciated that a deficiency of iodine in the diet leads to disturbances of the thyroid gland, particularly to the development of goiter. Burnt seaweed or sponge, both of which are rich in iodine, have been employed in the treatment of goiter from the days of Hippocrates. Following the discovery of the element in the early part of the 19th century, its administration for the cure of many ills, but especially of goiter, became the vogue. But as a result of its indiscriminate use, the true value of iodine was lost sight of. Studies of the geographical distribution of cases of goiter again indicated the importance of iodine. Goiter is not seen along the seaboard. The sea contains an inexhaustible supply of iodine which has been leached from the soil. Sea water contains about 0.02 mg. of iodine per liter; fresh water, as a rule, very much less. The further away from the ocean and the more mountainous the country, the lower is the concentration of iodine in food and water and the higher in consequence is the incidence of goiter.

The accompanying schema modified from

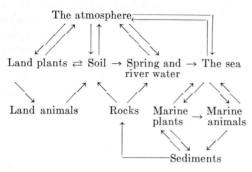

Lunde shows the distribution and circulation of iodine in Nature.

To Marine and his associates is due the credit for establishing the value of iodine in the prevention of goiter. They found that iodine or sea food prevented the thyroid enlargement in brook trout hatcheries. Marine and Kimball carried out experiments upon a large number of school children in Akron, Ohio, where goiter was endemic. They showed that of the group of children given iodine (2 grams of sodium iodide in 10 daily doses twice a year) those who developed goiter amounted to only a small fraction of the number of goitrous individuals in a control group in which the iodine intake was not increased above that of the general population. The employment of small amounts of iodine in goiter districts such as Switzerland, New Zealand, Derbyshire in England, and in parts of the United States and Canada has proved to be a preventive measure of the utmost value. Many preparations of table salt have this essential added in a proportion of 1 part in 10,000 or so. Once goiter has become established iodine administration is of much less value but, as already mentioned, a hyperplastic parenchymatous goiter may be converted thereby to the less severe colloid type. The ingestion of iodine in much larger amounts than those mentioned above may induce hyperactivity in a simple goiter.

Iodine in the form of Lugol's solution[3] (10 to 40 minims daily) produces temporary amelioration in cases of exophthalmic goiter, and for this reason is used, together with antithyroid drugs, in the preparation of patients for partial thyroidectomy. The amount of colloid in the gland increases and the vascularity decreases (fig. 57.4). Such treatment has markedly improved the operative mortality and almost eliminated the risk of a postoperative thyroid crisis. The bene-

[3] Iodine, 1 gram; potassium iodide, 2 grams; water, 30 cc.

ficial action of iodine in Graves' disease has been a puzzling problem and more than one theory has been proposed to account for it. It is possible that iodine inactivates thyrotrophin or interferes with the action of thyrotrophin on the thyroid, or that it inhibits a proteolytic enzyme involved in the release of thyroxine from the gland.

IODINE REQUIREMENTS AND METABOLISM. The following figures, quoted by Riggs, are representative for the normal adult: daily intake of iodine, 150 $\mu$g.; urinary excretion, 144 $\mu$g. per day, and fecal excretion, 6 $\mu$g. per day. Iodine is readily absorbed from the gastrointestinal tract and through the skin. The normal concentration of inorganic iodide in the serum is 1 $\mu$g. per 100 cc.

Studies on the metabolic path of iodine have been greatly aided by the use of radioactive iodine. Physiologically negligible amounts of the latter may be administered, too minute in themselves to affect the metabolism of iodine in the body, and the pathway of the isotope in the organism followed with ease by use of the sensitive counters and scaling equipment available. Following administration of tracer doses of $I^{131}$ it has been found that radioactive iodine distributes in the blood and extracellular fluids and is accumulated by the thyroid and excreted by the kidney. After oral administration the blood concentration reaches a peak in 1 hour and then declines exponentially; the rate of fall depending on thyroid activity and renal excretion. Both the thyroid and the kidney remove $I^{131}$ from the blood at a rate dependent on the plasma concentration. The amount excreted by the kidney varies with thyroidal activity. After thyroidectomy or administration of antithyroid drugs the renal excretion of $I^{131}$ may reach 98 per cent of the administered dose. On the other hand, in hyperthyroidism, the thyroid may accumulate a greater proportion of $I^{131}$ than the kidney. Iodide is also normally concentrated and secreted by the salivary glands and gastric mucosa, but little of this finds its way into the feces since it is reabsorbed in the intestines. After incorporation in the thyroid gland into hormonal form, it is secreted as part of the hormone molecule, a proportion of which will be degraded in the tissues with liberation of iodide. This iodide will then recirculate a second time, and is again partly accumulated by the thyroid and partly excreted by the kidneys.

A deficiency of iodine in the diet leads to the development of simple goiter. The deficiency may be (a) *an absolute deficiency* in drinking water and food, (b) *a relative deficiency*, the iodine of the food being sufficient for the elaboration of the amount of hormone required under the ordinary circumstances of life but insufficient under more exacting conditions, e.g., puberty, pregnancy, excessive protein of the diet, etc., and (c) it is also possible that certain microorganisms in the intestinal tract may reduce the quantity of iodine absorbed from the food; this would explain McCarrison's observations upon the relationship between the incidence of goiter in India and infected drinking water. It is more likely, however, that infected water, if it does sometimes play a part in the production of goiter, acts in some other way than by merely interfering with the absorption of iodine.

The quantity of iodine in the normal human thyroid is about 2 mg. per gram of dried tissue; the average total store in the gland is from 10 to 15 mg. A content below 1 mg. per gram of dry gland, according to Marine, is indicative of definite thyroid abnormality; in severe parenchymatous goiter, either simple or exophthalmic, it may be as low as 0.25 mg. or less per gram. In colloid goiters the general level is higher. Marine considers all goitrous enlargements, as examples of "a compensatory work hypertrophy," brought about by iodine deficiency. The demands made upon the gland to produce its hormone without an adequate iodine supply results in hypertrophy and hyperplasia, or adenomatous growth, and in some instances, final exhaustion and atrophy. The different types of simple goiter are looked upon as stages in a process which is responsive to the iodine supplies, the gland sometimes passing several times through a cycle of hypertrophic, hyperplastic, and colloid changes; or the cycle may end in atrophy. The successive stages are represented in the following schema after Marine. According to Rawson the thyroid may, in some instances, become restored to normal from the colloid goitrous state.

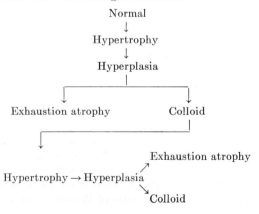

UPTAKE OF IODIDE BY THE THYROID GLAND. The thyroid gland was shown some years ago by Marine to have a remarkable affinity for iodine. Though constituting only about 0.05 per cent or so of the body weight, the gland contains about half of the body's entire iodine content. The rest of the body's iodine store is contained mainly in the skeletal muscles. The entire blood contains less than a milligram. Marine observed that when the thyroid was perfused with a solution of potassium iodide, relatively large quantities of iodine were taken up by the gland and could not be removed by subsequent washing. This result was not obtained by the perfusion of other organs, e.g., spleen, kidney, etc. The selective action of the intact thyroid for ingested iodine was also demonstrated. Over 18 per cent of iodine fed to normal animals was recovered from the gland; the fetal gland also stores iodine fed to the mother.

If a smaller tracer dose of $I^{131}$ (2 to 4 $\mu c.$) be administered to an animal such as a rabbit, an immediate, slow, steady increase of $I^{131}$ in the thyroid gland follows and reaches a peak after about 30 hours. The $I^{131}$ is taken up from the blood in the inorganic (iodide) form, converted into organic compounds and stored as thyroglobulin. If di-iodotyrosine or thyroxine is injected instead, then the uptake of iodine by the thyroid is delayed and occurs only after the organic compound is degraded and iodide released. The partial visualization of these processes has been made possible by the use of the radioautographic technique. Radioiodine in contact with a photographic emulsion acts upon it to give a dark mark: when the emulsion is spread upon a microscopic section of thyroid tissue which has taken up the isotope, the latter's position in relation to the histological structure can be observed (fig. 57.8). Leblond and Gross used this technique to investigate the site of $I^{131}$ in the thyroid at various time intervals after injection of the isotope into rats and guinea pigs. It was found that with animals on a high iodine diet the radioactivity in the thyroid was mostly present in the epithelial cells at 1 hour and in the colloid at 24 hours after injection. If the animals were placed on a low iodine diet, or thyroid activity was increased by injection of thyrotrophin, the deposition of radioactivity in the colloid was much accelerated since it was found there as early as 2 minutes after injection. These results imply that the chemical conversion of iodide to thyroglobulin occurs with rapidity in the thyroid gland. Two main steps may then be recognized in the formation of hor-

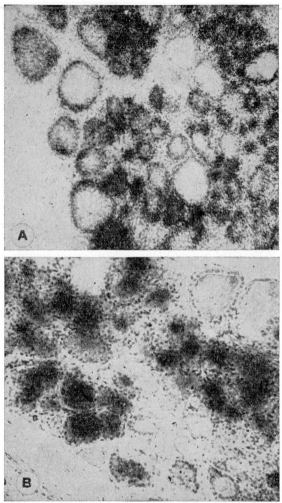

Fig. 57.8. Radioautographs of rat thyroids stained with hematoxylin and eosin. The location of radioactivity is indicated by the accumulations of black granules. In these sections the radioactivity is present as radioactive iodine incorporated in the thyroglobulin molecule. *A*, Thyroid of a rat sacrificed 1 hour after injection of radioiodine. In most of the follicles the radioactivity is arranged in the form of rings because the newly-formed radioactive thyroglobulin is present in the epithelium of the thyroid follicle. *B*, Thyroid of a rat sacrificed 24 hours after injection of radioiodine. The photographic reaction is present over the colloid of the thyroid follicles indicating that the thryoglobulin formed in the cells at 1 hour is deposited in the colloid some 24 hours later. (From Leblond and Gross; kindness of Dr. C. P. Leblond.)

mone in the thyroid. First, the accumulation of inorganic iodide from the blood stream by thyroid cells. This avidity of the gland for iodine occurs against a concentration gradient and is said to be due to an *iodide-trapping mechanism* on the part of the gland. And second, the conversion of the iodide into organic combination and storage as thyroglobulin. These two processes may be separately and individually blocked by different pharmacological agents. Thiocyanates, perchlorates, and other anions block the iodide-trapping activity of the thyroid, whereas various thiocarbonamides and other compounds (see pp.

1012–1013) do not interfere with the iodide-concentrating ability of the thyroid but do inhibit the organic binding of the iodide (therefore, any iodide taken up by the gland is not converted into hormonal form but remains as inorganic iodide). The use of an antithyroid drug of this latter type makes it possible to measure the iodide-trapping ability of the thyroid. After blocking organic binding by administration of a drug such as propylthiouracil, a dose of $I^{131}$ is given and, 1 hour later, the animal is killed and the concentration of $I^{131}$ measured in the serum and in the thyroid. The ratio of thyroid-serum $I^{131}$

concentration (T/S ratio) gives a measure of the ability of the gland to accumulate iodide. Blockage of organic binding is necessary, otherwise part of the $I^{131}$ accumulated by the thyroid would be secreted as hormone and lost to the gland. Typical values for the T/S ratio in the rat are about 50 in the normal animal, 250 for the animal under the influence of excess thyrotrophin, and about 2 after hypophysectomy.

### THE FORMATION OF THYROID HORMONE

A glycerine extract of sheep's thyroids was first employed successfully by the English physician George Murray in 1891, for the relief of myxedema. The thyroid tissue itself when given by mouth was shown subsequently to be physiologically active. Baumann in 1896, discovered that iodine was an important constituent of the thyroid extract. By acid hydrolysis of thyroid tissue, and later by peptic digestion, he obtained a brownish powder containing 10 per cent of iodine and possessing the physiological activity of the whole gland. He believed that the iodine was present in organic combination and named the compound *iodothyrin*. It was shown subsequently by Oswald (1899) that the active iodine constituent was attached to a protein, *thyroglobulin*, which is the chief component of the colloid material filling the alveoli of the gland. Thyroglobulin contains both di-iodotyrosine and thyroxine joined to the protein molecule by peptide linkages. It is looked upon as the storage form of the thyroid hormone.

The active principle of the thyroid was isolated in crystalline form by Kendall in 1919. He named the substance *thyroxin*[4] and found that it contained 65 per cent of iodine and an amino group. Harington and Barger in 1927, established the chemical form of thyroxine and effected its synthesis. It was found to be constituted of 2 benzene rings united by an oxygen bridge, and to contain four atoms of iodine and an amino acid (alanine) side chain. The synthesis required a number of separate steps.

3:5-Di-iodo-4-(4'-methoxyphenoxy)benzaldehyde contains iodine atoms in the same positions as two of those in natural thyroxine.

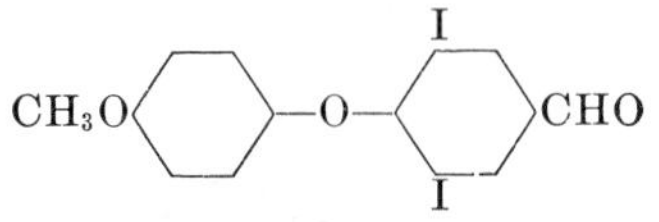

3:5-Di-iodo-4-(4'-methoxyphenoxy)benzaldehyde

This compound having been prepared, the amino group was attached by condensation with hippuric acid. The resulting compound was boiled with NaOH in alcohol and then with acetic anhydride and hydriodic acid. The product of these procedures, *3:5-di-iodothyronine*, readily takes up 2 additional atoms of iodine with the formation of thyroxine, when treated with a concentrated solution of iodine in potassium iodide (see formula).

Synthetic thyroxine possesses physiological properties identical with those of the natural product.

3:5:3'-Tri-iodothyronine has also been found to be physiologically active. It has in fact greater activity than thyroxine in preventing thiouracil-induced goiter in rats and in stimulating oxygen consumption in various forms. Gross and Pitt-Rivers in 1952, produced strong evidence that this compound was identical with an unknown factor previously found to be present in rat thyroid and blood. These same workers managed to isolate tri-iodothyronine from the thyroid. In simultaneous and independent studies, Roche and coworkers were able to synthesize 3:5:3'-tri-iodothyronine and also to detect its presence in hydrolysates of rat thyroid tissue. These studies have been confirmed and tri-iodothyronine has now been identified in the thyroid of the human and other forms, in human blood and in the venous blood from the thyroid of the sheep, horse, and calf. There can be no doubt that it should be included with thyroxine as a hormone secreted by the thyroid gland.

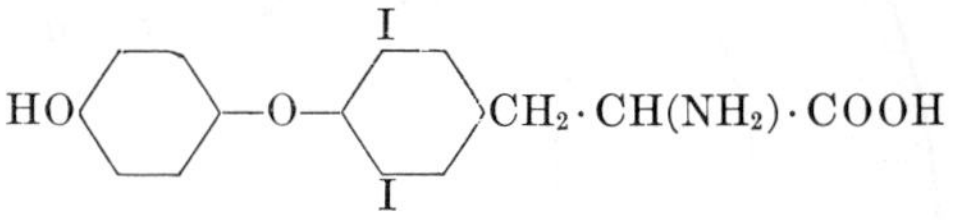

3:5-di-iodothyronine

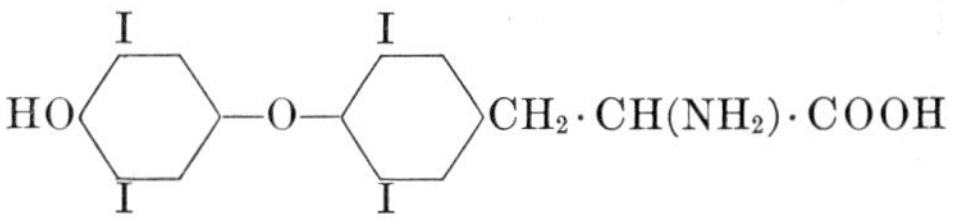

Thyroxine (3:5:3':5'-tetraiodothyronine)[5]

Thyroxine is formed in the thyroid gland from di-iodotyrosine.

[5] The numbering of the positions in the thyronine nucleus is shown below.

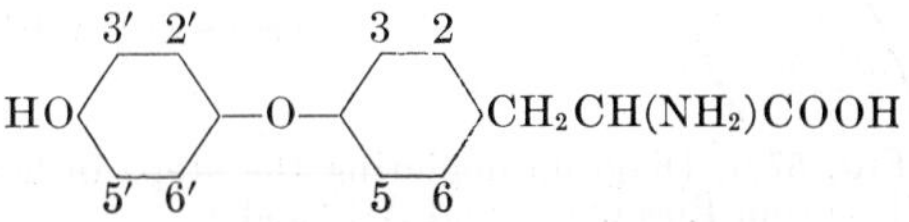

---

[4] Now spelled thyroxine.

HO⟨⟩CH₂CH(NH₂)COOH

(structure with I at top and I at bottom of ring)

### Di-iodotyrosine

This compound is formed in the body from tyrosine (fig. 57.9) and certainly represents a stage in the synthesis of thyroxine; when added to slices of surviving thyroid tissue di-iodotyrosine is converted to thyroxine. Di-iodotyrosine itself has only slight physiological activity. Most of the organic iodine in the thyroid is in this form, a much smaller part being present as thyroxine. Four separate processes (see fig. 57.9) or steps are required for the synthesis of thyroxine, (a) the concentration of iodide in the gland, (b) the oxidation of iodide to elemental iodine, (c) the combination of iodine with tyrosine, and (d) the oxidative coupling of di-iodotyrosine molecules, forming a diphenyl ether with the loss of one alanine side chain. The thyrotrophic hormone (TSH) of the pituitary gland appears to be neces-

sary for all four steps. The mechanism responsible for the oxidative reactions, second and third steps, is not definitely known, but the most probable theory which has been proposed is that both the iodination of tyrosine and the coupling of two molecules of di-iodotyrosine are effected through an enzyme system in which *peroxidase* plays an essential part. Fine granules in the thyroid cells which give the histochemical reaction characteristic of peroxidase have been described by Dempsey. The enzyme has not, so far, however, been extracted from thyroid tissue; but in support of this theory is the fact that such antithyroid drugs as thiourea and thiouracil inhibit peroxidase action. An experiment performed by Keston is of great interest and suggests the type of reaction that may take place in the thyroid gland. When radioactive iodide was added with xanthine to milk and the mixture incubated, thyroxine containing the isotope was formed. The xanthine oxidase in the milk, acting presumably upon the xanthine, liberated hydrogen peroxide which in

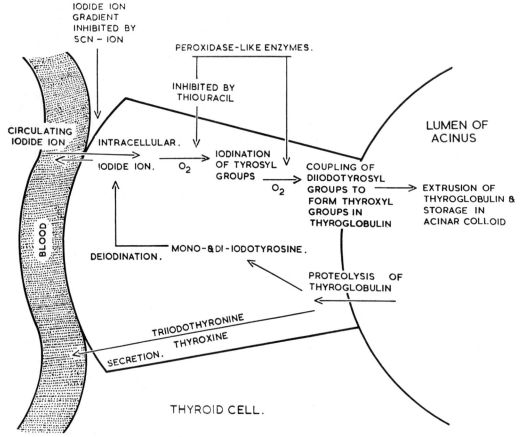

Fig. 57.9. Diagram depicting the steps in hormone synthesis, storage, and secretion by a thyroid cell. (From Rosenberg and Astwood.)

the presence of milk peroxidase oxidized the iodide to iodine which was introduced into tyrosine groups. Thyroxine was then formed by the coupling of di-iodotyrosine molecules. If thiourea were added before incubation no thyroxine was formed.

Additional evidence for the peroxidase theory is afforded by the observation of Harington that hydrogen peroxide hastens the *in vitro* iodination of protein (see below).

Other enzyme systems, e.g., cytochrome and tyrosinase, have been suggested as playing the chief role in thyroxine synthesis, but this is unlikely, for the cytochrome system is not inhibited by thiourea or thiouracil. Tyrosinase has not been demonstrated in thyroid tissue nor does the inhibition of its action by thiourea derivatives run parallel with the antithyroid activity of these drugs.

The formation of tri-iodothyronine in the thyroid could be effected by the coupling of one

$$HO\text{—}\langle\text{—}\rangle\text{—}O\text{—}\langle\text{—}\rangle\text{—}CH_2\cdot CH(NH_2)\cdot COOH$$

3:5:3'-tri-iodothyronine

molecule of monoiodotyrosine with one molecule of di-iodotyrosine, or by the removal of iodine from thyroxine.

For further information on the thyroid hormone the monograph of Pitt-Rivers and Tata may be consulted.

## EXTRATHYROIDAL SYNTHESIS OF HORMONE

It has been suggested that tissues in the body, other than the thyroid gland, can manufacture small amounts of thyroid hormone. Such a view was suggested on the grounds that thyroidectomized rats fed on a high iodine diet show a slightly higher consumption of oxygen than similar animals on a low iodine diet. It was also claimed that thyroxine could be isolated from tissues of thyroidectomized animals. However, these findings have not been substantiated. Although certain tissues, such as that of the lactating mammary gland and the gastric mucosa, concentrate iodine and may contain a fraction of this in organic form, it is to be doubted whether compounds with the activities of thyroid hormone are formed in this manner. Such a possibility is of little practical significance, since complete thyroidectomy is followed by myxedema.

## *The Iodination of Protein and the Artificial Synthesis of Thyroxine*

The remarkable discovery was made some years ago that the iodination of casein, serum protein, and other proteins, followed by hydrolysis, yielded crystals of thyroxine possessing the characteristic physiological activity. The first experiments in which the *in vitro* synthesis of thyroxine was demonstrated were performed by Abelin. His results were published in a series of papers from 1934 to 1938. His claim was not, however, generally accepted until the same result was obtained by Ludwig and Mutzenbecher in 1939. They gave an account of the method, a clear chemical description of the product obtained, and described its physiological property. It was also shown that a small amount of thyroxine was formed spontaneously simply by prolonged incubation in alkaline solution. These findings were soon confirmed by Harington and Rivers and in several other laboratories. Iodinized protein causes all the physiological effects of thyroid extract, relieves myxedema, and in large doses induces thyrotoxicosis.

## *The Storage and Release of Thyroid Hormone*

It is likely that the iodination of tyrosine in the thyroid gland occurs when the amino acid is incorporated in protein rather than when it is in the free state. Studies of the iodine containing compounds in the thyroid gland, after injection of $I^{131}$, suggest that thyroxine is first produced as the bound form in thyroglobulin and that the free hormone is formed subsequently. The characteristics of the thyroglobulin molecule may in some way facilitate the formation of hormonally active iodothyronines as end groups in the protein molecule, and their attachment in loose surface bonds may be related to the regulation of the rate of hormone secretion.

Thyroglobulin has a high molecular weight (about 650,000), a fairly constant amino acid composition, but an iodine content that varies with the functional state of the gland from which the protein was extracted. Recent studies indicate that even within the thyroid gland of a single animal the thyroglobulin is not completely homogenous. If different thyroglobulins exist it is possible that they are the products of different follicles in a gland, that are in varying states of functional activity.

The fact that the thyroid hormone is stored in combination with a protein and that simpler molecules, thyroxine and tri-iodothyronine, form

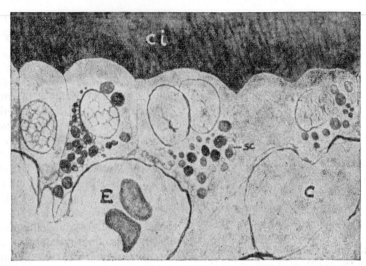

FIG. 57.10. Cells of the thyroid of a rat which had been injected 22 hours previously with the thyroid stimulating hormone (TSH) of the pituitary. The intracellular droplets of colloid are increased in number and are collected toward the basal part of the cell from where they are discharged into the capillaries. The first effect of TSH, within 30 minutes or so, is to cause an increase in intracellular colloid which is accumulated toward that part of the cell abutting on the follicular lumen. The reversal of the direction of the movement of the droplets, i.e., from the free to the basal part of the cell commences in about 6 hours after the administration of TSH. $ci$, Colloid in lumen of the follicle; $c$, capillary; $E$, erythrocyte in capillary. From De Robertis.)

the circulating hormone leads to the question whether a proteolytic enzyme exists in thyroid tissue by which the thyroglobulin is broken down to permit the smaller thyroxine molecule to enter the circulation. Such an enzyme has been demonstrated by De Robertis in the colloid of the gland, and was found to increase in activity by 100 per cent in thyrotoxicosis and to be reduced in hypothyroidism. The thyrotrophic hormone of the pituitary activates this enzyme as the researches of De Robertis have demonstrated. Within a few minutes after the injection of TSH, droplets appear in the cells lining the alveoli of the gland. These intracellular droplets appear to be different in composition from the colloid of the alveoli and are believed to be composed of smaller molecules derived from hydrolysis of the latter (fig. 57.10).

*Pharmacological Agents and Hormone Synthesis*

In 1928, Chesney and his associates observed that rabbits which were on a diet of cabbage became goitrous. Other members of the *Brassica* family, e.g., cauliflower, Brussels sprouts, etc., are also goitrogenic. Rape seed was also found by Kennedy and Purves to cause goiter in man. Cases of goiter in man resulting from a diet containing a large proportion of cabbage have been reported. A characteristic of vegetables of the *Brassica* family is their relatively high content of cyanogen compounds. Taking this hint Marine and his associates gave various cyanides to rabbits and obtained a marked thyroid enlargement; methyl cyanide was especially effective. The thyroid hyperplasia was accompanied by exophthalmos. Marine suggested that the goitrogenic effect of cyanides was dependent on their property of depressing tissue oxidations, increased thyroid function being a compensatory effect instituted to oppose this action. The effect of cyanide on the thyroid more probably reflects the fact that the iodide-trapping mechanism requires energy. *In vitro* studies with surviving thyroid tissue showed that cyanide inhibits this mechanism.

The goitrogenic activities of the above foodstuffs fall into at least two classes. The goitrogenic action of a cabbage diet may be inhibited by administration of iodide, whereas the goitrogenic action of brassica seeds is not reversed by iodide but can be inhibited by thyroxine administration.

It has been mentioned above (p. 1008) that the chemical processes concerned in the synthesis of hormone in the thyroid gland may be blocked at two separate points by different pharmacological agents: (a) Thiocyanates inhibit the process by which the thyroid gland extracts iodide ions from the blood. The goitrogenic action of thiocyanate is inhibited by iodide administration. (b) Drugs, such as thiouracil, block the process by which the gland binds iodide into organic combination. The goitrogenic action of these drugs is not inhibited by iodide administration but is reversed by giving thyroxine.

1. THIOCYANATES AND THE IODIDE-TRAPPING MECHANISM. Potassium thiocyanate is a more recently discovered goitrogen than the cyanide compounds of Marine. It is a normal metabolite and, it will be recalled, is excreted in the saliva. Its action on the thyroid was first observed by Barker in two patients under treatment with the drug for hypertension. Goiters developed in these cases. In rats, thiocyanate inhibits the uptake of iodide by the gland and thereby causes goiter. The primary action of this drug appears to be on the iodide-trapping mechanism. In spite of its avidity for iodide, the normal thyroid gland contains very little inorganic iodide since the iodide is rapidly incorporated into organic form. If this organic binding is blocked with a drug such as propylthiouracil, inorganic iodide accumulates in the thyroid. In such a gland, which has accumulated a quantity of inorganic $I^{131}$, thiocyanate evokes a prompt discharge of $I^{131}$ through the inhibitory effect it exerts on the iodide "pump" of the gland. Chronic administration of thiocyanate results in reduced iodide uptake by the thyroid, a reduced rate of hormone synthesis, a fall in blood level of thyroid hormone and, thereby, an increased secretion of TSH and the development of a goiter. It is of interest that the uptake of iodine and the rate of synthesis and release of hormone may be returned toward normal values in the thiocyanate-treated animal by increasing the iodine intake. Presumably, the increased concentration of iodide in the blood allows sufficient halogen to enter the gland by diffusion. Other anions, such as chlorate, perchlorate, hypochlorite, iodate, periodate, bi-iodate, and nitrate have a similar effect on the thyroid to thiocyanate.

2. ANTITHYROID DRUGS AND THE ORGANIC COMBINATION OF IODIDE. In 1941, Mackenzie and coworkers reported the goitrogenic action of sulfaguanidine, and in 1943, the same group, and also Astwood and his colleagues, gave an account of the effects of some sulfonamides and thioureas on

the thyroid. Because of the possible clinical significance of such compounds a great deal of work was undertaken to find antithyroid drugs that are nontoxic. Over 100 drugs possessing antithyroid activity to varying degrees have now been discovered. In general they fall into two groups, those with a thiocarbonamide grouping (thiourea, thiouracil) and those with a substituted benzene ring (p-aminobenzoic acid, sulfonamides, phloroglucinol).

These antithyroid drugs inhibit the synthesis of thyroid hormone by preventing the binding of iodide ions into organic compounds. This results in an increased concentration of inorganic iodide, and a fall in hormone content of the gland. A fall in concentration of thyroid hormone in the blood follows, with a consequent increased rate of secretion of pituitary thyrotrophin and all the anatomical and histological changes in the thyroid normally produced by excess TSH. That the goitrous and hyperplastic changes in the thyroid produced by antithyroid drugs are mediated by the pituitary is shown by the fact that they do not occur in hypophysectomized animals and that they are inhibited by simultaneous administration of exogenous thyroxine. The degree of inhibition is quantitatively related to the dose of thyroxine, and measurement of the least amount of thyroxine that prevents hyperplasia of the thyroid gives a method for estimating the normal daily secretion of thyroid hormone. Thyroxine and allied compounds are thus said to possess *antigoitrogenic properties*. However, the direct action of antithyroid drugs in blocking iodide-combining activity and their indirect goitrogenic action should be clearly distinguished. There is no evidence that these compounds affect the other actions of the thyroid such as the iodide-trapping mechanism or the release of preformed thyroid hormone. It has been suggested by Pitt-Rivers that the thiocarbonamide group of antithyroid drugs exert their direct effect by keeping the iodine in the gland in a reduced state. However, this view could not account for the action of the sulfonamides or resorcinol compounds, and it is now generally believed that all the antithyroid drugs act by inhibiting the peroxidase enzyme system in the thyroid.

A species difference exists in the action of the drugs of the benzene derivative class. Whereas the members of the thiocarbonamide group appear effective in all forms, those of the benzene group are active in the rat and mouse but much less so in the chick and human.

Rawson and his associates have produced evi-

Thiourea

2-Thiouracil

dence that the thiol compounds have a further direct effect on thyroid tissue, that is that they augment the action of TSH on the gland. The thyroids of rats given thiouracil for only 24 hours showed hyperplasia at the end of this period, yet no fall in the blood level of protein-bound iodine occurred. This finding would be compatible with the observed augmentation of the action of TSH already in the circulation. Further, TSH and thiouracil given simultaneously to cockerels produced a greater increase in acinar-cell height than TSH alone.

Antithyroid drugs are used clinically either on a short term basis, to prepare a thyrotoxic patient for operation, or on a long term basis, in an attempt to control hyperthyroidism without resource to surgery or radioactive iodine treatment. However, it should be remembered that prolonged treatment with these compounds [such as propylthiouracil or methimazole (1-methyl-2-mercaptoimidazole)] does result, in rare cases, in toxic effects such as agranulocytosis, and that even though the remission of the thyrotoxic state has been induced for several years by drug therapy, cessation of administration results in recurrence of hyperthyroidism in about half the cases.

### THE SECRETION AND TRANSPORT OF THYROID HORMONE

It has been mentioned above that thyroxine is formed in the thyroid gland as part of the thyroglobulin molecule. Only a small part of the thyroxine in the gland is in the free form (less than 1 per cent) and this probably represents the immediate source of serum thyroxine. The secretion of hormone from the gland to the blood seems to involve an enzymatic proteolysis of thyroglobulin in the gland, with liberation of free thyroxine which enters the blood stream. The rate of release of hormone from the thyroid is very largely regulated by pituitary thyrotrophin, and present data indicate that the first effect of TSH on thyroid function is to increase the rate of release of hormone. Studies on the radioactive content of thyroid vein blood have shown that, in such forms as the rabbit and cat, this may occur in less than half an hour. From this evidence it might be suggested that the primary action of TSH on the thyroid is to regulate the release of thyroidal hormone, and that the other effects are secondary to this. However, it should not be forgotten that TSH evokes thyroid hypertrophy when hormonal synthesis has been blocked with antithyroid drugs.

After the discovery of thyroglobulin and thyroxine in the thyroid gland it was thought that the hormone secreted into the blood might be a polypeptide. Harington discussed this possibility with the facts in mind that the physiological potency of whole thyroid substance did not seem explainable in terms of its thyroxine content (now explained by the presence of the more potent tri-iodothyronine in thyroid tissue), and that thyroid hormone in the blood is precipitated by protein precipitants (now explained by the binding of thyroxine to plasma protein; see below). Immunological studies showed that only in exceptional circumstances (associated with thyroid disease and damage) was thyroglobulin present in the circulation. In 1948, Taurog and Chaikoff showed that thyroid hormone labelled with $I^{131}$ in the circulation behaved in an identical way to thyroxine added to the blood. It is now generally accepted that the thyroid hormone in the circulation is thyroxine together with a small amount of tri-iodothyronine.

The normal rate of secretion of thyroid hormone has been estimated in a variety of ways; by measuring (a) the amount of thyroxine necessary to restore to a normal state the thyroidectomized animal, or thyroidectomized or myxedematous patient, (b) the smallest quantity of thyroxine to give a maximal depression of the thyroidal uptake of $I^{131}$ or of the thyroidal release of $I^{131}$-labelled hormone, (c) the minimum quantity of thyroxine necessary to prevent enlargement of the thyroid, or cytological changes in the pituitary after treatment with antithyroid drugs, and (d) the rate of accumulation of iodide by the gland. The most direct method of assessing thyroid activity (the amount of hormone liberated per unit time) would be to measure the blood flow through the gland and the hormone content of the arterial blood passing to, and the venous blood leaving, the gland. Such measurements can be made, but unfortunately the stress of the manipulations involved, anesthesia and manipulative trauma, result in a rapid reduction of thyroid function. Average figures for the daily secretion of thyroxine are 0.2 to 5.2 $\mu$g. per 100 grams of body weight per day in the chicken, rat, rabbit, goat, cow, and man. In absolute figures, the rat secretes about 8 $\mu$g. of thyroxine per day, the rabbit about 18 $\mu$g. per day, and the human about 200 to 300 $\mu$g. per day. The larger the animal, the less hormone (on a weight basis) is secreted per day. This may be correlated with the fact that the greater the body weight, the less the surface area of the body per unit weight and, thus, the less is the heat loss per unit weight. The amount of hormone secreted per day will of course vary widely in the normal animal according to environmental conditions. Thus, Dempsey and Astwood found that the normal rat secretes 9.5 μg. of thyroxine per 100 grams of body weight per day at an environmental temperature of 1°C., 5.2 μg. per 100 grams per day at 25°C., and 1.7 μg. per 100 grams per day at 35°C.

The concentration of thyroid hormone in the blood is probably maintained at a more constant level than is the rate of secretion of hormone from the gland. This is because the blood level represents a balance between the rate of secretion and the rate of metabolism or excretion of the hormone. Iodine exists in the blood stream as inorganic iodide and as organically-combined iodine. This latter is precipitated by protein precipitants and is commonly referred to as protein-bound iodine (PBI). The PBI represents largely hormonal iodine and has an average value in the normal human of 4 to 8 μg. per 100 cc. of serum. In cases of hyperthyroidism this figure may rise to 20 μg. per 100 cc. or over, and in myxedema fall to 1 μg. per 100 cc. It is important to note that misleadingly high figures are obtained if the patient has been treated previously with large quantities of iodide or with organic iodine compounds such as those used in X-ray diagnosis.

Thyroxine is carried in the blood stream bound to serum proteins. An $\alpha$-globulin has the highest binding affinity for thyroxine and is commonly referred to as thyroxine binding protein (TBP). If the amount of thyroxine in serum is raised, increasing amounts of thyroxine become bound to albumin. The "binding" of thyroxine to plasma proteins must be clearly distinguished from the peptide linkage uniting thyroxine to thyroglobulin in the thyroid gland. The fact that butanol extracts thyroxine from serum shows that only a relatively loose attachment between thyroxine and TBP occurs. The protein binding of thyroid hormones in serum may modify their peripheral action. It is possible that the lower affinity of TBP for tri-iodotyronine, than for thyroxine, may account for the faster, greater, and shorter-lived physiological activity of tri-iodothyronine. Also conditions in which the plasma proteins are decreased or increased in amounts may affect the blood concentration of thyroid hormone. Thus in nephrosis low blood levels of TBP and PBI coexist, and during pregnancy the reverse is the case. In nephrotic patients signs of hypothyroidism are commonly present; in pregnancy a diet relatively low in iodine may result in goiter.

## THE ACTIONS OF THYROID HORMONE

Many of the actions of thyroid hormone in the human were given at the beginning of this chapter when the clinical pictures of hyper- and hypothyroidism were described. The experimental investigation of the physiological effects exerted by the thyroid gland has likewise involved the study of hypothyroid states (produced by surgical or chemical thyroidectomy) and their repair, and hyperthyroid states (produced by administration of thyroxine or tri-iodothyronine). The qualitative effects produced by thyroxine and tri-iodothyronine are similar, but tri-iodothyronine acts more quickly, is usually (according to the effect studied) the more potent of the two compounds, and has a shorter-lived action. The long latent period of action of thyroxine at one time gave rise to the view that thyroxine was not the hormone secreted by the gland. After it was established that tri-iodothyronine is a normal secretion product of the thyroid the possibility was considered that thyroxine was converted into tri-iodothyronine in the tissues, and formed, therefore, a "precursor" of the hormone. However, the evidence is now strong that both thyroxine and tri-iodothyronine are secreted by the gland and that both substances act as such at a tissue level.

1. HEAT PRODUCTION; CALORIGENESIS. Magnus and Levy in 1895, first described the low oxygen consumption of patients with myxedema and showed that thyroid feeding raised the basal oxygen intake in the human. The effect of a single administration of thyroxine upon the basal metabolic rate is slowly developed but prolonged (fig. 57.11); it commences after a lapse of 12 to 48 hours, reaches its maximum in 8 to 10 days, and lasts for 5 or 6 weeks. Thyroxine brings about the combustion of a relatively enormous amount of material; 1 mg. causes the total $CO_2$ output to increase by some 400 grams and the heat production to increase by about 1000 calories. In the athyroid human the basal metabolic rate may be only one-half the normal value, whereas in severe thyrotoxicosis it may be double. To maintain a normal basal metabolic rate in myxedema requires the daily administration of about 200 to 300 μg. of *l*-thyroxine.

*In vitro* studies of the oxygen consumption of tissues taken from animals rendered hyper- or hypothyroid show that these tissues have an increased or decreased exchange, respectively. Thus the calorigenic action of thyroid hormone is exerted directly on the cells rather than through the

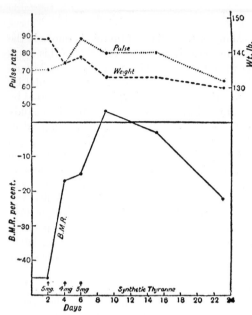

Fig. 57.11. Effect of thyroxine on a myxedematous patient. (From Harington.)

nervous system. It should be noted that if thyroxine is added to the incubation medium containing tissue taken from a normal animal, no calorigenic effect is observed.

Such obvious mental changes are observed in Graves' disease and myxedema that thyroxine might be expected to exert a marked effect on cerebral metabolism. However, this does not seem to be the case since the respiratory metabolism of tissue from the brains of rats rendered hyper-

or hypothyroid is normal. In this respect brain tissue behaves differently from other bodily tissues. Similarly, the cerebral oxygen consumption of thyrotoxic patients is not increased, although oxygen and glucose consumption of the brain has been reported as low in myxedema.

The various effects of the thyroid hormone upon the development and differentiation of skeletal, nervous, and other tissues cannot be explained by its property of increasing combustion in the cells; a substance such as dinitrophenol, which increases heat production, has no such action.

2. GROWTH AND DIFFERENTIATION. The earliest and clearest evidence that the thyroid is closely concerned with tissue differentiation came from the experiments of Gudernatsch in 1912. He showed that feeding thyroid tissue to frog tadpoles resulted in early metamorphosis and the production of small frogs. Later studies showed that thyroidectomized tadpoles fail to metamorphose and develop into abnormally large larval forms. The human cretin, besides showing retardation of growth, shows marked failure in the maturation of the skeletal and other bodily systems. The growth process is influenced both by growth hormone (STH) from the anterior pituitary and by thyroid hormone (fig. 57.12), whereas the process of maturation and differentiation (formation of ossification centers in the epiphyses, eruption of primary and secondary dentition) is more solely influenced by the thyroid hormone. For example, hypophysectomized young rats treated with growth hormone show

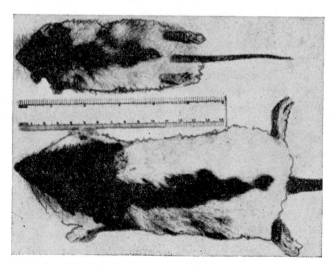

Fig. 57.12. Showing the effect of thiourea on growth. Above, 84-day-old cretin rat (50 grams) from a mother which had been treated with thiourea for the entire gestation period. Below, normal untreated animal (160 grams) of the same age. (From Goldsmith and associates.)

bony growth but abnormal development of epiphyses whereas treatment of similar animals with thyroxine results in slight growth of the bones but marked stimulation of epiphyseal development and bony maturation. The growth and development of the brain appears to be particularly dependent on thyroid hormone. The retarded mentality or imbecility of the cretin may not be completely reversible by treatment with thyroxine even though therapy is started in the first year of life. Experimental studies have shown that young animals rendered hypothyroid, surgically or with drugs, show impaired growth of the brain, decreased size of cortical neurones, a decreased density of the neuropile between the cortical neurones, and retarded myelination of cerebral nerve tracts.

3. METABOLIC PROCESSES. The increased basal metabolic rate typical of hyperthyroidism is associated with a normal fasting respiratory quotient. The ratio of the different foodstuffs metabolized remains within normal limits. Increased protein catabolism and an increased excretion of urinary nitrogen occurs in both hyper- and hypothyroidism. The administration of small doses of thyroxine to hypothyroid animals results in protein deposition. This may be correlated with the increased growth which occurs in young hypothyroid animals under therapy. Creatinuria is typical of the hyperthyroid state. An increased concentration of blood lipid and cholesterol occurs with thyroid deficiency, and has some diagnostic significance in suspected cases of myxedema. An increased excretion of calcium, sometimes in association with osteoporosis, occurs in hyperthyroidism; this may, though rarely, result in bony fractures. In the absence of the thyroid hormone the conversion of carotene to vitamin A is impaired, possibly through defective intestinal absorption of carotene. The occasional failure of night vision in cases of myxedema may be thus explained. Administration of thyroid hormone to the lactating animal results in a temporary increase in milk yield and an increase in the fat content of the milk. It is probable that this action is mediated by an increased blood flow to the mammary gland and by stimulation of the metabolic processes of the glandular cells themselves.

## THE CELLULAR ACTION, METABOLISM, AND EXCRETION OF THYROID HORMONE

The manner in which thyroxine exerts its effects on oxidative processes, growth, and differentiation, at a cellular level, is unknown. At one time it was thought very probable that thyroxine, and other hormones, owed their effects to an action on enzyme systems. At the present time more attention is being paid to the possibility that the hormones act by modifying the permeability of cellular and subcellular (mitochondrial) membranes.

Our knowledge of the metabolism of thyroid hormones has increased rapidly since the introduction of radioactive iodine and radioactive thyroxine. Chromatography has allowed the separation and identification of the different labelled iodine compounds from body fluids and tissues and provided a useful analytical tool. After injection of radioactive thyroxine, the blood concentration falls rapidly at first (as the hormone is distributed in the tissues) and then more slowly (as the hormone is metabolized and excreted). The half-life of thyroxine in the blood is about 8 days in man, 4 days in the rabbit and guinea pig, and only 18 hours in the rat. Thyroxine is taken up rapidly by the liver and bile, and accumulates more slowly in the intestines, muscle, and skin. These latter two tissues, though, ultimately contain a significant fraction of administered hormone owing to their large bulk. It is of interest that different parts of the brain and pituitary gland show a selective absorption of radioactive thyroxine and tri-iodothyronine. This occurs mainly in the nuclear areas of the brain (Ford and Gross), and especially in the neurosecretory nuclei of the hypothalamus (supraoptic and paraventricular nuclei) and in the neurohypophysis and pars distalis of the adenohypophysis. Although the total amounts of hormone taken up in these tissues is small the concentration of $I^{131}$-tri-iodothyronine in the neural lobe of the rabbit pituitary may reach 40 to 50 times the plasma concentration. It is tempting to speculate that the hypothalamic and hypophysial uptake of these compounds is related in some way to the homostatic effect exerted by the feed-back mechanism of thyroid hormone over TSH secretion.

It has long been known that the liver concentrates thyroxine and secretes it in the bile. Although part of the thyroxine appears as such in the bile, a greater part is conjugated in the liver with glucuronic acid and secreted as such. This is a process of some magnitude; after the injection of radiothyroxine into a rat, about half the radioactivity is found in the bile in the first 24 hours. The glucuronide is hydrolyzed by bacteria in the gut and free thyroxine liberated. The greater part of the thyroxine is then reabsorbed through the gut wall, once more to enter the blood stream, whereas the remainder is excreted in the feces. The cycling of thyroxine through the liver, gut, and back to blood is referred to as the enterohepatic circulation. The amount of thyroxine excreted in the feces varies with the species studied, and expressed as a percentage of an administered dose, is approximately 65 per cent in the rat, 50 per cent in the rabbit, and 10 per cent in man. The remainder of a dose of radiothyroxine is largely deiodinated in the tissues and the radioiodide so liberated is shared between thyroid and kidney. The main excretory path of thyroid hormone in man is, thus, the kidney; the urine containing largely inorganic iodide as a degradation product of the hormone.

### The Assay of Thyroid Hormone

*Chemical assay.* A given extract of thyroid tissue may be assayed by determining its content of iodine bound in thyroxine, according to the method of Harington and Randall. As indicated above the blood concentration of thyroid hormone is assayed by estimating the iodine in organic combination in the blood.

*Biological assay.* Several biological criteria have been used in testing the thyroid potency of an extract, e.g., the rate of carbon dioxide production in mice, the rate of oxygen consumption in rats, the sensitivity of rats to oxygen lack, and the rate of metamorphosis of tadpoles as described by Gudernatsch. With the introduction of radioactive iodine a more detailed method became available. The thyroid activity of different compounds may be assessed by their ability to inhibit TSH secretion, and, therefore, to inhibit the thyroidal uptake of $I^{131}$ or release of $I^{131}$-labelled hormone. A further method, also involving the feed-back mechanism, employs the antithyroid drugs. After blocking the release of endogenous thyroid hormone with these drugs, the least amount of an extract which prevents goiter formation is measured. Both these latter two methods assay hormone activity within the range of the normal daily secretion rate of the thyroid gland of the assay animal used.

### The Measurement of, and the Factors Regulating, Thyroid Activity

The measurement of thyroid activity may be made by observations on the gland itself, by assessing the blood concentration of thyroid hormone, or the magnitude of the peripheral effects exerted by the hormone. The requirements vary somewhat according to whether the test is to be applied to the human or to the laboratory animal.

*1. Thyroid uptake of iodine.* Following an injection of $I^{131}$ (half-life, 8 days) or $I^{132}$ (half-life, 2.26 hours) the rate of uptake of the isotope by the thyroid gland is followed. For acute experiments on the laboratory animal this is most accurately assessed by killing the animal 1 to 2 hours after injection, dissolving the thyroid in alkali, and counting an aliquot of the solution. In clinical studies the uptake is followed by external counting over the neck.

*2. Urinary excretion of $I^{131}$.* Since an injected dose of iodide is mainly shared by the thyroid and the kidney, measurement of the excretion rate of $I^{131}$ in the urine indirectly measures the thyroid accumulation of $I^{131}$.

*3. Release of $I^{131}$-labelled hormone from the thyroid.* The turn-over rate of thyroid hormone in the normal human gland is too slow for this method to be of value in man. In the experimental animal the amount of radioactive hormone in the thyroid is followed by external counting over the neck. After correcting for the physical decay of the $I^{131}$, the rate of decline of radioactivity in the gland is related to the rate of secretion of thyroid hormone.

*4. Thyroid histology.* Measurement of the average height of the acinar cells of the thyroid has been used to assess thyroid function in laboratory animals.

*5. Blood hormone.* As mentioned previously estimation of the protein-bound iodine ($I^{127}$) gives a measurement of the blood concentration of thyroid hormone. Following an injection of $I^{131}$ the rate of rise of radioactive hormone in the blood may be followed. This method has been found useful in distinguishing suspected cases of hyperthyroidism.

*6. Methods based on the peripheral action of thyroid hormone.* Measurements of the basal metabolic rate and the concentration of serum cholesterol or fasting serum creatinine are used clinically as indications of thyroid activity.

Many factors influence the activity of the thyroid gland. Some of these have been discussed elsewhere and will only be mentioned briefly below.

*Iodine deficiency* (see p. 1006). A deficiency of iodine in the diet leads to hyperplastic changes in the gland and, eventually, to a state of exhaustion atrophy. Between wide limits of iodine intake thyroid function proceeds normally. In the presence of excess iodine, however, the organic binding of iodine by the thyroid is inhibited for at least a temporary period.

*Diet.* It has been claimed that a faulty diet, such as one containing an excess of fat or fatty acids, an excess of protein, or a deficiency of vitamins A or C, may lead to goiter in animals, and presumably, therefore, in man.

*Thiocyanate, perchlorate, and the antithyroid drugs.* The effect of these compounds on thyroid function has been described on page 1013.

THE PHYSIOLOGICAL FACTORS WHICH REGULATE

THE THYROID GLAND in the normal animal on an adequate diet are its nerve supply, the thyrotrophic hormone from the anterior pituitary gland and possibly the steroid hormones from the gonads and adrenal cortex (fig. 57.13).

*1. Nerve supply.* The nerves to the thyroid probably supply only the blood vessels of the gland. The fact that transplanted thyroid tissue functions in an apparently normal fashion demonstrates the essential dependence of the thyroid on humoral, rather than nervous, factors. It is likely, though, that the vasomotor innervation acts to adjust the blood flow through the gland in accordance with its functional requirements. Söderberg has shown that acute changes in blood flow through the thyroid are reflected by changes in the rate of uptake of $I^{131}$ and that stimulation of the nerve supply of the thyroid modifies, in a transient fashion, the secretory response of the gland to administered TSH.

*2. Thyrotrophic hormone.* There can be no doubt that the main factor regulating thyroid activity is the thyrotrophic hormone. The control of the thyroid gland, therefore, becomes largely a problem of the control of TSH secretion by the anterior pituitary gland. The data relating to this topic has been given in chapter 56. In summary, the secretion of TSH by the adenohypophysis is *maintained* and *regulated* by the central nervous system acting through the hypothalamus and hypophysial portal vessels of the pituitary stalk. In all probability, the nervous system acts as an intermediary between environmental stimuli and pituitary and thyroid function. The stimulus of cold has been found to result in an increase of TSH concentration in the blood within 30 minutes after the beginning of cold exposure, and this occurred despite a previous injection of thyroxine (Bottari). The time relations, and the apparent independence from the feed-back system, afford strong evidence that the response is mediated by a nervous reflex. Similarly the evidence is good that environmental stimuli which cause emotional excitement or stress inhibit TSH secretion and thyroid activity by a central nervous mechanism. The secretion of TSH is also regulated by the blood level of thyroid hormone, although it is as yet undecided whether this exerts its effect directly on the pituitary gland or indirectly *via* the hypothalamus.

*3. Adrenal and gonadal steroids.* Administration of corticoids (e g., cortisone) or the adrenocorticotrophic hormone (ACTH) in small physiological doses inhibits thyroid hormone production. Since it has been found that similar treatment

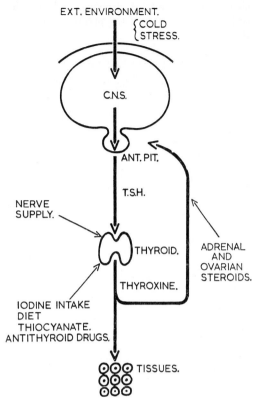

FIG. 57.13. Diagram to show the factors controlling thyroid function. Certain dietary factors (iodine intake) and drugs exert an action directly on the thyroid gland. The nerve supply is probably vasomotor in type and may modify the function of the gland by regulating its blood supply. The main physiological factor controlling thyroid activity is, without doubt, the thyrotrophic hormone. It is probable that environmental stimuli (cold, stress) exert their effects *via* central nervous reflexes modifying thyrotrophin secretion from the anterior pituitary. The blood concentration of thyroid hormone (and probably of ovarian and adrenal cortical hormone) acts by, in some way, regulating TSH release.

does not modify the action of a given dose of TSH on the thyroid, it is likely that the adrenal corticoids act at a pituitary, rather than thyroid, level as depicted in figure 57.13. The thyroid enlargement which occurs in the human at puberty, and during menstruation and pregnancy, is strong evidence of a thyroid-ovarian relationship. However, studies in experimental animals have failed to reveal any marked change in thyroid function during the different phases of the estrous cycle, pregnancy, or after ovariectomy, although a slight decrease in thyroid activity has been seen after castration in male rabbits. The increased level of plasma protein-bound iodine seen during pregnancy in the human is probably related to changes in the plasma proteins, and the thyroxine-binding power of the plasma, rather than thyroid activity *per se*.

# REFERENCES

ABELIN, A. Klin. Wochschr., 1934, 13, 940.

ABELIN, A. Arch. exper. Path. u. Pharmakol., 1934, 173, 146.

ABELIN, A. Arch. exper. Path. u. Pharmakol., 1934, 175, 151.

ABELIN, A. Arch. exper. Path. u. Pharmakol., 1936, 181, 250.

ABELIN, A. AND NEFTEL, A. Arch. exper. Path. u. Pharmakol., 1938, 189, 473.

ALBERT, A. Endocrinology, 1945, 37, 389.

ANDERSON, A. B., HARINGTON, C. R. AND LYON, D. M. Lancet, 1933, 2, 1081.

ANDRUS, E. C. Tr. A. Am. Physicians, 1932, 47, 47.

ASTWOOD, E. B. J. A. M. A., 1943, 122, 78.

ASTWOOD, E. B. J. Pharmacol. & Exper. Therap., 1943, 78, 79.

ASTWOOD, E. B. Harvey Lectures, 1944–1945, 40, 195.

ASTWOOD, E. B. Ann. New York Acad. Sc., 1949, 50, 419.

BAUMANN, C. Ztschr. physiol. Chem., 1896, 21, 319.

BAUMANN, C. Münch. med. Wchnschr., 1896, 43, 309 (Quoted by Harington).

BOOTHBY, W. M. AND ASSOCIATES. Tr. A. Am. Physicians, 1925, 40, 195.

BRAIN, R. Q. J. Med., 1938, N.S. 7, 293.

BRAIN, R. Q. Lancet, 1939, 2, 1217.

CHATIN, M. A. Series of papers in Compt. rend. Acad. sc., 1850, 30, to 1860, 50.

CHESNEY, A. M. AND ASSOCIATES. Bull. Johns Hopkins Hosp., 1928, 43, 261.

COINDET, I. R. Observations on the remarkable effects of iodine in Bronchocele and Scrofula. Longman, Hurst, Reese, Orme and Brown, London, 1921 (Quoted by Means).

DEMPSEY, E. W. Endocrinology, 1944, 34, 27.

DEMPSEY, E. W. Ann. New York Acad. Sc., 1949, 50, 336.

DEMPSEY, E. W. AND ASTWOOD, E. B. Endocrinology, 1943, 32, 509.

DOBYNS, B. M. AND WILSON, L. A. J. Clin. Endocrinol., 1954, 14, 1393.

ELMER, A. W. Endocrinology, 1934, 18, 487.

FAGGE, C. H. Tr. M. Chir. Soc. London, 1871, 54, 155.

FORD, D. H. AND GROSS, J. Endocrinology, 1958, 63, 549.

GALLI-MAININI, C. Endocrinology, 1941, 29, 674.

GOLDSMITH, E. D. AND ASSOCIATES. Am. J. Obst. & Gynec., 1945, 49, 197.

GUDERNATSCH, J. F. Am. J. Anat., 1914, 15, 431.

GULL, W. W. Tr. Clin. Soc. London, 1874, 7, 180.

HALSTED, W. S. Johns Hopkins Hosp. Rep., 1896, 1, 373.

HARINGTON, C. R. J. Chem. Soc., 1944, 193.

HARINGTON, C. R. Proc. Roy. Soc. London, Series B, 1944, 132, 223.

HARINGTON, C. R. AND BARGER, G. Biochem. J., 1927, 21, 169.

HARINGTON, C. R. AND RANDALL, S. S. Quart. J. Pharm., 1929, 2, 501.

HERCUS, C. E., BENSON, W. N. AND CARTER, C. L. J. Hyg., 1925, 24, 321.

HORSLEY, V. Proc. Roy. Soc., 1886, 40, 6.

HUNT, R. J. Biol. Chem., 1905, 1, 33.

HUNT, R. Am. J. Physiol., 1923, 63, 257.

HURXTHAL, L. M. Am. Heart J., 1928, 4, 103.

KENDALL, E. C. Tr. A. Am. Physicians, 1915, 30, 420.

KENDALL, E. C. J. Biol. Chem., 1919, 39, 125.

KENNEDY, T. H. AND PURVES, H. D. Brit. J. Exper. Path., 1941, 22, 241.

KIMBALL, O. P. Am. J. Pub. Health, 1928, 18, 587.

LEBLOND, C. P. Advances in biological and medical physics. Academic Press, Inc., New York, 1948.

LEBLOND, C. P. AND GROSS, J. Endocrinology, 1948, 43, 306.

LERMAN, J. J. Clin. Invest., 1940, 19, 555.

LERMAN, J. AND SALTER, W. T. Endocrinology, 1939, 25, 712.

LUDWIG, W. AND VON MUTZENBECHER, P. Ztschr. physiol. Chem., 1939, 25, 712.

LUNDE, G. Chem. Rev., 1929, 6, 45.

MACKENZIE, J. B. AND ASSOCIATES. Science, 1941, 94, 518.

MACKENZIE, J. B. AND ASSOCIATES. Endocrinology, 1943, 32, 185.

MAGNUS-LEVY, A. Berliner klin. Wchnschr., 1895, 32, 650.

MAHER, C. C. AND SITTLER, W. W. J. A. M. A., 1936, 106, 1546.

MARINE, D. J. Exper. Med., 1914, 19, 376.

MARINE, D. Am. J. M. Sc., 1930, 180, 767.

MARINE, D. Ann. Int. Med., 1930, 4, 423.

MARINE, D. Cowdry's special cytology, Vol. 2. 1932, p. 797.

MARINE, D. AND ASSOCIATES. Arch. Int. Med., 1908, 1, 349.

MARINE, D. AND ASSOCIATES. Arch. Int. Med., 1909, 3, 66.

MARINE, D. AND ASSOCIATES. Arch. Int. Med., 1909, 4, 440.

MARINE, D. AND ASSOCIATES. Bull. Johns Hopkins Hosp., 1909, 20, 131.

MARINE, D. AND ASSOCIATES. J. Pharmacol. & Exper. Therap., 1915, 7, 557.

MARINE, D. AND ASSOCIATES. J. Pharmacol. & Exper. Therap., 1916, 8, 439.

MARINE, D. AND ASSOCIATES. J. Lab. & Clin. Med., 1917, 3, 40.

MARINE, D. AND ASSOCIATES. Arch. Int. Med., 1920, 25, 661.

MARINE, D. AND ASSOCIATES. Am. J. Physiol., 1921, 57, 135.

MARINE, D. AND ASSOCIATES. Proc. Soc. Exper. Biol. & Med., 1932, 29, 772, 822, 976.

MARINE, D. AND ASSOCIATES. Proc. Soc. Exper. Biol. & Med., 1933, 30, 649, 910.

MARINE, D. AND ASSOCIATES. Am. J. M. Sc., 1934, 188, 565.

McCLENDON, J. F. Physiol. Rev., 1927, 7, 189.

McCLURE, R. D. Ann. Surg., 1934, 100, 924.

MORTON, M. E. AND ASSOCIATES. J. Biol. Chem., 1943, 147, 757.

MURRAY, G. R. Brit. M. J., 1891, **2**, 796.

NAFFZIGER, H. C. Arch. Ophth., 1933, **9**, 1.

NAFFZIGER, H. C. AND JONES, O. W. J. A. M. A., 1932, **99**, 638.

ORD, W. M. Tr. M. Chir. Soc. London, 1878, **61**, 57.

OSWALD, A. Ztschr. physiol. Chem., 1899, **27**, 14.

PERKIN, H. J., LAHEY, F. H. AND CATTELL, R. B. New England J. Med., 1936, **214**, 45.

PLUMMER, H. S. Tr. A. Am. Physicians, 1913, **28**, 587.

PLUMMER, H. S. Collected Papers Mayo Clin., 1925, **17**, 473.

PLUMMER, H. S. Tr. A. Am. Physicians, 1928, **43**, 159.

POCHIN, E. E. Clin. Sc. 1944, **5**, 51, 75.

POCHIN, E. E. Ciba Foundation Colloquia on Endocrinology, 1952, **4**, 316.

RAWSON, R. W. Endocrinology, 1942, **30**, 240.

RAWSON, R. W. Recent Progr. Hormone Res., 1947, **1**, 99.

RAWSON, R. W. Ann. New York Acad. Sc., 1949, **50**, 491.

RAWSON, R. W. Ciba Foundation Colloquia on Endocrinology, 1952, **4**, 294.

DE ROBERTIS, E. Anat. Rec., 1941, **80**, 219.

DE ROBERTIS, E. Ann. New York Acad. Sc., 1949, **50**, 317.

SCHOCKAERT, J. A. Proc. Soc. Exper. Biol. & Med., 1931, **29**, 306.

SEVERINGHAUS, A. E. Quoted by J. Lerman, *In* Symposium on glandular physiology and therapy. American Medical Association Publication, 1942, p. 380.

SMELTZER, G. K. Proc. Soc. Exper. Biol. & Med., 1936, **35**, 128.

SMELTZER, G. K. Am. J. Ophth., 1937, **20**, 1189.

SMELTZER, G. K. Endocrinology, 1938, **21**, 1208.

SMELTZER, G. K. Am. J. Anat., 1943, **72**, 2.

SMELTZER, G. K. Anat. Rec., 1943, **85**, 3.

SMELTZER, G. K. Am. J. Physiol., 1943, **140**, 308.

SMELTZER, G. K. Am. J. Physiol., 1944, **142**, 396.

SOFFER, L. T. AND ASSOCIATES. Proc. Am. Soc. Clin. Invest., 1947.

STANLEY, M. M. AND ASTWOOD, E. B. Endocrinology, 1947, **41**, 66.

SWINGLE, W. W. J. Exper. Zool., 1919, **27**, 397.

WEBSTER, E. Endocrinology, 1932, **16**, 617.

WEBSTER, B. AND CHESNEY, A. M. Bull. Johns Hopkins Hosp., 1928, 43, 261, 278, 291.

*Monographs and Reviews*

BROWN-GRANT, K. Ciba Foundation Colloquia on Endocrinology, 1957, **10**, 97.

BRUNTON, C. Physiol. Rev., 1949, **29**, 260.

CARGILL, S. L. AND LESSES, M. F. New England J. Med., 1946, **235**, 717.

DODDS, E. C. Harvey Lectures, 1934–1935, **30**, 119.

DODDS, E. C. *In* Symposium on glandular physiology and therapy. American Medical Association Publication, 1942.

GOLDSMITH, E. D. Ann. New York Acad. Sc., 1949, **50**, 283.

HARINGTON, C. R. The thyroid gland. Oxford University Press, London, 1933.

HARROW, B. AND SHERWIN, C. P. The chemistry of the hormones. The Williams & Wilkins Co., Baltimore, 1934.

HOGBEN, L. T. The comparative physiology of internal secretion. Cambridge University Press, London, 1927.

KENDALL, E. C. Thyroxine. Chemical Catalog Co., New York, 1929.

MANN, I. The orbital endocrine problem. Ophthalmic Literature, London, 1948.

MARINE, D. Physiol. Rev., 1922, **2**, 521.

MARINE, D. Medicine, 1927, **6**, 127.

MARINE, D. J. A. M. A., 1935, **104**, 2250, 2334.

McCARRISON, R., The etiology of endemic goitre. Bale, London, 1913.

McCLENDON, J. F. Iodine and the incidence of goiter. University of Minnesota Press, Minneapolis, 1939.

MEANS, J. H. Ann. Int. Med., 1945, **23**, 779.

MEANS, J. H. The thyroid gland, 2nd ed. Lippincott, Philadelphia, 1948.

MEANS, J. H. Ann. New York Acad. Sc., 1949, **50**, 279.

MULVANEY, J. H. Am. J. Ophth., 1944, **27**, 589, 693, 820.

ORR, J. B. Iodine supply and the incidence of endemic goitre, Special Report No. 154. Medical Research Council, London, 1951.

PINCUS, G. AND THIMANN, K. V. The hormones. Academic Press, Inc., New York, 1948.

PITT-RIVERS, R. Physiol. Rev., 1950, **30**, 194.

PITT-RIVERS, R. AND TATA, J. R. The thyroid hormones. Pergamon Press, Ltd., London, 1959.

RAWSON, R. W., RALL, J. E. AND SONENBERG, M. *In* The hormones, Vol. III, edited by G. Pincus and K. V. Thimann. Academic Press, Inc., New York, 1955, p. 433.

REINEKE, E. P. Ann. New York Acad. Sc., 1949, **50**, 450.

REINHOFF, W. F., Jr. Medicine, 1931, **10**, 257.

RIGGS, D. S. Pharmacol. Rev., 1952, **4**, 284.

ROSENBERG, I. N. AND ASTWOOD, E. B. *In* Glandular physiology and therapy, 5th ed. Lippincott, Philadelphia, 1954.

SALTER, W. T. The endocrine function of iodine. Harvard University Press, Cambridge, Mass., 1940.

SALTER, W. T. Ann. New York Acad. Sc., 1949, **50**, 358.

SCHÄFER, E. A. S. The endocrine organs: an introduction to the study of internal secretion. Longmans, London, 1926.

SÖDERBERG, U. Acta physiol. scandinav., 1958, **42**, Suppl. 147.

WERNER, S. C. *In* Glandular physiology and therapy, 5th ed. Lippincott, Philadelphia, 1954.

WOLF, W. Endocrinology in modern practice. Saunders, Philadelphia, 1957.

WOODS, A. C. Medicine, 1946, **25**, 113.

ZONDEK, H. The diseases of the endocrine glands Arnold, London, 1935.

# 58

# THE ADRENAL (SUPRARENAL) GLANDS

---

The mammalian adrenal gland, like the pituitary body and the thyroid-parathyroid apparatus, consists of two parts which, though closely associated anatomically, have separate origins and are structurally different. The central part of the gland is called the *medulla*: the outer enveloping rim of tissue is known as the *cortex*. In certain fishes (Elasmobranchs) the two parts are present but not combined as a single gland. Tissue corresponding to the mammalian medulla, for example, is found as a number of small discrete masses on either side of the spine in association with the sympathetic ganglia (*chromaffin tissue*), whereas an elongated structure lying between the kidneys (*inter-renal body*) corresponds to the adrenal cortex of mammals. In the amphibia and reptilia the two types of tissue have come together, but masses of cortical cells are intermingled with islets of medullary tissue and the two tissues are not segregated into a peripheral and a central zone, as in the mammalian adrenal.

In all animals the medullary tissue and the sympathetic ganglion cells have a common origin; they develop from primitive cell masses which have separated from the neural crest. Migrating from their sites of origin these masses of ectodermal cells undergo differentiation along two paths, some into sympathetic ganglion cells, others into *chromaffin tissue*. This latter term is derived from their reaction with chromic acid or its salts in which the cells are stained dark brown. Chromaffin or chromophil cells are also stained blue by ferric chloride and black by osmic acid. In the abdomen, on either side of the midline, a relatively large mass of chromaffin cells becomes enveloped by cortical tissue to constitute the adrenal medulla. Other smaller masses persist as accessory chromaffin tissue in association with the ganglia and plexuses of the sympathetic, and are called *paraganglia*. On the other hand, sympathetic ganglion cells may be found scattered among the cells of the adult adrenal medulla. The cortex is developed from mesoderm. It arises as a bud from the celomic epithelium covering the inner side of the fore part of the mesonephros. The celomic epithelium immediately behind this area gives rise to the germinal epithelium from which in turn the sex glands develop.

The medulla is composed of closely packed groups of polyhedral cells containing chromaffin granules which are looked upon as the mother substance of the medullary secretion. The cell groups are separated by blood sinuses which empty into a central vein. The cells of the cortex are arranged in three zones. These are, from without inward, the (1) *zona glomerulosa*, in which groups of cells are arranged in a circular or oval pattern, (2) *zona fasciculata*, in which the cells are arranged in columns, and (3) *zona reticularis*, which is composed of a network of cell cords (fig. 58.1). The cells of the cortex in a number of species contain fine lipid droplets which can be made apparent by a variety of histochemical or optical methods. Such lipid droplets appear to be associated with the secretion of the gland, but in some forms (e.g., the hamster, other hibernants and ruminants) these droplets are not visible microscopically.

The characteristic zonation of the adrenal cortex has led many workers to consider that the cells of the cortex originate at the periphery of the gland, in the zona glomerulosa just beneath the capsule or from the capsular cells. With increasing age the cells were believed to move inward, through, and as constituents of, the zona fasciculata to the zona reticularis where cellular death and absorption ensued. More recent opinion favors the view that the three zones of the cortex reflect differing functional activities, although it is well established that following an almost complete adrenalectomy a few zona glomerulosa cells are able to regenerate a new adrenal cortex with the normal zonation.

The adrenal gland of the human fetus is proportionally some 10 to 20 times larger by weight than that of the adult. Most of the gland is comprised of an enormously enlarged reticular (or fetal) zone which is destined to involute soon after birth. The function of the fetal zone is not clear; it may be developed under the influence of chorionic gonadotrophin.

A sex difference in the size and histological appearance of the adrenal cortex has been demonstrated in animals. The glands are larger in women than in men, a difference which is enhanced when the smaller female body is taken into account. In animals, the adrenals of the female are reduced to the size of the male glands under the influence of testosterone.

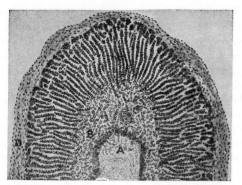

FIG. 58.1. Section of the human suprarenal capsule: *A*, medullary portion; *B*, zona reticularis; *C*, zona fasciculata; and *D*, capsule. The zona glomerulosa is situated just beneath the capsule. (From Maximow and Bloom.)

BLOOD AND NERVE SUPPLY. The adrenal is one of the most richly vascular organs in the body, receiving 6 to 7 cc. of blood per gram of tissue per minute. It is supplied by three small arteries which are derived, respectively, from the inferior phrenic artery, the renal artery, and the aorta. These form rich plexuses in the cortex. The plexuses are continuous with the sinuses of the medulla which drain into the central vein of the latter. The right adrenal vein empties directly into the inferior vena cava, the left vein into the renal vein. The nerves are derived from the splanchnic nerves and the lumbar sympathetic chain, the fibers passing through a plexus (suprarenal) before entering the gland. These fibers are medullated and have no cell stations in their course. That is, they are entirely preganglionic, the medullary cell itself taking the place of the ganglion cell and postganglionic fiber; they differ thus from all other sympathetic pathways (see ch. 71).

## The Adrenal Medulla

Thomas Addison's report in 1855 (p. 1042), and the experimental work of Brown-Séquard in 1856, gave the first hints concerning adrenal function. The last mentioned observer showed that complete removal of the glands from rabbits caused death. Not until many years later was it shown that the effects described by these pioneer investigators were due to loss of the adrenal *cortex*. The French physiologist Vulpian, working at about the same time as Addison and Brown-Séquard, discovered that the medulla, unlike any other tissue, was stained blue-green by ferric chloride and that the blood of the adrenal vein sometimes gave a similar reaction. The staining reaction, it is now known, is characteristic of the internal secretion of the medulla (adrenaline). In 1894, Oliver and Schäfer obtained an aqueous extract from the medulla which upon injection caused a pronounced rise in blood pressure.

The active principle of the extract was obtained in pure form, in 1901, by Takamine and by Aldrich. The substance has been given various names; *adrenaline* (or *adrenalin*), *epinephrine*, *adrenin*, and *suprarenin*, the first is most commonly used. More recently it has been established that the adrenal medulla contains a mixture of adrenaline and *noradrenaline*, and may release these substances in different proportions in different circumstances. Adrenaline and noradrenaline possess a close structural relationship to tyrosine, as may be seen from the following:

$$HO\!-\!\langle\!\!\bigcirc\!\!\rangle\!\!-\!CH_2\!-\!\underset{\underset{COOH}{|}}{CH}\!-\!NH_2$$

*Tyrosine*

$$\underset{HO}{\overset{HO}{\langle\bigcirc\rangle}}\!\!-\!\underset{\underset{OH}{|}}{CH}\!-\!CH_2\!-\!NH_2$$

*Noradrenaline*

$$\underset{HO}{\overset{HO}{\langle\bigcirc\rangle}}\!\!-\!\underset{\underset{OH}{|}}{CH}\!-\!CH_2\!-\!NH\!-\!CH_3$$

*Adrenaline or epinephrine*

Since they may also be said to be derived from catechol they are termed *catecholamines*.

ADRENALINE OR EPINEPHRINE. Adrenaline is a secondary alcohol, its full chemical name being 3,4-dihydroxy-$\alpha$-phenyl-$\beta$-methylaminoethanol. It was first prepared synthetically by Stoltz (1904) and later by Dakin (1905). Adrenaline possesses an asymmetric carbon atom, so two isomers are possible (i.e., a levo- and a dextrorotatory form). The natural levo- form is 15 times more powerful than the dextrorotatory form.

Adrenaline is probably synthesized in the adrenal medulla from the amino acid phenylalanine. However, although there are only five changes in the molecule involved in the process, there are 120 different ways of achieving the conversion with 30 possible intermediates. A likely pathway is that set out on the following page.

Evidence in favor of the following sequence is derived from a variety of experiments. Following the administration of isotopically labeled phenylalanine or tyrosine, radioactive adrenaline has been isolated from the adrenals. An enzyme system for the conversion of phenylalanine to tyrosine is known. With the introduction of a second hydroxyl group into the tyrosine molecule, *dihy-*

$$\text{C}_6\text{H}_5\text{—CH}_2\text{—CH—NH}_2$$
$$\text{COOH}$$

*Phenylalanine*

↓

$$\text{HO—C}_6\text{H}_4\text{—CH}_2\text{—CH—NH}_2$$
$$\text{COOH}$$

*Tyrosine*

↓

$$\text{(HO)}_2\text{C}_6\text{H}_3\text{—CH}_2\text{—CH—NH}_2$$
$$\text{COOH}$$

*Dihydroxyphenylalanine (dopa)*

↓

$$\text{(HO)}_2\text{C}_6\text{H}_3\text{—CH}_2\text{—CH}_2\text{—NH}_2$$

*Hydroxytyramine (dopamine)*

↓

$$\text{(HO)}_2\text{C}_6\text{H}_3\text{—CH—CH}_2\text{—NH}_2$$
$$\text{OH}$$

*Noradrenaline or levarterenol*

↓

$$\text{(HO)}_2\text{C}_6\text{H}_3\text{—CH—CH}_2\text{—NH—CH}_3$$
$$\text{OH}$$

*Adrenaline or epinephrine*

droxyphenylalanine *(dopa)* is produced which when decarboxylated by the enzyme dopadecarboxylase forms *hydroxytyramine* or *dopamine*. Dopa itself has been much studied and has been detected (like dopadecarboxylase) in the adrenal. Labeled adrenaline has been recovered from the adrenal after giving dopa-$\alpha$-$C^{14}$ or dopamine-$\alpha$-$C^{14}$. The methylation of noradrenaline yields adrenaline and this step has been demonstrated in minced adrenal tissue and perfused glands (Bulbring).

INACTIVATION OF ADRENALINE. Adrenaline disappears rapidly after injection due to its uptake by the tissues. The effects following subcutaneous injection are much less intense, though more prolonged, than those induced by intravenous administration. When given orally, adrenaline is inert. Adrenaline is rapidly inactivated in the body. Free adrenaline and noradrenaline are normally present in human urine, and according to von Euler, a 24 hour collection contains 5 to 10 $\mu$g. of adrenaline and 30 to 60 $\mu$g. of nor-

adrenaline. The rate of excretion falls away during sleep. Minor amounts of noradrenaline and adrenaline may be conjugated physiologically with glucuronic acid, but the majority is oxidized or eliminated as metabolites. Outside the body adrenaline is much more stable in blood and tissue fluids than in Ringer solution, in which it undergoes oxidation to form a pink compound (*adrenochrome*). The substances in blood and tissue fluids which have a stabilizing or protective action upon the adrenaline molecule are reducing agents such as glutathione and ascorbic acid (Welch). It is significant that the adrenal gland is especially rich in these substances.

### ACTIONS OF ADRENALINE AND NORADRENALINE

Although Oliver and Schäfer discovered the pressor effect of an extract of adrenal medulla as long ago as 1894, not until nearly 50 years later was it discovered that the gland contained noradrenaline (arterenol, norepinephrine) as well as adrenaline. Noradrenaline or levarterenol present in adrenergic nerve trunks, sympathetic ganglia and the hypothalamus, and other parts of the brain, but absent in nerve free tissues such as placenta and bone marrow. Adrenaline and noradrenaline are present in the adult human adrenal medulla in the proportion of about 5 to 1, but the reverse proportion is obtained in children and very large amounts of noradrenaline (up to 90 per cent) may be found in some adrenal tumors (pheochromocytomas). It is probable, as noted earlier, that noradrenaline is the immediate precursor of adrenaline but in addition to its importance from this point of view, the substance has physiological functions of its own. For many years the properties of extracts of adrenal medulla have been studied with the belief that the only active principle present was adrenaline. The discovery of noradrenaline, therefore, revolutionized thought in this field, and only now are signs of order emerging. In what follows an attempt will be made to compare and contrast the properties of the two amines. In general it may be said that the main function of noradrenaline seems to be the normal control of the circulation, whereas adrenaline produces a variety of 'metabolic' effects useful in an emergency. Both agents act upon structures innervated by sympathetic nerve fibers and because of this are called (like certain other drugs) *sympathomimetic* (Barger and Dale).

1. VASCULAR EFFECTS. Ordinary preparations of adrenaline (e.g., U.S.P. epinephrine) have a

pronounced pressor action causing widespread
vasoconstriction. But adrenaline itself is by no
means a general vasoconstrictor. Its over-all effect upon the vascular system is vasodilatation,
that is, it decreases rather than increases the
peripheral vascular resistance of the body as a
whole. It constricts powerfully the arterioles and
capillaries of the skin and the arterioles of the
kidney, but dilates the vessels of the skeletal
muscles and liver, and probably also of the coronary system. This vasodilator effect upon the
muscles and liver overshadows the vasoconstrictor effects with a consequent decrease in the total
peripheral resistance. The pronounced rise in
blood pressure (fig. 58.2), a true adrenaline effect,
is due entirely to its increasing the cardiac output.
The rise in blood pressure is confined to the
systolic phase, the diastolic phase showing no
change or a fall, an expression either of the absence of any increase in, or a reduction of the
total peripheral resistance (see table 58.1).

Noradrenaline is an over-all vasoconstrictor,
causing an increase in the total peripheral resist-

### TABLE 58.1

*Effects of adrenaline and noradrenaline
on blood flow (ml. per min.)*

(After Barcroft, modified)

|  | Before Adrenaline or Noradren- aline | During | |
|---|---|---|---|
|  |  | Adrenaline | Noradren- aline |
| Liver | 1500 | 3000 | 1500 |
| Kidneys | 1500 | 900 | 1200 |
| Muscles | 1000 | 2000 | 1000 |
| Brain | 750 | 900 | 675 |
| Over-all | 4750 | 6800 | 4375 |

ance, and a hypertensive effect which is from 30
to 70 per cent greater than that of adrenaline.
Noradrenaline constricts the cutaneous vessels,
but to a lesser degree than adrenaline, the latter
in man causing a much more pronounced pallor.
Noradrenaline causes a reduction in blood flow
through the brain of about 10 per cent, whereas
adrenaline increases it by 20 per cent or so.

2. HEART. Adrenaline (U.S.P. epinephrine)
exerts a direct stimulating effect upon the myocardium; it increases the oxygen consumption of
the heart and augments the cardiac output mainly
by an increase in stroke volume, this being responsible for the rise in systolic pressure. These
effects are apparently due to the action of adrenaline as such, for noradrenaline either has no
effect upon the cardiac output or decreases it.
Both drugs dilate the coronary vessels and increase the coronary flow. In animals with the
vagus nerves intact, adrenaline slows the heart
as a secondary effect of the hypertension (due to
reflex inhibition—Marey's law) but causes cardiac
acceleration after vagal section. In hearts protected from reflex inhibition by division of the
vagus nerves or atropine, the force and rate of
the heart are increased and conduction improved
by both drugs. In man, adrenaline accelerates the
heart whereas noradrenaline causes bradycardia.
Adrenaline also appears to increase the susceptibility of the ventricular muscle to the development of extrasystoles, or even of ventricular
fibrillation.

3. RESPIRATION. After a short initial period of
apnea the respirations are increased in rate and
depth, both by adrenaline and noradrenaline.
The apneic period is apparently secondary to the
rise in blood pressure and is brought about
through the carotid sinus mechanism.

4. SMOOTH MUSCLE. Adrenaline inhibits the

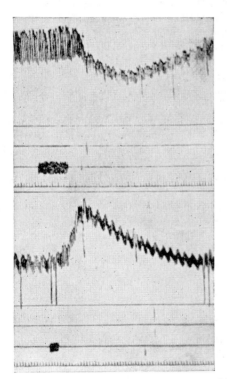

FIG. 58.2. Lower tracing shows the effect of intravenous injection of 0.02 mg. of adrenaline upon
blood pressure. Upper tracing from the same animal shows the fall in pressure produced by the
injection of 0.02 mg. of adrenaline following a
previous dose of 0.4 mg. per kilogram of ergotamine tartrate. (From Geiling.)

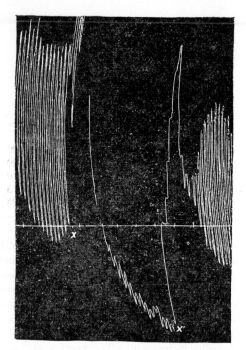

FIG. 58.3. Rabbit's intestine in Ringer's solution. At *X*, Ringer's solution plus adrenaline 1:100,000,000; at *X'*, Ringer's solution substituted. Time 30 seconds. (From Hoskins.)

muscle of the *stomach, intestine, bronchioles,* and *urinary bladder*. Both the tone and movements of the intestine are inhibited (fig. 58.3); the bronchioles are dilated. It excites the muscle of the *splenic capsule, ureter, trigone* and *sphincter of the bladder*, the *retractor penis*, and the *pyloric, ileocolic,* and *internal anal sphincters*. The *uterus*, whether pregnant or nonpregnant, is contracted in man and in many animals, but in the cat, rat, mouse, and guinea pig, the pregnant organ alone is contracted by adrenaline; the nonpregnant is relaxed. The contractions of the human uterus at term are often inhibited by adrenaline. Most of these effects are exhibited, though less strongly, by noradrenaline, with the exception of the excitation of the pregnant uterus of the cat upon which noradrenaline exerts a greater effect. As a result of the excitation of the radiating fibers of the *iris* (dilator pupillae) the pupil is dilated by adrenaline especially if the superior cervical ganglion has been previously excised. *Mueller's muscle* is stimulated and the eyeball protruded. Retraction of the *upper eyelid* is caused by the stimulation of its smooth muscle. The *nictitating membrane* of animals is retracted. Adrenaline also stimulates the *erectores pilae muscles* and other smooth muscle fibers in the skin. After denervation the

sensitivity of some tissues to noradrenaline (e.g., the nictitating membrane of the cat) is greatly increased, whereas that to adrenaline is only slightly affected. This may be due to disappearance of amine oxidase from this tissue which destroys noradrenaline more rapidly than adrenaline.

5. SKELETAL MUSCLE. Adrenaline postpones muscle fatigue and increases the tension developed in a twitch of skeletal muscle. It increases muscle tone, and may cause tremors or muscular twitching. The effects of noradrenaline upon muscle are much less pronounced. When the sympathetic supply to a muscle is excited during stimulation of the motor nerves, the contractions are increased. This effect is known as the *Orbeli phenomenon*.

6. CARBOHYDRATE METABOLISM. Adrenaline administered by injection causes hyperglycemia and glycosuria. It shows an antagonism to insulin; relieving hypoglycemic convulsions. These effects, which are also shown by noradrenaline, but to a lesser degree, are due to the mobilization of sugar from the liver whose glycogen stores are thus reduced. The hyperglycemic effect is, therefore, greatest in well fed animals with an abundant hepatic store of carbohydrate, and of course is not obtained in hepatectomized animals. The glycogen of the muscles is also reduced by adrenaline. On the other hand, there is evidence (Himsworth and Scott) that the rate of removal of glucose from the blood by the tissues is accelerated. When administered to animals after a prolonged fast or in other conditions which deplete the hepatic glycogen stores, adrenaline causes an *increase* in liver glycogen. The latter is due to the breakdown of muscle glycogen to lactic acid which, diffusing into the blood, is carried to the liver where resynthesis to glycogen occurs. There is a fall in the inorganic phosphate of the blood due apparently to the phosphorylation of glycogen and the formation of glucose monophosphate. If the adrenaline administration is continued the liver glycogen is converted in turn to glucose which passes into the blood, causing hyperglycemia; it is subsequently reconverted to glycogen in the muscles (Cori). The cycle may be represented in the following scheme:

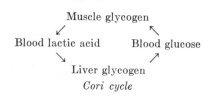

Muscle glycogen

Blood lactic acid        Blood glucose

Liver glycogen

*Cori cycle*

Noradrenaline exerts little effect upon the concentration of lactic acid in the peripheral blood (Bearn *et al.*).

7. GENERAL METABOLISM. Oxygen consumption is increased by from 20 to 40 per cent, and $CO_2$ production by from 30 to 50 per cent; the respiratory quotient is, therefore, raised. In man the increase in the basal metabolic rate occurs within a short time after the subcutaneous injection of 0.5 cc. of a 1:1000 solution; the temperature of the muscles rises. The effect of adrenaline upon heat production is known as its *calorigenic* action; it does not occur after removal of the liver (Soskin).

Boothby and Sandiford attributed the latter effect largely to stimulation of cellular oxidations throughout the tissues of the body generally, and in a major degree to the hyperglycemia ("carbohydrate plethora"), and the increased utilization of carbohydrate, that is, to the specific dynamic action of glucose. The extent to which each of these factors contribute to the increased heat production is a controversial question, but the consensus favors increased carbohydrate utilization as the predominant factor (see Griffith). Cutaneous vasoconstriction leading to diminished heat loss and its effect upon metabolism, as well as increased muscular tone, are probably contributing factors. The calorigenic effect is not brought about through an action upon the thyroid since it is obtained after thyroidectomy. Moreover, the rise in metabolic rate commences within a few minutes and returns to normal within 2 hours or so, whereas the effect of thyroxine upon heat production does not commence for some hours and is prolonged for several days (p. 1015).

8. OTHER EFFECTS OF ADRENALINE (U.S.P.). (a) Secretion of saliva; (b) lacrymation; (c) sweating in such animals as horses and sheep, but in most other animals the sweat glands, though innervated by the sympathetic, are not excited by adrenaline (see p. 1306). Sweating can be evoked in most human subjects by adrenaline or noradrenaline injected intradermally in very dilute solution; (d) contraction of the spleen (stimulation of the smooth muscle of its capsule and trabeculae) and consequent increase in the blood volume and in the red cell count (p. 517); (e) increase in the coagulability of the blood; (f) small doses increase the flow of urine as a result of constriction of efferent glomerular vessels (larger doses constrict both afferent and efferent vessels) and through reduction of the renal blood flow diminish the urinary flow (p. 546); (g) a fall, sometimes preceded by a rise, in the potassium

of the blood; (h) contraction of melanophores of certain cold blooded animals, e.g., frog and horned toad (Redfield)[1]; (i) increased output of the adrenocorticotrophic hormone of the pituitary gland; (j) affects the transmission in nerve; (k) enhances or depresses, according to the dosage, the action of acetylcholine at synaptic junctions (ch. 71); and (l) intravenous injection of adrenaline causes arousal and anxiety in man, whereas injection of adrenaline into the cerebral ventricles gives signs of depression and drowsiness.

## ASSAY OF ADRENALINE AND NORADRENALINE

The assay of adrenaline in blood, tissue fluids or extracts can be accomplished in many ways, and both biological and chemical methods are available. Since both adrenaline and noradrenaline are well established chemical entities, there is no international standard. All results are expressed in terms of the weight of pure amine.

With the growth of pharmacological knowledge, it has been realized that some of the earlier methods, such as that concerned with the effect of adrenaline on the amplitude of the frog heart, are not specific, and that it may be difficult to distinguish between adrenaline and noradrenaline. This difficulty is overcome by preliminary purification of the extract which increases both the specificity and the sensitivity of the final assay procedure. Adrenaline may be concentrated by adsorption on to aluminium hydroxide or an ion-exchange resin, whereas adrenaline and noradrenaline may be separated with the aid of paper chromatography and eluted from the paper prior to assay. In order to establish the relative concentration of adrenaline and noradrenaline in any extract, and in order to avoid the confusion introduced by interfering substances, it is advisable to use two or more methods in parallel.

BIOASSAYS. These include:

*Cat and rat blood pressure.* An assay involving the pressor effect of catechol amines in the anesthetized or spinal cat has long been used. The response to the sample and to standard solutions is measured and an attempt made to 'sandwich' the response of the unknown between a greater and a smaller dose of standard. The use of the hexamethonium treated rat provides a particularly sensitive preparation (Crawford and Outschoorn), and whereas the blood pressure of both the cat and rat

---

[1] The contraction of the melanophores of the horned toad which results from adrenaline administration, also occurs when the animal becomes excited. Since in the latter instance the effect is abolished if the circulation to the melanophores is occluded, but not when the skin nerves are cut, the effect must be due to a chemical substance, presumably adrenaline, in the blood.

is more sensitive to noradrenaline than to adrenaline, that of the rat is particularly so. Amounts of noradrenaline of the order of 0.050 of 1 $\mu$g. can be measured with accuracy.

*Rat uterus.* In this test the isolated rat uterus is suspended in a bath of modified Tyrode solution to which constant amounts of acetylcholine are added regularly. Contractions of the organ are induced which are readily inhibited by adrenaline. Unknown solutions are assayed by comparison of the effect observed with that produced by standard solutions. The rat uterus is much less sensitive to noradrenaline than to adrenaline and with good preparations less than 0.0001 of 1 $\mu$g. of adrenaline can be detected.

*Vasoconstriction in rabbit ear.* The vasoconstriction induced by adrenaline in the perfused rabbit ear provides by far the most sensitive assay for adrenaline available. The vessels are sensitized by denervation and the diameter of the central artery measured microscopically at intervals. Adrenaline can be detected in a concentration of $10^{-11}$ grams per milliliter or less. The rabbit ear is also sensitive to 5-hydroxytryptamine but this effect can be blocked with lysergic acid diethylamide.

*Intestinal muscle.* Catecholamines generally inhibit the smooth muscle of the gut and studies employing a segment of rabbit intestine were carried out over 40 years ago. Rat colon is particularly sensitive to noradrenaline, whereas the rectal cecum of the fowl is much better suited for the assay of adrenaline, since it is able to detect 0.002 of a microgram.

CHEMICAL ASSAYS. These are generally more convenient but less sensitive and specific than bioassays.

*Colorimetric.* Colorimetric assays are based on the oxidation of adrenaline to the pink adrenochrome and other pink indole compounds or the use of adrenaline as a reducing agent. Thus arsenomolybdic acid is reduced by adrenaline to a blue compound.

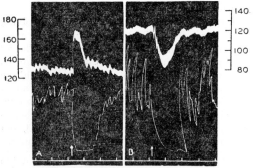

FIG. 58.4. Showing the effects of adrenaline upon the blood pressure and the uterus (*in situ*) of a pregnant cat before and after the administration of dibenamine. The intravenous injection of 2.5 mg. per kilogram is indicated by the arrows. (From Nickerson and Goodman.)

*Fluorimetric.* The observation that adrenaline became fluorescent in alkaline solution was made by Paget in 1930, and an assay utilizing this fact was proposed 4 years later (Gaddum and Schild). In recent years, with a revival of interest in fluorimetric methods, new assays have been described. Though sensitive, these assays are as yet nonspecific.

### THE EFFECTS OF CERTAIN SUBSTANCES UPON THE ACTION OF ADRENALINE

A number of terms are used in the discussion of the action of drugs which interfere with the action of adrenaline and like substances. Thus the abolition of the effect of sympathetic stimulation is called a *sympatholytic* action, whereas a drug which abolishes the excitor action of adrenaline is called *adrenolytic*. The term *adrenergic blocking agent* may be applied to a drug which has either an adrenolytic or a sympatholytic action or both.

The first adrenergic blocking agents to be discovered were derivatives of ergot. *Ergotoxine* or *ergotamine* block the pressor effects of adrenaline and sympathetic stimulation, but the vasodilator action is not interfered with. For this reason certain effects of adrenaline administration or of sympathetic stimulation appear to be reversed by the ergot alkaloids. Thus, as just noted, only a depressor effect is obtainable with adrenaline if ergotoxine has been administered previously. Also, after ergotoxine, adrenaline causes expansion of the melanophores of the frog instead of the usual contraction. The hyperglycemic response to adrenaline is abolished after treatment with ergot alkaloids. Ergotoxine is made up of three alkaloids, ergocornine, ergocristine, and ergocryptine, which are derivatives of lysergic acid. These substances also markedly increase the motor activity of the uterus. This property is lost upon hydrogenation to, respectively, dehydroergocornine, -cristine, and -cryptine, but the cardiovascular effects are little affected. The action on the capillaries, blood pressure, and bronchioles of *histamine* and adrenaline are antagonistic, and adrenalectomized animals show an increased susceptibility to histamine administration. The blood concentrating effect of histamine administration is lessened or prevented by a previous injection of adrenaline. There is also some evidence that histamine increases the output of adrenaline from the medulla.

Other antagonists of adrenaline and of sympathetic effects have been discovered more recently. The $\beta$-halo-alkylamines (of which *dibenamine* and *dibenzyline* are examples) possess particularly powerful adrenergic blocking properties (see fig. 58.4). The blockade develops slowly, due to the *in vivo* formation of active intermediates, but is then highly specific and persistent. Dibenamine and dibenzyline reverse the pressor effect of adrenaline although, unlike ergotoxine, the hyperglycemic action of adrenaline is little affected. Nor are the inhibitory effects of adrenaline upon the virgin cat's uterus or the intestine modified by these drugs. Dibenamine (N,N-dibenzyl-β-chloroethylamine) and dibenzyline (phenoxybenzamine) have the structures shown below:

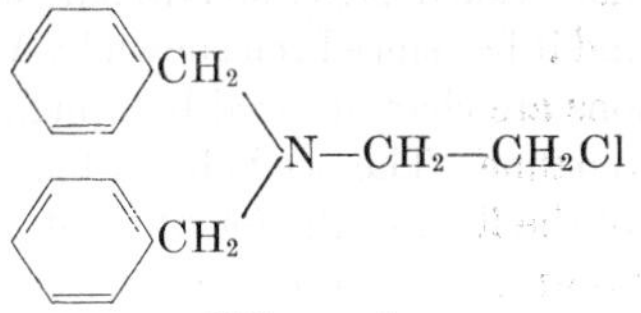

*Dibenamine*

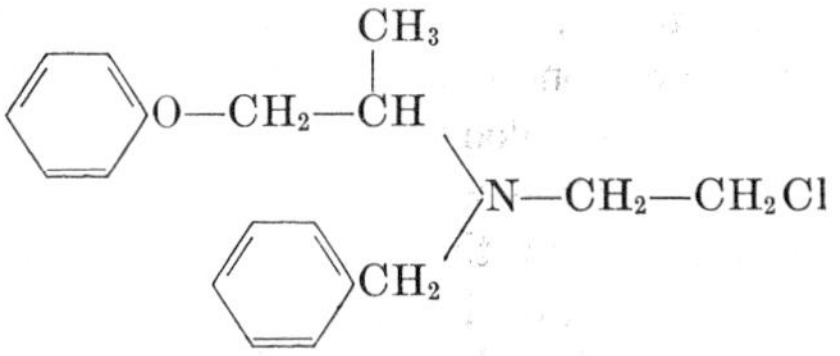

*Dibenzyline*

Adrenergic blocking activity is also possessed by the *benzodioxanes*, or Fourneau compounds, such as *933F* (piperoxan) and *883F* (prosympal) and the imidazolines. Of the imidazolines, tolazoline (priscoline, benzazoline, or priscol) and phentolamine (regitine, C-7337) are best known. The blockade produced by both series is relatively transient and they are useful in the diagnosis of pheochromocytoma.

Other compounds may be mentioned here which also block ganglionic transmission. *Nicotine* acts by depolarizing the ganglion cell, which it first stimulates and then paralyzes. The *methonium compounds* (hexa- and decamethonium) compete with naturally formed acetylcholine for "possession" of the ganglion cells, that is for the specific chemical receptors of the cell. Once in position, the postsynaptic membrane is stabilized and depolarization rendered more difficult. This ability of the methonium compounds depends upon their resemblance to acetylcholine, being also quaternary nitrogen compounds. The methonium compounds are useful clinically for the reduction of blood pressure and for their curarelike action.

### ADRENALINELIKE SUBSTANCES

An extract containing *ephedrine* has been used in Chinese medicine for thousands of years; the pure alkaloid was obtained by Nagai, who gave it its present name, in 1887. The chemical resemblance to adrenaline may be seen in the formula.

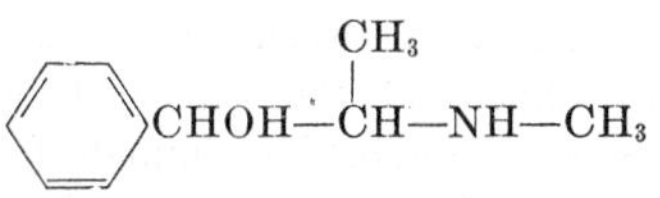

*Ephedrine (1-hydroxy-1-phenyl-2-methylaminopropane)*

This alkaloid is closely similar to adrenaline in its action, causing bronchiolar relaxation, vasoconstriction, hyperglycemia, inhibition of intestinal muscle, and excitation of other smooth muscle. It has also a calorigenic action; its pressor effect (Curtis) is reversed by ergotoxine and reduced by cocaine. Ephedrine is about 100 times less powerful than adrenaline, but its effects are more prolonged. Because of its more lasting effect, it is often combined with adrenaline in commercial preparations. Unlike adrenaline, it is active when taken by mouth. According to the theory of Gaddum and Kwiatkowski, ephedrine exerts its action after a fashion analogous to that by which eserine enhances the action of acetylcholine (ch. 71) namely, by inhibiting the oxidative deamination of adrenaline by amino oxidase. *Tyramine* is a sympathomimetic amine formed by the action of bacteria upon protein (decarboxylation of tyrosine). It is also secreted by the salivary glands of certain mollusks. It is chemically allied to adrenaline and resembles the latter in several of its actions, e.g., it elevates the blood pressure and stimulates the uterine muscle. Its structural formula is:

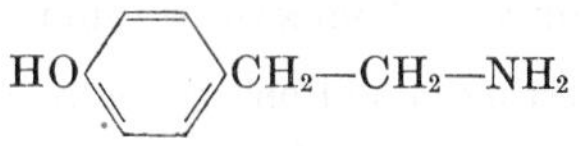

*Tyramine (1-(4'-hydroxyphenyl)-2-amino ethane)*

*Amphetamine* or *benzedrine* is a compound closely allied chemically to adrenaline, as shown in the following formula:

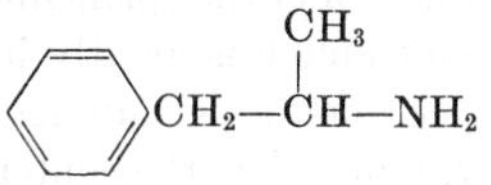

*Amphetamine (1-phenyl-2-aminopropane)*

This sympathomimetic amine has also a stimulating action upon the mental processes somewhat like that of caffeine, inducing wakefulness, postponing mental fatigue, and relieving nervous depression.

A number of other sympathomimetic amines are known. Details of these should be sought in the review by Beyer and in current textbooks of pharmacology.

The skins of certain toads secrete substances (*bufotenine* and *bufotenedine*) similar in action to adrenaline; the secretion of these substances is increased during nervous excitement.

### THE EMPLOYMENT OF ADRENALINE IN MEDICINE

Adrenaline is used (1) to staunch bleeding from accessible mucous surfaces (epistaxis, hematemesis) or from the skin. Because of its pressor effect it is of no value and may do harm in pulmonary hemorrhage and other forms of internal bleeding; (2) to shrink mucous surfaces, especially those of the nose, and is then frequently used in combination with ephedrine; (3) to relax the muscle of the bronchioles in asthma, the relief following its use is very striking; (4) to combat certain allergic conditions, e.g., serum sickness, and to antagonize the effects of the histaminelike substances supposedly liberated in the skin in such conditions as urticaria and giant edema; (5) to stimulate the respiration or to resuscitate the heart which has ceased to beat; in the latter event it may be given by injection into the cardiac musculature. Adrenaline is of value in syncope due to Stokes-Adams disease (p. 193). It should be mentioned that the administration of adrenaline during chloroform anesthesia is attended by the danger of inducing ventricular fibrillation (p. 200); (6) to enhance and prolong the action of cocaine and similar local anesthetics; the vasoconstriction thus induced retards the absorption of these substances, thus prolonging their effects and reducing their toxicity. It is also used as an aid in spinal anesthesia; and (7) noradrenaline has been used in certain hypotensive states for its vasoconstrictor action.

### The Regulation of the Secretions of the Adrenal Medulla

Under resting conditions the adrenal medulla releases very little secretion into the circulation; a recent estimate of the adrenaline equivalent for both adrenals in dogs is about 50 m$\mu$g. per kilogram per minute (Satake). On the other hand, in states of stress (see emergency function, below) or during stimulation of the splanchnic nerve, the output of pressor amine is greatly increased—to 50 to 75 $\mu$g. per minute per adrenal in the dog. Elliott in 1912, found that the content of pressor amines of innervated adrenals fell on stimulation of the splanchnic nerve. More detailed information has been obtained in the dog (Houssay and Rapela) for the output of adrenaline and noradrenaline under various conditions. The output of adrenaline at rest was 10 m$\mu$g. per kilogram per minute and 400 m$\mu$g. per kilogram per minute after stimulation of the splanchnic nerve. The corresponding figures for noradrenaline were 2 m$\mu$g. at rest and 80 m$\mu$g. per kilogram per minute after the nerve stimulation. Clearly the discharge of catechol amines is markedly increased.

There is little doubt that the activity of the adrenal medulla lies under direct nervous control. Denervation of the gland suppresses the release of hormone and the content of hormone declines. Procedures which normally cause the discharge of medullary hormone are ineffective in the denervated gland. Such factors as a fall in pressure in the carotid sinus, emotional excitement, asphyxia, and a fall in blood sugar appear to act

reflexly upon the adrenal through centers in the diencephalon and midbrain. The location of these centers has been investigated by Ranson and Magoun. They found that electrical stimulation of various sites in the hypothalamus, midbrain, and medulla evoked signs of adrenal medullary activity, and it has since been shown by Vogt that these regions are characterized by a high content of noradrenaline. The diabetes which follows puncture of the floor of the fourth ventricle (Bernard) has been found to be due, at least in part, to increased adrenal medullary activity.

In simple terms, the adrenal medulla may be considered to respond to a circulatory stress tending to lower the blood pressure by releasing largely noradrenaline which constricts the arterioles and increases the peripheral resistance. Metabolic stresses, on the other hand, such as a sudden fall in the blood sugar level, are countered by the discharge of adrenaline which frees sugar from the liver and bars the uptake of sugar by the muscles. In order to respond appropriately to such stimuli it might be expected that a dual mechanism exists in the medulla for the release of adrenaline and/or noradrenaline. Information in favor of such a mechanism is accumulating. Measurement of the proportion of adrenaline and noradrenaline in adrenal vein blood has shown that the relative amounts change in accordance with the above concept. Scandinavian histologists have obtained evidence which indicates that some cells of the medulla contain mainly adrenaline, whereas others contain mainly noradrenaline. There may also be special islets of noradrenaline secretory cells. Chromaffin cell tumors in man may contain predominantly adrenaline or noradrenaline, and some exclusively noradrenaline. Further, it has been shown that electrical excitation of different regions of the hypothalamus may liberate preferentially adrenaline or noradrenaline.

Emotional excitement is a strong stimulus to sympathetic and adrenal medullary activity. Studies by Elmadjian and his colleagues on the human indicate that active, *aggressive* emotional displays are related to increased excretion of noradrenaline, whereas tense anxious, but *passive* emotional displays are related to increased excretion of adrenaline in the urine. There also seems to be a relationship between the adrenal content of noradrenaline and the typical behavior in different species. Aggressive animals (cat, lion) have large amounts of nonadrenaline in the adrenal medulla, whereas timid animals (rabbit, guinea pig) have little. The indication exists then, that aggressive excitement leads mainly to an increased blood concentration of noradrenaline, and that emotion of a restrained or defensive type affects mainly the blood content of adrenaline.

The adrenal medulla is supplied by preganglionic sympathetic nerve fibers and the medullary cells themselves replace the ordinary ganglion cells. Because of this relationship, stimuli are transmitted to the medulla cholinergically. The pressor effect of splanchnic stimulation in cats, or of the close arterial injection of acetylcholine, can be almost completely abolished by large doses of nicotine, whereas pretreatment with the anticholinesterase eserine enhances the effect of such stimulation.

### The Role of the Adrenal Medulla in the Body

The adrenal medulla is not essential to life. In animals one adrenal may be removed completely and the medulla of the other excised without any apparent ill effect—the animal survives the operation indefinitely.

THE EMERGENCY THEORY OF ADRENAL FUNCTION. Cannon and his colleagues have furnished convincing evidence that the medulla liberates its secretion in significant amounts only under conditions which call for unusual effort on the part of the body to perform work, to prevent changes in its internal environment or to resist threatened dangers. In such times of stress the medullary secretion, it is believed, reinforces the sympathetic nervous system. Through this hormonal-nervous cooperation, the several bodily reactions associated with such states of emergency are raised to maximal efficiency. Cannon and his associates employed the denervated heart as an indicator of adrenaline liberation. The operation for denervation comprised section of the vagi and removal of the stellate and second thoracic ganglia of the sympathetic chain, so that the heart was completely isolated from nervous control. Inasmuch as in their experiments any effect due to a change in the temperature of the blood was excluded, a pronounced acceleration of a heart so prepared was taken to be the result of a chemical substance carried in the blood stream. Fright, rage, pain, asphyxia, anesthesia, muscular activity, exposure to cold, stimulation of a sensory nerve, and several other conditions, caused within 10 seconds an increase in heart rate of from 20 to 40 beats per minute. Removal of the adrenals, their denervation, or ligation of the adrenal veins, prevented this effect. The conclusion, therefore,

is justified that the various conditions mentioned cause the reflex liberation of the medullary hormone. The denervated heart responds to as little as 1 part of adrenaline in 1400 million parts of blood. In some of Cannon's experiments, cats were frightened by the barking of a dog; the rate of the denervated heart increased by from 15 to 30 beats per minute. The cardiac acceleration was accompanied by pupillary dilation, erection of the hairs, and spitting. When motor activity, e.g., struggling in the animal holder, accompanied the emotional excitement, the cardiac acceleration was more pronounced (40 to 80 beats per minute). Even minor muscular movements without emotion, e.g., extending the legs, walking, or turning the body, caused an acceleration of from 5 to 20 beats per minute.

The hyperglycemia and glycosuria resulting from emotional excitement in man and animals is probably associated with the discharge of adrenaline, since it has been shown that the continued rise in blood sugar which occurs during the emotional reactions (sham rage) following removal of the cerebral cortex (p. 1239) is dependent upon the adrenals. The blood sugar continues to rise after this operation, though the glycogen stores of the liver are removed from nervous control by sectioning the hepatic nerves. On the other hand, the effect does not occur after removal of the adrenals, even though the hepatic nerves are intact. In those instances in which the emotional state does not follow the operation of decortication, the hyperglycemic effect also fails to appear. Puncture of the floor of the fourth ventricle or stimulation of the adrenal nerves also causes hyperglycemia after the hepatic nerves have been previously cut.

Though direct evidence is difficult to obtain it is reasonable to assume that besides the effects mentioned above, adrenaline when secreted into the blood stream brings about other actions which we have seen to be characteristic of its action when injected.

A recapitulation of the actions of the sympathoadrenal system will show how useful these several actions are in fitting an animal for defense or flight; for attack or pursuit. (1) The rise in general blood pressure accompanied by dilation of the vessels of the contracting skeletal muscles, and of the coronary arteries, and the increased force and output of the heart, raise the circulatory system to a state of maximal efficiency. (2) Hyperglycemia indicates the mobilization of the carbohydrate stores of the liver: thus, an adequate supply of fuel for the active muscles is ensured; muscular fatigue occurs less readily. (3) Increased oxygen capacity of the blood is brought about by the discharge of red cells from the spleen. (4) Bronchiolar dilation and an increase in the rate and depth of respiration permit an increased oxygen intake to supply the tissue cells; at the same time the level of oxygen consumption of the latter is raised. (5) Shortened coagulation time of the blood lessens the danger from hemorrhage. (6) Finally, the emotional manifestations of man and the fighting attitudes or defense reactions of various animals are sympathoadrenal effects, e.g., pupillary dilation; and, possibly, the startled expression due to contraction of Mueller's orbital muscle which retracts the upper eyelid; cutaneous vasoconstriction; acceleration of the heart; contraction of smooth muscle in the skin causing "gooseflesh" in man, and the erection of the hairs, quills or feathers of animals; sweating; salivary secretion (cat),[2] and the color changes of some cold blooded animals.

However, it is important to bear in mind that the above reactions are not *essential* to survival. In Cannon's studies, completely sympathectomized cats with denervated adrenal medullae lived entirely normal lives in the laboratory. Only when the animals were placed in an emergency situation did the effects of the operation become evident. Then the changes set out in the preceding paragraph were reduced in intensity or absent.

THE TONUS THEORY OF ADRENAL FUNCTION. It has been suggested that the medulloadrenal secretion maintains the sympathetic nerve endings in a state of sensitivity or tone and that the height of the normal blood pressure is dependent upon the continuous discharge of the hormone into the blood. Low blood pressure has been ascribed to adrenaline deficiency (so-called hypoadrenalemia) and essential hypertension to the liberation of adrenaline in excess (hyperadrenalemia). But the evidence against such conjectures is conclusive; the theory has been entirely discredited. For example, if one adrenal is excised and the other cureted or burned away, no fall in blood pressure occurs, so long as a sufficient amount of cortical tissue is left intact. Furthermore, we have seen that adrenaline does not increase the peripheral resistance (which is the basis of essential hypertension), and neither noradrenaline nor adrenaline is found in greater than usual amounts in the ad-

[2] It is an interesting and perhaps a significant fact that in the cat, in which spitting is a defense reaction, sympathetic stimulation causes a profuse watery flow of juice from the salivary glands. In other animals sympathetic stimulation causes a scanty flow of viscid saliva, a watery secretion being caused by parasympathetic excitation.

renals of hypertensive subjects. There are, however, certain types of hypertension, namely those associated with pheochromocytomata or adrenal hyperplasia, which are due to hypersecretion of the hormones of the adrenal medulla.

PHEOCHROMOCYTOMA AND HYPERPLASIA OF THE ADRENAL MEDULLA. Pheochromocytoma is a tumor composed of chromaffin tissue arising either in the adrenal medulla itself or in an outlying collection of chromaffin cells (paraganglia, Zuckerkandl's organ). The secretion of one of these growths, or of a simple hyperplasia of the adrenal medulla, is a rare cause of hypertension, though not as rare as it once was thought to be. The hypertension may be due to the presence in the circulation of unusual amounts of adrenaline, or of noradrenaline, or of both hormones, of which the tumor or hyperplastic medullary tissue contains excessive amounts. Noradrenaline rather than adrenaline is usually in greatest concentration and may constitute 90 per cent of the gland's hormone content. Both hormones have been found in excess in the urine of subjects of this type of arterial hypertension. The hypertension may be paroxysmal, with sometimes a violent onset, or the excessive secretion of the hormones may be continuous, the high blood pressure then being sustained and indistinguishable, clinically, from essential hypertension. Hyperglycemia and glycosuria, especially when the disease is paroxysmal, may occur; pallor, rapid pulse and profuse sweating usually accompany the attack. Peripheral circulatory collapse may ensue during a paroxysm which is thought to be analogous to the shock in animals which follows the injection of large doses of adrenaline; or hypotension and circulatory collapse may result from surgical removal of the tumor. This is attributed to the depressed tone of the vasomotor center, made evident only after the abolition of the excessive adrenal secretion. Adrenal hypertension can be distinguished from essential and other hypertensive states by means of Goldenberg's benzodioxane test. Benzodioxanes temporarily abolish, through their adrenergic blocking action, hypertension of adrenal origin, but not that due to other causes. Alternatively, in cases of paroxysmal hypertension drugs which stimulate the adrenal medulla, such as histamine or methacholine, may be given in order to determine whether a paroxysm can be initiated.

SYMPATHIN

It has been mentioned that the *prompt* acceleration of the denervated heart does not occur in adrenalectomized animals during excitement, sensory nerve stimulation, etc. Cannon and his colleagues found, however, that a *slowly developing* acceleration of the denervated heart occurred during excitement or muscular activity though the adrenals had been extirpated. The increase in heart rate took about a minute to develop, reached its maximum in about 3 minutes and then gradually subsided. Its occurrence was not prevented by the removal of all accessory adrenal tissue, by hypophysectomy or by the excision of the thyroid, parathyroids, or gonads, or by denervation of the liver. It was abolished, however, by by removal of the sympathetic chains. It was also found that the characteristic slow acceleration of the heart occurred when the lower abdominal sympathetic chain was stimulated. The latter nerve contains fibers supplying the smooth muscle of the skin which are responsible for the erection of the tail hairs. Secretion of the denervated salivary glands, contraction of the nictitating membrane, a rise in blood pressure and of blood sugar also resulted from the stimulation of the abdominal sympathetic. These effects as well as the cardiac acceleration occurred though the cord had been divided in the thoracic region, and the sympathetic chain above this level removed. A material originating in the hind part of the animal was evidently conveyed in the blood stream to the heart and other structures mentioned. Blocking the blood flow returning from the area supplied by the stimulated nerve or removal of the patch of skin prevented the cardiac response. As a result of these researches, Cannon and his associates concluded that during sympathetic stimulation a chemical substance resembling adrenaline in its action was liberated from the sympathetic endings supplying the smooth muscle of the skin. They named this substance *sympathin.*

Cannon and Rosenblueth found that sympathin and adrenaline showed certain differences in action. Preparations of adrenaline (e.g., U.S.P. epinephrine) exhibited both excitatory and inhibitory actions, whereas there appeared to be two types of sympathin; one, which they named *sympathin E* (excitatory), was formed at the terminals of some sympathetic nerves, such as vasoconstrictors, whereas the other type, called *sympathin I* (inhibitory), was produced at other nerve terminals, such as those in the small intestine. But sympathin E was found to be not purely excitatory, and sympathin I not purely inhibitory. This rather confusing state of affairs has been clarified by the discovery of the existence of two hormones of the adrenal medulla. Sympathin E is now considered to be noradrenaline, as first suggested by Bacq; sympathin I is thought to be adrenaline itself. von Euler proposes that the qualifying letter E and I should be substituted by N (for noradrenaline) and A (for adrenaline).

It is clear that noradrenaline rather than adrenaline is the predominant humor liberated at nerve endings, and in this context it is interesting to find that the excretion of noradrenaline in the urine is within normal limits in patients following bilateral adrenalectomy, whereas the content of adrenaline falls markedly.

## The Adrenal Cortex

The cortex of the adrenal, unlike the medulla, is essential to life. Removal of more than about five-sixths of this part of the adrenal causes death within a few days unless replacement therapy is instituted. Removal of the interrenal body of Elasmobranch fishes (p. 1022) is also fatal, but comparative work on the amphibia is complicated by the difficulty of complete removal of the organ without serious damage to the kidney. Stewart and Rogoff found that the average survival time of dogs after complete double adrenalectomy was 10 days and the maximal time 15 days. They observed that pregnant or pseudopregnant animals survived much longer and suggested that some substance formed at this time substituted for the adrenal hormone. The substance in question is probably progesterone (p. 1086), and, indeed, it has since been shown that progesterone administration prolongs the life of adrenalectomized dogs, rats, and ferrets. Numerous attempts were made to extract some substance from the adrenal gland which was able to maintain life, and in 1927, Stewart and Rogoff, and Hartman announced the preparation of suitable extracts. Both groups used watery extracts of the organ, but in 1930, Swingle and Pfiffner demonstrated that with the aid of lipid solvents a very potent substance could be extracted from the cortex which maintained adrenalectomized animals indefinitely and could be used successfully in the treatment of patients suffering from a deficiency of adrenal cortical hormone (Addison's disease). At this time it was thought by Hartman that the adrenal cortex produced a single hormone, and he called this *cortin.* Subsequent work has established the existence of a number of active adrenal hormones which, since they are steroid compounds, are termed *adrenal steroids.*

### The Effects of Bilateral Adrenalectomy

During the short period of survival characteristic of the completely adrenalectomized animal, a variety of manifestations of adrenal cortical deficiency can be detected. These are also present in the patient suffering from reduced

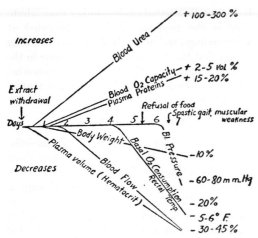

FIG. 58.5. Characteristic changes in metabolism, circulation, and blood concentration in a group of adrenalectomized animals following withdrawal of extract. (From Harrop and associates.)

adrenal function. There is a loss of appetite (particularly for fats), vomiting, diarrhea, rapid loss of weight, muscular weakness and prostration, pronounced diuresis until the later stages, a fall in body temperature, hypotension, and a reduction in the basal metabolic rate of about 20 per cent (see fig. 58.5). The blood becomes concentrated (due to loss of plasma water) and shows a fall in the serum sodium and glucose, and a rise in nonprotein nitrogen, phosphate, calcium, and especially potassium. The urinary excretion of sodium is increased (pp. 554–555) and that of potassium reduced. There is a reduced excretion of urinary nitrogen and other signs of renal failure. Although there is a spontaneous diuresis the elimination of ingested water is defective. The glycogen store of the liver and muscles is diminished. When placed in a cold environment the metabolic response of the adrenalectomized animal is less than normal and any form of stress is poorly met. Many of the above changes are detectable within 42 hours of the operation. Postmortem examination frequently shows congestion of the gastrointestinal tract and pancreas. There may be erosions in the mucosa of the stomach and intestine, and gastric ulcers may be observed; the gastric juice may lack hydrochloric acid—*achlorhydria*.

It will be seen that the adrenal cortex exerts an influence over a wide variety of bodily functions. As might be expected the individual suffering from adrenal cortical insufficiency is extremely susceptible to the damaging effects of a wide variety of stimuli such as changes in the environmental temperature, traumatic injuries, burns, severe muscular exercise, infections, and the ad-

ministration of toxic agents such as histamine and diphtheria toxin. Such stimuli may be grouped together as *stresses*. A supply of adrenal cortical hormones will greatly increase the resistance of an adrenalectomized individual to such noxious agents. The adrenal cortex also appears to be concerned in some way with the maintenance of the nutrition of certain nervous tissues; degenerative changes have been noted in autonomic ganglia (cervical, stellate, and celiac) following adrenalectomy, and almost complete loss of function of the vasomotor and cardiac accelerator nerves in adrenalectomized animals has been described. The relation of the adrenal cortical hormone to the development of renal hypertension is described in chapter 27, and the role of the adrenal cortex in lactation is mentioned in chapter 60.

Changes such as those outlined above can be prevented or reversed by the administration of adrenal cortical extracts, and even comatose animals can be restored to health. In treated adrenalectomized bitches, for example, heat will occur and pregnancy and lactation ensue normally. Adrenalectomized puppies given cortical extract will continue to grow.

The part played by adrenal hormones in salt and water metabolism merits a little more attention (see also ch. 34). In adrenalectomized animals, as well as in human adrenal insufficiency, there is a marked reduction in total base due mainly to the loss of sodium, apparently through diminished reabsorption by the renal tubules, whereas the potassium concentration of the serum is raised above normal. The renal excretion of potassium is reduced and, perhaps most important, there is a shift of potassium from the intracellular to the extracellular fluids. In combination with an increased elimination of water by the kidney marked dehydration results. Under these conditions the administration of sodium chloride to adrenalectomized animals and a reduction in the potassium intake exert a remarkably beneficial effect. On the other hand, the withdrawal of salt from the diet increases the severity of the condition. The sodium rather than the chloride ion is the important factor.

The reduction of blood sodium was observed originally by Bauman and Kurland, and the effects of transfusions of saline in sustaining adrenalectomized animals were described by Stewart and Rogoff, and by Hartman, but the importance of sodium loss in the development of the symptoms was first pointed out by Loeb and his associates, and by Harrop. The value of a low potassium content of the diet in the survival of adrenalectomized animals was shown by Allers and his associates. Completely adrenalectomized animals can be maintained in good health without treatment by a cortical hormone if placed upon a diet low in potassium but high in sodium chloride and, in order to prevent the acidosis which otherwise develops, containing sodium citrate. The tendency to hypoglycemia is controlled by a high carbohydrate diet. These measures, however, do not completely restore an animal to a physiological state, for they are unable to withstand stress or to perform work with full efficiency.

### The Physiological Actions of Adrenal Cortical Extract

Extracts of the adrenal cortex contain a large number of steroids, of which only a minority are of importance physiologically. In view of the wide spectrum of activity of the adrenal steroids it is convenient to classify them into three groups according to the characteristic action of each steroid. These are:

1. The *glucocorticoids*, which particularly affect carbohydrate metabolism.

2. The *mineralocorticoids*, which are highly active in the control of mineral and water metabolism.

3. The *androgenic corticoids*.

Before examining each group in more detail it must be pointed out that representatives of each group possess overlapping activities. Thus cortisone, which is classed as a glucocorticoid, also acts on salt and water metabolism, and conversely, aldosterone, which is a highly potent mineralocorticoid, possesses very definite glucocorticoid activity. It is possible, as Bush has suggested, that the adrenal steroids could be grouped according to whether they are secreted under 'steady state' conditions independently of pituitary control, or as a 'stress function,' being discharged in response to stress stimuli *via* pituitary adrenocorticotrophic hormone.

The *glucocorticoids* are characterized as a class by the presence of an oxygen atom at position 11 (see pp. 1038–1039) either as a doubly bound oxygen or as an hydroxyl group. In the absence of this grouping there is little or no effect on carbohydrate, fat, or protein metabolism, whereas an hydroxyl group in addition at position 17, as in cortisone, enhances the activity of the steroid. The most important compounds in this group are cortisone (or Kendall's compound E), 17-hydroxycorticosterone (compound F), and corticosterone (compound B).

The fundamental action of the glucocorticoids lies in the domain of glucose production and utilization for in the salt maintained adrenalectomized rat there is apparently little abnormality in the storage of carbohydrate until a period of fasting is instituted, when hypoglycemia develops and the store of glycogen in the liver is rapidly depleted. Administration of adrenal steroids is followed by a large increase in liver glycogen. The glucocorticoids exert their effects in a variety of ways. There is an increase in the catabolism of tissue protein with the carbon fraction of the amino acids being used for the production of glucose. Because of this stimulation of gluconeogenesis, the glucocorticoids exert a marked anti-insulin action. Administration of these corticoids exacerbates diabetes and will induce diabetes in the force fed normal individual; the diabetes so produced is ameliorated by insulin only with difficulty. There are indications that cortical extracts decrease the amount of glucose that is utilized. The daily administration of cortisone to rats fed a high carbohydrate diet results in a severe hyperglycemia and glycosuria, and the increased urinary nitrogen accounts for only a fraction of the glucose present in the urine (Ingle).

The glucocorticoids cause the mobilization of fat from the fat depots and increase the fat content of the liver. Nothing more need be said here concerning the role played by the adrenal cortex in the metabolism of carbohydrate and fat inasmuch as these subjects have been dealt with in chapters 48 and 49.

The point of action of the adrenal hormones in the metabolic processes touched upon above is not clear. Studies on the enzyme content of various tissues, before and after adrenalectomy, indicate that a variety of enzymes may be reduced in amount, but it has not yet been possible to go much further than this.

Under stressful conditions there is an increased liberation of glucocorticoids. This action is mediated *via* the adrenocorticotrophic hormone of the pituitary and does not occur in the hypophysectomized individual. Whereas the glucocorticoids are highly active in increasing resistance to stress, the mineralocorticoids are relatively ineffective. Allied to their protective action in stress is the effect the glucocorticoids exert on muscular efficiency. One characteristic of adrenal cortical insufficiency is the early onset of muscular weakness and fatigue. Administration of cortisone restores the normal work performance of muscles.

The *mineralocorticoids* exert their most striking action upon the kidney, although there is increasing evidence for a generalized effect in the body, possibly on cell surfaces. In the adrenalectomized animal there is an abnormally large excretion of sodium and chloride by the kidney and this phenomenon may be abolished by administration of adrenal cortical extract. Study of the individual steroids isolated from the cortex indicated, until quite recently, that desoxycorticosterone (desoxycorticosterone acetate = DOCA) was the most potent in the regulation of electrolyte metabolism. However, there always remained in the mother liquor of the extract an active, noncrystalline residue termed simply the *amorphous fraction*. Most of the biological activity effective in prolonging the life of adrenalectomized animals under low stress conditions remained in the amorphous fraction. In 1952, Simpson, Tait, Wettstein, Neher, von Euw, and Reichstein announced the crystallization of a new steroid from adrenal extracts which was from 30 to 100 times more active than desoxycorticosterone in promoting sodium retention and was effective in the rat in amounts of 0.1 μg. or less. Sodium retention in man can be demonstrated with doses of 100 μg. Initially the compound was termed electrocortin, but following the determination of the structure of the steroid, the name *aldosterone* was suggested in 1954, and has since been generally adopted. Aldosterone is unique among the adrenal steroids in possessing an aldehyde group at position 18 (p. 1039).

Among the "classical" adrenal steroids, *desoxycorticosterone* exhibits the greatest influence on the kidney. This compound increases the concentration of sodium in the body fluids, but reduces the concentration of potassium. It also reduces the intracellular concentration of potassium and increases that of sodium (fig. 58.6) and with prolonged administration, the concentration

of sodium may nearly equal that of potassium. The administration of potassium almost completely corrects the abnormal quantitative relationship of these electrolytes. Through its action in causing sodium and water retention, the administration of desoxycorticosterone may be followed by a great increase in plasma volume and edema, especially if the intake of sodium is increased. With overdosage, more serious effects may result such as hypertension, dilation of the right ventricle, and pulmonary congestion. Death from cardiac failure has resulted from its clinical use. The rapid increase in plasma volume, and, as a result of this, the extra burden thrown upon the cardiovascular system, are thought to be the most important factors leading to these ill effects although depression of the potassium concentration of the body fluids may be the lethal factor in some instances. Loeb and his associates have shown that administration of desoxycorticosterone to animals may lower the potassium level to the point where paralysis results. In dogs given desoxycorticosterone for several successive days, a condition resembling diabetes insipidus develops. The water intake, especially if salt is administered as well, is increased by from 6 to 10 fold. The output of urine rises accordingly and its specific gravity falls. The administration of potassium salts or a reduction in the sodium intake is undoubtedly of benefit in patients receiving large doses of desoxycorticosterone.

The actions of aldosterone differ in some respects from those of desoxycorticosterone. A comparison of the relative potency of the two hormones shows that aldosterone is about 25 times as active as desoxycorticosterone in maintaining life in adrenalectomized dogs, and about 5 times as effective in promoting potassium excretion in adrenalectomized rats. In the maintenance of sodium and potassium balance in human adrenal insufficiency, aldosterone is the more potent by a factor of 30 or so. Prolonged administration of aldosterone does not, at present, appear to produce hypertension or edema though, like desoxycorticosterone, it results in chloride retention and increased potassium excretion.

The production, and function, of the *androgenic corticoids* produced by the adrenal gland has occasioned much controversy. Typical of the observations that must be taken into consideration is the fact that adrenalectomy disrupts sexual function. In the rat, for example, there is a loss of libido in the male and a suppression of the estrous cycles in the female. Since normal sexual activity is restored in animals given salt, it may be pre-

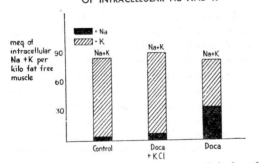

FIG. 58.6. The replacement intracellularly of potassium and sodium in the muscles of normal dogs under the influence of desoxycorticosterone acetate (DOCA). The effect is inhibited by the administration of KCl. (From Loeb.)

sumed that the adrenal steroids are not essential in reproductive processes. On the other hand, estrogens, androgens, and progesterone can be extracted from the adrenal cortex and are found not only in normal urine but that of eunuchs and of ovariectomized women. It is possible that the secretion of androgen by the adrenal is concerned in the persistence of libido after gonadal removal (p. 1075).

Among numerous observations concerning the possible relationship of adrenal hormones to reproduction, the following are of interest here. Special cells (the cells of Stilling) appear in the adrenal cortex of the frog during the mating season. The ovaries of hypophysectomized tadpoles are increased in weight by injections of cortical extract. Stimulation of the adrenal cortex in the castrated rat by administration of adrenocorticotrophic hormone has been found to increase the weight of the accessory reproductive organs. In women, the intermenstrual periods are said to be shortened by from 3 to 5 days by giving cortical extract (Hartman and associates). There is a marked increase in the excretion of adrenal androgens in both boys and girls at puberty. Sexual abnormalities are a striking feature of the syndrome associated with certain tumors of the adrenal gland (p. 1043).

In view of the common origin of the genital organs and the adrenal cortex from the celomic epithelium, and the closely similar chemical structure of the hormones derived from the two sources (see pp. 989 and 1039), it is perhaps not surprising that the steroids produced may overlap in their activities. Further, it is important to note that the adrenal glands of immature mice contain an *X-zone* of cells with an acidophilic cytoplasm and prominent basophilic nuclei; it immediately invests the medulla. In the male, the X-zone collapses as a result of the direct action of the androgens produced at puberty; if castration is performed, the X-zone persists and may enlarge. In the immature female the X-zone continues to develop up to puberty and can then persist for several months until it too disappears, possibly under the influence of androgen. The function of the X-zone is not clear. A somewhat similar zone is distinguishable as the *fetal cortex* in the newborn human. In this case the greater part of the cortex at birth (apart from a peripheral layer of cortical cells which develops into the definitive cortex) is destined to involute and disappear in the first months of extrauterine life. Despite considerable research, the function of the fetal cortex is also obscure although it is speculated that the cells produce androgen. According to Benirschke, and Lanman, to cite recent workers, it would seem that the fetal cortex is trophically stimulated by chorionic gonadotrophin (p. 1093), or possibly luteinizing hormone (p. 971) from the fetal pituitary, and that upon withdrawal of this hormone at birth, involution occurs.

The adrenal cortex possesses spheres of influence additional to those described above. In the rat it has been found that desoxycorticosterone will restore the rate of *growth* of young adrenalectomized rats to normal, and that the amorphous fraction is almost as active. Corticosterone and cortisone are not active in this respect and in general cortisone acts to suppress growth. Clinically, cortisone has frequently been found to induce a negative nitrogen balance; this effect may be modified by increasing the diet and supply of protein. Administration of adrenal cortical hormone, or the application of (stressful) stimuli leading to the discharge of cortical hormone, produces a *dissolution of lymphocytes and a fall in the lymphocyte count* in the blood. There is also an *eosinopenia*. With high dosage of cortisone there is an atrophy of the thymus, spleen, and lymph nodes. There may be an increase in the titer of circulating antibodies in certain species. Recent work has emphasized the effects of the adrenal steroids, and particularly cortisone, on mesodermal tissues. Inflammation of these tissues (connective tissue, synovial membranes, reticulum), which is prominent in the so-called *collagen diseases*, is abruptly arrested by cortisone. Cortisone also delays *wound healing* by interference with the formation of granulation tissue and fibrosis. Desoxycorticosterone, in contrast, markedly stimulates the fibroblasts and ground substance. Cortisone also appears to inhibit the enzyme hyaluronidase and thus to decrease cell permeability.

### OUTLINE OF THE BIOCHEMISTRY OF THE ADRENOCORTICAL HORMONES

There is good evidence that the adrenal cortical hormones are produced in the adrenal from cholesterol, which is in turn synthesized from acetate. This is indicated by the finding that when an adrenal gland is perfused with $C^{14}$-labeled cholesterol, labeled corticosterone and 17-hydroxycorticosterone are produced. Additionally, incubation of adrenal slices, or perfusion of isolated adrenal glands with labeled acetate, results in the formation of labeled cholesterol and corticosteroid. It has been found that the cholesterol content of the adrenal cortex is reduced by half by the injection of pituitary adrenocorticotrophic hormone, by trauma, or in states of stress (Long and associates). The fall is greatest some 5 to 6 hours after administration of ACTH and requires about 24 hours for the restoration of the normal level. No similar reduction in the cholesterol content of other organs has been observed to follow the injection of ACTH, so that the response appears to be specific to the adrenal cortex. An increase in liver glycogen accompanies the fall in adrenal cholesterol and is taken as an indication of the release of glucocorticoids.

The ascorbic acid content of the adrenal is reduced by 50 per cent or more by ACTH or by trauma. This finding has been much used as an index of the release of ACTH by various stimuli, and forms the basis of an assay method for ACTH. In the rat, injection of ACTH results in a depletion of adrenal ascorbic acid which is maximal in about 1 hour. The concentration of ascorbic acid is rising in 3 hours and is restored to normal or above in 12 hours. The significance of ascorbic acid with respect to adrenal cortical function is, however, unknown, since in the guinea pig elaboration of the adrenal corticoids has been found to continue in the scorbutic animal, that is in the absence of ascorbic acid.

Analysis of extracts of ox glands has established the existence of between 20 and 30 steroids in the adrenal. Seven are of major importance although others are probably essential as intermediates in the synthesis of the discharged hormone. The seven biologically active corticoids are: corticosterone, desoxycorticosterone, 11-dehydrocorticosterone, 17-hydroxycorticosterone (hydrocortisone), 17-hydroxy-11-dehydrocorticosterone (cortisone), 17-hydroxy-11-desoxycorticosterone, and aldosterone. Their formulas, and the various synonyms, are illustrated in figure 58.1.

Corticosterone was isolated by Reichstein and his associates, and by Kendall and his colleagues, in 1937, and was later synthesized by the former workers. It is also known as Kendall's compound B. Desoxycorticosterone, lacking the hydroxyl group at carbon 11, was later synthesized by Steiger and Reichstein from stigmasterol but is present in minor amount in the adrenal.

The adrenal corticoids are included in the group of $C_{21}$-steroids, that is steroids with 2 methyl groups as well as a side chain of 2 carbon atoms at $C_{17}$. They also have a $\Delta^4$-3-ketone grouping believed to be essential for corticoid

activity and a characteristic $\alpha$-ketol (—CO—$CH_2OH$) grouping in the side chain attached at $C_{17}$. The oxygen component on carbon 11 appears to confer on the molecule activity in relation to carbohydrate metabolism, for such properties are minimal in desoxycorticosterone. Aldosterone is unique in possessing an aldehyde grouping at carbon 18.

As recorded earlier, the adrenal gland secretes steroids which exert an effect upon the genital tract. These include *estrone, progesterone, 17-"$\beta$"-hydroxyprogesterone, $\Delta^4$-androstenedione-3-17* and *adrenosterone* ($\Delta^4$-androstenetrione-3,11,17). The last three of these compounds are androgenic and the last two have a ketone group at position 17 and are known as adrenal neutral *17-ketosteroids* (17-KS). The 17-ketosteroids excreted in normal urine are *adrenosterone, dehydroisoandrosterone,* and *11-hydroxyisoandrosterone.* Cortical steroids of both the 11-oxy and the 11-desoxy series are also excreted in the urine. These and the 17-KS are excreted in increased amount in adrenal tumors or following the administration of ACTH.

Adrenosterone is the most active androgen in the adrenal cortex, and has the formula:

*Adrenosterone*

THE NATURAL CORTICAL HORMONE. The corticoid content of human adrenal vein blood has now been studied by a number of workers, and it appears that the main constituents are hydrocortisone and corticosterone. Aldosterone is also secreted in low concentration, but in a potent amount. The human, monkey, sheep, and guinea pig secrete primarily hydrocortisone, the rabbit and rat primarily corticosterone, the dog and cat mainly hydrocortisone with some corticosterone, and the ferret, ox, and cow a mixture of both in roughly equal parts. There is, however, a considerable variation within any one species. For further information on this subject see the review by Hechter and Pincus.

URINARY EXCRETION AND ASSAY. A wide variety of steroids may be isolated from human urine, and it is well established that a number originate in the adrenal glands. They are excreted both in the free form and following conjugation with glu-

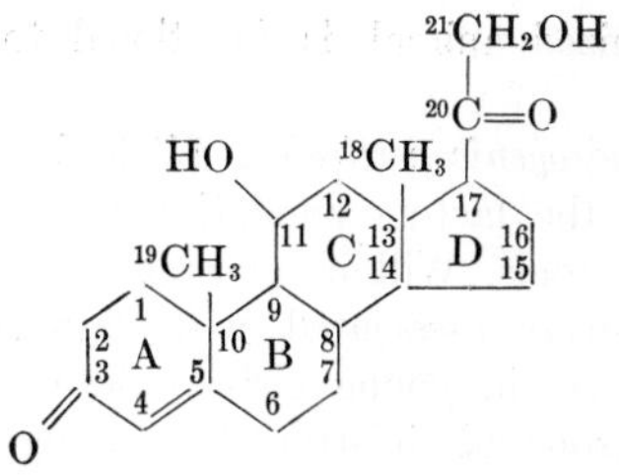

FIG. 58.1. Formulas of adrenocortical principles.

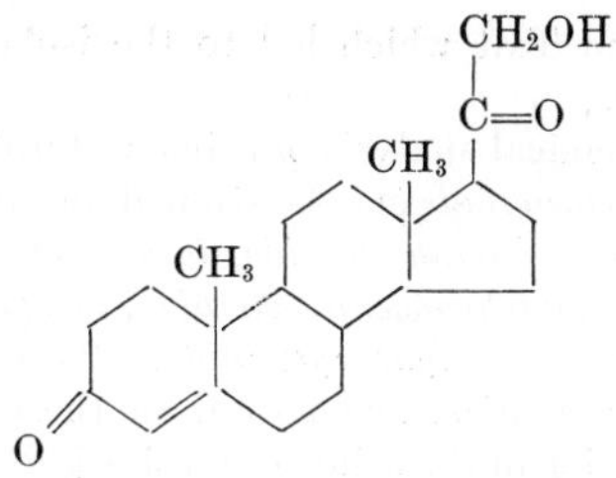

curonic acid to form water soluble glucuronides. Some may also be linked with sulfuric acid and excreted as sulfates. Before analysis of urine can be undertaken, it, therefore, becomes necessary to free the steroids from conjugation by hydrolysis with mineral acid or, better, by incubation with the enzyme β-glucuronidase. The steroids can then be extracted from the urine and subjected to analysis by a variety of procedures.

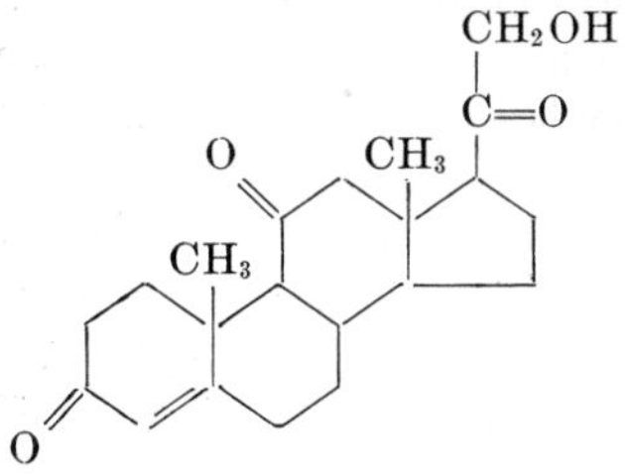

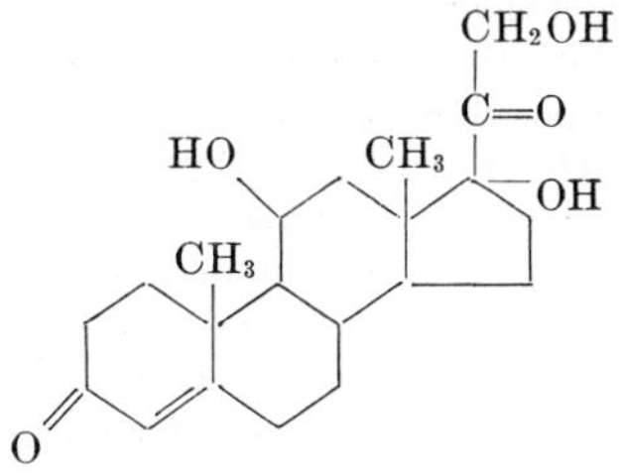

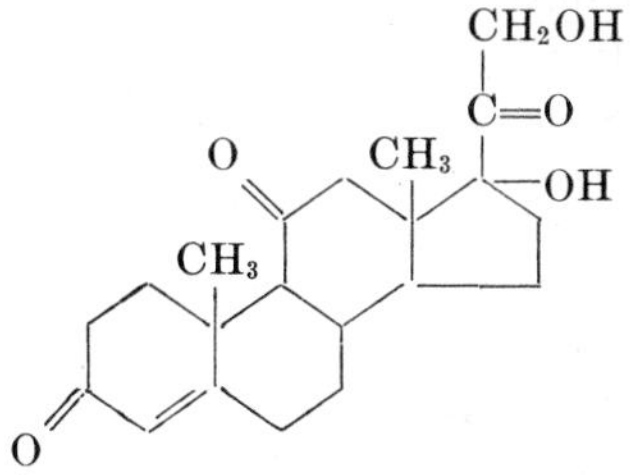

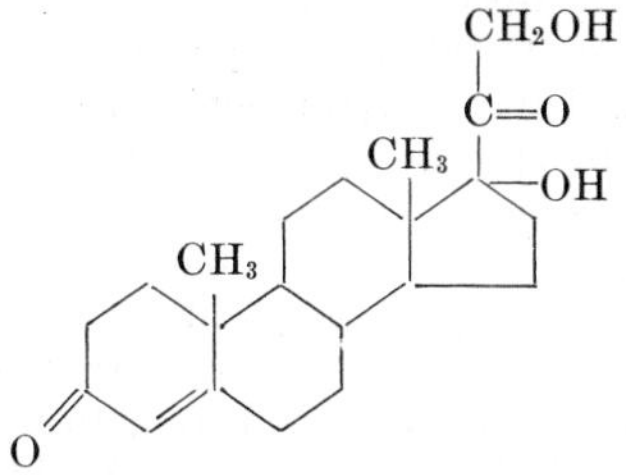

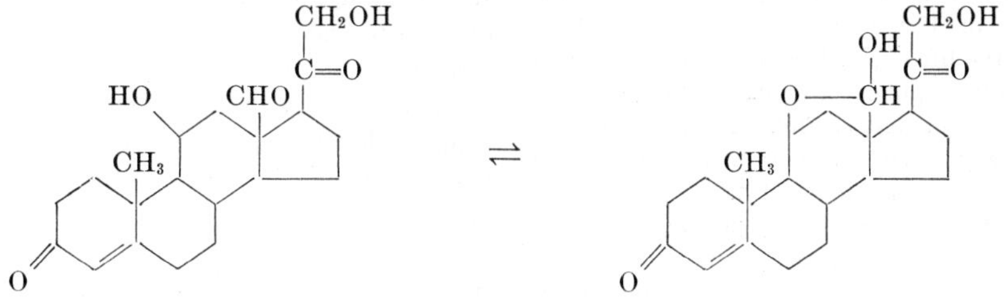

For assay of adrenal corticoids, a selection may be made from a great profusion of both biological and chemical techniques. The information gained is often complementary, but with a growing under-

standing of the relationship between structure and function of the adrenal hormones, emphasis is now being given to chemical methods. The bioassays utilize effects such as the glycogen deposition induced in the livers of adrenalectomized mice, the action of adrenal corticoids in prolonging the lives of adrenalectomized rats subjected to cold, the fall in blood eosinophils induced by adrenal steroids in the adrenalectomized mouse, and elimination of radioactive sodium and potassium. A procedure based on the ability of corticoids to depress the ratio of $Na^{24}/K^{42}$ in the urine of adrenalectomized rats proved of great value in the studies of

Simpson and Tait which led to the isolation of aldosterone.

In the chemical analysis of urinary steroids, the *neutral 17-ketosteroids* may be studied, or attention given to the *reducing steroids, formaldehydogenic steroids, acetaldehydogenic steroids, 17-ketogenic steroids, total 17-hydroxysteroids, Porter-Silber chromogenic steroids,* and so on. In these procedures a fraction of the urinary steroids is examined in detail but the data obtained seldom permits presentation of the results in terms of a particular substance. With the use of *paper chromatographic methods* it is possible to identify individual steroids in extracts of urine, but highly quantitative observations cannot yet be made. In the past much emphasis has been put on the analysis of urinary steroids for assessing adrenal cortical activity in the human patient. The recent introduction of radioactive hydrocortisone, labeled with $C^{14}$ in ring A, has made possible a more direct method (Peterson and Wyngaarden, Cope and Black) for measuring the rate of production of endogenous hydrocortisone.

The *neutral 17-ketosteroids* possess an oxygen atom attached at carbon 17: there is no side chain. They arise from precursors secreted largely by the adrenal cortex and testis, and only in a minor degree by the ovaries. In men, some two-thirds of the neutral 17-ketosteroids are derived from the adrenal cortex. Following the appropriate extraction procedure, the quantity of 17-ketosteroids is determined colorimetrically with the aid of the *Zimmerman reaction*. Here, steroids containing the group $—CO—CH_2$ give a purple color when treated with *m*-dinitrobenzene in the presence of alkali. The output of 17-ketosteroids is not constant throughout the life cycle. In both men and women it rises sharply at puberty, reaches a maximum at about 25 years of age (Hamburger), and subsequently slowly declines. The mean output in healthy 25-year-old males is 14 mg. per day, and in women of the same age 9 mg. per day. In cases of tumors of the adrenal cortex the excretion of 17-ketosteroids is generally increased, and values of more than 1000 mg. per day have been found. In Addison's disease (p. 1042) the output of 17-ketosteroids is usually abnormally low.

## The Regulation of Adrenal Cortical Hormone Secretion

It is clear that the adrenal cortex, unlike the medulla, is under humoral and not nervous control. This is indicated by the marked adrenal atrophy which follows removal of the hypophysis, and the enlargement of the gland which is produced by administration of ACTH. However, the fact that complete adrenalectomy is fatal, whereas hypophysectomy is compatible with life, shows that the adrenal cortex of the hypoph-

ysectomized animal is functional to some extent.

*1. Androgenic corticoids.* Little is known regarding the factors regulating the secretion of these steroids. Wilkins observed that the virilizing effects associated with adrenal cortical hyperplasia in young girls could be controlled by cortisone administration, and suggested that the cortisone was acting by depressing the pituitary release of ACTH and, therefore, the adrenal cortical release of androgenic substances. Such a view implies a dependence of adrenal androgen secretion on ACTH.

*2. Glucocorticoids.* The secretion of corticosterone and 17-hydroxycorticosterone is almost entirely dependent on the pituitary release of ACTH. Hypophysectomy markedly reduces the glucocorticoid content of adrenal vein blood, whereas injection of ACTH gives a rapid and dramatic increase in the concentration of hormone in this blood. The regulation of secretion of the adrenal glucocorticoids becomes a question of the regulation of the secretion of pituitary ACTH (see ch. 56).

*3. Mineralocorticoid (aldosterone).* Unlike other adrenal corticoids the secretion of aldosterone appears to be relatively free from hypophysial control. Evidence in favor of this conclusion includes the following: (a) in the hypophysectomized rat, the output of aldosterone will vary in response to changes in the electrolyte intake; (b) in the hypophysectomized dog, the secretion of aldosterone remains at about normal value whereas that of other steroids falls markedly; (c) similarly, in hypophysectomized man, the urinary aldosterone levels are nearly normal; (d) when cortisone is injected, the adrenal output of hydrocortisone is depressed, but not that of aldosterone. Nevertheless, it is known that ACTH stimulates the production of aldosterone by the adrenal cortex although the mechanism concerned is obscure. It has been suggested that the secretion of aldosterone is controlled directly by the blood level of circulating electrolytes, but Farrell points out that the secretory rate of aldosterone can be tripled during hemorrhage without any associated change in plasma electrolytes, or even in the presence of increasing plasma sodium levels. Further, ablation of the diencephalon in the dog results in a profound fall in aldosterone output without significant changes in serum electrolytes. This latter fact is in line with Farrell's view that the secretion of this steroid is controlled by a factor arising within the head, but not necessarily in the hypophysis. Rauschkolb and Farrell found that, in the dog, removal of the head greatly depresses the secretion rate of aldosterone, but section of the nervous connections between the head and trunk is without effect if the vascular connections are intact. In later work, Farrell has produced suggestive evidence that some humoral factor originating in the region of the dorsal diencephalon is directly concerned with the regulation of aldosterone release.

### Some Therapeutic Uses of Cortisone

Great interest has been aroused within recent years, and both laboratory and clinical research into the functions of the adrenal cortex have been intensified, by the dramatic discovery of Hench and his associates of the therapeutic value of compound E (cortisone) in acute rheumatism and rheumatoid arthritis. In acute rheumatism there is rapid reduction of fever, and of the swelling and pain in the joints, following the oral or parenteral administration of cortisone. The high sedimentation rate which occurs in this disease is restored to the normal by this steroid. Compound F (hydrocortisone) and the adrenotrophic hormone of the hypophysis, ACTH (through its stimulation of the production and liberation of the cortical hormones), have a similarly beneficial effect. Rheumatoid arthritis is in most cases benefitted by these compounds, sometimes dramatically, but improvement as a rule is not sustained after treatment has been discontinued.

The adrenal steroids effect amelioration of these arthritic diseases though there is no evidence of adrenal insufficiency. Inasmuch as such large doses are required, much greater than are employed in the treatment of Addison's disease, it is not credible that these compounds act by correcting a hormone deficiency. That they act pharmacologically, rather than by replacement, there can be little doubt. In the dosage employed they appear to exert a specific effect upon the metabolism of the collagenous tissues (connective tissue fibers embedded in cement or ground substance containing hyaluronic acid) of joints, skin, arteries, and many other structures. The results of Opsahl's experiments may provide a clue to this action. She found that in mice, adrenal cortical extracts inhibited the enzyme hyaluronidase, as shown by a reduction of the "spreading effect" of the enzyme. Compounds A, E, and F exhibit this inhibiting action, but compound E was the most effective.

The *therapeutic value* of cortisone and dehydrocortisone has been investigated in a large number of diseases, many of them apparently quite unrelated to one another. The diseases upon whose course cortisone, dehydrocortisone, or ACTH has been found to have a favorable effect though in many cases this has been slight or evanescent, can for the most part be grouped under three main headings, as shown below:

*Collagenous diseases (collagenoses):*
 Acute rheumatism (rheumatic fever)
 Rheumatoid arthritis
 Rheumatoid spondylitis
 Psoriatic arthritis
 Scleroderma
 Periarteritis nodosa
 Dermatomyositis
*Allergic diseases or diseases due to abnormal sensitivity of cells:*
 Bronchial asthma
 Allergic rhinitis (hay fever)
 Contact or atopic dermatitis
 Urticaria
*Lymphatic and myelogenous diseases:*
 Acute and chronic lymphatic leukemias
 Lymphosarcoma
 Hodgkin's disease
 Lymphoid thyroiditis (struma lymphomatosa)
 Myelogenous leukemia
 Sarcoidosis
 Multiple myeloma

In the following list are a number of other pathological states in which ACTH or cortisone has been employed with variable success and which cannot be placed in any of the above categories: ulcerative colitis, acute inflammatory eye diseases, alcoholism with delirium tremens or Korsakoff's psychosis, chronic nephrosis, Waterhouse-Friderichsen syndrome, Loeffler's syndrome, and the adrenogenital syndrome.

*Deleterious effects which may result from cortisone or ACTH treatment.* A number of serious adverse effects may result from treatment with these agents. Prolonged cortisone therapy may lead to adrenocortical atrophy. Collapse and death from acute adrenal insufficiency may follow cessation of treatment. Several instances of the development of Cushing's disease (ch. 56), e.g., hirsutism, rounding of the facial contours, osteoporosis, kyphosis, and hypertension have been reported from the continued administration of ACTH. Mental aberrations ranging from an exaggerated sense of well being (euphoria), moodiness, or mild anxiety states to definite psychoses, e.g., paranoia, have been reported following cortisone therapy. Wound healing is apparently delayed by cortisone, and resistance to certain infections is lowered. Hamsters can be infected with poliomyelitis virus by intraperitoneal injection, and develop a highly virulent form of the disease if pretreated with cortisone, but animals similarly injected, but not receiving the hormone, could not be infected (Shwartzman). The spread of a tuberculous infection from a previously localized focus is thought to be a serious complication which may follow cortisone therapy. Peptic ulcers are not uncommon with prolonged treatment and perforation of the bowel in cases of ulcerative colitis has sometimes occurred.

### DISEASE OF THE ADRENAL CORTEX IN MAN

#### *Addison's Disease*

The syndrome known today as Addison's disease was first described (in 1855) by Thomas Addison and ascribed by him to tuberculous disease of the adrenals. Experimental and clinical observations since that time have fully substantiated Addison's conclusion that the disease is due to adrenal involvement. Tuberculous disease of the gland is found, however, in only a proportion of the cases. It has also been shown that deficiency of the cortex and not of the medulla is the essential cause of the disease. The condition is most common between the ages of

30 and 50, and is found more often in men than in women. Its chief features, which closely resemble those seen in adrenalectomized animals, are: (a) muscular weakness and languor, (b) low blood pressure and reduced circulation rate, (c) gastrointestinal disturbances, loss of appetite (anorexia), hypochlorhydria, and vomiting, (d) pigmentation of the skin and mucous membranes, bronzing, or tanning—a dirty brown cutaneous discoloration being a classical symptom of the disease, (e) lowered metabolic rate, subnormal temperature, sodium loss and a rise in serum potassium, reduced blood volume (plasma loss), dehydration, and loss of weight, (f) renal insufficiency with consequent rise in blood nonprotein nitrogen, (g) depression of the sexual functions, (h) hypoglycemia, which may be an immediate cause of death, (i) abnormal electroencephalogram, slowing of $\alpha$ rhythm and reduced number of $\beta$ waves, and (j) changes in the electrocardiogram, e.g., low voltage, flat or inverted T, prolongation of P-R and QRS, and depression of RS-T. The pigmentation of the skin may be so deep that the patient is mistaken for a mulatto; it is most pronounced in those regions, nipples, abdomen, etc., where the normal pigmentation is greatest (fig. 58.7). The palms of the hands and soles of the feet remain pale. The discoloration is

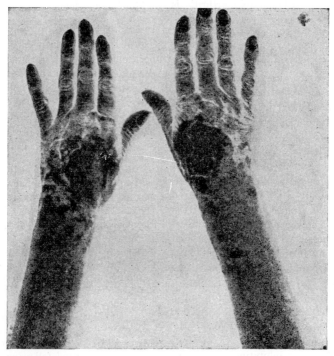

FIG. 58.7. Showing pigmentation of the skin together with patches of depigmentation in a patient with Addison's disease. (From Kepler.)

due to the excessive accumulation of the normal cutaneous pigment, *melanin*. This is deposited chiefly in the basal cells of the epidermis, but pigment granules are also found in the dermis. The change in pigment metabolism which causes the deposits is unknown.[3]

Addison's disease, unless treated with cortical hormone or with a diet of high salt and low potassium content, is almost invariably fatal within from 1 to 3 years. The high salt, low potassium diet exerts an almost specific effect in adrenal insufficiency, but desoxycorticosterone acetate is most usually employed; it is given in oil or as pellets inserted subcutaneously. However, as already mentioned, there are certain disadvantages associated with the use of this corticoid; a marked antidiuresis and edema with sodium retention and loss of potassium occurs when a certain dosage is exceeded. A high sodium and low potassium content of the diet enhances the adverse effects. Nor does the desoxy compound constitute a complete replacement therapy, for the tendency to hypo-

[3] Bloch found that sections of normal skin became deeply pigmented when placed in a dilute solution of 3:4-dihydroxyphenylalanine; albino skin treated similarly remained unpigmented. Solutions of other aromatic compounds (e.g., tyrosine, tryptophane, pyrogallol, etc.) did not cause pigmentation of skin sections. Bloch concluded that *di*hydroxyphenylalanine, which he called *dopa*, was the precursor of melanin, the conversion being brought about by an oxidizing enzyme (dopa oxidase) in the skin. Until recently tyrosinase, present in potato, fungi, and other plants, and which is capable of catalyzing the conversion of tyrosine to "dopa," has been believed to be absent from mammalian tissues. But since its discovery in animals, this enzyme has been assigned the role of catalyzing the reactions, tyrosine to "dopa," and "dopa" to melanin (see Lerner and Fitzpatrick). Tyrosinase is now believed or thought to be identical with Bloch's dopa oxidase (see scheme below).

$$HO\langle\bigcirc\rangle CH_2-CHNH_2-COOH$$

*Tyrosine*

↓

$$HO\langle\bigcirc\rangle CH_2-CHNH_2-COOH$$
$$HO$$

*3:4-Dihydroxyphenylalanine (dopa)*

↓

*Melanin*

*Tyrosinase*

The reactions resulting in melanin production are inhibited by ascorbic acid, and under certain circumstances, by cortical steroids. So far, the foregoing facts have not led to a satisfactory theory of the cause of the pigmentation in Addison's disease.

glycemia during fasting and the EEG and ECG abnormalities are not corrected. Cortisone given with DOCA provides a more complete replacement therapy in Addison's disease.

Acute adrenal cortical hypofunction may be encountered following adrenal surgery, or in patients with chronic adrenal insufficiency who have been subjected to a sudden stress. Bilateral adrenal hemorrhage may occur, most often in children, and the ensuing condition is known as the *Waterhouse-Frederichsen syndrome*.

### *Tumors of the Adrenal Cortex. Adrenogenital Syndrome, Pseudohermaphroditism*[4]

Tumors composed of cortical tissue which secretes an excess of androgenic compounds may arise in the adrenal itself or in aberrant collections of cortical cells (adrenal "rests") which are found in the broad ligament of the uterus, in the neighborhood of the testes or in the retroperitoneal tissue of the abdomen or pelvis. Such growths, or a diffuse hyperplasia of the adrenal cortex, may occur in children or adults, and are associated with extraordinary abnormalities of development, especially of the *accessory organs of sex* and of the *secondary sex characters* (p. 1072).

When cortical hyperplasia, or a tumor composed of cortical tissue, occurs in young children, puberty appears prematurely; a male child of 4 or 5 years, for example, may show the sexual development of an adult (fig. 58.8). The testes and penis are enlarged, hair may appear upon the chest, pubis, and face, and there may be precocious sexual desire. Often there is also unusual muscular development or extreme obesity. There is early ossification of the epiphyses. Male children showing these characteristics have been described as resembling "an infant Hercules" (Herculean type of Weber), or "a burly brewer's drayman" (Guthrie). Growth is rapid as a rule, but the epiphyses fuse early; young subjects of the disease, therefore, do not reach full stature.

In little girls, the breasts hypertrophy, hair appears on the mons veneris and around the vulva, the uterus develops prematurely, the clitoris is hypertrophied, and there is sometimes precocious menstruation. In appearance such children re-

[4] Pseudohermaphroditism is defined as a condition in which the gonads of one sex only are present but the external genitalia combine features of both sexes, so that from inspection of them alone it is difficult or impossible to determine the sex. In true hermaphroditism, both ovarian and testicular tissues are present; it is an embryological aberration and not due to a hyperfunctional adrenal cortex (see also ch. 60).

semble stout little women. Women who are subjects of this disease become mannish in appearance and disposition (virilism, fig. 58.9). The voice deepens, menstruation ceases, the breasts atrophy, and hair may grow upon the chest, face and limbs; homosexuality is a common feature. The urinary excretion of androgens (17-ketosteroids) is increased several fold. In some adult female subjects, the virilism is accompanied by glycosuria and decreased sugar tolerance, due apparently to an increased production of glucocorticoids. This type is known as the Achard-Tiers syndrome and was described by these authors as the "diabetes of bearded women." Adult male subjects of cortical tumors, as a rule, give no evidence of endocrine disturbances. In some, however, an exaggeration of the male characters is manifest, e.g., enlargement of the penis, a tendency to hirsutism, an increased sexual appetite. In others, the tumor secretes excessive amounts of estrogen when a certain degree of feminization is observed, e.g., enlargement of the mammae, atrophy of the testes, and a feminine distribution of fat.

It might be expected that with the increase in active adrenal cortical tissue, changes in electrolyte balance corresponding to those following injections of adrenal cortical hormone, namely, a rise in blood sodium and a fall in potassium, would be found. But actually such changes occur only in a proportion of cases and are, as a rule, moderate in degree. On the other hand, there may be an associated depression of adrenal salt retaining factors with the appearance of Addisonian symptoms, due to atrophy of the opposite adrenal. Surgical removal of the tumor or hyperplastic tissue is the preferred treatment when possible. Sometimes as a result of atrophy of the normal

FIG. 58.8. Enlarged abdomen and precocious sexual development of a boy aged 30 months. A mass palpated in the abdomen was probably a suprarenal cortical tumor. (From Rowntree and Ball.)

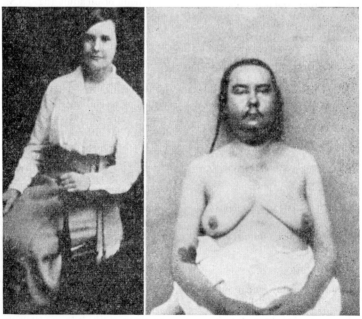

FIG. 58.9. Virilism due to adrenal tumor. On left, at age 28 years before the onset of the disease; on right, at age 35 years at the height of the disease. (From Lescher.)

adrenal tissue, acute cortical insufficiency develops after operation. In order to forestall such a crisis, treatment with a cortical hormone is instituted preoperatively. The administration of cortisone is sometimes successful in suppressing adrenal hyperplasia; the elevated blood level of this hormone tends to inhibit the output of ACTH and, as a consequence, to reduce its stimulating effect upon the hyperplastic tissue. This treatment, however, is of little benefit if the disease is due to a tumor whose activity is independent of pituitary control.

Broster and Vines have made the interesting discovery that hyperplastic adrenal cortical tissue or tumor tissue, in cases of virilism, contains large numbers of cells which have an affinity for fuchsin (fuchsinophil cells). Cells possessing this property are normally absent from the mature adrenal or present only in very small numbers. They are a characteristic feature, however, of the fetal adrenal of both sexes between the 10th and 17th weeks (in the case of the male) and between the 11th and 15th weeks (in the case of the female), but disappear thereafter. These observers suggest that virilism is due to the elaboration of a masculinizing hormone by the fuchsinophil cells, and that the female fetus normally passes through a male phase. The importance of the fuchsinophil cells in the production of hyperadrenocortical manifestations has been questioned, however, by Soffer.

### Primary Aldosteronism

With the isolation of aldosterone as a highly potent mineralocorticoid, and with the development of assays for this steroid, the existence of tumors primarily secreting aldosterone has been established. The syndrome of 'primary aldosteronism' was first described by Conn in 1954, and many cases have now been detected. The major clinical manifestations of the syndrome consist of periodic severe muscular weakness, intermittent tetany and paresthesia, polyuria and polydipsia, and hypertension. The blood sodium level is raised, that of potassium lowered; there is an alkalosis. Only mineral metabolism appears to be affected. Surgical treatment is advised at present.

### Clinical Tests of Adrenal Cortical Function

In mild or atypical cases of adrenocortical insufficiency the following tests may be employed for its detection:

*1. Eosinopenic response to ACTH* is one of the most sensitive tests. In normal persons, a 50 per cent reduction in circulating eosinophils results from the administration of a test dose of cortico-trophin, whereas the response is absent or much reduced in adrenocortical insufficiency.

*2. Robinson-Kepler-Power test* to ingested water. Normally diuresis commences within 30 to 45 minutes after drinking water: in adrenal insufficiency the excretion of the excess water is much delayed.

*3. Cutler-Power-Wilder test.* The urinary excretion of sodium chloride during a 53 hour period of rigidly restricted salt intake accompanied by the administration of potassium. Normally less than 150 mg. per 190 cc. of urine is excreted in the last 4 hours of the test. The subject of adrenal insufficiency excretes a much larger quantity. This test is potentially dangerous, for unless the adrenal insufficiency is of mild or moderate degree, an adrenal crisis may be precipitated.

Other determinations are, the tendency to hypoglycemia during fasting, the sensitivity to insulin, estimation of urinary 17-KS (which are reduced in adrenal insufficiency and increased in normals by ACTH administration), and the uric acid-creatinine ratio which is normally increased by cortical stimulation.

### REFERENCES

ADDISON, T. London, 1855. Reprinted by the New Sydenham Society, 1868.

ALDRICH, T. B. Am. J. Physiol., 1901, **5**, 457.

ALDRICH, T. B. J. Am. Chem. Soc., 1905, **27**, 1074.

ALLEN, W. J. AND ASSOCIATES. J. Physiol., 1946, **105**, 255.

ALLERS, W. D. AND ASSOCIATES. Proc. Staff Meet. Mayo Clin., 1935, **10**, 406.

ALLERS, W. D. AND ASSOCIATES. Proc. Staff Meet. Mayo Clin., 1936, **11**, 283.

BACQ, M. M. Ann. physiol., 1934, **10**, 467.

BAUMANN, E. J. AND KURLAND, S. J. Biol. Chem., 1926, **71**, 281.

BEARN, A. G. AND ASSOCIATES. J. Physiol., 1951, **115**, 430.

BENIRSCHKE, K. AND ASSOCIATES. Endocrinology, 1956, **58**, 598.

BLASCHKO, H. J. Physiol., 1942, **101**, 337.

BOOTHBY, W. M. AND SANDIFORD, I. Am. J. Physiol., 1923, **66**, 93.

BRITTON, S. W. AND SILVETTE, H. Am. J. Physiol., 1932, **100**, 701.

BRITTON, S. W. AND SILVETTE, H. Am. J. Physiol., 1934, **107**, 190.

BROSTER, L. R. AND VINES, H. W. C. The adrenal cortex, a surgical and physiological study. Lewis, London, 1933.

BROSTER, L. R. Lancet, 1934, 1, 830.

BROWN-SÉQUARD, C. E. Compt. rend. Acad. sc., 1856, **43**, 422.

BÜLBRING, E. J. Physiol., 1937, **91**, 18P.

BÜLBRING, E. Brit. J. Pharmacol., 1949, 4, 234.

BÜLBRING, E. AND BURN, J. H. J. Physiol., 1941, **100**, 337.

BÜLBRING, E. AND BURN, J. H. J. Physiol., 1949, **109**, 11P.

CANNON, W. B. Am. J. Physiol., 1914, **33**, 356.

CANNON, W. B. Am. J. Physiol., 1914, **34,** 232, 243, 251.

CANNON, W. B. Am. J. Physiol., 1919, **50,** 399.

CANNON, W. B. New England J. Med., 1928, **199,** 593.

CANNON, W. B. Endocrinology, 1931, **15,** 473.

CANNON, W. B. AND ASSOCIATES. Am. J. Physiol., 1911, **28,** 64.

CANNON, W. B. AND ASSOCIATES. Am. J. Physiol., 1921, **58,** 308, 338.

CANNON, W. B. AND ASSOCIATES. Am. J. Physiol., 1922, **61,** 215.

CANNON, W. B. AND ASSOCIATES. Am. J. Physiol., 1925, **72,** 283, 295.

CANNON, W. B. AND ASSOCIATES. Am. J. Physiol., 1926, **77,** 326.

CANNON, W. B. AND ASSOCIATES. Am. J. Physiol., 1927, **79,** 433, 466.

CANNON, W. B. AND ASSOCIATES. Am. J. Physiol., 1931, **96,** 377, 392.

CANNON, W. B. AND ASSOCIATES. Am. J. Physiol., 1933, **104,** 557.

CHAIKOFF, I. L. Quoted by C. N. H. LONG. Ciba Foundation Colloquia on Endocrinol., 1952, **4,** 379.

CHEN, K. K. J. Am. Pharm. A., 1924, **14,** 189.

CHEN, K. K. AND SCHMIDT, C. F. J. A. M. A., 1926, **87,** 836.

CLEGHORN, R. A. AND ASSOCIATES. Am. J. Physiol., 1939, **126,** 466.

CLEGHORN, R. A. AND ASSOCIATES. J. Physiol., 1939, **96,** 146.

CORI, C. F. AND CORI, G. T. J. Biol. Chem., 1928, **79,** 309.

DAKIN, H. E. J. Physiol., 1905, **32,** xxxiv.

DUNLOP, H. A. J. Physiol., 1929, **67,** 349.

ELLIOTT, T. R. J. Physiol., 1912, **44,** 374.

ELLIOTT, T. R. J. Physiol., 1914, **49,** 38.

VON EULER, U. S. Acta. med. scandinav., 1946, **12,** 73.

GADDUM, J. H. AND KWIATKOWSKI, H. J. Physiol., 1938, **94,** 87.

GOLDENBERG, M. AND ASSOCIATES. Science, 1949, **109,** 534.

GRIFFITH, F. R. Physiol. Rev., 1951, **31,** 151.

GROLLMAN, A. AND FIROR, W. M. J. Biol. Chem., 1933, **100,** 429.

GUTHRIE, L. AND EMERY, W. D'E. Tr. Clin. Soc. London, 1907, **40,** 175.

HARROP, G. A. Bull. Johns Hopkins Hosp., 1936, **59,** 11, 25.

HARROP, G. A. AND ASSOCIATES. J. Exper. Med., 1933, **58,** 1.

HARROP, G. A. AND ASSOCIATES. J. Exper. Med., 1935, **61,** 839.

HARTMAN, F. A. AND KILBORN, L. G. Am. J. Physiol., 1918, **45,** 111.

HARTMAN, F. A. AND ASSOCIATES. Proc. Soc. Exper. Biol. & Med., 1927, **25,** 69.

HARTMAN, F. A. AND ASSOCIATES. Am. J. Physiol., 1928, **86,** 353.

HARTMAN, F. A. AND ASSOCIATES. Am. J. Physiol., 1930, **95,** 670.

HARTMAN, F. A. AND ASSOCIATES. Proc. Soc. Exper. Biol. & Med., 1930, **28,** 94.

HARTMAN, F. A. AND ASSOCIATES. Proc. Soc. Exper. Biol. & Med., 1933, **30,** 560.

HARTMAN, F. A. AND ASSOCIATES. Am. J. Physiol., 1936, **117,** 553.

HECHTER, O. M. Transactions of the 3rd conference on the adrenal cortex, p. 115. Josiah Macy, Jr., Foundation, New York, 1951.

HENCH, P. S. AND ASSOCIATES. Proc. Staff Meet. Mayo Clin., 1949, **24,** 181, 277.

HENCH, P. S. AND ASSOCIATES. Ann. Rheumat. Dis., 1949, **8,** 90, 97.

HIMSWORTH, H. P. AND SCOTT, D. B. M. J. Physiol., 1938, **93,** 159.

HOSKINS, R. G. Am. J. Physiol., 1912, **29,** 363.

HOSKINS, R. G. J. A. M. A., 1927, **88,** 2011.

HOSKINS, R. G. AND MCCLURE, C. W. Arch. Int. Med., 1912, **10,** 343.

HOSKINS, R. G. AND MCCLURE, C. W. Am. J. Physiol., 1912, **30,** 192.

KENDALL, E. C. Proc. Staff Meet. Mayo Clin., 1938, **13,** 519.

KENDALL, E. C. Proc. Staff Meet. Mayo Clin., 1949, **24,** 298.

KENDALL, E. C. AND ASSOCIATES. Proc. Staff Meet. Mayo Clin., 1934, **9,** 245.

KENDALL, E. C. AND ASSOCIATES. Proc. Staff Meet. Mayo Clin., 1936, **11,** 351.

KENDALL, E. C. AND ASSOCIATES. J. Biol. Chem., 1936, **114,** 613.

KENDALL, E. C. AND ASSOCIATES. Proc. Staff Meet. Mayo Clin., 1937, **12,** 136.

LANNAN, J. T. Endocrinology, 1957, **61,** 684.

LESCHER, F. G. Quart. J. Med., 1935, N.S. 4, 23.

LI, C. H. AND ASSOCIATES. J. Biol. Chem., 1943, **149,** 413.

LI, C. H. AND ASSOCIATES. Harvey Lectures, 1951, **46,** 181.

LOEB, R. F. Proc. Soc. Exper. Biol. & Med., 1933, **30,** 808.

LOEB, R. F. J. A. M. A., 1935, **104,** 2177.

LOEB, R. F. Bull. New York Acad. Med., 1940, **16,** 347.

LOEB, R. F. AND ASSOCIATES. J. Exper. Med., 1933, **57,** 775.

LOEB, R. F. AND ASSOCIATES. Science, 1939, **90,** 496.

LONG, C. N. H. Bull. New York Acad. Med., 1947, **23,** 260.

LONG, C. N. H. Proc. Fed. Am. Soc. Exper. Biol., 1947, **6,** 461.

LONG, C. N. H., FRY, E. G. AND THOMPSON, K. W. Am. J. Physiol. Proc., 1938.

LONG, C. N. H. AND LUKENS, F. D. W. J. Exper. Med., 1936, **63,** 465.

MENKIN, V. Am. J. Physiol., 1940, **129,** 691.

NICKERSON, M. AND GOODMAN, L. S. Proc. Fed. Am. Soc. Exper. Biol., 1948, **7,** 397.

OLIVER, G. AND SCHÄFFER, E. A. J. Physiol., 1894, **16,** 1.

OLIVER, G. AND SCHÄFFER, E. A. J. Physiol., 1895, **18,** 230.

OPSAHL, J. C. Yale J. Biol. & Med., 1949, **21,** 255, 433.

OPSAHL, J. C. Transactions of the 2nd conference on the adrenal cortex, Josiah Macy, Jr., Foundation, New York, 1950.

REDFIELD, A. C. J. Exper. Zool., 1918, **26,** 275.

REICHSTEIN, T. AND ASSOCIATES. Helvet. chim. acta, 1936, **19,** 1107.

REICHSTEIN, T. AND ASSOCIATES. Nature, 1937, 139, 26, 925.

ROGOFF, J. M. Proc. California Acad. Med., 1930, 1, 7.

ROGOFF, J. M. Canad. M. A. J., 1931, 24, 43.

ROWNTREE, L. G. AND BALL, R. G. Endocrinology, 1933, 17, 263.

SCHWARTZMAN, G. Proc. Soc. Exper. Biol. & Med., 1952, 79, 573.

SIMPSON, S. A., TAIT, J. F., WETTSTEIN, A., NE-HER, R., VON EUW, J. AND REICHSTEIN, T. Experientia, 1953, 9, 333.

SMITHWICK, R. H., FREEMAN, N. E. AND WHITE, J. C. Arch. Surg., 1934, 29, 759.

SOFFER, L. J. Bull. New York Acad. Med., 1947, 23, 479.

SOSKIN, A. Am. J. Physiol., 1927, 83, 162.

STEWART, G. N. AND ROGOFF, J. M. Science, 1927, 66, 327.

STEWART, G. N. AND ROGOFF, J. M. Am. J. Physiol., 1928, 84, 660.

STEWART, G. N. AND ROGOFF, J. M. Am. J. Physiol., 1928, 86, 20.

STEWART, G. N. AND ROGOFF, J. M. Am. J. Physiol., 1929, 88, 162.

STEWART, G. N. AND ROGOFF, J. M. Am. J. Physiol., 1929, 91, 254.

STEWART, G. N. AND ROGOFF, J. M. J. A. M. A., 1929, 92, 1569.

STOLTZ, F. Ber. deutsch. chem. Gesellsch., 1904, 37, 4149.

SWINGLE, W. W. AND ASSOCIATES. Science, 1930, 71, 321, 489.

SWINGLE, W. W. AND ASSOCIATES. Science, 1930, 72, 75, 483.

SWINGLE, W. W. AND ASSOCIATES. Am. J. Physiol., 1931, 96, 153, 164.

SWINGLE, W. W. AND ASSOCIATES. Proc. Soc. Exper. Biol. & Med., 1932, 29, 1267.

SWINGLE, W. W. AND ASSOCIATES. Am. J. M. Sc., 1932, 183, 1.

SWINGLE, W. W. AND ASSOCIATES. J. Exper. Med., 1933, 58, 17.

SWINGLE, W. W. AND ASSOCIATES. Science, 1933, 77, 58.

SWINGLE, W. W. AND ASSOCIATES. Am. J. Physiol., 1934, 107, 259.

SWINGLE, W. W. AND ASSOCIATES. Am. J. Physiol., 1934, 108, 159.

SZENT-GYÖRGYI, A. Am. J. Physiol., 1929, 90, 536.

SZENT-GYÖRGYI, A. Science, 1930, 72, 125.

TAKAMINE, J. Am. J. Pharm., 1901, 73, 523.

THORN, G. W. AND ASSOCIATES. Proc. Soc. Exper. Biol. & Med., 1936, 35, 247.

VULPIAN, E. F. A. Compt. rend. Acad. sc., 1856, 43, 663.

WELCH, A. D. Am. J. Physiol., 1934, 108, 691.

WILDER, R. M. AND ASSOCIATES. J. A. M. A., 1938, 111, 117.

WILKINS, L., BONGIOVANNI, A. M., CLAYTON, G. W., GRUMBACH, M. M. AND VAN WYK, J. Ciba Foundation Colloquia on Endocrinol., 1955, 8, 460.

*Monographs and Reviews*

BEYER, K. H. Physiol. Rev., 1946, 26, 169.

BRITTON, S. W. Physiol. Rev., 1930, 10, 617.

BROSTER, L. R. AND ASSOCIATES. The adrenal cortex and intersexuality. Chapman, London, 1938.

BURN, J. H. Physiol. Rev., 1945, 25, 377.

CANNON, W. B. Bodily changes in pain, hunger, fear and rage. Appleton-Century-Crofts, New York, 1915.

CANNON, W. B. AND ROSENBLUETH, A. Autonomic neuro-effector systems. Macmillan, New York, 1937.

CONN, J. W. Arch. Int. Med., 1956, 97, 135.

ELMADJIAN, F., HOPE, J. M. AND LAMSON, E. T. Recent Progr. Hormone Res., 1958, 14, 513.

VON EULER, U. S. Noradrenaline. Charles C Thomas, Springfield, Ill., 1956.

FARRELL, G. Physiol. Rev., 1958, 38, 709.

GADDUM, J. H. AND HOLZBAUER, M. Vitamins & Hormones, 1957, 15, 151.

GROLLMAN, A. The adrenals. The Williams & Wilkins Co., Baltimore, 1936.

HECHTER, O. AND PINCUS, G. Physiol. Rev., 1954, 34, 459.

HOSKINS, R. G. Physiol. Rev., 1922, 2, 343.

LERNER, A. B. AND FITZPATRICK, T. B. Physiol. Rev., 1950, 30, 91.

LIEBERMAN, S. AND TEICH, S. Pharmacol. Rev., 1953, 5, 285.

LOEB, R. F. Harvey Lectures, 1941–1942, 37, 100.

LONG, C. N. H. Medicine, 1937, 16, 215.

LORAINE, J. A. The clinical application of hormone assay. E. & S. Livingstone, Edinburgh, 1958.

MINZ, B. The role of humoral agents in nervous activity. Charles C Thomas, Springfield, Ill., 1955.

NICKERSON, M. Pharmacol. Rev., 1949, 1, 27.

PARKES, A. G. Physiol. Rev., 1945, 25, 203.

SAYERS, G. Physiol. Rev., 1950, 30, 241.

SAYERS, G. Recent Progr. Hormone Research, 1948, 2, 81.

SIMPSON, S. A. AND TAIT, J. F. Recent Progr. Hormone Res., 1955, 11, 183.

STEWART, G. N. Physiol. Rev., 1924, 4, 163.

STEWART, G. N. Arch. Int. Med., 1929, 43, 753.

SWINGLE, W. W. AND PFIFFNER, J. J. Medicine, 1932, 11, 371.

See also references in chapter 57.

# 59

# THE PARATHYROID GLANDS

### DEVELOPMENT AND STRUCTURE

The parathyroid glands are the smallest endocrine organs in the body. They remained unrecognized as structures distinct from the thyroid gland (to which they are often closely applied) until Sandstrom's description in 1880. Although Sandstrom was of the view that the structures represented remnants of embryonic thyroid tissue, and named them accordingly, the glands actually arise quite independently of the thyroid as outgrowths of the endoderm of the third and fourth pharyngeal pouches. Typically there are two pairs of glands, frequently called parathyroids III and IV to indicate the gill clefts of origin. Inasmuch as parathyroids III tend to follow the thymus during development, whereas parathyroids IV become associated with the thyroid gland, the position of the two pairs in the adult becomes reversed from that in the embryo. It is of importance that in the human, parathyroid glands may occasionally be found in the anterior, or posterior, mediastinum not associated with remnants of the thymus. Parathyroids III are constantly found in all vertebrates above the fishes, whereas parathyroids IV are absent in some species. In the human, the superior pair of parathyroids (IV) are referred to as the external, whereas the inferior pair (III) are termed the internal parathyroids. The terms 'internal' and 'external' signify the proximity of the gland to the mesial, or to the lateral aspect, respectively, of the thyroid lobe. The human parathyroids are roughly oval in shape, about 6 mm. in length, and weigh about 35 mg. each. Pathologically, glands weighing as much as 250 grams have been reported.

The cells of the parathyroids are densely packed in masses separated by capillary blood sinuses; they sometimes form cords. Two main types of epithelial cell may be distinguished in the gland of the adult human: *chief*, or *principal* cells which contain glycogen and possess a clear cytoplasm, and *oxyphil* cells which have a granular cytoplasm which stains intensely with acid dyes, and lack glycogen. The principal cells are, apparently, the essential secreting cells of the gland inasmuch as they are the only ones present in the human gland up to the 10th year and, indeed, are the only ones present at any age in most animals. Curiously, there is no clear cytological evidence of secretory activity in these cells, although the physiological evidence of an endocrine function is irrefutable. The function of the oxyphil cells, which appear near puberty, is as yet unknown.

The rich blood supply of the parathyroids is derived from the superior and inferior thyroid arteries. Interference with these vessels during thyroidectomy may occasionally result in hypoparathyroidism. Branches of the recurrent and superior laryngeal nerves innervate the glands and are probably entirely vasomotor.

### EARLY STUDIES AND CONCEPTS

The most prominent indication of inadequate function of the parathyroid glands is the occurrence of tetany. This symptom was long known to occur rather frequently after surgical thyroidectomy but was attributed to infection of the operation wound (Kocher), or to thyroid deficiency (Reverden). Attempts to induce tetany experimentally introduced complications, for in 1884, Schiff observed that thyroid removal in cats and dogs produced tetany and proved fatal, whereas little effect was observed in the rabbit. The difficulty was resolved by Gley in 1891, who pointed out that the inferior parathyroids lie caudal to the thyroid in the rabbit and that they were not affected by thyroidectomy. However, it was left to Vassale and Generale (1900) to differentiate between thyroid and parathyroid function by showing that removal of all the parathyroids, while leaving the thyroids intact, led to a fatal tetany. The cause of the tetany is a fall in the blood calcium level, as discovered by MacCallum and Voegtlin (1909). The same workers showed that administration of calcium salts could avert the convulsions.

For a number of years it was believed that the tetany occurring after parathyroidectomy was due to the accumulation of a toxin within the body, but this view was confounded, and the endocrine nature of the parathyroids established, when several independent workers, Hanson, Berman, and Collip, succeeded, around 1923, in obtaining consistently potent extracts of parathyroid hormone. It then became possible to relate clinical observations to the effects produced experimentally by overdosage with the extract.

## EFFECTS OF PARATHYROIDECTOMY—TETANY

The effects observed following experimental removal of the parathyroid glands vary in intensity according to the species studied, although comparable metabolic changes occur in all. In general, young animals are more susceptible than older ones to the effects of parathyroid deprivation, and herbivores tolerate the operation better than carnivores. The existence of accessory parathyroids offers only a partial explanation, inasmuch as tetany is induced in the rat only with difficulty following complete parathyroidectomy. The high phosphorus and low calcium content of the meat diet of carnivores probably accentuates the effects of parathyroidectomy.

*In the dog*, which has been studied most extensively, signs of parathyroid hormone deficiency may appear within 24 hours of operation. These include: (1) a *fall in serum calcium* from the normal level of about 10 mg. per 100 ml. to 6 mg. or less. The fall may be very abrupt, reaching the latter value or lower in 24 hours, or may be delayed for 48 to 72 hours or so. (2) A *rise in serum inorganic phosphate* from a normal level of about 5 mg. per 100 ml. to 9 mg. or higher. (3) The *urinary excretion of calcium and phosphorus* is reduced: this despite an increase in the blood level of the latter mineral. (4) *Fibrillary twitchings* of the muscles appear, followed by tonic or clonic (jerking) muscular contractions. The jaws are clenched and the limbs are either stiffly extended or jerk violently; the head is dorsiflexed. Sometimes there are automatic swimminglike movements of the forelimbs. (5) The skeletal muscles show *increased excitability* to a galvanic stimulus (p. 1050) and to mechanical excitation. Cardiac muscle also displays hyperirritability. The time constant of accommodation is increased (see p. 1124). (6) The muscle *phosphocreatine* is reduced and its rate of resynthesis slower than normal. (7) There is *rapid, noisy breathing* (hyperpnea), hyperpyrexia and tachycardia, and salivation. (8) *Death* usually follows in the dog, and is due to asphyxia through spasm of the laryngeal and thoracic muscles.

The above symptoms constitute the condition known as *tetany* and because the complex can be produced in other ways, Erdheim designated it as *tetania parathyreopriva*. The tetanic symptoms are closely related to the serum calcium level. As this falls, the symptoms, mild at first (perhaps merely slight stiffness of the hind limbs), become gradually more severe and when the serum calcium has fallen to between 5 and 6 mg. per 100 ml., the tetanic state is usually fully developed. Chronically, the bones become denser and cataracts may develop in the eyes. As might be expected, the tetanic convulsions can be relieved or averted by injection of calcium salts.

*In man*, in infants and very young children, tetany is usually seen in association with rickets. It may occur in the new-born due to a temporary inadequate production of parathyroid hormone. In the adult, tetany may follow accidental removal of the parathyroid glands during thyroidectomy, or removal of a hyperfunctional adenoma. The symptoms are usually less intense than those seen in parathyroidectomized animals, and the condition runs a more chronic course. The serum calcium lies usually between 4 and 7 mg. per 100 ml.; rapid respirations and high temperature are not usually seen. The outstanding feature is the heightened neuromuscular excitability. Though jerking movements and generalized convulsions may occur in children, they are unusual in adults. The hypertonic state of the muscles causes the hands and feet to be drawn into typical attitudes which are spoken of as *carpopedal spasm* (fig. 59.1). The hands are flexed at the wrists, and the fingers flexed at the metacarpophalangeal but extended at the interphalangeal joints. The thumb is adducted into the palm. This position constitutes the so-called *accoucheur's hand* of tetany. The feet are extended at the ankles and the toes plantar-flexed. Spasms of the eye muscles may be seen, and, occasionally, spasmodic retention of urine occurs. In infantile tetany spasm of the muscles of the glottis is not uncommon, causing inspiratory stridor (*laryngismus stridulus*). When severe, the laryngeal spasm causes complete closure of the glottis for a time; cyanosis results and when asphyxiation seems imminent, a sharp inspiration occurs accompanied by a high pitched "crowing sound." These various forms of muscular spasm are grouped under the general term *spasmophilia*.

In association with the lack of parathyroid hormone, there is a tendency toward metastatic calcification. *Cataracts* frequently occur. The teeth are not affected in the adult, but if the condition sets in during infancy, the roots may be hypoplastic. Enamel defects are often seen.

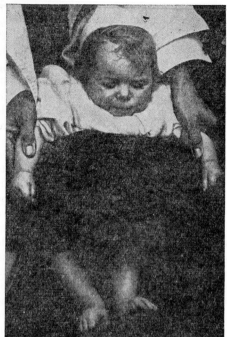

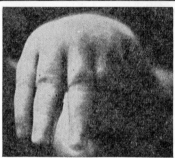

Fig. 59.1. Tetany (description in text). (Upper photograph from Purvis Stewart; lower photograph from Cabot.)

*Latent tetany.* Frequently the serum calcium remains just above the critical level at which definite tetanic symptoms appear. Emotion, some undue strain upon the organism, e.g., pregnancy, lactation, or a failure in general health, may, however, precipitate an attack of manifest tetany in a subject who has been suffering from the disease in latent form. Certain tests are employed to unmask this incipient form of the disease: (1) *Chvostek's sign,* tapping over the facial nerve in front of the ear causes twitching or spasm of the facial muscles; (2) *Trousseau's sign,* occlusion of the circulation in the arm by means of a blood pressure armlet causes the hand to assume the typical attitude (the effect is probably due to the anoxemia induced in the muscles of the hand and forearm); (3) *Von Bonsdorff's phenomenon,*

the facilitation of the muscular spasms caused by hyperventilation during the occlusion of the circulation to the arm; and (4) *Erb's sign,* increased excitability of the neuromuscular apparatus to a galvanic current. Stimulation of the median nerve in adults or the peroneal nerve in children produces muscular contraction with weaker currents than normal, and contraction may be preferentially elicited by an anodal opening current rather than the anodal closing current as is normally the case. In mild cases of tetany, numbness and tingling of the fingers and toes may be reported.

### Other Forms of Tetany

These with the chief changes in blood chemistry are shown in table 59.1.

Infantile and idiopathic tetany. Tetany occasionally arises spontaneously in infants and may then be due to parathyroid deficiency. Spontaneous, or idiopathic tetany as it is sometimes called, occurs also, though rarely, in adults as a result of defective parathyroid function. Tetany arising in this way does not differ essentially from that following parathyroidectomy. The tetany of infants is, usually, however, an accompaniment of rickets and, so far as is known, is then not due to parathyroid deficiency. During the active stage of rickets the serum calcium is little if at all depressed, but during the healing stage of the disease, calcium is diverted to the bones and the calcium of the serum falls. It is at this time that tetany occurs. Tetany may also be produced in rachitic rats by placing them upon an antirachitic diet (Hess and associates).

The tetanies of osteomalacia and sprue. Osteomalacia is a disease of the bones of adults. Its pathogenesis is essentially the same as that of rickets. The serum calcium is often very low; tetany is of common occurrence. Tetany occurs in *celiac rickets* and *nontropical sprue.* In the latter disease the absorption of fat and of calcium is defective and the serum calcium depressed. Tetany also sometimes occurs in tropical sprue.

Tetany associated with alkalosis (gastric, hyperpneic, and bicarbonate tetany). In pyloric obstruction, dilation of the stomach, or as a result of persistent vomiting from other causes, the loss of chloride in the vomitus causes a change in the acid-base balance toward the alkaline side. Tetany follows. Alkalosis is also the apparent cause of the tetany which results from increased pulmonary ventilation. In this case it is the excessive elimination of carbon dioxide which is the cause of the increased blood alkalinity. Alka-

TABLE 59.1*

*Types of tetany*

| | Calcium | Bicarbonate of Blood | Chlorine | pH | Phosphorus |
|---|---|---|---|---|---|
| Infantile or idiopathic tetany | Reduced | Normal | Normal | Normal | Normal or reduced |
| Tetany of osteomalacia | Reduced | Normal | | Normal | Normal or reduced |
| Tetanies of sprue and celiac rickets | Reduced | Normal | | | |
| Gastric tetany | Normal | Increased | Reduced | Increased | Increased |
| Bicarbonate tetany | Normal | Increased | Reduced | Increased | |
| Hyperpneic tetany | Normal | Increased | | Increased | |
| Parathyroid tetany | | | | | |
|    (1) Experimental | Reduced | Normal | | Normal | Increased |
|    (2) Postoperative | Reduced | Normal | | | |
| Phosphate tetany (Na₂HPO₄) | Reduced | Normal | Normal or increased | Normal or increased | Increased |
| Citrate tetany | Reduced | — | — | — | — |
| Tetany due to calcium and vitamin D deficiency | Reduced | — | — | — | — |
| Tetany due to magnesium deficiency | Normal | — | — | — | — |
| Guanidine tetany | Normal or slightly reduced | — | — | — | Increased |

* With modifications and additions from MacCallum.

losis is also evidently the cause of the tetanylike seizures which sometimes follow the administration of large quantities of sodium bicarbonate for therapeutic purposes.

PHOSPHATE TETANY Phosphate tetany is produced experimentally. The intravenous injection of 0.5 gram per kilogram of either the acid or the alkaline sodium (or potassium) phosphate into animals causes a profound and rapid fall in the serum calcium. In dogs, it is only after the injection of the alkaline salts, however, that tetany occurs. This difference is probably due to the different effects of the two salts upon the the acid-base balance—the one tending to cause alkalosis and a reduction in the ionization of calcium, the other acidosis and a relative increase in the concentration of calcium ions (see below). The injection of a neutral mixture of the two salts or of phosphoric acid itself does not cause tetany.

CITRATE TETANY. An intravenous injection of sodium citrate is a less sure way to induce tetany, but in a certain proportion of animals typical convulsions follow within 15 or 20 minutes after the injection. The serum calcium is lowered.

TETANY DUE TO CALCIUM AND VITAMIN D DEFICIENCY. The serum calcium of rats on a diet lacking in calcium, falls, after a period of from 3 to 7 weeks, to a low level, but tetany does not de-

velop unless the diet is also devoid of vitamin D. Even when both calcium and vitamin D are absent from the diet, tetany does not appear spontaneously, but typical convulsive seizures can be induced by stimulation with the galvanic current or by a sudden sound.

*Milk fever.* Hypocalcemia and tetany sometimes occur in cows after calving as a result of the loss of calcium in the milk. The condition is treated by inflating the udder with air, which suppresses milk secretion and causes a rise in the serum calcium, or by the intravenous injection of calcium. A similar condition is seen in sheep after lambing and is then referred to as "lambing sickness" or "ewe distemper."

MAGNESIUM DEFICIENCY TETANY. The general features of this type of tetany are indistinguishable from those due to calcium deficiency. It has been produced in rats, dogs, and young cattle by feeding diets deficient in magnesium. Calves reared on whole milk, which has a low magnesium content (0.01 per 100 ml.), frequently show severe tetany and may die in convulsions. The blood calcium and phosphorus are within normal limits but the magnesium is reduced to little more than half the normal value. This type of tetany is not known to occur in the human subject.

PATHOGENESIS OF TETANY

MacCallum and Voegtlin discovered (1909) that the serum calcium was invariably depressed in tetania parathyreopriva and that the condition was immediately relieved by the intravenous injection of calcium. In the years following the recognition of the connection between tetany and the parathyroids, and up to the work of Mac-Callum and Voegtlin, the tetanic state was believed to be due to some endogenous toxic metabolite (e.g., guanidine) which was destroyed in some way by the parathyroids, but accumulated in the blood and tissues after parathyroidectomy.

With the general recognition of these facts the *calcium deficiency theory* of tetany came into being. The low serum calcium found in other forms of tetany, that is, produced otherwise than by parathyroid deficiency, e.g., the tetanies of rickets, osteomalacia, and sprue, also indicates that calcium deficiency is the direct cause of the neuromuscular hyperexcitability in these conditions. Depression of the serum calcium also explains the convulsions following the injection of phosphate. It is generally accepted that the determining factor in the production of tetany is the concentration of *ionized* calcium in the plasma and extracellular fluids of the body, rather than the *total calcium* concentration. For example, in nephritis with a low serum protein, the total calcium of the serum may be reduced to 3 or 4 mg. per 100 ml., yet tetany does not occur presumably because the concentration of ionic calcium has not been reduced to the critical level. As shown by the experiments of Loeb upon frog muscle, the sodium and potassium ions tend to increase neuromuscular excitability, the calcium and magnesium ions to depress it. The calcium concentration of the tissues themselves (muscle or brain) is not altered in tetany; the increased neuromuscular excitability would, therefore, appear to be due to an imbalance between the concentration of ionic calcium in the extracellular and intracellular fluids.

It is difficult to assess the importance of hyperphosphatemia as a factor in the production of tetany, for a reciprocal relationship exists in the blood between the concentrations of calcium and phosphorus. Phosphate retention or phosphate injection causes a fall in the calcium of the serum; a rise in the concentration of the calcium of the serum, on the other hand, tends to depress the blood inorganic phosphorus. Nevertheless, tetany can result from a reduction in the serum calcium as in infantile rickets and osteomalacia with a normal concentration of blood phosphate. Hyperphosphatemia, therefore, though undoubtedly in-

creasing the severity of the tetanic symptoms, does not appear to play the primary role in their development.

The tetany of alkalosis cannot be explained upon the basis of calcium deficiency, inasmuch as in this type the serum calcium is not significantly lowered. It is suggested, however, that the shift of the acid-base balance of the blood toward the alkaline side causes a reduction in the ionic calcium fraction without altering the concentration of the total calcium of the serum. The following equation illustrates the possible relationship between the concentrations of calcium, bicarbonate, phosphate, and hydrogen ions.

$$\frac{[Ca^{++}]\,[HCO_3^-]\,[H^=PO_4]}{[H^+]} = K$$

According to this equation, an increase in the concentration of the bicarbonate ions or of phosphate ions, or a fall in the concentration of hydrogen ions would cause a reduction in the concentration of ionized calcium without a change in the total calcium level of the serum.

Certain observations are in conformity with such an hypothesis. The benificial effect upon tetany of the administration of an acidifying salt such as ammonium chloride, since it is not accompanied by a rise in the total calcium of the serum, and the difference, already mentioned, between the actions of the alkaline and acid phosphates may be explained upon such a basis.

The question of the neuromuscular mechanisms responsible for the tetanic seizures has not received a decisive answer. D. N. Paton and his associates sectioned the cord in parathyroidectomized dogs and observed cessation of the clonic and tonic spasms, but the tremors and the fibrillary twitchings were abolished only by section of the peripheral nerves. These results indicated that the tonic and clonic spasms were supraspinal in origin whereas the finer movements were dependent upon spinal centers. West more recently concluded that the supraspinal centers were not involved, since the characteristic tonic and clonic spasms persisted after section of the cord in the upper thoracic region. The integrity of the spinal reflex arcs was, however, considered to be essential for the tonic and clonic manifestations since they were abolished after section of the dorsal roots. The fibrillary movements and the increased electrical excitability of the muscles appeared to be dependent upon a peripheral mechanism. They persisted for at least 24 hours after section of both afferent and efferent nerves. In contradiction of West's conclusions. Greenberg and his colleagues state that in rats, tetanic movements of the hind limbs, but not of the forelimbs, are abolished by transection of the cord at the level of the seventh spinal segment. They conclude that activity of nervous centers above the spinal level is essential for the development of both the tonic and clonic seizures.

### TREATMENT OF TETANY

Though the symptoms of tetany are rapidly abolished by the intravenous administration of calcium salts, the beneficial effect is of short duration. Calcium by mouth is of little value in acute tetany, but is of some value in the more chronic forms. Acidifying salts, e.g., ammonium chloride, are also of benefit. A single injection of parathyroid extract will relieve the condition in a few hours and hold it in abeyance for several days. In chronic tetany (e.g., postoperative) irradiated ergosterol in the form of dihydrotachysterol or calciferol is of great value, especially when combined with a high calcium and a low phosphorus intake. The necessity of maintaining a high calcium, low phosphorus ratio prevents the use of a milk diet because of its high phosphorus content. According to Anderson and Lyall, adjustment of the calcium and phosphorus of the diet (0.5 to 0.65 gram of phosphorus, daily) is capable alone of controlling the symptoms. Lactose or dextrin in the diet tends to reduce tetanic neuromuscular hyperexcitability, for the organic acids produced during the fermentation of these carbohydrates lower intestinal pH, and thereby increase calcium absorption.

### THE ACTIONS OF PARATHYROID EXTRACT (PARATHORMONE)

The belief in the calcium regulating function of the parathyroids, which followed naturally upon the discovery that hypocalcemia was an accompaniment of parathyroid deficiency, was confirmed in 1924, when Hanson obtained an active extract of the gland. At about the same time, Collip obtained an extract from beef parathyroids which also possessed a powerful hypercalcemic effect. The intravenous or subcutaneous administration of this extract to parathyroidectomized dogs will maintain the serum calcium at the normal level. Violent tetanic symptoms are abolished within 3 or 4 hours after the injection of 10 or 20 units, and by the daily administration of considerably smaller doses than this the animal is maintained in good health indefinitely. If, after the calcium has been raised to normal, the administration of the hormone is

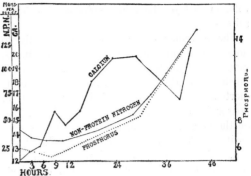

FIG. 59.2. Curves of serum calcium, blood phosphorus, and nonprotein nitrogen reproduced from Collip's article describing the effects of parathyroid extract. The curve representing the nonprotein nitrogen is not from the same animal as are the curves of serum calcium and blood phosphorus.

continued in frequently repeated doses (10 to 20 units twice daily, or oftener) or if given in such dosage to a normal animal, overdosage effects are produced. These are: (1) *Early changes in blood chemistry.* The serum calcium rises abruptly and within from 24 to 48 hours usually reaches a concentration of from 18 to 22 mg. per 100 cc. (fig. 59.2). During this time the inorganic phosphorus shows a moderate fall followed by a return to normal and a small rise. There is a slight rise in the potassium and magnesium of the serum. (2) *Early symptoms.* During the rise in serum calcium there is loss of appetite, depression and weakness, polyuria, vomiting, diarrhea, and dehydration. (3) The *urinary excretion of calcium and phosphorus* is greatly increased. The increased excretion of phosphorus precedes the rise in serum calcium and the increase in urinary calcium. There is little change in the fecal excretion of these elements. (4) *Later blood changes* are: a reduction in the hypercalcemia by 2 or 3 mg. per 100 ml.; a pronounced rise in the plasma inorganic phosphorus; a 4-fold increase in blood nonprotein nitrogen; a reduction in blood volume by 15 per cent due to plasma loss and, in consequence, concentration of the blood and a great increase in its viscosity. (5) *Later symptoms.* At the time that these blood changes are occurring urgent symptoms appear— vomiting of bloody fluid and sometimes the passage of blood stained stools, signs of renal failure, and great prostration ending in death. (6) *At autopsy* the gastrointestinal mucosa is found to be the seat of extensive hemorrhages, and the stomach and upper part of the intestinal canal contain a quantity of bloody fluid.

All the manifestations are intensified by a high

calcium diet or the administration of calcium salts.

The preceding description applies chiefly to dogs. The serum calcium of herbivorous animals, rats, mice, rabbits and guinea pigs, responds much less readily to the extract and the post-mortem picture so characteristic of its effects in dogs and cats is not seen. In herbivorous animals, on the other hand, repeated doses cause the deposit of calcium in the soft tissues (metastatic calcification), particularly of the arterial tree; this is infrequent in dogs. In the human subject, hypercalcemia is produced about as easily as it is in dogs. In both man and dogs tolerance to the hormone not infrequently becomes established after a certain number of doses.

Therapeutic (physiological) doses administered to a normal man, or to a subject of hypoparathyroidism, cause a moderate increase in phosphorus and calcium excretion, a fall in serum phosphorus, and a rise in serum calcium, i.e., a complete reversal of the biochemical abnormalities caused by parathyroidectomy (fig. 59.3).

The excess calcium in the serum following parathormone overdosage is derived from the skeleton; there is no increase in the absorption of

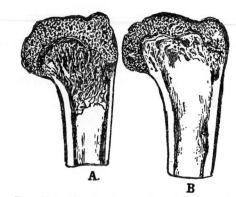

FIG. 59.4. Showing trabeculae of humeri of cat on (*A*) a high calcium diet and (*B*) on a low calcium diet. (Redrawn from Bauer, Aub, and Albright.)

calcium from the gut. Bauer, Aub, and Albright have shown that repeated doses of the extract to rabbits causes a reduction of the trabeculae of the epiphyses indicating that they serve as a store of calcium, which is rapidly mobilized by the hormone (fig. 59.4). By the administration of parathormone over long periods, a condition corresponding to osteitis fibrosa cystica of man (see below) has been produced by Bodansky and Jaffe in guinea pigs, and by others in rats and puppies. There is a marked demineralization and resorption of bone and replacement with fibrous tissue. Continued administration of the hormone to experimental animals results in gross and microscopical changes in the parathyroid glands; they become much reduced in size and their cells appear shrunken, show hydropic degeneration and a diminution in the number of mitotic figures. Such changes indicate that the administered hormone has depressed the functional activity of the glands.

### CHEMISTRY OF THE PARATHYROID HORMONE

The active principle contained in extracts of parathyroid glands (parathormone) has not been prepared in pure form. It is a water soluble protein which has still to be crystalized. The Collip preparation was obtained by boiling fresh glands for 1 hour with 5 per cent hydrochloric acid. The cooled solution was then made alkaline, to pH 8, by the addition of sodium hydroxide, followed by hydrochloric acid until a maximal isoelectric precipitation of protein, containing the active principle, occurred. Subsequent workers have modified this procedure and have obtained better yields and purer preparations. The hormone is soluble in water, 80 per cent alcohol, and warm 50 per cent glycerol, and is insoluble in absolute alcohol, ether, benzene, and acetone. Its potency is lost

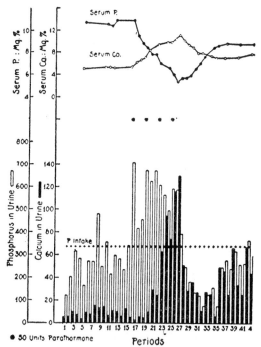

● 50 Units Parathormone

FIG. 59.3. Showing the effects of parathyroid hormone upon the serum calcium and phosphorus, and upon the urinary excretion of these minerals in a case of hypoparathyroidism. (From Albright and Ellsworth.)

upon acid hydrolysis, treatment with strong alkali, exposure to oxidizing agents, or incubation with the proteolytic enzymes pepsin and trypsin. Parathormone appears to possess no prosthetic group; it is not a glycoprotein. To be effective the hormone must be given by injection; it is inactive when given by mouth. Upon continued administration parathyroid hormone loses its effectiveness. This is generally believed to be due to the production of an antihormone, although Selye suggests the effect arises from a change in the reaction of the bones to the hormone. Clinically, an inability to respond to *endogenous* parathyroid hormone has been described, and is termed pseudohypoparathyroidism (Albright, Burnets, Smith, and Parson, 1942).

*Assay.* The standard assay procedures are based upon the changes in the level of serum calcium in normal or parathyroidectomized dogs. However, with the demonstration of independent actions of parathyroid hormone in the excretion of phosphate and the mobilization of calcium, methods based on the excretion of phosphate have been devised, as well as modified serum calcium assays. None has yet achieved wide application. One U.S.P. or Hanson unit is $\frac{1}{100}$ of the amount required to raise the calcium level of the blood serum of normal healthy male dogs, weighing 10 to 12 kg., by 1 mg. per 100 ml. This unit is $\frac{1}{5}$ of the Collip unit, which is also still in use.

## Calcium and Phosphorus Metabolism

Before proceeding to a discussion of the mode of action of parathyroid hormone, it will be advantageous at this point to review the metabolism of calcium and phosphorus.

Calcium is an indispensable mineral; it is a constituent of all animal fluids and solid tissues and is of importance in a variety of physiological processes. Among these may be listed: (1) coagulation of the blood (ch. 12), (2) formation of bone (p. 1062), (3) cardiac rhythmicity (ch. 14), (4) maintenance of normal neuromuscular excitability (p. 1052) and (5) milk production (p. 1099).

The Distribution of Calcium in the Body

Calcium constitutes about 2 per cent of the weight of the adult body, and about 99 per cent of the total quantity is contained in the skeleton. The muscles contain about 8 mg. per 100 grams net weight, plasma or serum from 9 to 11.5 mg. per 100 ml. The red corpuscles contain only minute amounts, so that the content of whole blood is between 4.5 and 6 mg. per 100 ml. The other body fluids, e.g., lymph, aqueous humor, ascitic and edema fluids, etc., contain it in some-

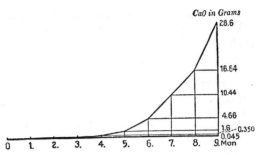

FIG. 59.5. Showing the increase in the calcium of human fetus in later months of gestation. (From Hess and Schmitz.)

what lower concentration, whereas the concentration in the cerebrospinal fluid is only about 5 mg. per 100 ml. Negligible amounts of calcium are deposited in the skeleton before the fifth month of intrauterine life, and nearly 70 per cent of the skeletal calcium of the new-born is the result of deposition during the last 2 months of prenatal life (fig. 59.5). The mother suffers a much greater loss of calcium to the suckling child. Whereas only about 20 grams of the element are lost during pregnancy, over 80 grams are secreted in the milk during a normal lactation period.

### The State of the Calcium in the Blood

Practically all the calcium of blood, as just mentioned, is contained in the plasma; after clotting it is all present in the serum, and it is upon this that determinations are usually made. The clot itself contains mere traces.

The calcium of blood exists in two main forms, *nondiffusible* and *diffusible*. The nondiffusible form is bound to the serum proteins, both albumin and globulin fractions (but chiefly to the albumin fraction) in the proportion of about 0.84 mg. per gram of protein. It remains in the serum when the latter is dialyzed or subjected to ultrafiltration. The nondiffusible part constitutes about 45 per cent (from 4 to 5 mg. per 100 cc.) of the total serum calcium. The diffusible portion amounts to 55 per cent or so (5 to 6.5 mg. per 100 cc.) of the total calcium; when the serum is ultrafiltered this fraction passes into the filtrate. *Nearly all the diffusible calcium of the serum is in the ionized form.* The previous low figures which have been given for the concentration of ionized calcium (1.5 to 2 mg. per 100 cc.) are, according to McLean and Hastings, erroneous. They state that only a very small amount of diffusible unionized calcium (about 0.25 mg. per 100 cc.) is present; it is in the form of a citratelike compound. The ionized calcium is in the form of calcium carbonate and phosphate. The following is a summary of the calcium fractions in serum:

| *Serum calcium* | *mg. per 100 cc.* |
|---|---|
| Nondiffusible | 4.0  to 5.0 |
| Diffusible | 5.0  to 6.5 |
|   Ionized | 4.75 to 6.25 |
|   Unionized | 0.25 |

The nondiffusible calcium, as might be expected, varies with the protein concentration of the plasma. For example, in Bright's disease (with low plasma protein, and without phosphate retention) the decline in serum calcium roughly parallels the fall in plasma albumin and the hypocalcemia is due mainly to a reduction in the nondiffusible fraction. Lymph, which has a lower concentration of protein than plasma, has also a lower calcium content.

The calcium of the cerebrospinal fluid, which is practically protein free, is almost entirely in the diffusible form, and has a concentration approximately equal to that of the diffusible fraction in the plasma. The calcium concentration of the cerebrospinal fluid has, therefore, been taken as an index of the diffusible fraction of the plasma calcium upon the assumption that the former fluid is simply an ultrafiltrate. This assumption is not warranted, inasmuch as it is more probable that the cerebrospinal fluid is *secreted* by the choroid plexus (ch. 70). Also, the administration of parathyroid extract or the injection of calcium salts, both of which raise the diffusible calcium of the plasma, causes little increase in the calcium concentration of the cerebrospinal fluid; it is little affected by parathyroidectomy.

McLean and Hastings have devised a biological method for the determination of the ionized calcium of the body fluids based upon the sensitivity of the frog's heart to the calcium ion concentration. In this method a modified Straub cannula is passed through the aorta into the ventricle, tied into position, and then filled with the unknown fluid (serum, edema fluid, cerebrospinal fluid, etc.). The amplitude of the contraction of the heart is recorded on a moving drum, and the cannula emptied and refilled with one of a series of standard calcium chloride solutions graded in concentration by 0.1 mmole per liter. If the amplitude of contraction given by the unknown is greater than that given by the standard, then a standard of higher concentration is tried, and *vice versa*. The calcium solution giving a contraction which just matches

that given with the unknown fluid is taken as having the same concentration as the unknown.

According to McLean and Hastings, the ionization of calcium in the body is determined primarily by an equilibrium between calcium and protein which may be expressed according to the law of mass action as:

$$\frac{(Ca^{++}) \times (Protein^{=})}{(Ca\ Protein)} = K = 10^{-2.22}$$

(at 25° C. and pH 7.35)

In other words, the calcium in protein containing fluids is considered to be present as calcium proteinate which ionizes as a weak electrolyte into calcium and protein ions, with a residue of protein bound calcium—the nondiffusible calcium fraction. The above equation may be used for the calculation of the calcium ion concentration in human serum or other protein containing fluids, providing that the total calcium and protein concentrations are known.

## The Absorption and Excretion of Calcium—Calcium Balance

Calcium is found in food as both organic and inorganic compounds, but probably it is absorbed only in the inorganic form. Absorption occurs mainly from the upper part of the small intestine. The reaction of the intestinal contents is an important condition in the absorption of this mineral, its salts, for the most part, being readily soluble in acid but insoluble in alkaline media. Sugars, especially lactose, which in their fermentation yield organic acids in the intestine, favor absorption. Fats (free from vitamin D) reduce calcium absorption on a high calcium, low phosphorus intake, owing most probably to the formation of insoluble calcium soaps; but for some reason, perhaps the production of soluble complexes with fatty acids, such fats increase the absorption of calcium on a diet with a low calcium-phosphorus ratio. Protein food tends to increase the absorption of calcium inasmuch as the latter forms soluble complexes with certain amino acids. Soluble calcium salts, such as the chloride, carbonate, lactate, and gluconate, but not the relatively insoluble phosphate, are readily and, in moderate dosage, almost completely absorbed. After the ingestion of a large dose of a soluble calcium salt, the serum calcium level rises, reaching its maximum value in about 2 hours. The normal serum concentration is reached again about 3 hours later. It is not possible to maintain the calcium level above normal for any considerable time by the administration of calcium salts.

Milk is the best dietary source of calcium, but important amounts (up to 0.2 gram daily) of available calcium may be obtained from "hard" drinking water. The calcium of many vegetables is well utilized by the rat; the calcium of carrots (and probably of certain other vegetables as well) is readily absorbed by the human intestine, being nearly as valuable as that in milk. Spinach and other plant foods containing oxalic or benzoic acid, which form relatively insoluble compounds with calcium, reduce calcium absorption. In cereals (wheat, oatmeal), owing to their content of phytic acid (inositolhexaphosphoric acid) which combines with calcium and magnesium to form an insoluble salt, much of of the mineral is unavailable. The action of phytic acid in the intestine depresses the absorption of calcium in other foods as well. Whole wheat flour has a higher phytic acid content than has white flour and, therefore, is a poorer source of absorbable calcium. As mentioned elsewhere (p. 908) the phosphorus of phytic acid is also largely unavailable. These facts explain the decalcifying action of certain cereals.

Calcium is secreted into the small intestine in various digestive juices, but little is eliminated through the wall of the colon. The excretion of calcium continues upon a calcium free diet or during a fast and, under these conditions, the body is in negative calcium balance. In man, on an ordinary mixed diet, the calcium of the feces amounts daily to from 0.4 to 0.8 gram; this, though a considerable amount is endogenous, is mainly the unabsorbable calcium of the food.

Smaller quantities of calcium are excreted in the urine, an average of 150 mg. being lost daily by this route, though there are rather wide variations. An increase or decrease in the absorption of calcium is reflected in parallel changes in the urinary excretion.

The *calcium balance*, that is the difference between the quantity of calcium ingested and that excreted in the urine and the feces, is *positive* (calcium retention) during *growth, pregnancy, acromegaly*, or after a period of *calcium starvation*. Sherman and Hawley found that children from 3 to 13 years of age, upon a daily calcium intake of from 0.74 to 1.02 grams of calcium, utilized (i.e., retained) from 0.15 to 0.62 gram per day; the quantity retained was in proportion to the size of the child (0.01 gram, daily per kilogram). In adults, Breiter and his colleagues found that the utilization of the calcium of milk varied from 15.3 to 30.3 per cent. *A negative calcium balance is observed in infantile rickets, celiac and renal*

Fig. 59.6. Front and side views of skeletons of twin brothers (albino rats), one of which had received a diet of normal calcium content (wheat, meat, and milk) whereas the other had received a low calcium diet (wheat and meat). (From Sherman and MacLeod.)

*rickets, sprue, osteomalacia, hyperparathyroidism, hyperthyroidism* (ch. 57), during *starvation* or *calcium deficiency*, and usually during *lactation*. In infantile rickets, celiac rickets, and osteomalacia (p. 908), vitamin D administration reduces the negative balance, establishes calcium equilibrium, or induces a positive balance. The chief effect of the vitamin is to increase the absorption of calcium through the alimentary tract. It also augments the calcification of bone and cartilage. Vitamins A and C are also concerned in normal bone formation (ch. 53 and 54). The daily calcium requirement and the calcium content of various foods are given in chapter 55 (see also fig. 59.6).

### Phosphorus Metabolism

The adult body contains about 700 grams of phosphorus of which some 80 to 85 per cent is found in the bones and teeth. The daily requirement (1.2 grams) is 1.5 times that of calcium. The mineral may be obtained from a wide variety of foods. Because the foods containing most phosphorus are also rich sources of calcium and protein, it can be assumed that a diet containing sufficient protein and calcium also contains sufficient phosphorus. However, if an excess of calcium is present, the absorption of phosphorus may be impeded due to the formation of insoluble calcium phosphates in the intestines.

Inorganic phosphates comprise about one-half of the total blood phosphate. In adults the normal blood level is $3.5 \pm 0.5$ mg. per 100 ml. In children the level is higher by 1 to 2 mg. per 100 ml. because of the activities of growth hormone. The serum levels of phosphorus and calcium are closely linked, the one varying inversely with the other. The relationship is such that the product of the total calcium in milligrams per

100 ml. and inorganic phosphorus in milligrams per 100 ml. is approximately constant. This *solubility product* ranges between 30 and 40 in adults and 40 and 55 in growing children. It was established by Howland and Kramer in 1922, that rickets occurs in children if the product falls below 35 and that healing takes place if it rises above 40. The serum phosphorus is also said to fluctuate directly with the blood sugar.

### The Function of Parathyroid Hormone

The primary concern of parathyroid hormone is the maintenance of a normal level of calcium in the blood. Following parathyroidectomy the blood calcium falls to a low level which is, however, maintained by residual homeostatic mechanisms. If the parathyroidectomized animal is subjected to bleeding and replacement with calcium free blood, then the blood calcium is restored to the low basal level. It is the function of parathyroid hormone to raise the blood calcium level to that prevailing normally.

The means by which parathyroid hormone is able to maintain a normal blood calcium level is not yet certain, although some features are becoming clear. At one time there was considerable argument over the question whether parathyroid hormone exerted its action mainly through the kidney, or by a direct effect on bone. It now appears that the hormone acts at both sites.

Because the first change observed following the administration of parathyroid hormone is a rise in the urinary excretion of phosphate, Albright and his associates adopted the view that the hormone exerted its primary action on phosphate metabolism. Ellsworth suggested that the reabsorption of phosphate from the kidney tubules was reduced, whereas in the opinion of Albright and Reifenstein, the phosphate dissolved in the tissue fluids was affected in such a way as to make it more readily excreted by the kidney. The ensuing fall in serum phosphate and change in the calcium-phosphorus solubility product produces reabsorption of bone salt to restore the equilibrium, and a rise in the level of serum calcium to maintain the solubility product produced in the face of a low serum phosphate. Since the hypercalcemia leads to a loss of calcium in the urine, there is a continued solution of bone salt.

Studies on nephrectomized animals have been prominent in experiments designed to test the above hypothesis. Thus, some workers (Tweedy, Neufeld, and Collip) found that parathyroid extracts were unable to raise the blood calcium level when given to dogs, cats, or rats following removal of both kidneys, ligation of the ureters, or ligation of the renal blood vessels. If the flow of urine was restored by opening the ureters, then the usual hypercalcemia followed injection of the hormone. Others (Ellsworth and Futcher, Stoerck, Monahan and Freeman, and Stewart and Bowen) have since recorded a characteristic hypercalcemia following intravenous parathyroid hormone administration to nephrectomized animals. Generally, when the kidneys are removed there is a steady rise in serum phosphate which, through the solubility product, will tend to reduce the serum calcium. When the parathyroids are further removed, there is a prompt fall in serum calcium, indicating that endogenous parathyroid hormone is able to keep up the serum calcium in the absence of the kidneys. The difficulties arising from the use of nephrectomized animals, and the reservations which must be made in the interpretation of the findings, are underlined by the work of Grollman, who found that if the blood levels of phosphate and calcium are maintained within normal limits by peritoneal dialysis, the nephrectomized dog will respond to parathyroid extract with an hypercalcemia. An extrarenal action of parathyroid hormone was thus established.

The evidence in favor of an extrarenal action of parathyroid hormone must not be taken to exclude a direct effect on the kidney, for recent work has shown that the reabsorption of phosphate is affected. Administration of parathyroid hormone depresses the tubular transfer maximum (ch. 34) of the kidney.

The production of experimental osteitis fibrosa following parathyroid hormone administration drew attention to the possibility of a direct action of the hormone on bone. Selye found in rats that correlated with the hypercalcemia and hypercalciuria, there was an increase in the number of osteoclasts in bone (p. 1063). With continued treatment, the osteoblasts increase in number whereas the osteoclasts are reduced, a change which accords with increased calcification of bone and a return of the serum calcium to normal. Osteoclast proliferation and resorption of bone have also been observed in nephrectomized animals following treatment with parathyroid hormone. Although nephrectomy itself elicits similar, though mild, bone changes, such changes are prevented by parathyroidectomy so that a direct action of the hormone on bone seems likely. Conclusive evidence to this effect was obtained by Barnicot, and subsequently by Chang. Barnicot transplanted pieces of parietal bone together with parathyroid tissue to the cranial cavity of mice. Intense osteoclastic activity and resorption of bone was observed; perforation of the bone sometimes occurred. Calciferol and Vitamin A, also known to affect bone metabolism, had a similar effect, but, as Chang showed, control grafts of cartilage, gastric mucosa, pancreas, bone marrow, thyroid, and other tissues had no effect. The histological changes in bone following parathyroid hormone administration occur quite rapidly; McLean and Bloom observed an extensive proliferation of osteoclasts and destruction of osteoblasts 6 hours after the administration of a large dose of hormone to rats.

Although it appears quite certain that parathyroid hormone acts directly on bone, the nature of this effect remains obscure. One early suggestion was that the solvent power of the plasma for calcium is increased, and McLean and co-workers have produced evidence for the view that supersaturation of the plasma with bone salt occurs. It now seems that calcium is mobilized from the deeper areas of bone and that citric acid may be involved in the metabolic processes concerned (Talmage). The possibility that the hormone may act upon the "uncalcified" bone matrix is also receiving attention.

In summary, then, it appears that the secretion of the parathyroid gland acts directly both upon bone and the kidneys.

### THE CONTROL OF PARATHYROID GLAND ACTIVITY

The secretion of parathyroid hormone is not subject to nervous control; attention must be directed instead to the concentration of calcium and phosphate ions in the plasma. There is little doubt that the secretion of hormone by the parathyroid is stimulated by a low level of calcium. Perfusion of the thyroid-parathyroid complex with decalcified blood and injection of the perfusate into normal dogs raised the serum calcium from 1.3 to 4.9 per cent within 3 hours or less. Hyperplasia of the parathyroid glands occurs in those conditions having a tendency toward a low serum calcium, such as rickets and pregnancy, and has also been produced experimentally by establishing a chronic hypocalcemia. Conversely, the elevation of the serum calcium by the intravenous infusion of calcium salts in normal man is followed by a diminished phosphate output by the kidney despite a rising blood phosphate concentration, a response associated with a low level of secretion of parathyroid hormone.

Currently, attention is also being paid to the proposal that elevation of the plasma concentration of phosphate may call forth an increased secretion of parathyroid hormone. There is evidence in favor of the suggestion, although the matter cannot be regarded as settled. However, if the point is established, then any action of ACTH and growth hormone on parathyroid function may be attributed to the changes in phosphate metabolism induced by these agents. The parathyroid glands of hypophysectomized animals have been found to be smaller than those of control animals, but as a lowered serum phosphate is also found in the hypophysectomized rabbit and rat, the changes in parathyroid size may be presumed to be associated with the altered blood levels of phosphate and perhaps of calcium. There is little evidence in favor of a pituitary parathyrotrophic factor.

No functional relationship between the thyroid, adrenals, or gonads and the parathyroids has been demonstrated.

### HYPERPARATHYROIDISM

Although the terms *osteitis fibrosa generalisata, osteitis fibrosa cystica,* or *von Recklinghausen's disease* are sometimes regarded as synonymous with hyperparathyroidism, in actuality they represent an advanced stage of the disease. The bone changes that occur include decalcification, the formation of cystlike cavities, and resorption of the bony tissue of the trabeculae and shaft, which become largely replaced by fibrous tissue (fig. 59.7). In severe cases there may be (1) pain in the bones, (2) extreme hypotonicity of the skeletal muscles, (3) elevation of serum calcium (sometimes up to 20 mg. per 100 ml. or more, but usually not above 15 or 16 mg.) (fig. 59.8), (4) fall in the serum inorganic phosphate (to below 3 mg. per 100 ml.) and a rise in serum alkaline phosphatase, (5) increased urinary elimination of calcium and phosphate, and polyuria, together with occurrence of renal cal-

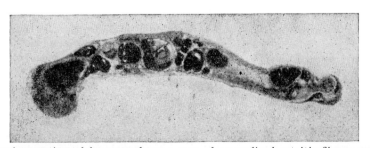

FIG. 59.7. Showing section of humerus from a case of generalized osteitis fibrosa cystica. (From Hunter and Turnbull after Hill and Lucey.)

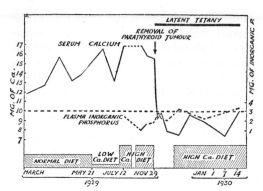

FIG. 59.8. Showing the chemistry of blood in hyperparathyroidism, and the effect of removal of the parathyroid tumor (From Hunter.)

culi and renal damage (this latter may take the form of peritubular calcium deposits leading to interstitial fibrosis and cystic dilation of the tubules (Anderson)), (6) metastatic calcification may be observed in the subconjunctival tissue, superficial layers of the cornea, lungs, arteries, and heart, (7) spontaneous fractures, deformity of the bones of the limbs or spine, and reduced or irregular density of bone is indicated by X-ray, and (8) some degree of anemia due to fibrosis of the bone marrow. However, as emphasized by Reifenstein and Howard, it is possible to have four kinds of hyperparathyroidism, namely, (1) chemical hyperparathyroidism without bone and kidney disease, (2) hyperparathyroidism with kidney, but without bone, disease, (3) hyperparathyroidism with bone, but without kidney involvement, and (4) classical hyperparathyroidism with both bone and kidney damage. These differential effects may possibly depend on such factors as the dietary supply of calcium and phosphorus.

*Primary hyperparathyroidism* is most frequently associated with the presence of an adenoma of one or more parathyroid glands. As shown by Mandl in 1926, the condition is relieved by removal of the tumor, but the operation may be followed by an episode of low serum calcium and tetany due partly to the inactivity of the residual parathyroid tissue (which had been compensatorily depressed by the overactive adenoma) and partly to an increased demand for minerals by the healing, mineralizing bones.

*Secondary hyperparathyroidism* generally follows procedures which tend to reduce the blood calcium level or raise the serum phosphate. It may be induced experimentally by (1) the provision of a low calcium diet (rats and rabbits), (2) lack of vitamin D (chicks), (3) daily injec-

tions of phosphate over a period of weeks, and (4) surgical reduction of renal tissue, of experimental nephritis—the former procedure producing dwarfing in rats and a condition resembling the renal rickets of children (Pappenheimer). In the human subject, hyperplasia of parathyroid tissue may occur physiologically in pregnancy and lactation, and pathologically in association with renal disease which reduces kidney function and produces a retention of phosphate.

### THERAPEUTIC USES OF PARATHYROID EXTRACT

Although the administration of parathyroid hormone would seem to be the treatment of choice in tetany, its use in the clinic is limited because of the production of antihormones with frequent injection. There is also the tendency toward demineralization of bone (which may be utilized clinically in the treatment of heavy metal poisoning) to be considered. In view of this, large doses of calcium (as chloride), lactate, or gluconate are given in tetany together with a high calcium diet and dihydrotachysterol.

Attempts to move extraskeletal deposits of calcium by means of parathormone have not met with success. This is not unexpected, inasmuch as the action of the hormone in mobilizing calcium and phosphorus is confined to the skeleton and may actually induce calcification of soft tissues (see p. 1069).

### THE RELATION OF VITAMIN D TO PARATHYROID FUNCTION

The actions of parathyroid hormone and of vitamin D share many points in common. This is probably due to the fact that both agents act to maintain a normal blood calcium level. In the absence of vitamin D the parathyroid glands become hyperactive. Higgins and Sheard found that the parathyroids of chicks deprived of ultraviolet light became hyperplastic, but were restored to normal appearance by the administration of cod liver oil. Also, the effects of overdosage of vitamin D are reduced by elimination of parathyroid function. Hess, Weinstock, and Rivkin found, in monkeys, that hypercalcemia is less readily induced by irradiated ergosterol after parathyroidectomy. In dogs, Taylor, Weld, Branion, and Kay found that the toxic overdosage effects of irradiated ergosterol were less severe than usual in parathyroidectomized dogs. They also showed that the overdosage effects of parathyroid hormone and irradiated ergosterol were similar in that both substances cause the same degree of hypercalcemia (fig. 59.9) and hyperphosphatemia, and a rise in the nonprotein nitrogen of the blood. The symptoms during

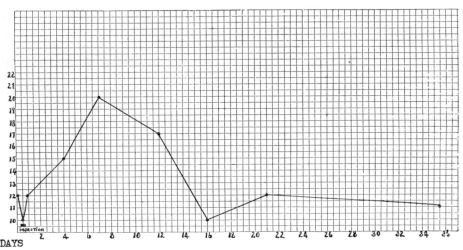

DAYS

FIG. 59.9. Serum calcium curve of a dog illustrating the effect of a large dose of irradiated ergosterol given intravenously in divided doses over a period of 4 hours. Note the prolonged effect upon the serum calcium. (From Taylor, Weld, Branion, and Kay.)

life and the postmortem findings after poisoning with either material are identical and those species (herbivora) resistant to parathormone are similarly resistant to overdosage with vitamin D. It has also been shown that either parathyroid hormone or irradiated ergosterol gives rise to metastatic calcification and to bony changes analagous to osteitis fibrosa cystica. The effect of the vitamin upon the serum calcium is slower to appear than that of the hormone. The hypercalcemia of the vitamin, once established, persists for some weeks (fig. 59.9).

Clinically, a product of irradiated ergosterol, dihydrotachysterol (AT 10), is used as a substitute for parathyroid hormone, since its effect does not diminish on repeated administration. Dihydrotachysterol is less potent in promoting the absorption of calcium from the alimentary canal than calciferol (vitamin $D_2$), and is also favored for that reason.

Unlike vitamin D, parathyroid hormone does not increase the absorption of calcium from the intestine.

## Bone

### The Composition of Bone

Osseous tissue freed from fatty marrow is composed of organic material (mainly protein), water, and minerals. The chief protein constituent is *ossein*, but there are also small quantities of *osseomucoid* and an *albuminoid*. Water constitutes about 25 per cent of the bone weight, 30 per cent organic material, and 45 per cent inorganic constituents. The minerals consist of calcium, phosphorus, and magnesium, and small quantities of potassium, sodium, chlorine, fluorine, and iron. Citrate is present in bone; indeed, 70 per cent of the body's entire store of citrate is contained in the skeleton. The existence of a diffusible citratelike compound of calcium in serum has been mentioned. That citrate and calcium metabolism are intimately associated seems established, but the nature of the relationship is unknown. Recent work suggests that citrate may be involved in the mechanism through which parathyroid hormone releases calcium from bone (see also pp. 1054 and 1058).

Calcium makes up from 15 to 18 per cent of the weight of fresh osseous tissue and from 20 to 25 per cent of the weight of bone which has been dried and extracted with ether.

Bone calcium exists in two forms, calcium carbonate ($CaCO_3$) and tricalcium phosphate $Ca_3(PO_4)_2$.[1] The ash of bone amounts to about 60 per cent of its dry weight. Calcium constitutes about 36 per cent of the ash, phosphorus about 16 per cent, magnesium 0.5 per cent, and $CO_2$ 5.5 per cent. The ratio of calcium to phosphorus is approximately 2.2:1. The ratio of residual calcium (i.e., calcium other than that present as carbonate) to residual phosphorus (phosphorus not combined with magnesium) is about 2:1. This is, approximately, the ratio of the two minerals in tricalcium phosphate. Magnesium is present mainly as $Mg_3(PO_4)_2$. The proportions of the three chief compounds in bone ash are $Ca_3(PO_4)_2$ 80 per cent, $CaCO_3$ 13 per

[1] Small amounts of calcium chloride and calcium fluoride are also present.

TABLE 59.2

*Calcium of bone (dog)*

| | Whole Bone | | Bone Ash | Calcium-Phosphorus Ratio |
|---|---|---|---|---|
| | Fresh | Dry, ether extracted | | |
| Total calcium (per cent) | 18 | 25 | 36 | 2.2:1 |
| Residual calcium (per cent) | — | — | 31 | 2:1 |

cent, and $Mg_3(PO_4)_2$ 2 per cent. Some of the foregoing data are given in table 59.2.

Rickety bone contains a lower percentage of ash and larger proportions of water and organic material. The ratio of calcium to phosphorus, however, remains unchanged whether the rickets (experimental) develops upon a low calcium or a low phosphorus diet. The magnesium content of bone is said to be increased in rickets and in osteomalacia.

It is now generally believed that the calcium carbonate and calcium phosphate of bone are present not as separate compounds simply mixed together with smaller amounts of other mineral salts, but as a complex chemical structure.

From a comparison of the refractive indices and X-ray diffraction patterns of bone and dental enamel on the one hand, and certain crystalline minerals composed mainly of calcium and phosphorus, Taylor and Sheard concluded that the inorganic solid phase of bone and of dental enamel resembled the apatite series (podolite, fluorapatite, etc.). Fluorapatite, which many considered to be nearest in chemical structure to the bone salt, has the formula $Ca_{10}(PO_4)_6F_2$. In bone, *hydroxyapatite*, $Ca_{10}(PO_4)_6(OH)_2$ in which OH replaces F, or a closely similar compound, is very generally, though not unanimously, accepted as the predominant compound in bone. The bone salt is laid down in the form of minute crystals. Compounds in which sodium, magnesium, and other minerals are substituted for calcium are also found in bone.

The ratio of total calcium to phosphorus, 2.2:1 (or 10 atoms of calcium to 6 of phosphorus) and that of residual calcium to residual phosphorus, 2:1 (9 atoms of calcium to 6 of phosphorus) which exist in bone also support this conclusion.

Pathological calcifications, e.g., salivary calculi, arterial or pulmonary calcifications, are believed to be similar in chemical composition to bone. Hastings and his associates hold a similar view in respect to a crystalline compound related to the apatite series as being the main mineral constituent of bone.

It should be emphasized that adult bone is not simply an inert structural material, but living tissue whose mineral composition fluctuates under the influence of other body functions. The trabeculae of the bone, as shown by Aub and associates, constitute a calcium store readily available when necessary for the maintenance of the calcium requirements of other tissues when the exogenous supplies are deficient. For this reason, though calcium continues to be excreted when an animal is kept, even for a long period, upon a calcium free diet, no change in the serum calcium level occurs. Parathyroid extract, as mentioned elsewhere, raised the serum calcium through its action in mobilizing these calcium stores.

In birds, the extraordinary demand made upon calcium metabolism for the production of the egg shell has been provided for by the development of osseous tissue within the marrow spaces of the long bones. Weakening of the essential skeletal structure which otherwise might result from the withdrawal of the mineral during the egg laying season, is thus avoided. The growth of this socalled *medullary bone* is stimulated by estrogens. Normally, its growth appears to be under the control of the ovarian secretion; it is cyclical or seasonal in character, and is associated with other phenomena of the mating season of birds, e.g., the appearance of serum vitellin in the circulation, an increase in plasma fat and phospholipid, and pronounced hypercalcemia.

The bones also serve a detoxicating function, elements such as lead, radium, fluorine, and arsenic, being removed from circulation and deposited in the bones and teeth. "Mottled enamel" (chalky white patches upon the surfaces of the teeth) is attributed to an excess of fluorine in the food or drinking water, though smaller amounts of fluorine are said to be beneficial for the development of the teeth and to prevent dental caries. The mobilization of bone calcium plays a very minor role in maintaining the normal blood reaction against the ingestion or production of excess acid. Some reduction in bone calcium can be detected, however, in animals after the administration of hydrochloric acid.

### BONE FORMATION

*The Histology of Developing Bone*

There are two types of ossification, *intramembranous* and *intracartilaginous* or *endochondral*. The bones of the cranial vault, the maxilla, and the mandible are formed through the ossification of membranes. The bones of the limbs and trunk, and the base of the skull are first modeled in cartilage which becomes transformed into bone by both endochondral and intramembranous (i.e., periosteal) forms of ossification. Studies with radioactive isotopes have shown that calcium and phosphorus are first laid down in the epiphysis of the developing bone, and are later transferred to the shaft (diaphysis) where a *primary center* of ossification appears, and, enlarging, spreads toward both ends of the bone. Secondary centers appear subsequently in the epiphysis. The deposition of calcium is hastened by vitamin D. The cartilage cells just ahead of the spreading zone of calcification show active proliferation, and become arranged in longitudinal rows (fig. 59.10). The transformation of the calcified cartilage into true bone is brought about in the following fashion. The cells of the deeper layers of the membrane covering the cartilage (perichondrium) give off long processes to form a meshwork of interlacing fibers. These cells are referred to as *osteoblasts*. The fibrous framework thus laid down soon becomes impregnated with calcium salts with the formation of a layer of true bone just beneath the perichondrium, or periosteum as it must now be called. The subperiosteal process, which is essentially the same as that whereby the cranial bones are developed from membrane, is well advanced, whereas the interior of the bone still consists merely of calcified cartilage. The latter, however, soon becomes invaded by blood vessels from the periosteum and by large multinucleated cells (20 to 40 $\mu$) known as *osteoclasts*. These cells, which have a pronounced eroding action upon the mineralized cartilage, probably through the production of an enzyme, tunnel channels through it for the conveyance of the blood vessels and excavate small cavities. The excavations in which the osteoclasts lie are known as *Howship's lacunae*. Osteoblasts which have advanced into the interior of the blood vessels cause the formation of true osseous tissue in the walls of the spaces formed by the osteoclasts.

At a somewhat later date than that at which the primary ossification center appears in the shaft, a secondary or epiphyseal center appears in one or both ends of the bone. The calcification process and subsequent ossification follow the same course as that described for the diaphysis. The epiphyseal and diaphyseal areas, however, remain separated from one another by a layer of uncalcified cartilage, the *epiphyseal plate*, until a certain age, which varies between different bones.

Through the combined action of osteoclasts and osteoblasts, a complete replacement of the calcified cartilage results, and the structure characteristic of bone gradually evolves. The center of the shaft becomes hollowed out to form the medullary canal. The spaces which have been formed by the osteoclasts in the shaft of the bone itself become joined together and constructed into the system of *Haversian canals* which serve as conduits for the transmission of blood vessels. In the ends of the

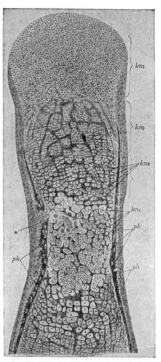

Fig. 59.10. Developing bone; proximal phalanx of a 3 month human fetus. $kn_1$, Unchanged cartilage; $kn_2$, columns of cartilage cells; $kn_3$, zone of calcifying cartilage; $kn_4$, vestiges of walls of broken down cartilage cavities; *pk*, perichondral (periosteal) bone (black); *ph*, perichondrium (periosteum); and *, connection between periosteum and primary marrow. As yet, no endochondral bone formation. (From Maximow and Bloom after Sobotta.)

bones the spaces are much larger and irregular; and becoming filled with red marrow constitute the characteristic spongy or cancellous bone of this region. The walls of these spaces appear in cross section as interlacing bars of osseous tissue and are usually referred to as trabeculae. The bone forming the walls of the Haversian canals is laid down in a series of concentric tubular lamellae. As each lamella is completed, it imprisons the osteoblasts within small lacunae from which numerous fine canals are given off; into these the processes of the osteoblasts penetrate. The osteoblasts in these situations lose their osteogenetic function but do not disappear. In the developed bone they are referred to simply as *osseous cells* or *osteocytes*.

A long bone grows in length at the junction of the epiphysis with the diaphysis, and in thickness through the activity of the osteoblasts of the deeper layers of the periosteum. The Haversian canals and the marrow cavity are also lined with a membrane (the *endosteum*) containing osteoblasts through which increased width of the bone is also brought about.

The osteoblasts and osteoclasts are concerned not only with the development and growth of bone, but are active throughout life and are responsible, it is believed, to a large extent at any rate, for the lability of adult osseous tissue (p. 1062). Healthy bone is constantly being broken down, resorbed, and repaired. Several conditions may alter the balance one way or the other between these two processes, e.g., the relation of the calcium intake to the calcium requirement and the activities of various ductless glands—parathyroid, thyroid, pituitary etc. Large numbers of osteoclasts are in evidence when bone resorption is taking place. Osteoclastic activity is, therefore, pronounced when remodeling of bone is occurring, as in the removal of excess callus or in the restoration to normal dimensions of the enlarged end of a bone in healing rickets, in certain bone diseases, and in wasting diseases. In old age also, the resorptive process outstrips the processes of repair; the bones become rarefied (*senile osteoporosis*) and more fragile. Ham and some other authorities deny that the osteoclasts are active agents in the removal of the bone tissue, claiming that the appearance of these cells is merely incidental or sequential to the resorption process.

When bone formation is in the ascendancy, as during the repair of a fracture, the osteoblasts show active proliferation.

Newly formed bone is stained selectively *in vivo* by madder, a red dye, or by alizarin, a derivative of it. These are, therefore, valuable agents for the investigation of the growth of bone in the living animal or of the action of parathyroid hormone and other influences upon bone metabolism. The dye, which is given orally, is deposited with the mineral constituents, calcium and phosphorus.

A CONSIDERATION OF THE FACTORS UNDERLYING THE CALCIFICATION PROCESS. Several theories have been advanced in attempts to picture the processes underlying the deposition of calcium salts in the cartilaginous matrix.

1. A protein constituent of cartilage, it has been supposed, adsorbs calcium, for which it exhibits a special affinity; the calcium subsequently combines with phosphorus to form tricalcium phosphate. Wells showed, for example, that bone salts were deposited in a piece of boiled cartilage placed in the abdominal cavity.

2. The saturation of a solution with a salt such as calcium phosphate and the precipitation of the latter in solid form is determined by the product of the concentrations of the $Ca^{++}$ and $PO_4^{\equiv}$ ions in the solution, i.e., upon the *ion product* $(Ca^{++}) \times (PO_4^{\equiv})$, and not upon the total quantities of calcium and phosphorus present. The ion product at which the solution is just saturated is called the *solubility product*. The presence of protein in the solution reduces the degree of ionization, part of the calcium, as we have seen, becoming bound to form calcium proteinate, a weak electrolyte. The body fluids are, therefore, capable of dissolving more calcium phosphate than is a protein free solution similar in its salt composition to that of plasma. The $CO_2$ dissolved in the body fluids also increases their ability to hold calcium salts in solution. Any reduction in the protein concentration or in the $CO_2$ tension in the body fluids would, therefore, be expected to favor the deposition of calcium salts.

An explanation of the calcification process upon a basis afforded by the foregoing considerations has been advanced by Howland. It is assumed that the fluids bathing the cartilage cells have, in common with other extravascular fluids, a lower protein concentration than has plasma. It is further suggested that since the cartilaginous matrix has a low metabolism, the $CO_2$ tension of the fluids bathing its cells is lower than that of plasma; the pH of these fluids will, therefore, tend to be higher. Such conditions, it is argued, must favor the deposition of calcium salts. A low concentration of inorganic phosphorus and of calcium in the plasma will, on the other hand, tend to retard calcification; this would be completely arrested if the ion product were below the value at which precipitation occurs. In practice, Howland and his associates have employed the product of the *total* calcium and inorganic phosphorus, each expressed in milligrams per 100 ml., as an index of the calcification process in infantile rickets. They state that in children with active rickets the product is practically always below 40, and when the disease is severe, below 30, whereas in normal children it is between 50 and 60 (i.e., 11 mg. of Ca × 5 mg. of P = 55). It is obvious that a fall in either inorganic phosphorus or calcium would tend to lower the Ca × P product; actually two varieties of rickets were distinguished—a low phosphorus and a low calcium type. It is now recognized, however, that these are simply different stages of the disease and that the level of the inorganic phosphorus alone is a more useful criterion by which to judge the extent of the calcification defect than the Ca × P product. For example, when rickets is progressing, the inorganic phosphorus of the plasma is lowered to between 3 and 4 mg. or less per 100 ml., but the serum calcium is not far from the normal level. During the stage of healing, i.e., of active calcification, the inorganic phosphorus of the blood tends to rise and the serum calcium to fall; there might, therefore, be little change in the Ca × P product.

Another factor considered to be of importance in the calcification process is the *supersaturation* of the body fluids with calcium salts. That is, quite apart from the greater solubility of calcium salts in fluids containing protein and $CO_2$, the concentrations of calcium phosphate and calcium carbonate in the body fluids are constantly maintained above their saturation limits, owing to the extreme slowness with which final equilibrium between the solid and liquid phases is established. Precipitation of these salts from solution will continue so long as the ion product is above that of the saturation level.

Calcification, however, cannot be explained upon a physicochemical basis alone; the activity of living cells is also involved in the process. Shipley, Howland, and Kramer showed, for example, that in experiments *in vitro*, calcification was inhibited by a protoplasmic poison such as HCN. Two views have been expressed as to the nature of the vital processes concerned.

3. Watt, from a comparison of the shapes of calcium phosphate particles precipitated in certain inert colloids with those formed in bone, concluded that calcification was not a simple precipitation of calcium phosphate from solution but was due to the active *secretion* by the osteoblasts of bone salts derived from the calcium and phosphorus of the blood.

4. According to Robison and his colleagues, calcification is primarily dependent upon enzyme action through which the fluids in immediate relation to cartilage cells become highly supersaturated with calcium phosphate. These observers have accumulated much evidence in favor of their view. They have demonstrated the presence in bone (and also in plasma and other tissues, see below) of an enzyme capable of hydrolyzing various phosphoric esters, e.g., hexosemonophosphate, glycerophosphate, etc. This enzyme is called *phosphatase*. It is believed to be a product of the osteoblasts, the proliferating cartilage cells and the cells of the inner layer of the periosteum. According to this conception of the calcification process, the enzyme liberates inorganic phosphate from phosphoric esters and raises, locally, the concentration of the $PO_4^=$ ion. The product of the concentrations of the $Ca^{++}$ and $PO_4^=$ ions then exceeds the solubility product of calcium phosphate, which is in consequence deposited in the cartilagenous matrix.

Evidence bearing upon this hypothesis is as follows:

1. It was shown by Robison that when the head of a bone from a rachitic rat was immersed in a solution of calcium hexosemonophosphate at body temperature, a deposit of calcium phosphate occurred in the zone of preparatory calcification (p. 1062). This was attributed to the liberation by phosphatase of inorganic phosphate from a phosphoric ester, thus raising the product of the concentrations of $PO_4^=$ and $Ca^{++}$ ions.

2. Shipley, Kramer, and Howland found that calcification of a rachitic bone occurred if placed in normal serum. Calcification also resulted if the bone were placed in a sterile solution of inorganic salts containing sodium chloride, sodium bicarbonate, and magnesium sulfate, together with calcium and inorganic phosphate in the same concentrations as in normal serum. They concluded that living processes were concerned, since calcification was inhibited by HCN. They believed, however, that phosphatase could have played no part in the process for the artificial solution did not, of course, contain a phosphoric ester.

3. Robison claimed that the result of the experiment just described was dependent upon the fact that in the solution used, the concentration of the calcium phosphorus compound was near the point at which spontaneous precipitation might be expected to occur. In normal plasma, as already mentioned, calcium and phosphorus remain in solution at these concentrations because it contains protein which depresses the ionization of calcium; the ion product upon which precipitation depends is, therefore, considerably lower. Robison and Soames showed that calcium phosphate precipitates after a few days from a solution such as that employed by Shipley and associates if simply allowed to stand. It was found indeed by the latter workers that the addition of protein to the extent of 1 or 2 per cent inhibited the calcification of the immersed bone. Robison and Soames showed later that though calcification of rachitic bone will occur when immersed in a solution containing calcium and phosphorus if the concentrations are sufficiently high, i.e., Ca × P product over 40 (4 mg. of phosphorous and 10 mg. of calcium per 100 cc.), calcification will not occur if the product is lower than this unless a phosphoric ester is added. Quite small amounts of the ester (glycerophosphate) were sufficient to cause calcification.

4. Phosphatase is present in bone in largest amounts when and where active calcification is taking place (see below), which strongly suggests that it plays an essential role in the calcification process.

5. Certain facts have been cited as opposed to the phosphatase hypothesis: (a) in rickets the phosphatase activity of bone and plasma is increased rather than the reverse, and in the blood of rachitic rats the percentage of phosphoric esters hydrolyzable by phosphatase is not below normal; (b) normal plasma contains only very small quantities of phosphoric esters, which seem inadequate to supply the inorganic phosphate necessary for the calcification process; and (c) certain tissues which do not calcify normally are rich in phosphatase whereas other tissues, such as the arteries, which are frequently the site of pathological calcification, do not contain the enzyme.

Robison did not contend, however, that the phosphatase mechanism is the only one concerned in the calcification process for, as mentioned above, calcification will occur in the absence of a phosphoric ester provided the concentrations of calcium and inorganic phosphate are sufficiently high. He and his colleagues found that when bone slices were treated with KCN or with certain fat solvents (alcohol, chloroform, or acetone) before placing them in the supersaturated solution, calcification did not occur in the absence of glycerophosphate. These substances, however, exerted little or no inhibitory effect if glycerophosphate were present, i.e., the phosphatase mechanism was not paralyzed and calcification proceeded. Formalin, on the contrary, prevented calcification whether a phosphoric ester was present or not. These results, in Robison's view, point to two distinct mechanisms governing the calcification process. (1) The phosphatase mechanism, poisoned by formalin, which produces in the fluids bathing the cartilage cells a state of supersaturation in respect to bone salt. (2) A mechanism poisoned by several agents, especially cyanide, which is responsible for the deposition of bone salts from a supersaturated solution, whether this is the result of phosphatase action or is brought to the cartilage matrix from another source. The nature of the second mechanism is unknown. It may be due, Robison suggests, to a "slight increase in the pH of the matrix fluid brought about by some membrane equilibrium." Since this mechanism is inhibited or paralyzed by cyanide, it is evidently dependent also upon the activity of living cells.

At the present time a satisfactory description of the processes underlying the calcification of bone cannot be provided. Among the factors contributing to the prevailing uncertainty two are prominent:

1. There is no agreement concerning the precise structure of bone salt or of the identity of the mineral deposited during calcification. Although it is accepted that the material is of the general nature of an apatite, a complex of tricalcium phosphate and calcium hydroxide, there is also the presence of carbonate and its variable composition in different areas to be accounted for. Perhaps the bone salt may be precipitated in one form and then remodeled to another.

2. The function of alkaline phosphatase remains obscure. Although there is little doubt that the enzyme is concerned in some way with calcification, the view that the phosphatase may be concerned with the production and maturation of the bone matrix prior to calcification, rather than with the deposition of bone salt, is now thought possible. In this connection, it is of interest that ossifying areas of cartilage display a particular affinity for calcium and phosphate, even after boiling (Waldman).

Additional suggestions are that the enzyme might be concerned with the formation of a phosphate ester acting as a template for the catalytic

crystalization of bone salt, or that it keeps the surface of bone crystals free of ester phosphate, thus permitting continued crystal growth.

The distribution and properties of "alkaline" phosphatase. Phosphatase[2] is present in greatest amount in ossifying cartilage, in smaller amount in formed bone, but is absent from resting epiphyseal cartilage and from nonossifying cartilage in other situations. It was shown by Robison to be absent from the patella before the appearance of the ossification center in this bone, but present thereafter. The teeth of young animals contain it in relatively large amounts. It is present in milk[3] and also in the floral parts of plants.

The optimum pH for phosphatase activity is around 9.0. Magnesium ions greatly increase the activity of the enzyme, whereas calcium ions are mildly inhibitory. Phosphatase activity has been demonstrated in a number of tissues (see table 59.3). The "alkaline" phosphatase in plasma, kidney, and intestine are not necessarily identical with that found in bone, inasmuch as the bone and kidney phosphatase, but not intestinal phosphatase, are inhibited by bile acids. Bone is apparently the main if not the sole source of plasma phosphatase, since this is not appreciably reduced after the removal of various organs (intestine, kidney, spleen, pancreas, etc.). Phosphatase is excreted by the liver; a marked rise in plasma phosphatase, therefore, occurs in obstructive jaundice and in jaundice due to liver damage, but not in the purely hemolytic type (ch. 39).

The pathological calcification of arteries such as the aorta, which Kay states does not contain the enzyme, cannot be satisfactorily explained upon the phosphatase hypothesis of Robison. The phosphatase in bone and the other solid tissues mentioned is reduced by the administration of irradiated ergosterol in amounts which cause the withdrawal of calcium from the bones and calcification of the tissues, whereas small doses cause an increase. On the other hand, it has been shown by Kay that the plasma phosphatase is increased, often markedly, in diseases involving extensive changes in bone structure (see table 59.4). Bone and certain other tissues, e.g., kidney, serum, and semen, but especially the human prostate, contain

---

[2] Phosphatase activity is expressed as the number of milligrams of inorganic phosphorus liberated per gram of tissue from sodium $\beta$-glycerophosphate after 48 hours hydrolysis at the optimum pH and at a temperature of 38°C.

[3] Kay and Graham have introduced a test by which one may determine whether a given sample of milk has been properly pasteurized. The test is based upon the fact that the temperature used in the pasteurization process destroys the activity of the enzyme.

TABLE 59.3*

*Relative phosphatase activity of tissue extracts prepared under similar conditions from various mammalian tissues†*

| Tissue | Forrai (1923) Man | Robison (1923) Young rabbit | Kay (1928) Adult Rabbit | Kay (1928) Adult Cat | Kay (1928) Adult Man | Kay (1931) Adult rat —average of 4 |
|---|---|---|---|---|---|---|
| Intestine | 100 | | | | | |
|   Duodenum | | | 50‡ | 93‡ | 57‡ | 46 |
|   Jejunum | | | 100‡ | 100‡ | 85‡ | 33 |
|   Ileum | | | 53‡ | 81‡ | 100‡ | 15 |
|   Colon | | | 17‡ | 34‡ | 27‡ | 6 |
| Kidney | 58 | 36 | 33 | 38 | 35 | 100 |
| Ossifying cartilage | | 100 | | | | |
| Whole bone | | | 20 | 10 | | 76 |
| Liver | 16 | 43 | 12 | 4 | | 4 |
| Pancreas | 8 | 11 | | | 6 | |
| Lung | | | 10 | 26 | 7 | 20 |
| Blood | | 14 | | | | 1 |
| Testis | 12 | | | | | 13 |
| Brain cerebrum | | | 3 | 3 | 4 | 7 |
| Cardiac muscle | | | 1 | 1 | | 5 |
| Skeletal muscle | | 4 | 1 | 1 | | 2 |
| Artery | | | | Nil | Nil | |

\* Modified from Kay, H. D., Physiol. Rev., 1932, **12**, 388.

† The figures in each column are relative one to the other, but the different columns cannot be compared quantitatively.

‡ Mucosa only.

TABLE 59.4*

*Changes in the phosphatase content of the plasma in disease*

| Disease | Number of Cases | Phosphatase Content of Plasma Highest | Lowest | Mean |
|---|---|---|---|---|
| | | unit | unit | unit |
| Arthritis without bony changes | 11 | 0.33 | 0.11 | 0.17 |
| Arthritis with bony changes | 7 | 0.25 | 0.09 | 0.17 |
| Exophthalmic goiter | 7 | 0.75 | 0.27 | 0.47 |
| | 8† | 0.53† | 0.19† | 0.36† |
| Osteomyelitis | 8 | 0.41 | 0.14 | 0.27 |
| Fragilitas osseum (infants or children) | 6 | 0.66 | 0.16 | 0.41 |
| Acromegaly | 2 | 0.32 | 0.22 | 0.27 |
| Rickets (infantile)‡ | 13 | 1.7 | 0.42 | 1.03 |
| Rickets (renal) | 2 | 1.5 | 0.9 | 1.2 |
| Adolescent rickets | 1 | | | >2.4 |
| Osteitis fibrosa (generalized) | 3 | >2.5 | 1.5 | >1.8 |
| | 3† | 1.8† | 1.06† | >1.31† |
| Osteitis deformans | 24 | 3.4 | 0.65 | >1.7 |

\* Modified from Kay H. D., Physiol. Rev., 1932, **12**, 412.

† Hunter (1930).

‡ Average for normal infants approximately same age = 0.32 arbitrary unit. Average for normal adults = 0.10 to 0.21 unit.

an "acid" phosphatase. Its optimum pH is between 4 and 5.4. Its concentration in the serum is increased in prostatic cancer with metastases.

### DEFECTS OF OSSIFICATION AND PATHOLOGICAL CALCIFICATIONS

#### Diseases of Bone

Several of these have already been considered in other parts of the text—*infantile rickets*, on pages 447, 453, and 454, *osteomalacia* on page 908, and *osteitis fibrosa cystica* on page 1059.

The hardness, strength, and rigidity of healthy bone depend upon the proportions of the organic and inorganic constituents incorporated into its structure, much as the properties of a plaster bandage depend upon the impregnation of the cotton mesh with plaster of Paris. The mineral and fibrous components are of equal importance; each reinforces the other. The cotton bandage has a certain tensile strength but lacks rigidity; a cast of plaster of Paris alone has maximum rigidity, but is brittle and readily broken or crushed. In most bone diseases the normal proportions between these two components are altered. In rickets and osteomalacia, for example, the bone salts are reduced in relation to the organic material. In these diseases, as also in *osteitis fibrosa cystica*, the bones are in consequence softer and more yielding than the normal. In certain other bone conditions the proportion of mineral to organic material is increased. The bone as a result is brittle and easily fractured. In other instances again there may be little change in the proportion of these two materials but the mass of the bone is increased or diminished with corresponding variations in strength.

*Osteitis deformans* (Paget's disease) is a disease of the skeleton involving mainly the bones of the skull, pelvis, limbs, and spine. The cranium is enlarged and its wall greatly thickened, the long bones of the limbs are massive and curved, the back is bowed (kyphosis) and its movements restricted. The organic matter of the bones is increased and the calcium content decreased, but the total amount of phosphorus is not far from normal. A pronounced degree of arteriosclerosis is frequently a feature. There is good evidence that the overgrowth of osseous tissue is secondary to a primary bone destruction. Metabolic studies in this disease have yielded little information though there is said to be a retention of calcium and phosphorus; the blood alkaline phosphatase level is high.

*Fragilitas ossium* (*osteogenesis imperfecta*) is a congenital disease characterized by thinness and extreme fragility of the skeleton, especially of the long bones and ribs. The cranium shows defective calcification. Fractures result from the most trivial injuries or may occur without any apparent cause. Union and healing of the fractures occur, however, as readily as in a normal bone. The bones have a low calcium content, the cortex is very thin, and the medullary cavity dilated.

*Achondroplasia* is a congenital disease in which endochondral ossification (p. 1062) of the limb bones, especially the humeri and femora, is defective. Periosteal ossification is active. The long bones are, therefore, much shorter and thicker than normal, strong, and dense. A characteristic type of dwarf results; short arms and legs with a trunk and head of almost normal dimensions. The bones of the base of the skull fuse prematurely and the development of certain facial bones is abnormal. Achondroplastic dwarfs develop, as a result of these abnormalities, a distinctive facies; depressed nasal bridge (pug nose), a broad forehead, and prominent lower jaw.

*Marble or chalky bone (Albers-Schönbergs disease).* In this condition the density of the bone is greatly increased; the cancellous tissue is filled with a chalky material and the medullary canal may be almost obliterated by the concentric thickening of the shaft. The excessive calcification, however, renders the bones soft and brittle. Calcification of soft tissues (arteries, lungs, tendons) is often a feature. The disease is exceedingly rare.

The cause or causes of the foregoing osseous abnormalities is unknown. The possibility of some endocrine disorder, of course, comes to mind, but there is little or no evidence of such.

*Renal rickets, renal osteitis fibrosa cystica,* or *generalisata.* This is a condition commencing most usually in childhood and associated with chronic nephritis, rarefaction of the skeleton, dwarfism, low serum calcium, and, sometimes, calcium deposits in the soft tissues, especially in the kidneys; there are also acidosis and phosphate retention. The parathyroids show hyperplasia. We have seen that a rise in serum phosphate causes a reciprocal reduction in serum calcium and it is usually held that the hypocalcemia seen in this disease is due to the retention of phosphate resulting from the renal insufficiency. The hypocalcemia so produced causes, it is presumed, a drain of calcium from the bones. Increased excretion of phosphate into the intestine as a result of the diminished excretion by the kidney, with consequent depression of calcium absorption is possibly a contributory factor in the production of the low serum calcium. Albright and his colleagues suggest that renal osteitis fibrosacystica or generalisata is a more appropriate name for this disease than renal rickets inasmuch as the histological changes in the bones are indistinguishable from *primary* hyperparathyroidism (p. 1060). This brings up the question as to whether the demineralization of the skeleton is due to the hyperparathyroidism induced as a compensatory reaction to the low serum calcium. In the opinion of Albright and his associates, the withdrawal of calcium from the skeleton is not directly due to the parathyroid hyperplasia, i.e., to the parathyroid hormone itself, but to the acidosis which results from the failure of the diseased renal tubules to produce ammonia. Calcium is used as a base for the neutralization of acid; the tendency toward a fall in serum calcium is met by the withdrawal of calcium from the bones. Parathyroid hyperplasia occurs as a compensatory reaction to the hypocalcemia. The effect upon the bones was found to respond to measures which reduce the acidosis.

### Calcification of Soft Tissues

*Dystrophic calcification* is the term applied to the deposition of calcium salts in dead, dying, or chronically inflamed tissues, and in areas of fatty or hyaline degeneration. Thus areas of necrosis, infarcts, scar tissue, caseous tuberculous areas, and degenerated nerve cells, tend to undergo calcification. Calcification also occurs in the infarcts of the placenta which appear in the later half of pregnancy. Many of the examples of pathological calcifications to be described are simply special examples of dystrophic calcification. The factors determining the deposition of calcium salts in devitalized tissues are obscure. It has been suggested that since the $CO_2$ production in such tissue is minimal or entirely absent they will have a more alkaline reaction; this, of course, would tend to cause the deposition of calcium salts.

*Calcinosis* is the name given to conditions in which (1) calcified areas are scattered throughout the skin and subcutaneous tissues (*calcinosis circumscripta*) or (2) a more generalized calcification of skin interstitial tissues, tendons, fascia, or muscles occurs (*calcinosis universalis*). When the calcification process involves predominantly the interstitial tissues of the muscles the condition is usually referred to as *myositis ossificans*. In calcinosis the calcium and phosphorus levels of the blood are normal. Metabolic studies have in some instances revealed a retention of calcium. In the region of the calcified areas true bone formation may occur. Calcinosis of the superficial tissues is in many cases associated with scleroderma (a condition characterized by induration of the skin due to an increase in the intercellular collagenous tissue). The cause of calcinosis is obscure; the calcification process may be secondary to degenerative changes in the tissues themselves. There is no evidence that it is dependent upon an abnormality of parathyroid function, though Selye has reported a condition in rats resembling scleroderma following the administration of parathyroid extract.

ARTERIAL CALCIFICATION. *Arteriosclerosis* is seen in two main forms: (1) the *atherosclerosis* (athere = crushed grain, porridge) of *Marchand*, (2) the *medial sclerosis* of *Mönckeberg*.

METASTATIC CALCIFICATION. This term connotes a transference of calcium from the skeleton to the soft tissues. It occurs in animals treated with excessive doses of parathyroid extract or irradiated ergosterol. Though the calcium deposits may be found in any of the soft tissues, the arteries, kidneys, and lungs are especially susceptible to calcification. The fundus of the stomach is also a common site. It will be noted that the three last mentioned organs eliminate acid; and it has been suggested that since this will leave the cells more alkaline in reaction, a condition favorable to calcium deposition is created. Metastatic calcification also occurs occasionally clinically. It has been reported in hyperparathyroidism (p. 1060), renal rickets, and in certain bone diseases, e.g., multiple myelomata. It is very natural to assume that in conditions of disturbed calcium metabolism and destructive disease of bone the calcium deposits are simply the result of the excess calcium in the circulation. It is quite possible, however, that in some instances at any rate, it is secondary to tissue injury and may therefore be, in reality, a type of dystrophic calcification induced by a toxic agent. Parathyroid extract and irradiated ergosterol, for example, besides their effects upon calcium metabolism have a definitely toxic action. Furthermore, metastatic calcification is in some instances associated with hypocalcemia.

It is a fact of great interest that the calcium deposits in the arteries and in other soft tissues in the various types of pathological calcification have the same composition as the main mineral compounds of bone. Evidence obtained by both chemical and physical methods support this conclusion. In certain instances actual bone formation occurs, even to the extent of producing red marrow tissue. Areas of ossification have been observed in the aorta and in the neighborhood of calcium deposits in the necrotic kidney of the rabbit. Also, as shown by Huggins, if a section of the mucosa of the bladder be transplanted into the subcutaneous tissues it becomes the site of bone formation.

*Renal calculi (nephrolithiasis, urolithiasis)*. Kidney and bladder stones composed largely of calcium phosphate have been produced in experimental animals (rats) by the administration of irradiated ergosterol or parathyroid extract in excess. They are apparently the result of the excretion in the urine of large amounts of calcium liberated from the bones.

Renal or vesical calculi are also associated with various bone diseases of a destructive nature; they are quite frequent in hyperparathyroidism. Renal calculi may be composed of calcium oxalate (in acid urine), or of calcium carbonate or phosphate (in alkaline urine), or of urates, uric acid or cystine. There is an undoubted relationship between the urinary excretion of citrate and the production of calcium stones. Citrate excretion is reduced in those suffering from renal calcium deposits even though the intake of citrate is greatly increased. In normal persons, the urinary excretion of citrate runs parallel with the calcium excretion and varies with the calcium of the diet. It is suggested that citrate in some way reduces the tendency toward the precipitation of calcium. Nephrolithiasis is particularly prevalent in the tropics and the possibility has been suggested that hypervitaminosis D, due to overirradiation with ultraviolet light and, possibly, deficiency of vitamin A are causative factors. The production of renal calculi in animals by hypervitaminosis D, as mentioned above, occurs only, however, when doses are employed which cause bone resorption and an increased concentration of calcium in the urine. Such results have, therefore, little bearing upon the question of the production of urinary calculi in the human subject. Also, though there is some evidence that avitaminosis A is conducive to the development of urinary calculi in animals (the cornification of the epithelium of the urinary tract being, apparently, a predisposing factor), there is little warrant for applying the results of animal experiments to the question of urinary lithiasis in man.

*Albright's syndrome (polyostotic fibrous displasia, osteitis fibrosa disseminata).* This is a rare disease with bizarre manifestations, consisting of bone cysts, fractures, patches of brown pigmentation in the skin, outward bowing of the femur, and, in female children only, precocious puberty. The bony changes resemble those of osteitis fibrosa cystica but are more localized; they, as well as the cutaneous pigmentation, often show a segmental distribution, suggesting a neurological or developmental origin. There is no evidence of parathyroid overactivity or of a fault in any other endocrine.

### REFERENCES

ALBRIGHT, F., DRAKE, T. G. AND SULKOWITCH, H. W. Bull Johns Hopkins Hosp., 1937, 60, 377.

ANDERSON, I. A. AND LYALL, A. Quart. J. Med., 1939, 8, 209.

ANDERSON, W. A. D. Endocrinology, 1939, 24, 372.

BARNICOT, N. A. Nature, 1948, 162, 848.

BAUER, W., AUB, J. C. AND ALBRIGHT, F. J. Exper. Med., 1929, 49, 145.

BINGER, C. J. Pharmacol. & Exper. Therap., 1917, 10, 105.

BODANSKY, A., BLAIR, J. E. AND JAFFE, H. L. J. Biol. Chem., 1930, 88, 629.

BODANSKY, A. AND JAFFE, H. L. J. Exper. Med., 1931, 53, 591.

BREITER, H. AND ASSOCIATES. J. Nutrition, 1941, 21, 351.

CAMERON, A. T. AND MOORHOUSE, V. H. K. J. Biol. Chem., 1925, 63, 687.

CAMERON, A. T. AND MOORHOUSE, V. H. K. Tr. Roy. Soc. Canada, 1925, 19, Section V, 39.

CHANG, H. Y. Anat. Rec., 1951, 111, 23.

COLLIP, J. B. J. Biol. Chem., 1925, 63, 395.

COLLIP, J. B. AND CLARK, E. P. J. Biol. Chem., 1925, 64, 485.

COLLIP, J. B., CLARK, E. P. AND SCOTT, J. W. J. Biol. Chem., 1925, 63, 439.

ELLSWORTH, R. J. Clin. Invest., 1932, 11, 1011.

GLEY, D. Arch. physiol., 1893, 5, 5 Série, 766.

GREENBERG, D. M. AND ASSOCIATES. Am. J. Physiol., 1942, 137, 459.

GREENWALD, I. J. Biol. Chem., 1924, 61, 33.

GROLLMAN, A. Endocrinology, 1954, 55, 166.

HASTINGS, A. B., ROSEBERRY, H. H. AND MORSE, J. K. J. Biol. Chem., 1931, 90, 395.

HIGGINS, G. M. AND SHEARD, C. Am. J. Physiol., 1928, 85, 299.

HOLTZ, F. Klin. Wchnschr., 1934, 13, 104.

HUGGINS, C. B. Arch. Surg., 1931, 22, 377.

HUNTER, D. Brit. J. Surg., 1931, 19, 203.

IMRIE, C. G. AND JENKINSON, C. N. J. Physiol., 1933, 79, 218.

JAFFE, H. L. AND BODANSKY, A. J. Exper. Med., 1930, 52, 669.

JAFFE, H. L., BODANSKY, A. AND BLAIR, J. E. J. Exper. Med., 1932, 55, 695.

KAY, H. D. J. Biol. Chem., 1930, 89, 249.

KAY, H. D. AND GRAHAM, W. R. J. Dairy Res., 1933, 5, 54.

LOEB, J. Am. J. Physiol., 1900, 3, 383.

LOEB, J. Am. J. Physiol., 1901, 5, 362.

LOEB, J. J. Biol. Chem., 1915, 23, 423.

MACCALLUM, W. G. AND VOEGTLIN, C. J. Exper. Med., 1909, 11, 118.

MCLEAN, F. C. AND HASTINGS, A. B. J. Biol. Chem., 1934, 107, 337.

MCLEAN, F. C. AND HASTINGS, A. B. J. Biol. Chem., 1935, 108, 285.

MACLEOD, J. J. R. AND TAYLOR, N. B. Tr. Roy. Soc. Canada, 1925, 19, Section V, 27.

MANDL, F. Zentralbl. Chir., 1926, 53, 260. (Quoted by Hunter.)

PAPPENHEIMER, A. M. J. Exper. Med., 1936, 64, 965.

PATON, D. N. AND FINDLAY, J. Quart. J. Exper. Physiol., 1916, 10, 203, 233, 315, 377.

PATT, H. M. AND LUCKHARDT, A. B. Endocrinology, 1942, 31, 384.

PUGSLEY, L. I. AND SELYE, H. J. Physiol., 1933, 79, 113.

ROBISON, R. Biochem. J., 1923, 17, 286.

ROBISON, R. AND SOAMES, K. M. Biochem. J., 1924, 18, 740.

ROBISON, R. AND SOAMES, K. M. Biochem. J., 1925, **19**, 153.

SCHOUR, I. AND HAM, A. Arch. Path., 1934, **17**, 22.

SELYE, H. Endocrinology, 1932, **16**, 547.

SELYE, H. Arch. Path., 1932, **14**, 60.

SELYE, H. J.A.M.A., 1932, **99**, 108.

SHERMAN, H. C. AND HAWLEY, E. J. Biol. Chem., 1922, **53**, 375.

SHIPLEY, P. G. AND HOLT, L. E. Bull. Johns Hopkins Hosp., 1927, **40**, 1.

SHIPLEY, P. G. AND HOLT, L. E. Bull. Johns Hopkins Hosp., 1927, **41**, 437.

SHIPLEY, P. G., KRAMER, B. AND HOWLAND, J. Biochem. J., 1926, **20**, 379.

SNAPPER, I. Arch. Int. Med., 1930, **46**, 506.

TALMAGE, R. V. AND ELLIOTT, J. R. Endocrinology, 1958, **62**, 717.

TAYLOR, H. Brit. J. Surg., 1934, **22**, 561.

TAYLOR, N. D., WELD, C. B., BRANION, H. D. AND KAY, H. D. Canad. M. A. J., 1931, **24**, 763.

TAYLOR, N. D., WELD, C. B., BRANION, H. D. AND KAY, H. D. Canad. M. A. J., 1931, **25**, 20.

TAYLOR, N. W. AND SHEARD, C. J. Biol. Chem., 1929, **81**, 479.

THOMPSON, D. L. AND PUGSLEY, L. I. Am. J. Physiol., 1932, **102**, 350.

WATT, J. C. Arch. Surg., 1925, **10**, 983.

WEST, R. Brain, 1935, **58**, 1.

*Monographs and Reviews*

ALBRIGHT, F. AND REIFENSTEIN, E. C. The parathyroid glands and metabolic bone disease. The Williams & Wilkins Co., Baltimore, 1948.

AUB, J. C. Medicine, 1925, **4**, 1.

AUB, J. C. Harvey Lectures, 1928–1929, **24**, 151.

BARR, D. P. Physiol. Rev., 1932, **12**, 593.

BOURNE, G. H. The biochemistry and physiology of bone. Academic Press, New York, 1956.

COLLIP, J. B. Medicine, 1926, **5**, 1.

DRAGSTEDT, L. R. Physiol. Rev., 1927, **7**, 499.

HAM, A. Cowdry's Special Cytol., 1932, **2**, 981.

HAM, A. J. Am. Dent. A., 1934, **21**, 3.

HAM, A. W. Histology, 2nd ed., Chapter 16. Pitman Medical Publishing Co., London, 1953.

HARRISON, H. E. AND HARRISON, H. C. J. Clin. Invest., 1941, **20**, 47.

HESS, A. F. Rickets, including osteomalacia and tetany. Lea & Febiger, Philadelphia, 1929.

HUGGINS, C. Physiol. Rev., 1937, **17**, 119.

HUNTER, D. Lancet, 1930, **1**, 897, 947, 999.

HUNTER, D. AND AUB, J. C. Quart. J. Med., 1926, **20**, 123.

KAY, H. D. Physiol. Rev., 1932, **12**, 384.

LOGAN, M. A. Physiol. Rev., 1940, **20**, 522.

MacCALLUM, W. G. Medicine, 1924, **3**, 137.

McLEAN, F. C. Ann. Rev. Physiol., 1943, **5**, 79.

McLEAN, F. C. AND BLOOM, W. Science, 1937, **85**, 24.

McLEAN, F. C. AND URIST, M. R. Bone. University of Chicago Press, Chicago, 1955.

ROBISON, R. The significance of phosphoric esters in metabolism. New York University Press, New York, 1932.

SCHMIDT, C. L. A. AND GREENBERG, D. M. Physiol. Rev., 1935, **15**, 297.

THOMPSON, D. L. AND COLLIP, J. B. Physiol. Rev., 1932, **12**, 309.

WEINMAN, J. P. AND SICHER, H. Bone and bones; fundamentals of bone biology, 2nd ed. C. V. Mosby Co., St. Louis, 1955.

See also references in chapter 57.

# 60

# THE ENDOCRINE ORGANS OF SEX

## The Genetic Basis of Sex

The sex glands—testes and ovaries—are known also as the *gonads* and are the *primary organs of sex*. They furnish the male or female sex cells (spermatozoa or ova) and the hormones upon which the *ultimate* maleness or femaleness of the individual depend. Associated with the sex glands are organs which are essential for procreation but whose activities are governed by the secretions of the sex glands. These are the *accessory sex organs* and include the external genitalia, as well as the uterus, fallopian tubes and vagina in the female and the seminal vesicles and prostate glands of the male. Certain sexual characteristics, the *secondary sex characters*, make their appearance at the time of sexual maturity (puberty). They include the occurrence of hair on the pubis of the human male or female, the deepening of the voice in men, the development of the mammary glands in women and the psychic manifestations in both sexes. In certain other forms the secondary sex characters differ even more noticeably, (e.g., the development of the antlers of stags, the distinctive plumage of birds, the comb and wattles of the cockerel). The genetic sex of an animal is determined at the time of conjugation of the *gametes* (spermatozoon and ovum), and depends upon which one of two types of chromosome is contained in the sperm cell. The cells of the human body contain 23 pairs of chromosomes. During gametogenesis the pairs are split so that each gamete contains a single representative of each of the 23 pairs of chromosomes, in other words 23 chromosomes instead of 46. This is the process of *meiosis*. The partners in one pair of chromosomes of the male, the sex chromosomes, are dissimilar; one, X, is larger than the other, Y, and during meiosis these are separated so that one male gamete will contain an X-chromosome and the other a Y. In the female two X chromosomes are in combination as the sex chromosomes, so that on meiotic division to form ova, each ovum comes to possess one X-chromosome. It will be seen that the chromosomes determining sex are carried by the gametes produced by the male. If an ovum is fertilized by a sperm bearing an X-chromosome then the combination XX will be produced and result in the development of a female. On the other hand, if the fertilizing sperm bears a Y-chromosome, then the XY com-

bination produces a male. It is perhaps worth noting that in birds the heterogametic sex (XY) is female, whereas the sex possessing two X-chromosomes (XX) is male.

Besides carrying the genes concerned with sex determination the sex chromosomes may also contain the genes controlling certain diseases and defects. Hemophilia, color-blindness and fishskin disease (ichthyosis) are examples of such abnormalities. Hemophilia and color-blindness are transmitted from grandfather to grandson, through the intermediary of a normal carrier female and are conveyed on the X-chromosome, whereas ichthyosis passes from father to son *via* the Y-chromosome. If a man afflicted with hemophilia marries a normal woman the disease is not transmitted to his sons (XY), for the X-chromosome received from the mother does not carry the defect and neither does the Y-chromosome received from the father. The daughters, however, have received an abnormal factor in the X-chromosome from the father as well as a normal one from the mother but remain free of the disease since the abnormal character is 'recessive' and is suppressed by the dominant normal character. Should the daughters marry and a Y-sperm fertilize an ovum, then a male (XY) zygote results and the child will show the disease for one of the abnormal X-chromosomes of the mother has paired with the Y of the father. The Y-chromosome does not offset the effect of the abnormal X-chromosome. It should be remembered that since the mother possesses two X-chromosomes, a normal and an abnormal one, it is an even chance which one the child will receive. A classic series of cases of the disease may be found among the descendants of Queen Victoria who was a carrier. Eleven hemophilics are to be found in the three succeeding generations.

*Sex chromatin.* Since every cell of a male individual differs from that of a female, in that it possesses a dissimilar sex chromosome, it might be postulated that suitably refined cytological techniques would prove capable of distinguishing between male and female cells. Such is so. In 1949 Barr and Bertram reported the discovery of a sexual dimorphism in the neurone of the cat; since then their findings have been extended to a

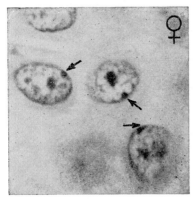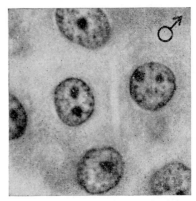

Fig. 60.1. Nuclei of cells in epidermal spinous cell layer of a chromosomal female (left) and chromosomal male (right). Note the sex chromatin indicated by arrows in the female. (From Grumbach and Barr.)

variety of tissues and a variety of species, including man. The difference between male and female cells lies in a special mass of chromatin, known as the *sex chromatin* which is characteristic of the female. In man, skin biopsy preparations, smears from the oral mucous membrane, and blood films yield satisfactory preparations for study. The sex chromatin is typically a planoconvex mass, about 1 micron in diameter lying close to or in contact with the nuclear membrane (fig. 60.1). It stains readily with basic dyes and is Feulgen-positive, indicating the presence of desoxyribose nucleic acid. The sex chromatin appears to be a chromosomal derivative since, like the chromosomes, it is consistently Feulgen-positive, whereas the nucleolus (with which the sex chromatin might be associated) is Fuelgen-negative. There is no evidence that the sex hormones influence the chromatin; typical sexual dimorphism has been found in the nuclei of individuals of all ages, from the early embryo to senility. It is likely, although not proven, that the sex chromatin of female cells represents certain regions of the two X-chromosomes that adhere together. The importance of the discovery of sex chromatin, apart from its theoretical significance, lies in the diagnosis of the genetic sex of individuals with sexual anomalies, such as in cases of pseudohermaphroditism, gonadal agenesis, etc. These will be examined further below.

*Sex ratio.* If spermatozoa carrying X-chromosomes and spermatozoa carrying Y-chromosomes are produced in equal numbers in the testis, and if each has an equal chance of fertilizing an ovum then equal numbers of male and female individuals should be conceived. In actual fact, in the human more male embryos than female develop; the *primary sex ratio* is greater than one. Precise

figures are difficult to obtain for man, but in the pig Parkes concluded that the ratio must be about 160:100; in cattle it is about 130:100. Between conception and delivery there is an appreciable mortality which preferentially affects the male so that the proportion at birth, the *secondary sex ratio* is lower, being in the pig about 105:100. In Britain the human secondary sex ratio is about 106:100. Through childhood and in adult life the male mortality exceeds that of the female so that numerical equality of the sexes is reached during adolescence, and thereafter the females outnumber the males. At around 85 years or so there are twice as many women as men. The cause of the primary sex ratio is uncertain. It has been suggested that the spermatozoa bearing the smaller Y-chromosomes are more active than those carrying the larger X-chromosome, so that more "male" spermatozoa than "female" reach the ovum. Alternatively the environment of the genital tract could favor one kind of spermatozoon—attempts to control the primary sex ratio have been made on this basis.

## The Hormonal Factors in Development of the Genital System

Although the sex of an individual has been seen to be determined genetically, a variety of factors may intervene to modify embryonic sexual development. The gonads are derived from mesodermal primordia arising in the genital ridges along the dorsal surface of the celomic cavity. Essentially they are bipotential organs which can become testes or ovaries. The testicular and ovarian components are antagonistic, and the balance normally becomes tipped so that the resultant gonad conforms to the genetic sex of the individual. Experimentally, in lower forms such as amphibia and birds, treatment with sex hormones can reverse gonadal development so that a presumptive testis becomes an ovary, and vice versa. In mammals, gonadal reversal has not been achieved experimentally but evidence in favor of a hormonal effect on gonadal development has long been derived from study of the bovine *freemartin*. Here a sterile female calf (a freemartin) is born as a twin with a normal male. The sexual abnormalities of the freemartin include a small undeveloped uterus and an enlarged clitoris. The gonads are intraabdominal and resemble testes to a variable extent. It is well established that the freemartin is a genetic female (this has recently been confirmed by sex chromatin studies) and that the condition is caused by a hormone that reaches the female embryo from the male twin through vascular anastomoses between the partially fused placentas (Keller and Tandler, Lillie). In the unusual case when fusion of the chorion did not occur, and the female embryo remained free from masculinization by the male, the female twin remained normal. Modification of the development of the accessory sex structures is more easily achieved. Following castration of the male rabbit fetus the male tubular system (Wolffian ducts) regresses whereas the coexistent female (Müllerian) system persists and differentiates into a female reproductive tract together with female external genitalia (Jost). Removal of the fetal ovary, on the other hand, does not interfere with the differentiation of a female genital tract. Testosterone given to castrated males or to females stimulates the development of the masculine characters but does not inhibit the uterine horns or tubes. There is thus good evidence for the existence of a hormone secreted by the testis at a very early stage of development which results in the repression of the female primordia. The early observation of Bouin and Ancel that the interstitial cells (p. 1101) of the testis are well developed at this time supports this view, but the identity of the embryonic testicular hormone is unknown.

The facts summarized above are of importance in the study of a variety of sexual abnormalities. These include true and pseudohermaphroditism, and gonadal dysgenesis. In cases of *true hermaphroditism* the individual possesses both ovarian and testicular tissue. There is generally some degree of ambisexual development of the genital tract but this, and the development of the secondary sexual characteristics, is highly variable. The chromosomal sex may be male or female. Two variations of *pseudohermaphroditism* exist: the male and the female type. In the male type the individual has testes only but exhibits development of the female genital duct system to a variable degree. The patients may appear male or female, but are genetically male. Female pseudohermaphrodites possess only ovaries and show variable masculine genital development. The sex chromatin is female. A variety of causes underlie these defects but, in the female, congenital viriliz-

ing adrenal hyperplasia is the most common. In typical cases of *gonadal dysgenesis* the internal and external genital structures are female but remain infantile, and there is little development of the secondary sexual characteristics. Congenital anomalies may be present including webbed neck, lymphedema of the extremities, coarctation of the aorta, and various skeletal deformities. Following the description by H. H. Turner of a series of cases in 1938 the condition gained the name of *Turner's syndrome*. Patients with this syndrome do not possess gonads as such but in the position of the ovary there is a narrow ridge of fibrous connective tissue. On the basis of experimental studies on the effect of gonadectomy in rabbit and mouse fetus Jost and Wilkins independently predicted in 1950 that some patients with gonadal dysgenesis should be genetically male. This prediction was proved correct when study of the sex chromatin revealed that more than 80 per cent of cases had male nuclei. The factors underlying this condition are obscure.

## The Effect of Excision of the Gonads— Castration—Spaying

Removal of the gonads of a young animal prevents the development of the accessory sex organs and the secondary sex characters fail to appear. The effects of castration upon the secondary characters are evident even in such simple forms as the earthworm and hermit crab. Castration of the male frog prevents the appearance of the sexual changes which normally occur during the mating season. The thumb-pad and fore-limb muscles do not hypertrophy, the clasping reflex cannot be elicited and the animal does not emit its characteristic croak. The sexual development of birds and mammals is profoundly affected by castration. The castrated cockerel (capon), for example, has a greater proportion of body fat than does the normal bird, whereas the comb, wattles and spurs, and the sex instincts, do not develop. Development of the spurs and plumage, however, is not prevented. Corresponding effects of gonadectomy are seen in the young turkey cock and in the young of other avian species. Removal of the ovaries (spaying) causes the development of spurs, a comb resembling that of a cock, and male plumage. The spayed duck assumed the plumage of the drake.[1]

[1] Male plumage is considered to be the basic or neutral type. Its development is suppressed by the female sex hormone, when the female type of plumage appears. Hence the male plumage appears after ovariectomy and persists after testicular removal.

The effects of castration upon young cattle, horses and stags are well known. Castration of young bulls causes an increase in the size of the skeleton and a greater deposition of fat. The mature development of the accessory organs is prevented. The antlers of young stags do not develop after castration. Castration of boys before puberty retards ossification of the epiphyses of the long bones with consequent enlargement of the stature due to disproportionate lengthening of the lower limbs. There is also adiposity, with a tendency toward a feminine distribution of the fat. The larynx is not prominent, as in the mature male, and the voice remains high-pitched. Hair fails to grow upon the face and body, but is unusually plentiful on the head. The penis remains infantile and sexual feeling is suppressed. Such a state is called *eunuchism.* Ovariectomy in women is followed by changes characteristic of the menopause (p. 1080), namely, amenorrhea, atrophy of the secondary sex organs and obesity. If performed before puberty the characteristic feminine attributes do not appear; the girl tends to become somewhat mannish in type whereas the accessory organs fail to develop fully and menstruation does not occur.

Sexual desire in higher animals and in the human subject is not necessarily entirely dependent upon the gonads, particularly in the male. Ovariectomized adult female chimpanzees show few signs of desire for intercourse, but ovariectomized women may show as much erotic behavior after the operation as was exhibited previously. Castration of male primates often produces no diminution in the capacity to mate or (in man) to achieve sexual climax during coitus (Ford and Beach). In lower mammals, such as the cat, removal of the ovaries abolishes sexual behavior. It may be recalled that, following removal of the gonads, androgens produced by the adrenal gland may be responsible for some of the sexual responses observed.

*Transplantation or grafting experiments.* If the excised gonad (testis or ovary) is transplanted to another situation in the body and survives, the otherwise inevitable endocrine effects of castration are prevented. This fact, first demonstrated by Berthold in the cock in 1849, proves conclusively that the gonad furnishes an internal secretion. The studies of homotransplants show that feminization of the capon, or masculinization of the ovariectomized hen, can be induced by transplantation of the gonad of the opposite sex.

## The Ovaries

*Development of the ovaries.* The ovaries, as well as the testes, arise from the celomic epithelium covering the inner aspect of the Wolffian body. The epithelial cells of this region assume a columnar form and proliferate to form several layers which constitute the *germinal epithelium,* whereas the mesenchymal stroma underlying the germinal epithelium becomes thickened to form the *genital ridge.* By means of a localized multiplication of cells in the germinal epithelium, fingerlike processes arise which penetrate into the mesenchymal stroma. These processes are known as the *primary sex cords* and contain both germinal and supporting tissue. Up to this point there is no difference in the differentiation of an ovary or testis. If the gonad is destined to become an ovary then the germinal epithelium remains thickened and proliferates a set of *secondary sex cords* or *cortical cords* which form the definitive cortex of the adult ovary. The primary sex cords become the adult medulla. In the process of testis formation the germinal epithelium becomes reduced in thickness and the primary sex cords progress to become the seminiferous tubules.

*Structure of the ovary.* The adult ovary is a flattened oval structure (about 3.4 cm. long) with one of its edges, the *hilus,* attached *via* the mesovarium to the broad ligament. It consists of a dense stroma of connective tissue which carries blood vessels and in which are embedded the oocytes and *Graafian follicles* in all stages of development. The stroma also contains smooth muscle fibers and small numbers of large polyhedral epithelial cells —the *interstitial cells.* The surface of the ovary is covered with a layer of epithelial cells, the germinal epithelium, which is continuous with the epithelium of the general peritoneum.

*The Graafian follicles.* It is possible that the germinal epithelium covering the ovary retains its embryonic character and proclivities after birth—until the end of the reproductive period (to about the 45th year in women). The question of postnatal formation of ova has been the subject of much debate. The general opinion is that the ovary continues to form sex cells after birth although at a diminishing rate. A *primordial follicle* is formed by invagination of a cord of cells from the germinal epithelium. An island of cells becomes separated; one of the group develops into a *primitive ovum* whereas the rest form a surrounding layer of *granulosa cells.* At this time the primordial follicle is about 45 microns in diameter and becomes displaced towards the deeper regions of the cortex. It appears that the orderly arrangement of cells in the development of primordial follicles is governed by the ovum itself, for when the ova are destroyed by X-ray treatment the germinal epithelium forms cords and clumps instead of follicles.

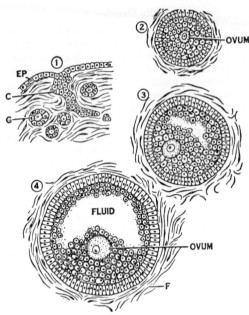

FIG. 60.2. Successive stages in the development of the ovum and Graafian follicle (diagrammatic). EP, germinal epithelium covering the surface of the ovary; C, a cord of cells growing from the germinal epithelium into the ovarian substance; G, primordial ovum encircled by a single layer of (granulosa) cells. In 4, the *membrana granulosa* and the *cumulus oophorus* are shown but the follicle has not yet reached full development; F, ovarian stroma.

The infantile ovary contains some 400,000 primordial follicles, but subsequent development requires the participation of pituitary activity which becomes manifest at puberty. As follicles develop two more layers of cells are produced from the ovarian stroma. The inner layer—the *theca interna* —is thought to be formed by some influence exerted upon the stroma cells by the granulosa cells. This layer is vascular and more cellular than the outer layer—the *theca externa*—which is fibrous in character. At the same time that these changes are occurring the granulosa cells multiply to form a cell mass several layers deep, now known as the *membrana granulosa* in which two concentric zones can be distinguished. These become separated by the accumulation of fluid (liquor folliculi) and a cavity or *antrum* is formed. It is at this time that the follicle may be called a Graafian follicle. The cells of the inner zone of membrana granulosa surround the ovum and these are piled in pyramid fashion in contrast with part of the wall of the follicle. This mass protruding into the antrum of the follicle is the *cumulus oophorus*, or *discus proligerus*.

The growth of the follicle and the changes just described represent follicular maturation or ripening and during this process the follicle extends outwards so that when mature the follicular wall projects from the surface of the ovary. A mature follicle may have a diameter of up to 10 mm. and contains an ovum some 100 to 150 microns across, bounded by a clear membrane, the *zona pellucida*. Full maturity of the ovum is heralded by the extrusion of the first polar body and following this the follicular wall ruptures and the ovum, together with some discus proligerus cells forming the *corona radiata*, is discharged. It passes along the Fallopian tube to the uterus.

After discharge of the ovum the cavity of the ruptured Graafian follicle may become filled with a clot of blood. The small body formed in this way is sometimes spoken of as the *corpus hemorrhagicum*. The clot is soon replaced by a mass of cells containing a yellow lipid material (*luteal cells*). These are derived from the proliferation of the epithelial cells of the membrana granulosa (*granulosa lutein cells*) and of the theca interna (*theca lutein cells*). The follicle with its content of luteal cells constitutes the *corpus luteum* (fig. 60.3). The circumference of the follicle by this time has become more vascular and capillaries penetrate into the yellow cell mass. The transformed follicle may now be looked upon as a temporary organ of internal secretion. If fertilization of the ovum does not occur, the life of the corpus luteum is short. In the human it persists for about 10 days and then regresses. Its vessels become obliterated; the luteal cells disintegrate and are replaced by fibrous tissue; nothing then remains of the follicle but a pale scar—the *corpus albicans*. On the other hand, if fertilization of the ovum occurs the corpus luteum continues to grow and in women attains a diameter of three-quarters of an inch or more by the middle of pregnancy. It then commences to

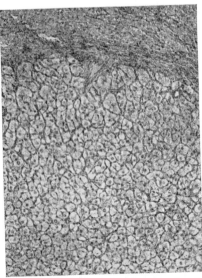

FIG. 60.3. Section of corpus luteum showing luteal tissue under high magnification. (From Parkes, *The Internal Secretions of the Ovary*, by permission of Longmans, Green & Co.)

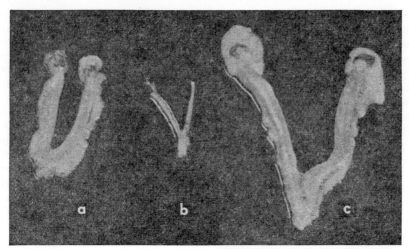

Fig. 60.4. Showing uterus (a) in anestrus, (b) one month after ovariectomy, (c) in estrus. (After d'Amour and Blood.)

shrink and is finally absorbed by the seventh month.

Of the vast number of ova and primordial follicles in the ovary only a few ever reach the Graafian follicle stage. In women, not more than one or two ova are as a rule discharged each month, or a total of 400 or so during the entire reproductive period. The remaining follicles develop to some extent and then undergo degenerative changes to become *atretic follicles*. Each of the latter is finally replaced by fibrous tissue derived from the theca and only a small scar, a *corpus fibrosum*, remains.

The factors which determine the rupture of the ripe follicle are not definitely known but clearly involve the effects of the rhythmic secretions of the pituitary gland. The accumulation of fluid and the consequent increase in intrafollicular pressure is probably a factor in some animals, or the contraction of the smooth muscle fibers of the stroma may play a part. In most species, including man, the follicle ruptures "spontaneously," but in the rabbit, cat and ferret ovulation occurs only after copulation.

### The Sexual Life of Females

Three sexual periods of different lengths occur in female mammals:

1. A single long period occupying the greater part of the animal's life. It commences at *puberty*, at which time the first ovulation occurs. The accessory organs of reproduction mature, sex desire is aroused and the secondary sex characters appear. It ends with atrophic changes in the ovary and accessory organs. In women the termination of this period is called the *menopause* (p. 1080).

2. A period which recurs once or oftener each year, known as the *mating, sexual,* or *breeding season*. In most species it is only during this time, or during a part of it, that the female will receive the male.[2] The duration of the mating season and the number of times it occurs annually vary in different species. In the dog, for instance, it is generally said that two such periods of about six weeks' duration occur each year (spring and autum), whereas in certain other species they occur more frequently, and in others again only once, and may be of long or short duration. In the human, reproduction is not confined to any one part of the year, although a study of birth statistics shows that fertility is greatest at certain periods (April to June). It has been suggested that in primitive man a mating season corresponding to this time of year did exist.

3. *The estrus cycles.* These are periods of sexual activity in animals which occur once or oftener in each breeding season. The first cycle commences at puberty. Animals such as the bitch, in which a single estrus cycle extends throughout the breeding season, are called *monestrus. Polyestrus* animals, on the other hand, are those such as the domestic cat, the mare, cow, sow, rat and mouse, in which two or more cycles, separated by short periods of sexual quiescence, occur in succession during the breeding season. In a monestrus animal the following phases of the estrus cycle are distinguished. (a) *Proestrus*, or period of "coming on heat." There is usually swelling and congestion of the external genitalia together with growth and increased vascularity of the uterus (fig. 60.4).

[2] The corresponding period which occurs in the males of some species is known as the *rutting season.* In many species however, the male is capable of copulation at any time.

There is, as a rule, some enlargement of the mammary glands and, in the dog and mare, bleeding from the vagina. During this stage of the cycle the Graafian follicles are undergoing maturation preparatory to rupture. (b) *Estrus,*[3] or "period of desire." The female receives the male and ovulation occurs. The term "heat" is commonly applied to the combined periods, proestrus and estrus. (c) *Pseudopregnancy* or *pregnancy.* During this phase there occurs pronounced proliferation and secretory activity of the uterine glands, hypertrophy of the mucosa and a great increase of the uterine blood supply. It will be seen presently that these phenomena are dependent upon the formation of a corpus luteum. The growth of the mammary glands is stimulated. The uterine changes are looked upon as anticipating the arrival of, and providing nourishment for, a fertilized ovum. (d) *Anestrus* is the period of sexual quiescence between the mating seasons. In the cycle of those animals in which pseudopregnancy does not occur, the short period following estrus and during which the phenomena of estrus subside, is called *metestrus.* The monestrus cycle may be illustrated as follows.

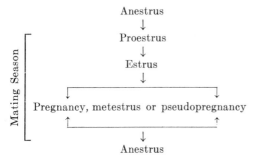

In polyestrus animals the short intervals of quiescence separating the estrous cycles are called *diestrous* periods. The term anestrus, as in the case of monestrus species, refers to the longer periods of rest between the mating seasons.

Although the onset of estrus in some species is quite obvious, in others, such as the rodents, it is difficult to detect by the ordinary means. Stockard and Papanicolaou discovered that the vaginal mucosa of the guinea pig underwent certain changes (cornification of the epithelium) coinciding with estrus. Similar changes occur in the vagina of the rat and mouse as well as in the human vagina (fig. 60.5). By the examination of a smear of the vaginal secretions the stages of the estrus cycle can be readily followed in these animals.

---

[3] *Estrus,* L. = *gad-fly,* with figurative meaning of frenzy or intense desire.

Leukocytes which are present in smears taken during the diestrus or anestrus period are absent from the vaginal secretions during proestrus and estrus, but large squamous (cornified) cells, with small pyknotic nuclei, appear. The intact vaginal epithelium becomes stratified squamous in character.

*The menstrual cycle and sexual life in the human.* The sexual cycle of primates is termed a *menstrual cycle.* This differs from that of lower forms in so far as the period of desire is not localized to any one phase of the cycle (such as estrus), and that external bleeding occurs roughly midway between two ovulations rather than at the time of ovulation. Therefore in equating the typical 28-day menstrual cycle of the human with the estrous cycle of an animal such as the bitch, it may be said that the first 14 days of the menstrual cycle (day 1 being the first day of the flow) are represented by the phases of diestrus and proestrus during which follicular ripening occurs, whereas the last 14 days of the menstrual cycle correspond to the phases of metestrus and pseudopregnancy associated with the development of corpora lutea. The ovarian and uterine changes which occur in the menstrual cycle, and the hormonal factors regulating the cycle, afford evidence in support of this relationship and are described further below (p. 1089). It may also be mentioned that slight bleeding does rarely occur in the human at about the time of ovulation, that is midway between the menstrual periods proper.

The sexual life of the human female usually commences between the 12th and 15th years, when the first menstruation or *menarche* occurs. This period of sexual awakening which is seen in animals and man of both sexes is referred to as *puberty,* with the periods before and after being called *pre-* and *postpubertal,* respectively. Some year or more before the appearance of the overt signs of puberty in girls gonadal hormone can be detected in the urine in amounts which are found to vary cyclically. At this time the ovaries show increased growth. The growth of the uterus is accelerated, the breasts enlarge and, in both girls and boys, hair appears upon the pubis and in the axillae. Deepening of the voice, enlargement of the genitalia (penis and testes) and growth of hair on the face are characteristic features of this period in boys. In both sexes, somatic growth is accelerated. The first menstrual cycles are frequently irregular and may be prolonged, with intervals of amenorrhea. During the next two or three years a menstrual rhythm becomes established but during this phase fertility has not

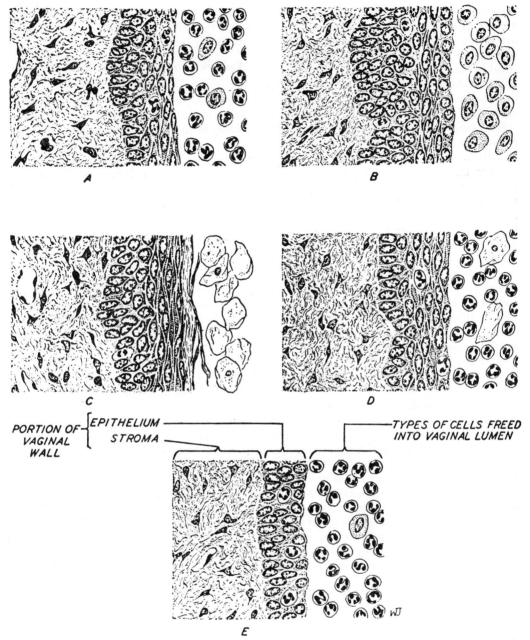

*PORTION OF VAGINAL WALL*    { *EPITHELIUM*    *STROMA* }    *TYPES OF CELLS FREED INTO VAGINAL LUMEN*

Fig. 60.5. The vaginal epithelium and smear at various stages of the estrus cycle of the rat. A, diestrus; B, proestrus; C, estrus; D, metestrus; E, ovariectomized. (From Turner.)

reached the 'adult' level and the girl passes through a period of *"adolescent sterility."*

The length of the menstrual cycle has been measured on numerous occasions, with variable results. Most commonly the cycle lasts 26 to 29 days, with a mean close to 28 days. However, only 10 to 15 per cent of the cycles examined are of this duration and a normal range may be said to be 24 to 35 days. Studies on individual women

show that two consecutive cycles may differ in length by several days; this could be due to the operation of psychic factor.

Ovulation occurs usually, but not invariably, about the middle of the intermenstrual period, that is some 13 to 17 days after the first day of the last menstruation. Evidence in favor of this timing has been derived from the recovery of ova and early embryos from the tubes of women with known menstrual histories; from pregnancies following a single artificial insemination on a known day of the cycle; from the results of coitus at known times; from the occurrence of midmenstrual bleeding, which is associated with ovulation; and from the study of vaginal changes, hormone excretion, and variations in basal temperature.

For a variety of reasons it is sometimes of importance to establish the day of ovulation in an individual. A number of approaches have been made to this problem. In 1935 Burr, Hill and Allen discovered that ovulation in the rabbit was accompanied by a sharp rise in *electrical potential* across the pelvis just before rupture of the follicle, and this observation was confirmed in the human. However, subsequent work indicated that the effect was an indirect one only remotely due to ovarian influences, and unsuitable for the detection of ovulation. The *blood levels of hormones* and their excretion in the urine has been studied. Briefly, the maximum concentration of estrogen (p. 1081) in blood and urine occurs at about the time of ovulation, whereas a metabolic product of progesterone (p. 1091), pregnanediol, is demonstrable in the urine a day or so after ovulation. There is also an increase in the concentration of gonadotrophin (p. 974) in the urine at about the time of ovulation. Studies of the *cervical mucus* have revealed cyclic changes in the character and composition of this secretion. It becomes less viscous and more plentiful about the time of ovulation, whereas on drying the mucus a characteristic crystallization pattern appears. By far the most convenient index of ovulation is the change in *basal temperature* that occurs about this time. The body temperature, recorded daily during the menstrual cycle, shows an abrupt fall at about the time of ovulation (13 to 17th day). It then rises sharply and is maintained at a level about 0.8° F. above that seen during the first half of the cycle until the commencement of the menstrual flow.

Information as to the time of ovulation in women has a practical value in contraception. The so-called "safe period" during which conception presumably cannot occur, has been placed in those parts of the cycle before and after ovulation. However, the time of ovulation varies considerably in different women and may occur several days before or after the 15th day of the cycle. The "safe period," therefore, cannot be predicted in any individual case without preliminary study although the least likely time for conception to occur is within the last eight days or so of the cycle, that is, eight days before menstruation.

## Factors Concerned in the Fertilization of the Ovum

The ovum, if unfertilized, degenerates within a few hours after its discharge from the ovary, probably in the Fallopian tube. For this reason, and because only one ovum is discharged each cycle, the period during which fertilization can occur is very short, probably not longer than 6 or 7 hours. Yet the period during which coitus may lead to conception is relatively long, for the spermatozoa may retain their capacity to fertilize the ovum for some 48 hours or so, although this varies from species to species. In the rabbit the fertilizing capacity of sperm in the female tract may be retained for 32 hours, whereas in the mouse the corresponding period is only 6 hours. In the guinea pig this period is 22 hours, in the rat 14 hours, and perhaps remarkably, in the mare 5 to 6 days. The sperm shows motility for some time after it has lost its ability to fertilize. The former property is therefore not a reliable index of the latter.

As mentioned in the preceding section, if the sperm do not penetrate the ovum within a few hours after ovulation, they cannot do so at all. Fertilization is effected in the Fallopian (uterine) tube and here also the earlier stages in the maturation of the ovum take place. When discharged, the ovum is surrounded by the *cumulus oophorus*. It has been thought that this covering could not be penetrated by the sperm, and must first be destroyed by the enzyme *hyaluronidase* contained in the sperm of most mammalian species; however, there has been a misconception in this regard for the mammalian spermatozoan can reach the ovum through an intact cumulus. It is possible, however, that the enzyme aids the sperm in some other way in its approach and penetration of the ovum. A hyaluronidase inhibitor, such as tri-gentisic acid (rehibin) added to rabbit semen before insemination was found by Parkes to prevent fertilization—an effect not due merely to a nonspecific spermicidal action.

*The menopause.* Between the ages of 42 and 52 (average 47 years) the menstrual cycles become irregular and finally cease. This time is known as the *menopause* or *climacteric*. As menstruation ends retrogressive changes gradually set in in the accessory organs of reproduction, e.g., atrophy of the uterus, shortening and narrowing of the vagina with loss of its epithelium and replacement by fibrous tissue, and shrinkage of the mammary glands. These results are due to atrophic changes in the ovary—disappearance of the Graafian follicles together with a general fibrosis and shrinkage of the organ. Similar changes in the uterus and vagina follow the removal of the ovaries in earlier life, and constitute an *artificial menopause*. Psychic disturbances quite often occur during this "change of life" and occasionally may progress to melancholia and hysteria. Vasomotor and other autonomic disturbances, hot flushes, sweating, etc., are very common features of the climacteric. The effect of the natural menopause upon the sex libido varies in different subjects. In married women it shows little alteration as a rule. It would seem that the menopause occurs through a failure on the part of the ovary to secrete estrogen (p. 1084).

## The Ovarian Hormones

In addition to its gametogenic function the ovary produces hormones which regulate the reproductive processes. These are (1) the *estrogenic*, or follicular hormone, *estradiol*; (2) the hormone of the corpus luteum, *progesterone*, and (3) *relaxin*. The exact status of the latter hormone is doubtful since under certain conditions it can be formed by other parts of the reproductive tract. It has been isolated from the corpus luteum of the pig. The estrogenic hormone exerts its effect primarily during the first part of the estrus cycle, whereas the corpus luteum hormone is concerned particularly with the latter part, with pseudopregnancy and pregnancy.

### The Estrogenic Hormone

During the first twenty years of this century the evidence derived from ovariectomy and transplantation experiments had made it clear that the ovaries furnished an internal secretion which was responsible for the sexual development of the female. However the use of whole ovaries, and the use of rather uncertain biological indicators, confused the results available until the work of Allen and Doisy in 1923. These workers aspirated the liquor folliculi from sows' ovaries and found that it was capable of inducing estrus in immature animals. The success of these workers was due to a large extent to the use of a precise method for the determination of estrus, namely the vaginal smear technique described above. Other investigators had mostly studied the effects of their extracts upon the uterus. With a sensitive test

available the next step was to isolate the active constituent of follicular fluid. It was soon found that the material was extractable by fat solvents and could be concentrated, but another twelve years passed before the hormone was characterized. Meanwhile other estrogens had been isolated from the urine of pregnant women, pregnant mares, human placentas, and, surprisingly, the urine of stallions, and in 1929 Doisy, Veler and Thayer, and Butenandt independently announced the crystallization of an estrogen in pure form from the urine of pregnant women. It was believed at this time that there was only one estrogen and the workers concerned were generous in bestowing names upon it. Unfortunately, this led to confusion, particularly when the existence of other estrogens came to light; therefore many of the early names have been discarded and a formal nomenclature is now used.

### The Origin and Distribution of Estrogen

The elements of the ovary responsible for the production of the follicular hormone are not definitely known. Its presence in high concentration in liquor folliculi, and the fact that follicular maturation coincides with the onset of estrus, point to the follicular cells (probably the theca interna) as being the chief source. Yet these cells cannot be solely responsible, for Parkes showed that estrus continues at regular intervals after the follicles have been completely destroyed by X-rays; moreover the hormone can be extracted from the stroma alone. The interstitial cells in the latter situation may be a source of the hormone. One of the most remarkable features of estrogen is its very wide distribution in animal tissues. It or a similarly acting estrogen is found in the blood and urine of both pregnant and nonpregnant females, in the urine of adult males, and in the testes, with the testes and urine of stallions being among the richest known sources (Zondek). It is present in very high concentration in the urine of pregnant women after the first 2 or 3 months. In the later months around 300,000 or more international units (see below) are excreted daily. It is also obtainable in large amounts from the urines of pregnant mares and monkeys. The human placenta contains large quantities of estrogen which are believed to be manufactured by this organ, for women ovariectomized during the later months of pregnancy continue to excrete large amounts of the hormone in the urine. An estrogen is present in the corpus luteum, in the fetal membranes and amniotic fluid, and in the adrenal cortex; it has been demonstrated in a human chorionic vesicle containing an embryo 12.5 mm. in length.

### Chemistry and Terminology

There are three well established natural estrogens. These are *estradiol, estrone* and *estriol*. Two others, epiestriol and hydroxyestrone have recently been isolated from human pregnancy urine. Of these estradiol is now generally believed to be the true estrogenic hormone, i.e., the estrogen formed in, and secreted by the ovary. Doisy and coworkers, and Butenandt were able to isolate estrone from the urine in 1929, whereas estradiol was obtained by MacCorquodale, Thayer and Doisy in 1935—after the use of 2 tons of ovaries as starting material. Estriol was first isolated in 1930 from human pregnancy urine independently by Doisy and associates and by Marrian. Estrone was named theelin by Doisy and modifications of this name were subsequently applied to the compounds later discovered.

The estrogens possess a basic steroid nucleus like the hormones of the adrenal cortex. They dif-

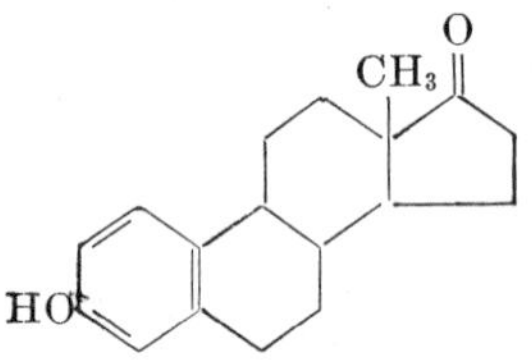

Ketohydroxyestrin
(Theelin or estrone)

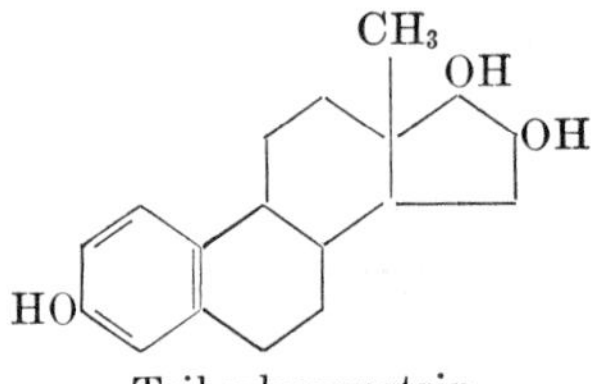

Trihydroxyestrin
(Theelol or estriol)

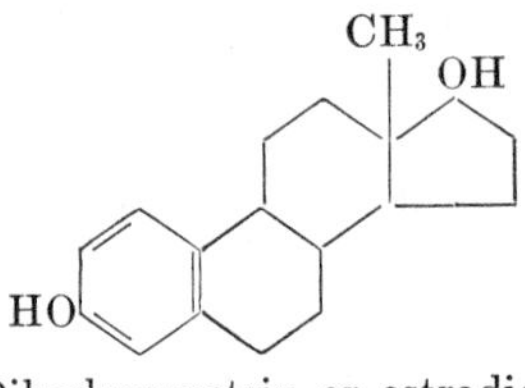

Dihydroxyestrin or estradiol

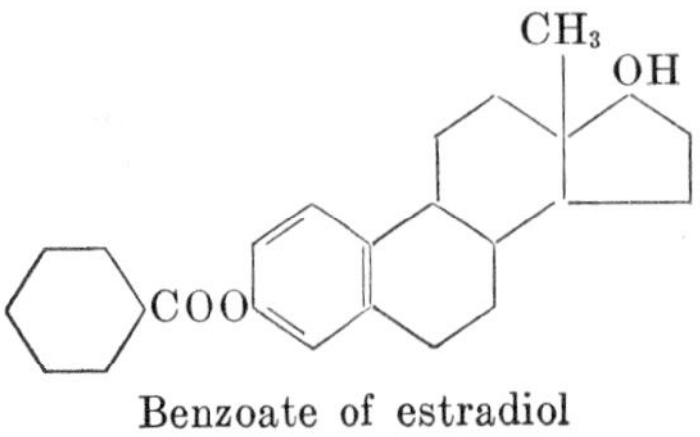

Benzoate of estradiol

fer in that ring A is benzenoid or aromatic in character so that the phenolic hydroxyl group attached to carbon 3 has weakly acidic properties. This feature implies a solubility in alkaline solution and has been utilized in the separation of the hormones. In addition the estrogens possess an oxygen, or an hydroxyl group linked to carbon 17, and thus possess the capacity to exhibit stereoisomerism.

*Estradiol* (dihydrotheelin, dihydroxyestrin). Estradiol was first obtained in the laboratory by reduction of the ketone group in estrone to an hydroxyl group, and was only later isolated from ovarian tissue. Two stereoisomers of estradiol are possible: estradiol-17$\alpha$, and estradiol-17$\beta$, depending on the relative position of the hydroxyl group. There has been confusion over the relative biological activity of the two isomers but it is now established that the active one is estradiol-17$\beta$, or the cis form. The replacement of the hydroxyl group in the 3 position with benzoic acid gives a product possessing more prolonged physiological action than the original compound due to a slowed rate of inactivation. This compound *estradiol benzoate*, is known commercially by various names. *Estradiol dipropionate* and *ethinyl estradiol* exert an even more prolonged effect.

*Estrone.* This was the first estrogen to be crystallized and was given a variety of names. These include *theelin* (Doisy), *estrin* (Parkes and Bellerby), *folliculin* and *estrone*. It has been isolated from human pregnancy urine, human male urine, human placental tissue, bovine adrenal glands and the bile of pregnant cows. It differs from estradiol in possessing an oxygen atom instead of an hydroxyl group at carbon 17.

*Estriol* (*theelol*, Doisy; trihydroxyestrin) has been obtained from human pregnancy urine, and from human placental tissue. Despite the reported isolation of this hormone from the placenta of the chimpanzee and from the female pussy willow, the hormone is believed to be characteristic of the human species. Since estriol contains three hydroxyl groups it is more soluble in water than the other estrogens.

### The Metabolism of Estrogens

Like the adrenal cortical hormones the estrogens appear to be synthesized in the body from cholesterol. A fall in the ovarian cholesterol has been observed to occur following stimulation with pituitary gonad-stimulating hormones. Certainly cholesterol can be used as a starting material in the laboratory synthesis. Starting with ergosterol, estrone was synthesized in 1936 by

Marker and his associates; others have synthesized estradiol from cholesterol.

The estrogens seem to be converted one to the other in the body according to this relationship:

$$\text{estradiol} \rightleftharpoons \text{estrone} \rightarrow \text{estriol}$$

Administration of estradiol or estrone results in an increased excretion of estriol, whereas administration of estriol does not increase the output of the other two hormones. Radioactive estrone and estradiol are converted to radioactive estriol. Estriol may be the main estrogen in human plasma.

There is little doubt that estrogens are inactivated by the liver. Incubation of estradiol and estrone with liver slices caused loss of activity; use of a heart-lung-liver preparation has revealed loss of estrogen in the perfusing fluid, whereas the activity was retained when perfusing a heart-lung preparation. Liver damage, such as follows the administration of carbon tetrachloride, is associated with an increased effect of estrogens, as well as a greater urinary excretion of these materials. In rats if pellets of estrogen are implanted into the spleen so that the estrogen drains directly into the portal system no estrogen activity is detected. If the spleen is transplanted elsewhere in the body, or adhesions of the spleen to the stomach or body wall form, allowing escape of estrogens from the portal circulation, then full estrogenic activity appears. Clinical observations fully support the above experimental findings. Increased estrogen excretion often occurs in association with liver disease. Gynecomastia, loss of chest and axillary hair, testicular atrophy and loss of libido have all been described in men with cirrhosis of the liver, although the significance of these findings has recently been questioned. The inactivation of estrogens also appears to be impaired in cases of malnutrition and inanition; it has been argued that a deficiency of vitamin $B_2$ is also of importance in this respect. Normally, estrogens are rapidly destroyed in the body.

Estrogens are excreted in the urine in the form of water-soluble conjugates; little is eliminated through the feces. They are combined mainly with glucuronic acid, as well as with sulfuric acid, and in this form are physiologically inert. Upon hydrolysis with acid, or enzymically with glucuronidase or phenol sulfatase, the conjugates are split and estrogenic activity reappears.

*Synthetic estrogens.* Estrogenic materials are not restricted to animal sources. Estrogens can be obtained from petroleum, peat and lignite, rape seeds and pussy willow. Estrogen has been demonstrated in the mud at the bottom of the Dead Sea. It is not necessary for such substances to possess a similar chemical structure to that of the natural compounds. Thus Dodds and his associates found active estrogens among the derivatives of diphenylethane and diphenylethylene and one of them *stilbestrol* (4,4'-dihydroxy-$\alpha$-$\beta$-diethylstilbene), introduced in 1938, has been of great clinical value for many years. It is as active as the natural estrogens but, unlike the estrogens, it retains its potency when given by mouth. The success of stilbestrol greatly stimulated work in this field and now a wide range of synthetic estrogens is available for clinical use. Two other synthetic compounds widely used clinically are *dihydroethylstilbestrol*, or *hexestrol*, and *dienestrol*.

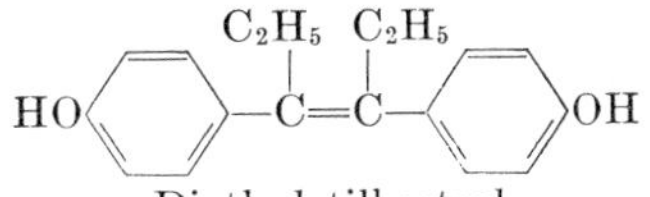

Diethylstilbestrol

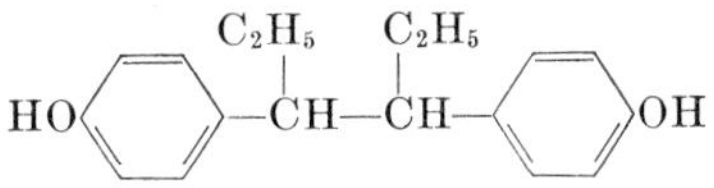

Hexestrol

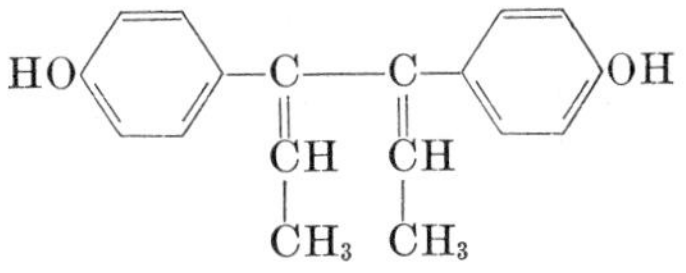

Dienestrol

On the basis of estrogen withdrawal bleeding (p. 1084) dienestrol possessed 90 per cent of the potency of stilbestrol and hexestrol possessed about 10 per cent. This finding reveals an order of potency quite different from that observed in animals.

The reasons underlying the estrogenic effect of the synthetic compounds are not well understood. One structural relationship between stilbestrol and estradiol was pointed out by Dodds and is shown below, but when the structures are com-

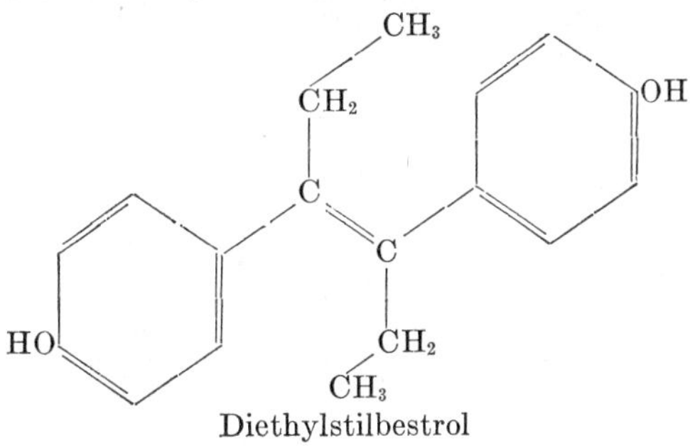

Diethylstilbestrol

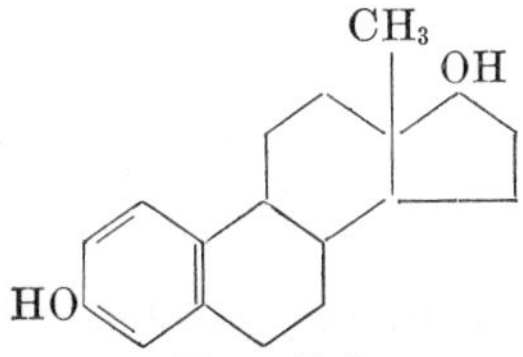

Estradiol

pared three-dimensionally there is not the same degree of similarity.

## The Physiology of Estrogen

For descriptive purposes the actions of estradiol, estrone and estriol are identical, for these compounds differ only in relative potency. When used without qualification 'estrogen' implies any or all of these materials and may include stilbestrol.

The main effects of estrogen are as follows:

1. It induces estrus in immature animals, or in normal adult animals during anestrus; there result in consequence hypertrophy of the uterus (fig. 60.6), and development of a proliferative type of endometrium, vaginal changes (cornification), growth of the mammary glands (p. 1095), and rhythmical contraction of the muscle of the uterus and Fallopian tubes, as well as the psychic phenomena associated with estrus. Prolonged treatment with estrogen causes pronounced hyperplasia of the endometrium which may come to resemble the clinical condition known as "Swiss cheese" endometrium.

2. It prevents the otherwise inevitable atrophy of the accessory reproductive organs in ovariectomized animals.

3. It is responsible for the development of the secondary sex characters which in some species are such prominent features of the mature female.

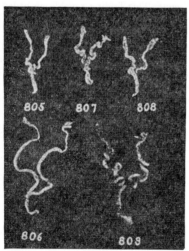

Fig. 60.6. Effect of injection of follicular extract into 8-week-old rabbits. Animals were litter sisters. No. 807 received 2 mg. of extract. No. 805 was not injected and was killed at the same time as No. 807 for control. No. 806 received 1 mg. of extract daily for 4 days and No. 809 received 1 mg. daily for 8 days. No. 808, uninjected control, was killed on the same day as No. 809. (After Doisy, Ralls, Allen and Johnston.)

4. It prevents nidation of the fertilized ovum or induces abortion in early pregnancy.

5. Estrogen is largely responsible for the enormous growth of the uterus during pregnancy. When pregnancy is confined to one horn of the rabbit's uterus, that horn alone increases in size. It is thought, therefore, that estrogen produced by the placenta may act locally on the uterine tissue rather than through the general circulation.

6. Estrogen exerts a direct effect upon the ovary. Since estrogen stimulates mitosis the hormone present in the liquor folliculi itself promotes the growth of the follicle. The administration of large doses of estrogen has been found to prevent ovarian atrophy in immature hypophysectomized rats. It has also been suggested that on ovulation the follicular fluid comes into contact with the germinal epithelium of the ovary and promotes a burst of mitoses which produces a new crop of oogonia ready for a future cycle.

7. With more moderate dosage estrogen induces ovarian atrophy, as well as testicular atrophy in the male, by suppressing the release of the pituitary gonad stimulating principles.

8. If, after menstruation has been abolished in monkeys by ovariectomy, a series of injections of estrogen is given and then stopped abruptly, menstruation occurs a few days later. During the treatment of these ovariectomized monkeys phenomena appear analogous to those seen during the estrus period of lower animals, i.e., endometrial changes, reddening and swelling of the external genitalia, and the production of a vaginal smear showing cornified cells and lacking leukocytes. The induction of uterine bleeding by the above "estrogen withdrawal" has been utilized in the human, for artificial menstrual cycles can be produced in this way in women suffering from amenorrhea.

9. Estrogen appears to be concerned in the production and maintenance of corpora lutea. In rats the administration of estrogen leads to the formation of many corpora lutea, and in rabbits estrogen will maintain the corpora lutea in the ovaries of the hypophysectomized pseudopregnant animal.

10. A synergic action between the follicular hormone and the oxytocic hormone of the posterior pituitary (ch. 56) has been demonstrated. After estrogen is administered to a mouse toward the end of pregnancy, a dose of oxytocin (which is ordinarily ineffective) causes a powerful uterine contraction (fig. 60.7).

11. This ovarian hormone induces water reten-

tion, an increase in blood volume and of the water content of the muscles. Ovariectomy results in a loss of water and a diminished volume of blood which is restored to normal by estrogen administration.

12. Estrogen presumably acts upon the nasal mucous membrane (see p. 1092).

13. In the male, estrogen in physiological dosage, or derived endogenously (testicular estrogen) may act synergistically with androgen in the development of the secondary sex characters. Protracted treatment with estrogen causes hypertrophy of the fibromuscular tissues of the prostate, but has little or no effect upon the glandular elements. Growth of the male mammary glands may be stimulated. In young males other feminizing effects are produced.

14. Estrogen causes hypertrophy of the adrenal cortex, apparently by stimulating the output of ACTH.

15. Prolonged treatment with estrogen raises the blood calcium, particularly in pigeons and fowls.

16. Estrogen exerts a variety of additional effects throughout the body, e.g., on the skeleton. These actions are best discussed elsewhere in relation to the end-organ concerned.

### Assay and Standardization of Estrogens

It has been the practice to assay the activity of estrogenic preparations upon ovariectomized rats or mice, with a unit being defined as the minimal quantity of the material required to induce estrus in 50 per cent of a group of test animals as shown by the vaginal smear. This is basically the technique of Allen and Doisy, but can be made quite sensitive by applying the estrogen directly to the vagina of the test animal. Alternatively, the increase of uterine weight produced by estrogen in ovariectomized or intact immature rats or mice has been used as an index of activity. Although there may be a linear relationship between the logarithm of the dose of estrogen and the increase in uterine weight, the dose response curves of the separate estrogens differ one from the other so that it becomes difficult to assay mixtures of estrogens, such as occur in the urine. Further, the use of such methods is complicated by the finding that results vary with the mode and frequency of administration of the hormone, as well as by the presence in urine of materials which may augment the action of estrogen.

Initially, in work on the assay of estrogens, a rat or mouse unit on the lines outlined above was used, but there were wide discrepancies between the results of different laboratories and in 1932 the Commission on Biological Standardization of

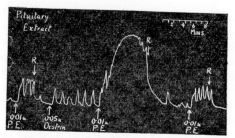

Fig. 60.7. Action of estrin in sensitizing an isolated uterus to pitocin. P.E., pituitary extract. (After Bourne and Burn.)

the League of Nations defined an international unit. This was expressed in terms of estrone and was the activity exhibited by 0.1 $\mu$g. of the standard preparation. Later, with the use of esters of estrogen an additional standard was set up, and one international unit was constituted by the activity of 0.1 $\mu$g. of estradiol-17$\beta$-monobenzoate.

Currently, most attention is being given to the development of chemical procedures for the assay of estrogen. These are essentially colorimetric or fluorimetric, in which the color or fluorescence is developed after a somewhat complex extraction and purification sequence. In the colorimetric method, when a pink color, which can be measured, is developed, the estrogens are heated with phenol and sulfuric acid, diluted with water and reheated. This is the Kober reaction, first described in 1931 and altered in detail since. The fluorimetric method is more sensitive but less specific than the colorimetric; it depends on the fact than an intense yellowish green fluorescence develops when an estrogen is heated with sulfuric or phosphoric acid.

### Estrogens and Cancer

Since estrogens powerfully stimulate the growth of the uterus, vagina and mammary gland, it is not surprising that with continued administration benign proliferation may develop into malignant growth. As long ago as 1916, before the isolation of estrogens, Leo Loeb noted that spontaneous mammary cancer occurred in mice and was confined to the female, whereas in 1932 Lacassagne succeeded in producing mammary cancer in the male mouse by the prolonged administration of estrogen. However, there are important species differences in the occurrence of mammary cancer. For instance, dogs and rabbits never develop breast cancer following administration of estrogen; neither does the rhesus monkey. But such a carcinoma can develop in dogs and rabbits following pregnancy toxemia which may damage the liver and interfere with the inactivation of estrogen. Rats never develop mammary cancer spontaneously, but will do so when subjected to treatment with estrogen. In women carcinoma of the breast is quite common but according to Bishop there is surprisingly little evidence that cancers develop with the administration of estrogen, particularly when the enormous number of women given estrogen at one time or other is taken into account.

From the present point of view there are two kinds of cancer; those that are *hormone-dependent* and those that are *hormone-independent* (Huggins and Scott). As the classification implies, the hormone-dependent carcinoma requires a particular hormone or hormone complex for its development. Denial of this need frequently inhibits the growth and promotes regression. In the male, cancer of the prostate gland (p. 1108) provides an instance of this class of tumor, which is dependent upon androgen for its continued growth. Removal of endogenous androgen by orchidectomy generally produces a remission although in some cases the adrenals may provide an alternative supply of androgen. *Hormone-independent* tumors are not subject to control by any endocrine secretion and develop in such tissues as the skin, stomach and lung. However, a hormone-dependent tumor can become independent of a particular hormone and so become autonomous. It should be pointed out that in a number of cases an optimal endocrine environment may be necessary for tumor growth. Thus it appears that following hypophysectomy certain chemical carcinogens failed to induce cancers of the liver, whereas they continue to do so in other parts of the body. The full carcinogenic effect is restored by ACTH or growth hormone administration.

The mode of action of carcinogens remains obscure. Interest was aroused when it was found that the causative agents in coal tar which induced cancer when painted on the skin were benzanthracene compounds possessing a structure akin to that of the steroid hormones. This finding greatly stimulated studies with estrogens but the nature of mechanism underlying the process is uncertain, although it appears to involve the genetic material of the cell.

### The Luteal Hormone

The suspicion that the corpus luteum might be a gland of internal secretion which functions during gestation has long been held. Indeed, Corner relates that when Gustav Born lay dying in 1900 he imparted this idea to Ludwig Fraenkel for subsequent experimental test. Three years later (1903) Fraenkel reported that destruction of the corpora lutea in the ovaries of the rabbit was not compatible with the continuance of pregnancy,

whereas Ancel and Bouin (1910) found that the cycle of growth and regression of the corpus luteum was closely linked with a series of (progestational) changes which take place in the uterus. Also about this time Loeb discovered (1909) that stimulation of the uterine mucosa of the nonpregnant guinea pig by means of a glass bead or a silk thread, or merely by scratching the endometrium with a needle during the development of the corpora lutea resulted in the growth of a small mass of decidual tissue (*deciduoma*) at the point of stimulation. This *Loeb reaction* could not be obtained after the corpora lutea had been excised or during a phase of the estrus cycle when they were absent. Even transplanted uterine tissue responded to stimulation if the ovary contained corpora lutea. Other observers have since obtained corresponding results in the rat, rabbit and dog. Thus it appears that the contact of the fertilized ovum with the endometrium is the natural stimulus which in the presence of a corpus luteum causes the formation of decidual tissue.

Corner first showed that the corpus luteum was necessary for the survival and implantation of the rabbit embryo and, in collaboration with W. M. Allen, he obtained a crude extract which was active in maintaining pregnancy in ovariectomized rabbits. Within five years (1934) the active constituent of the extract was obtained in chemically pure form by several groups of workers, and had been synthesized from stigmasterol by Butenandt and his associates. The hormone is now known as *progesterone*, with Corner's original name *progestin* being used as a general term for any substance possessing similar actions.

Corpora lutea are not restricted to the mammalia, nor are they invariably associated with viviparity since they have been described in oviparous and ovoviviparous selachians, teleosts and reptiles, and in mammals they first appear in the oviparous Monotremata. However, any hormone produced is not necessarily progesterone.

### Progesterone

Progesterone has the structure shown below. It occurs in two crystalline forms, the $\alpha$ and $\beta$, but these are about equal in physiological activity. Comparison with the estrogens (p. 1082) and the adrenal cortical hormones (p. 1039) shows that it is more closely allied to the adrenal hormones and that it belongs to the carbon-21 or pregnane group of steroids. This relationship is underlined by the fact that progesterone can be transformed *in vitro* to corticosterone and 17-hydroxycorticosterone.

Progesterone

Pregnanediol

Progesterone can be isolated from ox adrenal tissue, and administration of ACTH to ovariectomized women has been found to increase the urinary output of pregnanediol, a metabolic product of progesterone. It would appear that progesterone is formed from cholesterol since Bloch found that when isotopically-labelled cholesterol was given to a pregnant woman, the pregnanediol in the urine contained the isotope. A decline in ovarian cholesterol has been demonstrated to follow stimulation with gonadotrophin.

Progesterone is produced by luteal tissue, by the adrenal cortex and by the placenta. During pregnancy in women the corpus luteum gradually ceases production of progesterone, and the placenta takes over this function. For this reason gestation can continue after ovariectomy if the latter operation is carried out after 4 or 5 months. A similar situation exists in the monkey, cat and guinea pig, but in the rabbit, rat, goat and cow, abortion occurs if the corpora lutea are destroyed at any time during pregnancy.

Progesterone is rapidly metabolized *in vivo* and normally cannot be detected in the urine. There appears instead the reduced form, *pregnanediol,* as a glucuronide. *Sodium pregnanediol glucuronide* is water soluble. Measurement of this steroid in the urine provides a useful index of the rate of production of progesterone. However, caution is necessary in the interpretation of results since, according to Loraine, less than 20 per cent of a dose of administered progesterone may be ex-

creted in the urine as pregnanediol. Also a rise in urinary pregnanediol has been reported to follow the administration of desoxycorticosterone and, in certain cases of adrenocortical hyperplasia or tumor, the pregnanediol output may be increased so that the possible participation of adrenal steroids should be borne in mind. It seems fairly clear that the liver is involved in the metabolism of progesterone, and its conversion to pregnanediol glucuronide. This has been shown by studies (with isotopically labelled progesterone) of patients with liver disease, by studies of the constituents of human bile, and by a comparison of the effects of progesterone in normal and partially hepatectomized rabbits. Pregnanediol is physiologically inert and is readily converted to progesterone in the laboratory. It was isolated from the urine of pregnancy in 1929 by Marrian and in 1930 by Butenandt, before the characterization of progesterone.

THE PHYSIOLOGY OF PROGESTERONE. This hormone produced by the corpus luteum possesses a spectrum of activity which includes (1) effects on the uterus, (2) the maintenance of pregnancy, (3) participation in the control of the growth of the mammary gland and (4) suppression of estrus and ovulation. These actions will now be examined.

*Effects on the uterus.* It was previously shown, as described above, that progesterone treatment develops the endometrium. In the rabbit this is marked by a typical arborization of the glands which is identical to that appearing during pregnancy or pseudopregnancy. Corresponding changes have been observed in other species during treatment with progesterone, and under these conditions deciduomas (p. 1086) are readily induced. In the immature rabbit treatment with progesterone fails to produce the endometrial changes outlined above, nor is the treatment effective in adult rabbits which have been ovariectomized for some time. However, administration of estrogen for several days before the progesterone treatment results in the appearance of progestational changes. It is clear that the uterus must be *"primed"* with estrogen before it can respond to progesterone. This effect is not confined to the rabbit; it is also well marked in the monkey, where progesterone has little effect in the ovariectomized animal. When preceded by estrogen, progesterone will produce a typical premenstrual endometrium in 7 to 10 days. Two other aspects of this process must be emphasized. First, it is possible for progesterone to produce proliferative changes in the uterus by itself, but enormous doses must be given; and second, estrogen also antagonizes some effects of progesterone. This latter effect appears when the ratio of estrogen to progesterone, optimal for uterine development, is altered in favor of estrogen. Under these circumstances the action of progesterone is inhibited. Conversely, progesterone will block the action of estrogen; the coloration and edema of the sexual skin of a spayed monkey, developed by treatment with estrogen, is lost following a single injection of progesterone. It will be seen that, depending upon the relative amounts of these hormones, estrogen and progesterone can interact to produce a variety of effects. This is of importance in a number of reproductive processes.

The deciduoma reaction (which can be elicited under the influence of progesterone) has been described previously. This can be inhibited by treatment with estrogen.

In addition to the effects on the mucosa of the uterus, progesterone also exerts an action on the muscle. In the castrate rabbit the uterus is flaccid and quiescent and does not display any motility, although when estrogenized, regular rhythmic contractions appear. These are also seen in the estrous rabbit, rat or sow; however, administration of progesterone abolishes such activity. The oxytocic hormone of the posterior pituitary (ch. 56) is probably implicated in the uterine response to estrogen, for it has been shown that the activity of the uterus of the estrus animal is greatly increased by the oxytocic hormone. Following treatment with progesterone, oxytocin can no longer produce this effect upon the uterus which is then said to be "desensitized." Such phenomena would seem to be of value in the normal individual since a motile estrous uterus would aid the transport of sperm toward the ova, and the movement of ova along the tubes. In agreement with this concept oxytocin has been found to be released at coitus (p. 987). Further, once the uterus contains blastocysts, the uterine contractions, which would be detrimental to their implantation and survival, are blocked by progesterone. Toward the end of pregnancy uterine reactivity to oxytocin reappears, possibly due to the increasing amounts of circulating estrogen, and discharge of the fetuses is facilitated.

*Maintenance of pregnancy.* This function of progesterone has previously been noted (p. 1086). In ovariectomized rabbits about 1 mg. of progesterone daily will compensate for the absence of corpora lutea and maintain pregnancy, although in the later stages up to 5 mg. may be necessary. In the rhesus monkey the corpus luteum may be removed as early as the 25th day without disturbing pregnancy, whereas in women gestation can continue following ovariectomy after the first weeks. In the latter species the placenta becomes responsible for the production of progesterone. Administration of progesterone toward the end of pregnancy in rabbits prolongs the gestation period and results in the delivery of larger young.

*Suppression of estrus and ovulation.* The estrous cycle or menstrual cycle does not continue during pregnancy; ovarian follicles do not mature and ovulation does not occur. This change is brought about by progesterone, which interrupts the normal sexual cycles in nonpregnant individuals. If the corpora lutea are removed during a pseudopregnancy then estrus and ovulation quickly follow; whereas if the corpora lutea are extirpated from the guinea pig ovary early in the estrous cycle then the next ovulation occurs sooner than usual (Loeb). Elimination of the corpora lutea of the cow's ovary by manipulation through the rectum hastens the onset of the next estrous period. The ovulation which normally follows copulation in the rabbit is blocked by the administration of progesterone. Such effects are brought about by the inhibition of the secretion of gonadotrophin from the pituitary (p. 971). During pregnancy or pseudopregnancy the superficial layer of cells in the vagina lose their squamous and cornified character and become rounded and filled with a mucus-like substance. This change occurs under the influence of progesterone, acting in cooperation with estrogen.

*Growth of the mammary glands.* The part played by progesterone in the development and function of the mammary glands will be discussed on page 1095.

ASSAY AND STANDARDIZATION OF PROGESTERONE. The *international standard* of progesterone is defined as the progestational activity of 1 mg. of the international standard crystalline preparation. The test animal is an adult female rabbit which has been mated and then castrated, or an immature female rabbit which has been primed for 5 days previously with estrogen. These preparations are relatively insensitive and do not permit the detection of progesterone in blood. Hooker and Forbes (1947) used intrauterine injection of the hormone in ovariectomized mice and examined the endometrium histologically. This procedure will measure "progestogenic activity" in the blood of pregnant women but is not very specific. Recently Zander and Simmer (1954) have developed a chemical method, using ultraviolet spectroscopy, which will measure the progesterone concentration in blood.

Since pregnanediol is regarded as a metabolic product of progesterone and is present in relatively large amounts in the urine, assay of this steroid has been used as an index of progesterone production. The first method, described by Venning in 1937, involved extraction of the urine with butanol, precipitation with acetone, and weighing the precipitate. During the past 10 years a variety of procedures have been developed which generally involve chromatography, and colorimetry. The technique of Klopper, Michie and Brown (1955) is sensitive enough to measure the pregnanediol derived from the adrenals of men.

## RELAXIN

One of the many adaptive processes occurring in pregnancy is the relaxation of the ligaments of the symphysis pubis which takes place in a variety of species. This "pubic relaxation" occurs in women, monkeys, guinea pigs, mice, dogs, cows and ewes, among others. In 1926 Hisaw discovered that the blood serum of the pregnant rabbit contains a substance which produced this effect in nonpregnant guinea pigs. It was called *relaxin* and has now been detected in the serum of women, mares, sows, dogs and cats. Relaxin differs from other ovarian hormones in that it appears to be peptide or polypeptide in nature, is readily soluble in water, and is destroyed by proteolytic enzymes. It has been extracted from the corpora lutea of sows, whole ovaries, blood serum, urine and placenta. The relaxin content of the sow ovary begins to increase early in pregnancy and reaches its highest concentration by the time the fetuses are from 12 to 15 cm. long.

For a time the existence of relaxin was questioned, for it was claimed by some workers that pubic relaxation could be induced by estrogen or progesterone or a combination of the two. Abramowitz and his associates found, however, that an extract prepared from sows' ovaries, when given in a dosage far below that necessary for an estrogenic or progestational effect caused relaxation of the pubic ligaments. It would seem that relaxin is formed in the uterus under the influence of estrogen and progesterone as removal of this organ greatly reduces the action of these steroids on the pelvis, whereas the potency of relaxin is retained. Even in the intact guinea pig relaxin acts much faster (within 12 hours) than progesterone or estrogen. Further, histological studies have shown that estrogen relaxes the pubic symphysis by promoting resorption of the bone, and a

proliferation of loose fibrous connective tissue whereas relaxin produces a dissolution and splitting of the collagenous fibers into thin threads. The changes following progesterone treatment are similar to those induced by relaxin.

## THE HORMONAL CONTROL OF THE MENSTRUAL CYCLE

Although essentially similar to the estrous cycle of lower animals the menstrual cycle of primates possesses several features which must be examined. The hormonal basis of the process has also to be discussed.

### Uterine Changes in the Menstrual Cycle

The occurrence of uterine bleeding marks the end of a menstrual cycle, although it is customary to describe the period of hemorrhage as days 1 to 4, i.e., the first stage of the cycle. The remainder of the cycle is usually divided into two stages—the stage of repair and proliferation (days 5 to 14) and the days of secretion (days 15 to 28). However since ovulation and any corpora lutea formed thereby exert a regulating influence on the succeeding menstrual flow, it is more logical to describe the cycle as commencing with the stage of repair and proliferation.

*The stage of repair and proliferation—follicular phase.* During the 10 days or so after the end of the menstrual flow the epithelium of the endometrium which was shed at that time is restored by rapid outgrowths from the mouths of the glands. The epithelial lining then hypertrophies and the glands show proliferative changes. The uterus enlarges as a result of the growth of its stroma and as it becomes more vascular the arteries which supply the inner third of the endometrium—the *spiral arteries*—become coiled. In the ovary the Graafian follicle has been undergoing maturation and ovulation occurs at the end of the proliferative stage. The proliferative changes in the uterus occur under the influence of estrogen.

*The premenstrual or secretory stage—luteal phase.* This stage, following the follicular phase, lasts for 13 or 14 days. The uterine mucosa shows marked hypertrophy and is highly vascular; its glands become elongated and assume a coiled or corkscrew form. The glandular secretion becomes greatly increased and more mucoid in character and toward the end of the premenstrual stage the endometrium resembles the decidua of early pregnancy, with the appearance of typical decidual cells in the uterine stroma. During this phase the

spiral arteries continue to lengthen disproportionately to the growth of the endometrium. Some
time before menstruation there is a reduction in
the blood supply to the endometrium which
shrinks and compresses the spiral arteries. The
blood is then further slowed until there is a state
of stasis. Finally the spiral arteries constrict and
ischemia of the endometrium occurs. The stage
is set for menstruation.

The uterine changes occurring in the luteal
phase are produced by progesterone secreted by
the corpus luteum, and to this extent the stage
corresponds to that of pseudopregnancy observed
in some lower species. If fertilization of the ovum
does not occur the corpus luteum does not persist,
its influence upon the endometrium wanes, and
this change is marked by shrinkage of the endometrium. At the end of the premenstrual stage
swelling of the mammary glands may be noted
and mild psychic disturbances (irritability, nervousness, depression, etc.) may appear.

*The destructive stage* or *stage of menstrual flow*
lasts for about 4 days. After a period of ischemia
of the endometrium individual spiral arteries relax and hemorrhage occurs through rupture of the
wall of an arteriole or capillary. The blood may
escape through the epithelium or may collect in
the underlying tissues to form a hematoma which
eventually discharges into the lumen of the
uterus. Hemorrhage ceases locally through vasoconstriction of the spiral arteries, but constriction
and relaxation of these vessels does not occur
synchronously throughout the uterus so that some
bleeding continues. During the process fragments
of the epithelium become desquamated and blood
vessels may be observed to project freely into the
lumen. Gradually the vessels close permanently
and an intact circulation becomes reestablished
through the basal arteries. This heralds the end
of menstruation and the commencement of a new
follicular phase.

The blood discharged during menstruation differs from normal blood in that it does not clot.
This is apparently due to its passage through the
endometrium, for blood that escapes during arterial hemorrhage clots rapidly.

Markee has followed the process of menstruation microscopically in pieces of endometrium
transplanted into the anterior chamber of the eye
of monkeys. Bleeding occurred from the transplanted tissue during menstruation, but preceded
the appearance of blood in the vagina by about
3 hours. His observations emphasize the essentially endocrine nature of the uterine changes occurring during the menstrual cycle. In the human

subject patches or tumors of endometrial tissue
are sometimes found in extrauterine situations,
e.g., surface of the broad ligament or ovary; in the
omentum, pelvic peritoneum or subcutaneous tissue of the vulva or perineum, or in the tissue in
the neighborhood of a laparotomy scar. The ectopic tissue bleeds during menstruation. The condition is not uncommon and is known as *endo-
metriosis.*

### Effects of Estrogen—Progesterone Interactions on the Menstrual Cycle

It is evident that estrogen-progesterone interactions underly many of the changes observed
during the menstrual cycle. However, although
the changes seen are well accounted for on this
basis, the precise mode of action of the ovarian
hormones merits further examination.

It is not necessary for a luteal phase to precede
menstruation. This is shown by the fact that in
monkeys, as well as in women, ovariectomy during the follicular phase is followed in a few days
by a premature menstrual period. Such postoperative bleeding can be postponed by administration
of estrogen. Markee showed that an intraocular
transplant of endometrium menstruated when a
crystal of estrone inserted into that eye was removed, and also that while the crystal was present, the graft in that eye did not bleed at a time
when the uterus did so. Also, in monkeys and
young women, menstrual cycles can occur without
ovulation and the formation of luteal tissue. In
these cases cyclic changes in the blood level of
estrogen alone presumably are responsible for the
flow. Evidence for this view is the finding that
ovariectomized monkeys, subjected to a course of
estrogen treatment, menstruate soon after the
withdrawal of the hormone. This is the estrogen
withdrawal effect alluded to earlier (p. 1084).
Bleeding may also follow if the dose of estrogen is
suddenly reduced although continued at a low
level.

Cessation of progesterone administration results in similar effects to estrogen withdrawal. If
a short series of progesterone injections is superimposed upon a long course of treatment with
estrogen in an ovariectomized monkey, then
menstruation ensues shortly after the withdrawal
of the progesterone. Alternatively progesterone
will prevent estrogen-withdrawal bleeding when
given immediately following the estrogen. On
stopping the progesterone then a progesterone-
withdrawal menstrual period ensues. Menstruation follows the end of progesterone treatment in
a recently ovariectomized monkey not given es-

trogen. Progesterone delays menstruation when given during the normal menstrual cycle.

It would seem from the observations above that menstruation follows a reduction in the hormonal stimulus applied to the uterus—whether progestational or estrogenic. In the usual menstrual cycle bleeding normally follows a decline in the circulating level of progesterone (fig. 60.8) for the urinary excretion of pregnanediol begins to fall a few days before the onset of menstruation. With regard to estrogen the recent observations of Brown (1955) on the excretion of the hormone during the menstrual cycle give the following picture: The excretion of estrogens increases steadily up to about the 13th day when an *ovulation peak* is reached. It then suddenly falls, remains low for several days, and thereafter slowly increases to reach a *luteal maximum* at about the 21st day. Finally, immediately prior to the onset of menstruation the excretion of estrogen falls once more.

So far the menstrual cycle has been discussed as if it were a process lying entirely under the sway of the ovary. This is not so, for the participation of the gonadotrophic hormones of the pituitary gland in regulating the cyclic activity of the ovary has been neglected. These are discussed on page 971, so that here the interactions may be tentatively summarized:

The estrogen content of the blood rises when the ovary is stimulated by the follicle-stimulating hormone of the pituitary, and when the concentration of this ovarian hormone reaches a certain level it, in turn, acts to suppress the output of follicle-stimulating hormone and excite the release of luteinizing hormone. The concentration of estrogen upon which the proliferative stage of menstruation depends is thus reduced. Next the hypophysis releases its luteinizing principle which stimulates the development of the corpus luteum, but as the concentration of progesterone in the blood rises the production of the luteinizing principle is in turn suppressed, with the result that the integrity of the luteal tissue cannot be maintained. With the fall in the concentration of estrogen and progesterone menstrual bleeding occurs and the secretion of follicle-stimulating hormone is then resumed—with commencement of another cycle.

### Menstrual Irregularities

The nonoccurrence of the menstrual periods in postpubertal life is called *amenorrhea*; except during pregnancy, when suppression of the menses is a physiological phenomenon, the failure of the

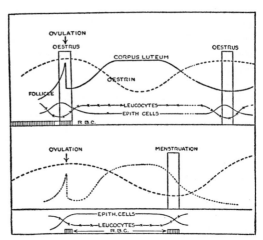

Fig. 60.8. Upper diagram, estrous cycle; lower diagram, menstrual cycle. (After Corner.)

menstrual cycles at any time between puberty and the menopause is abnormal. Amenorrhea may be either *primary* or *secondary*. In the former instance the menses have never occurred, in the latter they appeared but were subsequently suppressed. Primary amenorrhea is in many instances associated with arrested development of the reproductive organs. Scanty menstruation is termed *oligomenorrhea*, whereas *menorrhagia* is excessive bleeding. *Metrorrhagia* is the loss of blood from the uterus in the intermenstrual periods. A large proportion of these menstrual irregularities, when unaccompanied by some gross disease (e.g., tumor in the uterus), have an endocrine basis.

Amenorrhea is frequently the result of ovarian hypofunction. *Dysmenorrhea*, painful menstruation, is the result of irregular and spasmodic contractions of the uterine muscle which may in many cases have an hormonal origin. In the past, excessive bleeding in the absence of some obvious uterine disease has been put down to inflammation of the uterine mucosa (endometritis). Before the physiological changes in the endometrium were correlated with the stages of the ovarian cycle (p. 1089) the normal premenstrual characters of the uterine mucosa were considered to be pathological evidence of endometritis!

With the knowledge currently available it is clear that disorders of the menstrual cycle, such as amenorrhea, can result from a variety of causes which will operate through the ovaries or through the pituitary. The operation of psychological or neurological factors which act on the pituitary gland through the hypothalamus must not be neglected in this regard. It is well known that *gross* diseases of the anterior pituitary gland such as acromegaly, Simmonds' disease, and dystrophia adiposogenitalis are associated with menstrual irregularities which usually appear as oligomenorrhea or amenorrhea. Amenorrhea also occurs as an accompaniment of hyperthyroidism and as a symptom of several general diseases, notably anemia, tuberculosis and malnutrition.

The treatment of menstrual disorders depends, of course, upon the nature of the factors precipitating the condition.

*The nasogenital relationship.* A number of observations suggest a physiological relationship between the sex processes and the nose. In the first place the mucosa covering the nasal conchae has a cavernous structure suggestive of the erectile tissue of the penis and clitoris, and olfactory stimuli and psychic aspects of sex are very closely associated. Nasal congestion, often associated with epistaxis, occurs regularly in many women at the time of the menses, and in both sexes it is not unusual for nasal bleeding to occur at puberty. Sometimes the nasal hemorrhage in girls or women has seemed to replace menstruation which was coincidentally suppressed, and for this reason was termed erroneously *"vicarious menstruation."* Swelling and reddening of the nasal mucosa is a common finding in women during pregnancy and in monkeys during the menstrual cycles. Stimulation of the interior of nose has been reported to alter the periodicity of estrous cycles in rats, whereas excision of the conchae in young animals is said to result in hypoplasia of the sex organs. On the other hand, degenerative changes in the nasal mucosa have been observed as a sequence to castration, which could be reversed by estrogen injections.

## The Endocrine Functions of the Placenta

The human placenta has been found to contain (a) *estrogens*, (b) *progesterone*, and (c) a *gonadotrophin*; it is now clear that it acts as an endocrine gland.

*Estrogen.* Following ovariectomy in pregnant women large amounts of estrogen continue to be excreted in the urine. This observation clearly points to the existence of an ancillary source of estrogen. The fact that the output of estrogen falls abruptly at parturition, and that this hormone can be extracted from the placenta, indicates that it is produced in this organ. Although placental tissue grown *in vitro* does not appear to produce estrogen, Stewart has demonstrated estrogenic stimulation of the uterus of ovariectomized rabbits with intraocular implants of full term human placenta.

*Estrone, estradiol and estriol* have all been isolated from placental tissue, and are probably produced by the syncytial trophoblast. Of these estriol is the most important from the quantitative point of view. During pregnancy the placenta takes over much of the function of the ovary in the human. During gestation the output of estrogen in the urine rises fairly sharply in the first trimester and then remains more constant. At term the 24-hour excretion of the various estrogens is approximately as follows: estriol, 30 mg.; estrone, 2.0 mg.; estradiol, 0.75 mg.; whereas 2 mg. of hydroxyestrone and 0.75 mg. of epiestrol are also eliminated. Such large amounts of estrogen are not excreted in the free form but are conjugated with glucuronic acid (p. 1083). Toward the end of pregnancy it has been found that the proportion of combined to free estrogen, normally of the order of 99:1, falls as more free estrogen appears in the urine, and this has been taken to indicate a change in the metabolism of estrogen at this time. However, a fairly recent study by Clayton and Marrian indicates that the presence of unconjugated estrogen is due to the action of $\beta$-glucuronidase in the urine with consequent hydrolysis of the glucuronides. At delivery, with expulsion of the placenta, the urinary output of estrogen falls sharply to the levels found in nonpregnant individuals.

*Progesterone.* The production of progesterone by the placenta is implied in the finding that pregnancy continues in certain species following ovariectomy (p. 1088). In other species, such as the rat, "pregnancy" will continue in the ovariectomized animal provided that the number of fetuses is reduced to a minimum. If the fetuses alone are removed, the placentas will survive and be delivered at term; meanwhile all the signs of pregnancy will continue.

The excretory product of progesterone, pregnanediol, was first obtained from human pregnancy urine in 1929. According to Venning the amount of pregnanediol excreted during pregnancy steadily increases from about 5 or 10 mg. daily to around 80 mg. per 24 hours at term. Following delivery the pregnanediol in the urine falls sharply to reach nonpregnant levels in a few days. Recent applications of more specific assays for pregnanediol indicate that the peak output may not be as great as that noted above.

*Gonadotrophin.* The existence of a gonadotrophic principle in the blood and urine of pregnant women was established in 1927 by Ascheim and Zondek, but it was left to later workers to show that the principle was derived from the placenta. Since the hormone concerned has been shown to possess actions similar to those of the pituitary hormones it has been termed "anterior-pituitary-like" (APL), or "pregnancy prolan." However, as it is now known to be produced by the chorionic villi, the name *"human chorionic gonadotrophin"* (HCG), or simply *"chorionic gonadotrophin"* (CG) has been adopted and is in general use.

The hormonal secretions of the pituitary are required during pregnancy in the rabbit and dog, whereas in other species, monkey, mouse, guinea pig and rat, pregnancy is interrupted only if pituitary ablation is performed early. This, in conjunction with the evidence that in the rat the ovaries are essential for the maintenance of pregnancy, implies that the placenta produces a gonadotrophic (luteotrophic) hormone.

In the human, chorionic gonadotrophin appears in the urine very shortly after conception, in a fortnight or so, and the amount rapidly increases to reach a peak about 50 to 70 days after the last menstrual period. Thereafter there is an equally rapid fall until the 112th day when a low level is reached which is maintained until the end of gestation. In the chimpanzee and monkey chorionic gonadotrophin is excreted for only a short time during pregnancy.

It is clear that chorionic gonadotrophin is produced by the Langhans' cells of the fetal chorion. In addition to the extraction of the hormone from the human placenta, fragments of this tissue implanted into the eyes of rabbits have been found to liberate gonadotrophin. Chorionic gonadotrophin is also produced by tissue cultures of the placenta. Further, gonadotrophin is detectable in the urine in all conditions in which normal or abnormal chorionic tissue is present, and disappears with its complete removal. In cases in which the placenta is retained after expulsion of the fetus, gonadotrophin excretion continues. Chorionepitheliomas of the uterus, or of the testis, are also characterized by the excretion of chorionic gonadotrophin in the urine, as is hydatidiform mole (a cystic degenerative disease of chorionic tissue).

In its actions chorionic gonadotrophin differs from any of the pituitary hormones. When immature female rats are treated with chorionic gonadotrophin prepared from human placenta, placental implants, or extracts of human pregnancy urine, follicular maturation, estrus and the formation of corpora lutea result; the luteinizing action is the predominant effect. LH is ineffective in immature animals. The failure of the pituitary

principle is believed to be due to the absence of FSH whose synergistic action is required by both HCG and LH. The placental hormone appears to stimulate the release of FSH from the hypophysis of the rat, whereas the pituitary hormone does not. Human chorionic gonadotrophin causes enlargement of the ovaries, but to a lesser degree than the pituitary principle, and hypertrophy of the interstitial (Leydig) cells of the testes. In the latter case the output of male sex hormone is increased and the growth of the accessory sex organs is stimulated. This action may be of value in the treatment of undescended testes and eunuchoidism. Chorionic gonadotrophin will also maintain the integrity of the seminiferous tubules in hypophysectomized animals, but will not prevent ovarian atrophy after hypophysectomy, for here the synergistic action of FSH is required.

In summary, it would seem that the function of chorionic gonadotrophin is to supplement the action of the pituitary in maintaining the corpus luteum during pregnancy, and from this point of view the hormone is luteotrophic in effect. Support for this concept may be obtained from the finding that the life of the corpus luteum in women can be prolonged by chorionic gonadotrophin.

A wide variety of techniques has been used in the *assay* of *human chorionic gonadotrophin*. Those performed on the rat include the increase in ovarian weight, the production of ovarian hyperemia, the increase in uterine weight, changes in the vaginal smear, and increase in the weight of the accessory reproductive organs of the male. The production of ovulation in the rabbit and toad, as well as spermiation in the male toad, are also used. For comparative purposes the international unit represents the activity contained in 0.1 mg. of the international standard preparation.

### Pregnancy Tests

Quite apart from strictly quantitative or assay purposes a number of the tests noted above are of value in the diagnosis of pregnancy. Since chorionic gonadotrophin appears in the urine some 2 or 3 weeks after conception, detection of the hormone permits an early diagnosis of the presence or absence of pregnancy. Such tests are also of importance in cases of suspected chorionepithelioma and hydatidiform mole.

The more important pregnancy tests are:

1. *The Ascheim-Zondek test.* This was the first procedure devised and depends on the changes induced by HCG in the ovaries of immature mice.

Two milliliters of urine are given over 2 days and the ovaries examined on the 5th day. The presence of hemorrhagic follicles and luteinized follicles indicates that the urine contains chorionic gonadotrophin.

2. *The Kupperman test.* In order to save time the immature rat may be used. Here 2 ml. of urine are injected subcutaneously into each of three immature females, which are killed 6 hours later. If the urine contains HCG a marked hyperemia of the ovaries is observed. Alternatively the response may be read after 2 hours following intraperitoneal administration of the hormone.

3. *The Friedman test* depends on the production of ovulation in the rabbit following the intravenous injection of 10 to 15 ml. of urine. The ovaries are examined 24 to 48 hours later.

4. *The Hogben test* utilizes the South African clawed toad, *Xenopus laevis.* A mature female is isolated and a concentrate, prepared from 20 to 30 ml. of urine, is instilled into the dorsal lymph sac. If the urine contains HCG ovulation follows between 6 and 12 hours later.

5. *The Galli-Mainini test* employs the male amphibian and is the most recently developed method. It depends upon the expulsion of spermatozoa and the result can usually be read within 2 hours. A variety of species may be used, including *Bufo arenarum* (which was the first tested), *Rana pipiens, Bufo bufo, Bufo marinus* and *Xenopus laevis.*

Finally, it is perhaps worth recalling that as Ascheim has pointed out, tests for pregnancy are not a modern innovation. In an Egyptian papyrus some 3000 or 4000 years old it is directed that should a woman wish to know whether she is pregnant she should place some earth and barley in a vessel and add a little of her urine each day. Should the barley grow she is pregnant. It has since been found that estrogen, which is present in quite high concentration in the urine after the first month or two of pregnancy, is a stimulant to plant growth.

*Pregnant mare serum gonadotrophin.* The existence of a gonadotrophin in the serum of the pregnant mare was discovered in 1930 by Cole and Hart. This hormone appears about the time of implantation of the blastocyst and its concentration in the blood reaches a peak at about the 80th day, although, unlike HCG, only very small amounts appear in the urine. It seems fairly clear that pregnant mare serum gonadotrophin (PMS) is produced by specialized structures in the mucosa of the uterus—the endometrial cups, and the production of PMS may be correlated with the appearance of a number of accessory corpora lutea in the ovary.

In hypophysectomized rats, PMS causes a marked increase in ovarian weight, in follicular growth, and, with large doses, in luteinization.

The interstitial cells in the testes of the male are markedly stimulated.

The hormone is seldom used clinically in view of its limited effect on the human gonad and the ease with which antigenic reactions are stimulated.

## The Structure and Development of the Mammary Glands and the Secretion of Milk

### *The Structure of the Mammary Glands*

The secretory tissue of the mammary glands consists of elongated slender sacs or ducts— the *alveolar ducts*—whose walls show numerous pouches—the *alveoli.* The walls of the alveoli are composed of a basement membrane, a layer of myoepithelial cells, and an inner layer of columnar epithelium. The epithelial cells are the secreting elements.

The gland is composed of some 15 to 25 lobes marked off by connective tissue septa containing much fat and derived from the mantle of adipose tissue which envelops it. A lobe is subdivided into lobules which are variable in size, shape and number. Each lobule gives rise to a narrow duct which is the continuation of an alveolar duct but whose wall is quite devoid of alveoli. By the successive junctions of these lobular ducts a single *lactiferous duct* is formed which serves an entire lobe; it is lined by stratified epithelium. The lactiferous ducts converge toward the nipple, become dilated beneath the areola and then constrict again. Near the base of the nipple they turn abruptly to run vertically toward the skin surface. Each opens separately at the apex of the nipple by a minute mouth called the *galactopore.* In the nonlactating gland few alveoli, if any, are to be found and the gland consists of ducts, connective tissue and fat. Preparatory to lactation the glandular tissue shows active growth, leading to the development of the lobular-alveolar system which completely transforms the histological appearance.

The nipple and an area of the skin (the *areola*) surrounding it are darkly pigmented. The pigmentation deepens in the early months of pregnancy, a sign recognized from the earliest times, and only partially fades after gestation. As in other cutaneous pigmented areas the color is due mainly to the accumulation of granules of pigment in the squamous epithelial cells of the skin; but the actual production of pigment is a function of cells called *melanoblasts* lying just below the epithelial layers. These are the cells which give the "dopa" reaction (p. 1043), but they themselves may contain little pigment. The function of this pigment is unknown but its increase during pregnancy appears to be causally related to the functional activity of the underlying gland, an influence being conveyed from the active tissues to the melanoblasts through the rich sympathetic innervation (Cathcart and associates). There is possibly also a hormonal factor carried to the melanoblasts in the general blood stream.

The nipple contains smooth muscle which is arranged circularly as well as vertically. The vertical fibers are in close relation to the lactiferous ducts. The stiffening and erection of the nipple which results from mild stimulation is caused by the contraction of these strands of muscle. The nipple is one of the most richly innervated structures in the body. Nerve fibers both medullated (somatic) and nonmedullated (sympathetic) are found in profusion in and beneath the skin, and especially in relation to the openings of the lactiferous ducts. In the dermis, nerve fibers form a loose open network without encapsulation, or enter end-organs of various forms. Pacinian and Meissner's corpuscles commonly found in other cutaneous and subcutaneous areas are absent, and Krause's end-organs are scarce. The sensations aroused from the nipple and areola are, apparently like those of the glans penis, of the diffuse protopathic or thalamic type. Light touch with cotton wool or von Frey's hairs is not appreciated.

### *The Roles of the Ovaries and Anterior Pituitary in Mammary Development*

There are three phases in the development and activity of the mammary glands. These are seen as (a) the period up to and including puberty, (b) the phase during which the action of the corpus luteum is prominent, that is during pregnancy and pseudopregnancy, and (c) the final secretory phase of lactation when milk is secreted and discharged.

The building of the framework upon which the mechanism of lactation is to be hung, begins before puberty, for it has been shown that growth of the mammary glands of the rat becomes faster than that of the body as a whole at about the 22nd day (Cowie). At this time it would appear that estrogen is largely responsible for the growth changes seen. It is generally true that estrogen is responsible for the growth of the mammary duct system whereas progesterone, acting synergistically with estrogen, promotes full alveolar development. But the above is a generalization and in the mouse, rat and monkey progesterone alone, in sufficiently high dosage, will cause alveolar development in spayed animals lacking estrogen. Further, it is possible to group various species according to the effect estrogen has on the undeveloped mammary gland. In some species, the dog and probably the ferret, estrogen alone causes little or no mammary development, whereas in the next group, which includes the mouse, rat, rabbit and cat, estrogen in physiological dosage evokes primarily and mainly duct growth. In the third group, which includes the monkey, guinea pig, cow and goat, estrogen produces extensive growth of the alveolar system—lobular-alveolar development—as well as of the ducts.

Surprisingly little is known about the relative roles of estrogen and progesterone in the development of the human mammary gland. Mammary development has been produced clinically by the topical administration of estrogen. A number of workers have described cyclic changes in the tissues of the breast during the menstrual cycle, with growth occurring in the luteal phase and regression after menstruation. However such reports have been contested. Physiologically, the enlargement of the mammary glands seen during pregnancy is due to the growth of the corpus luteum which superimposes the alveolar developing action of progesterone upon the basically ductal action of estrogen.

It has long been thought that an intact anterior pituitary gland is essential for the stimulating actions of the ovarian hormones on the mammary gland. In hypophysectomized rats, mice or guinea pigs, estrogen exerts little or no effect upon duct development unless anterior pituitary replacement therapy is initiated. The nature of the pituitary principle necessary for the response to estrogen and progesterone has provided a controversial topic over many years. Turner and his associates produced evidence for the view that the pituitary produced two mammogenic principles, distinct from any known hormone. *Mammogen I* was thought to stimulate the duct system and to be liberated under the influence of estrogen; and *Mammogen II*, was believed to produce the growth of the lobular-alveolar system and to be secreted under the influence of progesterone. Thus the ovarian hormones acted, not directly on the mammary gland, but through the hypophysis. However, the theory has failed to find general favor. It has recently proved possible to obtain full mammary development, typical of late pregnancy, in the hypophysectomized rat by giving estrogen, progesterone and the anterior pituitary hormones, prolactin, growth hormone and adrenocorticotrophin (Lyons). Further, Ahrén and Jacobsohn have shown that if insulin is supplied to the hypophysectomized immature female rat (together with estrogen and progesterone), then mammary growth and differentiation will follow. This observation underlines the importance of general metabolic activities in mammary development.

The direct action of prolactin in promoting mammary growth (as distinct from its lactogenic effect described below) was shown by Lyons who induced localized hyperplasia of the glandular epithelium by injections of prolactin into the mammary ducts of rabbits previously treated with ovarian hormones.

### Prolactin

The existence of a lactogenic hormone in the pituitary has already been mentioned, and is discussed elsewhere, in chapter 56. However, certain points are of interest here. The first evidence of the existence of such a hormone was provided by Stricker and Grueter in 1928 who found that crude anterior pituitary extracts induced lactation in ovariectomized, pseudopregnant rabbits. The material would also restore lactation in rabbits which had ceased lactating 10 to 15 days previously, and was later found to act similarly in bitches. In 1930 Corner showed that injections of anterior lobe extract caused enlargement of the mammary glands and lactation in ovariectomized virgin rabbits. Many workers quickly confirmed that anterior pituitary extracts were able to initiate lactation in the adequately developed glands of a wide variety of species. Within a few years it was established that the extracts contained a separate hormone which had pronounced lactogenic effects (Riddle and Bates), and was called *prolactin, galacin,* or *mammotropin.*

### The Role of the Placenta in Mammary Growth

The work of Lyons on the hypophysectomized rat showed that mammary development could be obtained after replacing prolactin administration by placental extracts. This finding is in accord with the results of rather different work performed some 20 years ago. It was then found that removal of the ovaries and fetuses from rats together with hypophysectomy causes mammary regression if the placentas are also removed, but mammary growth continues if the placentas are left. It appears then that the placenta can substitute for the ovaries as well as the pituitary. The production of estrogen and progesterone by the placenta should be recalled in this connection (see also p. 1092).

### The Initiation of Lactation

Although lactation is generally held to start at the end of pregnancy, the secretion of milk sets in long before this, at about the fifth month. Nevertheless the initiation of a copious lactation is a striking consequence of delivery.

The factors underlying this event have excited comment for many years, and a variety of explanations have been put forward. Thus it was supposed that lactation resulted as a natural consequence of the end of pregnancy and mammary development, so that when the growth stimulus was removed, secretion began. Support for this view came from experiments in which, for example, lactation followed the end of a course of estrogen injections in the guinea pig. With the discovery of prolactin, attention was directed to the pituitary gland, as well as to the endocrine activities of the placenta, and Nelson in 1936 put forward a new concept. This was that during pregnancy the ovarian hormones induced proliferative changes in the mammary glands and in addition, and particularly during the latter half, inhibited the actual secretion of milk. The restraining influence was visualized as acting (a) by suppressing the secretion or release of the pituitary lactogenic hormone, and (b) by a direct inhibitory effect on the mammary glands. Thus the high ovarian hormone levels during pregnancy would promote glandular development, whereas the sharp fall in concentration at parturition would permit lactation to begin. It is known that lactation is inhibited in most animals by estrogen, or by measures which stimulate estrogen liberation, and is also promptly suppressed by human chorionic gonadotropin (HCG) which stimulates the production of luteal tissue. Collip and his colleagues reported that if the luteinized ovaries induced in virgin rats by the administration of HCG were removed, then the hypertrophied mammae secreted profusely. Removal of the pituitary, however, together with the ovaries prevented this result. When lactating cows become pregnant, milk production declines progressively during gestation but rises abruptly after calving. In guinea pigs, removal of the ovaries and embryos, although leaving the placentas intact, does not induce lactation, but lactation occurs following expulsion of the placentas. Observations of the above nature lend strong support to the view of Nelson. Evans also explained the milk secretion which occasionally occurs in the child shortly after birth ("witches milk") on this basis, for the fetus is exposed to ovarian hormones and the elimination of these after birth might result in the liberation of prolactin from the pituitary of the infant.

The theory as described above, with an emphasis on the inhibitory action of estrogen, has limitations. Thus the amounts of estrogen required to suppress established lactation probably are greater than those produced during pregnancy, and the typical signs of high estrogen levels (cornified vagina, estrous behavior) are not seen during pregnancy. Further, low doses of estrogen actually stimulate mammary secretion in some forms (goat and cow). It was to account for difficulties of this nature that Meites and Turner in 1942 drew attention to the possible role of progesterone. These workers suggested that during pregnancy progesterone inhibited a stimulating effect of estrogen on the secretion of prolactin, but at the time of parturition estrogen became dominant and was able to evoke a quick rise in the output of prolactin and so initiate lactation. In support of this view it was found that in rats and guinea pigs the prolactin content of the hypophysis began to rise a few days before the birth of the young, and that the urinary excretion of prolactin after parturition was from 8 to 16 times greater than that during pregnancy. Estrogen was found to increase the content of prolactin in the hypophysis, so that the low prolactin content during pregnancy was attributed to the relatively high progestin content of the blood, and its antagonistic effect on the action of estrogen. It was found that estrogen and progesterone given in appropriate proportion had no effect on the prolactin content of the pituitary.

In turn, the view of Meites and Turner has been subjected to criticism, notably by Folley, who was not convinced that increases in pituitary prolactin content (assumed to reflect pituitary secretion rate by Meites and Turner) were accompanied by an increased secretion of prolactin into the blood, and objected to the key position assigned to prolactin in the initiation of lactation. He suggested, as a modification of the Nelson theory, that low levels of circulating estrogen stimulate the secretion of anterior pituitary hormones concerned in lactogenesis, whereas high levels inhibit such secretion. At about the time of parturition the level of circulating estrogen, previously above the threshold for pituitary inhibition, falls and in passing through the range between the two thresholds will cause functional activation of the anterior pituitary with respect to the production of lactogenic hormones and so initiate full lactation.

More recently it has been found (Meites and Sgouris) that estrogen and progesterone exert an antagonistic effect toward prolactin at the mammary gland level. Thus the ability of a moderate dose of prolactin to initiate milk secretion in ovariectomized rabbits with well developed glands could be effectively inhibited if optimal mammary growth-promoting doses of estrone and progesterone were given at the same time. In the absence of either or both steroids prolactin elicited a good lactational response. Variation of the amounts of gonadal or hypophysial hormones given showed that the occurrence of mammary growth (or of lactation) depended on the balance achieved. In the light of this work it is clear that to focus attention solely upon the hypophysis at the onset of lactation is to neglect other important factors. Although retaining his "double threshold" theory, Folley now believes that 'lactogenic' doses of estrogen may be deprived of their lactogenic action by suitable doses of progesterone, and that the combination of the two hormones may act as a potent inhibitor of lactation during pregnancy. At parturition the fall in the ratio of progesterone to estrogen would remove the inhibition, and the positive "lactogenic" effect of estrogen would act unopposed.

An entirely different viewpoint is that of Petersen, who does not concern himself with estrogen-progesterone-prolactin interrelationships. It is now clear that milk production, i.e., the formation of milk and its secretion into the alveoli, begins some time before parturition. The question, therefore, is not a matter of *secretion* after childbirth, but of the discharge or *ejection* of milk from the gland. As pointed out by Petersen, the low water content of the first milk secreted, the *colostrum*, strongly suggests a retained secretion which tends by distention of the alveoli to depress secretory activity, but with the emptying of the alveoli the inhibitory effect of distention is removed and a continuous profuse secretion is maintained by the lactogenic hormone.

### The Maintenance of Lactation

With parturition the operation of a number of as yet imperfectly understood factors results in lactation, a process which is maintained in many forms for months.

*Neural factors.* The mechanism underlying the continuance of lactation is not clear, although it is certain that the pituitary is involved since lactation is arrested abruptly by hypophysectomy. It is common knowledge that weaning is followed by rapid involution of the mammary gland and cessation of milk production. This might be due to the retention of milk within the gland, with consequent deleterious effects on its secretory activity, or to loss of a stimulus which promotes lactation—the stimulus of suckling. The latter alternative is more likely, for there are numerous cases in which suckling has been shown to induce lactation in male individuals of various species (bull, goat, wether, man). Lactation has often been induced in this way in virgin girls, as well as experimentally in the rat. Selye and his coworkers showed that suckling tended to delay the involution of the mammary glands in rats in which the galactophores were tied (to prevent the egress of milk), and suggested that the suckling stimulus caused a nervous reflex release of lactogenic hormone from the pituitary which maintained lactation. In lactating mice deprived of their litters the mammary involution which normally occurs may be retarded by painting the nipples with an irritant such as turpentine. The prolactin content of the hypophysis of lactating rats has been observed to fall over a 30-minute nursing period. In nonpuerperal women lactation may follow extensive operations involving the thoracic wall, probably through irritation of the intercostal nerves. Such observations indicate that nervous factors play an important part in the maintenance of lactation. The operation of psychic factors in women is not to be neglected; their operation is well seen in relation to milk ejection (see below).

*Hormonal factors.* The precise nature of the hormonal systems activated by neural stimuli has not been elucidated. It is presumed that the stimulus is transmitted to the hypothalamus and from there to the hypophysis by the portal vessels. But the nature of the response of the anterior pituitary gland is not certain. With the availability of purified pituitary hormones the maintenance of lactation in hypophysectomized rats has been attempted. Cowie found that, using growth hormone, prolactin and ACTH singly and in combination, the best result was given by prolactin plus ACTH. Oxytocin was also given to make certain that the litters obtained any milk produced. Lyons, in rather similar work, found that prolactin and hydrocortisone together were able to raise the milk production to about half of normal.

When pure pituitary hormones are given to lactating animals, and the effect on the milk output is studied, it is found that growth hormone augments the secretion of milk (*galactopoiesis*) to the greatest extent. This effect can be observed, not only toward the the end of lactation, when the milk yield is declining, but also at the height of milk secretion. It is further significant that upon cessation of treatment the milk yield does not fall below the expected level—the action of growth hormone is thus not due to mobilization of reserves. Prolactin exerts very little galactopoietic activity although its continued secretion is probably necessary for the maintenance of lactation. Injection of ACTH in cows has been found to temporarily depress the milk yield, although it is evident from work involving adrenalectomy and replacement therapy that the adrenal corticoids are essential for the maintenance of lactation. In adrenalectomized rats cortisone and desoxycorticosterone acetate (DCA) together provided the best maintenance of lactation (Cowie), whereas later work showed that chlorohydrocortisone gave virtually complete maintenance. The effects of thyroidectomy on lactation, although depressive, do not appear to be particularly striking. It was found more than 60 years ago that thyroid feeding increased the milk yield of women and cows. This has been confirmed, and similar responses demonstrated in the rat. Pituitary thyrotrophic hormone is also active in this regard. Besides increasing the weight of milk produced, L-thyroxine increases the percentage of fat and nonfatty solids in the milk, whereas the concentration of alkaline phosphatase drops markedly. Recent work has shown that triiodothyronine (ch. 57) is about twice as active as L-thyroxine. Unlike thyroxine, triiodothyronine is not effective when given orally to cows. Dried thyroid and L-thyroxine have been used with benefit in the treatment of human hypogalactia, but cannot be regarded as a panacea.

## Milk Ejection

The production of milk by the maternal mammary gland forms only one step in the process of lactation. For lactation to be successful the milk must be transferred to the young. It is not possible to empty a mammary gland passively, by compression or by suction, since the milk is retained in the small ducts and alveoli. Physiologically, emptying of the gland is achieved by the operation of a neurohormonal reflex referred to as the milk ejection reflex. It consists of an afferent nervous pathway, which begins with the sensory end-organs in the nipple and areola, passes up the spinal cord to the hypothalamus, and to the posterior lobe of the hypophysis through the supraoptico-hypophysial tract. That is the neural part of the reflex. In the posterior pituitary the neurohypophysial hormone, oxytocin, is discharged into the blood stream whence it is carried to cause the contraction of myoepithelial cells embracing the alveoli. There is little doubt that this is the reflex activated by milking in cattle which results in *"let-down,"* or by suckling in women, which results in the *"draught."* The reflex is highly susceptible to conditioning, and is easily inhibited by fright or, in women, by embarrassment. Experimentally, milk ejection can be produced by electrical stimulation of the supraopticohypophysial tract, and blocked by lesions of this nerve pathway. In the latter case milk ejection may be restored by injection of oxytocin.

It follows from the above that interference with the process of milk ejection will stop or prevent lactation just as surely as disturbance of the formation of milk. Neglect of this consideration has in the past led to much confusion in both experimental and clinical investigations.

The fact that both oxytocic hormone and lactogenic hormone are secreted in response to the same physiological stimuli has led several investigators to suggest that oxytocin released from the neurohypophysis acts on the anterior pituitary to cause the release of lactogenic hormone. In support of this concept it has been found that the administration of oxytocin to rats whose litters had been removed retarded mammary involution. This effect was not apparent in the hypophysectomized animal. However, it must also be pointed out that lactogenic hormone appears to be released from the hypophysis isolated from neural influences by transplantation away from the sella turcica.

### The Composition of Milk, the Origins and Secretion of Its Constituents

With the onset of lactation, the epithelial cells lining the alveoli become loaded with fine droplets of fat which soon coalesce to form large globules in the part of the cell lying next to the alveolar lumen. The fat, with other constituents of the milk, may then be discharged into the alveolus as droplets, or the inner part of the cell is pinched off as it were from the larger portion and is freed into the lumen. The latter represents the process of *apocrine* secretion.

*Colostrum.* At the end of pregnancy and the beginning of lactation the secretion contained in the mammary gland is unlike normal milk. It is known as *colostrum*. Colostrum contains numerous globules and cell fragments, together with *colostrum bodies*, which are large ameboid cells. Colostrum contains little fat, but a larger amount of antibodies than are present in milk proper. It is presumed that colostrum formation occurs when there is an imbalance between the secretion of milk and its removal. Thus it is found at the end of pregnancy and at the end of lactation.

*Milk.* Milk consists essentially of an emulsion of fat globules in a colloidal solution of protein, together with crystalloids in true solution. It contains two substances not found elsewhere in the body, casein and lactose; the combination of glycerides forming milk fat is peculiar to it.

The composition of human milk is compared with that of cow's milk in Table 60.1. The quantity of protein in cow's milk is more than double that in human milk; the difference is largely confied to the casein content. The sugar and fat content of cow's milk is lower than that of the human. Calcium is the mineral present in largest amount. Both human milk and cow's milk vary greatly in composition and in quality due to the operation of many factors; psychic, dietary, hormonal, period of lactation, time of day (greater volume during night), etc. The daily output increases up to a maximum of from 1000 to 3000 ml. at about the 25th week after childbirth and then gradually declines. Human milk of good quality contains all the elements essential for building body tissue, and adequate amounts of vitamins A (as well as carotene), the B complex and C. Vitamins $B_1$ and D are in low concentration and may be present in inadequate amounts. Raising the protein in the diet tends to increase the total milk yield, and a high fat diet increases the yield, as well as the fat content, of the milk. Carbohydrates, if in high proportion in the diet, reduce both the yield and the quality of the milk.

*The milk protein.* The proteins of milk consist largely of casein, lactalbumin and lactoglobulin. Since the phosphoprotein, casein, occurs in no place other than the mammary gland, it is clear that it must be synthesized there. The details of the synthesis have not yet been worked out. According to Folley, milk protein may be synthesized entirely from the amino acids of the circulating blood, or partly from these and partly from degradation of plasma protein in the mammary gland. Alternatively the milk proteins might arise from plasma proteins by rearrangement of peptide chains, or partly in this manner and partly from blood amino acids. From measurement of

TABLE 60.1

| | Total protein | Casein | Lact-albumin | Lacto-globulin | Lactose | Fat | Ash | Water |
|---|---|---|---|---|---|---|---|---|
| | % | % | % | % | % | % | % | % |
| Cow's milk...... | 3.6 | 3.0 | 0.5 | 0.08 | 5 | 3.5 | 0.7 | 87.2 |
| Human milk...... | 1.5 | 1.1 | 0.4 | — | 6.8 | 4.0 | 0.2 | 87.5 |

the arteriovenous difference of blood amino acids in the lactating udder, it is clear that some amino acids are utilized by the mammary gland. However, it has been claimed that the uptake is sufficient to account for only about half of the casein in milk. For this reason attention has been directed to the plasma proteins and it was thought that a glycoprotein present in small amounts in blood represented the precursor. Quite recent work with udder perfusion methods and with labelled amino acids indicates that casein is indeed synthesized from plasma amino acids, and that a similar conclusion may well be reached in the case of lactoglobulin.

*Milk fat.* Milk fat differs in composition from the neutral fat of the blood in that it contains a relatively high proportion of short chain fatty acids of the series $C_4$ to $C_{12}$. The fatty acids, e.g., butyric, caproic, caprylic, lauric, and myristic, constitute about 30 per cent of the total fat of milk. The fat of milk therefore cannot be simply neutral fat transferred from the circulation to the gland and there concentrated. Of the long chain fatty acids, oleic (35 per cent) and palmitic (30 per cent) are present in greatest quantity. Stearic acid constitutes only about 2 per cent. Much of our knowledge of the synthesis of milk fat is derived from work on the ruminant, where it is probable that most of the fatty acids up to, and including, palmitic acid are formed in the udder from small molecules, mainly acetate and possibly β-hydroxybutyrate. In other species, e.g., the rat and rabbit, considerable quantities of glucose may be used in addition for fat synthesis.

*Lactose.* Like the other constituents of milk just discussed, lactose is found only in the mammary gland. This disaccharide, galactose-glucose, must therefore be formed in that organ. Lactose could be produced from small molecules taken up from the blood, like lactic acid and pyruvate, or from the blood glucose. Most evidence favors glucose as a precursor. Thus perfusion of a bovine udder with blood containing labelled glucose, followed by extraction and hydrolysis of the lactose resulted in isolation of labelled glucose and galactose. This result implies that galactose is derived from glucose and is supported by experiments in which slices of mammary tissue, incubated with glucose, formed lactose. It has also proved possible to synthesize lactose from glucose in homogenates of mammary gland tissue. It is perhaps worth noting here that procedures which lower the blood sugar tend to decrease the concentration of lactose in milk whereas hyperglycemic procedures have the reverse effect.

## The Testes

### THE STRUCTURE OF THE TESTES

The testes are ovoid glands suspended in the scrotum by the spermatic cords. Each is surrounded by a firm, thick capsule—the *tunica albuginea*, which is in turn enclosed by a double layer of peritoneum. The layers of the *tunica vaginalis communis* slide freely upon one another, enabling the testis to move easily within its scrotal sac.

The substance of the testis consists of a mass of coiled tubules, the *convoluted seminiferous tubules*, bound together by a stroma of connective tissue. Each seminiferous tubule is a rather closely coiled tube between 35 and 70 cm. long and from 150 to 300 microns in diameter. They are held in wedge-shaped compartments or *lobules* by incomplete connective tissue septa. Through the gaps in the septa they are joined to one another by short tubular connections. The combined length of the convoluted tubules of man has been estimated at over 300 yards. At the apices of the lobules the seminiferous tubules join the first elements of the excretory duct system. These are narrow straight tubules—the *tubuli recti*—which in turn empty into a system of irregular cavernous spaces, the *rete testis* in the hilum or mediastinum in the posterior part of the testis. At the upper part of the rete testis some dozen or more ducts, the *ductuli efferentes*, arise; passing to the upper part or *caput* of the epididymis, these ducts become confluent to form the *ductus epididymis*. The latter is a long, greatly tortuous tube which forms the body and tail of the epididymis. At the lower extremity of the epididymis the ductus bends abruptly upon itself to be continued as the *vas* or *ductus deferens*. The vas deferens on each side, after a devious course, is joined by the duct of the corresponding seminal vesicle, and terminates as an *ejaculatory duct* which opens into the urethra.

The convoluted tubules are lined by several layers of cells, the *spermatogenic* cells, which produce the spermatozoa. Among the spermatogenic or sex cells are a small number of *cells of Sertoli*—long cells attached perpendicularly to the basement membrane. The spermatogenic cells undergo well defined changes in the course of transformation into spermatozoa. In the mature testis these can be distinguished, for the primitive stages lie close to the basement membrane and develop on passage toward the lumen of the tubule. Initially the germ cells are large round cells at the periphery of the tubule and are called *spermatogonia*. They alone are present in the immature testis. Spermatogonia multiply mitotically, giving rise to *primary spermatocytes*. These are larger than the spermatogonia. Each divides into two smaller *secondary spermatocytes*, and each of these in turn divides to produce two *spermatids*. The latter transformation involves a *reduction* or *meiotic division* of the nucleus, so that each spermatid contains only half the normal number of chromosomes in its nucleus. The spermatids which are found near the lumen of the tubule are transformed directly, i.e., without division, into the free *spermatozoa* (see figure 60.9). About half the number of spermatids or spermatozoa contain a Y-chromosome and half an X-chromosome.

*Sertoli cells.* The Sertoli or sustentacular cells occur fairly regularly at intervals around the tubules. The nucleus of a Sertoli cell is large, but division has not been seen under normal conditions. In the human testis, the Sertoli cell contains a spindle-shaped crystalloid near the nucleus. The Sertoli cells are believed to perform a nutritive and supporting function toward the developing spermatozoa; the spermatids are found to be attached to them. Unlike the spermatogenic cells, the cells of Sertoli are highly resistant toward a variety of noxious factors. To judge from the findings in cases of Sertoli cell tumors of the testis, the sustentacular cells may secrete estrogen.

*The interstitial cells.* The tubules of the testis lie in a stroma of connective tissue, and in this connective tissue are found clumps of irregularly polyhedral cells—the *interstitial cells of Leydig.* The Leydig cells appear to be differentiated from fibroblasts, and contain many granules of lipoid material and pigment. In the fetus and newborn the Leydig cells are remarkably prominent due to stimulation by chorionic gonadotrophin. After birth they atrophy but become conspicuous once more at puberty. The Leydig cells are known to secrete androgen.

*The accessory sex glands.* Linked in functional association with the testis are a number of glands which produce secretions which, with the sperm of the testis, together make up the *semen.* They are functionally dependent upon the endocrine secretion of the testis, for they display atrophy in its absence. The most important are the *seminal vesicles, prostate gland,* and the *bulbo-urethral or Cowper's glands.*

The *seminal vesicles* are paired organs lying dorsal to the bladder; their ducts join the vas deferens. They are absent in many mammals (e.g., the whale and dog) and so are not considered essential in reproduction. On the other hand they are greatly developed in boars, hedgehogs, rats and guinea pigs, and their secretion increases the volume of the ejaculate in these species. They do not act as reservoirs for the spermatozoa. The secretion of the seminal vesicles is a yellowish

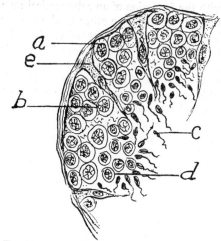

Fig. 60.9. Spermatogenesis; *a*, spermatogonia; *b*, primary spermatocytes; *c*, spermatozoa; *d*, spermatids; *e*, cells of Sertoli.

viscous fluid which is marked by its content of fructose. The level of fructose is closely associated with the blood titer of male sex hormone, and falls sharply in its absence (as after castration). The fructose appears to be derived from blood glucose since it is increased in diabetic rabbits or in humans, and falls after the administration of insulin.

*The semen.* The fluid ejaculated from the male genital tract is known as *semen.* It contains about 60,000,000 spermatozoa per cu. ml., although the normal limits range from 25,000,000 to 225,000,000. In the assessment of fertility from a sample of semen the motility and viability are often regarded as more important than the sperm count. The average volume of an ejaculate is about 3 ml. and immediately after expulsion the semen coagulates, to liquefy again in a few minutes. The spermatozoa in the seminiferous tubules are non-motile and appear to be carried along the ductuli efferentia by the cilia of the cells lining these channels. They are stored in the epididymis. Ejaculation of the semen during coitus is brought about by contractions of the deferentia and the ejaculatory ducts.

## THE PHYSIOLOGY OF THE TESTIS

The function of the testis is two-fold, namely, the production of germ cells, *spermatogenesis,* and the elaboration of the male sex hormone, its *endocrine function.*

### *The Gametogenic Function of the Testis*

In man the production of spermatozoa in the testes is carried on continuously throughout adult life, with the formation of an astronomical number of germ cells. In some other species the production of sperm occurs seasonally, at a time when conception of young will lead to their delivery at an auspicious time of the year. The sheep, deer, ferret and many classes of birds display this condition; sheep, for example, breed in autumn and the young are delivered in spring. During the remainder of the year, outside the breeding season, little sign of germinal activity is seen in the testis. Experimentally, however, spermatogenesis may be promoted by administration of pituitary gonadotrophic hormones.[4]

The testis, like the ovary, is functionally dependent on the pituitary gland. The removal of the hypophysis is followed by arrest of spermatogenesis and testicular atrophy; these changes can be reversed by implantation of pituitary tissue or suitable extracts of anterior pituitary glands. Upon hypophysectomy the testes soften and lose weight. Differentiation of the gametes does not proceed beyond early spermatocyte formation and thus spermatids and spermatozoa disappear from the organ. The Leydig cells become inactive and androgen production ceases, with consequent atrophy of the accessory sexual organs and accessory sex characters. Implantation of pituitary tissue or injection of gonadotrophic extracts of the pituitary speedily results in the onset of spermatogenesis in the immature individual, whether mouse or man. The effect is sometimes seen clinically in cases where pituitary overactivity advances puberty in boys. It is believed that the follicle-stimulating hormone (FSH) of the hypophysis is mainly concerned with spermatogenesis, as injection of purified FSH into hypophysectomized male rats prevents atrophy of the seminiferous tubules and will restore gametogenic activity. Similar effects have been reported in studies employing purified FSH in man. The luteinizing hormone (LH) of the pituitary also exerts an effect on spermatogenesis. Here it is believed, mainly from studies on rats, that the action is initially on the Leydig cells to promote androgen secretion, which in turn stimulates sperm formation. It has been found that androgen (testosterone) will support gametogenesis in the hypophysectomized male rat but it should be borne in mind that in normal individuals large doses of testosterone suppress spermatogenesis and, *via* its suppressive action of the secretion of pituitary gonadotrophin, causes testicular atrophy.

In man and many other mammals, but not in the sloth, whale or elephant, the testes are contained extraabdominally in the scrotum. In many of these the testes descend into the scrotum at puberty and remain there permanently; in others again the testes occupy a scrotal position only during the breeding season. It is now evident that the scrotum exerts a thermo-regulating function (Moore). This has been established in a variety of studies. In the developmental anomaly known as *cryptorchidism* the testis fails to descend into the scrotum and spermatogenesis does not occur in the undescended organ. This condition can be reproduced experimentally by returning the testis of the normal adult animal from the scrotum to the abdomen; degeneration of the seminiferous tubules will follow in a few days. Upon replacement of the testis in the scrotum there is a restoration of normal testicular appearance and function provided that the stay in the abdomen has not been too long. It is possible to produce this effect in the ram by enclosing the testis in a bag of heat-insulating material which raises the temperature of the testis by a few degrees. Such an observation ensures that the result of moving the testis to the abdomen was not an artifact due to operative procedures. Measurement of the temperature of the scrotum has shown that it is several degrees lower than that of the abdomen. It has also been found that exposure for 15 minutes or so to a temperature of 6° C. above the normal body temperature leads within some 10 days to degeneration of the sperm producing cells. The human testis may suffer in febrile illnesses, as a result of the high temperature, but as a rule the loss of function is only temporary. The requirement for a lower temperature than that prevailing in the rest of the body explains why testicular transplantation has seldom been associated with continuing spermatogenesis, unless a cool location (such as the anterior chamber of the eye) is chosen. Normally it appears that the descent of the testis is dependent upon the secretion of androgen, although in cases of cryptorchidism gonadotrophin is used to produce descent in order to avoid the depressive effects on the pituitary of androgen alone.

Ligation of the vas deferens has been stated by some (e.g., Steinach) to cause degeneration of the spermatogenic cells, and further, to increase the

[4] Spermatogenesis can also be advanced in seasonally breeding species by modifying the external environment, such as by altering the period of illumination during the day. This latter effect is mediated by the nervous system which brings about an increase in the secretion of pituitary hormones.

production of sex hormone. These claims have been conclusively disproved. Vasoligation has been advocated as a means of increasing the output of male hormone and so causing "rejuvenation," but it is based on error. It exerts no lasting effect upon either the sperm-producing cells or upon those of internal secretion. Ligation, or resection of a portion of the vas deferens, results in sterility by preventing the egress of the male germ cells but does not interfere with the sexual drive of the male.

The spermatogenic function of the testis is affected adversely by several conditions, such as exposure to X-rays or radioactivity, alcoholism, vitamin E and $B_1$ deficiency and (in some species) close confinement. Following irradiation of the testes there is a marked destruction of spermatogonia whereas the Sertoli and Leydig cells survive. This effect would seem to be due to the operation of the principle that the most actively dividing cells are those most adversely affected by ionizing radiations. The effect of vitamin B deficiency may be exerted through the pituitary, whereas lack of vitamin E would seem to act directly. Testicular function is depressed in cases of simple starvation.

### The Endocrine Function of the Testis

The effects of castration have long been known. Aristotle described the changes following castration in the bird more than 2000 years ago, and before that testicular tissue was used as a treatment for impotence in India. More recently John Hunter showed that the normal function of the prostate and seminal vesicles was maintained only in the presence of the testes, and Berthold, in 1849, demonstrated that the testes discharged some material into the blood stream essential for the growth of the cock's comb. Among the first to attempt the preparation of an active material was the noted physiologist Brown-Séquard (1889) who administered testicular extracts to himself and thought that he acquired an increase of vigor and a greater capacity for work after the treatment. This concept was later revived by Voronoff in France and Steinach in Germany who believed that senescence was related to testicular atrophy and consequent reduction or loss of male hormone. However this idea has been discredited and it is only necessary to point out that although in the female ovarian function ceases at the menopause (p. 1080) senile changes are not prominent at this time. Eunuchs did not show premature senility, and, in any case, the sexual functions in the male often continue well into senility.

The effects of castration have been discussed at the beginning of this chapter (p. 1074), and it will be recalled that in the male the accessory sexual organs are developed and maintained under the influence of androgen, as are certain characters, including the pattern of pubic and facial hair, and the pitch of the voice. In lower mammals other features can be studied, such as the presence of horns in the stag, the cape of long hair in the male baboon, and the male odor of the billy goat. These male features may be maintained in the castrated animal by the transplantation of testicular tissue, or androgen therapy.

When the testes are transplanted from the scrotum to a situation elsewhere in the body germinal activity ceases (p. 1102) but the endocrine function continues. A similar finding is made following destruction of the germinal elements with X-rays and it then becomes evident that germinal cells are not concerned with the production of androgen. This function is exercised by the Leydig cells. Apart from the evidence which denies this function to other testicular constituents it has been found that in rats with vitamin B deficiency there is a loss of androgenic activity and the interstitial cells are atrophic, but normal production of sperm continues. Injections of pitch dissolved in olive oil have been found to cause atrophy of the interstitial cells and involution of the accessory sexual organs although the tubular epithelium appeared unaffected. In man, tumors of the interstitial tissue of the testis produce excessive quantities of androgen and, in boys, cause a premature appearance of masculine characteristics.

An active androgen-containing extract of testis was obtained by Pézard in 1911 who produced comb growth in capons with a saline extract. McGee in 1927 obtained an active lipoid extract of bull's testes, but it was not until 1935 that the pure hormone, *testosterone*, was separated in crystalline form by Laqueur and his colleagues. Meanwhile more success had been achieved with extracts of human urine for between 1931 and 1934 two androgenic substances had been isolated. These were androsterone and dehydroandrosterone, and were found to differ from the hormone in testicular extracts in being less potent and more stable to alkali.

THE ANDROGENS In recent years the efforts of the biochemists in isolating steroids from organs such as the adrenal cortex, ovary and testis have resulted in the identification of a wide variety of androgens.

Of the steroids isolated from the testis, *testosterone* is the most important and is regarded as the true male hormone. It has been synthesized from cholesterol. When the testis is perfused, or incubated, with isotopically labelled acetate and gonadotrophic hormone, labelled testosterone appears, together with another androgen, $\Delta^4$-androsterone-3,17-dione. A further constituent of the testis is pregnenolone ($\Delta^5$-pregnen-3$\beta$-ol-20-one) which, although lacking androgenic activity, maintains testicular weight and spermatogenesis in the hypophysectomized rat.

Testosterone

Androsterone

Dehydroandrosterone

The urine provides a ready source of androgens. Here the first androgen isolated, *androsterone*, is also the principal androgen, and it is about one-tenth as potent as testosterone. It has been synthesized from cholesterol by Ruzicka and coworkers. Two isomers of androsterone exist and are found in urine. Epiandrosterone is about five times less active than androsterone, whereas the other isomer etiocholan-3$\alpha$-ol-17-one is almost inactive. It has been shown that the principal metabolites of testosterone in urine are androsterone and its isomers. The testicular androgen $\Delta^4$-androsterone-3,17-dione is also found in urine. A further androgen, dehydroepiandrosterone, with an activity of the order of that of epiandrosterone, also occurs in urine.

At least five androgens have been isolated from the adrenal gland. These are 17$\alpha$-hydroxyprogesterone, adrenosterone, $\Delta^4$-androstene-3,17-dione,

androstane-3$\beta$,11$\beta$-diol-17-one and 11$\beta$-hydroxy-$\Delta^4$-androstene-3,17-dione.

Most of the androgens found in the urine possess a ketone group attached to carbon-17, and are thus *17-ketosteroids*. On the other hand, certain urinary 17-ketosteroids which possess a ketone group at this site lack androgenic activity. Etiocholan-3$\alpha$-ol-17-one and dehydroepiandrosterone are examples of such compounds. This is in part due to the fact that the adrenal makes a major contribution to the output of 17-ketosteroids. Therefore measurement of these compounds by chemical methods (Zimmerman reaction) does not necessarily coincide with the amounts as measured by biological assay of androgenic activity. However a reasonable correlation exists between the results of the two methods.

Only very small amounts of androgens or 17-ketosteroids are found in the urine of children. At puberty the output increases and it reaches a maximum in men of about 25 years of age when the excretion is 12 to 17 mg. of 17-ketosteroids daily. In women the daily excretion is 7 to 12 mg. per day, much of which comes from the adrenal, and which does not exert any androgenic effect physiologically. Androgen has been extracted from ovarian tissue and the production of androgens by the ovaries has been demonstrated experimentally. Clinically, virilism (p. 1044) has been found in association with several kinds of ovarian tumors (arrhenoblastoma, "Leydig cell" tumor, "theca cell" tumor, "adrenal-like" tumor). These tumors thus seem to produce androgens, although it should be borne in mind that progesterone in large doses is androgenic and will maintain spermatogenesis and the accessory sexual organs in the castrate.

In general the actions of androgen may be summarized as follows.

1. They promote the growth of many tissues. Besides that of the accessory sex organs such as the seminal vesicles and prostate glands, there is a general increase in body mass with growth of muscle, kidneys and bone. This action is marked by an increased blood supply to the various organs, which obviously follows application of androgen in the cock's comb.

2. Perhaps as part of the growth-promoting action, androgens are remarkably anabolic and cause nitrogen retention. This response is of clinical value and compounds allied to testosterone are being studied in the hope of finding one with high anabolic activity but little androgenic potency.

3. They act directly upon the nervous system to shape the sexual behavior of the individual. This is clearly shown by the effects of castration

on masculine sexual behavior and the return to normal with androgen treatment, perhaps before effects on the sex accessories are observed. In the intact female androgens may result in a bisexual pattern of behavior. In women, moderate doses of androgen appear to heighten, but not alter, the sexual interests.

*The actions of androgens.* Androgens exert an effect upon the genital system from the earliest period of life. When frog larvae (or tadpoles) are treated with testosterone, genetic females are transformed into apparently normal males which will produce normal spermatozoa. In the mammalian fetus, such as that of the rat, the injection of androgens markedly stimulates the Wolffian (male) structures, both in the male and female, without promoting the disappearance of the Müllerian system. This effect can also be observed when large amounts of male sex hormone are given to the pregnant cat or mouse. Here also, alongside the development of the Wolffian system in the female, the Müllerian ducts persist.

The effects of androgen in the fowl have been long studied. In the castrated cock, or capon, androgens restore the size of the comb and wattles, and enlarge those of the female (figure 60.10). The ability to crow is regained and male sexual behavior becomes manifest. Continued administration of androgen to hens enables them to assume dominance over other members of the flock and so assume a higher rank in the "social scale" or peck-order.

Castration atrophy of the accessory male organs (seminal vesicles, prostate gland, Cowper's glands, scrotum and penis) is prevented by testosterone or other androgens (figure 60.11). The

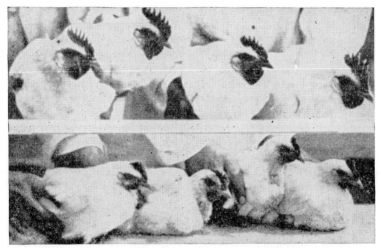

Fig. 60.10. Showing the effect of testis hormone (from urine) upon the comb growth of capons. The birds in the upper photograph received daily injections over a period of 15 days. Lower photograph, untreated controls. (After Funk, Harrow and Lejwa.)

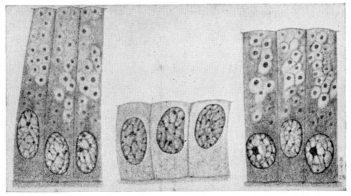

Fig. 60.11. Effect of castration and testis hormone on epithelium of seminal vesicles. (Moore, Hughes and Gallagher.) 1, cells from normal animal, showing secretion granules; 2, cells from 20-day castrate; 3, cells from 20-day castrate treated with male hormone.

epithelium of the seminal vesicles is restored to its normal condition and the level of fructose in the gland is raised. Involution of the prostate gland is prevented and there is stimulation of the secretion of the gland with elevation of the concentration of acid phosphatase.

The effect of androgens upon the testis seems to be largely dependent upon the amount given. With a moderate dose there is testicular atrophy together with arrest of spermatogenesis and atrophy of the Leydig cells. The pituitary is involved in this response, for when gonadotrophic hormone is given with the androgen there is no atrophy. High doses of androgen stimulate the seminiferous tubules and will partially prevent the results of hypophysectomy, but the Leydig cells still undergo degeneration, for they are solely under the control of the hypophysis. Androgens do not exhibit the seminiferous tubule maintenance to the same degree. The most potent in this regard is 17-methyl-$\Delta^5$-androstene-3$\beta$,17$\beta$-diol (methylandrostenediol), whereas testosterone is much less effective.

In the female small doses of testosterone modify the secretion of gonadotrophin by the pituitary in favor of FSH so that mainly follicular activity is observed in the ovaries. When testicular tissue is implanted into an intact prepubertal female rat, the animal displays constant estrus on reaching sexual maturity (Pfeiffer). The effect of male hormone would seem to be exerted at an hypothalamic level since transplantation of the pituitary of a male rat under the median eminence of an hypophysectomized female permits the restoration of normal estrous cycles. In large doses androgens inhibit the gonadotrophic function of the hypophysis and so produce ovarian atrophy. Testosterone exhibits progesteronelike effects in the female, as seen by the changes induced in the endometrium of the uterus. However, deciduomas cannot be produced or pregnancy maintained.

### Regulation of Testicular Function

There is much evidence to show that the testis and pituitary interact with one another. Besides the striking effect of hypophysectomy upon the testis (p. 961) it is well known that removal of the testes results in enlargement of the hypophysis and the appearance of characteristic signet ring cells or *castration cells*. This change is prevented by the administration of androgen. Further, assay of the gonadotrophic hormone in the urine after castration shows that the excretion of gonadotrophic hormone is increased, but can be reduced

by the administration of sex hormones. This phenomenon is observed clinically in cases of primary testicular deficiency in which the gonad is defective. Here too the output of pituitary hormone can be limited by administration of testosterone.

However, a variety of observations indicate that the normal regulation of testicular function is not a simple matter of a depressive action of testosterone on the pituitary. For example, in cases of primary testicular failure more testosterone is required to inhibit the secretion of gonadotrophin than to restore the secondary sex characters. Mottram and Cramer in 1923 found that although radium treatment caused atrophy of the the tubular epithelium of the rat testis without apparently harming the interstitial cells, castration cells nevertheless appeared in the hypophysis. This observation indicated that the tubular epithelium might produce a hormone which inhibited the pituitary, and search for it began. Although an aqueous extract which caused disappearance of castration cells in the hypophysis without stimulating the accessory sex organs was prepared and was called "inhibin," this work has not been confirmed. Albright and his colleagues direct attention to a close analogy between testis-pituitary and ovary-pituitary function. In their view an "X-hormone" produced by the Sertoli cells of the testis takes the place of the estrogen secreted by the analogous granulosa cells of the ovary. The identity of the postulated "X-hormone" is not established although it is likely that the Sertoli cells produce estrogen (p. 1044). Estrogen will inhibit the secretion of gonadotrophin in the male in smaller dosage than testosterone. Nelson and his coworkers find little to favor in the inhibitory concept. Although they agree that the testis produces estrogen (but locate its origin in the Leydig cells) they put forward the hypothesis that the germinal cells inactivate pituitary gonadotrophin during spermatogenesis and so keep down the level of hormone in the blood. They suggest that when spermatogenesis stops, as in radiation damage, cryptorchidism, or castration, the gonadotrophins are not removed from the blood, accumulate and are then excreted in the urine in abnormal quantity. Evidence in favor of each theory has been brought forward by its supporters, and at the present time both find adherents.

ASSAY OF ANDROGENS. Androgen may be assayed biologically, using the growth of the comb of the fowl or changes in the accessory sex organs of mammals, or it may be assayed chemically by measurement of the 17-ketosteroids. In the assays utilizing the fowl, the capon or chick is used and the test material is given intramuscularly or applied directly to the comb. Measurement of the blood or urinary neutral 17-ketosteroids (p. 1040) is becoming more frequently used an an index of androgenic activity but it should be borne in mind that the androgenic potency of a given urine extract will not necessarily parallel 17-ketosteroid concentration.

HYPOGONADISM AND HYPERGONADISM IN THE MALE. Tumors of the testis in young boys may result in the precocious development of the secondary sex characters—growth of hair upon the pubis, in the axillae and over the face, deepening of the voice and enlargment of the penis. These effects are evidently due to hypersecretion of the male hormone, for they tend to subside after excision of the tumor. Hypergenitalism with closely similar features occurs as a result of hyperfunctioning of the adrenal cortex (p. 1043). Failure of development of the accessory male sex organs and of the secondary sexual characters, a condition referred to as *hypogonadism* or *eunuchoidism*, is in most cases due primarily to a pituitary disorder. This can be tested by measurement of the FSH excreted in the urine. In other instances of eunuchoidism the testes are the primary site of disease, e.g., destructive new growths, mumps, typhoid fever, syphilis, etc. Here, in the postpuberal individual the output of FSH in the urine will be higher than normal. Testicular atrophy occasionally results from prolonged and severe inanition or vitamin B$_1$ deficiency. Hypofunctioning of the testes may commence at any time during postpuberal life as a result of pituitary disease or of any of the conditions just mentioned. In this *deferred type of eunuchoidism* regressive changes, although usually of mild degree in the accessory organs of sex and in the secondary sex characters may result.

### The Prostate Gland

The prostate which surrounds the first inch or so of the urethra is composed of branched tubuloalveolar glands, grouped into about 20 lobules. Its stroma is fibroelastic in nature and contains many bundles of smooth muscle. The alveoli of the glands drain into some 20 ducts which discharge into the urethra. The gland is traversed by the ejaculatory ducts. Within the lumina of some of the alveoli, small concretions known as *corpora amylacea* are found (especially in older men). They are composed of a calcium-phosphorus compound similar in chemical structure to apatite (p. 1062).

Glands lying in relation to the wall of the up-

per part of the urethra are present in the female. They are analogous to the male organ and are referred to as the *female prostate*.

The prostate does not appear to have any endocrine function. It secretes small amounts of fluid continuously into the urethra (from 0.5 to 2 cc. per hour in man), and much larger amounts during coitus. This occurs before the seminal vesicles discharge their secretion. Both secretions are added to the sperm; of the two, the secretion of the seminal vesicles appears to be of the greater importance for the viability of the spermatozoa, or at any rate for fertilization.

The secretion of prostatic fluid is increased by stimulation of parasympathetic (sacral outflow) and sympathetic nerves (hypogastric).

*Prostatic hypertrophy.* The cause of prostatic hypertrophy is still a matter for speculation. The theory has been advanced that the production of a male hormone in excess is a factor. It is unquestionable that testosterone stimulates prostatic growth as castration causes prostatic involution. It is improbable, however, that hyperactivity of the testicular interstitial cells is a cause of prostatic enlargement in man; secretion of male hormone tends to decrease rather than to increase with advancing years. It has been suggested that the threshold of the prostatic tissue for the action of testosterone is lowered as age advances to an extent which more than compensates for the diminished production of the male hormone.

It has been mentioned that estrogen is excreted in the urine of the male and can be isolated from testicular tissue; it has also been shown by Zuckerman and Parkes that injections of estrogen into monkeys cause prostatic hypertrophy by fibromuscular over-growth of the whole prostate together with epithelial stratification and distension of the uterus masculinus. Such effects can be counteracted by injections of male hormones. These facts, taken in conjunction with the observation that the concentration of the male hormone in the urine of elderly men may be reduced whereas the excretion of estrogen remains unchanged, have led some (de Jongh, Laqueur) to the conclusion that prostatic hypertrophy in man is based upon an imbalance between androgen and estrogen—a *diminished* production of the former, and , in consequence, a relative *excess* of the latter. In support of this hypothesis de Jongh states that injections of the male hormone in cases of prostatic enlargement prevents further hypertrophy and may actually cause shrinkage of the organ. Moreover, R. A. Moore and his associates observed that prostatic tissue of the rabbit transplanted into the anterior chamber of the eye showed a greater growth response to estrogen than to male hormone administration. However, observations opposed to this theory can be cited, e.g., the absence of excessive amounts of estrogen in the blood or urine of subjects of prostatic hypertrophy, and the fact that injections of estrogen do not, apparently, aggravate the condition. Moreover, the effect of estrogen is mainly on the stroma, whereas the male hormone stimulates the epithelial element which is chiefly affected in hypertrophy of the prostate. The whole question of the causative factors in prostatic hypertrophy is rife with speculation and beset with contradictory observations and opinions. Established facts are few and difficult to obtain.

The epithelial cells of a prostatic adenocarcinoma are dependent for their growth and activity upon the male hormone, as is the normal epithelium of the prostate. It is upon this basis that castration has been employed in the treatment of prostatic cancer, the malignant growth, in many cases, undergoing regression after operation. Since androgen activity is antagonized or neutralized by estrogens, inhibition of the cancerous growth can also be induced by the administration of estrogens such as stilbestrol.

*The hormonal treatment of male sex disorders.* Although the testis hormone, in accordance with the principles of hormone action in general does not stimulate the interstitial cells of the testes it provides the perfect substitution therapy in cases of underdevelopment or regression of the accessory male sex organs. Methyltestosterone, testosterone cyclopentylpropionate, or testosterone pellets may all be used.

The gonadotrophic principle derived from pregnancy urine (p. 1092) has been employed to stimulate spermatogenesis in an undeveloped testis or to restore the normal spermatogenic function which had been suppressed as a result of disease. Sterility in man is said to have been cured by this means; spermatozoa which before treatment were few and nonmotile have, according to report, been increased in number and rendered actively motile after a series of injections of the anterior-pituitary-like hormone. Notable success has followed the use of the gonadotrophic hormone of pregnancy urine in cryptorchidism, descent of the testes being induced. It has also been employed in various types of hypogonadism. The gonado-

trophic principle of the pituitary itself would be expected to give the best results but so far a reliable commercial preparation of this hormone has not been available.

### Erection and Ejaculation

In order to carry to completion the sexual function of the male, semen must be deposited in the female genital tract. For this purpose the flaccid penis is converted into a rigid intromittent organ and at the orgasm expulsion of semen occurs through it. Thus two phases can be distinguished: erection and ejaculation. Both provide good examples of sympathetic-parasympathetic interaction although, since the nerve plexuses involved contain both sympathetic and parasympathetic fibers, it is difficult to study each system in isolation.

*Erection* is brought about by a vascular engorgement of the penis, produced by dilation of the arteries which supply the spongelike erectile tissue in the corpora cavernosa penis and the corpus cavernosum urethrae. This reaction was observed nearly a hundred years ago by Eckhard (1863) who found that electrical stimulation of the visceral rami of the sacral nerves in the dog induced penile erection *via* the vasodilator action. He called these fibers the "nervi erigentes" and the name has been retained. However, the integrity of the nervi erigentes is not essential for erection, for in the dog and cat destruction of the origin of the nervi erigentes in the spinal cord does not prevent erection following suitable stimuli such as manipulation of the glans or psychic stimulation. In the latter case erection does not occur when the lumbar part of the spinal cord is destroyed. It would seem that, in addition to the action of the parasympathetic nervi erigentes, sympathetic fibers arising in the lumbar cord are involved in the erectile process, although sympathetic stimulation, by its vasoconstrictor effect, may interfere with erection. Eckhard also found that mechanical stimulation of the glans would bring about erection only if the pudendal nerve was intact. Thus the pudendal nerve is afferent to glans stimulation. Efferent fibers from the hypogastric plexus also pass in the pudendal nerve to exert a vasoconstrictor action on the penis.

*Ejaculation* of semen is a frequent accompaniment of erection although the *emission* of semen can occur through a flaccid penis. In man stimulation of the pelvic sympathetic nerves produces discharge of semen from the ejaculating ducts due to seminal vesicle and prostatic contraction.

Following lumbar sympathectomy semen is no longer discharged from the urethra. Ejaculation still occurs but the semen may enter the bladder instead of the urethra because of nonclosure of the internal vesical sphincter. During physiological ejaculation the smooth muscle of the genital system is probably constricted by both parasympathetic and sympathetic impulses propagated under the control of the spinal cord. Contraction of the voluntary muscles, such as the bulbo-cavernosus and ischio-cavernosus muscles also occurs at this time.

### Sexual Behavior

The gonadal hormones, in addition to their actions upon the reproductive system, act upon the nervous system to elicit characteristic patterns of behavior—sexual behavior. It may perhaps be taken for granted that the sexual behavior is invariably associated with fully functional gonads. Such may be deduced from the fact that the term "estrous cycle" has a behavioral basis. However, in the sheep one or more estrous cycles—*silent heats*—may pass at the commencement of the breeding season before the occurrence of overt estrous behavior. In the monkey, ovulation may not occur during the summer, although the menstrual cycles continue. Sexual activity does not appear to be diminished.

There is no question that the removal of the gonads may depress sexual activity, although to an extent which varies between the sexes and from one species to another. In the female rat sexual activity is abolished whereas in the female rabbit coitus may occasionally take place. In the ovariectomized chimpanzee there is little sign of desire for intercourse but it is said that ovariectomized women may show as much erotic behavior after the operation as before. With regard to the male primate, castration often fails to diminish the capacity to mate (chimpanzee) or to abolish the orgasm (man).

Full sexual activity in the ovariectomized or castrated individual may be restored by treatment with the appropriate sex hormones. Further, it is possible to evoke components of the pattern of sexual behavior of the opposite sex by administration of androgen, e.g., to a spayed female, and *vice versa*. Basically, overt sexual behavior does not appear to depend upon a learned response but is due to a fundamental action of the sex hormones upon the nervous system. (Young has shown that in guinea pigs the performance of the male is improved by experi-

ence; the sexual activity of males reared in isolation is inferior to that of animals reared in a group, and may be permanently impaired.)

The gonadal hormones might produce their behavioral actions either by an effect on the peripheral receptors, or by a direct action on some integrating center in the central nervous system. In the former case the hormone could act by sensitizing the genitalia to excitation, but this possibility has been eliminated by the finding that removal or denervation of the genitalia does not inhibit sexual behavior or reduce sexual aggression.

The second possibility, that of a direct action of the gonadal hormones upon the central nervous system, has received detailed examination. It is now clear that "normal" estrous behavior can continue in the cat, rabbit, guinea pig and rat following removal of the cerebral cortex, although none appears in the spinal animal. It may therefore be presumed that some subcortical but supraspinal neural structure is involved in the behavioral mechanism. Dempsey and Rioch in 1939 studied the guinea pig and found that a transection of the brain which passed through the rostral end of the mammillary bodies did not abolish estrous reflexes, but that transection posterior to the mammillary bodies did cause lose of these reflexes. This observation implies that some area in the region of the hypothalamus may be concerned in the production of sexual behavior in the guinea pig, and since that time evidence has accrued which indicates that the hypothalamus itself is of importance. Among the salient observations we may note that (a) sexual behavior may be abolished by hypothalamic lesions, (b) reproducible electrical activity has been recorded in the hypothalamus following artificial stimulation of the vagina of the cat, and (c) the application of estrogen to the posterior hypothalamus of the spayed cat has been found to induce full and typical sexual behavior at a time when no effects of the estrogen upon the reproductive organs could be found. The insertion of similar amounts of estrogen into the cerebellum, preoptic region, caudate nucleus, thalamus or amygdaloid nucleus did not evoke sexual behavior in similar circumstances.

In summary, it appears that some integrating mechanism exists in the upper midbrain or hypothalamus which is sensitive to the blood concentration of gonadal hormones. If these hormones are present in amounts above a certain threshold level, then specific sensory stimuli (e.g., visual, auditory, olfactory), normally derived from a possible mate, act through this mechanism to excite reflexly the pattern of sexual behavior typical of the species. In the human, it seems that this basic neural mechanism has become largely dominated by cortical factors, so that learning and conditioning play an increasingly important role. The continuance of active sexual behavior after castration in the adult human may well be dependent on this latter fact.

### The Thymus

*Structure.* The thymus arises from the third branchial cleft (and sometimes the fourth) on either side, each anlage going to form one of the lobes of the thymus. Each thymic lobe is composed of a number of lobules in which an outer portion or *cortex* and a central portion or *medulla* may be distinguished. The *cortex* resembles lymphoid tissue, being constituted of masses of small round cells—*thymocytes*—identical in appearance with small lymphocytes. The epithelial element of the embryonic structure is almost entirely replaced during development by the ingrowth of these lymphoid cells from the surrounding mesenchyme. A small number of elongated reticular cells are seen scattered among the lymphoid elements. The *medulla* also contains lymphocytes but in fewer numbers; the reticular cells are thus shown up more prominently and are seen to form a definite reticular stroma. Scattered throughout the medulla are round or oval elements from 30 to 100 microns in diameter known as *Hassall's corpuscles*. These bodies, which are the remnants of the original epithelial elements, are composed of cells arranged concentrically; they stain with acid dyes and therefore stand out conspicuously against the surrounding basophilic substance.

*Possible functions.* The thymus of the infant is of relatively large size but during later childhood its weight in relation to body weight gradually decreases; little change in its absolute weight (25 to 40 grams) occurs; after the age of puberty a definite involutionary process commences. Although the involutionary changes, which consist of a reduction in the number of lymphocytes and reticular cells and their replacement by fat, are most marked during adolescence, they continue slowly throughout the rest of life. The corpuscles of Hassall disappear more slowly than the other elements.

It is admitted by most observers that the thymus serves a lymphopoietic function. Beyond this, little is definitely known concerning its physiological role. It is enlarged in exophthalmic goiter, myasthenia gravis, adrenal insufficiency and in certain leukemic states. Thymic enlargement has also been considered to be a feature of the so-called *status thymicolymphaticus*, a condition believed to consist of hypoplasia of the vascular system, a general increase in lymphoid tissue throughout the body, and a tendency to fatal syncope. Infants and young children who have died suddenly as a result of some trifling shock or during anesthesia have been thought to be subjects of this disease; it has been thought that enlargment of the thymus was in some way responsible. An investigation carried out in 1931, by Turnbull and Young, for the Medical Research Committee of Great Britain failed to substantiate this belief. In the post-mortem examination of a number of children's bodies no relationship was found between the size of the thymus and vascular hypoplasia to the amount of lymphoid tissue in other parts of the body. In subjects dying suddenly as a result of shock or during anesthesia the thymus was not larger than in subjects dying from other causes. These investigators conclude that there is "no evidence that so-called status thymicolymphaticus has any existence as a pathological entity." The possibility has been suggested that such cases of sudden death in infants are due to failure in function of the adrenal cortex (p. 1043).

The great body of experimental work which has been carried out in the past in efforts to elucidate the functions of the thymus has yielded little evidence which would enable it to be classed definitely among the glands of internal secretion. There is certainly no feature of its minute structure which suggests a glandular function. Numerous investigators, nevertheless, have claimed that their findings pointed to the thymus as playing an endocrine role. The problem has been studied both by the use of extracts of thymic tissue and by observing the effects of extirpation of the organ. Among the functions claimed for the thymus as a result of these two lines of investigation are the regulation of calcium metabolism and the control of skeletal growth. Defective mineralization of the bones has been described following thymectomy; others believe that this operation results in dwarfing. Gudernatsch found that feeding thymus tissue to tadpoles stimulated their growth but delayed metamorphosis. Thymectomy in pullets and pigeons is said to result in their laying eggs with uncalcified shells.

Much of the earlier work on the thymus is very difficult to appraise, owing to the indecisive nature of the data or to the conflict between the results obtained by different workers in the field.

Andersen has made the intersting observation that rats exercised to the point of exhaustion show atrophy of the thymus and hypertrophy of the adrenal cortex. Selye has described similar changes following a variety of injurious agencies as part of what he has termed the "alarm reaction."

### The Pineal Body or Epiphysis

*Origin and structure.* This is a small glandlike structure (about 10 mm. long in man) somewhat resembling a pine cone (pinea) in shape, situated just beneath the splenium of the corpus callosum and resting in the groove between the superior colliculi. The pineal arises as a diverticulum of the roof of the third ventricle. The cavity of the original pouch eventually disappears, the fully developed gland being composed of a solid mass of cells. The histological features of the pineal are very diverse, the picture varying from species to species and with age. In general however, it may be said to have a pseudoalveolar structure, the cells being arranged in masses or lobules surrounded by a highly vascular connective tissue.

Involutionary changes are said to commence in the human pineal body about the seventh year. In children past the age of seven laminated bodies composed of phosphates and carbonates of calcium and magnesium—the so-called "brain sand"—make their appearance.

The *functions* of the pineal body are quite unknown. Its structure has suggested an endocrine function but there is really little definite evidence from which such a conclusion may be drawn. It may be merely vestigial.

## REFERENCES

ABRAMOWITZ, A. A. AND ASSOCIATES. Endocrinology, 1944, 34, 103.

AHRÉN, K. AND JACOBSOHN, D. Acta Physiol. scand., 1956, 51, 190.

ALBRIGHT, F. AND ASSOCIATES. J. Clin. Endocrinol., 1950, 10, 121.

ALLAN, H. AND WILES, P. J. Physiol., 1932, 75, 23.

ALLEN, E. AND DOISY, E. A. J. A. M. A., 1923, 81, 819; Am. J. Physiol., 1924, 69, 577.

ALLEN, E., PRATT, J. P. AND DOISY, E. A. J. A. M. A., 1925, 85, 399.

ALLEN, W. M. Am. J. Physiol., 1930, 92, 174, 612; J. Biol. Chem., 1932, 98, 591; Am. J. Physiol., 1932, 100, 650.

ANCEL, P. AND BOUIN, P. J. physiol. et path. gen. 1910, 12, 1.

ANDERSEN, D H., J. Physiol., 1935, 85, 162.

ANDERSEN, D. H. AND WOLF, A. J. Physiol., 1934, 81, 49.

ASCHHEIM, S. J. A. M. A., 1935, 104, 1324; Am. J. Obst. & Gynec., 1930, 19, 335.

ASCHHEIM, S. AND ZONDEK, B. Geburtsh. Gynäk., 1926, 90, 372, 387 (quoted by P. Smith.) Klin. Woch., 1927, 6, 248, 1322; 1928, 7, 1404, 1453.

BARR, M. L. AND BERTRAM, E. G. Nature, 1949, 163, 676; J. Anat., 1951, 85, 171.

BELLERBY, C. W. J. Physiol., 1929, 67, xxxii.

BLOCH, K., J. Biol. Chem., 1945, 157, 661.

BOUIN, P. AND ANCEL, P. Compt. rend. Soc. biol., 1903, 55, 1882.

BRADBURY, J. T. Endocrinology, 1941, 29, 393.

BROWN, J. B. Lancet, 1955, 1, 320.

BROWN-SÉQUARD, C. E. Lancet, 1889, 2, 105.

BROWNE, J. S. L., HENRY, J. S. AND VENNING, E. H. J. Clin. Invest., 1937, 16, 678.

BROOKS, C. McC. Am. J. Physiol., 1937, 120, 544; 1938, 121, 157.

BURR, H. S., HILL, R. T. AND ALLEN, E. Proc. Soc. Exper. Biol. & Med., 1935, 33, 109.

BUTENANDT, A. Deutsche med. Wchnschr., 1929, 55, 2171; Naturwissenschaften, 1929, 17, 879; 1933, 21, 49; 1935, 23, 44.

CAMPBELL, A. D., Lancet, 1932, 2, 561. Ann. Int. Med., 1933, 7, 330.

CANNON, W. B. AND BRIGHT, E. M. Am. J. Physiol., 1931, 97, 319.

CATHCART, E. P. AND ASSOCIATES. Proc. Roy. Soc. Edin., 1948, 61, 699.

CHANG, M. C. AND PINCUS, G. Science, 1953, 117, 274.

COHEN, S. L. AND MARRIAN, G. F. Biochem. J., 1936, 29, 1577; 30, 57.

COHEN, S. L., MARRIAN, G. F. AND ODELL., A. D. Biochem. J., 1936, 30, 2250.

COLE, H. H. AND HART, G. H. Am. J. Physiol., 1930, 93, 57.

COLLIP, J. B. Canad. M. A. J., 1930, 22, 761. Proc. Calif. Acad. Med., 1930, 1, 38. Trans. Roy. Soc. Can., 1932, 26, Sec. V. 1. Ann. Int. Med., 1934, 8, 10; 1935, 9, 150.

COLLIP, J. B., SELYE, H., THOMSON, D. L. AND ASSOCIATES. Endocrin., 1931, 15, 315; J. A. M. A., 1933, 101, 1553; Proc. Soc. Exper. Biol. & Med., 1933, 30, 588, 647, 665, 780, 913; 31, 82; 1934, 32, 544; 1935, 32, 851; Endocrinology, 1934, 18, 237.

COOK, J. W. AND DODDS, E. C. Nature, 1933, 131, 205.

CORI, C. F. J. Exper. Med., 1927, 45, 983.

CORNER, G. W. Carnegie Inst., Washington. Pub. No. 332, 1923, 15, 73; Am. J. Physiol., 1930, 95, 43.

CORNER, G. W. AND ALLEN, W. M. Am. J. Physiol., 1929, 88, 326, 340.

COWIE, A. T. J. Endocrinol., 1949, 6, 145.

COWIE, A. T. J. Endocrinol., 1957, 16, 135.

CUSHING, H. Pituitary body and hypothalamus, p. 29. Charles C Thomas, Springfield, Ill., 1932.

DANTCHAKOFF, V. Bull. biol. France et Belg., 1937, 71, 269.

DANDY, W. E. J. Exper. Med., 1915, 22, 237.

DE JONGH, S. E. Arch. internat. pharmacodyn., 1935, 50, 348.

DEMPSEY, E. W. AND RIOCH, D. M. J. Neurophysiol., 1939, 2, 9.

DODDS, E. C. AND ASSOCIATES. Nature, 1938, 144, 247.

DOISY, E. A., VELER, C. D. AND THAYER, S. Am. J. Physiol., 1929, 90, 329; J. Biol. Chem., 1930, 86, 499; J. Biol. Chem., 1939, 130, 431.

ECKHARD, C. 1863, cited by Marshall, F. H. A., 1922.

ELY, F. AND PETERSEN, W. E. J. Dairy Sc., 1941, 24, 211.

EVANS, H. M. AND ASSOCIATES. Proc. Nat. Acad. Sc., 1922, 8, 38. Am. J. Physiol., 1931, 98, 511; 1932, 100, 141. Endocrin., 1934, 18, 601, 607. J. Exper. Med., 1933, 57, 897; 58, 545.

FEE, A. R. AND PARKES, A. S. J. Physiol., 1929, 67, 383; 1930, 70, 385.

FEVOLD, H. L. AND HISAW, F. L. Am. J. Physiol., 1934, 109, 655.

Folley, S. J., Brit. M. Bull., 1947, 5, 1100, 1102.

Folley, S. J. and Young, F. G. Lancet, 1940, 1, 380.

Fraenkel, L. Arch. Gynäk., 1903, 68, 438 (quoted by Asdell).

Friedman, M. H., Am. J. Physiol., 1929, 90, 617.

Funk, C., Harrow, B. and Lejwa, A. Am. J. Physiol., 1930, 92, 440.

Gallagher, T. F. and associates. J. Clin. Invest., 1937, 16, 695, 705.

Gallagher, T. F. and Koch, F. C. J. Biol. Chem., 1929, 84, 495.

Graham, W. R. J. Nutrition, 1934, 7, 407; Biochem. J., 1934, 28, 1368.

Graham, W. R. and associates. Proc. Roy. Soc. London, ser. B., 1936, 120, 330.

Greene, R. R. Endocrinology, 1941, 29, 1026.

Harris, G. W., Michael, R. P. and Scott, P. P. Ciba Foundation Symposium on the Neurological Basis of Behaviour. J. and A. Churchill, Ltd., London, 1958, 236.

Haterius, H. O. Proc. Soc. Exper. Biol. & Med., 1935, 33, 101.

Heape, W. Phil. Trans. Roy. Soc., 1897, B 188, 135. Quart. J. Microscop. Sc., 1900, 44, 1.

Hill, R. T. Endocrinology, 1937, 21, 633.

Hisaw, F. L. Proc. Soc. Exper. Biol. & Med., 1926, 23, 661.

Hisaw, F. L. and associates. Endocrinology, 1944, 34, 122.

Hitschmann, F. and Adler, L., Montasschr. Geburtsh. u. Gynäkol., 1908, 27, 1 (quoted by Dodds and Dickens).

Hooker, C. W. and Forbes, T. R. Endocrinology, 1947, 41, 158.

Horrax, G. Arch. Int. Med., 1916, 17, 607, 627.

Huggins, C. and Scott, W. W. Ann. Surg., 1945, 122, 1031.

Ivy and colleagues. See Greene, R. R., Burrill, M. W. and Ivy, A. C. Proc. Soc. Exper. Biol. & Med., 1939, 41, 169.

Jost, A. Gynécol. et obstet., 1950, 49, 44.

Juhn, M., D'Amour, F. and Womack, E. B. Am. J. Physiol., 1930, 95, 641.

Kaufmann, C. J. Obst. & Gynaec. Brit. Emp., 1935, 42, 409.

Keller and Tandler. Wien. tieräztl. Wchnschr., 1916, 3, 513. (Quoted by Lipschutz).

Klopper, A., Michie, E. A. and Brown, J. B. J. Endocrinol., 1955, 12, 209.

Knaus, H. Arch. exper. Path. u. Pharmakol., 1930, 151, 371; Klin. Wchnschr., 1930, 9, 939; J. Physiol., 1926, 61, 383.

Koch, F. C. J. A. M. A., 1931, 96, 937.

Kurzrok, R., Bates, R. W., Riddle, O. and Miller, E. G. J., Jr. Endocrinology, 1934, 18, 17.

Lacassagne, A. Comp. rend. Acad. sci., 1932, 195, 630. Compt. rend. Soc. biol., 1934, 115, 937.

Laqueur, E. Schweiz. med. Wchnschr., 1934, 64, 1116.

League of Nations. Report of the permanent commission on biological standardization. Quart. Bull., Health Organization, Spec. No. January, 1935.

Lillie, F. R. J. Exper. Zool., 1917, 23, 371.

Lillie, F. R. and Bascom, K. F. Science, 1922, 55, 624.

Loeb, L. J. A. M. A., 1908, 50, 1897. Proc. Soc. Exper. Biol. & Med., 1908, 5, 102.

Loeb, L. and Genther, I. T. Proc. Soc. Exper. Biol. & Med., 1928, 25, 809.

Long, J. A. and Evans, H. M. Memoirs Univ. Calif., University of California Press, 1922.

Lyons, W. R. Proc. Soc. Exper. Biol. & Med., 1942, 51, 308.

MacCorquodale, D. W., Thayer, A. S. and Doisy, E. A. J. Biol. Chem., 1936, 115, 435.

Malpress, F. H. Unpublished observation cited by H. D. Kay, Brit. M. Bull., 1947, 5, 1099.

Marker, R. E., Kamm, O. et al. J. Am. Chem. Soc., 1936, 58, 1503.

Markee, J. E. Anat. Rec., 1933, 55, 66.

Martin, G. J. and Beiler, J. M. J. Biol. Chem., 1947, 174, 31; Science, 1952, 115, 402.

Marrian, G. F. Biochem. J., 1929, 23, 1090; 1930, 24, 435.

Marshall, F. H. A. Quart. J. Exper. Physiol., 1927, 17, 205.

Marshall, F. H. A. and Verney, E. B. J. Physiol, 1936, 86, 327.

Martins, T. and Rocha, A. Endocrin., 1931, 15, 421.

McCullagh, D. R. and associates. Science, 1932, N.S. 76, 19. Tr. A. Genito-Urin. Surgeons, 1934, 27, 15.

McGee, L. C. Ph.D. thesis, Univ. Chicago, 1927.

McGee, L. C., Juhn, M. and Domm, L. V. Am. J. Physiol., 1928, 87, 406.

Meites, J. and Sgouris, J. T. Endocrinology, 1953, 53, 17; 1954, 55, 530.

Meites, J. and Turner, C. W. Endocrinol., 30, 711, 719, 726; 31, 340. Res. Bull. Missouri Agric. Sta., No. 415, 1948.

Mixner, J. P. and Turner, C. W. Univ. Miss. Coll. Agric. Res. Bull. No. 378, 1943.

Moore, C. R. J. A. M. A., 1935, 104, 1405.

Moore, C. R. and Gallagher, T. F. Am. J. Anat., 1930, 45, 39.

Moore, C. R. and McGee, L. C. Am. J. Physiol., 1928, 87, 436.

Moore, C. R., Price, D. and Gallagher, T. F. Am. J. Anat., 1930, 45, 71.

Moore, K. L., Graham, M. A. and Barr, M. L. Surg. Gynec. & Obst., 1953, 96, 641.

Moore, R. A. and Melchionna, R. H. Am. J. Cancer, 1937, 30, 731.

Moore, R. A. and Smith, A. J. Exper. Med., 1937, 66, 291.

Mortimer, H., Wright, R. P. and Collip, J. B. Canad. M. A. J., 1936, 25, 503, 615.

Mottram, J. C. and Cramer, W. Quart. J. Exper. Physiol., 1923, 13, 209.

Nelson, W. O. and Gallagher, T. F. Anat. Rec., 1936, 64, 129.

Nelson, W. O. Cold Spring Harbor Symposia Quant. Biol., 1937, 5, 123; Physiol. Rev., 1936, 16, 488.

Newell, Q. V., Allen, E., Pratt, J. P. and Bland, L. J. Carnegie Inst., Washington, 1930, 22, 45.

ODELL, A. D. AND MARRIAN, G. F. Biochem. J., 1936, **30**, 1533.

PARKES, A. S. Proc. Roy. Soc. London, ser. B, 1926, **100**, 151; 1927, **101**, 421. Lancet, 1936, **2**, 674; Lancet, 1953, **2**, 1285.

PARKES, A. S. AND BELLERBY, C. W. J. Physiol., 1926, **61**, 562; 1927, **64**, 233.

PETERSEN, W. E. Rec. Prog. Horm. Res., 1948, vol., **2**, Acad. Press, New York.

PETERSEN, E., AND LUDWICK, T. M. Fed. Proc. 1942, **1**, 66.

PÉZARD, A. Compt. rend. Acad. Sc., 1911, **153**, 1037; Bull. biol. Franc. et Belge, 1918, **52**, 1.

RIDDLE, O., BATES, R. W. AND DYKSHORN, S. W. Proc. Soc. Exper. Biol. & Med., 1932, **29**, 1211. Anat. Rec., 1932, **54**, 25. Am. J. Physiol., 1933, **105**, 191.

ROWNTREE, L. G., CLARK, J. H. AND HANSON, A. M. Am. J. Physiol., 1934, **109**, 90 (Proc.). Science 1934, N.S. **80**, 274. J. Am. Med. Assoc., 1934, **103**, 1425.

ROWNTREE, L. G., CLARK, J. H., STEINBERG, A., EINHORN, N. H. AND HANSON, A. M. Am. J. Physiol., 1936, **116**, 132 (Proc.).

RUZICKA, L. AND ASSOCIATES. Schweiz. med. Wchnschr., 1934, **64**, 1118; Helvet. chim. acta., 1935, **17**, 1389 (quoted by Moore); Naturwissenschaften, 1935, **23**, 44.

SELYE, H. Am. J. Physiol., 1934, **107**, 535.

SELYE, H. AND McKEOWN, T. Proc. Soc. Exper. Biol. & Med., 1934, **31**, 683; Anat. Rec., 1934, **60**, 323; Brit. J. Path., 1936, **17**, 234.

SHAW, W. J. J. Obstet. & Gynaec. Brit. Emp., 1929, **36**, 1; Brit. M. J., 1933, **1**, 907.

SIEVE, B. F. Science, 1952, **116**, 373.

SMITH, P. E. Am. J. Anat., 1930, **45**, 205.

SMITH, P. E. AND ENGLE, E. T. Am. J. Anat., 1927, **40**, 159.

SNYDER, F. F. Bull. Johns Hopkins Hosp., 1934, **54**, 1.

STOCKARD, C. R. AND PAPANICOLAOU, G. N. Am. J. Anat., 1917, **22**, 225.

STONE, C. P. J. Comp. Psychol., 1927, **7**, 369.

STRICKER, P. AND GRUETER, F. Compt. rend. Soc. biol., 1928, **99**, 1978; Klin. Wchnschr., 1929, **8**, 2322.

TEEL, H. M. Am. J. Physiol., 1926, **79**, 184.

TURNBULL, H. M. AND YOUNG, W. J. Path. Bact., 1931, **34**, 212.

TURNER, C. W. 9th Ann. Rep. Internat. Cancer Res. Found., 1941.

TURNER, H. H. Endocrinology, 1938, **23**, 566.

VENNING, E. H. J. Biol. Chem., 1937, **119**, 473.

VENNING, E. H. Brit. M. Bull., 1955, **11**, 140.

VENNING, E. H. AND BROWNE, J. S. L. Proc. Soc. Exper. Biol. & Med., 1936, **34**, 792.

WALKER, A. T. Am. J. Physiol., 1925, **74**, 249.

WALLEN-LAWRENCE, Z. J. Pharm. Exper. Therap., 1934, **51**, 263.

WEISNER, B. P. Edinburgh M. J., 1930, **37**, 73.

WERNER, A. A. AND COLLIER, W. D. J. A. M. A., 1933, **101**, 1466.

WINTERSTEIN, O., J. Biol. Chem., 1937, **118**, 789.

WOMACH, E. B. AND KOCH, F. C. Endocrin., 1932, **16**, 273.

ZANDER, J. AND SIMMER, H. Klin. Wchnschr., 1954, **32**, 529.

ZUCKERMAN, S. AND PARKES, A. S. Lancet, 1935, **1**, 925; 1936, **1**, 242. Proc. Roy. Soc. Med., 1936, **29**, 81.

*Monographs and Reviews*

ALLEN, E. Sex and internal secretions. 2nd Ed. The Williams & Wilkins Co., Baltimore, 1939.

ANDERSEN, D. H. Physiol. Rev., 1932, **12**, 1.

ASDELL, S. A. Physiol. Rev., 1928, **8**, 313.

BARD, P. Research Publ., A. Research Nervous Mental Disease, 1940, **20**, 551.

BARTELMEZ, G. W. Physiol. Rev., 1937, **17**, 28.

BIELSCHOWSKY, F. AND HORNING, E. S. Brit. M. Bull, 1958, **14**, 106.

BISHOP, P. M. F. Recent advances in endocrinology, 7th Ed., Blakiston Co., New York 1954.

CHANG, M. C. AND PINCUS, G. Physiol. Rev., 1951, **31**, 1.

CORNER, G. W. Medicine, 1933, **12**, 61. Physiol. Rev., 1923, **3**, 457; 1938, **18**, 154.

CORNER, G. W. The hormones in human reproduction. Princeton University Press, Princeton, 1942.

DODDS, E. C. AND DICKENS, F. J. Obst. & Gynaec. Brit. Emp., 1929, **36**, 92.

DOISY, E. A. Harvey Lectures, 1933–1934, **29**, 158.

DORFMAN, R. I. AND SHIPLEY, R. A. The androgens. John Wiley & Sons, New York, 1956.

EVANS, H. M. Harvey Lectures, 1923–1924, **19**, 212; J. A. M. A., 1935, **104**, 464, 1232.

EVANS, H. M., MEYER, K. AND SIMPSON, M. E. Memoirs Univ. Calif. Vol. 11. University of California Press, 1933.

FOLLEY, S. J. Marshall's physiology of reproduction. Edited by Parkes, A. S. Vol. II, Chapter 20. Longmans, Green, & Co., London, 1952.

FOLLEY, S. J. The physiology and biochemistry of lactation. Oliver and Boyd, Edinburgh, 1956.

FRIEDEN, E. H. AND HISAW, F. L. The biochemistry of relaxin. Recent Progr. Hormone Research, 1953, **8**, 333.

GRUMBACH, M. M. AND BARR, M. L. Recent Progr. Hormone Research, 1958, **14**, 255.

HARRIS, G. W. Proc. Roy. Soc. London, ser. B., 1958, **149**, 336.

HARTMAN, C. G. Time of ovulation in women. The Williams & Wilkins Co., Baltimore, 1936.

HISAW, F. L. AND ZARROW, M. X. Vitamins & Hormones, 1950, **8**, 151.

JOST, A. Hormones in Reproduction. Recent Progr. Hormone Research, 1953, **8**, 379.

KITAY, J. I. AND ALTSCHULE, M. D. The Pineal Gland, Harvard University Press, Cambridge, Mass., 1954.

KOCH, F. C. Harvey Lectures, 1937–38, **33**, 205; Physiol. Rev., 1937, **17**, 153.

LAQUEUR, E. Harvey Lectures, 1945–46, **41**, 216.

LIPSCHUTZ, A. The internal secretions of the sex glands. The Williams & Wilkins Co., Baltimore, 1924.

LORAINE, J. A. The clinical application of hormone assay. E. & S. Livingstone, Ltd., Edinburgh, 1958.

LYONS, W. R., LI, C. H. AND JOHNSON, R. E. Recent Progr. Hormone Research, 1958, 14, 219.

MANN, T. The biochemistry of semen. Methuen & Co., Ltd., London 1954.

MARRIAN, G F. Physiol. Rev., 1933, 13, 185.

MARSHALL, F. H. A. The physiology of reproduction. Longmans, London, 1922; An introduction to sexual physiology. Longmans, London, 1925.

MEIGS, E. B. Physiol. Rev., 1922, 2, 204.

MERRILL, R. C. Physiol. Rev., 1958, 38, 463.

McCULLAGH, E. P. AND SCHAFFENBURG, C. A. Glandular physiology and therapy, 5th Ed., Chapter 9, 1954. J. B. Lippincott Co., Philadelphia.

MOORE, C. R. Hormones in relation to reproduction. Am. J. Obst. & Gynec., 1935, 29, 1.

NELSON, W. O. Physiol. Rev., 1936, 16, 488.

PARKES, A. S. Brit. M. Bull., 1955, 11, No. 2.

RIDDLE, O. AND BATES, R. W. Sex and Internal Secretions. Baillière, Tindall & Cox, London, 1939, 1088.

ROBSON, J. M. Recent advances in sex and reproductive physiology, 3rd Ed., Churchill, London, 1947.

TURNER, C. D. General endocrinology, 1st Ed., W. B. Saunders Co., Philadelphia, 1948.

WILKINS, L. The Diagnosis and Treatment of Endocrine Disorders in Childhood and Adolescence, Charles C Thomas, Springfield, Ill., 1950.

YOUNG, W. C. *in* Hormones, Brain Function and Behavior, p. 75. Edited by H. Hoagland. Academic Press, N. Y., 1957.

# THE NERVOUS SYSTEM

# 61

## INTRODUCTORY: THE PHYSIOLOGICAL PROPERTIES OF NERVE

### The Structure of Nervous Tissue

The structural unit of the nervous system is the *nerve cell* or *neuron*. Other elements—*neuroglial cells*—lying among the nerve cells provide a supporting framework.

The neuroglial cells possess numerous branching processes which interlace with one another to form a dense-felt-work between the neurons (fig. 61.1). These interstitial cells of the central nervous system are present in both the gray and white matter; they vary greatly in size and shape and their processes in number and arrangement. Upon a basis of these differences they have been classified into three main types—*astrocytes, microglia* and *oligodendroglia*. The microglia are considered by most observers to be reticuloendothelial elements (ch. 11). They are migratory and phagocytic, wandering into the nervous tissue from the meninges along the blood vessels. In inflammatory processes involving the central nervous system these cells are increased in number. The oligodendroglia are believed to play a part in the formation of the myelin material which sheathes the nerve fibers. Though neurons do not multiply in the adult body and when destroyed are not replaced, certain neuroglial cells possess the power of active proliferation. This may occur to a marked degree in pathological processes. The recent observations by Tasaki that neuroglial cells grown in tissue culture produce slow action potentials suggests caution in assuming that functions of these are restricted to mechanical and metabolic actions.

### The Neuron

The neuron consists of a *body* or *soma*, and two types of process—the *dendrite* and the *axon* (axis-cylinder process, fig. 61.2). In vertebrates, the bodies of the nerve cells lie within the gray matter of the central nervous system or in outlying ganglia, e.g., posterior spinal root, cranial or sympathetic ganglia. The white matter of the brain and spinal cord and of the peripheral nerves is composed of bundles of nerve fibers. The core of each nerve fiber is formed by a process of a nerve cell, and many of them are surrounded by a sheath of myelin which gives them a white appearance. The gray matter receives a rich blood supply from the vessels of the pia mater (1000 mm/mm³ of capillaries); the blood supply to the white substance is much less profuse (300 mm/mm³ of capillaries).

There are a number of different types of nerve cell; those in which axon and dendrite arise by a common stem are called *unipolar*, and those in which the axon and the dendrite or dendrites spring from opposite or at least different parts of

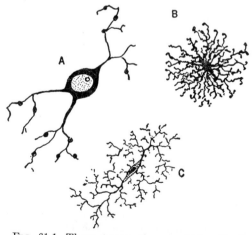

Fig. 61.1. Three types of neuroglial cell. A, oligodendroglia; B, astrocyte; C, microglia.

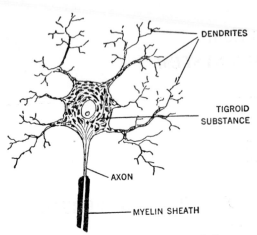

FIG. 61.2. Showing different parts of the neuron.

the soma are called *bipolar* or *multipolar*. The cell bodies or somata are of various sizes and forms— stellate, round, pyramidal, fusiform, etc.

After fixation and staining by special techniques, various structures are seen in the cytoplasm or *perikaryon* of the nerve cell body; (a) *neurofibrils*, (b) *Nissl bodies* or *tigroid substance*, (c) *Golgi* apparatus and (d) *mitochondria*. The neurofibrils appear as fine filaments which stream through the cytoplasm from dendrites to axon (fig. 61.3); they enter the latter process and extend to its terminations. The Nissl bodies are granular masses stainable with basic dyes. They give a striped or tigroid appearance to the cell. They are absent from the region of origin of the axon and vary in size and number with the state of the neuron; they undergo disintegration (chromatolysis) in a fatigued or injured cell or in one whose axon has been sectioned (p. 1118). The internal reticular apparatus of Golgi is a coarse network seen within the cells when special methods—e.g., impregnation with silver chromate—are employed which leave the Nissl bodies and the neurofibrils invisible. It is a debatable question whether the Nissl substance is present in the living cell in the particulate form observed, or whether the latter represents the precipitation from colloidal solution of some material—probably a nucleoprotein— by the methods of fixation employed.

The mitochondria are minute bodies scattered through the cytoplasm. They take the form of short rods, filaments or beads; they are not peculiar to nerve cells, and appear to be centers of metabolic activity. The surfaces of most cell bodies are covered by a fine network—the *superficial reticulum of Golgi*. The *nucleus* of the nerve cell contains one and sometimes two nucleoli but, as a rule, no centrosome. The nucleus stains poorly, as a rule, due apparently to its paucity in chromatin. The absence of a centrosome indicates

that the highly specialized nerve cell has lost its power of division. Nerve cells once destroyed are replaced merely by neuroglia.

The arrangement in series of neurons to form conducting pathways of two or more links and of variable lengths is effected by the contact (but not union) of the axon terminal of one nerve cell with the body or dendritic process of another. This functional union is called a *synapse* (ch. 63).

Though the nerve cell frequently possesses more than one dendrite the axon is single. The axon may be long and contribute to one of the tracts of the central nervous system forming the white matter, or terminate as a peripheral nerve fiber. Such cells are referred to as *Golgi I type*. In the *Golgi II* type cell, the axon is short and ends within the gray matter by making contact with another neuron. The axon arises from a small elevation on the surface of the cell body—the *axon hillock*. It may give off short collateral branches or may run as an unbranched fiber, not dividing until it has reached its destination. The dendrite is the receptive process of the neuron, the axon the discharging process, i.e., the former transmits the impulse toward,

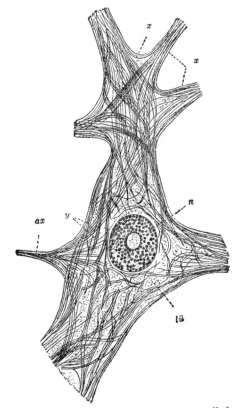

FIG. 61.3. Showing neurofibrils in a cell from the anterior gray column of the human spinal cord. *ax*, axon; *lü*, interfibrillar spaces; *n*, nucleus; *x*, neurofibrils passing from one dendrite to another; *y*, neurofibrils passing through the body of the cell (from Ranson, after Bethe and Heidenhain).

the latter away from the cell body. Nerve fibers which carry impulses to the central nervous system are termed *afferent*; those conveying impulses from the central nervous system to the periphery are called *efferent*. Purely sensory (afferent) nerves are therefore composed, strictly speaking, of dendrites, and purely motor (efferent) nerves of axons. A mixed nerve contains fibers of both types. This unidirectional conduction is due to the properties of synapses for nerve fibers can be made to conduct in either direction.

### Structure of the Nerve Fiber

The axons and dendrites so long as they remain within the gray matter are protoplasmic extensions of the cell body, but upon entering the white matter they become invested by a layer of lipoid material called *myelin*. This covering is known as the *myelin sheath* (fig. 61.2). In the peripheral nerves, but not in the central nervous system, the myelin sheath is enclosed in turn by a nucleated membrane, the *neurilemma* or *sheath of Schwann*. The myelin sheath is interrupted at regular intervals at the nodes of Ranvier where the neurolemma dips in to the axon. In peripheral nerves, each internode is invested by a single Schwann cell.

Toward its termination the nerve fiber loses its myelin covering, being then clothed simply by the neurilemma; the fiber may terminate as a naked axis cylinder or become enclosed within some form of specialized end organ (ch. 62). The processes arising from sympathetic nerve cells (postganglionic fibers) are devoid of a myelin covering. They are invested simply by a sheath of Schwann and are therefore called *amyelinated* or *nonmedullated* fibers. In invertebrates, large (giant) nonmedullated fibers are found sometimes 500 $\mu$ in diameter. Myelinated fibers conduct much faster than nonmyelinated fibers of the same diameter. There is a relationship between the diameter of nerve fibers and the speed at which they conduct nerve impulses (p. 1125).

### Myelination of Fiber Tracts in the Central Nervous System

The nerve fibers in the various conducting pathways receive their myelin sheaths at different ages and it is generally believed that the myelination of a given tract and the time at which it commences to function coincide. The sensory tracts become myelinated first, those of the posterior columns of the spinal cord between the fourth and fifth months of fetal life (human). The spinocerebellar tracts are myelinated later and the motor paths, e.g., corticospinal (pyramidal) tracts do not commence to receive their myelin sheaths until the second month of life and are not completely myelinated until about the second year, or about the time when the child has learned to walk. The

fibers of association paths, for the most part, myelinate at still later dates.

### Neurotropism

The nerve fiber grows by extrusion of filiopodia much as the protoplasm of an amoeba is thrust out in filiform and lamellar pseudopodia. The guiding of growth along a particular orientation has received much attention in the last half century. This, called *Neurotropism*, is found to be closely bound up with the structure of the medium in which growth occurs; for an axon will not grow into a structureless fluid but will follow the submicroscopic structure in gelled protein or creep along any surface of separation of two suitable components in the medium. *Contact guidance* appears to direct the fiber on its way; its immediate surroundings determine the direction of the developing filament, and distant action suggested as *galvanotropism* (following electrical gradients) or *chemotropism* (following chemical gradients) do not appear to be very important factors except in so far as they may orientate the matrix. This partly explains the great importance of the tube of Schwann cells in regeneration, but some kind of symbiosis also exists between Schwann cells and the fibers which they surround. Many problems of development in the central nervous system remain unanswered. In the central nervous system the orientation of growth is orderly and this for contact guidance requires order in the medium through which it is taking place. In tissue culture, fibers will follow the strains imposed on a blood clot since these produce structural orientation of its fibrin filaments. The relative movement of parts which occurs in development leaves orientated strains and structures in the ground substance and this may be an important factor in determining the direction of nerve outgrowth.

### Nerve Degeneration and Regeneration

When a nerve fiber is divided, the portion separated from the body of the cell, undergoes degenerative changes. The degenerative process does not start first at the point of section and progress to the periphery but all parts of the nerve fiber even to its finest terminals are involved virtually simultaneously. The first change is noted in the neurofibrils which become tortuous and show irregular thickenings. The myelin sheath next becomes swollen and breaks up into small ovoid segments (fig. 61.4). Later, decomposition of the myelin occurs; droplets of kephalin and leci-

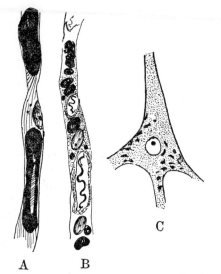

FIG. 61.4. Degenerating nerve stained with osmic acid. A, shows appearance of distal segment of nerve fiber 2 days after section, note large masses of myelin derived from medullary sheath; B, 5 days after section, smaller myelin particles together with droplets of fatty acids and fragmented neurofibrils; C, retrograde degeneration in cell body, disintegration of Nissl bodies.

thin appear; derivatives of the latter—choline, glycerophosphoric acid and unsaturated fatty acids—can be detected. There is a progressive and rather rapid fall in the acetylcholine (ch. 71), cholinesterase and thiamine contents of the degenerating nerve. The fatty acids are responsible for the brown staining of the degenerated nerve when treated with osmic acid. The nuclei of the neurilemma proliferate, and the cytoplasm becomes swollen and vacuolated. The neurofibrils undergo fragmentation; they and the protoplasm surrounding them finally undergo complete disintegration, the débris intermingling with the material of the disorganized myelin sheath. Subsequently the degenerated materials disappear, and all that remains of the nerve fiber is the empty neurilemma tube. The foregoing changes were first observed by Waller and are spoken of as *Wallerian degeneration*. Alterations which were not recognized by Waller also occur in the neuron on the proximal side of the section (*retrograde degeneration*). The nerve fiber as far centrally as the first node of Ranvier shows changes similar in nature to those just described. In the cell body itself, swelling of the cytoplasm and nucleus occurs and the Nissl granules undergo disintegration (*chromatolysis*). Atrophy of the cell body may ultimately result.

*Regeneration.* This occurs in peripheral nerve fibers, but not in those of the central nervous system, the presence of a neurilemma being essential for the process. Section of the sensory root of the trigeminal nerve, for example, for the relief of severe neuralgia of the face, is not followed by regeneration of the fibers within the brain. Nor does regeneration of the optic nerve, whose fibers do not possess neurilemma sheaths, occur.

Regeneration is accomplished by a downgrowth of the neurofibrils from the proximal segment of the cut nerve. These enter the empty neurilemma sheath of the distal segment and in time traverse its entire length. The rate of growth in man varies from 1.0 to 4.5 mm. per day; it is influenced by many factors, namely, the nerve involved, whether there is complete severance of the nerve (*neurotmesis*), the distance separating the sections, and whether the axons alone are crushed, the supporting structure remaining intact (*axonotmesis*). The cells of the neurilemma form a protoplasmic matrix for the sprouting neurofibrils. The neurilemma of the lower segment grows upwards, and if the gap is not too long joins that of the upper segment which has formed around the developing axis cylinder. The myelin sheath is developed some time later. The young axis cylinders may traverse the tissues for relatively long distances in order to enter the neurilemma of the lower segment. The force responsible for this remarkable phenomenon (neurotropism) is unknown. The attraction may be due to the liberation of chemical substances by the proliferating neurilemma cells of the lower segment. If the gap separating the two segments is wide and occupied by scar tissue, an effectual block may be offered to the regenerating fibers; these nevertheless continue to grow in a tangled, curled fashion and may produce a localized mass of tissue composed of nerve fibers embedded in connective tissue (*neuroma*). In those cases of nerve injury in which, as a result of pressure or crushing, the axis cylinder is interrupted without division of the neurilemma, the conditions for regeneration are the most favorable.

The remarkable rapidity of regeneration of preganglionic sympathetic fibers has been demonstrated by Haimovici and Hodes. In a three-stage operation upon cats large sections of the sympathetic chains below their cervical portions were excised. Stimulation of the cephalic end of a cervical sympathetic stump as early as 54 days after the last stage of the operation caused pupillary dilation and retraction of the nictitating membrane.

The regenerating fibers of one nerve will grow into the sheath of the lower segment of another, though less readily than into its own sheath, and even the fibrils of a sensory nerve will grow into the distal segment of a motor nerve or vice versa. The central stump of one nerve will not, however, grow into the central stump of another. The proximal end of the hypoglossal or spinal accessory, for example, has on many occasions been anastomosed to the distal end of a paralyzed facial nerve with a successful functional result. Balance and Duel, experimenting with cats, anastomosed the central end of the hypoglossal to the peripheral cut end of the cervical sympathetic, and reported that the normal pupillary reactions were restored. Restoration of function does not follow the union of a motor with a sensory nerve, nor of a cholinergic with an adrenergic nerve (ch. 71).

It has been shown by Tello in animals and by Duel in man that when a nerve has been severed a much better functional result is obtained if from 2 to 3 weeks are allowed to elapse before the divided nerve is sutured. The reason for this is that the degenerated material in the distal segment has had time to be cleared away; thus, an unobstructed neurilemma tube is left for the downward growth of the neurofibrils of the upper segment. Otherwise, apparently, some of the neurofibrils upon meeting the degenerated débris are diverted from their course.

Degeneration of the facial nerve in the facial canal as a result of middle ear disease (Bell's palsy, ch. 1201), trauma, etc., has been treated with outstanding success by Duel. The affected portion of the nerve is excised and a graft, constituted of a section of the anterior femoral cutaneous nerve, is used to fill the gap. For the reason just given the latter nerve is sectioned and left in place for 2 or 3 weeks before it is employed in the grafting operation.

## The Physiological Properties of the Nerve Fiber

### EXCITABILITY AND CONDUCTIVITY

The nerve fiber may be stimulated electrically, thermally, chemically or mechanically. Any one of these types of stimulus causes a change in the nerve at the point of stimulation which may be termed the *local excitatory state*. If this attains a certain value a wave of excitation is transmitted along the nerve fiber. The propagated disturbance is referred to as the *nerve impulse*, and its passage from point to point along the fiber as *conduction*.

### THE CHARACTERS OF A STIMULUS

A stimulus may be defined as any change in the environment of a tissue which causes it to react. In experimental work the electric current is usually employed as the stimulus on account of its convenience and the accuracy with which it can be measured. It also leaves the tissue undamaged. A stimulus produces a local change of state in the nerve; if this is of sufficient strength to set up propagated activity which spreads over the cell surface, it is said to be adequate. For this to occur, a stimulus must reach a certain (a) strength, (b) duration, (c) rate of change.

*Intensity or strength.* The least stimulus which excites is said to have threshold intensity. Stimuli of less strength are subthreshold (subliminal). When an electrical stimulus is used, the intensity is the current sent through the tissues, and under many conditions, as resistance is substantially constant, it may also be measured in terms of voltage.

The subthreshold stimulus produces a local change which persists for a few milliseconds after the stimulus, and if a second sub-threshold stimulus occurs during this time, a nerve impulse may be set up. The local excitatory state is accompanied by a local electrical change which can be recorded close to the stimulating electrodes (fig. 61.5).

*Duration.* If a constant current is passed through medullated nerve (or muscle), excitation occurs when the circuit is made or broken; but in order to excite at make, the current must flow for a certain period of time to bring about the local changes that culminate in a nerve impulse. For brief current pulses, there is a reciprocal relationship between strength of current and duration of its flow. This can be determined as a strength/duration curve (fig. 61.6). The strength can be varied with a simple potentiometer and the duration determined by a rheotome which allows current to flow through the tissue for a brief period.

The strength/duration curve shows that for brief current pulses the strength must be very great to excite. If a brief, ineffective pulse is followed by another in the reverse direction, any ionic changes produced by the first are reversed by the second. As a result, alternating currents of high frequency may be passed through a tissue without producing sufficient movement of ions to culminate in excitation even though they are sufficiently strong to produce considerable heating of the tissue. This is made use of in a number of ways as *diathermy*. Currents from a diathermy

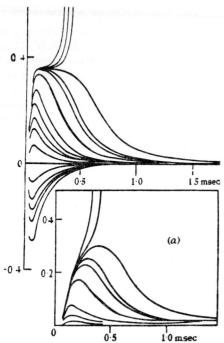

FIG. 61.5. Electrical changes at stimulating electrode produced by shocks with relative strengths, successively from above, 1.00 (upper 6 curves), 0.96, 0.85, 0.71, 0.57, 0.43, 0.21, −0.21, −0.43, −0.57, −0.71, −1.00. The ordinate scale gives the potential as a fraction of the propagated spike, which was about 40 mV in amplitude. The 0.96 curve is thicker than the others, because the local response had begun to fluctuate very slightly at this strength. The width of the line indicates the extent of fluctuation. (Inset) Responses produced by shocks with strengths, successively from above, 1.00 (upper 5 curves), 0.96, 0.85, 0.71, 0.57; obtained from curves in upper figure by subtracting anodic changes from corresponding cathodic curves. Ordinate as above. (From A. L. Hodgkin, Proc. Roy. Soc. Lond. (1938–39), 126, 87–121.

generator producing alternating current (a million or more cycles per second) may be passed between electrodes on the two hands, and body temperature can be raised using the internal resistance of the tissue between the electrodes to evolve heat as it does in the radiant in an electric stove. Diathermy currents are also used in surgery to produce coagulation of bleeding points and to cut soft tissues; when a small electrode is drawn through the tissue the local release of steam within the cells gives a clean heat-sealed cut. It has been widely employed in brain surgery.

The period throughout which there is a reciprocal relationship between strength of current and the duration of its flow is called the *serviceable* or *utilization time* (*temps utile*). It is measured in thousandths of a second. When, for instance, a current of a certain voltage and having a duration

of say 3 milliseconds (msec.) just fails to excite the tissue, then either increasing the voltage or prolonging the duration of the current causes a response. Or, if a current of a certain voltage and duration is just capable of exciting the tissue, reducing either of these factors renders the stimulus ineffective. The length of the utilization time varies in different tissues, but for the frog's striated muscle it is about 50 msec. Beyond the utilization period the relationship between intensity and duration no longer holds. Therefore when the current is of long duration its effectiveness depends entirely upon its intensity. The intensity of a current which when allowed to flow for an indefinitely long period is just capable of exciting the tissue (intensity threshold) is called the *rheobase*. The relationship between strength and duration of current is shown in figure 61.6.

CHRONAXIE. The strength/duration curves from various tissues are of similar shape but differ in their time-scale, and it is convenient to be able to define this time-scale for any tissue. The *chronaxie* is the measure normally employed and is obtained by finding the minimal current which will excite if of long duration, the *rheobase*; next finding the time which a stimulus twice this strength must last to be effective. The factor 2 is arbitrarily chosen by convention and gives a convenient point at about the middle of the strength/duration curve. *The chronaxie may therefore be briefly defined as the shortest duration of a current necessary for excitation when its strength is twice the rheobase.*

Determinations of chronaxie may be carried out by the use of (a) *a steady current* which by means of a special type of rheotome is allowed to flow through the tissue for a very brief accurately

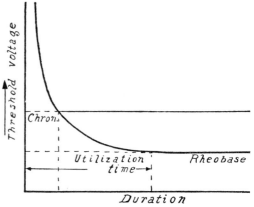

FIG. 61.6. Strength-duration curve; chron., chronaxie.

measured period, (b) *condenser discharges*. The duration of a condenser discharge is proportional to the capacity (C) of the condenser, provided the resistance (R) in the discharge circuit remains constant. By charging condensers of different capacities (measured in farads) to different potentials, currents of any desired duration or voltage can be employed. In order to render any variation in the resistance of different tissues negligible a high resistance (15,000 to 20,000 ohms) is introduced into the discharge circuit. In determining the chronaxie by means of condenser discharges the current of minimal voltage required for excitation is first determined, a very high capacity, i.e., one with a long discharge, being used. The threshold voltage (rheobase) is then doubled and the lowest capacity is found (shortest duration of discharge) which will produce a response at the higher voltage. The result is obtained in microfarads. Since the time, or chronaxie, is proportional to the product of the capacity and the resistance in the discharge circuit, the result can be converted into seconds by the following formula:

$$\text{Chronaxie} = \text{C (farads)} \times \text{R (ohms)} \times \text{K}.$$

$$(\text{K} = 0.37)$$

Rapidly reacting tissues have a shorter chronaxie than the more slowly acting. The chronaxies of smooth muscle and its nerves are longer than those of skeletal muscle and somatic nerves. The tissues of cold-blooded animals have, in general, longer chronaxies than the tissues of higher forms. Flexor muscles have shorter chronaxies than extensors and the chronaxies of the more rapidly acting white muscles are shorter than those of the red. Nerve fibers of larger diameter and of more rapid conduction respond to shorter durations of current than do the thinner and slower fibers. The chronaxies of sensory nerves are in general about the same as those of the motor nerves of the same size. The chronaxie of the ventricular muscle, contrary to expectation, is shortened by vagus stimulation, or by drugs such as acetylcholine which slow the cardiac rate, and lengthened by accelerator stimulation or by drugs, e.g., atropine and adrenaline, which cause acceleration. The chronaxie of the junctional tissues is about three times longer than that of auricular or ventricular muscle. The chronaxie of the gastric muscle is also shortened by vagal stimulation. The chronaxie is lengthened by cold and shortened by a rise in temperature. Stretching cardiac or smooth muscle reduces the chronaxie; and that of skeletal muscle is lengthened by fatigue and shortened by adrenaline. The utilization time (*temps utile*) of a tissue varies with its chronaxie, being about 10 times the value of the latter. Thus the chronaxie of the frog's sciatic nerve is 0.3 msec; the rheobase is reached in 3 msec.

Chronaxie is altered by temperature, by ionic changes, and by many substances of physiological activity, but is stable if conditions are kept constant.

For the motor fibers of the frog's sciatic nerve, it is about 0.3 msec. at 17°C., frog's striated muscle 3 msec., frog's cardiac muscle 20 to 30 msec., frog's stomach 100 msec. In mammals, chronaxie of large nerve fibers may be as short as 0.1 msec.

*Electrode size.* The chronaxie depends upon the rapidity with which electrical charge can diffuse away from the site excited. This will be much more rapid if the site is small than when it is large. Thus the chronaxie of muscle is shorter when measured by electrodes ten microns in diameter than when large electrodes are used. With medullated nerve fibers stimulation occurs at the nodes of Ranvier; the myelin sheath restricts the current flow to these, which form in effect small electrode sites of anatomically fixed size and the size of the external electrode makes little difference.

Following investigations of this by Watts and by Rushton, chronaxie measurements are usually taken with large electrodes to give a figure related to the tissue constants and independent of the electrode used.

*Chronaxies in the human subject* have been investigated under various physiological conditions and in many pathological states by Bourguignon and others. Condenser discharges are employed, an indifferent electrode being placed upon the skin over the sternum and the stimulating electrode, as the cathode, upon the skin overlying the nerve or muscle to be investigated. The chronaxies in the newborn child are about 10 times longer than those of the adult. The longer chronaxies are in agreement with the much slower movements of the infant. In diseases of the central nervous system all muscles which are the seat of paralysis show lengthened chronaxies and in progressive nervous disease those groups of muscles of similar chronaxies are usually attacked more or less simultaneously.

### Reaction of Degeneration

The reaction of degeneration is a phenomenon commonly seen following nerve injuries in man and gives a valuable index of the abnormalities which are present. A motor nerve may be stimulated through the skin by either the faradic (interrupted) or the galvanic (constant) current. The muscle contracts so long as the faradic current flows but only during the make (closure) or break (opening) of the galvanic current, for a given strength of current closure shocks are more effective than opening shocks. In testing the reactions one electrode is placed upon the skin of some indistant part of the body (*indifferent electrode*) and another smaller electrode (*stimulating electrode*) is placed upon the skin overlying the nerve trunk or muscle which it is desired to stimulate. In the latter instance the nerve terminals within the muscle are stimulated, not the muscle fibers themselves. The stimulating electrode is applied over that part of the muscle which gives a response with the least strength of current, this is spoken of as the *motor point* and corresponds to the point of entrance into the muscle of the motor nerve. When the stimulating electrode is attached to the positive pole of the battery it is called the *anode*. The current enters the muscle by this electrode and leaves the body by the indifferent electrode which is called the *cathode*. When the galvanic current is reversed, the stimulating electrode becomes the cathode and the indifferent electrode the anode. Normally the least strength of current is required when the cathode overlies the muscle and the circuit is closed. The response which follows such a shock is called the *cathodal closing contraction* (abbreviated C.C.C.). The next most easily elicited response is the *anodal closing contraction* (A.C.C.), i.e., when the stimulating electrode in the anode and the current is closed. The *anodal opening contraction* (A.O.C.) is less easily evoked than the last, and the *cathodal opening contraction* (C.O.C.) requires the strongest current of all. The four reactions in the order of the strength of current required for their elicitation may be expressed thus:

$$C.C.C. < A.C.C. < A.O.C. < C.O.C.$$

The normal relationship between current strength and these responses is also shown in table 61.1.

The investigation of these reactions is of considerable value in the detection of degeneration of a motor nerve and in the diagnosis of a lower from an "upper neuron" lesion (ch. 65). Lengthening of the chronaxie of a nerve occurs during the earlier stages of its degeneration; it therefore fails to respond to the brief shocks of faradic stimulation but a sluggish contraction of the muscle follows

TABLE 61.1

| Strength of current | Reaction |
|---|---|
| Weak.............. | C.C.C. |
| Medium........... | C.C.C. and A.C.C. |
| Strong............. | C.C.C., A.C.C., A.O.C. |
| Very strong....... | C.C. tetanus, A.C.C., A.O.C. and C.O.C. |

stimulation with the galvanic current. Later the nerve becomes quite incapable of being excited by either the faradic or the galvanic current. When the nerve terminals have degenerated the chronaxie of the muscle is lengthened and the faradic current applied directly to the muscle causes no response; the muscle responds, however, though in an abnormal manner, to the galvanic current, the fibers being *directly* stimulated. The response of the muscle shows the following features. (a) Sluggishness of contraction and relaxation. (b) The response is elicited with a weaker current than normally, i.e., the muscle is hyperexcitable to the galvanic current. (c) The anodal closing contraction (A.C.C.) may often be elicited more readily, i.e., with a weaker current, than the cathodal closing contraction (C.C.C.). Thus, A.C.C. < C.C.C.

These changes in the electrical responses of nerve and muscle, namely, loss of excitability of nerve to faradic and galvanic stimulation, failure of the muscle to respond to faradic stimulation and the abnormalities of the reaction to galvanic stimulation just described constitute the *complete reaction of degeneration* (C.R.D.). When the nerve is still capable of being excited by galvanic but not by faradic stimulation, but the muscle responds weakly or not at all to the faradic current, the reaction of degeneration is said to be incomplete—*partial reaction of degeneration* (P.R.D.).

### Electrotonus, Electrotonic Currents, the Rate of Change in the Intensity of the Stimulus —Accommodation in Nerve

ELECTROTONUS. It was shown many years ago (1859) by Pfluger that the passage of a constant electric current through a nerve altered the properties of the nerve in respect to *excitability*, *conductivity*, and *electrical state*. The effects are produced both at the *anode* (positive pole) and at the *cathode*, and are referred to as *electrotonus*; the anodal effect is called specifically *anelectrotonus*, while the effect at the cathode is called *catelectrotonus*.

The effects occur in sensory as well as in motor nerves, but they can be demonstrated most conveniently in a motor nerve attached to its muscle (fig. 61.7). If the electrodes are placed upon the nerve with the cathode nearer the muscle, i.e., the current is *descending*, and the nerve then stimulated near the cathode with induction shocks which, ordinarily, are submaximal, the muscle gives a maximal contraction owing to the increased excitability of the nerve. The excitability at the anode can be shown in a similar way to be reduced. When the electrodes are reversed, the anode being the nearer the muscle and the current *ascending*, the nerve again shows increased excitability in the region of the cathode and reduced excitability in

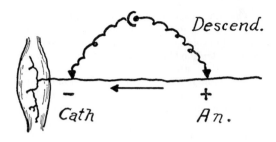

FIG. 61.7. Diagram illustrating the arrangement for demonstrating anelectrotonus and cat-electrotonus. With a strong descending current (*upper figure*), break excitation at the anode is blocked at the cathode, and with a strong ascending current make excitation at the cathode is blocked at the anode. An., anode; cath., cathode.

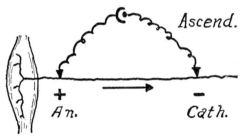

FIG. 61.8. Illustrating altered excitability of nerve during the passage through it of a weak ($y^1$), medium ($y^2$) and strong ($y^3$) constant (polarizing) current. A, anode; B, cathode. The horizontal line represents the normal excitability of the nerve; the curves above and below this line indicate increased and decreased excitability, respectively, of the nerve. The crossings of the horizontal line by the curves, $x^1$, $x^2$ and $x^3$, indicate the points where anelectrotonic and catelectrotonic effects neutralize one another, i.e., they represent indifferent points in the interpolar region A–B. (From Lombard after Pfluger.)

trotonus; with weak currents it is nearer the anode (fig. 61.8).

The effect of the constant current upon *conduction* can be shown by stimulating the nerve in the interpolar region. When the anode is nearer the muscle, anelectrotonic depression of conductivity tends to block the impulse from reaching the muscle; complete block is produced by a strong current. There is no interference with the passage of the impulse toward the muscle when the electrodes are reversed.

The stimulating effects of making and breaking a constant current vary with the strength of the current. With a current of moderate strength stimulation of the nerve occurs at the cathode when the current is "made" (or closed) and at the anode when it is "broken" (or opened), for excitation is increased at the cathode in the one instance and at the anode in the other. The cathodal "make" effect is always greater than the anodal "break" effect, so that, with weak currents the excitation at the anode does not occur; a response is obtained only upon making the current. With very *strong descending currents*, a response is obtained only on the "make" because on the "break" the impulses set up at the anode are blocked by catelectronic depression near the muscle. With *strong ascending currents* excitation occurs only on the "break" because on the "make" the impulses are blocked by anelectrotonus depression near the muscle (see table 61.2 and fig. 61.8).

*Electronic currents*. During the passage of a constant current through a nerve the resistance of its membranes causes the current to spread laterally along their surfaces as well as toward the core of the nerve. The change in the electrical state within the nerve is thus diffused for a distance on either side of the electrode (fig. 61.9). If a galvanometer be led off from the outer side of either electrode, i.e., in the extrapolar region, a current flows through the instrument in the same direction as the constant current. The current flows toward the anode and away from the cathode (and from anode to cathode in the interpolar region). These *electrotonic currents* are due to changes in polarization of the membranes or interfaces within the

the anodal region. When the current is interrupted, opposite effects are produced before the nerve returns to its normal state, namely, a rise in excitability at the anode and a depression of excitability at the cathode.

The anelectrotonic and catelectrotonic effects spread along the nerve on either side of the electrodes. At a certain indifferent point between the poles one effect neutralizes the other. With strong currents the indifferent region is nearer the cathode than the anode, i.e., anelectrotonus extends farther into the interpolar region than does catelec-

TABLE 61.2

|  | Ascending Current | | Descending Current | |
|---|---|---|---|---|
|  | *Making* | *Breaking* | *Making* | *Breaking* |
| Very weak currents.. | C | O | C | O |
| Moderate currents... | C | C | C | C |
| Very strong currents.............. | O | C | C | O |

C = contraction; O = failure to contract.

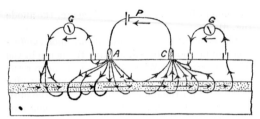

Fig. 61.9. Electrotonic currents. P, constant current; A, anode; C, cathode; G, galvanometer. (After Schafer.)

nerve structure by the constant (polarizing) current. When the polarizing current is broken the electrotonic currents flow in the opposite direction. The production of electrotonic currents by a constant current can also be shown in an artificial moist conductor model consisting of a conducting wire running down the center of a glass tube filled with saline. The changes in the electrical state of the nerve are the cause of catelectrotonus and anelectrotonus described in the preceding section.

When the current is "made", and the "local potential" at the cathode, which may be designated $V$, reaches a certain value, excitation of the nerve occurs. The critical value of $V$ at which the nerve is excited, i.e., the threshold of excitation, may be designated $U$. The decay in the "local or cathode potential" upon cessation of the current, i.e., the rate of return of $V$ to its original or resting value $V_0$,[1] is expressed by the formula $dV/dt = (V - V_0)/K$. $K$ is the time constant for the return of $V$ to $V_0$; it has a value of around 0.35 msec. for frog's nerve and is related to the chronaxie which equals $0.693 \times K$. In order for excitation to result a certain rate of change in the intensity of the stimulus is required. The nerve "accommodates" itself to the stimulus if the change in intensity of the latter is not sufficiently rapid. A stronger stimulus is therefore required for excitation when the rate of rise in intensity is slow than when it is rapid. Hill has introduced a second time factor which he calls the *time constant of accommodation* ($\lambda$). If the critical value of $V$ for excitation, i.e., the threshold, designated $U$, and substituting $U$ and $U_0$ for $V$ and $V_0$, and $\lambda$ for $K$, in the above formula, we have $dV/dt = (U - U_0)/\lambda$. For the calculation of the time constant of accommodation ($\lambda$) the reader is referred to the original paper.

---

[1] The reason for measuring the decline of $V$ to $V_0$ is given by Hill in the following words. "We might have defined the time constant in terms of the rate of change of $V$ when a current is put into the nerve. This would have required the choice of a particular form of current. There would have been no difficulty, but it might have given the impression that $K$ has something to do with the current; it has not; it is a property of the nerve itself; it expresses the time factor in the tendency of the nerve to revert to its resting condition."

The time constant of accommodation is altered by several conditions, the most notable being changes in calcium ion concentration. An increase in concentration of ionic calcium reduces the value of $\lambda$, that is, the neuromuscular tissues accommodate more readily, which means that more rapid changes in stimulus strength are required for excitation. Reduction in ionized Ca, as in tetanic states, exerts the reverse effect—increased value of $\lambda$, and reduced accommodation of the neuromuscular tissues which are in consequence excited by relatively slow rates of change in the strength of the stimulating current. If the calcium ion concentration is sufficiently low there may be a complete absence of the phenomenon of "accommodation."

## THE NERVE IMPULSE

The nerve impulse is a self-propagated disturbance. That is to say, the energy for the transmission of the impulse is derived from the nerve fiber over which it passes. Nervous conduction therefore depends upon the state of the fiber at successive points reached by the impulse. The impulse resembles a spark traveling actively along a train of gunpowder rather than a wave transmitted passively through air or water. In either of the latter two instances in contrast to the first, the energy is derived from a source other than the medium through which the wave travels and the force and amplitude of the wave become gradually reduced with distance. To carry further the analogy drawn between the impulse and the burning train of gunpowder—if a section of the powder fuse is dampened in advance of the spark, the latter becomes less intense as it passes through the dampened section, and travels more slowly. Upon reaching a succeeding dry portion the spark flares up again to its previous intensity and velocity, and, so long as the powder remains dry, is transmitted without change to the end of the fuse. In a comparable way, if the activity of a segment of nerve is depressed by treatment in a chamber with a narcotic (alcohol or ether vapor) the impulse undergoes a reduction in amplitude and velocity in its passage through the narcotized region, but upon reaching the untreated nerve beyond, regains its original value, and is transmitted unchanged to the termination of the nerve. The question then arises whether the strength of the impulse in its passage through the narcotized section of nerve is suddenly reduced or whether the reduction is progressive. In other words, would the impulse suffer a greater reduction if it were made to traverse a long section of narcotized nerve than if it passed through a short stretch?

Formerly it was thought that a gradual or progressive impairment of conduction, i.e., *conduction with a decrement*, occurred. The mode of propagation of the impulse over narcotized nerve was, therefore, supposed to be essentially different from that along a normal nerve. If, for example, the narcotized section were long enough, complete extinction of the impulse would result; in this region, therefore, the impulse would resemble a wave transmitted through air or water. From his experiments, in which the long nerve of the Japanese toad was employed, Kato could obtain no evidence that there was a progressive decline in the strength of the impulse. He came to the conclusion that the impulse suffered sudden reduction upon entering the region of narcosis and underwent no further reduction during its transmission along the narcotized section. Conduction was therefore *decrementless*. Kato's findings have been confirmed by Davis, Forbes, Brunswick and Hopkins (see fig. 61.10) but it is pointed out that on theoretical grounds there must exist a short transitional portion of the nerve at the junction of the normal and the narcotized section, where progressive decline in the impulse occurs. Beyond this the impulse is conducted throughout the length of the narcotized section without further reduction.

### Conduction Rates

The velocity of the nerve impulse varies in different nerve fibers in accordance with their diameters, the thicker fibers conducting more rapidly than those of smaller diameter. In the large motor fibers of the mammal the rate is from 80 to 120 meters per second. Sensory nerves of the skin being of smaller diameter have slower conduction rates. Nonmedullated fibers conduct more slowly than medullated. Some of the fibers subserving pain sensation and those of the sympathetic nervous system have a very slow conduction rate (see also pp. 1129 and 1143).

The following table from Hill gives the conduction rates in the nerves of several different animals.

Medullated nerve, mammal, 37°C., about 120 m. per sec.

Medullated nerve, dogfish, 20°C., about 35 m. per sec.

Medullated nerve, frog, 20°C., about 30 m. per sec.

Nonmedullated nerve, crab, 22°C., and 1.5 m. per sec.

Nonmedullated nerve, mammal, 37°C., about 1 m. per sec.

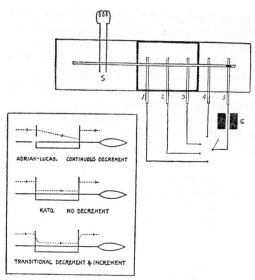

Fig. 61.10. Upper drawing, diagram of nerve (peroneal of cat) in narcotizing chamber to illustrate "set up" of an experiment on conduction of impulses through narcotized nerve. S, stimulating electrodes. Leadoff electrodes at 1, 2, and 3 within the chamber and 4 outside. Circuit completed through an indifferent electrode at 5. G, galvanometer for recording action currents. Nerve in chamber exposed to alcohol vapor. The results of this experiment gave no evidence of conduction with a decrement. The action currents from all three leads within the chamber were reduced to practically the same degree. Lower drawing contrasts the different views advanced regarding conduction of the impulse through a narcotized region of nerve. It will be noted that in all three the impulse regains its full value upon entering normal nerve. (From Davis, Forbes, Brunswick and Hopkins.)

Nonmedullated nerve, olfactory of pike, 20°C., 0.2 m. per sec.

Nonmedullated nerve, in fishing filament of *Physalia*, 26°C., average 0.12 m. per sec.

Nonmedullated nerve, in Anadon, 0.05 m. per sec.

Compare the velocity of sound in air at 0°C., 331 m. per sec.

By an indirect method of measurement Carmichael and his associates found the rates of conduction in various human postganglionic sympathetic nerves to be from 0.85 to 2.30 m. per sec. The lower figures were obtained for the nerves of the leg, the higher ones for the nerves of the chest.

### The "All or None" Principle

A stimulus which is just capable of exciting a nerve fiber (threshold stimulus) sets up an impulse which is no different from one set up by a much stronger stimulus. The impulse set up by the weak stimulus is conducted just as rapidly and is just as strong, when judged by the action current developed or the mechanical response of the muscle, as one set up by the strong stimulus. Briefly, the propagated disturbance set up in a single nerve fiber cannot be graded by grading the intensity or duration of the stimulus—the nerve fiber gives a maximal response or none at all. To make use again of the train of gunpowder analogy —the flame of a match applied to the powder fuse will start a traveling spark no less intense than one started by the flame of a torch. The restoration of the strength of the impulse to its original value after passing from a narcotized region into normal nerve (p. 1124) also shows the "all or none" nature of nervous conduction. The well known fact that a strong stimulus applied to a nerve trunk causes an action current of greater amplitude, and a greater muscular response than a weaker stimulus is due to the fact that the nerve trunk is composed of many fibers each of which supplies a group of muscle fibers. The weak stimulus excites only a proportion of the units of the nerve, a maximal stimulus excites them all. For example, the *cutaneous dorsi muscle* of the frog is supplied by a nerve which contains only 8 or 9 fibers; each of these innervates about 20 muscle fibers. Keith Lucas found that when the nerve was stimulated by shocks, gradually increasing in intensity, the muscular responses did not show a similar continuous rise in amplitude; on the contrary, the responses of the muscle increased in a series of well-defined steps; that is, increasing the stimulus intensity produced no effect for a time upon the amplitude of the muscular response, but then a slight increase in strength of stimulus produced a sudden rise in amplitude. The steps were never greater in number than the number of fibers, and were due, it was concluded, to additional fibers becoming excited as the strength of stimulus reached a certain value.

It must also be remembered that the all or none principle applies only for the condition of the

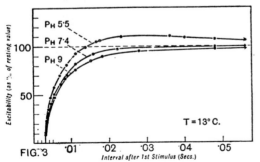

FIG. 61.11. Recovery of excitability in nerve perfused with fluids of different pH. (After Adrian.)

nerve at the point where, and the moment when, the impulse arises. A stimulus which will give rise to a response of a certain magnitude under one condition of the nerve may give a much smaller response under other conditions, e.g., during the relative refractory period (see below), narcosis, oxygen lack, etc.

### The Absolute and Relative Refractory Periods of Nerve

For a brief interval following the passage of an impulse along the nerve fiber a second stimulus, however strong, is unable to evoke a response. This interval is called the absolute refractory period. In a frog's sciatic nerve at a temperature of about 15°C. the absolute refractory period has a duration of between 2 and 3 msec. Its duration is roughly the same as the action potential "spike" (see pp. 1127–1128). It is much shorter in mammalian nerve (1.0 to 0.4 msec. in large medullated nerve fibers).

This period during which the nerve is absolutely refractory is succeeded by one in which the nerve, though it will not respond to as weak a stimulus as it did before the passage of the impulse, will respond to a somewhat stronger one. The excitability of the nerve gradually increases and the strength of stimulus necessary for excitation becomes progressively less (fig. 61.11). In the end, the restoration of excitability is complete and the nerve responds to a stimulus of no greater strength than that which is capable of exciting a resting nerve. This period following the absolute refractory phase and during which the excitability gradually rises to normal is called the *relative refractory period*. It lasts for from 10 to 20 msec. or at any rate the excitability of the nerve has returned to about 95 per cent of the resting value by this time. (Full recovery however may not be attained until the lapse of 100 msec.) It should be pointed out that the failure of the nerve to conduct a second impulse is not due simply to lowered excitability at the *point in the nerve where the original stimulus was applied*, for during the absolute refractory period a stimulus applied to any other point upon the nerve likewise fails to set up an impulse. The passage of the impulse along the nerve leaves in its wake a change of state like a trail of ash after the ignition of a powder fuse. For the moment the impulse consumes the entire resources of the nerve fiber (Adrian). The burned fuse must have its store of energy replenished by laying a fresh train of powder grains before a second spark can traverse the path of the first. So also, a certain time is required for the changes associated with the passage of the impulse to become reversed and the nerve restored to its resting condition (polarized state, see also p. 1130).

The refractory period renders a continuous excitatory state of the nerve impossible just as the corresponding period in cardiac muscle assures rhythmical contractions and prevents summation and tetanus. Fusion or summation of impulses does not occur. The refractory period obviously must also limit the frequency of the impulses. In the mammal the absolute refractory period is about 1.0 to 0.4 msec. The intervals between impulses cannot be shorter than the absolute refractory period; the maximum impulse frequency is therefore around 1000 per sec. At this rate the impulses are travelling in the *relative* refractory period of their predecessors and are weaker and more slowly conducted. In frog nerve with its refractory period of from 2 to 3 msec., the maximal impulse frequency is between 250 and 300 per second.

## THE ELECTRICAL CHANGES IN NERVE

### *The Current of Injury*

When a pair of electrodes are placed a short distance apart upon the surface of an uninjured and resting nerve (or muscle) and connected through a galvanometer, no current flows and no deflection of the instrument occurs, since the entire surface of the nerve (or muscle), and, therefore, the tissue beneath each electrode, is of the same electrical potential. When, however, one part of the tissue is injured the membrane at this point becomes depolarized (see membrane theory, p. 1130) and, in consequence, negative to the uninjured surface. When the two electrodes are now placed one on the injured and the other on the uninjured part and connected through a galvanometer a constant current flows through the instrument from the uninjured (+) to the injured (−) section and in the opposite direction through the length of the tissue. This is known as the *current of injury* (or *demarcation current*) (fig. 61.12, I).

Very large nonmedullated nerve fibers are found in some invertebrates and Hodgkin and Huxley were able to thread an electrode into the giant axon of the squid from the cut end.

The electrode inside the fiber is found to have a resting potential 80 mv. below that of one on the outer surface of the fiber. Glass micropipettes about ½ micron in diameter at the tip, filled

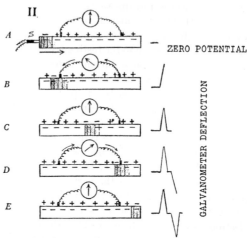

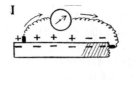

FIG. 61.12. I, current of injury; II, current of action. Description in text. The small arrows indicate the flow of the current in the galvanometer leads; the large arrow, in II A, indicates the direction of spread of the wave of contraction which is represented by the stippled area.

with saline, can be used as electrodes; puncturing cells with such very small electrodes does not lead to a rapid deterioration of the cell; by this means similar resting potentials have been found across the surface of many cells, including vertebrate nerve cells and fibers.

### *The Current of Action*

Active tissue is also relatively negative to resting tissue. If, therefore, two electrodes are placed upon a section of nerve and connected through a galvanometer, as shown in fig. 61.12 II, A, stimulation of the nerve at S causes a movement of the galvanometer indicator first in one direction and then in the other.[2] The movement may be photographed, when a diphasic curve—a wave above the base line followed by one in the opposite direction—is obtained. This is the result of the propagation of the wave of excitation along the nerve from one electrode to the other. When the wave reaches the tissue beneath the first electrode this region becomes negative to the resting tissue beneath the second electrode. A current flows through the galvanometer from the resting

[2] Today a cathode ray oscillograph is employed (p. 1128) which, when combined with a valve amplifier, enables weak currents of short duration to be measured and recorded.

to the active region. A wave above the base line is inscribed in the record (fig. 61.12 II, B). During the lapse of time from the passage of the wave from beneath the first electrode to its arrival at the second no current flows, and the galvanometer indicator returns to the zero position (fig. 61.12 II, C). The arrival of the excitation wave beneath the second electrode now renders the tissue here negative to the resting tissue under the first electrode, and a current flows through the galvanometer, but in a direction opposite to that of the current previously set up. As the nerve beneath the second electrode returns to the inactive state the galvanometer comes to rest. A wave below the base line is thus recorded (fig. 61.12 II, D and E). The diphasic electrical change is called the *current of action*. If a current of injury is set up by crushing the nerve beneath the second electrode, an action current initiated by stimulating the nerve on the side near the first electrode, since it will be opposite in direction to the current of injury, will cause a reduction in the strength of the latter, as indicated by a movement of the galvanometer. The reduction thus caused in the strength of the current of injury is spoken of as the *negative variation*. The excitation wave does not reach the tissue beneath the second electrode since it is blocked by the injured tissue so a second oppositely directed wave does not appear, i.e., the variation is *monophasic*. The injury potential can be compensated for by balancing against it an opposing current; a record of a monophasic action potential—the "spike potential"—is thus obtained.

When the giant nerve fiber of the squid is stimulated, the action potential recorded between electrodes inside and outside the fiber obliterates the resting potential and continues to a reversed potential or overshoot giving a total 'spike' potential of about 110 mv. Similar results are obtained with vertebrate nerves pierced by microelectrodes.

The action potential of the nerve cannot be separated from the propagated disturbance and plays an essential role in exciting the nerve ahead of the active region. Hodgkin showed that if a local anaesthetic were used to block conduction, when an impulse arrived at the blocked region, the excitability to electrical stimulation beyond the block increased. This coincided with the current flow ahead of the nerve impulse. The impulse normally propagates owing to the excitation of regions ahead of the impulse by their passive depolarization by current from the active region.

Moreover, in medullated nerve, Huxley and Stämpfli showed that the current flow is restricted to the nodes of Ranvier and so propagation occurs by activation jumping from node to node. This is called saltatory conduction; it enables medullated nerve fibers to conduct much faster than nonmedullated axons of the same size.

*After-potentials.* Following the main action potential or *"spike" potential* as it is now usually called, a series of smaller electrical changes appear in tracings obtained by the more sensitive methods of recording. These are known as *after-potentials.* They appear following a series of spikes, but in their simplest form, after a single response. They consist of an initial negative potential (i.e., of the same direction as the spike) followed by a positive potential of much smaller magnitude (about 0.2 per cent of the height of the spike), but of longer duration. The negative after-potential has a duration in rapidly conducting fibers of about 15 msec., the positive after-potential of 70 msec. or more. The after-potentials show much greater variability with experimental conditions than does the spike.

### The Compound Nature of the Action Current Recorded from a Nerve Trunk

Erlanger, Bishop and Gasser studied the action potential of mixed nerve trunks by means of the cathode ray oscillograph.

Unlike any instrument previously employed for this purpose, e.g., the string galvanometer or the capillary electrometer, the moving part of this instrument—a stream of electrons—possesses practically no mass and is in consequence inertialess. It is therefore capable of recording very rapid changes in electrical potential. The instrument consists of an evacuated tube; an electron stream from a hot cathode strikes a fluorescent screen upon which it produces a spot of light. On either side of the electron stream is placed a vertical plate. A potential difference is created between the pair of plates; the electric field thereby set up across the path of the stream deflects it horizontally, and sweeps it across the screen. The spot of light is thereby converted into a horizontal streak. By means of a rotating commutator the deflections are repeated from 10 to 20 times per second. A second pair of horizontal plates is placed one above, the other below, the electron stream. These are connected with the nerve whose action current is timed to reach them at the instant that the stream is deflected horizontally by the vertical plates. A vertical deflection of the electron stream results with the production of a standing wave which is photographed and a permanent record thus obtained. The speed of the horizontal movement of the spot of light enables the time scale to be calculated, and can be varied by altering the potential applied to the horizontal pair of plates; the horizontal movement corresponds to the movement of a kymograph, though of course its rate is very many times faster. The upward deflection is analogous to the rise of a muscle lever. The magnitude of the action potential is determined from the height of the wave. Before reaching the recording system the action current is amplified several thousand times by passing it through a valve amplifier.

Upon analysis of the electrical potentials of mammalian nerves, Erlanger and Gasser showed that the "spike" is actually compound and represents the fusion of the potentials of three main types of nerve fiber, which are referred to as the A, B, and C groups. Several properties of nerve are correlated with the diameters of the fibers, the larger the fiber diameter, the higher is the conduction velocity, the lower the threshold of excitation, the greater the magnitude of electrical response, but the shorter its duration, and the shorter the refractory period, latent addition[3] and chronaxie. The relationship of conduction velocity to diameter of the nerve fiber is a linear one (fig. 61.13). The amplitude of the recorded potential is also linearly related to the fiber diameter.

The A group is composed of the largest fibers, 1 to 20 micra in diameter, with conduction rates from 5 m. per sec. or less for the smallest fiber to 100 m. per sec. for the largest. This group has been analyzed into four subsidiary groups labelled $\alpha, \beta, \gamma, \delta$ in accordance with and in this order of fiber diameter (fig. 61.14). The A groups are all myelinated, are both sensory and motor and are found in such somatic nerves as the sciatic and saphenous nerves. The alpha fibers of this group are absent from cutaneous nerves.

Less study has been made of the B and C groups. The B fibers are myelinated and have diameters from 1 to 3 micra, and conduction velocities from about 3 m. per sec. to 14 m. per sec. The B fibers are found solely in autonomic (preganglionic and in some myelinated postganglionic) nerves. The C group, composed of the smallest fibers (less than 1 micron in diameter), are unmyelinated and have a conduction rate of around 2 m. per sec. or less; many are found in cutaneous and visceral nerves. The A group of fibers make by far the greatest contribution to the compound spike potential, and the C group the

---

[3] This is the period during which a subliminal stimulus is capable of summing with a previous one and of raising excitation to threshold value.

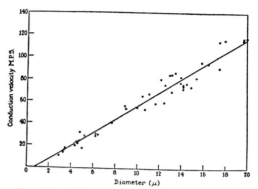

FIG. 61.13. Linear relation between diameter and conduction velocity of mammalian nerve fibers. Each point represents a determination of the maximum conduction velocity of meters per sec. and of the diameter in micra of the largest fiber of an individual nerve. Dots = adult nerves. Circles = immature nerves. (After Hursh.)

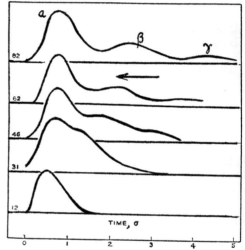

FIG. 61.14. Cathode ray oscillograph records of the action currents in the sciatic nerve of the bull-frog after conduction from the point of stimulation through the distances (in millimeters) shown at the left. The action potentials might be compared to runners in a race who become separated along the course as the faster contestants outstrip the slower; thus in a record at 82 mm. from the point of stimulation three waves are shown, whereas at 12 mm. the potentials are fused, and only one large wave appears. The delta wave is not shown in the record. (Modified from Erlanger, Bishop and Gasser.)

least. The electrical potentials recorded from both A and C fibers show both negative and positive after-potentials, but the B group shows no negative after potential with a single response, though it appears upon repetitive stimulation. The B fibers are the most susceptible to asphyxia; the C fibers the least so.

The linear relationship between fiber diameter

and conduction velocity holds also for growing nerves of young animals (Hursh). During growth the diameters of the nerve fibers in the nerve of the leg, for example, increase as the nerve lengthens. Conduction velocity increaes proportionately so that the time taken for an impulse to travel from the toes of a kitten a few days old to the spinal cord is the same as for a full grown cat. Thus the kitten and the cat react to stimulation with about equal promptness.

The diameters of the regenerating fibers in a sectioned or crushed nerve also enlarge gradually and conduction velocities increase accordingly (Berry and associates); the relationship again being a linear one. The maximum conduction velocity is not reached until maximum diameter of the fiber is attained. If the axons of the nerve alone are interrupted, the sheaths of the nerve fibers remaining intact, the diameters and conduction velocities may reach those of the normal nerve; this rarely occurs if the nerve has been completely severed.

### The Membrane Theory (Bernstein) of Nervous Conduction

Conduction, according to this theory, is a surface phenomenon. The nerve fiber is surrounded by a semipermeable membrane or surface film which is polarized when the nerve is at rest. That is, the surface film separates a layer of cations on its outer side from a layer of anions on its inner side. A stimulus applied to the nerve increases the permeability of the membrane at the point of stimulation with the result that a redistribution of ions and depolarization of the membrane occur. This point of the nerve becomes thereby relatively negative to the inactive (polarized) section of nerve immediately adjacent. A potential differ-

ence is set up and a current flows between the active and inactive sections. This secondary current in turn causes depolarization and activation of the adjoining region which, being now relatively negative to the next section, results in a current being again set up between these two which depolarizes the latter. The currents set up between contiguous, inactive and active regions serve as successive stimuli and the wave of depolarization spreads down the nerve; the disturbance set up by the original artificial stimulus is in this way propagated automatically (see fig. 61.15). Thus, nerve impulses are "transient self-mending electrical leaks travelling along nerve fibers" (Sherrington). The depolarized state persists for a short time after the passage of the impulse; during this time the nerve is refractory. The return of excitability is dependent upon the restoration of the polarized state. According to the membrane theory the nerve impulse is a propagated wave of depolarization.

In recent years the membrane theory has become more firmly established by the experiments above, showing the role of the action potential in propagation; it had, however, to be elaborated to cover the experimental finding of overshoot, where the action potential exceeds the resting potential so that a transient reversal of potential occurs. The axon contains a great excess of K ions over the surrounding fluid and a deficit of Na ions; these differences are maintained in the resting nerve by metabolic activity.

The use of radioactive sodium and potassium to replace part of the normal potassium and sodium in a giant axon from the squid, or fluids round it, has enabled the ionic changes to be followed in detail, and it is possible to detect and measure very small quantities of these substances by the radiation emitted from radioactive breakdown. When the nerve is conducting impulses, the escape of potassium ions is greatly accelerated into the surrounding fluids and sodium ions enter the fibers. The concentrations are restored to normal after activity; but the permeabilities for potassium and sodium do not change together. The reaction of the surface membrane is much more complex than postulated in the simple Bernstein theory.

By placing an iron wire in strong nitric acid a model can be made along the surface of which a physicochemical change can propagate. The wire becomes coated with a thin film of oxide which prevents its solution in the acid (the iron becomes "passive"). If the oxified film is scratched or re-

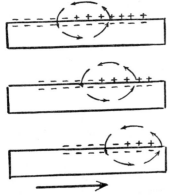

Fig. 61.15. Illustrating nervous conduction according to the membrane theory (see text).

moved electrolitically by an adequate electric stimulus, the protective film is removed and the wire is attacked by the acid. Gas is evolved, and the change propagates along the wire at a speed of several meters per second (varying with temperature). After this activity, a thick oxide film is left on the wire which is refractory to further stimulation for a few seconds until it has slowly dissolved, to leave a thin oxide film that gives the passive state, when it can be reactivated. The propagation resembles that in nerve, for the reaction oxidizing the exposed wire causes local currents to flow, reducing the film in neighboring regions by electrolysis and so causes the activity to propagate in the same sort of way as does the action potential in nerve. An action potential can be recorded from two electrodes near the iron wire which give a diphasic variation as the active region passes. If short lengths of glass tubing are threaded on the wire to restrict the current flow to "nodes", "saltatory" activation occurs, greatly accelerating the conduction of activity along the wire.

## METABOLISM OF NERVE AND BRAIN

It has been thought until comparatively recent years that a negligible expenditure of energy accompanies the transmission of the nerve impulse; the latter was believed to be immediately dependent upon physical rather than upon chemical processes. Though it was recognized that conduction eventually failed in the absence of oxygen this fact did not prove that conduction itself was due to oxidative processes. In order to show this it would be necessary to demonstrate an *increase* in the oxygen consumption and in the carbon dioxide production during *activity*. An increased carbon dioxide production of active nerve over that of resting nerve was observed by Tashiro in 1913. This was confirmed by Parker, and an increased oxygen consumption during excitation was shown by Fenn. Earlier attempts (Helmholtz, 1848) to demonstrate heat production in active nerve were unsuccessful, but in 1926 Hill, using a thermopile composed of over two hundred thermocouples, detected a rise of $\frac{7}{10,000}$ °C. in the temperature of a nerve as a result of stimulation lasting 10 seconds.

## HEAT PRODUCTION IN NERVE

The resting sciatic nerve of the frog in oxygen at 20°C. was found by Beresina to generate 4.14 calories[4] per gram of nerve per minute. In nitrogen

[4] Small calories.

the resting heat production falls gradually, reaching, at the end of about 3 hours, to 20 or 25 per cent of the value in oxygen, and remains steady at this low level. Upon the readmission of oxygen to the asphyxiated nerve, heat production rises rapidly, extra heat being produced over that produced previously by the nerve in oxygen. This extra heat amounts to some 15 or 20 per cent of the "missed" heat in nitrogen (i.e., of the amount equal to the difference between heat production in oxygen and in nitrogen). The heat generated in nitrogen is attributed mainly to an oxidative process dependent upon a store of oxygen in the nerve tissue, and to the breakdown of carbohydrate to lactic acid, and possibly also to phosphocreatine breakdown. In the steady state the heat production is attributed to lactic acid production from carbohydrate. The extra heat produced upon the readmission of oxygen is probably in part waste heat in the process of phosphocreatine resynthesis, and possibly also due to the oxidation of some of the lactic acid accumulated during the anaerobic period.

During stimulation of the nerve in oxygen, at the rate of 280 shocks per second, an increase in heat production occurs of $40 \times 10^{-4}$ calories per gram of nerve per second. At this rate of stimulation the heat resulting from a single impulse is about $1.4 \times 10^{-7}$ calories per gram of nerve fiber. Though the heat production per gram of resting nerve is nearly as great as that of resting muscle, during activity the heat produced by nerve is only $\frac{1}{400,000}$ of that generated by muscle of equal weight and stimulated to the same degree.

As in the case of muscle, the heat produced during activity is given off in two batches—the *initial heat* and the *delayed* or *recovery heat*. The initial heat is less than 4 per cent of the total heat,[5] the ratio of initial to delayed heat being 1:30. The rate of generation of the initial heat is some 5000 times greater than that of the delayed heat (fig. 61.16). The former coincides with or follows immediately upon the "spike" potential being an intense explosive outburst which, with a single stimulus, lasts for only a few milliseconds. The delayed or recovery heat which is given out after the period of activity declines rapidly at first and then more slowly.

The delayed heat is accompanied by the consumption of oxygen and is evolved in two stages. The first of these lasts for a few seconds, and the

[5] Hill found that the initial heat of crab nerve was only 2.25 per cent of the total heat, which, however, was much greater ($2.5 \times 10^{-3}$ per second per gram of fiber) than that of frog nerve. Beresina and Feng obtained similar values for crab nerve.

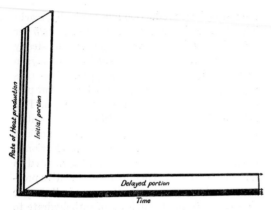

FIG. 61.16. Diagrammatic representation (not to scale) of the heat production due to each nervous impulse, indicating how the observed heat resulting from a tetanic stimulation is built up of these units. The horizontal lines represent the delayed heat, starting at a maximum rate of 0.05 "C" units and slowly falling to zero in about 10 mins. The vertical lines represent the initial heat which probably is largely produced during less than 4 sec. at a rate 5000 times greater than that at the start of the delayed phase. (After Gerhard.)

quantity of heat is of small magnitude; the second lasts for form 10 to 30 minutes and contributes the greater proportion of the delayed heat.[6] Increase in the *strength* of the stimulus does not increase the heat production, whereas increase in the *frequency* of stimulation causes an increase in heat production up to 25 per cent. The heat per second, however, does not increase proportionately with the increase in frequency of stimulation, so the heat per impulse is actually reduced. When the shocks are at the rate of 280 per second the heat production per second is maximal and the heat per impulse (since each impulse is travelling in the relative refractory period of its predecessor) is only a quarter of that generated by a single isolated impulse. The heat production of the central nervous system is enormously greater than that of nerve fibers amounting to from 600 to over 2000 $\times$ $10^{-6}$ per gram per second for the spinal cord of the frog.

### Carbon Dioxide Production and Oxygen Consumption

The resting sciatic of the frog produces in the neighborhood of 0.6 cu. mm. $CO_2$ per gram of nerve per minute. The corresponding $O_2$ consumption is about 0.7 cu. mm. The resting respiratory

[6] The cause of the initial heat is unknown. It may be chemical in nature and due to the breakdown of phosphocreatinine or may be derived, as Hill suggests, from an electrical source, namely, the discharge of an electric double layer—a condenser—located at the surface of the fiber. See A. V. Hill, "Chemical wave transmission in nerve." Cambridge, University Press, 1932.

quotient is therefore around 0.8. During activity an extra 0.25 cu. mm. of $O_2$ per gram of nerve per minute is consumed and a somewhat smaller quantity of extra $CO_2$ produced. The extra metabolism of the nerve resulting from activity has an R.Q. of about 0.90 (Meyerhof and Schmidt).

The extra oxygen consumption resulting from nerve activity occurs during the period of delayed heat. It continues for a considerable time—15 minutes or more after the impulse has passed. The quantity of oxygen consumed agrees well with the heat produced at this time, upon the basis that the latter is the result of the oxidation of ordinary food materials. Like the heat production the oxygen consumption per impulse falls with a rise of frequency of stimulation, though of course the total consumption per minute increases. Increasing the strength of the stimulus beyond that necessary to excite all the fibers does not increase the oxygen consumption.

### Chemical Changes in Nerve[7]

(1) IN THE ABSENCE OF OXYGEN. Placed in nitrogen a *resting* nerve undergoes a reduction in its glycogen and free sugar contents and an accumulation of lactic acid. The lactic acid production proceeds slowly and in about 3 hours has reached a maximum rate of 7 mg. per 100 grams of nerve per hour; it then falls gradually to zero. The total acid production is about 100 mg. per 100 grams of nerve (0.1 per cent). This is not attained until the end of 24 hours, at which time the carbohydrate store of the nerve becomes exhausted. Immersion of the nerve in a solution of glucose (but not of galactose or fructose) causes lactic acid production to continue at the maximum rate (7 mg. per cent) for days—or until conversion of the added glucose has occurred. When the nerve is *stimulated* in nitrogen there does not result, however, as in the case of muscle deprived of oxygen, an increased accumulation of lactic acid. Also when oxygen is readmitted lactic acid does not disappear or does so very slowly. Oxygen consumption of the nerve is somewhat greater than usual after a period in nitrogen—an indication that nerve runs into debt for oxygen during a period of anoxia. In the absence of oxygen, nerve, unlike muscle, continues to respond to stimulation for a considerable time. It shows a progressive fall in excitability but does not fail to conduct until the lapse of about 3 hours. The action current or the current of injury is gradually reduced during

[7] The formation of acetylcholine in nervous tissue is dealt with in Chapter 71.

this time but rises again when oxygen is readmitted. A fall in phosphocreatine content and a rise in inorganic phosphorus also occur.

In the asphyxiated nerve the delayed heat production declines no more rapidly (if anything less so) than the initial heat, whereas in the case of a muscle contracting in the absence of oxygen most of the recovery heat is abolished (p. 877). In nerve, therefore, *both conduction and the recovery process can apparently be accomplished for a time after the external oxygen supply has been cut off*.

(2) IN THE PRESENCE OF OXYGEN. In the case of the excised *resting nerve* free sugar gradually disappears but the glycogen content remains unchanged and *no lactic acid is formed*. These observations indicate that the function of the resting nerve is probably maintained in part by energy derived from the combustion of sugar. Energy is also probably derived from the breakdown of phospholipins. *During activity* phosphocreatine is broken down but the glycogen content of the nerve remains unaltered. Sugar does not disappear more rapidly than during rest, nor is lactic acid produced. The glycogen-lactic acid cycle which is so prominent in the metabolism of muscle therefore appears to play no part in nerve fiber conduction. The immediate source of the energy for conduction is believed to be derived from the breakdown of phosphocreatine which is resynthesized after the passage of the impulse. The ultimate source of the energy for the recovery process in nerve is unknown.

It has been thought that the nerve fiber was incapable of oxidizing lactic acid or of synthesizing lactic acid to glycogen, but, as mentioned above, when an accumulation of lactic acid occurs as a result of asphyxia small amounts do disappear upon the readmission of oxygen. Also, in a nerve soaked in sodium iodoacetate the phosphocreatine disappears and the nerve soon fails to respond, but if lactate be supplied the survival time is considerably lengthened and oxygen consumption increased (Feng). (The addition of lactate causes no increased oxygen consumption by normal nerve.) These and other observations indicate that the inability of the nerve to oxidize lactic acid is not absolute but that, under certain circumstances at any rate, such does occur.

Small quantities of *ammonia* (about 0.3 mg. per cent per hour) are produced by resting nerve and about double this amount during activity. The source of the ammonia is probably adenylpyrophosphate. The *inorganic phosphate* also increases during activity as a result of the breakdown of phosphocreatine and adenylpyrophosphate and, possibly, of phospholipins.

*Potassium of nerve.* The nerve fiber is exceptionally rich in potassium; Cowan found that the potassium concentration in the nerve of the crab is some 13 times greater than that in crab's blood. Ratios as high as 65:1 for the potassium concentrations on the inner and outer sides of the membrane have been reported for vertebrate nerve. It is upon this difference in the potassium concentrations that the resting potential (polarization) of the nerve is believed, according to the Bernstein hypothesis, to depend. But when the nerve is stimulated or deprived of oxygen, potassium diffuses rapidly into the surrounding fluid, but is restored again (repolarized) during rest or, in the case of the asphyxiated nerve, after the readmission of oxygen. A nerve at rest and adequately supplied with oxygen does not lose potassium and a potential difference between the surface of the fiber and its interior is maintained. Increasing the concentration of potassium in the fluid bathing the nerve will tend to reduce the potential difference; this procedure also reduces the excitability of the nerve and with high concentrations excitability is completely lost but is restored again when the nerve is placed in sea water. The amplitude of the action current or of the current of injury is also markedly reduced by raising the potassium concentration on the outer side of the nerve. Furthermore, when the nerve is exposed to cold, "blocking" of the impulse occurs at a higher temperature than usual if the nerve has been soaked in a solution containing a high percentage of potassium.

The metabolism of the resting nerve may be considered in terms of the membrane theory (p. 1130) to be directed toward securing a certain degree of impermeability of the surface film for the maintenance of the polarized state. The chemical changes associated with activity result in increased permeability and depolarization. During recovery the membrane is repolarized, the energy being furnished by oxidative processes. The potassium is returned to the fiber and the sodium that has entered is "pumped" out.

The *brain* (gray matter) when supplied with oxygen oxidizes glucose and, unlike the nerve fiber under the same conditions, produces lactic acid, though in small amounts. Lactic acid is also produced slowly when glucose is added to brain slices *in vitro* with free access to oxygen. Glucose is present in brain tissue in about the same concentration as in blood, and is the main substrate for the respiration of the gray matter. The respiratory quotient of the brain is around unity. As compared with muscle the gray matter contains only small amounts of glycogen. When the latter is added to brain slices it is broken down very slowly to lactic acid. Hexosephosphate, according to Ashford and Holmes, is not an intermediary in the oxidation of glucose by brain tissue, but the production of pyruvic acid appears to be an essential step. The utilization of glucose by brain tissue is made evident by its addition to brain slices, an increased consumption of oxygen then occurs. The oxygen consumption of brain tissue *in vitro* is also increased by the addition of fructose, mannose, galactose, and hexose diphosphate and monophosphate, and to a much less extent by other sugars. Next to glucose, fructose and mannose are most readily oxidized by brain slices. Lactate and pyruvate are utilized about as readily as glucose. Glutamic acid and alcohol are utilized by brain tissue to a small extent.

In hypoxia and during convulsive seizures, large quantities of lactate are produced by brain tissues, but as already mentioned, only minimal amounts when the oxygen supply is adequate. The large production of lactate under anaerobic conditions and the minimal amounts produced when the oxygen supply is adequate raises the question whether the formation of lactic acid plays any role in the normal function of the brain. It appears, at any rate, that it does not play an indispensable part in the oxidation of glucose, for nicotine, iodoacetate or hydroxymalonate inhibits the oxidation of lactate but permits glucose to be oxidized. During convulsions, or when from any cause the oxygen supply is inadequate, the brain, like muscle, uses phosphocreatine. Similar changes are produced by injury to brain tissue. Though other fuel can be oxidized by the brain, glucose, lactic acid and pyruvate are the only ones, and especially glucose, which are utilized normally to any significant extent. In excised brain tissue "the utilization of glucose is faster than that observed in hepatic, cardiac, or renal slices" (Himwich). A respiratory quotient of unity supports the conclusion that the main fuel of the brain is carbohydrate, but more direct evidence for the oxidation of glucose can be cited. Himwich and Fazekas, for example, determined the glucose and oxygen contents of the arterial blood and of blood drawn from the superior longitudinal sinus of anesthetized dogs. They obtained a figure of 13 mg. per 100 cc. of blood for the glucose utilization. The quantity of oxygen which by calculation

would be required to oxidize this quantity of glucose is 9.7 cc. The oxygen consumption actually observed was 9.3 cc. These figures are, of course, for the brain as a whole.

The gray matter shows a much higher oxygen consumption than does the white matter which is composed mainly of nerve fibers. Though the nerve fiber can contract a small oxygen debt, the gray matter cannot and, in consequence, is highly susceptible to oxygen deprivation. It has been estimated that the adult brain accounts for about one-quarter of the basal metabolism of the entire body at rest, or over 3 liters per hour, yet mental work increases the general metabolism to a negligible extent (ch. 44). The infant brain which, as compared with the adult brain, forms a larger part of the body has a relatively greater consumption of oxygen; its oxygen consumption is about half the total oxygen consumption of the body. Considering the high oxygen requirement of the gray matter, especially of the cerebral cortex, it is not surprising that it is so vulnerable to anoxia. Mental confusion, delirium and unconsciousness follow any considerable reduction in the oxygen supply to the brain. The delirium of pneumonia is due largely to anoxia rather than to toxemia, and the mental aberrations associated with high altitudes are well known. The metabolism of the cerebellar cortex, according to some investigators, is higher than that of the cerebral cortex. Himwich and Fazekas have made the interesting observation that in week-old puppies the medulla and midbrain have a higher oxygen consumption than has the cerebral cortex but the reverse relationship holds true in adult dogs. The increased oxygen consumption of the higher centers of grown animals appears related to their having acquired greater functional importance and assumed a position of dominance over the lower centers.

The very high oxygen consumption of gray matter as compared to white matter (nerve fibers) is not due to the presence of cell-bodies, but apparently to the great number of synapses (ch. 63), for the posterior root ganglia, which are made up of unipolar cells without synaptic connections, have not a high vascularity or oxygen consumption, and are not more susceptible to ischemia than are nerve fibers.

The brain is also very sensitive to a reduction in its supply of glucose, and when the blood sugar level falls to a certain point, mental confusion, muscular incoordination, convulsions and loss of consciousness result. The hypoglycemic symptoms are quickly relieved by the administration of glucose, fructose or mannose but not by pyruvate or lactate. In the human subject insulin hypoglycemia greatly reduces the oxygen consumption of the brain, but this is quickly restored to normal by the injection of glucose (Himwich and associates). The reduction of the metabolism of the brain and its restoration to normal are closely associated in time with the hypoglycemic symptoms and their relief. Yet, strangely enough, the brain continues to utilize glucose in the absence of insulin; the respiratory quotient remains at unity and the arteriovenous oxygen difference is unaltered after pancreatectomy.

As might be expected from the relationship between the blood glucose level and the oxygen consumption, the effects of anoxia and of hypoglycemia are in certain respects closely similar, and are supplementary to one another. Hypoglycemic convulsions are induced more readily in the presence of anoxia, and the effects of the latter are more severe if the blood sugar is depressed.

There is no evidence that the lipids—*cholesterol, lecithin, cephalin* and *sphingomyelin*—which enter so largely into the composition of brain substance serve any special metabolic need; their function is probably to insulate neighboring nerve fibers from one another. Nor are fats or amino acids, with the exception of glutamic acid, utilized by the brain. This amino acid is capable of restoring consciousness to a subject of hypoglycemia; it is probably oxidized directly by the brain, but may also cause, through an adrenalinelike action, the liberation of glucose from the liver.

### Theories of the Action of Anesthetics and Narcotics

There has been much speculation as to the manner in which certain drugs induce anesthesia or narcosis, but no theory is entirely satisfactory. There are three main theories, which may be termed the *lipid solubility, membrane permeability* and *metabolic theories*. The lipid solubility (Meyer-Overton) theory is concerned mainly with the manner in which the anesthetic enters the neuron, rather than with its mode of action upon the function of nervous tissue after it has penetrated the cell. This theory is founded upon a certain, but far from perfect, correlation between the action of anesthetic agents, and their solubility in lipid (which the cell membrane and other structures of the cell contain) but low solubility in water. The narcotic effects of the chemically inert gases,

argon, krypton and xenon are attributed to their ready solubility in lipid.

It was proposed by Lillie that the permeability of the cell membrane, with the consequent prevention of depolarization, upon which excitability depends, was reduced by anesthetic drugs.

The metabolic theory is based largely on the work of Quastel and Wheatly, who have shown that many narcotic drugs, notably the barbiturates, paraldehyde and urethane, depress the oxygen consumption of brain tissue *in vitro*, and reduce the oxidation of glucose. The metabolic activity of the brain *in vivo* is also inhibited in anesthesia. These inhibitory effects upon brain metabolism are dependent, presumably, upon the interference with the function of oxidative enzyme systems, possibly by blocking the interaction between flavoprotein and cytochrome *b*. An important objection to this theory is the failure to establish a satisfactory correlation between the concentrations of drugs which are effective in inhibiting oxidation *in vitro*, and the concentrations which cause anesthesia. Ether, for example, causes insignificant effects upon the oxygen consumption of brain slices in concentrations which induce general anesthesia. It is possible, however, that the concentrations of anesthetic drugs in the brain as a whole may be much lower than in certain special and restricted regions, and that they have specific effects on the reticular system.

One point seems to be generally agreed upon with respect to anesthetic and narcotic agents, namely, that they act through a physical rather than through a chemical mechanism. All the evidence points in this direction. No consistent chemical structure is associated with their anesthetic or narcotic property; their actions are reversible; they do not appear to enter into any chemical reaction, and they can be recovered almost quantitatively from the tissues unchanged.

### REFERENCES

ADRIAN, E. D. and BRONK, D. W. J. Physiol., 1928, **66,** 81; 1929, **67,** 119.

ASHFORD, C. A. and HOLMES, E. G. Biochem. J., 1929, **23,** 748.

BALLANCE, C. and DUEL, A. B. Brain, 1932, **55,** 226.

BARR, M. L. and BERTRAM, E. G. Nature, 1949, **163,** 677.

BERESINA, M. J. Physiol., 1932, **76,** 170.

BERESINA, M. and FENG, T. P. J. Physiol., 1933, **77,** 111.

BERRY, C. M. and assoc. J. Neurophysiol., 1944, **7,** 103.

BROOKS, C. McC. and ECCLES, J. C., Nature, 1947, **159,** 760.

CANNON, W. B., BINGER, C. A. L. and FITZ, R. Am. J. Physiol., 1915, **36**, 363.

CHUTE, A. L. and SMYTH, D. H. Quart J. Exper. Physiol., 1939, **29**, 379.

COWAN, S. L. Proc. Roy. Soc., London. ser. B., 1934, **115**, 216.

DAVIS, F., FORBES, A., BRUNSWICK, D. and HOPKINS, A. McH. Am. J. Physiol., 1925, **72**, 177 (Proc.). Ibid., 1926, **76**, 448.

DOWNING, A. C., GERARD, R. W. and HILL, A. V. Proc. Roy. Soc., London. ser. B., 1926, **100**, 223.

DUEL, A. B. Brit. M. J., 1934, **2**, 1027.

EMERSON, G. A. Proc. Soc. Exp. Biol. & Med., 1935, **33**, 171.

ERLANGER, J., BISHOP, G. H. and GASSER, H. S. Am. J. Physiol., 1926, **78**, 537. Ibid., p. 574.

ERLANGER, J. and GASSER, H. S. Am. J. Physiol., 1924, **70**, 624. Ibid., 1930, **92**, 43.

FENG, T. P. J. Physiol., 1932, **76**, 477.

FRIEDGOOD, H. B. and CANNON, W. B. Endocrinology, 1940, **26**, 142.

GASSER, H. S. Harvey Lectures, 1936–1937, p. 169.

GERARD, R. W., HILL, A. V. and ZOTTERMAN, Y. J. Physiol., 1927, **63**, 130.

GRUNDFEST, H. Am. J. Physiol., 1930, **127**, 252; Ann. Rev. Physiol., 1940, **2**, 213.

GRUNDFEST, H., and GASSER, H. S. Am. J. Physiol. 1938, **123**, 307.

HAIMOVICI, H. and HODES, R. Am. J. Physiol., 1940, **128**, 463.

HILL, A. V. Proc. Roy. Soc., London. ser. B., 1936, **119**, 305.

HIMWICH, H. E. Brain Metabolism and Cerebral Disorders. The Williams and Wilkins Co., Baltimore, 1951.

HIMWICH, H. E. and associates. Am. J. Physiol., 1932, **101**, 446. Endocrinology, 1937, **21**, 800. Am. J. Physiol., 1941, **132**, 454.

HORRAX, G. cited by CUSHING, H. in "Studies in intracranial physiology and surgery." Oxford Univ. Press, 1926, p. 76.

HURSH, J. B. Am. J. Physiol., 1939, **127**, 131, 140.

LUCAS, K. J. Physiol., 1909, **38**, 113.

PARKER, G. H. J. Gen. Physiol., 1925, **7**, 641. Ibid., p. 671, Ibid., 1925, **8**, 21.

QUASTEL, J. H. Proc. Roy. Soc. Med., 1936, **29**, 200.

QUASTEL, J. H. and WHEATLEY, A. H. M. Proc. Roy. Soc., London. ser. B., 1932, **112**, 60. Biochem. J., 1932, **26**, 725. Ibid., 1933, **27**, 1609.

RUSHTON, W. A. H. J. Physiol., 1933, **77**, 337.

SOLANDT, D. Y. Proc. Roy. Soc. London. ser. B., 1936, **119**, 355.

TASHIRO, S. Am. J. Physiol., 1913, **32**, 107.

TELLO. Quoted by Ramon y Cajal's Degeneration and regeneration of nervous tissue. Oxford University Press, 1928.

*Monographs and Reviews*

ADRIAN, E. D. The basis of sensation. Christophers, London, 1928. The mechanism of nervous action. University of Pennsylvania Press, 1932. Messages in sensory nerve fibers. Harvey Lectures, 1931–32, **27**, 57. The mechanisms of the sense organs. Physiol. Rev., 1930, **10**, 336.

BUTLER, T. C. Theories of general anesthesia. Pharmacol. Rev., 1950, **2**, 121.

DAVIS, H. The conduction of the nerve impulse. Physiol. Rev., 1926, **6**, 547.

DAVIS, H. and FORBES, A. Chronaxie. Physiol. Rev. 1936, **16**, 407.

ERLANGER, J. Analysis of the action potential in nerve. Harvey Lectures, 1926–27, **22**, 90.

FENN, W. O. The metabolism of nerves. Harvey Lectures, 1927–28, **23**, 115. Medicine, 1928, **7**, 433.

FREDERICQ, H. Chronaxie. Physiol. Rev., 1928, **8**, 501.

GASSER, H. S. The control of excitation in the nervous system. Harvey Lectures, 1936–37, p. 169.

GERARD, R. W. Nerve metabolism. Physiol. Rev., 1932, **12**, 469. Metabolism of brain and nerve. Ann. Rev. Biochem., 1937, **6**, 419.

HILL, A. V. Chemical wave transmission in nerve. Cambridge University Press, 1932.

HOLMES, E. G. The metabolism of brain and nerve. Ann. Rev. Biochem., 1932, **1**, 487. Ibid., 1934, **3**, 381. Ibid., 1935, **4**, 435. Metabolism of living tissues. Cambridge University Press, 1937.

KAPPERS, A. C. U. Three lectures on neurobiotaxis and other subjects delivered at the University of Copenhagen. Heinemann, London, 1928.

KATO, G. The theory of decrementless conduction in narcotized region of nerve. Kodachi, Tokyo, 1924.

LEE, F. C. The regeneration of nervous tissue. Physiol. Rev., 1929, **9**, 575. The regeneration of sympathetic nerve-fibres. Assoc. Res. Nerv. Mental Dis., The Williams & Wilkins Co., Baltimore, 1930, **9**, 417.

LILLIE, R. S. Transmission of physiological influences in protoplasmic systems, especially nerves. Physiol. Rev., 1922, **2**, 1.

LUCAS, K. The conduction of the nervous impulse. Longmans London, 1917.

PENFIELD, W. Cytology and cellular pathology of the nervous system. Hoeber, New York, 1932.

RAMON Y CAJAL, S. Degeneration and regeneration of nervous tissue. Oxford University Press, 1928.

# 62

# THE REFLEX ARC. RECEPTOR ORGANS. CUTANEOUS AND KINESTHETIC SENSATIONS

The involuntary muscular contraction which results from the stimulation of a sense organ is known as a reflex. The quick withdrawal of the hand from some agent which has inflicted pain or the contraction of the pupil when a light is thrown into the eye are familiar examples of reflex action. Control of the activities of various glands is also largely reflex in nature as are many of the reactions of the vascular, respiratory and digestive systems. The causal agent of the reflex may make an impression upon consciousness, as when a group of skeletal muscles contracts as a result of a painful stimulus; or the initiating stimulus as well as the reflex act itself may be entirely unperceived, as in the case of reflexes involving the secretion of glands or the activities of smooth muscle, e.g., of the blood vessels, heart or digestive tract. In some mammals many reflexes are present at birth, but in others (including man) only a few are present, and development of the central nervous system is very far from complete. The basic reflexes appear to be genetically determined, and provide a groundwork of inherited behavior that blends with control by higher centers.

## The Reflex Arc

The anatomical basis of reflex action is the reflex arc which in its simplest form consists of:

(a) *An afferent limb* composed of the *receptor organ*, which upon excitation, gives rise to nerve impulses and the *neuron* whose processes transmit the impulse to the central nervous system. In the case of the spinal reflex arc the cell bodies of the afferent neurons are situated in the posterior root ganglia.

(b) *An efferent limb* constituted of a motor neuron which conducts impulses from the central nervous system to an *effector organ*—muscle or gland. In the case of motor spinal reflex arcs, the axons of the efferent neurons leave the cord by the anterior nerve roots and travel in the peripheral nerves; their cell bodies are situated in the anterior horns.

(c) *A center* situated in the gray matter of the central nervous system and consisting of the cell body and dendrites of the efferent neuron and its junction (synapse) with the central process of the afferent neuron.

The afferent and efferent limbs may connect directly in the center, or one or more nerve cells may be interposed between the two. These are spoken of as *connector, internuncial,* or *intercalated neurons* (fig. 62.1). The stretch reflex (p. 1162) as shown by Lloyd is carried out through a reflex arc of only two neurons, but the great majority of the spinal reflex arcs in higher animals consist of several neurons, and in most reflexes each afferent neuron makes connection through collateral branches and internuncial neurons with a large number of motoneurons.

Injury, leading to loss of function of any one part of the reflex arc, is sufficient to destroy the function of the whole.

## The Receptor Organs

The afferent fibers end peripherally either as bare unmyelinated filaments or in accessory structures called *receptors* (fig. 62.2). These are specialized to respond most effectively to one or other type of stimulus. When stimulated appropriately an impulse or a series of impulses is sent along the afferent fiber. Receptors are situated in the skin, muscles, tendons, etc., and in such special organs as those of sight, hearing, smell and taste. They are also contained in the walls of the respiratory and digestive tracts, mesentery, carotid sinus and other internal structures. Through receptors in these various situations messages (nerve impulses) are continually being transmitted over somatic and autonomic pathways to the central nervous system.

Those receptors which respond to stimuli arising outside the body, e.g., in the skin, eye, ear, etc., are called *exteroceptors*. Of these, ones which make perception at a distince possible, i.e., those situated in the visual, auditory or olfactory sense

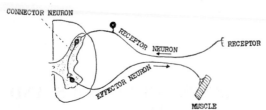

FIG. 62.1. Diagram of a simple reflex arc

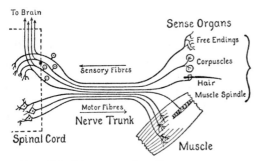

FIG. 62.2. Diagram to show the nervous connections between the central nervous system and the periphery (muscle and cutaneous receptors) (from Adrian, *The Basis of Sensation*).

organs, are sometimes referred to as *distance receptors* (telereceptors). Receptors lying in the mucous linings of the respiratory or digestive tracts are spoken of as *interoceptors*. *Proprioceptors* are those which respond to stimuli originating within the body itself, e.g., in the skeletal muscles, (p. 1146) tendons, joints, heart, carotid sinus, gastrointestinal wall, etc. Though each variety of receptor responds most readily to one particular type of stimulus—*adequate stimulus*—many will respond in some degree to stimuli of other types. The retina, for instance, can be stimulated mechanically or electrically and the receptors of taste, though responding most effectively to chemical stimuli, may also be stimulated by an electric shock applied to the tongue. A terminology based upon the type of stimulus which excites them adequately is sometimes used to designate different varieties of reception organ. Thus, *tango-* (touch), *chemo-* (taste, smell and the receptors of the carotid and aortic bodies) and *photo-* (light) *receptors* are spoken of.

## ANALYSIS OF SENSATION

The problems of the senses have been studied by two approaches. First, by using human subjects much can be learned by investigating what physical and chemical events they are able to detect and discriminate, but this involves much more than the sense organs; for example, a subjec-

tive threshold may depend on the state of the central nervous system as much as on the sensory receptors concerned. Secondly, objective methods of analysis can be used. Investigation of the action of receptors in setting up nerve impulses has received a great impetus in the last forty years by the improved methods of detecting nervous activity electrically. Much of this has been done in animal experiment, but structural similarities of sense organs in man and animals make it possible to apply this knowledge to interpret human sensory problems.

## CUTANEOUS SENSATIONS

The sensations which may be aroused by stimulation of the skin are *touch, cold, warmth* and *pain* Each of these sensations, except the last, is evoked from regions where sense organs possessing distinctive structural features are found. Small areas are mapped out upon the skin which are specific for one or other sensation. The areas are called touch, cold, heat or pain "spots" respectively in accordance with the sensation which their stimulation arouses (fig. 62.3). It must be emphasized that these spots are outlined by subjective methods, and maps vary from time to time in the same individual. They must not be confused with objectively demonstrable nerve endings. The latter are the basis from which 'spots' reach consciousness, but the central nervous system may select or reject components of the sensory discharge during transmission to the cortex. It must, also, be pointed out that it has recently been demonstrated that parts of the human skin which contain few endings that can be differentiated histologically, nevertheless have a wide range of subjective sensation that can be evoked by appropriate stimulation. It is possible that the site of the nerve ending within the skin may confer some specificity on it or that as yet unrecognised features of its structure may be concerned; but the elaborate encapsulated endings are found in skin surfaces of high sensory significance, e.g. finger tips etc.

If the mixed *nerve* supplying receptor organs is excited *directly* by the application of the type of stimulus, e.g., touch, heat, etc., for which the receptor itself is adapted to respond, the characteristic sensation is not, as a rule, aroused; a painful sensation usually results.[1] Moreover, reflexes

[1] Heinbecker, Bishop and O'Leary have reported that tactile as well as painful sensations may be aroused by the electrical stimulation of the nerve trunk. The experiments were carried out upon the exposed nerves of human subjects. Stim-

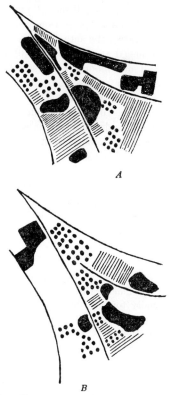

*A*

*B*

FIG. 62.3. Showing cold spots (A) and hot spots (B) within an area on the palm of the hand. The sensation in each case was most intense in the black areas, less intense in the lined and mildest in the dotted areas. In the blank portions no definite sensation was aroused (after Goldscheider).

can usually be elicited much more readily by stimulating the receptors than by applying the stimulus directly to the afferent nerve, and certain reflexes cannot be evoked at all by direct excitation of the nerve fiber. Pressure upon the pad of the hind foot of the "spinal dog", for example, causes a strong extension of the whole limb—the *extensor thrust*—whereas no form of stimulus applied directly to the afferent nerve itself will produce this reflex (Sherrington). The afferent fiber before terminating in the receptor organ or as a free nerve filament loses its myelin sheath and neurilemma and ends as a naked axis cylinder often branched or convoluted.

LIGHT TOUCH. Tactile sensation—the sensation aroused by light contact—is subserved by three types of receptor, *Meissner's corpuscles, Merkel's disks* and a basketlike arrangement of nerve fibers

surrounding the base of hair follicle (fig. 62.4). Meissner's corpuscles are situated in the papillae of the skin, just beneath the epidermis. They are unevenly distributed, being sparsely scattered over such a region as the volar aspect of the forearm but numerous in the skin of the hand, foot, nipple and lips, and in the mucous membrane of the tip of the tongue. They are well organized structures, consisting of irregularly coiled nerve endings with capsules of connective tissue. *Merkel's disks* consist of groups of three or more cup-shaped disks with a reticulated appearance (Fig. 62.4F). The nerve fiber upon approaching a group of such structures breaks up into branches, one going to each disk. Merkel's disks are found in the skin of the snouts of pigs and other mammals and in the fingertips, lips and mouth of man. The basketlike arrangement, surrounding the base of a hair follicle consists of a number of short, vertical, nerve filaments which end in small bulbous expansions. They are stimulated by any slight movements of the hairs.

Inequality of pressure with consequent deformation of the skin surface is the essential factor in the stimulation of touch receptors. If the pressure is distributed equally, and, therefore, no deformation of the skin occurs, a tactile sensation is not

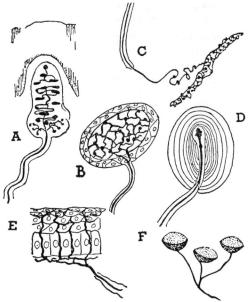

FIG. 62.4. Cutaneous receptors. A, Meissner's corpuscle (touch); B, Krause's end bulb (cold); C, Ruffini's end organs (warmth); D, Pacinian corpuscle (deep pressure); E, bare nerve endings in cornea (pain); F, Merkel's disks (touch) (in part from Bainbridge and Menzie, *Essentials of Physiology*, Longmann, Green and Co.).

uli of low intensity applied to the nerve aroused the sensation of touch, those of greater intensity a sensation of pain. No other type of sensation was experienced by the subjects.

experienced; when, for example, a finger is dipped into mercury a sensation is aroused only in the narrow band of skin where it is deformed as a result of unequal pressures at the interface between the mercury and air.

The sensation of light touch is tested by bringing a wisp of absorbent cotton in contact with the skin, or by the use of von Frey's esthesiometers. These consist of a series of hairs of graded thickness attached at right angles to wooden holders. The pressure in grams required to bend each hair is known. In order, therefore, to express the sensitivity of the skin to touch in terms of pressure the hair is found by trial which, when pressed vertically upon the skin until bending occurs, causes the sensation. The sensitivity of the skin to touch varies widely in different regions. The minimal pressures required are given in table 62.1. When hairy parts, such as the back of the hand, are lightly brushed with a tuft of cotton wool the hairs serving as levers deform the skin, and thus cause stimulation of touch receptors situated in the neighborhood of the hair follicles. Shaving the hairs over such parts greatly reduces the sensitivity to touch. Other regions quite devoid of hairs such as the finger tips and lips, on the other hand, possess tactile sensibility.

TACTILE LOCALIZATION. When a tactile stimulus is applied to a point upon the skin the normal subject is capable of recognizing the location of the stimulus with a high degree of accuracy. This faculty is termed *topognosia*. A tactile sensation has, thus, associated with it a localizing quality in addition to its specific characteristic, which has

TABLE 62.1

*The minimal pressures required for the elicitation of the sensation of touch from various cutaneous regions*

(After Meyers)

| Region | Grams per Square Millimeter |
|---|---|
| Nose | 2 |
| Lips | 2.5 |
| Tip of finger | 3 |
| Back of finger | 5 |
| Upper arm, inner surface of thigh | 7 |
| Back of hand | 12 |
| Calf, shoulder | 16 |
| Abdomen | 26 |
| Front of leg, sole of foot | 28 |
| Back of forearm | 33 |
| Loin | 48 |

been called "local sign". Though there is a neural basis for point to point projection of skin areas to the cerebral cortex, the actual faculty of locating the point touched appears to be acquired by experience and not inborn. Localization is much more precise over some regions, such as lips and tips of the fingers, than over others, such as the forearm or thigh. In some nervous diseases this localization is grossly impaired. In certain lesions of the cerebral cortex the subject usually, according to Horsley, when asked to locate the stimulus indicates a point some distance from it on the *proximal* side. In some diseases, notably hysteria, the subject feels the stimulus at a corresponding point on the opposite side of the body; or in a limb on the side opposite to that to which the stimulus was applied; this phenomenon is called *allocheiria*.

The localization of a cold, hot or painful sensation is very inaccurate unless the stimulating agent actually touches the skin. Thus, heat radiated from a small object about 1 mm. from the cutaneous surface gives rise to a diffuse sensation. The more accurate localization when contact is made with the skin is evident though the subject experiences no sensation of touch. It is likely, nevertheless, that the tactile receptors are excited, that the failure to appreciate touch is due to masking by the stronger stimulus, and that impulses arising in the touch endings are responsible for the more accurate localization of the other types of stimulus when these are applied directly to the skin.

TACTILE DISCRIMINATION (TWO-POINT SENSIBILITY, COMPASS TEST). If two stimuli are applied simultaneously, two distinct sensations are felt, provided the distance between the two stimulated points is sufficiently great. Thus, when the points of a pair of compasses are blunted or covered with cotton wool and applied to the finger tip, the subject recognizes the duality of the stimulus if the points are more than about 2.3 mm. apart. When they are separated by a shorter distance a single sensation is experienced. The minimal distance at which the recognition of two stimuli is possible varies in different regions, as shown in table 62.2.

In the case of the limbs the power of discrimination diminishes progressively from the distal to the more proximal segments, and hairless regions in general have a higher discriminating ability than those covered with hair.

A correspondence is also exhibited between the mobility of a part and its discriminating ability. For example, the minimal distance necessary for two stimuli to give rise to a double sensation is less for the fingers and hand than for the arm, shoulder and back, and diminishes progressively over the skin of the face from the region of the ear to the lips.

It should be pointed out that the values given in the foregoing table do not represent the distances separating individual touch receptors, and tactile sensation can be evoked from single stimuli applied successively from points only 0.1 mm. apart. The density of receptors in the surface is only one of the factors enabling the central nervous system to discriminate characteristics of the stimulus.

TICKLING AND ITCHING. There has been much discussion concerning the origins of these sensations. The *tickling* sensation caused by light stimulation of the skin, as by a straw, appears to be due to the summed effects of stimulating both touch and pain endings. Section of the lateral spinothalamic tract (which conveys pain impulses) results in the loss of the appreciation of pain but retention of the sense of touch; a tickling sensation cannot be aroused over the analgesic skin. On the other hand, the sense of touch is lost while that of pain is retained, when the skin is rendered moderately ischemic; again, the tickling sensation cannot be elicited. The *itchiness* which is experienced in the region adjacent to a slight injury, or during the healing of a more severe injury when the skin is rubbed, is also dependent upon impulses travelling by both tactile and pain fibers, but the *spontaneous* itching (i.e., in the absence of any external stimulus) which is felt under the same circumstances, may be due to the mild stimulation of pain endings alone. This type of itchiness is affected relatively little by ischemia. Both types of itching are attributed to a chemical

### TABLE 62.2

*Different cutaneous areas compared with regard to the minimal distance which must separate two stimulated points in order to arouse a double sensation*

(After Meyers)

| Region | Minimal Distance |
|---|---|
| | *mm.* |
| Volar surface of finger tip | 2.3 |
| Dorsal surface of third phalanx | 6.8 |
| Palm of hand | 11.3 |
| Sole of foot | 16.0 |
| Back of hand | 31.6 |
| Back of neck | 54.0 |
| Middle of back, upper arm and thigh | 67.1 |

stimulator acting upon nerve endings and liberated by the damaged cells of the skin. This substance appears to be the same as that which causes the triple response. An extract of skin showing this response when injected into normal skin induces both types of itching. Histamine introduced into the skin has a similar effect. Rothman believes that itching is mediated by the C group of nerve fibers.

COLD may be mediated by the end organs of Krause (fig. 62.4B) and *warmth* probably by the end organs of Ruffini (fig. 62.4C).[2] Mechanical or electrical stimulation, as well as the application of heat itself, will stimulate the latter end organs and give rise to the sensation of warmth. The receptors for warmth (Ruffini's) are situated in close proximity to the deep plexus of blood vessels; when these latter dilate the endings are stimulated by the warmer blood coming from deeper regions. The cold receptors are also stimulated at temperatures above 112°F. giving rise to a sensation, not of heat but of cold. Cold, of course, is a negative quality—the sensation being due to the withdrawal of heat. It would be more correct, therefore, to say that the cold receptors are stimulated at extremes of temperature, above 112°F. or below that at which the warm receptors respond. When mapped on the skin, cold and touch spots are much less numerous than touch and pain spots.

PRESSURE upon the skin considerably greater than that which elicits the sensation of touch stimulates the more deeply lying receptors including the *Pacinian corpuscles* (fig. 62.4 D). The

---

[2] Waterston and others have questioned the existence of definite heat and cold spots since it has been found that the points from which these sensations can be aroused change from time to time in number as well as in pattern. He states that when the skin is hyperemic the entire surface responds to warmth (punctate distribution being abolished) and he believes that the entire skin surface is potentially sensitive to this sensation, the apparent punctate distribution being due simply to fluctuations in the activity of different areas. The variability in sensation, it has been suggested, may possibly be related to a corresponding fluctuation in the capillary circulation. The observations of Bazett and associates indicate, however, that the diffuse nature of the temperature sensations in hyperemic skin can be best explained upon the basis of a more ready conduction of heat through the blood stream to neighboring end organs; thus, when the cutaneous blood flow is profuse, heat applied to a nonsensitive point in the skin would be conducted rapidly to adjacent warm spots. The observations of Bazett and his colleagues upon the sensitivity of the prepuce support the conception of heat and cold spots and the existence of discrete receptor organs for these sensations as well as for touch (Arch. Neur. Psych. 1932, 27, 489).

sensation of pressure is not, however, a true cutaneous sensation; the Pacinian corpuscles are situated in the subcutaneous tissues or inner layers of the dermis as well as in tendons, periosteum and other deep-seated structures; their nerve fibers run chiefly, not in the cutaneous nerves, but in the sensory fibers of mixed nerves supplying muscles, tendons, joints and blood vessels. Since the sense of deep pressure is preserved after sectioning the cutaneous nerves, the loss of light touch, a purely cutaneous sense, may, therefore, be undetected in a lesion affecting this sensation, unless the contact is made very lightly, as by a wisp of cotton wool, with the skin; otherwise receptors in the subcutaneous tissues may be stimulated.

PAIN is subserved by naked nerve endings, there being no organized end organ for this sensation. The pain nerves of the skin are described by Woollard as consisting mostly of non-medullated fibers which terminate in the superficial layers of the dermis in delicate loops lying parallel to the skin surface, or as long naked neurofibrillae. Only occasionally do fibrils penetrate the epidermis. Bare nerve endings mediating pain are also present in the cornea (fig. 62.4E) and in serous surfaces (peritoneum, pleura, etc.); touch, cold and warm endings are absent and the corresponding sensations cannot be aroused from these locations. Although it has been the general belief that the cornea contains only pain endings and that any stimulus, if intense enough to evoke a response at all, causes pain. The sensation of cold can, however, be elicited from the cornea, and according to some, the sensation of touch without pain can be aroused by a very mild stimulus such as a jet of isotonic saline. Certain structures, e.g., the tooth pulp, the middle meningeal artery, the arteries at the base of the brain and some of the vessels of the scalp contain no sensory fibers except those which give rise to pain. Other structures, on the contrary, e.g., the substance of the brain and the mucosa of the cheek opposite the second lower molar tooth, are insensitive to pain.

Most of the pain impulses arising in the skin travel to the central nervous system in the somatic nerves, but some of those from deeper structures join autonomic nerves. All enter the central nervous system by the lateral divisions of the posterior spinal nerve roots or the cranial nerves.

The pain endings do not respond selectively to one variety of stimulus but to any type whether mechanical, chemical or thermal, provided it is sufficiently intense. The pain stimulus, whatever

it may be, has one property in common, namely, that it is of a nature to cause injury. The sensation of pain therefore serves a protective purpose, giving warning of injurious stimuli. Stimuli which arouse painful sensations also provoke reflex actions which have the following features. (a) They comprise movements for *protection* or *defense*, or for the withdrawal of the part from the noxious agent. (b) They are *prepotent*, other less urgent reflexes being for the time inhibited. (c) They are *imperative* and can override voluntary control. Such reflexes are called *nociceptive*.

### PERCEPTION OF AND REACTION TO PAIN

*Pain thresholds.* A distinction should be drawn between the *perception of pain* and the *reaction* which results, e.g., contraction of facial muscles, vocalization, narrowing of eyelids, changes in pulse rate or rise in blood pressure, sweating, and vasomotor responses. The threshold can be conveniently measured by focussing heat from a lamp on the forehead for 3 sec. and measuring the intensity which becomes painful. The subject indicates the perception threshold verbally and the reactivity threshold may be found by detecting when a change of skin resistance occurs by a wheatstone bridge and galvanometer.

In man the *perception threshold*, under similar conditions, remains remarkably constant between normal persons, and for the same person from day to day, or from hour to hour of the day. The threshold is altered, however, by such extraneous influences as a loud noise, gripping some object or clenching the jaws, which may raise it by 40 per cent. The threshold may be definitely raised by a placebo, and some distraction, such as pain or discomfort, in one situation may reduce the perception of pain in another. The twitch applied to a horse's nose during a minor operation is a familiar example. Even other sensations, e.g., touch, pressure (rubbing), warmth, etc., may raise the pain threshold. The analgesic action of counterirritation is, in some instances, dependent upon such an effect. Hypnosis also raises very considerably the perception threshold, as do alcohol and, of course, other analgesic drugs.

The *threshold of reaction* to pain varies widely between different subjects. In those of a stoical, phlegmatic temperament, in prize-fighters, Negroes and North American Indians the threshold is high whereas in "high-strung", neurotic persons it is low. Alcohol and analgesic drugs raise the reaction threshold to a greater degree than they do the perception threshold (Wolff and Haryd).

*Cutaneous pain.* A blindfolded subject is unable to distinguish between the pain caused by a pin prick, a hot point, a punctate electrical stimulus or the plucking of a hair, provided no associated nonpainful sensation gives the patient a clue as to the nature of the stimulating agent. These pains would all be described as sharp, "bright" or pricking. A burning pain is experienced when the sensation is more prolonged, whether caused by heat or ulta-violet light or by a chemical or mechanical irritant. There is no spatial summation of pain stimuli, i.e., the threshold for pain is not influenced by the extent of the area stimulated. Nor, in contrast to stimulation by touch or warmth, adaptation to a painful stimulus does not occur; pain continues to be felt as long as the stimulus is applied. The biological significance of this is obvious.

*First and second pain.* It is a common experience that a single painful stimulus applied to the skin, if intense enough, may give rise to two sensations separated by a short interval. The first pain is short and sharp, the second, more prolonged and severe. The observations of Lewis and Pochin upon this phenomenon indicate that pain impulses are conveyed from the skin by two sets of nerve fibers, one of which is rapidly conducting, the other with a much slower conduction rate. They found that ischemia of the skin of the arm, induced by arresting the circulation, abolished the first response to the needle prick, the second response being unaltered for a time but later becoming reduced. Cocaine, on the other hand, abolished the second response before the first. It was shown moreover, that the time interval between the two responses was prolonged as the length of the nerve between the point of stimulation and the central nervous system was increased, a fact which seems to demonstrate decisively the existence of a fast and slow pathway for the transmission of cutaneous pain. The time interval between the two responses is 1.9 sec. when the stimulus is applied to the toe, 1.3 sec. to the knee and only 0.9 sec. to the upper limit of the thigh.

The first painful sensation of the dual response appears to travel by fibers conducting at 30–8 M. per sec. and is mediated by myelinated fibers; they are more susceptible to asphyxia; the second pain response is transmitted by the slowly conducting C group of fibers (conduction rate of less than 2 m. per sec.); they are more readily affected by cocaine.

The rapidly transmitted pain appears to be the sensory basis for protective reflexes. Pochin found that the "fast pain" is abolished in tabes but the "slow pain" is retained. In this disease the response to pin prick is delayed, the withdrawal reflex abolished, and the larger fibers are the first to be destroyed.

A third type of pain response follows some little time after certain forms of injury, e.g., scorching, scalding, sunburn or the application of an irritating agent, and persists for a variable period. Even a slight burn may cause a dull pain which continues for many minutes. This pain evidently is caused by the release of a chemical substance from the damaged tissues and not by direct action of the stimulating agent upon the nerve terminals. Arresting the blood supply to the part intensifies and prolongs the pain. The chemical excitant does not appear to be potassium, nor acetylcholine; nor is it due to altered pH. It has not yet been isolated chemically.

*Dissociation of cutaneous sensations.* In disease, the several modalities of sensation, touch, cold, warmth, and pain may be lost separately, or they may be temporarily dissociated by artificial means as by asphyxia, cocaine or the application of cold. Thus, the cutaneous sensations, touch, cold, warmth and pain are lost in this order when the skin is made ischemic. If the skin is cocainized, the appreciation of cold is lost first; then follow in order the senses of warmth, pain and touch. Cooling the skin causes first, failure of cold sensations, then in succession the sensations of touch, pain and warmth are lost. Also, after section of a cutaneous nerve, the area of pain loss is smaller than that of touch; there is thus a boundary zone from which a response to a painful stimulus, such as that of a pin prick, can be obtained but which is insensitive to light touch.

*Deep sensibility.* Pain in the deep structures, muscles, bones and joints, etc., the sense of pressure in the subcutaneous tissues, and sense of position and movement (e.g., kinesthetic sense) of joints, come in to the category of deep sensibility. Deep sensibility is mediated by afferent fibers in the mixed nerves. Pain arising in deep structures differs in certain respects from superficial pain. It is poorly localized (ch. 43), and is often of a dull, aching or "sickening" character as compared with superficial pain which tends more usually to have a "bright", sharp or burning quality. Deep pain is more often accompanied by nausea and vomiting, slowing of the pulse, and a fall in blood pressure, whereas cutaneous pain is more commonly associated with a quickening of the pulse and a rise in blood pressure.

Muscles, tendons and fasciae are especially susceptible to painful stimulation by chemical agents. The injection of a few drops of a 6 per cent saline solution into one of these structures causes pain. Muscle is relatively insensitive to pricking or cutting but pain is aroused by pressure, e.g., pinching or squeezing, or by exercising under ischemic conditions (p. 1143). Severe tension acts also as a pain stimulus for muscle, tendon or fascia. Pain occurring in ischemic muscle during activity is due to a chemical irritant produced by active tissues and which accumulates and stimulates the pain endings when the circulation to the part is arrested or considerably reduced. This substance is referred to as factor P by Lewis and his associates. The soreness of healthy muscles which comes on some hours after exercise may be of the same nature.

Periosteum and cancellous bone are very sensitive to the various types of mechanical stimulation, but compact bone is insensitive to drilling or sawing. The arteries give rise to painful sensations when pricked, but the walls of the veins, except the larger intracranial veins, are usually insensitive.

*Visceral pain* and *referred pain* are dealt with in chapter 43, *central pain* in chapters 66 and 67, and *headache* in chapter 67.

*Hyperalgesia.* In many persons an area of tenderness develops around even a small cutaneous injury and spreads for a considerable distance in all directions. The soreness starts within a few seconds, increases to a maximum in from 15 to 30 minutes and lasts for hours or, with a more severe injury, for days. The threshold for pain as tested by a needle prick is lowered only slightly over the area, but the pain when aroused is diffuse, and unusually intense and prolonged. This phenomenon has been studied by Lewis and his associates. Injury was produced by prolonged faradic stimulation of the skin, by crushing a small cutaneous fold with forceps or by direct stimulation of a cutaneous nerve trunk or one of its branches. A similar area of cutaneous hyperalgesia may result from an injury or an inflammatory process involving deep-lying tissue or mucous membrane. Thus, stimulation of a dental nerve or of the mucous membrane of the maxillary antrum is followed by tenderness of the overlying skin of the cheek. Lewis' experiments point to a specific system of nerves in the skin as being responsible for the hyperalgesia. They are not sympathetic filaments,

for the phenomenon is observed in skin completely deprived of its sympathetic innervation. Lewis concluded that the nerve fibers responsible were distinct from pain fibers and suggested a separate innervation of 'nocifensor' fibers; this has not been supported by more recent work such as that of Weddel on the distribution and sensitivity of fibers in human skin. It is now thought that the nocifensor fibers are the same as the fine branching fibers subserving slow pain. Impulses arising in the damaged region spread via branching fibers to release a chemical excitant in neighboring areas; this alters the responsiveness of the endings of other fibers round the area of damage.

A similar process has been demonstrated in animal experiments by recording the action potentials from small skin nerves.

### Epicritic, Protopathic and Deep Sensibilities

Head and his associates, from the study of a large number of peripheral nerve injuries, grouped the several superficial sensations into two classes: (1) *epicritic*, and (2) *protopathic*. The sensations grouped under *epicritic sensibility* included light touch over hairless parts, the power of localizing the point touched, the detection of two individual sensations when two points are touched simultaneously, and the appreciation of finer grades of temperature, cool and warm, i.e., temperatures ranging between about 40° and 25°C. *Protopathic sensibility* is a more primitive type of sensation and more widely distributed. It includes pain and the temperature sensations aroused by extremes of heat and cold—above 40° to 50°C. and below 20° to 25°C. In other words, protopathic sensibility possesses a high threshold; but, though the stimulus must be strong in order to arouse a sensation, this once aroused is intense, diffuse, poorly localized and peculiarly unpleasant in quality. These latter qualities of protopathic sensibility are particularly prominent in the absence of epicritic sensibility, which therefore has been considered to exert a restraining influence upon the former. The glans penis possesses only portopathic and deep sensibilities.

For the purpose of studying these two types of sensation, Head underwent an operation in which his radial nerve and the cutaneous branches of the musculocutaneous nerve were severed at the elbow. After the operation there was *complete* loss of cutaneous sensation over the radial half of the back of the hand. Surrounding this was a narrow zone in which epicritic sensibility alone was lost; protopathic was retained. This is due to over-lapping of the protopathic innervation of the adjacent unaffected skin area. Over a small triangular area of skin at the wrist the relationship between these two sensations was reversed; protopathic sensibility was lost but epicritic retained. Stopford has since shown that this latter type of dissociation of the two groups of sensations is also characteristic of section of a posterior root—the area of protopathic loss being much greater than epicritic. In Head's experiment evidence of returning sensation (due to regeneration of the nerves) was noticed on the 43rd day after operation when the zone of protopathic sensation was found to have become broader and to have encroached upon the totally insensitive area. The original area insensitive to light touch remained unreduced. Within about six months *protopathic* sensibility had returned over nearly the entire area, yet the extent of the *epicritic* loss remained unaltered. The first signs of the return of epicritic sensation was not observed until a year after the operation and was not complete after the lapse of two years. Deep sensibility was not affected by the nerve section referred to above; it is not mediated by fibers running in superficial nerves. Moderate pressure could be everywhere appreciated. This is an important point to remember in the investigation of nerve lesions since it shows that crude methods for studying the sensations of touch may fail to reveal any loss. The superficial touch receptors are stimulated by light contact with a wisp of cotton or by the pressure of a fine hair, whereas a pressure not very much greater, as with the point of a pencil, will stimulate the deeper lying pressure receptors whose nerve fibers may be intact. As a result of these experiments in which dissociation of the three types of sensation were clearly demonstrated, Head and his associates concluded that each sensation was mediated by a separate and structurally distinct group of fibers. Unquestionably, a deep sensibility is conveyed by fibers separate from those responsible for cutaneous sensations, but that epicritic and protopathic sensations has each its specific fiber group has been seriously questioned. The work of Erlanger and Gasser and of Ranson appeared to lend support to Head's interpretation. The C fibers of the former authors were suggested as the possible mediators of protopathic sensation, and the A group, of epicritic Ranson had previously described unmyelinated fibers in the cutaneous nerves which, since they were believed to mediate pain might offer an anatomical basis for the primitive protopathic sensations. The existence of protopathic sensation only in the glans penis and the dissociation of the two sensations, which as shown by Stopford result from section of the posterior roots, also supported Head's conception of two distinct sets of fibers. Experiments by other neurologists, on the other hand, have failed to substantiate this contention (see Trotter and Davies). Some would explain the two classes of cutaneous sensation following nerve section upon the basis of different rates of regeneration of the receptor organs, the terminals of the pain fibers being thought to regenerate first. Fine discrimination, according to Heinbecker, is dependent upon the *number* of active end organs within a given area. The zone of protopathic sensibility surrounding an anesthetic area caused by nerve section is ascribed simply to the presence, in reduced numbers, of intact afferent endings which have overlapped the field of distribution of the sectioned fibers.

The recognition of these two types of sensation is of distinct value from a clinical standpoint, and reflects the fact that conscious appreciation of a sensory message depends on all its components; removal of part of the message leads to the appearance of abnormal sensations such as isolated protopathic pain.

*Vibration sense, pallesthesia.* This is the ability to perceive stimuli of a vibratory nature applied to the body surface, as by means of a low-pitched tuning fork, or other vibrating instrument. They arise if the stimulus is applied to bone tendon and muscle and are therefore part of the system of deep sensibility. Pollock has shown that the vibration sense is retained though the superficial sensations have been lost, which indicates that it is conveyed by fibers other than those mediating the latter sensations, namely by the deep system. Receptors for vibration sense are probably also situated in the deeper layers of the skin, and in the subcutaneous tissues. Though the sense is usually elicited by placing a vibrating tuning fork upon a bone, e.g. the shin or some other superficial bone, it can be aroused by applying the instrument to the soft tissues. The structures which respond to vibration are the proprioceptors of tendon and muscle. The basis of this sense is probably the stimulation of receptors by rapid mechanical changes in pressure which will cause many receptors to set up impulses together in time with the tuning fork.

Testing the vibration sense is an important diagnostic aid in neurological conditions. It is impaired or lost (and often before the sensation of touch or kinesthetic sense is affected) in lesions of the peripheral nerves, or of the posterior columns of the cord, but is not affected if both tactile and kinesthetic senses are intact—a fact that supports the view that it is mediated by the same receptors which subserve both of these sensations.

*Stereognosis* (G. *sterio*, solid + *gnosis*, knowledge), *stereognostic perception*. This is the ability to recognize, with the eyes closed, the size, weight and shape of objects placed in the hand or upon some other part. The absence of this sense is called *astereognosis*. When placed in the hand of a normal person while his eyes are closed, a coin, button, chain, ball or cube is easily identified from its size, weight, shape, texture (fur, wool, mesh) etc. Recognition may be made, though less readily, even if the object is laid upon the foot or pressed against the toes. Stereognosis is not a separate sense, but depends upon the senses of touch, spatial discrimination, cutaneous localization, and the kinesthetic sense. It is impaired or lost in lesions of the peripheral nerves or posterior columns of the cord, or of the somesthetic area of the cerebral cortex.

### THE PROPRIOCEPTORS OF MUSCLES, TENDONS AND JOINTS

The receptors situated in skeletal muscles and in the tendons and joints furnish information to the central nervous system concerning the movements and positions of the limbs and other parts. Afferent fibers carrying this information make up from $\frac{1}{3}$ to $\frac{1}{2}$ of the fibers in a so-called motor nerve. As a result of the messages received by the nervous centers, the contractions of individual muscles and groups of muscles are coördinated to produce smooth, finely adjusted and effective movements which would be impossible in the absence of such guidance from the periphery. For this reason the term *kinesthetic* is applied to this group of receptors. A proportion of these afferent impulses arouse no sensation, their information being delivered to centers lying beneath consciousness. To others are due the sensations grouped in the section under deep sensibility. The receptors in the situations mentioned respond to mechanical stimulation, e.g., pressure or stretch. These types of stimulus are furnished by the strains and stresses set up in the muscles, tendons and joints during muscular contraction.

The sensory endings in the various situations mentioned above are of four main types: (1) *muscle spindles*, (2) *Golgi corpuscles*, (3) *Pacinian corpuscles*, and (4) *unencapsulated nerve endings*.

(1) *The muscle spindle* is a fusiform body from 0.75 to 4 mm. long and from 0.1 to 0.2 mm. broad lying parallel to and between the muscle fibers (fig. 62.5). It is constituted of a bundle of from 3 to 10 muscle fibers (*intrafusal fibers*) enclosed in a fibrous capsule. The latter is separated from

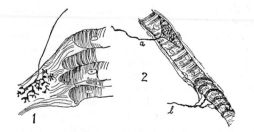

FIG. 62.5. 1. Golgi ending in tendon; 2. intrafusal fiber showing, *a*, muscle flower-spray and *b*, annulo-spiral endings.

the intrafusal fibers by a lymph space bridged across by delicate septa. The intrafusal fibers differ from the ordinary fibers of the muscle in being smaller and more circular on cross section, and in having a greater number of nuclei and coarser striations. The nerve supply of the spindle is double—afferent and efferent. The former enters the spindle about its center, the latter more toward one or other end. The efferent fibers are mostly small (7 to 10 $\mu$) and go to end plates on the intrafusal muscle fibers. They are designated $\gamma$ fibers to distinguish them from the larger $\alpha$ motor fibers supplying the rest of a muscle. The afferent fibers end in two ways. The large (17–18 $\mu$) fibers coil round the middle of an intrafusal fiber to form an annulospinal ending. Smaller fibers go towards the ends of the spindle and ramify to form endings, called from their appearance, flower spray endings of Ruffini.

(2) *The Golgi corpuscles* (fig. 62.5) are situated in tendons and consist of a bundle of tendinous fibers surrounded by a lymph space and enclosed within a fibrous capsule. Afferent nerve fibers enter the organ near its center and ramify upon its constituent fibers. Tension is the adequate stimulus for these receptors.

(3) *The Pacinian corpuscles* are oval bodies composed of concentric laminae, like the "skins" of a sectioned onion. The afferent fiber penetrates to the center of the corpuscle. Pressure is the adequate stimulus. These receptor organs are found in tendons, joints, periosteum, especially beneath tendinous insertions, in fasciae covering muscles and in subcutaneous tissues (fig. 62.4D). They are also found in the mesentery.

(4) *Free nerve endings* lie between the muscle fibers, in tendons and in the fasciae and joints. They mediate deep pain.

### THE RESPONSES OF RECEPTORS

When the action potential of a nerve trunk, e.g., frog sciatic, is recorded following maximal stimulation, the potential recorded is a substantial fraction of that occurring across the membranes of the axons. About 30 mv. may appear at electrodes on the surface; from experiments with microelectrodes it is known that the action potential of each fiber is of the order of 100 mv.; the difference is due to the partial shortcircuiting of the action potentials by interstitial fluids and connective tissue, and because the internal resistance of the fibers is high, the potential at the nerve surface is lowered. When only a single fiber in a nerve trunk is active, the action potential recorded from electrodes on the surface may be only a few microvolts. The impulses occurring naturally in sensory nerves are not synchronized in the different units, and hence it was not possible to analyze them by recording action potentials until the invention of the valve amplifier enabled them to be magnified, and then recorded, with insensitive but rapidly deflecting instruments such as oscillographs; for the last 20 years the cathode ray oscillograph has been generally used for this purpose. Adrian and his associates at Cambridge first recorded the activity of individual sensory fibers in various mixed nerves, e.g., in the frog's sciatic, set up by stretching the gastrocnemius, from fibers supplying touch receptors in the frog's skin, and from digital nerves of the cat during stimulation of receptors in the toe pad.

*Sense organs in muscle.* The response of a single muscle spindle to stretch was first investigated by Adrian and Zotterman. They employed the sterno-cutaneous muscle of the frog which arises from the abdominal wall and is inserted into the skin. The whole muscle contains only three or four muscle spindles and by removal of portions of the muscle, a preparation containing a single spindle with intact nerve fiber, was obtained. Stretching the muscle caused a *rhythmic* discharge of impulses up the nerve fiber. Increasing the stimulation by greater stretch did not increase the magnitude of the action potentials but the frequency with which they recurred increased up to over 100 per sec. This behavior has been found to be general and seen in many types of sensory receptor. The intensity of the stimulus is signalled by the frequency of impulses and these following the all-or-nothing law are all the same size. When groups of receptors are studied they vary in threshold and an increasing stimulus leads to a greater total nerve impulse discharge both by more units coming into action and by the response increasing in frequency. Matthews employed the small extensor muscle situated on the side of the middle

toe of the frog which often contains only one muscle spindle. Impulses can be recorded from a branch of the peroneal nerve supplying it. The muscle spindle was stimulated by loading the muscle at various rates with different weights. It was found that (a) the frequency of impulses set up was roughly proportional to the logarithm of the load; (b) the frequency was much higher during rapid extension than if the load were applied slowly; (c) at 16°C. the maximum impulse frequency was about 290 per sec. Upon altering the temperature the maximum frequency of impulses varied in much the same way as the refractory period of nerve. Matthews, by dividing muscle nerves until only one sensory fiber was active, found in mammalian muscle that the flower-spray and annulo-spiral endings in the spindles and the Golgi tendon organs are all stimulated by passive stretch. Those in the spindle responded to the rate of extension as well as its magnitude while those in the tendon were little affected by rapid stretch. The response of some endings ceased during active contraction which relieves the strain upon them (see fig. 62.5); but some endings, thought to be the annulo-spiral type, which cease to respond if contraction is just maximal, accelerate their discharge if the stimulus to the nerve is supramaximal for contraction. This was attributed to contraction of the intrafusal muscle fibers increasing the stress upon the nerve endings. The high threshold agreed with the known small size of the motor fibers ending within the spindles now designated as gamma fibers. Hunt and Kuffler have since confirmed that the sensitivity of the muscle spindle is controlled by the activity of the gamma fibers; these have been found to be activated from the central nervous system under a number of conditions.

The Golgi endings respond to stretch of the tendons whether passive or induced by contraction of the muscle and can thus signal the total tension in the muscle.

*Adaptation.* The rhythmic discharge of impulses set up by the stimulation of a receptor diminishes in frequency and may cease entirely though the stimulus remains at constant intensity. For instance, if a weight is placed on tactile receptors in the frog's skin, a burst of impulses in many fibers occurs during deformation of the skin, but after one or two seconds this discharge may cease entirely. This phenomenon is spoken of as *adaptation* (see fig. 62.6). Adaptation occurs at a very different rate in different types of receptor (see fig. 62.7). Adaptation must be distinguished

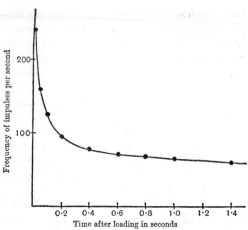

Fig. 62.6. Adaptation. Graph of response during first second after sudden loading with a large load. 100 gm. Temperature 14°C. (After Matthews).

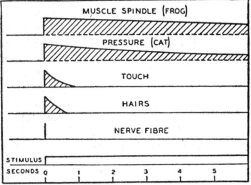

Fig. 62.7. Showing the response of nerve fiber and of different types of receptor to a continued stimulus. Adaptation is most rapid in the nerve fiber and slowest in the muscle spindle (from Adrian, *The Basis of Sensation*, Christophers, London).

from fatigue. If the stimulus is removed and re-applied, even after a very short interval, a new outburst of impulses appears. Adaptation is not produced by the setting up of impulses, for it may be shown that if electrically evoked impulses are backfired into a muscle spindle, no adaptation is produced. Adaptation is associated with the presence of the stimulus rather than with the activity of the tissue. End organs are not easy to fatigue, but fatigue is hastened by oxygen lack whereas adaptation is less altered.

The physiological importance of adaptation is very great. The unchanging state of the environment is of much less importance to an organism than new stimuli; adaptation acts to make new events in the environment have a major stimulating effect on the sense organs and leaves only a small inflow to the nervous system under stationary states. This emphasis on new components in the sensory environment may be further enhanced by transformations within the central nervous system. We can see the result of such processes in human sensation and we speak of "becoming accustomed" to some environmental change which initially caused a large effect. We do not feel the contact of our clothes; a hot bath feels much hotter on first contact with it than a short time later. Only the nerve endings subserving slow pain appear not to adapt.

Some very slowly-adapting nerve endings are found, for example the otolithic organs of crustacea, and many of the vertebrate muscle proprioceptors adapt very slowly and a discharge continues for an hour or more if the stimulus is maintained. Again, the endings of carotid sinus, aorta and those excited by inflation of the lung, all have slow rates of adaptation. At the other extreme the endings surrounding hair follicles adapt so rapidly that when a hair is moved, impulses cease as soon as the hair comes to rest though displaced to a new position. A Pacinian corpuscle deformed suddenly may set up only one impulse.

*The genesis of rhythmic discharge.* At the nerve ending the stimulus operates to produce a state in which the axon is excited at regular intervals. In terms of the membrane theory of nerve, it is supposed that the appropriate stimulus acts by producing a partial depolarisation of the terminations, so allowing current to flow from more distant regions. This is confirmed by the recent demonstration of *generator potentials* occurring in simple sense organs. Thus Katz has demonstrated that in the frog's muscle spindle a long-lasting change of potential occurs near the terminations when stretch is applied, and that this remains after impulse generation and conduction by the axon are abolished by anaesthesia. Similar potentials have been demonstrated by Gray in the Pacinian corpuscle. In the crustacean stretch receptor the cell body lies peripherally, and microelectrodes within it have been shown by Kuffler to record the local changes accompanying stretch of the muscle which initiated a rhythmic discharge. Rhythmic discharges can be evoked by constant current stimulation of many nonmedullated and some medullated nerve fibers; in some sensory end organs applied steady currents raise or lower the rate of rhythmic response by summing algebraically with the normal generator potential.

*Specific sensations.* Accessory nonneural portions of the sense organ act to raise the threshold to some types of stimulation and lower it to others, and thus confer specificity in the sensitivity of the receptor. Thus, for example, chemical agents are unable to penetrate the lamellae of the Pacinian corpuscle at all rapidly, so ensuring insensitivity to chemical stimuli, while transmitting the effect of mechanical deformation. This specificity is rarely complete and, for example in the dog, pressure on the thermal endings will increase the response to a thermal stimulus, and pressure on taste buds will increase the response to chemical stimuli. It has long been known that structures in the retina can be stimulated by pressing on the eyeball and give a sensation of a light stimulus. The taste buds can also be stimulated electrically. The pain endings which have no encapsulation are most readily reached by chemical agents, and on injury occurring, cell breakdown products appear to be the normal stimulus.

In conscious sensations the quality ascribed depends largely on the pathway by which impulses arrive at the higher levels of the central nervous system. Thus impulses in the VIIIth nerve, whether set up by an electric stimulus applied via fluid in the external meatus or by air borne pressure patterns, are appreciated as sound, those from the IInd nerve as light, whether due to light or pressure on the eyeball. Cutting Gower's tract abolishes pain sensations from areas one segment below the lesion (contralateral); only impulses ascending by this pathway arouse pain.

The various pathways to the brain come from receptors protected from some of the physical or chemical events in the environment and organised to be very sensitive to others, so conferring a specificity which enables the brain to separate events into recognisable categories.

## REFERENCES

ADRIAN, E. D., CATTELL, McK. and HOAGLAND, H. J. Physiol., 1931, 72, 377.

ADRIAN, E. D. and UMRATH, K. J. Physiol., 1929, 68, 139.

CATTELL, McK. and HOAGLAND, H. J. Physiol., 1931, 72, 392.

HEAD, H., RIVERS, W. H. R. and SHERREN, J. Brain, 1905, 28, 99. RIVERS, W. H. R. and HEAD, H. Brain, 1908, 31, 323. See also, BORING, E. G. Quart. J. Exper. Physiol., 1916, 10, 1. SHARPEY-SCHAFER, E. Brain, 1927, 50, 538. Quart. J. Exper. Physiol., 1928, 19, 85. TROTTER, W. and DAVIES, H. M. J. Physiol., 1909, 38, 134.

HEINBECKER, P., BISHOP, G. H. and O'LEARY, J. Arch. Neur. Psychiat., 1933, 29, 771. Ibid., 1934, 31, 34.

LEWIS, T. Clin. Sc., 1936, 2, 373. Brit. M. J., 1938, 1, 321.

LEWIS, T. and POCHIN, E. E. Clin. Sc., 1937, 3, 67.

LLOYD, D. J. Neurophysiol., 1943, 6, 111; 293; 317.

MATTHEWS, B. H. C. J. Physiol., 1931, 71, 64. Ibid., 72, 153.

POCHIN, E. E., Clinical Sc., 1938, 3, 191.

POLLOCK, L. J. Arch. Neur. Psych., 1937, 37, 1383.

RANSON, S. W. Am. J. Anat., 1911, 12, 97. Ibid., 1914, 16, 97. RANSON, S. W. and VON HESS, C. L. Am. J. Physiol., 1915, 38, 128. RANSON, S. W. and DAVENPORT, H. K. Am. J. Anat., 1931, 48, 331.

ROTHMAN, S. Physiol. Rev., 1941, 21, 357.

RUFFINI, A. J. Physiol., 1898, 23, 190.

TROTTER, W. and DAVIES, H. M. J. Physiol., 1909, 38, 134.

WATERSTON, D. Brain, 1923, 46, 200.

WEDELL, G. J. Anat., 1941, 75, 346, 441; Brit. M. Bull., 1945, 3, 167.

WOOLLARD, H. H. and assoc. J. Anat., 1940, 74, 413.

*Monographs and Reviews*

ADRIAN, E. D. Basis of sensation. Christophers, London, 1928. The mechanism of sense organs. Physiol. Rev., 1930, 10, 336. The mechanism of nervous action. University of Pennsylvania Press, 1932.

BRONK, D. W. The mechanism of sensory end organs. Proc. A. Res. Nerv. & Ment. Dis., 1934, 15, 60.

GERARD, R. W. and TAYLOR, R. E. A general survey of muscle and nerve—physiological orientation. Am. J. Med., 1953, 15, 83.

HEAD, H. Studies in neurology. Vol. I. Frowde, London, 1920.

LEWIS, SIR T. Pain. Macmillan, N. Y., 1942.

ROTHMAN, S. Physiology of itching. Physiol. Rev., 1941, 21, 357.

STOPFORD, J. S. B. Sensation and the sensory pathway. Longmans, London, 1930.

WOLFF, H. G. and HARDY, J. D. On the nature of pain. Physiol. Rev., 1947, 27, 167.

WOLFF, H. G. and WOLF, S. Pain, Am. Lecture Series, Charles C Thomas, Springfield, Ill.

# 63

## REFLEX ACTION

---

In peripheral nerve the individual fibers conduct independently and little interaction occurs, but in their central terminations interaction becomes the important process. It depends partly on proximity (fig. 63.1) and the absence of myelin at terminations but also on the release of transmitter substances and the movements of ions along electrical gradients.

In a complete animal any reaction depends in greater or less degree on many factors in its environment which affect its senses. In analysis of the mode of action of the central nervous system, components of central activity can be partially isolated as reflexes. This isolation may be assisted by surgical section of the central nervous system, as in the spinal or decerebrate preparation; or by anesthetics such as barbiturates which suppress differentially the activity of particular parts; or by controlling the environment so that a simple stimulus is presented in isolation as in testing the knee jerk.

In the intact animal or man, the reflexes that can be isolated are limited, e.g., pupil reflexes to light, the blink reflex, the knee jerk, and certain pain reflexes. More detailed and quantitative information has been derived from animals by methods which simplify the nervous system and where stimulus and response are capable of accurate measurement, as in the classical experiments by Sherrington and his collaborators, where the response was measured as contraction of a particular muscle or group. In the last 30 years, in addition, analysis of the impulse discharges entering and leaving the central nervous system has added much detail; the nature of electric changes accompanying reflex activity at electrodes inserted within the central nervous system have assisted the development of theories of the mechanisms concerned. All the simpler reflex pathways appear to be genetically determined, but the delay in development of the central nervous system after birth enables interaction of genetic and environmental factors to occur. In many species highly elaborate reflexes are present at birth and can be regarded as "race learning" in evolution, as without many of these survival is impossible.

### The Spinal Preparation

Many reflexes can be studied in the spinal preparation. If this is made by decapitation under anesthesia after ligature of the blood vessels to the head, the respiratory center in the midbrain is removed, and, consequently, ventilation to the lungs must be maintained by means of a pump. This can replace the function of respiration in oxygenating the blood, but not that of controlling the elimination of $CO_2$ to maintain constant pH. This is grossly disturbed by loss of control by the respiratory center. In addition, the loss of the controlling centers for blood pressure, heart rate, the vasomotor center in the midbrain, all lead to circulatory abnormality and greatly lowered blood pressure due to loss of tone of the blood vessels. However, the knee jerk, flexion reflex, and scratch reflex can all be seen for some hours after decapitation. If the spinal cord is severed below the outflow to the respiratory muscles, the animal can survive for long periods with hindlegs isolated from the rest of the central nervous system. When such severance of the cord occurs in man by accidents or gunshot wounds, there is loss of all normal sensation and voluntary control below the lesion.

### Spinal Shock

Immediately after severance of the spinal cord, all activity below the lesion is completely absent but is followed by a progressive return of reflexes. In laboratory animals reflexes begin to return in a few minutes and continue to increase in activity and number for some weeks; the flexor reflex and knee jerk are the first to return. In primates, including man, recovery occurs much more slowly and imperfectly and is still continuing six months after the lesion. This depression is known as spinal shock; it is not due simply to the injuries produced in transection for after recovery of reflexes a second section lower down does not reabolish them. It appears to be a sign of functional disorganization and insensitivity due to the absence of impulse discharges from the higher levels which normally reach many centers in the spinal cord.

### The Knee Jerk (See also Ch. 64)

The contraction of the knee extensors when the patella tendon is tapped is found in most mammals and similar reflexes occur in many muscles; in man, the ankle jerk seen in the gastrocnemius on tapping the tendo achillis. The jerk reflex is not of obvious purpose, but it is an exhibition of fundamental purposive mechanism by which muscles contract reflexly as a load is imposed on them mechanically. It is of great value in clinical examination and in elucidating reflex mechanisms. A tap causes an abnormal, brief activation of the mechanism by which muscular movement is related to the mechanics of the environment, which is especially seen as postural contraction in muscles called on to support the body, often referred to as *antigravity muscles* (p. 1164).

Tendon jerks in man can be studied conveniently by recording the mechanical and electric changes in the gastrocnemius following a tap, a timed and calibrated blow to the tendons, delivered by a mechanical tendon striker. The record of action potentials from the muscle gives the time of the start of activity in the muscle with more precision than a mechanical record. Some 30 msec. after a blow to the tendon, the action potential appears in the muscle, and the contraction develops 3 or 4 msec. later. Most of the delay or latency of the response is time occupied in conduction to the spinal cord and back to the muscle; there are small latencies between the tap and the initiation of impulses in the afferent neurons, and between the arrival of nerve impulses at the muscle and the development and spread of action potential within it. The reflex can be graded by grading the tap on the tendon; it cannot be suppressed voluntarily, but can be increased by contracting other muscles, e.g., reinforcement by gripping the hands together. The motor impulses leave the spinal cord long before any reach the cortex to produce awareness of the tap.

HOFFMANN REFLEX. If electrodes are placed at A (fig. 63.2) over the course of the popliteal nerve, the same reflex can be set up by stimulating the sensory fibers electrically. The electrically evoked reflex is spoken of as the Hoffmann reflex after its discoverer. The sensory fibers concerned are of low threshold. By gradually increasing the stim-

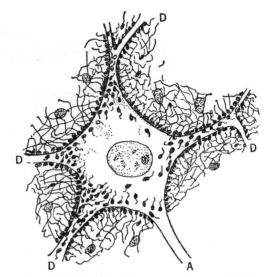

FIG. 63.1. End-feet (represented by small black ovals) or *pieds termineaux* making contact with the body and the dendrites of a nerve cell; *A*, axon; *D*, dendrites. (From *Living Body*, Holt and Company, New York.)

ulus A, a point is reached where a Hoffmann reflex is obtained, preceded much earlier, by a direct response from stimulating a few of the motor fibers. With a strong stimulus the direct response becomes very large, and the reflex disappears because of impulses also travelling antidromically to the spinal cord and producing a refractory state in the motor neurons. The delay between excitation at A and the direct motor response gives a value for the conduction time and endplate delay between A and the start of response in the muscle. Similarly, the reduction in reflex time when the stimulus at A replaces the tendon tap, gives a value for initiation and conduction of impulses to A, so that with the electrically evoked reflex, the time of conduction to the spinal cord, plus central delay, plus conduction back to A, is the interval on the record between the start of the direct response and that of the reflex response (Y, fig. 63.2). This interval (18 to 25 msec.) is largely made up of conduction time, and allowing for this, leaves about 2 msec. for the time taken between the arrival of sensory impulses at the spinal cord and the appearance of motor impulses leaving it. This is called the *reduced reflex time* and comprises conduction time within the spinal cord (partly in small branches of neurons which may conduct quite slowly) and also of true delay at the synapse.

In man the nerve action potentials have been recorded from the roots close to the cord by in-

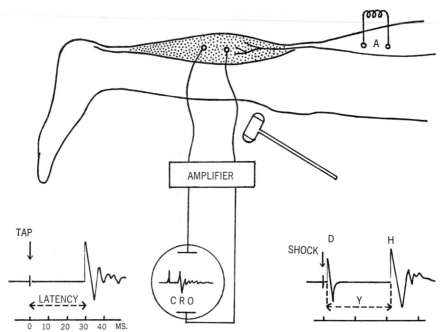

Fig. 63.2. Diagram showing elicitation of the patellar and Hoffmann reflexes, *inset left*, oscillographic tracing of the muscle action potential in knee jerk; *inset right*, the Hoffmann reflex elicited by a shock delivered at *A*.

serting needle electrodes by lumbar puncture. This method was successfully used by Magladery and coworkers on the spinal cords of medical student volunteers at Johns Hopkins University. However, the central delays can be more conveniently measured at the exposed cord in spinal or decerebrate animals, and it has been so analyzed with increasingly accurate methods during the last forty years. Lloyd found a reduced reflex time of about 1.6 msec. in the cat. In Lloyd's experiments the reflex could be set up either by a sharp tug from an electromagnet pulling the tendon of a muscle, or by an electrical stimulus to activate the same fibers. The fibers concerned are the large (16 to 18$\mu$) axons from which the annulospiral endings of muscle spindles are innervated; they can be selectively excited because their threshold is lower than that of smaller fibers. It is now thought that the earliest impulses to leave the cord in the jerk reflex have been interrupted by only a single synapse. It is known from degeneration experiments that many of the afferent fibers go directly to motor neurons and end in *boutons terminaux* scattered on their surface. Allowing for the conduction within the spinal cord, the delay between the arrival of impulses at the boutons and the initiation of impulses in the motor neurons is 0.6 to 0.9 msec.; in some circumstances, e.g., occulo-motor neurons, studied

by Lorente de Nó, a synaptic delay may be as low as 0.5 msec. It will be seen later that it can vary from these values when the excitation only just reaches threshold for motor discharge and is a minimum of 0.5 msec., when a previous volley has just entered the cord.

So far we have only considered the earliest component of the knee jerk reflex when a synchronous or nearly synchronous volley of impulses reaches the spinal cord. The initial response is often followed by further discharges of impulses which may travel by interneurons and arrive later at the motor neurons. While the knee jerk enables the activity of the monosynaptic pathway to be uncovered, it is not a pure monosynaptic reflex as normally evoked; and while it is convenient to speak of monosynaptic reflexes, they are a simplification arrived at by neglecting the later activity or suppressing it by anesthetics. In the decapitate spinal preparation the muscles are flaccid and cannot support the animal's weight against gravity; in contrast, in *decerebrate rigidity* (ch. 64) the limbs are vigorously extended by reflex contraction more than adequate to support the animal's weight. It was shown by Sherrington that this rigidity of muscles depended on a reflex action elicited by a stretch stimulus, for division of either sensory or motor roots abolished it, and it is inhibited by stimulating a cutaneous nerve.

Stretch reflexes are exaggerated in decerebrate rigidity and absent during spinal shock; they return after some days in animals with divided spinal cords.

Sherrington recorded the tension in the soleus muscle of the cat when the muscle was stretched (see fig. 63.3). The principal structures responsible are the muscle spindles; the tendon organs are not the source of excitation for these can be anesthetized by infiltrating the tendon with novocaine without abolishing the stretch reflex. The spindles activate the motor neurons by the monosynaptic pathway and also by less simple paths. Sherrington gave the name *plastic tonus* to the condition of muscles exhibiting stretch reflexes, because when an attempt is made to flex the limb, the stretch reflex causes the muscle to resist displacement until considerable force is exercised. Then the tonus melts away (clasp knife reflex), the limb moves easily to a new position; but tested in the new position, again it resists flexion.

The position of the muscle spindles and their behavior when the muscle contracts (see ch. 62) fits them to provide automatic self-regulating behavior; the spindle is situated in parallel with the rest of the muscle (see fig. 63.4). When the muscle contracts, it takes the strain off the spindle and so reduces excitation of the reflex; lengthening the muscle increases the stretch reflex which resists the force causing the extension. This simple basis is refined by two additions; the small ($\gamma$) motor neurons which innervate the muscle spindle itself can accelerate its response and so act as control on the sensitivity of the reflex. It has recently been shown by Granit and Merton that many factors which alter the stretch reflex in decerebrate animals modify the activity of the $\gamma$ motor neurons. We thus have a self-regulating action using the $\alpha$ motor neurons with delicate control exercised by the gamma fiber control of the muscle spindle itself. The other addition leads the plastic tonus to vanish with forced flexion; this appears to be due to the tendon organs.

The most important structures in the stretch reflex (chap. 64) are the *annulo-spiral endings* (ch. 62) and the large nerve fibers which innervate them. The role of the *flower-spray endings* is not yet fully understood. All normal muscular reactions and reflexes are superimposed on the background of the stretch reflex. This means that other activation arriving at the motor neurons finds them in a condition appropriate to the external mechanical load, and the requirements for control of muscular action are thus delegated to a very simple reflex pathway which, by its speed of

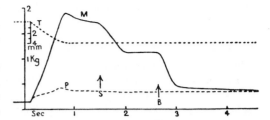

Fig. 63.3. Response of quadriceps to stretch $T$ of 4 mm., before $M$, and after $P$ severance of its nerve. During the response $M$, a stretch of semitendinosus begins approximately at $S$, followed by a stretch of biceps at $B$. (After Creed, Denny-Brown et al., *Reflex Activity of the Spinal Cord*, Clarendon Press, Oxford.)

action, can co-ordinate muscular action to produce the same movement when a wide range of different conditions of resistance are encountered.

In engineering we speak of a *servo-system* when action is controlled by a mechanism designed to keep that action constant; for example, a centrifugal governor controls an engine to run at constant speed with changing load by regulating the throttle. The centrifugal governor imitates a sense organ and the throttle valve the motor neurons, and the feedback of information about the action to the controlling mechanism is the essential feature. Thus the simple proprioceptive reflex is present under all normal conditions, and other reflexes blend with it and so produce action

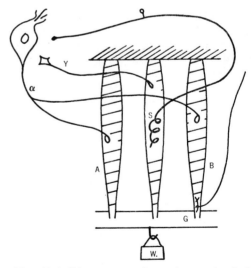

Fig. 63.4. Diagram to show the mechanical conditions when a sensory end organ lies "in parallel" with the muscle fibers. $A$ and $B$, skeletal muscle fibers. $S$, afferent end organ on an intrafusal fiber innervated by a $Y$ fiber. $G$, Golgi tendon organs in series with contractile elements. $W$, weight. (After Fulton and Pi-Suñer.)

related to the mechanical reaction met with in the movement.

## Phasic and Postural Contraction

The steady contraction of muscle in the stretch reflex is maintained for long periods, and when the activity of individual motor units is studied, it is found that impulses are set up by individual motor neurons at frequencies up to nearly 50 per sec., and may remain substantially regular down to 1 or 2 per sec. A motor unit consists of a neuron in the spinal cord providing the axon, which runs to the muscle and divides there, to innervate many muscle fibers (10 to 100). A single activation of a motor unit is the least response that can occur via the spinal cord. The tension exerted by a single motor unit when its nerve fiber is tetanized may amount to as much as 30 grams. The activity of single units has been studied by subdividing motor nerves until the activity of a single fiber can be recorded electrically, but a valuable indirect method was evolved by Adrian and Bronk. They found that when concentric electrodes consisting of a hypodermic needle with a wire, insulated except at its tip, running down its center, was thrust into a muscle, the muscle action potentials of the group of fibers comprising the motor unit, could be recorded. This technique makes it possible to find how a single motor neuron discharges under a variety of conditions. The method has been widely used in man as well as animals, and much of our understanding of human muscle control has been derived from it. The slowly repeated discharge of motor neurons in tonic contraction would give tremor in the contraction were it not for the fact that different units fire independently and at differing rates so that the asynchronous activation of the individual units becomes fused into an apparently steady contraction. Increasing voluntary or reflex contraction in man (and animals) is brought about by an increasing number of units being excited and also by an increase in the rate of firing of impulses to individual units. Thus an asynchronous motor discharge is evoked by asynchronous bombardment of the motor neurons by simple or indirect pathways from a large number of sensory receptors. The phasic jerk reflex and the tonic postural contraction depend on common structures and when a tap is given to the tendon of a tonic muscle, many units are activated synchronously; after the jerk is over there is a brief absence of tonic activity— *"the silent period"*—while the muscle re-extends

to the original length; the tonic discharge and contraction then continue as before. We thus have a self-regulating action using the $\alpha$ motor neurons with delicate control exercised by the $\gamma$ fiber control of the muscle spindle itself.

## Grading of Reflex Response

Sherrington found in many types of reflex that the response could be graded by grading the strength of the stimulus, and this is also seen in the knee jerk in man and tendon reflexes in animals. As the stimulus is increased, there is a threshold at which a *liminal response* is obtained with further increase the reflex grows to a *maximal response*. Further increase may reduce or alter the response. It is, however, found that with the threshold stimulation which just fails to produce any reflex response, impulses are in fact being set up in a number of afferent fibers, and there is a central threshold requiring simultaneous arrival of impulses in a number of fibers before a reflex occurs.

## Summation and Occlusion

These facts, well known from Sherrington's studies on numerous reflexes, are clearly seen in the simplest form in Lloyd's experiments stimulating dorsal roots in the spinal cord with gradually increasing shocks, and recording the size of the action potential both of the sensory fibers and of the motor fibers; the magnitudes are closely related to the number of sensory fibers activated and the number of motor neurons excited to carry impulses out to the muscles (see fig. 63.5). The graph in figure 63.6 shows that a certain number of sensory fibers must be activated before any reflex occurs; the reflex grows rapidly with further addition of active sensory fibers and gradually reaches a maximum when all of the large fibers are excited. The relationship is clearly not a linear one and underlies the properties described by Sherrington as "spatial summation" and "occlusion".

When two afferent nerves give a reflex in the same muscle, convergence is said to occur; if both are stimulated simultaneously the contraction is not the sum of the two separate reflexes. If stimulation is near threshold it is greater, i.e., *spacial summation* takes place; if both are maximal, it is less than their sum: *occlusion* is present.

If in figure 63.6 we imagine the sensory fibers divided in two and placed on two pairs of stimulating electrodes, the case closely resembles Sherrington's investigation of volleys set up in two

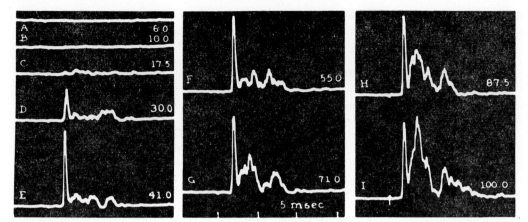

FIG. 63.5. Dorsal root-ventral reflex discharges from the first sacral segment. The successive records illustrate the growth of the reflex discharge as the afferent (dorsal root) volley is increased in size. The figures to the right hand of each observation give the relative size of the afferent volley employed for that observation. Time = 5 msec. (After Lloyd.)

nerve branches reaching the spinal cord together. If both stimuli are set to the threshold in isolation, each may activate 10 per cent of the total ingoing fibers which fail to evoke a reflex. When both are stimulated together, 20 per cent of the fibers will be activated, and from the graph it is clear there will now be a large reflex owing to summation. For stimuli close to the threshold the summated response may be many times that of either alone.

If, on the other hand, both stimuli are set to activate all the fibers in each nerve, each alone will produce a 50 per cent maximal volley, and this as may be seen from the graph will activate 90 per cent of the efferent units. However, both activated together cannot produce 180 per cent of the maximal response. The deficit between the actual response and the response calculated from the sum of the two, namely 80 per cent, is due to "occlusion" and reflects the anatomical fact that many neurons receive afferent excitation from fibers that branch and supply many others. It is known that any motor neuron may receive some hundreds of boutons terminaux from different fibers; it is deduced that for an impulse to be set up a minimum number of boutons must be simultaneously active. If a neuron has sufficient boutons activated, it fires a motor impulse, but further addition of more from the other nerve cannot lead the all-or-nothing structure to do more immediately. Hence it is usual to see summation between reflexes evoked by near threshold stimuli while occlusion is often seen with stimuli activating a higher proportion of the fibers.

Something of the organization of boutons from different nerves is learned by finding the nerves

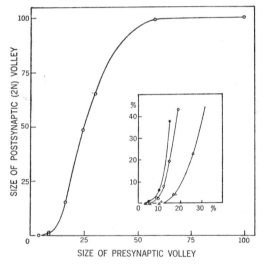

FIG. 63.6. Dorsal root-ventral root reflex preparation. The size of the two-neuron-arc (2N) reflex discharge is plotted against the size of the afferent volley evoking the reflex. *Inset*; The initial portions of similar curves from other experiments to illustrate the variation in onset of the reflex discharge from one experiment to another. (After Lloyd.)

between which summation can occur. In general, sensory fibers from muscles that act synergically at the same joint produce summation while those from antagonistic muscles do not and may produce a depression of the reflex response known as inhibition. The response occurs primarily in the motor neurons supplying parts of the muscle close to the origin (muscle spindles) of the sensory fibers concerned. Thus the jerk reflex utilizing a monosynaptic pathway is anatomically localized and restricted by the pattern of central connections, and the flexibility of response is not nearly as great as when interneurons are concerned in reflexes considered later.

### Facilitation—Temporal Summation

When a volley of impulses is subliminal, no reflex takes place. Yet we cannot assume that no effect has been produced within the central nervous system, for as described above, two subliminal volleys together may produce a substantial reflex response. However, the two volleys do not need to arrive simultaneously to produce summation. It also occurs when the same nerve fibers are activated twice in quick succession; *temporal summation* can occur. The change of state in the central nervous system by which the second subliminal volley is rendered liminal is spoken of as *facilitation*. To study facilitation, a volley may be sent into the spinal cord, referred to as the conditioning volley, followed by a second, the test volley, to see how the response differs from that obtained when the test volley is used in isolation. Temporal summation has been studied in many reflexes since the beginning of the century, but will be first considered in relation to the simple monosynaptic activity as in the tendon jerk. If the test volley and conditioning volley are simultaneous, and applied to different

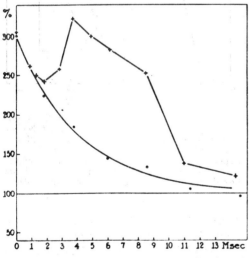

FIG. 63.7. Facilitation of biceps reflex by afferent volleys in semitendinosus nerve. Amplitude of the test reflex, expressed as per cent of control amplitude, is plotted as function of the time interval between conditioning and test volleys. To obtain the curve represented by dots, conditioning volleys of near reflex threshold strength were used. Stronger conditioning volleys caused the appearance of a second period of facilitation (crosses). (After Lloyd.)

portions of the nerve, we have *spatial summation*. As the two volleys are separated in time, the response to the test volley becomes less; the time course is shown in figure 63.7, obtained by Lloyd from the cat; the later activity of the polysynaptic pathways is evident in the upper curve. It will be seen that the response has fallen to about half at 3 msec.; the facilitation continues to decay exponentially. The later part of this curve can only be obtained with weak stimuli for the activity of interneurons leads to additional phenomena which are responsible for the upper curve. It is clear that under these conditions, the change of state at the motor neurons outlasts the arrival of the afferent volley, and something persists for a number of milliseconds which is able to make a later volley more effective. Sherrington named the change of state in facilitation "the central excitatory state", and suggested that excitation had to accumulate somewhere in the pathway and reach a certain level before discharge of the motor neurons occurred. This has been substantiated in more concrete terms by recent investigations described later.

### Flexor Reflexes

The purposive significance of these reflexes is clear. A noxious stimulus, such as pinching, applied to a limb leads to its rapid withdrawal and concurrently a crossed extensor reflex is often seen with it. The flexor reflexes can be obtained in many mammals and man by a painful or noxious stimulus. The afferent fibers are those from the skin, and the response can be obtained by stimulating wide regions of a limb by pin prick or an electrical stimulus. Stimulating a mixed nerve trunk is often followed by reflexes of flexion. The stimulus is abnormal in that fibers from different regions and of diverse function may be stimulated simultaneously; this does not normally occur with sensory stimuli. The limb is rapidly withdrawn and may be maintained flexed for several seconds following a strong stimulus.

As in the stretch reflex, phasic and sustained components in the reflex can be identified (fig. 63.8); after nearly synchronous activity in rapid withdrawal, the motor units fire at rates of 5 to 40 per sec during the maintained flexion.

Facilitation may be readily demonstrated in flexor reflexes. Using an electric stimulus to a nerve to elicit the phasic component of the reflex, Sherrington and Eccles showed that as the stimulus was increased in strength, the latency shortened; when a threshold response was obtained, it occurred later than when a stronger stimulus was used to evoke a large reflex. The reduced reflex time for the flexor reflex in the cat is about 2.5 msec., and a greater synaptic delay than in the jerk reflex is to be anticipated, for the fibers innervating the skin do not appear to possess boutons on the motor neurons themselves, but all end on interneurons so that at least two synapses must occur in the path used by the flexor reflex. Temporal summation for this pathway is found over much greater intervals than in the monosynaptic pathway. With facilitation, the delay suffered by a volley of impulses reaching the spinal cord shortly after each other may be reduced to a minimum of a little over a millisecond. From such effects Sherrington formed his theory of a gradable central excitatory state which caused motor neurons to fire when sufficiently intense, and which persisted some time after the afferent impulses were over. Such a theory immediately suggests an interpretation of the reduction in latency when facilitation occurs. This is illustrated in figure 63.9. The central excitatory state postulated by Sherrington has since been shown to be closely related to electrical changes that can be recorded from central structures during activity.

## Inhibition

Impulses travelling in sensory fibers from antagonist muscles may produce a reflex response in those muscles but depress the response of the agonist. For this to occur, they must arrive at the spinal cord at least 0.5 msec. before the impulses producing the reflex. We are no longer dealing with simple, invariable conduction, such as is seen in peripheral nerve; even in these simple, direct reflex pathways, reflex response may be prevented by nerve impulses of different origin. Such inhibition, which will be considered in detail later, may be prolonged; for instance, a single excitation of a nerve supplying the skin can abolish the knee jerk completely in a spinal cat for up to $\frac{1}{2}$ sec.

## Crossed Extensor Reflex

As the pathway in the central nervous system becomes more complicated, there is an increasing modification of the impulse patterns in travelling through the spinal cord. In the crossed extensor reflex the latency may be many times longer than in reflexes considered above. With a weak stimulus repetition at $\frac{1}{10}$-sec. intervals for a second or more may elicit the reflex. The discharge of

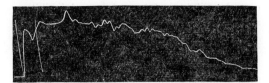

FIG. 63.8. Flexion reflex, showing *after discharge*. The duration of the stimulus is indicated by the pair of nearly vertical lines. (After Sherrington.)

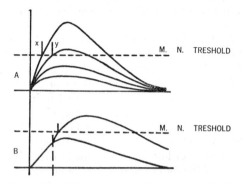

FIG. 63.9. Diagram of graded central excitatory state reaching a motor neuron threshold, giving earlier response to a large volley. *cf.* X, Y and maximum shortening of latency with facilitation by a previous subliminal stimulus.

impulses by the motor nerves is no longer closely related to each volley of afferent impulses but the firing rate of the motor neurons is independent and often asynchronous in different units. The reflex builds up slowly over several seconds and on cessation of the stimulus dies away slowly with after-discharge occurring in the motor neurons.

The crossed extensor reflex is normally seen blended with the tonic stretch reflex in the muscle examined, and there is co-operation between the two reflexes. Thus when the stimulus is made so weak that no reflex occurs in the slack muscle, when repeated with the stretched muscle, a reflex may result. Similarly when the muscle is stretched, a contraction results if a contralateral skin nerve is stimulated subliminally for producing a reflex. If the muscle be deafferented by cutting the sensory roots, the crossed extensor reflex can still be elicited by stimulating a skin nerve on the other side. However, now threshold is raised, the onset is more abrupt, and the after discharge shortened. With the stretch reflex blending with it, the response is less explosive.

The crossed extensor reflex is inhibited by stimulating a skin nerve on the same side, and may thus be replaced by a flexor reflex. There is then said to be algebraic summation of the central excitatory state and central inhibitory state produced.

## Reciprocal Innervation

It has been seen above that afferent fibers from a muscle excite it monosynaptically, while those from antagonists inhibit it. Such reciprocal effects are found from many muscles, but the interconnection of central neurons, on which reciprocal innervation rests, are not solely or even primarily functions of the afferent fibers from the limb.

At the beginning of the century, Graham-Brown showed that under very deep anesthesia alternating movements of the limbs may occur. This was given the name of narcosis progression. Study of such phenomena shows that reciprocity occurs between the centers of antagonistic muscles even when all the sensory roots supplying them are cut. For instance, in the spinal cord of a cat with all lumbar sensory roots cut, stimulation of the cord or of roots above or below the lumbar enlargement provokes alternating movements of the limbs, and even under such conditions reciprocal contraction still holds. Activity ceases in one muscle when at its height in the antagonistic muscle. It becomes clear then that central connections must underlie reciprocal innervation as well as specific effects elicited via fibers from a particular muscle when these are intact. When the motor neurons of any muscle are excited, a diminution of excitability occurs in the motor neurons of the antagonist. The detailed nature of these central interconnections is not yet fully understood.

## Fractionation

The reflexes considered above fall into the class of segmental reflexes in that they are largely determined by fibers entering a segment and exciting or inhibiting the motor neurons within that same segment. Normally, intersegmental connections by propriospinal fibers co-ordinate activities at different levels and in the flexor reflex evoked by a pinch stimulus to the skin, excitation will reach two or three segments from the sensory fibers but may spread far outside these. The reflex flexion occurring in any particular muscle changes when the position of the sensory stimulation is altered. The motor neurons to a particular muscle form the final common path for many reflexes, and when different sensory nerves are stimulated, the activation varies considerably. This is spoken of as *fractionation*, and typical results are given in table 63.1.

## Scratch Reflex

The scratch reflex is elicited by light stimulation of the flank and is readily elicited from a spinal (or normal) dog. Its purposive nature is obvious. Sherrington used a small star-wheel or mechanical flea which, when rolled along the skin, would evoke reflex scratching. Alternatively the skin may be stimulated with a weak electric shock. When the stimulus is moved on the skin, the balance of activity in the muscles alters to make the limb scratch close to the stimulated spot. Incoming sensory nerve impulse discharges thus possess *local sign* which determines the exact pattern of activity distributed among the motor neurons of the several muscles that are involved. Many reflexes require alternating movements, scratching, walking, swimming, etc., and alternating activity is easily provoked in the spinal centers. Such movements are spoken of as *clonic*, and the second movement is often assisted by sensory stimulation produced during the first movement. The interconnection of centers which underlies reciprocal innervation is also involved.

The propriospinal pathways link not only neighboring segments but also the lumbar and brachial enlargements in quadrupeds, and in narcosis progression there may be alternating activity in flexors and extensors in opposing phase on opposite sides, co-ordinated with similar movements in the forelimbs. The appearance of spinal shock below a section has already been mentioned, but when the cord is divided there are also modifications of reflex activity spreading forward from the section. The best known of these is the "Sherrington-Schiff phenomenon". If in a decerebrate animal the spinal cord be divided between the lumbar and cervical enlargment, the hindlimbs immediately become flaccid and recover

### TABLE 63.1

*The tensions of the reflex responses for each nerve are expressed as percentages of the strongest contraction*

| Nerve | Hip flexor (tensor fasciae femoris) | Knee flexor. (Semi-tendin-inosus) | Ankle flexor. (Tibialis anticus) |
|---|---|---|---|
| Internal saphenous | 100 | 56 | 87 |
| Popliteal | 3 or less | 42 | 100 |
| Peroneal distal to tibialis anticus | 14 | 100 | 69 |

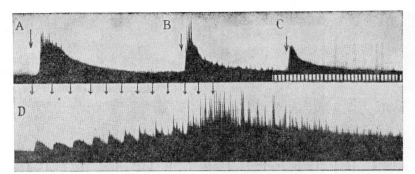

Fig. 63.10. Electrical changes in anterior roots of the frog in response to shock excitation. Ventral roots cut. *A*, 14° C, electrodes 1.5 and 11 mm. Single shock to ipsilateral sciatic at arrow. *B*, 16° C, electrodes 2 and 11 mm. Single shock to ipsilateral dorsal root. Cord cut through about 2.5 mm. above and below exit of root. *C*, 16° C, electrodes 1.3 and 10 mm. Single shock to ipsilateral peroneal nerve. *D*, 15° C, electrodes 2.5 and 11 mm. Repeated shocks to ipsilateral peroneal nerve marked by arrows. (Time marker $\frac{1}{50}$ sec. for A-C at foot of C. $\frac{1}{10}$ sec. on D) (From Barron and Matthews.)

from shock slowly; the forelimbs become even more active in decerebrate rigidity, and all reflexes in front of the section are enhanced and more easily elicited. This is attributed to removal of forward travelling impulses that have an inhibitory action on the forward centers.

### Visceral Reflexes

In addition to the somatic reflexes underlying locomotion and protection, a number of reflex actions involving the viscera can be elicited in animals with the spinal cord divided. Immediately following a spinal section there is loss of vasomotor tone, and it appears that continual tonic discharges from the vasomotor center in the medulla are necessary for the normal contraction of capillaries and arteries. With recovery from spinal shock, however, tone gradually returns to the vessels, and it is supposed that the lower neurons concerned (in the lateral columns) which supply the sympathetic system gradually accommodate until their activity is maintained without supraspinal impulses reaching them. The sacral outflow is normally the final common path for the reflexes of defecation and urination, and these reflexes can be elicited in the chronic spinal dog by distention of the bladder or rectum although the pattern is abnormal. Similarly some sexual reflexes are also present. Goltz and Sherrington showed that with the spinal cord divided, impregnation and parturition took place. Stimulation of the genitalia was followed by erection and copulation with the accompanying muscular activity. The reflexes of pilo-erection are mediated via the sympathetic system but cannot easily be elicited in the spinal preparation. When a spinal preparation is asphyxiated by stopping the respiration pump, many neurons concerned discharge

vigorously and reflex co-ordination is disrupted. A mass discharge of motor impulses may occur with convulsive movements, which no longer show reciprocal innervation; these are followed by defecation, urination, and pilo-erection.

### Electrical Activity of Central Nervous Tissue

Electrical changes can be led off from electrodes in or close to the spinal cord in a number of ways, and different components are emphasized with different arrangements of electrodes.

(a) *Electrodes* on the surface yield a negative and positive complex when any volley of impulses enters the cord which long outlasts the action potentials of the impulses.

(b) *Electro-tonic potentials* observed from the roots of the spinal cord indicate changes occurring within the cord in the fibers examined. Thus when an afferent volley reaches the spinal cord, a sequence of changes is recorded from the dorsal roots lasting some 100 msec. and a different sequence of changes from the ventral roots. The latter are closely related to the discharge of impulses from motor neurons (fig. 63.10).

(c) *Focal potentials.* When a fine insulated wire or a saline-filled micropipette is thrust into the central nervous system and records are made between this electrode and a distant electrode on non-active tissues, a record is obtained which varies with the position of the electrode in the cord and shows a correlation with reflex activity.

(d) *Intracellular electrodes.* If fine glass micropipettes are drawn with a tip diameter of $\frac{1}{2}$ to 1 $\mu$ and are filled with a saline or strong KCl solution, single cells may be punctured without their normal activity ceasing immediately—although in many cases the injury produces a characteristic

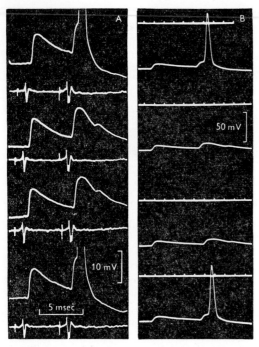

FIG. 63.11. Intracellular potentials set up in a BSt. motoneuron by two afferent volleys in BSt. nerve, the first being submaximal for group I fibers, the second being set up by a supramaximal stimulus. Note that summation to set up a spike occurred at the shortest interval (first record), the intervals of the second and fourth, which are equal, being just critical. *A* and *B* show precisely the same responses but at high and low amplifications respectively. (From Brock and associates.)

rapid discharge of impulses if they are severely damaged.

From observations by these methods it is clear that the arrival of a volley of sensory impulses results in a depolarizarion of some part of the motor neuron surface which, if sufficiently intense, culminates in a propagated impulse.

With asynchronous bombardment of the motor neurons, long-lasting depolarization of motor neurons occurs, and the rate of rhythmic discharge is related to the magnitude of the local potential.

When the monosynaptic reflex was studied by Eccles and his collaborators with intracellular electrodes, the local synaptic potential corresponding to Sherrington's C.E.S. had a rapid rise and lasted some 5 or 6 msec. (fig. 63.11). Summation between successive local changes could be seen to occur. When impulses from an antagonistic muscle were set up, which caused inhibition, the depolarization was counteracted by a hyperpolarization having about the same time course as the depolarization. However, stud-

ies both of intracellular and root potentials have shown that the volley-producing inhibition sent in isolation produces little or no hyperpolarization, but is effective in neutralizing depolarization caused by an excitation of the reflex.

It is thus possible to consider Sherrington's concepts, C.E.S. and C.I.S., as an index of the electrical state at the motor neurons which is closely related to their excitability. It should be emphasized that electrical changes in fluids imply movements of ions but that ions have a chemical nature as well as an electrical charge, and that the electrical and chemical aspect of events at the synapse are complimentary and represent descriptions in the terms of charge or chemical nature of the same processes.

## Theories of Reflex Action

The concepts of a central excitatory state and central inhibitory state, derived from reflex experiments, can be related to the depolarization and hyperpolarization of the neuron surface demonstrated for some components of simple reflexes. These demonstrate changes of state which outlast the action potential of the afferent volley. In the periphery, e.g. at the motor endplate, the importance of humoral transmitter substances is fully established, and clearly the central changes of state are consistent with long-lasting transmitter substances being released on the synaptic surfaces. The presence of humoral agents or chemical transmitters has been sought within the central nervous system. Owing to the complexity of the situation it will be a long time before we can describe the processes of the various synapses in very exact chemical terms but a number of agents, including acetylcholine and adrenaline, have profound effects on central structures.

In many quarters it is held that as a neuron appears to be a pharmacological unit producing the same transmitter at all its terminations, the same incoming volley could only produce an exciter substance at one point and an inhibitory substance at another if an additional neuron were located in the second pathway. There is some evidence that this may be the case, e.g., the .5 msec. by which an inhibitory volley must precede a testing volley to produce direct inhibition. Chemical transmission provides a simple basis for long-lasting changes which can be extremely prolonged in regions where the enzymes destroying the transmitter are in low concentration, and it offers an explanation of the very prolonged effects (several seconds) that may follow a single inhibitory afferent volley.

However, a second theory has been developed (see Lorente de Nó) to account for long-lasting activity. It suggests that closed chains of neurons have impulse activity circulating around them and may produce re-excitation of other neurons for long periods (see Wall). While this is an attractive idea which is consistent with many of the phenomena observed, no direct evidence of the reverberating chains has yet been found, and the stability of long-lasting changes after gross surgical interference with parts of the spinal cord makes it difficult to accept this hypothesis for some of the common long-lasting electrical and reflex events observed. However, it is clear that centers in the cord can interact by internal connections as in reciprocal innervation after de-afferentation.

## REFERENCES

ADRIAN, E. D. AND BRONK, D., J. Physiol., 1929, 67, 119.

BARRON, D. H. AND MATTHEWS, B. H. C., J. Physiol., 1938, 92, 276.

BROCK, L. G., COOMBS, J. S. AND ECCLES, J. C., J. Physiol., 1952, 177, 431.

COHEN, L. A., J. Neurophysiol., 1953, 16, 272.

DENNY BROWN, D., Proc. Roy. Soc. London, ser. B, 1929, 104, 252.

ECCLES, J. C. AND SHERRINGTON, C. S., Proc. Roy. Soc. London, ser. B, 1931, 107, 511.

FRANK, K. AND FUORTES, M. G. F., J. Physiol., 1955, 130, 625.

FULTON, J. F. AND PI-SUÑER, J., Am. J. Physiol., 1928, 83, 554.

GASSER, H. S. AND GRAHAM, H. T., Am. J. Physiol. 1933, 103, 303.

GRAHAM BROWN, T., J. Physiol., 1914, 48, 18.

GRANITE, R. AND MERTON, P., J. Physiol., 1953–1955, 122, 498; 130, 213.

HOFFMAN, P., Ergebn. Physiol., 1934, 36, 15.

LLOYD, D. P. C., J. Neurophysiol., 1943, 6, 111.

LORENTE DE NO, R., J. Neurophysiol., 1938, 1, 195; 2, 404.

MAGLADERY, J. W., PATER, W. E., PARK, A. M. AND TEASDALL, R. D., Bull. Johns Hopkins Hosp., 1951, 88, 499.

RENSHAW, B., J. Neurophysiol., 1940, 3, 373.

WALL, P. D., J. Neurophysiol., 1959, 22, 305.

### Monographs and Reviews

CREED, R. S. *Et. Al.*, Reflex activity of the spinal cord. Clarendon Press, Oxford, 1932.

PATON, W. D. M., Ann. Rev. Physiol., 1958, 20, 431.

SHERRINGTON, C. S., The integrative action of the nervous system.

# *64*

# THE PHYSIOLOGICAL MECHANISMS GOVERNING
# POSTURE AND EQUILIBRIUM

## Stretch or Myotatic Reflexes

One of the basic reflexes is the stretch reflex. It is present in all healthy skeletal muscles, but it is more pronounced in some muscles than in others and is more readily elicited and more pronounced under certain circumstances. When a muscle is stretched it responds by contracting. This is the stretch reflex. Pulling on the muscles stimulates the muscle-spindles (see ch. 62 and p. 699) which are specialized sensory end-organs lying among the muscle fibers. These spindles send afferent nervous impulses up the muscular nerve and into the spinal cord over the posterior spinal root. Within the spinal cord these impulses are transferred over a single synapse to the $\alpha$ motor cells of the anterior gray column of the spinal cord. These $\alpha$ cells, in turn, send impulses out over the anterior spinal roots, down the muscular nerve and into the skeletal muscle where they cause the muscle to contract. This reflex is normally present and serves particularly to maintain the body of the animal in an upright position. Such reflexes are, therefore, more pronounced in the extensor muscles. These reflexes become exaggerated after the cerebrum is removed by transecting the brainstem through the mesencephalon (decerebration). This produces a state known as *decerebrate rigidity* in which stretch reflexes are more easily elicited; these stretch reflexes are commonly studied under the abnormal circumstances of decerebrate rigidity. Naturally, section of either the related anterior or posterior spinal root, or dividing the muscular nerve, or destroying the related portion of the spinal cord interrupts the reflex arc and abolishes the response. The muscular response is proportionate, within limits, to the stretching force, and persists as long as the stretching is maintained. The muscular contraction ceases as soon as the stretching force is withdrawn, i.e., there is no after-discharge. The latent period of the stretch reflex is short—less than 20 msec. This reflex is readily inhibited by stimuli to the extremity which would ordinarily be painful (noci-

ceptive stimuli), or by stimulation of the afferent nerves from the skin, or by stretching the antagonistic flexor muscles, or by applying excessive stretching force to the muscle itself or to its tendon. This latter inhibition gives rise to the lengthening reaction (see below). These forms of inhibition are largely devices to protect the muscle from overextension, and the animal from injury. In figure 64.1 are the graphic results of the classical experiments of Liddell and Sherrington demonstrating some of these points.

As noted above the stretch reflex is enhanced by decerebration. Such transection of the midbrain abolishes controlling inhibitory impulses from the cerebral cortex, the basal ganglia and the anterior lobe of the cerebellum which are transmitted down the spinal cord from the bulbar reticular formation, while leaving intact the facilitatory mechanism in the more caudal portions of the reticular formation. Even with fixed lesions of the central nervous system the intensity of the muscular responses to the stretch reflex wax and wane under varying circumstances. This modulation of the reflex response may be brought about by changes in these facilitatory impulses which affect the stretch reflex directly, or by descending impulses which vary the response of the muscle spindle to stretch. This latter effect is produced over small neurons known as gamma efferents which arise in the anterior gray columns of the spinal cord and innervate the intrafusal muscle fibers within the muscle spindle. This control of the responsiveness of the peripheral sensory endorgan is in considerable measure exercised by the reticular formation of the brain stem. By varying the tension within the muscle spindle, its response to stretch is varied and, in turn, the reflex muscular contraction.

The afferent fibers of the myotatic reflex arcs are large calibered, myelinated, rapidly conducting fibers of the A group. The dark muscle fibers of the extensors, upon which the maintenance of posture depends, are also more plentifully sup-

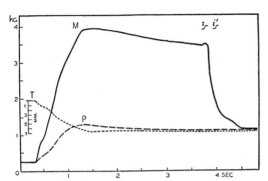

FIG. 64.1. The stretch reflex of the quadriceps (cat). Muscular response (M) before and (P) after cutting nerve to the muscle. T is a record of the table-fall which stretches the muscle. At the right is shown the effect of reflex inhibition, evoked between *i* and *i'* by stimulation of afferent fibers in the ipsilateral peroneopopliteal nerve (from Liddell and Sherrington).

plied with large diameter nerve fibers than are the pale fibers of flexor muscles. The stretch reflexes show reciprocal innervation; when a muscle reacts by contraction to a stretching force its antagonist relaxes: the *myotatic unit* which consists of muscle receptor, afferent nerve fiber, spinal center and motoneuron, "exhibits within itself in full measure the elementary mechanism of reciprocal innervation" (Lloyd).

### THE KNEE AND ANKLE JERKS

A sharp tap upon the patellar tendon, when the knee joint is semi-flexed stretches the quadriceps extensor muscle and causes it to contract. Similarly a blow upon the tendo-Achilles causes a quick contraction of the calf muscles. These brief contractions or jerks, as well as those described below for the upper limb, are "fractional examples of the stretch reflex" and are not due to stimulation of the tendon but stretching the muscle. A stretch of 0.05 mm. or less in $\frac{1}{20}$ second being sufficient to elicit the response. A voluntary action, such as clasping the hands together, reinforces the reflex and increases the force of the jerk. The center for the knee jerk in the human subject lies in the 2nd, 3rd and 4th lumbar segments of the cord; it is innervated through the anterior crural nerve. The center for the ankle jerk is situated in the 1st sacral segment; the peripheral nerve is the sciatic. Lloyd has shown that only two neurons are involved in the reflex arc of the knee and ankle jerks, and of other myotatic reflexes, i.e., the impulse passes from afferent fiber to motor neuron without traversing an internuncial neuron (see also ch. 62).

Any condition, such as decerebration or injury

to the descending motor pathways (ch. 65), which enhances the stretch reflexes increases the tendon jerks.[1] They are abolished by an injury or disease involving the efferent or afferent limb of the reflex arc or the center itself (anterior horn cells). On account of its brief twitchlike character the knee jerk is sometimes spoken of as the "phasic reaction" of the stretch reflex, whereas the sustained contraction resulting from a continuous pull upon the tendon, and which is concerned in the maintenance of posture, is referred to as the "static or postural reaction" of the stretch reflex. The knee jerk is less subject to abnormal states, e.g., spinal transection, anesthetics, circulatory failures, etc., than are the postural reactions. In an animal such as the dog or rabbit, the knee jerk returns in a few minutes after spinal transection, in the monkey after some days. In man, though postural reflex activity is entirely lost, the muscles being quite flaccid, the knee jerk is elicitable in some degree in some 3 weeks or even earlier after a complete transverse lesion of the spinal cord (see ch. 65).

The smooth and steady character of the contractions brought about through the ordinary stretch reflexes concerned with the maintenance of posture, is due to the asynchronous nature of the impulses set up by the numerous stretch receptors and the asynchronous reflex discharge of impulses down the motoneurons to the muscles. The muscle fibers are, therefore, never all relaxed nor all contracted at the same time. The sharp contraction of the quadriceps characteristic of the knee jerk, on the contrary, is brought about by the discharge of a volley of synchronous impulses and therefore by the fibers of the muscle contracting in unison.

*Clonus.* Under certain conditions a muscle or group of muscles instead of contracting smoothly and continuously may do so rhythmically in a series of rapidly repeated movements or jerks. Thus, in lesions of the central nervous system associated with hypertonus, sharp passive dorsiflexion at the ankle joint with maintenance of the foot in the dorsiflexed position by light pressure upon the sole, evokes a stretch reflex which con-

---

[1] When the electrical responses are recorded from the muscle of an animal during the elicitation of a tendon jerk, cessation of the action currents is found to occur during the actual contraction of the muscle. This, the so-called *"silent period"* is probably due to the muscle spindles being relieved of stretch as the muscle shortens (see p. 1154). An additional factor is the synchronous nature of the discharge down the motoneurons, for, the latter being all excited in unison pass also simultaneously into the subnormal phase.

sists of a series of rhythmical contractions of the stretched muscles (ankle clonus). The sudden dorsiflexion causes a sufficient number of stretch receptors to discharge a synchronous volley of impulses along the afferent nerve to the spinal centers and a synchronous efferent volley to be discharged to the muscles. The continued stretch of the muscle caused by keeping the ankle in the dorsiflexed position sets up another synchronous volley as soon as the motoneurons have recovered each time from the subnormal phase of the preceding one. Thus, the clonic movements continue so long as the muscles are kept upon the stretch. Clonus can be evoked in a similar fashion in other situations.

## SOME OTHER STRETCH REFLEXES (DEEP OR TENDON REFLEXES) OF CLINICAL IMPORTANCE

The *jaw jerk*. Tapping the chin with the mouth partly open, and jaw supported, stretches the masseters which contract and jerk the jaw. The reflex center is in the pons.

The *biceps jerk* is elicited by a sharp tap upon the biceps tendon in front of the elbow joint; the response consists of a quick contraction of the biceps with flexion of the elbow. The center for the reflex is situated in the 5th and 6th cervical segments of the cord; it is innervated through the musculocutaneous nerve.

The *triceps jerk* is evoked by a blow upon the triceps muscle just above the olecranon process of the ulna; contraction of the muscle and extension of the elbow result. The center for the response lies in the 6th and 7th cervical segments; the peripheral nerve is the musculospiral (radial).

The *supinator jerk* consists of contraction of the supinator muscle and flexion of the elbow; it follows a blow upon the styloid process of the radius. The center lies in the 5th and 6th cervical segments of the cord; the peripheral nerve is the musculospiral.

*Rossolimo's reflex* which is seen with hyperactivity of the stretch reflexes in the lower extremity, consists of flexion of the toes, including the hallux, when the toes are flicked on their plantar surfaces. A similar response (*Hoffmann's reflex*) which consists of a sudden flexion of the terminal phalanx of the thumb can be evoked by flicking the finger tips.

### The Tone of Skeletal Muscle

As a result chiefly of the work of the Sherrington school the word "tone" or "tonus" as applied to skeletal muscle has acquired a clearly defined meaning. Muscle tone is the steady reflex contraction of the muscles concerned in maintaining the posture characteristic of a given animal species. To use Sherrington's words "reflex tonus is postural contraction." Tonus has its basis in the "static reactions" of the stretch reflexes, and its seat is therefore mainly in the *antigravity muscles*. In most mammals these are extensor muscles and in decerebrate rigidity the animal exhibits an attitude which is a caricature of standing, due to an exaggeration of the tone of the extensors.

In man the antigravity muscles and consequently those which exhibit the greatest degree of tone are the retractors of the neck, the elevators of the jaw (masseters), the supraspinatus, the extensors of the back, the ventral muscles of the abdominal wall (probably), and the extensors of the knee and ankle (vastocrureus, gastrocnemius and soleus). When these muscles are completely relaxed, as in an unconscious person, the body collapses. In the healthy conscious person, stretch reflexes are largely instrumental in preventing this occurrence.

Though the fundamental basis of tonus in voluntary muscle is the myotatic reflex centered in the spinal cord, the tonic state is influenced profoundly by higher centers. Impulses from labyrinthine and neck muscle receptors (pp. 1166 and 1170) exert their influence upon this background of tonus established through lower spinal centers. Similarly, pathways from cerebellar, midbrain and cerebral centers convey impulses which, impinging upon the final common path, are capable of altering the degree of tonus, or effecting finer adjustments in the tonic state and of maintaining its normal distribution between groups of muscles (fig. 64.8, p. 1173). The tone of a given group of muscles may also be influenced through the spinal centers by impulses arising in other muscle groups (e.g., neck muscles and the muscles of the digits, ankle and wrist, as in the positive supporting reaction) and in skin receptors.

When the spinal centers are separated from higher centers there is an areflexic state of muscular flaccidity. Gradually this gives way to a state of hyperreflexia. The extensor tone, however, never is as pronounced as in decerebrate rigidity whereas the flexor reflexes are more active.

A feature of tonic contraction is its economy in the expenditure of energy. Posture is maintained for long periods with little or no evidence of fatigue, e.g., in decerebrate rigidity; in the maintained closure of the jaws, standing or sitting in the normal person; and in the clasping reflex of

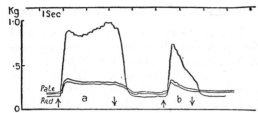

FIG. 64.2. The reflex effect of the labyrinthine and neck reflexes on red and pale muscle. Preparation with section of brain-stem slightly anterior to superior colliculi. M. triceps, short lateral head (pale), double traced line; short medial head (red), single line. Neck dorsiflexed at ↑ and ventriflexed at ↓. Labyrinth in intermediate position in each neck posture. (From Creed, Denny-Brown, Eccles, Liddell and Sherrington *Reflex Activity of the Spinal Cord*, Clarendon Press.)

the frog. The increase in metabolism is less than in the case of those ordinary contractions which result in movement, though the difference is not as great as was once supposed.[2] The work of Forbes and of Adrian and their associates indicates that the economy of energy is effected through different groups of muscle fibers contracting in relays, only a proportion of the total number of fiber groups of the muscle being active at any moment. Thus, active fiber groups mingled with inactive groups are scattered throughout the muscle. The alternating periods of rest and activity of the muscle groups explains the ability of the tonic contraction to be maintained for so long without showing fatigue.

### RED AND WHITE MUSCLE

The skeletal muscles of many animals, e.g., birds, rabbit, cat, etc., can be clearly divided into two types, (a) *red or dark*, and (b) *white or pale*. The former, as compared with the latter, are composed of smaller fibers having a granular and more opaque appearance, possessing more distinct longitudinal striations but less pronounced cross striations, and containing a larger proportion of sarcoplasm.[3] These *red* fibers contract more slowly, fatigue less readily, and are tetanized at a slower rate of stimulation than are the pale fibers. The *pale* fibers are translucent, show prominent cross striations and a small quantity of sarcoplasm.

[2] In the normal human subject postural contractions cause a rise of from 50 to 70 per cent in the basal metabolism. In certain nervous states, in which the body is maintained in fixed attitudes for long periods (catatonia), the increase in metabolism resulting from the tonic contraction of the muscles is less (20 per cent) than in the normal subject. The circulatory effects of sustained posture are also less pronounced in the pathological cases.

[3] They resemble the intrafusal fibers of the muscle spindle (p. 1146).

FIG. 64.3. A suspended decerebrate cat showing extensor rigidity. In A, the labyrinths are intact. B, a decerebrate and labyrinthectomized animal. As a result of the destruction of the labyrinths the head has dropped; this position of the head induces reflex flexion of the forelimbs and extension of the hindlimbs (tonic neck reflexes, p. 1171). (After Pollock and Davis.)

Those muscles which execute rapid movements are usually, though not invariably, of the pale variety, whereas the slower movements are carried out chiefly by the dark muscles. It is probable that all muscles are a mixture of the two types of fiber, but that in some the red, in others the pale type, predominates. The segregation of the two types of fiber in different muscles is much more pronounced in some animals, e.g., the fowl and rabbit, than in others. In birds capable of soaring, or of long flight the wing muscles are mainly of the red type. In man and the monkey the two kinds of muscle can be distinguished with the naked eye, though the differences are not very pronounced. The predominance of one or other type of fiber, can, however, be readily made out under the microscope. The rapidly contracting flexor muscles are largely composed of the pale fibers, whereas each of the extensors usually has a superficially placed, rapidly contracting, pale component (or head) and a deep, slowly acting dark head. No hard and fast line, however, can be drawn, since both types of extensor muscle exhibit tone, and both take part in phasic contractions (fig. 64.2).

### Decerebrate Rigidity

This is the term applied to the sustained contraction of the extensor muscles which supervenes upon transection of the brain stem at any level between the superior colliculi and the vestibular nuclei.[4] It was first studied and described in de-

[4] Decerebration can also be produced by tying the common carotids and the basilar artery at the center of the pons and thereby depriving the forebrain of its blood supply.

tail by Sherrington. The animal assumes a characteristic attitude with limbs stiffly extended, head retracted, jaws closed, and tail horizontal or erect. When placed upon its feet the limbs support the weight of the body (fig. 64.3.A). *The position is a caricature of the normal standing position.* The knee jerk and other stretch reflexes (pp. 1162, 1163) are exaggerated. The righting reflexes are abolished; tonic neck and labyrinthine reflexes are retained.

In some instances there is increased reflex excitability of the flexor muscles as well, but the characteristic feature of decerebrate rigidity is the tonic contraction of the muscles which maintain the posture of the body against gravity (p. 1152), the *antigravity muscles*. It may be pointed out that in the frog whose natural posture is squatting with flexed thighs, legs and arms, it is the flexor muscles which are the site of decerebrate rigidity. Also in the sloth, whose habit it is to remain for long periods suspended from a tree branch, flexor rigidity is the characteristic result of decerebration. In the pigeon the flexor muscles which maintain the resting (folded) position of the wing exhibit rigidity, and in the ape the muscles which hold the elbow semiflexed when the body is erect show increased tone. In man abolition of the function of the cerebral motor cortex results in a state of increased tone in the flexors of the arms and in the extensors in the lower extremities, whereas decerebration at the mesencephalic level is associated with extensor spasticity in all four extremities.

## Tonic Labyrinthine and Neck Reflexes in the Decerebrate Preparation (see also p. 1171)

Labyrinthine proprioceptors are responsible for the tone of the neck extensors; consequently, after destruction of the labyrinths in the decerebrate preparation the head is no longer held erect but falls into the fully flexed position. The rigidity in the forelimbs in turn is maintained through proprioceptive reflexes initiated in the extended neck muscles as well as directly through labyrinthine reflexes (p. 1171). After labyrinthectomy, therefore, the flexed position assumed by the head sets up proprioceptive impulses from the neck muscles which lead to a reduction in the extensor tone of the forelimbs; these then become strongly flexed upon the chest (fig. 64.3B). If the neck muscles of the labyrinthectomized animal are deafferented, movements of the head are without effect upon the extensor muscles of either fore or hind limbs.

## Lengthening and Shortening Reactions

Attempts at passive flexion of the extended limb of the decerebrate (or chronic spinal) preparation are met with considerable resistance. If the force is increased beyond a certain point the stretch reflex (upon which the resistance depends) is inhibited and the limb gives way suddenly (*clasp-knife effect*). It may then be easily flexed to any degree and remains in the new position. The elongation of the extensor muscles which permits the flexion of the limb is called the "*lengthening reaction*". Upon moving the limb again into the extended position the extensor muscle shortens adaptively, and again resists the limb being bent. This is the "*shortening reaction*". These reactions give the muscles a certain plastic quality. The giving way of the extensor spasm in the lengthening reaction has been ascribed to the setting up of inhibitory impulses in the tendon and the muscle when the stretch stimulus reaches a certain intensity. The knee extensor is inhibited also by a contraction of the opposite knee extensor; this is known as the *crossed extensor* or *Phillipson's reflex*.

## A Consideration of the Central Mechanisms Concerned in the Production of Decerebrate Rigidity

Bazett and Penfield succeeded in keeping animals (cats) alive for from two to three weeks after aseptic section through the midbrain. The animals showed extensor rigidity up to the day of death, though as time elapsed the condition tended to be less constant, intervals of reduced extensor tone and increased flexor tone alternating with periods showing the typical decerebrate posture. The fact that extensor rigidity was present so long after operation makes it clear that the condition is not due to the irritation of fibers at the line of section, for these must have undergone degeneration before the end of the survival period. In a more recent investigation Bard and Macht demonstrated that if the hypothalamus is left intact, even though severed from the midbrain and bulb, and if the animals are given intensive care they may recover some useful movement of their extremities following transection through the upper mesencephalon.

Decerebrate rigidity is evidently due to the release from higher control of a center or centers situated below the level of the transection. This control of the stretch reflex (postural reflexes; muscular tone) is complex. The precentral motor cortex exerts the most marked inhibitory effect upon these reflex muscular activities. In this portion of the cerebral cortex a narrow strip originally described by Marion Hines and commonly known as 4s is particularly active in this regard. Area 4s lies just anterior to area 4 or the area gigantopyramidalis which contains the Betz cells and immediately behind area 6, an agranular precentral area which contains no Betz cells. Neighboring cortical areas are probably also similarly although less effectively active. The opinion once held that this inhibitory effect over the postural reflexes is exercised by the gigantic cells of Betz in area 4 of the precentral gyrus and the corticospinal tract which arises from the precentral gyrus (the "pyramidal tract") is certainly erroneous. There is also evidence that some of the basal ganglia exercise a certain controlling influence, probably both inhibitory and facilitatory, over the postural reflexes but detailed information regarding the anatomy and physiology of this mechanism is lacking. In animals the anterior lobe of the cerebellum exercises an inhibitory control over the stretch reflexes. Destruction of this portion of the cerebellum in the cat results in a state akin to decerebrate rigidity, whereas in a decerebrate cat electrical stimulation of this portion of the cerebellum causes a pronounced relaxation of the decerebrate rigidity. In man it appears that this cerebellar inhibitory mechanism is either far less effective than in animals or is absent altogether for no one has ever demonstrated any human cases in which cerebellar lesions have resulted in spasticity. The only alteration in muscular tone seen in human beings with cerebellar lesions is hypotonia.

In any consideration of the control of muscular activity by the central nervous system one is repeatedly impressed with the important differences between the organization of the nervous system of man as compared with lower animals. If one removes the precentral motor cortex (areas 4 and 6, or the frontal agranular cortex) from man, a severe and enduring spastic paralysis of the contralateral extremities develops. If, on the other hand, the "motor" cortex or the cortex of the sigmoid gyrus is removed from the cat, or even if the entire cerebral cortex is removed any paralysis is fleeting and slight, and any alteration in the tonic state of the skeletal musculature is of little moment. These facts illustrate the constant care which must be exerted in interpreting any facts demonstrated in animal experiments in explanation of phenomena observed in man.

Area 4s exercises its *inhibitory* influence over

muscular activity by transmitting impulses to a centrally placed bulbar portion of the reticular formation. It is likely that the basal ganglia and the cerebellum also send their impulses there. The reticular formation also contains a laterally placed *facilitatory* mechanism which is capable of *enhancing* the postural reflexes. This facilitatory mechanism is connected with various other central neural structures but most notably with the vestibular apparatus and the vestibular nuclei. These nuclei may augment reflex activity either directly over the vestibulo-spinal pathways or by way of the reticular formation. It is obvious then that the reticular formation which contains both inhibitory and facilitatory mechanisms is capable of acting as a center for the regulation of the stretch and other postural reflexes and of muscular activity in general.

The view that spasticity is not merely the result of excessive spinal reflex activity released by the removal of suprasegmental inhibitory control but is due to an imbalance of the reticular formation between inhibition and facilitation is a distinct advance in our physiological thinking, but it represents an incomplete understanding of the problem and ignores many clinical facts. Some of the most striking examples of muscular spasticity from disturbances in the human central nervous system are seen in patients with traumatic or neoplastic lesions of the spinal cord. In such cases the entire brain, including the reticular formation of the brain-stem, has been excluded so far as concerns the skeletal musculature which is innervated by the spinal cord below the level of the lesion. Obviously in such cases the mechanism giving rise to the spasticity is a purely spinal one, and the condition must represent a removal of descending inhibitory influences and a release of spinal mechanisms from suprasegmental control.

### Decerebrate Rigidity in Man

In certain neurological disorders in man one encounters disturbances in muscular tone and of the postural reflexes, including the stretch reflex. With lesions in the region of the midbrain one sees a state very akin to decerebrate rigidity in the laboratory animals. All four extremities are rigidly extended. The forearms are pronated. The muscles show the lengthening and shortening reactions, and the tonic neck and labyrinthine reflexes are elicitable. When the head is flexed on the neck the legs are rigidly extended and the arms become flexed at the elbows. When the head is rotated to one side the extremities on that side become rigidly extended while those on the opposite side relax or flex. When the head is rotated to the opposite side the pattern is reversed (fig. 64.5). With decortication rather than decerebration the picture is somewhat different. The lower extremity is still usually spastic in extension but the upper extremity is usually flexed at the elbow, wrist and fingers. This is the situation usually seen in patients with a spastic hemiplegia caused by a destructive lesion in the internal capsule.

Diseases affecting the basal ganglia are commonly associated with increased muscular tone. This differs from spasticity in that it affects both flexors and extensors more nearly equally, and the degree of resistance to passive manipulation is more nearly constant throughout the range of motion. This rigidity seems to be dependent upon proprioceptive afferent impulses, as it disappears when the posterior spinal roots are divided. Thus it resembles the spasticity of decerebrate rigidity which is dependent upon the stretch reflex for its existence.

### The Spinal State

Transection of the cord produces an immediate flaccid paralysis of the muscles below the point of section. Immediately after section in the lower cervical region the limbs hang limply, the muscles being quite toneless; the stretch reflexes and other extensor responses cannot be elicited; the knee jerk is abolished. The blood pressure falls and vascular and visceral reflexes are unobtainable. This condition is called *spinal shock*. Its duration varies with the species. The higher the position of the latter in the phylogenetic scale the more profound is the shock and the slower is the recovery. In the frog its duration is brief; in the rabbit, cat and dog the knee jerk returns within a few minutes (rabbit); or in an hour (cat) or longer (dog); but in the monkey, not for several days. Other extensor reflexes, however, remain in abeyance for a much longer time. In the cat and dog the picture immediately following spinal transection is different from that seen after decerebration. The extensor stretch reflexes are less active while the flexor responses to nociceptive stimuli are more easily elicited. Consequently, if the spinal cord of a decerebrate preparation is sectioned, the exaggerated extensor tone characteristic of the latter is replaced (behind the section) by an imbalance in favor of the flexor muscles.

Spinal shock also follows section through the medulla below the vestibular nuclei (*decapitate preparation*) (see also p. 1150).

In the cat and dog recovery from spinal shock gradually takes place in a few days. The blood pressure is restored to normal and the vascular reflexes can again be obtained. The reactions of the extensor muscles return, and the animal is able, though imperfectly and very briefly to support the weight of the body when placed upon its feet (chronic spinal animal).

Spinal shock is attributed to the removal of impulses which in the intact animal descend from higher centers to reinforce the spinal centers. That it is due to this and not simply to an inhibitory effect of the local injury itself seems clear from the fact that after an animal has recovered from spinal shock, a second transection made behind (lower than the original one) does not cause a return of the shock state. In *the cat and dog* the flexor reflexes are evidently dependent only to a minor extent upon the higher centers, since they are capable of being executed by the spinal centers alone and are seen in their most exaggerated form in animals or human beings with a complete transection of the spinal cord. The fact that the extensor stretch reflexes are less active in the spinal animal is due to the loss of facilitatory impulses from the reticular formation and the vestibular nuclei, but these reactions can also eventually be carried out by the spinal centers. In *primates* in which a greater degree of motor function is represented in the cerebral cortex, the immediate effect of cord section upon reflex activity is much more profound than in the cat or dog. Recovery of reflex activity following transection of the spinal cord is in considerable measure dependent upon the condition of the animal or patient. Infection or impaired nutrition greatly retard recovery.

### The "Thalamus" Animal

This term is given to an animal whose cerebral hemispheres have been removed, leaving the optic thalami intact (see fig. 64.9, Section I). Such preparations retain their righting reflexes and can regulate their body temperature. They are also capable of carrying out coordinated reflex acts and show, often to an exaggerated degree, reactions which in the intact animal are associated with emotional states (fright, anger). Such reactions, which are termed pseudoaffective, are also exhibited by an animal whose cortex alone has been ablated (see ch. 66). In contrast to the decerebrate animal, the distribution of muscular tone in the thalamic cat or dog shows little departure from the normal, though pronounced extensor rigidity becomes evident when the animal is held suspended in mid-air.

Primates, on the contrary, are usually unable

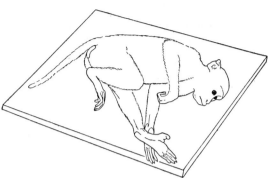

FIG. 64.4. Showing posture of a "thalamus" monkey. The underneath limbs are extended and the uppermost flexed. When the animal is turned over, the previously extended limbs (being now uppermost) are flexed, and those which were flexed (now underneath) are extended. (After Bieber and Fulton.)

to walk after bilateral decortication, and there are profound alterations in the muscular tone of the limbs. The animal generally assumes a characteristic attitude. When lying upon its side the limbs of the under part of the body are extended and the uppermost limbs flexed. The uppermost limbs show a pronounced grasp reflex. Turning the animal on to its opposite side reverses the picture. The limbs which were underneath and extended are now flexed and show the grasp reflex, while the limbs previously uppermost, being now underneath, are extended. Righting reflexes (except those dependent upon vision) and the tonic labyrinthine and neck reflexes of Magnus and de

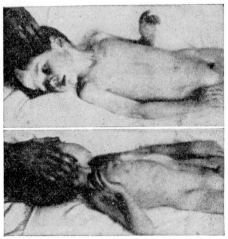

FIG. 64.5. Decerebrate child. Suprasellar cyst causing interruption of descending pathways at the level of the midbrain. Turning the head to one side causes extension of the arm of that side and increased flexion of the opposite arm. (Modified after L. E. Davis.)

Kleijn are shown in a striking fashion (figs. 64.4 and 64.5).

If the extirpation of the cerebral cortex is carried out piecemeal over a considerable period of time, and if the animal is given meticulous care as to nutrition and manipulation of its extremities, it is possible occasionally to produce an animal which can stand briefly and awkwardly and even take a few steps, but in general such an animal is quite disabled. The disability is much more profound than that seen in a decorticate cat.

### Static and Statokinetic Reflexes of Magnus and de Kleijn

The reflex mechanisms governing the orientation of the head in space, the position of the head in relation to the trunk and the appropriate adjustments of limbs and eyes to the position of the head, are called into action by afferent impulses discharged from receptors situated in (a) the vestibular apparatus (semicircular canals or utricle), (b) the neck muscles, (c) the retina, and (d) in the body wall or limb muscles.

These are complex reflexes which are concerned with the posture of entire extremities and of the trunk as they are influenced by movements of other extremities, of the trunk and of the head and neck. They aid in maintaining the position of the body in space, in restoring the body to an upright position when its position has been disturbed, in progression forward, etc. A more detailed account of these postural reflexes follows.

#### General Static Reflexes

##### THE RIGHTING REFLEXES

The orientation of the head in space, and the ability to maintain the body in a certain definite (normal) relation to the head is a characteristic of animal life. A cat held back downwards and then allowed to fall through the air lands upon its feet, its head and body assuming, in a flash, the normal attitude. A fish resists any attempt to turn it from its natural position and if placed in the water upon its back flips almost instantly into the normal swimming position. Even a cray fish rights itself from the back-down position.[5] These

[5] The otocyst of the prawn is homologous to the utricle of mammals. It is open to the exterior and at moulting time its lining is shed. The otoliths consist of grains of sand which the animal itself introduces into the otocyst. If, after moulting, the animals are placed in a dish containing fine iron filings these are inserted and various forced movements of the head and body can be induced by bringing a magnet into relation with the ear.

Fig. 64.6. On left, position taken up by a thalamus rabbit with intact labyrinths. As it possesses the labyrinthine righting reflexes, it carries its head in the normal position. On the right, position taken up by a rabbit like the preceding but deprived of its labyrinths. The head is not raised towards the normal position. (After Magnus.)

righting reactions are complex and involve five separate types of reflex.

(a) Labyrinthine righting reflexes acting upon the neck muscles.

(b) Neck righting reflexes acting upon the body.

(c) Body righting reflexes acting upon the head.

(d) Body righting reflexes acting upon the body.

(e) Optical righting reflexes.

The first four of these are demonstrated best upon a "thalamus" animal (p. 1168). When a "thalamus" rabbit or a blindfold normal animal is suspended from the pelvis (fig. 64.6) the head turns until it assumes its normal position in space i.e., into the position it would occupy were the animal in its natural position. The maintenance of the head in the new position is due to *labyrinthine righting reflexes* acting upon the neck muscles. Turning the body of the animal through the air into different positions is followed by compensatory movements of the head, its orientation in space being thereby maintained. After extirpation of the labyrinths or destruction of the utricle alone, and suspension of the animal as before, the head shows no compensatory movements; it hangs limply like that of a dead rabbit.

When the blindfold or thalamic animal is laid resting upon its side on a table the head is raised into the usual upright position as a result of the labyrinthine reflexes just mentioned. The contraction of the neck muscles which rotate the head sets up in turn, proprioceptive impulses, which through a center in the upper cervical cord exert an influence upon the muscles of the body which rotate it (thorax first, then pelvis) into the normal relationship to the head. This is the *neck righting*

*reflex acting upon the body.* A labyrinthectomized animal when laid upon its side behaves in a somewhat similar manner. The reaction under the latter circumstances is due, however, to the asymmetrical stimulation (pressure of one side of the body upon the table) of exteroceptors in the body wall, and the reflex contraction of the neck muscles. This is the *body righting reflex acting upon the head.* If a board of a weight equal to that of the animal is laid upon its upper surface, the pressure being thereby disposed equally on the two sides, the compensatory movement of the head does not occur.

Again, when a blindfold animal or one which has been decorticated is laid upon its side, and its head held down to the table, to eliminate the righting reflexes of labyrinthine and cervical origins, as well as the body righting reflex acting upon the head, the body nevertheless attempts to right itself by raising the hindquarters. This must be due to the asymmetrical pressure upon the body exerting a reflex effect upon the skeletal musculature, i.e., a *body righting reflex acting upon the body.*

This reflex is well shown by the labyrinthectomized dogfish, especially after blinding. When placed in the water (pressure being equal on all sides) upon its side or back the fish deprived of its labyrinths swims away in the false position. When, however, it comes into contact with the bottom or side of the tank (pressure then being exerted unequally) the righting reaction immediately occurs. Even worms possess this means of orientation.

The *optical righting reflexes* are initiated through retinal impressions. They are absent in the thalamic animal since their center is cortical (occipital lobes). Visual impressions play a prominent role in the orientation of the head in some animals, such as the monkey, dog and cat. If a labyrinthectomized dog is held in the air in order to exclude the body righting reflexes, it is capable of orienting the head, but is not able to do so if blindfolded. The optical righting reflexes are of minor importance as compared with the labyrinthine in animals such as the rabbit and guinea pig whose cortical development is more rudimentary, and who depend to a large extent upon subcortical visual centers. In the more intelligent animals the optical righting reflexes are abolished by decortication. Yet even the crayfish deprived of its otocyst, which is the homologue of the utricle of mammals, rights itself, though with less facility than normally, when placed upside down in water. In this medium righting reflexes due to unequally distributed pressures upon the body surface must obviously be in abeyance; the righting reaction, then, is apparently entirely of retinal origin. That this is so is proved by blinding the animal; then the righting reaction is lost completely.

To sum up, the righting reflexes may now be given in their natural sequence. When the animal is placed upon its back the labyrinthine reflex acting upon the neck muscles turns the head into its normal relationship to the dimensions of space; the proprioceptive reflexes of the neck muscles then bring the body into its normal relation to the head. When resting upon a rigid support these reflexes are reinforced by body righting reflexes (on head and body). When the animal falls through air or water, these latter reflexes of course do not come into play. A labyrinthectomized but otherwise normal animal, such as the cat or dog, recovers its upright position when allowed to fall through the air, as a result of the operation of the optical righting reactions; the righting ability is lost, however, if the eyes are covered with a hood. Also, an air-breathing animal deprived of its labyrinths, though a good swimmer, drowns if thrown into deep water, since it cannot orient itself by the sight of surrounding objects. Deaf mutes, whose labyrinths are very frequently undeveloped, though able to swim may become disoriented and drown if they fall or dive into deep water.

Righting reflexes may be demonstrated in the human subject. A baby a few weeks old, for example, when lying prone raises the head into a nearly vertical position. When blindfolded and held by the pelvis in different positions in the air the head is moved toward the normal position.

## Local and Segmental Static Reactions. Supporting Reactions

Magnus speaks of the simultaneous reflex contractions of both extensor and flexor muscles and other opposing muscles whereby the joints are fixed and the limbs converted into rigid pillars for the support of the body against gravity as the *positive supporting reaction*. This reaction is initiated by:—

(a) Impulses discharged from the proprioceptors of the flexor muscles of the terminal segments of the limbs—digits and ankle or wrist; the pressure of an animal's paw upon the ground by stretching these muscles provides the adequate stimulus which calls forth simultaneous reflex

contractions of the flexors and extensors of the knee (or elbow).

(b) Myotatic reflexes set up in the flexors of ankle and toes (plantar flexors), and of the corresponding forelimb joints; excessive extension at these joints is thus counteracted. Any tendency toward over-extension at the knee or elbow is also provided against through the reflex set up when the flexors of these joints are stretched. Similarly, any tendency of the knee or elbow to bend under the weight of the body calls forth a myotatic reflex from the extensors, which prevents any weakening of the supporting action of the limb.

(c) Impulses set up in the pressure receptors in the deeper layers of the skin of the sole when in contact with the ground; thus exteroceptive reflexes reinforce those of proprioceptive origin. The exteroceptor element is well shown in a decerebellated dog. When such a preparation is placed upon its back and the head strongly flexed, the hindlimbs are flexed in all joints. Light pressure with the finger upon the toe pad then causes an extension of the limb, and if the finger be moved with the limb as it extends so that only very light pressure upon the pad is maintained, one has the sensation of the limb being drawn out by the finger. For this reason the movement has been called the "magnet reaction."

The relaxation of the muscles and the unfixing of the joints which enables the limb to be flexed and moved to a new position is called the *negative supporting reaction*. It is brought about by raising the pad off the ground and plantar flexing the toes and ankle. The exteroceptive stimulus and the stretch stimulus to the *plantar flexors* are thus removed. The reflex "unlocking" of the limb is not, however, simply due to the removal of these stimuli, but has in addition a positive element, namely, the stimulus provided by plantar flexion and the consequent stretching of the dorsi-flexors of the toes and ankle—relaxation of the extensors of the knee or elbow and contraction of the flexors result.

The supporting reactions, though seen best in a decerebellate animal, can also be demonstrated in the decorticate preparation or in one whose brain-stem has been divided above the medulla oblongata. Segmental static reactions, e.g., flexion reflex and the crossed extension reflex have been described in chapter 63.

### Statotonic or Attitudinal Reflexes

(1) *Tonic labyrinthine and neck reflexes acting upon the limbs.* These reflexes influence the tone

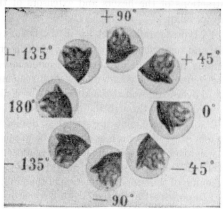

Fig. 64.7. Diagrammatic representation of the positions of an animal's head, each marked with the angle which the mouth cleft makes with the horizontal plane. (After Magnus.)

of the skeletal muscles and thereby maintain the different parts of the body in an attitude appropriate to a given position of the head. They are investigated best in the decerebrate animal (p. 1165), the righting reflexes being then largely abolished. The proprioceptors concerned are in: (a) the *labyrinth* (tonic labyrinthine (utricular) reflexes) which are brought into play by alterations in the position of the head in space, (b) the *neck muscles* (tonic neck reflexes) which come into action when the position of the head is altered relatively to the body. In order to study separately the part played by each of these reflexes in any given reaction, the following procedures are adopted.

A. *To exclude the neck reflexes:*

(a) Immobilization of the neck of an animal by means of a plaster of Paris bandage in order to prevent movement of the head in relation to the trunk. Any tonic effects resulting from a change in the animal's position must then be due solely to alterations in the position of the head in space (labyrinthine reflexes); or (b) section of the posterior roots of the first three of four pairs of cervical nerves.

B. *To exclude tonic labyrinthine reflexes:*

(a) Fixation of the head alone in some suitable apparatus. The tonic effect resulting from movement of the body must then be due to an alteration in the position of the body in relation to the head, i.e., to movements of the neck; or (b) destruction of the labyrinths or section of the 8th cranial nerves.

The labyrinthine reflexes exert an influence upon the tone of the extensor muscles which is in the *same* direction (increase or decrease) in all four

limbs. The influence of the neck reflexes, on the other hand, is usually in *opposite* directions in the fore and hind pairs of limbs. The greatest degree of extensor tone is exerted through the labyrinth mechanism when the animal is supine and the mouth cleft inclined at an angle of 45° above the horizontal plane (fig. 64.7), and is least when the mouth cleft makes an angle of 45° below the horizontal plane.

Extensor tone diminishes as the angle increases; it is minimal in the prone position with the mouth cleft at an angle of 45° below the horizontal plane.

In an animal on all fours the labyrinthine effect is, therefore, to increase or decrease the extensor tone in the muscles of all four limbs when the head is strongly extended or flexed, respectively. In the decerebrate labyrinthectomized animal, the neck reflexes alone operating, flexion of the forelimbs and extension of the hindlimbs occur when the neck is flexed toward the sternum (ventriflexion) (see fig. 64.3, p. 1165). Extension of the neck (dorsiflexion) produces the converse picture, i.e., extension of the forelimbs and flexion of the hindlimbs. When, therefore, the neck is ventriflexed in the decerebrate animal with intact labyrinths, the neck reflexes reinforce the tonic labyrinthine effect upon the forelimbs but antagonize that upon the hindlimbs; the usual result is relaxation of the forelimbs with strong extension of the hindlimbs. When the neck is extended the neck reflexes reinforce the labyrinthine effect upon the tone of the forelimbs but antagonize that upon the hindlimbs. The effect of the neck reflexes upon the extensor tone of the latter again predominates; the extension of the forelimbs is maintained but definite relaxation of the hindlimbs occurs.

Rotation of an animal's head (turning in the frontal plane of the skull) causes increased extensor tone of the fore and hindlimbs on the side of the body toward which the jaw is rotated (*jaw limbs*)[6] and reduces the extensor tone of the opposite limbs (*skull limbs*).[6] Inclination of the head toward one shoulder (lateral flexion) as when an animal turns a corner is accompanied by similar effects—extension of the limbs on the side of the body toward which the jaw (or snout) is inclined (jaw limbs) and flexion of the limbs on the opposite side (skull limbs).

Pressure upon the last cervical vertebra reduces the tone in all four limbs (*vertebra prominens reflex*).

[6] Magnus has introduced the term jaw limbs to indicate the limbs toward which the chin of man or the jaw of animals is rotated or inclined. The opposite limbs, i.e., the limbs to which the vertex of the skull is rotated, are called skull limbs.

FIG. 64.8. Photographs of a normal cat, showing the animal's posture (on left) when its attention is attracted by an object placed above it. Photograph of the same animal (on right) when its attention is drawn to an object below it. The difference between the two positions of the forelimbs is very marked, because in them the neck and labyrinthine reflexes reinforce one another; the hindlimbs are in much the same position in both cases, since the two sets of reflexes cancel one another. (After Magnus.)

The significance of these reflexes and their importance in the coördination of the postural muscles may be realized when the attitudes of the intact animal are observed. Thus when an animal turns to one side the limbs of that side are stiffened in order to support the body's weight. A cat looking upwards to a bird in a tree extends the forelimbs and flexes the hindlimbs, thus giving the back a suitable inclination which improves the position of the head and eyes, and places the body in a position preparatory for a spring (fig. 64.8). When looking into a hole or beneath a cupboard the flexion of the forelimbs and extension of the hindquarters gives an opposite but no less advantageous inclination to the body. Depression of the back in the region of the last cervical vertebra brings the animal into a crouching attitude.

Stato-tonic effects may be demonstrated in certain nervous lesions associated with a state analogous to decerebrate rigidity of animals (pp. 1165, 1166). Turning the head to one side, for example, causes an increase in tone of the extensors of the jaw limbs and hypotonicity in the limb muscles of the opposite side.[7] When the head is in the position for maximal labyrinthine tone, i.e., when the patient is supine, and the neck extended the extensor tone of the paralyzed limbs increases, but becomes reduced in the prone position.

(2) *Tonic labyrinthine and cervical reflexes acting upon the eyes.* Tonic effects upon the eye muscles, analogous to those described for the skeletal muscles, result from changes in the position of the head. Labyrinthine and neck reflexes are responsible. Alteration in the position of the head with neck immobilized, or movement of the head in relation to the body after labyrinthectomy, is fol-

[7] This, according to Magnus, can also be shown in a certain percentage of normal infants, and in hydrocephalus it may be well marked.

lowed by compensatory eye movements. Turning the head downwards causes an upward movement of the eyes which are held in this position so long as the head position is maintained, the tone of the superior recti and inferior oblique being increased while that of the inferior recti and superior oblique is reduced. A corresponding compensatory movement of the eyes occurs when the head is turned upward. Similarly, when the head is turned to one side the internal and external recti of the two eyes cooperate to deviate the eyes outward or inward in relation to the head. Briefly, the eyes are moved in a direction opposite to that taken by the head; thus their original positions in space are maintained and the visual field existing prior to the head movement remains unaltered. It should be pointed out that the actual *movement* of the eyes is a stato-kinetic reflex (p. 1174) and due to a different mechanism (semicircular canals) from that which maintains the eye *position* while the head is held in the altered attitude. The latter is a stato-tonic reflex, dependent upon the utricle.

## SUMMARY OF THE CENTERS FOR GENERAL STATIC REFLEXES

Magnus found that all the static reactions mentioned in the foregoing section could be obtained unaltered after removal of the cerebellum, as could also most of the stato-kinetic reflexes to be described in the next section. Nevertheless, this rather surprising fact does not necessarily imply that in the normal intact animal the cerebellum plays no part in these reactions. A contrary conclusion must be drawn from anatomical considerations and from observations in cerebellar disease in which disturbances referable to the labyrinth (e.g., abnormal positions of head, falling, etc.) are

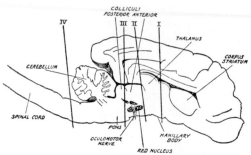

FIG. 64.9. Diagram to illustrate the effects of sections through cat's brain at various levels. Line I, thalamic animal, righting, tonic labyrinthine and neck reflexes retained; little disturbance of muscular tone; Lines II and III, decerebrate rigidity; Line IV, behind vestibular nucleus, decapitate animal, extensor rigidity less marked, tonic neck reflexes retained. Section at level of second or third cervical segment of the cord—spinal animal—abolishes the tonic neck reflexes (after Magnus); III indicates Sherrington's original section.

manifest. Moreover, numerous connections between the labyrinths, the vestibular nuclei and the cerebellum have been demonstrated.

(a) *The righting reflexes*. All the labyrinthine righting reflexes, as well as the body righting reflexes acting upon the head, have their centers in the midbrain. The center for the optical righting reflexes is cortical, that for the body righting reflexes acting upon the head have their centers in the midbrain.

(b) *The stato-tonic labyrinthine reflexes* acting upon the skeletal muscles have their center in the vestibular nuclei.

(c) *The neck reflexes* are centered in the upper two or three cervical segments of the spinal cord (see fig. 64.9).

(d) The centers for the *tonic labyrinthine and cervical reflexes acting upon the eyes* are situated between the vestibular nuclei and the oculomotor nuclei.

*Placing and hopping reactions*. These have been thoroughly investigated by Bard. Bard and Brooks describe five *placing reactions*.

(1) If a cat is held in mid-air with legs dependent and chin held up so that it cannot see anything below or in front, contact of the backs of the forepaws with the table's edge is followed by a quick movement of the limbs which brings the paws, soles down, precisely upon the surface of the table. (2) If the forelimbs of a cat are held down while the chin in brought in contact with the table near its edge, the forepaws when released are instantly raised and placed upon the table beside the chin, a movement which is usually followed by extension of the limbs and the assumption of a standing position. (3) If the fore-or hindlimbs of a cat standing or sitting upon a

table are pushed over the table's edge, they are immediately lifted and placed in their original positions. (4) If one abducts, without holding, the limb of a standing cat, it is instantly returned to its previous position. (5) If a blindfolded cat is suspended in the air with forelimbs free, and its head brought toward some obstacle, at the instant that the vibrissae come into contact with the object the forepaws are raised and accurately planted upon the surface of the object. The first three of these reactions are due to stimulation of receptors upon the body surface (exteroceptors) and probably also of proprioceptors in muscles and tendons. The fourth is a purely proprioceptive reflex; the last is initiated from tactile receptors. The *hopping reactions* consist of limb movements which serve to maintain the standing position against any force acting upon it in a horizontal plane. When, for example, a cat is held so that its body is supported upon one fore- or hindlimb and is then pushed in one or other direction, the supporting limb hops quickly in the direction of the displacement, the foot being kept directly under the corresponding shoulder or hip. The hopping reactions are probably dependent upon myotatic (stretch) reflexes (p. 1162).

The placing and hopping reactions are controlled from the sensorimotor area of the cerebral cortex. Removal of this region from both cerebral hemispheres by Bard and Brooks was found to abolish the placing reactions, and to produce an extreme degree of deficiency in the hopping reactions. Decortication (complete removal of the neocortex) produce no greater deficiency. The control exerted by the cerebral cortex is entirely contralateral, i.e., the component movements of the reactions on one side of the body are governed solely by the opposite side of the brain.

### Kinetic, Statokinetic or Accelerator Reflexes

The term kinetic is attached to these labyrin-

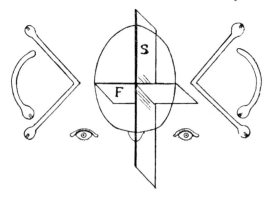

FIG. 64.10. Diagram showing the semicircular canals and their relation to the planes of the skull. S, median sagittal plane; F, transverse frontal plane (see text).

FIG. 64.11. Diagram of the labyrinth: C, cochlea; C.R., canalis reuniens; S, saccule; U, utricle. Receptor areas indicated in heavy black.

thine reflexes because they are caused by the *movement* of the head, but since it is not the movement itself, but *acceleration* above a certain rate, angular (rotary) or linear (progressive), that is the adequate stimulus, *acceleratory reflexes* is a better name.

### ANATOMY OF THE LABYRINTH

Before a description of other labyrinthine functions, e.g., the stato-kinetic reflexes, can be undertaken, a brief description of the structure of the labyrinth must be given. This structure consists of an auditory (cochlear) and a nonauditory portion. We are concerned here only with the latter which we shall refer to simply as the labyrinth. The *bony labyrinth* comprises a series of cavities tunnelled in the petrous part of the temporal bone. The cavities are the three semicircular canals, each of which opens by its two extremities into a ovoid chamber known as the *vestibule*. The bony labyrinth lodges a series of hollow membranous structures—the *membranous labyrinth*. The membranous labyrinth consists of: (a) *Three semi-circular*

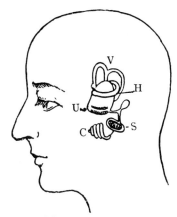

FIG. 64.12. Diagram (not to scale) giving a lateral view of the internal ear within the skull. V, vertical canals; H, horizontal canal; U, utricle; S, saccule; C, cochlea. (Redrawn fom Quix.)

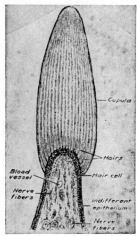

FIG. 64.13. Drawing of crista. (From *Bailey's Histology,* after Schafer.)

canals lying in the corresponding bony canals. (b) Two sacs, the *utricle* and *saccule* situated in the vestibules (fig. 64.11).

THE SEMICIRCULAR CANALS. One extremity of each canal shows an expansion known as the *ampulla* wherein is situated the specific sense organ. The membranous labyrinth is filled with fluid —the *endolymph:* a similar fluid—the *perilymph*— lies between its walls and the walls of the bony labyrinth. The canals lie in planes approximately at right angles to one another and are called respectively *external* or *lateral* (horizontal), *anterior* or *superior* (vertical) and *posterior* (vertical) (see fig. 64.10). It will be noted that the nonexpanded extremities of the vertical canals join to form a common stem through which they communicate with the utricle (figs. 64.10, 64.11 and 64.12).

The external canal is directed with its convexity outwards and backwards. When the head is in the erect position this canal is only approximately horizontal; it is inclined backwards and downwards at an angle of about 30° to the horizontal plane. The vertical (anterior and posterior) canals both make an angle of about 45° with the frontal and the sagittal planes of the skull.[8] The anterior canal of one ear is therefore nearly in the same plane as the posterior canal of the other ear, whereas the posterior or anterior canal of one ear is at right angles to its fellow of the opposite side as well as to the other two canals of the same ear. The external (horizontal) canals of the two sides lie in the same plane.

THE CRISTA. This is the receptor organ of a semicircular canal. It is situated in the ampulla and consists of a mound of sensory hair cells between which are nonsensory supporting cells. The sen-

[8] That is, their planes cross both the frontal and sagittal planes diagonally.

sory cells are surmounted by a gelatinous dome-shaped structure—the *cupula;* this contains fine longitudinal channels in which the hairs or cilia lodged (fig. 64.13).

### THE OTOLITH ORGANS—THE UTRICLE AND SACCULE

In the wall of the *utricle* lie the openings of the semicircular canals. The utricle communicates through a fine canal with the cochlea and by a second small channel—the *ductus utriculosaccularis*—with the saccule. The sense organs of the utricle and saccule are called *macula*. Each macula is a plaque of sensitive hair-cells covered by a gelatinous material—the *otolith membrane*—containing crystals or concretions of a calcareous substance—the *otoliths*. The macula of the utricle is situated on its anterior and medial walls, the two portions being joined at an angle of 140°. The sensitive hair-cells are directed laterally and posteriorly. The saccule communicates with the cochlea through the *canalis reuniens*. The saccular maculae are situated obliquely, forming an angle of 27° with the vertical plane and 22° with the horizontal. The saccular maculae of the two sides incline towards each other so that if continued backwards they would meet behind the head. The dorsal lobe of the saccule also contains a macula whose hair-cells face downwards. The *saccule* communicates with the utricle on the one hand and with the cochlea on the other. Its communication with the latter is through the duct of Henson. The sense organ of the saccule is also given the name of macula[9] and is constructed upon a plan similar to that of the utricle.

### THE NERVOUS CONNECTIONS OF THE LABYRINTH

The central connections of the vestibular mechanism are very widely distributed throughout the central nervous system, and are far from being fully known, but the following connections are fairly well established.

The impulses from the proprioceptors of the different parts of the non-auditory labyrinth are con-

[9] The term "lapillus" is sometimes applied to the otolithic organ of the utricle while that of the saccule is spoken of as the "sagitta."

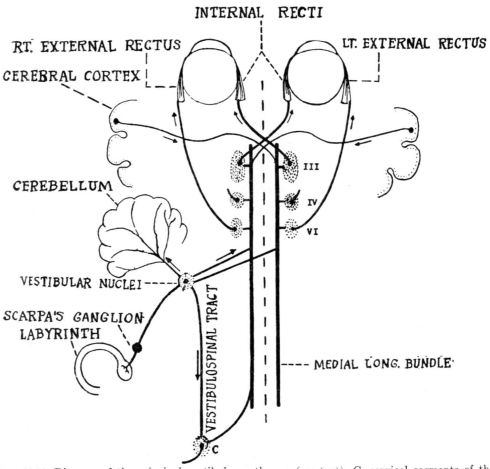

FIG. 64.14. Diagram of the principal vestibular pathways (see text). C, cervical segments of the spinal cord.

veyed to the medulla by the vestibular branch of the 8th nerve. The cell bodies of the vestibular fibers lie in Scarpa's ganglion situated at the bottom of the internal auditory meatus. These cells are bipolar. Their afferent processes (dendrites) are distributed to the sense organs of the utricle, saccule and semicircular canals, and terminate in the hair cells. Their axons pass for the most part to the *superior, lateral, medial* and *inferior vestibular nuclei* in the medulla (a few go directly to the flocculo-nodular lobe and the fastigial nuclei of the cerebellum) from which relay fibers follow three pathways (fig. 64.14). Thus there are:

(a) Ascending fibers from the superior vestibular neucleus which join the medial longitudinal bundle of the same side. From the medial vestibular nucleus impulses are relayed to the medial longitudinal fasciculus of the opposite side; from the inferior vestibular nucleus fibers ascend in the medial longitudinal fasciculus of both sides. The fibers from these nuclei terminate in the nuclei of the 3rd, 4th and 6th cranial nerves and constitute the vesibulo-ocular tract. Through these connections, reflex movements of the eyes are brought about.

(b) Fibers descend from the lateral (Dieter's) and the inferior vestibular nuclei. Those from the lateral nucleus constitute the vestibulospinal tract (ch. 65), while those from the inferior nucleus descend in the spinal extension of the medial longitudinal fasciculus as far as the upper cervical region of the cord, where they synapse with the anterior horn cells. Through these connections impulses are conveyed to the skeletal muscles.

(c) Fibers pass via the inferior cerebellar peduncle mainly to the flocculonodular lobe of the cerebellum on the same side, but also to the fastigial nucleus of the same side. These constitute the vestibulo-cerebellar tract.

As a result of his clinical findings I. H. Jones concludes that the fibers from the vertical and from the horizontal canals follow different paths. Those from the vertical canals do not according to this observer, enter the vestibular nuclei but ascend to the pons where they divide into two diverging paths; one arm of the Y so formed joins the medial longitudinal bundle and is distributed to the ocular nuclei; the other passes to the cerebellum via the middle cerebellar peduncle.

### Effects Following Labyrinthectomy (in the Dog)

*Unilateral labyrinthectomy.* (1) *Ocular.* Both eyes are turned toward the side of the operation. The eye of this side also shows a downward deviation while the eye of the sound side deviates upwards (skew deviation). *Horizontal nystagmus* (pp. 1179, 1180) with the slow movement toward the operated side.

(2) *Lateral flexion and rotation of the occiput* to the operated side together with flexion of the thorax on the pelvis toward this side.

(3) *The extensor tone of the limb muscles* is greater on the sound side than on the operated side, the limbs of this side being flexed and adducted, whereas those of the opposite side are extended and abducted.

(4) *Spontaneous movements.* These are all toward the operated side and consist of (a) circling, i.e., turning of the body around a vertical axis, (b) rolling, i.e., rotation around a horizontal axis; in the rabbit the rolling movements are very violent, (c) side to side movements of the head (head nystagmus), (d) falling to operated side, (e) stepping gait.

Many of the foregoing features, e.g., nystagmus, rolling and circling movements, are *irritative* in nature, i.e., the result of irritation of nerve endings by the operative trauma. They, therefore, improve with time. The others, e.g., oscillating movements of the head, head torsion, stepping gait, falling and asymmetrical distribution of tone, are deficiency phenomena.[10] These, for the most part, also improve since they tend to be compensated by visual and other nonlabyrinthine reflexes, especially in higher animals, who also learn to exercise cerebral control over the abnormal muscular activity.

Bilateral labyrinthectomy produces irritative effects similar to those described above, the direction of the movements being variable and dependent upon which ear shows the greatest degree of irritation. The labyrinthine static reflexes are, of course, abolished but in the more intelligent animals the defects of orientation are largely compensated for by visual reactions. The normal reactions to rotation (p. 1179) are abolished.

It is surprising that such striking manifestations were seen in the dog following destruction of the labyrinth, as section of the eighth cranial nerve in man is not followed by any such symptom complex. In fact such a section is usually followed by no symptoms or signs of any moment. The question must therefore be raised as to whether the manifestations described above might have arisen as the result of some complication of the operation, or as the result of an incomplete destruction of the labyrinth which resulted in stimulation. The different results may

---

[10] Cocaine injected into the labyrinth produces the deficiency phenomena characteristic of labyrinthectomy, but when applied to the nerve stump after removal of the labyrinth it prevents the occurrence of the irritative phenomena.

TABLE 64.1

| Semicircular Canal | Rotation About the: | | | | | |
|---|---|---|---|---|---|---|
| | Longitudinal axis | | Transverse axis | | Vertical axis | |
| | Right | Left | Forwards | Backwards | Clockwise | Anticlockwise |
| Right ant. vert...... | ● | ⊗ | ● | ⊗ | ⊗ | ● |
| Left ant. vert........ | ⊗ | ● | ● | ⊗ | ● | ⊗ |
| Right post. vert..... | ● | ⊗ | ⊗ | ● | ● | ⊗ |
| Left post. vert....... | ⊗ | ● | ⊗ | ● | ⊗ | ● |
| Right horizontal..... | ○ | ○ | ○ | ○ | ● | ⊗ |
| Left horizontal...... | ○ | ○ | ○ | ○ | ⊗ | ● |

Responses of the six semicircular canals (of fish, the thornback ray) to rotation. ● excited; ⊗ inhibited; ○ unaffected. ant. vert. = anterior vertical; post. vert. = posterior vertical. (After Löwenstein and Sand.)

be dependent upon variations in function and importance of the labyrinths in different animals.

### Labyrinthine Function

The semicircular canals are organs of dynamic sense, the otolithic organs subserve both dynamic and static senses. The hair cells of the cristae in the canals respond to angular acceleration (rotation), and are therefore called *rotary receptors*. The hair-cells of the macula on the medial wall of the utricle, and probably the macula of the saccule, as well, are stimulated mainly by changes in position of the head, and by linear acceleration. They are called *gravity receptors*.[11]

*The semicircular canals.* The rotary receptors of the cristae respond and give rise to a sensation at the commencement and at the cessation of a rapid rotary movement. Though impulses at low frequency are discharged along the nerve fibers while the head is at rest, a sharp increase in impulse frequency occurs at the commencement of the rotary movement, and at its end. The rapid discharge lasts for about 25 seconds. The rotary receptors, therefore, give no information of a continuous rotary motion of unvarying speed, though any alteration in speed of rotation (angular acceleration) arouses a sensation. The reason for this will be evident upon consideration of the stimulating mechanism.

Stimulation of the sensitive hair-cells of the

[11] Breuer (1874 to 1891) was the first to point out the difference in function between the semicircular canals and the utricle.

cristae is brought about through the effect which the movement of the head exerts upon the endolymph within the canal, the particular canal which is stimulated depending upon the plane in which the rotation occurs. The canals are of capillary diameter (0.1 to 0.2 mm. in man), and the endolymph is of relatively high viscosity (2 to 3 times that of water). The membraneous labyrinth is a practically closed system and is supported on the outside by perilymph, and the unyielding walls of the osseous labyrinth.

When the head turns quickly from a position of rest, say to the right (see fig. 64.16 and table 64.1), i.e., in a clockwise direction, and in the plane of the horizontal canals (around a vertical axis), the endolymph within the canal, owing to its inertia, does not move at first with the walls of the canal. This lag is equivalent to a movement or flow of endolymph to the left—anticlockwise—in both canals. But owing to the relative positions of the two ampullae such a flow of endolymph causes the cupula—the gelatinous mass surmounting the crista, and in which the hair-cells are embedded—to swing toward the utricle in the right ampulla and away from the utricle in the left ampulla. Deflection of the cupula causes, in turn, deformation of the hair-cells which acts as a stimulus when the swing is toward the utricle (right) but is "inhibitory" if it is away from the utricle (left). These events are reversed when the rotation is to the left—anticlockwise.

Thus, a clockwise rotary movement of the head (e.g., a quick turn) around a vertical axis stimulates the right horizontal canal; an anticlockwise motion excites the left, or, put in another way, the rotary receptors are stimulated only when the narrow part of the canal is leading and the ampulla trailing.

The receptors of the vertical canals, on the other hand, are stimulated only when the ampulla is leading and the narrow part of the canal bringing up the rear. There is no explanation for this difference between the horizontal and vertical canals.

The maximal response is given by a canal when it is rotated in its own plane.[12] No response is aroused from a horizontal canal by rotation in a

[12] It will be recalled that the vertical canals are placed diagonally in the head, and that an anterior vertical canal is in the same plane with the posterior canal of the opposite side, therefore, in a manner analogous to that of the horizontal canals, a *diagonal* rotary movement forward will maximally stimulate an anterior canal and suppress the activity in the opposite posterior canal. A backward rotary movement would act in the opposite way.

plane at right angles to this. But a vertical canal, though most effectively stimulated by rotation in its own plane (diagonal) also gives a lesser response when rotated in other planes. Thus a quick tilt of the head, forward or backward (rotation around a transverse axis), or laterally toward a shoulder (rotation around an anteroposterior axis) stimulates the vertical canals. The threshold of excitation of a horizontal canal is an angular acceleration between 2° and 3° per sec.

When any rotary movement is continued for longer than a few seconds, and the inertia of the endolymph is overcome, the cupula regains its resting (umbent) position; at the cessation of the movement the momentum of the fluid causes bending of the cupula in a direction opposite to that at the commencement of the movement. This is why no sensation occurs, during prolonged rotation, but a sensation of turning in the opposite direction is felt when the rotation suddenly ceases.

The mechanism of the semicircular canals is admirably suited to signal rapid turns of the head, i.e., a rotary movement in one or other plane. But it is poorly adapted to report continuous rotation at a constant speed (for, as Adrian points out, this is a movement to which the body throughout its life is rarely if every subjected, and has therefore not developed suitable receptors for recording it). Continuous rotation tends to confuse rather than to inform, and also, because of the swing of the cupula in the reverse direction when the rotary movement ceases, an illusion of rotation (in the opposite direction) is created. The ballet dancer avoids the confusion in a pirouette by making a series of alternating acceleration and deceleration.

*A brief outline of the experiments on vestibular function.* The foregoing account of vestibular mechanisms is based upon the work of many investigators. Some of the more recent experiments will be briefly outlined.

Tait and McNally studied the effect on frogs of tilting and rotation after denervation of one or more canals in various combinations, and after destruction of the utricle or saccule. Steinhausen elucidated especially the movements of the cupula in the canals of the pike whose labyrinth can be visualized in the living fish after the introduction of India ink, the cupula showing up clearly against the darker background. This structure was shown to completely partition the cavity of the ampulla, being in contact everywhere around its free circumference with the membranous wall.

It was shown to move during caloric stimulation as well as during angular acceleration, but not during electrical stimulation. Later, similar studies were made by Dohlman which confirmed Steinhausen's findings. Dohlman followed the endolymph movements by means of a drop of oil introduced into a canal. Ross employed the *right half* of a frog's head held in an apparatus, whereby the labyrinth could be turned and fixed in any desired plane, and subjected to rotation. The electrical changes were recorded from a filament of the auditory nerve. Clockwise rotation caused a response from the horizontal canal, whereas an anticlockwise movement was ineffective. Steinhausen's conception of a deflected cupula caused by an endolymph movement was verified. Lowenstein and Sand employed the surviving isolated labyrinths of the pike and ray (Raya clavata) and recorded the electrical potentials from individual canals and found that the nerve endings of the cristae discharged impulses continuously during rest at a low rate but at increased frequency during angular acceleration and deceleration. Adrian, experimenting with cats, recorded the potentials from single units by means of a fine wire electrode inserted into the medulla in close proximity to the vestibular nuclei. The main findings of others in cold blood animals were confirmed.

### EFFECTS OF STIMULATION OF THE SEMICIRCULAR CANALS

The semicircular canals respond to any one of the following forms of stimulation: (1) *Rotation* (angular acceleration) of the head on a vertical, transverse or anteroposterior axis. (2) *Caloric—* syringing the ear with a hot or cold solution. (3) *Galvanic.* (4) *Mechanical.*

#### *Rotation*

The effects produced by rotation are: (a) *eye movements*, (b) *vertigo*, (c) *reactions of the neck and limb muscles*, (d) *reactions of the autonomic nervous system*.

(a) *Eye movements.* When an animal's head is turned sharply on a vertical axis, i.e., in the plane of the horizontal canals, the eyes deviate in the opposite direction, and then return with a quick jerk to the original forward-looking position. The movement causing the slow deviation of the eyes is really a rotary one through a small arc.

If the horizontal rotation is continuous, a rhythmical to and fro movement of the eyes occurs when the rotary movement ceases. This is called *nystagmus*. It can be easily demonstrated

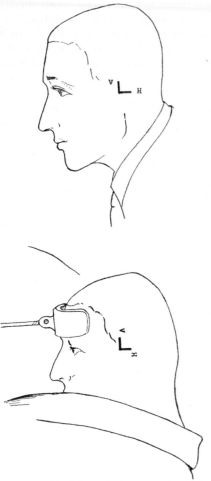

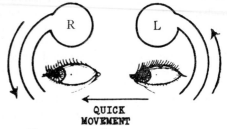

QUICK
MOVEMENT

FIG. 64.17. Postrotary nystagmus.

FIG. 64.15. Positions during rotation. Upper, horizontal canals in plane of rotation. Lower, vertical canals in plane of rotation. V, vertical canals; H, horizontal canals.

in man by rotating him with eyes closed, in a revolving chair, at a rate of about 10 complete turns in 20 seconds. In order to stimulate the canals maximally, the head should be inclined

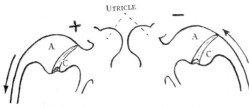

FIG. 64.16. Diagram of ampullae (A) of horizontal canals and utricle, showing deflection of the cupula during rotation. Plus and minus signs indicate increase and decrease, respectively, in the impulse frequency from the hair cells; arrows indicate the direction of rotation; C, cupula.

forward about 15° when the rotary movement is almost exactly in the plane of the horizontal canals. When the rotation is suddenly stopped (angular deceleration), and the subject opens his eyes, the rapid to and fro motion of the eyes is seen. It consists of a slow deviation to one side, and a quick return to the normal position. This post-rotary nystagmus lasts for about 20 sec. in a normal person; its quick component is in a direction opposite to that of the rotary movement. By convention *the quick movement or jerk to the normal position is taken to designate the direction of nystagmus from whatever cause.* Thus, a right horizontal post-rotary nystagmus is caused by rotation to the left. At the beginning of the rotation to the left the nystagmus would be in the opposite direction—quick movement to the right (figs. 64.15 and 64.17).

There are two other forms of nystagmus—*vertical* and *rotary*—in which the eyes oscillate up and down, and round and anteroposterior axis, respectively. These types result from the simultaneous excitation of both vertical canals. Vertical nystagmus is induced when the canals are stimulated with the sagittal plane of the head in the plane of rotation, that is with the head inclined about 90° to one or other shoulder. The rotary type follows when the frontal plane of the head is bent forward 90° or more, or backward 30° to 60°. In each instance the post-rotary nystagmus is observed after the head has been brought upright.

*Central connections responsible for nystagmus.* The slow phase of nystagmus is initiated from the semicircular canals and has its center in the vestibular nuclei, from which impulses are discharged, in part at least, through the median longitudinal bundle to the eye muscles. The quick movement is entirely central, but the nervous pathways upon which it depends are uncertain. However, its neural mechanism must lie in the brain stem between and including the nuclei for the third nerves and the vestibuli nuclei, for nystagmus occurs after transections of the brain above and below these

levels, respectively. It is not abolished by ablation of the cerebellum. Even the nuclei of the 3rd
and 4th nerves may not be necessary, for in the
rabbit nystagmus can be induced after section just
above the abducent nucleus. Lorente de Nó has
located the center for the rapid phase in the formatio reticularis in the region of the abducent
nucleus. He also found that nystagmus could still
be produced after section of both median longitudinal bundles. There may be a double pathway
from the vestibular nucleus to the nuclei of the
ocular nerves—through the medial longitudinal
bundle and through the formatio reticularis.

(b) *Vertigo.* Vertigo consists of a sensation that
the environment is whirling, that objects at which
the person is looking are moving, of a feeling of
unsteadiness and of an actual disturbance of the
equilibrium of the individual so that he is unsteady and staggers. He may fall. When the subject is rotated with head erect, his vertigo is in
the horizontal plane, i.e., in the plane of the external canals but in the direction opposite to that
of the previous rotation (sensation of counter-
rotation).

If the subject is rotated with the head bowed
forward at an angle of about 90°, in order to stimulate the vertical canals, and the head maintained
in this position after rotation, the sensation is the
same as if the head position had been upright during rotation, i.e., one of counter-rotation in the
horizontal plane. If, however, the head is brought
upright after rotation there is then a sensation of
falling to one or the other side, i.e., of rotation of
the body in the frontal plane; the sensation is of
falling to the side away from that toward which
the body had been rotated. Rotation with the head
bent backwards to an angle of 60° and then brought
upright gives a sensation of falling to the same side
as that toward which the body had been rotated
(see table 64.2). A sensation of falling forward or
backward (i.e., rotation in the sagittal plane) results from rotation with the head flexed on one
shoulder and then brought upright.

Vertigo arises from other causes than rotation.
It is a common symptom in disease, constitutional
or neurological, and occurs in alcoholic intoxication, seasickness, swinging, etc. Also, just as the
labyrinth influences the movements of the ocular
muscles, so, conversely, labyrinthine function
may be disturbed and vertigo produced as a result
of some unusual or abnormal action of the eye
muscles. Vertigo and its associated phenomena
are, therefore, common effects of eye strain or of
viewing the landscape from a moving train; an
ocular element is also an important contributory
factor in the causation of seasickness. For ex-

ample, if one sees a moving picture, which if actually experienced would cause giddiness, a sensation of vertigo is aroused. But with whatever
condition vertigo is associated, whether cardiovascular, renal, toxic, gastrointestinal or neurological, its immediate cause is excitation of the
semicircular canals or of their central connections.

(c) *Reactions of the neck and limb muscles.* In
animals stimulation of the horizontal canals by a
rotary motion causes alterations in tone and
movements on both sides of the body which tend
to resist the rotary movement, and enable the
animal to maintain its balance. When, for example, a frog is rotated on a round table, say to
the *left*, the tone of the neck muscles is increased
on the right side and reduced on the left, the head
turning to the *right*. The limbs, especially the
hindlimb, on the left are extended; those on the
right are flexed: the animal may move around to
the right. Cessation of the rotary motion causes a
reversal of these effects upon the neck and limbs.
In the snake, lizard, and reptiles with very long
necks, the head may deviate to one or other side
by as much as 100° or more. Sometimes a quick
return to the normal position occurs, as in nystagmus.

Dusser de Barenne, who first described these reflexes, cites a simple means for their demonstration. When a frog is rotated, say to the left, around
its long axis by suspending it by a thread fixed to
its jaw, and giving the thread a twist between the
finger and thumb, the animal's right hindlimb is
extended and abducted, and the toes spread, while
the left hindlimb is bent at knee and ankle, and
the toes flexed. As the movement to the left comes
to an end, and turning to the right begins the limb
movements are reversed. Similar movements may
occur in the forelimbs.

Corresponding effects follow rotation, e.g., a
quick tilt, in the plane of a vertical canal. Tait and
McNally described the respective vertical canals
as affecting the limb muscles on one or other
"corner" of the body. Thus, stimulation of the
right anterior vertical canal by a quick tilt diagonally forward and to the right causes contraction of the right forelimb: stimulation of the left
anterior vertical canal by tilting forward and to
the left causes a corresponding movement of the
left forelimb. Backward tilting to right or left
causes, respectively, contraction of the muscles
of the right and of the left hindlimbs.

*The past-pointing test of Barany.* Under ordinary circumstances a normal person if he places
his finger upon a certain spot has no difficult in
hitting the mark again with his eyes closed. After

TABLE 64.2

| Position of Head | Stimulus | Type and Direction of Nystagmus (Rapid Phase) | Sensation of Vertigo, Head Upright after Rotation | Past-Pointing | Falling (after Bringing Head Upright) |
|---|---|---|---|---|---|
| Upright or forward | Rotation right | Horizontal, left | Turning left | To right | To right |
| Forward 120° | Rotation right | Rotary, left | Falling to left | To right | To right |
| Backward 30°–60° | Rotation right | Rotary, right | Falling to right | To left | To left |
| Inclined to right shoulder | Rotation right | Vertical, downward | Falling forward | Upward | Backward |
| Inclined to left shoulder | Rotation right | Vertical, upward | Falling backward | Downward | Forward |
| Backward 30°–60° | Caloric 112°F. to ear or 68°F. to left | Horizontal, right | Falling to right | To left | To left |
| Forward 90°–120° | Caloric 112°F. to left ear or 68°F. to left | Horizontal, left | Falling to left | To right | To right |
| | Galvanic | Mixture of horizontal and rotary. Direction same as that of current | | | |

With stimuli opposite to sign to those given in the table, the reactions are reversed.

rotation, though able to place his finger upon a mark with his eyes open, he cannot find it again when his eyes are closed. The finger *deviates* or *past-points* to one or other side, or above or below the mark, the direction of the miss-aim being dependent upon the direction of the previous rotation and upon the position of the head during rotation (see table 64.2). Past-pointing is not reflex in nature but is a voluntary motor act, the error in judgment is the result of the associated subjective phenomenon, a subconscious correction being made in the opposite direction for the false sensation. The deviation of the finger and the vertigo are in opposite directions.

*Other post-rotary reactions.* If the body is rotated in the plane of the horizontal canals and the movement stopped, the head (eyes closed) then turns in the direction of the rotation. If rotation is carried out with the head in one or other plane of the vertical canals and the head after rotation is brought upright while the eyes are closed, the body leans to one or other side, backward or forward, according to the position of the head during rotation. The subject may actually fall in the direction to which the body leans. The phenomenon is virtually a past-pointing of the entire body. The actual fall is, therefore, opposite in

FIG. 64.18. So-called 'discobolus' position resulting from caloric or galvanic excitation of the labyrinth. (From Camis after Wodak and Fischer.)

direction to the vertiginous sensation of falling. That is, the subject has the illusion that he is leaning to one side (i.e., a sense of being rotated in the frontal plane of the skull), and in order to correct his supposed false position and retain his balance, leans actually in the *opposite* direction, and therefore falls if he leans too far.

One particularly interesting reaction resulting from excitation of the semicircular canals is that which has been appropriately called the *disc throwing* or *discobolus* attitude (fig. 64.18). Though occurring after rotation it is evoked most readily by caloric (especially cold) or galvanic stimulation of the canals. A stimulus applied, say to the left ear, causes a twisting of the thorax upon the pelvis and rotation of the head to the stimulated side. When the arms are raised they are also turned toward this side with the left limb lower than the right. After a short time the attitude is reversed, the body swings round and takes up a position in the opposite direction. The attitude may reverse its direction several times. It is due to reflex alterations in tone of the musculature on the two sides of the body.

(d) *Reactions of the autonomic nervous system.* Excitation of the semicircular canals in man is not uncommonly followed by nausea, vomiting and pallor. A fall in blood pressure of 10 mm. or so may occur, together with slowing of the heart by 8 or 10 beats per min. In the rabbit, syringing the ear causes vasodilatation and a fall in blood pressure. During rotation the pupil constricts; pupillary dilatation occurs upon cessation of the rotary movement.

### Caloric Stimulation

The effects of caloric stimulation are similar to those following rotation but possess an advantage in that one or other ear can be examined separately. The ear to be tested is syringed with hot (112°F.) or with cold (68°F.) water.[13] (In clinical practice much colder water is often used in examining the labyrinths.) When the head is bent backward through 60° the horizontal canals are brought into a vertical position. The douche causes a greater change in the temperature of the endolymph in the part of the canal lying nearer to the external meatus than in the part more deeply situated. Convection currents are set up which stimulate the receptors of the cristae, horizontal nystagmus and vertigo result. The change in temperature in the canal follows the irrigation of the external meatus by about 3 seconds. The direction of the convection currents, which of course are due to

[13] Douches much nearer the body temperature than these will stimulate.

changes in the specific gravity of the endolymph resulting from heating or cooling, is determined by the temperature of the douche fluid. Thus a cold douche causes currents away from the ampulla, a hot douche causes ones toward the ampulla (see table 64.2). Caloric stimulation of the vertical canals is effected by douching with the head upright.

### Galvanic Stimulation

In the employment of this method of stimulating the canals electrodes are placed one upon each mastoid process or, more usually, one on a mastoid process and the other on some indifferent part of the body. The current required in normal persons is from 2 to 7 ma. Owing to current spread all six canals are excited usually by electrical stimulation. The nystagmus has a rotary movement as well as a horizontal. The horizontal movement is with the current. Thus, when the cathode is over the right labyrinth the nystagmus is to the right, though the head may turn to the left. The resulting nystagmus is a mixture of the horizontal and rotary forms, its direction being the same as that of the current. Thus, when the cathode is over the right labyrinth, the nystagmus is to the right and vice versa. The effects occur only during the make and break of the current. In the absence of the labyrinth the galvanic current produces its effects by stimulation of the vestibular nerve. Consequently when, as the result of disease, labyrinthine function has been destroyed, this method affords a means of determining the condition of the nerve. Whereas rotary, caloric and direct mechanical stimulation involve essentially the same mechanism—movement of the cupula—the galvanic current is a direct electrical stimulation of the cristae. Steinhausen observed no movement of the cupula during this form of stimulation.

Galvanic stimulation does not have the reliability of caloric stimulation and has not found wide acceptance in clinical practice.

### Direct Mechanical Stimulation of the Canals in Animals

Ewald cemented a metal cylinder over a hole made in the bony wall of the horizontal canal. A piston fitted into the cylinder could be operated by air pressure. During the descent and ascent of the pneumatic hammer the membranous canal was compressed and decompressed respectively. The endolymph during compression and decompression moved, respectively, toward and away from the ampulla. An endolymph movement toward the ampulla caused a movement of the head and eyes to the opposite side. Decompression caused a weaker movement in the reverse direction.

*The otolithic organs, utricle and saccule, gravity receptors.* The role played by the utricle in the static reflexes has been dealt with in previous

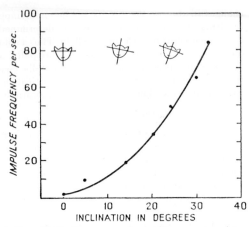

F ɪ ɢ. 64.19. Response of gravity receptor (otolith organ), showing the relationship between degree of tilt of head and frequency of impulses in vestibular nerve. (After Adrian.)

sections (see righting reflexes). But the gravity receptors respond also to linear acceleration, that is, to movements in a straight line forward, backward, up or down, or laterally, as well as to slow tilting of the head on its transverse or its anteroposterior axis. The gravity receptors are also stimulated by a sudden cessation of a linear movement (deceleration), or a sharp change in the speed of such a movement. The receptors are stimulated when the otoliths are hanging down, and thus exerting a gravitational pull upon the sensitive hairs. It is possible that bending the hairs also acts as a stimulus. The utricular organs are also stimulated by centrifugal force, and under certain conditions by angular acceleration.

In the cat, when the head is level the receptors cause a discharge of impulses at a relatively low frequency (at about 6 per sec.). When the head is tilted laterally (on its anteroposterior axis— cheek down) from the level position to an angle of 20°, the impulse frequency increases up to 95 per sec. in the nerve on the side to which the head is tilted, but the resting discharge on the opposite side ceases. Thus, in a lateral tilt to the right the otoliths on that side (cheek down) are dependent and presumably exert a gravitational pull, whereas those on the opposite side are *resting* on the maculae, and are inactive. The greater the degree of downward tilt from the level position the higher is the impulse frequency (see fig. 64.19). If the head is held in the tilted position the impulse frequency declines slowly, for the gravity receptors are of the slow-adapting type. Tilting around a transverse axis (snout up or down) also evokes a response, though less readily than does a lateral tilt.

A pull upon the otoliths as a result of their inertia should also be caused by linear acceleration, i.e., a progressive or translatory movement in any of three directions, fore and aft, up or down (vertical linear acceleration),[14] or sideways. Records of the action currents from the labyrinth show that this actually occurs, horizontal or vertical acceleration stimulates the gravity receptors in a lateral movement on the side from which the movement is made. Thus, a quick movement to the left stimulates the receptors on the right, owing to the inertia of the otoliths, acceleration laterally and to the left acting like a gravitational pull upon the receptors of the right side. Adrian found that rapid fore or aft, or up or down (vertical linear acceleration) also caused responses from the labyrinth. The threshold of excitation of the otolith organs by linear acceleration is around 12 cm. per sec. per sec.

*The saccule.* The role played by the saccule in the responses just described has not been settled unequivocally. Though anatomically this structure appears to be part of the vestibular mechanism it has been thought by many to have a cochlear rather than a vestibular function. McNally and Tait observed no loss of any known vestibular function after denervation of the saccules. The auditory nerve from a frog's labyrinth which has been denervated except for the saccule does not respond to vestibular stimuli by a discharge of impulses, but gives a response when a vibrating tuning fork is brought near it. Lorente de Nó, on the other hand, traced saccular fibers to the vestibular nucleus, but none could be found connecting this organ with the cochlear nucleus. Adrian considers that the saccules rather than the utricles are more likely responsible for the responses caused by lateral tilting and for upward linear acceleration, while the utricles are excited by downward and horizontal accelerations and tilting around a transverse axis. A macula is situated on the medial wall of the saccule and faces laterally, a position suitable for stimulation of gravity receptors by a lateral tilt. Another macula lies in the roof of the saccule and faces downward and could be stimulated by upward linear acceleration.

In the guinea-pig the otolith membranes can be

[14] In a quick linear movement forward or backward, or vertically, the gravity receptors would be in the same plane as that of the movement, which implies that they can respond to a pull acting in their own plane, though probably less effectively than to one acting at right angles. But in this case bending of the hairs rather than a pull upon them may be the effective stimulus.

detached by centrifuging the animal (at a speed of 1000 m. per min.). All responses to linear acceleration or to different positions of the head are then lost, but those caused by angular acceleration are retained.

### Vestibular Reactions in Disease

Abnormal vestibular reactions are seen in various diseased conditions involving (a) the labyrinth, (b) the vestibular nerve, or (c) the vestibular centers or central pathways (e.g., Deiter's nucleus, medial longitudinal bundle, cerebellum). Normally, some slight nystagmus may occur upon looking for a time to the right or left, but if nystagmus is present when looking forward or if pronounced when the eyes are turned to one side, it is pathological. A spontaneous vertical nystagmus suggests a lesion of the brain-stem; it is not seen in disease of the labyrinth itself or of the vestibular nerve. The phenomenon of past-pointing, unless induced artificially, is always pathological and suggests a cerebellar lesion. Spontaneous vertigo most commonly occurs as a result of labyrinthine disease but may be seen with disorders of the medulla oblongata. Disturbance of equilibration may be seen with diseases of the labyrinth, the brain-stem or the cerebellum. On the other hand, a lesion in one or other of these situations may cause a failure of the usual reactions following rotary or caloric stimulation. In deaf mutes, the labyrinthine reactions, as a rule, are absent. Again, the reactions to artificial stimulation may be abnormal; for example, in a lesion of the brain-stem vertical nystagmus may occur in response to a stimulus which normally causes nystagmus of the horizontal type.

### Ménière's Syndrome

The features of this condition are paroxysmal attacks of vertigo, noises in the ears (tinnitus) and a progressive impairment of hearing of the inner ear type (ch. 78). The sense organs of the cochlea (organ of Corti) as well as those of the semicircular canals are affected in this disease. There are various pathological processes in the inner ear which may give rise to this symptom complex, but labyrinthine hydrops is the most common one. Medical therapy directed toward the reduction of the sodium content of the body has been effective in relieving the victims of this condition. The surgical treatment of the condition consists of severing the vestibular portion of the 8th nerve intracranially, leaving the cochlear division intact (McKenzie; Dandy), or of destroying the labyrinth with ultrasonic waves.

### REFERENCES

Adrian, E. D. J. Physiol., 1943, **101,** 389.

Bard, P. and Macht, M. B. The behavior of chronically decerebrate cats. Ciba Foundation Symposium on the Neurological Basis of Behavior. Pp. 55–75. Edited by G. E. W. Wolstenholme and C. M. O'Connor. Little, Brown & Co., Boston, 1958.

Bazett, H. C. and Penfield, W. G. Brain, 1922, **45,** 185.

Breuer, J., quoted by McNally and Stewart.

Corkill, A. B. and Tiegs, O. W. J. Physiol., 1933, **78,** 161.

Dandy, W. E. Am. J. Surg., 1933, N.S. **20,** 693. Bull. Johns Hopkins Hosp., 1933, **53,** 52.

Davis, L. E. Arch. Neurol. Psych. 1925, **13,** 569.

Dohlman, G. Proc. Roy. Soc. Med., 1935, **28,** 1371.

de Kleijn, A. J. Laryng. & Otol., 1923, **38,** 646.

de Kleijn, A. and Versteegh, C. J. Laryng. & Otol., 1927, **42,** 649.

Liddell, E. G. T. and Sherrington, C. S. Proc. Roy. Soc., London. ser. B., 1924, **96,** 212; 1925, **97,** 267.

Lloyd, D. P. C. J. Neurophysiol., 1941, **4,** 115.

Lowenstein, O. and Sand, A. Proc. Roy. Soc., London. ser. B., 1940, **129,** 256.

Mackenzie, K. G. Canad. M. A. J., 1936, 34, 369.

McNally, W. J. and Stewart, E. A. War Med., I(42), **2,** 1683.

Pollock, L. J. and Davis, L. E. J. Comp. Neurol., 1930, **50,** 377. Am. J. Physiol., 1931, **98,** 47.

Ross, D. A. J. Physiol., 1936, **86,** 117.

Sherrington, C. S. J. Physiol., 1898, **22,** 319.

Steinhausen, W., Arch. ges. Physiol., 1927, **217,** 747. Ztschr. f. Hals-, Nasen-u. Ohrenh., 1931, **29,** 211; ibid, 1933, **34,** 201.

Tait, J. Ann. Otol. Rhin. & Laryng., 1932, 41, 681.

Tait, J. and McNally, W. J. Am. J. Physiol., 1925, **75,** 155. Quart. J. Exper. Physiol., 1933, **23,** 147.

*Monographs and Reviews*

Camis, M. The physiology of the vestibular apparatus. (Translated by Creed.) Clarendon Press, Oxford, 1930.

Creed, R. S., Denny-Brown, D., Eccles, J. C., Liddell, E. G. T. and Sherrington, C. S. Reflex activity of the spinal cord. Clarendon Press, Oxford, 1932.

Jones, I. H. Equilibrium and vertigo. Lippincott, Philadelphia, 1918.

Magnus, R. Körperstellung. Springer, Berlin, 1924. Animal posture. Proc. Roy. Soc., London. ser. B., 1925, **98,** 339. Studies on the physiology of posture. Lancet, 1926, **2,** 531: 585.

Needham, D. M. Red and white muscle. Physiol. Rev., 1926, **6,** 1.

# 65

# THE SPINAL CORD AND BRAIN STEM (MEDULLA OBLONGATA, PONS AND MIDBRAIN) AND THE RETICULAR FORMATION

## Outline of the Internal Structure of the Spinal Cord

In figure 65.1 the spinal cords is shown in cross-section. The *gray matter*, centrally placed, is in the form roughly of an H or the two wings of a butterfly. It is composed of a mass of nerve cell bodies and nerve fibers (dendrons and axons), mostly unmyelinated, supported by a framework of neuroglia. The ventral and dorsal portions of each lateral half of the gray mass (i.e., each arm of the H) are commonly referred to, respectively, as the ventral (or anterior) and dorsal (or posterior) horns; but since the gray matter extends throughout the length of the cord "column" is a more suitable term than "horn." In the ventral columns are situated the large bodies ($100\mu$ in diameter) of the motor neurons whose axons leave the cord by the ventral roots. Each axon ends in a group of skeletal muscle fibers—the neuromuscular structure constituting the so-called motor unit. The large multipolar cells are known as $\alpha$ cells and innervate the ordinary striated muscle fibers. The small $\gamma$ cells innervate the intrafusal fibers of the muscle spindles and thus regulate the threshold of these important proprioceptive end-organs (see ch. 62). In the thoracic and upper lumbar segments, the gray mass lying between the ventral and dorsal columns shows a small lateral projection. This is the lateral column or horn; it contains a cluster of nerve cells (the *intermediolateral cell column*) they give origin to sympathetic (preganglionic) fibers which leave the cord by the anterior (ventral) nerve roots. The well defined collection of cells occupying the inner part of the base of the posterior horn is known as *Clarke's column;* this group, since it is confined almost entirely to the thoracic region of the cord, is also known as the *dorsal nucleus.* It is homologous with the nucleus cuneatus of the medulla oblongata (p. 1193). To the outer side of the base of the posterior column is an area where strands of white matter and prolongations from the main mass of gray matter intermingle to form a delicate interlacement. This is known as the *reticular formation* (formatio reticularis) and is most prominent in the cervical region. It is continuous with the reticular formation of the medulla oblongata and pons. At the apex of the dorsal horn is a cap of gelatinous material containing groups of small nerve cells possessing many dendrites and named the *substantia gelatinosa of Rolando.* It is believed to receive the finest fibers (myelinated and unmyelinated) of the posterior roots. The remaining part of the substance of the dorsal horns constitutes the *chief sensory nucleus.* A canal pierces the bar or isthmus connecting the two lateral masses of gray matter across the midline; it is known as the *central canal.* The gray isthmus itself is called the *gray commissure.* Sometimes the parts in front and behind the central canal are referred to as the anterior and posterior gray commissures, respectively (fig. 65.2).

The *white matter,* which completely surrounds the gray matter is composed of bundles of fibers both myelinated and unmyelinated, the former predominating. A deep cleft on the ventral aspect of the spinal cord (the *anterior median fissure*) and a septum on the dorsal aspect (*posterior median septum*) together, incompletely divide the white matter into two lateral halves. The bands of white matter lying in front of the gray commissure are called the *anterior (ventral) white commissure;* a few strands of white matter lying behind or within the posterior part of the gray commissure are sometimes called the *posterior (dorsal) white commissure.* Each half is further marked out, by the fibers of the ventral and dorsal nerve roots, into three white columns or funiculi, ventral (anterior), lateral and dorsal (posterior). The *anterior*

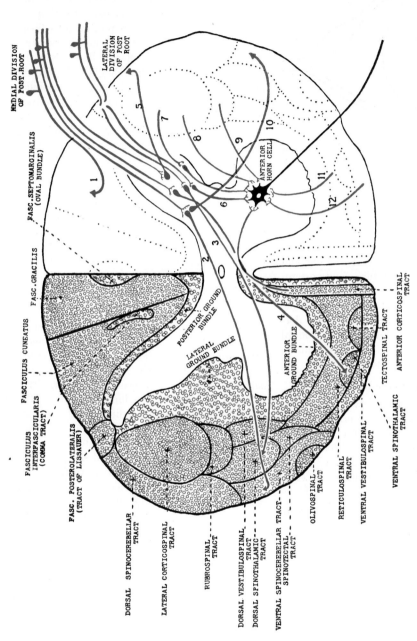

Fig. 65.1. Diagram to show tracts of the cord. Ascending fibers shown in blue, descending in red, spinal motoneuron in black. 1, represents fibers ascending in posterior columns (mediating sensations of touch, spatial discrimination, and of position and movement); 2 and 10, represent fibers entering the contralateral and homolateral ventral spinocerebellar tracts, respectively; 3, represents fibers entering dorsal spinothalamic tract of the opposite side (mediating pain and thermal sensations); 4, represents fibers entering ventral spinothalamic tract of the opposite side (mediating touch and tactile localization); 5, fiber entering dorsal spinocerebellar tract; 6, internuncial neuron connecting a posterior root fiber with anterior horn cell (reflex arc); 7 and 8, crossed corticospinal fibers connecting, respectively, through an internuncial neuron and directly, with anterior horn cell; fiber of anterior corticospinal tract (not numbered) also shown; 9, rubrospinal fiber; 11, reticulospinal fiber; 12, vestibulospinal fiber. The student must recognize that this is a very schematic representation of the fiber systems in the spinal cord. These various bundles of fibers do not occupy such circumscribed compartments as this diagram might lead one to believe.

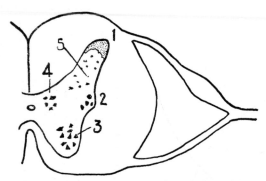

FIG. 65.2. Main cell groups in the thoracic region of the spinal cord. 1, substantia gelatinosa of Rolando; 2, intermedio-lateral cell column (sympathetic); 3, cells (motoneurons) of anterior horn; 4, Clarke's column (dorsal nucleus) of posterior horn; 5, chief sensory nucleus.

*(ventral) funiculus* lies between the anterior median fisure on the one hand, and the ventral gray column (anterior horn) and the fibers of the ventral roots on the other. Bounded in front and medially by the last two structures, and posteromedially by the dorsal gray column and the fibers of the dorsal roots lies the *lateral funiculus*. The *dorsal funiculus* is situated between the dorsal gray column (posterior horn) and the dorsal root fibers which form its anterolateral boundary, and the posterior median septum.

### The Spinal Nerve Roots

There are 31 pairs of spinal nerve roots, a pair from each spinal segment. The anterior and posterior roots join within the vertebral canal just beyond the posterior root ganglion to form a corresponding number of spinal nerves.

The *anterior roots* of the spinal nerves are composed entirely of efferent fibers (p. 1117).[1] These

[1] Although doubt has been expressed from time to time concerning the purely efferent nature of the fibers composing the anterior roots, no substantial evidence has been ever brought forward to show that this is not so. It is true that stimulation of the central end of an anterior root sometimes gives rise to pain, but this is due to the presence of recurrent fibers from the posterior roots and in no way invalidates the Bell-Magendie law. Neurons have been found in the anterior roots resembling those of the posterior root ganglia, but there is no evidence that they are sensory in function. Some authors have been led to believe that the anterior roots transmit sensory impulses because pain is not always relieved by section of the posterior roots. There are three possible reasons for the failure of this operation. In the first place, the pain may arise within the central nervous system itself, a filament of a posterior root may have escaped division, or innervation from adjacent spinal segments may overlap to an unusual extent; pain would then continue to be registered from the area innervated by the severed roots.

are (a) coarse, heavily myelinated, the axons of cells of the anterior horns, which are conveyed in the peripheral nerves to the skeletal muscles, and (b) fine, lightly myelinated fibers, in the thoracic and lumbar regions; these are preganglionic fibers of the sympathetic nervous system. The *posterior roots* are constituted of afferent fibers from the skin, muscles and viscera. They are the central processes of the large unipolar cells of the spinal ganglia. There is no important evidence that they contain efferent fibers. These statements regarding the efferent and afferent nature, respectively, of the anterior and posterior roots are called the Bell-Magendie law. Two divisions of the posterior root, a medial and a lateral, are distinguished. The lateral division is largely composed of small unmyelinated fibers; these, after entering the cord form the small triglangular area at the tip of the posterior horn known as Lissauer's tract. The fibers of the medial division enter the posterior columns of the cord (see fig. 65.1).

### The Segmental Distribution of the Spinal Nerves

In the young mammalian embryo and in certain adult lower forms, e.g., fishes, the body is demarcated into a regular series of transverse segments or *metameres*. The muscles (*myotomes*), skin (*dermatomes*) and viscera of each of these primitive blocks eventually receive innervation from the nerve roots of a corresponding spinal segment. The anterior root of each spinal nerve supplies motor fibers to the respective myotome, and autonomic fibers to the viscera and skin; the posterior root supplies sensory fibers to the corresponding dermatome as well as to the muscles and viscera. As a result of the outgrowth of the embryonic limbs the orderly arrangement of the metameres from before backwards becomes altered. In the adult mammal, the primitive metameric disposition is observed only in the trunk. The fibers of the spinal nerves supplying the limbs have joined to form the brachial and lumbosacral plexuses and, after intermingling freely, issue again as the peripheral nerves. The latter, in consequence, are composed of fibers derived from two or more spinal segments, and fibers from a given segment pass into several peripheral nerves. The muscles supplied by a given spinal segment do not necessarily lie in close proximity to one another (the coracobrachialis, for example, is innervated by the same segments as those which supply the muscles of the thumb) and a single muscle may derive its nerve supply from more

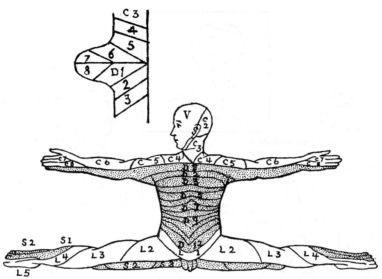

Fig. 65.3. *Upper:* Showing the drawing out of the metameres of the embryo with the development of the upper limb-bud. *Lower:* Showing the segmental arrangement of the dermatomes. (From Strong and Elwyn, after Luciani.)

than one spinal segment. As development proceeds and the limbs grow out from the trunk, the dermatomes become arranged in a series of narrow areas lying for the most part in the long axis of the limb (fig. 65.3). The skin and muscles of the limbs also tend to move away from the visceral structures with which they were originally associated and, in the adult, structures innervated by a common spinal segment may be widely separated. Thus, the diaphragm is innervated (through the phrenic) from the 3, 4 and 5 cervical segments which also supply skin and muscle in the region of the neck and shoulder. The heart receives sensory and autonomic fibers from the upper thoracic segments; these segments also supply sensory fibers to the skin over the inner aspect of the arm and hand and upper part of the thorax. The distribution of the dermatomes and cutaneous nerves in the human subject are shown in figure 65.4.

Several methods have been employed by different investigators in mapping out the dermatomes in animals and in the human subject. The *anatomical* method is laborious and consists in tracing the fibers of a spinal root to their terminations in the skin. A *physiological* method ("isolation" or "sensory remainder" method) was employed by Sherrington in cats and monkeys and Foerster in man. The area of skin supplied by a given segment was demarcated by dividing the sensory roots above and below it. The sensitive area of skin bounded above and below by an anesthetic zone indicated the area of distribution of the undivided

roots. Owing to the overlap of fibers from adjacent segments, it is not possible to produce an anesthetic area by the division of the sensory roots of a single segment (fig. 65.5). Head mapped out the segmental distribution of the cutaneous nerves in the human subject from studies of cases of herpes zoster, a condition due to a lesion of the ganglion cells of the posterior roots. Within more recent years Foerster, using Sherrington's method has mapped out the dermatomes in man. He also stimulated the posterior roots at operation and used the resulting vascular reaction (vasodilatation) as the means of demarcating the dermatomes.

### The Tracts of the Spinal Cord

The fiber tracts of the cord are divisible into two main groups. (a) *Long tracts* (projection tracts) connect the cord with other parts of the central nervous system. Some of these (ascending tracts) carry impulses to higher centers; other tracts (descending) conduct in the reverse direction—from higher centers to spinal neurons. (b) *Short tracts* (intersegmental or association tracts, ground bundles) begin and end within the spinal cord and connect different segments. The fiber tracts making up the substance of the respective funiculi are listed in table 65.1 and shown diagrammatically in figure 65.6.

### Ascending Tracts of the Spinal Cord

5. Dorsolateral fasciculus (tract of Lissauer). This is seen in cross section as a small

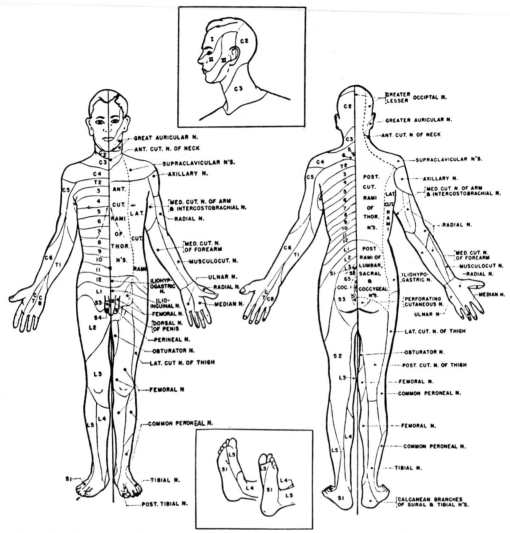

FIG. 65.4. Showing distribution of cutaneous nerves (right halves of figures) and the dermatomes (left halves). (After Wolff.) The student must recognize that these are schematic outlines and that the actual areas of innervation vary considerably from person to person.

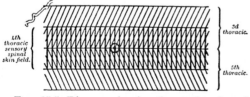

FIG. 65.5. Diagram showing the overlapping of the skin area innervated through the fourth thoracic spinal nerve root by those supplied by the third and fifth. The small circle indicates the position of the nipple. (After Sherrington.)

area lying between the tip of the posterior horn and the periphery of the spinal cord (fig. 65.6). It is composed of fibers derived from the lateral division of the posterior nerve roots. These fibers upon entering the spinal cord connect immediately, or after a very short upward or downward course, with cells occupying the tip of the posterior horn, i.e., in the substantia gelatinosa of Rolando (p. 1186). The fibers of this tract are mostly of small diameter and for the most part unmyelinated, and from both pathological and experimental evidence there is little doubt but that they constitute the primary neurons in the pathway for pain and crude thermal sensations. The axons of the secondary neurons (axons of the cells in the substantia gelatinosa of Rolando just mentioned) go to form the lateral spinothalamic tract of the opposite side, to be immediately described.

TABLE 65.1

| Funiculus | Ascending Tracts | Descending Tracts | Intersegmental Tracts (Ground Bundles) |
|---|---|---|---|
| Ventral (anterior) | Ventral (anterior) spino-thalamic | Ventral (anterior) corti-cospinal<br>Ventral vestibulospinal<br>Ventral (anterior) tecto-spinal<br>Reticulospinal | Ventral (anterior) inter-segmental fasciculus |
| Lateral | Lateral spinothalamic<br>Dorsal (posterior) spino-cerebellar (Flechsig)<br>Ventral (anterior) spino-cerebellar<br>Spinotectal<br>Dorsolateral (posterolat-eral) fasciculus (Lis-sauer) | Lateral corticospinal<br>Rubrospinal<br>Olivospinal (Helweg)<br>Dorsal tectospinal<br>Lateral vestibulospinal | Lateral intersegmental fasciculus |
| Dorsal (posterior) | Fasciculus gracilis<br>Fasciculus cuneatus | | Septomarginal fasciculus<br>Dorsal (posterior) inter-segmental fasciculus |

2. ANTEROLATERAL AND VENTRAL (ANTERIOR) SPINOTHALAMIC TRACTS. These tracts occupy, respectively, the lateral and ventral columns of the cord. The fibers of the *lateral* tract arise, as mentioned above, from cells in the substantia gelatinosa of Rolando; of the opposite side of the cord. Those of the *ventral* tract are the axons of cells in the chief sensory nucleus of the opposite dorsal horn of gray matter.

In order to reach the ventral spinothalamic tract of the opposite side, the fibers arising from the chief sensory nucleus ascend in the posterior columns for two or three spinal segments, and then cross in the anterior white commissure. This tract is a crossed pathway for the sensations of *touch*, and probably also for *tactile localization*. These sensations have, therefore, a double path to consciousness for they are also conveyed uncrossed in the posterior columns of the cord.

The fibers going to form the lateral spinothalamic tract (secondary neurons from cells of substantia gelatinosa of Rolando of the opposite side) ascend for a short way (within a single segment), and then cross in the anterior white commissure. This tract transmits impulses aroused by all forms of thermal and painful stimuli.

The two tracts—anterior and lateral—come together in the medulla oblongata to constitute the spinal lemniscus which joins the medial lemniscus in the upper part of the medulla oblongata to enter the thalamus (ch. 66).

3. SPINOTECTAL TRACT. This is placed in the lateral column ventral to the lateral spinothalamic tract. Its fibers arise from cells in the posterior horn of the opposite side and terminate in the superior colliculus. It subserves spinovisual reflexes.

4. SPINO-OLIVARY TRACT. The fibers of this tract are the axons of cells in the dorsal horn of gray matter; they run with olivospinal fibers and end in the inferior olivary nucleus of the opposite side. They probably transmit proprioceptive impulses which are relayed from the olivary nucleus to the cerebellum. Some anatomists have expressed doubts as to the existence of an olivospinal tract.

5. SPINOCEREBELLAR TRACTS. (a) The *dorsal (posterior) spinocerebellar tract* (direct cerebellar or tract of Flechsig) is situated in the posterior part of the lateral funiculus to the outer side of the lateral corticospinal tract. It is composed of the axons of the cells of Clarke's column (p. 1186) of the same side and, possibly, to some extent of the opposite side. The direct cerebellar tract reaches the cerebellum via the inferior cerebellar peduncle; its fibers end mainly in the cortex of the anterior and posterior lobes of the cerebellum (ch. 69). (b) The *ventral (anterior* or *indirect) spinocerebellar tract* arises from cells in the base of the dorsal horn, mainly of the same side, but also of the opposite side of the cord. It ascends in front of the dorsal spinocerebellar tract and is con-

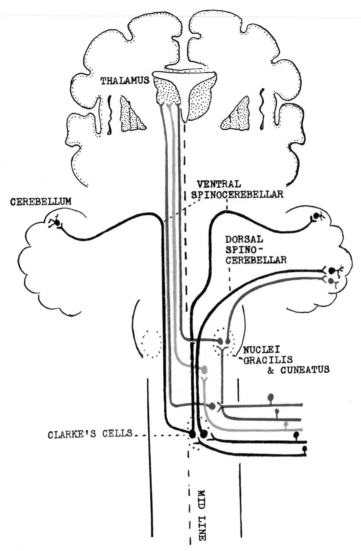

Fɪɢ. 65.6. Diagram showing the course of afferent impulses after their entrance into the cord. *Red*, pathway for pain and thermal sensations (ascend in ventrolateral spinothalamic tract of opposite side). *Blue*, pathway for touch, sense of position and movement, and spatial discrimination (ascend in posterior columns); external arcuate fibers from posterior column nuclei to cerebellum also shown. *Green*, pathway for touch, and tactile localization (after travelling for variable distances in posterior columns, fibers cross to ventral spinothalamic tract of opposite side). *Black*, ventral and dorsal spinocerebellar tracts, some fibers of latter (not shown) also cross to opposite side.

tinued upwards through the brain stem as far as the midbrain where it arches backwards (arciform fibers) to reach the cerebellum via its superior peduncle. Its constituent fibers end in the cortex of the anterior and posterior cerebellar lobes. The spinocerebellar tracts carry impulses arising in the proprioceptors of the muscles, tendons and joints. The information thus conveyed to the cerebellum is essential for the latter's function in adjusting the tone of the skeletal muscles and synergizing their movements (ch. 69).

6. Fᴀsᴄɪᴄᴜʟɪ ɢʀᴀᴄɪʟɪs (ᴛʀᴀᴄᴛ ᴏғ Gᴏʟʟ) ᴀɴᴅ ᴄᴜɴᴇᴀᴛᴜs (ᴛʀᴀᴄᴛ ᴏғ Bᴜʀᴅᴀᴄʜ). These occupy the dorsal (posterior) funiculus of the spinal cord. In the upper part of the spinal cord the former tract lies on the medial side of the latter.

Both tracts are composed of heavily myelinated fibers which are the continuation upwards of the fibers of the medial division of the posterior nerve roots of the same side. The nerve cell bodies from which these fibers arise lie outside of the spinal cord in the posterior root ganglia. The fasciculus gracilis commences in the lowest level of the spinal cord. After their entrance into the cord, its fibers divide into long ascending and short descending branches. A few of the former fibers and all the latter, after a short course, enter the gray matter. The long divisions become displaced medially as they ascend, with the result that fibers arising at lower levels (e.g., sacral region) come to lie nearer the midline than those entering the spinal cord higher up: the fasciculus cuneatus first appears in the midthoracic region. Therefore, from the midthoracic region upwards, the more medially placed tract (fasciculus gracilis) is derived from the lower thoracic, and the lumbar and sacral nerve roots, in this order, from the lateral to the medial border of the tract. The ascending fibers of both tracts pass uncrossed to the medulla oblongata, ending, respectively, in the nucleus gracilis and the nucleus cuneatus. However, this division into two tracts and two nuclei is an artificial one. We are dealing here with only one tract with fibers serving different parts of the body. From the nuclei gracilis and cuneatus the axons of secondary neurons emerge and, passing medially as the *internal arcuate fibers*, decussate with those of the opposite side (sensory decussation). They ascend through the brain stem as the *medial lemniscus* (see below) to terminate in the postero-ventral part of the lateral nucleus of the thalamus. Other fibers (*external arcuate*) from the nuclei gracilis and cuneatus relay impulses to the cerebellum from these same posterior columns. They are concerned with reflex activity and not with sensory perception.

## SUMMARY OF THE PRINCIPAL PATHWAYS ASCENDING THROUGH THE SPINAL CORD

1. SENSORY (conveying impulses to consciousness). (a) The fibers mediating thermal and painful sensations enter the cord in the lateral divisions of the posterior nerve roots. According to Ranson they are unmyelinated. Within the spinal cord they constitute Lissauer's tract. Immediately, or after a very short upward or downward course, they enter the dorsal horn and connect with nerve cells in the substantia gelatinosa of Rolando. The axons of the latter secondary neurons cross to the opposite side in the white commissures and ascend as the ventrolateral spinothalamic tract. This tract occupies a position in the brain stem lateral to the medial lemniscus and ends in the posterolateral part of the ventral nucleus of the thalamus (cf. figs. 65.1 and 65.6).

(b) The fibers conveying all other sensory impulses, e.g., from the muscles and joints (sense of movement and position), and those mediating the senses of vibration, touch, pressure, tactile localization and spatial discrimination (compass test), enter the cord in the medial division of the posterior roots and ascend in the fasciculus gracilis and fasciculus cuneatus. The fibers mediating all these sensations, except *some* of those concerned with touch and probably with tactile localization, pass without crossing to the nuclei in the medulla oblongata where they connect with secondary neurons. The axons of the latter constitute the *internal arcuate* fibers; they decussate with those of the opposite side and ascend to the thalamus as the medial lemniscus (or fillet). Tertiary neurons convey the impulses to the cerebral cortex.

In a transverse spinal lesion interrupting solely the posterior fasciculi, vibratory and position senses are lost but the sensation of touch is retained, since the fibers which have entered the gray matter and crossed below the level of the lesion to ascend in the ventral spinothalamic tract have escaped injury. Likewise, although a hemisection of the spinal cord destroys vibratory and position senses on the same side and pain and temperature sensibilities on the opposite side it does not abolish tactile sensibility as this is conveyed in both crossed and uncrossed pathways (see hemisection of the cord).

2. NONSENSORY impulses from the muscles, tendons and joints as well as nonsensory impulses aroused by a tactile stimulus, are conveyed into the spinal cord by fibers composing the medial divisions of the posterior roots. These fibers connect immediately with the cells of Clarke's column and are continued upwards in the dorsal (direct) and ventral (indirect) cerebellar tracts of the same side, mainly, but also of the opposite side. Some of these impulses, viz., those which enter the cervical cord, are conveyed by fibers of the cuneate fasciculus to the cuneate nucleus, to be relayed by secondary neurons (*external arcuate fibers*) via the inferior peduncles to the cerebellum (see fig. 65.6).

### Sensory Paths in the Brain Stem (Medulla Oblongata, Pons and Midbrain)

The *medial lemniscus* (or fillet) is composed of fibers arising in the nuclei gracilis and cuneatus. The fibers leave the ventral aspects of these nuclei and arch forward and medially (as *internal arcuate fibers*) to the midline where they cross

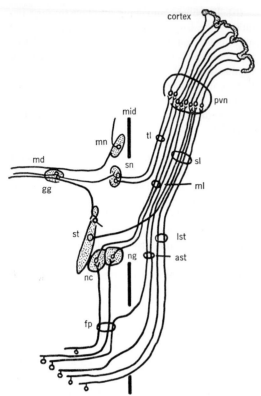

FIG. 65.7. Diagram of the trigeminal, medial and spinal lemnisci. *mn*, mesencephalic motor nucleus of trigeminal nerve; *sn*, sensory nuc. of trigeminal; *st*, spinal tract and nucleus of trigeminal; *md*, motor fibers passing into mandibular nerve; *gg*. gasserian ganglion; *nc*, nuc. cuneatus; *fp*, posterior columns of the cord; *ng*, nuc. gracillis; *tl*, trigeminal lemniscus; *pvn*, posterior ventral nuc. of the thalamus; *sl*, spinal lemniscus; *ml*, medial lemniscus; *lst*, lateral spinothalamic tract; *ast*, anterior spinothalamic tract; *mid*, midline. The trigeminal is on the medial side of the medial lemniscus, only in the medulla; it comes to lie on the outer side in the pons, and in close relation to the spinal lemniscus.

The *trigeminal lemniscus* (or fillet) conveys impulses from the area of distribution of the trigeminal nerve of the opposite side (p. 1199).

The fibers of the medial, spinal and trigeminal lemnisci terminate in the thalamus, from where tertiary neurons pass to the cerebral cortex (see fig. 65.7).

The *lateral lemniscus* constitutes the pathway for auditory impulses from the cochlear nuclei to the inferior colliculus and the medial geniculate body.

The sensory pathways are constituted of three neurons. For example, the pathway traversed by the sensory impulses for touch or kinesthetic sense consists of a primary neuron whose cell body lies in the posterior root ganglion, a secondary neuron originating in a posterior column nucleus (gracilis or cuneatus) and a tertiary neuron arising in the thalamus which convey impulses to the somesthetic area of the cerebral cortex (ch. 67). The cells of the Gasserian ganglia are the primary neurons of the trigeminal pathway; secondary neurons lie in the sensory nucleus and in the spinal nucleus of the nerve (p. 1198); tertiary neuron fibers ascend to the cortex from the thalamus. In the upper part of the pons and in the midbrain these several sensory pathways become fused together into a compact bundle. But a lesion in the lower part of the brain stem may involve one of the sensory pathways exclusively of the others. Thus an injury localized to the outer part of the lower pons or of the medulla oblongata may by injuring the spinal lemniscus cause loss of sensation to pain, heat and cold over the *opposite half* of the body leaving muscle sense and tactile discrimination intact. Sensory loss of this nature accompanied by ipsilateral cerebellar symptoms occurs as a result of the occlusion (as by thrombosis or embolism) of the posterior inferior cerebellar artery. Usually also, as a result of the involvement of the bulbospinal tract of the trigeminal nerve (p. 1198) the face on the *same side* as the occluded vessel shows a loss of pain and temperature sensibilities whereas tactile sensation which is transmitted by the main sensory nucleus is largely unaffected. A lesion more centrally placed may, by implicating the medial lemniscus alone, cause the converse type of dissociated sensory defect, namely, loss of the sense of position of the limbs and of spatial discrimination with retention of sensibility to pain, heat and cold. In lesions at higher levels in the brain stem all forms of sensation are likely to be involved more or less equally.

with corresponding fibers of the opposite side (*sensory decussation*). They then turn upwards as a compact bundle known as the medial lemniscus or fillet. This ascends through the medulla oblongata and pons dorsal to the corticospinal tracts, and through the tegmentum of the midbrain.

The *spinal lemniscus* (or fillet) is formed by the fusion of the anterior and lateral spinothalamic tracts and is therefore a crossed path for impulses aroused by light touch, pressure, pain, heat and cold. In the upper part of the medulla oblongata the spinal lemniscus joins the medial lemniscus on its outer side, and is joined in the pons by the trigeminal lemniscus.

### Descending Tracts of the Spinal Cord

1. CORTICOSPINAL (CEREBROSPINAL) TRACTS. From their origins in the cerebral cortex these tracts descend through the cerebrum and brain stem on each side to the lower border of the medulla oblongata. Here each tract divides into two bundles of unequal size, the larger of which crosses to the opposite side and descends in the posterior part of the lateral funiculus of the cord as the *lateral corticospinal tract*. The remaining fibers uncrossed, descend in the anterior funiculus as the *anterior corticospinal tract*. In most instances the direct or anterior corticospinal tract is but a small part of the total number of corticospinal fibers (usually not over 10 per cent), but the number of fibers in the anterior tract varies and in rare instances most of the corticospinal fibers lie in this position. In most cases these anteriorly placed fibers descend only as far as the cervical spinal cord. Even these fibers cross to the opposite side

before terminating on the ganglion cells of the anterior gray column (*cf.* figs. 65.1 and 65.8). There are also direct corticospinal fibers lying in the lateral columns of the spinal cord which do not cross to the opposite side. Through these the precentral motor cortex sends impulses to ipsilateral skeletal muscles.

All corticospinal fibers whether crossed or uncrossed connect with the large motor cells of the ventral gray columns (anterior horn cells). The connections are of two types, (a) direct synapses (20 to 30 per cent) with the motor neurons, (b) indirect connections with these cells through an internuncial neuron whose cell body is also in communication with a posterior root fiber on each side. It has been estimated that from 75 to 90 per cent of the corticospinal fibers terminate in the cervical (55 per cent) and thoracic (20 per cent) regions of the spinal cord, and about 25 per cent in the lumbar and sacral regions.

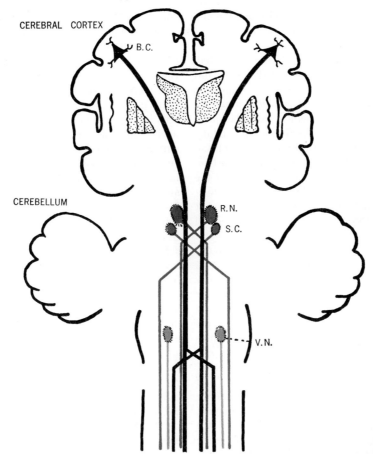

FIG. 65.8. Diagram of the descending tracts of the cord showing corticospinal tracts (black), rubrospinal tracts (red), tectospinal tracts (blue) and vestibulospinal tracts (green). B.C., Betz cell of motor cortex; R.N., red nucleus; S.C., superior colliculus; V.N., vestibular nucleus. The implication of this figure that the corticospinal tract arises exclusively from the Betz cells is erroneous.

For many years an erroneous belief was entertained that all of the fibers in the pyramids on the ventral surface of the medulla oblongata arose from the Betz cells of the precentral gyrus and were responsible for all voluntary activity of the skeletal musculature. It is now known that this concept contains many errors. Only a very small percentage of the corticospinal fibers arise from the gigantic Betz cells of the precentral gyrus, approximately 3 to 4 per cent. The remainder of the corticospinal fibers arise from other cells in the precentral gyrus, from cells in the parietal cortex and perhaps other areas. There is a question as to whether all of the fibers in the medullary pyramids are of cortical origin, and some investigators have even questioned as to whether they are all descending fibers. Certainly all voluntary muscular activity is not achieved exclusively by corticospinal fibers or by fibers contained in the medullary pyramids. There are multisynaptic fiber pathways from the cortex down to the anterior horn cells of the spinal cord which are also capable of producing voluntary movement.

2. VESTIBULOSPINAL TRACTS. Two tracts, a ventral and a lateral, are commonly designated, although there is no evidence that they serve different functions or that there is any significant difference between them. The *ventral vestibulospinal tract* arises predominantly from the spinal or inferior vestibular nucleus (in the cat) and descends in the forepart of the anterior funiculus of the spinal cord just lateral to the anterior corticospinal tract. It is a downward extension of the medial longitudinal fasciculus of the brain stem. The *lateral vestibulospinal tract* is a prominent descending pathway lying in the anterolateral part of the spinal cord. It arises from the lateral vestibular or Deiter's nucleus and extends throughout the entire length of the spinal cord. Most of its fibers are uncrossed although a few arise from the contralateral lateral vestibular nucleus. The vestibulospinal fibers terminate either upon the anterior horn cells or upon small internuncial neurons which in turn form synapses with the motor cells of the anterior gray horns of the spinal cord.

3. TECTOSPINAL TRACTS of each spinal half arise from the contralateral superior and inferior colliculi and descend at first as a single compact bundle through the reticular formation of the brain stem. Upon reaching the cord the fibers are segregated into two fasciculi, a ventral and a dorsal, which descend in the ventral and lateral white columns respectively. The fibers synapse with the spinal motonureons, either directly or through internuncial neurons, especially in the cervical region, wherein are situated the centers for the neck muscles. Impulses from the retina are received by the superior colliculus which through such impulses, and its spinal connections serves as a center for the integration of visual impressions with body movement, especially of the head (*visuospinal reflexes*). This center is probably of less importance in man, with his highly developed visual cortex, than in animals. Auditory reflexes may also be mediated by this tract and the inferior colliculus.

4. RUBROSPINAL TRACT arises from the large cells (nucleus magnocellularis) in the posterior part of the red nucleus (p. 1215). The fibers immediately upon leaving the red nucleus cross to the opposite side (*Forel's decussation*) and descend through the reticular formation of the pons and medulla to enter the lateral funiculus of the cord ventral to the lateral corticospinal tract. In carnivorous animals, e.g., cat and dog, the rubrospinal tract is large and important. In the primates, particularly in man, the rubrospinal tract is so small that its existence has been questioned; at any rate it has little if any functional significance.

5. OLIVOSPINAL (BULBOSPINAL) TRACT OF HELWEG. Its fibers are presumed to arise from cells in the neighborhood of the inferior olivary nucleus and descend in the ventral and lateral part of the lateral funiculus. However, its existence has been seriously questioned. It descends no farther than the cervical region. The fibers synapse with motor neurons. The functions of this tract are unknown. It and the thalamo-olivary tract constitute a possible path whereby impulses from the thalamus may reach the spinal centers.

6. RETICULOSPINAL TRACTS arise from cells scattered through the reticular formation of the brain stem. They are two in number, one in which crossed fibers predominate descends in the anterior funiculus, the other composed mainly of uncrossed fibers, in the lateral funiculus. They connect with the motor neurons in the anterior horns and probably with cells in the lateral horn. Impulses conveyed over this complex pathway are concerned with the regulation of the reflex activity of the skeletal musculature, the control of the vegetative nervous system, adjustment of the threshold of peripheral end-organs such as the muscle spindles and of the sensory pathways.

## Intersegmental Tracts of the Spinal Cord

There is in each funiculus of the cord lying close to the gray matter an intersegmental fasciculus or ground bundle. These, as already mentioned, serve to link spinal segments of different levels. Their fibers arise from cells in the gray matter and after an ascending or descending course of variable length end around cells of the same or of the opposite side at a higher or a lower level. A proportion of the fibers constituting the inter-segmental fasciculus of the lateral column of the spinal cord (*lateral intersegmental fasciculus* or *lateral ground bundle*) are continued upwards into the medial longitudinal fasciculus (or bundle) of the brain stem. The ground bundle of the anterior funiculus (*anterior intersegmental* or *sulcomarginal fasciculus*) is composed of fibers which connect the anterior horn cells of one side with those of the opposite side both at the same and at different levels. In the cervical region, it is composed largely of the spinal fibers of the medial longitudinal fasciculus.

The posterior funiculus contains (a) the septo-marginal fasciculus and (b) the posterior intersegmental fasciculus (or posterior ground bundle).

The *septomarginal fasciculus* is composed of (a) intersegmental fibers which arise from cells of the posterior horn and synapse with corresponding cells at lower levels and (b) descending fibers of the medial divisions of the posterior nerve roots. Septomarginal fasciculus is a term applicable to these fibers only in the lumbar region where they abut on each side against the posterior median septum. They are also known here as the *oval area* or *bundle of Fleichsig*. These fibers form areas of different sizes and shapes on cross section at various spinal levels. In the cervical and upper thoracic regions the fibers appear on section as a

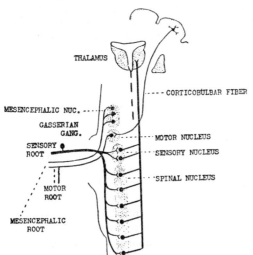

FIG. 65.9. Diagram of the central connections of the trigeminal nerve.

crescentic area at about the center of the posterior funiculus. Here they are spoken of as the *comma tract of Schultz*, or *tractus interfascicularis*. In the lower thoracic region they form a narrow zone bounding the posterior aspect of the cord and are known as the *dorsal peripheral strand*. In the sacral region this tract lies against the posterior part of the median septum and is called the triangular area of Philippe-Gombault. The descending fibers of the branches of the medial division of the posterior roots as they descend also, like the long ascending branches, become displaced toward the midline.

The *posterior intersegmental fasciculus* is seen in cross section as a small area lying behind the posterior gray commissure. Its fibers connect the posterior horn cells of different segments (see fig. 65.1).

## The Longitudinal Fasciculus (or Bundle)

The medial (posterior) longitudinal fasciculus (or bundle) is a tract of great physiological importance and is present in all vertebrates. It is composed of fibers which connect the 3rd, 4th and 6th cranial nerves with one another and with the vestibular nuclei, and makes connections with the motoneurons of the cervical segments of the spinal cord (fig. 65.15). The tract lies near the midline and extends from the cervical segments of the spinal cord, where it is continuous with the anterior intersegmental fasciculus (anterior ground bundle) to the floor of the 3rd ventricle. In the medulla oblongata it lies immediately subjacent to the floor of the 4th ventricle; in the pons it courses through the formatio reticularis, and in the midbrain, lies in relation to the gray matter of the floor of the Sylvian (cerebral) aqueduct. It also received fibers from the lateral lemniscus (auditory path, p. 1194) and from the superior colliculus, through which it is in communication with the optic pathway (ch. 75). The essential function of the medial longitudinal bundle is the coordination of reflex movements of the ocular and neck muscles in response to labyrinthine, auditory and visual stimuli.

## The Central Connections of the Trigeminal, Facial, Glossopharyngeal, Vagus, Accessory and Hypoglossal Nerves

### THE TRIGEMINAL PATHWAY

The trigeminal nerve appears on the lateral surface of the pons. The nerve has three roots (a) a large *sensory*, (b) a small *motor*, and (c) a *mesencephalic* (fig. 65.9).

The fibers of the *sensory root* convey impulses from the anterior part of the scalp, from the skin of the forehead and face, with the exception of an area over the lower border of the mandible. It also supplies the mucous membrane of the mouth, anterior two-thirds of tongue and nose, the cornea and conjunctivae and part of the intracranial dura mater. This root arises from the cells of the gasserian (semilunar) ganglion, which corresponds to a spinal posterior root ganglion. The processes of the ganglion cells divide into peripheral and central branches. The former enter into the composition of the peripheral divisions (ophthalmic, maxillary and mandibular) of the nerve; the central branches (which constitute the sensory root of the nerve) enter the pons in close association with the fibers of the motor root and divide into an ascending and a descending group in a manner homologous with a spinal root fiber. The *ascending fibers* convey impulses of light touch, tactile discrimination and localization, and of the sense of position and passive movement. They end in a nucleus (*main or upper sensory nucleus of the trigeminal nerve*) situated in the pons, deep and lateral to the motor nucleus. The axons of cells in this nucleus ascend with those from the spinal nucleus of the trigeminal nerve (see below) to form the *trigeminal lemniscus*. The *descending fibers* constitute the *bulbospinal tract of the trigeminal nerve.* They subserve sensations of pain and temperature over the entire trigeminal area. They descend through the pons and medulla oblongata and may be traced as far as the 2nd cervical segment. This tract dwindles gradually in its descent, its fibers terminating around cells in the substantia gelatinosa of Rolando which in this situation is referred to as the *spinal nucleus of the trigeminal nerve.* From the spinal nucleus the axons of secondary neurons swing downward in the spinal tract of the trigeminal nerve as far as the upper cervical spinal cord. They then cross the midline and turn upward. In the upper part of the medulla oblongata they join fibers arising from the upper sensory nucleus to form the *trigeminal lemniscus* (or fillet). The trigeminal lemniscus lies in close association with the medial and the spinal lemnisci (spinothalamic tracts) (p. 1191); its fibers terminate in the posteroventral nucleus of the thalamus.

A number of reflexes are mediated through the afferent fibers of the trigeminal nerve, e.g., corneal, winking, sneezing and oculocardiac.

The main sensory nucleus of the trigeminal cor-responds to the nuclei of the posterior columns of the spinal cord (nuclei gracilis and cuneatus) and like the latter sends fibers to the cerebellum through the inferior cerebellar peduncle. The spinal tract of the trigeminal nerve may be looked upon as corresponding to the tract of Lissauer (p. 1189), and the spinal nucleus as an extension upwards of the substantia gelatinosa of Rolando whose cells, as we have seen, give rise to the lateral spinothalamic tract.

The *motor root* fibers arise from a nucleus in the upper part of the pons underlying the lateral part of the floor of the 4th ventricle. The nucleus receives fibers from the corticobulbar tract of the opposite side and also probably from the same side. The motor root after its emergence from the brain stem, travels peripherally with the sensory root and, passing deep to the gasserian ganglion, joins the mandibular (3rd) division of the trigeminal nerve to supply the muscles of mastication (temporal, masseter and pterygoids).

The *mesencephalic root* consists of a small bundle of fibers which run in company with the fibers of the motor root. Entering the pons they ascend to the *mesencephalic nucleus* of the trigeminal, an elongated collection of nerve cells extending from the level of the motor nucleus to the upper region of the midbrain. It was thought at one time that the mesencephalic root and nucleus were motor in function, but it is now generally admitted that they are composed of afferent neurons. The nucleus is looked upon as a group of cells homologous with the gasserian (semilunar) ganglion and the posterior root ganglia of the spinal nerves, but which has migrated or been "drawn" into the brain stem at an early period of phylogenetic development. It is believed to receive proprioceptive impulses from the muscles of mastication and possibly from the ocular muscles.

LESIONS INVOLVING THE TRIGEMINAL PATHWAYS. Either the peripheral portions or the central connections of the nerve may be the seat of disease. A lesion of the nerve peripheral to the ganglion is more likely to involve only one of its three divisions. Pain, or loss of sensibility over the distribution of the division affected, may result. If the gasserian ganglion is involved the disturbance of sensation usually involves the area of distribution of more than one division, often of the entire nerve. If as a result the eye is rendered anesthetic the patient may develop an ulceration of the cornea and an inflammation of the cornea and conjunctiva. This has often been referred to as a neuroparalytic keratitis and has been attributed to the loss of some obscure trophic influence of the nerve. Actually it results from the fact that the eye is anesthetic and can be injured easily by a foreign body or by scratching without any discomfort to the patient. The eye is then likely to be neglected by the patient because it is not painful. As a result he may lose his sight or even his eye.

Herpetic eruptions may result from the involvement of the gasserian ganglion. Spontaneous herpes zoster usually involves the area of distribution of the ophthalmic division and is often serious because the lesions on the cornea may lead to corneal opacity and loss of vision. Such herpes is also commonly followed by a very distressing post-herpetic neuralgia which is very difficult to treat satisfactorily.

Paralysis of the muscles of mastication with reduction in the strength of the bite on the affected side and deviation of the mandible toward the paralyzed side when it is opened occurs when the motor division is involved. Such paralysis is commonoy seen in association with affections of the mandibular division which the motor root joins, or of the gasserian ganglion which lies directly over the motor root.

Loss of sensation of taste (as well as of ordinary sensibility) over the anterior two-thirds of the tongue on the corresponding side is a common accompaniment of degenerative changes affecting the mandibular division of the 5th nerve. The taste fibers to this part of the tongue are derived from the chorda tympani branch of the facial, but travel via the lingual branch of the mandibular division of the trigeminal nerve. Removal of the gasserian ganglion does not result in a loss of taste.

Lesions (e.g., tumors, vascular changes) in the pons, medulla or upper cervical spinal cord may injure the upper sensory nucleus, the motor nucleus, the trigeminal lemniscus (crossed) or the bulbospinal tract of the nerve. When the motor nucleus is involved weakness and wasting of the muscles of mastication result; implication of the ascending sensory fibers, or of the main sensory nucleus in the pons, is followed by loss of the sensation of light touch and the discriminative aspects of cutaneous sensibility over the same side of the face, but the retention of sensibility to pain, heat and cold. The neighboring spinothalamic tract (crossed) may suffer coincidently with the ascending sensory fibers, when thermanesthesia and analgesia over the trunk and limbs of the opposite side combined with loss of tactile sensation

over the face of the same side will result (see also p. 1193). Syringomyelia extending into the upper cervical region or into the bulb (syringobulbia) is likely to cause, as a result of pressure upon the spinal tract of the nerve, a loss of the appreciation of pain and changes in temperature, with retention of tactile sensibility.

The trigeminal nerve, or one of its divisions, is sometimes the seat of a severe and intractable type of pain which recurs in paroxysms (*trigeminal neuralgia; tic douloureux*). The cause of the affection is unknown. In treating the condition, injections of alcohol into the division of the nerve involved are sometimes employed. The injection is made into the nerve at the infraorbital foramen in the case of involvement of the maxillary division, and at the foramen ovale of the sphenoid or at the supraorbital notch, respectively, in disease of the mandibular or ophthalmic division. Injection or section of the peripheral branches result in only temporary remission of the pain whereas the section of the nerve between the gasserian ganglion and the pons provides permanent relief. The motor root can be spared in such an operation.

### THE FACIAL NERVE

The facial nerve consists of a large *motor* and a small *sensory* portion. The two portions or roots appear at the lower border of the pons and enter the internal auditory meatus in company with the auditory nerve.

The *sensory* root of the facial, which is also known as the *nervus intermedius of Wrisberg*, contains not only afferent fibers but secretory and vasodilator (parasympathetic) fibers as well.

The *sensory fibers* arise from the cells of the geniculate ganglion (fig. 65.10). The peripheral processes of these cells are distributed through the chorda tympani branch of the facial nerve to the taste buds and mucous membrane of the anterior two-thirds of the tongue, and through the nerve to the pterygoid canal (formed by the union of the greater superficial petrosal and the deep petrosal nerves), and the sphenopalatine ganglion to the lacrimal gland and the mucosa of the soft palate and posterior part of the nose. The chorda tympani branch joins the trunk of the lingual nerve through which it is conveyed to the floor of the mouth.[2] The central processes of the gan-

---

[2] The nervus intermedius, the geniculate ganglion, the chorda tympani and part of the great superficial petrosal nerve are sometimes grouped together under the name *glossopalatine nerve*. The origin and distribution of the secretory and sensory fibers of which this nerve is composed are

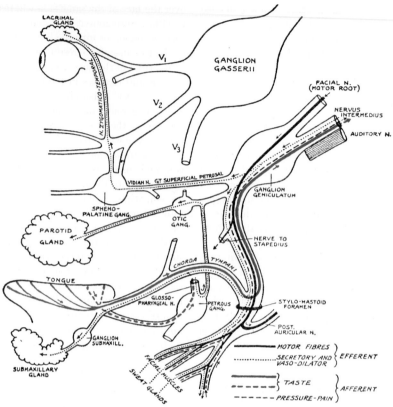

Fig. 65.10. Diagram of the facial nerve; afferent and efferent paths, including taste (red) and secretory fibers (dotted lines). (After Purves-Stewart.)

glion cells end in the *sensory nucleus* situated in the upper part of the tractus solitarius. Fibers arise from the latter and ascend in the medial fillet of the opposite side to reach the thalamus.

The *parasympathetic fibers* arise from the *superior salivatory nucleus* (p. 588) which lies in close relation to the motor nucleus of the facial. After leaving the brain stem in the sensory root the parasympathetic secretory and vasodilator fibers pass via the *great superficial petrosal* nerve and *nerve to pterygoid canal* (formed by the union of the great superficial and deep petrosal nerves) to the *sphenopalatine ganglion* from where they are relayed to the lacrymal gland, and to the vessels and glands of the palate and posterior part of the nose. The secretory and vasodilator fibers to the submaxillary and sublingual glands leave the

closely similar to those of the glossopharyngeal, and it is considered by some as an aberrant part of the latter nerve.

A small proportion of taste fibers may take an alternative route, namely, via the chorda tympani to the otic ganglion and thence by way of the internal sphenoidal and great superficial petrosal nerves, genicular ganglion and nervus intermedius to the brain stem (Schwartz and Weddell).

facial with the taste fibers in the chorda tympani branch.

The *motor part* of the facial is conveyed through the facial canal of the temporal bone to the stylomastoid foramen. After its emergence from the latter it is distributed to muscles of the face, auricle, and forehead. The motor fibers arise from a nucleus in the lower part of the pons and pass backwards to the lower end of the nucleus of the abducent nerve. Then ascending to the upper end of the latter they bend and sweep downwards and forward to where they leave the brain. As the facial fibers take this arched course to the point of their emergence from the brain stem, they, together with the abducent nucleus, form a prominence in the floor of the 4th ventricle, known as the *facial colliculus*.

*Connections:* the motor nucleus of the facial nerve receives:

1. Fibers from the corticobulbar tract of the same and of the opposite side.
2. Fibers from the lateral, trigeminal and medial lemnisci, and from the spinothalamic tracts. Through these connections reflex facial move-

ments in animals may be initiated from various receptive areas of the body.

FACIAL PARALYSIS. The effects of interruption of the facial pathway vary in certain important features according to the level at which the injury occurs. The nature of the motor loss following a lesion of the supranuclear (corticobulbar) fibers is described on page 1206. In the paralysis resulting from division to the trunk of the facial nerve all the muscles of the affected side of the face are completely paralyzed. The subject is unable to close the eye owing to paralysis of the orbicularis oculi, or to frown; the eyebrow droops. The mouth is drawn over to the sound side by the unparalyzed muscles and the muscles of the affected side do not take part in the facial expression of emotional states, e.g., laughing or crying.

Facial paralysis may result from a lesion involving:

1. The motor nucleus or the intra-pontine course of the motor fibers (tumors, hemorrhage, etc.).

2. The nerve as it crosses the posterior fossa of the skull to reach the internal auditory meatus, as in fractures of the skull or tumors in this situation; the sensory portion and the auditory nerve are commonly involved as well, when loss of the sensation of taste over the anterior two-thirds of the tongue, and deafness on the affected side will result.

3. The nerve in its course through the temporal bone as in fracture of the skull or in otitis media; inflammation of the nerve within the facial canal (aqueduct of Fallopius)—*Bell's palsy*—may occur.

4. The nerve after its emergence from the stylomastoid foramen, as it lies behind the angle of the jaw; inflammation, parotid tumors, or accidental injuries may implicate the nerve in this situation.

## THE GLOSSOPHARYNGEAL NERVE

The glossopharyngeal nerve contains motor, secretory, vasodilator and sensory fibers. The nerve emerges from the side of the upper part of the medulla oblongata in the groove between the olive and the restiform body. The motor fibers are distributed almost entirely to the stylopharyngeus muscle; a few terminate in the circular and longitudinal muscle of the upper part of the pharynx. However, division of the glossopharyngeal nerve which is done for glossopharyngeal neuralgia produces no motor disability so far as the patient is concerned. The secretory and vasodilator fibers (via its tympanic branch, the tympanic plexus, the small superficial petrosal

nerve and the otic ganglion) (p. 589) supply the parotid gland. The *sensory* fibers arise from cells in the superior (jugular) and inferior (petrous) ganglia of the glossopharyngeal nerve. The peripheral processes of the cells of the latter ganglion supply the taste buds of the posterior third of the tongue. Those from cells of the *superior* ganglion mediate *ordinary sensations* (touch, thermal, etc.), from this part of the tongue and the mucosa of the pharynx and posterior part of the mouth; the central processes (superior ganglion) terminate in the *dorsal nucleus* of the vagus and (inferior ganglion) in the lower part of the *tractus solitarius*. Fibers (secondary neurons) pass from the latter nucleus and, crossing to the medial fillet of the opposite side, ascend to the thalamus, from where axons of tertiary neurons pass to the cortical area for taste. The motor fibers arise from the upper part of the *nucleus ambiguus* situated in the reticular formation of the medulla oblongata. Secretory fibers are the axons of cells lying in the *inferior salivatory* nucleus which lies below the superior nucleus of the same name. The carotid sinus nerve is another important afferent branch of the glossopharyngeal nerve. It is concerned with the conduction of impulses from the carotid body and the carotid sinus to the medulla oblongata. These impulses and their frequency are determined by chemical changes in the blood which are detected by the carotid body and by changes in the blood pressure which are detected by the carotid sinus. These afferent impulses are concerned in reflex activities which take part in controlling the pulse rate, the respiratory rate and the blood pressure.

## THE VAGUS NERVE

The vagus nerve contains motor, secretory, vasodilator and sensory fibers. The secretory and vasodilator fibers and the fibers to the involuntary muscle of the bronchi, heart, esophagus, stomach, small intestine, gall-bladder, etc. (parasympathetic fibers, ch. 71) arise from cells in the *dorsal nucleus of the vagus* (principal autonomic nucleus). This gray mass extends upwards from the lower, closed part of the medulla oblongata to beneath the floor of the 4th ventricle at the level of the striae medullares. The voluntary motor fibers arise in close relationship with the motor fibers of the glossopharyngeal nerve, namely, from the cells of the *nucleus ambiguus* lying below the glossopharyngeal neurons. They supply (through the superior laryngeal branch) the cricothyroid and arytenoid muscles of the larynx, and the inferior constrictor of the pharynx. The pharyngeal and recurrent laryngeal branches of the vagus also convey voluntary motor fibers many of which are derived from the bulbar nucleus of the accessory nerve (see below) to the pharyngeal muscles (with the exception of the stylopharyngeus), and to the muscles of the soft palate (except the tensor palati) and larynx (except the cricothyroid). The cell bodies of the *sensory fibers* lie in the inferior ganglion of the vagus (ganglion nodosum). The peripheral processes of these cells convey impulses from the lungs, heart, larynx, pharynx, esophagus, stomach, small intestine and gall-bladder. They also, through the anterior laryngeal branch, innervate the taste buds of the epiglottis and valleculae (the depressions lying at the sides of the fold running from the epiglottis to the base of the tongue). The taste fibers end centrally by synapsing with cells in the *gustatory nucleus* lying in the upper and medial part of the *tractus solitarius*. These impulses are relayed upwards along the same paths as those conveying other taste impulses. Afferent vagal fibers from visceral structures terminate in the dorsal nucleus. This latter is, therefore, both motor and sensory in function and constitutes an important visceral reflex center. It contains the cardio-inhibitory and vomiting centers.

Vagal afferent filaments travelling in Arnold's nerve mediate the general sensations of the skin lining the external auditory meatus and a small area behind the auricle. Irritation of these fibers may cause reflex coughing (p. 477). These sensory fibers have their cell stations in the jugular ganglion.

## The Spinal Accessory Nerve

The spinal accessory nerve is entirely motor and is made up of a bulbar and a spinal root. The *bulbar* root arises from the lower (caudal) end of the nucleus ambiguous from cells situated below those which give origin to the motor fibers of the vagus. The bulbar fibers join the vagus within and below the jugular foramen and are distributed, as already mentioned, in the pharyngeal and recurrent branches of the latter nerve; these fibers of the spinal accessory nerve innervate the muscles of the larynx, with the exception of the cricothyroid, the muscles of the pharynx and those of the soft palate, with the exception of the tensor palati (which is supplied by the 5th cranial nerve). The *spinal* root is composed of the axons of a group of cells in the anterior gray column of the spinal cord extending

from the 1st to the 4th or 5th cervical segment inclusive. These fibers supply the sternocleidomastoid and trapezius muscles. The spinal part of the nerve exchanges fibers with the bulbar part in the jugular foramen.

## The Hypoglossal Nerve

The hypoglossal nerve is also purely motor. Its fibers are derived from a nucleus situated near the midline in the floor of the posterior part of the 4th ventricle and medial to the nucleus ambiguus. It supplies the thyrohyoid, styloglossus, hyoglossus and genioglossus muscles, and the intrinsic muscles of the tongue.

## The Pathways for the Control of Muscular Activity

The neural mechanism controlling the activity of the skeletal musculature is extremely complex and as yet incompletely understood. Voluntary movements are dependent in primates (monkeys, apes and man) upon the precentral motor cortex. The same is not true for lower animals. Birds and reptiles have practically no cerebral cortex and their well organized movements are controlled by nuclear masses more or less comparable to the basal ganglia of the primate brain. In higher animal forms such as rodents the cerebral cortex is present but of relatively little importance so far as muscular activity is concerned. In the carnivores, e.g., cat and dog, a specialized portion of the cerebral cortex (the sigmoid gyrus) has developed into a "motor" cortex. If it is stimulated electrically movements can be produced in the contralateral extremities and if the sigmoid gyrus is removed a transitory contralateral paralysis ensues. However, the cerebral cortex is not essential for useful movement of the skeletal musculature. The sigmoid gyri can be removed from both sides with only a temporary paralysis. In fact, the entire cortex can be removed and the animal still be able to sit, stand, walk or run. In primates the situation is quite different. Here the cerebral cortex is much more important but there still exists a considerable difference between the various animals. If one removes the precentral motor cortex or even the entire cortex from one cerebral hemisphere in a monkey, a complete paralysis of the opposite side of the face and of the opposite arm and leg will result. Useful movement will soon begin to return and in a few weeks the animal will be running about, climbing the walls of his cage and hopping about on his trapeze in an agile fashion, although a partial paralysis of the involved arm and leg will be obvious. The ape, too, will recover, though not as completely as the monkey, whereas removal of the precentral motor cortex in man will result in a contralateral paralysis which, though it will improve, will always be severely disabling. After such an operation a man will become able to walk, although with a limping gait dragging and circumducting his leg. He will never recover useful movement in his upper extremity and will probably have no movement at all in his hand and fingers.

The recovery in primates following removal of the precentral motor cortex is due almost entirely to ipsilateral innervation from the intact cerebral hemisphere, for if the remaining precentral motor cortex is removed a severe and enduring paralysis *in all four extremities* is the immediate result. It is true that if the cortex is removed piecemeal in several operations over months of time and if the animal is given very special care occasionally it is possible to produce a bilaterally decorticate monkey that has a few awkward but very limited voluntary movements. At best such an animal is almost completely disabled. In most instances he is totally paralyzed except for a few useless stereotyped grasping movements. In view of the demonstrably greater importance of the precentral motor cortex in man as compared with the motor cortex of cats it is obvious that in the human being the production of useful voluntary movements is dependent upon this important area of the cerebral cortex. It is evident that the subcortical centers (basal ganglia, red nucleus, substantia nigra, reticular formation, cerebellum and spinal cord) are important in the production of well coordinated, useful muscular activity, but in man these centers cannot function adequately in the absence of the precentral motor cortex.

The precentral motor cortex gives rise to corticospinal fibers which arise from the precentral gyrus and descend to the anterior gray horns of the spinal cord. These fibers are concerned with voluntary muscular activity and primarily with delicate, precise, well coordinated movements of the distal parts of the extremities, particularly the digits. The relationship of the corticospinal fibers which arise in the parietal cortex to voluntary muscular activity is unkuown. It is certain, however, that this parietal component of the corticospinal system is not capable of producing useful coordinated movements independent of the precentral motor cortex.

The precentral motor cortex gives rise to many more descending fibers with motor functions than just the corticospinal fibers. There are fibers to the basal ganglia, the red nucleus, the substantia nigra, the reticular formation and the pontine nuclei (and through them impulses pass to the cerebellum). These, too, are concerned with the production of voluntary muscular activity. In the absence of the corticospinal tract such movement is apt to be cruder and less delicate but still useful. Exactly which of these many fiber systems —corticocaudate; corticopallidal; corticonigral; corticopontine, etc.—is concerned in the production of voluntary muscular activity is unknown.

This neural mechanism is also concerned with other functions of great concern in the organization of muscular activity. These include (1) the control by inhibition and facilitation of the various postural reflexes (see ch. 64); (2) the control of various automatic and associated movements, such as swinging of the arms when walking; (3) various visceral and vasomotor activities such as respiratory movements, blood pressure, pulse rate, the vascular bed, gastrointestinal motility, etc.

### CORTICOBULBAR FIBERS

The fibers passing from the lower part of the motor area of the cortex to the cranial nuclei constitute an important part of the *corticobular tract*. These bear precisely the same relationship to the cells of the cranial motor nuclei as does the corticospinal tract to the anterior horn cells of the cord. The corticobulbar fibers, however, cross at various levels throughout the brain stem.

### THE INTERNAL CAPSULE

In a horizontal section of the cerebrum, the internal capsule is seen as a compact band of white matter lying between the thalamus and caudate nucleus on its inner aspect and the lenticular nucleus on its lateral aspect (cf. fig. 65.11). It is the broad highway of communication in both directions between the cerebral cortex and subcortical and spinal centers. In addition to the corticospinal and corticobulbar tracts the following are the principal tracts which compose it:

I. *Descending*
  a. *Corticopontine tracts* consisting of three bundles of fibers, *frontopontine, parietopontine* and *occipitopontine* from the corresponding areas of the cerebral cortex to the nuclei of the pons.
  b. *Corticorubral tract*, from the frontal lobe to the red nucleus.

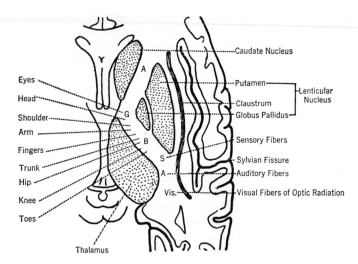

FIG. 65.11. Horizontal section of right hemisphere, showing corticobulbar and corticospinal fibers, and the location of the visual and sensory fibers. A, anterior limb of capsule; B, posterior limb; G, genu.

c. *Corticothalamic* from almost all areas of the cortex to various nuclei of the thalamus.

d. *Corticostriatal fibers* from the precentral area of the cortex to the caudate nucleus and the globus pallidus.

e. *Occipitotectal fibers* from the para- and peristriate cortex to the tectum of the midbrain.

f. *Corticonigral fibers* from the precentral and temporal areas to the substantia nigra.

II. *Ascending*

a. *Thalamic radiations* consist of four bundles ascending from the thalamus, *anterior*, *superior*, *posterior* and *inferior*, which connect the thalamus with various parts of the cerebral cortex. The anterior group terminate in prefrontal areas, and the superior group in the somesthetic area (postcentral gyrus).

b. *Auditory radiations fibers* ascending from the medial geniculate body to the temporal cortex (geniculo-temporal fibers).

c. *Optic radiation fibers* ascending from the lateral geniculate body to the visual area in the occipital cortex (geniculocalcarine) fibers.

d. *Rubrocortical fibers* from the red nucleus to the cortex.

The internal capsule is bent in the horizontal plane to form a convexity directed medially. The region of the angle so produced is called the *knee* (*genu*); the portions in front and behind this are known, respectively, as the *anterior* and *posterior* *limbs*. The shorter anterior limb lies between the caudate nucleus and the lenticular nucleus; the posterior limb between the lenticular nucleus and the thalamus. The extension backwards of the posterior limb is known as the *retrolenticular part*.

The anterior limb is occupied by the *frontopontine* fibers and the *anterior thalamic radiation* (thalamofrontal fibers), the *frontothalamic tract*, *corticostriatal* and *corticorubral tracts*. In the anterior three-fifths of the posterior limb are transmitted the *corticobulbar* and *corticospinal* fibers. The fibers of these two tracts are organized in accordance with the portions of the body which they innervate, those carrying impulses for the eye muscles, the muscles of the tongue, and face and upper and lower extremities arranged in this order from before backwards; and those transmitting impulses destined for the proximal part of an extremity are placed in front of those for the more distal muscles. The remaining part of the posterior limb, and the retrolenticular part carry in anteroposterior order the *superior* and *posterior* *thalamic radiations*, the *auditory* (*geniculotemporal*), and the *inferior thalamic radiations*, *corticothalamic*, and *parietopontine* fibers, and the *optic* (*geniculo-occipital*) *radiations*.

The internal capsule is supplied with blood through the lateral striate branches of the middle cerebral artery, by the recurrent artery of Hubner from the anterior cerebral artery, and the anterior choriodal artery from the internal carotid artery.

## A Comparison of the Effects Produced by Injury of Supraspinal Paths with Those of the Spinal Centers or Peripheral Nerves (Motoneurons)

It is obvious that lesions at various points in the nervous system are likely to produce different manifestations. This is particularly true in the field of muscular activity. In view of the intricacy of the neural mechanism responsible for muscular activity which has been briefly outlined above, it must be obvious that the patterns of muscular disturbances which may develop can vary through a wide range. There are no simple syndromes upon which the student may rely. Rather he must familiarize himself, as completely as is possible in our present state of knowledge and ignorance, with the neural mechanisms responsible for muscular activity and then must attempt to understand and interpret what he finds in the patient in the light of that knowledge.

Destruction of the peripheral nerves supplying a skeletal muscle produces an easily understood clinical picture. The muscle is (1) totally paralyzed, it is beyond the patient's control and he cannot move it; (2) no reflex activity of any sort is possible, although in the early stages the muscle may still contract in response to direct percussion or direct stimulation with a galvanic current; and (3) the muscle wastes away to a useless fibrous cord because it is devoid of innervation and completely without use. Involvement of this sort is often spoken of as a "lower motor neuron" paralysis and it may develop following destruction of the anterior horn cells in the spinal cord, or following division of the anterior spinal roots or of the muscular nerve. One must never forget, however, that not all paralyses are complete. Some innervation may remain and then the muscle is weakened but not completely paralyzed, the reflexes are diminished but not abolished and the wasting is incomplete.

Although the term "lower motor neuron" paralysis is accurate for the condition described above, it has the disadvantage that it implies that there is a counterpart, an "upper motor neuron" paralysis. This is misleading for there is no constant reliable entity which can be so designated. The manifestations of involvement of the many neurons which lie above the anterior horn cell which are responsible in one way or another for some phase of muscular activity vary widely depending upon which such neurons or groups of neurons are involved. Thus we may have a severe paralysis with spasticity and hyperactivity of the stretch reflexes if the descending motor pathways in the internal capsule are involved. If on the other hand the lesion is limited to the corticospinal fibers in the central portion of the cerebral peduncle one sees a loss of some fineness and delicacy of movement with little or no spasticity and little increase in tendon reflexes. Lesions of the globus pallidus combined with destruction of the substantia nigra are, on the other hand, characterized by increased resistance to passive manipulation of the extremities, with a generalized rigidity of the body and a loss of the facial movements of expression and of many automatic associated muscular movements but with little or no true paralysis and little if any change in the tendon reflexes. As we have noted before a paralysis arising from a lesion in the internal capsule is commonly associated with a flexor spasticity in the upper extremity and an extensor spasticity in the lower extremity, whereas a severe lesion in the mesencephalon is likely to produce a paralysis with extensor spasticity in all four extremities. In contrast with this a paralysis due to a transverse lesion of the spinal cord will produce a complete paralysis of the skeletal musculature below the level of the lesion with a variable reflex pattern. In some cases, or even only at some times in a given case, the paralyzed extremities may show a severe extensor spasm while at other times a severe flexor pattern may develop. In contrast with "lower motor neuron" lesions, paralysis due to involvement of motor neurons above the anterior horn cells are almost always associated with some type of reflex activity. Often this reflex activity is exaggerated beyond that which one would expect in normal muscles. However, the nature and pattern of the reflex activity will vary depending upon the location of the lesion and the pathways which are involved. One reflex seems to have its own specific significance—the *sign of Babinski*. This reflex is elicited by stroking the outer margin of the sole of the foot from the heel toward the little toe. Normally, such stimulation is associated with a flexion of all of the toes. However, if the corticospinal fibers from the "foot" area of the upper part of the precentral gyrus are interrupted the great toe will extend or dorsiflex. The other toes may or may not "fan" outward laterally. It must be remembered that such a "positive" response is dependent upon an intact peripheral mechanism. Regardless of the nature or location of the central lesion the sign of Babinski will not be elicited if the great toe is ankylosed, if the extensor tendon is severed or

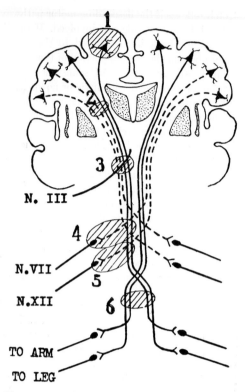

N. III

N.VII

N.XII

TO ARM

TO LEG

FIG. 65.12. Diagram illustrating the effects of lesions at various levels. 1, lesion of cerebral cortex causing monoplegia or hemiplegia, depending upon its extent; 2, lesion of internal capsule, hemiplegia; 3, lesion of midbrain involving descending motor fibers and nucleus or tract of the third nerve (Weber's paralysis); 4, lesion in pons destroying descending motor fibers and nucleus of facial nerve, crossed hemiplegia with homolateral facial paralysis; 5, lesion in medulla oblongata involving descending motor fibers and the hypoglossal nucleus, crossed hemiplegia and homolateral paralysis of lingual muscles; 6, transection of spinal cord, paraplegia. (In part from Villiger and from Ranson.)

the extensor hallucis muscle destroyed, or the muscular nerve to this muscle interrupted or the related anterior spinal root or anterior horn cells seriously damaged. It must also be remembered that this is a sign only of interruption of the corticospinal fibers which innervate the musculature of the great toe. It is not a sign of damage to any other corticospinal fibers.

Both "upper" and "lower" motor neuron paralyses may be associated with atrophy or wasting of the involved muscles. Muscular wasting is in general proportionate to the degree of loss of use of the muscle rather than to loss of innervation. Because the paralysis resulting from a complete "lower" motor neuron lesion is complete both as

to voluntary and reflex activity the atrophy is likewise complete. Wasting from "upper motor neuron" lesions is never that severe because even with a complete paralysis of voluntary activity some reflex activity persists.

Lesions at various levels are likely to involve other structures and thus indicate their location by the nature of the other clinical manifestations which the patient develops (fig. 65.12). Thus a massive lesion of the internal capsule will produce a contralateral hemihypesthesia and possibly a homonymous hemianopia as well as a hemiplegia. A unilateral lesion in the midbrain often will produce a third cranial nerve palsy (with a ptosis of the upper eyelid, a paralysis of several ocular muscles, a dilatation of the pupil and a loss of the pupillary light reflex) on the side of involvement in addition to a contralateral spastic hemiplegia. Lesions involving one half of the lower brain stem may be associated with a paralysis of one or more cranial nerves (e.g., facial, vagus or hypoglossal) on that side of the body and a hemiplegia and hemianesthesia on the opposite side of the body. In contrast with this unilateral lesions of the spinal cord produce what is known as a Brown-Sequard syndrome—a paralysis of the skeletal muscles of the trunk and extremities and a loss of position and vibratory sensibilities below the level of the lesion and on the same side with a loss of pain and thermal sensibilities on the opposite side (fig. 65.13). Obviously the possible combinations of symptoms and signs are numerous and cannot all be discussed in detail here. Their recognition and proper interpretation are dependent

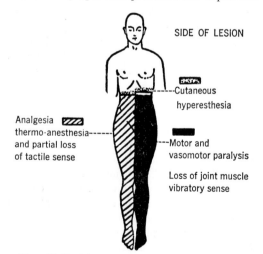

FIG. 65.13. Diagram showing effects following hemisection of the spinal cord in the lower thoracic region. Narrow white band at level of lesion indicates total anesthesia and analgesia.

upon a thorough understanding of the structure and function of the nervous system.

It is evident that the paralysis is more likely to be bilateral if the lesion is situated in a region where, as in the brain stem or spinal cord, the descending motor tracts of the two sides are approximated, than if it is located at a level where these tracts are widely separated, as in the corona radiata or internal capsule; then unilateral effects are usual. Complete interruption of the spinal cord will of course result in paralysis on both sides of the body below the level of the lesion—*paraplegia* (p. 1210).

## FUNCTIONAL, MORPHOLOGICAL AND CHEMICAL CHANGES IN DENERVATED MUSCLE

A lesion which involves any part of the lower motor neuron—anterior horn cell—such as may result from anterior poliomyelitis or peripheral nerve injury, is followed by degenerative changes which extend to and include the nerve terminals within the muscle. A muscle thus completely denervated exhibits constant, fine, rapid, rhythmical contractions. This so-called fibrillation of the denervated muscle does not appear until several days after the abnormal electrical reactions (reaction of degeneration, ch. 61) have already developed and complete degeneration of the nerve has occurred. The muscle fibers contract asynchronously; the contractions involve only a part of the length (0.5 to 1 mm.) of the fiber and give rise to small irregular action potentials. The fibrillation can sometimes, though not commonly, be seen through the skin. Having once appeared, fibrillation persists for a year or more and until the contractile elements have undergone complete atrophy. According to Denny-Brown, a reduction in tension developed by the muscle when stimulated maximally can be detected within 2 minutes after section of the nerve, but other investigators have been unable to observe any loss of contractile force until after a much longer interval (30 to 40 hours). An outstanding functional effect of denervation is the great increase in the sensitivity of the muscle to the intravenous or intra-arterial injection of acetylcholine. Normal muscle is excited by the intra-arterial injection of from 0.2 to 2.0 mg. of acetylcholine, whereas denervated muscle responds to a dose of from 0.002 to 0.02 $\gamma$. It is generally believed that this hypersensitivity to acetylcholine is responsible for the Vulpian and Sherrington effects, and most probably also for the "fright reaction" described by Bender. The denervated muscle is also hyperexcitable, though to a less pronounced degree, to potassium chloride.

The denervated muscle soon commences to atrophy, reduction in its bulk becoming apparent

within a few days after section of the nerve. Atrophy progresses rapidly and is followed by degeneration of the contractile elements. Microscopic changes in the muscle fibers consist of swelling and vesiculation of the nuclei, a reduction in sarcoplasm, and fading, followed by disappearance of the striations of the myofibrillae. Ultimately all contractile tissue disappears and is replaced by fibrous tissue and fat. As these morphological changes are occurring, the muscle gradually loses its plastic or ductile quality, flexors and adductors shorten and become more or less "set" in their new positions. The antagonistic muscles lengthen adaptively. This state of the muscles is called *contracture*. This disappearance of the denervated muscle fibers and their replacement by fibrous tissue is important in considering when a divided muscular nerve should be sutured or replaced by transplantation of another nerve. Obviously if such operations are delayed until only fibrous tissue remains they will be unsuccessful. If they are to succeed they should be performed within a year after the muscular nerve has been damaged.

The chemical changes in denervated muscle comprise a reduction in glycogen, phosphocreatine and adenosine triphosphate, but they do not become pronounced until the onset of fibrillation. The breakdown and subsequent resynthesis of glycogen by the denervated muscle during a work period is normal for a time following nerve section but when fibrillation supervenes, the ability of the muscle to restore its glycogen after contraction is greatly impaired. The atrophying muscle shows a large increase in calcium, a smaller increase in chloride, and a decrease in potassium. The changes in chloride and potassium can be accounted for by the reduction in muscle mass and its replacement by interstitial tissue and fluid. The increase in calcium is too great, however, to be explained entirely in this way.

The cause of fibrillation in denervated muscle is unknown, but it is not improbable that it is a manifestation of its hypersensitivity to acetylcholine. The observation of Magladery and Solandt that quinidine, which abolishes acetylcholine hypersensitivity, also suppresses fibrillation is highly suggestive; yet as Dale and his associates have shown, direct stimulation of denervated muscle does not cause the release of acetylcholine. It follows, therefore, that if the stimulating effect of this agent is responsible for fibrillation it must be carried to the muscle in the blood stream. The increased sensitivity to acetylcholine may be due to a lack of cholinesterase for, according to Marnay and Nachmansohn, this enzyme, which normally is concentrated in the neighborhood of the nerve endings in skeletal muscle, disappears after denervation. The lack of cholinesterase might also explain the failure of eserine to cause anything more than a transient augmentation of fibrillation.

## SYRINGOMYELIA

This condition is characterized by a cavitation of the spinal cord surrounded by an area of gliosis. The disease process involves the central gray matter primarily and the surrounding white matter to a variable degree. The process may extend for considerable distances up and down the spinal cord. The lower cervical and upper thoracic regions are most commonly affected. The disease may extend into the bulb (syringobulbia) when signs of implication of the nuclei of the cranial nerves appear.

A loss of pain and temperature sensibilities, muscular weakness and changes due to involvement of the central sympathetic fibers are among the characteristic features of the disease. Owing to the site of the changes, the fibers mediating pain, heat and cold, where they make connections with the cells of the posterior horns, are first destroyed. If the lesion is unilateral, thermoanesthesia and analgesia of the skin supplied by, and on the same side as the diseased segments result. Other sensations, e.g., touch, muscle sense, are unaffected until later in the disease. Involvement of the spinal nucleus of the trigeminal results in the characteristic sensory loss over the face. When the disease involves both dorsal horns or the anterior gray commissure where the fibers subserving pain and temperature sensibilities cross the thermoanesthesia and analgesia are bilateral. The muscles innervated by the anterior horn cells of the diseased segments become weak and wasted; these effects often appear first in the small muscles of the hand. So long as the disease does not cause injury to the white matter, the sensory and motor effects are limited and have a segmental distribution. Involvement of the descending motor pathways will result in a spastic paralysis below the level of the lesion, while pressure upon the spinothalamic tracts and dorsal columns will be followed by sensory loss below the level of the lesion. The degree of sensory loss, its type and distribution and whether homolateral or contralateral vary according to the extent to which the individual tracts are affected by the disease. As a result of the loss of the protective sensations (pain and (temperature), patients with syringomyelia are prone to suffer injuries which, not being perceived at the time, are neglected and ultimately lead to serious lesions, e.g., painless burns or the disorganization of a joint (arthropathy, Charcot's joint). Involvement of the sympathetic centers in the lateral columns leads to vasomotor disturbances, excessive sweating or absence of sweating, cyanosis, etc. So-called trophic disturbances, e..g, ulcers, whitlows, gangrene, etc., are largely the result of vasomotor abnormalities and the loss of

sensation which, as just mentioned, permits an injury, trivial perhaps at first, to be disregarded.

## SUBACUTE COMBINED DEGENERATION OF THE SPINAL CORD

This condition involves the white matter of the cord and is almost always associated sooner or later with pernicious anemia. The degenerative process consists of a breakdown of the myelin sheaths, subsequent destruction of the axons and their replacement by newly formed glial tissue. The changes are most pronounced in the corticospinal and cerebellar tracts and in the posterior columns. The chief clinical features are, therefore: (a) muscular weakness and spasticity, (b) impairment of the sense of position and of passive movement of the limbs with consequent ataxia and a positive Romberg sign, (c) loss or impairment of spatial discrimination, and vibratory sensibility. The relative extent to which these sensations are lost is variable. Paresthesias (tingling, pricking and burning sensations) frequently precede the sensory loss, and are usually the result of an associated peripheral neuropathy. The reflexes vary. The tendon jerks are frequently exaggerated as a result of involvement of the descending motor pathways, but they may disappear as the disease progresses if the peripheral neuropathy becomes sufficiently severe. The plantar response is usually of the "extensor" type.

The severity of the nervous manifestations do not always run parallel with that of the blood picture; the neurological features may be pronounced though the anemia is of mild degree, or vice versa. Subacute combined degeneration of the cord, though associated with pernicious anemia, is not due to the anemia itself. This is shown by the well recognized fact that the blood picture may be restored to normal by the administration of folic acid, but the neurological condition progresses unchecked, whereas the latter is arrested by the hematinic principle (vitamin $B_{12}$). See also p. 931.

## TABES DORSALIS, LOCOMOTOR ATAXIA

In this condition, which is the result of syphilis, the fibers of the dorsal roots at their point of entry into the spinal cord (i.e., the central processes of the primary sensory neurons) are attacked. The ganglion cell bodies of the dorsal roots, as a rule, are not affected. The essential lesion within the spinal cord, therefore, involves the entrance zone of the lateral division of the dorsal roots (dorsolateral fasciculus of Lissauer), and the dorsal fasciculi (gracilis and cuneatus). The endogenous fibers of the spinal cord escape, but although it is those tracts composed of exogenous fibers which are specifically attacked by the disease, the functions of the cerebellar and spinothalamic tracts are also seriously disturbed as a result of degeneration of the primary neurons leading to them. The descending tracts remain as a rule practically unaffected. The reason for the selective destruction of the exogenous fibers of the cord is unknown; possibly it is compression of the fibers by proliferation or inflammatory swelling of the meninges at the point of entrance of the posterior root.

The sensory changes are those which might be expected to result from a gradual degeneration of dorsal root fibers. Somewhat similar effects are produced in monkeys by section of the posterior nerve roots.

The chief manifestations are as follows: (a) During the degenerative process paresthesias of various types, hyperesthesia and stabbing pains are common. (b) Impairment, or loss to a variable degree, of all forms of sensation follows. Loss of the rapid conduction component of deep pain occurs early. Loss of the sense of position and of passive movement, and blockage of afferent cerebellar impulses result in marked incoördination of the muscles—ataxia. Movements are jerky, exaggerated and imperfectly controlled, the subject being unable to move his feet in the desired direction or to assume a given position at will, e.g., placing the heel of one foot upon the toes of the other. The gait is ataxic, the feet are kept wide apart, raised unnecessarily high and brought down in a stamping fashion; the patient may learn to overcome this tendency by shuffling.

The loss of sense of position is in large measure responsible for the patient's difficulties. When standing with the eyes closed the patient, being thus deprived of an important aid in maintaining his equilibrium, tends to sway and may fall (Romberg's sign). (c) The interruption of the pathways for proprioceptive impulses from the skeletal muscles (p. 1146) results in extreme *hypotonia*, but there is no true paralysis. (d) The *tendon reflexes* are abolished as a result of the destruction of the afferent limb of the proprioceptive reflex arc. The abdominal reflexes may or may not be present. (e) "*Lightning pains*" and *trophic disturbances.* The former are severe stabbing paroxysmal pains usually localized to an area supplied by one or more spinal segments. They are commonly in the abdomen or in the lower extremities. Vasodilatation, small hemorrhages or herpes zoster may occur in the painful area. These vascular and cutaneous effects have been attributed to antidromic impulses reaching the periphery via sensory fibers. The skin of the affected area may break down with the formation of so-called trophic ulcers. Painless destruction of joints (Charcot's joint) is not uncommon in tabes. The loss of the sense of pain which causes the patient to suffer injuries of which he is unaware, the extreme hypotonia of the muscles which normally support the joint, and the vascular disturbances resulting

from damage to autonomic fibers combine to produce such joint conditions. They are usually classed among the trophic disturbances, the term implying that the interruption of trophic impulses is responsible. However, the existence of true trophic fibers, i.e., specific fibers which preside over the nutrition of the peripheral tissues, is questionable. (f) *Tabetic crises.* These are apparently the result of the involvement of afferent autonomic fibers which enter the spinal cord by the dorsal roots. They consist of paroxysmal attacks of pain and functional disturbances in one or other of the viscera. Gastric crises are the commonest. They consist of severe epigastric pain and vomiting. *Rectal crises* consisting of pain in and increased activity of the rectum, *vesical crises* with bladder pain and difficult urination or *laryngeal crises*, in which spasm of the adductors of the larynx with dyspnea may occur. (g) *Ocular signs.* The pupils are as a rule constricted and often unequal. The Argyll-Robertson pupil (p. 1412) in which the reflex to accommodation is retained but the reaction to light is lost, is a characteristic ocular feature of tabes dorsalis. The pupil also frequently fails to respond by dilatation to stimulation of the skin of the neck (ciliospinal reflex). The loss of this reflex is usually attributed to degeneration of the central sympathetic pathway through which the dilator pupillae muscle is innervated. Some drooping of the upper lid (ptosis) may also result from the blockage of sympathetic pathways which normally transmit impulses to the smooth muscle in this situation; compensatory contraction of the frontalis muscle with wrinkling of the skin of the forehead results. Damage to the fibers of the 3rd, 4th or 6th nerves results in paralysis of the ocular muscles, the external rectus most commonly. Squint and double vision (diplopia (p. 1418)) are consequences. Primary optic atrophy often occurs.

### DISSEMINATED (MULTIPLE) SCLEROSIS

This is a chronic disease of the nervous system characterized anatomically by the occurrence of small patches of demyelination followed by overgrowth of glial tissue throughout the white substance of the brain (especially in the regions beneath the lateral ventricles), and spinal cord. The lesions in the cord are most numerous in the corticospinal tracts and in the posterior columns. Clinically, the disease is marked by an insidious onset, irregular course, with remissions and relapses of unpredictable duration, and a great variability of signs and symptoms between individual cases. Progressive spastic weakness of the muscles of the legs, with increased tendon jerks, "extensor" plantar response (Babinski) and loss of abdominal reflexes, is a common manifestation of this disease. Many patients also complain of paresthesias and have a loss of vibration and muscle senses from lesions in the posterior columns. The loss of tactile and pain and thermal sensibilities are seldom striking and rarely of an enduring nature. Impairment of vision, or even blindness, may result from involvement of the optic nerve, chiasma or tract. Nystagmus, slurring of speech and intention tremor, once regarded as diagnostic of the disease, appear late if at all and are manifestations of involvement of cerebellar pathways.

## COMPLETE TRANSVERSE DIVISION OF THE SPINAL CORD

A sudden, or rapidly progressive, complete interruption of the continuity of the cord may result from injury (e.g., gunshot nound, fracture-dislocation of the spine, etc.) or from acute inflammation (e.g., transverse myelitis). Immediate and complete loss of voluntary power below the level of the lesion results. Paralysis of both lower limbs resulting from this or any other nervous lesion is spoken of as *paraplegia*. Complete division of the cord in the lower cervical region will result in paralysis of all four limbs, *quadriplegia*. A lesion of this nature in the upper cervical region is of course rapidly fatal since the diaphragm and other respiratory muscles are isolated from the respiratory center.

*Stage of spinal shock.* Immediately following the injury there are complete loss of visceral and somatic sensations, and flaccid paralysis below the level of the lesion. The skeletal muscles are quite toneless. The tendon jerks, plantar response and abdominal reflexes are abolished. The cremasteric and bulbocavernosus reflexes, though absent as a rule, may at times be elicited. The anal reflex is present. A zone of heightened sensitivity (hyperesthesia) immediately above the level of the lesion may be present and spontaneous pains in this region, or a feeling of tightness encircling the body may be experienced by the patient. There is retention of urine and feces. This stage is analogous to the state of spinal shock in lower animals but is much more severe and prolonged (ch. 67). In man spinal shock lasts for from one to three weeks.

*Stage of reflex activity.* After a variable period of time, depending largely upon the general health of the patient, reflex activity begins to return to the isolated spinal cord below the level of the lesion. The first reflex to appear is usually the sign of Babinski, the extensor response of the great toe to stimulation of the sole of the foot. This reflex is actually a part of the flexor reflex pattern of the lower extremities. Both exaggerated extensor and flexor reflex patterns are usually present with lesions of the descending motor pathways. They vary in intensity and in relation to each other. If the lesion lies above the pons the extensor reflexes usually predominate. If the lesion is in the spinal cord the flexor reflexes are usually more prominent than when the lesion lies at higher levels and they may exceed the extensor reflexes in intensity. Then a paraplegia in flexion is present. However, this balance between extensor and flexor reflexes fluctuates from time to time in the same patient and is quite variable from one patient to another. After the sign of Babinski has become elicitable other flexor reflexes, dorsiflexion of the foot, flexion of the knee and hip gradually become more marked and more easily elicited. At first they are usually seen only with stimuli which except for the interruption of the pain pathways in the spinal cord would be painful, i.e., nociceptive stimuli. Later less intense stimuli such as passive flexion of the toes or mere touching of the foot or leg may be sufficient to provoke a violent flexion of the leg. When this stage is reached the patient usually has a paraplegia in flexion. The extensor reflexes begin to return after variable periods. At first the only demonstrable reflex of this type may be the patellar tendon reflex (knee jerk). Later the Achilles tendon reflex (ankle jerk) will return, ankle and patellar clonus may be elicited. At times the patient may develop severe extensor spasms and the muscles may be involved by severe clonic contractions with little or no external stimulation. At other times the extremities may lie quietly without either extensor or flexor reflexes causing any striking disturbances. Elicitation of the flexor reflexes will immediately result in a subsidence of ankle clonus or other manifestations of the extensor reflexes, and *vice versa*. This inhibition of the one when the other is produced is due to reciprocal innervation. On occasion elicitation of the flexor reflexes will be associated with evacuation of the bowel and bladder. This Head and Riddock termed the *"mass reflex."* However, reflex or automatic evacuation of the bowel and bladder need not be associated with a violent flexion of both lower extremities. Such reflex evacuation may result from distention of the bladder or rectum as the case may be, or may be induced by the patient. He may produce emptying of the bladder by stimulating the skin on the inner aspect of the upper thigh or reflex defecation by stimulating the rectal musoca at and just above the anal ring. These reflexes are often used to great advantage by the paraplegic patient. The time of development of these various reflexes and their vigor depend in large measure upon the condition of the patient and his paralyzed extremities. A poor state of nutrition or the presence of infection in the urinary tract or in decubitus ulcers, the development of severe muscular wasting or of fibrous changes in the muscles or about the joints will all mitigate against the development of active reflex activity.

### INCOMPLETE INTERRUPTION OF THE CORD

A bilateral lesion of gradual onset which impairs the activity of the descending motor pathways usually causes *paraplegia in extension*. The muscles are spastic and extensor activity predominates. The tendon jerks are exaggerated and patellar and ankle clonus can be readily elicited. Paraplegia in extension is more or less comparable to decerebrate extensor rigidity. The "extensor" plantar response, which is in reality a part of the flexor reflex pattern, is present, but much less intense than in paraplegia in flexion. It is associated with much less contraction in other flexor muscles and may be accompanied by a crossed extensor reflex. The mass reflex is absent. The abdominal reflexes are lost.

### THE PLANTAR REFLEXES

This is the most appropriate place to consider these and other superficial reflexes.

The *normal plantar response* to a light scratch applied to the skin of the sole is plantar flexion of the four outer toes with no movement, or, more usually, plantar flexion of the great toe. The center for the reflex lies in the first sacral segment; its physiological significance is unknown. With a lesion of the corticospinal fibers from the precentral region to the foot (see also p. 1205) at any level above the first sacral segment, the normal response is replaced by one in which *dorsiflexion* of the great toe and often spreading or fanning of the outer toes occurs. It is elicited best from the outer border of the sole. This response is called after its discoverer the *sign of Babinski* (fig. 65.14). From the dorsiflexion of the great toe, which is due to the contraction of the extensor longus hallucis, this reflex is also frequently referred to as the extensor response.[3] This term, however, is incorrect since the upward movement of the great toe is part of a general

---

[3] An "extensor" plantar response is present normally in infants up to the first year or so, i.e., to the age of walking, and is then probably due to the undeveloped state of the corticospinal tracts. It is also present in normal adults during deep sleep (p. 1270) and in the apneic stage of Cheyne-Stokes respiration, being apparently due in the latter instance, to anoxemia of the motor cortex.

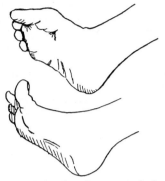

FIG. 65.14. Upper drawing, normal plantar response, lower drawing, Babinski response.

flexor response homologous with the flexor reflex elicitable from the hind limb of a lower animal (p. 1156) (see Walshe). The dorsiflexors of the toes, although classed anatomically as extensors must, when compared physiologically with similar muscles in the limb of an animal such as the dog, be included among the flexors. In lesions of descending spinal tracts in which extensor reflex activity overshadows the flexor reactions, the so-called extensor plantar response is less active and less readily elicited than when flexor patterns predominate. Nevertheless the flexor nature of the reflex is shown by the associated contraction of the hamstrings, i.e., semitendinosus, semimembranosus and biceps femoris, which usually occurs (see also p. 1210). Its flexor nature is also indicated by the fact that an undoubted extensor reflex such as ankle clonus is readily inhibited by evoking the Babinski reaction (reciprocal inhibition).

In the restricted forms of the extensor response as seen in hemiplegia, the receptive field of the reflex is also strictly circumscribed, being elicitable only from the sole—the outer border especially.

In paraplegia-in-flexion in which flexor activity predominates the so-called "extensor" response is maximal and, as we have seen, is simply part of a widespread flexor reaction. The receptive field of the reflex is extensive and the application of a stimulus is followed by contraction not only of the extensor longus hallucis (with dorsiflexion of the hallux) and hamstrings but by an associated contraction of the true flexors of the lower limb, the extensor longus digitorum, tibialis anticus, gracilis, sartorius, rectus femoris and iliopsoas.

### OTHER SUPERFICIAL REFLEXES

1. *Oppenheim's reflex* is simply a modified Babinski response; it is associated with the same

conditions as the latter and has a similar significance. It consists in dorsiflexion of the hallux which results when a firm downward sliding pressure is applied to the skin over the anterior border of the tibia. The Gordon, Chaddock and Gonda reflexes are other modifications of the Babinski response.

2. *Abdominal reflexes.* Lightly scratching the skin of the abdomen of a normal person causes a reflex contraction of the abdominal muscles. They do not appear until between the 6th and 8th months of age when the infant can sit up unsupported. These reflexes are, of course, abolished by any lesion which interrupts afferent conduction from the skin of the abdomen or destroys the anterior horn cells or the motor pathways concerned with the abdominal musculature. These reflexes also are often abolished by a lesion which interrupts the corticospinal pathways above the 7th thoracic segment, but they are *not* permanently abolished by extirpation of the precentral gyrus. These confusing facts have thrown serious doubt on all current physiological explanations of the abdominal reflexes.

3. *Cremasteric reflex* consists of contraction of the cremaster muscle and elevation of testicle which results from a light stroke applied to the skin on the inner aspect of the upper part of the thigh. It is often abolished by corticospinal lesions or as a result of destruction of the center in the 1st or 2nd lumbar segment.

4. *Bulbocavernosus reflex* has its center in the 3rd and 4th sacral segments. It consists of contraction of the bulbocavernosus muscle (detected by palpation) in response to stimulation of the glans penis. It is absent in a lesion involving any part of its reflex arc, motor or sensory limb, or center.

5. *Anal reflex* is the contraction of the external anal sphincter in response to scratching the neighboring skin. Its center is situated in the 4th and 5th sacral segments and the coccygeal segment; it is lost after interruption of its reflex arc.

6. *Gluteal reflex.* Scratching the skin of the buttock causes contraction of the gluteal muscles. It depends upon the integrity of the 4th and 5th lumbar and upper sacral segments.

The *deep* or *tendon reflexes*, such as the knee jerk, ankle jerk, etc., have been discussed in chapters 63 and 64.

## The Reticular Formation

The central portion of the brain stem is occupied by a diffuse ill defined mass of nerve cells and fibers known as the *reticular formation*. It extends downward into the spinal cord and upward into the thalamus and subthalamus. In the following discussion we shall not be concerned with the spinal reticular formation. The reticular forma-

tion in the brain stem can be subdivided into numerous nuclei or cell masses. However, as these have not been shown to have functional significance no cognizance of these cellular groups will be taken here. The reticular formation has been defined (see Segundo, 1956) as including all areas within the brain stem (excepting primary afferent pathways) which when stimulated will produce "arousal." This includes the bulbar reticular formation, the pontomesencephalic tegmentum, the hypothalamus, the subthalamus, and the ventromedial portion (including the intralaminar nuclei) and the reticular nucleus of the thalamus. There appears to be little doubt but that the reticular formation constitutes one, if not the most important regulatory mechanism within the central nervous system. As will be discussed below it is concerned with such general effects as the arousal of the entire organism, alerting the animal, maintaining attention, or, on the other hand, with the production of sleep or in cases of injury to the reticular formation the development of stupor or coma. It is also concerned with such specific effects as the control of muscular activity, the regulation of the receptivity of peripheral sensory end-organs, the control of the threshold of central sensory pathways, the regulation of vegetative visceral and vasomotor responses and of emotional expression. (The reader who is interested in the extensive literature concerning the reticular formation, and in more detailed information is referred to the summarizing articles by Segundo (1956) and French (1958) and to the Henry Ford Hospital symposium on the reticular formation of the brain (1958)).

The reticular formation is subject to a wide variety of afferent impulses. Every afferent pathway bearing information to the brain concerning the outside world, its relation to the organism itself and activities within the organism also sends afferents into the reticular formation. These connections are by means of both direct afferent fibers and collaterals from the main afferent pathways to the cerebellum and thalamus. Thus the reticular formation receives afferent impulses from the optic, the olfactory, the auditory and the gustatory systems as well as from the spinal and trigeminal pathways which bear impulses concerned with tactile, painful, thermal and vibratory sensibilities and sensations from the muscles, joints and tendons, and afferent impulses from the viscera and other internal structures of the body. In addition afferent fibers converge on the reticular formation from the cerebellum, the basal ganglia, the thalamus, the rhinencephalon and the cerebral cortex. Peculiarly, only certain specific portions of the cerebral neocortex seem to send afferent impulses to the reticular formation. These are the orbital, oculomotor, sensorimotor and posterior parietal cortices, the superior temporal and cingular gyri and the temporal pole. In addition the activity of the reticular formation is influenced by certain hormonal and chemical changes (adrenalin, acetylcholine, carbon dioxide, etc.) and by many drugs (barbiturates, anesthetics, tranquilizing compounds, etc.).

In turn, efferent impulses from the reticular formation are conducted cephalad into the brain, particularly to all parts of the cerebral cortex, and caudad into the spinal cord. Because of the multisynaptic character of the pathways to and from the reticular formation and the small caliber of many of the fibers connected with it reticulocortical conduction is much slower than in the primary sensory system. The reticulospinal fibers run bilaterally in the lateral and ventral white columns of the spinal cord and transmission in this system is thought to be quite rapid.

One of the first effects shown to result from excitation of the reticular formation was that of arousal. This may be demonstrated in two ways, electroencephalographically and by the animal's behavior. In general these two parallel one another but that is not invariably true. There are circumstances under which the electroencephalographic pattern may be changed from that characteristic of the waking state (desynchronized, irregular waves of low amplitude), to that characteristic of sleep (slow, regular waves of high amplitude) without the animal's actually going to sleep, e.g., in the atropinized animal. The changes characteristic of arousal which are induced by stimulation of the reticular formation are the same as those brought about by physiological stimuli. In addition to actual arousal from sleep, stimulation of the reticular formation also has a very definite effect upon the awake animal in that it appears to "alert" him for possible changes in his environment, or serves to make him more attentive to such changes. Thus it may be said that the reticular formation is indispensable for the initiation and maintenance of wakefulness. On the other hand, lesions of the reticular formation impair the wakefulness of the organism. Experimental lesions in the cephalic end of the reticular formation in the mesencephalic tegmentum and basal portion of the diencephalon of the cat produces sleep while destructive lesions in this same portion of the human brain result in coma. Likewise, small lesions in this same portion of the reticular formation of the cat are associated with a state which Ingram, Barris and Ranson referred to as "catalepsy."

The reticular formation is also concerned with more specific activities. Early Magoun and Rhines showed that the bulbar reticular formation is capable of inhibiting the spinal mechanism responsible for the stretch reflex of the skeletal muscles. It is through this mechanism in the brain stem that the cortical inhibitory mechanism finds expression. In addition the reticular formation is also capable of facilitation of the more peripheral motor mechanism. These effects are produced through the large motor cells of the anterior gray column of the spinal cord, the alpha cells, which innervate the ordinary striated muscle fibers, and also by controlling the receptivity of the muscle spindle (the sensory end-organ within skeletal muscle which responds to stretching) through the small gamma cells of the anterior horn.

In addition to controlling the receptivity of the stretch receptors in skeletal muscles, it also appears that the reticular formation is able to control the sensitivity of certain other sensory receptors such as those in the retina and the cochlea, and of tactile receptors, and is capable of modifying conduction along various sensory pathways, in the thalamus and in the sensory cortex. In this way the reticular formation is able to regulate the threshold of sensory perception and to control the level of attention to sensory stimuli. In all likelihood the reticular formation is not the only neural mechanism concerned in such control but it appears to be an important one.

The reticular formation is also capable of exerting extensive influence over many autonomic, or viscerovascular vegetative functions, such as cardiac, vascular, respiratory, gastrointestinal, metabolic and the control of the temperature of the body.

## REFERENCES

FOERSTER, O. Brain, 1933, **56**, 1.

FRENCH, J. D.   J. Neurosurg., 1958, **15**, 97.

HEAD, H. Brain, 1893, **16**, 339. Brain, 1894, **17**, 339. Brain, 1896, **19**, 153.

INGRAM, W. R., BARRIS, R. W., AND RANSOM, S. W. Arch. Neurol. & Psychiat., 1936, **35**, 1175.

MAGLADERY, J. W. AND SOLANDT, D. Y. Neurophysiology, 1942, **5**, 357.

MAGOUN, H. W. AND RHINES, R. J. Neurophysiol., 1946, **9**, 165.

MARNAY, A. AND NACHMANSOHN, D. J. Phisoly., 1932, **92**, 37.

SEGUNDO, J. P. Acta Neurol. Latinoam., 1956, **3**, 245.

Swartz, H. G. and Weddell, G. Brain, 1938, **61,** 99.

Walshe, F. M. R. Brain, 1956, **79,** 529.

*Monographs and Reviews*

Fulton, J. F. and Keller, A. D. The sign of Babinski: a study of the evolution of cortical dominance in primates. Charles C Thomas, Springfield, Ill., 1932.

Harris, W. Brain, 1927, **50,** 399.

Jasper, H. H., Proctor, L. D., Knighton, R. S., Noshay, W. C., and Costello, R. T. (Eds.) Reticular formation of the brain. Henry Ford Hospital International Symposium. Little, Brown & Co., Boston, 1958.

Ranson, S. W. The anatomy of the nervous system from the standpoint of development and function. W. B. Saunders Co., Philadelphia, 1928.

Tower, S. S. Physiol. Rev., 1939, **19,** 1.

# *66*

# THE BASAL GANGLIA. THE THALAMUS
# AND HYPOTHALAMUS

---

## The Basal Ganglia

The basal ganglia form a large and prominent part of the human brain, and in lower animal forms are a very important part of the nervous mechanism controlling muscular activity. Destructive lesions in the human basal ganglia are associated with several well known, common, severe motor disorders which are fairly constant in their clinical pattern, yet our knowledge of the nervous connections and of the functional activity of the human basal ganglia is grossly deficient. At one time it was denied (erroneously) that the basal ganglia had any connections with the cerebral cortex or that there was any functional or somatotopic localization within them. The thalamic connections are imperfectly understood. There is no known *direct* connection by which afferent impulses from the various sense organs can send information regarding the outside world or the body itself to the basal ganglia. Experimental stimulation or destruction of the basal ganglia in laboratory animals produces very little effect. Then, what is the function of the basal ganglia in the human brain? What do they do and how? Are they merely vestigial remnants from earlier animal forms? That seems most unlikely. They form a large part of the brain and they have grown proportionally from the lower primates to man, so that whereas the globus pallidus, putamen and caudate nucleus occupy 980 cu. mm. in the rhesus monkey, they measure 2775 cu. mm. in the chimpanzee and have a volume of 14,912 cu. mm. in man (Harman and Carpenter, 1950). There have been some discussions of the possibility that the basal ganglia may be related to perceptual functions (Mettler, 1955) but the evidence in support of such a possibility is most tenuous. There also is some reason to believe that the basal ganglia may be related to vegetative or autonomic functions but the evidence is inadequate to establish such a relationship or to permit us to understand it if it exists. At this time we have reliable evidence only that the basal ganglia are intimately concerned in the activity of the skeletal musculature. At present no one can answer the question as to what the basal ganglia do or how they do it in man. It may prove profitable, however, to summarize what we do know.

The term "basal ganglia" is a loose one which defies accurate definition. There certainly is no uniformity of opinion even as to what the term includes. Perhaps the term is meaningless in modern neurology and will be discarded shortly, but for the moment it is so deeply embedded in our literature and in our thinking that it cannot be discarded. For the purpose of this discussion the term will include the *caudate nucleus*, the *putamen*, the *globus pallidus*, the *subthalamic body of Luys*, the *red nucleus* and the *substantia nigra*. (The caudate nucleus and putamen are often referred to as the *striatum* and the globus pallidus as the *pallidum*. The putamen and globus pallidus are sometimes referred to as the *lenticular nucleus*.) The *claustrum* should also be included in the basal ganglia but as practically nothing is known of its connections or functions it need not be considered further. It might be argued that the subthalamic body, the red nucleus and the substantia nigra should not be included; but their anatomical relationships, their numerous connections and their apparent close functional relationships with the other nuclei of the basal ganglia make their inclusion natural and reasonable. One might also include the substantia reticularis of the brain stem, the pontine nuclei, the inferior olive, the cerebellum and the amygdala. They certainly form part of this subcortical motor mechanism. But the reticular formation is related not only to muscular activities as are the basal ganglia (Magoun and Rhines, 1947) but it also has what are perhaps even more important functions concerned with the alerting reaction, the control of spinal reflexes, of sensory threshold and of visceral regulation (Magoun and his coworkers). The pontine nuclei, inferior olive, and cerebellum, although related in an important fashion to muscular activity (Bailey, 1949) are too far removed to be included in the term "basal ganglia." The amygdala has no known connections with the functions of the skeletal muscular system and seems more likely to be related to vegetative activities.

The cytology of the various nuclei under discussion offers little assistance in understanding their functional activity. For the most part the nuclei seem to be divided into two groups—the small-celled and the large-celled parts. As is true of the cerebral cortex the small-celled parts appear to be the receptive divisions of the basal ganglia, whereas the large-celled parts have a predominantly motor function. The caudate nucleus and the putamen constitute the receptive portion and so far as is known at this time receive their afferent innervation from the precentral motor cortex (areas 4, 4s, and 6), the

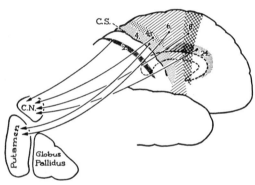

FIG. 66.1. The connections from the cerebral cortex to the caudate nucleus and putamen.

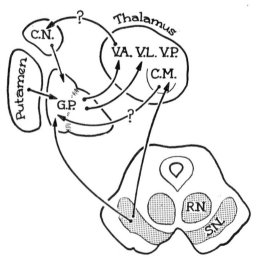

FIG. 66.2. Some of the intrinsic connections within the basal ganglia.

suppressor strips of Dusser de Barenne and his coworkers (areas 4s, 8, 2, and 24), (Fig. 66.1) and in a small way from the thalamus. In turn the caudate nucleus and putamen send their efferent fibers mainly to the large-celled or "motor" portion of the lenticular nucleus, the globus pallidus, (Fig. 66.2) with a much smaller group of efferent fibers going to the substantia nigra. Similarly the substantia nigra is divided into a large-celled (pigmented) dorsal portion and a small-celled (unpigmented) ventral portion which lies just above the cerebral peduncle. And the red nucleus is divided into a small-celled anterior portion and a large-celled posterior portion which gives rise to the rubrospinal tract. Here we must call attention to the fact that a material change has occurred in the red nucleus in primates as compared with that in the carnivora. In the dog and cat the magnocellular portion of the red nucleus and the rubrospinal tract are large and presumably important structures, whereas in the primates this portion of the red nucleus and the rubrospinal tract which arises from it are small and apparently insignificant (Stern, 1936). It is obvious that the experimental evidence which has indicated a place of great importance for the magnocellular portion of the red nucleus and the rubrospinal tract in the neural mechanism controlling muscular tone in the carnivora (Rademaker, 1926) is not applicable to the monkey, the ape or man. Another structure, the reticular formation of the brain stem, has apparently taken over that function. In fact, the reticular formation and the inferior olive are probably the principal effector or efferent structures of the subcortical motor system in primates.

Within the basal ganglia almost all parts are connected with all other parts (Fig. 66.2), i.e., the globus pallidus sends fibers to the red nucleus, the substantia nigra and the subthalamic nucleus; the substantia nigra sends fibers to the red nucleus, the globus pallidus and the subthalamic nucleus; the subthalamic nucleus sends fibers to the globus pallidus, red nucleus and the substantia nigra. Within the basal ganglia there are also circular systems, such as the projection from the caudate nucleus to the globus pallidus, the globus pallidus to the ventral anterior nucleus of the thalamus, and from this thalamic nucleus back to the caudate nucleus (Fig. 66.2). Two parts of the basal ganglia, however, remain more or less aloof from this intranuclear activity. They are the caudate nucleus and putamen, and the red nucleus. The caudate nucleus and puta-

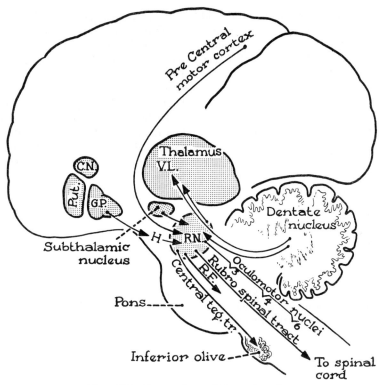

FIG. 66.3. Connections of the red nucleus.

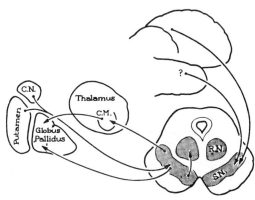

FIG. 66.4. Some connections of the substantia nigra with other parts of the basal ganglia.

ganglia, to the spinal cord, the reticular substance of the brain stem, the ventrolateral nucleus of the thalamus, the inferior olive and the oculomotor nuclei (Fig. 66.3). Thus the caudate nucleus and the putamen appear to be acting as the primary receiving station of the basal ganglia whereas the red nucleus and the globus pallidus are acting as the principal sending stations. In addition to their efferent fibers there are fibers from the substantia nigra and the subthalamic nucleus to the substantia reticularis and the center-median nucleus of the thalamus (Ranson, Ranson and Ranson, 1941; Glees, 1945; Brodal, 1948) (Fig. 66.4).

men on the one hand receive their afferent innervation largely from the cerebral cortex (with additional afferent connections from the substantia nigra (Ranson and Ranson, 1939) and from the ventral anterior nucleus of the thalamus), and they distribute their efferents to the globus pallidus and the substantia nigra. The red nucleus receives from all of the other nuclei of the basal ganglia (and from the precentral motor cortex and the cerebellum) but sends all of its efferent fibers to structures outside of the basal

## FUNCTION

What do the basal ganglia do with this complicated neural mechanism? Here again our knowledge is very incomplete. The location of the basal ganglia in the interior of the cerebral hemisphere, covered with the cerebral cortex and white matter, in very intimate relationship with the Island of Reil, the internal capsule, the thalamus and the hypothalamus has made discrete stimulation or destruction difficult. In any event the many experiments carried out on the basal ganglia have shed surprisingly little light on their activity. Furthermore, in man the functional activity of the basal ganglia is apparently quite different from the lower animal forms, even monkeys. Whether this or some other factors are the reason, it is a fact that it has been almost impossible to duplicate in animals the clinical pictures associated with diseases of the basal ganglia in man. The only exception is the intention tremor produced in both man and monkey by section of the superior cerebellar peduncle (Walker and Botterell, 1937). It is true that Richter (1945) produced a parkinsonianlike state in monkeys by destruction of the globus pallidus and substantia nigra by chronic intoxication with carbon disulfide. But as Richter noted, the experimentally produced state was not the same as that seen in man because, "The characteristic tremor, in particular, is lacking." As a result we must turn to the experiments conducted in man by nature herself for what limited knowledge we have of the functions of the human basal ganglia.

It has been repeatedly said that there is no localization of function, somatotopic or otherwise, in the basal ganglia. Clinical experience leaves no doubt that this statement is untrue. Disease in different parts of the basal ganglia give rise to vastly different clinical pictures. Destruction at any point in the dentato-rubro-thalamic projection (Fig. 66.5) causes an intention tremor. Lesions of the substantia nigra and globus pallidus are associated with parkinsonism and a tremor at rest. Destruction of the caudate nucleus and putamen is seen in patients with choreoathetosis. Obviously there must be some functional differences between these various nuclei. Every clinical neurologist is aware of how the tremor of parkinsonism may begin in the head and neck, or in the foot, or in a finger, and then later gradually spread to other parts of the body on the same or opposite side. Obviously there is somatotopic localization in the basal ganglia in man, otherwise such localized manifestations of disease would not be possible.

What are the specific manifestations of disease

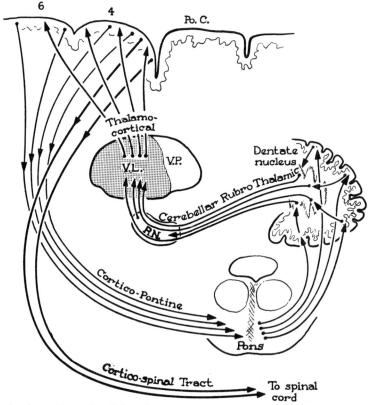

Fig. 66.5. A circular pathway involving the cerebral cortex and the cerebellum. Interruption of this pathway between the dentate nucleus, red nucleus and thalamus results in the appearnace of an intention tremor. This probably is the result of the loss of controlling impulses from the cerebellum to the precentral motor cortex.

of the basal ganglia and what do they signify in terms of normal physiological activity? Diseases of the basal ganglia and experimental studies indicate at least four principal functions of the basal ganglia: (a) the production of useful voluntary muscular activity; (b) the control of reflex muscular activity; (c) the production of automatic associated movements; and (d) the control of the precentral motor cortex in its function of producing muscular activity.

*Voluntary muscular activity.* For years it was thought that the production of voluntary muscular activity occurred exclusively as the result of the activity of the corticospinal tract. It is now obvious that that is incorrect. In the birds and reptiles there is no "motor cortex" (Ariens Kappers, 1929). The basal ganglia function as the "head ganglia" of the neural mechanism controlling movement; it is a detailed and exquisite control, as one can see by studying a bird in the air. In the dog and cat there is a "motor" cortex but if it (or even the entire cerebral cortex) is removed the animal still sits, stands and walks. It appears that the animal does this largely with its basal ganglia but even if the basal ganglia and the diencephalon are removed useful movements are not completely abolished in cats. Bard and Macht (1958) decerebrated a small series of cats. In some animals the transection was immediately above the pons, in others it was through the mesencephalon producing a "low mesencephalic cat," whereas in the remainder it was through the upper midbrain producing a "high mesencephalic cat." The "pontile cats" never stood or walked. The "low mesencephalic cats" never walked spontaneously but unsteady walking could be induced by "strong" stimulation. The "high mesencephalic cats" spontaneously assumed a crouching or sitting position and walked in response to such stimuli as a light slap, a whistle or a tweak of the tail. One such animal "frequently" walked spontaneously. Unfortunately we are not supplied with detailed information regarding the character of the walking and other muscular activities, nor do we know how the activity of these animals compared with that of a decorticate cat with the basal ganglia intact. That there was a considerable difference seems obvious.

In primates the situation is quite different from what it is in the carnivora and other lower animal forms. If the precentral motor cortex (areas 4 and 6) is removed from both cerebral hemispheres the animal becomes almost totally paralyzed. Such voluntary movement as an occasional animal may reacquire is possible only if the cortex is removed piecemeal over months of time and if the animal is given painstaking care in retraining and repeated manipulation of his extremities. Even under the most optimum circumstances the movement which is recovered is very limited and stereotyped (Bucy and Fulton, 1933; Woolsey and Bard, 1943; Travis and Woolsey, 1956). Does this mean that in primates the basal ganglia and other subcortical centers have lost their ability to produce useful voluntary movements? This seems unlikely, but it does appear that they have lost their ability to produce such movements in the absence of the precentral motor cortex. Area 4 of the precentral cortex gives rise to corticospinal fibers whereas area 6 does not (Verhaart and Kennard, 1940). If we remove area 4 from the precentral motor cortex of monkeys bilaterally, leaving area 6 on one or both sides, the animal is still able to walk, sit, climb and feed himself but the movements are limited and awkward and reside more about the proximal joints than in the digits (Bucy and Fulton, 1933). Similarly, if the medullary pyramids on the under surface of the medulla oblongata are sectioned in the monkey, the fine, delicate, precise movements of the digits are lost but crude awkward movements of the extremities, particularly those which are more stereotyped and which are related to standing, to progression, etc., are retained (Tower, 1940). Likewise, and somewhat surprisingly, destruction of the corticospinal fibers in the cerebral peduncle in man does not completely paralyze the contralateral extremities, nor is such an operation necessarily associated with the severely incapacitating hemiplegia of a destructive lesion in the motor cortex or in the internal capsule (Walker, 1949 and 1952; White; Swanson; Bucy, 1957). These patients are able to walk and to use their upper extremities for many useful purposes. Although final decisive proof is lacking it seems probable that these voluntary movements present in the absence of the corticospinal fibers are produced over the multisynaptic system of the precentral motor cortex and the basal ganglia and other subcortical centers functioning together.

*Reflex muscular activity.* Rigidity is one of the characteristics of disease of the basal ganglia, notably Parkinson's paralysis agitans. Clinicians frequently attempt to make a sharp distinction between the rigidity of diseases of the basal ganglia and the spasticity associated with decerebration and capsular hemiplegia. However, the differences appear to be rather superficial. As Fulton and his coworkers were the first to emphasize, both result from the loss of supraspinal inhibition which is not concerned with the corticospinal fibers. Furthermore, as Foerster (1921), Walshe (1924), and Pollock and Davis (1930) have shown, the rigidity of paralysis agitans, like the spasticity of decerebration, is abolished by interrupting afferent impulses from the involved muscle to the spinal cord. This demonstrates that both rigidity and spasticity result primarily from activity of the local, spinal reflex arc which is released to hyperactivity by removal of descending, inhibitory influences. Thus it appears likely that the basal ganglia as well as the precentral motor cortex, area 4s and the bulbar reticular formation, exert an inhibitory influence over the spinal reflexes which control the muscular activity responsible for posture and reflex standing. Recent clinical observations reported by Narabayashi (1956), Guiot (1957), and Cooper (1956) that lesions in the globus pallidus produced surgically in the treatment of various diseases result in the reduction of rigidity indicate the possibility that the basal ganglia exert an excitatory as well as an inhibitory influence upon the spinal reflex mechanism responsible for rigidity. However, the physiological explanation of these clinical observations are as yet unknown and anatomical controls are meager. This serves further to emphasize our ignorance in this field.

*Automatic associated movements.* One thing that characterizes parkinsonism perhaps even more than tremor or rigidity is the loss of automatic associated movements. Commonly this term is regarded as indicating only the swinging of the arms in walking—a type of movement which is abolished by various destructive lesions in the precentral motor cortex, in the cerebellum, as well as in the substantia nigra and globus pallidus in parkinsonism. However, in parkinsonism far more is lost than automatic swinging of the arms. There is a general poverty of movement. The loss of expressional movements of the face results in the familiar masklike face. There is also a generalized loss of movements throughout the body so that the victim is described as being "statuesque." It thus appears that the basal ganglia are responsible for a wide variety of automatic and associated movements.

*Abnormal involuntary movements.* Lesions of the basal ganglia are commonly associated with various abnormal involuntary movements, the nature of which vary depending upon the part of the basal ganglia which is involved. It is generally agreed that these movements develop because some inhibitory influence is removed allowing some part of the remaining intact neural mechanism concerned with the control of muscular activity to develop increased and abnormal activity. It seems likely that the corticospinal tract is probably the mechanism responsible for tremor and that some other motor neural mechanism stemming from the precentral motor cortex is responsible for the abnormal movements of choreoathetosis (Bucy, 1949, 1957). Possible inhibitory circuits involving different subcortical nuclei, including the basal ganglia which probably are concerned in the development of these abnormal movements, have been described and discussed (Figs. 66.5, 66.6 and 66.7) (Bucy, 1942). The connections and pathways outlined in these figures exist but whether their destruction is responsible for the appearance of these diseases is hypothetical.

It is known that destruction of the cerebello-dentato-rubro-thalamic system results in intention tremor (Walker and Botterell, 1937). This system ends in the ventrolateral nucleus of the thalamus which in turn sends its efferent fibers to the precentral motor cortex. This system may well exert a controlling influence over the precentral motor cortex which when removed releases the corticospinal tract to the abnormal activity which results in intention tremor (Fig. 66.5).

Destruction of the substantia nigra and globus pallidus is associated with the tremor at rest of parkinsonism. These nuclei are intimately related. The substantia nigra projects onto the globus pallidus directly and *via* the center-median of the thalamus (Fig. 66.4). The globus pallidus projects onto the anterior part of the ventrolateral nucleus of the thalamus which in turn sends its fibers to the precentral motor cortex. Again it is thought that this mechanism may exert control over the corticospinal fibers (Fig. 66.6).

*Choreoathetosis* is associated with destruction of the caudate nucleus and putamen. These project directly to the globus pallidus, which again sends impulses to the precentral motor cortex *via* the thalamus. It is thought that this mechanism probably exerts control over that part of the precentral motor cortex which sends its efferent impulses to the skeletal musculature over one or more synapses in the various subcortical

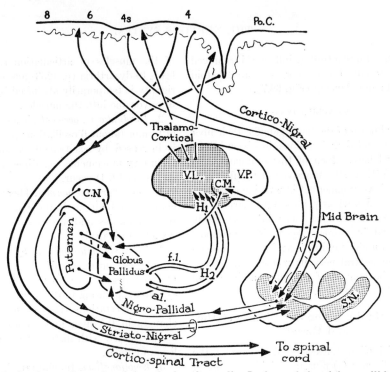

FIG. 66.6. A circular pathway involving the basal ganglia. Lesions of the globus pallidus and substantia nigra in man may be associated with parkinsonian tremor at rest. This diagram shows how impulse from these areas may reach and exert a controlling influence on the precentral motor cortex. The loss of such influence may permit tremor at rest to appear.

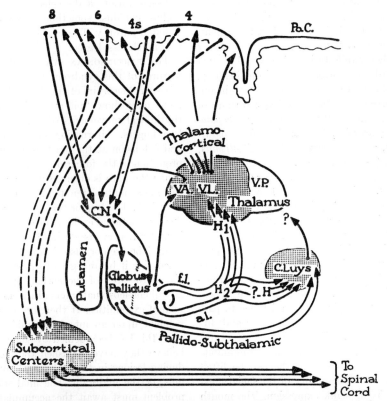

FIG. 66.7. Another circular pathway involving the basal ganglia. Lesions of the caudate nucleus and putamen in man may be associated with choreoathetosis. Such lesions might so distort or disorganize the impulses from the basal ganglia to the precentral motor cortex as to cause the abnormal movements of choreo-athetosis to appear.

nuclei. When this controlling influence is removed from the precentral motor cortex choreoathetoid movements may develop (Fig. 66.7).

### Conclusions

What is known of the basal ganglia, their fiber connections and their functions, has been briefly summarized here. Much of this is unconfirmed and not a little has been arrived at by inference. The result is very imperfect knowledge regarding this large and obviously important part of the brain. The basal ganglia merit intensive study in man and in animals by various methods. Until better understanding is achieved our knowledge of the central nervous mechanism responsible for the control of muscular activity will continue to be imperfect.

### Clinical Manifestations of Disease of the Basal Ganglia

The chief clinical features of disease of the basal ganglia are: (a) muscular rigidity resulting in disturbances of posture and movement, (b) involuntary movements, e.g., tremor, athetosis, chorea, (c) a loss of automatic and associated movements such as those of emotional expression, the swinging of the arms in walking, etc., and (d) absence of a paralysis of voluntary movement, although it may be distinctly impaired by one or all of the other manifestations. The basal ganglia are particularly susceptible to certain toxins (e.g., carbon disulfide), to anoxia, and to certain encephalitic processes. The following are some of the syndromes met with: (a) *Progressive hepatolenticular degeneration*, (b) *parkinsonism*—paralysis agitans, etc., (c) *chorea*, (d) *hemiballismus*, (e) *athetosis*, (f) *torsion spasm*.

*Progressive hepatolenticular degeneration (Wilson's disease)*. This was described by Wilson in 1912. It invariably terminates fatally but its duration varies from a few months to several years. The following are its chief features:

1. *Muscular rigidity* is widespread and progressive; it involves face, trunk and limbs. Flexors as well as extensors are affected, but the former more conspicuously than the latter. The hypertonus offers a "lead-pipe-like" resistance to passive movement and results in slowness and difficulty of movement. Eventually, contractures occur and the patient is rendered almost immobile as though carved from stone; he can be lifted or moved *en bloc*. The rigidity of the facial muscles gives a fixed, blank expression. The mouth is sometimes held widely open; the smile or laugh is peculiarly stiff and vacuous. The hypertonus

of the muscles of articulation and deglutition leads to dysarthria (p. 1253) and dysphagia. The rigidity is temporarily abolished by the injection of novocaine into the muscles.

2. *Involuntary movements*. These consist chiefly of tremor (about 6 oscillations per second) which is increased by excitement or any attempt at voluntary movement; sometimes athetoid movements (p. 1224) occur.

3. *The reflexes are normal*. There are no sensory changes and although the muscles often show some weakness and are easily fatigued there is no actual paralysis.

4. *Cirrhosis (multilobular) of the liver* is found at autopsy, but during life there may be no signs of liver disease. In some instances, however, symptoms pointing to the liver precede the nervous manifestations. There is evidence that the changes in the liver and possibly in the brain are associated with disturbances in the metabolism of copper.

5. *Emotionalism*. Involuntary laughing or crying, and some mental deterioration.

6. *Greenish brown pigmentation of the cornea (in Descemet's membrane) occurs in most cases*.

Degeneration of the cells of the putamen and globus pallidus, sometimes with cavitation, is found at autopsy. The caudate nucleus is affected to a much less degree.

THE PARKINSONIAN SYNDROME. The principal features of this syndrome are the following: (a) A *coarse tremor* involving head and limbs. The hand may show "pill-rolling" movements, i.e., rhythmical movements of thumb upon the first two fingers. Alternating movements of flexion and extension at the wrist, or of supination and pronation of the forearm, are frequently present. When the limb is engaged in some voluntary act the movements often temporarily disappear in that limb. The tremor becomes more pronounced during emotional excitement or when the patient is under a nervous strain. It disappears during sleep. The tremor also disappears on the paralyzed side if hemiplegia supervenes. Ablation of the motor area of the cortex, or section of the lateral corticospinal tracts also abolishes it in the related extremities. It therefore seems to be dependent upon an intact pyramidal tract. However, this has been denied by some surgeons who believe they have abolished the tremor by producing lesions in the globus pallidus, the thalamus, or the midbrain. The final solution of the problem must await the accumulation of more accurate anatomical and physiological information. (b) *Muscular rigidity* which leads to slowness and stiffness of movement. The rigidity is different both in its quality and distribution from that characteristic of the decerebrate animal (p. 1165) or of the hemiplegic patient. Flexors and extensor muscles are affected about equally, and the resistance of a limb to passive movements has been described as resembling cogwheels moving slowly upon one another, as though groups of muscles gave way in succession to the stretching force. This cogwheel phenomenon is undoubtedly merely a manifestation of the rhythmical innervation of the involved muscles which also gives rise to the tremor. The upper limbs are held in characteristic attitudes of adduction at the shoulders, flexion at the elbows, flexion or slight extension at the wrists, flexion at the metacarpophalangeal joints and slight flexion at the interphalangeal joints. (c) The *gait* is slow and shuffling with short steps, or it may be "festinating" in character, i.e., the patient is bent forward and hastens along with short quick steps as though trying to "catch up to his center of gravity" and prevent his falling. When pushed forward or backward he cannot stop quickly but moves by a series of small rapidly repeated steps in the direction in which he is pushed. *Propulsion* and *retropulsion* are the respective terms applied to these forward and backward movements. There is no true paralysis; the reflexes and sensation are unaffected. (d) One of the most constant manifestations of parkinsonism is the loss of certain automatic and associated movements. As a result the patient does not swing his arms as he walks, the typical facial expressions of various emotions are decreased or absent and the face is said to be masklike. Because the many little movements of the body which characterize normal human activity are absent the patient stands rigidly and without moving, "like a statue."

Parkinsonism appears to be the result of destructive lesions in the globus pallidus or the substantia nigra or both. These lesions may appear as the result of a primary idiopathic degeneration, of toxic processes, of anoxemia, of arteriosclerosis or of encephalitis.

All of the manifestations of parkinsonism are not necessarily present in all cases, or if present they are not of the same intensity. Some patients have the parkinsonian rigidity and lack of automatic and associated movements with little or no tremor. Some have tremor with relatively little rigidity. Some patients, particularly the postencephalitic group, have associated disturbances of ocular movements known as oculogyric crises,

and of vegetative functions such as sialorrhea and excessive oiliness of the skin. Others, particularly those in the arteriosclerotic group, may have exaggerated tendon reflexes, the sign of Babinski and impairment of psychological processes. These disturbances are, of course, due to involvement of other structures and pathways in the internal capsule, the cerebral cortex, the hypothalamus, the midbrain, etc.

*Chorea.* There are two principal forms of this condition.

1. SYDENHAM'S CHOREA (or St. Vitus's dance) is one of the manifestations of rheumatic fever. Its chief feature is involuntary jerky movements, semipurposeful in character, involving the muscles of the limbs and face. Facial grimacing, an inability to remain quiet, the frequent dropping of objects from the hands, and the inability to maintain sustained muscular contractions characterize the disease.

Sydenham's chorea may be bilateral or unilateral. Death is rare and there is consequently uncertainty concerning its neuropathology. In those few cases where examinations have been made the lesions have been multiple and diffuse, involving both cerebral cortex and subcortical structures.

2. HUNTINGTON'S CHOREA is a rare familial disease which results in severe disability and ultimately terminates fatally. It is transmitted as a dominant characteristic but the onset is usually late in the fourth decade of life. Pathologically one finds severe degeneration and atrophy of the caudate and lenticular nuclei. The small cells of the caudate nucleus and putamen are particularly affected. However, the large cells are not entirely spared and changes are seen in the globus pallidus and cerebral cortex. The disease is characterized by facial grimacing, jerky gesticulating movements of the upper extremities and a lurching, uncertain gait. Speech is dysarthric. The motor disturbances steadily increase until the patient is incapacitated. There is mental deterioration with irritability and occasional homicidal and suicidal tendencies.

3. HEMIBALLISMUS or HEMICHOREA usually results from vascular lesions in the subthalamic nucleus of Luys. It is, therefore, seen most often in older people with cerebral arteriosclerosis. It is characterized by wild flinging movements of the extremities on one side of the body. In some cases the condition subsides spontaneously (Hyland and Forman), in others the violent movements continue unremitting during the patient's every waking moment but subside during sleep

In such cases the patient may injure his extremities and may die of exhaustion. The movements can be abolished by dividing the corticospinal fibers which arise in the precentral gyrus. This can be accomplished at the cortical level, in the cerebral peduncle or in the spinal cord. Pedunculotomy is the simplest of these procedures and should be considered in any case in which the movements show no evidence of subsiding spontaneously and are violent enough to warrant surgical intervention. It has been reported that these movements have been abolished by section of the anterior white column of the spinal cord but this observation needs confirmation. Physiologically it is difficult to understand why section of the corticospinal tract and an anterior cordotomy should both be effective.

ATHETOSIS is a form of abnormal involuntary movements beginning most often in childhood. It is associated with damage to the basal ganglia, particularly the caudate nucleus and the putamen. This damage may result from asphyxia or injury at birth, or from injury or encephalitis subsequently. Pure athetosis consists of slow, writhing, twisting movements of the involved extremities and the face. In many cases there are also quicker, jerky involuntary movements and the condition is then termed *choreoathetosis*. As with most other abnormal involuntary movements these are present during all waking hours and are absent during sleep. They are aggravated by nervous tension and are diminished or abolished by the ingestion of alcohol. In many patients choreoathetoid movements are unilateral and are associated with a hemiparesis on the same side. In some cases with bilateral involvement, or *athetose double*, examination of the brain

will reveal congenital changes in the basal ganglia known as *status marmoratus*. Unilateral choreoathetosis can be abolished by removal of the contralateral precentral motor cortex (areas 4 and 6). They can also be diminished by section of the central portion of the contralateral cerebral peduncle which contains the corticospinal fibers from the precentral gyrus. A few cases have been reported in which the movements have been decreased after surgical lesions have been placed in the region of the internal segment of the globus pallidus or the ansa lenticularis. However, these observations lack anatomical confirmation. It appears likely that both corticospinal fibers and multisynaptic neuron chains from the precentral motor cortex which pass downward through subcortical centers to the spinal cord mediate the impulses which are responsible for the abnormal involuntary movements of choreoathetosis.

TORSION SPASM is very rare condition and need only be defined. It consists of abnormal involuntary turning, twisting movements of the neck, trunk, and extremities which distort the body into bizarre postures. Pathological changes in various parts of the basal ganglia have been described.

### The Thalamus

This large gray mass is related medially to the third ventricle which lies between the thalami of the two sides. The thalami are joined across the midline by an isthmus, the *massa intermedia*. The posterior limb of the internal capsule lies upon the outer side of the thalamus and separates it from the lentiform nucleus. Above the thalamus is the lateral ventricle, a part of whose floor it forms. In front is the head of the caudate nucleus; the arched *body* of the latter is related to the upper part of the lateral surface of the thalamus. Below the thalamus are the corpus of Luys (subthalamic nucleus) and the forepart of the red nucleus.

There are five main nuclear masses in the thalamus.

A vertical septum of fibers known as the *internal medullary lamina* divides the principal part of the thalamus into: A, a *medial* and B, a *lateral* mass, each of which contains two main nuclear groups. C, In the massa intermedia and the adjacent part of the medial mass are discrete groups of nerve cells known as the *nuclei of the midline*. D, Clusters of nerve cells are present in the internal medullary lamina itself—the *intralaminar nuclei*. E, *Pulvinar*.

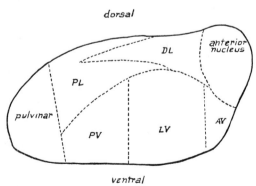

FIG. 66.8. Showing the anterior nucleus and the divisions of the lateral nuclear mass of the thalamus. DL, dorsal lateral nucleus; PL, posterior lateral nucleus; PV, posterior ventral nucleus; LV, lateral nucleus; AV, anterior ventral nucleus. (Courtesy of Dr. Murray Barr.)

A. *Nuclei of the medial mass.* (*1*) *Anterior nuclei.* These form a mass which bulges into the lateral ventricle. They receive fibers from the mammillary bodies (mamillothalamic tract of Vicq d'Azyr) which convey olfactory impulses. They send fibers to the paracentral lobule and the posterior part of the cingular gyrus on the medial aspect of hemisphere. (*2*) *Dorsomedial nuclei.* These consist of a dorsolateral group of small cells, and a medial collection of large cells. The former projects to prefrontal areas of the cerebral cortex. The large-celled portion is connected by both afferent and efferent fibers with the hypothalamus; it also projects to the corpus striatum, and has rich afferent connections with other thalamic nuclei. The dorsomedial nuclei are thought to serve as an association center where visceral and crude somatic sensations are synthesized. It is thought to be a conscious center for the cruder (protopathic) sensations, and where sensations are integrated into "feelings", both pleasant and unpleasant.

B. *Nuclei of the lateral mass.* (*1*) *Ventral group.* This consists of; (a) *Anterior ventral nucleus* which receives fibers from the globus pallidus and projects to different parts of the corpus striatum, but not to the cerebral cortex. This nucleus occupies the most anterior (rostral) extremity of the lateral mass. (b) *Lateral ventral nucleus.* The fibers entering the anterolateral part of this nucleus arises in the globus pallidus, whereas those ending in the posterior and medial part of this nucleus are derived mainly from the dentate nucleus of the contralateral half of the cerebellum (*via* the dentatothalamic and the dentatorubrothalamic tracts). Its efferent fibers pass to area 4, and in much smaller numbers to area 6 of the precentral motor cortex. Thus a pathway is established through which voluntary movements can be brought under the influence of the basal ganglia and the cerebellum. (c) The *posterior ventral nucleus* is the main subcortical center for sensory impulses ascending in the trigeminal, medial and spinal lemnisci (proprioceptive from muscles and joints, light touch, discrimination of two points, pain, heat and cold). It projects to the post central gyrus (somesthetic area), areas 1, 3, 2, 5 and 7. This nucleus also sends fibers to the hypothalamus and corpus striatum. The posterior ventral nucleus is composed of two subsidiary parts: (i) the *posteromedial nucleus*, which receives the trigeminal fibers, and (ii) the *posterolateral nucleus* which is the thalamic station for the medial and the spinal lemnisci.

(*2*) *Dorsal group.* This is also called the *lateral*

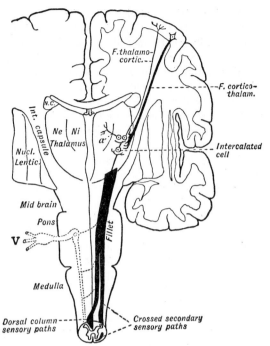

FIG. 66.9. Diagram showing the paths and centers concerned in sensation. All sensory impulses ascend to the lateral part of the thalamus, where regrouping occurs; the cruder sensations (e.g., those of pain and extremes of temperature) are relayed to the medial portion of the thalamus, the remainder (e.g., light touch, discrimination of two points, sense of position and movement, etc.) to the cerebral cortex. The cortico-thalamic fibers, which terminate in the lateral nucleus of the thalamus are also shown. (Modified from Head.)

*nucleus of the thalamus.* It is subdivided into an anterior and a posterior portion, designated, respectively, the *dorsolateral* and *posterolateral nuclei.*

C. *The nuclei of the midline* are, as mentioned above, situated in the massa intermedia, and in the adjacent part of the medial mass forming the upper part of the wall of the third ventricle. They are phylogenetically the oldest of the thalamic nuclei and are a center for the most primitive forms of sensation, e.g., from the viscera and other structures occupying the axial regions of the body. The midline nuclei are connected by many fine myelinated fibers with other subcortical centers, namely, the hypothalamus and midbrain nuclei. They also receive fibers from the corpus striatum. These nuclei have many intrathalamic connections but few if any fibers pass to the cerebral cortex, corpus of Luys (subthalamic nucleus) and the forepart of the red nucleus.

D. *The intralaminar nuclei* are scattered groups of cells within the internal medullary lamina. The connections of these nuclei are imperfectly known, but they are thought to receive both trigeminal fibers and fibers of the medial lemniscus; they project to the globus pallidus and have many connections with neighboring thalamic nuclei. A well defined nucleus in the middle of the thalamus, and usually classed with this group is known as the *central* or *centromedian nucleus*. It is especially well marked in primates, as is possibly an intrathalamic integrating center.

E. *The pulvinar* is the expanded continuation posteriorly of the lateral nuclear mass. It overhangs the superior colliculus. It projects to the cortex, its inferior part to an area comprising part of the temporal lobe, and the anterior part of the occipital lobe. The rest of the pulvinar projects mainly to the parietal and temporal lobes.

The *medial* and *lateral geniculate bodies* are usually included as part of the thalamus or referred to as the *metathalamus*; they are dealt with in chapters 75 and 76.

It will be seen from the foregoing account that the nuclei of the thalamus can be divided upon a functional basis into three categories, namely, (a) those which serve as relay stations of afferent impulses from the periphery to the cortex, (b) those which are connected mainly with other subcortical centers and (c) those whose chief function is associative.

## FUNCTIONS

We have seen that the corpus striatum is a part of an old or primitive motor system. The thalamus, on the other hand, is a primitive receptive center wherein sensory impulses give rise to a *crude uncritical form of consciousness*; a consciousness which is greatly elaborated upon, especially in man, by the cerebral cortex (see ch. 67). Sensory localization in the thalamus has been demonstrated by Dusser de Barenne and Sager by means of local strychninization. The injection of a minute quantity of the drug into the thalamus in cats is followed by hyperesthesia and hyperalgesia to cutaneous and deep (muscle, tendon and periosteum) stimuli. The cutaneous hypersensitivity is most pronounced on the contralateral side of the body; increased sensitivity to deep stimuli occurs only on the contralateral side. By this method, and other methods of investigation it has been shown that there is a definite somatotopic organization in the posterior ventral nucleus of the thalamus, which serves the conscious perception of sensory stimuli. The leg is represented most laterally, the face most medially, and the trunk and upper extremity in between.

The thalamus is not, however, entirely sensory in function. In animals possessed of little or no cortex, or in higher mammals (e.g., cat or dog) after decortication, it and the corpus striatum serve for the execution of complex movements of an automatic or reflex nature. Furthermore, the reticular nucleus and the ventromedial portion of the thalamus (including the intralaminar nuclei) form part of the reticular formation of the brain stem and take part in the arousal and alerting reactions produced by that mechanism, as well as other functions referred to on pages 1224 to 1226.

## THALAMIC LESIONS

The effects resulting from a lesion involving the lateral thalamic nuclei will resemble those following an interruption of ascending pathways in the brain stem above their decussation. That is, all types of sensation on the opposite side of the body tend to be lost or grossly affected, or there may be severe pain as a result of destruction of inhibitory mechanisms or possibly of the direct stimulation (irritation) of pain fibers. In addition to the loss or diminution of sensation, lesions of the thalamus are not infrequently associated with spontaneous pain and with marked hypersensitivity which has a very unpleasant quality. These manifestations are part of the thalamic syndrome described below and are not well understood.

THE THALAMIC SYNDROME OF DEJERINE AND ROUSSY. This is a characteristic picture occasionally seen in thalamic disease. The following are its chief features:

(1) Asterognosis and sensory ataxia, due to the impairment of cutaneous and kinesthetic senses. These and the other effects given below are mainly on the contralateral side of the body.

(2) Some loss of tactile and thermal sensations over the body and face. The threshold for these sensations, and for pain, is frequently raised. Sometimes the patient with a thalamic lesion is unable with closed eyes to localize the position of a limb, and must grope in the air in order to find it (*thalamic phantom limb*); or he may have the illusion that the limb is not there at all (*amelognosia*). He also is commonly unable to localize a point which has been stimulated even though he recognizes the stimulus.

(3) Spontaneous pain occurring in paroxysms and often excruciating. The pain may be so intense as to resist the action of powerful sedatives, e.g., morphine. A painful stimulus is felt much more acutely than is normal (hyperalgesia) and

although, as mentioned above, the threshold for pain is often raised, the sensation when once aroused (by increasing the strength of stimulus) is excessively severe. Other stimuli are often associated with an unpleasant sensation. Cold in particular may be most disagreeable but light touch may also be unpleasant. These spontaneous discomforts and unusual reactions to various stimuli are usually referred to as *thalamic over-reaction.*

(4) Lesions in the thalamus are frequently associated with various abnormal involuntary movements. Choreoathetosis and intention tremor are the more common. It is believed that choreoathetosis results from the involvement of the projection system from the basal ganglia to the anterior part of the ventrolateral nucleus of the thalamus and that intention tremor arises when the pathway from the dentate nucleus of the cerebellum and the red nucleus is damaged at its point of termination in the posterior part of the ventrolateral nucleus. This nucleus in turn projects to the precentral motor cortex and it is thought possible that these abnormal involuntary movements arise because regulating impulses from the thalamus to the motor cortex have been destroyed (Bucy, 1942). Furthermore, such lesions commonly give rise to an abnormal posture of the extended hand known as the *"thalamic hand."* This is characterized by a moderate flexion of the wrist and a hyperextension of the fingers. The same posture of the outstretched hand is also referred to by some as the "athetoid hand."

(5) Hemiparesis and defects in the visual fields which may be seen in some patients exhibiting the thalamic syndrome are not the result of thalamic involvement but are due to damage to the neighboring internal capsule.

The thalamic syndrome may also be associated with disturbances of sensation which are associated with certain emotional reactions. Thus one of Head's patients was so affected by music that he "could not stand the hymns on his affected side," another said that when the choir sang "a horrid feeling came on the affected side and the leg ... started to shake." In another patient pleasant feelings of a psychic nature were referred to the abnormal side. He said "I seem to crave for sympathy on my right side," and "My right hand seems to be more artistic."

### The Hypothalamus

The hypothalamus is the basal part of the diencephalon (interbrain). It forms the floor and lower parts of the walls of the 3rd ventricle (fig. 66.10).

Of the *nuclei of the hypothalamus* the greatest interest from the physiological point of view centers around the following.

The *supraoptic nucleus* lies anteriorly, lateral to the optic chiasma and above the commencement of the corresponding optic tract. The *preoptic nucleus* is situated most anteriorly above and in front of the supraoptic nucleus, and immediately behind the lamina terminalis. The *paraventricular nucleus* is found above the supraoptic nucleus and is in close relationship medially to the wall of the 3rd ventricle. It is richly vascular, and its large vacuolated cells contain numerous granules, possibly the mother substance of a secretory product. The *posterior hypothalamic group of nuclei* lie in the posterior part of the hypothalamus in relation to the wall of the 3rd ventricle, and include the mammillary nuclei. Cells of this group send fibers to the medulla oblongata and the lateral horns of the spinal cord, which constitute the spinal sympathetic center. The *tuber cinereum (nucleus tuber)* is a small eminence of gray matter situated at the base of the brain between the optic chiasma and the mammillary bodies, i.e., in the midregion of the hypothal-

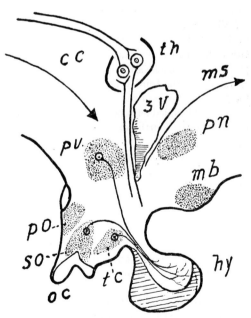

FIG. 66.10. Diagram of the nuclei and connections of the hypothalamus. *cc*, corticohypothalamic fiber; *pv*, paraventricular nucl.; *po*, preoptic nucl.; *so*, supraoptic nucl.; *oc*, optic chiasma; *tc*, tuber cinereum; *hy*, hypophysis; *mb*, mammallary body; *pn*, posterior nucl.; *ms*, fiber to midbrain and brain stem; *3V*, third ventricle; *th*, thalamus.

amus; from its vicinity grows the pituitary stalk. Two groups of cells can be clearly defined within it; they are known as the *dorsomedial* and *ventromedial hypothalamic nuclei*. The slight swelling caused by these nuclei and covered by the pars tuberalis of the adenohypophysis (ch. 56), is called the "median eminence." The tuber cinereum is a center of the parasympathetic nervous system.

*Fiber connections*. The hypothalamus receives fibers from the globus pallidus (pallidohypothalamic tract), from the amygdaloid nucleus and through the *medial forebrain bundle*, from the olfactory lobe and the parolfactory area. The medial forebrain bundle sweeps through the hypothalamus and in its course gives off fibers to several of the hypothalamic nuclei. The hypothalamus, especially the supraoptic and paraventricular nuclei, also receives fibers from prefrontal areas and the precentral motor area (6) of the cerebral cortex (ch. 67) both directly and indirectly through the thalamus. There are probably afferent fibers from the spinal cord, doubtless similar to the direct and collateral ascending afferents which go to the reticular formation. It also projects through the anterior and the dorsomedial nuclei of the thalamus to prefrontal areas. The most prominent tract from the hypothalamus to the thalamus is the mammillo-thalamic tract (of Vicq d'Azyr) from the medial mammillary nucleus to the anterior nuclei of the thalamus. Other efferent tracts (sympathetic and parasympathetic) pass backwards in close relation to the ependyma of the third ventricle, and descend in the gray substance of the midbrain (surrounding the cerebral aqueduct), pons, medulla (beneath the floor of the fourth ventricle) and spinal cord (sympathetic).

The various hypothalamic nuclei are in communication with one another through fiber tracts; the best known of these is the paraventricular-supraoptic tract, but others undoubtedly exist.

The supraoptic, and tuberal nuclei, and probably the paraventricular nuclei as well, are linked with the hypophysis by efferent fibers which descend the infundibular stalk (hypothalamo-hypophyseal tract). The majority of these fibers terminate around the pituicytes of the pars nervosa but some can be traced into the pars intermedia.

Thus, there exists a pathway, through the hypothalamus, from the cerebral cortex to the cells (pituicytes) of the neural lobe of the hypophysis.

## THE PHYSIOLOGY OF THE HYPOTHALAMIC NUCLEI

Modern experimental and clinical investigations have revealed the hypothalamus as a region of great physiological importance. Our knowledge of the functions of this part of the cerebrum is still, nevertheless, very incomplete. Much of the evidence is suggestive rather than conclusive and permits only tentative views to be held concerning many of its activities. It is the general opinion, however, that in this part of the diencephalon are contained the mechanisms for the control of certain primitive reactions (visceral and somatic) associated in animals with defense or attack, and in man with emotional states (fear, anger, etc.). This region is also believed to contain centers for the regulation of certain fundamental and vital processes, e.g., fat, carbohydrate and water metabolism, and to exert a governing influence upon the body temperature, the gastric movements, the genital functions and the sleep rhythm (ch. 68), hunger and thirst (ch. 43).

It is now generally conceded that important centers governing the activities of the autonomic nervous system are situated in the hypothalamus. Those cell groups in the anterior part of the hypothalamus and in the tuberal region were at one time believed to constitute a parasympathetic center, whereas the posterior part was thought to be concerned with sympathetic functions. It is now recognized that our knowledge concerning the localization of function in the hypothalamus is still defective.

The pituitary and the nervous structures of the hypothalamus are intimately associated in function; indeed, they should be considered together as constituting a closely integrated neuroglandular mechanism rather than as possessing distinct and independent functions. It will be recalled that the pars nervosa of the pituitary is developed as a downgrowth from the floor of the third ventricle, and that the pituicytes are modified neuroglial cells. On the other hand, the cells of the supraoptic and paraventricular nuclei of the hypothalamus show evidence of possible secretory activity.

A brief summary of the experimental evidence relating to hypothalamic functions will be given in the following paragraphs.

(1) Karplus and Kreidl were the first to furnish evidence of a sympathetic center in the hypothalamus. Upon electrical stimulation of this region they obtained pupillary dilation, sweating and a rise in blood pressure. Inhibition of intestinal movements also results. Liberation of adrenaline has also been reported to follow stimulation of the hypothalamus. By means of needle electrodes inserted into the region of the lateral nucleus Bronk and his colleagues have recorded im-

pulses from sympathetic efferent nerves during stimulation of the hypothalamus. On the other hand, rhythmical variations in potential were produced in the hypothalamus by the stimulation of certain afferent nerves through which reflex sympathetic responses may be elicited.

(2) Beattie, Brow and Long found that extrasystols produced in the cat by means of chloroform anesthesia, and which had been shown by Levy to be dependent upon sympathetic impulses (ch. 71), were abolished by a destructive lesion placed in the posterior hypothalamic nuclei or by a section of the brain behind this region. Stimulation of the posterior hypothalamic region, on the other hand, caused extrasystoles to appear in an animal which previously had been free from these cardiac irregularities. Animals subjected to such lesions also showed hyperglycemia and glycosuria. Drowsiness for two or three days following the operation was a noticeable feature in some animals; they also showed a change in behavior, being more docile and "tamer" after the operation (see "sham rage" below). The nervous system of animals examined histologically some time after the lesions in the posterior hypothalamic nuclei had been made showed degenerating fibers which entered the midbrain and descended through the brain stem and cord. Those in the latter situation entered the lateral column of gray matter at different levels down to the third or fourth lumbar segment.

(3) Decerebration by a section through the midbrain causes a profound fall in body temperature. No such loss of temperature control follows the removal of the cerebral cortex and thalamus, provided the hypothalamus is left intact. It is significant that sympathetic effects, e.g., adrenaline liberation, ruffling of feathers or hairs, constriction of vessels and goose flesh, result from exposure to cold. Moreover, Cushing has called attention to the high temperature which frequently follows operations upon tumors in the region of the third ventricle of the brain.

(4) Hess fixed electrodes in the hypothalamus of cats. After the animals had recovered from the operation, a weak electric current passed through the hypothalamus induced a state indistinguishable from normal sleep. More recently Akert, Koella and R. Hess, Jr. were all able to produce sleep in cats by stimulation of the intralaminar thalamic nuclei. Both of these observations are difficult to reconcile with the fact that stimulation of the reticular formation arouses the animal from sleep.

(5) Kabat and associates by means of an electrode fixed in the hypothalamus stimulated this region in the unanesthetized animal. Pupillary dilation, erection of hair, inhibition of gastrointestinal peristalsis, clawing and urination resulted. Stimulation of other parts of the brain produced none of these effects.

(6) Gastric lesions associated with hypothalamic damage have been reported, and ovulation following stimulation of the hypothalamus has been mentioned (p. 620). Evidence for hypothalamic control of gastric secretion has been cited on p. 975. There is also some evidence of a hypothalamic center for gastric motility.

### Quasi-emotional State—"Sham Rage"

It was first demonstrated by Goltz that the reactions which usually accompany displeasure and anger are more readily evoked in an animal deprived of its cerebral cortex (decorticated) than in the normal animal. In Goltz's classical experiment the hemispheres and a large part of the thalamus were removed from a dog. The disposition of the animal was greatly altered by the operation, it being very readily aroused to anger. Barking, growling, baring the teeth or snapping occurred upon the least provocation. Cannon and Britton produced a similar state in cats by removal of the cortex, the decortication being performed by means of a pointed stilet inserted through the orbital cavities. Immediately following recovery from the anesthetic the animals showed the following remarkable phemonena which these observers termed "sham rage"— lashing of the tail, erection of the hairs, protrusion of the claws, dilatation of the pupils, sweating, struggling and biting, greatly increased rate of respiration and a rise in blood pressure. Most of these manifestations will be recognized as being of sympathetic origin. In many instances the picture is a combination of fear and anger. Liberation of adrenaline, as indicated by an increase in the rate of the denervated heart (p. 1032), also occurred. The mildest stimulus such as jarring the table or lightly touching the animal was sufficient to evoke a paroxysm of rage.[1] In his decortication experiments Bard found that the posterior and ventral portion of the diencephalon was essentially responsible for the development of "sham rage." The typical quasi-emotional behavior occurred after decortication and section through the hypothalamus at about the middle of the tubercinereum. It also resulted from an operation which

---

[1] Pseudoaffective states—displeasure, anger or rage, can be evoked in animals after a section caudal to the hypothalamus, but much less readily than after decortication, and they do not constitute the fully integrated response of the animal with hypothalamus intact.

removed the basal ganglia and the dorsal half of the diencephalon, i.e., the thalamus, but left the hypothalamus connected with the midbrain. The condition failed to appear if the section separated the caudal part of the hypothalamus.

In view of the excessive display of emotional reactions which can so easily be induced in the cat (or dog) from which the forebrain has been removed, leaving the posterior part of the hypothalamus intact, it was only natural to conclude that the cerebral cortex exerted a regulatory influence over this hypothalamic mechanism. However, Bard and Mountcastle have shown in cats that the restraining influence of higher levels of the cerebrum upon hypothalamic activity is not exerted by the neocortex, but by certain parts of the rhinencephalon (cortex of the pyriform lobe, amygdaloid nucleus and hippocampal formation) and an area of cortex on the medial aspect of the hemisphere lying ventral to the cingular sulcus in front and below the rostrum of the corpus callosum. This latter area of cortex is believed to be a transitional zone between the rhinencephalon and the neocortex. An operation which removed the neocortex alone, leaving the rhinencephalon and the area of transitional cortex uninjured, was performed upon cats whose behavior and temperament had been studied for some time previously. The manifestations of animals prepared in this way were the reverse of those which had been subjected to complete decortication. They showed extraordinary placidity. Responses expressive of of pleasure were predominant and often exaggerated. Procedures, which in a normal animal provoke resentment, anger or even rage, such as, pinching the tail strongly with surgical forceps, tying the animal down on its back, strong electric shocks applied to the skin, etc., evoked no sign of anger or even of resentment. The animals responded to mild nociceptive stimulation by purring or with other expressions of pleasure. An animal which before operation resented handling or petting, became affectionate, purred when stroked and submitted to being tied to the animal board "as though it enjoyed the maneuver." Removal of those parts of the rhinencephalon mentioned above or of the transitional area of cortex, transformed animals deprived of their neocortex, i.e., abnormally placid animals, into ones which, upon the slightest provocation, exhibited all the signs of rage.

It is apparent from these experiments that some part of the rhinencephalon and the transitional area of cortex exerts a restraining influ-

ence upon those hypothalamic mechanisms governing the expressions displeasure, resentment and anger in carnivores (e.g., cats and dogs).

Repeatedly attention has been called to the danger in transferring information found to be true for one animal to another species of animal without carefully controlled investigations. Nowhere could this precaution be more appropriate than in connection with the amygdala. Although removal of this nucleus bilaterally renders the dog and cat savage and aggressive, it converts the normally intractable Norway wild rat into a gentle animal; bilateral temporal lobectomy, including removal of both amygdaloid nuclei, converts vicious and aggressive rhesus monkeys into relatively tame animals. There are obviously wide species differences and we cannot conclude that what is true for the hypothalamus or the amygdala or the neocortex of the cat is necessarily true for man unless the fact is established.

*Emotion.* This is an appropriate place to consider the mental state with its accompanying reactions which is generally referred to as emotion. The word emotion is derived from the Latin meaning a "moving out." But there is an inward as well as an outward component of the emotional state. It can be analyzed into subjective and objective elements—emotional feeling or experience, and certain visceral and somatic manifestations, e.g., pallor, blushing, cardiac acceleration, facial expression, etc.

According to the James-Lange theory, the emotional feeling is not aroused *primarily* in consciousness but is the result of the bodily reactions. Briefly, for example, we are frightened because the heart accelerates, the vessels constrict, the respiration quickens and the skeletal muscles increase their tone, or contract for purposes of defense, or in order that one may run away; the afferent impulses initiated by these various activities impinging upon consciousness arouse the feeling of fear. Sherrington showed, however, that the emotional state of a dog remained unaltered after a high spinal transection and section of the vagus nerves, afferent impulses from the viscera and skeletal muscles being thus largely removed.

The modern view, which was advanced by Cannon and by Dana, proposes that emotional feeling, and the associated bodily reactions are the result of interaction between the cerebral cortex and the diencephalon—hypothalamus and thalamus (anterior nucleus)—visceral and somatic responses being *secondary* to the feeling of rage, delight, grief, etc., rather than the cause, which is dependent upon the cortex, probably of the orbital and cingular gyri and the hippocampus, [2] but the emotional manifestations are initiated in subcortical levels. As we have seen, there is much experimental support for such a view. Also, clinically, outbursts of uncontrollable laughter or crying are sometimes associated with lesions of the diencephalon.

### DISORDERS OF THE HYPOTHALAMUS

The effects which may result from lesions (e.g., tumors, encephalitis, etc.) involving the hypothalamic region fall into the following groups: (a) disturbances in fat in carbohydrate or in water metabolism and (b) disorders of sleep, drowsiness, somnolence and, less commonly, abnormal wakefulness, or reversal of the sleep rhythm,[3] (c) emotional manifestations, laughing, crying, or a state resembling "sham rage" in animals, may result, (d) phenomena attributable to sympathetic or parasympathetic stimulation, (e) disorders of the sexual functions.

Any one of the foregoing groups of effects may dominate the clinical condition to give rise to one or other of the following syndromes: (a) diabetes insipidus, (b) dystrophia adiposogenitalis, (c) the Laurence-Biedl-Moon syndrome, and (d) narcolepsy.

These several conditions, with the exception of the last (d), have been considered in chapter 56.

*Narcolepsy (see also p. 1272).* This is the term applied to a disturbance in the sleep mechanism in which sudden attacks of an irresistible desire for sleep occur during the daytime. The duration of the attacks, which resemble normal sleep, is quite brief—from a few seconds to 20 minutes or so. It is only to such sudden and brief naps, and not to persistent drowsiness or to prolonged periods of pathological sleep that the term is applicable. Nocturnal sleep may be normal but it is often disturbed or there may be insomnia. Sleep may overcome the subject of narcolepsy while he is going about his usual occupation, while walking, in the middle of a conversation, during a meal, driving a car, etc. But commonly they occur at times when anyone would be inclined to sleep. There may be many attacks during the day. A few cases were discovered during the war in sol-

diers under trial by court-martial for falling asleep on sentry duty. The condition may be a sequel to influenza or to epidemic encephalitis involving the hypothalamus or may result from a tumor or injury in this region. In other instances the condition appears without known cause (idiopathic narcolepsy). Although evidence is not conclusive, it is very likely that in these latter, also, disordered hypothalamic function is responsible, for other features, e.g., obesity, polyuria or impairment of the sexual functions, pointing to an abnormality of this region are frequently present. *Ritalin*, ephedrine sulfate and amphetamine (benzedrine) have been used with benefit in idiopathic narcolepsy. *Cataplexy*[4] is the term given to a condition allied to, and very frequently associated with narcolepsy, in which the patient as a result of some emotion—amusement, anger, fear, embarrassment or surprise—is seized with complete muscular relaxation and weakness. The attack is brief, lasting for a few seconds, or for a minute or two at the most. Consciousness is not lost but the muscles are completely toneless and powerless for the time, and if the attack supervenes while the subject is standing his knees fail him and he sinks to the ground. The deep reflexes are lost. A somewhat similar situation may develop in a normal person who may become "weak with laughter," be "struck all of a heap," or "transfixed" when surprised or shocked. Or his jaw may "drop" when confronted with some unexpected occurrence. Cataplexy is regarded as an exaggeration of this normal tendency, just as narcolepsy is an intensification of the desire of many normal persons to drop into a doze under certain circumstances. Mirth is especially likely to precipitate a cataplectic attack. One victim reported by Adie remarked, "At the scout's camp the boys used to amuse themselves by making me laugh and then running away leaving me helpless on the ground." Though narcolepsy occurs without cataplexy the converse is extremely rare. This association of the two conditions at once suggests a common pathogenesis, but the muscular atonicity characterizing the cataplectic attack cannot be explained upon any physiological basis. An interesting speculation has been made by Wilson, who compares the attacks to the defense reaction of certain animals whereby they fall into immobility when frightened, and suggests for them a certain biological significance, namely, that they are the relic of a primitive reaction uncovered by disease.

---

[2] von Bonin speaks of a reverberating circuit—hypothalamus (mammillary body) to anterior thalamic nuclei *via* mammillo-thalamic tract; thence to anterior part of cingular gyrus; thence to cornu Ammonis, and finally back to the mammillary body through the fornix and fimbria.

[3] See Fulton and Bremer.

[4] This should not be confused with catalepsy, an entirely different condition.

## REFERENCES

BAILEY, P. The precentral motor cortex, Ed. 2, p. 227. Edited by P. C. Bucy, Univ. of Ill. Press, Urbana, Ill., 1949.

BARD, P. Am. J. Physiol., 1928, **84**, 490.

BARD, P., Psychol. Rev., 1934, **41**, 309.

BARD, P. AND MOUNTCASTLE, V. B. A. Res. Nerv. & Ment. Dis., 1948, **27**, 362.

BEATTIE, J. Canad. M. A. J., 1932, **26**, 278.

BEATTIE, J., BROW, G. R. AND LONG, C. N. H. Proc. Roy. Soc., London, Ser. B, 1930, **106**, 253.

BRONK, D. W. AND ASSOCIATES. Am. J. Physiol., 1936, **116**, 15.

BUCY, P. C., AND FULTON, J. F. Brain, 1933, **56**, 318.

BUCY, P. C. J. Neuropath. & Exper. Neurol., 1942. **1**, 224.

COOPER, I. S. Clinical results and follow-up studies in a personal series of 300 operations for parkinsonism. St. Barnabas Symposium on Surgical Therapy of Extrapyramidal Disorders, p. 3, 1956.

DUSSER DE BARENNE, J. G. AND SAGER, O. Arch. Neurol. & Phsyciat., 1937 **38**, 913.

FOERSTER, O. Ztschr. ges. Neurol. u. Psychiat., 1921, **73**, 1–169.

GLEES, P. Brain, 1945, **68**, 331.

GUIOT, G. Semaine d. hôp. Paris, 1957, **33**, 3711.

HARMON, P. J. AND CARPENTER, M. B. J. Comp. Neurol., 1950, **93**, 125.

HESS, W. R. Lancet, 1932, **2**, 1199; 1259.

KABAT, H., ANSON, B. J. AND MAGOUN, H. W. Am. J. Physiol., 1935, **113**, 74.

KARPLUS, J. P. AND KREIDL, A. Pflüger's Arch. ges. Physiol., 1911, **143**, 109; 1927, **215**, 667.

METTLER, F. A. J. Neuropath. & Exper. Neurol., 1955, **14**, 115.

NARABAYASHI, H. Arch. Neurol. & Psychiat., 1956, **75**, 36.

POLLOCK, L. J. AND DAVIS, L. Arch. Neurol. & Psychiat., 1930, **23**, 303.

RANSON, S. W. AND RANSON, M. Arch. Neurol. & Psychiat., 1939, **42**, 1059.

RANSON, S. W., RANSON, S. W., JR. AND RANSON, M. Arch. Neurol. & Psychiat., 1941, **46**, 230.

RICHTER, R. J. Neuropath. & Exper. Neurol., 1945, **4**, 324.

RIOCH, D. M. Psychiatry, 1940, **3**, 119.

STERN, K. Brain, 1936, **61**, 284.

SWANSON, H. S. Personal communication.

TOWER, S. S. Brain, 1940, **63**, 36–90.

TRAVIS, A. M. AND WOOLSEY, C. N. Am. J. Phys. Med., 1956, **35**, 273–310.

VERHAART, W. J. C. AND KENNARD, M. A. J. Anat., 1940, **74**, 239.

WALKER, A. E. AND BOTTERELL, E. H. Brain, 1937, **60**, 329–353.

WALKER, A. E. Acta psychiat. et neurol., 1949, **24**, 723.

WALKER, A. E. J. Nerv. & Ment. Dis., 1952, **116**, 766.

WALSHE, F. M. R. Brain, 1924, **47**, 159.

WHITE, J. C. Personal communication.

WOOLSEY, C. N. AND BARD, P. Fed. Proc., 1943, **2**, 55.

### Monographs and Reviews

ARIENS KAPPERS, C. U. The evolution of the nervous system in invertebrates, vertebrates and man. Erven F. Bohn, Haarlem, The Netherlands, 1929.

BARD, P. A. Res. Nerv. & Ment. Dis., 1930, **9**, 67.

BARD, P. AND MACHT, M. B. Neurological basis of behaviour, p. 55. Edited by G. E. W. Wolstenholme and C. M. O'Connor. Little, Brown and Co., Boston, 1958.

BRODAL, A. Neurological anatomy in relation to clinical medicine. Oxford Univ. Press, London, 1948.

BUCY, P. C., (Ed.) The precentral motor cortex Univ. Illinois Press, 1959.

CUSHING, H. W. Papers relating to the pituitary body, hypothalamus and parasympathetic nervous system. Charles C Thomas, Springfield, Ill., 1932.

DANIELS, L. E. Medicine, 1934, **13**, 1.

HEAD, H. Studies in neurology, Vol. II. Frowde, London, 1920.

MAGOUN, H. W. AND RHINES, R. Spasticity: the stretch reflex and extrapyramidal systems. Chas. C Thomas, Springfield, Ill., 1947.

RADEMAKER, G. G. Die Bedeutung der roten Kerne und des übrigen Mittelhirns für Muskeltonus, Körperstellung und Labyrinthreflexe. J. Springer, Berlin, 1926.

WALKER, A. E. The primate thalamus. Chicago Univ. Press, Chicago, 1938.

WILSON, S. A. K. Brain, 1928, **51**, 63.

WILSON, S. A. K. Modern problems in neurology. Arnold, London, 1928.

# 67

# THE CEREBRAL CORTEX. THE PHYSIOLOGY OF SPEECH AND SOME OF ITS DISORDERS. APRAXIA AND AGNOSIA. EPILEPSY. HEADACHE

## Minute Structure of the Cortex

The human cerebral cortex (or *pallium*) has a total area of about 220,000 sq. mm.; not more than a third of this lies upon the free surface or crown of the convolutions. The remaining two-thirds of the gray mantle of the cerebrum occupy the walls of the sulci. The total number of nerve cells in the human cerebral cortex has been estimated at around $10^{10}$. The number of fibers received from and projected to lower levels of the nervous system is in the neighborhood of 200 million. Added to these are fibers, many times more, which connect cells within the cortex (association fibers). On the basis of cellular structure the major part of the cortical gray matter is divisible into *six layers* or *laminae*. But these layers do not show identical histological appearances throughout the extent of the cortex. Characteristic differences in the depth of the individual layers and in their cellular components are found in the various regions. The six layers from the surface inwards with a general description of their cellular features as given by Economo[1] follows (see fig. 67.1).

I. MOLECULAR (OR PLEXIFORM LAYER). In this, the most superficial layer, the terminal filaments of numerous dendrites from cells of deeper layers, as well as from the axons of Martinotti cells form a dense felted network. Its cells are sparse; they are small (4 to $6\mu$) and pear-shaped or fusiform.

II. EXTERNAL GRANULAR LAYER consists of large numbers of small round, polygonal or triangular cells closely packed together. Their afferent processes pass into the overlying layer; their axons end mainly in deeper layers, but some enter the white substance of the hemispheres.

III. PYRAMIDAL CELL LAYER. Medium-sized pyramidal cells are contained in the outer part of this layer; pyramidal cells of larger size and more sparsely distributed are present in the deeper part. It is customary, therefore, to subdivide this layer into an outer and an inner portion; Campbell refers to them as separate layers.

IV. INTERNAL GRANULAR LAYER resembles the external granular layer in being composed of closely packed masses of small stellate cells, but unlike the outer granular layer it is rich in nerve fibers. This layer contains many horizontal fibers which show as a white stripe, or band known as the outer stripe or line of Baillarger, which is especially well marked in the calcarine cortex, but in this situation it is more usually referred to as the line of Vicq d'Azyr or of Gennari.

V. GANGLIONIC LAYER (or internal pyramidal layer) consists of pyramidal cells of graded sizes. This layer is particularly well-developed in the precentral (motor) cortex where giant pyramidal cells (Betz) are conspicuous. It contains, also, cells of Martinotti; these cells are peculiar in that their axons pass *outwards* toward the surface of the cortex and arborize in their own layer, or in overlying layers. Some of these cells can be found in nearly all layers of the cortex. Its deeper strata contain a dense network of fibers which forms the inner line of Baillarger.

VI. FUSIFORM CELL LAYER, in contact with the white matter, is composed of closely packed small spindle-shaped cells with their long diameters perpendicular. Cells of Martinotti and small stellate cells are present also in this layer but fewer in number.

It should be emphasized that the foregoing is no more than a general description of the histological structure of the cortex and that marked regional differences exist. Even the lamination itself is not a feature common to the entire cortex. In man one-twelfth of the cortical area shows little or no lamination; this portion, which is called the *allocortex* or *archipallium* comprises the

---

[1] For a detailed description, this author, or the earlier works of Campbell and of Bolton, should be consulted.

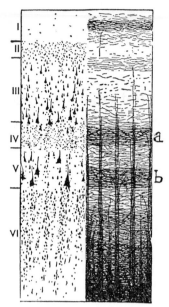

FIG. 67.1. Showing layers of area 4 of human cerebral cortex (agranular); *left*, cell-bodies, Nissl stain; *right*, nerve fibers, Weigert stain; a, outer band of Baillarger; b, inner band of Baillarger. Note the large cells of Betz in the fifth layer. (After Brodmann.)

cortex of the olfactory lobe (i.e., the pyriform area and the hippocampal, supracallosal and olfactory gyri, etc.). The laminated cortex, which in man constitutes the remaining eleven-twelfths, but which in lower mammals is a much smaller fraction of the whole, is called the *isocortex* or *neopallium.*

The greater part of the human laminated cortex shows the cytoarchitectural features described above, and is therefore sometimes referred to as the *homotypical* cortex. In other more restricted areas, the cortex departs from the typical cytological appearance, chiefly in the preponderances of the small granular cells or of the pyramidal elements, and is called *heterotypical.* In areas in which the internal granular layer is absent or practically so and in which pyramidal cells predominate, the cortex is called *agranular*, and when the small granulelike cells form a prominent internal granular layer with few pyramidal cells, it is called the *granular* cortex. The agranular cortex is thicker than the granular which is particularly thin at the frontal and occipital poles of the hemispheres.

The cortex of the precentral region (areas 4 and 6) is of the agranular type. The granular layers (II and IV) are shallow, being encroached upon by the expansion of the pyramidal layers III and

V. In the deep part of layer V of area 4 (the area gigantopyramidalis) are situated the characteristic giant cells of Betz (60 to 80 microns in their greatest diameters) (see below). These cells contribute fibers to the corticospinal tracts (ch. 65). In area 6 in front of area 4 the granular layers are also inconspicuous but the large cells of Betz are absent.

In the cortex of the walls of, and surrounding the calcarine fissure—the *area striata* or *visual area*—the outer and inner granular layers (II and IV) are expanded at the expense of the pyramidal layers (III and V). This very finely *granular* type of cortex, also called from its "dusty" appearance under the microscope the *koniocortex*, is characteristic of sensory areas. It is present, though to a less fully specialized degree than in the visual cortex, in the postcentral gyrus (somesthetic area) and in Heschl's gyrus (auditory cortex, p. 1445).

Upon gross examination of a section of the brain two lighter bands can be seen in the cortex against the darker gray matter. These are produced by nerve fibers running parallel to the surface of the convolutions. They are known respectively as the outer (already mentioned) and inner bands of Baillarger. In the visual area the outer band is broad and prominent and is usually referred to in this part of the cortex as the band of Vicq d'Azyr or of Gennari, who had described it previously. The inner band is less dense than the outer, particularly in this area.

### Localization of Function in the Cerebral Cortex

Campbell mapped the cortex into 20 areas which could be differentiated on the basis of their cytoarchitectural characters. This number was raised to 47 by Brodmann, and subsequent workers (Vogts) have subdivided these again to make a total of 200.[2] Bailey and von Bonin (1951) in a careful reappraisal of the matter of the subdivision of the cerebral cortex on the basis of cytoarchitectonic studies concluded that most of the divisions of the cortex which had been devised previously were unsupportable. They were able to divide the cerebral cortex into the allocortex of the hippocampal region and the pyriform lobe, the agranular cortex of the precentral region and the anterior limbic area, the koniocortex of the primary sensory areas (the somesthetic areas of

[2] The microscopical study of the cortex and mapping it into areas according to the cytological characteristics is called *cytoarchitectonics.*

the postcentral gyrus, the visual cortex of the calcarine area, and the auditory cortex of Heschl's convolution on the superior surface of the first temporal gyrus), and the eulaminate cortex of most of the remainder of the mantle of the cerebral hemisphere.

Differences, most of them minor, within this broad outline were demonstrable. Thus in the precentral agranular cortex there are two areas—the area gigantopyramidalis (area 4) which lies just in front of the central fissure and contains the large cells of Betz, and the other which Brodmann designated area 6 and which lies immediately in front of area 4 and is devoid of gigantic pyramidal cells. The agranular cortex of the anterior limbic area partakes of some of the characteristics of the allocortex. The koniocortex of the visual area is more complex than that of the somesthetic and auditory areas and there are minor variations in different parts of the eulaminate cortex which need not concern us here. In the following discussion we shall refer to the numerically designated areas described by Brodmann as they are well established in neurological literature and teaching, but his finer subdivisions will not be dwelt upon.

### The Frontal Lobe

*The Precentral Cortex, Areas 4, 4s, 6, 8 and 44*

*Area 4* is a tapering strip of agranular cortex lying with its wider end at the upper border of the hemisphere, in front of the central fissure (Rolandic), and occupying the posterior part of the precentral convolution. A good part of this area is buried, for it covers the anterior wall of the central fissure. It also turns over the upper border of the hemisphere and extends down the mesial aspect as far as the cingulate sulcus. Area 4 is a center for voluntary movement. It gives origin to an important part of the corticospinal tracts, and also projects to the pons (frontopontine tract), corpus striatum, red nucleus, and the subthalamus. Areas 4 and 6 are also connected by intracortical fibers. The muscles of the various parts of the body are represented in this area on the mesial and the lateral surfaces, in an order which is, in general, the inverse of that in the body itself, namely, toes, ankle, knee, hip, trunk, shoulder, arm, elbow, wrist, hand, fingers, brow, eyes, face, larynx, jaw and tongue (fig. 67.2). The parts of the face are not inverted. By suitable electrical stimulation of different parts of this area, movements of muscles on the opposite side of the body can be evoked.

The careful studies of Woolsey (on the monkey) have demonstrated that the distal parts of the extremities, i.e., the hands and feet, are represented near the central fissure while the more proximal joints, i.e., shoulders and hips, and the trunk, are represented somewhat more anteriorly. With suitably controlled stimuli discrete movements limited to a small part of the extremity or even to a single muscle may be elicited. Although most of the control of the precentral cortex over the muscular activities of the body are exerted contralaterally, there is also some control over muscles on the same side of the body. This ipsi-

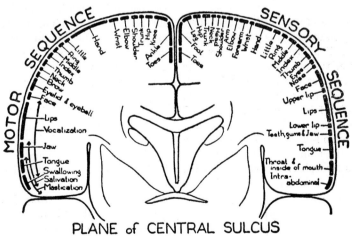

PLANE of CENTRAL SULCUS

Fig. 67.2. Coronal section through the hemispheres to show the motor and sensory representations in the cerebral cortex. (From Rasmussen and Penfield.)

lateral innervation is greater in the proximal joints of the extremities than in the distal parts and is greater in the lower than in the upper extremity. Furthermore, this ipsilateral innervation by the precentral motor cortex is greater in monkeys than in man. Electrical stimulation of the cerebral cortex, although a valuable tool for the study of cortical activity, is a poor substitute for normal physiological activity. The range and extent of movement produced by such stimulation represents but a small fraction of the motor activity which the intact cerebral cortex is able to produce under normal circumstances. Furthermore, the movements which are induced by electrical stimulation are crude and limited compared with the well coordinated, smoothly executed movements of the normal animal. One must never fall into the error of concluding that the results of electrical stimulation are a measure of the extent or nature of the normal activity of the areas stimulated.

Penfield and Welch, and Woolsey and his associates have demonstrated a *supplementary motor area* lying on the medial surface of the hemisphere in both man and monkey. This area lies anteriorly and ventrally to the primary motor area described above. In it the entire body is again represented. The head and upper extremity are represented farther forward and closer to the edge of the hemisphere while the lower extremity is represented more posteriorly and nearer to the corpus callosum. The threshold of this supplementary motor area is somewhat higher than that of the primary motor area which lies immediately anterior to the central fissure. The function of this supplementary area has not yet been well defined.

A large percentage of the corticospinal fibers arise from the precentral gyrus (area 4 in the monkey), whereas it is questionable if any corticospinal fibers arise from area 6. However, as both of these areas give rise to fibers which descend to subcortical centers (e.g., basal ganglia, thalamus, reticular formation, pontine nuclei, etc.) destructive lesions of neither area 4 nor area 6 is comparable to an isolated lesion of either the corticospinal or the multisynaptic motor pathways which pass through the subcortical nuclei. Thus any idea that a lesion of area 4 which gives rise to both types of motor fibers is comparable to a section of the corticospinal fibers in the cerebral peduncle or the medullary pyramid is false, as is the thought that a lesion of area 6, which gives rise to much fewer fibers to the subcortical nuclei

than does area 4, will give rise to a clinical picture typical of destruction of the motor pathways through the basal ganglia, etc.

Destructive lesions of the various parts of the precentral motor cortex do have certain important characteristics. First, it is obvious that the precentral motor cortex is essential to normal activity of the skeletal musculature in primates. If one removes the excitable motor cortex (the sigmoid gyrus) from both cerebral hemispheres of a dog or cat, or even if all of the cerebral cortex is removed, there is some interference with motor activity, especially with certain stereotyped reactions, such as the placing and hopping reactions, but the animal is not paralyzed. He can still sit, stand, walk, or run in a very creditable manner. If the precentral motor cortex is removed from both hemispheres of a monkey he is permanently and severely incapacitated and only a few stereotyped movements are possible. It is true that if the precentral motor cortex is removed piecemeal over months of time and if the animal is given intensive care with massage, manipulation and re-education he can in a few instances become able to stand in a very uncertain fashion and take a few halting awkward steps. These observations indicate clearly that in dogs and cats some subcortical mechanism (the basal ganglia?) is capable of producing useful, well coordinated movements, but that in the monkey the motor cortex has assumed much greater importance and the subcortical mechanism is almost totally unable to function in the absence of the cortex. Naturally the precentral motor cortex has rarely been removed bilaterally in man, and in one case observed by Walker the patient's condition and short postoperative survival did not permit of any study of value. The evidence available indicates that the precentral motor cortex in man is of even greater importance and that functions are even more localized and even more contralaterally represented than in the monkey.

In the cat and dog the unilateral removal of the motor cortex (sigmoid gyrus) or even the removal of all of the cortex from one cerebral hemisphere causes little motor disturbance. Even in the monkey the motor deficiency resulting from such an operation is not profound. The animal still uses all four extremities. He sits, stands, runs and hops about in his cage from one wall to another and back and forth on his trapeze. The extremities contralateral to the hemidecortication are more awkward than the normal ones. In jumping the animal misses the bars of his cage occasionally with the involved digits, and often rests on the backs of the fingers or toes rather than on the palmar and volar surfaces as the normal animal does. So long as his normal extremities are available he seldom uses the involved ones to pick up food, but he can do so in case of necessity. In other words, although the contralateral extremities are not normal, they are far from being paralyzed. Naturally one asks what is the source of the innervation of these extremities. There can be little doubt that it is from the intact ipsilateral cerebral hemisphere, for if it is removed, the animal not only becomes pralyzed in the extremities contralateral to it but in those affected by the original decortication as well. In other words, removal of the cortex from the remaining hemisphere results in a severe paralysis of all four extremities. There are other evidences that the precentral motor cortex is capable of ipsilateral innervation. Homes and May, and later Bucy and Fulton presented definite evidence that ipsilateral movements, particularly in the lower extremity and particularly in the more proximal joints could be produced by electrical stimulation of the precentral motor cortex.

In man the situation is similar but not identical. If the precentral motor cortex is removed from one hemisphere the contralateral extremities are severely incapacitated but not completely paralyzed. Movements at the distal joints—the wrist, hand and fingers, the ankle, foot and toes—are entirely or nearly completely abolished. In some cases a slow and rather weak simultaneous flexion of all the digits of the hand can be produced voluntarily. Movements at the shoulder and elbow and at the hip and knee are much fuller and stronger. In the upper extremity the flexor movements tend to be better, whereas in the lower extremity extension at both the hip and knee is more extensive and stronger than flexion. Such movements in the upper extremity are less than in the lower, but this does not account for all of the differences from the standpoint of usefulness. The upper extremity is primarily a prehensile one, designed to bring things to the individual or to pull him to them. Thus a condition in which the fingers, hand and wrist are paralyzed and only movements at the elbow and shoulder are possible does not result in a useful extremity. On the other hand, the lower extremity is used for standing and walking. It is primarily a supporting pillar. The fact that the toes and foot can not be moved is of relatively little importance while the ability

to move the extremity at the knee and hip, especially at the latter, enables the patient with his his precentral motor cortex destroyed or its pathways severed to walk in a very useful fashion, even though he limps and has to circumduct the involved foot with each step. Evidence is not available to prove the source of the innervation which accounts for the remaining muscular activity in the involved extremities in man, but reasoning by analogy from the monkey it would seem most likely that it is from the ipsilateral cerebral hemisphere. The few bits of evidence available to us support this view. For instance, in a few human cases in which the upper part of the precentral motor cortex has been destroyed bilaterally by a tumor or by injury, both legs have been paralyzed. If the movement in the lower extremities seen in hemiplegics were produced by the subcortical centers, then such a paraplegia would not be expected as the result of purely cortical lesions. Furthermore, Bates has been able to produce ipsilateral movements by electrical stimulation of the medial surface of the cerebral hemisphere in man.

As noted above there are differences in function between the various parts of the precentral motor cortex. Lesions of area 4 produce more severe motor deficiencies than do lesions of area 6. While lesions of both together produce the most severe deficiency. However, either area 4 or area 6 alone in one hemisphere of the monkey, all other parts of the precentral motor cortices having been removed, is able to produce useful movements in all four extremities. This is evidence of the presence of ipsilateral as well as contralateral motor innervation from both area 4 and area 6, and is also evidence that useful movements can be produced over the multisynaptic neuronal pathways from the precentral motor cortex through the various subcortical centers (the so-called extrapyramidal pathways) as well as over the corticospinal tract direct from the precentral gyrus to the spinal cord. Other evidence in confirmation of this fact is the demonstration that useful voluntary movement is still possible in the monkey after the medullary pyramids have been divided (Tower, 1940) and in man after the central portion of the cerebral peduncle has been cut (Bucy, 1957). There is one interesting and as yet enigmatic fact concerned with these two observations, the one on the monkey and the other in man. When the medullary pyramid is divided in the monkey, the greatest defect in movement is seen in the distal parts of the extremities, that is, in the fingers, hand, toes and foot. This is similar to the deficiency which develops when the precentral motor cortex is destroyed. Surprisingly when the cerebral peduncle is cut in man movement of the digits and the distal part of the extremity remain good and in a recent case were the first movements to recover and the strongest.

Alteration in only one reflex can be attributed to destruction of the corticospinal tract from the precentral gyrus. If the "foot" area in the uppermost part of area 4 on the medial surface of the hemisphere is destroyed or if the corticospinal fibers to the muscles of the great toe are divided it will become possible to elicit the sign of Babinski. Destruction of other parts of the precentral region or section of other corticospinal fibers, of course, does not have such an effect. Furthermore, this reflex can only appear if the peripheral mechanism is intact. Thus the necessary anterior horn cells, anterior spinal roots, peripheral nerves, and muscles must be present and functioning and the great toe and its joints must be in condition to respond properly if the reflex is to appear.

Destruction of area 4 results in a weakness of the contralateral extremities which is relatively flaccid as compared with that resulting from a lesion of both areas 4 and 6. This led Fulton and his associates to conclude correctly that destruction of the corticospinal tract which arises from the precentral gyrus is not the cause of the spasticity so commonly seen in animals or men with capsular hemiplegias. Hines demonstrated that spasticity tended to appear most prominently when a narrow strip lying just in front of area 4 was removed. This area which has been called "the strip" of Marion Hines or area 4s appears to be the part of the precentral motor cortex particularly concerned with the control of the postural and the stretch reflexes. Its destruction causes these reflexes to become exaggerated and spasticity with hyperactive tendon reflexes to appear. McCulloch, Graf and Magoun showed that area 4s projects to the bulbar reticular formation and exerts its controlling influence on these reflexes through that important mechanism. In addition Dusser de Barenne and his coworkers have demonstrated that area 4s is capable of inhibiting other forms of peripheral motor activity in addition to these reflexes. They have also shown that under certain special circumstances the area 4s (and certain other "strip" areas, areas 8, 2, 19 and 24) is capable by means of connections which pass through the caudate nucleus to suppress the electrical activity of the remainder of the cerebral cortex. Various other investigators have questioned the accuracy of these observations, but peculiarly no one of them has ever repeated the experiments of Dusser de Barenne and his coworkers. It is recognized that this suppressor function can be demonstrated only under certain special conditions as to anesthesia, stimulation of the suppressor strips, and that we do not know what, if any, function these suppressor strips and their effect upon other cortical areas play in the normal physiological activity of the animal.

Lesions of area 6, in contrast with those of area 4, give rise to an awkwardness in the performance of skilled acts with little loss of strength, spasticity and increase in the tendon reflexes (possibly due to involvement of area 4s which lies so close), forced grasping and groping and in some cases disturbances in autonomic functions. These effects are all contralateral to the lesion. Woolsey would view these facts somewhat differently. It is his opinion that lesions in area 4 near the central fissure would affect the distal parts of the extremities (hand and fingers, foot and toes), whereas those lesions farther forward in area 6 would produce changes in movements of the trunk and proximal joints.

Irritative lesions involving area 4 give rise to localized clonic convulsive seizures. The convulsive movement usually begins focally in some part of the body depending upon which part of area 4 is irritated. There may be a localized twitching of the face, or of one or more fingers, or of the foot or of the leg. This convulsive movement may remain localized or it may spread to neighboring parts of the body or even become generalized. This "march" of the convulsive involvement is typical of what is known as a Jacksonian epileptic seizure and is dependent upon a spread of the irritation in the motor cortex. A convulsive seizure produced by irritation of area 6 is characterized by what Foerster termed an adversive seizure. These begin with a turning of the head and eyes and often of the body toward the side opposite the involved cerebral cortex. Bucy and Pribram described a case in which a tumor in the "face" area of the precentral motor cortex was associated with localized convulsions of the contralateral side of the face and with localized sweating of that side of the face and to a lesser extent of the upper extremity. Such paroxysmal outbursts of autonomic activity are far from common but indicate the relationship of this part of the cerebral cortex to vegetative functions.

There is other definite evidence that the precentral motor cortex also exerts some control over various visceral and vascular activities, such as heart rate, vasomotor activities, gastrointestinal motility, perspiration. There is also evidence, at least in the cat, that these activities are also controlled in some measure by the cortex on the mesial surface of the hemisphere, and that of the orbital surface of the frontal lobe.

It has been noted above that destruction of the precentral motor cortex (areas 4 and 6) results in a spastic hemiplegia. However, it is not to be assumed that this condition is identical with the spastic paralysis which results from lesions at lower levels. The spasticity resulting from lesions of the internal capsule is in general greater than that seen with cortical lesions. In all probability this is due at least in part to the fact that in the internal capsule the fibers are drawn close together in a compact bundle and the damage is, therefore, greater than with the usual cortical lesion. There is also the possibility that the greater spasticity commonly seen with hemiplegias of capsular origin is the result of some destruction in the basal ganglia, which is common with such lesions, as well as the destruction of the fibers descending from the precentral motor cortex. In any event the *pattern* of the increased tone is similar with hemiplegias of both cortical and capsular origin, i.e., the increase in tone in the upper extremity is in the flexor muscles. With severe lesions at the mesencephalic level it is common to see spasticity even greater than is commonly seen with capsular or cortical lesions but the pattern in both the upper and lower extremities is an extensor one. If the lesion is in the spinal cord, one may see either a paralysis with very severe extensor rigidity or a paraplegia in flexion, as has been discussed elsewhere.

### Grasping Movements and Tonic Innervation

Involvement of the anterior part of the precentral motor cortex, i.e., of area 6, is not uncommonly associated with a group of phenomena to which various terms have been applied, e.g., "forced grasping and groping", "grasp reflex", "tonic innervation" and so forth. A description of these phenomena follows.

(1) Merely touching the skin between the finger and thumb with a pencil results in slow flexion of the fingers. If the stimulating agent is withdrawn gently without disturbing the position of the patient's fingers no tightening of the grasp results but his hand and arm sometimes move

through space (grope) in the direction of the moving object, as if drawn by a magnet.

(2) *Grasp reflex.* When an object is placed in the involved hand of the patient the fingers close slowly and gently around it, but any attempt made by the observer to withdraw the object often results in its being grasped more firmly. Nevertheless, when the patient clenches his empty fist he can relax the fingers again without difficulty.

(3) Any attempt to bend the arm or leg is met by an active resistance exerted by the antagonistic (stretched) muscles; this differs from the resistance offered by the ordinary spastic limb in that there is no sudden giving way with a "clasp-knife effect".

Walshe and Robertson have made a critical study of these phenomena and find that they are separable into two distinct components: (a) the *grasp movement* and (b) *tonic innervation.*

The *gentle* grasp and the groping movements just described (see (1) above) are voluntary and not reflex acts. That is to say, though they are automatic in nature and are taken to indicate deterioration of the psychomotor functions, the patient can prevent their occurrence if asked to do so. They disappear in stupor or in coma. The gentle grasping movement follows tactile stimuli alone or visual and tactile stimuli acting together. The groping movements can be elicited by visual stimuli alone but not by tactile stimuli alone.

*Tonic innervation* (see (3) above) is a stretch reflex (ch. 64). The *strong* grasp (2) which results when an attempt is made to remove an object from the hand is simply one phase—an incident— of this reflex. It is quite distinct from the gentle grasp movement. It results from the passive stretching of the flexor muscles of the fingers caused by the observer's attempt to extricate the object. The patient cannot relax the grasp and release the grasped object. It occurs in the unconscious patient. The grasp reflex is most pronounced when the patient is on his side and the affected arm uppermost (Fulton).

Richter and Hines produced the "tonic grasp reflex" in adult monkeys by removal of area 6. Excision of the motor areas or the prefrontal areas from both hemispheres did not cause the effect. A similar reflex is present in normal infants, Robinson showing that in these it is sufficiently strong to suspend the body from a bar for 2 minutes. A grasping reflex has also been described for the foot in lesions of area 6; it occurs in the normal infant up to the end of the first year and is said to occur in 50 per cent of Mongolian idiots. It is elicited by stroking the sole.

*Area 8* is called the *frontal eye field.* It lies in front of area 6. Stimulation of the cortex here causes a conjugate movement of the eyes to the opposite side, opening and closing of the eyelids, and sometimes dilation of the pupils and lacrymation. No visual hallucinations occur in man, but an epileptiform seizure may be provoked which spreads to the adversive field (area 6).[3] Ablation of area 8 of one side in monkeys or involvement of this area or its projection fibers in man causes the eyes to be turned up toward the side of the lesion, and paralysis of the conjugate eye movement. These effects are temporary. The animal in walking circles toward the side of the lesion. No abnormalities are observed in the pupils or in the movements of the lids. Area 8 is one of the "suppressor" areas. This area receives fibers from the dorsomedial nucleus of the thalamus, through which it is connected with the hypothalamus. It also connects by long association tracts, both afferent and efferent, with the occipital lobe (visual area, 18) and with the tegmentum of the midbrain (probably with the oculomotor nuclei).[4]

*Area 44* in the region of the posterior part of the frontal operculum in the *dominant hemisphere* (which is the left in right-handed persons) is the motor area for speech (Broca's area). Stimulation of this area in conscious patients causes their speech to be abruptly arrested.

### Prefrontal or Orbitofrontal Region

The prefrontal region embraces the part of the frontal lobe in front of areas 8 and 44, but it includes the orbital as well as the lateral aspect of the lobe, and for this reason is also known as the orbitofrontal region. It was divided by Brodmann into several different areas (9, 10, 11, 12, 13 and 14) but Bailey and von Bonin do not believe that

---

[3] Stimulation of area 8 in man also causes conjugate deviation of the eyes and turning of the head to the opposite side.

[4] Unilateral ablation of this area in monkeys is followed by a visual defect in the form of failure to recognize objects in the opposite homonymous halves of the visual fields—*a pseudohemianopia*—results. When area 8 is destroyed on both sides the animal does not react in a normal manner to visual stimuli. It may appear to be blind for it walks into or stumbles over obstructions in its path, and tends to stare straight ahead with an immobile "wooden" expression (see Kennard and Ectors). Yet, an animal will follow an object with its eyes and will seize anything offered to it though failing, apparently, to recognize it or to understand what to do with it.

such subdivision of this area is supportable by a careful study of the cytoarchitecture. These areas until recent years have been thought to be inexcitable, and were therefore referred to as "silent" or association areas. But upon stimulation by a suitable electric current having pulses of low frequency, autonomic, respiratory, circulatory, renal, and gastrointestinal responses can be elicited. After bilateral removal of these areas the blood pressure is reduced, gastric secretion suppressed, and gastrointestinal movements increased. In man, suffering from intractable pain is relieved. These areas receive important fibers from the dorsomedial nucleus of the thalamus, which in turn receives impulses from the hypothalamus. These orbitofrontal areas, especially those of the orbital surface, are thought also to be closely associated with emotional feeling. Their part in the scheme of cortical representation of sensation is uncertain, but they are probably concerned with visceral rather than with somatic sensations through the hypothalamus and dorsomedial thalamic nucleus.

*Area 24,* anterior part of the cingular gyrus on the mesial aspect of the hemisphere, is a powerful suppressor area. Various autonomic responses follow stimulation of this area including pupillary dilation, pilo-erection, acceleration of the heart, and a fall in blood pressure. Arrest of respiration in expiration also results.

The prefrontal areas have extensive subcortical and cortical connections. Areas from 9 to 12 in the monkey receive fibers from the dorsomedial nucleus of the thalamus. Fibers ascending to the orbital areas 11 and 12 from this nucleus have also been demonstrated in man from a study of retrograde degeneration in the nucleus following section of white matter. The anterior nucleus of the thalamus also sends fibers to the prefrontal area (area 23), and both dorsomedial and anterior thalamic nuclei receive fibers from the hypothalamus. The pathway from hypothalamus to the cortex through the dorsomedial nucleus was established by stimulation of the posterior hypothalamic region and observing the action potentials in the thalamic nucleus and the cortex. The greater part of the prefrontal cortex is considered by Le Gros Clark as a projection area for the hypothalamus, just as the occipital cortex and auditory cortex are projection areas, respectively, for the retina and the cochlea (fig. 67.3).

The prefrontal areas are connected by efferent fibers with (a) the hypothalamus through the dorsomedial nucleus of the thalamus; (b) there is also good evidence for the existence of a direct efferent connection with the hypothalamus both in animals and in man; (c) with the caudate nucleus; (d) nuclei of the pons (from area 10); (e) tegmentum of the midbrain.

Unilateral or bilateral removal of the *prefrontal area* does not cause paralysis either in the monkey or in man. Unilateral removal of the human prefrontal area produces a definite if rather subtle alteration in mental processes. Some loss of initiative and mental alertness are the most outstanding results of the operation. Memory, judgment and intellect often show little or no deterioration. Removal of the prefrontal area of the dominant hemisphere (i.e., the left in right-handed and the right in left-handed persons) is sometimes thought to produce somewhat greater alterations in character or intellect than does a similar operation upon the nondominant side. Even the bilateral excision of prefrontal areas is followed by a sur-

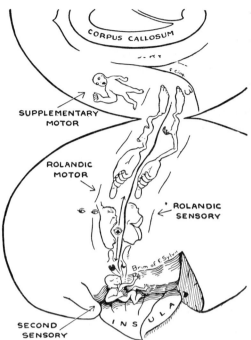

FIG. 67.4. Showing figurines of motor and sensory representation in the cerebral cortex, slightly modified. (From Penfield and Jasper, *Epilepsy and the Functional Anatomy of the Human Brain,* courtesy of Dr. Penfield.)

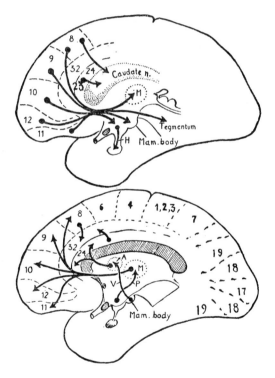

FIG. 67.3. Connections of prefrontal areas. (After Le Gros Clark, with minor additions). *Lower sketch*, right cerebral hemisphere from the medial aspect, showing afferent connections; A, anterior nucleus of the thalamus; M, dorsomedial nucleus of the thalamus; P, periventricular system of fibers ascending from the hypothalamus to the thalamus; v, mammillothalamic tract of Vicq D'Azyr. *Upper sketch*, efferent connections; M, dorsomedial nucleus of the thalamus; H, hypothalamicohypophyseal tract.

prisingly moderate mental defect, so far as superficial observation and examinations are concerned. However, we must not be misled by such inadequate observations. The fact that the patient following a unilateral or even a bilateral prefrontal lobectomy appears normal, functions as a normal individual during casual associations, or passes the usual psychometric tests with flying colors does not mean that the frontal lobes are without important functions so far as mental activity and behavior are concerned. Halstead has discussed this matter in detail and has developed tests which indicate with amazing accuracy the damage to the frontal lobes. These tests have been elaborated into a battery of very objective tests, the results of which give an impairment index of the functions of the frontal lobes. Damage to other parts of the brain does not give rise to comparable changes in these tests. Subcortical lesions involving the white matter of the frontal lobes do not disturb these functions as do lesions of the frontal cortex. Many of these tests are based upon the ability of the patient to classify and categorize a large number of familiar objects and to recall them once they have been taken from him. In an operation for the eradication of a tumor, Dandy excised the frontal lobes on both sides in front of the motor areas (reported by Brickner). The subject of this extensive extirpation appeared of normal intelligence upon a casual acquaintance. It is reported that for an hour he toured the hospital with two visiting neurologists who failed to notice in him any mental abnormality. A more intimate knowledge of the patient, however, revealed very definite defects of character and mentality. His mental age was about thirteen years; his intelligence quotient eighty. The main features shown by this subject and which may be taken generally as representative of the effects of extensive prefrontal destruction are listed below. They constitute what has been called the *frontal lobe syndrome.*[5]

(1) *Lack of restraint* leading to boasting, self-aggrandizement, hostility, aggressiveness.

(2) *Distractibility* and *restlessness*—difficulty in fixing attention.

(3) *Hypermotility* which appears to be due to the loss especially of area 13.

(4) *Flight of ideas*, puerile fantasies, emotional instability, facetiousness, punning.

(5) *Lack of initiative*, and difficulty in planning any course of action.

(6) *Impairment of memory* for recent events but not for remote events.

(7) *Impairment of moral and social sense*, loss of love for family.

(8) *Failure to realize*, or indifference to, the seriousness of his condition, and a sense of well-being (euphoria).

Among some of the other manifestations which may follow a prefrontal defect are: (a) increased appetite, (b) impaired control of the sphincter

---

[5] The classical example of a severe prefrontal injury which resulted in surprisingly little mental defect, is the case of the American, Phineas Gage (1848), who suffered extensive damage of his frontal lobes by an iron tamping bar driven through his head by an explosion. The bar penetrated the left orbit and emerged from the midline of the head just anterior to the coronal suture. He was stunned for only an hour and was able with assistance to walk to a surgeon's office. He lived for 12 years after the accident and showed in general these mental changes. A case has also been reported in which the prefrontal cortex on both sides were absent or degenerated. The condition existed from early childhood yet, at adult age the subject of this defect, after a careful psychologic and psychiatric examination, was reported to be of normal intelligence, though some defect in planning capacity and in the ability "to organize his behavior toward a relatively remote goal" were revealed.

of the bladder or rectum, (c) disturbances of orientation in time and space, and (d) tremor.

Chimpanzees which have had both prefrontal areas removed show restlessness and are easily distracted, though they remain alert and evince a keen interest in things around them. Fulton and Jacobson reported in 1935 that after this operation chimpanzees failed to show temper tantrums and other neurotic effects of frustration (experimental neurosis (p. 1266). This observation formed the basis for the surgical treatment of certain psychoneuroses in man, first employed by the Portuguese neurologist, Egaz Moniz in 1936. The operation, called frontal lobotomy consists in severing the fibers connecting prefrontal areas with subcortical centers (probably the thalamus and hypothalamus). With the introduction of the various drugs which are capable of reducing nervous tension and rendering the aggressive, agitated patient more tractable the need for this type of operation has been greatly diminished.

*The frontal lobes and intelligence.* The development of the frontal lobes bears in general a direct relationship to the level of an animal in the phylogenetic scale and to its intelligence. This has led to the belief that this part of the cerebrum is the seat of the intelligence of animals and the "center" or "organ" of the mind of man. Within this region those processes underlying intellectual, as well as moral and emotional attributes were supposedly carried out. The absence of any overt effect from stimulation of these so-called silent areas seemed to confirm this belief. Extirpation experiments and lobectomy or injury in man, however, show decisively that the prefrontal area cannot be looked upon as a region where these higher mental qualities reside exclusively or even predominantly. Intelligence depends upon a knowledge of the external world received through various channels. Visual, auditory, somesthetic perceptions, etc., are received and stored as memories in cortical areas situated in the occipital, temporal and parietal lobes. Tracts of association fibers in turn link together these several primary areas; sensations of various types are thereby brought into relationship, and synthesized into more complex memories. Thus, as time passes, the fabric of our experience is woven in patterns of greater and greater intricacy.

The progressive increase in size of the frontal lobes through the upper levels of the phylogenetic scale is not as great as that of the parietal lobe, which supports the conclusion derived from extirpation experiments that intelligence, memory, control of behavior, etc. are not solely or even predominantly dependent upon the prefrontal areas.

It is probable that the prefrontal area merely represents a region of relatively high associative or synthetic capabilities. The subcortical connections of this area, as well as the effects upon behavior resulting from its injury, strongly suggest that it is concerned with emotional feeling. After its bilateral removal the cerebrum deprived of the synthesizing faculty of this region is incapable of the more elaborate association of those experiences required for the formulation of abstract ideas and more accurate judgment, and for the guidance of conduct in conformity with social customs. Here also are mainly located those mental processes relating to "prediction," forecasting, or to any planned action. A person deprived of these areas would have little ability as a strategist; even a housewife after the loss of these parts of the cortex experiences some difficulty in planning a meal. Nevertheless, synthesis at somewhat lower levels is still possible of achievement through the remaining cerebral tissue. Mental capacity according to this conception is a function of the cerebral cortex as a whole rather than of any particular region.

## The Parietal Lobe

### The Somesthetic (Somatesthetic) Area

*The postcentral gyrus,* i.e., the band of cortex lying behind and including the posterior lip and wall of the fissure of Rolando (areas 3, 1 and 2) is sensory in function and is known as the *somesthetic area.* This band of sensory cortex turns over the upper border of the hemisphere, and extends down the mesial surface as far as the cingulate gyrus. As in the case of the primary motor area, the sensory areas of the body are, in a general way, represented mainly in inverted order, from the lowest part of the mesial surface to a corresponding part of the lateral surface. Thus, the area for the toes is at the lower part of the mesial surface, that for the leg near the upper border of the hemisphere, while the face, mouth and tongue areas are found in the lower part of the lateral surface. The parts of the face, however, are represented in uninverted sequence—brow, eyelids, nose, lips, in this order from above downward

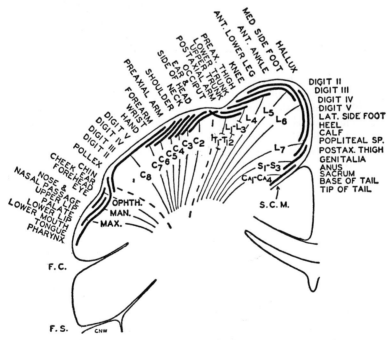

Fig. 67.5. Diagram of a section through the somesthetic area to show cortical representation of the dermatomes. F.S., sylvian fissure; F.C., central fissure; s.c.m., callosomarginal sulcus; MAX., maxillary division of the trigeminal nerve; MAN., mandibular; OPHTH., ophthalmic; C., cervical; T., thoracic; L., lumbar; S., sacral; Ca., caudal. (From Woolsey, Marshall and Bard, Bull. Johns Hopkins Hosp., 70: 399–441, 1942.)

(fig. 67.2). Though broadly speaking, sensory representation in the cortex has this regional representation, when the topography of the different parts is examined in greater detail it is found that the order of cortical representation conforms closely to that of the dermatomes, i.e., to the spinal innervation. For example, the cortical sequence for the upper limb (monkey) is postaxial arm, occiput, ear, side of head, neck, shoulder (C2–C6); preaxial arm, forearm, wrist, hand, digits (C7, C8, T1). But it will be seen from figure 67.5 that the dermatomal representation is not in continuous numerical sequence from head to tail. For example, if the sensory band of cortex (which turns over the upper border of the hemisphere) were straightened out, it would appear quite clearly that the projection of the dermatomes from the upper thorax to the tail (Thoracic 1 to Caudal 4) was in an order the inverse of that of the spinal segments, whereas, the representations of the head and neck were uninverted, the cervical segments being represented in ascending numerical order from above down, and the ophthalmic division of the 5th nerve following C8. There is no obvious explanation for this arrangement. Excisions from the somesthetic cortex are followed by disturbances of cutaneous and kinesthetic sensations on the opposite side of the body. These subside to a greater or lesser degree with the passage of time.

Cushing, and later, Penfield and his associates have stimulated different parts of the area in conscious patients; sensations on the contralateral half of the body were experienced, their locations bearing a constant relationship to the point stimulated. Dusser de Barenne discovered that the application of a strychnine solution to the postcentral gyrus in monkeys caused sensory effects (paresthesias, hyperesthesis and hyperalgesia) on the opposite side of the body, but also to some extent on the same side.

The sensory area of the cortex is not confined to the postcentral gyrus but extends forward into the precentral gyrus. Penfield and his associates found that 25 per cent of stimulations of the latter area in patients caused a sensation, with or without a motor response. On the other hand, 20 per cent of stimulations of the postcentral gyrus gave a motor response, instead of or accompanied by a sensation. Also ablations of postcentral areas cause motor defects which are not due simply to loss of kinesthetic sense. It appears that the precentral and postcentral areas are knit together by connecting neurons, and are so interrelated functionally as to be called appropriately, taken as a whole, the *sensorimotor area*. The question of the sensory function of the precentral gyrus and the motor functions of the postcentral still require accurate definition.

Marshall, Woolsey and Bard have used a method to map out the cortical representation of tactile sensibility in monkeys, based upon the fact that impulses set up by stimuli applied peripherally can be recorded as action currents from the surface of the hemisphere (fig. 67.6). This is known as the *method of evoked potentials*. They found tactile sensations represented contralaterally in the postcentral gyrus (areas 3, 1 and 2). Ipsilateral representation was not observed, except for a part of the face (e.g., lips, tongue and lower cheek). In no instance was evidence obtained for the precentral representation of this sensation.

As in the motor area the extent of the sensory representation in the postcentral gyrus is greatest for those parts of the body which are of most importance in acquiring information concerning surrounding objects. Thus, in man and in the monkey, the cortical area for the hand and arm is larger than that for the trunk or leg, while in such animals as the rabbit, cat or pig, the area for the face, lips, snout and vibrissae is much larger

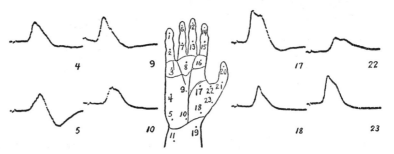

Fig. 67.6. Action potentials recorded from postcentral gyrus during tactile stimulation of points on palm. (Part of figure from Marshall, Woolsey and Bard.)

than that for the paws. In the pig the representation for the snout takes up a large part of the postcentral gyrus, whereas that for the feet is insignificant. In the Shetland pony the cortical area receiving impulses from the nostril is nearly as large as that representing the rest of the body surface. The large facial representation in man appears to be an exception for, after infancy, we do not gain information by feeling objects with the lips or by putting them into the mouth. It is looked upon, however, as an inheritance from our animal ancestry.

Somatic sensation as well as the visual and auditory senses have a double representation in the cortex of each hemisphere. This dual somatic representation was first observed by Adrian, in the case of the claws of the cat. The somesthetic area described above and long recognized, is now called the "primary" sensory area, or, as Woolsey has suggested, *somatic area I*. The more recently discovered sensory area is called *somatic area II*. Corresponding terms for the dual visual and auditory areas are employed, namely auditory and visual areas I and II. Somatic area II lies in the upper wall of the Sylvian fissure, that is, below the face area of somatic area I, which is much larger in extent. The order of representation in sensory area II is the inverse of that of sensory area I, the face being above the arm in the upper part of the wall of the fissure and the representation of the foot at the bottom. The significance of the dual cortical representation is unknown. Area II is thought to be the more primitive of the two, that is, to have been developed at a much earlier phylogenetic period. It is possible that it receives fibers subserving the cruder forms of sensation, (the protopathic system of Head) while the primary area receives impulses upon which more critical perception (epicritic) is based.

All somatic sensory impulses ascend in the medial, spinal and trigeminal lemnisci to the thalamus, which is the subcortical destination of crude sensations. Though rather vague sensations described as tingling, numbness, tickling, prickling, or as the movement of a limb, are aroused by stimulation of the postcentral gyrus, and are referred to some part of the body depending upon the area stimulated, pain is never aroused and rarely even discomfort. There does not appear to be an area of the cortex essential for the perception of pain for "no removal of the cortex anywhere prevents pain from being felt" (Penfield). Impulses for pain reaching the thalamus can arouse this feeling without being transmitted to the cortex. Though, as mentioned earlier, severe intractable pain, usually associated with disease of internal structures is relieved by frontal lobotomy or lobectomy, the perception of pain is not abolished; but the patient ceases to suffer and complain; he no longer worries about it.

The finer sensations of touch and temperature and the sense of position and movement are relayed to the cortex by fibers which ascend through the internal capsule and corona radiata. The function of the somesthetic cortex, according to the theory of Head and his associates, is not, however, simply to record these several primary sensations. Its activity lies in the psychic sphere; cortical sensation, to quote these observers, is one of the "elementary processes of the mind". The somesthetic area brings its discriminative and synthesizing abilities to bear upon the primary sensations which it receives, and from these are formed our perceptions of the qualities of external objects, such as their size, shape, weight, texture, etc., and of the positions of our limbs in space. Through cortical activity a particular sensation is subjected to critical appraisal and compared with or related to another simultaneous or consecutive sensation; thereby, its intensity and nature are accurately judged. Thus, according to Head, the somesthetic area of the cortex, through the integration of the primary sensations, becomes endowed with three discriminative faculties.[6] These are:

(a) SPATIAL RECOGNITION—the appreciation of relationships in space, e.g., the recognition of position and passive movement of the limb, the discrimination of two points, and the localization of a point which has been touched.

(b) RECOGNITION OF THE RELATIVE INTENSITY of different stimuli, e.g., that one object is warmer or cooler.

(c) RECOGNITION OF SIMILARITY AND DIFFERENCES—appreciation of the shape, relative size and texture of objects, and the estimation of their weights—*stereognosis*.

With a *lesion* involving the cortical somesthetic area, one or the other, but usually all three, of these faculties are disturbed. Spatial recognition shows the greatest disturbance the farther forward the lesion lies in the somesthetic area. Appreciation of intensity is disturbed most by lesions involving the foot of the postcentral gyrus and the

---

[6] According to the conception of Penfield and Jasper, impulses received in the sensorimotor cortex return to the thalamus and other parts of the centrencephalic system where the highest level of functional integration is situated.

supramarginal and angular gyri. Recognition of similarity and difference is affected most by lesions of the middle of the postcentral gyrus.

If with lesions confined to the cortex, the related nuclei of the thalamus which are concerned with the *primary* sensations, e.g., light touch, temperature, passive movement and position, etc., are intact and the sensations will be appreciated. The patient with such a lesion has difficulty, however, in bringing the necessary discriminative ability to bear upon the sensation in order to judge it, and he is unable to synthesize different sensations into a composite impression which will enable him readily to identify an object. When tested, he is uncertain in his answers, which tend to vary from moment to moment, and it is difficult for the examiner to determine the threshold for a given sensation. For example, though he recognizes that an object is warm, he cannot say whether it is warmer or less warm than another object which he has felt previously or at the same time. He responds to tactile stimuli, but also with inconstancy, and he is often even less consistent in his answers when the strength of the stimulus is increased. He cannot locate the point touched and may respond when not touched (hallucination of touch). The weights of objects placed upon the hand cannot be estimated, and a fabric (e.g., silk or tweed), though felt to be smooth or rough cannot be recognized.

It is not to be assumed that sensation is simply a matter of nervous conduction, that all stimuli of equal intensity are equally perceived by the person stimulated. The perception of a given stimulus is not always the same; the threshold varies. This in part is due to attention or inattention. If a person's attention is concentrated upon one part of his body he will become more acutely aware of stimulation of that part while at the same time he becomes less aware of stimuli received elsewhere. This is common everyday human experience. It also plays an important role in the symptomatology of disease. The patient whose attention is constantly focused upon a diseased or injured part is keenly aware of unpleasant sensations from that area, whereas another patient with a similar disease or injury who is busily engaged with other activities and does not concentrate upon his disease or injury suffers much less discomfort. Likewise, it is a matter of common experience on the part of physicians that some patients have a much lower threshold for pain than others. In general, the patient who is introspective, who concentrates his attention

upon himself, his body and its ailments is the one with the lowest threshold for pain and the one who suffers and complains more. What is the physiological explanation for these differences between patients, and from time to time in the same patient. It seems likely that several neural mechanisms are at work here. One of these is the reticular formation in the brain stem. There is ample evidence that it can influence sensory thresholds both peripherally and centrally. Other mechanisms which may be concerned are the corticothalamic, corticobulbar and corticospinal fibers. We have mentioned the projection of thalamic fibers to almost every area of the cerebral cortex. Sensory perception is the primary concern of those from the nucleus ventralis posterior of the thalamus to the postcentral gyrus. It has also been pointed out that there is also an extensive projection system from the cerebral cortex back to the thalamus. In general a given area of the cortex projects back to the same thalamic nucleus as that from which it receives fibers. It seems entirely reasonable that this corticothalamic system is a mechanism for controlling the threshold of the thalamus and thus for regulating sensory attention. There is also a corticobulbar system which extends from the postcentral sensory cortex to the spinal root of the trigeminal nerve, and corticospinal fibers from the postcentral gyrus to the posterior gray horn of the spinal cord in the monkey (Kuypers, 1958). This same investigator also found evidence of a cortical projection from the "leg" areas of both the pre- and postcentral gyri to the nucleus gracilis. Projection from the pericentral cortex to the nucleus cuneatus was also found. Although conclusive evidence that these connections are concerned with modulation of sensory perception has not yet been presented, Hagbarth and Kerr (1954) have shown that stimulation of the postcentral sensory cortex (in the cat) will depress afferent responses from the spinal dorsal root transmitted over pathways in the spinal cord and the midbrain.

Hypotonia may also be a symptom of lesions of the sensory cortex; it corresponds in distribution to the loss of the sense of position and passive movement.

The cortex at the lower end of the somesthetic area (tongue and face area) appears from the studies of Bornstein to be the *area for taste*. This area lies adjacent to the motor cortex governing the muscles of mastication.[7] It had been generally

---

[7] This area probably extends into the upper bank of the Sylvian (lateral) fissure, for the sensa-

taught, but on doubtful evidence, that the center for taste lay close to that for smell, namely, in the region of the hippocampal gyrus. It appears from the results of the stimulation of the human cortex during operations that the taste area extends deeply into the fissure of Sylvius. An electrical stimulus applied to the cortex above the circular sulcus (surrounding the insula), or the surface of the insula itself causes a sensation of taste—a "terrific tight sensation of taste" as one patient expressed it (Penfield).

*Motor effects* of a generalized type are produced by electrical stimulation of the posterior part of the superior parietal lobule (area 5, parietal adversive field). These are movements of the head and eyes to the opposite side. Stimulation of the angular gyrus causes conjugate deviation of the eyes to the opposite side.

Attacks of Jacksonian epilepsy, due to lesions of the sensory cortex, may be preceded by sensory aurae—comprising pricking sensations, "pins and needles," sensation of cold, etc.

### THE TEMPORAL LOBE. THE CENTERS FOR HEARING AND SMELL

The primary cortical center for hearing is situated in the transverse gyrus of Heschl lying in the floor of the lateral cerebral (Sylvian) fissure, and an adjoining small area of the superior temporal gyrus. Fibers from the medial geniculate body reach this *auditosensory* area (area 41) via the posterior limb of the internal capsule; they constitute the *auditory radiation* (p. 1205). In the auditosensory area the fundamental auditory sensations—intensity, quality and pitch—are appreciated. The area is bilaterally represented.

Equilibratory sense is represented in the posterior part of the first temporal convolution. Stimulation of this region in conscious patients causes dizziness or nausea, a sense of swaying, falling, or of rotation.

It has been asserted that memory resides in the temporal region, either in the neocortex or in the amygdala. It is certainly true that defects in memory occur with lesions of the temporal lobe, but the concept that "memory" is localized there is much too superficial and simplified a view of this complex neural process. Memory is composed of many things—the retention of various types of sensory experiences, the recollection of ones own thoughts, ideas and expressions,

and the recall of ones motor acts, to ennumerate the more obvious categories. To postulate that the memory traces of these many varied things are stored in any one part of the brain is unsupportable. It can be shown readily that memory is often disturbed by disease processes in many different parts of the brain but it is unlikely that "memory" is *localized* anywhere.

As in the case of the somesthetic (p. 1243) and visual senses, auditory sensations have a dual representation in each cerebral hemisphere—*auditory areas I and II*. Woolsey and Walzl stimulated electrically the different levels of the exposed cochlea in cats and found a point to point projection on to the temporal cortex. In auditory area I, the apical turns of the cochlea were projected posteriorly, the basal turns anteriorly, whereas in the "secondary" area, which lies adjacent and ventral to the "primary" area, the different points of the cochlea showed the reverse distribution, apical turns anterior, basal turns posterior (fig. 67.7). A large part of the cortex of the superior temporal gyrus lying outside these auditosensory areas is considered to be *audito-psychic* in function. Herein the analysis and interpretation of auditory sensations, and their integration into more complex perceptions take place. The auditopsychic area is mainly unilateral, being on the left side in right-handed individuals and vice versa.

Fibers descend from the cortex of the temporal lobe to the *medial geniculate* body and *inferior colliculus*; the former is therefore connected with the auditory area by both ascending and descending paths.

It has been taught for many years that fibers

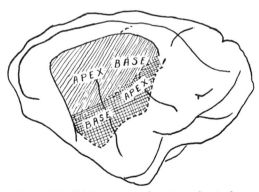

FIG. 67.7. Right temporal cortex of cat showing the representation of the right (ipsilateral) cochlea. This is a composite figure from data of a number of experiments. *Upper hatched region*, primary auditory area; *lower cross-hatched region*, secondary auditory area. (After Woolsey and Walzl, redrawn with minor modifications.)

---

tion has been aroused in patients by stimulation of the upper bank where it joins the insula (Penfield and Rasmussen).

descend from the temporal lobe through the internal capsule and the lateral segment of the cerebral peduncle to the pons—the so-called *temporo-pontine* or Türck's bundle. However, in detailed studies of the brains of monkeys following temporal lobectomies neither Rundles and Papez nor Bucy and Klüver were able to demonstrate any such tract. It is possible that these fibers in the lateral part of the cerebral peduncle are parieto-pontine fibers as Mettler suggested. The temporal lobe also receives fibers from the posterior pole of the pulvinar of the thalamus (Bucy and Klüver), and it appears that these terminate in the anterior part of the cortex of the lateral surface of the temporal lobe (Simpson, 1952 and Chow, 1954). There is also a large bundle of fibers (Arnold's) which has an uncertain origin in the anterior part of the temporal lobe and which passes backward to end in the pulvinar of the thalamus. The functions of these connections are unknown.

THE CENTER FOR SMELL is situated in the uncus and the anterior part of the hippocampal gyrus (pyriform area). In man, stimulation of the uncus, olfactory lobe or the region of the amygdaloid nucleus causes an olfactory sensation. Owing to the close relationship of these parts of the rhinencephalon to the temporal lobe, lesions of the latter (e.g., tumor, abscess, etc.) are not uncommonly associated with disturbances of the olfactory sense.

A LESION OF THE TEMPORAL LOBE may result in:

*1. Aphasia.* Disturbances of the speech function—understanding, expression, recall of the names of objects, etc.—commonly occur with lesions of the dominant (usually the left) temporal lobe. Frazier and Rowe found aphasic disturbances in 36 per cent of such cases; Kolodny reported 57 per cent. The occurrence of aphasic difficulties will depend upon the location of the lesion. They are unlikely with lesions in the anterior or ventral part of the left temporal lobe and likely with lesions in the postero-superior part near the posterior part of the Sylvian fissure.

*2. Auditory disorders* may occur with lesions of the temporal lobes. Paroxysmal attacks of tinnitus (buzzing, ringing, etc.) or even of auditory hallucinations may occur. These are often associated with other manifestations of "temporal lobe seizures" or of uncinate attacks or dreamy states. Epileptic attacks induced by various auditory stimuli have also been described. Because of the extensive bilateral representation of both cochleae in both auditory cortices deafness never occurs as the result of a unilateral cortical lesion and is very rare with bilateral ones because involvement of the auditory cortices in both cerebral hemispheres is most uncommon.

*3. Disturbances of smell and taste* in the form of paroxysmal hallucinations in these sensory fields occur commonly with lesions, especially tumors in the anterior temporal region. These smells and tastes are more often unpleasant. Such attacks are commonly called *uncinate seizures.* Impairment of the sense of smell occurs most often as the result of lesions of the olfactory bulb and tract, rather than from involvement of the so-called rhinencephalon. In fact, the rhinencephalon is much more concerned with the control of emotions and emotional expression and of vegetative functions than it is with the elementary sensations of smell and taste.

*4. Dreamy states.* Lesions of the anterior part of the temporal lobe are not infrequently associated with peculiar attacks known as dreamy states. In these attacks the patient has a feeling of unreality, a sense of familiarity of his surroundings (*deja vu*). He may describe these attacks as being similar to a dream. They may be associated with certain activities on the part of the patient over which he appears to have no control and of which he subsequently has no memory. In these attacks he may remove his own clothing, or tear off the clothing of others. He may be destructive or he may merely wander about aimlessly as though looking for something. Because of this combination of psychological disturbance with certain motor activities these have been referred to as *psychomotor seizures.* These seizures may be associated with auditory, olfactory or visual hallucinations. Individuals with temporal lobe seizures not infrequently suffer from generalized convulsions as well.

*5. Visual symptoms.* Lesions of the temporal lobes, particularly tumors, may be associated with visual hallucinations. Although these hallucinations may take almost any form they commonly are of formed objects,—people, animals, etc. On occasion these may be smaller than normal or the figures may be incomplete. In some cases the hallucinations may be unformed, that is flashes of light. Lesions in the posterior part of the temporal lobe commonly involve the visual radiations which run from the lateral geniculate body to the calcarine cortex, and thus give rise to a defect in the contralateral halves of the visual fields—a homonymous hemianopia. If the hemianopia is incomplete, it is usually the upper contralateral quadrants of the visual fields which are involved.

*6. Extensive lesions* of the temporal lobes may be associated with defects in memory but it would not be correct to conclude that memory is "localized" in the temporal lobes.

In monkeys bilateral extirpation of the temporal lobes including both the neocortex and the rhinencephalon on the medial surface of the temporal lobes gives rise to a most interesting group of symptoms (Klüver and Bucy, 1939). (*1*) *Visual agnosia.* These animals seem to have lost the ability to recognize and to detect the meaning of objects on the basis of visual criteria alone. There also seems to be a similar agnosia in the auditory and tactile fields. (*2*) *Oral tendencies.* There is a very strong tendency to examine all objects with the mouth. (*3*) *"Hypermetamorphosis."* There is a marked tendency to take notice of and to attend to every visual stimulus. (*4*) *Tameness.* These animals seem to have lost their sense of fear, and there is a marked diminution in their emotional responses. (*5*) *Hypersexuality.* There is a striking increase in various sexual activities and in their diversity. This change does not occur until several weeks after the operation. Females may show a complete lack of maternal behavior. (*6*) *Changes in dietary habits.* Monkeys do not ordinarily eat meat but after the removal of both temporal lobes they do so without hesitation. There is also an increase in the amount of food consumed. In some animals some "tameness" may be produced by a unilateral temporal lobectomy, but the other manifestations appear only following a bilateral removal. In a few cases some of these symptoms have been observed in human beings following bilateral temporal lobectomy.

### The Occipital Lobe

The gray matter forming the walls of, and surrounding the calcarine fissure (on the medial aspect of the occipital lobe) constitutes the primary cortical center for vision—the *visuosensory area.* From the broad stripe of Gennari which can be seen with the naked eye this area is commonly known as the *area striata* or, following the numerical terminology, as area 17. It will be considered in more detail in chapter 75. Its histological features have already been touched upon.

It is commonly said that the *second visual area* wherein the visual sensations are interpreted and integrated into more complex perceptions is contiguous to the area striata and lies on the lateral

aspect of the occipital lobe (area 18). Definite confirmation of this hypothesis is lacking.

Stimulation of the anterior part of the lateral surface of the occipital lobe causes conjugate deviation of the eyes to the opposite side (occipital motor eye field, area 19). In man, visual hallucinations, such as, flashes of light of different colors, or definite images have been evoked by the electrical stimulation of area 18 or 19.

### The Physiology of Speech and Some of Its Disorders

The first stage in the development of speech is the association of certain sounds—(words)—with visual, tactile and other sensations aroused by objects in the external world. These associations are "stored" as memories. After definite meanings have been attached to certain words, pathways between the auditory area of the cortex and the motor area for the muscles of articulation become established, and the child attempts to formulate and pronounce the words which he has heard. This act of verbal expression involves the co-ordinated movements of a large group of respiratory, laryngeal, lingual, pharyngeal and labial muscles. Later, as the child is taught to read, auditory speech is associated with the visual symbols of speech, and finally, through an association between these and the motor area for the hand, the child learns to express his auditory and visual impressions by the written word.

#### Aphasia

This term is applied to those disorders of speech resulting from defects in the nervous mechanisms underlying the comprehension and use of symbols (words, numerals) for the formulation, transmission and reception of ideas. General intelligence may be little impaired. Yet aphasia is not a defect in the pronunciation of words as a result of the paralysis of the muscles of articulation. The innervation of the latter—motor area, corticobulbar fibers, cranial nuclei or peripheral nerves—is not necessarily affected. The defects in aphasia involve higher neural levels; they lie in the psychical sphere.

The faculty of speech is based upon a highly complex neural mechanism and being one possessed by the human brain alone cannot, of course, be investigated in animals. In conscious patients electrical stimulation of the cortex of either hemisphere within the lower part of the precentral gyrus (lips, jaw and tongue areas), or

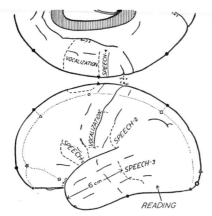

F𝐈𝐆. 67.8. Showing speech areas in the left (dominant) cerebral cortex. (From Penfield and Jasper, *Epilepsy and the Functional Anatomy of the Human Brain,* courtesy of Dr. Penfield.)

in the upper part of the supplementary motor area on the mesial aspect of the hemisphere, causes the emission of a crude vocal sound like the cry of an infant or of an epileptic at the beginning of an attack. The vocal response elicited from the lip, jaw and tongue region never even remotely resembles a spoken word, but that evoked from the supplementary motor area is more compli-cated. Ablation of one or other of these areas causes only temporary speech defects. If the cortex in the lower part of the precentral gyrus of the dominant hemisphere (left in the great majority of persons) is excised a temporary apha-sia results which is probably due to some inter-ference with the blood supply to area 44 (Broca's area). If while the patient is speaking, certain cortical areas are stimulated electrically, speech is arrested; he cannot think of a word or words which he wished to use. There are four such areas situated in the dominant hemisphere: (5) *lower frontal,* area 44; (2) *upper frontal,* motor cortex an-terior to the foot area on the mesial aspect of the hemisphere; (3) *parietal,* posterior to the lower part of the postcentral gyrus; (4) *temporal,* pos-terior part of temporal lobe. Injury to one or other of these areas, with the possible exception of (2), causes persistent aphasia (see fig. 67.8).

Before giving Head's views on aphasia, a short account of previous ideas on the subject may be helpful to the reader.

The views of the neurologists of the 19th cen-tury had the merit of simplicity. These observers, to whom Head refers as the "diagram makers," conceived of the language faculty as built up of four separate components. Each of these, sup-

posedly, was represented by a definite anatomi-cally circumscribed area of the cortex, and could be affected independently of the others.

Two of these centers were *sensory* and two *motor.* All four were linked together by association tracts. In such a scheme, memories of spoken words were stored in the superior temporal con-volution—the auditopsychic center; the cortex in the region of the angular gyrus was the reposi-tory of visual word memories. These two receptive areas comprised what was referred to as Wer-nicke's zone. The pair of motor centers, i.e., those presiding over the coördinated movements concerned in vocalization and writing were called respectively the glossokinesthetic and cheiro-kinesthetic centers. The former was located in the posterior part of the left 3rd frontal convolu-tion (area 44); the latter in the hind part of the left 2nd frontal convolution, in most instances on the left side. Diagrams were drawn confidently to show these four centers with their interconnec-tions, and the type of aphasia which would result from the destruction of one or other component part of the neural mechanism. Broca (1861) be-lieved that *motor aphasia* (see below) was the result of a lesion of the glossokinesthetic area (Broca's area), especially of the left side. Defects in the ability to write—*agraphia*—were held to be the result of the involvement of the cheiro-kinesthetic center. *Sensory* aphasias were classed as *auditory*—loss of the comprehension of audible speech—and *visual*—the inability to understand written or printed words. The former was held to be due to injury of the second temporal gyrus; the latter to injury of the angular gyrus. The most extreme proponents of this view even con-sidered that every memory, auditory or visual, had its anatomical representation, so that a lesion limited to a small group of nerve cells would cause the loss of only those word memories for which they served as centers.

The different types of aphasia which were rec-ognized may be briefly described.

1. M𝐨𝐭𝐨𝐫 𝐚𝐩𝐡𝐚𝐬𝐢𝐚 (Broca's). This term was applied to the type of speech defect in which the patient is almost speechless, but there is no paral-ysis of the muscles of articulation. Though un-able to express his thoughts in words, he can understand what is said to him and can read. He is usually able to utter a few words of an ejacula-tory nature, e.g., "oh my," "dear me," "damn," etc. Sometimes he is able to say the last words which he had spoken just before the onset of his

illness, as in the oft cited case of the librarian whose only words were, "lists complete".

2. AGRAPHIA. This term indicated that the patient was unable to write though motor speech and the comprehension of written or spoken words were possible. The movements of the hand and arm for other acts were not impaired.

3. AUDITORY APHASIA OR "WORD DEAFNESS" were the names given to those defects of the language faculty in which the subject, though able to hear, does not understand spoken words. He is as a person listening to a strange language. The power of speech, writing and the comprehension of written or printed words are retained. He may be able to repeat words spoken to him, and instead of answering a question may simply repeat the questioner's words; this phenomenon is called *echolalia*.

4. VISUAL APHASIA OR "WORD BLINDNESS" (ALEXIA). Vision is unaffected yet the recognition of written words or numerals and the appreciation of their meanings are defective or lost.

In 1906 these mechanical conceptions of the speech faculty and the production of aphasia were challenged by Pierre Marie. He claimed that there was only one true type of aphasia—sensory aphasia—due to a lesion in Wernicke's zone, and associated with a lowering of those intellectual capacities upon which were based the use of symbols in the expression of ideas. Thus, not only was the comprehension of written or spoken words defective but the ability to solve problems in arithmetic, and to perform certain other mental tasks were impaired. He maintained that the classical motor aphasia of Broca was simply anarthria (see below) due to involvement of the motor cortex governing the muscles of articulation plus sensory aphasia, and that a pure motor aphasia, i.e., a defect of speech due to the loss of "motor images" did not exist. Marie denied the existence of isolated cortical centers governing the different aspects of the speech faculty, and attacked the belief that aphasia was the result of the destruction of images—motor, auditory or visual—in such specific areas. He re-examined the brains of Broca's first two patients, which had been preserved in the Musée Dupuytren in Paris, and found no confirmation of the view of Broca that the posterior part of the third frontal convolution was necessarily involved in aphasia. In the first brain, the lesion was not confined to Broca's area but involved Wernicke's zone. The second specimen did not show a circumscribed lesion but, on the contrary, a generalized wasting; the posterior part of the third frontal convolution was not especially implicated.

The terms in the classification given above, e.g., motor asphasia, agraphia, "word deafness," etc., are still sometimes employed, but it is understood they refer to the outstanding features of a given case rather than that they denote clear-cut types.

### Head's Classification of the Aphasias

Head's views, based upon an exhaustive study of patients suffering from gunshot wounds of the cortex, are also strongly opposed to the conception of the speech faculty being dependent upon circumscribed anatomical centers. He considers speech to be a highly integrated cortical process—a special aspect of intelligence—yet one which can suffer with little lowering of the general intellectual level. The different components of the speech faculty, he decides, cannot be separated from one another by disease. Nor, consequently, can the types of aphasia be classed as "motor" or "sensory," but in any type, deficiencies on both the receptive and the executive side can be demonstrated. Head concluded that cortical representation of speech mechanisms was more diffuse than had been supposed and that strict localization was impossible. Aphasia is a state in which the power to use words and other symbols as instruments of thought and expression is affected or, as he expresses it, "aphasia is a defect in symbolic formation and expression." The more complicated or abstract the idea which must be understood or expressed, the greater is the difficulty. Thus an aphasic may be able to name *objects* correctly but fails to find the word for a more *abstract idea*, e.g., color. Shown a black object, for instance, and asked to name its color he fails to do so, yet indicates that he recognizes that it is black by saying "what you do for the dead." An aphasic soldier when shown a red object said, "what the staff wear."

Head, as a result of his investigation of aphasic patients, devised a series of six tests of graded severity. These tests are briefly as follows:

*1. Naming and recognition of common objects.* Six objects, e.g., a pencil, key, knife, etc. The patient is asked to name each object as it is pointed out to him. Next he is asked to point to each object as its name is called out. He is then given cards upon each of which the name of one of the objects is written. He is asked to indicate the object named.

*2. Naming and recognition of colors.* This test is

carried out in a manner similar to that described for test (1) except that eight strips of differently colored silk are substituted for the six objects.

*3. Man, cat and dog test* is designed to investigate the powers of reading and writing in their most elementary forms. The printed words "man," "cat" and "dog" are employed. The subject is asked to read these words; to write them from dictation; to copy them or to repeat them after hearing them spoken. Pictures of a man, a cat and a dog are also shown and the patient asked to write or to speak their names.

*4. The clock tests.* The patient is requested to set the hands of a clock in the same positions as those of a similar one set by the observer. He is then told to set the clock from verbal or printed commands. Again, he is asked to state the time aloud or by writing, of a clock set by the observer.

*5. Coin bowl tests.* Pennies are placed one in front of each of four bowls. The patient is asked verbally and in writing to place a coin in one or other of the bowls according to their number in the row. He is then asked to give an order himself and to carry it out according to his own words.

*6. The hand, eye and ear tests.* The patient is requested to repeat the movements of the observer which consist in touching an eye or an ear with one or other hand. When this is done correctly the patient's hand which moves is of course diagonally opposite to the hand of the observer. A much easier form of this test is the imitation of the observers movement as reflected in a mirror. This simply requires matching without calculation.

The aphasic frequently fails to recognize that when the one hand is brought to his contralateral eye or ear the hand crosses the face. A further part of the test is to ask him to imitate the positions shown in pictorial form upon cards or to carry out the movements from printed and verbal instructions. Finally, he is asked to write down movements made by the observer.

Employing these tests Head divided aphasia into four types, as follows:

1. VERBAL DEFECTS. The outstanding feature is a defect in the utterance of individual words of all kinds. The power to express an idea in words is practically lost. The patient, however is not entirely speechless but can usually utter a few monosyllables, "yes" or "no", etc., or ejaculations and emotional expressions, such as, "damn", "oh dear me". When the disorder is less severe, the words are mispronounced but sentences are correctly constructed. For example, one patient said that he had trouble with "tenical terms" (technical terms) and that he "had *diffulty* in remembering what you do with a skull, *tri-tre-tripine*"

(trepan). Another spoke of "*claration* of war by the *Ollies*" (declaration . . . Allies). Another would say "pyramerad" (pyramid), "sissiors" (scissors) and "oboid" (ovoid). Such patients read with difficulty and writing is very defective or impossible. They usually understand printed or oral commands. This form of aphasia resembles the classical motor aphasia described on page 1250.

2. SYNTACTICAL DEFECTS (agrammatism, jargon dysphasia). The patient is voluble but speaks a jargon in which, though the individual words may be fairly accurately pronounced, they are strung into short phrases or badly constructed sentences without articles, prepositions or conjunctions. The ability to read aloud is impaired, and curiously enough such a patient, though he can write a well constructed letter, may be quite unable to read it coherently. Such a one when asked the contents of a letter which he had just written replied, "I can't; I know, I suppose in time, not now, funny thing, why." In other instances the words themselves are often slurred over, mutilated and may be unrecognizable. Speech sometimes resembles "baby talk". Thus one patient when asked what his right arm felt like replied "Tiffrent from uffer um" (different from other arm). The understanding of ordinary conversation is defective.

3. NOMINAL (NAMING) DEFECTS. In this form of speech disorder the patient has difficulty in finding the right word to express his meaning or in naming a well known object. He will often employ a descriptive phrase in substitution for the word which he cannot recall. For example, a painter when asked to name a series of colors could not say "violet" but instead explained that "it was made with black, red and a bit of blue." Another when asked to tell the time from a clock which had both hands at 12 replied "That is when you eat." These patients can draw from a model either directly or from memory, after it has been shown and then removed, but are usually unable to draw from imagination. They write a coherent letter with difficulty, usually fail to carry out simple arithmetical exercises and confuse the values of coins.

4. SEMANTIC[8] DEFECTS. A patient suffering from this type experiences little difficulty in articulate speech, can name objects, understands individual words and some sentences, but the general meaning of what he hears escapes him.

[8] Semainein = to signify.

He often fails to follow his own utterances to an intelligent conclusion, his sentences trailing off as though he had forgotten what he had started out to say. When shown a picture he picks out the details but fails to grasp the meaning which it conveys to others. Such a patient therefore misses the point of a joke whether this is printed, told to him, or is in pictorial form. He fails to comprehend the significance of much that he sees and hears. There is no impairment in the pronunciation of words and, though speech tends to be in short jerky sentences, syntax and intonation are not disturbed.

Head, though he discards the conception that the neural basis of speech consists of strictly localized anatomical "centers" wherein resides *exclusively* one or other of the speech functions—auditory, visual or motor—believes that regions exist in the cortex "where the progress of some mode of action can be reinforced, deviated or inhibited." These regions constitute foci of integration—convergence points for association paths. Destruction of one or other of such foci or "knots" of association paths will depress *as a whole* the psychological processes underlying speech. The speech faculty is disabled; certain faculties are lost, while others are retained. Yet he points out that it is not logical to conclude that the abilities which remain and those which have been abolished constitute essentially separate and distinct functions from which the normal processes of speech have been synthesized, or that they are represented in specific circumscribed areas. To make a rather crude comparison—a person who has injured his foot, knee or hip, adjusts his locomotor apparatus as best he can. He hops or limps, yet it cannot be argued that the hopping or the limping motion which he employs is simply one of the component movements employed in the normal act of walking and which the injury has left intact. Nevertheless, the form which the disability assumes is undoubtedly influenced by the site of the injury. The ambulatory abnormality, for example, which results from an injury to the foot is different from that resulting from injury to the knee or hip. So too the nature of the speech disability is influenced by the particular region of the cortex involved. Thus if the lesion is in the neighborhood of the lower part of the precentral and postcentral convolutions of the dominant hemisphere the speech defect tends to be of the *verbal* type. In injury to the temporal lobe the speech defect tends to be of the *syntactical* type.

In a lesion in the region of the angular gyrus of the dominant hemisphere the patient has difficulty, particularly, in finding names for things (*nominal defect*); damage to the cortex in the region of the supramarginal gyrus results in a *semantic defect*.

*Anarthria or dysarthria* is loss or difficulty of speech due to paresis, paralysis or ataxia of the muscles concerned in articulation. There is no impairment of the psychical aspects of speech, i.e., "internal speech" is unaffected; there is no difficulty in the comprehension of spoken or written speech. Other functions, e.g., swallowing, which are dependent upon the same groups of muscles as those used in speech, are also frequently affected. The condition may result from a lesion in the internal capsule or corpus striatum, bulbar nuclei or peripheral fibers, or from disease of the muscles themselves. Since the muscular mechanism of speech is innervated from both sides of the brain unilateral central lesions are not followed by permanent anarthria. A lesion of the cerebellum or of its connections may also cause disordered control of the muscles of articulation (p. 1288).

### Apraxia and Agnosia

*Apraxia* (unable to act) is the inability to perform purposeful movements at will, either at command or in imitation, though the muscles normally engaged in the act are not paralysed. It is allied to aphasia, which might be called apraxia of the speech faculty. Apraxia may be sensory or motor. In the former, the patient does not recognize the significance of an object (visual agnosia), and therefore cannot put it to its proper use; this is simply visual agnosia. When, for example, he is given a pencil he may, upon a request to use it, attempt to clean his teeth with it or smoke it like a pipe. In motor apraxia the patient has no conception, or a very defective one, of the pattern of muscular movement required to perform a purposeful act. For example, apraxia of the tongue is frequently seen in hemiplegic patients. The tongue cannot be protruded upon request, but a moment later the patient may without thought lick his lips. When given an object, and asked to use it, though he recognizes it and knows its use, he cannot form the "motor picture" required to execute the act but manipulates the object in an awkward aimless manner. The defect is evidently in the physical sphere and not due to disease of the cells of the motor area or of the corticospinal fibers. It is thought to be due to the interruption of association tracts connecting the precentral gyrus with higher psychical regions of the cortex where impressions of the movements of muscles are received, synthesized and stored as kinesthetic memories. This higher ideational area probably lies in the region of the left supramarginal gyrus in right-handed persons. A lesion of this region may cause bilateral apraxia; one confined to the anterior part of the corpus callosum is likely to interrupt fibers passing from the left hemisphere to the right precentral convolution and may cause apraxia of the left side.

*Agnosia* (not knowing) is a defect of a higher level of consciousness than the mere inability to perceive tactile, visual, auditory or other forms of sensation; it results rather from the failure to interpret sensory impressions which enable an object, sound, symbol, etc., to be recognized and have meaning. A patient suffering from auditory agnosia, for example, cannot appreciate music or the meaning of other sounds. "Word blindness" and "word deafness" are forms of auditory and visual agnosia, respectively. The subject of visual agnosia is unable to name an object, not that he is aphasic in the true sense, but simply because the object is quite strange to him. When shown an object and asked to use it he behaves quite differently from the patient with motor apraxia who recognizes it but is unable to perform the necessary movement.

*Astereognosis* is a disorder in which though sensations of touch and muscle sense are retained, the patient cannot recognize an object placed in his hand if his eyes are closed. Visual agnosia is seen in lesions of the occipital lobe of the dominant hemisphere, auditory agnosia in injury to the temporal cortex, and astereognosis in lesions of the parietal lobe posterior to the postcentral gyrus.

*Agraphia* or *dysgraphia*, the inability to write or difficulty in writing, is usually associated with visual agnosia in so far as the recognition of written words is concerned, i.e., word blindness.

## Epilepsy

Epilepsy is a disorder arising as the result of an abnormal and severe discharge of nervous energy from some part of the central nervous system, usually the cerebral cortex. Epilepsy may be generalized, involving the entire organism or localized. Generalized seizures are of three types, grand mal, petit mal and psychomotor. In *grand mal* there is an abrupt loss of consciousness and a generalized convulsion. Two stages of the attack or seizure are recognized. In the first or *tonic stage* the muscles contract tonically, the spasms often twisting the facial features and holding the head and limbs in distorted positions. The arms are most commonly flexed and the lower limbs rigidly extended. After a few seconds the tonic spasm gives place to jerking movements, often violent,

of the limbs, face and muscles of mastication. This is spoken of as the *clonic stage*. Either during this stage or in the tonic stage the tongue may be bitten. Before the onset of the convulsion a large proportion of epileptics receive a warning in the form of a sensation or hallucination, the character of which varies in individual cases. The warning sensation or *aura*, as it is called, may be auditory, e.g., voices, music, etc., visual, e.g., flashes of light, sparks, etc., olfactory, gustatory, cutaneous, visceral or vasomotor, equilibratory, or anesthetic, i.e., a numbness in some part of the body. Turning of the head and trunk to one side and deviation of the eyes are commonly observed. The patient sometimes utters a cry or scream— the epileptic cry—just before consciousness is lost. After the convulsion the subject remains for a time in a stupor. Sometimes a number of convulsive seizures occur in rapid succession, the patient failing to regain consciousness in the intervals between them. This very serious condition is called *status epilepticus*. Minor seizures known as *petit mal* are characterized by brief periods during which the patient loses contact with his environment. He stares into space. There are no convulsive movements. A third form known as *psychomotor* epilepsy is marked by automatic movements, such as smacking of the lips, chewing, together with a clouded, "dreamy" feeling of unreality, or of having seen or heard before some sight or auditory impression which is actually happening at the moment ("déja vu" or "déja entendu" phenomenon, respectively). Or there may be a confused mental state persisting for a minute or two, or for a longer period. During this time the patient may perform automatic acts of which he is quite unaware and does not remember. Generalized convulsions do not occur nor does the subject fall to the ground during the psychomotor seizure, but patients who have such seizures may also suffer from generalized convulsions. Psychomotor seizures are most commonly due to disturbances in the temporal lobe.

A tumor in the hypothalamic region may cause an outburst of autonomic phenomena.

*Localized epilepsy* may occur in several different forms. These are often referred to as *Jacksonian epilepsy* because they are indicative of an abnormality in a particular part of the brain. Thus motor Jacksonian seizures are indicative of a disturbance in the precentral motor cortex, hallucinations of taste and smell are indicative of an abnormal nervous discharge from the uncus on the medial surface of the temporal lobe, sensory Jacksonian seizures indicate disease in the parietal region, etc.

Motor Jacksonian seizures commonly begin by a turning of the head and eyes toward the side opposite the lesion in the brain if it is located in the anterior part of the precentral motor cortex, or by a twitching of the foot or leg if it is in the upper part of the precentral region. Such attacks may also begin with a twitching of a finger, or of the hand or the face depending upon the seat of the irritation in the cortex which initiates the attack. These convulsions may remain localized to the part of the body in which they start or they may spread by a steady march to neighboring parts as portions of the cortex lying near to the original focus become involved in the irritative process. The spreading convulsion may cease after extending to all of one extremity or to one side of the body or it may continue until a generalized convulsion has occurred.

Such focal or localized convulsive seizures or seizures with localized onsets may develop as the result of many different kinds of disease processes in the brain. Tumors, abscesses, traumatic scars, vascular abnormalities are among the more common processes found to be responsible for such attacks. It must be noted that not all patients who have such disease processes suffer from epileptic attacks and that even in those patients who do have them the attacks occur at relatively infrequent intervals although the disease process is constantly present. It is thus obvious that some other process, neurological or metabolic, is essential to the development of such seizures. The tumor or scar alone is not enough.

*Idiopathic or cryptogenic epilepsy.* Epilepsy which cannot be explained by the presence of a demonstrable lesion of the brain is called idiopathic or cryptogenic. Though many theories have been advanced, the cause of this type of the disease remains obscure. There is a tendency today to look upon epilepsy as a symptom, or rather a group of symptoms common to several rather than to a single primary pathological state. Convulsions, whose features are indistinguishable from those of the epileptic seizure, occur in a number of conditions. In animals convulsions may be produced by injections of absinthe or caffeine. Hypocalcemia (ch. 59), hypoglycemia (ch. 48), cerebral edema or anemia and other states may be accompanied by generalized convulsions of an epileptiform character.

With regard to the neural mechanism through which the fits are produced, some authorities have thought that the convulsions are the result of *increased excitability of the cortex* and, therefore, comparable in their mode of production to those of the Jacksonian type, or to those produced by experimental stimulation of the cortex. Others view the convulsions as a *release phenomenon* due to the inhibition of cortical areas which normally exert a controlling influence upon lower motor centers, e.g., weakening of suppressor action. Finally, there is the view of Penfield and his colleagues that the primary disturbance in idiopathic epilepsy has its origin in a subcortical mechanism.

The close correspondence between the convulsive seizure as seen in focal epilepsy or to artificial stimulation of the cortex, and the fits of idiopathic epilepsy appears to support the first alternative as a cause of the generalized seizure known as grand mal. However, the *primary* disturbance responsible for the cortical discharge in idiopathic epilepsy probably lies outside the cortex. Evidence for a subcortical origin of petit mal attacks is provided by electroencephalographic studies. During such an attack, electrical potentials of the wave—spike type (fig. 67.10)—appear synchronously over prefrontal areas as well as from other widely separated cortical areas. This suggests that the cortical discharges are initiated in a common subcortical region (centrencephalic system) connected with extensive areas of the cortex. Jasper and Drooglever-Fortuyn, experimenting with cats produced electrical potentials from wide spread areas of the cortex synchronously in both hemispheres by rhythmical stimulation of a small area (2 mm. in diameter) in the anterior part of the massa intermedia of the thalamus. The cortical potentials were of the wave-spike form characteristic of petit mal.

Moreover the general convulsions which occur with focal epilepsy are thought to be due to the discharge of impulses from the cortical focus into the subcortical mechanism and causes unconsciousness. The subcortical structures then fire back and cause widespread excitation of the cortex of both hemispheres.

The nature of the underlying bodily state responsible for the convulsive seizures of idiopathic epilepsy are unknown. There are a number of drugs, e.g., metrazol, which are capable of inducing convulsions, and several others, e.g., phenobarbital and tridione, which are anticonvulsive, but they have not led to an understanding of the

TABLE 67.1

| | Conditions Which May Tend To | |
| --- | --- | --- |
| | Prevent seizures | Precipitate seizures |
| Oxygen | Rich supply | Poor supply |
| Acid-base equilibrium | Acidosis Ingestion of acids or acid-forming salts Breathing CO₂ | Alkalosis Hyperpnea— "blowing off" CO₂ |
| Water balance | Dehydration | Edema |
| Serum calcium | Increase | Decrease (hypocalcemia) |
| Blood glucose | Normal level | Decrease (hypoglycemia) |
| Acetylcholine | — | Increase |
| Cholinesterase | — | Decrease |
| Body temperature | — | Increase |

FIG. 67.9. Normal electroencephalogram taken from the occipital region. O and C refer, respectively, to open and closed eyes. (After Adrian and Matthews.)

pathogenesis of the convulsive seizures of epilepsy. Susceptibility to an epileptic seizure is influenced by several physiological and biochemical factors which are given in table 67.1, but they do not bear a specific relationship to the cause of idiopathic epilepsy, but merely affect the tendency to convulsive seizures of any kind.

The view that the actual seizure was initiated by cerebral ischemia resulting from a spasm of the cortical vessels has not been sustained. The blood flow through the brain of epileptics and the oxygen consumption have been found to be no different from that of nonepileptics. In focal epilepsy, however, local ischemia may play a part. Biochemical studies of such epileptogenic areas have not however revealed any important abnormality. The pH of the extracellular fluid shows no change from the normal, or a slight rise.

The induction of a dehydrated state of acidosis (by means of a ketogenic diet) has been employed to reduce the susceptibility of epileptics to seizures but not very effectively, and pitressin combined with an increase in the water intake is used as a test (*water-pitressin test*) in diagnosis. But in only about 30 per cent of epileptics is a seizure precipitated, so a negative result does not exclude epilepsy.

### The Electroencephalogram (EEG)

In 1929 Berger reported his discovery that changes in electrical potential could be recorded from the head of the human subject by means of electrodes applied to the scalp or needle electrodes placed in contact with the periosteum of the skull. These brain potentials were later studied by Adrian and Matthews. In normal subjects three wave frequencies may be recorded, the *alpha, beta* and *delta* rhythms.[9] The alpha rhythm consists of rhythmical oscillations in electrical potential occurring at the rate of 8 to 10 per second (fig. 67.9). The waves have a voltage of about 50 microvolts on the average. The beta rhythm has a frequency of 15 to 60 per second, and the waves are of lower voltage (5 to 10 microvolts); the frequency of the delta waves is from 1 to 5 per second and the voltage is relatively high (20 to 200 microvolts). No precise cytoarchitectural area can be said to have a characteristic rhythm as was once supposed, but differences are found between rather large areas of the cortex. Thus the alpha rhythm dominates records from the occipital region or from the posterior parts of the parietal and temporal lobes. The sensorimotor region emits waves with a frequency of from 20 to 25 per second; the anterior frontal areas give out waves at the rate of from 8 to 5 per second.

The alpha rhythm occurs in the *inattentive* brain, as in drowsiness or light sleep, narcosis or when the eyes are closed; it is abolished by visual and other types of stimulus or by mental effort (e.g., mathematical calculation). It, therefore diminishes when the eyes are open. This is true even if the subject opens his eyes in the dark and tries to see. It is apparent, therefore, that it is the attention rather than the visual stimulus itself that abolishes the alpha rhythm when the eyes are opened. On the other hand if

[9] A faster rhythm (*gamma*) appears in rare instances.

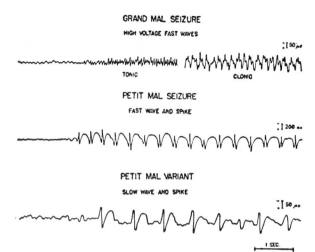

GRAND MAL SEIZURE
HIGH VOLTAGE FAST WAVES

TONIC          CLONIC

PETIT MAL SEIZURE
FAST WAVE AND SPIKE

PETIT MAL VARIANT
SLOW WAVE AND SPIKE

FIG. 67.10. Showing electroencephalograms in epilepsy. (Modified after Gibbs and associates.)

the visual field is uniform, that is without pattern, or glasses are worn which blur the visual image so that it has no meaning, the rhythm is not abolished. An attempt to discern any detail causes the alpha wave to disappear immediately. A visual field that flickers causes the waves to assume the same rate as that of the flicker within certain definite limits. The delta waves can be recorded very rarely from a normal adult while awake, but appear normally during deep sleep or during the waking hours in early childhood. Generally speaking, their presence in an adult, except during sleep, indicates some pathological process in the brain—tumor, epilepsy, raised intracranial pressure, mental deficiency or depression of consciousness by toxic or other factors. When present they tend to displace the alpha rhythm. Neither the beta nor the delta waves are affected by opening or closing the eyes.

There has been a difference of opinion as to the origin of the potential changes as recorded in the EEG. Whether they are inherent in the cortex, or are dependent upon subcortical structures has been argued. Definite conclusions as to the source and significance of the alterations in electrical potential recorded in the electroencephalogram can not yet be drawn. Certainly the electroencephalogram is to a considerable degree dependent upon the activity of neurons in subcortical centers, notably the reticular formation.

The EEG is affected profoundly by certain general states. *Hypoxia* causes at first a moderate slowing of the rhythm, but as the oxygen lack becomes more severe large delta waves appear; with persistent and severe hypoxia the amplitude

of the waves declines and may reach almost the vanishing point. *Hypoglycemia* causes an effect somewhat similar to that of hypoxia; when the blood sugar falls below about 60 mg. per cent, delta waves (1 to 3 per second) are seen, though the alpha rhythm is not abolished entirely. The effects of hypoxia and hypoglycemia enhance one another, their summed effects being much greater than the effect of each alone. Hyperglycemia has little effect upon the cortical potentials. Increase in carbon dioxide tension increases the rate, but reduces the amplitude of the waves. Blowing off of $CO_2$, as by overbreathing, has the opposite effect.

Abnormalities of the electroencephalogram in brain tumor, especially of so-called silent areas of the brain, and in epilepsy, may be of diagnostic value. In cerebral tumor or brain abscess, as shown by Walter and by Case, the functionally depressed brain tissue surrounding the lesion gives out waves of slow rhythm (delta waves) which, combined with a loss or diminution in the alpha rhythm over the occipital region may be of considerable aid in localization. However, the electroencephalogram may give misleading information as to the location of a brain tumor and a "normal" electroencephalogram in the presence of a brain tumor is not rare.

Epileptic seizures are characterized by pronounced departures from the normal rhythm. In *petit mal* attacks, large slow waves appear about a second before the attack is clinically manifest, and displace the previous rhythm. Each large wave is followed by a sharp spike deflection (fig. 67.10). In the tonic stage of a *grand mal* seizure, waves of relatively high frequency (10 to 30 per second) and of low voltage appear, but as the attack progresses into the clonic phase these fast waves give place to slower and large waves which continue into the stage of stupor following the seizure. Delta waves may be a prominent feature of the electroencephalogram of epileptics between seizures (fig. 67.10). Approximately one-third of epileptic adults have "normal" electroencephalograms.

In normal sleep the pattern of the electrical potentials recorded from the brain varies with the depth of unconsciousness. During light sleep delta waves make their appearance while the alpha waves superimposed upon the slower rhythm of the latter persist. In deep sleep the alpha rhythm disappears being replaced by delta waves, or in some instances by a faster rhythm with a frequency of about 14 per second. During the light sleep before awakening the record shows only an odd slow wave. As consciousness returns the tracing consists of an intermittent alpha rhythm which becomes continuous upon waking.

### Headache

Headache is one of the commonest of symptoms and occurs in a great variety of diseased states, e.g., arterial hypertension, chronic nephritis, eye strain, chronic disease of the paranasal sinuses, brain tumor, etc.

Headache may also be due to disturbances in the scalp or in the skull, such as osteitis, periostitis, osteomyelitis, tumor of the bone, etc. The temporary but severe pain felt in the frontal region by a normal person after eating ice cream is an example of a referred pain. The pain is most probably due to a stimulation of sensory nerve endings in the roof of the mouth producing reflex vasomotor changes, or it may be referred to the forehead through central connections with the sensory nucleus of the trigeminal nerve.

The two principal causes of the more common types of headache are either vascular in nature (stimulation of sensory nerves which accompany the vessels in the scalp or in the meninges) or a sustained reflex contraction of the posterior muscles of the neck which insert into the scalp and the skull. This latter reflex mechanism is mainly responsible for the headache of eyestrain—refractive errors, or unbalanced action of the extraocular muscles, excessive and prolonged accommodation—increased intraocular pressure also may contribute to the pain. Disease of the cervical spine may also induce reflex protective spasm of the muscles of the posterior neck and produce headaches.

The headache associated with an intracranial tumor, and with hypertension, are of vascular origin. The arteries and smaller veins on the convexity of the human hemispheres have been shown by neurosurgeons to be insensitive, but the larger arteries in the Sylvian (lateral) fissure and at the base of the brain, e.g., circle of Willis, vertebral, basilar, the larger of cerebral vessels of the dura, the branches of the anterior and posterior meningeals, as well as the arteries of the scalp, are accompanied by pain fibers which are stimulated by any stretching force. The larger veins where they empty into the dural sinuses are also sensitive. The brain substance itself is painless. The headache of intracranial tumor or abscess is not due primarily to the high intracranial pressure itself, but is the result of the displacement of the brain, local mechanical effect of the tumor, or to blockage of some part of the ventricular system. In this way traction or distortion of the vessels with consequent stretching of the sensitive vascular nerve endings, and, in some cases, of cranial nerves, results. In a large proportion of cases of headache due to brain tumor, the intracranial pressure is not elevated (Wolff and Wolff), and when headache exists, lowering the pressure within the skull does not always relieve it. Raising the intracranial pressure in a normal person or one with an intracranial growth does not necessarily cause headache. In fact intracranial tumors may be present with a considerable increase in intracranial pressure and still be unassociated with headache. On the other hand, lowering the intracranial pressure below the usual level as by drainage of cerebrospinal fluid causes severe headache. A normal subject experiences headache when about 20 cc. of fluid are withdrawn by lumbar puncture, and he is raised into the erect position. In the horizontal position, or if the fluid removed is replaced by an equal quantity of saline, the head pain is abolished or at least reduced.

Headache, presumably of vascular origin, can be produced in any normal person, as was shown by Wolff and his associates, by a sudden sharp rotary movement of the head. When a subject with headache due, apparently, to overdistension of the cerebral vessels was centrifuged, so as to drive blood out of the vessels, the pain was relieved. The intense headache caused by an injection of *histamine* appears to be due to cerebral vasodilation and distension of the vessels; it is relieved by increasing the cerebrospinal fluid pressure, and thus providing a circumferential support for the vessels, and protecting the pain endings from stretch. The headaches of fever and toxic states are similar in their origins to histamine headache; they, too, are ameliorated by raising the cerebrospinal fluid pressure.

*Hypertensive headache* is not due essentially to the high blood pressure (Wolff and Wolff), but rather to the amplitude of the movement of the arterial wall at each pulse beat which varies with the contractile state of the vascular wall itself. When the latter is relaxed and resilient, a given distending force will exert a greater degree of stretch upon the pain endings than when the walls are firmer and do not so readily permit stretching of the nerve terminals. The headache of arterial hypertension therefore varies with the amplitude of the movement of the arterial wall and is relieved by pressure upon the common carotid which reduces the pulse amplitude. Though the headache is not directly related to the height of the blood pressure, (since it may occur with equal intensity when the pressure is high, moderate or relatively low), with any given degree of relaxation of the vascular wall, the pain will of course be more intense when the pressure is high than when low, because a greater excursion of the vascular wall will occur in the former instance. Ergotamine, while it tends to increase the blood pressure rather than to reduce it, diminishes the amplitude of the arterial pulsations and, as a consequence, has a moderating effect upon the intensity of the headache.

The site of the headache in brain tumor may be of some value as a localizing symptom. The pain overlies the tumor or is on the same side in about 60 per cent of cases. In tumors of a cerebral hemisphere (supratentorial tumors) the pain is usually in the front of the head, the pain impulses being transmitted through branches of the 5th nerve, whereas in those of the posterior fossa the pain is felt in the occipital region, the impulses travelling by branches of the 9th and 10th cranial and upper cervical nerves.

MIGRAINE. (Synonyms, megrim; hemicrania; sick headache.) This is a type of headache whose special features entitle it to be placed in a class by itself. The headache is periodic, severe and often accompanied by nausea and vomiting. In many instances some type of sensory disturbance (aura) ushers in the attack. This frequently takes the form of scintillating colored lights or the so-called fortification figures, that is, zig-zag luminous bands which are suggestive of the walls of a turret. The visual hallucinations have a homonymous distribution, that is, they occur in the right or the left halves of the visual fields (ch. 75). Temporary hemianopia may follow or blindness of the central part of the retina may accompany the visual sensations. Cutaneous, auditory or gustatory aurae occasionally occur. The headache is localized at first but soon spreads to involve the entire half of the head; the pain is then on the side opposite to that of the hallucinations. Not unusually, however, the headache is bilateral, or is unilateral to start with, and later spreads to involve the opposite side of the head. In most cases of migraine, the pain has its origin in extracranial vessels; the branches of the external carotid, such as, the temporal or occipital artery being most commonly involved. When the pain originates intracranially the anterior and middle meningeal arteries are probably implicated.

The mechanism underlying the migrainous headache is not universally agreed upon. It is thought by some (Wolff and Wolff) to have a vascular origin, similar in nature to that causing hypertensive headache, namely a relaxed state of the vascular wall, and a resulting pulsatile movement of greater than usual amplitude. The pain varies in intensity with the amplitude of the arterial pulsations, and is reduced in intensity by compression of the common carotid or by ergotamine which, as mentioned above, reduces the pulse amplitude. In other cases the headache of migraine appears to be due to cortical vasodilation (like the histamine headache) which follows upon a period of vasoconstriction. The ischemia of the cortex during the vasoconstrictor phase would explain the visual hallucinations mentioned above, which an increase in pulse amplitude is unable to do; though the phase of vasodilation might quite well be associated with a relaxed state of the larger cerebral vessels. It has been suggested that migraine may sometimes be of allergic origin, dilation of the cortical vessels being the result of the local liberation of histamine (H-substance). The relatively high incidence of eosinophilia in migraine lends support to the idea of an allergic reaction.

## REFERENCES

ADRIAN, E. D. J. Physiol., 1941, **100**, 159.

ADRIAN, E. D. AND MATTHEWS, B. H. C. Brain, 1934, **57**, 355.

ALVAREZ, W. C. Physiol. Rev., 1924, **4**, 352.

BAILEY, P. AND VON BONIN, G. The isocortex of man. University of Illinois Press, Urbana, Ill. 1951.

BUCY, P. C. Brain, 1957, **80**, 376.

BUCY, P. C. AND FULTON, J. F. Brain, 1933, **56**, 318.

BUCY, P. C. AND KLUVER, H. Arch. Neurol. & Psychiat., 1940, 44, 1142. J. Comp. Neurol., 1955, 103, 151.

BUCY, P. C. AND PRIBRAM, K. H. Arch. Neurol. & Psychiat., 1943, 50, 456.

BORNSTEIN, W. S. Yale J. Biol. & Med., 1940, 12, 719.

BRICKNER, R. M. A. Res. Nerv. & Ment. Dis., Proc., 1934, 13, 259.

CASE, T. J. J. Nerv. & Ment. Dis., 1938, 87, 598.

CHOW, K. L. J. Comp. Neurol., 1950, 93, 313.

CLARK, W. E. LE G. Lancet, 1948, 1, 353.

DUSSER DE BARENNE, J. G., McCULLOCK, W. S. AND NIMS, L. F. J. Neurophysiol., 1941, 4, 311.

GIBBS, F. A., GIBBS, E. L. AND LENNOX, W. G Brain, 1935, 58, 44.

HAGBARTH, K. E. AND KERR, D. I. B. J. Neurophysiol., 1954, 17, 295.

HALSTEAD, W. C. Brain and intelligence; a quantitative study of the frontal lobes. University of Chicago Press, Chicago, 1947.

HINES, M. Bull. Johns Hopkins Hosp., 1937, 60, 313. Am. J. Physiol., 1936, 116, 76.

HOLMES, G. AND MAY, W. P. Brain, 1909, 32, 1.

KENNARD, M. A. Arch. Neurol. & Psychiat., 1935, 33, 698.

KENNARD, M. A. AND ECTORS, L. J. Neurophysiol., 1938, 1, 45.

KUYPERS, H. Science, 1958, 128, 662.

MARSHALL, W. H., WOOLSEY, C. N. AND BARD, P. Science, 1937, 85, 388. J. Neurophysiol., 1941, 4, 1.

McCULLOCH, W. S., GRAF, C. AND MAGOUN, H. W. J. Neurophysiol. 1946, 9, 127.

PENFIELD, W. Arch. Neurol. & Psychiat., 1932, 27, 30. Ann. Int. Med., 1933, 7, 303. A. Res. Nerv. Ment. Dis., Proc., 1947, 27, 519. Ibid., 1950, 30, 513.

PENFIELD, W. AND BOLDREY, E. Brain, 1937, 60, 389.

PENFIELD, W. AND JASPER, H. H. See under Monographs and Reviews.

PENFIELD, W. AND RASMUSSEN, T. Fed. Proc., 1947, 6, 452; see also under Monographs and Reviews.

PENFIELD, W. AND WELCH, K. Arch. Neurol. & Psychiat., 1951, 66, 289.

RICHTER, C. P. AND HINES, M. A. Nerv. & Ment. Dis., 1934, 13, 211.

ROBINSON, L. Nineteenth Century, 1891, 30, 831. Brit. M. J., 1891, 2, 1226.

RUNDLES, R. W. AND PAPEZ, J. W. J. Comp. Neurol., 1938, 68, 267.

SIMPSON, D. A. J. Anat., 1952, 86, 20.

TOWER, S. S. Brain, 1940, 63, 36.

WALSHE, F. M. R. AND ROBERTSON, E. G. Brain, 1933, 56, 40.

WALTER, W. G. Lancet, 1936, 2, 305.

WOOLSEY, C. N., SETTLAGE, P. H., MEYER, D. R., SENCER, W., HAMUY, T. P. AND TRAVIS, A. M. A. Res. Nerv. & Ment. Dis., Proc., 1950, 30, 238.

### Monographs and Reviews

ADRIAN, E. D. The physical background of perception. Oxford University Press, 1947.

Association for research in Nervous and Mental Disease. Vol. 7. Epilepsy and the convulsive state. The Williams & Wilkins Co., Baltimore, 1931.

VON BONIN, G. Essay on the cerebral cortex. Am. Lecture Series. Charles C Thomas, Springfield, Ill., 1950.

BRICKNER, R. M. The intellectual functions of the frontal lobes. Macmillan, New York, 1936.

BUCY, P. C. Editor. The precentral motor cortex. 2nd ed., University of Illinois Press, 1949.

CAMPBELL, A. W. Histological studies on the localisation of cerebral function. Cambridge University Press, 1905.

CLARK, W. E. LE G. Lancet, 1948, 1, 354.

COBB, S. Arch. Neurol. & Psychiat., 1932, 27, 1245.

CRITCHLEY, M. The parietal lobes. Edward Arnold & Co., London, 1953.

DUSSER DE BARENNE, J. B. A. Res. Nerv. & Mental Dis., Proc., 1934, 15, 274.

ECONOMO, C. VON. The cytoarchitectonics of the human cerebral cortex. Oxford University Press, 1929.

EWING, A. W. G. Aphasia in children. Oxford University Press, 1930.

FULTON, J. F. AND KELLER, A. D. The sign of Babinski. A study of the evolution of cortical dominance in primates. Charles C Thomas, Springfield, Ill. 1932.

HEAD, H. Studies in neurology. Vol. II. Oxford University Press, 1920.

HEAD, H. Aphasia and kindred disorders of speech (2 vols.). Cambridge University Press, 1926.

HINES, M. Physiol. Rev., 1929, 9, 362. Bull. Johns Hopkins Hosp., 1937, 60, 313.

HOLMES, G. Brain, 1927, 50, 413.

JACOBSEN, C. F. Physiol. Rev., 1939, 19, 303.

LASHLEY, K. S. Harvey Lectures, 1930–31, 26, 46. Physiol. Rev., 1933, 13, 1.

LENNOX, W. G. AND COBB, S. Medicine, 1928, 7, 105.

MONIZ, E. Tentatives opératoires dans le traitement de certaines psychoses. Masson et Cie., Paris, 1936.

OGILVIE, R. S. Handbook of electroencephalography. Addison Wesley Press, Cambridge, Mass., 1949.

PENFIELD, W. AND GAGE, L. A. Res. Nerv. & Ment. Dis., Proc., 1934, 13, 211.

PENFIELD, W. AND JASPER, H. H. Epilepsy and the functional anatomy of the human brain. Little, Brown & Co., Boston, 1954.

PENFIELD, W. AND RASMUSSEN, T. The cerebral cortex of man. Macmillan, N. Y., 1950.

WILSON, S. A. K. Problems in neurology. Ch. I and II. Edward Arnold & Co., London, 1928.

# 68

# CONDITIONED REFLEXES. SLEEP

## Definitions

The ordinary reflex with which we are all familiar is an inherited characteristic of the species and is not dependent upon previous experience. Its pathways are established at birth. This type Pavlov termed an *inborn* or *unconditioned reflex*. For example, food placed in the mouth of a new-born puppy evokes a scretion of saliva. The reaction depends solely upon the stimulation of receptors (taste, touch, etc.) in the mouth, the afferent and efferent nerves and the salivary centers in the medulla oblongata. When, on the other hand, the young animal sees or smells a piece of meat for the *first* time no secretion of saliva results. Yet if an animal who has eaten meat on previous occasions sees a morsel, a profuse secretion of saliva occurs. This reaction, which depends upon previous experience, Pavlov has termed a *conditioned* or *acquired reflex*. Its pathways are not fully established at birth but are developed by training. Quite evidently the reaction of the older animal is the result of an association established in the past between the stimulus applied to the receptors of the mouth, and the appearance of the food, i.e., a visual stimulus. The former is called the *unconditioned*, the latter the *conditioned stimulus*. Not only the qualities of the food itself but changes in the environment extraneous to the food, if they occur in association with feeding, can serve as conditioned stimuli.

Conditioned reflexes may be either of an excitatory character, e.g., the secretion of saliva, or have an inhibitory action. The former are termed *positive* or *excitatory*, the latter *negative* or *inhibitory*.

## Positive or Excitatory Conditioned Reflexes

In the great majority of the experiments performed by Pavlov and his school, the secretion of saliva was chosen as the indicator of the conditioned response. In order to follow the secretory reaction with precision the opening of the parotid or submaxillary duct was transplanted to the cheek or chin, respectively. The saliva is collected by means of a special apparatus consisting of a funnel sealed over the duct opening and leading into a system of tubes. The secretion is measured in drops by means of an electrical recorder. The animal is held in a stand by means of straps and occupies a sound-proof chamber separate from that of the experimenter (fig. 68.1).

The reflex is established in the following way. While the animal is being fed (unconditioned stimulus) a stimulus, e.g., a flash of light (conditioned stimulus) which is quite alien to the food itself is applied. After this association of the two stimuli has been repeated a number of times, the flash of light alone (i.e., food is withheld) evokes a secretion of saliva. This is called a *conditioned alimentary reflex*. Motor reactions, e.g., movements of the lips and jaws, snapping, whining or barking, and movements of the limbs, accompany the salivary secretion and constitute an integral part of the reflex. The number of repetitions of the experimental procedure, or "lessons," necessary to establish the reflex varies in different animals and in experiments of different types. Many types of conditioned stimulus (visual, auditory, olfactory and cutaneous) have been employed by Pavlov and his associates.[1] In establishing the reflex the conditioned stimulus must precede or accompany the unconditioned stimulus and, except in the case of secondary and trace reflexes, to be presently described, must overlap it for at least a brief period. If the conditioned stimulus *follows* the actual feeding it is quite ineffective, i.e., it will not evoke a reflex when subsequently applied alone. After the period of training, in order to demonstrate the conditioned response satisfacto-

[1] Among these are the following—the sound of a metronome, horn, bell, buzzer, tuning fork, organ pipe or of bubbling water; variously shaped objects, lights, figures or rotating disks; thermal, tactile and painful cutaneous stimuli; the odor of such chemicals as amyl acetate or vanillin. The cessation of a previously continuous stimulus, e.g., a buzzer; the rapid change in the intensity of a stimulus, or even the change in the rate of a rhythmical sound, e.g., a beating metronome, may serve as a conditioned stimulus (see also p. 594).

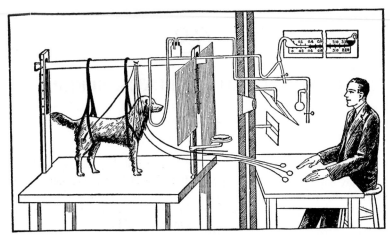

FIG. 68.1. Illustrating arrangements for experiments upon conditioned reflexes. (From Pavlov, *Lectures on Conditioned Reflexes*, International Publishing Company, New York.)

rily, the animal should be alert, not drowsy, and preferably hungry; furthermore it should not be distracted by extraneous stimuli, e.g, a strange sound or light.

### OTHER TYPES OF POSITIVE CONDITIONED REFLEXES

CONDITIONED DEFENSE REFLEXES. Acid injected into an animal's mouth (unconditioned stimulus) causes a profuse secretion of saliva which washes away the offending material. A conditioned reflex to acid is readily established by a series of trials in which a conditioned stimulus, e.g., a light, and the unconditioned stimulus (acid) are applied in combination. Or if an animal has been given a colored acid, it salivates when shown water of the same color. Also, if a painful stimulus is applied to the animal's paw (unconditioned stimulus) during some form of conditioned stimulation (e.g., sound of a buzzer) the motor reactions (e.g., drawing up the limb, turning the head towards the injured part, etc.) which follow the application of the combined stimuli occur, after a few trials, when the conditioned stimulus is employed alone. The painful stimulus may serve also as a conditioned stimulus for a salivary reflex; then, unless the painful stimulus is intense the usual defense reactions are suppressed, salivation alone resulting when the stimulus is applied. The alimentary reflex is in this case stronger than the defense reflex. Pavlov points out that the subordination of the defense reaction by the alimentary reflex is seen when dogs are struggling among themselves for food. Minor injuries (e.g., of the skin) may then be sustained, but they do not evoke a reaction of defense; this is suppressed by the domi-

nant food reflex. On the other hand, if the stimulus (such as one applied to bone) signals a more severe type of injury, or threatens the life of the animal, the defense reaction becomes prepotent.

Of great practical interest is the reflex which becomes established to the repeated injection of morphine. In the dog, morphine administration causes vomiting and salivation, followed by sleep. After a series of injections, these effects result from the mere sight of the syringe, or the approach of the attendant who had previously administered the drug.

SECONDARY AND TERTIARY CONDITIONED REFLEXES. A second stimulus may be conditioned by linking it up with a conditioned stimulus already firmly established. A defense conditioned reflex, let it be supposed, has been established with an electric shock to the front paw as the unconditioned and a touch upon the hind paw as the conditioned stimulus. A second neutral stimulus (e.g., the sound of bubbling water) is now applied and withdrawn a few seconds before the application of the primary conditioned stimulus (touching the hind paw) but the unconditioned stimulus (electric shock) is omitted. If the two stimuli are associated in this way a number of times it is found that the second stimulus (sound of bubbling water) has itself acquired conditioned properties; when applied alone the defense reaction occurs. If a third stimulus (e.g., the sound of a tuning fork) is applied a short time before the second, but the primary conditioned and the unconditioned stimuli are omitted, it now, when employed alone, causes the conditioned response. It has not been found possible to establish a conditioned reflex of the fourth order, and conditioned reflexes beyond the second order cannot be established for alimentary conditioned reflexes.

TRACE CONDITIONED REFLEXES. In establishing this reflex the unconditioned stimulus is made to follow the conditioned stimulus after an interval; when the reflex has been established the conditioned response follows the conditioned stimulus by an interval of the same duration. For example, a tactile stimulus is applied to the skin for half a minute and then withdrawn; one minute later acid is injected into the mouth. After a number of repetitions it is found that when the tactile stimulus is applied alone, although no secretion occurs during its application, a response follows after a minute's interval. Also, if an animal is fed at regular intervals, say every 30 minutes, it is found that after a series of such feedings secretion occurs spontaneously, thereafter, at intervals of approximately 30 minutes, although no food is given. In these instances the time interval itself has evidently acquired the properties of a conditioned stimulus.

## The Biological Significance of Conditioned Responses

Conditioned reflexes enter very largely into animal and human behavior. Many such reflexes are developed naturally as the experiences of everyday life become enriched, and associations accumulate. Stimuli arising in the environment are constantly calling forth conditioned responses of various types serving as signals to guide the animal in its choice of action. By training and discipline more complicated reflexes can be established, such as those forming the basis for the tricks of performing animals. In such instances the sound of a word (command) or a movement made by the trainer serves as a conditioned stimulus to some motor reaction of the animal. In the training and education of the child conditioned reflexes also play a prominent role. Animals with more highly developed nervous systems are capable of the more complicated reflexes, and although one can scarcely speak of certain conditioned reflexes, such as the secretion of saliva following the flash of a light or the sound of a tuning fork, as an intelligent act, the ability of an animal to develop conditioned responses is, nevertheless, a measure of its intelligence. Conditioned reflexes also play an important role in the psychology of sex and, according to Pavlov, in the induction of sleep (p. 1270). Conditioned reflexes which are established under the ordinary circumstances of life are termed *natural*. Those which are established experimentally or by special methods of training are called *artificial*. There is, however, no essential difference between the two. Gantt has enrolled the aid of the conditioned reflex in the investigation of psychiatric conditions. In organic mental disease there was impairment or failure to establish conditioned motor responses to an electric shock, whereas in the psychogenic (functional) types, the responses may be impaired but are not abolished. The conditioned reflex is also used to test sensations, especially hearing, in very young children before they can talk.

## Inhibition of Conditioned Reflexes

Inhibition as applied to conditioned reflexes is divided by Pavlov into *external* or *indirect* and *internal* or *direct*.

EXTERNAL INHIBITION. The conditioned reflex is inhibited by some form of stimulation quite apart from the conditioned stimulus itself. The inhibition arises in a part of the brain other than that in which the conditioned reflex is initiated. For instance, some disturbing factor, a sudden noise, a strange smell, a light, a fresh object in the room, or the entrance of a stranger tends to abolish a conditioned reflex, which in quiet surroundings can be elicited readily. The extraneous stimulus arouses the animal's curiosity and distracts its attention or, in Pavlov's words, evokes an *investigatory reflex*. This purely unconditioned reflex consists of what its name implies—pricking of the ears and turning the eye and head toward the source of the distraction. If the extraneous stimulus is repeated often enough its inhibitory effect is weakened or abolished; the conditioned responses of an animal placed in strange surroundings are at first inhibited but return later. A painful stimulus also sets up an *unconditioned defense reflex*—barking, struggling and other motor reactions which exert an inhibitory effect upon the conditioned response.

INTERNAL INHIBITION. This will be considered under the following headings: (1) *extinction of the conditioned reflex*, (2) *conditioned inhibition*, (3) *inhibition of delay*, and (4) *differential inhibition*.

(1) *Extinction of the conditioned reflex*. If a conditioned reflex is repeated a number of times and the unconditioned stimulus (e.g., feeding in the case of an alimentary reflex) always omitted, the response becomes weaker with each repetition, its latent period lengthens progressively and the reflex finally disappears. The reflex is said to have undergone *extinction*. If, however, after every few repetitions of the reflex the conditioned stimulus is followed by the unconditioned stimulus, extinction does not occur. The former stimulus is then

said to have been *reinforced* by the latter. For example, if a conditioned alimentary reflex has been established to the sound of a buzzer, the application of the latter alone calls forth at first a prompt and ample secretion of saliva. After a variable number of repetitions in which the conditioned stimulus is not followed by feeding, i.e., not reinforced, the secretion becomes less each time and finally ceases. After an hour or two the reflex recovers spontaneously. Extinction is due to inhibition of the cortical elements of the reflex. That is not due simply to fatigue of the salivary gland or of the medullary centers is shown by the fact that after complete extinction, reinforcement of the conditioned stimulus causes the reestablishment of the reflex. Moreover, the reflex continues at full strength after a great number of repetitions if it is followed every few times by reinforcement.

After a reflex has undergone extinction, some external stimulus may temporarily remove the inhibition. That is, just as an extraneous stimulus can inhibit the excitatory phase of a conditioned reflex, so also can it inhibit the inhibitory state. This is called *disinhibition* or the *"inhibition of inhibition"*.

(2) *Conditioned inhibition.* If, after a positive conditioned reflex has been firmly established another stimulus is combined with the conditoned stimulus for a number of trials but reinforcement is always omitted, then, though the conditioned stimulus still causes the customary response when applied alone (and regularly reinforced), it is quite ineffective when in combination with the extra stimulus. For example, an alimentary conditioned stimulus is established to the beat of a metronome. Later, a buzzer is sounded with the metronome, but the combination is not followed by feeding. After a series of such trials the metronome causes a secretion, but the combined stimuli, metronome plus buzzer, are without effect. The sound of the buzzer is termed a *conditioned inhibitor*, and the inhibitory effect which it produces, a *negative* or *inhibitory conditioned reflex*. Usually, in order to demonstrate the inhibitory effect, the primary conditioned stimulus and the conditioned inhibitor must overlap.

(3) *Inhibition of delay.* If during the establishment of a conditioned alimentary reflex, the conditioned stimulus is continued for only a brief period, 1 to 5 seconds, before the unconditioned stimulus is applied, then the conditioned response (secretion of saliva) follows almost immediately upon the commencement of the conditioned stimulus. That is, the reflex has a very short latent

period. If after such a *simultaneous reflex* has been established, it is repeated day after day, but the conditioned stimulus is continued a little longer each time before the reflex is reinforced, the latent period becomes lengthened in proportion to the interval between the application of the two stimuli. The almost simultaneous reflex has been converted into a *delayed reflex*. In other words, postponement of reinforcement has caused the conditioned response to be inhibited during the first part of the action of the conditioned stimulus; during the latter part of the action of the conditioned stimulus the secretion of saliva commences and increases in amount up to the moment when reinforcement ordinarily would have occurred.

(4) *Differential inhibition.* This will be described in the next section.

The examples of internal inhibition just given show the high degree of discriminative and adaptive powers of which the cerebral cortex ia capable. Although such adjustments are purely automatic they are effected with great delicacy and an apparent purpose. In the case of extinction, for instance, the futility of secreting saliva for food which does not follow appears to have been "recognized." The purpose in conditioned inhibition is quite as evident as in positive conditioned reflexes and the inhibition of delay is clearly an adjustment which economically times the secretory response to the moment when food is "expected."

It is not in these special instances that internal inhibition occurs, for all positive conditioned reflexes, although reinforced regularly, undergo inhibition if repeated over a period varying in different animals from weeks to months or even years. They become progressively weaker, the latent period lengthens out and they ultimately disappear. The tendency of conditioned reflexes to undergo inhibition is an inherent property.

### Analyzing and Synthesizing Functions of the Cerebral Cortex

Of the numerous agencies in the environment to which the organism is exposed the great majority might be termed neutral in that they exert neither a beneficial nor an injurious effect. The actions of others are either of definite physiologic value or detrimental to the animal's existence. Through the analyzing mechanism possessed by the nervous system the stimuli to which the latter types of agent give rise are given conditioned properties. Such stimuli are picked out to serve as signals for reactions on the part of the animal appropriate to the respective agents (beneficial or nocuous); they are therefore of the utmost biological importance. The cerebral cortex also possesses synthesizing mechanisms whereby individual stimuli are fused into conditioned complexes (p. 1266).

### The Analyzers

Pavlov divides the neural mechanism of the organism upon which the discriminative faculties depend into a number of *nervous analyzers*. These are constituted of the nerves of special sense, and the afferent nerves of the joints and skeletal muscles, together with their respective receptors and central connections. Thus he speaks of *visual, auditory, olfactory, gustatory, cutaneous* and *motor analyzers*. The receptor of each class is especially responsive to its own type of stimulus—light, sound, etc. The central part of each analyzer, i.e., its terminations in the cerebral cortex, is capable of a very fine discrimination between the different intensities and qualities of stimuli within its own class. The visual analyzer, for example, discriminates between the intensity and quality of different visual stimuli, the auditory analyzer between the intensity, pitch and quality of sounds, the motor analyzer between the various messages (proprioceptive) received from the muscles and joints—and so on for the other analyzers.

In the past, the study of these analyzers, i.e., of the sense organs, has been based very largely upon subjective data gleaned from experiments upon the human subject. The discovery of conditioned reflexes, however, has provided a reliable method for the study of the analyzing functions which being purely objective can in consequence be employed in animal experimentation; the conditioned salivary secretion, for example, is a reaction which readily lends itself to precise measurement and timing.

### Generalization and Differentiation

If a conditioned reflex is established, say to the sound of a tuning fork of 800 cycles per second (c.p.s.), it is found that tones somewhat higher or lower in the scale have also acquired conditioned properties. Also, after a conditioned reflex has been established to a tactile stimulus applied to a certain definite skin area, the stimulation of neighboring areas is also effective. The response, however, becomes weaker the farther away from the original area that the stimulus is applied. This *generalization of stimuli*, as Pavlov calls the

phenomenon, is seen also in the case of olfactory, visual and other analyzers. If, however, the original definite stimulus, for example the tone of 800 c.p.s., is always followed by reinforcement whereas other tones having a higher or lower frequency are employed without reinforcement, then only the tone of 800 c.p.s. evokes a response. The allied stimuli are said to have undergone *differentiation* from the primary stimulus. Pavlov ascribes the phenomenon to a form of internal inhibition— *differential inhibition*. He believes that originally the excitatory process in the cortical part of the analyzer is widespread, but through the antagonism offered by the internal inhibition set up by nonreinforcement of the allied stimuli, it becomes localized to only a minute cortical area corresponding to the receptors affected by the primary stimulus.

The degree to which differentiation between various types of stimulus can be developed is a measure of the analyzing ability of the cerebral hemispheres and is often amazing. The following examples are taken from Pavlov's monograph.

1. Auditory stimuli. (a) *Differentiation of pitch.* Primary stimulus 800 c.p.s. Differentiated stimulus 812 c.p.s. (b) *Differentiation of rhythm.* Primary stimulus 120 beats per minute of a metronome. Differentiated stimulus 118 beats per minute of a metronome (Andreyev). (c) *Differentiation of intensity.* The difference in the intensity of two sounds was so slight that it was detectable by the human ear only when one stimulus was followed immediately by the other. Differentiation was perfectly effected by the dog when the two stimuli were separated by an interval of 17 hours.

2. Visual stimuli. (a) *Differentiation of direction of movement or of the position of an object.* Primary stimulus, clockwise rotation of a disk. Differentiated stimulus. Anticlockwise rotation of the disk. (b) *Differentiation of figures and shapes.* Some of the figures which were differentiated are shown in figure 68.2. A luminous circle thrown upon a screen was readily differentiated from a series of ellipses of the same luminosity; the series started with one having its axes in the ratio of 1:2; of the remainder each successive one approached a little nearer to the circular shape. Differentiation just failed when the ratio of the axes was 8:9. (c) *Differentiation of luminosity.* Two shades of gray which to the human eye appeared exactly the same, even when viewed simultaneously, were perfectly differentiated by the dog when an interval of a minute separated the primary from the differentiated stimulus. (d) *Differentiation of colors* failed in all but one animal investigated, and even it gave a doubtful

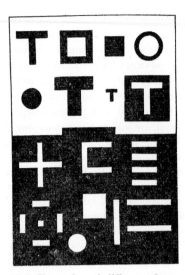

FIG. 68.2. Examples of different figures which were successfully differentiated in experiments upon a dog. The letter T, shown in the upper left-hand corner of the figure, served for the positive stimulus; the other black figures and the white letter T were differentiated from the positive stimulus. In another dog the white cross was the positive stimulus from which the other white figures were differentiated. (From Pavlov, *Conditioned Reflexes*, Oxford University Press.)

result. Color vision in the dog is therefore either absent or very rudimentary.

3. DIFFERENTIATION OF CUTANEOUS AND PROPRIOCEPTIVE STIMULI. Differentiation was obtained for various types of tactile stimuli, e.g., contact with rough or smooth surfaces, pressure with blunt points arranged in different patterns, scratching with a small brush in different directions. Differentiation was also demonstrated between stimuli applied to different areas, for variations in temperature, and between various passive movements, e.g., flexion of ankle as against extension.

4. DIFFERENTIATION OF OLFACTORY AND GUSTATORY STIMULI. Corresponding differentiations were established for various odors (e.g., vanillin, amyl acetate, camphor, etc.) and for taste sensations e.g., meat powders, sugar, cheese, etc.

Conditioned vasomotor responses have been established in human subjects, the unconditioned response (vasoconstriction of the opposite hand) being induced by immersion of one hand in ice-cold water. Ringing of a bell, a light pattern or a word spoken aloud by the experimenter and whispered by the subject were used as conditioned stimuli.

*"Experimental neurosis."* When an animal is presented with a problem which requires a fine degree of differentiating ability, i.e., when a con-

flict between inhibitory and excitatory processes is set up, either inhibition or excitation may gain the upper hand with the suppression of the opposite process. In the former event the animal may become drowsy and fall into a deep sleep (p. 1273), whereas in the latter a nervous disturbance may develop during which even gross differentiation cannot be accomplished. To give an example, a dog was required to discriminate between two visual stimuli, a circle and an oval, the former being followed by feeding (positive stimulus), whereas the latter was not reinforced (negative stimulus). Differentiation was made more and more difficult by making the oval at each successive trial more nearly circular. The experiment proceeded smoothly until the axes of the two figures had a ratio of 8:9. The animal then became fractious, howled and whined in its cage, struggled with its harness and became incapable of discriminating between any oval shape and a circle. Not until after a prolonged rest was the animal's power of discrimination between the two shapes restored, but upon being then confronted with the same problem the nervous disorder returned. *"Experimental neurosis,"* as this state was termed by Pavlov, has also been induced in sheep and pigs by Anderson and Liddell. In some instances the condition was permanent, and Gantt has reported such a state which has persisted for 12 years. The neurosis in this latter instance developed as a result of a conflict aroused in the differentiation of two auditory conditioned stimuli—two closely similar tones. These observations upon experimental neuroses have important psychiatric implications and may give a lead in the interpretation of certain nervous conditions in the human subject. Sexual excitement, as manifested by erections, are not uncommonly associated with the neurosis (see Gantt).

### SYNTHESIS OF STIMULI

The development of the conditioned response is, in itself, evidence of the synthesizing or associative ability of the cortex. Further evidence is afforded by experiments with compound stimuli, i.e., the fusion of separate individual stimuli, whether these act upon the same or upon different analyzers, into a conditioned complex.

As an example of simultaneous stimuli acting upon the same analyzer—an alimentary conditioned reflex was established to a chord of three tones of equal intensity but having a frequency of 85, 256 and 786 c.p.s., respectively. Later each tone when sounded separately caused a response.

The responses to the different tones were approximately equal but weaker than that caused by the chord.

A conditioned reflex may be established to a compound stimulus made up of two stimuli acting *simultaneously* but upon different analyzers. If the component stimuli are then applied separately and without reinforcement, it is found that one of the pair is effective but not the other. For example, a conditioned reflex to acid was established to a compound stimulus consisting of the simultaneous application of a tactile stimulus and a thermal stimulus of 0°C. The tactile stimulus when applied alone was found to be about as effective as the compound stimulus, whereas the thermal stimulus was quite ineffective. The results of experiments in which the component stimuli of the compound stimulus were of unequal strengths, and applied to the same analyzer, indicate that the factor determining the effectiveness of the stimuli, when applied separately, is their relative intensity. The thermal stimulus used in the foregoing experiment may therefore be regarded as being the weaker of the two stimuli. Visual stimuli are also weaker than those acting upon the auditory analyzer. For example, after a conditioned reflex had been established to a compound stimulus made up of a tone and a light, the tone by itself caused a response, whereas the visual stimulus was quite ineffective. However, the weaker stimulus undoubtedly plays its part in the combination, for if the stronger component is applied repeatedly without reinforcement by the unconditioned stimulus, but the compound stimulus is constantly reinforced, the stronger stimulus by itself becomes ineffective, whereas the compound stimulus retains its full effect.

The cortex is also able to synthesize *successive* stimuli into a compound conditioned stimulus. For instance, a flash of light (L), a cutaneous stimulus (C) and the sound of bubbling water (S) when applied in the order (L—C—S) were compounded into a positive conditioned stimulus. The reverse order (S—C—L) after differentiation (by nonreinforcement) was entirely without effect.

Similarly, four tones having vibration frequencies of 290, 325, 370 and 413 c.p.s. respectively when sounded in this order (1, 2, 3, 4) were successfully differentiated by a dog from all other sequences (e.g., 4, 3, 2, 1; 4, 3, 1, 2; 4, 1, 3, 2; 4, 2, 3, 1, etc., etc.).

The series of sounds in a word (e.g., a dog's name) or in a command is a familiar example of a successive compound conditioned stimulus.

### IRRADIATION AND CONCENTRATION

These features are best illustrated by citing an actual experiment. The skin of the hind limb was stimulated at five separate places. One of these situated upon the paw was differentiated by non-reinforcement in the usual way from the other four. That is, the place upon the paw was given inhibitory properties (p. 1263). The other four places, which through reinforcement were given positive conditioned properties, were placed at progressively further distances along the limb from the inhibitory place. It was found that if the latter was stimulated three times in succession, and one minute after the last stimulation, the positive place nearest the inhibitory place was then stimulated, there was complete failure of the usual conditioned response. Stimulation of the next (second) excitatory place one minute after the last application of the inhibitory stimulus was followed by a response half as great as usual. The remaining two places (third and fourth) gave a normal or somewhat greater than normal response (see positive induction, p. 1268). When the number of the previous stimulations of the inhibitory place was increased, and the interval following the last one shortened to 15 seconds, all four excitatory places gave a reduced response. As time elapsed the furthest place was first freed from the inhibitory influence, and the others in the order of their positions from the inhibitory place. The point nearest to the latter in some cases did not give a full response until the lapse of 10 minutes after the application of the last stimulus to the inhibitory place. It can also be shown that if, by means of extinction, inhibitory properties are given to one of the four excitatory places the inhibitory process spreads to involve the others.

These results are taken to indicate that each stimulated area has its circumscribed representation in the cortex. Inhibition initiated in the cortical cells to which the inhibitory place is projected *irradiates* to involve the cortical projection areas of the positive places. The gradual release of the cortical areas from the inhibitory influence, and its retreat to the original cortical cells corresponding to the inhibitory place is called the *concentration of inhibition*. Irradiation and concentration are antagonistic processes. These processes can also be shown for the acoustic analyzer and they most probably exist for other analyzers as well. The following is an illustration of irradiation within the acoustic analyzer. Positive conditioned reflexes were established respectively to the beat of a metronome, to a musical tone and to a buzzing sound. When the reflex to the buzzing sound or to the metronome was extinguished the inhibitory process spread to involve the reflex to the musical tone.

Irradiation is not always confined to the analyzer in which the inhibitory process originates. It can be shown that the inhibitory process initiated in one analyzer spreads to others and may involve the entire cortex. For example, a positive alimentary conditioned reflex was established to a tone of 4000 c.p.s.; a note a semitone lower than this was given inhibitory properties. When the inhibitory stimulus was applied a short time before a visual conditioned stimulus, the reflex which had been established to the latter, as well as that established for the positive auditory stimulus (tone of 4000 c.p.s.) was inhibited.

*Irradiation and concentration of excitation* occur in a manner analogous to that described for inhibition. Generalization (p. 1265) is ascribed to the irradiation of excitation from the primary cortical focus. Differential inhibition, on the other hand, antagonizes the excitatory process and concentrates it within the original cortical area.

### INDUCTION

Induction is a feature of conditioned reflex action analogous to the phenomenon of the same name described as occurring in spinal reflexes, namely, the increase of inhibition caused by a preceding state of excitation (*negative induction*) or an increase of excitation caused by a previous state of inhibition (*positive induction*). Induction is therefore a reciprocal process.

*Negative induction.* The inhibitory properties of a stimulus developed by means of differentiation can be readily destroyed again (disinhibition) by repeated reinforcement. If, however, each application of the inhibitory stimulus is *preceded* by a

positive one, and both are reinforced, the inhibitory properties of the former are strengthened and can be abolished only after a great number of trials. Thus, a metronome beating at a rate of 120 beats per minute served as a positive conditioned stimulus and a rate of 60 beats per minute was differentiated (differential inhibition). The inhibition was then almost abolished (disinhibition) by reinforcement but was restored again when the differentiated stimulus (rate of 60 beats per minute) was preceded by the positive stimulus (rate of 120 beats per minute). The data are shown in table 68.1, as given by Pavlov.

*Positive induction* in its simplest form may be illustrated as follows. A positive conditioned reflex was established to stimulation of the forepaw. A stimulus to the hind paw was given inhibitory properties by differentiation. When the excitatory place (forepaw) was stimulated *immediately* after the application of the stimulus to the inhibitory place, the positive conditioned reflex was enhanced (salivary secretion increased by 50 per cent). The excitability of the cortical area receiving impulses from the forepaw had evidently been increased as a result of inhibition of the cortical area corresponding to the hind paw. Thus the excitability of the cortex in proximity to the inhibited area is enhanced for the moment but later becomes depressed as a result of the irradiation of the inhibitory process. When dealing with irradiation it was pointed out that the inhibitory effect was demonstrable for several seconds or minutes after the inhibitory place had been stimulated. Positive induction occurs *during* the application of the inhibitory stimulus. Pavlov holds the view that these two processes, positive induction and irradiation of inhibition (or negative induction and the irradiation of excitation), are constantly interacting with one another and spread wavelike over the cortex. Positive or negative induction precedes, respectively, the spread of the inhibitory or excitatory process.

THE EMPLOYMENT OF CONDITIONED REFLEXES IN THE STUDY OF CORTICAL FUNCTION. Information concerning the localization of function in the cortex was obtained by, first, firmly establishing a conditioned reflex involving one or other analyzer, then excising a certain portion of the cortex and studying the effects of the operation upon the conditioned response.

### REMOVAL OF THE ENTIRE CORTEX

It was reported that in the dog removal of the entire cortex results in the complete and perma-

TABLE 68.1

| Time | Conditioned Stimulus Applied during 30 Seconds | Salivary Secretion in Dogs during 30 Seconds (Drops) | |
|------|------|------|------|
| 11.25 a.m. | 60 beats | 0 | |
| 11.30 a.m. | 60 beats | 0 | |
| 11.42 a.m. | 60 beats | 3 | All the stimuli |
| 11.49 a.m. | 60 beats | 4 | were accompa- |
| 11.56 a.m. | 120 beats | 8½ | nied by rein- |
| 12.06 p.m. | 60 beats | 0 | forcement |

nent loss of all conditioned responses, natural or artificial; new conditioned reflexes cannot be established. The decorticated animal responds to crude *unconditioned* stimuli, e.g., a bright light or sound, its reactions being frequently those of resentment or anger (p. 1168). The unconditioned salivary reflex is lost at first but eventually becomes stronger than the normal. More recent work has demonstrated that in a limited way and with considerable difficulty it is possible to establish some simple conditioned reflexes in both the decorticate dog and cat. This does not alter the fact that basically these reflexes are dependent upon the cerebral cortex. In addition we must not lose sight of the fact that in the dog and cat the cerebral cortex is not comparable to the cortex in man or even in the subhuman primates. There can be little doubt but that in the primate brain conditioned reflexes are developed only in the presence of the cerebral cortex.

REMOVAL OF A LIMITED PORTION OF THE CORTEX

Removal of a limited portion of the cortex, e.g., the temporal or occipital lobes, causes the disappearance for a time of all "artificial" conditioned reflexes, and sometimes of the "natural" ones as well. Unconditioned reflexes, which are dependent upon subcortical centers, remain in abeyance for only a few hours or may not disappear at all. Complete recovery of conditioned reflexes dependent upon analyzers, other than the one which has been directly injured, occurs after a few days, analyzers nearest to the excised area recovering later than those farther removed. Incomplete recovery of the injured analyzer eventually takes place.

THE ACOUSTIC ANALYZER is centered in the temporal lobe. Extirpation of both temporal lobes is followed by a very temporary loss, if any, of the auditory unconditioned reflexes (e.g., pricking of the ears to sound). The auditory conditioned reflexes may not return for several weeks or even months, and are never fully restored. The finer and more discriminating reactions are permanently lost. Discrimination of the intensity, pitch and quality of sound is possible, but the powers for more complicated analyses and syntheses are not regained. The animal, for example, never answers to its name, and the differentiation of other types of compound auditory stimuli (p. 1266), e.g., a descending from an ascending scale of tones, cannot be established.[2]

[2] An experiment upon the peripheral portion of the acoustic analyzer may be mentioned here, since it has a bearing upon Helmholtz' theory of

THE VISUAL ANALYZER is situated mainly but not exclusively in the occipital lobe. According to Pavlov the visual analyzer is probably spread over the entire cortex. Complete bilateral extirpation of the occipital lobes causes effects upon the visual conditioned reflexes corresponding to those upon the auditory reflexes which follow removal of the temporal lobes. Conditioned responses to changes in the intensity of illumination (e.g., switching on a high power lamp) established before operation returned upon the fifth day following the extirpation of the occipital lobes as well as of a considerable area of the cortex lying anterior to them. Differentiation was established between a luminous cross and a circle illuminated to the same intensity. It was found impossible, however, to establish conditioned reflexes to specific objects, for the reason, most probably, that the appearance of an object changes with the illumination, with its distance from the eye and the angle from which it is observed. Its recognition under different conditions of lighting, position, etc., therefore requires a much greater power of analysis and synthesis than that required for the differentiation of a flat luminous shape. The animal deprived of its occipital lobes is able, nevertheless, to avoid objects placed in its path. They are detected simply by the changes in illumination (lights and shadows) which their presence creates.

The findings described above, namely, that complete decortication in the dog abolishes all conditioned reflexes, and that removal of the temporal or occipital lobes impairs, respectively, auditory, and visual conditioned reflexes, but does not destroy them permanently and completely, lead to the following conclusions concerning the functions of the cortex, so far at any rate as the auditory and visual senses are concerned. (a) Although rudimentary reactions can be carried out through subcortical connections, the processes underlying conditioned reflexes are dependent upon the activity of the cerebral cortex. (b) The highest powers of analysis and synthesis are localized to definite areas, each of which may be regarded as the "nucleus" of a given analyzer. (c) The analyzer, however, is not rigidly confined to this area but extends into other cortical regions in which less complicated types of analysis can be

hearing. Destruction of the organ of Corti in the upper part of the cochlea (receptors for lower tones) resulted in a loss of conditioned reflexes which had been established to tones of the lower part of the musical scale (frequencies lower than 600 d.b. per minute). Reflexes to higher tones were unaffected.

undertaken. Experiments involving other ana-lyzers have yielded evidence pointing in the same direction.

These results of cortical extirpation cannot be directly applied to the human subject since the functions of subcortical centers of hearing, sight, etc., in lower animals have not, as in man, been so largely usurped by the cortex. Nevertheless, Pavlov's observations are, broadly speaking, in harmony with modern conceptions of cortical functions (see ch. 67). A given sensory function, although primarily "centered" in a certain corti-cal area, is, through association tracts, dependent for its full development upon other areas as well.

### The Effects of Drugs upon Conditioned Reflexes

*Caffeine and strychnine* increase the effects of positive conditioned stimuli and weaken internal inhibition. After a dose of less than 1 grain (0.025 to 0.05 gram) of the former drug, extinction (in-hibition) of a conditioned reflex is effected with the greatest difficulty. *Bromides* act by strengthen-ing internal inhibition, and not by directly de-pressing excitatory processes; under their influ-ence the extinction of positive conditioned reflexes is facilitated. *Alcohol* in moderate doses weakens internal inhibition. Andreyev and Pugsley have found that the *hypercalcemia* resulting from para-thormone or ergosterol overdosage causes an exag-geration of inhibitory processes; the after effect of inhibitory stimuli is enhanced and extinction of positive conditioned reflexes accelerated.

### The Physiology of Sleep
### The Depth of Sleep

The depth of sleep is not constant throughout the sleeping period but varies from hour to hour. Experiments upon man in which auditory stimuli were employed to arouse the subject at different times, or the movements of the sleeper were re-corded (the depth of sleep being assumed to be inversely related to the amount of muscular movement) indicate that the depth of sleep fol-lows a characteristic curve. In most adults sleep deepens rapidly to the end of the first hour, after which it lessens sharply for a time, and then more slowly till the time of waking. In children the sleep curve shows two maxima, i.e., two periods of the deepest sleep; one of these is reached in the first or second hour, the other between the eighth and ninth hours; the curve then falls rapidly to the time of waking. Generally speaking, sleep taken during the daytime is lighter than that during the night. Deep sleep is dreamless; dreams occur only during light sleep and chiefly in the

period which just precedes waking. In sleep, un-consciousness is not uniform for all senses; the depth of sleep is greatest for the sensations of smell and least for those of pain, hearing and touch.

The *sleep requirement* of different persons varies widely; it also alters with age. The following are average figures for the hours of sleep required at different periods of life.

|  | hours |
| --- | --- |
| New-born infant | 18 to 20 |
| Growing children | 12 to 14 |
| Adults | 7 to 9 |
| Old persons | 5 to 7 |

PHYSIOLOGICAL CHANGES ACCOMPANYING SLEEP

During sleep most bodily functions are reduced to their basal levels. The *blood pressure* is lowered; the systolic pressure showing a decline of from 10 to 30 mm. Hg. The lowest level is reached about the fourth hour of sleep, and remains at this level until a short time before awakening, when the pressure commences to rise again. Mac-William found that if the sleep was disturbed by exciting dreams the blood pressure might be ele-vated well above the normal waking level, of 125 or 130 mm. Hg. The *pulse rate* is slowed by from 10 to 30 beats. The *metabolic rate* is reduced by from 10 to 15 per cent below the basal level and the *rectal temperature* by a fraction of a degree Fahrenheit. The heat-regulating mechanisms are depressed. The *respirations* are slowed as a rule, and are said to become more costal in character; they also tend to become irregular or periodic. *Muscle tone* is minimal; the knee jerk is abolished, and a positive Babinski may be present. The thresholds for most *somatic reflexes* are definitely raised. Vasomotor reflexes, however, are more ac-tive. In most animals the *righting reflexes* are abolished. The pupils are usually constricted; the *light reflex* is retained. The eyeballs are turned upwards and outwards. *Urine volume* is reduced, but the absolute excretion of urinary phosphate is increased, and the specific gravity raised. The *secretion of the sweat glands* is considerably in-creased; according to Hartridge the quantity of fluid lost per hour in sleep is nearly equal to that lost during a corresponding period of strenuous muscular exercise. *Plasma volume* is reduced by about 10 per cent. *Gastric secretion* is increased or little altered during sleep. The contractions of the empty stomach continue and may be more vigor-ous than usual; the rate of digestion is about the same as during the waking state. *Lacrymal* and *salivary* secretions are reduced. The EEG during sleep is described in chapter 67.

It may be of interest to give an account of the effects upon the nervous system of prolonged wakefulness. In Kleitman's human experiments the subjects were kept awake for periods ranging from 60 to 114 hours. The knee jerk remained unaffected but disappeared promptly when the subject went to sleep at the termination of the period of forced insomnia, and a positive Babinski was obtainable. The latter was attributed to the establishment of a block in the corticospinal pathway. The *pupillary* response remained brisk throughout the wakeful period. There seemed to be little impairment of the mental processes, and the reactions to auditory and visual stimuli were as prompt as usual. The threshold for pain stimuli was definitely lowered, whereas that for touch was unaltered. The power to maintain *equilibrium*, as judged by the ability to stand with the eyes closed, was grossly impaired. This defect was attributed to neuromuscular fatigue and the consequent reduction in muscle tone, rather than to any impairment of labyrinthine function itself.

Tyler, in more recent experiments upon some 600 human subjects who went for periods of up to 112 hours without sleep, found no significant changes in blood chemistry, hemoglobin, red or white blood cell count, body weight or temperature, and only slight changes in blood pressure, respirations and heart rate. Notable psychological changes, however, were observed, e.g., loss of memory, irritability, inattention and hallucinations or illusions. These alterations in behavior, were noticeable after from 30 to 60 hours of sleeplessness, and, although mild in most subjects, in a few, they were severe and resembled those of acute schizophrenia.

The period of wakefulness which would be lethal for the human subject is not definitely known. Dogs may die after being kept awake continuously for 14 days, although they may survive for much longer periods. Young animals are much more susceptible to loss of sleep than older ones. Changes in the nerve cells of the cortex, e.g., chromatolysis and shrinkage of the cell bodies, have been described as resulting from prolonged periods of enforced wakefulness in animals.

### THEORIES OF SLEEP

The cause and nature of sleep have aroused speculation from the time of the Greek philosophers, but although hypotheses are many and often ill-founded, facts which might throw light upon the underlying processes are few and difficult to obtain. A discussion of only some of the many theories will be undertaken.

NEURON THEORY (Lépine, Duval). This theory arose from the demonstration by Cajal that there was not anatomical continuity between adjacent neurons but merely points of contact, for which the term *synapse* was later suggested by Foster. The neuron theory postulated that the function of the cells of the higher cortical centers was suspended as a result of the retraction of the dendritic processes, and the consequent break in contact between neurons. Although some histological evidence was cited in support of this conception, the theory was mainly speculative.

CEREBRAL ISCHEMIA THEORY. Howell suggested that fatigue of the vasomotor center with consequent vasodilatation of the peripheral vessels, especially of the skin, and reduction in cerebral blood flow was the primary change responsible for the onset of sleep. The flushed skin of the sleeping subject, the fall in blood pressure and the well-known feeling of drowsiness following a meal (which presumably was the result of the diversion of blood to the splanchnic area) lent plausibility to the theory. From ancient times the carotid artery (karoō = I sleep) has been believed to be connected in some way with the mechanism of sleep, for it was recognized that compression of this vessel was not uncommonly followed by unconsciousness. In later times the loss of consciousness following pressure upon the neck was attributed to vagal stimulation, with consequent inhibition of the heart and a reduction in intracranial blood flow. Unconsciousness may be produced by the fall in blood pressure and the cardiac asystole brough about by the compression of a hyperactive carotid sinus on one side or as the result of cerebral ischemia and anoxia produced by bilateral occlusion of the carotid arteries.

The unconscious states caused by a reduction in cerebral blood flow are not, however, akin to normal sleep. Vulpian observed some years ago that, although stimulation of the cervical sympathetic in animals caused cerebral ischemia, sleep was not induced. Moreover, Gibbs has shown by means of an electrically heated stylet that no diminution in blood flow through the brain occurs during natural sleep. It is possible, nevertheless, that there may occur a reduction in the blood supply to a limited area of the brain whose activity is essential for the waking state. A limited vascular change of this nature might not be revealed by observations upon the total intracranial blood flow.

CHEMICAL THEORIES. Several chemical theories of sleep have been proposed. One of the earliest of these was that fatigue products, especially lactic acid, formed in the tissues generally, acted by depressing the function of the cortex. Against this view is the well-known fact that one need not be fatigued in order to sleep; on the other hand, a person may be unable to sleep although utterly fatigued. Furthermore, the brain tissue actually derives energy from the oxidation of lactic acid.

Another chemical theory is that of Piéron. This observer claims that a substance, which he terms *hypnotoxin*, is produced by the brain tissue and acts as a soporific. He claims that the cerebrospinal fluid of a dog killed during sleep induces sleep when injected into another animal. Kroll makes similar claims, stating that an acetene extract of the brain of a sleeping or hibernating animal will cause sleep when injected into another. Holmes has been unable to confirm Kroll's findings. An extract prepared by Kroll's method either from sleeping or waking animals was found to be lethal through its toxic effect upon the heart. Ivy and Schnedorf have repeated Pieron's experiments and confirmed his observation. They found that the injection of cerebrospinal fluid of a dog kept awake for several days induced a state of depression resembling deep sleep in rested dogs, when introduced into the cisterna magna or cerebral ventricle. The effect, however, is probably due, not to the presence of a sleep-inducing substance in the "fatigued" cerebrospinal fluid, but to a rise in intracranial pressure, since the injection of cerebrospinal fluid from rested dogs had a depressing action not considerably less than that of the "fatigued" fluid. No evidence in support of the theory (Dikshit) that *acetycholine* liberation by the brain tissue is a factor in sleep was secured by these observers.

Zondek and Bier have advanced an interesting, but unsubstantiated theory in which the pituitary plays a leading role. They state that the pituitary during the waking state has a higher concentration in bromine than any other tissue but that during sleep the bromide concentration of the gland diminishes whereas that of the medulla increases. These observers therefore believe that sleep is induced through the liberation of a bromine compound from the hypophysis. They have named this substance *bromhormone*. The evidence upon which this theory is based is far from convincing.

Other chemical theories, based upon the supposed affinity of a subcortical area for certain ions, especially calcium whose depressant action upon nervous tissue is well known, have been advanced, but little substantial evidence has been secured for their support.

THE DIENCEPHALON AND SLEEP. Several observations both clinical and experimental point to the existence of a sleep center in the diencephalon. Hypersomnolence is a frequent accompaniment of tumors of the structures in the floor and walls of the third ventricle, or of inflammatory lesions involving the hypothalamic region. Hess claims to be able to cause sleep in animals by mild electrical stimulation of the diencephalon towards the anterior end of the cerebral aqueduct, and Gagel reported the production of sleep in human subjects during operations by mechanical stimulation of the posterior part of the hypothalamus. Hess also reported that ergotamine injected directly into the third ventricle induces sleep. Ergotamine paralyzes the motor and secretory fibers of the sympathetic. Since parasympathetic and sympathetic centers are apparently situated in the hypothalamus, Hess argued that the drug by suspending the activity of the sympathetic center caused a preponderance of parasympathetic effects. Sleep, he concluded, was a parasympathetic function. He also draws support for his theory from certain manifestations of parasympathetic activity, namely, the pupillary constriction, bradycardia and vasodilatation which accompany sleep. Although this observer's idea that sleep is a parasympathetic function requires further experimental support before it can be accepted, the evidence for the participation of the hypothalamus in the sleep mechanism is strong. Yet, contrary to the idea that sleep is caused by excitation of some part of the hypothalamus, other investigators believe that it results from the *depression* of hypothalamic activity. The hypothalamus is thus regarded as containing a waking center, sleep following its destruction or inhibition.[3] Ranson and his associates, for example, have reported that sleep can be readily induced in cats by lesions placed in the posterior and lateral part of the hypothalamus or by injury confined to the mammillary bodies, but

---

[3] The electroencephalogram recorded from the cortex of the cat after transection at the lowermost limit of the medulla is essentially that of the normal waking state; after section at the upper border of the pons the electroencephalographic pattern is that characteristic of sleep. From this it could be inferred that the latter section interfered with the transmission of "alerting" impulses to the cerebral cortex.

that it did not result from the *stimulation* of any part of the hypothalamus. Harrison also found that electrical stimulation of the hypothalamus caused somnolence only when the current exerted a destructive action.

Whether the thalamus plays a role in the sleep mechanism is unknown. Although unconsciousness may result from manipulations in the region of the thalamus, and a stuporous state may be associated with a thalamic lesion, true sleep has not been produced by either stimulation or injury.

PAVLOV'S THEORY. Pavlov believes sleep and internal inhibition to be essentially one and the same process, i.e., sleep is simply the spread (irradiation) of internal inhibition over the entire cortex with the subsequent involvement of subcortical levels; and internal inhibition confined within the boundaries of a single analyzer is a localized sleep. He was led to this conclusion by the behavior of animals during his investigations of conditioned reflex action. Drowsiness and sleep were frequent accompaniments of all forms of internal inhibition, e. g., inhibition of extinction and of delay (p. 1264), conditioned and differential inhibition, or the inhibition which ensued spontaneously after the repetition of positive conditioned reflexes over a long period of time. An animal, for example, which is quite alert during the establishment of a reflex to a definite musical tone becomes drowsy and falls alseep in the stand during attempts to develop differentiation (p. 1265) of a closely similar tone; its muscles relax, it may snore loudly and other positive conditioned stimuli fail to awake it. Moreover, drugs such as caffeine (p. 1270) which reduce internal inhibition, and those such as bromides which increase it, have corresponding effects upon the mechanism of sleep. As mentioned previously, positive conditioned reflexes after having been repeated over a long period ultimately undergo inhibition. At this stage in the investigations the experiment is frequently terminated by the animal falling asleep. Experiments involving the use of thermal and tactile stimuli are most frequently interrupted by the onset of sleep; auditory conditioned stimuli are the least likely to have this effect.

Protracted, mild stimulation of an extraneous nature was also found to cause cortical inhibition and lead to sleep. It has been mentioned (p. 1263) that an extraneous stimulus induces inhibition through setting up an investigatory reflex; upon repetition, the inhibitory effect disappears, and the conditioned responses return. With further repetition, however, the extraneous stimulus again causes inhibition; this time, it exerts, of itself, a direct inhibitory effect upon the cortex.

Pavlov's theory has much to recommend it. The drowsiness which results from some oft-repeated form of monotonous stimulation, e.g., reading or being read to in a low even voice, a dull lecture, or boredom from whatever cause, is well known. Also, the preparations for sleep—the various agencies in a familiar environment—probably serve themselves as inhibitory conditioned stimuli. A dog, for example, which has fallen asleep during previous experiments may do the same when merely brought into the room where the experiments have been performed or when preparations are being made to repeat them. The customary hour for retiring probably acts also as a time conditioned stimulus.

For a critique of Pavlov's theory see Denny-Brown.

In some experiments described by Pavlov the inhibitory process involved the cortex but did not descend to subcortical levels governing equilibrium and the postural reactions of the skeletal muscles. The animal assumed a trancelike or cataleptic state in which muscular tone was retained, the general attitude being one of alertness. It stood with wide-open eyes but was quite unresponsive to all ordinary forms of stimulation. Pavlov looks upon this state as a transition stage between wakefulness and deep sleep, due to a less widespread diffusion of the inhibitory process, and similar in nature to hypnosis. It is suggested that during sleep, also, all cortical areas, analyzers as Pavlov terms them, are not necessarily under the inhibitory influence. The alertness of a mother, apparently in deep sleep, to the slightest noise made by her baby, is a case in point. In such an instance it is the auditory analyzer, or a part of it, which has remained apparently outside the inhibitory influence.

These observations have undoubtedly some bearing upon the production of *dreams*. Dreams are evidently due to cortical activity especially of the temporal lobes (ch. 67), since they involve vivid memory, and the ability to recall and bring together various sensory impressions. It would seem, however, that the activity of other regions possessing a more critical ability—those areas endowed with a higher analytic and synthesizing capacity—is in abeyance. The illogical, uncritical and often grotesquely absurd character of dreams is well known, yet the mental pictures are often drawn with great vividness, and a stimulus which in the waking state would leave little imprint upon consciousness is sometimes magnified enormously during sleep. As Descartes says, "A flea bit me and I dreamt of a sword cut!" Sensations arising in the viscera, such as those due to hunger, a distended stomach or bladder, thirst, etc., which during the day may cause no more than a passing thought may give rise to dreams filled with the most exciting events. It has been mentioned that dreams occur only during light sleep, that is, at a time when one would expect the internal inhibitory process to be restricted to the more highly specialized parts of the analyzers and before it has spread to involve the entire cortex. Dreaming may therefore be reasonably looked upon as being dependent upon a state of partial sleep—certain areas of the cortex being freed from the restraint which during the day is exercised by more critical regions.

KLEITMAN'S THEORY. According to Kleitman, sleep is due to the inactivity of the cerebral cortex resulting from a reduction in the number of afferent impulses, especially from the muscles, reaching the sensorium. Fatigue of the neuromuscular mechanism mediating muscle tone, with consequent suppression of impulses from muscle proprioceptors, is considered to be the most important factor in the onset of sleep. According to this author loss of muscle tone is an invariable prelude to sleep.

Kleitman claims to have demonstrated a diurnal variation in the speed, accuracy and steadiness with which certain muscular acts are performed. The efficiency of performance was maximal in the afternoon and minimal late at night and in the early morning. It is suggested that the variability is due to a corresponding rhythm in the tone of the skeletal musculature. But quite apart from these experiments, many observations give credence to the theory that cortical inactivity resulting from the blockage of afferent impulses is an important element in the onset of sleep. The exclusion of stimuli from visual, auditory and cutaneous receptors and the diminution of the flow of proprioceptor impulses as a result of muscular relaxation, are well-known means employed to induce sleep, whereas cortical activity, whether from psychic causes—anxiety, worry, excitement, etc.—or as a result of impulses set up in exteroceptors or muscle receptors, prevents sleep. In extreme fatigue when muscle tone is presumably at a minimum and the threshold of other afferent paths also probably raised as well, sleep comes on irresistibly. Kleitman and his associates found that after a prolonged period of wakefulness the only way in which they could keep from falling asleep was by moving about, or at least remaining in a standing or sitting position. Upon lying down and permitting their muscles to relax they were immediately overpowered by sleep.

An attempt has been made by Kleitman to reconcile the cortical theories of sleep with the undoubted fact that the hypothalamus is in some way concerned in the sleep process.

That sleep is not solely dependent upon the cortex is evident from the fact that decorticated dogs show periods of sleep alternating with intervals of wakefulness. The sleep rhythm in these animals is not, however, related in any way with night and day but consists of a number of shorter or longer periods throughout the 24 hours. The sleep periods occur most constantly after feeding. During the waking periods the animals walk around almost incessantly. Lower orders in the animal scale in which the cortex is rudimentary and which, in consequence, are unable to develop a wide variety of conditioned responses show a similar sleep rhythm. This more primitive sleep mechanism is dependent conceivably upon a center located at a subcortical level, and most probably in the hypothalamus. We may regard it as presiding over vegetative functions and acting continuously to keep the animal asleep unless inhibited by impulses arising out of the more primitive processes and reactions, e.g., hunger, thirst, cold or distention of the bladder or rectum.

The diurnal sleep rhythm, that is, the ability to keep awake throughout the day, is dependent, on the other hand, upon the development of conditioned reflexes. So long as the cortex can bring its analyzing ability to bear upon the stream of impulses received from the different distance receptors, muscles, skin, etc., the functions of the primitive sleep center are held in abeyance. With the spread of internal inhibition over the cortex, or as a result of the elimination of stimuli from the periphery, the center asserts itself, and the subject is unable to remain awake. The diurnal sleep rhythm is therefore an acquired phenomenon—not inborn. Infants and very young animals do not show it but, like decorticated animals, have several sleeping periods throughout the day.

Those who believe that sleep results from the inhibition of a waking center in the hypothalamus take a somewhat different view. According to them sleep is a negative rather than a positive state, that is, it is due to the inactivity of the waking center. The activity of this center it is conceived is maintained by impulses received from the cortex. Cortical function is dependent in turn upon a flow of impulses along various afferent channels.

RETICULAR FORMATION. The common observation, noted above by Kleitman, that sleep is often produced by a reduction in exteroceptive and proprioceptive stimuli correlates well with what is known regarding the reticular formation in the brain stem. This mechanism receives afferent impulses set up by various forms of external stimuli (e.g., light, sound, touch and pain) as well as by impulses set into motion by muscular tension. Furthermore, this mechanism when stimulated by afferent impulses (or electrically) in turn arouses or alerts the animal and converts the electroencephalographic pattern from one characteristic of sleep to that typical of the waking state. In addition states resembling sleep are produced by certain drugs which decrease the activity of the reticular formation.

Although it appears likely that the activity or inactivity of the reticular formation are important in the production of wakefulness or sleep, it is equally obvious that many other parts of the nervous system are also concerned with this phenomenon. The peripheral nerves and the spinal cord are important in bringing afferent impulses which activate the reticular formation; the cerebral cortex is the structure which is aroused; whereas the diencephalon (the hypothalamus and the intralaminar nuclei of the thalamus) exercise an influence on the cortex exactly opposite to that of the reticular formation.

## REFERENCES

ANDREYEV, L. A. J. Comp. Psychol., 1934, **18,** 315.

ANDREYEV, L. AND PUGSLEY, L. I. Quart. J. Exper. Physiol., 1934, **24,** 189.

ANDERSON, O. D. AND LIDDELL, H. Arch. Neurol. & Psychiat., 1935, **34,** 330.

DENNY-BROWN, D. J. Neurol. & Psychopath., 1932, **13,** 52.

DIKSHIT, B. B. J. Physiol., 1934, **80,** 409.

DUVAL, Compt. rend. Soc. biol., 1895.

GAGEL, O. Bumke u. Forster's Handbk. Neurol., 1936, **5,** 482, quoted by Harrison.

GANTT, W. H. Contributions dedicated to Adolph Meyer, 1937, p. 78; see also under Monographs and Reviews.

GIBBS, F. A., GIBBS, E. L. AND LENNOX, W. G. Brain, 1935, **58,** 44.

HARRISON, F. Proc. Assoc. Res. Nerv. Ment. Dis., 1940, **20,** 635.

HESS, W. R. Lancet, 1932, **2,** 1199: 1259.

HESS, W. R. Am. J. Physiol., 1929, **90,** 386.

HOLMES, E. J. Physiol., 1935, **85,** 400.

HOWELL, W. H. J. Exper. Med., 1897, **2,** 313.

IVY, A. C. AND SCHNEDORF, J. G. Am. J. Physiol., 1937, **119,** 342.

KLEITMAN, N. AND ASSOCIATES. Am. J. Physiol., 1933, **104,** 449; **105,** 574; **106,** 478; **107,** 589.

KOCH, E. Z. Kreislaufforsch, 1932, **24,** 251 Neurol. (Quoted by Hess).

KROLL, F. W. Ztschr. ges Neurol. Psychiat., 1933, **143,** 780; **146,** 208; **147,** 316.

LEPINE. Compt. rend. Soc. biol., 1895. Quoted in Schäfer's text-book of physiology, 1900, **2,** 608.

MacWILLIAM, J. A. Quart. J. Exper. Physiol., 1923, **13,** Supp. 178.

RANSON, S. W. ET AL. Am. J. Physiol., 1935, **112,** 214.

RANSON, S. W. ET AL. Arch. Neurol. Psychiat., 1939, **41,** 1.

RANSON, S. W. ET AL. Trans. Coll. Physicians, Phila., 1934, Ser. 4, 2, 222.

ZONDEK, H. AND BIER, A. Klin. Wchnschr., 1932, **11,** 633, 759, 760.

*Monographs and Reviews*

GANTT, W. H., in Relation of psychological tests to psychiatry. Grune & Stratton, N. Y., 1950.

GANTT, W. H. Experimental Basis of Neurotic Behavior. Hoeber, N. Y., 1944.

GILLESPIE, R. D. Sleep and the treatment of its disorders. Baillière, London, 1929.

Henry Ford Hospital Internation Symposium; Reticular Formation of the Brain. Edited by H. H. Jasper *et al.* Little, Brown & Co., Boston.

KLEITMAN, N. The physiology of sleep. Physiol. Rev., 1929, **9,** 624.

KLEITMAN, N. Sleep and wakefulness. Univ. Chicago Press, Chicago, 1939.

PAVLOV, I. P. Conditioned reflexes. Oxford University Press, 1927.

PAVLOV, I. P. Lectures on conditioned reflexes. New York International Publishers, New York, 1928.

PIÉRON, H. Le problème physiologique du sommeil. Masson, Paris, 1913.

TYLER, D. B. Fed. Proc., 1947, **6,** 218.

# 69

# THE CEREBELLUM[1]

## General Structure and Divisions

The cerebellum consists of a narrow central body, the *vermis* (or worm) and two lateral masses, the *right* and *left cerebellar hemispheres*. On its upper surface the demarcation between the vermis (*superior vermis*) and the hemispheres is slight. Upon the under surface the hemispheres are separated by a deep depression—the *vallecula;* the floor of the latter is formed by the inferior surface of the vermis. The inferior aspect of the vermis (*inferior vermis*) consists of four subdivisions, these are called (in order from the front backwards) the *nodule, uvula, pyramid* and *tuber*. On either side and continuous with the nodule, is an elongated, somewhat lobulated structure called the *flocculus*. It should be noted that these gross subdivisions of the cerebellum are *not* related to either the developmental or the functional divisions of the cerebellum and are useful only as descriptive terms.

The cerebellar surface is not convoluted like the cerebral cortex but is divided by parallel and curved furrows into numerous laminae or folia (leaves). The total cortical area of the human cerebellum is about 100,000 sq. mm., or less than half that of the cerebral cortex.

Although the division of the cerebellum into the vermis and two hemispheres possesses considerable descriptive value, comparative neurologists (chiefly Bolk, Ingvar, Elliott Smith and Larsell), have suggested other divisions which possess greater significance from a phylogenetic and functional point of view. In Larsell's description the cerebellum is divided into two fundamental or primary parts, (a) the small flocculonodular lobe or vestibular part, and (b) the corpus cerebelli. These two parts are separated by a deep fissure—the *posterolateral fissure*—which is present in all vertebrate brains.

The *flocculonodular lobe* (or archicerebellum) the most ancient part of the cerebellum, comprises the flocculus and the nodule. It is developed from the structures in the region of the vestibular nuclei. The *corpus cerebelli*, which includes the rest of the cerebellum, is separated from the flocculonodular lobe by the *fissura posterolateralis*, and is divided by a well marked fissure—the *fissura prima* of Elliot-Smith—into a small anterior and a large posterior lobe. The *anterior lobe* (or paleocerebellum) consists of three subdivisions, the lingula, lobulus centralis and culmen. The *posterior lobe* (or neocerebellum) includes the lobulus simplex, declive, tuber, pyramid and uvula, together with the associated parts of the hemispheres (lobulus ansiformis and lobulus paramedianus, see below) and the paraflocculus (fig. 69.1). In higher forms a fissure appears in front of the pyramid, known as the *sulcus* or *fissura prepyramidalis*. The part of the posterior lobe between this sulcus behind and the fissura prima in front is sometimes referred to as the middle lobe of Ingvar (fig. 69.1); from the functional view this is a convenient subdivision. The flocculonodular lobe,[2] the anterior lobe, and the lobulus simplex, pyramid, uvala and paraflocculus of the posterior lobe are the phylogenetically old parts of the cerebellum and are referred to as the *archicerebellum* and *paleocerebellum*. The remainder of the cerebellum, i.e., the lateral expansions or hemispheres (ansiform lobules) declive and tuber (superior vermis) are late acquisitions, and constitute the *neocerebellum*; they correspond to most of Ingvar's middle lobe, and appear in phylogenetic development at about the same time as the cerebral cortex and the corticospinal tracts, and the pons. The neocerebellum, cerebral cortex and pons are absent or rudimentary in submammalian forms.

The *paramedian lobule* (or *tonsil*) is a small compact mass lying on either side of the inferior vermis. The ansiform lobule, which constitutes a large proportion of the posterior lobe and forms the expanded lateral mass of the hemisphere, reaches its greatest development in the human brain; its function is concerned with the tonus ad-

---

[1] Those interested in a more detailed review of the anatomy of the cerebellum are referred to Larsell, O., "The Cerebellum from Myxinoids to Man" (In press), Univ. of Minnesota Press, and for physiology and pathology of the cerebellum to Dow, R. S. and Moruzzi, G., "The Physiology and Pathology of the Cerebellum", Univ. of Minnesota Press, Minneapolis, 1958.

[2] The first appearance of a cerebellum, phylogenetically, is in the primitive fish *Petromyzon* (lamprey), and consists merely of a bridge of nervous tissue formed by an outgrowth from either side of the medulla which fuse in the midline over the fourth ventricle. This is the forerunner of the flocculonodular lobe of higher forms.

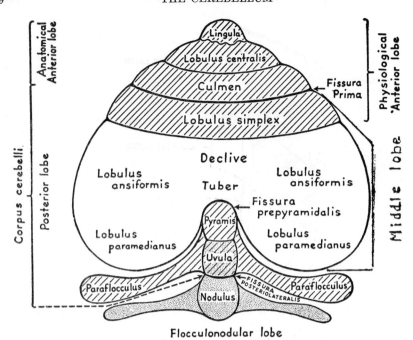

FIG. 69.1. Divisions of the human cerebellum. (After Larsell, modified.) Afferent fiber connections *stippled* vestibular paleocerebellum; *diagonals*, spinal paleocerebellum; *clear*, corticopontocerebellar, neocerebellum.

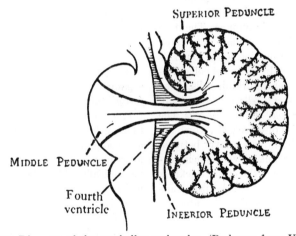

FIG. 69.2. Diagram of the cerebellar peduncles. (Redrawn from Villiger.)

justments and the muscular coordination required in the performance of skilled movements.

### INTERNAL STRUCTURE

When sectioned in the sagittal plane each hemisphere of the cerebellum presents a branching core of white matter which from its foliagelike appearance, has been named the *arbor vitae*. The terminal branches of the white matter are covered with a coating of gray substance which constitutes the cerebellar cortex. The leaflike structures so formed are spoken of as folia, and are responsible for the laminated appearance of the cerebellar surface (fig. 69.2). Unlike the cortex of the cerebrum all areas of the cerebellar cortex show a uniform histologic structure.

### The Gray Matter

THE CORTEX. Three cell layers are distinguished.

(1) *The molecular (or plexiform) layer* is outermost and consists largely of unmyelinated nerve fibers derived from (a) the white substance, (b) the cells of the two underlying layers, and (c) the

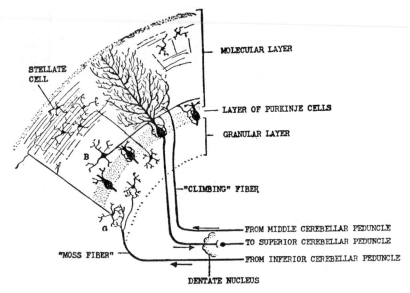

FIG. 69.3. Diagram to show structure of cerebellar cortex. G, granule cell; B, "basket" cell.

cells within this layer itself. The cells of the molecular layer are arranged in a deep and a superficial stratum, their axons synapse with the Purkinje cells, whose dendrites arborize throughout this layer. The cells of the superficial stratum are small, star-shaped and few in number. The deep stratum is composed of larger stellate cells whose axons run transversely in relation to the long axis of the folium and arborize by means of collaterals around the bodies of several Purkinje cells. They are referred to as *"basket" cells* (see fig. 69.3).

(2) *The intermediate layer of Purkinje cells.* The large flask-shaped bodies of these cells, which are peculiar to the cerebellum, form a layer between the molecular and the granular layers. Their dendrites pass outwards through the entire thickness of the molecular layer where they arborize luxuriantly. The axons of the Purkinje cells enter the white substance, and end by synapsing with cells in the cerebellar nuclei.

The Purkinje cells have been referred to as the "final common pathway" of the cerebellar cortex. It is through these cells that the efferent impulses of the cerebellum pass to the central nuclei of the cerebellum (dentatus, emboliformis, globosus and fastigii) and thence to other parts of the central nervous system.

(3) *The granular layer*, which rests upon the white matter, is composed of small, round, closely packed cells, and numerous nerve fibers. The cells possess four or five dendrites which end in a tuft of branches close to the cell body and connect with those of neighboring cells. One long process

(axon) of each extends into the molecular layer where it connects with the dendrites of a large number of Purkinje cells. Afferent fibers ("moss fibers," p. 1281) arriving *via* the inferior cerebellar peduncles make connections with the granule cells.

### The Cerebellar Nuclei

The cerebellum contains on either side four separate gray masses. These are: (a) *nucleus fastigii* (nucleus of the roof), (b) *nucleus globosus*, (c) *nucleus emboliformis*, and (d) *nucleus dentatus*. (The nuclei globosus and emboliformis of primates are comparable to the nucleus interpositus of lower mammals.) The first three of these are phylogenetically older than the nucleus dentatus, which is found only in mammals. The fastigial nuclei, which are the most ancient of all, lie near the midline on either side in the roof of the fourth ventricle. They receive fibers from the paleocerebellum (anterior lobe, pyramid, uvula and flocculonodular lobe), and from the vestibular nuclei and eighth nerve through the inferior peduncle; they also project to the vestibular nuclei. The globose and emboliform nuclei, which are placed more laterally than the roof nuclei receive fibers chiefly from the anterior lobe. The globose nucleus also receives fibers from the flocculonodular lobe. Both nuclei project through the superior peduncles to the large-celled portion of the red nucleus. The more lately acquired dentate nucleus, which is placed most laterally, is a large, crenated mass of gray matter, bent acutely upon itself. It

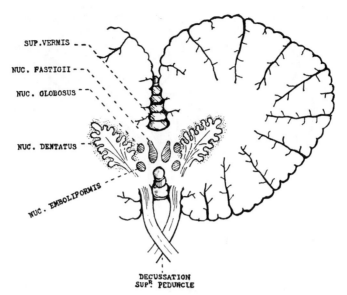

SUP. VERMIS

NUC. FASTIGII

NUC. GLOBOSUS

NUC. DENTATUS

NUC. EMBOLIFORMIS

DECUSSATION
SUP^R PEDUNCLE

Fig. 69.4. Diagram of a horizontal section through the cerebellum to show the cerebellar nuclei (viewed from in front).

receives fibers from the neocerebellum, chiefly from the Purkinje cells of the ansiform lobule. It projects through the superior cerebellar peduncle to the small-celled portion of the red nucleus (and to some extent also to the large-celled part), and to the ventrolateral group of the thalamic nuclei (fig. 69.4).

*The White Matter; Connections of the Cerebellum with Other Parts of the Central Nervous System—Cerebellar Peduncles*

The white matter of the hemispheres is composed of: (a) *projection fibers*, i.e., fibers which leave or enter the cerebellum *via* the peduncles, (b) *association fibers*, which connect different regions of the same hemisphere, and (c) *commissural fibers* connecting cortical areas of the two hemispheres.

The flocculonodular lobe, mainly the nodule, is connected by both afferent and efferent fibers (some of which are relayed in the fastigial and globose nuclei) with the vestibular nuclei and the vestibular nerve. The anterior lobes and the ansiform lobules receive spinocerebellar and pontocerebellar fibers, respectively, and project to brain stem and thalamic nuclei. The fibers, afferent and efferent, connecting the cerebellum with extracerebellar regions are all carried in three large bundles called the *inferior, middle* and *superior cerebellar peduncles.*

THE INFERIOR PEDUNCLES (RESTIFORM BODIES). Its fibers are predominantly afferent and convey nonsensory impulses from the labyrinth, joints,

voluntary muscles and skin (tactile). Its constituent fiber tracts are (figs. 69.2 and 69.5):

### A. Afferent (Entering) Fibers

(1) *Dorsal (posterior) spinocerebellar (direct cerebellar) tract.* The fibers of this tract end in the cortex of the anterior and posterior lobes of both sides but mainly of the same side. Some fibers also end in the nodule.

(2) *Dorsal external arcuate fibers* (p. 1193) from the nuclei gracilis and cuneatus of the same side, and the *ventral external arcuate fibers* from the corresponding nuclei of the opposite side. These fibers carry impulses aroused by tactile stimuli to the cortex of the paramedian lobule of the posterior lobe and to the lobulus simplex of the anterior lobe.

(3) *Vestibulocerebellar tract* from the vestibular nuclei of the same side, and also directly from the vestibular nerve. They pass to the three cerebellar nuclei (nucleus globosus, nucleus emboliformis and mainly to nuclei fastigii) and are relayed to the cortex of the flocculonodular lobe and of the uvula.

(4) *Olivocerebellar tract* arising in the inferior olive of the opposite side and to some extent in the nucleus of the same side; the fibers of this tract end in the cortex of those portions of the vermis and hemispheres constituting the posterior lobe.

(5) Fibers of the fifth nerve and possibly of the ninth and tenth nerves which terminate in the pyramid, uvula and paraflocculus.

(6) *Tectocerebellar,* from the colliculi of the midbrain to the cerebellum; the exact course and termination of this tract is unknown.

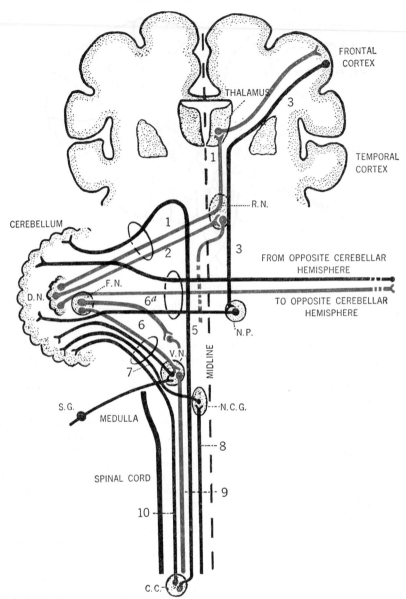

Fig. 69.5. Diagram of chief cerebellar connections. Afferent fibers, black; efferent fibers, red. R. N., red nucleus; D. N., dentate nucleus; F. N., fastigial nucleus; N. P., pontine nuclei; V. N., vestibular nucleus; N.C.G., nuclei cuneatus and gracilis; S.G., cell of Scarpa's ganglion; C.C., Clarke's column (dorsal nucleus). 1, dentato-rubro-thalamic tract, 1ᵃ dentatothalamic fibers which pass through the red nucleus; 2, cerebellorubral tract; 3, frontopontine tract; 4, rubrospinal tract; 5, ventral (indirect) spino-cerebellar tract; 6, fastigiovestibular tract; 6ᵃ, fastigiobulbar tract; 7, external arcuate fibers passing from N.C.G. to cerebelum; 8, fasciculi gracilis and cuneatus; 9, vestibulospinal tract; 10, dorsal (direct) spinocerebellar tract.

### B. *Efferent (Leaving) Fibers*

(1) *Fastigiobulbar (or cerebellovestibular) tract.* This is a pathway from the flocculonodular lobe and the roof nucleus to the vestibular nuclei, and the reticular formation of the medulla. Impulses are relayed from the medulla *via* (i) the reticulospinal and the vestibulospinal tracts to the spinal centers, and (ii) the medial longitudinal

fasciculus to the nuclei of the ocular nerves and into the anterior ground bundle of the cord.

(2) *Cerebello-olivary tract* to the inferior olives of both sides. The latter may be connected with the spinal centers through the olivospinal tracts (p. 1196).

THE MIDDLE PEDUNCLES (BRACHIA PONTIS) are also mainly afferent. Each contains:

(a) fibers which arise from cells of the pontine nuclei and end in the cortex of the posterior cerebellar lobe (declive, tuber, and the ansiform and paramedian lobules) of the opposite side, but also in smaller numbers in the homolateral hemisphere and vermis. These fibers constitute the secondary neurons of the *corticopontine* tracts, particularly the *frontopontine-cerebellar* tracts (b) fibers which pass from the cerebellar nuclei to the hemisphere of the opposite side (see fig. 69.5).

THE SUPERIOR PEDUNCLES (BRACHIA CONJUNCTIVAE) enter into the formation of the upper part of the roof of the fourth ventricle and plunge into the midbrain just beneath the inferior colliculi. The superior cerebellar peduncle contains both efferent and afferent fibers but is composed predominantly of the former. It is through the superior peduncle that the cerebellum exerts its main influence upon the cerebral cortex and upon voluntary movement.

*A. The efferent fibers* arise chiefly from the dentate nucleus, but a few are also derived from the nuclei globosus and emboliformis. The Purkinje cells of the cerebellar cortex constitute the primary neurons of these paths. The fibers decussate in the midbrain with those of the opposite side and then divide into an ascending and a descending group.

*(1) The ascending fibers* pass (a) directly to the lateral ventral nucleus of the thalamus where the impulses are relayed to areas 4 and 6 of the cerebral cortex; (b) from the dentate nucleus to the small-celled nucleus (*n. parvocellularis*) of the red nucleus, and from the globose and emboliform nuclei to the large-celled nucleus (*n. magnocellularis*). The impulses reaching the small-celled nucleus (from dentate nucleus) are relayed *via* the rubrothalamic tract to areas 4 and 6 of the cerebral cortex.

It will be noted that the ascending fibers connect one cerebellar hemisphere with the red nucleus, thalamus and cerebral cortex of the opposite side, but, as a result of the crossing of the rubrospinal and corticospinal and corticobulbar tracts, each cerebellar hemisphere is ultimately connected with the same side of the brain stem and spinal cord.

*(2) The descending fibers* terminate around cells of the reticular formation of the pons, medulla and cervical cord.

*B. The afferent fibers* of the superior cerebellar peduncle are:

(1) The ventral (indirect) spinocerebellar tract. This ascends through the spinal cord, the medulla oblongata and pons and, reaching the upper level of the latter, turns backwards, arches over the peduncle, enters the anterior medullary velum, and passes within this to the cerebellum. The fibers end in the cortex of the anterior lobe mainly of the same side.

*(2) The tectocerebellar tract*, composed of fibers which originate in the superior colliculus. It probably conveys retinal impulses and so constitutes a pathway for visuocerebellar reflexes.

*Afferent-efferent (cerebro-cerebello-cerebral) circuit.* This consists of fibers (frontopontine) from areas 4 and 6 of the precentral motor cortex to the pontine nuclei; and from the latter through the opposite middle cerebellar peduncle to the cerebellar cortex. The activity of the cerebellar cortex is finally centered in the Purkinje cells. Their impulses are transmitted to the dentate nucleus; from this nucleus (described on p. 1278) *via* the superior peduncle to the brain stem where they cross to the red nucleus of the opposite side; thence to the lateral ventral nucleus of the thalamus, whence they return to areas 4 and 6 of the cerebral cortex. Through these paths a steadying action is exerted upon voluntary movements initiated through the precentral motor cortex.

The fibers reaching the cerebellar cortex *via* the peduncles are of two main types: (a) *"moss fibers,"* which end in mosslike appendages around the cells of the granular layer (fig. 69.3) and (b) *climbing fibers*, which pass outward to the molecular layer; here they give off collaterals resembling the tendrils of a vine which appear to cling to the arborizations of the Purkinje cells. According to Cajal the climbing fibers are derived from the vestibular and pontine nuclei; whereas the direct spinocerebellar and olivocerebellar tracts are constituted of moss fibers. Through their connections with the cells of the granular layer each moss fiber is connected indirectly with a large number of Purkinje cells, whereas a climbing fiber is in communication with only one or two Purkinje cells.

In the foregoing paragraphs the anatomical connections of the cerebellum have been outlined, as far as they are known at the present time. Over these many pathways a multitude of afferent impulses bring information to the cerebellum. These different types of afferent impulses are distributed variously to the different lobes of the cerebellum. Thus the vestibular impulses concerned with the position of the body in space pass largely to the flocculonodular lobe, with some going to other parts of the cerebellum.

The impulses from the spinal cord pass over the dorsal and ventral spinocerebellar pathways and the posterior columns (fasciculi gracilis and cuneatus) particularly to the anterior lobe. These bear proprioceptive impulses from muscles, joints and tendons to the cerebellum and in view of this organ's predominant preoccupation with the regulation of reflex muscular activity this is as one would anticipate. But, in addition, impulses of tactile origin arrive in large numbers in both the anterior lobe and in the cortex of the neocerebellum or posterior lobe. Furthermore, there is a strict topographic localization of the termination of these impulses. The "tactile" area of the anterior lobe lies near the midline with each side of the body represented ipsilaterally. The impulses from the lower extremity are received more anteriorly; those from the upper extremity farther back and those from the face most posteriorly. Tactile impulses are received in the neocerebellum on either side of the vermis. Here the face is represented most anteriorly, then the upper extremity and finally the lower extremity, just the reverse of the representation in the anterior lobe. It is doubtless significant that there are both afferent and efferent connections between these same areas of the neocerebellum and the pre- and postcentral gyri of the cerebral cortex. Although there is no evidence that the cerebellum is in any way concerned with the conscious perception of tactile or other external stimuli, such a possibility cannot be excluded. The significance of the arrival of these tactile impulses in the cerebellum and of the connection of the same areas of the cerebellum with the sensory areas (postcentral) of the cerebral cortex are not understood at the present time.

The cerebellum also receives afferent impulses produced by visual and auditory stimuli and is connected with the cortical centers subserving auditory and visual functions. The auditory and visual center of the cerebellum occupies the midline at the junction of the anterior and posterior lobes. This auditory-visual area overlaps the "face" area of the tactile center in the cortex of the anterior lobe. Again the significance of these connections is not fully understood.

As we have indicated above there are many afferent connections from the cerebral cortex to the cerebellum. Those from the precentral motor cortex which are very numerous are easily understood. They are essential for the cerebellum's prominent role in the regulation of movement and they pass predominantly to the neocerebellum. The other connections are with the postcentral gyrus, the auditory cortex in Heschl's gyrus and the visual cortex along the calcarine fissure. It is also interesting and doubtless very significant that the connections between all of these areas of

the cerebral and cerebellar cortices are circular ones, i.e., each area of the cerebral cortex projects to a localized area of cerebellar cortex and the latter in turn projects back to the same cerebral area.

In addition to the prominent vestibular connections from the brain stem the cerebellum also has extensive connections with other nuclear structures in the midbrain, pons and bulb. Probably the most important of these, other than the vestibular nuclei, is the reticular formation. This important part of the brain stem has both afferent and efferent connections with all lobes of the cerebellum. There are also extensive connections with the red nucleus, the nuclei of the fifth cranial nerve and with the inferior olive. Through these the cerebellum is able to exert its great influence over the control of muscular tone, postural reflexes, righting reflexes and even over the $\gamma$-fibers and the innervation of the intrafusal fibers of the skeletal muscles. It has been demonstrated that the cerebellum is also capable of exerting a controlling influence over various visceral and vasomotor phenomenon as well.

## The Experimental Study of the Cerebellum

### Effects of Excision of the Cerebellum and of Section of the Peduncles

The earliest experiments upon the cerebellum were performed by Rolando (1809) and the French neurologist Flourens (1822). The latter removed the cerebellum of pigeons in which he observed, as a result of the ablation, grave disturbances of equilibrium and abnormal postures of the wings, neck and limbs. Luciani, in the later part of the 19th century, carried out cerebellar ablations upon dogs and observed three cardinal effects: (a) muscular weakness or *asthenia*; (b) a reduction in muscle tone, which he called *atonia* (really hypotonia), and (c) unsteadiness of voluntary movement, to which he gave the name *astasia*. These defects which appeared about a month after the operation gave rise to a coarse, jerky *tremor* when an attempt was made to perform any voluntary act.

Disequilibrium, due to the removal of the vestibular impulses, which is readily demonstrated in monkeys, causes a staggering, reeling, drunkenlike gait. The animal—dog or monkey—stands with limbs spread in order to provide a broad base, sways from side to side with oscillations of the head.

Another characteristic symptom of cerebellar ablation, and which is also seen with lesions of the cerebellum in man, is *dysmetria*—the inability to gauge the strength or duration of the muscular contraction required to execute a certain voluntary act. For example, if the arm reaches for an object it may overshoot the mark (*hypermetria*) or fall short of it (*hypometria*).

The effect of the cerebellum upon muscular tone and muscular reflexes varies with the animal concerned. In the cat and dog the anterior lobe forms a large part of the cerebellum. In these animals excision of the anterior lobe gives rise to a state of increased muscular tone similar to decerebrate rigidity and if decerebrate rigidity has already been produced ablation of this portion of the cerebellum will increase the already existing rigidity. On the other hand stimulation of the anterior lobe of the cerebellum will cause the rigidity characteristic of the decerebrate state to relax. From this evidence it has been concluded that the anterior lobe of the cerebellum is concerned with the inhibition of the stretch reflexes and the postural reflexes of the skeletal musculature. Certainly this is an important part of the function of this part of the cerebellum in these animals, but it has now been shown that stimulation of the cortex of the anterior lobe and of the fastigial nuclei to which it projects can produce *both* inhibition and enhancement of muscular rigidity. It thus appears that the anterior lobe of the cerebellum is an organ for the *regulation* of muscular tone rather than merely an inhibitor of reflex muscular activity. It should be noted, however, that these effects upon muscular tone and muscular reflexes are most marked in the carnivores. They are much less pronounced in subhuman primates and still less so in man. In fact, nothing resembling decerebrate rigidity or enhancement of pre-existing rigidity has ever been reported as the result of a cerebellar lesion in man. In human beings if there is any alteration in muscular tone as the result of a cerebellar lesion it is in the direction of a decrease. The involved extremities tend to become flaccid or hypotonic and tendon reflexes may become pendular.

*Unilateral* destruction or damage of the cerebellum causes a reduction in tone of the muscles of the same side and a tendency to fall to that side.

*Section of the peduncles.* Section of all six peduncles causes effects identical with those of complete decerebellation, and division of the three of one side results in effects described for unilateral

ablation. In the chimpanzee, *asynergia, hypotonia, easy fatigability,* and a *coarse tremor* appear on the same side as the section. Severance of one superior peduncle causes at first defects somewhat similar although less severe than those following unilateral section of all three peduncles, and is later compensated for through those which have been left intact. Little is known with respect to the disabilities following section of one or both middle peduncles. A lesion interupting the fibers of the inferior peduncles causes, mainly, equilibratory disturbances (due to division of vestibular connections), and ataxia as a result of the interruption of spinocerebellar fibers. Compensation through the intact cerebellum tends to occur later, so that the effects become progressively less severe.

Even after unilateral section of the three peduncles, compensation is brought about after a time through the remaining half of the cerebellum and through the frontal lobes (Botterell and Fulton).

The experiments of Aring and Fulton indicate that the nervous mechanism involved in the production of cerebellar tremor lies in the excitable part of the cerebral cortex (area 4 and the upper part of area 6); removal of these areas after contralateral section of the cerebellar peduncles abolished the tremor. Large parts of the cortex of the cerebellum can be removed with little permanent neurologic deficit, so long as all of the cortex of one hemisphere is not removed. On the other hand damage to the central nuclei or the cerebellar peduncles produces much more severe and lasting disturbances.

### STIMULATION OF THE CEREBELLUM

Electrical stimulation of the cerebellum, both of the cortex and of the central nuclei, has supplied relatively little information concerning the functions of this important structure. The results are far less than those produced by stimulation of the precentral motor cortex of the cerebral hemispheres. This is rather surprising in view of the fact that the cerebellum is primarily concerned with muscular activities. In general the responses to stimulation of both the cerebellar cortex and the nuclei are slow and tonic in character. They are also diffuse and complex in contrast with the well localized discrete movements which can be obtained by stimulating the precentral gyrus. It is also common to obtain diphasic responses, i.e., one type of response during stimulation which is followed by an opposite type of response after the stimulation has ceased. Many of the responses concern movements of the eyes toward the same side as that to which the stimulus is applied, or a movement of the eyes to a position in which they gaze forward. If there is a "rebound" response following the termination of stimulation the eyes turn toward the side opposite that on which the stimulus is applied. Such movements of the eyes may or may not be associated with similar movements of the head either to the side or straight ahead. Stimulation may give rise to movements involving the head, extremities, trunk and tail in the long axis of the body producing a concavity of the body on the side stimulated. Stimulation of the cortex of the anterior lobe and of the fastigial and globose nuclei sometimes causes flexion of the ipsilateral limbs and extension of the contralateral ones. It is interesting to note that most responses are obtained by stimulating the anterior lobe and the fastigial and globose nuclei. Stimulation of the posterior lobe or neocerebellum or of the dentate or emboliform nuclei is far less effective. This is surprising in view of the fact that these latter structures are the ones connected with the precentral motor cortex and primarily concerned with the regulation and integration of voluntary muscular activity.

### Localization in Cerebellar Cortex

In recent years representation in the cerebellum, afferent and efferent, have been shown to be much more circumscribed than had been supposed. Yet, even so, localization has not been found to be as precisely discrete as in certain regions of the cerebral cortex, e.g., in the motor area. Owing to the double crossing of the pathway for impulses from the cerebellum, as they ascend in the midbrain (dentatorubral tract) and as they descend to the spinal cord (rubrospinal tract), each half of the cerebellum exerts its influence mainly on the musculature of the same side of the body.

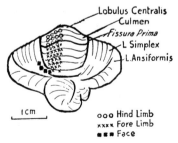

FIG. 69.6. Spinocerebellar receiving areas for hind-limb, fore-limb and face (vibrissae) in the cat, as determined by the method of evoked potentials. (From Adrian.)

Representation in the cerebellar cortex of somatic receptive areas has been studied by Dow, by Snider and his associates, and by Adrian by means of the method of evoked potentials. Adrian recorded the potentials evoked in the cortex of the *anterior lobe* of cats and monkeys by means of a fine wire electrode inserted beneath the surface. Various areas over the limbs and face were stimulated by touch, pressure, joint movement, or stretching of muscles (fig. 69.6).

The representation in the anterior lobe of the different somatic areas is in reverse order. That it to say, the hindlimb area is placed anteriorly to the areas for the forelimbs and face. Thus, stimulation of the hindlimb evoked potentials from the lobulus centralis and an anterior strip of the culmen, stimulation of the forelimb induced responses from the remainder of the culmen, and stimulation of the face (vibrissae in cat) from the lobulus simplex. The spinocerebellar impulses from the tail are probably received by the most anteriorly situated part of the anterior lobe, namely, in the lingula.[3] An even, more precise localization was mapped out within these areas; in the area for the hindlimb, the foot is in front of the knee and the knee in front of the thigh; in the forelimb representation the shoulder is in front of the wrist, with the wrist and hand following in corresponding order.

Potentials were also evoked from the anterior lobe by stimulation (electrical or local application of strychnine) of the motor area of the cerebral cortex, i.e., by causing a discharge over corticopontine and pontocerebellar pathways. The anterior part of the precentral motor cortex (area 6) projects to the lateral part of the neocerebellum, where the posterior part (area 4) projects to more medial structures in both the anterior and posterior lobes. Most of this cerebro-cerebellar projection is crossed but some of it is to the ipsilateral cerebellar hemisphere. The projections of area 4 to the cerebellar cortex correspond closely with the termination of tactile impulses. The topographic representation of the face, arm and leg of impulses from the precentral motor cortex followed the same pattern as that for tactile impulses. In the anterior lobe the "leg" area lies most anteriorly and the "face" area most posteriorly. In the posterior lobe the reverse is true. Stimulation of the caudate nucleus will evoke alterations in electrical potentials in the posterior lobe.

[3] In the giraffe the lobulus simplex is greatly enlarged, and in monkeys with a prehensile tail the lingula is elongated.

Impulses from the auditory and visual systems, from the olfactory bulbs and from the vagi are also conveyed to the cerebellum. Sound, or flashes of light, evoke potentials from an area covering the lobulus simplex, declive and tuber, and extending laterally into the ansiform lobule. The visual impulses are relayed to the cerebellum from the superior colliculus, the auditory from the inferior colliculus. The tectocerebellar tracts probably provide the pathways for these impulses. The auditory and visual cortices project to the same areas.

From ablation experiments topographical localization similar in character to that described above for the spinocerebellar and corticopontine-cerebellar systems has been demonstrated for the efferent side. The tail muscles are represented in the lingula, the muscles for the hindlimbs in the lobulus centralis, the forelimb muscles in the culmen, and the cervical and facial muscles in the lobulus simplex. Representation of the limbs in the middle lobe of Ingvar (ansiform lobule, declive and tuber) has not been demonstrated, but from the relatively enormous size of this part of the cerebellum in higher mammals and from the fact that it (ansiform lobule) is the chief receiving station for corticopontocerebellar impulses, it cannot be doubted that it is of paramount importance in volitional movement.

*The flocculonodular lobe,* through its vestibular connections, is concerned with equilibratory function, severe disturbances of balance resulting from its ablation. Ablation of the nodule in dogs confers complete immunity to motion sickness (Bard and associates. Removal of no other part of the cerebellum or of the cerebral cortex has this protective action (ch. 64). Ablation of the *nodule* and *flocculus* (flocculonodular lobe, p. 1276, 1277) in monkeys or of the nodule and part of the uvula (Dow) which causes injury to vestibular paths, is followed by pronounced disturbances of balance. In man a lesion of this part of the vermis is also associated with disturbances of equilibrium. Removal of the *nodule* alone in monkeys is followed by oscillation of the head and neck (and, in some instances of the whole trunk) falling backwards and an unsteady gait with the extremities spread widely apart to provide a broader and thus more certain base.

The functions of the *uvula* are largely obscure; its destruction alone is followed by some transient disturbance of equilibrium. Very little is known of the function of the *pyramid*, although it appears to be concerned in some way with vision or eye movement. Its excision causes no defect of bal-

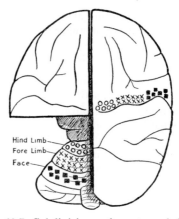

Fig. 69.7. Subdivisions of pontocerebellar receiving area in the monkey, showing their connection with different parts of the motor cortex. (From Adrian.)

ance. Ablation of the pyramid in the monkey results in an inability to halt its forward progression in time to prevent it from crashing into some obstacle. Faradic stimulation of the pyramid elicits an upward movement of the eyes, and Fulton suggests from this fact and the preceding observation the possibility of the pyramid being concerned in some way with the integration of proprioceptive impulses essential in judging distance.

### Summary of Functional Localization

(1) All cerebellar activities, afferent and efferent, are carried out beneath consciousness.

(2) In the anterior lobe are represented in regular order the various receptive and muscular regions of the body. It is concerned mainly with the adjustments of muscle tone and synergic action necessary for posture in subprimate mammals, but appears to be much less important in primates.

(3) The posterior lobe (middle lobe of Ingvar) (neocerebellum) is the chief receptive region for corticopontocerebellar tracts. It is most highly developed in the primates. It is concerned with the integration and regulation of well coordinated muscular activities.

(4) The flocculonodular lobe, the most ancient part of the cerebellum, is intimately connected with the vestibular apparatus both through the vestibular nuclei and directly by fibers from the vestibular nerve, and therefore constitutes an important part of the neural mechanisms underlying equilibratory function.

(5) The functions of the uvula and pyramid are little known, although the latter probably has to

do with eye movements and the former, to a minor degree, with equilibrium.

## GENERAL SUMMARY OF CEREBELLAR FUNCTION

The cerebellum is concerned primarily with the regulation of muscular activity. It does not initiate movement and its removal does not result in paralysis but it does coordinate the various muscles concerned in any given act to produce smooth, efficient movement. When the precentral motor cortex initiates a voluntary movement it simultaneously "informs" the cerebellum over the frontopontocerebellar pathway. The cerebellum has also been "informed" regarding the position of the body in space over the vestibulocerebellar connections, of the position of the muscles and of the trunk and extremities over the spinocerebellar pathways and of the *contact* of the body with other structures by means of tactile impulses. The cerebellum is then able to regulate reflexes and the contraction or relaxation of the various muscles concerned by means of its connections with the precentral motor cortex, the reticular formation, the vestibular nuclei and perhaps the inferior olive. Beevor has classified the muscles concerned in voluntary muscular activity as follows:

(a) PRIME MOVERS OR AGONISTS, those whose contraction is essentially responsible for the movement of the part.

(b) ANTAGONISTS, those which oppose the prime movers.

(c) SYNERGISTS, those which assist the prime movers and reduce unnecessary movements to a minimum.

(d) FIXATION MUSCLES, those whose contraction causes the fixation of the neighboring joints and maintains the limb or body in a position appropriate for carrying out the particular movement.

Normally these muscle groups act as a unit. The contraction of the prime mover, e.g., the biceps, is accompanied by inhibition of the contraction of its antagonist, i.e., the triceps. The reciprocal inhibition, however, is not absolute; the antagonistic muscle as shown by Tilney and Pike, gives a coincident but weaker contraction, and thus serves the function of a "brake" or "snubber" to check the action of the agonist. At the same time the fixation muscles of the neighboring joint contract, thus enabling the agonist to exert its force with a minimum of waste effort. Any increase in the force of contraction of the agonist is accompanied by a corresponding rise in

tone of its opponent (antagonist). Also, the muscles of fixation and the synergists contract more powerfully as the contraction of the prime movers increases, whereas groups of fixation muscles and synergists, which in a weaker movement remain quiescent, may be called into play. To give an example, when the fingers are closed with moderate force the only fixation muscles which show activity are the extensors of the wrist. When, however, the fist is clenched forcibly, muscles of the elbow and even those of the shoulder contract to fix these joints. Through such action between the various muscles taking part in a given act, smoothness and steadiness of movement are ensured and muscular force thereby economized. After destruction of the cerebellum these nice coöperative actions are lost. The asynergia results in jerkiness, overaction and imperfect muscular control (ataxia).[4] The force of a given muscular movement is not graded with precision for the work to be done, but "overshoots the mark." This led Babinski to suggest originally, that cerebellar activity (through the cerebral cortex) served as a "brake" to check such a tendency, that is, to overcome the inertia of the moving part.

It has also been shown that the cerebellum exerts some controlling or regulatory influence over various visceral and vasomotor phenomena. This influence does not appear to be great. The possibility exists that the cerebellum may exert some control over the perception of stimuli but this has never been conclusively demonstrated. There is evidence that the cerebellum, like the reticular formation, exerts some influence over the $\gamma$-motorneurons and thus over the muscle spindles which are proprioceptive end-organs.

## The Manifestations of Cerebellar Disease

The signs of cerebellar disease are much more pronounced in acute lesions, e.g., abscess, hemorrhage or trauma, than in those, e.g., tumor, which develop more gradually. In slowly developing lesions or after the subsidence of acute cerebellar disease a certain degree of compensation for the cerebellar defect always occurs. The majority of the signs of cerebellar disease are the result fundamentally of asynergia of the voluntary muscles.

[4] Holmes denies that the cerebellum exerts any specific function in respect to the distribution of tone among various muscles acting synergically. The steadying action which tonic muscles normally exert over their antagonists is absent in cerebellar disease but Holmes maintains that this is due merely to the general hypotonicity.

According to Holmes the chief features of cerebellar lesions are (1) *hypotonia*, (2) *asthenia, fatigability and slowness of movement*, (3) *tremor*, (4) *asynergia*, (5) *decomposition of movement*, (6) *dysmetria*, (7) *rebound phenomenon*, (8) *adiadochokinesis*, (9) *vertigo and past-pointing*, (10) *deviation of the eyes and nystagmus*, (11) *attitude and gait*, (12) *disturbances of speech*, (13) *reflexes*.

HYPOTONIA. This is usually a prominent feature in acute cerebellar lesions. The muscles are flabby. The limbs for this reason assume unnatural attitudes and can be moved passively into positions of extreme flexion or extension. The extremities flop about when shaken vigorously and, if the patient is suddenly rotated when standing, the arms swing loosely from the shoulders.

ASTHENIA, FATIGABILITY AND SLOWNESS OF MOVEMENT. The muscles on the affected side are definitely weakened and tire easily. The commencement of any voluntary movement is delayed, and both contraction and relaxation phases are abnormally slow. Neither hypotonia nor asthenia are notable features in chronic lesions. Some also question whether weakness is a manifestation of cerebellar deficit, but Holmes considers it to be due to involvement of the cerebellar nuclei.

TREMOR. This is a coarse involuntary rhythmical oscillation which supervenes upon any attempt at voluntary movement (*intention tremor*), or when the muscles are engaged in maintaining a steady posture (*static tremor*), as in holding the head erect on the arms outstretched. Removal of the precentral gyrus will abolish such a tremor. This probably is due to the destruction of the corticospinal fibers which arise there.

ASYNERGIA. It should be pointed out that this term as used by Holmes has a much more restricted meaning than that which is usually given to it. This observer applied the term especially to the asynchronism observed between the actions of the fixation muscles and the prime movers, as well as to the lack of coöperation which normally exists between the muscles of the limbs, trunk and neck during walking and standing, and other acts necessitating postural adjustments of the various members of the body against gravity. For example, when the patient is asked to clench his fist, the extensors which normally fix the wrist as the fingers are flexed, either contract to early, and so over-extend the joint, or too late. In the latter event the wrist is flexed as the fist closes. Also, the patient may fall when he throws his head back owing to his failure to flex his knees, and so maintain his center of gravity over his base. Similarly when he attempts to sit upon a low stool he may fall backwards because he cannot at the same time flex his trunk at the hips.

DECOMPOSITION OF MOVEMENT. The patient "breaks down" a given movement into its parts. When, for example, he is asked, as he lies in bed, to extend his arm vertically, and then to touch his nose with his forefinger, the latter movement is not performed naturally by simultaneously lowering the arm and bending the elbow. The extended arm is first lowered to the side; not until this position is reached is the elbow flexed and the finger brought to the nose.

DYSMETRIA is the lack of ability to adjust the force of the contraction necessary for the accomplishment of a given act. For example, when asked to touch a point with his finger the patient overshoots the mark or, less commonly, fails to reach it. Dysmetria in a lower limb may be demonstrated by the heel to knee test; when the patient, while recumbent, is directed to rest the heel of the affected side upon the opposite knee, he brings it in contact with the thigh or with the leg below the knee. Dysmetria is another manifestation of the general lack of synergic muscular control.

REBOUND PHENOMENON. If the patient is asked to attempt a movement against a resistance which is then suddenly removed, the limb moves forcibly in the direction towards which the effort was made. For example, if the observer holds the wrist of the patient, then asks him to bend the elbow, and, while he is making the effort, the forearm is suddenly released, flexion, of the arm occurs with an unusual degree of force. This rebound phenomenon can be attributed to the absence of the "braking" action (p. 1286) of the antagonistic muscles.

ADIADOCHOKINESIS (a = privative; diadocho = succession, kinesis = movement) is the name given by Babinski to the inability to execute alternating movements rapidly, e.g., pronation and supination of the forearm, or flexion and extension of the fingers.

PAST-POINTING AND VERTIGO (p. 1181). When the patient with his eyes closed is asked to *raise* the arm of the affected side and to touch a prescribed mark, the arm deviates outwards, rarely inwards. When directed to move the finger in the *horizontal* plane and touch the mark the arm in some cases, deviates upwards, in others downwards. Vertigo, the sensation that the environment is rotating, is not a symptom of cerebellar disease but of involvement of the vestibular nuclei or of the labyrinth in the inner ear.

DEVIATION OF THE EYES AND NYSTAGMUS. In

an acute unilateral lesion there may be conjugate deviation of the eyes to the uninjured side. In all probability this is the result of involvement of or pressure on the brain stem and not of the cerebellar involvement *per se*. When the patient is asked to look at an object in front of him the eyes move into position but then slowly deviate again to the uninjured side; after full deviation the eyes may return again to the central position with a sharp jerk. These alternate horizontal movements occur repeatedly and are known as nystagmus (p. 1179). Although no deviation of the eyes is evident, nystagmus can sometimes be demonstrated in a patient with a cerebellar lesion when he is asked to turn his eyes towards either the injured or the uninjured side; the eyes are moved in the direction indicated and then deviate slowly towards the midline, only to be returned in a series of jerks toward the point in which he is attempting to look. The nystagmus is due to injury of vestibulocerebellar paths (see also p. 1279).

Skew deviation of the eyes is sometimes observed with acute cerebellar disease but is probably the result of involvement of the brain stem.

ATTITUDE AND GAIT. Cerebellar disease sometimes results in abnormal attitudes. The trunk may be concave towards the affected side and sometimes rotated with the affected shoulder advanced. Rotation of the head with the chin towards the sound side, and flexed towards the shoulder of the affected side is not uncommonly seen in unilateral cerebellar disease. (This attitude is probably due to an associated lesion of the vestibular paths in the brain stem.) In standing the body is inclined towards the side of the lesion and tends to fall to that side. Falling backwards or forwards may occur (especially in lesions of the vermis). The abnormal attitudes of the limbs resulting from the muscular hypotonicity when this is present, have been mentioned.

The gait is often staggering, reeling or lurching in character. The patient's line of travel is not straight but tends to be curved; the deviation is towards the affected side. When he is able to see his way he attempts to correct his tendency to deviate to one side by bringing himself back from time to time to his intended line of travel. Thus he follows a zig-zag course to his objective. The movements of the lower limbs are ataxic; they are often thrown about in an awkward, uncontrolled manner. The upper extremity on the affected side does not swing as the patient walks as does the normal one.

DISTURBANCES OF SPEECH are due to asynergia of the muscles of phonation and articulation. It is seen most frequently with diffuse degenerative lesions rather than with localized ones. The speech may be drawling, scanning, singsong or explosive in type.

THE REFLEXES. The cutaneous reflexes are normal and the deep reflexes, with the exception of the knee jerk, show as a rule no marked departure from the normal. The knee jerk is not uncommonly pendular in character. That is to say, when the leg is hanging free a tap on the patellar tendon causes a slower, less brisk response than normal, but one of greater amplitude. Also, unlike the response of the sound side, the return excursion of the leg is not arrested when, as a result of the influence of gravity, it reaches the resting position, but swings beyond. Several to and fro movements follow before the limb finally comes to rest. This behavior is evidently due to the hypotonicity of the flexor and extensor muscles and thus to a lack of the restraining effect which they normally exert upon one another to prevent exaggerated excursions of the limb in either direction.

Muscle sense and other forms of sensation are unaffected in cerebellar disease. The following are the principal types of cerebellar lesion: (1) *tumor*, (2) *abscess*, (3) *injury*, e.g., gunshot wounds, (4) *degenerations* of (a) the cerebellar cortex, (b) the middle and inferior peduncles, (c) more rarely, of the cerebellar nuclei and superior peduncles, (d) of the spinocerebellar tracts, e.g., Friedreich's ataxia, a hereditary condition.

A lesion involving the neocerebellum (superior vermis and hemispheres) is associated with hypotonia; dysmetria; weakness, slowness and irregularity of voluntary movement; tremor and nystagmus. In disease of the flocculonodular lobe, there are marked disturbances of balance with a swaying, staggering gait and a tendency to fall backwards. There is no syndrome of the anterior lobe in man.

## REFERENCES

ADRIAN, E. D. Brain, 1943, **66**, 289.

ARING, C. D. AND FULTON, J. F. Arch. Neurol. & Psychiat., 1936, **35**, 439.

BARD, P. AND ASSOCIATES. Fed. Proc., 1947, **6**, 72.

BOTTERELL, E. H. AND FULTON, J. F. J. Comp. Neurol., 1938, **69**, 31.

Dow, R. G. Biol. Rev., 1942, **17**, 179.

Dow, R. G. J. Neurophysiol., 1942, **5**, 121.

HOLMES, G. Brain, 1917, **40**, 461; 1939, **62**, 1.

HOLMES, G., Lancet, 1922, **1**, 1177, 1231; 1922, **2**, 59, 111.

INGVAR, S. Brain, 1923, **46,** 301.

JACKSON, J. HUGHLINGS. Collected Writings, London, 1932, **1,** 8. (Quoted by Holmes, G.)

KELLER, A. D., ROY, R. S. AND CHASE, W. P. Am. J. Physiol., 1937, **118,** 720.

LARSELL, O. Arch. Neurol. & Psychiat., 1937, **38,** 580.

MILLER, F. R. AND BANTING, F. G. Am. J. Physiol., 1922, **59,** 478 (Proc.).

MILLER, F. R. AND BANTING, F. G., Am. Brain, 1922, **45,** 104.

MILLER, F. R. AND LAUGHTON, N. B. Arch. Neurol. & Psychiat, 1928, **19,** 47.

POLLOCK, L. J. AND DAVIS, L. Assoc. Res. Nerv. & Ment. Dis., 1929, **6,** 424.

SNIDER, R. S. Arch. Neurol. & Psychiat., 1950, **64,** 196.

SNIDER, R. S. AND STOWELL, A. J. Neurophysiol., 1944, **7,** 331.

TILNEY, F. AND PIKE, F. H. Arch. Neurol. & Psychiat., 925, **13,** 289.

WALKER, A. E. AND BOTTERELL, E. H. Brain, 1937, **60,** 329.

WEISENBURG, T. H. Cerebellar localization. Assoc. Res. Nerv. & Ment. Dis., 1929, **6,** 497.

### Monographs and Reviews

Association for Research in Nervous and Mental Disease. Vol. 6. The cerebellum. The Williams & Wilkins Co., Baltimore, 1929.

BOLK, L. Das Cerebellum der Säugetiere. Haarlem, 1906. Quoted by Miller.

DOW, R. S. AND MORUZZI, G., The physiology and pathology of the cerebellum. University of Minnesota Press, Minneapolis, 1958.

FULTON, J. F. Physiology of the nervous system. Oxford Univ. Press, London, 1938.

FULTON, J. F. Medicine, 1936, 15, 247.

LARSELL, O. The cerebellum from myxinoids to man. University of Minnesota Press, Minneapolis. In Press.

LUCIANI, L. Human physiology. Vol. 3, Macmillan, London, 1915.

MILLER, F. R. The physiology of the cerebellum. Physiol. Rev., 1926, **6,** 124.

RANSON, S. W. The anatomy of the nervous system from the standpoint of development and function. Saunders, Philadelphia, 1921.

SHERRINGTON, C. S. The integrative action of the nervous system. Yale University Press, New Haven, Conn., 1920.

SMITH, G. E. The nervous system. In Cunningham's text-book of anatomy, p. 505, Oxford University Press, London, 1931.

TILNEY, F., RILEY, H. A., POLLOCK, L. J. AND DAVIS, L. Brain, 1927, **50,** 275.

VILLIGER, E. Brain and spinal cord. Lippincott, Philadelphia, 1931.

WILSON, S. A. K. Modern problems in neurology. Arnold, London, 1928.

# 70

# THE CEREBROSPINAL FLUID (C.S.F.)

The discovery of the cerebrospinal fluid is generally ascribed to Cotugno (Liquor Cotunnii), but the first clear description was provided some fifty years after Cotugno's report by Magendie (1825).

### Anatomical Considerations

The dura mater and the arachnoid membrane form the sac which contains the cerebrospinal fluid. The inner wall of this sac is formed by the pia mater. The fluid circulates in the subarachnoid space which is for the most part narrow but is widened into larger spaces (cisternae) at several points. The principal dilations are the cisterna magna below and behind the cerebellum and above the medulla oblongata, the cisterna pontis on the ventral aspect of the pons and the cisterna basalis, which contains the circle of Willis.

### Site of Formation

In 1853 Faivre reported the results of a histological study of the villous projections of the chorioid plexuses into the ventricles of the brain. He found evidence of secretory activity in the cells covering these vascular structures. Whereas this observation served to turn the attention of physiologists from the concept of Haller and Magendie, who believed that the fluid was formed by the leptomeninges, the evidence that the choroid plexuses are the principal structures concerned was not obtained until quite recently. Although further histological and pharmacological studies gave additional support for this view, physiological experiments and observations on human cases have provided more conclusive results. Some of the more significant results will be cited: (1) when the aqueduct of Sylvius is occluded, an internal hydrocephalus is produced (Dandy and Blackfan; Frazier and Peet); (2) during an operation on a human case a clear fluid was observed exuding from a choroid plexus (Cushing); (3) a sustained outflow of fluid, similar in volume to that obtained from the subarachnoid space was secured from a catheter inserted into the aqueduct of Sylvius (Weed); (4) a unilateral internal hydrocephalus can be produced by obstructing one foramen of Monro (Dandy), but there is no excess accumulation of fluid when the choroid plexus is removed from the lateral ventricle before the obstruction is produced. These points leave no doubt of the importance of the plexuses in the elaboration of the fluid, but there is suggestive anatomical evidence that the perivascular spaces (Virchow-Robin), and the ependymal cells of the ventricles and the spinal canal may participate to some degree in this process. Studies of the formation of the cerebrospinal fluid using substances which have been "tagged" radioactively have thrown some doubt upon the formation of the cerebrospinal fluid by the choroid plexus but have not as yet supplied a completely satisfactory answer to the problem. Each blood vessel entering the nervous system is surrounded by a channel formed by the pia mater. The depth to which it penetrates the nervous system varies with the caliber of the vessel. This perivascular area provides a means of communication for fluid between the subarachnoid space and nervous tissue.

### Circulation

The fluid formed in the lateral ventricles passes through the foramen of Monro to join that produced in the third ventricle and thence through the aqueduct of Sylvius to the fourth ventricle. From the fourth ventricle the fluid passes into the cisternae magna and lateralis through three openings. The central one is the foramen of Magendie and the lateral openings bear the name of Luschka. From the cisternae in the posterior fossa a small amount of the fluid passes downward in the spinal subarachnoid space. Most of the fluid flows upward along the brain stem and then outward and upward over the surface of the cerebral hemispheres. In the subarachnoid spaces additional fluid with a somewhat higher protein con-

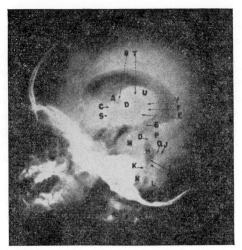

Fig. 70.1. Lateral, horizontal view of the ventricular system. A, intraventricular foramina; B, posterior margin of intraventricular foramen; C, anterior commissure; D, massa intermedia; E, posterior commissure; F, pineal gland; G, aqueduct of Sylvius; H, fourth ventricle; I, (darker shadow) lateral recesses superimposed on the shadow of the fourth ventricle; J, superior posterior recess of the fourth ventricle; K, foramen of Magendie; L, tonsils of cerebellum; M, pons; N, medulla oblongata; O, anterior medullary velum; P, lingula of vermis of cerebellum; Q, posterior medullary velum; R, nodulus of vermis of cerebellum; S, lamina terminalis; T, choroid plexus and ependyma of roof of third ventricle; U, fornix; V, suprapineal recess. (From Davidoff and Dyke.)

ent is added, probably by transudation from the various blood vessels.

## Absorption

When a readily diffusible dye is introduced into the subarachnoid space its rapid appearance in the blood of the venous sinuses under certain conditions demonstrates a possible path of absorption of the fluid. When the dye is injected into the cisternae magna and the spinal canal is blocked, the absorption is not significantly lessened. This indicates that the fluid is largely absorbed from the cranial subarachnoid spaces. Key and Retzius believed that the fluid was absorbed through the Pacchionian granulations, but these are absent from the brains of infants and are now regarded as pathological enlargements of a few of the arachnoid villi. By long-continued slow injection of an isotonic solution of a mixture of potassium ferrocyanide and iron ammonium citrate, Weed was able to demonstrate that the particles of Prussian-blue, formed when the tissue was subsequently fixed in acid medium, precipitated in the mesothelial cells of the tips of the arachnoid villi and within the dural sinuses into which these

villi project. A relatively slow absorption by way of the perineural spaces into the lymphatic system was also demonstrated. These findings have been confirmed, and it may be accepted that the main absorption of the cerebrospinal fluid is through the arachnoid villi into the great venous sinuses. The pathway postulated by Key and Retzius has therefore been established, but the numerous microscopic arachnoid villi have been substituted for the Pacchionian granulations.

MECHANISM OF ABSORPTION. Since the hydrostatic pressure in the subarachnoid space is always greater than that in the dural sinuses, filtration is apparently adequate to account for the flow of liquid into the venous blood stream. True solutions readily pass through the arachnoid villi, colloids more slowly, the rate depending upon the size of the molecules; particulate matter does not pass. No evidence of any secretory activity of the arachnoid villi has been obtained.

## Composition and Mechanism of Formation

In table 70.1 the amounts of the components of the cerebrospinal fluid are compared with those of blood plasma. The values given were obtained from analyses of lumbar fluid; that obtained from the ventricles may be slightly different. This is particularly true of the protein content which is about 5 mg. per 100 cc. of ventricular fluid. The

TABLE 70.1*

*Comparisons of amounts of main constituents of blood plasma and cerebrospinal fluid*

|  | Blood Plasma | Cerebrospinal Fluid |
|---|---|---|
|  | *mg. per 100 cc.* | *mg. per 100 cc.* |
| Protein................. | 6300–8500 | 16–38 |
| Amino acids........... | 4.5–9 | 1.5–3 |
| Creatinine............. | 0.7–2.0 | 0.45–2.20 |
| Uric acid.............. | 2.9–6.9 | 0.5–2.8 |
| Cholesterol........... | 100–150 | 0.06–0.22 |
| Urea.................. | 20–42 | 5–39 |
| Sugar.................. | 70–120 | 45–80 |
| Chloride (NaCl)....... | 560–630 | 720–750 |
| Inorganic phosphate... | 2–5 | 1.25–2.0 |
| Bicarbonate (volumes per cent $CO_2$)........ | 40–60 | 40–60 |
| Hydrogen ions (pH)... | 7.35–7.40 | 7.35–7.40 |
| Sodium................ | 325 | 325 |
| Potassium............. | 20 | 12–17 |
| Magnesium............ | 1–3 | 3–3.6 |
| Calcium............... | 9.0–11.5 | 4.0–7.0 |
| Lactic acid............ | 10–32 | 8–27 |

* Data largely that compiled by Flexner.

water content of a unit weight of spinal fluid is somewhat greater than that of blood.

The question arises, how is the fluid formed? It will be apparent from the table that if certain constituents are investigated, diffusion from the blood plasma will be sufficient to account for the findings. However, before a decision can be reached as to whether the process is one of simple diffusion or of secretion, the concentrations of all the substances on both sides of the semipermeable membrane (the choroid plexus) must be determined. This was done by Flexner whose findings indicate that work must be done to form this fluid, i.e., that it is not merely a filtrate from blood plasma. Since the hydrostatic pressure of the capillary blood is believed to be greater than that of the spinal fluid, except under grossly abnormal conditions, this factor and the secretory power of the cells of the plexus are the two forces to be considered. Thermodynamic considerations indicate that the hydrostatic pressure difference would provide only a small fraction (about one-thirteenth) of the energy necessary. This leads to the conclusion that ultrafiltration will not account for the formation of the cerebrospinal fluid and that the cells of the choroid plexus perform work in this process.

### The Amount and Pressure

Accurate figures for the volume of the fluid in the various age groups are not available. The methods used to investigate the problem involve a change of conditions which invalidate the results secured. The total volume in healthy adults has been given as approximately 200 cc. The normal rate of formation has not been established. When artificial drainage is provided very large volumes, several liters per day, may drain away. The results of the urinary excretion of dye injected into the cerebrospinal space suggest that the volume of fluid is renewed every three or four hours but this rate of formation is probably too high. In experiments in which precautions were taken to interfere as little as possible with normal pressure conditions, Flexner and Winters found in experiments with adult cats, that approximately 12 cc. of fluid per day could be collected from a cannula fixed in the aqueduct. Of course, this figure bears no relationship to the amount formed in man. The pressure of the cerebrospinal fluid may be taken as 110 to 175 mm. of cerebrospinal fluid for man in the recumbent position. Pressure on the internal jugular vein or the rise of venous pressure produced by crying or cough-

ing causes an increase in pressure of the fluid because of the direct transmission of the venous pressure to the cerebrospinal fluid.

EFFECT OF FLUID AND SALT INJECTIONS ON PRESSURE (WEED AND HUGHSON). When large volumes of isotonic solutions are injected intravenously there is a transient rise in venous and cerebrospinal pressure. Hypotonic solutions cause a prolonged rise in fluid pressure due presumably to the passage of fluid into the brain. There is a less marked and more transient rise of venous pressure.

Hypertonic solutions (30 per cent NaCl) administered intravenously, produce a fall in cerebrospinal pressure which may persist for a considerable period. Fluid is attracted by the raised osmotic pressure of the blood from the brain substance, perivascular spaces, etc., into the blood stream. Such a dehydration is not limited to the brain; other tissues react similarly. As the blood volume is thus increased, urinary output is also increased, and the patient is soon dehydrated. Accordingly, the use of hypertonic solutions or of urea injected intravenously is very limited. Such treatment may be useful as an emergency measure in preparing a patient for operation or in tiding him over until a surgical decompression can be made or in reversing a vicious circle of cerebral edema and venous congestion.

EFFECT OF CHANGE OF POSITION ON PRESSURE. It is important to realize that the fluid in the subarachnoid space of the brain and spinal cord may be regarded as a single column (approximately 600 mm. long in the man of medium height). There are no structures to act as valves, and restrictions of flow are not sufficient to interfere appreciably with this relationship. The change in pressure produced by a change of position can largely be predicted by hydrostatic considerations. The pressures in the lumbar and occipital regions are identical when the subject is horizontal. When the patient is sitting the pressure of the fluid in the lumbar region will vary with the length of his back and his posture. Using a water manometer the upper level of the fluid will reach to the midcervical region. Accordingly, with the patient sitting, the intracranial pressure and the pressure in the cisterna magna will be below atmospheric pressure under normal conditions.

### Function of the Cerebrospinal Fluid

The fluid within the elastic meningeal sac serves as a protective covering for the central nervous system. By change in its volume, compensation for change in the amount of blood is effected, and the contents of the cranium thus tend to remain of constant volume. It is doubtful if there is any considerable exchange of metabolic materials between the nerve cells and the fluid.

### Ventriculograms and Encephalograms

The location of air injected into the cerebral ventricles (ventriculography) or through a lumbar puncture (pneumoencephalography) can be visualized by the X-rays. By thus outlining the ventricular system alterations in the size and position of the ventricles can be detected. This is often of great value in neurological diagnosis.

Radio-opaque oils (pantopaque) may be injected into the ventricles of the brain or into the spinal subarachnoid spaces. In this way these spaces may be visualized roentgenographically. This is particularly useful in the diagnosis of space-occupying intraspinal lesions.

### Hydrocephalus

A consideration of the formation, circulation and absorption of the spinal fluid leads to the assumption that hydrocephalus might be produced by (1) Increased rate of formation of fluid. A very definite increase can be produced by the administration of hypotonic solutions (Weed), but the decreased tonicity of the blood cannot be maintained long enough to permit the develop-

ment of hydrocephalus. Clinically papillomas of the choroid plexuses might produce this condition and suggestive cases have been reported (Davis). (2) Obstruction to the passage of the fluid. An obstruction by tumor or inflammation in the right foramen of Monro, for example, would produce a right internal hydrocephalus. Blockage of the aqueduct of Sylvius would produce a bilateral internal hydrocephalus as would an obstruction in the fourth ventricle or at the foramina of Magendie and Luschka. (3) Interference with the absorption of fluid by way of the arachnoid villi. Blockage of many of these villi or interference with their function by other means may lead to an external hydrocephalus. Increased intracerebral venous pressure may produce a temporary decrease in absorption of fluid.

### REFERENCES

Association for Research in Nervous and Mental Disease. Vol. 4. The human cerebrospinal fluid. The Williams & Wilkins Co., Baltimore, 1926.

Association for Research in Nervous and Mental Disease. Vol. 8. The intracranial pressure in health and disease. The Williams & Wilkins Co., Baltimore, 1929.

FLEXNER, L. B. Physiol. Rev., 1934, 14, 161.

GREENFIELD, J. G. AND CARMICHAEL, E. A. Cerebrospinal fluid in clinical diagnosis. Macmillan Company, London, 1925.

WEED, L. H. Physiol. Rev., 1922, 2, 171.

WEED, L. H. Physiol. Rev., 1933, 13, 80.

# 71

# THE AUTONOMIC NERVOUS SYSTEM

(Synonyms—involuntary nervous system, vegetative nervous system)

The autonomic nervous system has been touched upon in many of its aspects in other sections of this book. There remains to be given an account of the structural plan of this system as a whole, a general summary of its functions and of the structures which it innervates. From anatomical, physiological and pharmacological viewpoints the autonomic system falls naturally into two main divisions—the *sympathetic* or *thoracicolumbar outflow* and the *parasympathetic* or *craniosacral outflow* (see fig. 71.1).

## The Sympathetic Division

The cells of origin of the sympathetic division are situated in the lateral horns of the spinal cord (intermediolateral cell column) from the 8th cervical or 1st thoracic to the 2nd or 3rd lumbar segments. The axons of these cells leave the cord by the corresponding anterior nerve roots and synapse with nerve cells in one or another of the outlying ganglia. The fibers arising from the spinal cord are medullated and are called *preganglionic*; those arising from cells of the ganglia are nonmedullated, and are called *postganglionic*. Evidence for the existence of a higher center in the posterior region of the hypothalamus has been considered in chapter 66, and in the cerebral cortex in chapter 67.

The ganglion cells are all motor or secretory in function (p. 1301). They have no afferent connections from the periphery. However, many afferent fibers from the various visceral and blood vessels pass through the sympathetic nervous system. They have their ganglion cells in the posterior root ganglia as have the somatic afferent fibers.

The ganglia are arranged in three systems or groups: (A) *paravertebral*, (B) *prevertebral* (or *collateral*) and (C) *terminal* (or *peripheral*).

## A. The Paravertebral Ganglia and the Gangliated Cord

The paravertebral group lies in close relation to the vertebral bodies and consists, on each side, of a series of some 22 ganglia connected together by intervening fiber tracts to form a nodular cord extending from the base of the skull to the front of the coccyx. This is known as the *sympathetic chain* or the *gangliated cord of the sympathetic nervous system*. It will be described in sections.

### The Cervical Part of the Sympathetic Chain

The cervical part of the sympathetic chain possesses three ganglia—the *superior, middle* and *inferior cervical ganglia*. They are relatively large and are believed to result from the fusion of two or more smaller ganglia.

THE SUPERIOR CERVICAL GANGLION, situated below the base of the skull, is the largest of the three. It receives preganglionic fibers from the upper thoracic segments of the spinal cord, and its cells supply fibers (postganglionic) to the vessels, glands and cutaneous muscle of the head. It is probably formed by the fusion of the uppermost three or four cervical ganglias. Its branches are:

(1) THE INTERNAL CAROTID NERVE. This nerve' composed of postganglionic fibers, arises from the upper pole of the superior cervical ganglion and, passing into the cranium with the artery of the same name, forms the internal carotid and cavernous plexuses.

(i) The *internal carotid plexus*, situated on the lateral side of the internal carotid artery sends branches to the following:

(a) The abducent nerve.

(b) The tympanic branch of the glossopharyngeal nerve.

(c) The sphenopalatine ganglion. These fibers pass by way of the deep petrosal nerve and the nerve to the pterygoid canal which is formed by the union of the former nerve with the great superficial petrosal nerve. Orbital branches of the sphenopalatin ganglion convey sympathetic fibers to the lacrymal gland; the soft palate, nasopharynx and pharynx receive fibers through the palatine and pharyngeal branches of the ganglion.

(d) The semilunar (trigeminal) ganglion.

The sympathetic fibers pass through the sphenopalatine and semilunar ganglia without interruption.

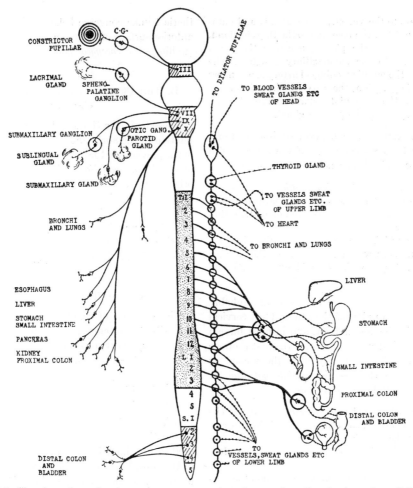

Fig. 71.1. Showing plan of autonomic nervous system from a functional viewpoint. C.G., ciliary ganglion. The celiac, inferior mesenteric and hypogastric ganglia are represented, in this order from above downwards, by the circles in the lower right portion of the diagram.

(ii) The *cavernous plexus*, situated on the inner side of the internal carotid artery as it lies in the cavernous sinus, sends branches to the following:

(a) The oculomotor, trochlear and abducent nerves and the nasociliary branch of the ophthalmic division of the trigeminal nerve. Through the long ciliary nerves (twigs of the nasociliary nerve), sympathetic fibers are conveyed to the dilator pupillae muscle (see also p. 1410).

(b) The ciliary ganglion, through which the sympathetic fibers pass without interruption into the short ciliary nerves. These fibers provide an additional pathway for sympathetic impulses to the dilator of the pupil.

(c) The pituitary body (vasomotor).

Through the communicating branches of the cavernous plexus the vessels of the eyeball and nasal mucosa are supplied with constrictor fibers, and the skin of the nose with vasoconstrictor, motor (smooth muscle) and secretory (sweat) fibers. The terminal filaments of the internal carotid

and cavernous plexuses are continued as delicate networks over the anterior and middle cerebral arteries to the minute vessels of the pia mater, and along the ophthalmic artery to the structures of the orbit.

(2) Branches to and distributed with the UPPER FOUR CERVICAL NERVES.

(3) Twigs to the GANGLION JUGULAR AND GANGLION NODOSUM OF THE VAGUS, to the PETROUS GANGLION OF THE GLOSSOPHARYNGEAL NERVE and to the HYPOGLOSSAL NERVE.

(4) Filaments to the CAROTID SINUS and CAROTID BODY.

(5) Fibers to LARYNGEAL and PHARYNGEAL PLEXUSES.

(6) The SUPERIOR CARDIAC NERVE to the cardiac plexuses.

(7) Branches which ramify in a plexiform manner upon the external carotid artery—the EXTERNAL CAROTID PLEXUS. This plexus is continued over the branches of the external carotid and sup-

plies fibers to the vessels, sweat glands and cutaneous muscles of the face, and to the thyroid gland. Filaments from the plexus investing the facial artery pass to the submaxillary ganglion. The plexus on the middle meningeal artery sends fibers to the otic ganglion; these pass without interruption into the auriculotemporal nerve through which they reach the parotid gland.

THE MIDDLE CERVICAL GANGLION is formed presumably by the coalescence of the 5th and 6th cervical ganglia. Its branches are as follows:

(1) Branches to the *5th and 6th cervical nerves* and thence to the blood vessels, sweat glands and cutaneous muscle within the area of distribution of these nerves.
(2) *The middle cardiac nerve* to cardiac plexuses.
(3) Branches which extend along the inferior thyroid artery to the *thyroid* and *parathyroid glands.*

THE INFERIOR CERVICAL GANGLION probably represents the union of the 7th and 8th cervical ganglia; in the dog and cat, and in most human subjects, it is usually fused with the first thoracic ganglion, and occasionally with the second as well, to form the so-called *stellate ganglion.* It gives off the following branches:

(1) Branches to the *7th and 8th cervical* and the *1st thoracic nerves,* sometimes also to the 6th cervical and the 2nd thoracic.
(2) The *inferior cardiac nerve* to cardiac plexuses.
(3) Branches which form plexuses upon the subclavian artery and its branches. Sympathetic fibers are thus carried into the cranial cavity along the vertebral artery, and over the axillary and commencement of the brachial.

### The Thoracic, Lumbar and Sacral Ganglia

The *thoracic ganglia* are 10 or 12 in number on each side. They are evenly spaced, one to each spinal segment. As mentioned above the first thoracic and inferior cervical ganglia are commonly partially or completely fused to form an irregularly shaped mass, called the *stellate ganglion.* There are usually 4 *lumbar* and 4 or 5 *sacral* ganglia.[1] The sacral portions of the two sympathetic trunks converge below and fuse upon the anterior surface of the coccyx to form a terminal swelling—the *coccygeal ganglion* or *ganglion impar.*

### B. THE PREVERTEBRAL (OR COLLATERAL) GANGLIA

These lie in the thorax, abdomen and pelvis in relation to the aorta and its branches. The larger of the prevertebral ganglia are: (a) the *celiac (solar or semilunar) ganglion,* lying in relation to the origin of the celiac artery, (b) the *superior mesenteric ganglion,* situated below the origin of the superior mesenteric artery, and (c) the *inferior mesenteric ganglion,* which bears a corresponding relation to the inferior mesenteric artery; this ganglion is rarely present in man (see also p. 1300).

### C. THE TERMINAL GANGLIA

These consist of small collections of ganglion cells situated in close relation to the innervated organs, especially those of the pelvis, e.g., the bladder and rectum.

### THE OUTFLOW OF SYMPATHETIC FIBERS FROM THE CENTRAL NERVOUS SYSTEM

It has already been stated that the cells giving rise to the sympathetic fibers (p. 1294) are situated in the thoracic and upper lumbar segments of the cord. It is from this limited region (8th C. or 1st T. to 2nd or 3rd L. inclusive) that the sympathetic (preganglionic) fibers emerge. *This region constitutes the only outlet for sympathetic impulses.* So the term thoracicolumbar outflow simply means the sympathetic division of the autonomic nervous system. The fibers emerge from the spinal cord through the anterior root of the spinal segment in which their cell bodies are placed. In a cross section of the anterior root they appear as fine medullated fibers ($2.5\mu$ or less in diameter) intermingled with the larger, medullated, somatic (motor) fibers. They separate almost immediately, however, from the motor fibers of the anterior root—which are concerned with movement of the skeletal musculature—and enter the corresponding ganglion of the sympathetic chain. Thus, the spinal nerves from the 8th cervical or 1st thoracic to the 2nd or 3rd lumbar,

[1] Small accessory ganglia, called *intermediate ganglia,* are found outside the sympathetic chain proper, attached to the rami communicantes close to the spinal nerve roots in the cervicothoracic and lumbar regions. From these ganglia sympathetic postganglionic fibers proceed for distribution by the brachial and lumbar plexuses to the limb vessels. Preganglionic fibers leaving the cord by the anterior roots and entering the intermediate ganglia without passing through the sympathetic chain offer a possible alternative pathway for sympathetic impulses to the limbs. Such fibers would remain intact though the sympathetic chain were excised; their presence would, thus, offer an explanation in some instances for the failure of sympatheticectomy to completely denervate the vessels of the limbs.

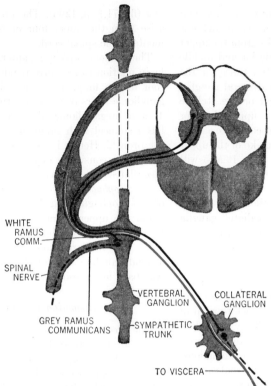

FIG. 71.2. Diagram showing the connections of sympathetic fibers. Efferent fibers in black; preganglionic, solid lines; postganglionic, interrupted lines. Afferent visceral fiber in red.

WHITE RAMUS COMM.

SPINAL NERVE

VERTEBRAL GANGLION

COLLATERAL GANGLION

GREY RAMUS COMMUNICANS

SYMPATHETIC TRUNK

TO VISCERA

but not others, are connected each to a paravertebral ganglion by a delicate white strand composed of preganglionic fibers and known as the *white ramus communicans* (plural, *rami communicantes*, fig. 71.2 and fig. 71.1, p. 1295). A preganglionic fiber after entering the ganglion may pursue one of three courses: (a) form synapses with cells in the ganglion which it first enters, (b) pass up or down the sympathetic trunk for some distance to terminate in a ganglion at a level higher or lower than that of the segment from which it originated. It may give off collateral branches to ganglion cells along its course. In any event, the preganglionic fibers issuing from a given segment connect with several ganglia (from five to nine). Furthermore, each preganglionic fiber may form a large number of synapses within a given ganglion. Ranson and Billingsley found that in the case of the superior cervical ganglion each fiber communicated with some thirty-two ganglion cells; this accounts for the diffuse nature of the sympathetic discharge. (c) Traverse the gangliated cord without interruption to find a cell station in either a prevertebral or a terminal ganglion.

PLAN OF DISTRIBUTION OF SYMPATHETIC FIBERS TO THE PERIPHERY

*To the Limbs and Trunk*

The ganglia of the sympathetic chain are connected with the spinal nerves supplying the limbs and trunk by delicate filaments called *gray rami communicantes*. They are composed of the axons of the ganglion cells in the paravertebral ganglia, and are therefore called *postganglionic*. The gray rami in the thoracic and upper lumbar regions join the spinal nerves close to the points at which the white rami arise. Their constituent fibers are continued in the peripheral nerves for the supply of the blood vessels, sweat glands and smooth muscle of the skin. Whereas, as already mentioned, only a limited number of spinal nerves possess white rami, *every spinal nerve receives a gray ramus*. It therefore follows that sympathetic impulses going to parts supplied by upper cervical, lower lumbar or sacral somatic nerves, must travel considerable distances up or down the sympathetic trunk before reaching an outlet through a gray ramus. The preganglionic fibers to the upper limb arise from the 2nd to the 7th thoracic spinal segments; most of these fibers are contained in the white rami of the 2nd and 3rd thoracic anterior roots. The postganglionic fibers to the upper limb may arise from the upper 1st to 4th thoracic, and the inferior and middle cervical ganglia (see also ch. 21); those for the lower limb from the lumbar and sacral ganglia. Excision of the inferior cervical or the stellate ganglion when present and the upper three or four thoracic ganglia provides as complete a sympathectomy as it is possible to make of the upper limb, as well as the head and neck. It also will destroy most of the sympathetic nerves to the heart. This operation may fail, however, to remove completely the sympathetic supply to the arm since there may be "intermediate" ganglia which are not removed in such an operation.

### To the Head and Neck

Sympathetic impulses to the structures of the neck, face, scalp and intracranial cavity are conveyed from the spinal cord in the white rami of the upper two thoracic nerves. They ascend to connect with cells in the middle and superior cervical ganglia. From the latter postganglionic fibers are distributed through the internal carotid, cavernous and external carotid plexuses as described on page 1295. The sympathetic nervous system as well as supplying the blood vessels, sweat glands and pilomotor muscles of the head and neck also innervates the salivary glands, the dilator pupillae muscles, Mueller's muscle and the smooth muscle component of the levator palpebrae superioris. The spinal center for the dilator pupillae is situated (in man) in the 8th cervical or 1st thoracic segment. The preganglionic fibers are found in the white rami of the first thoracic nerve, and are distributed, as already stated through the internal carotid and ciliary nerves.

### To the Thoracic Viscera

The sympathetic postganglionic fibers join with the branches from the vagus to form the *cardiac, pulmonary* and *esophageal plexuses.*

The *cardiac plexus* lies in relation to the origins of the aorta and pulmonary artery. It consists of a superficial and a deep portion, and is formed by the interlacement of fibers from the cardiac branches of the vagus (parasympathetic) and sympathetic nerves. The vagus fibers are preganglionic. They terminate around ganglion cells in the walls of the heart (p. 302). The sympathetic fibers derived from the superior, middle and inferior cardiac nerves are postganglionic, their cell stations lying in the corresponding cervical gan-

glia (fig. 71.1, p. 1295). The preganglionic fibers arise from the upper four or five thoracic segments of the spinal cord.

The *pulmonary plexuses*, anterior and posterior, lie in relation to the corresponding aspects of the root of the lung. They are formed from postganglionic fibers of the sympathetic (T. 2, 3 and 4) and preganglionic fibers of the vagus. The latter connect with ganglion cells in the walls of the bronchi. Herein is situated an intrinsic nervous plexus consisting of these ganglion cells and medullated and nonmedullated fibers.

The *esophageal plexus* embraces the lower half of the esophagus. Vagal and sympathetic fibers (from the upper thoracic ganglia and from the thoracic portion of the great splanchnic nerve) enter into its formation. The vagal fibers end around ganglion cells of the intrinsic plexus of Auerbach in the esophageal wall.

### To the Abdominal and Pelvic Viscera

The *greater, lesser and least splanchnic nerves.* These are composed of preganglionic fibers, and may be looked upon as elongated white rami. They connect with cells in the prevertebral (collateral) ganglia. The postganglionic fibers after emerging from the latter join the neighboring plexuses. The *greater splanchnic* nerve arises from the spinal cord from as high as the 4th or 5th thoracic segment, and as low as the 9th or 10th. Its fibers end in the upper part of the celiac ganglion; from here postganglionic fibers are continued into the celiac plexus. The *lesser splanchnic* and the *least* (or *lowest*) *splanchnic* nerves are much smaller. The former arises from the 9th and 10th or the 10th and 11th thoracic segments and its fibers, after passing without interruption through the vertebral ganglia at these levels, end in the lower portion of the celiac (or aorticorenal) ganglion. The least splanchnic nerve arises from the last one or two thoracic segments and first lumbar segment; it joins the renal plexus (fig. 71.3). Postganglionic fibers arising from small ganglia within the plexus are distributed to the kidney and ureter.

The *lumbar splanchnic nerves* are three or four strands which arise from the second and third lumbar segments. Their fibers pass through the lumbar portion of the sympathetic chain and enter the inferior mesenteric ganglion; here some are relayed, others are continued without interruption and find their cell stations in peripheral ganglia.

THE PLEXUSES OF THE ABDOMEN AND PELVIS.

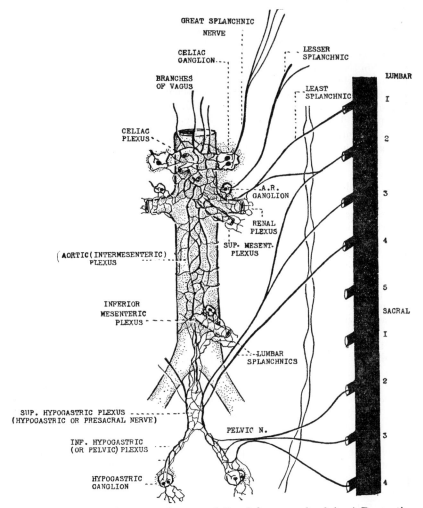

FIG. 71.3. Diagram of the nerve plexuses of the abdomen and pelvis. A.R., aortico-renal.

The sympathetic fibers form rich plexuses in relation to the aorta and its branches from which filaments pass to the abdominal and pelvic viscera. Parasympathetic fibers also enter into the constitution of these plexuses.

The *celiac* (or *solar*) *plexus* lies upon the abdominal aorta at the origin of the celiac artery. The *celiac ganglia*, right and left, lie embedded within the plexus, which is made up of fibers arising in the ganglion (i.e., postganglionic fibers of the greater and lesser splanchnic nerves) together with preganglionic fibers of the vagus. The lower part of the celiac ganglion is often detached and is then referred to as the *aorticorenal ganglion*. The plexus invests the celiac artery throughout its course and gives rise to several subordinate plexuses—the *hepatic, gastric, splenic, renal* and *adrenal plexuses*—which invest the corresponding arteries and their branches.

The *superior mesenteric plexus* is continuous above with the celiac plexus. It surrounds the superior mesenteric artery, along the branches of which it is prolonged as subsidiary plexuses. The plexus is composed of postganglionic fibers which arise in an aggregation of nerve cells—the *superior mesenteric ganglion*—lying within it, of preganglionic fibers derived from the lumbar segments of the cord, and from the celiac plexus. It and the other plexuses to be described also contain parasympathetic fibers. The superior mesenteric plexus supplies the pancreas, and the small intestine and the large intestines as far as the commencement of the descending colon.

The *aortic* or *intermesenteric plexus* lies upon the aorta between the origins of the superior and inferior mesenteric arteries. It receives fibers from the celiac plexus and from the upper lumbar ganglia. The aortic plexus gives rise secondarily to the *spermatic* and *ovarian* plexuses which supply the testes and ovary with autonomic fibers. It is connected below with the *inferior mesenteric plexus* which invests the artery of the same name. The *inferior mesenteric ganglion*, a collection of ganglion cells lying within the latter plexus, receives the lumbar splanchnics; this ganglion is not present, as a rule, in the human subject (Learmonth), but a number of smaller ganglia are found scattered through the plexus. The plexus is formed of fibers derived from the aortic plexus from the inferior mesenteric ganglion when this is present. From it secondary plexuses arise which invest the branches of the inferior mesenteric artery and carry sympathetic impulses to the descending colon, iliac colon, pelvic colon and rectum.

The *superior hypogastric plexus* is the downward extension of the aortic plexus. It lies over the lower end of the aorta, and in the angle formed by the aortic bifurcation. Though rarely condensed into a single bundle it is sometimes referred to as the *hypogastric nerve* or the *presacral nerve*. It transmits inhibitory impulses to the pelvic colon and via the pelvic plexuses to the rectum, bladder and other pelvic viscera. It divides below into the right and left *pelvic* or *inferior hypogastric plexuses*. These lie one on either side of the rectum and are composed of medullated and non-medullated fibers among which are scattered numerous small ganglia which are sometimes referred to collectively as the *hypogastric ganglion*. Parasympathetic fibers enter the inferior hypogastric plexuses through the pelvic nerve (sacral outflow). The sympathetic fibers contributing to the pelvic plexuses have their ultimate source in the lumbar segments of the cord. They reach the plexuses via the hypogastric plexuses as well as more directly from the sacral part of the sympathetic chain. Through subsidiary plexuses—*hemorrhoidal, vesical, uterine, vaginal* and *prostatic*—fibers (sympathetic and parasympathetic) are conveyed from the pelvic plexuses to the pelvic viscera.

### THE PARASYMPATHETIC OR CRANIOSACRAL DIVISION OF THE AUTONOMIC NERVOUS SYSTEM

The cells giving rise to parasympathetic fibers are situated at three different levels of the central nervous system—the *midbrain*, the *medulla oblongata* and the *sacral region of the spinal cord*. The axons of these cells leave the central nervous system to connect with ganglion cells lying within or in close relation to the innervated organ (see fig. 71.1). As in the case of the sympathetic division the axons of the central cells are called *preganglionic*; those of the ganglion cells, *postganglionic*. The former are medullated, the latter nonmedullated. The three levels from which parasympathetic fibers emerge will be referred to

as the *tectal* (or *midbrain*), the *bulbar* and the *sacral* outflows, respectively.

### A. THE TECTAL OR MIDBRAIN OUTFLOW

The group of cells composing the Edinger-Westphal nucleus of the oculomotor nerve (p. 1416), in the floor of the cerebral aqueduct, are believed to give rise to the tectal fibers.

The autonomic fibers are conveyed in the third nerve as far as the ciliary ganglion where they find their cell stations. Postganglionic fibers emerge from the ganglion in the short ciliary nerves, and terminate in the sphincter pupillae and the ciliary muscles (p. 1410).

### B. THE BULBAR OUTFLOW

These fibers leave the brain in the *facial, glossopharyngeal* and *vagus nerves*.

(1) The parasympathetic fibers (secretory and vasodilator) entering the *facial nerve* arise from the *superior salivatory (salivary) nucleus*, which lies dorsal and lateral to the lower end of the motor nucleus of the facial.[2] These fibers emerge from the brain in the sensory root of the facial nerve (*nervus intermedius*, ch. 65) and travel with the latter to the facial canal of the temporal bone. Here they leave the facial, (i) in its *chorda tympani* branch which later joins the lingual to be conveyed to the floor of the mouth. At this point some of the chorda fibers (secretory and vasodilator in function) separate from the lingual again to enter the *submaxillary (submandibular) ganglion* from where they are relayed; the postganglionic fibers pass to the submaxillary and submandibular glands, and the mucous membrane of the mouth. (ii) In the great superficial petrosal nerve and nerve of the pterygoid canal (Vidian nerve) to the sphenopalatine ganglion. From here postganglionic fibers pass via orbital branches of the ganglion to the lacrymal gland, and to the mucous membrane of the soft palate, nasopharynx and pharynx via the palatine nerves. Vasodilator fibers also leave the facial by the great superficial petrosal nerve, and entering the cranium are conveyed along the middle meningeal artery and its branches.

(2) The parasympathetic fibers (secretory and vasodilator) of the *glossopharyngeal nerve* arise from cells of the *inferior salivatory (salivary) nucleus*. This nucleus lies in the uppermost part of the medulla oblongata immediately below the superior salivatory nucleus, and lateral to the motor nucleus of the glossopharyngeal nerve. The autonomic fibers leave the brain with the latter nerve but separate from it again in its tympanic

---

[2] This nucleus is actually in the lowest part of the pons.

branch (Jacobson's nerve) which joins a twig from the geniculate ganglion (g. of facial nerve) and filaments from the internal carotid plexus to form the *tympanic plexus*. From this plexus emerges the *small superficial petrosal nerve* through which parasympathetic fibers are continued to the otic ganglion. From this ganglion postganglionic fibers are conveyed to the parotid gland via the auriculo-temporal nerve (p. 589). The tympanic plexus itself sends filaments to the mucous membrane of the tympanic cavity, the mastoid air-cells, auditory (Eustachian) tube and the internal ear.

(3) The *vagus nerve* contains the greater proportion of the fibers of the bulbar outflow. They arise from the *dorsal nucleus* of the vagus and are distributed through the latter's numerous branches to the thoracic and abdominal viscera (ch. 65). Unlike those in the other two cranial nerves, the preganglionic fibers of the vagus connect with ganglion cells situated within the innervated organs. Thus the vagal fibers to the heart connect with ganglion cells in the cardiac walls: those to the bronchi with the nerve cells of the intrinsic plexus in the bronchial walls; those to the esophagus, stomach and intestine form synapses with the ganglion cells of the myenteric plexus of Auerbach and the submucous plexus of Meissner. The preganglionic fibers are therefore quite long, the postganglionic very short. The cells of origin of most of the cardiac fibers of the vagus form a discrete group (cardio-inhibitory center) lying alongside the dorsal nucleus of the vagus.

### C. The Sacral Outflow

The cells of origin lie in the anterior horns of the 2nd, 3rd and 4th and sometimes the 1st sacral segments of the spinal cord. The preganglionic fibers emerge in the anterior roots of the corresponding sacral nerves. The fibers leave the spinal nerves again and, proceeding peripherally as the *pelvic nerve* (or *nervus erigens*), on each side, enter into the formation of the pelvic plexus. The fibers terminate around ganglion cells lying in close relation to the pelvic organs. They carry motor impulses to the walls of the descending colon, rectum and bladder; inhibitory impulses to the internal anal and vesical sphincters and to the uterus; and dilator impulses to the blood vessels of the bladder, rectum and genitalia.

### The Afferent Visceral Nerves

Impulses are transmitted from the viscera by afferent fibers which pass through the various plexuses and reach the central nervous system via the vagus, pelvic, splanchnics and other autonomic nerves.

The *afferent fibers of the sympathetic division* are the peripheral processes of ganglion cells in the posterior spinal root ganglia from the 1st thoracic to the 3rd lumbar segments. *None arise from sympathetic ganglia.* They reach the sympathetic trunk via the white rami communicantes and are distributed to the viscera along with the corresponding efferent fibers (fig. 71.2). Though some of these afferent fibers are nonmedullated, the majority are medullated, and of larger size than the efferent fibers. The ganglion cells of the posterior roots which give origin to the afferent fibers of the sympathetic (or of the pelvic nerve) have not been shown definitely to differ from those giving rise to the ordinary somatic sensory fibers. For this reason the sympathetic system proper is sometimes regarded, though perhaps irrationally, as consisting solely of efferent neurons. The afferent fibers pass to their destinations without interruption in any of the sympathetic ganglia, passing directly to the viscera in the splanchnics or the other visceral nerves. A certain proportion also enter the spinal nerves for distribution to the limbs via the gray rami.

The *afferent fibers of the vagus* are the peripheral processes of cells in the ganglion jugulare and the ganglion nodosum. The central processes of these neurons terminate in the dorsal nucleus of the vagus (ch. 65). Therein connections are made with efferent parasympathetic neurons to complete the reflex arc. The *afferent fibers of the pelvic nerve* arise from cells in the posterior root ganglia of the 2nd, 3rd and 4th sacral nerves. They pass peripherally with the efferent autonomic fibers.

*The visceral reflex arc*, as pointed out by Gaskell, is formed upon a plan similar to that upon which somatic reflexes are based. The afferent fiber in the latter instance is connected to the anterior horn cell through the intermediary of an intraspinal (internuncial) neuron or a series of such neurons. These are spoken of as connector neurons. In the case of visceral reflexes, the afferent fiber makes contact with a cell in the lateral horn of gray matter. The axon of this cell connects with a ganglion cell of the sympathetic system. This ganglion cell and its postganglionic fiber corresponds to the motor neuron of the somatic reflex arc.

A certain degree of independent reflex activity can be carried out through the intrinsic plexuses, e.g., of the intestine, when these are separated from the central nervous system by division of the main autonomic nerves. It is also true that some independent activity can be carried out through axon reflexes or possibly through some of the more peripherally placed ganglion cells. Other parts of the autonomic system, however, cannot function apart from the central nervous system. The larger ganglia of the parasympathetic or sympathetic, for instance, do not serve as reflex centers. It is clear from the description of the origin and course of the visceral afferent nerves given above that no anatomical basis for such action exists.

## The Functions of the Autonomic Nervous System

The autonomic nervous system governs the activities of cardiac and smooth muscle, of the digestive glands and sweat glands of the adrenal medulla and possibly of certain endocrine organs. It is concerned with those processes which normally are beyond voluntary control and are for the most part beneath consciousness. The term autonomic as applied to this system is not altogether suitable since, as we have seen, it is under the control of centers within the central nervous system, and cannot function as an independent unit.

Through its various activities the autonomic system exercises the important function of maintaining the constancy of the fluid environment of the body's cells; it serves to combat forces, acting either from within or without, which tend to cause variations in this environment. Regulation of the composition of the body fluids, of their temperature, quantity and distribution, is effected through the actions of the autonomic nerves upon circulatory, respiratory, excretory and glandular organs. For example, of glandular structures under autonomic influence, the liver, pancreas and adrenal medulla are of especial importance in the regulation of blood sugar; the sweat glands aid in the control of body temperature. The neural lobe of the pituitary is partially under autonomic nervous control. The thyroid gland, adrenal cortex, adenohypophysis and probably also the parathyroid glands, are governed by hormones liberated by the pituitary (ch. 56); though it is not improbable that they may be influenced also by impulses received through autonomic paths. The stability of the internal environment (the *milieu interne* of Claude Bernard) which is so characteristic of the healthy body, is spoken of by Cannon as *homeostasis*. According to Cannon, the essential and particular function of the autonomic system is to bring about the internal adjustments upon which this constant state depends. He therefore refers to the autonomic nerves as the *interofective* system. He speaks of the voluntary system (i.e., the central nervous system and the somatic

nerves) as the *exterofective* system, since through its exteroceptors and effectors a direct relationship is established with the external environment.

The great majority of the effector organs of the autonomic system are innervated by both sympathetic and parasympathetic divisions (see table 71.1), and the effects exerted by the two types of fiber going to a given organ are antagonistic. Thus the heart's action is inhibited by the vagus but augmented by the sympathetic. In the intestine the effects of the two nerves are reversed, the parasympathetic (vagus nerve to the small bowel and upper half of the colon, and the pelvic nerve to the lower half of the latter) are augmentor; the sympathetic is inhibitory. The removal of the effects of one set of fibers, as by section, results, as a rule, in the effects of the other set becoming more prominent. This fact indicates that each type of fiber exerts a constant or tonic action and suggests that the two effects are delicately balanced one against the other. Thus, section of the vagus nerves causes an increase in the cardiac rate, and section of the parasympathetic or of the sympathetic fibers to the iris causes, respectively, dilation or constriction of the pupil. See pupillary reactions, (p. 1409).

Taken as a whole the actions of the sympathetic division and its ally the medulla of the adrenal gland (sympathoadrenal system, ch. 58) are directed towards strengthening an animal's defenses against the various dangers which beset it, e.g., extremes of temperature, deprivation of water or the attacks of its enemies. It has been shown by Cannon, however, that the sympathetic system is not indispensable; both gangliated cords may be completely removed yet the animal remains in good health provided it is kept in the sheltered environment of the laboratory. Sympathectomized cats if kept warm and carefully tended will live indefinitely. Kittens deprived of their sympathetic trunks grow normally, female cats become pregnant and give birth to young, though the mammary glands do not function normally and the maternal instinct is lacking. Sympathectomized animals are, however, incapable of arduous work, sugar is not mobilized from the liver on demand, an increase of circulating red blood cells does not occur during excitement or exercise (p. 68, 69), the usual reactions to cold (elevation of the hairs and vasoconstriction) fail, and adrenaline is not liberated in an emergency. They are also less able to withstand oxygen lack or hemorrhage than are normal animals. It is evident that the sympathectomized animal could not fend for it-

TABLE 71.1

| Organ | Parasympathetic Effects | Origin of Sympathetic Postganglionic Fibers | Sympathetic Effects |
|---|---|---|---|
| *Heart* (p. 302): | Inhibition | Superior middle and inferior cervical ganglia | Acceleration |
| *Vessels:* | | | |
| Cutaneous (ch. 21 and 25) | — | Various paravertebral ganglia | Constriction |
| Muscular (see pp. 252–7 and 351) | | | |
| Coronary (see p. 329) | | | |
| Salivary glands (ch. 36) | Dilation | Superior cervical ganglion | Constriction |
| Buccal mucosa | — | Superior cervical ganglion | Dilation |
| Pulmonary (see p. 298) | | | |
| Cerebral (see p. 344) | | | |
| Abdominal and pelvic viscera | — | Prevertebral ganglia | Constriction |
| External genitalia (pp. 1108, 1301) | Dilation | Prevertebral ganglia | Constriction |
| *Eye:* | | | |
| Iris (ch. 75) | Constriction | Superior cervical ganglion | Dilation |
| Ciliary muscle (ch. 75) | Contraction | Superior cervical ganglion | Relaxation |
| Smooth muscle of orbit and upper lid (ch. 75) | — | Superior cervical ganglion | Contraction |
| Nictitating membrane (cat and dog) | — | Superior cervical ganglion | Retraction |
| *Bronchi:* | Constriction | Thoracic ganglia | Dilation |
| *Glands:* | | | |
| Sweat (ch. 52) | — | Paravertebral ganglia | Secretion |
| Salivary (ch. 36) | Secretion | Superior cervical ganglia | Secretion |
| Gastric (p. 599) | Secretion | Celiac ganglion | Inhibition? Secretion of mucus |
| Pancreas (p. 629) | | | |
| Acini | Secretion | Celiac ganglion | — |
| Islets | Secretion | Celiac ganglion | — |
| Liver | — | Celiac ganglion | Glycogenolysis |
| Adrenal (pp. 1030–31) medulla | — | No postganglionic fibers | Secretion |
| *Smooth muscle:* | | | |
| Of skin | — | Paravertebral ganglia | Contraction |
| Of stomach wall (pp. 717–18) | Contraction or inhibition | Celiac ganglion | Contraction or inhibition |
| Of small intestine (pp. 717–19) | Increased tone and motility | Celiac and superior mesenteric ganglia | Inhibition |
| Of large intestine (pp. 717–19) | Increased tone and motility | Inferior mesenteric and hypogastric ganglia | Inhibition |
| Of bladder wall (ch. 35) (detrusor muscle) | Contraction | Inferior mesenteric and hypogastric ganglia | Inhibition |
| Of trigone and sphincter | Inhibition | Inferior mesenteric and hypogastric ganglia | Contraction |
| Of uterus, pregnant | nil | Inferior mesenteric and hypogastric ganglia | Contraction |
| Of uterus, nonpregnant | nil | | Inhibition |

* With certain exceptions, e.g., those supplying the sublingual and parotid glands and the sphincter pupillae, the postganglionic fibers of the parasympathetic arise from cells situated in, or in close proximity to, the innervated organ itself.

self, and, in the struggle for existence, would soon succumb to the hazards of the environment. The sympathetic ganglionated chain has also been completely removed in man, thus abolishing all connection of the peripheral sympathetic system with the central nervous system without producing any serious consequences.

Parasympathetic effects, rather than being characterized by a diffuse outburst of activity, as may result from sympathetic stimulation, are more localized in character. It has also been suggested that they are concerned with conservative and restorative processes, and the sympathetic with processes involving the expenditure of energy. Inhibition of the heart, contraction of the pupil for the protection of the eye from intense light and the activities of the digestive tract, through which the energy stores of the body are replenished, are frequently given as examples of acts of conservation presided over by the parasympathetic. These apparent differences in the activities of the two divisions have led some (following Gaskell) to speak of the functions of the sympathetic and parasympathetic divisions as *catabolic* and *anabolic*, respectively. It is an interesting but perhaps a too speculative generalization.

A summary of the actions of the autonomic system upon various structures is given in table 71.1.

### Chemical (Humoral) Transmission of Nervous Impulses[3]

Transmission of impulses from neuron to neuron, and from neuron to effector cell is accomplished by the elaboration of chemical substances by the nerves. The classical experiments of Otto Loewi, in 1921, first clearly demonstrated the existence of humoral mediators. Two frog hearts, arranged in standard fashion for recording contractions, were prepared so that the fluid perfusing one heart could come in contact with the second. Upon stimulation of the vagus nerve to the first heart, its rate of contraction was reduced. When the fluid perfusing this heart came in contact with the second it also slowed in rate although its vagus had not been stimulated. Some substance had obviously been released in the first heart which could be carried by the perfusing fluid to the second. Loewi termed this material *"Vagusstuffe."* By the same technique, stimulation of the cardiac accelerator nerve to the first heart

increased its rate and also the rate of the second heart when the perfusing fluid reached the latter. This response Loewi attributed to the release of *"Acceleransstuffe."*

By various techniques, described below, "Vagusstuffe" has been shown to be acetylcholine, and "Acceleransstuffe" is identical with or related to epinephrine (adrenaline). In 1933, Sir Henry Dale proposed the terms *cholinergic* and *adrenergic* to describe the nerves which liberated acetylcholine or epinephrine (or related substances). The adjectives are also used to describe agents which cause effects similar to those produced by acetylcholine and epinephrine. Dale has also proposed that cells stimulated by cholinergic or adrenergic nerves be termed cholinoceptive and adrenoceptive respectively.

*Acetylcholine* is now recognized as the mediator of impulses at all autonomic ganglia, all parasympathetic postganglionic terminations, sympathetic postganglionic endings at sweat glands, and motor nerve endings at skeletal muscle. In these cholinergic nerve fibers acetylcholine is present in an inactive form (probably bound loosely with a protein or a lipoprotein). Upon stimulation of the nerve the acetylcholine is set free and diffuses down the nerve fiber and from the terminations. These same nerve fibers contain an enzyme, *choline acetylase*, which is capable of synthesizing acetylcholine with great rapidity.[4] Which of these two mechanisms is the more important in releasing free acetylcholine remains unsolved.

Free acetylcholine is unstable; it is readily hydrolyzed to choline and acetic acid. This hydrolysis occurs almost instantaneously in the presence of *acetylcholinesterase*, an enzyme present at the termination of cholinergic nerves.[5] The enzyme is one of a group of hydrolytic enzymes, often referred to as cholinesterases, found in the body. Acetylcholinesterase, or *true* or *specific cholinesterase*, has acetylcholine as its preferred or only substrate, and is most effective when the amount of acetylcholine is small. The other (pseudo- or nonspecific) cholinesterases will utilize acetylcholine and other choline and non-choline esters

---

[3] We are indebted to Dr. William C. North of the Department of Anesthesiology of Duke University for the preparation of this section.

[4] Choline acetylase is very widely distributed in the nervous tissues, being found in brain, ganglia and peripheral nerves; it is also present in the placenta, but is absent from liver and kidney. For optimal activity this enzyme requires Mg, K and Ca ions. The concentration of choline acetylase in nerve fibers declines during their degeneration, but some still remains even after the nerve has ceased to conduct.

[5] Acetylcholinesterase is also present in large amounts in erythrocytes, the chief source of the enzyme for experimental studies.

as a substrate and are most effective in the presence of large quantities of acetylcholine.

Cholinesterases may be inhibited by a variety of substances. Much of the knowledge about acetylcholine and nerve impulse transmission has been obtained only thrugh the ability of these agents to inhibit acetylcholinesterase. Physostigmine (eserine), an alkaloid extracted from the Calabar bean (*Physostigma venenosum*) was the first substance shown to inhibit these enzymes. Subsequently many synthetic inhibitors have been prepared, among them neostigmine (Prostigmin), di-isopropylfluorophosphate (DFP) and tetraethylpyrophosphate (TEPP). Physostigmine and neostigmine are reversible inhibitors; the enzyme is inactivated only so long as it is in combination with the inhibitor. As the latter is eliminated by the body, the enzyme once more becomes active. DFP and TEPP combine irreversibly with the enzyme, permanently inactivating it. Hence, for cholinesterase activity to be restored new enzyme must be synthesized.

Such minute amounts of the cholinergic mediator are liberated during impulse transmission, and the mediator is so rapidly broken down by acetylcholinesterase, that the identification of the mediator as acetylcholine is still largely indirect. The experimental methods used to identify acetylcholine are, however, sufficiently instructive to consider briefly. First, the effects of nerve stimulation may be compared with those of acetylcholine administration. Second, a modification of Loewi's original experiment, i.e., stimulation of the autonomic nerve to an organ or ganglion and testing the venous blood leaving it, or the fluid perfusing it, for acetylcholine activity on a suitable test preparation. In order to prevent hydrolysis of the acetylcholine after its liberation from the nerve terminals the animal must be given physostigmine or some other inhibitor, or the perfusing fluid must contain it. Five common qualitative tests for the detection of the mediator may be mentioned.

(1) Blood pressure of the cat. Dilation of the arterioles and a fall in blood pressure. The effect should be annulled by atropine. (2) Inhibition of the perfused frog's heart or rabbit's auricle annulled by atropine. (3) Contraction of the voluntary muscle (rectus abdominis) of the frog. (4) Contraction of the muscle in body wall of the eserinized leech. This test is sensitive to 2 $\mu$g. (gamma) of acetylcholine per liter. (5) The active substance should be inactivated by alkali or by blood (which contains cholinesterase). Comparison of the response of the test system (i.e., the

blood pressure fall in the cat) to the perfusuate with the response to known amounts of acetylcholine makes it possible to quantitatively estimate the amount of acetylcholine actually liberated. Results of such studies coupled with the knowledge that acetylcholine is actually found in cholinergic nerves leaves little doubt that acetylcholine is the mediator.

*Summary of Experimental Work Relating to the Role Played by Acetylcholine in the Transmission of Nervous Effects*

*1. Stimulation of the chorda tympani nerve to salivary glands.* Babkin and his associates found that when the chorda of one side was stimulated a substance entered the blood which caused a fall in blood pressure and secretion from the denervated salivary gland of the opposite side. These effects were abolished by atropine. Similar results have been obtained by others. During stimulation of the chorda of a perfused salivary gland, for example, a substance identical in action with acetylcholine was found by Henderson and Roepke in the perfusion fluid.

*2. The liberation of acetylcholine from parasympathetic endings in the iris.* When a strong light was thrown into one eye, the other eye being shaded, an acetylcholinelike substance was obtained from the aqueous humor of the illuminated eye but not from the darkened eye (Engelhart).

*3. Acetylcholine as an intermediary of parasympathetic effects to the alimentary tract and bladder.* It has been shown that Ringer's solution in which a beating loop of intestine is immersed is capable of augmenting the activity of another similar loop (Weiland). It has also been found that if the vagus nerve to the intestine is stimulated and a loop then removed and suspended in Ringer's solution, the contractions of this loop are greater than those of a similar one which had not been previously excited in this manner. These experiments suggest that during intestinal activity a substance is liberated by the vagal endings which has an augmenting effect upon the contractions. Evidence for the liberation of acetylcholine by the gastric vagus has been obtained by Dale and Feldberg. A substance identical in action with acetylcholine was detected in the venous blood leaving the resting stomach or in the eserinized fluid perfusing its wall. During vagal stimulation the quantity of the active material was increased fourfold.

An acetylcholinelike substance has also been identified by Henderson and Roepke in the fluid perfusing the bladder during stimulation of its parasympathetic nerves. In the case of the intestine and bladder as in the case of vasodilator nerves, the same discrepancy exists between the action of atropine upon the effects of nerve stimulation and the action of the drug upon the effects of acetylcholine administration. Atropine abolishes the action of acetylcholine when applied artificially to these organs but does not depress the contractions set up by parasympathetic stimulation. Henderson and Roepke conclude from the results of their experiments that, whereas the tone of the intestine and of the bladder is dependent upon the liberation of a choline ester, another mechanism is responsible for the phasic contractions. Atropine, as is well known depresses the tone of the intestinal and vesical musculatures but exerts no direct effect upon the contractile mechanism.

*4. The liberation of acetylcholine from sympathetic preganglionic fibers.* Feldberg and Gaddum perfused the superior cervical ganglion with eserinized fluid. The inflow cannula was inserted into the common carotid artery, all branches of which had been tied except the one to the ganglion. The fluid was collected from the internal jugular vein, all its tributaries except that from the ganglion having been occluded. During stimulation of the cervical sympathetic trunk below the ganglion the fluid issuing from the vein was found to possess an action identical with that of acetylcholine. When the collected fluid was passed through the ganglion of the opposite side its stimulant action upon this structure was evidenced by a contraction of the nictitating membrane. Fluid collected before or after the period of stimulation showed no such activity.

*5. Acetlycholine liberation during the discharge of adrenaline.* Stimulation of the sympathetic fibers supplying the adrenal medulla causes an acetylcholinelike substance to appear in the blood of the adrenal vein. It has therefore been concluded that acetylcholine acts as a chemical transmitter from the nerve terminals to the medullary cells. It will be recalled that the sympathetic fibers ending in the adrenal are preganglionic, the adrenal cell itself taking the place of the ganglion cell.

*6. Acetylcholine as the transmitter of effects to the sweat glands.* Although the human sweat glands are innervated by the sympathetic, their behavior to drugs is similar to that of structures supplied by the parasympathetic; they are unaffected by adrenaline, stimulated by pilocarpine, and paralyzed by atropine. An experiment by Dale and Feldberg gives an explanation of these discrepancies, or at any rate brings the mechanism of sweat secretion into the general scheme. Excitation of the sympathetic fibers to the foot pads of the cat was followed by sweating and the appearance of acetylcholine in the eserinized fluid perfusing the paw.

The chemical identity of the adrenergic mediator is not so well characterized as that of the cholinergic mediator. Cannon and Bacq, in 1931, demonstrated that stimulation of adrenergic nerves liberated a substance into the circulation which they called "sympathin." Although many of the effects of sympathetic stimulation could be produced by the administration of epinephrine, Cannon and Rosenblueth were unable to demonstrate complete qualitative and quantitative identity between the two types of stimulation. They proposed the "sympathin theory" which is discussed elsewhere (ch. 58). Subsequent work has confirmed their idea that there is more than one type of adrenergic effector. However, it has been shown that epinephrine is not the only mediator released on sympathetic stimulation.

Epinephrine was crystalized from adrenal medullary extracts by Abel in 1901. Since then it has been identified in other nervous tissue and found to be secreted at adrenoceptive effector cells. In 1946, Euler reported that adrenergic fibers contained another catechol amine, levarterenol (norephinephrine, noradrenaline); the following year Bacq and Fischer found that some adrenergic fibers liberate only epinephrine, others only levarterenol, and still others both epinephrine and levarterenol. Isoproterenol (isopropylnorepinephrine, isopropylnoradrenaline) was found by Lockett, in 1956, in pulmonary venous blood following stimulation of the upper thoracic sympathetic chain.

The properties of the first two of these substances, found in the adrenal medulla, are described in chapter 58. The response of the effector cells is the same whether the mediators arrive by way of the circulation or whether they are released by nerve terminal endings on the cells.

The mechanisms whereby the adrenergic mediators are formed, or by which they are released, are not known. However, once released upon stimulation of adrenergic neurons, the mediators are, compared to acetylcholine, slowly inactivated. At least four possible pathways of epinephrine metabolism have been described. (1) An enzyme, *monoamine oxidase*, is present throughout the body which is capable of oxidatively deaminating primary amines. Epinephrine and arterenol are substrates for this enzyme, although the reaction proceeds rather slowly. (2) Conjugation of epinephrine with glucuronic or sulfuric acid at the hydroxyl groups occurs, primarily in the liver and intestines. (3) The phenolic hydroxyl groups of epinephrine are readily oxidized, forming a quinone which in turn forms a cyclic structure *adrenochrome*. (4) Recently Axelrod has demonstrated that the phenolic group in the meta position is methylated to a considerable extent in the body. There is as yet, however, no evidence that any of these inactivating mechanisms is the one primarily responsible for terminating adrenergic effects.

The concept of specific receptors, first proposed by Dale in 1906, aids in understanding the rather complex responses to sympathetic stimulation or epinephrine administration. Noting that epinephrine caused some smooth muscle to contract, while it relaxed others, he proposed that the former had "motor" type receptors while the latter had "inhibitory" type receptors. Ahlquist has divided the adrenergic receptors into two types. Alpha receptors are those associated with vasoconstriction, myocardial ectopic excitation, myometrial contraction, nictitating membrane contraction, intestinal relaxation, iris dilator muscle contraction, pilomotor contraction, and glycogenolysis. Beta receptors are those concerned with vasodilation, cardioacceleration, myocardial augmentation, myometrial relaxation and bronchial relaxation. Furchgott has presented evidence which indicates that with vascular smooth muscle, at least, individual cells may contain both $\alpha$ and $\beta$ *receptors.*

Levarterenol appears to stimulate only alpha receptors, isoproterenol only beta receptors, and epinephrine is capable of stimulating both. Epinephrine is 2 to 10 times more potent than levarterenol in stimulating the alpha receptors. Isoproterenol is 2 to 10 times more potent than epinephrine in stimulating the beta receptors and 100 or more times more active than levarterenol. Therefore, although epinephrine is the more potent agent as a vasoconstrictor, levarterenol may produce a greater rise in blood pressure for a given dose, since it has no or little effect on vasodilator fibers.

Euler claims that levarterenol is most commonly found as the mediator in adrenergic nerves. If this is true it readily explains the observed discrepancies between the effects of epinephrine administration and sympathetic nerve stimulation.

From the information now available it is possible to construct the mechanism by which the autonomically innervated effectors are stimulated (fig. 71.4). Impulses leave the central nervous system by way of cholinergic preganglionic fibers which terminate at ganglionic cells. In the sympathetic division these neurons are collected in anatomically discrete bodies. The parasympathetic ganglion cells are rarely discrete, being located usually within the organ innervated. In either case, acetylcholine is liberated from the preganglionic terminals where it is free to act upon the

receptor sites of the ganglion cell. This combination of acetylcholine with receptor results in a loss of membrane integrity and the potential difference between the interior and exterior of the cell disappears. The electrical activity associated with this "depolarization" is of sufficient intensity to disrupt the continuity of the adjacent membrane, and the impulse is propagated along the postganglionic fiber. As long as the acetylcholine is bound to the receptor site, the membrane at that point remains depolorized. However, the acetylcholinesterase present at the synapse immediately (less than 1 msec.) destroys the acetylcholine and the polarity of the neuronal membrane is restored. By this mechanism each preganglionic impulse liberates acetylcholine which in turn initiates a postganglionic impulse. The limiting factor in rate of transmission seems to be the refractory period of the nerve fiber.

Obviously, substances which will prevent access of acetylcholine to the ganglion cell receptors, or which will cause prolonged depolarization of the nerve membrane will block ganglionic synaptic transmission.

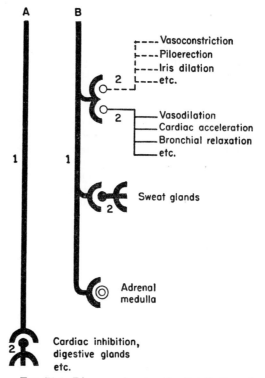

FIG. 71.4. Diagram showing the distribution of cholinergic and adrenergic fibers, A, parasympathetic; B, sympathetic; 1, preganglionic; 2, postganglionic, heavy lines, cholinergic; light lines, adrenergic.

The impulse travels down the postganglionic fiber as described and releases a humoral agent at its terminal. If the fiber is parasympathetic or sympathetic to the sweat glands, acetylcholine is the mediator released. This substance then combines with specific receptors on the effector cell to produce the characteristic response of that cell.

If the postganglionic fiber supplies other sympathetically innervated structures, epinephrine, levarterenol or isoproterenol is liberated from the terminals. The agent liberated is apparently characteristic for a specific neuron. In the case of the adrenal medulla, which may be considered to be composed of ganglion cells without axons, the adrenergic mediators are liberated into the blood. The other postganglionic sympathetic neurons liberate the mediator in close proximity to the effector cell. The mechanism whereby epinephrine, levarterenol, or isoproterenol stimulate the effector is unknown. Since there is apparently no specific instantaneous mechanism for destroying the substance, its action is probably somewhat different from that suggested for acetylcholine.

### Drugs Acting on the Autonomic Nervous System

Many agents are capable of eliciting or modifying responses of the autonomic nervous system. A brief survey of the types of drugs used for these effects may help further to understand the function of the autonomic nervous system.

#### DRUGS ACTING AT THE GANGLION

The alkaloid *nicotine* was the first compound found to stimulate postganglionic fibers. The delineation of this effect led to the term "nicotinic" used to describe the effect of acetylcholine on the ganglion cell. In recent years, a number of synthetic compounds have been found to possess ganglion stimulating properties including *carbaminoylcholine, decamethonium* and *tetramethylammonium bromide*. Obviously little therapeutic advantage would be obtained from the stimulation of all postganglionic fibers which would result from the administration of such an agent. However, these substances are useful as experimental tools.

The blockade of ganglionic transmission is a more desirable therapeutic end. Again *nicotine* was the first substance known to cause such an effect. The paradox of the same substance causing two opposing effects is resolved when it is understood that far larger quantities of the drug are necessary to block than to stimulate. The mechanism of action in both cases seems to be that nicotine, like acetylcholine, initiates a response in the postganglionic fibers by depolarizing the nerve membrane.

With large amounts of the alkaloid the depolarization is prolonged, preventing repolarization of the neuron, and hence preventing subsequent discharges. Even though acetylcholine is released by the preganglionic termination, it cannot initiate transmission in the postganglionic fiber. The dual nature of the action of nicotine, as well as its effect on skeletal muscle, makes it of little clinical usefulness. Its ganglionic actions are responsible for many of the side effects of the use of tobacco.

*Tetraethylammonium chloride* (TEA) blocks ganglionic transmission by combining with the acetylcholine receptors of the postganglionic neuron without depolarizing the cell membrane. In this instance the liberated acetylcholine cannot gain access to the receptor site to initiate depolarization. Other ganglionic blocking agents, hexamethonium, pentamethonium, pentolinium (Ansolysen), mecamylamine (Inversine), trimethaphan (Arfonad) and others, produce effects similar to those of TEA. There may be minor differences in mechanisms of action, and they may vary in the duration of their action; however, the qualitative nature of their responses is similar.

The effects of ganglionic blockade can be predicted readily. Depending upon the degree of blockage there will be depression to complete paralysis of autonomic function. This will result in such effects as interference with vision (accomodation and pupillary size), postural hypotension, etc. It must be remembered that the autonomic system is composed of two functional units which frequently antagonize each other to varying extent depending upon the demands made upon the body. No response to the administration of a ganglionic blocker may be observed until some demand is placed upon the autonomic system (e.g., hypotension following change from a recumbent to a standing position). On the other hand, where there is a great deal of autonomic activity (as in hypertension of sympathetic origin) the administration of a drug such as tetraethylammonium may produce a dramatic and immediate response (in this case a decrease in blood pressure). This is not the result of the drug initiating a response but rather of blocking existing physiological activity.

#### DRUGS ACTING AT CHOLINOCEPTIVE EFFECTORS

There are relatively few substances which will mimic the effects of acetylcholine liberation at autonomic effectors. The alkaloid *muscarine* from the poisonous mushroom *Amanita muscaria* was the first such substance isolated. From its effect came the adjective *muscarinic* which has been used to describe the actions of acetylcholine at the effector cells. It is now of only toxicological importance. *Acetyl-β-methacholine* (Methacholine, Mecholyl), possesses the actions of acetylcholine. It is destroyed by acetylcholinesterase but not by the nonspecific cholinesterase. When given in sufficiently large amounts its effects are, therefore, somewhat more prolonged than those of acetylcholine. *Carbaminoyl-β-methylcholine* (bethanecol, Urecholine) is similar to methacholine in its actions (at cholinoceptive effector cells) with the exception that it is not destroyed by cholinesterase. Consequently its actions may persist for hours. *Carbaminoylcholine* (Carbachol, Doryl) also stimulates cholinergically innervated effectors. In addition, as mentioned above, it also stimulates ganglionic cells. Like bethanecol, it is not subject to hydrolysis by cholinesterase. *Pilocarpine,* a naturally occurring alkaloid, was at one time an important therapeutic agent that stimulates cholinoceptive effectors directly. Like muscarine, it was of great help in elucidating the dynamics of autonomic function. Despite its long history relatively little is known of its mechanism of action, and its use today is limited chiefly to its local effects upon the eyes.

Many drugs block the stimulation of effector cells by cholinergic agents. The prototype of the group is *atropine,* an alkaloid found in several species of the potato family. The classical source is *Atropa belladonna* (deadly nightshade). A chemical isomer, *scopolamine,* also occurs naturally and has the same effect upon cholinergic transmission. These two agents are essentially interchangeable both quantitatively and qualitatively in their effects upon the autonomic nervous system. Dozens of synthetic compounds, similar to atropine in action, are available. None is as potent (in terms of amount required to produce a given effect) as the natural alkaloids, and they vary one from another in their duration of action and affinity for certain types of effectors. This permits some selectivity in blocking cholinergic responses.

Atropine and its congeners combine reversibly with the receptor site to prevent access of cholinergic substances to the effector cell. As with the ganglionic blockers, acetylcholine is released from their nerve endings, but no response is elicited. The effects produced by atropine are those of interference with parasympathetic function and sweating. Consequently a patient who has received atropine shows exaggerated sympathetic effects, such as tachycardia, decreased intestinal motility, mydirasis, etc. These are not direct responses to atropine but rather the result of blockade of normal physiological antagonism to sympathetic functions.

### DRUGS ACTING AT ADRENOCEPTIVE EFFECTORS

The effects of epinephrine and levarterenol (norepinephrine) have already been discussed (ch. 58). Unlike acetylcholine, these substances are inactivated relatively slowly and hence may be administered exogenously to produce their characteristic responses. However, the administration of a single dose of one of these drugs produces, therapeutically speaking, a transient response. Other drugs are available which produce various adrenergic responses for longer duration.

Ephedrine is an alkaloid from the Asiatic plant *ma huang.* It causes many of the cardiovascular effects of sympathetic stimulation, apparently affecting both alpha and beta receptors for it will increase blood pressure, dilate the pupil, relax the bronchioles, etc. Enough differences exist between the actions of ephedrine and epinephrine to suggest that ephedrine may act by some mechanism different from that of epinephrine, but no definitive statement can be made on the basis of information now available. It also produces central nervous system excitation, and is at times used to counteract central depression.

Many other adrenergic compounds have been synthesized. Minor chemical variations in some cases cause marked changes in the nature of the response produced. By making appropriate chemical modifications, drugs have been prepared which have primarily only one or two of the actions of epinephrine. The variety of drugs employed and the relationships involved in their actions is properly the scope of pharmacology and is too extensive a subject for review here.

Certain alkaloids (ergotamine, ergocristine, etc.) found in ergot were found by Dale early in this century to block the pressor effects of epinephrine. In recent years a number of synthetic cholinergic blocking agents have been prepared. Most widely used of this group are *piperoxan* (Benodaine) *phenoxybenzamine* (Dibenzyline), *phentolamine* (Regitene), and *azapetine* (Ilidar).[6]

Not all adrenergic effects are blocked by these agents. Vasoconstriction is most readily inhibited by these blockers. On the other hand, no known drug will inhibit sympathetic cardioacceleration. As with atropinelike drugs, the adrenergic blockers do not of themselves initiate responses, but effects are seen following their administration which are the result of disrupting the balance between the two divisions of the autonomic system or reducing excessive sympathetic activity.

### Transmission at the Myoneural Junction

The transmission of impulses at the myoneural junction is accomplished in much the same fashion as synaptic transmission. Acetylcholine, liberated from the nerve ending, reacts with the muscle end-plate to depolarize it and initiate contraction of the actomyosin fibers (fig. 71.5). Acetylcholinesterase immediately inactivates the acetylcholine, the muscle end-plate repolarizes,

[6] Many other compounds recently introduced into therapeutics produced limited adrenergic blockade which causes "undesirable side effects" at times.

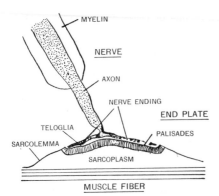

FIG. 71.5. Diagram of the region of the muscle end-plate (from Acheson after Couteaux).

and the situation is favorable for reception of another nerve impulse and initiation of another muscular contraction (p. 1304, 1305).

Evidence that acetylcholine is liberated from the terminals of motor nerves and serves as a transmitter of impulses to the muscle fibers has been obtained by Dale and his associates.

1. Upon rhythmical stimulation of the hypoglossal nerve of the perfused tongue of the cat, acetylcholine appeared consistently in the venous fluid. Similar results were secured with the perfused leg muscles of the dog during stimulation of the ventral spinal roots after excision of the lumbar sympathetic chain.

2. The sudden injection of a small dose (2 to 10μg.) of acetylcholine into the artery supplying the gastrocnemius of the cat during circulatory arrest caused a sharp contraction of the muscle. It is annulled by curarine but not by atropine. The direct application of a minute amount ($5 \times 10^{-6}$ μg.) of acetylcholine to the motor end-plate of the muscle fiber causes a short sharp tetanic contraction. Ten times this quantity applied elsewhere to the fiber is ineffective (Buchthal and Lindhard).

3. The intravenous administration of eserine (0.2 to 0.3 mg. per kg.) to a spinal cat caused an increase of 130 per cent in tension of a gastrocnemius twitch provoked by stimulation of the motor nerve. Eserine had no such effect upon the response of denervated muscle to direct stimulation.

## Drugs Acting at the Myoneural Junction

Although acetylcholine is the humoral mediator at the junction of motor nerves with skeletal muscle, the other choline esters mentioned above, muscarine, and pilocarpine have no effect at this site. Nicotine is capable of both stimulating and paralyzing the motor end-plate in a manner similar to its action at the ganglia. Neostigmine and *edrophonium* (Tensilon) are capable of potentiating muscular activity, and in larger doses will produce

fasciculations as a result of direct stimulation (depolarization) of the motor end-plate. Obviously direct chemical stimulation of muscle fibers is not of therapeutic, but only of toxicologic, importance.

The inhibitors of myoneural conduction are of more importance. The inhibition may be of two types. *d*-Tubo-curarine and its derivatives, as well as the synthetic drugs *gallamine* (Flaxedil) and Mytolon paralyze skeletal muscle by blocking access of acetylcholine to the motor endplate. Depolarization cannot occur and contraction cannot be initiated. This blockage is reversible, and to a limited extent paralysis with these agents can be overcome by the administration of a cholinesterase inhibitor (such as physostigmine or neostigmine) which will permit the released acetylcholine to increase to the point that it will "drive the curare molecules from the receptors." *Neostigmine* and *edrophonium*, in addition to their cholinesterase inhibiting action, are direct stimulants to these cholinergic receptors and will reverse curare paralysis directly. A second type of inhibitor, or muscle relaxant, is exemplified by compounds such as *succinylcholine* (Anectine) or *decamethonium* (Syncurine). These agents combine with the receptor site and cause depolarization. Since the compounds are relatively slowly inactivated, the membrane does not repolarize so that impulses cannot be transmitted from the nerve ending, even though acetylcholine is being released. There is no way in which this blockade may be reversed other than permitting the drug to be inactivated. Both succinylcholine and decamethonium are rather promptly inactivated by the tissues.

*Myasthenia gravis.* This condition, as its name implies, is a condition of profound weakness of the muscles, those of the eyes, face and throat being, as a rule, involved first. Collections of lymphocytes (lymphorrhages) and degenerative changes occur in the muscles. The disease is accompanied by a high degree of creatinuria and a reduction in the excretion of creatinine. The thymus is frequently enlarged, and myasthenia gravis is a frequent accompaniment of thymic tumors. Administered creatine is practically all excreted as such. Death results from involvement of the respiratory muscles. Myasthenia gravis is associated sometimes with thyrotoxicosis in which enlargement of the thymus is also commonly seen.

In 1934 Walker described a dramatic improvement in a case of myasthenia gravis following the administration of eserine; later prostigmine was found to confer even greater benefit. The effect, unfortunately, is transient, lasting for no longer than 3 or 4 hours. Other anticholinesterases like diisopropylfluorophosphate (DFP) have since been employed; the latter agent, though it has a more lasting effect is otherwise inferior to prostigmine or neostigmine. The first drug to be used with benefit was ephedrine, introduced by Edgeworth in 1930, who was herself a victim of the disease.

The muscular weakness is myasthenia gravis is not due to any disease of the central nervous system, nerve trunks, or muscles but, as shown by Harvey and his associates, to some defect at the myoneural junction. With regard to the nature of the junctional disorder, the action of cholinesterases suggests three possibilities, namely (a) deficiency of acetylcholine production, (b) the presence of excessive amounts of cholinesterase, or (c) the production of a substance with a curarelike action. The investigations of Wilson and Stoner point to the last mentioned as the most likely factor. They found no increase in the cholinesterase content of the blood in subjects of the disease, nor any evidence of a failure in acetylcholine synthesis, but the serum of patients suffering from the disease, but not under treatment with prostigmine, caused neuromuscular block in the nerve-muscle preparation of the frog. Serum from patients receiving prostigmine treatment exerted no curarelike action. With the idea that the primary fault originates in the thymus, thymectomy has been resorted to in some instances, with apparently beneficial results.

## The Role of Humoral Transmission in the Central Nervous System

There is currently much controversy over the nature of synaptic transmission in the central nervous system. Acetylcholine is involved, but is apparently not the only transmitter. The prevailing concept is that where acetylcholine is involved its mechanism of action is similar to that at the autonomic ganglia. Where acetylcholine is not the transmitter, other substances have been suggested; including levarterenol (or "sympathin"), 5-hydroxytryptamine, histamine and adenosine triphosphate (ATP).

The role of acetylcholine is suggested by the following observations.

1. Feldberg and Vogt found varying concentrations of choline acetylase in different regions of the central nervous system belonging to the same afferent or efferent pathway. They attributed this variation to alternate distribution of cholinergic and noncholinergic neurons. For example, the retina of the dog contains large amounts of choline acetylase, the optic nerve very little, and the lateral geniculate body (where next neuron in the pathway begins) again large amounts.

2. Acetylcholine content of the brain varies with the degree of functional activity. Richter and Crossland have shown that during deep anesthesia the concentration of acetylcholine in rat brains is three times as great as during convulsions. The concentration returned to normal in 10 seconds after cessation of the convulsions.

3. Acetylcholine has been found in the eserinized venous outflow of the isolated cat's brain and in eserinized Ringer's solution which was perfused through the lower end of the spinal cord of the dog. In the latter instance, stimulation of the central end of the divided sciatic nerve increased the concentration of acetylcholine during the period of reflex activity (Bülbring and Burn).

4. Acetylcholine is found in cerebrospinal fluid by a variety of techniques, and it has been observed to transude from the cerebral cortex. This transudation decreases concomitantly with a decrease in electrical activity of the cortex as the depth of anesthesia is increased. Undercutting of the cortex (leading to a "silent cortex") stops the production of acetylcholine (MacIntosh and Oborin).

The evidence for the existence of noncholinergic chemical transmission is more tenuous.

1. Eccles has demonstrated, by intracellular recording, that the electrical activity at synapses can be accounted for only on the basis of a mediator and that this mediator at certain synapses is not acetylcholine.

2. As mentioned, Feldberg and Vogt have demonstrated uneven distribution of acetylcholine in the central nervous system. The cerebellum is notably deficient in both acetylcholine and choline acetylase. Yet extracts of cerebellum injected into the carotid artery have been found to increase electrical activity of the cerebellum. No claim is made that this substance, as yet unidentified, is a mediator, but it seemingly would fulfill the requirements of a central transmitter.

3. 5-Hydroxytryptamine (serotonin) is irregularly distributed in the brain. This agent, as well as drugs which will liberate it and drugs which antagonize its actions peripherally, can elicit pronounced central effects. The objections to its role as a mediator result first from the fact that it is found in those areas also high in acetylcholine concentration, where presumably acetylcholine is functioning as a mediator. Second, drugs which have opposing central effects (such as amphetamine which is a stimulant and reserpine which is a depressant) produce identical quantitative changes in 5-hydroxytryptamine concentrations in the brain.

4. Levarterenol is also irregularly distributed in the brain. Like 5-hydroxytryptamine it is found in highest concentrations in those areas rich in acetylcholine. It has been demonstrated to modify synaptic transmission, but there is little evidence to justify assigning it a primary role in noncholinergic transmission.

No unifying statement may be made of the mechanism of humoral transmission within the central nervous system. That such transmission must exist seems assured. Likewise, it must in part be cholinergic. The identity of other mediators, or what functions are served by the substances found in the brain which are active elsewhere in the body, remains to be elucidated.

## REFERENCES

AHLQUIST, R. P. Am. J. Physiol., 1948, 153, 586.

AXELROD, J. Science, 1957, 126, 400.

BABKIN, B. P., ALLEY, A. AND STAVRAKY, G. W. Trans. Roy. Soc. Can., 1932, 26, Sec. V, 89.

BACQ, Z. M. AND FISCHER, P. Arch. internat. physiol., 1947, 55, 73.

BEUTNER, R. AND BARNES, T. C. Science, 1941, 94, 211. Biodynamics, 1942, 4, 47.

BEYER, K. H. AND SHAPIRO, S. H. Am. J. Physiol., 1945, 144, 321.

BEZNÁK, A. B. L. J. Physiol., 1934, 82, 129.

BROCK, L. C., COOMBS, J. S. AND ECCLES, J. C. J. Physiol., 1952, 117, 431.

BRONK, D. W. AND ASSOCIATES. Am. J. Physiol., 1938, 123, 24. J. Neurophysiol., 1939, 2, 380.

BUCHTHAL, F. AND LINDHARD, J. J. Physiol., 1937, 90, 82 P.

BULBRING, E. AND BURN, J. H. J. Physiol., 1941, 100.

CANNON, W. B. Lancet, 1930, 1, 1109. CANNON, W. B. AND ASSOCIATES. Am. J. Physiol., 1929, 89, 84. Ibid., 1931, 97, 319, also, MOORE, R. M. A. Res. Nerv. & Ment. Dis., Proc., 1930, 9, 385.

CANNON, W. B. AND BACQ, Z. M. Am. J. Physiol., 1931, 96, 392.

CANNON, W. B. AND ROSENBLUETH, A. Am. J. Physiol., 1933, 104, 557.

CANTONI, G. L. AND LOEWI, O. J. Pharmac., 1944, 81, 67.

CHANG, H. C. AND ASSOCIATES. Chinese J. Physiol., 1938, 13, 153.

CHUTE, A. L., FELDBERG, W. AND SMYTH, D. H. Quart. J. Exper. Physiol., 1940, 30, 65.

COLE, K. S. AND CURTIS, H. J. J. Gen. Physiol., 1940, 24, 551.

CROSSLAND, J. The problem of non-cholinergic transmission in the central nervous system, in Metabolism of the Nervous System, D. Richter, Ed., Pergamon Press, 1957.

DALE, H. H. J. Physiol., 1906, 34, 163. Pharmacol. Rev., 1954, 6, 7. Lancet, 1929, 1, 1179: 1233, 1285. J. Physiol., 1933, 80, 10 P. Brit. M. J., 1934, 2, 1161.

DALE, H. H. AND DUDLEY, H. W. J. Physiol., 1929, 68, 97.

DALE, H. H. AND FELDBERG, W. J. Physiol., 1934, 81, 320. Ibid., 82, 121.

DALE, H. H. AND ASSOCIATES. J. Physiol., 81, 39 P. Ibid., 1936, 86, 353. Ibid., 87, 394. Ibid., p. 42 P.

DU BOIS-REYMOND, E. H. Gesamelte Abhandl. Z. Muskel-u. Nervenphysik. Leipzig, 1877. (Quoted by Dale.)

ECCLES, J. C. Ann. Rev. Physiol., 1948, 10, 93.

EDGEWORTH, H. J. A. M. A., 1930, 94, 1136; 1933, 100, 1401.

ELLIOTT, T. R. J. Physiol., 1904, 31, 20; 1905, 32, 401.

ENGELHART, E. Arch. ges. Physiol., 1931, 227, 220.

ERLANGER, J. J. Neurophysiol., 1939, 2, 370.

EULER, U. S. v. Acta physiol. scandinav., 1946, 12, 73.

EULER, U. S. v. Nor adrenaline. In Metabolism of the Nervous System, D. Richter, Ed., Pergamon Press, 1957.

FELDBERG, W., see under Monographs and Reviews.

FELDBERG, W. AND BROWN, G. L. Ibid., 1935, 84, 12 P. Differential paralysis of the superior cervical ganglion. Ibid., 1936, 86, 10 P. Ibid., p. 290.

FELDBERG, W. AND GADDUM, J. H. J. Physiol., 1934, 81, 305.

FELDBERG, W. AND VARTAINEN, A. J. Physiol., 1934, 83, 103.

FELDBERG, W. AND VOGT, M. J. Physiol., 1948, 107, 372.

FORBES, A. J. Neurophysiol., 1939, 2, 465.

FURCHGOTT, R. F. J. Pharmacol. & Exper. Therap. 1954, 111, 265.

GERARD, R. W. Ann. New York Acad. Sc., 1946, 47, 575.

HARVEY, A. M. AND ASSOCIATES. Bull. Johns Hopkins Hosp., 1941, 69, 1, 529, 546.

HARVEY, A. M. AND MACINTOSH, F C. J. Physiol., 1938, 97, 408.

HAWKINS, R. D. AND MENDEL, B. J. Cell. & Comp. Physiol., 1946, 27, 69.

HENDERSON, V. E. AND ROEPKE, M. H. J. Pharmacol. & Exper. Therap., 1933, 47, 193. Ibid., 1934, 51, 97.

HENDERSON, W. R. AND WILSON, W. C. Quart. J. Exper. Physiol., 1936, 26, 83.

HOET, J. C. J. Physiol., 1925, 60, x.

LABROSSE, E. H., AXELROD, J. AND KETY, S. S. Science, 1958, 128, 573.

LEARMONTH, J. R. Brain, 1931, 54, 147.

LOCKETT, M. F. Brit. J. Pharmacol., 1954, 9, 498.

LOCKETT, M. F. J. Physiol., 1956, 133, 73 P.

LORENTE DE NÓ, R. J. Cell. & Comp. Physiol., 1944, 24, 85.

MACINTOSH, F. C. AND OBORIN, P. E. Abstr. 15th Int. Physiol. Cong. 1953, 380.

MARNEY, A. AND NACHMANSOHN, D. J. Physiol., 1938, 92, 37.

NACHMANSOHN, D. Yale J. Biol. & Med., 1940, 12, 565. Vitamins and Hormones. 1945, 3, 337. Ann. New York Acad. Sc., 1946, 47, 392. Rôle of acetylcholine in conduction. Bull. Johns Hopkins Hosp., 1948, 85, 463. See also under Monographs and Reviews.

QUASTEL, J. H., TENNEBAUM, M. AND WHEATLEY, A. H. M. Biochem. J., 1936, 30, 1668.

RANSON, S. W. AND BILLINGSLEY, P. R. J. Comp. Neurol. 1918, 29, 313: 359.

RICHTER, D. AND CROSSLAND, J. Am. J. Physiol., 1949, 159, 247.

SMITHWICK, R. H. New England J. Med., 1947, 236, 662.

WILSON, A. AND STONER, H. B. Quart. J. Med., 1944, 13, 1.

*Monographs and Reviews*

Association for Research in Nervous and Mental Disease. Vol. 9. The vegetative nervous system.

The Williams & Wilkins Company, Baltimore, 1930.

BAYLISS, W. M. The vaso-motor system. Longmans, Green & Company, London, 1923.

BLASCHKO, H. Pharmacol. Rev., 1952, 4, 415.

BROWN, G. L. Physiol. Rev., 1937, 17, 486.

BURN, J. H. Physiol. Rev., 1945, 25, 377.

CANNON, W. B. The wisdom of the body. W. W. Norton & Company, Inc., New York, 1932.

CANNON, W. B. Bodily changes in pain, hunger, fear and rage. Appleton, New York, 1920.

CANNON, W. B. Physiol. Rev., 1929, 9, 399.

COMROE, J. H. AND ASSOC., Am. J. Med. Sc., 1946, 212, 641.

DALE, H. H. Bull. Johns Hopkins Hosp., 1933, 53, 297. Harvey Lectures, 1936-7, Ser. 32, 229.

ECCLES, J. C. Physiol. Rev., 1937, 17, 538. Ann. New York Acad. Sc., 1946, 47, 429. Ann. Rev. Physiol., 1948, 10, 93.

EULER, U. S. v. Pharmacol. Rev., 1954, 6, 1.

FELDBERG, W. Physiol. Rev., 1945, 25, 596. Brit. M. Bull., 1949-50, 6, 1531.

FURCHGOTT, R. F. Pharmacol. Rev., 1955, 7, 183.

GASK, G. E. AND ROSS, J. P. The surgery of the sympathetic nervous system. The Williams & Wilkins Company, Baltimore, 1934.

GASKELL, W. H. The involuntary nervous system. Longmans, Green & Company, London, 1920.

GASSER, H. S. Physiol. Rev., 1930, 10, 35.

KUNTZ, A. The autonomic nervous sytem. Lea & Febiger, Philadelphia, 1934.

LANDS, A. M. Pharmacol. Rev., 1949, 1, 279.

LANGLEY, J. N. The autonomic nervous system. Heffer, Cambridge University Press, 1921.

LOEWI, O. Harvey Lectures, 1932-33, 28, 218.

LOEWI, O. Proc. Roy. Soc., London. ser. B 1935, 118, 229.

NACHMANSOHN, D., in The Hormones, PINCUS, G. AND THIMANN, K. V., Eds. Academic Press, 1948.

NACHMANSOHN, D. AND ASSOCIATES. Bull. Johns Hopkins Hosp., 1948, 85, 463.

PARKER, G. H. Humoral agents in nervous activity. Cambridge University Press, 1932.

RANSON, S. W. Physiol. Rev., 1921, 1, 477.

RIKER, W. F., JR. Pharmacol. Rev., 1953, 5, 1.

ROSENBLUETH, A. The transmission of sympathetic nerve impulses. Physiol. Rev., 1937, 17, 514.

Symposium on Neurohumoral Transmission, Pharmacol. Rev., 1954, 6, 1.

TAYLOR, D. B. Pharmacol. Rev., 1951, 3, 412.

WELSH AND ASSOCIATES. Fed. Proc., 1948, 7, 435.

WHITE, J. C. The autonomic nervous system. Macmillan Company, New York, 1935.

WHITTERIDGE, D. J. Neurol. Neurosurg. & Psychiat., 1948, 9, 134.

# 72

# THE PHYSIOLOGY OF VISION

## Structure of the Eye

ANATOMICAL OUTLINE OF THE EYE

The human eyeball (bulb or globe of the eye) is approximately spherical, being slightly flattened from above down (see figure 72.1). In the adult it measures about 24 mm. in its anteroposterior and transverse diameters and 23.5 mm. in its vertical diameter. It is compounded of the segments of two spheres, its posterior five-sixths being the large segment of a sphere with a radius of about 8 mm. The center of the anterior curvature of the eyeball is called its *anterior pole* and the corresponding point on the posterior surface the *posterior pole*. A straight line joining the two poles is known as the *optic axis*. The visual axis passes through the cornea a little to the nasal side of its center of curvature and the fovea centralis; the optic and visual axes therefore cross at a point a little behind the center of the lens.[1] The circumference of the eyeball midway between the two poles is termed the *equator*. Any imaginary circle drawn to pass through both poles of the eye is called a *meridian*. The *optic nerve* (p. 1395) enters the eyeball a little to the inner side of the posterior pole. The optic axes are nearly parallel, converging only slightly behind, whereas the axes of the optic nerves followed backward converge more sharply to the optic chiasma.

A thin fibrous membrane—the *fascia bulbi* or *capsule of Tenon*—encloses the globe from the entrance of the optic nerve to just behind the circumference of the cornea, where it blends with the outer (sclerotic) coat of the eyeball. The fascia bulbi is pierced a little in front of the equator of the globe by the ocular muscles; it blends with the sheaths of these muscles. Fascial slips (*check ligaments*) pass from the muscle sheaths, especially those of the external and internal recti, to the walls of the orbit and serve, it is believed, to check the movements of the muscles. In the region surrounding the optic nerve entrance the fascia bulbi is pierced by the ciliary vessels and nerves and just behind the equator by the vortex veins. The space between the fascia bulbi and the globe is occupied by a meshwork of fine areolar tissue, the

[1] The angle formed by the intersection of the optic axis with the visual axis is about 5° and is referred to as the *angle alpha*.

eyeball thus lies in a cushioned socket, separated from the other contents of the orbit.

The exposed part of the eyeball is covered by delicate mucous membrane—the *conjunctiva*—which is reflected onto the inner surfaces of the eyelids. The conjunctival surfaces are lubricated and kept clean by a film of fluid secreted by the *lacrimal gland* (fig. 72.2). The lacrimal gland is about the size and shape of a shelled almond. It lies under the shelter of the bone forming the upper and outer part of the orbit (i.e., the zygomatic process of the frontal bone). It is of the racemose type, somewhat resembling in structure a serous salivary gland; its secretion—the tears—is delivered through a number of fine ducts into the conjunctival fornix. The secretion is a clear watery, slightly hypertonic fluid having, according to Ridley, the following composition.

|  | *per cent* |
|---|---|
| Water | 98.2 |
| Total solids | 1.8 |
| Ash | 1.05 |
| Total N | 0.158 |
| Nonprotein N | 0.051 |
| Urea | 0.03 |
| Protein (albumin and globulin) | 0.669 |
| Sugar | 0.65 |
| Chlorides (as NaCl) | 0.658 |
| Sodium as $Na_2O$ | 0.60 |
| Potassium as $K_2O$ | 0.14 |
| Ammonia | 0.005 |

A sample of tears collected from the conjunctival surface contains traces of mucus secreted by the conjunctiva itself. The tears also contain the bacteriolytic enzyme lysozyme (ch. 36).

Several small accessory lacrimal glands are situated in the conjunctival fornices: their secretion suffices for lubrication and cleansing under ordinary circumstances. The main glands are called into play only upon special occasions, e.g., irritation of the conjunctiva, as a result of pain, certain emotional states, such as grief, disappointment, anger, etc., and during the acts of yawning and coughing.

The blinking movements of the lids spread the tears over the conjunctival surfaces; the fluid is directed into the *lacrimal lake*—a small triangular area lying in the angle bounded by the innermost portions of the lids. The center of the lacrimal lake is occupied by a small pink structure, the lacrimal caruncle, composed of modified skin and containing sebaceous glands and a few slender hairs. The tears are drained from the lacrimal lake by two small tubes—the *lacrimal ducts*. The minute orifices of the latter—the *puncta lacrimalia*—may be seen, one on the margin of each lid. The lacrimal ducts lead into the upper part of the *nasolacrimal duct*; this opens into the inferior meatus of the nose; its upper blind end is termed the *lacrimal sac*.

The drainage of tears into the nose does not depend merely upon gravity. Fluid enters and passes along the lacrimal ducts by capillary attraction aided by aspiration caused by contraction of a part of the orbicularis oculi muscle which is inserted into the lacrimal sac (pars lacrimalis muscle). When the lids close, contraction of this muscle causes dilation of the upper part of the sac and compression of its lower portion. Tears are thus aspirated into the sac, and any which have collected in its lower part are forced down the nasolacrimal duct towards its opening into the inferior meatus of the nose. As the lids open, the muscle relaxes. The upper part of the sac then collapses and forces fluid into the lower part which at the same time is released from compression. Thus, the act of blinking exerts a suction-force-pump action in removing the tears from the lacrimal lake and emptying them into the nasal cavity.

The secretory fibers to the lacrimal gland are derived from the parasympathetic. They arise from the superior salivatory nucleus, or, according to some, from a separate group of cells (*lacrimal nucleus*) in close relation to the latter. The fibers leave the brain in the nervus intermedius of Wrisberg, the sensory root of the facial. They pass to the geniculate ganglion which they leave in the great superficial petrosal nerve (see fig. 65.10, p. 1200). This nerve joins the deep petrosal nerve to form the nerve of the pterygoid canal (Vidian nerve). The fibers are conveyed in the latter nerve to the sphenopalatine ganglion and thence into the zygomatic branch of the maxillary nerve. A branch of the zygomatic nerve (zygomaticotemporal) anastomoses with the lacrimal nerve—a branch of the ophthalmic. The lacrimal nerve thus receives the parasympathetic fibers and delivers them to the lacrimal gland; it also carries sensory fibers to the gland.

The sympathetic fibers are derived from the cervical sympathetic; they pass into the carotid plexus and travel in the deep petrosal nerve to the great superficial petrosal nerve. They accompany the parasympathetic fibers to the gland. The sympathetic is probably purely vasomotor in function; it does not appear to furnish secretory fibers to the lacrimal gland.

Lacrimation is induced reflexly by stimulation

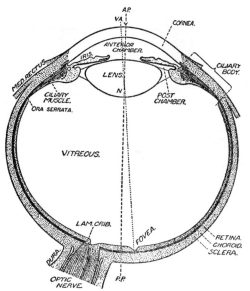

FIG. 72.1. Horizontal section of the right eye. P. P. posterior pole; A. P., anterior pole; V. A., visual axis. (From Wolff, modified from Salzmann.)

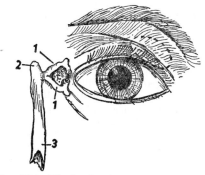

FIG. 72.2. The lacrimal apparatus. 1, Lacrimal ducts; 2, lacrimal sac; 3, nasolacrimal duct. Region marked off by interrupted line indicates the position of the lacrimal gland.

of nerve endings of the cornea or conjunctiva (ophthalmic division of the fifth nerve). The reflex is annulled by anesthetization of the surface of the eye, by section of the sensory nerves or of the great superficial petrosal nerve, or by blockage of the sphenopalatine ganglion. Emotional lacrimation is not affected by local anesthetization nor by section of the ophthalmic division of the fifth nerve, but is abolished by section of the great superficial petrosal nerve or by blockage of the sphenopalatine ganglion. Defective or complete absence of a lacrimatory response, either psychic or reflex is seen, although very rarely, as a congenital anomaly.

### The Tunics of the Eyeball

The wall of the eye is composed of three concentric layers or tunics. (1) An outer or fibrous

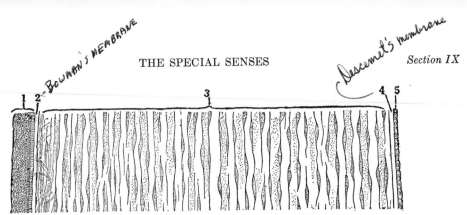

FIG. 72.3. Vertical section of human cornea (lying horizontally); *1*, corneal epithelium; *2*, anterior elastic lamina; *3*, substantia propria; *4*, posterior elastic lamina; *5*, endothelium of the anterior chamber. (After Waldeyer, modified.) - *see* WOLFF, 'ANATOMY OF THE EYE & ORBIT'

tunic—the *sclera and cornea*, (2) a middle vascular tunic—the *choroid, ciliary body* and *iris*, and (3) a nervous tunic—the *retina* (see fig. 72.1).

THE OUTER OR FIBROUS TUNIC. The posterior five-sixths of this coat is opaque and is called the *sclera*; it is composed of white fibrous tissue and fine elastic fibers. Its anterior one-sixth is perfectly transparent and is called the *cornea*. The sclera appears in front as the so-called "white of the eye." The point where it joins the cornea—the *sclerocorneal junction*—is marked by a faint groove (see p. 1399). The sclera where it is pierced by the optic nerve is reduced to a thin membrane containing perforations for the transmission of the retinal vessels and the bundles of nerve fibers. This part of the outer tunic, known as the *lamina cribrosa*, is the weakest part of the wall of the globe and is the first to yield to a persistently high intraocular pressure (see Glaucoma, p. 1401), producing the so-called "cupping" of the optic disc. The cornea is convex anteriorly, being the small segment of a sphere having a radius of about 7.7 mm.[2] It is almost circular in circumference, measuring 11 mm. and 12 mm. respectively in its vertical and horizontal meridians. It is from 0.5 mm. to 1 mm. in thickness. The cornea is composed of five layers in the following order (from the front backward); (a) the corneal epithelium, (b) the anterior elastic lamina of Bowman, (c) the substantia propria, (d) the posterior elastic lamina of Descemet, and (e) a layer of endothelial cells (fig. 72.3).

The *corneal epithelium* is continuous with that of the conjunctiva; it consists of several strata of cells of different sizes and shapes. Columnar cells compose the deepest layer; this is overlaid by two or three layers of polyhedral cells. The cells of the superficial three or four layers are of the squamous type. The *substantia propria* is a tough transparent membrane consisting of a number of flattened lamellas composed of bundles of modified connective tissue fibers continuous with those of the sclera and lying in a mucoprotein ground-substance (keratosulfate). The *anterior elastic lamina of Bowman* and the *posterior elastic lamina of*

*Descemet* bound the corresponding aspects of the substantia propria. At the circumference of the cornea the posterior elastic lamina breaks up into fibers which are continued into the pectinate ligament (ch. 74). The cornea is devoid of blood vessels which is an important feature in relation to surgical grafting. The cornea is one of the few tissues which can be successfully grafted from one person to another. It receives nourishment from lymph (derived from vessels at its margin) which percolates through the spaces between its cells. It is supplied around its circumference by a rich plexus of pain fibers. Fine nonmedullated filaments derived from this plexus pass through the posterior elastic lamina and form a second plexus in the substantia propria (stroma plexus). From the stroma, plexus fibers proceed outward through the anterior elastic lamina where they form a subepithelial plexus; nerve filaments can be traced from the latter to the epithelial cells. The pain fibers have a very low threshold being aroused by very mild forms of stimulation. This has led to the general belief that the cornea is devoid of touch receptors and that stimuli which give a sensation of touch when applied to the skin are painful if applied to the cornea. It is claimed, however, that certain weak and innocuous stimulating agents, such as a jet of fluid impinging upon the cornea, arouse a sensation of touch alone.

THE MIDDLE OR VASCULAR LAYER consists from behind forwards of the *choroid, ciliary body* and the *iris*. The choroid is composed of a rich capillary plexus and the numerous small arteries and veins leading to and from it. It is dark brown in color, due to the presence of pigment cells, and forms the middle layer of the posterior five-sixths of the globe; it terminates anteriorly at the level of the ora serrata of the retina. The ciliary body and iris are described elsewhere.

THE NERVOUS TUNIC OR RETINA. The retina proper extends from the margins of the optic papilla (see below) to just behind the ciliary body. At this point it ends abruptly in a dentated border —the *ora serrata* (see figs. 72.1, and 74.28, p. 1386). Its thickness diminishes progressively from the optic papilla (where it is about 0.4 mm.) to the dentate border where it is only 0.09 mm.

---

[2] The peripheral zone is somewhat flattened as compared with the central portion.

The *optic disc* is situated about 3 mm. to the nasal side of and a little above the posterior pole of the eyeball; it has a diameter of about 1.5 mm. in man. As viewed in the human eye by means of the ophthalmoscope (p. 1381) it appears as a pink circular area fading to a creamy white toward the center. It is pierced near its center by the retinal vessels—*arteria centralis retinae* and its accompanying vein (Pl. III, ch. 74). The circumference of the optic disc is elevated to form the *optic papilla*. The central depressed part is known as the *physiological cup* or the *excavation of the optic nerve*. The vessels climb up the inside of the cup to reach the retina. All layers of the retina except the nerve fiber layer are absent from the optic disc. It is therefore totally insensitive to light and is known as the *blind spot* of the retina. The reader is referred to figure 75.3, p. 1404, for a demonstration of the blind spot in his own eye.

In order to clarify the relationships of the outer tunics of the eyeball to the retina and to facilitate the description and interpretation of the retina itself, its mode of development will first be outlined.

The rudiment of the eye is first visible in the embryo as a vesicular outgrowth of the neural tube (fig. 72.4). This vesicle grows larger and bulges outward until it meets the epidermis, in which, in some species at least, it is responsible for the induction of a *lens*. At this stage, the walls of the optic vesicle are formed of neuroblastic tissue precisely similar to that of the rest of the neural tube. The vesicle is lined on the inside by cells which are of the same kind as those which, elsewhere in the neural tube, will form the ependyma. To the outside of the neural tissue of the neural tube, neural crest cells will, at a later stage, apply themselves as the pia mater, and blood vessels will ramify among them and form the arachnoid layer. Outside this, the mesenchymal tissues will condense as the dura mater. As the optic vesicle grows out, the same layers are found in it as in the rest of the neural tube, and when the outer pole invaginates and begins to form the optic cup, the lining layer of the vesicle becomes opposed to itself so that the space between the two parts of it (i.e., the cavity of the vesicle) is almost obliterated. The covering layers of the vesicle (i.e., the dura mater which over the vesicle becomes the sclera and cornea, the pia mater and arachnoid, which become the choroid) on the other hand do not follow that part of the vesicle which actually invaginates. The sclera and cornea remain as though surrounding the original sphere and there is a space left in the pia mater and arachnoid which roughly corresponds with the cavity which will form the pupil, and through which the lens (which is now separated from the epidermis and lying within the future cornea) penetrates into the cup, together with the connec-

tive tissues for the formation of the vitreous body. The invagination of the optic vesicle is not a symmetrical invagination and the cup is formed partly by the folded sides or margins of the cup growing toward each other until they eventually meet and enclose the arteries which will supply the inner surface of the retina and the vitreous body. The method of this invagination is best understood by reference to Figure 72.4.

In the neural tube, the neural tissue, consisting of neuroblasts and neuroglia, arises by cell multiplication which occurs mostly in or near the ependymal layer. In the optic vesicle, the part of this layer which, after the invagination, forms the outer part of the optic cup, does not give rise to neural tissue but remains as a single layer of cells, which eventually forms the *pigment layer of the retina* and a pigmented covering for the ciliary processes (fig. 72.5). Because of the invagination, this layer is reflected back on itself at the rim of the *iris*, thus lining the posterior surface of the iris with a double layer of pigment epithelium. In this region the outer layer not only forms an epithelium covering the posterior surface of the iris but also gives rise to the *sphincter* and *dilator pupillae muscles*. Continuing towards the retina, this pigment layer (after again covering the ciliary processes, but this time as the colorless columnar epithelium responsible for the secretion of the aqueous humour) reaches the *ora serrata* and the *pars optica retinae*. Here it again gives rise to true neural tissue in a manner which is almost precisely similar to that found in the rest of the nervous system.

Because of the absence of neural tissue on the outside of the optic cup, the ependymal layer (i.e., the pigment layer of the retina) is brought into immediate contact with the pia mater and the arachnoid (which together constitute the choroid coat). Outside the choroid lies the sclera which can thus be seen to correspond to the dura mater. These relationships are set out in figures 72.4 and 72.5.

Thus the retina itself appears as a true part of the central nervous system, and its cells have exactly the same origin as those of other cells of the central nervous system. During the development of the retina there are, in essence, two main waves of cell production. The 'ependymal' and embryonic layer first gives rise to cells which migrate outwards to become the eventual *ganglion cells*. Because of the invagination, 'outwards' now means toward the center of the optic cup. This wave is then followed by a second wave whose cells mainly constitute the layer of *bipolar cells*, and the cells which are left behind in the 'ependymal' layer differentiate to become the sensory layer of the retina, the layer

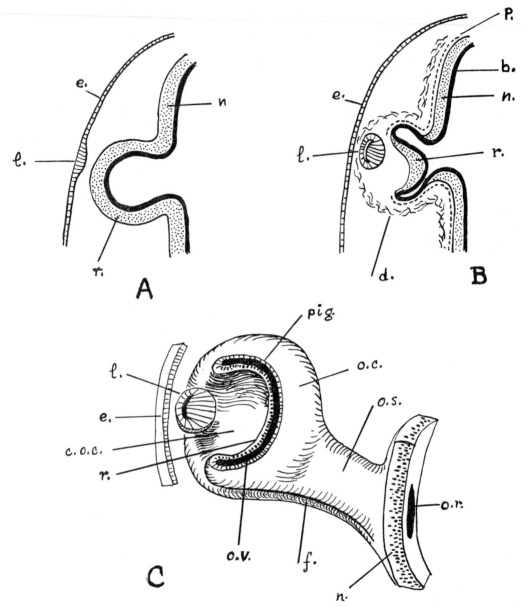

Fig. 72.4. Diagrams of developing eye. (*A*) Sagittal section through left optic vesicle; (*B*) same section at a later stage; (*C*) semisolid diagram to show the method of invagination and the development of the optic stalk.

c.o.c., cavity of optic cup; d, dura mater; e, epidermis; f, fissure; l, lens; n, neural tissue; o.c., optic cup; o.r., optic recess; o.s., optic stalk; o.v., optic vesicle; p, pia mater; pig., pigment epithelium; r, retina.

of *rod* and *cone cells*. Thus, basically, the retina is built up of three layers of cells, their processes, and the synaptic connections which they make with each other and with the rest of the nervous system; this last connection with the central nervous system is established by nerve fibers growing away from the ganglion cells along the inner surface of the retina to the point known as the *optic disc* (see above) and flowing thence along the fold of neural tissue which encloses the retinal arteries and constitutes the optic stalk and eventually the optic nerve to the brain proper.

Thus a needle pushed into the eye from any point in the posterior half, i.e., behind the ora serrata or rim of the retina, would pass through the following layers (Fig. 72.6).

Sclera: specialized connective tissue.

Choroid: blood vessels mingled with branching and heavily pigmented cells of the pia mater.

Pigment epithelium of the retina: cells arranged as a single layer of hexagonally packed cells, corresponding to the outer fold of ependyma.

(The cavity of the original optic vesicle.)

Rods and cones: these are the processes of rod and cone cells (see pp. 1321–1323).

External limiting membrane: original 'cuticle' of the neural tube, partly composed of processes of neuroglial cells.

Cell bodies and nuclei of rod and cone cells.

Outer synaptic layer: the connections between rod and cone cells and bipolar cells.

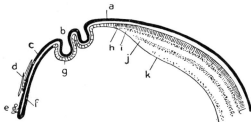

FIG. 72.5. Diagram to show the genetic relationships between the cells of the retina, iris, etc. (*a*) Pigment layer of the retina; (*b*) pigment layer over the ciliary processes; (*c*) anterior pigment layer of the iris; (*d*) dilator pupillae muscle; (*e*) sphincter pupillae muscle; (*f*) posterior pigment layer of the iris; (*g*) columnar epithelium over the ciliary processes; (*h*) rods and cones; (*i*) nuclei of the rods and cones; (*j*) bipolar, horizontal and amacrine cell nuclei; (*k*) ganglion cell nuclei. (From Willmer.)

Bipolar cells and their nuclei: this layer also includes the nuclei of *horizontal cells, amacrine cells* and the cells of *Muller's fibers.*

Inner synaptic layer: the connection between bipolar cells and ganglion cells.

Ganglion cells.

Optic nerve fibers.

Internal limiting membrane: partly composed of the processes or products of the neuroglial cells, the Muller's fibers.

The light which penetrates the eye after passing through the cornea and lens obviously passes through the retina in the reverse order of that just given, i.e., it passes in the direction of the arrow in Figure 72.7. During life, the retina is practically transparent, so that light readily penetrates almost unimpeded to the rods and cones, where some of it is absorbed and initiates the visual processes. In the region of the *fovea*, which is the point on the visual axis at which the most distinct vision occurs, the thickness of the retinal layers is nevertheless reduced by dispersing the bipolar cells and ganglion cells to the sides and so producing a depression in the inner surface of the retina at that point (*fovea* (Latin) means a depression or hearth) and allowing the light to reach the receptors with as little interference as possible (Fig. 72.8).

The light that is not absorbed by the rods and cones is absorbed partly by the pigment layer and partly by the choroid. Only a very small part of the entering light escapes absorption and is reflected back; in this way the pig-

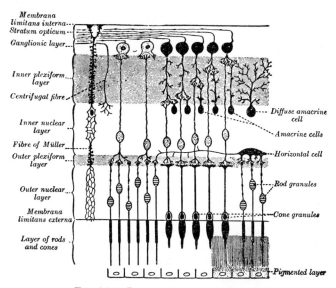

FIG. 72.6. Layers of retina. (After Cajal.)

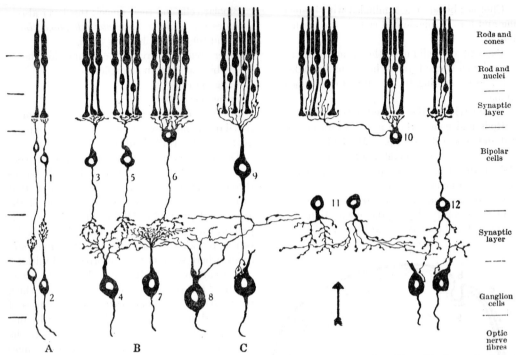

Rods and
cones

Rod and
nuclei

Synaptic
layer

Bipolar
cells

Synaptic
layer

Ganglion
cells

Optic
nerve
fibres

A          B          C

FIG. 72.7. Chief synaptic connections of rods and cones A. Pure cone path, midget bipolar and midget ganglion cells. B. Mainly cone paths, flat and brush bipolar cells. C. Mainly rod path, mop bipolar cells. 1. Midget bipolar cell; 2. Midget ganglion cell; 3. Flat bipolar supplying cones only; 4. Shrub ganglion cell; 5. Flat bipolar cell supplying rods and cones; 6. Brush bipolar supplying rods and cones; 7. Parasol ganglion cells; 8. Garland ganglion cells; 9. Mop bipolar cell; 10. Horizontal cell; 11. Amacrine cells; 12. Centrifugal bipolar cell. (After Polyak.)

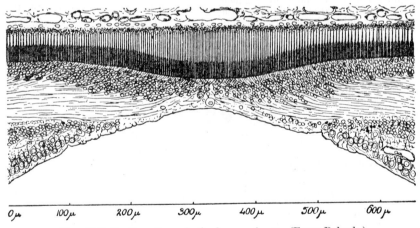

0μ      100μ      200μ      300μ      400μ      500μ      600μ

FIG. 72.8. Section through the human fovea. (From Polyak.)

ment layers act like the black paint inside a camera. The absorbing pigment in the epithelium and in the choroid is the inert derivative of tyrosine, *melanin*; although it may be bleached by prolonged exposure to bright light, it is not a visual pigment in the true sense.

In certain nocturnal animals there may, however, be considerable reflection either from minute fibers or crystals in the cells of the pigment layer, or from special fibers in the choroid coat. These reflecting surfaces (*tapeta*) are the cause of the eyeshine in cats and other animals. The tapetum is essentially a device for making use of whatever light is available at night by allowing it to pass first in one direction and then in the other through the visual pigments in the photoreceptor cells.

*The rod and cone cells.* In the normal eye, the

PLATE II

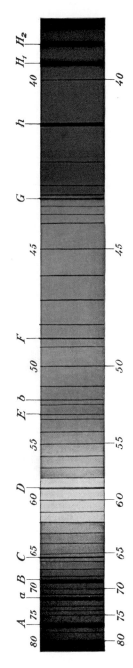

Spectrum as seen by light adapted eye (Photopic vision). (Figures form Duke-Elder *Text-book of Ophthalmology*, by permission of Henry Kimpton, London.)

Spectrum as seen by the dark adapted eye (Scotopic vision).

curved surface of the cornea and the lens cause an image of the outside world to be cast on the layer of the actual rods and cones, that is, the elongated projections of the rod and cone cells which extend beyond the external limiting membrane and each of which is divisible into an outer and inner segment. It is the outer segment which is believed to be the sensitive part. In some animals (e.g., the frog), one class of these structures (the rods) can be seen (if the preparation has been made from an animal previously kept in the dark and only dim red light has been used during the dissection) to contain a reddish pigment called *visual purple* or *rhodopsin*. This pigment is readily bleached by all wave lengths of visible light except those in the far red, e.g., those longer than 650 m$\mu$ and so, under the microscope the pink outer segments can be seen to fade rapidly.

If the eye of a rabbit is excised in darkness or in red light and then exposed to an object clearly defined in light and shade, e.g., a window sash against the sky, an image of the object will be found to have been impressed upon the retina when it is examined in the dark room. The image is caused by the bleaching of the visual purple where the bright parts of the image fell upon the rods. The retina thus behaves like a photographic film; the image so obtained is called an *optogram* (see fig. 72.9).

When a light from a small but intense source is shone obliquely through the sclera into the human eye, shadows of the blood vessels, which course over the inner surface of the retina, can be seen by the subject, and these shadows (Purkinje's figures) appear to move as the position of the light source is changed. From measurements of the relative movement of the image in relation to that of the light source, it can be shown that the image which is seen must be falling on the outer segments of the rods and cones at a distance of between 0.2 and 0.3 mm.

FIG. 72.9. Optogram formed upon the retina of a rabbit by exposing the eye to an object made of a glass plate and strips of black paper. (After Stewart.)

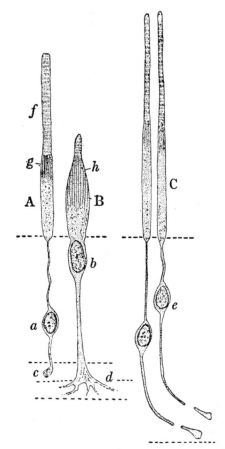

FIG. 72.10. Human rods and cones. (*A*) Rod—*a*, nucleus; *c*, central connection; *g*, ellipsoid; *f*, outer segment. (*B*) Cone—*b*, nucleus; *d*, central pedicle; *h*, ellipsoid. (*C*) Cones in the fovea centralis—*e*, nucleus. (From Cajal.)

from the retinal vessels (see p. 1326 and fig. 72.10). For these and other reasons, the outer segments of the rods and cones are now accepted as the most probable seat of the initial processes which convert radiant energy into something which is capable of being transmitted along the neural mechanisms in the rest of the retina and so to the brain.

The shapes of the outer segments of the rods and cones are extremely variable in different species and often also within the same animal. In man, those of the rods are fairly uniform cylinders (about 24 $\mu$ long and 3 $\mu$ wide), whereas those of the cones are short (6 $\mu$) and conical in the periphery, but become longer (up to 34 $\mu$), thinner (2 $\mu$) and much more cylindrical toward the center, reaching their extreme limits in this direction in the floor of the foveal depression (fig. 72.10).

In many animals (e.g., perch, frog, guinea pig and rat) evidence from the optical properties,

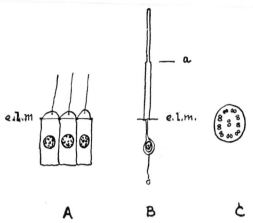

Fig. 72.11. The origin of rods from flagella. (*A*) The flagellar structure of the rod and cone cells in the developing retina; (*B*) a fully developed rod showing outer and inner segments; (*C*) a transverse section of a flagellum or cilium as seen with the electron microscope, showing the usual arrangement of internal fibers. a, The junction between inner and outer segments (*cf.* Fig. 72.12); e.l.m., external limiting membrane.

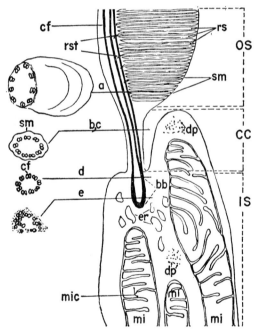

Fig. 72.12. Diagram of the structures at the junction between inner and outer segments of a rod as seen by the electron microscope. OS, outer segment; rs, platelike arrangement of flattened rod sacs; rst, junction of rod sacs with ciliary fibers; cf, ciliary fibers; sm, surface membrane; a, transverse section. CC, cilium connecting the inner and outer segments (*cf.* Fig. 72.11). b.c., transverse section. IS, inner segment; bb, basal body; dp, dense particles; e, transverse section; er, endoplasmic reticulum; mi, mitochondria; mic, mitochondrial cristae. (From de Robertis.)

particularly as obtained with the use of the polarizing microscope, and also from electron-microscopy indicates that the outer segments of rods are subdivided into a series of leaflike structures, each composed of a flattened vesicle enclosing a space between a pair of membranes, and piled one above the other like a stack of plates. The visual purple molecules are orientated with their long axes at right angles to the axis of the rod, in the same plane as these membranes. The outer segments of cones appear to have a somewhat similar structure but, in the one animal, the perch, for which there is detailed information, the membranes appear to be single instead of double and are thus likely to have a different origin. The pigment in the cones is not rhodopsin, nor is it known exactly where it is situated in each cone.

Recent work on rods and cones with the electron microscope has abundantly confirmed the older observations based on embryological development that the photosensitive part of the rod process, and with less certainty of the cone process also, are each derived from a modified flagellum. The inner and outer segments of the rod are connected by a fine fiber which, in transverse section shows a fibrillar structure very similar to that which is characteristic of all flagella (figs. 72.11 and 72.12). It will be remembered that many of the cells of the neural tube elsewhere, i.e., the ependymal cells, are flagellate, so, from the embryological point of view, it is not surprising to find flagella appearing in a modified form in this 'ependymal' layer of the retina.

The inner segments of rods and cones again show differences, although they are both very rich in mitochondria and metabolic enzymes, e.g., succinic dehydrogenase. In many animals, e.g., amphibia, reptiles, birds and monkeys, the cones may have oil globules in the inner segments at their junction with the outer segments. These globules in birds and turtles are sometimes colored with carotenoid pigments of which xanthophyll and astaxanthine are the most usual. Such globules do not occur in human cones but there is evidence that xanthophyll occurs in the cytoplasm of the cones and their centrally directed fibrous processes and gives rise to the yellowish pigmentation which occurs around the fovea for a distance of about 4° in all directions. This area is known as the *yellow spot* or *macula lutea*. The effect of this yellow pigmentation (macular pigment) can be seen, entoptically, if a uniform white surface is viewed alternately through a purple (i.e., transmitting blue and red) filter and a neutral grey filter of about the same optical density. The fovea then appears as a reddish spot often surrounded by another reddish ring on a bluish background, and this pattern is always seen at the point in the purple field to which the gaze is directed. The pigment appears to be to some extent orientated with respect to the axis of the cone cell and is probably the agent responsible for the appearance of "blue arcs" or "Haidinger's brushes" sometimes seen when a uniform field of blue polarized light is examined.

Cone cells generally have their nuclei near the external limiting membrane and each has a conspicuous nucleolus. Rod nuclei are smaller, without definite nucleoli, and generally are situated more centrally. The cones tend to make their synaptic connections with bipolar cells in the form of extended 'pedicles,' whereas rods end centrally in knoblike endings (see Fig. 72.10). The electron microscope shows vesicular invaginations into these endings and the processes of the bipolar cells penetrating into them. The cytoplasm of the knob is also filled with minute closed vesicles, and it has been suggested that these may be concerned with the production of the chemical transmitter.

In man, rods occur all over the retina except for a small area (about 0.44 mm. in diameter and corresponding to a visual field of rather less than 1°) on the visual axis at the center of the fovea. This important area is known as the *fovea centralis*. The receptors present in this area are almost certainly cones, but they are very elongated. Rods are most abundant at about 20° from the foveal center. The distribution of rods and cones is illustrated in figure 72.13, and it will be seen that cones are enormously concentrated around and in the fovea. The intimate

pattern of the distribution of rods and cones is often very regular, e.g., in certain areas one cone is surrounded by six rods, and, near the fovea, the cones appear, in histological sections cut transversely to the long axis of the cones, to be arranged in regular rows.

From the structural point of view there are very good reasons for considering rods and cones to be the processes belonging to two distinct (but closely related) races of cells. It will be seen that experiments on visual performance endorse this view. For example Stiles and Crawford have shown that a pencil of light which enters the eye through the center of the pupil causes a more intense sensation than does one of equal physical brightness passing through the pupil nearer its circumference. This phenomenon is most pronounced at the fovea. The smaller effect caused by the peripheral beam is not due to greater absorption by the ocular media, but to the direction of the beam in relation to the position of the cones, a smaller photochemical change being caused by light passing obliquely across the receptors than by that which traverses their lengths.

This phenomenon is very much more in evidence with the cones than it is with the rods and probably indicates structural differences between the two types of receptor. Not all the wave lengths of light are affected equally. The blue rays are affected most, then the red end of the spectrum. The directional effect is least with the green rays.

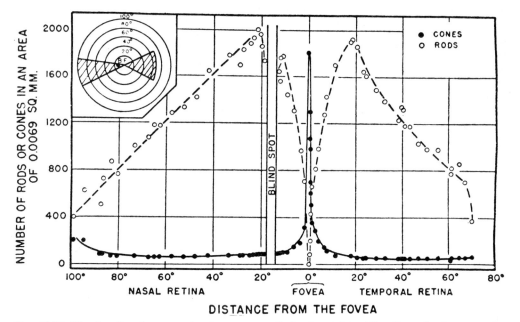

FIG. 72.13. The density of cones and rods on or near the horizontal meridian through a human retina. The inset is a schematic map of the retina showing the fovea (*F*) and the blind spot (*B*). The striped area represents the regions of the retina which were sampled in obtaining the counts plotted here. (From Chapanis after Østerberg.)

There are also slight color differences to be observed between monochromatic rays which have entered the pupil centrally and those entering at the periphery and thus falling obliquely on the receptors.

The outer segments of the rods and cones are often intimately surrounded by the processes of the cells of the pigment epithelium which interdigitate with them across the vanished space of the original lumen of the optic vesicle. This vanished but still potential space may become an actual space as the result of trauma, e.g., detached retina, or very frequently in histological preparations. In some animals, as for example, the frog, although not in man, the brown or black melanin granules in the pigment cells can move up and down the cell processes in relation to the intensity of the illumination. In the frog the granules are caused to extend along the cell processes by the action of adrenaline, as well as by light, and in this way these cells contrast with other melanin-containing cells which generally aggregate their pigment under the influence of adrenaline. The pigment epithelium is generally more highly developed in relation to cones than to rods and in the human eye is most noticeable in the region of the fovea.

Each rod or cone acts as a separate photosensitive element and, since in each human eye there are some 120 million rods and 6 million cones, the visual image cast on this layer is subdivided into some 126 million separate fragments, rather in the same way as when printing from photographs the picture is divided into innumerable separate points and the greater the number of points the better the quality of the reproduction. Half-tone reproductions obtained with a very fine screen are clearer and more precise than illustrations in the cheap press where coarse screens are used. Since a certain quantity of light has to be absorbed before any photochemical change can be initiated, the photoreceptors have to contain a certain mass of absorbing pigment within them. Consequently, if they have to be made as thin as possible in order to produce the necessary fine grain in the picture, they may also have to be correspondingly elongated. Attention has already been called to this change of form in the cones of the human eye between the periphery of the retina and the point of most distinct vision which lies at the fovea centralis (see fig. 72.10). The rods show much less change in their dimensions in different parts of the retina. Probably the underlying reason for this difference between rods and cones is related to the roles which the two types of

unit play in vision and these are, in turn, related to the manner in which rods and cones are connected with the visual centers. The subdivision of the image into many millions of separate photosensitive stimuli all of about the same order of magnitude might for some purposes be ideal and one might expect, at first sight, that all the information provided in this way would be relayed to the brain along separate channels. This, however, is not so. There are only about one million fibers in each optic nerve of man, and since there is no evidence for any qualitative difference in types of nerve impulse, only this number of separate trains of messages can reach the lateral geniculate body and visual centers. Clearly then there is considerable pooling and funneling of information into the optic pathway and this takes place through the bipolar cells and ganglion cells. Probably these layers of cells sift and integrate the information which the photoreceptors provide and send on only a summary of the most important information. A study of the bipolar and ganglion cells in different parts of the retina shows that their distribution is by no means uniform and that it correlates rather closely with the visual performance of the retina in its different regions. In the first place, the number of ganglion cells per sq. mm. in the retinal periphery (about 80° from the visual axis) is only measured in hundreds whereas in the central region of the eye, near the fovea, the density may rise to hundreds of thousands per sq. mm. Thus the number of receptor cells per ganglion cell progressively diminishes from the periphery towards the center of the eye, but it never reaches equality, although it begins to approach it in the fovea. This is one reason why peripheral vision is blurred and incomplete as compared with that at the fovea.

Histological studies of the retina, mostly by means of Golgi silver impregnation methods, indicate that there are three main varieties of bipolar cell, and a rather indefinite grouping of ganglion cells into two main classes. Again the distribution of these two classes of cells differs in different parts of the retina. Golgi preparations have to be carefully interpreted. The method only picks out a few cells at a time for impregnation and then apparently coats them in their entirety. All other cells remain almost completely untouched. The cellular architecture can therefore only be surmised from piecing together very fragmentary pictures. The main types of cell detected by this method are illustrated in figure 72.7 which also shows the shapes and relative positions of two other types of cell, the *horizontal cell* and the *amacrine cell*. The *mop bipolar* (or rod bipolar as it was originally called by Cajal) is distinguished from the others by the 'vertical' orientation of its dendrites and by the fact that it connects with the cell bodies as well as with the dendrites of the ganglion cells. It is present over most of the retina but is rare or absent from among the bipolar cells which relay from the foveal region. The *flat* and *brush bipolars*, or the cone bipolars of Cajal, are found in all regions of the retina including the foveal region (fig. 72.14). They are characterized by horizontally distributed dendrites which all end at the level of the internal endings of the cones, i.e., the cone pedicles. In this way they differ from the mop bipolars whose dendrites extend further and enter the little invaginations in the end knobs of the rods, many of which do not reach centrally as far as those of the cones. Centrally, the cone bipolars mostly appear to terminate among the dendrites of the ganglion cells and, distally, they probably make synaptic connections with about a dozen cones. The third

class of bipolar cell, the *midget bipolar*, is probably a specialization of the cone bipolar and becomes most numerous in the center of the retina in the region of the fovea. Members of this class have very restricted dendritic branchings and probably make contact with one or two cones only. Similarly at their opposite pole they each connect with one small ganglion cell only. Thus these midget bipolars and *midget ganglion cells* appear to provide private connections from individual cones to neurons in the lateral geniculate body at least. It should be remembered, however, that although these cells are most numerous near the fovea, they are always mingled with flat and brush bipolars also. There is probably very considerable overlap among the fields covered by the flat and brush bipolars and both probably collect information from cones which are also transmitting along the "midget pathway." Similarly, there is also likely to be overlapping of the fields of the ganglion cells. Among these ganglion cells there is, in addition to the numerous rather small and histologically featureless cells, a rather distinct class of very large cells, each with a large vesicular nucleus

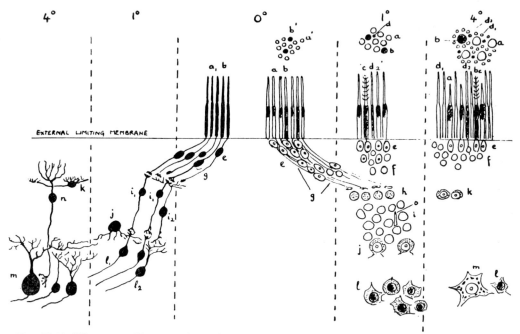

FIG. 72.14. Diagram to illustrate the main features of the foveal center. (On the right) the information obtained by the usual cytological and histological methods; (on the left) information obtained by Golgi methods.

a, light-staining cone; b, dark-staining cone; c, spiral process surrounding some cones; d, rod; $d_1$, light-staining rods; $d_2$, dark-staining rod; e, cone nuclei; f, rod nuclei; g, Henlé's fibers; h, midget bipolar cells; i, bipolar cells; $i_1$, midget; $i_2$, flat and brush; j, amacrine cells; k, horizontal cells; l, small ganglion cells; $l_1$, midget; $l_2$, other types; m, large ganglion cells; n, rod or mop bipolar cells; o, nucleus of cell of Müller's fiber. (From Willmer.)

and prominent nucleolus and whose cytoplasm is filled with large Nissl's granules. These cells are readily stained supravitally with methylene blue or neutral red and are evenly distributed all over the retina, but become scarce in, or absent from, the foveal region. These cells possess a very wide arborization of dendrites which may extend over an area with a diameter of more than 1 mm. in the synaptic layer between the bipolar cells and the ganglion cells. The overlap of these cells with the fields of other ganglion cells must therefore be very considerable. Microelectrodes placed near these large cells in the eyes of decerebrate animals (see p. 1334) record large spike potentials and, partly for this reason, most of the electrical recording of such spikes which has been possible from the inner surface of the living retina has been localized to these cells. The electrical properties of the small ganglion cells and the bipolar cells still remain somewhat problematical.

Acetylcholinesterase is present in the inner synaptic layer, suggesting that some at least of the cells in the bipolar cell layer transmit by means of acetylcholine. On the other hand, the outer synaptic layer between the rods and cones and the bipolar cells is histochemically negative in this respect and there is as yet nothing to indicate the nature of the transmitter substances, if any, in that layer.

Horizontal cells are most abundant in eyes with many rods, e.g., in the cat. Their terminals end in the outer synaptic layer but opinions differ on their exact distribution. Presumably they are concerned with the various processes of lateral interaction which go on in the eye.

The processes of the amacrine cells end in the inner synaptic layer. In Golgi preparations of the retina of some birds they branch at certain particular levels and spread laterally for long distances within the synaptic layer so that they impart to it a horizontal stratification. This same stratification also appears in sections treated to show acetylcholinesterase and this again is suggestive of acetylcholine transmission in these synapses. Amacrine cells are particularly numerous in retinas in which cones preponderate, e.g., in pigeons, and these retinas are the ones that show conspicuous stratification of acetylcholinesterase in the synaptic layer whereas, for example, the retina of the guinea pig which is very rich in rods, shows an even distribution of cholinesterase in the synaptic layer.

Neither the horizontal cells nor the amacrine cells have any processes running 'vertically' in the retina, i.e., in the direction of the main neural path.

THE OCULAR CIRCULATION. Thirty-three separate arteries enter the eyeball. The *retina* is supplied by the *arteria centralis retinae*, a branch of the ophthalmic artery. The central artery with its companion vein pierces the optic nerve about 1.25 cm. behind the eyeball and, bending sharply, runs forwards in the center of the nerve. Perforating the lamina cribrosa it appears inside the eyeball at the center of the optic disc. It immediately divides into two main branches which redivide to form a vascular network, the finer channels ending in a capillary plexus which extends outwards as far as the inner nuclear layer. The fovea itself is devoid of vessels. The *choroid, iris* and *ciliary body* are supplied by a separate system of vessels derived from the long and short posterior ciliary arteries, branches of the ophthalmic, and from the anterior ciliary arteries which are twigs of the lacrimal branch of the ophthalmic. The two long posterior ciliary arteries pierce the sclera a short distance from the optic nerve and, running forward on either side of the globe between the choroid and the sclera, anastomose with branches of the short posterior ciliary arteries and of the anterior ciliary artery to form a vascular ring (*circulus arteriosus major*) which encircles the periphery of the iris. Branches pass from this vascular circle along converging lines through the tissue of the iris to the pupillary margin; here they join to form a smaller arterial ring (*circulus arteriosus minor*). The short posterior ciliary arteries perforate the sclera around the optic nerve and supply the choroid and ciliary process. The anterior ciliary arteries and their companion veins pierce the globe a little behind the sclerocorneal junction. The blood is returned from the choroid by a system of veins in the outer choroidal layer. From their whorl-like arrangement they are termed the *vortex veins (venae vorticae)*. The smaller and medium sized vessels of this system become confluent to form four trunks which penetrate the sclera and appear on the surface of the globe equidistant from one another just behind its equator. These vessels and the anterior ciliary veins drain into the ophthalmic veins. The central vein of the retina empties into the cavernous sinus either directly or through one of the ophthalmic veins.

In man the pressure in the central artery of the retina is from 70 to 85 mm. Hg systolic and from 40 to 50 mm. diastolic. But owing to the presence of the intraocular fluid and the resistant nature of the sclerotic coat, pulsation of the retinal artery as observed by ophthalmoscopic examination is slight. The pressure in the retinal artery of the intact globe may be determined by the method of

Bailliart which consists in observing the vessel with the ophthalmoscope while a measured pressure is made upon the globe. Maximal pulsation is taken as indicating the diastolic level and the disappearance of pulsation as an index of the systolic pressure. There are several fallacies in this or any other indirect method, the results being far from reliable. The pressure in the central vein of the retina is around 25 mm. Hg. A venous pulse is also observed; it is attributed to the transmission of the impulse from the artery through the intraocular fluid to the veins. That is to say, with each expansion of the artery the veins (for a short distance proximal to where they leave the orbit) are compressed and an extra quantity of blood is ejected from the eyeball.

The lens and ciliary body are described in chapter 74, the visual pathway and ocular muscles in chapter 75.

### The Photochemistry of Vision

It was suggested as long ago as 1866 by Max Schultze that the retina is a duplex organ, dependent on the activity of its two types of receptor, namely rods and cones. This idea has been abundantly confirmed and it is now generally agreed (for reasons that will appear later) that at ordinary levels of illumination (*photopic conditions*) the activity of the cones predominates, but below an illumination of about 0.01 millilamberts (*scotopic conditions*) the cones cease to contribute; vision then becomes exclusively dependent on rods. This phenomenon obviously simplifies the problem of investigating certain aspects of the visual processes, particularly those which are associated with the action of the rods, since at low light intensities the cones no longer complicate the issue.

In 1922, Hecht and Williams amplified the earlier work of König and Abney, and measured the *absolute scotopic sensitivity* of the human eye to the different wave lengths of the spectrum under more thoroughly standardized conditions than had hitherto been used. Before such measurements are made the subjects must remain in total darkness for at least an hour (see p. 1342) and then the intensity of the light of each wave length, illuminating an area of standard size for a given time, and just causing a sensation of light in 50% of the trials is determined. In order to eliminate the effects of the dilation of the pupil which occurs in darkness, the subject views the test field through an artificial pupil of about 3 mm. diameter.

When the necessary calibrations of the light source, neutral filters, etc., have been made, a

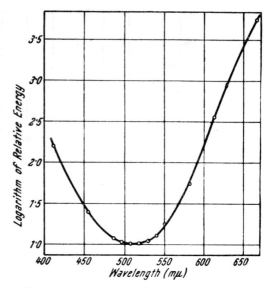

Fig. 72.15. Relation between energy for scotopic vision and wave length. (From Hecht & Williams.)

curve is plotted to relate the threshold energy in ergs of the light entering the eye to wave length (fig. 72.15). This *scotopic visibility curve* shows that under these conditions the threshold energy is least, i.e., the eye is most sensitive, at a wave length of about 507 m$\mu$. At this wave length the minimal energy entering the eye was found to be between 2.1 and 5.7 $\times$ 10$^{-10}$ ergs as measured at the cornea. On the other hand, the curve indicates that the threshold energy rises enormously beyond about 400 m$\mu$ and 650 m$\mu$, at the ends of the visible spectrum.

As already mentioned, the outer segments of the rods of some animals can be seen to contain a reddish pigment which bleaches on exposure to light. The pigment itself can be extracted from excised retinas, including that of man, by the action of bile salts, digitonin or by supersonic disruption of the rods. This visual purple or rhodopsin was first discovered by Boll in 1876 and extracted from the retina by Kühne in 1878. Such solutions are readily bleached by light within the visible range of wave lengths from about 380 m$\mu$ to 650 m$\mu$ and very much less readily by wave lengths beyond these limits. When the absorption of light by the pigment at different wave lengths is plotted against wave length, a curve is obtained which, when suitably corrected for absorption by breakdown products, etc., is strikingly similar to the visibility curve for the dark-adapted eye, although there are

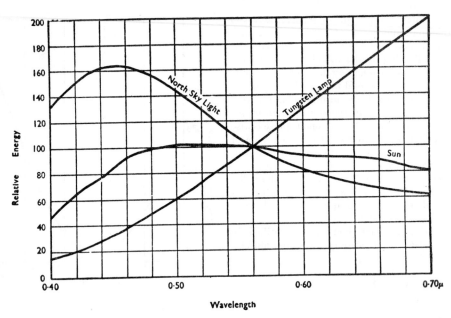

FIG. 72.16. Energy distribution curves for light from a gas-filled tungsten lamp, the sun, and average north sky light. (From Wright.)

slight differences in shape and in the positions of the maxima.

These observations clearly indicate that vision by the rods is fundamentally a photochemical reaction with visual purple as the photosensitive pigment, a hypothesis which is made even more probable by the fact that vision, up to about 0.03 sec., obeys the Bunsen-Roscoe law formulated for photochemical processes in general, namely, that for the production of a given photochemical effect a constant quantity of energy is required which can be distributed within certain limits by varying either the illumination or its duration. In other words, the product of the illumination (I) and the time of exposure (T) is constant, Energy $= k$IT.

Nevertheless, if the hypothesis is valid, then various discrepancies between the scotopic visibility curve and absorption spectrum of visual purple must be satisfactorily removed.

In making comparisons between the visual performance and the absorption spectrum of the supposed visual pigment there are several points to be considered. First, it is necessary to take note of the energy distribution of the light source used in each case and of its photochemical efficiency at different wave lengths.

Different sources of light have not the same spectral composition. For example, electric (incandescent tungsten) light is relatively rich in rays from the red end of the spectrum and poor in rays from the blue end; sunlight is much more uniformly distributed throughout the spectrum, whereas "north sky" light is more powerful in the blue region than in the red (Fig. 72.16). Fluorescent tubes generally have, in addition to a fairly uniform background, large peaks of radiation corresponding to the lines of the original mercury arc. It is customary, therefore, to express all visibility and absorption curves in terms of an "equal energy spectrum." This is a purely hypothetical concept. It means simply that the light source must be calibrated in terms of the energy which it emits at different wave lengths so that the sensitivity or absorption can be standardized for each wave length and so made independent of the particular form of illuminant. If, for example, the amounts of light required to reach threshold at, let us say, wave lengths 470 m$\mu$ and 550 m$\mu$ were determined by either the densities of neutral filters or by the apertures required in rotating sectors in the path of the light, first with incandescent electric light and second with "north sky" daylight the ratios would be entirely different in the two cases. In electric light, far less red would be required than in daylight. When, however, the data are corrected in terms of the actual energy required (as measured by a suitably calibrated photocell) the two sets of figures become comparable. All modern visibility, absorption and threshold measurements starting with those of Hecht and

Williams, make not only this correction but also one other similar and necessary correction. The photochemical effects on the pigment depend not so directly on the energy absorbed as on the number of quanta absorbed, so that the energy values at each wave length next have to be converted into quanta. Probably the most accurate scotopic visibility curve so far produced is that of Crawford (1949).

Radiant energy is expressed in *ergs*. The erg is a purely objective or physical unit, being quite independent of visual sensations. The energy is measured by means of a thermopile, bolometer or radiometer. Light is radiated in elementary units called *quanta*. The energy content of a quantum of light is proportional to the frequency of the radiation, $\nu$, and equal to $h\nu$, where $h$ is Planck's *constant of action*, $6.62 \times 10^{-27}$ erg $\times$ second. The frequency $\nu$ is equal to the velocity of light $(2.998 \times 10^{10}$ cm./sec.) $c$, divided by the wave length $\lambda$. The energy content of a quantum of light is, therefore, inversely proportional to the wave length of the radiation. Thus the quantum of green light is $3.84 \times 10^{-12}$ ergs and it has a greater energy content than one of orange or red. The *meter candle* is a unit which is in part subjective and in part objective. It is a measure of surface illumination, being defined as the light *incident* per second per sq. cm. of a surface placed at right angles to the beams from a standard (international) candle 1 meter distant (a standard candle is made of spermaceti, weighs $\frac{1}{6}$ lb., and burns 120 grains of wax per hour with a flame 45 mm. high). Illumination is measured by means of a photometer. If, for example, the illumination of a lamp is to be measured, a photometer is set up at this point, and a standard candle is moved until its light just matches that of the lamp. If the candle's distance in meters is $d$, then the surface illumination is $1/d^2$. The meter candle is thus a measure of the visual stimulus, not of the sensation itself. The quantity of light *reflected* from a perfectly diffusing surface (e.g., of magnesium oxide) 10,000 meter candles is termed a *lambert*; a millilambert is 1/1000 lambert. The *lumen* is the unit of *emitted* light (*luminous flux*). One lumen is the light emitted in a *unit of solid angle* by a uniform point source of 1 standard candle. A point source is regarded as occupying the center of a sphere; a unit solid angle is the angle subtended at the center of the sphere by an area on its surface equal to the square of the radius. The area of a sphere is $4\pi r^2$, therefore one stand-

ard candle emits $4\pi$ lumens. The intensity of a light source is expressed in lumens, i.e., the luminous flux emitted in any direction per unit of solid angle.

In recent years the photometric unit system has been revised. The unit of luminous intensity is now called the *candela* which is approximately equal to the obsolete "standard candle." A *full radiator* (black body) at the melting point of platinum emits 60 candelas per square centimeter. The popular unit of illumination is now the *lux* or meter-candle, which is the illumination falling on a surface placed one meter from a point source of one candela. The units of luminance have also altered. The internationally recognized unit of luminance is the *nit* or candela per square meter ($cd$/sq. mm.). The millilambert equals $10/\pi$ or 3.183 $cd$/sq. mm. The *stilb* is another unit of luminance sometimes used and it is a $cd$/sq. cm.

The unit of retinal illumination is called the *photon*, or, preferably, the *troland*. The amount of light which illuminates the retina depends not only upon the brightness of the object but also upon the size of the pupil. A troland is, therefore, defined as the illumination of the retina by light from a surface having the brightness of one standard candle per square meter, as seen through a pupil having an area of 1 sq. mm.

Such comparisons as those between the scotopic visibility curve and the absorption spectrum of rhodopsin are only legitimate when the data are fully corrected to an equal quantum spectrum. When this is done the two curves become practically coincident over a large part of the spectrum, but still they are not identical (Fig. 72.17). They still diverge somewhat widely and rather inconstantly in the short-wave (blue) part of the spectrum, but this discrepancy can be explained partly on physiological grounds. The amount of light which actually reaches the visual cells of the retina is of course only that which is not absorbed by the ocular structures on its way. It is therefore important to know the absorptive properties of the cornea, aqueous humor, lens, vitreous humor and the neural layers of the retina.

The cornea transmits rays from $\lambda$ 295 m$\mu$ to $\lambda$ 2,500 m$\mu$, but above 1,800 m$\mu$ the transmission is slight. Maximum transmission occurs at around 1,000 m$\mu$ and continues high at lower wave-lengths until the ultraviolet is reached. Absorption then becomes pronounced and is com-

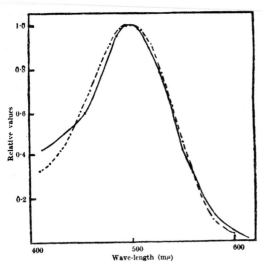

FIG. 72.17. Comparison of the absorption curve of pure visual purple (interrupted line) with the scotopic luminosity curve (continuous line) as obtained with an equal quantum spectrum. (After Ludvigh.)

plete at about 295 m$\mu$. The aqueous humor and vitreous body are somewhat less transparent than the cornea. All rays above 2700 m$\mu$ are absorbed by the aqueous humor and all above about 1,600 m$\mu$ by the vitreous. The lens absorbs all rays below 300 m$\mu$, or above 2500 m$\mu$; most of the rays longer than 1300 m$\mu$ are absorbed. Maximal transparency is between 400 and 1200 m$\mu$. That is, most of the rays outside this range are absorbed by the lens. Wave lengths between 350 m$\mu$ and 400 m$\mu$ cause fluorescence in the lens. The phenomenon of fluorescence, in general, is attributed to the transference of the energy of the incident radiations to particles of the substance absorbing them. The particles then act as independent light sources, emitting waves which are, for the most part, longer than the original radiation. Thus, the lens converts the harmful shorter waves to longer ones which are permitted to reach the retina. That wave lengths shorter than those which are transmitted by the lens are capable of stimulating the retina is shown by the fact that the visible spectrum is extended towards the blue end after removal of a lens of normal transparency. The lower limit of transparency of the lens rises with age. This is partly caused by increased pigmentation and partly by more scattering by the lens structures. In the aged it is opaque to rays shorter than about 400 m$\mu$. In the early stages of cataract the lower limit is around 450 m$\mu$.

When the corrections for loss in the optical media are made, the agreement between the two curves becomes very much closer. Not all the light which falls on the rods is absorbed by the rhodopsin. Indeed most of it (80%) passes through the rods to be absorbed by the pigment layers of the retina and the choroid; however, a small fraction is reflected back. When allowances are made for this, it can be stated with some confidence that the maximum sensitivity of the retina is such that only from 2 to 14 quanta of light need to be absorbed by the rods in a given area and within a given time for a sensation of light to be evoked. This means that a stimulated rod must give its signal to the bipolar cell when only a single quantum of light has been absorbed and as the result of the breakdown of a single molecule. Several such discharges must be combined (2 to 14) on to one optic nerve fiber to cause sufficient impulses for the stimulus to be perceived. The retina has thus achieved almost the highest sensitivity physically possible for the amount of photopigment which it contains. The extraordinary sensitivity of the retina to light may be expressed in simpler terms by saying that light emitted by a standard candle at a distance of nearly a mile would be visible if the air were perfectly transparent. Pirenne has made the interesting calculation that the mechanical energy of a pea falling from a height of 1 inch, if converted to luminous energy would be sufficient to cause a faint visual sensation "to every man that ever lived." The minimum quantity of light energy required to evoke a visual sensation increases progressively towards either end of the spectrum, being several thousand times greater for red and blue than for green light.

In this account of the determination of the absolute threshold at various wave lengths the field of view has been considered as being large and no restrictions have been placed on the part of the retina stimulated. With small fields, and with fixed positions on the retina the results in terms of threshold may be very different, and will be discussed later. Nevertheless, it is important to emphasize that processes of summation go on extensively in the retina. For example, when the field is small it can be shown that all the light falling within a certain area, the *summation area*, within a given time, the *summation time*, is summed in order to give the response. With very small fields the eye cannot distinguish between an intense point-source and a less intense but larger area of light, provided it falls within the limits of the summation area. Up to a certain size of field (which depends on the wave length of the light used and on the position on the retina) $IA$ is constant, where $I$ is the light intensity and $A$ is the area of the field. This is known as *Riccò's Law*. With larger fields and in the retinal periphery the relationship is much more nearly $I \times \sqrt{A} = K$ and this is known as *Piper's Law*. These are only approximations, and various other formulas have been suggested as describing the relationship in the extra-foveal area more accurately.

From what has already been said about the characteristics of vision as mediated by the rods, the essential visual process is the photochemical breakdown of rhodopsin, and reasons will be advanced for the belief that something very similar is the basis for vision by the cones.

Rhodopsin is one of a large class of photosensitive pigments which are formed by combination of a carotenoid derivative with a protein. Such pigments are widely distributed throughout the animal kingdom and indeed almost all the responses of animals (and also of plants) to light which have been investigated have been found to have carotenoid pigments involved in them at some stage.

Rhodopsin, itself, ($\lambda$ max. 497–500 m$\mu$) is formed from *retinene*$_1$ , which is the aldehyde of vitamin $A_1$ and as such is a derivative of $\beta$-carotene, the yellow pigment widely distributed in vegetables and fruits, e.g., carrots, tomatoes, oranges etc.

When it is acted upon by light, it first breaks down to yellowish substances, which were originally called *transient orange* and *indicator yellow*,

duce the photosensitive pigment and has to be isomerized before it can do so. The breakdown from rhodopsin to retinene appears to be fairly readily reversible, but if the light acts more thoroughly, the retinene changes to vitamin A, i.e., from the aldehyde to the alcohol, and metabolic processes involving the oxidizing systems, e.g., the dehydrogenases, so richly present in the ellipsoids of the inner segments of the rods, are required to reconvert the vitamin to retinene once more. Fig. 72.18 shows some of the main features of the process as it is at present understood. The nature of the link with the protein is still under investigation, but an increase in free SH-groups can be detected when rhodopsin yields retinene. There is now thought to be one chromophore group, i.e., one retinene molecule, in each unit of rhodopsin and the molecular weight of the whole has been estimated at about 40,000.

When the retinas of many fresh-water vertebrates are extracted in the dark with digitonin a variant of rhodopsin is found, and, in life, the retinas of these animals appear much more purple than the reddish retinas of most marine and terrestrial vertebrates. This variant, which is named *porphyropsin*, has its maximum sensitivity at about 523 m$\mu$ (*cf.* rhodopsin at 500 m$\mu$) and the photosensitivity of the eyes is correspondingly shifted towards the long-wave end of the spectrum. This pigment yields retinene$_2$ , differing from retinene$_1$ by the presence of an extra double bond in the ionone ring and yielding vitamin $A_2$ on further bleaching.

Vitamin $A_2$

the latter being so called because its color changes with pH. Eventually it forms the colorless retinene$_1$ and the protein. If retinene is extracted from bleached retinas, it can again be combined with a protein also extracted from rods and unspecifically called *opsin*, and a photosensitive rhodopsin is regenerated if the reaction takes place in the dark. There are several isomers of vitamin A and of retinene and for the regeneration of the photosensitive pigment the 11-cis isomer (neo-retinene b) is required. The all-trans form, in which vitamin A usually occurs, cannot pro-

The significance of this variation in the structure of the vitamin is still an unsolved problem. It appears to be connected in some way with the ionic content of the animal's environment. Although it may be some advantage to fish living in the deeper waters of the sea to have a pigment that is more sensitive to the blue rays—the only rays which penetrate through any depth of water—it is a little difficult to see that this can apply to the change in the character of the pigment in the eye of the bullfrog when this animal leaves the water and emerges on dry land.

When either of these retinenes, of the correct

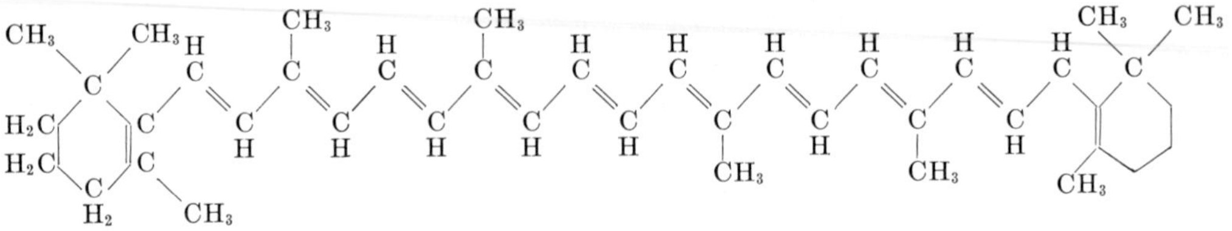

β Carotene

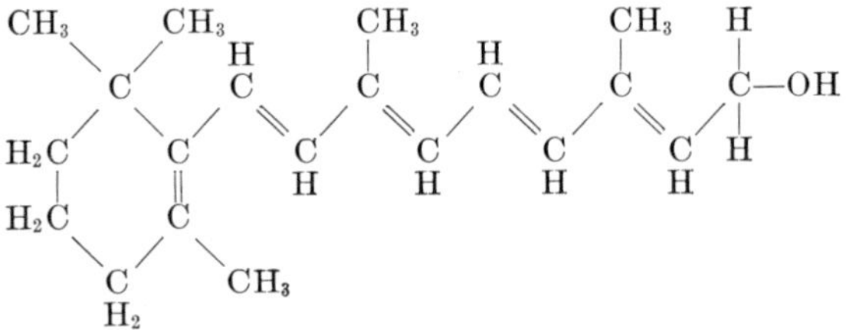

Vitamin A₁

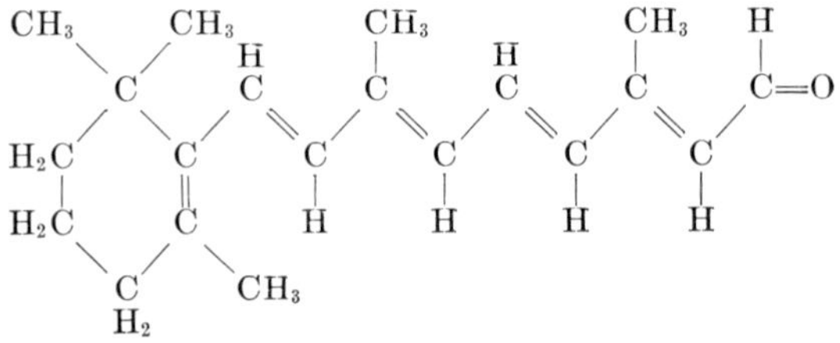

Retinene₁

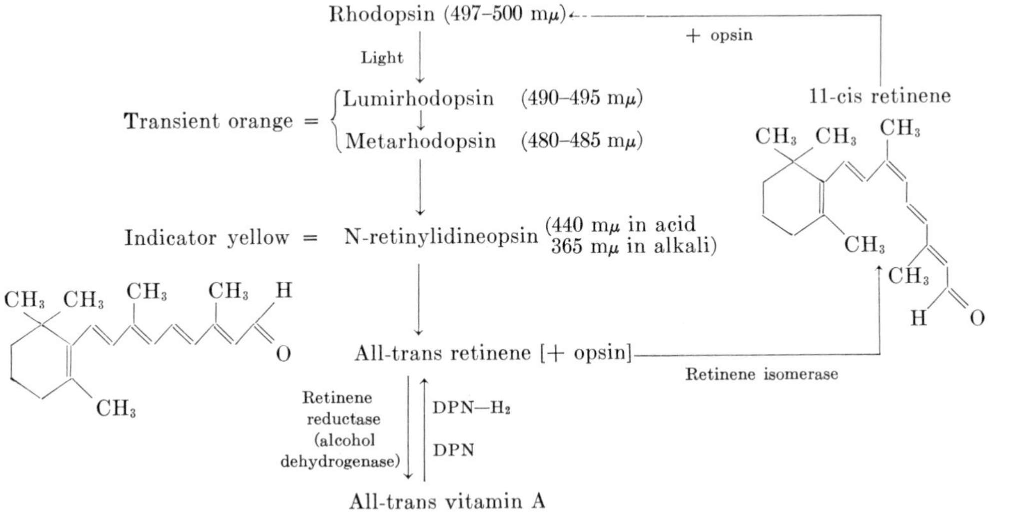

FIG. 72.18. Chart showing the main features of the Rhodopsin cycle. (After Morton and Pitt.)

isomeric form, is mixed in the dark with proteins suitably extracted from eyes in which cones can be seen, histologically, to preponderate, e.g., certain birds, then other photosensitive pigments are obtained whose maxima are located more towards the red end of the spectrum. For example, retinene₁ combined with the cone opsin from chicken retinas gives a violet pigment *iodopsin* with maximum sensitivity at about 560 mμ, whereas retinene₂ combined with 'opsin' from the eye of the chicken gives *cyanopsin*, with its maximum at about 609 mμ. The difference spectrum of iodopsin corresponds rather closely to the spectral sensitivity of the chicken, and pigments with maxima near 610 mμ also occur in nature, e.g., in turtles where cones again dominate the retina. It thus appears that there are four main classes of visual pigments related to the retinenes.

| Pigment | Composition | λ max.[3] | Animals |
|---|---|---|---|
| Rhodopsin | Retinene₁ + rod opsin | 500 mμ | Frog and mammals |
| Iodopsin | Retinene₁ + cone opsin | 560 mμ | Birds |
| Porphyropsin | Retinene₂ + rod opsin | 522 mμ | Fresh-water fish |
| Cyanopsin | Retinene₂ + cone opsin | 609 mμ | (? turtles) |

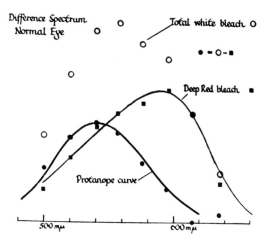

FIG. 72.19. Pigments in the fovea of the normal eye analyzed by bleaching with colored lights. The total pigment is made up of chlorolabe (protanope curve) and erythrolabe (deep red bleach) in the proportions shown. In the particular form of red-green color-blindness known as protanopia (see p. 1355) only one pigment (chlorolabe) appears to be present in the fovea. This has the difference spectrum indicated by the curve labelled "protanope curve"; this same curve (indicated by the filled circles) is obtained as the difference between the effects of bleaching with deep red light and with white light. (From Rushton.)

This is undoubtedly an oversimplification, in the sense that the opsins are not to be considered as single substances, and just as the properties of hemoglobinlike compounds may differ not only with changes in the prosthetic (hæm) group but also with the particular globin, so it appears that visual pigments may differ not only (as above) in the retinene part of the molecule, but also, more specifically, in the protein part also. Analysis of the retinas of a wide variety of animals suggests the existence of several families of pigments, each based on one of the four main ones indicated, but differing in λ max. by virtue of their different proteins. For example, rhodopsinlike pigments have been obtained with maxima lying between 483 mμ and 510 mμ. It is thus theoretically possible that almost any maximum between about 470 mμ and 620 mμ could be obtained by suitable variations of the molecules in the systems so far revealed. Nor does this rule out other possibilities for visual pigments, because other carotenoids, e.g., xanthophyll, are known to combine with proteins to produce pigments which are photosensitive. Ovoverdin, the blue-green pigment of lobsters and certain marine eggs, is a compound of the carotenoid astaxanthin and a protein and is unstable both to heat and light.

Although there is now no doubt that human rods contain and depend upon rhodopsin, the visual pigment or pigments in the human cones have not been extracted in the same way, although they must obviously be present in the living eye. The only objective evidence as to their nature comes from some recent work of exceptional precision by Rushton, who has made use of

[3] There are often small differences in the position of λ max. in all these pigments. They are probably dependent on the specific characters of the opsins.

the minute amount of light which is reflected back from the foveal region of the eye and which comes from the pigment layer and the choroid and has thus passed twice through the retina (once on its way in and once on its way out). He has observed that after exposing the eye to strong monochromatic lights the composition of the emergent light differs from the same light before the eye had been exposed; presumably this means that some pigment, probably that contained in the foveal cones, has been bleached or altered. Moreover, after bleaching with red light the composition of the emergent beam is different from its composition after bleaching with blue-green light or with white light. By this technique, which is neither as simple nor unfortunately as accurate as it sounds (because of the incredibly small amounts of pigment present and of the reflected light available), Rushton has demonstrated the probable existence of two cone pigments in the normal eye. These he has christened *chlorolabe* and *erythrolabe* because they absorb most actively in the green and in the red parts of the spectrum respectively. The estimates for their spectral sensitivities obtained as difference spectra are shown in figure 72.19 and their significance will be further considered in relation to color vision (see p. 1347).

## Electrical Records from the Eye and Optic Nerve

Electrical records from eyes fall into two main categories. The first includes the *electroretinogram*, which is a more or less generalized electrical response which the eye makes to illumination. It can be picked up from the living intact eye even in man and, like the electrocardiogram and electroencephalogram, has considerable value and importance in diagnosing abnormalities, but is too generalized a response to be easy to interpret in detail. It seems to have its origin primarily in the layer of rods and cones.

The second category includes the records that can be obtained from the eyes of animals by applying microelectrodes to individual cells or nerve fibers. These give much more precise information but cannot be obtained from man. From other animals they can only be obtained after anesthetization or decerebration, and, in any case, under rather unphysiological conditions, but nevertheless they do provide direct evidence as to how some of the neural elements in the retina behave.

RETINAL ACTION CURRENTS; THE ELECTRORETINOGRAM (ERG). When the cornea and the optic nerve or the posterior pole of the darkened eyeball are connected through a galvanometer, a current is set up with the cornea as the positive pole. A steady deflection of the galvanometer results. The cause of this resting potential is not clearly understood. When a light is thrown into the eye a series of potential changes is produced which can be recorded as a corresponding sequence of waves. These are the retinal action currents, the record is called an *electroretinogram* (fig. 72.20). A steady current is also set up when the inner and outer surfaces of the eyeball are connected.

Holmgren, the Swedish physiologist, was the first (in 1866) to demonstrate retinal action currents when the eye is stimulated by a beam of light. From then to the beginning of the present century they were studied by a number of investigators, including Dewar and McKendrick, Waller and Gotch. They were recorded with the string galvanometer by Einthoven and Jolly in 1908 and by Piper, by means of the capillary electrometer, in a series of studies from 1908 to 1911. In recent years with the development of more delicate methods of recording the subject has been reinvestigated by Chaffee, Bovie and Hampson, by Hartline, by Granit and his associates, and by numerous others.

In the earlier experiments, records were obtained from the surviving excised eye, and in many instances after removal of the anterior half of the globe, or from preparations in which dissection had caused a considerable degree of trauma. Although it was necessary to place one electrode directly upon the retina in order to prove the retinal origin of the currents, better results can be obtained by leaving the eye *in situ* and placing one electrode, which may take the form of a contact lens, upon the cornea of the illuminated eye and the other (indifferent electrode) upon the eye of the opposite side or upon any moist surface of the body. Typical electroretinograms are obtained in this way. In another method employed by Hartline and Adrian for man, a cotton-tipped electrode is applied directly to the illuminated eye after anesthetization with a 2% solution of holocaine; the indifferent electrode is placed in the mouth.

The most satisfactory preparation from which to record the electroretinogram is the decerebrate animal, since perfect immobilization is thus secured, as well as full pupillary dilation. The indifferent electrode is placed upon brain tissue on the proximal side of the decerebration cut, and the other electrode on the cornea. The recording instrument most commonly employed is the string galvanometer or some type of oscillograph, the currents being first conducted through a valve amplifier.

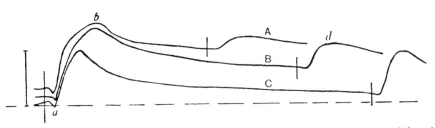

FIG. 72.20. Electroretinograms from the eye of the frog with three different durations of the stimulus. (*A*, 1 sec.; *B*, 1.5 sec.; *C*, 2 sec.) and at two different states of adaptation. In *A* and *B* the frog had been dark-adapted for 4 hr; in *C* it had been adapted to 1800 mc. Strength of stimulus, 1800 mc; calibration 0.673 mv. (From Granit.)

The latent period of the electroretinogram is shorter than that for any impulses which have ever been picked up directly from the retina. When an electrode is slowly and carefully passed through the retina large potential changes occur at about the level of the external limiting membrane and these are affected by illumination. For these and a variety of other reasons the electroretinogram is thought to originate in the layer of the rods and cones. During embryonic development the ERG first appears when the rod and cone layer differentiates and, later in life, damage localized to the rod and cone layer alters or abolishes the ERG. For this reason the electroretinogram is often a rather sensitive clinical sign of degeneration in the receptor layers.

The form of the electroretinogram varies with the state of adaptation of the eye and with the wave length of the light used to produce it (fig. 72.20). The large positive b-wave is probably mostly produced by the rods; it is largest in poor illumination and with blue light. In light-adaptation and with red light the negative a-wave becomes more conspicuous, and an earlier rise occurs in the b-wave often constituting a separate X-wave. This X-wave is absent in cases of total color-blindness and is much reduced in that form of red-green color-blindness which is known as protanopia (see p. 1355). This suggests that it is associated with the activity of those cones which are most sensitive to the red end of the spectrum. The ordinary response seems likely to be compounded of two diphasic variations each with an early negative phase followed by a later positive phase. The quicker response is associated with the cone mechanism, which also seems to have the greater negative component.

NERVE IMPULSES IN THE OPTIC NERVE. Action currents in the optic nerve were first investigated by Adrian and Matthews in the optic nerve of the conger eel. This animal was selected because it has a very long optic nerve and few nerve fibers in it, thus facilitating experimentation. The nerve was found to be almost 'quiet' in the dark but when light shone into the eye there was a burst of impulses after a latent period of 0.1 to 0.5 sec. according to the strength of the stimulus. After an initial high frequency of discharge, impulses continued at a decreased frequency for as long as the illumination lasted and then, when the light was turned off, another burst of impulses was recorded (the *off-effect*) (fig. 72.21).

*Nerve impulses in the eye of Limulus.* Since these early experiments much basic information about the relationship between stimulus and response in a photoreceptor unit has been learned from a study of the eye, not of a vertebrate, but of the king crab (*Limulus polyphemus*), mostly by Hartline and his colleagues. This compound eye is built on very different lines from that of the eye of all vertebrates in that it consists of numerous ommatidia, each comprising a group of 10–20 elongated retinula cells, with which one large central nerve cell is functionally connected, and this cell transmits impulses to the optic ganglion which lies at some distance from the photoreceptors. This eye is therefore somewhat simpler than that of any vertebrate, since the photoreceptors stimulate the central cell directly and impulses can be picked up from that cell or its nerve fiber, whereas in the eyes of vertebrates at least two synapses intervene between the receptor and the first place where impulses can be easily recorded. In the vertebrate eye, potential changes can be recorded in the rod and cone layer and probably even from single cells in it, but the first place where definite nerve impulses appear is in the ganglion-cell layer and the emergent nerve fibers. The evidence as to the nature of the conduction through the bipolar cell layer is somewhat conflicting. Some cells in it appear to produce spikes, but there are also large slow potentials. Limulus is therefore a much more suitable animal than any vertebrate would be in which to investigate the relationship between stimulus and response in a photoreceptor unit.

In Limulus, again, the nerve is practically silent in the dark. When a light is shone on the ommatidium there is a short latent period (about 0.1 sec.) and then the frequency of impulses in the neural discharge varies with the intensity of the stimulus and with the state of adaptation of the eye, i.e., on whether the eye has recently been exposed to light (fig. 72.22). The ommatidium, like the receptors in the human eye, can also be stimulated mechanically or electrically and it is interesting to note that the latent period in electrical stimulation is shorter than it is for stimulation by light. Presumably the photochemi-

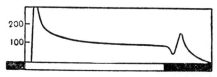

FIG. 72.21. Curve of frequencies of impulses in optic nerve. Duration of stimulus indicated by space in the base line (several seconds). (After Adrian & Matthews.)

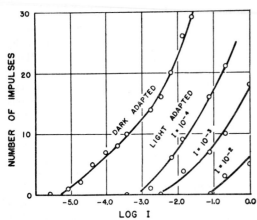

FIG. 72.22. Number of impulses in single nerve fibers in the eye of Limulus in response to test flashes (0.01 sec. duration) of different intensities (abscissae) given when the eye was adapted to darkness or to three different light intensities. (From Hartline & McDonald.)

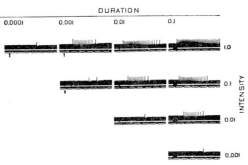

FIG. 72.23. Oscillograph records of impulses from a single optic nerve fiber of Limulus caused by brief flashes of light of varying intensity and duration. Note that the frequency of the impulses is a function of the product of these two variables. When the products are equal, the frequency of the impulses is virtually the same. (After Hartline.)

cal changes take time to complete. The amplitude of the impulses, as in other nerve fibers is constant (pp. 1125, 1126) and independent of the strength of the stimulus. As in the eel, the onset of illumination produces a high initial frequency, which rather rapidly dies down to a slower and relatively constant frequency. With short flashes, the impulse frequency varies with the product of the duration of the flash and its intensity, i.e., with the total amount of photochemical change, and thus this system also obeys the Bunsen Roscoe law (fig. 72.23). Within a limited time, therefore, it is possible to record a given frequency of impulses either by using an intense flash of short duration or a longer flash of lower intensity. The summation time, within which this is possible is about 0.2 sec.

The retina of Limulus shows considerable powers of adaptation and becomes more sensitive, discharging more impulses at a higher frequency for a given stimulus, when it has previously been kept in the dark.

Similarly, when the eye is placed in darkness and the intensity of light which will just produce a single impulse is measured, it is found that the necessary intensity falls rapidly at first and then more slowly and the ommatidium increases its sensitivity continuously and asymptotically for a period of about an hour. This is an important observation in any consideration of the mechanism for the rather similar phenomenon which occurs in the human eye when the subject remains in the dark and where the possibility of the adaptation occurring in the neural mechanism of the retina has to be considered. The relationship between impulse frequency and strength of the stimulus at different states of adaptation in the ommatidium of Limulus is shown in figure 72.22.

Under constant background conditions, and with a given duration of flash the frequency of impulses in the initial discharge varies more nearly with the logarithm of the intensity of the stimulus than with its intensity directly. This does not apply at very low intensities, near the threshold, nor at very high intensities, but over several $\log_{10}$ units in the middle range of intensities the logarithmic relationship is approximately true. Very much the same remarks apply also to the frequency of the sustained discharge, but the frequencies are then much lower.

If monochromatic light is used, it is found that the frequency of discharge varies with the wave length. By using different intensities of light of different wave lengths it is possible to elicit any given frequency of impulses and when these measurements of intensity are recorded for the different wave lengths it is found that the lowest intensity occurs at about 500 m$\mu$ and the curve obtained is almost identical with that obtained by plotting the light intensities necessary to reach threshold in the dark-adapted human eye (fig. 72.24). The probability is therefore very high that the ommatidium in Limulus depends on the same pigment (rhodopsin) and on the same photochemical process as does the human rod. The information obtainable from Limulus is therefore directly relevant to human vision and can be used in trying to analyze the process involved in the much more complex system of the human retina from which direct information of the same type cannot be obtained.

In Limulus it is clearly impossible for the animal to distinguish between the wave length and the intensity of a light on the basis of the information supplied by the frequency of impulses in a single optic nerve fiber. A given frequency of impulses can arise from stimulation by a low intensity of light to which the ommatidium is very sensitive (e.g., green) or by a high intensity of a light to which it is rather insensitive (e.g., red or violet) and, without further assistance from some other independent source, there can be no means of distinguishing between the two stimuli.

All that has been said so far about Limulus has referred to the stimulation of a single ommatidium. However, if a neighboring ommatidium is stimulated simultaneously, then there is some interaction between the two. They inhibit each other, and the more so the nearer they are together in the eye. Each gives a response which is less than it would give if it were stimulated separately and the impulse-frequencies are almost directly subtractive. The activity of each ommatidium is then the resultant of its own direct excitation and the inhibition exerted upon it by ommatidia simultaneously stimulated in its immediate neighborhood. An interesting example of the effects of this lateral inhibition is seen when three ommatidia more or less in line are investigated. If the first ommatidium ($A$) is stimulated alone it gives a response ($a$). When the second ommatidium ($B$) is simultaneously stimulated the response of the first falls to some value ($a - kb$), where $b$ is the initial response of receptor $B$ and $k$ is a factor depending on the distance between receptors $A$ and $B$. If now receptor $C$ is stimulated in such a way that it tends to inhibit $B$ but is too far away from $A$ to affect the response of $A$ directly, then the response of $A$ rises owing to the decreased inhibition exerted upon it by $B$, whose response has fallen from $b$ to ($b - lc$) because of the inhibitory effect of $C$ ($c$ is the original response of $C$ and $l$ is again a constant depending on the distance between $B$ and $C$). The response of $A$ is then something more like $a - k(b - lc)$, so that the effect of stimulating the third ommatidium is to increase the response from the first.

Since in such systems the interaction is mutual, the relationship is expressed by the pair of simultaneous equations:

$$R_a = E_a - K_{ab} (R_b - R^o{}_b)$$
$$R_b = E_b - K_{ba} (R_a - R^o{}_a)$$

where the subscripts $a$ and $b$ designate the respec-

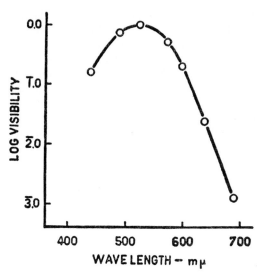

FIG. 72.24. Visibility curve for a single visual cell in the eye of Limulus. (From Graham & Hartline.)

tive receptor units, $R$ is the final response, $E$ is the response of the receptor when stimulated alone and $K$ is the coefficient of the action of the one receptor on the other, which, as stated earlier, is at least partly dependent upon the distance separating the two receptors. $R^o$ is the minimum response required to initiate the inhibition.

These observations on this relatively simple eye are clearly of the utmost importance in showing that the units are not entirely independent of each other and that there is mutual inhibition occurring between them. How this inhibition is brought about is not yet certain. There is a network of fine interlacing fibers at the base of the ommatidia which could be responsible, but it is not known how the impulse frequencies are caused to interfere in this curiously subtractive manner. The interference must occur at a stage when the stimulus has already been converted to something that varies more nearly with the logarithm of the intensity of the stimulus than with the intensity directly. This principle of mutual interference may obviously have important implications not only in relation to the performance of the human eye but also to other sense organs and parts of the central nervous system.

*Nerve impulses in the eyes of vertebrates.* When the lens and cornea of the eye of a vertebrate (e.g., the decerebrate cat, rabbit or monkey) are removed, microelectrodes can be gently applied to the inner surface of the retina. Provided that Ringer's solution is not used, but only the natural fluids of the eye itself, the isolated eye of the frog may be used in the same way. Under these conditions, single uniform spike-potentials can be obtained, and the majority of these spikes can be localized to the discharges from the large ganglion cells. The frequency and distribution of the impulses that are obtained are very variable and do not always bear any easily discernible relationship to the strength and duration of the stimulus. It seems to be fairly clear that the synaptic connections in the retina itself carry out a large amount of coding and sifting of the information provided by the photoreceptors.

Sometimes, even in complete darkness there may be an almost continuous and not necessarily regular discharge of impulses, and there is some indication from the results of decerebrate preparations in the cat that the better the preparation the more of this resting discharge is obtained. Presumably therefore it is something that is normal to the eye of the cat at least. The application of a stimulus of light may either increase or decrease the resting discharge. At other times, ganglion cells remain silent unless they are stimulated by light falling on the retina in their neighborhood. In this case the response may be very like those recorded in Limulus and correspond reasonably closely with the strength and duration of the stimulus. This type of discharge has been called the *on-discharge* and the fiber has been called an *on-fiber.* Alternatively the cell or fiber may give a rapid discharge of impulses when the light is turned on, then may go silent or at least reduce its frequency of discharge very considerably while the light remains on, and then give another outburst when the light is turned off. This is the *on-off type of discharge.* Thirdly it may sometimes happen that the on-effect is missing altogether and the cell only responds when the light is turned off. Such a unit is called an *off-fiber.*

There is considerable evidence that on-off- and off-effects are the result of inhibitory processes occurring within the retina itself. Nevertheless it has to be remembered that in the eye of the mollusk *Pecten* some nerve fibers yield only off-effects and in this eye the histological structure is such that the opportunity for inhibitory process to occur would appear to be small. It is of course conceivable that the build-up of rhodopsin in darkness could be turned to advantage as a means of exciting a receptor unit in the same way as its breakdown in light has been used.

From a study of the relationship between the wave length of the stimulating light and the character of the response obtained, there is strong evidence that some of these inhibitory effects are caused by interaction between the pathways in the retina activated by rods on the one hand or cones on the other. On-off-units and pure off-units are in general far more frequent in those retinas where there is a good mixture of rods and cones than in the more purely rod-retinas such as that of the guinea pig. However, this interaction between dissimilar units cannot account for the whole phenomenon, because there is, as in Limulus, much evidence for the existence of lateral inhibition when only one class of receptors, in this case rods, are in action. If, for example, a light source is so arranged that it can deliver into the retina just that intensity of monochromatic light at each wave length which would be necessary to stimulate a receptor that was dependent on rhodopsin only to give a standard and constant response, i.e., with intensities corresponding to the ordinates of figure 72.15, then a ganglion cell which gave the same response at all wave lengths would clearly be one which, under the conditions of the experiment, was being activated by receptors dependent on rhodopsin only. If some other class of receptor intervened, e.g., the cones, then the rhodopsin-equated stimulus would no longer give a uniform response from the ganglion cell throughout the spectrum. It is therefore possible to pick out ganglion cells whose response is apparently confined to rhodopsin-activated receptors (rods). Even among these units there may be "on-," "on-off-" and "off-"elements and, what is even more important, there are some which respond to low light intensities with a pure on-effect, then as the intensity is raised they change to the on-off type and with increasing intensity again become more and more "off," until finally they respond only whenever the light is turned off. If, as seems probable, these effects arise by some sort of lateral inhibition in the retina, then such interaction must occur as the result of the stimulation of one type of receptor only, i.e., the rod, and it would seem to be the direct counterpart of the lateral inhibition discussed in relation to the responses in Limulus.

Further information on the nature of events within the retina itself has been gained by studying the responses of single ganglion cells, not to general illumination of the retina as in the above examples, but to localized stimulation by small points of light (about 0.1 mm. or less in radius). By this means it is possible to investigate directly the area of the retina which feeds its information on to any particular ganglion cell, or in other words to determine in an objective way the *receptive field* of that cell. Histological preparations indicated that such receptive fields might have a diameter of about 1 mm and the electrical records confirm this conjecture. Around the center of the receptive field there may be a plateau of high sensitivity (0.6 mm. in diameter in some peripheral ganglion cells, 0.2 mm. in those nearer the center of the eye). This is surrounded by an area with much lower sensitivity. The response in the central area may be an on-effect, an on-off-effect or even an off-effect, which is a point of some interest in relation to the earlier discussion of the nature of these effects. Even more interesting, however, is the fact that stimulation in the periphery of the field, or even of an area outside it, may alter the response from the center. Thus as with larger stimuli, the ganglion cells can be subdivided into on-center, off-center and on-off-center cells and it is again noteworthy that the threshold for evoking the on-effect is not necessarily the same as that for evoking the off-effect and, moreover, they are not constantly related to each other in different parts of a receptive field.

If two spots of light, each giving a subliminal stimulus are applied simultaneously to the receptive field of a single ganglion cell the effects are usually additive, indicating that Riccò's law is followed within the receptive field. On the other hand when one of the spots falls outside the receptive field of a ganglion cell that cell may be inhibited. This inhibition from external sources does not usually affect off-center cells but strongly affects on-off center cells, in which case the on- and the off-responses may react differently. In on-off units the inhibitory effects of peripheral stimuli may be produced from within the margins of the receptive field itself. These rather elaborate and complicated results may help to emphasize the complexity of events within the retina. This complexity is all too easily overlooked in attempts to correlate stimulus and response in visual phenomena. Even so it should be remembered that, small as are these stimuli which have been used to explore the receptive fields of ganglion cells, they still cover hundreds of photoreceptors.

By the insertion of microelectrodes into the unopened eye of the decerebrate cat, where incidentally all effects of light are superimposed on a continuous spontaneous discharge of impulses, the effects of changes in the adaptation of the eye on isolated ganglion cells have been studied. It is clear from these results that many ganglion cells receive information from both rods and cones. For example, the wave length of maximum sensitivity of a cell may change with the light intensity, indicating a change-over from the preponderance of one type of receptor to that of another (see Purkinje shift, p. 1343). Dark-adaptation curves, i.e., curves relating the intensity of the threshold stimulus to time in the dark, indicate events arising in both cones and rods. If red light (to which the cones are relatively more sensitive than the rods) is used, a simple curve is obtained and the threshold does not sink as far as if green light were used when the curve acquires a knee in it which probably indicates the point at which the rod mechanism begins to determine the threshold rather than the cones (see p. 1343). Even in the thoroughly dark-adapted state both on- and off-center units are found, and, in both cases, an increase in the area of receptive field stimulated lowers the threshold, but, in this state, stimulation outside the receptive field no longer exerts inhibitory effects. This change in the effects of stimulation outside the receptive field between the dark-adapted and light-adapted states takes place at lower levels of illumination than that at which the cones are thought to operate, so it is probably a change in retinal organisation rather than the introduction of a different type of receptor. The receptive field becomes smaller in light-adaptation and this effect is probably caused by the increasing effects of lateral inhibition rather than by a decrease in the area of effective synaptic connections made by the ganglion cell. As emphasized already, the lateral inhibition, while it may be partly caused by cones is certainly not entirely dependent on their action.

The results obtained by such electrical recordings in the retinas of various animals are obviously of the highest importance to the understanding of the physiology of the retina. Nevertheless, at this stage, the utmost caution is required in their interpretation; much further experimental analysis with improved methods will be needed before the relationships between receptors, bipolars and ganglion cells are understood. Apart from some of the more complex situations outlined above, the meaning to be attached to on-center cells and off-center cells is still quite obscure, so also is the significance to be attached to stimulation of the dendrites of a ganglion cell as opposed to stimulation of its cell body. When constant currents are passed through the retina it has been found possible to alter a ganglion cell which normally responds only at "on" to one which responds only at "off," and *vice versa*.

Finally there exist many ganglion cells in the retina of the cat which apparently contribute nothing in the way of trains of impulses (or at least nothing which has so far been picked up). It is conceivable that they do not exert their effects by means of measurable impulses, but perhaps in the form of slow potentials, electrotonic effects or even chemically. Any analysis of retinal function based on the responses which have so far been recorded, and on those alone, is likely to be extremely incomplete and probably fallacious. Impulses have not been recorded with certainty from the receptors themselves except possibly in some fish but considerable potentials develop in or near the rod and cone layer during illumination as noted in connection with the electroretinogram. Intracellular recording from what are either large receptors or horizontal cells present in certain fish have recently been made and the results may be of great significance in relation to color vision (see ch. 75).

## REFERENCES

ADRIAN, E. D. J. Physiol., 1945, **104**, 84; 1946, **105**, 24.

ADRIAN, E. D. AND MATTHEWS, R. J. Physiol., 1927, **63**, 378; **64**, 279; 1928, **65**, 273.

ARMINGTON, J. C. J. Opt. Soc. Am., 1952, **42**, 393.

BARLOW, H. B. J. Physiol., 1953, **119**, 58, 69.

BARLOW, H. B., FITZHUGH, R. AND KUFFLER, S. W. J. Physiol., 1957, **137**, 327, 338.

BRINDLEY, G. S. J. Physiol., 1956, **134**, 360; 1958, **140**, 247.

CHAFFEE, E. L., BOVIE, W. T. AND HAMPSON, A. J. Opt. Soc. Am., 1923, **7**, 1.

DE ROBERTIS, E. J. Biophys. Biochem. Cytol., 1956, **2**, 319.

CRAWFORD, B. H. Proc. Phys. Soc. (London), 1949, **62B**, 321.

DEWAR, J. AND MCKENDRICK, J. G. Tr. Roy. Soc. Edinburgh, 1873, p. 141.

EINTHOVEN, W. AND JOLLY, W. A. Quart. J. Exper. Physiol., 1908, **1**, 373.

GRAHAM, C. H. AND HARTLINE, H. K. J. Gen. Physiol., 1935, **18**, 917.

HARTLINE, H. K. Am. J. Physiol., 1938, **121**, 400; 1940, **130**, 690, 700.

HARTLINE, H. K. AND GRAHAM, C. H. J. Cell. & Comp. Physiol., 1932, **19**, 277.

HARTLINE, H. K. AND MCDONALD, P. R. J. Cell. & Comp. Physiol., 1947, **30**, 225.

HARTLINE, H. K. AND RATLIFF, F. J. Gen. Physiol., 1957, **40**, 357.

HARTLINE, H. K., WAGNER, H. G. AND RATLIFF, F. J. Gen. Physiol., 1956, **39**, 651.

HECHT, S., SHLAER, S. AND PIRENNE, M. H. J. Gen. Physiol., 1942, **25**, 819.

HECHT, S. AND WILLIAMS, R. E. J. Gen. Physiol., 1922, **5**, 1.

HOLMGREN, G. Centralbl. med. Wissensch., 1871, p. 423 (cited by Waller).

HUBBARD, R. AND WALD, G. J. Gen. Physiol., 1952, **36**, 269.

KUFFLER, S. W. J. Neurophysiol., 1953, **16**, 37.

KÜHNE, W. Untersuch. physiol. Inst. Heidelberg, 1883, **2**, 89.

LUDVIGH, E. Arch. Ophth., 1938, **20**, 713.

LYTHGOE, R. J. J. Physiol., 1937, **89**, 331.

ØSTERBERG, G. Acta ophth., 1935, Suppl. 6.

RIDLEY, F. Brit. J. Exper. Path., 1930, **11**, 217.

RUSHTON, W. A. H. Nature, 1949, **164**, 743; 1957, **179**, 571; 1958, **182**, 690.

RUSHTON, W. A. H. AND CAMPBELL, F. W. Nature, 1954, **174**, 1096.

SCHULTZE, M. Arch. mikr. Anat., 1866, **2**, 175.

SJÖSTRAND, F. S. J. Cell. & Comp. Physiol., 1953, **42**, 15, 45.

STILES, W. S. Proc. Roy Soc., London, ser. B., 1937, **123**, 90.

STILES, W. S. AND CRAWFORD, B. H. Proc. Roy. Soc. London, ser. B., 1933, **112**, 428.

WALD, G., BROWN, P. K. AND SMITH, P. H. Science, 1953, **118**, 505.

WALLER, A. D. Quart. J. Exper. Physiol., 1909, **2**, 169.

*Monographs and Reviews*

See Chapter 73

# 73

## INTENSITY DISCRIMINATION AND THE DUPLICITY THEORY OF VISION; COLOR VISION; VISUAL ACUITY; FLICKER; AFTER IMAGES; OPTICAL ILLUSIONS

### Intensity Discrimination and the Duplicity Theory of Vision

With this background of more or less objective data concerning the structure of the retina, the distribution of its cells, the nature of its pigments and the electrical records obtainable from retinal structures, it will now be appropriate to examine retinal performance and the so-called psychophysical aspects of vision.

One of the most remarkable features of the human eye is the incredibly wide range of intensities of light over which it is capable of discriminating differences in intensity. This is much the same as saying that the eye performs almost equally well in light of very different absolute intensities. Basically the two main problems of vision are those connected with *intensity-discrimination* on the one hand and with *hue-discrimination* on the other.

At its most sensitive, the eye can detect light when only a very few quanta are absorbed by the retina and, at the other extreme, it can still detect differences in intensity when the light is more than 10,000,000 times stronger than the minimum required to reach its absolute threshold. It will be noticed that the word intensity has so far been used in this discussion, and not brightness. The reason for this is that brightness is a purely subjective phenomenon and is always more or less relative either to what has gone before or to what is simultaneously presented to the eye. It is well known that when black is placed against white, or *vice versa*, they set one another off; the black looks blacker and the white appears to be a purer white than if either were placed against a gray or colored ground. Gray also appears darker against a white than against a black ground (fig. 73.1). This is known as *simultaneous contrast*. Another example will illustrate a different aspect of the same phenomenon. If one eye, after being kept in darkness,

views a field whose *luminance* or luminous intensity is 3 millilamberts while the other eye continues to view a field whose luminance is 15,000 millilamberts the two fields may give the same sensation of brightness, even though one has 5000 times the physical intensity of the other. In other words, the eye as a whole adapts to changes of intensity in much the same way as it was shown in the last chapter that the individual units in the eye of Limulus could adapt. It is largely a consequence of this capacity for adaptation that the eye can work efficiently over such wide ranges of intensity, and this is combined with the fact that there are two distinct mechanisms, the rod and the cone mechanisms, which share the intensity range. Cones predominate at higher intensities whereas the rods begin to take over when the intensity falls below about 0.01 millilamberts. This essential duality of the retinal receptor system was recognized as long ago as 1866 by Max Schultze and the suggestions for the division of labor between the two systems have become collectively known as

Fig. 73.1. Illustrating contrast (Hering). Observe through tissue paper.

1341

the *Duplicity Theory of Vision* largely connected with the name of von Kries.

*Intensity discrimination.* This faculty was first investigated by Bouguer in 1760 and later by Weber (1834) and Fechner (1858). The latter observer found that, when the light intensity is gradually increased, the least change in illumination which can be perceived by the subject occurs in a series of steps. This relationship is expressed in the Weber-Fechner law which is applicable not only to vision but to other senses as well. The law states that the least perceptible difference between a series of stimuli is in each instance a certain constant fraction of the preceding stimulus. For example, let us suppose that for vision the fraction is $1/100$ and the initial illumination is 100 candles. Then, if the light of one more candle is added, the difference in illumination will be recognized; that is, the light of 101 candles is perceived to be greater than that of 100. If there were 1000 candles to start with, 10 more would need to be added before any difference could be noticed. If, therefore, the logarithms of the intensities are plotted (abscissas) against the least perceptible differences in sensation (ordinates) a straight line should result. The law may be stated in another way, namely, that in order to cause a series of equal increments in sensation the strength of the stimulus must increase in geometrical proportion. Or again, the added intensity ($\Delta I$) necessary to cause a just perceptible difference in sensation ($\Delta S$) bears a constant ratio ($\Delta I/I$) to the preceding intensity (I). Thus, $\Delta S = K (\Delta I/I)$.

When the logarithms of the light intensity are plotted against the just perceptible differences, the curve shown in fig. 73.2 is obtained. The curve is composed of three parts. It is only section A representing the relationship at moderate light intensities that accords even approximately with the Weber-Fechner law. At intensities below and above this limited range marked deviations from the law occur (sections B and C). The whole curve covers a range from the lowest intensity to one of dazzling strength and comprises 572 steps of just perceptible differences. Starting with the very lowest intensities, e.g., 0.0000484 millilamberts (I) the least absolute increment of the stimulus which is effective ($\Delta I$) is very small (König and Brodhun's data), namely, 0.000031 millilamberts, and increases progressively as the intensity rises, so that at an illumination of 147.0 $\Delta I$ has a value of 3.803 ml. The fraction $\Delta I/I$, therefore, is not constant, nor does it show a continuous change in one direction, for it diminishes from about $2/3$ at the lowest intensity to about $1/65$ at moderate ranges and then rises again to $1/25$ at the highest intensity. More recent observations indicate that this increase with higher intensities does not occur if the eye is fully adapted to the basic level of intensity (I), the fraction remaining at the lowest value even though the illumination is unpleasantly intense (see Craik). Hecht considers that the low intensity part of the curve (B) represents rod function and the high intensity portion (C), the activity of the cones. The cones are therefore more sensitive to *differences* in illumination than the rods, although their threshold for light perception (intensity threshold) is higher.

It is interesting to compare these observations with those obtained by Hartline on the eye of Limulus (see p. 1335 and fig.72.22). Impulse frequency, upon which intensity discrimination presumably depends, was there found to be rather closely related to the logarithm of the intensity of the stimulus over quite a wide range of intensity levels. However, the state of adaptation of the eye was also found to be a very important factor in determining the frequency of impulses. Thus, in these psychophysical measurements of intensity-discrimination, the changing state of adaptation of the eye certainly cannot be neglected and probably it is a very large factor in determining the apparent value of $\Delta I/I$ more particularly in the rod part (B) of the curve in figure 73.2.

## DARK ADAPTATION

The process of dark adaptation is clearly seen when a subject enters a dark or dimly lighted room after being out in ordinary daylight. In the light, he can see objects clearly and in color. He can read small print and, if tested with a spectroscope, he would find the yellow-green part of the spectrum to be the brightest. On entering a very dimly lighted room his pupils dilate, but at first he can see nothing. After a time, however, the room appears to him to become brighter and he may be able to discern large shapes. His vision

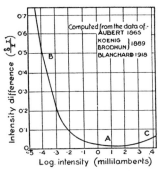

FIG. 73.2. Curve of the intensity discrimination of light. (After Hecht.)

will continue to improve for a period of half an hour or more. Nevertheless, if the light intensity is below that which will excite his cone mechanism, the room will only be seen in terms of light and shade and it will be without color; he will not be able to read small print and the spectroscope will show that he now considers the blue-green region of the spectrum to be its brightest part; he will be completely blind to the red end of the spectrum (see Plate II). This change in the relative sensitivity of the eye to different wavelengths which occurs at the lower ranges of intensity is known as the *Purkinje shift* and accounts for the well known phenomenon that, at twilight in a garden, the red flowers appear black, whereas the blue flowers appear grey or white. In this process of dark adaptation there are four main factors at work in the human eye; (a) dilation of the pupil, (b) change-over from cone to rod vision, (c) adaptation of the actual receptors, probably involving the regeneration of rhodopsin, and (d) reorganization of the neural connections in the retina with a probable reduction in the extent of lateral inhibition.

In other animals, other factors may also enter into the process. For example, in the frog there is retraction of the pigment from between the photoreceptors; in the catfish the rods and the cones interchange their positions so that the inner segments of the rods shorten and the outer segments approach the external limiting membrane, whereas the cones move in the opposite direction toward the pigment layer; in the cat, which can become about eight times more sensitive in the dark than the human being, the reflecting tapetum of the retina adds its effect to the relatively greater size of the pupil.

The process of dark adaptation is usually followed experimentally by presenting the subject, in an otherwise completely dark room, with an illuminated field, often in the form of a Landolt C or other similar test letter, at decreasing light intensities. The Landolt C (see p. 1366) is merely an illuminated field in the form of the letter C which can be placed with the opening of the C up, down, or to the right or left, and the subject has to report on the position of the opening. The field is presented in brief flashes at different intensity levels; the threshold is determined by the lowest level at which it is just visible to the subject and at which his diagnoses are more than 50 per cent correct. A curve is then plotted, relating the threshold intensities to the time in the dark. This is known as the *dark adaptation curve*. When

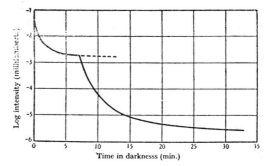

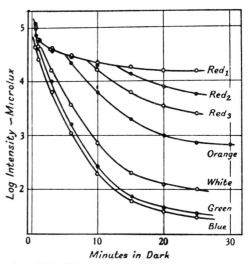

Fig. 73.3. (*Upper*) Dark adaptation curve. The dotted line—continuation of the upper section of the curve—is the cone adaptation curve obtained when a centrally fixated red stimulus is used. The lower part of the curve indicates rod adaptation. Only the upper part of the curve and its extension is obtained in night blindness. (After Rawdon-Smith.) (*Lower*) Dark adaptation curves plotted for different wave-lengths. Only extreme red (Red₁) confines the stimulus to the cones. (From Hecht, after Kohlrausch.)

a white light is used, a curve with a definite break or "knee" in it is obtained (fig. 73.3). The threshold drops (i.e., the sensitivity rises) very quickly at first and after about five to seven minutes in the dark, it stabilizes for a time. It then drops suddenly again and does not reach a final steady state for about another 30 minutes, at which time the sensitivity will be found to be well over 100 times that achieved at the first plateau and possibly more than 10,000 times that at the start of the observations. In constructing such a curve the effects of the dilation of the pupil are eliminated by using an artificial pupil of about 3 mm. in diameter. Such dark-adaptation curves are

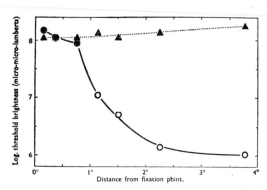

FIG. 73.4. Threshold values for extreme blue (small circles) and extreme red light (triangles) in various parts of the retina near the fovea. The full circles and triangles indicate that the lights give rise to sensations of color, the open circles indicate a colorless sensation. Diameter of test field subtends 10 minutes at the eye. (From Pirenne.)

purely relative and the absolute values obtained depend upon many factors, such as the area of the test stimulus, the position of the test stimulus on the retina, the duration of exposure of the test stimulus, the wave length of the test stimulus and the physical and mental condition of the subject including the extent and duration of his previous exposure to light.

If, instead of white light, the extreme red end of the spectrum is used, then the second drop in threshold does not occur and the absolute threshold is approached after about 10 minutes. Similarly if white light is used, but only a very small field subtending about 30 minutes is presented and also if a small red point-source is provided to assist the subject to fixate the test field on the central fovea, i.e., to help him to look straight at the test field and not allow his gaze to wander, then a curve precisely similar to that obtained with red light is again found. These two observations are interpreted to mean that vision is confined to the cone mechanism in each case and that the shoulder of the ordinary dark adaptation curve represents the threshold of the cone mechanism and the take-over point for the rods. The extent to which the rod threshold drops below this point, of course, varies with the wave-lengths used, in a manner which is directly related to the spectral sensitivity curve of rhodopsin, and the lowest thresholds are found with blue-green light. It is clear therefore from these curves that both rods and cones have the power to adapt, but the cones adapt much more quickly than the rods and they do not adapt to such low intensities. The absolute thresholds for red and blue stimuli at different positions on the retina are shown in

figure 73.4. It will be seen that the threshold for blue (rod threshold) is higher than that for red (cone threshold) in the fovea, but very much lower elsewhere. The threshold for red on the other hand is much more uniform over the retina, but is slightly lower in the fovea than elsewhere. The insensitivity of the foveal center under scotopic conditions, caused by the scarcity of rods and the yellow pigmentation in that area (figs. 73.5 and 73.6), is the reason why it is necessary to look slightly to one side of such a group of stars as the Pleiades when attempting to determine their number with the naked eye.

When the size of the field is reduced to such an extent that it is commensurate with the size of the receptor units, and spatial summation over an area of the retina is thereby eliminated, the process of adaptation is slower and the ultimate threshold reached is very little different in the periphery from its value in the fovea, which strongly suggests that the absolute thresholds of rods and cones themselves, as individuals, are not very different, and that quite a large part of the normal dark adaptation process is concerned with the sort of neural reorganization which was discussed in the last chapter (p. 1317). The other factor which is important in the process is the accumulation of rhodopsin in the rods, and presumably of the cone pigments in the cones although until recently there was no direct evidence for the latter. At one time it was thought that this regeneration of visual pigment would account for the whole process of adaptation but this now seems unlikely. As the result of measurements of the light reflected back from the fundus of the eye by extremely sensitive methods it is now possible to estimate the amount of rhodopsin actually present in the rods at any given stage of dark adaptation and to be certain that rhodopsin not only accumulates in the dark but also that it is not entirely bleached away under conditions of light adaptation. Similar changes in the amounts of light reflected from the fovea probably also indicate bleaching and regeneration of cone pigments (see p. 1333).

It is not at all clear what part, if any, rods play at photopic levels of light intensity. It is a little difficult to believe that they become entirely insensitive to light in the upper ranges of intensity, so long as they contain unbleached rhodopsin. If they do not contribute at all to photopic vision, this must be due either to the breakdown of the mechanism which connects the photochemical process with neural excitation or to some com-

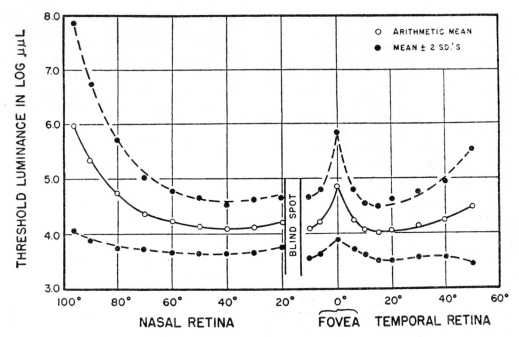

Fig. 73.5. The threshold for white light in different parts of the retina. The solid curve is the average curve for 101 subjects, 95% of whose measurements fall within the broken curves. (From Chapanis, after Sloan.)

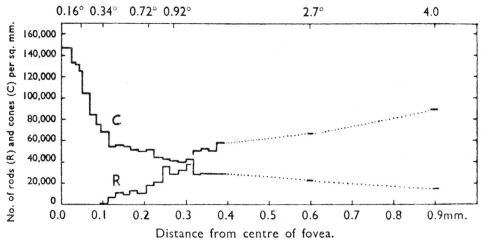

Fig. 73.6. The distribution of rods and cones near the center of the human retina. This figure obtained from histological preparations may be compared with figure 74.4, since blue light stimulates rods at threshold, and red light stimulates cones. (From Pirenne, after Østerberg.)

plete inhibition of their effects in the neural mechanism itself.

It is interesting to compare the figures for the thresholds for red and blue stimuli, since these are undoubtedly determined by the cone and rod mechanisms respectively, in the different parts of the retina. These figures may then be compared with the estimated distribution of the rods and cones themselves in the same areas. The relevant data are set out in figures 73.4 and 73.6. The more rods there are in a given area the lower the threshold for blue becomes. The threshold for red, i.e., of the cones, is not, however, affected so much by the density of the cones per unit area. Thus spatial summation is probably of far more importance in rod vision than in cone vision.

Occasionally, people are found who are described as night blind, meaning that they have very limited powers of dark adaptation (see fig. 73.3) and are unable to see at all when the light intensity falls much below that required for cone vision. In extreme cases of vitamin A deficiency, the threshold of the rods rises and the subject may then become completely night blind. This condition, when severe enough, may involve atrophy of the rods and of the pigment epithelium, and ultimately may involve destruction of the cones also. The eye, however, holds on to its vitamin for longer than most tissues in the body and the deficiency has to be very severe and of long duration before the visual symptoms appear. The congenital and progressive disease, known as retinitis pigmentosa, brings about similar retinal changes with similar effects, but in this case there is also an accumulation of melanin in the damaged tissues. Once again the cones may become involved at a later stage.

Among animals, the type of eye and retina which is found differs according to the way of life of the animal. Nocturnal creatures, e.g., the bat, the rat and the owl, have a preponderance of rods very often associated with a tapetum and a large pupil. Strictly diurnal animals, e.g., the pigeon and the lizard, have retinas with very few or even no rods. These observations are further indications of the essential duality of the retina, but it should be remembered that many animals which have a very heavy preponderance of rods in their retinas are by no means blind by day.

When a person comes out of a dark room into the light, the processes of dark adaptation are all reversed; the pupil constricts, the retina loses its sensitivity and the rhodopsin concentration is lowered, the spectral sensitivity-maximum moves towards the yellow (reversed Purkinje shift) and

all this happens very much more quickly than the dark adaptation. After the first few moments of dazzle, the sense of color and the ability to read small print are restored. Moreover, if the adaptation to light is not too prolonged, the return to the darkroom will be followed by a much more rapid dark adaptation than follows a prolonged period of light adaptation.

### Photopic Visibility (Sensitivity) Curve

Although the scotopic spectral sensitivity or visibility curve (see fig. 72.15) is a reasonably accurate expression of the sensitivity of the rods to the different parts of the spectrum since it is obtained by determining absolute thresholds, it is much more difficult to obtain any similar expression for the cones. The problem may be approached in one of two ways. Evidence has been presented to show that the very center of the fovea is a part of the retina where cones only are present. A threshold visibility curve for this area therefore should give a good indication of the spectral sensitivity of the cones. Such a curve is plotted in figure 73.7, where it can be compared with the visibility curve for the rods, and some of the reasons for the Purkinje shift become obvious. By the other approach, the sensitivity of the eye to the different parts of the spectrum can be gauged by comparing the intensities of light of different wave-lengths which match a given standard white light in brightness. Since this involves the rather difficult feat of heterochromatic matching, it is inclined to be rather inaccurate, although this difficulty can be overcome to some extent by altering the wave-length of the field to be matched from white to yellow and to the other spectral colors in a stepwise manner so that

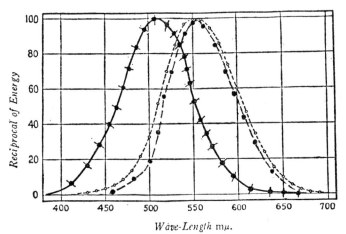

Fig. 73.7. Visibility curves for scotopic and photopic vision. ●——● = scotopic vision; ○-----○ = photopic vision; ●– –● = foveal photopic vision. (After Hecht, Thomson and Wright.)

the color differences between the fields are minimized. For example, instead of matching red with white directly a standard yellow field is first chosen and an orange field first matched against the yellow; the orange is then used as the standard for the red. If the steps in such a matching procedure are made small enough the matches are almost homochromatic but there is then, of course, still the possibility of a cumulative error. The method of flicker photometry (see p. 1371) can also be used. In determining the *photopic visibility curve* by the process of matching brightnesses, a field subtending 2° at the eye is traditionally used. Errors or difficulties are introduced with fields that are much larger or much smaller than this.

The photopic visibility curve, although interesting in itself, has not the same objective reality as the scotopic curve. It varies with the size of the matching fields, with the position of the field on the retina, with the brightness level which is used as a standard, and with the direction in which the light impinges upon the receptors. Light falling obliquely on the cones is less efficient than that which traverses their length in an axial direction. Different wave-lengths are affected to different extents. Since there are known to be at least two types of cone (with different pigments in each) in the human eye, the curve must inevitably be composite.

Another and rather inaccurate method of attempting to assess the spectral sensitivity of the cones is to determine the *chromatic threshold*, i.e., the intensity of light at each wave-length which is just sufficient to produce a sensation of color. For most parts of the spectrum, there is a large *achromatic interval*. This means that at some very low intensity the colorless rod threshold is reached, then, as the intensity is raised, the field begins to appear colored, presumably at about the threshold of the cones. The range of intensities between the threshold for light and that for color is known as the achromatic interval. It is very large in the blue region of the spectrum and absent in the red part. In the central fovea there is no achromatic interval in the true sense, although light from the middle of the spectrum tends to appear colorless at threshold levels. Both violet and red are either seen in full saturation or not at all.

Like the electroretinogram, the photopic visibility curve or curves give a general summary of retinal performance but their analysis is beset with difficulties. Consequently, they are only of limited physiological importance, until more is known of the exact meaning to be attached to

the sensation of brightness when several types of retinal receptors and pathways may be contributing to it.

## Color Vision; The Nature of Color

Before discussing the physiological basis for color vision, it may be desirable to recapitulate some of the main facts about color in general. In the first place, color is entirely a subjective phenomenon, and there can be no such thing as color except for those animals, including man, which have the necessary sensory and analytical apparatus with which to discriminate between the wave-lengths of visible light as well as differences in light-intensity. Lights of different wave-lengths excite the receptor mechanisms in the human eye to different extents, and two colors appear to be identical when they excite the receptor mechanisms in the same way and to equal extents. For example, the sensation of yellow can be evoked either by a narrow spectral band centered around a wave-length of 580 mμ or by a suitable mixture of red (620–700 mμ) and green (500–570 mμ), without any spectral yellow whatsoever. It is almost certainly true that when the receptors are stimulated equally by the lights illuminating two fields, those two fields will match in all respects; however, the reverse is not necessarily true, and certainly not when one field is viewed with one eye and the other with the other eye. A sensation of white is obtained when a suitable mixture of wave-lengths impinges on one eye and an equally colorless sensation of white can simultaneously be obtained in the other eye if it is dark adapted and illuminated by a narrow wave-band at 500 mμ. In the one case, the whole photopic cone mechanism is being activated and, in the other, the scotopic rod mechanism; but the brain produces very much the same sensation in each case.

Each spectral color excites the receptor mechanisms in a characteristic pattern, but quite different patterns of stimulation can be provided when mixtures of spectral wave-bands are used so that there are numerous 'extra-spectral' colors. Similarly when one, or more, of the receptor mechanisms themselves have had their performance modified by such means as adaptation (e.g., to one color), fatigue or even by the action of hormones or drugs, the responses which they can give may be greatly altered. In other words, the number of detectable hues depends upon the number of possible patterns of response from the receptors which can be distinguished by the interpreting neural mechanism. Physiologically, there is no distinction to be drawn between spectral and "extra-spectral" colors. Even so-called spectral colors can produce different sensations under different conditions. For example, when two fields are equally illuminated by wave-length 590 mμ they both appear to be orange yellow, but if one of the fields has its physical intensity reduced to about one half, that field will then appear brown in comparison with the other, but will appear yellow again when the brighter field is turned down in intensity or extinguished. Similarly, if two yellow fields are matched by binocular vision (one field being seen by each eye) and then one eye is adapted to red light, by looking at a bright red light for a few minutes, the yellow field will subsequently appear to be green to that eye. Or, again, if one eye is adapted to red light and then a field illuminated by spectral green (about 530 mμ) is observed by each eye in turn, it will be found to appear as a far more vivid, intense, or "saturated" green to the adapted eye than to the normal eye.

Any color sensation has three main attributes or qualities. They are *hue, brightness* and *saturation.*

Hue is the actual color, to be described by "red," "blue," "green," etc.

Brightness or luminosity is the amount of light which is involved. A color can always be described as being lighter, darker or equal in brightness to a given white standard. Alternatively it can always be matched in brightness or be given the same "tone value" as a particular and colorless gray; in other words, its luminosity can be measured by comparison with white standards of known intensity. The relative luminosities or brightnesses of the spectral colors are described by the ordinates of the photopic luminosity curve.

The saturation of a color is very much the same as the "purity" of the color, although this can be misleading. It is perhaps better defined as the extent to which a given color departs from a colorless gray of equal brightness. It can be measured in one of two ways. First, it can be measured in terms of the amount of it which has to be added to a given white light in order to make the white deviate perceptibly in hue from the original white. This can best be done by comparing two adjacent white fields and adding the test color to one, whereas the other may be altered in brightness in order to compensate for any changes in luminosity caused in the first field by adding the test color. The alternative method, which yields similar results, is to proceed in the opposite way, i.e., by adding white to the color until it is noticeably less saturated. Two fields are illuminated with the color to be tested; to one field (A) white light is added until it is detectably different, the luminance of the other field (B) being altered to compensate for the added white. When this first step has been fixed, the field B is desaturated until the two fields again match in all respects. White is then added to field A as before and another step established. The process is repeated until the further addition of white makes no more difference. The number of steps between the original color and white is recorded as the measure of the saturation of that color. The saturation of the spectral colors as determined by these two methods is depicted in figure 73.8. It will be seen that the spectral colors vary greatly in saturation from the intensely saturated violet and red at one extreme to the very unsaturated yellow-green at the other. Mixtures of spectral lights, in general, produce colors which are less saturated than the original separate hues, e.g., mixtures of red and blue-green. Multiple mixtures of many bands, of course, approach white, since white is the sensation evoked by the whole undivided spectrum. Some mixtures of spectral colors can, however, produce very saturated hues, e.g., mixtures of red and blue which produce purples. These observations do not mean that it is impossible for a color to be more saturated that the correspond-

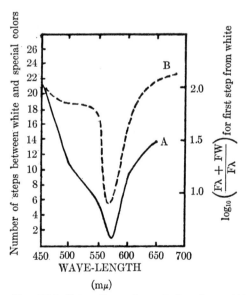

FIG. 73.8. Saturation of spectral colors. (*A*) Log of reciprocal of colorimetric purity of colors which differ from white by one perceptible step. (Ordinates on the right.) $F$ = flux of spectral color, $F_w$ = flux of white light. (*B*) Number of perceptible steps between the spectral colors and white. (Ordinates on the left.) (After Wright.)

ing spectral hue. The eye can certainly be persuaded into giving sensations of hue which are far more saturated than any spectral color normally appears. This can be done by suitable alterations to the sensitivities of the intrinsic mechanisms of the retina (or visual path), e.g., by adaptation, or by suitable mixtures of stimuli.

The pigments in a paint box are generally fairly saturated colors, although, spectroscopically, they seldom reflect only narrow spectral bands and are usually very "impure." In most cases, as any one who has attempted to paint in water colors knows, when the colors are mixed, they tend to lose their purity and become more grey and less colored. There are however, exceptions to this, since pigment mixtures are "subtractive" in character. For example, when blue and yellow pigments are mixed, the result may be a green which is more saturated than either of the original hues. A yellow pigment tends to be yellow because it absorbs very strongly in the blue part of the spectrum and only reflects green, yellow and red. The green and the red rays combine in their effects on the eye to produce a reinforcement of the pure yellow; this probably accounts for the greater saturation of yellow pigments as compared with spectral yellow. The blue pigment, on the other hand, is blue because it absorbs all the red and yellow part of the spectrum. Therefore, when the two pigments, yellow and blue, are mixed, the only light which is not absorbed by one or other of them, and which therefore continues to be reflected back, is the green light which escapes as a rather narrow spectral band. In contrast to this mixture of pigments which act in a subtractive way, the addition of the right amount of yellow light ($\lambda$ = 580 m$\mu$) to blue light ($\lambda$ = 479 m$\mu$.) so stimulates the receptor mechanisms that they give almost the same response as they would if stimulated by the whole spectrum and the mixture appears white.

This reconstitution of white light from blue and yellow is an example from the series of *complementary colors*. White can always be reconstituted from three spectral bands, widely spaced through the spectrum, when they are mixed in the right proportions; in addition to this, there are a number of pairs of wave-bands which when mixed in the correct amounts also make white. Such pairs are called complementary colors and a list of specific examples is given in Table 73.1 together with the requisite intensities of each for the match with a standard white. Physiologically, the interpretation usually given for this phenomenon is that these pairs stimulate the receptor mecha-

nisms in the eye in exactly the same manner as does white light. Although probably correct, this is not absolutely necessary since there are many different conditions under which the eye yields a colorless or white sensation, e.g., when rods only are functioning (*scotopic white*), when wave-length 574 m$\mu$ falls on the very center of the fovea (see p. 1358), as well as under ordinary conditions when a white surface is examined (*photopic white*). The complementary colors to the green part of the spectrum ($\lambda$ 495 m$\mu$ to 565 m$\mu$) are not spectral colors, but purples.

The hues produced by the different wave-bands of course change progressively throughout the spectrum, but the rate of change with wave-length is not constant. Yellow changes to orange when the wave-length is changed from 590 m$\mu$ to 600 m$\mu$, but there is very little change of hue between 460 m$\mu$ and 470 m$\mu$. The spectrum can be divided into a series of steps, over each one of which the hue is effectively constant. These steps (the hue-discrimination steps) are long in some parts and short in others. A curve relating the length (in m$\mu$) of the step to the mean wave-length of the step is called a hue-discrimination curve and is plotted in figure 73.9. It will be seen that hue discrimination is good, i.e., the steps are small, in the yellow and blue-green regions of the spectrum and very poor in the far red, green and violet, where much longer steps occur.

From the physiological point of view, too much accent need not be placed on these character-

TABLE 73.1

*Complementary Colors*

| Wave-length | Log Energy to Match White |
|---|---|
| *m$\mu$* | |
| 700 | 2.20 |
| 492 | 0.70 |
| | |
| 650 | 0.81 |
| 492 | 0.71 |
| | |
| 600 | 0.30 |
| 489 | 0.68 |
| | |
| 580 | 0.495 |
| 479 | 0.586 |
| | |
| 570 | 0.720 |
| 450 | 0.430 |
| | |
| 568.5 | 0.77 |
| 410 | 1.398 |

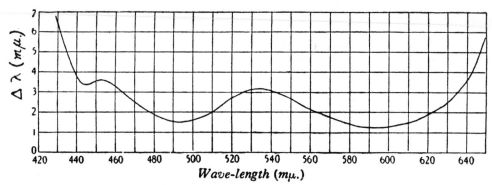

FIG. 73.9. Hue discrimination curve. (From Wright.)

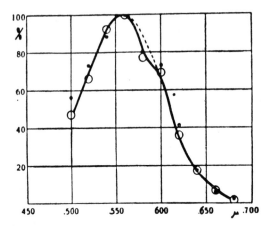

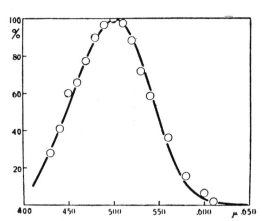

FIG. 73.10. Dominator curves in the retina of vertebrates. (*Upper*) Photopic dominator curve; (*Lower*) scotopic dominator curve. Equal quantum intensity spectrum. Ordinates, sensitivity; abscissas, wave-length. (From Granit.)

istics of the spectrum since there is nothing physiologically peculiar about spectral colors as distinct from nonspectral purples and browns. Spectral colors are physiologically interesting only in the fact that they can be used as repeat-

able and defined stimuli, which can be easily mixed and can therefore be used as a starting point for defining other colors. The basis of color sensation is more profitably sought in the pattern of nerve impulses arising from different receptors in the retina than in the wave-lengths of light which produce them.

This suggests that the first approach to the analysis of color vision should be made by recording, objectively, the impulses which pass up the optic nerve fibers as the result of stimulation of the retina by different wave-lengths. Granit and his coworkers took up this challenge and for a number of years studied the problem by this technique with extremely interesting, but puzzling, results. They found that a great many nerve cells or fibers gave an impulse-frequency versus wave-length curve (the photopic dominator curve) figure 73.10 very similar in shape to the photopic sensitivity curve of many animals, including man. At lower brightness levels some of these fibers showed a Purkinje shift and then yielded a "*scotopic dominator curve.*" By means of selective adaptation to particular wave-lengths and by various other devices, Granit and his colleagues were able to establish that many nerve fibers give responses which are greatly affected by wave-length over quite narrow ranges of the spectrum. Fibers from which this type of information could be extracted were called *modulators* (fig. 73.11) and they are clearly of great importance as indicating the presence in the retina of elements whose responses change rapidly with wave-length and which could therefore participate in hue-discrimination, but how they are to be interpreted is still very much an open question. Modulator curves, on a restricted scale have been obtained from the retinas of both rats and guinea pigs (animals in which rods very heavily preponderate among the receptors to the almost complete exclusion of cones). There are, indeed, so

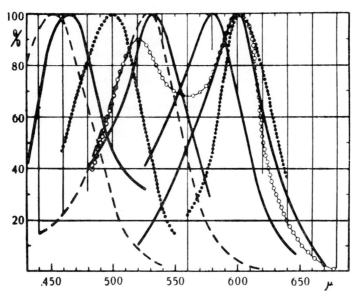

F<small>IG</small>. 73.11. Modulator curves in various animals. Dots = rats; broken lines = guinea pigs; continuous line = frogs; circles = snakes. Equal quantum intensity spectrum. Ordinates, sensitivity; abscissas, wave-length. (From Granit.)

many possible ways in which these modulators could arise in the retina, either directly from receptors or by interaction between cells in different parts of the organization, that further discussion of them at this time is hardly profitable. This becomes even more evident when the numbers of different types of cell in the retina, on the one hand, and the number of different types of information, e.g., concerning brightness, form, contrast and edges, color, saturation, movement etc., on the other, are both considered as part of retinal physiology. The codes used by the retina for transmitting all this information economically constitute a fascinating problem in the theory of communication.

In 1807, Thomas Young emphasized the trichromatic character of color vision and Helmholtz elaborated and developed the so-called trichromatic theory of color vision by his immense researches on the eye during the course of the nineteenth century. All colors, including the 'nonspectral' colors, can be matched by using three primary stimuli, i.e., three wave-bands well separated in the spectrum, e.g., blue, green and red, and mixing them in different proportions. Every color then requires its own unique mixture. There is only one set of intensities of each of those particular primaries which will make the exact match in hue, brightness and saturation. Any color can therefore be expressed by the formula:

$$aC = xB + yG + zR$$

where $a$ is the luminosity of color C and $x$, $y$ and $z$ are the luminosities of the three primaries chosen, e.g., blue, green and red. If a different set of primaries were used, a similar expression could be written:

$$aC = x_1B' + y_1G' + z_1R'$$

where the symbols have similar meanings with respect to the new primaries.

This formula applies to all colors and it does not matter whether C is a spectral color. If each of the second set of primaries (B', G' and R') is expressed in terms of its "tri-stimulus" values when the first primaries are used, it is clearly possible to convert from one set of primaries to another:

$$x_1B' = pB + qG + rR$$
$$y_1G' = p_1B + q_1G + r_1R$$
$$z_1R' = p_2B + q_2G + r_2R$$

and $aC$ can be expressed as the sum of these three.

When two or more lights are mixed, as in all colorimetrical experiments, the luminosity of the mixture is the sum of the luminosities of the separate stimuli, i.e., if $aC_1$ is one color and $bC_2$ is another color, each can be expressed as above in terms of $x_1B + y_1G + z_1R$ and $x_2B + y_2G + z_2R$. Then the new color $C_3$ can be expressed as $aC_1 + bC_2$ where the luminosity of the new color will be $a + b$:

$$(a + b)\mathrm{C}_3$$

$$= (x_1 + x_2)\mathrm{B} + (y_1 + y_2)\mathrm{G} + (z_1 + z_2)\mathrm{R}$$

These two findings, that all colors can be expressed in terms of the luminosities of three primaries and that when colors are mixed by means of spectral lights the luminosities of the components are for all practical purposes additive, are the cardinal features of all color measurement and specification. There are, indeed some minor deviations of the strictly additive law under certain special conditions, e.g., with very small centrally fixated fields and at very high or very low brightness levels, but, in general, the additivity of color mixtures is basic to colorimetry. There are certain colors which can only be matched in saturation by a mixture of three primaries by desaturating the color to be matched on the control side, i.e., by using a negative component of the match. Color mixture, using spectral lights, always tends to give colors which are somewhat less saturated than might be expected. In spite of these minor difficulties the essentially trichromatic character of all color matching is, however, no longer seriously disputed, and it is thought that the trichromacy reflects the existence of three basic mechanisms, if not actually of three different classes of receptors, in the retina.

If the three spectral primaries are so chosen, as they must be, that a particular mixture of them matches white, then the luminosities of the primaries in the match with white can be conveniently regarded as the units of the red, green and blue stimuli, and all other colors can be expressed in terms of these units. If, for example, the spectral colors are matched, one by one, with the use of the three primaries (650 m$\mu$, 530 m$\mu$ and 460 m$\mu$), the units of these having first been determined by the match on white, then all the colors can be expressed in terms of these units and a result like that shown in figure 73.12 can be obtained. Each color can be obtained by mixing the three primaries in the proportions indicated by the ordinates in this figure. It will be noticed that, in the blue region of the spectrum, the green stimuli are negative and, in the green region, the red stimulus has to be transferred to the matching field. Other units, based on the amounts of red and green necessary to match yellow and the amounts of blue and green necessary to match blue green, are sometimes used as more satisfactory units than the luminosities of each primary in the match on white. *Whiteness* has subjective qualities whereas spectral yellow and blue-green can be determined precisely by specific wave-bands (582.5 and 494 m$\mu$ respectively).

If the figures shown in figure 73.12 are converted back to luminosities, i.e., into terms of the absolute amounts of blue, green and red radiations, then the matches on the spectral colors are represented by figure 73.13 in which, owing to the very low luminosity values of the blue stimulus, the figures for the blue primary have been multiplied by 10. The blue stimulus always has a great effect on hue and saturation, but very little effect on luminosity. Since the coefficients plotted in figure 73.12 are all expressed as fractions of 1 they can

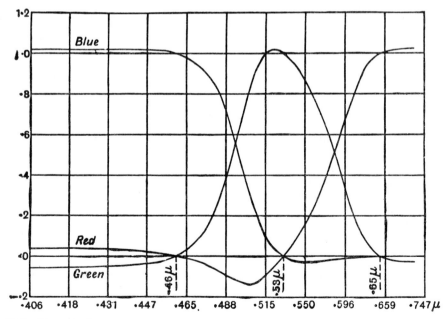

Fig. 73.12. Mean coefficient curves for matches on the spectral colors. Ordinates, coefficients; abscissas, wave-length. (From Wright.)

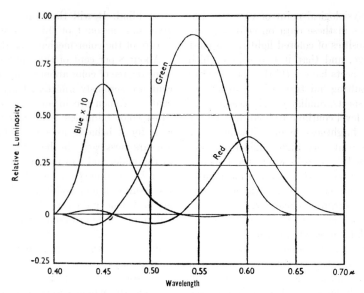

FIG. 73.13. The spectral mixture curves for the equal energy spectrum, in terms of radiations of wavelengths 650 m$\mu$, 530 m$\mu$ and 460 m$\mu$ as matching stimuli, the amounts of the stimuli being expressed as luminosity units. (From Wright.)

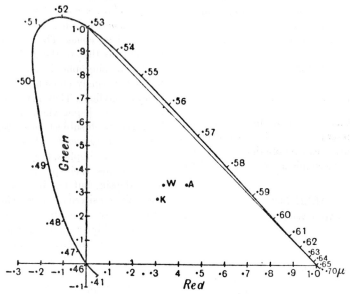

FIG. 73.14. The spectrum locus on a chromaticity chart. The point W is the white point. The coefficient for the blue stimulus can be calculated by subtracting the sum of the red and green coefficients from unity. The primaries used were 650 m$\mu$, 530 m$\mu$ and 460 m$\mu$. (From Wright.)

be replotted as figure 73.14 where the red and green coefficients (R and G) of the spectral colors are plotted against each other and the blue coefficient (B) can be obtained by difference from 1 (since R + G + B = 1). This figure is of interest because it forms the basis for many standard color charts like the one adopted by the Commission Internationale d'Eclairage, the so-called C.I.E. chart, upon which any color can be specified by its posi-

tion on the chart. The white point is represented by the point 0.33, 0.33 and colors increase in saturation from that point towards the spectral locus. On such a chart, the areas occupied by the colors are unfortunately rather irregular in size, most of the chart being occupied by greens, and various modifications have been suggested in order to obtain a more even distribution. The chart is really the modern version of the original color triangle.

From the physiological point of view, the important features in these data on color mixture are that luminosities of colored lights are almost strictly additive, and that if two colors which match in all respects have a third color added to them, the resulting mixture will continue to match in all respects. Similarly, matches made at one brightness level continue to hold over a very wide range of brightness levels, although they may break down at very high brightnesses and also at very low brightnesses where the Purkinje effect and the entry of the scotopic mechanism begin to desaturate colors in the blue and green regions of the spectrum particularly.

The trichromatic coefficients for each color and all the other data on color mixture are of great practical and commercial importance in standardization of colors but they cannot yet be translated into physiological terms. Ideally, a color chart of the form shown in figure 73.14 but recording the response of the three receptor mechansims, instead of the intensities of the three primary colors used, is how the physiologist would wish to be able to describe colors. But this aim has not yet been achieved, except perhaps to some extent in the restricted form of color vision found in the central fovea, where some approach to it is now possible (see pp. 1357, 1358).

## COLOR BLINDNESS

As Young realized, when he investigated the color blindness described by Dalton, the chemist, in 1807, information can be obtained on the nature of the color mechanisms by a study of the

### TABLE 73.2
### (After Wright)

| Type of Color Defect | Percentage |
|---|---|
| Anomalous trichromatism | |
| Protanomaly.............. | 1.0 |
| Deuteranomaly........... | 4.6 |
| Tritanomaly.............. | 0.0001 |
| | 5.6 |
| Dichromatism | |
| Protanopia................ | 1.2 |
| Deuteranopia............. | 1.4 |
| Tritanopia................ | 0.0001 |
| | 2.6 |
| Monochromatism........... | 0.003 |
| Total................. | 8.2 |

color blind. It will therefore be appropriate to give some account of this before discussing the nature of the color mechanisms themselves.

About 8 per cent of the male population have some degree of color abnormality and about 1 per cent are seriously affected. Only about 0.4 per cent of women are in any way color-abnormal. Most color blindness is inherited and since the gene for it behaves as a sex-linked recessive, it appears most easily in the heterogametic sex, i.e., in the male, and can only be inherited by a son from his mother. Occasionally, color blindness is the result of injury and it may then appear in one eye only. One of the rarer forms of color blindness, tritanopia or blue blindness (see p. 1356), is inherited in a different way from the others.

Subjects with abnormal color vision fall into several classes:

MONOCHROMATS. These are totally color blind and see the whole spectrum in shades of grey. Their vision therefore resembles that provided by black and white cinephotography. They fall into two main groups according to their spectral sensitivity and other characters.

*Rod monochromats.* These behave as if they possessed no cones. Their spectral sensitivity is the same as that of the dark adapted eye. They tend to be photophobic and are dazzled by light, but, interestingly enough, they are certainly not blind in daylight. They may have a "central scotoma" or blind spot where the normal person has his fovea. Such subjects are rare.

*Cone monochromats.* These are very rare and, as their name implies, they apparently depend on cones, because their spectral sensitivity is not that of rhodopsin, but has its peak near that of the photopic sensitivity curve. Comparatively few subjects have been investigated with sufficient accuracy to be certain, but there are indications of two groups among them, one with maximum sensitivity at about 530–540 m$\mu$ and the other with maximum sensitivity at about 560–570 m$\mu$. The former appear to be the more common and, in them, rod vision (i.e., night vision) is apparently normal.

DICHROMATS. All these subjects require only two primary colors with which to match all colors in the spectrum. There are certainly three and perhaps four groups of them. They, and other color-abnormal types, are readily picked out from the normal population by the use of one or more of the standard tests which have been devised for the purpose, such as the Ishihara test, the Stilling test, Holmgren's wool test, or the 100 hue test of Farnsworth. The Ishihara test is perhaps the one most frequently used as a preliminary screen. It consists of a series of colored plates each composed of a field of colored dots. The dots are so selected and arranged as to constitute patterns visible either to the normal person or to the color blind but seldom to both. For example, a figure composed partly of red and partly of green dots may be lost to the normal observer in a background of other multicolored dots, however it may be quite easily distinguishable for the color blind person who sees no difference between the red and the green dots. Alternatively a red figure on a background of green dots is clearly seen by the normal person but may be invisible to the color blind. The wool test depends upon the inability of the color blind to differentiate between certain pairs of colored wools, and the 100 hue test consists of arranging colored chips in an orderly sequence of hues. From the particular confusions or irregularities in these tests, it is possible to

classify the color blind to a limited extent on the tests alone, but further and more searching tests are generally necessary to determine the exact type of defect which is present.

*Protanopes.* These subjects confuse red with green, and on a 2° field can match these two colors in all respects. They are relatively insensitive to red light and their photopic sensitivity curve is noticeably displaced from the normal curve and has its maximum at about 540 m$\mu$. They see the whole spectrum in terms of blue and yellow (brown?) except for a region near 495 m$\mu$ which they match with white. They confuse the colors which lie along the lines in the color chart shown in figure 73.15. Their foveal center apparently is monochromatic and, when their vision is restricted to this area, they see all colors as shades of grey.

*Deuteranopes.* These subjects also confuse red with green, but the particular reds and greens

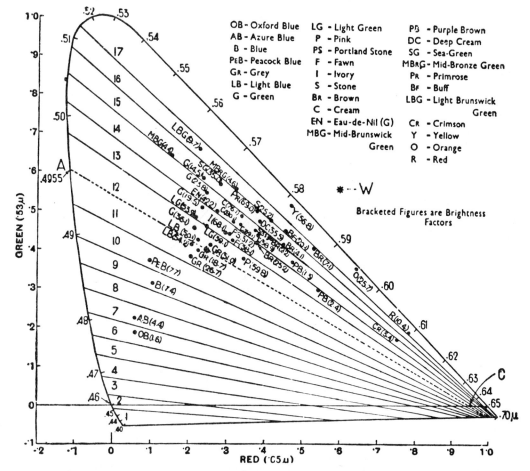

FIG. 73.15. Chromaticity chart similar to that shown in figure 73.14. The lines divide the chart into areas within each of which there is no hue-discrimination and colors are likely to be confused by the protanope. Thus the protanope has 17 color steps in the spectrum. (From Wright, after Pitt.)

which they confuse are different from those which the protanopes confuse. Unlike the protanopes they can see the whole spectrum to the same limits as the normal person. Their photopic sensitivity curve, which is somewhat variable in position is not always significantly different from that of the normal subject. Like the protanopes they become completely color blind when their vision is restricted to the central fovea, and there is some suggestion that there are two classes of deuteranopes. Again like the protanopes they see the whole spectrum in shades of blue and yellow and they have a neutral point at about 497–500 m$\mu$ which they see as white. The colors which they confuse are those lying on the lines of the color chart in figure 73.16.

*Tritanopes.* These are very rare and, in some cases at least, the defect is the result of injury or damage. Such subjects see colors with their whole retina in very much the same way as normal subjects see them when their vision is restricted to the foveal center (see pp. 1357, 1358). The spectrum is divided for them into a blue-green part and an orange-red part by a neutral point at about 574 m$\mu$, which can be matched with white. Colors which they confuse lie along lines radiating from the origin in the color chart (fig. 73.14).

*Tetartanopes.* A few, rather ill-defined cases of blue-yellow confusion have been included under this heading, but they are not sufficiently standardized or categorized to be of much significance either in elucidating the problems of color vision or as medical cases. Two neutral points, one at 470 m$\mu$ and another at 580 m$\mu$, are reported.

ANOMALOUS TRICHROMATS. If a normal subject examines a yellow field which is subdivided down

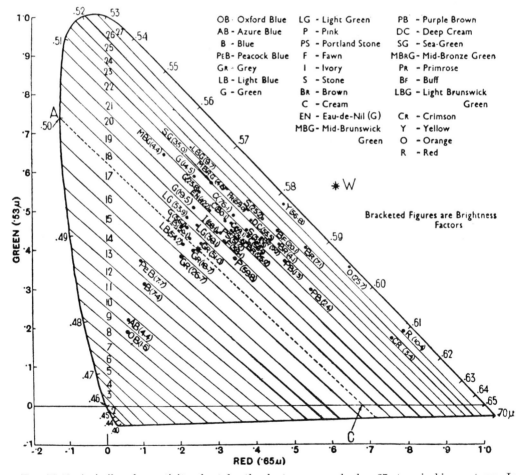

FIG. 73.16. A similar chromaticity chart for the deuteranope, who has 27 steps in his spectrum. In both these cases the steps are based more on differences in saturation than on hue. It is probable that both protanopes and deuteranopes see the spectrum in shades of blue from 400 m$\mu$ to the neutral point and in shades of yellow from the neutral point to the red end of the spectrum. The dotted lines represent the real division of the hues. (From Wright, after Pitt.)

the middle so that one half is illuminated by a narrow spectral band of yellow (about 585 mμ) and the other by a mixture of red and green, it will be found that, in order to match the yellow, he requires a particular ratio of red to green within rather narrow limits. The instrument is called the Nagel *anomaloscope* and the match is called the Rayleigh match.

There is, however, a large group of people who either make different settings from the normal or who have a much greater tolerance for "incorrect" settings than the normal in what they consider to be satisfactory matches. The subjects who make abnormal Rayleigh matches range form the nearly normal to the frank dichromats who have complete tolerance and so can match the yellow either with pure green or with pure red, provided that the brightnesses of the two fields are adjusted.

Anomalous trichromats require three primary colors with which to match the whole spectrum, but the contributions made by each seem to differ from the normal. Some subjects in this class tend towards the deuteranope (*deuteranomalous*), others towards the protanope (*protanomalous*). It is, however, improbable that there is a complete gradation from the normal to the deuteranopes and the protanopes. These extremes seem to differ qualitatively as well as quantitatively from the normal. Although normal people obviously do not accept, in general, matches which are made by the color-blind, color-blind subjects generally accept matches made by normal people. This, however is not true for anomalous trichromats who sometimes reject matches made by normal subjects.

## The Physiological Basis for Color Vision

Emphasis has been placed on the fact that at low light intensities, when rods alone are believed to be in action, the eye produces no sensation of color. From the spectral sensitivity curve in the dark adapted state the evidence is very strong that no pigment other than rhodopsin is involved in rod vision. The position is exactly comparable with that in the eye of Limulus where it was shown (p. 1335) that there was no possibility for this animal to discriminate between intensity and wave-length, since the same frequency of impulses could result from suitable adjustment of either. The colorless sensation associated with rod vision and the observations on Limulus make it quite clear that a single set of receptors, containing one pigment only, cannot provide a basis for color vision. Therefore, in any color-sensitive

mechanism, there must be at least two (if not more) classes of receptor, each containing a mechanism or pigment for providing it with a specific spectral sensitivity.

In man, as soon as the light intensity is raised to the threshold for the cones, sensations of color arise. This must mean that at least two classes of receptor are then in action. These two classes could theoretically be the rods and the cones, or two or more classes of cones, and the main physiological problem of color vision is to determine the nature of the color receptors.

Attention has already been called to the fact that birds have the photopigment, iodopsin, probably in their cones and that some of them also have oil droplet of different colors in the inner segments of their cones. There is also experimental evidence that these colored droplets alter the spectral sensitivity of the iodopsin of the cones in which they occur sufficiently to provide a basis for color discrimination. Man, however, does not possess such colored droplets in his cones and so must depend upon some other mechanism. Indeed, it seems probable that the problem of providing a mechanism for color vision has been solved more than once in evolution, and probably by several different methods. Color vision occurs sporadically in the animal kingdom, in bees and butterflies, fish, amphibia, some reptiles, some birds and in very few, if any, mammals outside the Primates. In deciding whether an animal has color vision it is necessary to be absolutely certain that apparent discrimination between colors is not really discrimination between shapes, brightnesses etc., or even between smells, or differences of texture.

Apart from some unexplained differences in staining properties and a progressive elongation of those situated nearer the center of the retina, human cones all appear to be histologically the same. Rushton's work on the differential bleaching of the pigments of the fovea certainly indicates the presence of at least two cone pigments, although exactly how these results are to be interpreted is a little uncertain in view of the fact that the field size which was used in these experiments would almost certainly include within it a large number of rods.

### The Foveal Center and the Nature of the Color Mechanisms

Since it is known that color vision does not occur in man without the intervention of the cones, and since it is suspected that cones may be entirely responsible for color vision, and since cones occur alone and apparently unmixed with rods in the foveal center, it is logical to examine the performance of this part of the retina to see how much these central cones can achieve on their own. Unfortunately the rod-free area is very small and eye movements are relatively large, so that very small fields (less that 30′ in diameter) have to be used. Rigid fixation also has to be maintained. In spite of these precautions the opportunity for error is large and great will-power has to be exerted by the subject to prevent the eye from moving its point of fixation to other regions in order to gain information. In normal vision constant small eye movements are habitual and really steady fixation is an unnatural form of behavior.

However, when all these conditions are fulfilled, there can be no doubt that although the central fovea is capable of a limited discrimination of color, somewhat surprisingly, it does not have the complete color vision which is characteristic of the retina as a whole. When experiments in matching colors are performed with these small centrally fixated fields, it is found that all the spectral colors can be matched with mixtures of two primaries only, i.e., with mixtures of red and blue. Moreover, certain well defined color confusions occur, such as matching blue with green, pink with orange and so on; spectral yellow becomes indistinguishable from white when seen

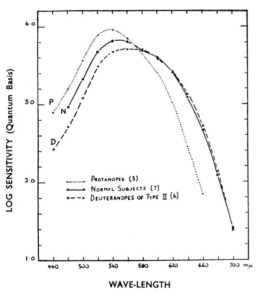

Fig. 73.17. Central foveal luminosity curves. N = Luminosity curve for normal central fovea; P = luminosity curve for the protanope and probable sensitivity curve for one type of receptor in the normal fovea; D = luminosity curve for certain deuteranopes and probable sensitivity curve for the other type of receptor in the normal fovea. (From Willmer.)

with the foveal center alone. These are all properties which are to be expected in a system which is based on two types of receptor only, and, what is more, they are identical with the properties of the color vision of the tritanope (see p. 1356). Central foveal vision, dependent upon a population of cones only, is therefore a form of dichromatic vision and is probably most easily explained by reference to the curves shown in figure 73.17.

If it is supposed that there are two kinds of receptor in the central fovea, which are functional under the conditions of the color-matching just described, and if it is supposed that their spectral sensitivities are as depicted in figure 73.17, curves P and D, then it is clear that each wavelength must evoke a different ratio of responses from the two classes of receptors. Theoretically therefore, this difference could be used to indicate wave-length; and some property of the total response could give information about brightness. Moreover a study of the figure shows that, if suitable intensities of red (stimulating one class of receptor (D) much more than the other) and of blue (stimulating mainly the other class (P)) are mixed together it should be possible to produce almost any desired ratio of responses from the two classes of receptors, including the ratios which are normally produced by the different wave-lengths of the spectrum, and so to match all the spectral colors. Wherever the two curves cross, both classes of receptor might be expected to give the same response, i.e., at this wave-length they would all behave as if they were alike, thus constituting a uniform population, and, just as the rods (which are another uniform population of receptors) give no sensation of color when they are functioning alone in scotopic vision, so it is the spectral wave-length which the central fovea matches with white, and which evokes a sensation of light but no color.

It is evident therefore that the color properties of the central fovea can be adequately described in terms of two types of receptor and two only, whose spectral sensitivities are similar to those depicted in figure 73.17. The normal central fovea thus behaves as if it were partly color blind, dichromatic and tritanopic. Fixation within this area allows all spectral colors between violet and yellow-green to be matched with blue-green and all colors between red and yellow-green to be matched with orange, provided that the brightness of the matching fields is equalized. If, in the foveal center there is a simpler form of color vision than elsewhere, in fact a two-unit system instead of the full three unit system, its further investigation is likely to be somewhat easier and more immediately rewarding than that of the whole eye. A system with only two variables is always simpler than one with three.

Now it so happens that in certain forms of color blindness (e.g., deuteranopia and protanopia, see p. 1355) the subjects are, as indicated above (figs. 74.15 and 74.16) normally unable to distinguish between the two main colors associated with central foveal vision, namely blue-green and orange, provided that the colors are equalized in brightness. As might be expected therefore, such subjects, when they have their vision restricted to the central fovea, are found to be totally colorblind in that area. Once again, the simplest interpretation of this observation is that such subjects have only one type of receptor in the central fovea, or, if they have more than one type of receptor, the information which the two or more types provide is lost before it is used for color discrimination. In other words, either there is only type of receptor or all types relay on to the same optic nerve fiber. If the first assumption is made, namely that red-green blind subjects have only one type of receptor in the foveal center, then as with rod vision, the spectral sensitivity curve must be a close approximation to the spectral sensitivity of the visual pigment in the receptor. Another very significant fact from the point of view of the subjective interpretation of color is the fact that these color blind subjects who are monochromatic in the foveal center have a sensation of "no color," colorlessness or white, for all wave-lengths, as soon as foveal fixation is obtained. This is not to be confused with another equally important observation that as soon as an image is stabilized on any one part of the retina of a normal person, the color very soon disappears and then the whole image fades away. The time relationships of the two phenomena are quite different. Monochromacy and central fixation are almost simultaneous in the color blind subject who is trained to observe without eye movements. Since it is known that the red-green blind subject can normally receive sensations of color with large fields, probably in shades of blue and yellow, the suggestion is very strong, since color disappears at the foveal center where one type of receptor is working on its own, that color does not depend on the stimulation of one particular form of receptor alone, but rather on the difference between the responses of two or more classes of receptors.

The curves shown in figure 73.17 are actually the spectral sensitivity curves for the foveal centers of protanopes (P) and deuteranopes (D). The justification for this is that very similar curves are obtained by strongly adapting the fovea of the normal subject first to strong red light and then to strong blue-green light and determining the spectral sensitivity immediately after each type of adaptation. (At the central fovea, since there are no rods, threshold measurements of cone sensitivity can be obtained.) By the first adaptation, the mechanism for the perception of the red end of the spectrum is rendered relatively insensitive and the fovea then becomes dependent upon the "blue-green" mechanism alone at threshold level. This gives the P-curve or something closely approaching it. After the second adaptation, the "blue-green" mechanism is similarly desensitized and the "red" mechanism can be investigated in isolation yielding a close approximation to the D-curve. These facts, all taken together, indicate that in all probability the receptors of the central fovea, or at least those which are active under these conditions, fall into two classes with sensitivities not very different from those depicted in figure 73.17.

The question therefore arises as to how these two curves can be reconciled with the two curves shown in figure 72.19 and obtained by direct bleaching of the pigments in and around the fovea. Protanopes, who give the P-curve of figure 73.17 also give the *chlorolabe curve* of figure 72.19, and it is therefore extremely probable that, although the agreement is not perfect, these subjects have only one type of receptor and one photo-pigment in their foveal center. In making comparisons between such curves, account must be taken of colored photo-products, macular pigment (see p. 1322) and other factors which affect the transmission through the various ocular media. Difference spectra are therefore used. Although the situation in protanopes appears to be relatively simple, there is a much greater discrepancy between the D-curve, expressing the spectral sensitivity of the monochromatic foveal center of the deuteranope and the difference spectrum of *erythrolabe* (see p. 1333). However, in this case there is some evidence from bleaching and ocular reflection observations on the fovea of the deuteranope that his cones may contain a mixture of erythrolabe and chlorolabe so that the sensitivity curve is likely to depend upon both these pigments. Since differential bleaching with lights from either end of the spectrum which are subjectively equally bright produces the same degree of insensitivity in the central cones of some deuteranopes at least, quite irrespective of wave-length, these subjects appear to have only one type of cone and it would seem likely that the pigments must therefore occur mixed within each cone.

Although it is too early to be certain, it is probable that the central fovea of the normal person contains two classes of receptors and that these are both cones; one of the classes is dependent upon a single pigment, conveniently called chlorolabe, which has its maximum sensitivity between 530 and 540 m$\mu$. From the shape of the sensitivity curve of the protanope duly corrected for the effects of macular and ocular pigmentation) it may be surmised that chlorolabe is probably a carotenoid-protein akin to other members of the rhodopsin group. The receptors of the other class appear to contain a mixture of chlorolabe and erythrolabe which is possibly a similar pigment, but the matter is still very much under investigation.

Although in some ways it is easier to investigate, this central foveal vision is peculiar and very different from normal color vision, which occurs either when larger fields are being used or when the eye is allowed free movement and the use of other parts of the retina. Under these more normal conditions human color vision is trichromatic, as suggested by Thomas Young, and dependent upon three receptor mechanisms, as emphasized by Helmholtz. Some third factor must therefore intervene to prevent the sorts of confusion which must inevitably occur with any dichromatic system like the one just described for the central fovea.

Although it seems probable that the two classes of receptor in the central fovea are both cones, there is much less certainty about the nature of the third mechanism, whose activities are mostly concerned with the blue end of the spectrum and which therefore is conveniently called the "blue" mechanism.

The effects of this third factor are fourfold. First, three primary colors are required in order to make mixtures which will match each of the colors of the spectrum and all extra-spectral colors. Second, three primary colors are sufficient. Third, the sorts of confusion found in the dichromatic foveal center no longer occur. Fourth, trichromatic color mixtures are unique, i.e., there is only one combination of the three primaries that are chosen which will make an exact match with any other particular color. This has the important practical applications already discussed (p. 1354) and allows deductions to be made from

color mixture data as to the probable sensitivities of the three basic mechanisms involved.

Attempts have therefore been made to estimate the sensitivity of the three mechanisms responsible for color vision by assuming that the sensation depends upon stimulating the three mechanisms, each of which gives its specific contribution, i.e., blueness, greenness, or redness, in very much the same way as the color mixture itself is made by compounding blue, green and red primaries. In other words, the mixture data for one set of primaries have been converted to another set of primaries, one of which is deemed to be the spectral sensitivity of one of the receptors. How far this is legitimate is somewhat dubious, since color sensations, as determined by the simpler conditions of the central fovea, seem to depend upon the differences between the responses in two pathways rather than on the response in any one path. Nevertheless, the problem of the nature of the third factor has to be approached by any means that are available.

Stiles has tackled the problem of the sensitivities of the color mechanisms in general by a study of what may be termed increment thresholds. In the description of the dark adaptation curve for the whole eye (p. 1343) attention was drawn to the "knee" in the curve and this was related to the dropping out of the cone mechanism at that particular level of illumination, which thus allowed the threshold light-intensity for the cones to be determined.

Stiles has adopted a somewhat similar method for detecting the thresholds for the various cone or photopic mechanisms. If a small test patch of monochromatic light is superimposed momentarily on a uniform background of the same or of a different color (i.e. monochromatic spectral band), a subject can say whether or not he sees the test patch. If then the minimum visible intensity of the test patch is recorded with different intensities of the background field, a curve relating the two intensities can be plotted. As the brightness of the background increases, the brightness of the test patch has to be increased in a corresponding way. The amount of the increase is presumably related to the extent to which the background light alters the sensitivities of the receptors required for the perception of the test light. For example, one might suppose that a dim blue background would have little effect upon the threshold for seeing a red test patch, since the "red mechanism" is unlikely to be stimulated to any great extent by the blue light. When, however, the blue light becomes strong enough, it would begin to affect the receptors concerned with red vision and the threshold for red would then begin to rise. The intensity at which this occurs therefore indicates the threshold of some part of the red receptive mechanism for blue light of the particular wave-length used to illuminate the background. When this is done systematically throughout the spectrum with different wave-lengths in the background, the sensitivity of this part of the red mechanism to all other wave-lengths can be plotted. If the red mechanism depends on two or more receptors or pathways then a further rise in the blue background intensity may produce another break in the regular increment threshold curve for a red test flash at the point where the second mechanism begins to be affected by the blue (or other colored) stimulus.

As a result of a detailed analysis made in this manner, in which numerous wave-lengths have been used both for the test flash and for the background, Stiles has obtained evidence for five separate mechanisms in addition to the rods. The estimated spectral sensitivities of the three main ones ($\pi_1$, $\pi_4$, $\pi_5$) are plotted in figure 73.18. They provide a very important body of concrete information with regard to the color mechanisms in the normal eye. The problem, however, remains as to how these curves should be interpreted and how they can be integrated into the other data on color vision.

Stiles is cautious on this subject and prefers to label the curves $\pi_1$ to $\pi_5$ and to use the word mechanism rather than receptor, or even pathway. The point that has been determined in each case is the intensity which is required at each wave-length for some process involved in the perception of the test flash to be affected by the conditioning stimulus. On structural and physiological grounds this new process which becomes affected could be: (a) the threshold of a new type of receptor; (b) the threshold of a bipolar cell; (c) the threshold of a ganglion cell; or (d) the threshold at which some inhibitory process came into action. There is nothing as yet to indicate which, if any of these processes is the effective one in any of the $\pi_1$ to $\pi_5$ mechanisms. When more information is available, this analysis of increment thresholds will undoubtedly prove of the utmost value. Meanwhile $\pi_1$ (blue mechanism) $\pi_4$ (green mechanism) and $\pi_5$ (red mechanism) agree very well with estimates which have been made of the sensitivity of these color mechanisms from the data obtained by color mixture. $\pi_4$ and $\pi_5$ are closely similar to the curves obtained from the foveal center and described above. Thus there now seems to be approaching some certainty that the sensitivity of the two mechanisms of the central fovea is very much as has been suggested, but there is still doubt as to what physiological characters determine the sensitivities of these two mechanisms. Among the various possibilities the following may be mentioned: (a) Single pigments in single cones; (b) mixed pigments in single cones; (c) single pigments in single cones, but relaying on to combined

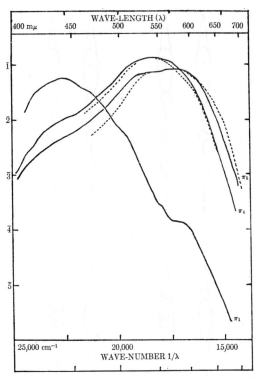

Fig. 73.18. Sensitivity curves for the $\pi_1$, $\pi_4$ and $\pi_5$ mechanisms. The dotted lines represent the P and the D curves from figure 73.17. See text. (After Stiles and Willmer.)

pathways; or (d) mixed pigments in single cones relaying on to mixed pathways (see figure 73.19). In addition to this simple pattern it could be postulated that other retinal nerve cells could also send information about the difference in responses between the receptors and these nerve cells might have very different thresholds from the receptors themselves. Figure 73.20 indicates one such possibility. The thresholds of cells 1, 2, 3, and 4 might be very different and very differently affected by adaptation, and so show up by the increment threshold technique, which, after all, depends on information supplied to the brain by the optic nerve and not necessarily only on the degree of stimulation of the receptors themselves. This hypothesis should be regarded as only a suggestion regarding the manner in which it is now becoming possible to think about retinal physiology; however, since retinal physiology is, in a sense, the physiology of the central nervous system, its implications are far-reaching.

THE BLUE MECHANISM AND $\pi$ 1. Although some finality appears to be approaching in relation to the identification of the red and green mechanisms, the nature of the blue mechanism remains an unsolved problem. From color-mixture data obtained from both normal and color-blind subjects and from the increment threshold data of Stiles (the

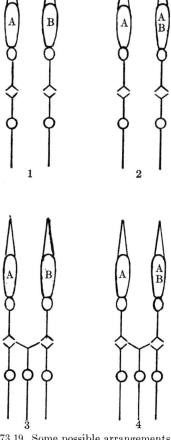

FIG. 73.19. Some possible arrangements for the use of two types of pigment and two types of cone and for the transmission of their photochemical responses to the brain. See text.

$\pi_1$ curve) it appears to have its maximum sensitivity at about 450 m$\mu$. In several ways, it appears to differ in kind from the other two mechanisms. Some of these differences are listed below.

1. Blue contributes very little to the luminosity of any color mixture, and the responses from the green and red mechanisms ($\pi_4$ and $\pi_5$) account for nearly all the luminosity of the spectrum.

2. The blue mechanism does not operate with very small fields, and it may actually be absent from the central fovea.

3. The receptive field of the blue mechanism is about 13' in diameter, whereas for the red and the green mechanisms it is of the order of 1'.

4. Extrafoveally, a fairly large field has to be stimulated (or eye movements allowed) in order to allow the mechanism full play.

5. The normal eye can be reduced to a state of monochromatism by sufficient adaptation to violet and blue-green, or to violet and red. When this is

done, the eye yields only colorless or very desaturated sensations in response to subsequent test fields over a large part of the spectrum. If, on the other hand, it is reduced to monochromatism by intense stimulation by yellow light (which, incidentally, has very little influence on color sensations in the central fovea, other than raising their threshold) then all wave-lengths from 400–500 m$\mu$ subsequently appear as a very saturated violet (which can be matched with 447 m$\mu$). Under these conditions of "violet monochromatism" induced by intense adaptation to yellow light, as distinct from the more usual colorless monochromatisms, intensity discrimination becomes very bad and the visual acuity (see p. 1364) becomes very low; black bars on a uniform field have to be separated by more than 7.5' before they can be resolved, whereas in comparable "red" and "green" monochromatisms visual acuity is little impaired from the normal (bars can be seen as separate entities when only about 1' apart). This low visual acuity of the blue mechanism is comparable with the low acuity of the rod mechanism, although it is definitely somewhat higher.

6. When the eye is adapted to various colored lights, the effect of the adaptations on subsequent color matches can be recorded and the rate of the recovery of the different mechanisms from the

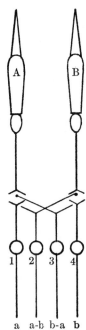

FIG. 73.20. Some possible ways in which receptors could be linked to optic nerve fibers. Cell 1 transmits $a$, which is some function of $A$. Cell 2 transmits $a$-$fb$, where $fb$ is some function of $B$, but not necessarily equal to $b$, which is the response transmitted by cell 4. Cell 3 transmits $b$-$fa$, where, similarly, $fa$ is some function of $A$ but not necessarily equal to $a$.

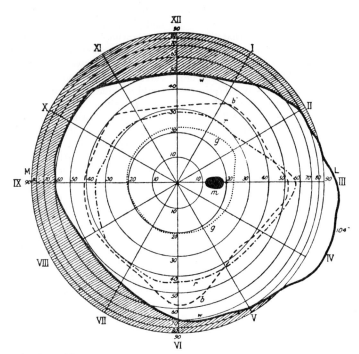

FIG. 73.21. Fields for white, blue, red and green for a normal right eye. (From Hartridge.)

adaptation can be investigated. It is nearly always found that although the red and the green components in the mixture tend to follow similar and rapid recovery curves, the recovery of the blue mechanism is definitely slower and follows a different time course.

7. The estimated spectral sensitivity curve for the blue mechanism $(\pi_1)$ has an unique kink in it between about 550 m$\mu$ and 600 m$\mu$ which is not found in other sensitivity curves nor in the absorption spectrum of carotenoid-protein pigments.

8. Tritanopia (blue blindness) is inherited separately from the other forms of color-blindness.

Several features of the blue mechanism suggest that it may be associated in some way with the function of the rods.

1. Neither the blue mechanism nor the rods are present in the foveal center, whereas the blue mechanism, unlike the red and green mechanisms, is in operation almost to the extreme periphery of the eye (see p. 1323), or at least as far out as color is recognized at all (fig. 73.21).

2. The blue mechanism is often the first of the color mechanisms to be affected in cases of retinitis pigmentosa. Tritanopia or failure of the blue mechanism often follows any retinal damage or degeneration which involves the destruction of the rods.

3. When light of any wave-length from 400 to 570 m$\mu$ illuminates one half of a divided field (about 4° in diameter) at such a low level of in-

tensity that no sensation of color is aroused, one presumes that only rods are being stimulated. However, the illumination of the other half of the field with light of any wave-length between 570 and 700 m$\mu$, of sufficient intensity to arouse a sensation of color in that half, i.e., to stimulate cones, immediately causes the first half of the field to darken and to appear blue. If the divided field is viewed monocularly, the blue can be matched by a spectral wave-band centered on 464 m$\mu$ viewed by the unstimulated eye. The suggestion is very strong that rods are involved in this blue sensation.

4. Twilight vision often has a subjective quality of blueness.

There are, equally, several features which argue against the blue mechanism being dependent upon the rods:

1. The spectral sensitivity of the blue mechanism is not that of rhodopsin; it is more nearly that of indicator yellow, although this is not a photosensitive pigment in the ordinary sense.

2. The color mixture data are incompatible with rhodopsin as one of the primary pigments used for color vision if the curves for the other $(\pi_4$ and $\pi_5)$ mechanisms are valid.

3. The visual acuity in violet monochromatism, although low, is higher than that with ordinary rod vision.

4. Trichromatic matches made at photopic levels should not break down at scotopic levels if

rods are involved in both. In practice such matches do sometimes break down.

It is clear from these summaries that, if rods are involved in the blue mechanism, they are acting in some rather different way from their more clearly recognized action. Although man has developed from nocturnal ancestors in whose eyes rods undoubtedly preponderated, it is rather extraordinary that his retina should still possess some twenty rods to every cone, if they are of no significance in his apparatus for vision under ordinary daylight conditions, for he has now become such a definitely diurnal animal.

Moreover, there is something very attractive about the "opponent color theories" that have been developed in various forms by Hering, Houstoun, Ladd-Franklin, Gothlin and, more recently, by Hurvich and Jamieson, some of which could well be reconciled with an antagonism between rods and cones. The essence of these theories, all of which vary in detail, is the idea of opposition between blue and yellow, and between red and green. Indeed there are many arguments which can be brought in support of such an interpretation of color vision, particularly if the antagonisms are thought of as not necessarily arising at the receptor level but at some higher level in the neural pathway.

Some of the electrical potentials recorded by Svaetichin and MacNichol (1958) in the horizontal cells (?) of fish in response to stimulation of the photopic receptors by different wave-lengths of light suggest that they result from mutually antagonistic events. Negative potentials develop in the blue-green part of the spectrum, positive potentials in the orange-red.

The concept of one neural pathway or mechanism opposing another has much to recommend it as a means of reducing the information entering the central nervous system to manageable proportions and at the same time insuring that the specific qualities of the stimulus are maintained. Redundant information can be eliminated in this manner. For example, and as a pure hypothesis, if both rods and cones are being stimulated, the complete response of the less strongly stimulated together with the excess response from the other provide all the necessary information for recording both luminosity and a limited sensation of hue.

The general hypothesis that the most primitive form of color vision was based on some feature or modification of rod function opposing cone function (or *vice versa*) and giving rise to sensations of blue when the rod function was dominant and to yellow when the cones were in the ascendant is certainly attractive in its simplicity. It also suggests that the red-green blind (protanopes and deuteranopes) who have these two sensations only, may still possess something akin to this more primitive evolutionary condition of the visual system. If some of the cones then acquired a second pigment, just as, among the chromatophores, the xanthophores often acquire a red pigment in addition to their normal xanthophyll and become erythrophores, two groups of cones could then result, and the responses from these two groups could provide the means of subdividing the sensation of yellow into one of blue-green and one of orange-red according to which type of cone gave the greater response. This concept is consistent with the restricted retinal fields over which the red and green sensations are evoked in the normal light-adapted eye, whereas the yellow sensation can be evoked, either by green or red light, as far out in the retinal periphery as any color sensations can be recognized (fig. 73.21). However, in the dark-adapted eye, red is seen, as red, in the extreme periphery; yellow and green then generally appear as white because they excite the dark adapted rods. The physiological interpretation of these receptive fields is presumably to be sought partly in the distribution of the receptors themselves and partly in the distribution of the various bipolar cells and ganglion cells which integrate and code the information provided by the receptors. Protanopia and deuteranopia may in some cases depend on defective transmitting systems rather than defective receptor systems. Two tentative schemes for retinal function could be summarized as follows (see Diagrams I and II). Both have their difficulties, but they may help to provide some mental picture of present trends in color-vision theory. Future research alone can clarify the position.

## Visual Acuity

THE RESOLVING POWER OF THE EYE. The acuteness of vision (or visual acuity) is dependent upon several retinal functions, e.g., the sensitivity to light (intensity threshold), the minimum visible and the ability to recognize the separateness of two closely approximated or parallel lines. The threshold of the latter faculty is commonly referred to as the *minimum separable*[1] or the *resolution threshold*. Visual acuity is the basis of the *form sense*, by which is meant the power of determining by sight the shape, form, outline and minute detail of our surroundings. Visual acuity is customarily expressed in terms of the minimum separable or, to be more explicit, as the reciprocal of the angle subtended at the nodal point of the eye—the *visual angle*—by the space between two points situated at the minimum distance apart at which their duality can be recognized. For example, if the visual angle is 1.321

---

[1] The minimum separable is analogous to two point discrimination in cutaneous sensation (p. 1140).

DIAGRAM I

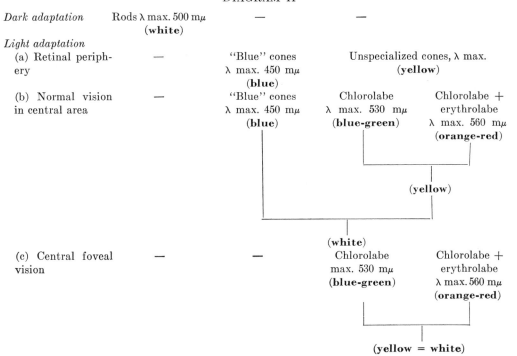

*Dark adaptation*      Rods, λ max. 500 mµ
                **(white)**

*Light adaptation*
  (a) In primitive state and   φ(Rods), max. 450 mµ      Cones (unspecialized)
  in retinal periphery              **(blue)**            λ maxi. 560 mµ
  (b) Normal vision in cen-   φ(Rods), max. 450 mµ            **(yellow)**
  tral area                    **(blue)**     Chlorolabe cones   Chlorolabe + erythro-
                                     λ max. 530 mµ    labe cones
                                                λ max. 560 mµ
                               **(blue-green)**      **(orange-red)**

                                            **(yellow)**

                         **(white)**
  (c) Central foveal vision                      as above
                             **(yellow = white)**

*Note:* 1. The separation of chlorolabe from chlorolabe + erythrolabe cones may have involved only a separation of the neural pathways, the two types of pigment being always present except in the protanopes.

2. φ(Rods) indicates some, as yet undetermined, modification either of the photochemistry of rod vision or in the spectral distribution of the rod response which remains effective under photopic conditions (i.e., which survives inhibition by cones or other similar process).


DIAGRAM II

*Dark adaptation*      Rods λ max. 500 mµ      —           —
                   **(white)**

*Light adaptation*
  (a) Retinal periph-       —        "Blue" cones     Unspecialized cones, λ max.
  ery                         λ max. 450 mµ           **(yellow)**
                            **(blue)**
  (b) Normal vision      —        "Blue" cones      Chlorolabe      Chlorolabe +
  in central area                λ max. 450 mµ    λ max. 530 mµ      erythrolabe
                          **(blue)**      **(blue-green)**    λ max. 560 mµ
                                             **(orange-red)**

                                        **(yellow)**

                         **(white)**
  (c) Central foveal      —        —      Chlorolabe      Chlorolabe +
  vision                              max. 530 mµ       erythrolabe
                                   **(blue-green)**    λ max. 560 mµ
                                             **(orange-red)**

                                 **(yellow = white)**

FIG. 73.22. See text.

FIG. 73.23. See text.

minute, then the visual acuity is $(1/1.321 =)$ 0.756. The average normal eye can resolve two points when the visual angle is 1 minute (60 seconds). The maximum acuity measured with a Landolt C (see below) is about 2.1. As an object is moved away from the eye its visual angle becomes progressively smaller. Consequently, those details of form and structure which subtend an angle of a minute or more at the nearer point and are therefore visible, gradually become imperceptible with increasing distance. In other words, in order to see an object at a distance as clearly as when it is near the eye, it would need to be increased proportionately in size (see fig. 73.22).

In determining the visual acuity, figures such as the broken circle **C** of Landolt or Snellen's prong, **E**, painted black on a white ground and in graded sizes are employed. The subject is seated at a distance of 6 meters (20 feet) and a figure is placed with the gap of the **C** or the prongs of the **E** turned to the right or left; he is asked to say in which position the figure is directed. The width of the lines composing the figures and the gap in the **C**, or the spaces between the prongs of the **E**, subtend angles of various degrees, depending on the size of the figure, when placed at a distance of 6 meters. The width of the whole figure is five times the thickness of its parts. By finding the smallest figure whose position can be recognized the visual acuity of the subject (in terms of the visual angle) is ascertained. In testing the visual acuity for the fitting of glasses Snellen's *test type* is most commonly employed. This test is devised upon the basis that two points or lines separated by a space having a visual angle of 1 minute can be resolved by the average normal eye. The test type comprises nine rows of block letters printed in black upon a white card. The rows are arranged in descending order of size from above down. The width of the lines forming the letters of the first row subtends an angle of 1 minute at 60 meters from the eye, whereas that of the letters in the other rows, two to nine, have a visual angle of 1 minute at 36, 24, 18, 12, 9, 6, 5 and 4 meters, respectively. The card is placed in a good light, the patient is seated facing it at a distance of 6 meters and asked to read down as many rows as he can. The visual acuity is expressed as a fraction, the numerator being the distance at which the subject is seated from the card and the de-

nominator the distance at which the letters could be read by the normal eye. Thus, if he reads the seventh row of letters, i.e., those with a visual angle of 1 minute at 6 meters his vision is 6/6 or normal. If, on the other hand, he can see distinctly only as far as the fourth row, which the normal eye can read at 18 meters, his vision is 6/18; if as far as the third row his vision is 6/24, and so on, for any other row which he is just able to read.

Knowing the distance of the nodal point of the eye from the retina and the visual angle, the size of the retinal image of an object can be calculated (p. 1380, 1381). With a visual angle of 1 minute the space on the retina separating two point images is 4.4 $\mu$. The diameter of the space occupied by a foveal cone is given by different observers as between 2.5 and 4.0 $\mu$. Even if the higher of these figures is taken, then the image of two dots separated by 4.4 $\mu$ would fall upon two cones separated by a single unstimulated cone or by one stimulated differently, i.e., by the image of the interspace (fig. 73.23).

From such calculations it has been argued that the distance between cone centers is the limiting factor in discriminating two points or thin lines, for obviously with an interspace less than a cone width the two dots would fall upon a single cell, and from what is known of the nerve impulse it cannot be admitted that two parts of a visual receptor, upon receiving simultaneously different types of stimulus, can give rise to dissimilar sensations.

Difficulties stand in the way of so simple an explanation. The eyes, even with the most exact fixation, are constantly executing fine movements (subtending as much as 10'), and this means that the retinal image does not stimulate only one group of cones, but must be constantly shifting its position. This theory must also make the assumption that when the angular distance separating two points is about the diameter of a cone the two images must be dodged about with almost incredible precision, so that they come to lie not on adjacent cones (see fig. 73.23) but on two cones separated by an unstimulated cone or by one stimulated differently. Adler concluded from his experiments, in which fixation as exact as possible was secured, that a point image moves over from 2 to 4 cones at least. Furthermore, the size of the image on the retina cannot, owing to the diffusion of light, be calculated with the precision implied by the foregoing calculations (see below). It is true that the smallest visual angle recorded (28") for the space between two visually discrete objects

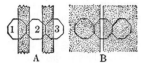

FIG. 73.24. Description in text.

would give a retinal image of the same order of magnitude as the diameter of a cone—a fact which fits the theory that the latter is the limiting factor. Nevertheless, it is probable that the correlation is little more than a coincidence.

Wilcox and Purdy suggest that the essential factor is the total illumination of the central cone as compared with its fellow on either side. Thus, in figure 73.24 A, cone 2 receives more light than cones 1 and 3. There is no reason then theoretically why the interspace separating two lines could not be narrower than the width of a single cone and still be recognizable. A limit would be reached, however, when the white interspace was reduced to about half the width of a cone; then all three cones must be illuminated equally. It may be asked, what essential difference is there between the minimum visible (p. 1364) and the minimum separable, that the minimum visual angle should be so much greater in the one instance than in the other? Two parallel black lines upon a white surface are recognized as separate because a third white line is seen between them. Why then, provided it is bright enough can it not be seen, even though reduced to an almost infinitesimal width? The difference in the two instances appears to be a matter of the background and may be illustrated by fig. 73.24 B. A bright light upon an extensive background illuminates a single row of cones, whereas all cones for a distance on either side are unilluminated. According therefore to the conception of Wilcox and Purdy, no difference exists, in so far as the fundamental retinal process is concerned, between the minimum visible and the minimum separable.

There is one aspect of visual acuity which is probably of far more importance than appears at first sight. It might be supposed that the highest visual acuity would only be obtained if there existed an exactly one to one relationship between each receptor and its optic nerve fiber. It must be remembered, however, that there are, in and around the central fovea, not only midget bipolar cells but numerous flat and brush types also and that these presumably collect information from numerous receptors. Moreover, ganglion cells may again collect information from several of these bipolar cells. The fields of these cells certainly overlap, which incidentally may have considerable advantaged in preventing the development of blind spots or scotomas when individual cells

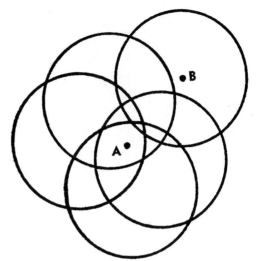

FIG. 73.25. Diagram illustrating the effect of overlapping receptive fields on visual acuity. For explanation see text.

degenerate. The situation is diagrammatically represented in figure 73.25 where the circles represent the overlapping fields of five bipolar cells. A study of this figure shows that the field in question must be covered by at least these five fields, and that it can be subdivided into numerous areas in which from one to five of the receptive fields in question may be affected. For example, a receptor situated at point A would affect four out of the five bipolars, but one situated at point B would affect only one. Thus position on the retina is specified by the particular pattern of bipolar cells which are stimulated. Moreover it has been shown that within any one receptive field the center is generally the most sensitive part and that a greater stimulus becomes necessary to elicit a response from the margins of the field; this means that a still greater specificity can be achieved in the pattern of response to stimulation of any particular point in the retina. The point A lies on the margins of fields 1, 2, 4, and 5 and therefore stimulates them all rather weakly, but point B affects field 3 maximally and the other fields not at all. Every point stimulated in the area under discussion thus evokes a particular and specific pattern of responses from the bipolar cells both with respect to the grouping of cells affected and also with respect to the frequency of impulses generated, since these depend on the intensity of the stimulus and the position within the receptive field.

As with other faculties of the eye, no absolute and constant value can be given for the minimum separable. It varies greatly with several factors, viz., (a) the *intensity of illumination* of the test

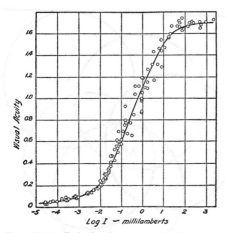

Fig. 73.26. Relation between visual acuity and illumination. (After Hecht.)

object, (b) the spectral character of the light, (c) the region of the retina stimulated and (d) the size of the pupil.

The resolving power of the eye for two points increases with the illumination, as illustrated in fig. 73.26. This is a fact difficult to explain. It might be thought that as long as the illumination was above the threshold for a just perceptible sensation, increase in the intensity of the light would be without influence upon the threshold for the minimum separable. Two theories which have been proposed to account for the phenomenon will be mentioned, not because they give any final answer to the problem, but because they bring up some interesting points.

Hartridge proposes a theory based upon the aberrations of the optical system of the eye and the ability of the retina to discriminate between small differences of light intensity (p. 1341). The retinal image is not clearly defined but is blurred by diffusion circles or bands, caused by the diffraction of light at the pupillary margin and to colored fringes (chromatic aberration, p. 1394). Assuming the pupil to be 3 mm. in diameter and a foveal cone $3.2\mu$. across, he made the following calculations of the light distribution on the retina caused by a white line separating two dark areas. The illumination of the row of cones corresponding to the center of the line image was taken as 100. The illumination of the next row was 31%, of the next 9%. The diffusion bands thus virtually increase the width of the image of the white line beyond that indicated by calculations from the visual angle, and encroach upon the dark boundaries. The fine movements of the eyes are continually shifting the image and even the slightest movement will cause the line of junction between the outermost diffusion band and the dark area to move from one row

of cones to another. A row of cones is therefore stimulated at one instant at a different intensity from that at the next. If the difference in light intensity is greater than 10% it is appreciated, and thus a gap between the two dark areas is detected. Now the threshold for discrimination of differences in light intensity varies with the illumination (p. 1342). Consequently, when the illumination is reduced, the difference between the intensity of the outermost diffusion bands and of the dark areas is not perceived, i.e., the shift of the line of junction from one cone to the next causes no sensation. The difference between the illumination of the inner and outer bands may be still detectable, but the width of the bright line will be reduced. With further reduction in the illumination and the consequent raising of the threshold for intensity discrimination the white image becomes still narrower and finally, when the angular width is about 1″, the dark areas fuse across it.

Hecht's theory postulates a change in the "grain" of the retina as a result of variations in illumination. The retina, according to Hecht, is made up of sensitive elements of different intensity thresholds distributed in a statistical manner similar to that of other populations. At low levels of illumination only a proportion of these elements (i.e., rods with the lowest threshold) are excited. The active elements are therefore farther apart and the "grain" of the sensitive surface is relatively coarse. As the light intensity increases, the thresholds of more and more elements are exceeded. More rods function, that is, the number of active elements is increased and the "grain" of the retina is finer. As the illumination rises further, cones, first those with the lowest thresholds and later less sensitive ones, become active. The maximal effect of increasing the illumination upon the resolving power is reached when the entire rod and cone population is responding (see fig. 73.26). Objections to both of the theories just outlined could be cited; several observations indicate that the threshold for the minimum separable is not dependent entirely upon retinal factors but that central processes play an important part.

The influences of such processes as the lateral inhibition already mentioned in sharpening up edges and increasing contrast between illuminated and unilluminated areas must also be important in determining visual acuity at different brightness levels.

The resolving power of the eye is greater for monochromatic light than for a mixed light source such as daylight when the two have equal illuminating values. This fact is due to the absence of chromatic aberration in the former instance. Monochromatic yellow light (575 m$\mu$) gives the highest value, next in order come green, red and blue.

Theoretically the resolving power must .be limited by half the wave-length of the light and should therefore be higher in the short-wave end of the spectrum. However, the amount of light visible in the short-wave end falls off very rapidly and as shown on pp. 1362, 1363 the visual acuity of the blue mechanism is conspicuously lower than that of either the green or the red mechanisms. For these reasons, the middle region of the spectrum in practice shows the highest acuity. Hartridge has suggested that the visual acuities in white light and in monochromatic lights remain approximately the same, in spite of the fact that there may be blue, green and red-sensitive cones, because the cones of the different types may be grouped together in clusters in a more or less random way and the eye tends to fixate the image on the most appropriate cluster.

Three factors are involved in the effect of pupillary size upon the resolving power of the retina. Increase in diameter allows more light to enter the eye and therefore increases the illumination of the retinal image and raises the visual acuity. Diffraction is also reduced by widening the pupillary aperture which will tend to improve the definition of the image. On the other hand, narrowing the pupil diminishes chromatic aberration. The optimum pupillary size lies between maximum constriction and full dilation, namely, at a diameter of about 3 mm.

With ordinary illuminations the visual acuity is some twenty times greater at the fovea than in any outlying part of the retina. In the dark adapted eye (p. 1342) the peripheral retina has a much higher value than the fovea.

The illumination of the field surrounding the test object (the surround) has an important influence upon the resolving power of the eye. A uniform increase in the illumination of the surround up to one-tenth that of the test object progressively increases visual acuity. Raising the illumination of the surround from this point to equality with the test object causes a slight reduction in visual acuity and, when the surround becomes brighter than the test object, there is a decided depression. A very bright but small light source situated in the neighborhood of the test object, e.g., a motor head light, causes a very marked lowering of the visual acuity. The effects caused by such concentrated sources of light are referred to as "glare." If the small light source is not too bright and especially if the surround is dark, little depressing effect upon the acuteness of vision is produced, indeed there may be an improvement due to the accompanying pupillary constriction.

Fig. 73.27. See text. (After Adler.)

THE DISPLACEMENT THRESHOLD OR THE VERNIER ACUITY. These terms are applied to the visual faculty of recognizing a break in the contour of a border, a variation in width of a line or the lack of alignment of two straight lines placed end to end. This power of the eye is some ten times greater than its ability to resolve two points. A break in a line subtending an angle as small as 5″ or even 1″ can be detected under optimal conditions. It seems quite certain that this visual faculty is not limited by cone diameter, for the break must lie on a single cone, and the lines on both sides of the break on the same row of cones (fig. 73.27). It is probable that the underlying mechanism is different from that governing the threshold for the discrimination of two points. For example, its threshold is only slightly raised by increasing the illumination (p. 1368).

Anderson and Weymouth offer an interesting theory to account for the extraordinary accuracy of the vernier acuity. They suggest that the slight but continuous eye movements shift the line image over the retina, causing successive stimulus patterns. The averaging of the successive patterns gives a sense of position which they call *retinal local sign*. The longer the lines the greater are the number of patterns presented to consciousness and, consequently, the more accurate is the averaging process. For details of the view of these authors the reader is referred to their original paper.

Hubel and Wiesel have recently (1959) shown by electrical recording from single cells in the visual cortex of the cat that some of these cells respond only to linear patterns of light on the retina, and that the orientation of these linear patterns may determine whether a given cell will discharge.

SOME PRACTICAL CONSIDERATIONS WITH REGARD TO LIGHTING. Besides reducing visual acuity, glare causes discomfort and one instinctively attempts to protect the eyes by closing the lids or raising the hand as a shield; the pupil constricts. A constant source of glare, even of mild degree, results in eye strain. Glare has been classified into three types—veiling, dazzling and blinding. *Veiling glare* is that due to strong light which, being uniformly superimposed upon the retinal image, reduces contrast. The light reflected from a printed page under a bright sky is an example. *Dazzling glare* is due to scattered light in the ocular media which does not form part of the retinal image. Such glare can be produced by a strong light shining into the eye from an angle of about 45°. *Blinding glare* results when one looks directly at a very bright light. It is due to an actual reduction of retinal sensitivity.

For moderately fine work, such as reading, sewing, typesetting, etc., the illumination of the objects should not be less than from 10 to 20 foot candles. An illumination of 10 foot candles is sufficient for reading ordinary black type on good paper, but the higher illumination is necessary if the printing or the paper is of poor quality. The effect of lighting upon the performance of typesetters, mail sorters and others engaged in fine work has been the subject of a number of investigations. Raising the illumination has been found to increase the rapidity and accuracy of the work by from 10 to 16 per cent and to reduce eye strain and general fatigue. The maximum efficiency appears to be reached when the illumination is about 20 foot candles. The lighting should be diffuse, and naked bright light sources which could cause glare eliminated. The central field should receive additional lighting so that its illumination will be from 5 to 10 times that of the surround. The constant use of the eyes in poor lighting leads to ocular strain and fatigue with consequent headache. It may cause increase in pulse rate and even nausea; ultimately serious eye defects, especially in the young, may result. The quality of the light is also an important factor. The nitrogen light, being more homogeneous, gives a higher visual acuity than the ordinary electric light bulb; the kerosene lamp lies between the two.

THE PERCEPTION OF MOVEMENT. This is the most primitive of the visual functions; in disease it is the last to fail and is the first to return should any improvement in vision occur. The peripheral (extrafoveal) retina is more specially differentiated for the perception of movement than for other purposes. It is a familiar fact that a slight movement is readily detected even if the moving object is not in the direct line of vision, i.e., when its image falls upon the peripheral retina, and the eyes are not fixed upon it. The most sensitive part of the retina is from 10° to 15° from the fovea, but sensitivity diminishes progressively towards the periphery. In the region of maximum sensitivity the angular velocity of a just perceptible movement is from one half to one minute per second, provided that there are stationary objects in the visual field to serve as reference points.

When such are absent the angular velocity must be from 10 to 20 times as great in order for the movement to be perceived. On the other hand, if the angular velocity is very great the movement is not perceived; owing to visual persistence a very rapidly moving object appears as a stationary streak. The total distance travelled, i.e., the displacement of the object, as well as the angular velocity is, of course, a factor in movement perception. The minimum displacement is about 17 seconds of arc, under optimal conditions. The sensitivity of the retina to movement is lower in the dark-adapted than in the light adapted eye. Barlow has suggested that the on-off fibers play a large part in the detection of movement.

When the eyes are stationary but the body or head is moved, an *apparent* movement is given to objects in the visual field. To a subject travelling in a train, near objects often appear to move in the opposite direction to the direction of travel, whereas those in the background appear to move with the moving vehicle. Apparent movements of surrounding objects also occur when the eye is displaced slightly by pressure upon it with the finger tip, or as a result of involuntary contraction of the eye muscles. These apparent movements are attributed to the successive stimulation of groups of receptors as the images move over the retina. When the eyes are moved voluntarily from one object to another in the visual field, images must sweep over the retina in a similar fashion, yet there is no apparent movement of stationary objects. An allied phenomenon and one which offers a similar problem to be solved is seen in cutaneous sensation. We are able, for example, to distinguish between the movement of the finger over a stationary object and the movement of an object over a motionless finger. In both instances receptors are stimulated successively. Conversely, the movement of an object is perceived when it is followed by the eyes, although the position of its retinal image does not alter. It is quite evident that the perception of movement is very complex and cannot yet be explained in all its aspects upon physiological grounds. It is suggested that the absence of an apparent movement of stationary objects when the eyes are turned from one part of the visual field to another is to be explained upon the basis of *attention*. The attention exercised by the observer in changing the fixation of his eyes from the one to the other point compensates, it is believed, for the movements of the images over the retina. In other words, the successive stimulation of visual receptors is ignored because the point to which the eyes are to be turned engages the attention at the moment that the eye movement takes place, or even before. The perception of the movement of an object pursued by the eyes must also depend upon cerebral processes.

Apparent movement is also produced by the stimulation of closely approximated retinal areas in rapid succession by a series of images of a stationary object. The two main factors determining this so-called *stroboscopic illusion* of movement are the time interval between the stimuli and the *angular separation* of the successive retinal images. A visual sensation of smooth motion is produced when the angular separation is about 1 degree or less and the intervals between the stimuli about $\frac{1}{10}$ second. At intervals of $\frac{1}{30}$ second or less no sensation of movement is produced. The illusion of motion is also lost if the time intervals are lengthened to $\frac{1}{5}$ second or greater, the impressions then becoming discrete.

*Irradiation.* Owing to chromatic and spherical aberration the images on the retina are not formed of geometrical points of light, but rather of bright points surrounded by diffusion circles. For this reason, and also probably as a result of the spread of the effect of the stimulus (*irradiation*) to neighboring neural elements of the retina, or even within the visual area in the brain, a bright area on a dark ground appears larger than a dark one of the same size upon a bright ground. In either instance the image of the bright area encroaches upon that of the black area (see fig. 73.1).

INTERMITTENT RETINAL STIMULATION; FLICKER. When the retina is stimulated intermittently by a series of light flashes as may be produced by interrupting a continuous light by a rotating notched disc or by reflecting light from a rotating disc divided into alternate black and white sectors, a characteristic flickering or unpleasant glittering sensation is experienced when the periodic stimulation reaches a certain frequency. This is due to each light stimulus falling upon the retina during the time of the positive after image (p. 1372) of its predecessor. The suppression of the after image by the second stimulus causes the first sensation to end more abruptly, and, through contrast, to render the succeeding one more brilliant. Upon further increasing the speed of rotation and, in consequence, the frequency (number per second) of the light stimuli, fusion results and the flicker disappears, to be replaced by a continuous sensation having a brilliance equal to the mean of the two (bright and dark) impressions; the frequency at which this occurs is called the *critical fusion frequency* (C.F.F.). If at the instant of fusion the illumination of the bright patch in millilamberts

be designated $a$, its area designated $b$, and the total area of the disc, $c$, then the sensation produced is equal to that which would result from a continuous stimulus having the value $(a \times b)/c$. This is known as the Talbot-Plateau law. It accounts for the well-known fact that a gray sensation of any depth can be matched by throwing black and white images alternately and at a suitable frequency upon the retina. Similarly, at the critical fusion frequency, white and red images give a sensation of pink; blue and red, a sensation of purple; yellow and green, yellowish green, and so on. These effects are simply explained by *visual persistence*, that is, the sensation evoked by one stimulus has not ceased before the next one is produced, thus a blend of the two sensations in consciousness results. The law holds true only for moderate light intensities.

The value of the C.F.F. is variable, depending upon several conditions the most influential of which is the intensity of the light, the value rising as the intensity increases. That is, a higher rate of stimulation is required for fusion as the intensity of the illumination is increased. The influence of light intensity is embodied in the Ferry (1892)-Porter (1906) law which states that the *critical fusion frequency is directly proportional to the logarithm of the light intensity*. Thus, $n = k \log I + k'$ where $n$ equals flashes per second at the instant of fusion, and I the light intensity; $k$ and $k'$ are constants involving the size of the stimulated area and the sensitivity of the observer's eye.[2]

The Ferry-Porter law is valid, however, only under certain special conditions; it holds over moderate ranges of illumination of the test object when the image is restricted to the fovea. Above and below this middle range the linear relationship between the logarithm of the intensity and the critical fusion frequency does not hold. When the value of $n$ is plotted against log I at low and at high intensities the points fall on two straight lines, one at low the other at high intensities. It is believed that these represent respectively rod and cone function, a conception borne out by the results of Hecht and associates and of Lythgoe and Tansley.

Hecht found that with a stimulus restricted to the fovea (cones) the relationship was linear for a middle range of illumination, but above this the curve flattened out, below, it formed a very gentle

[2] Determination of the critical fusion frequency (C.F.F.) offers an accurate and convenient method for comparing the brightness of differently colored lights. It is especially valuable in this regard because of our natural tendency to confuse the brightness of a color with its hue or saturation.

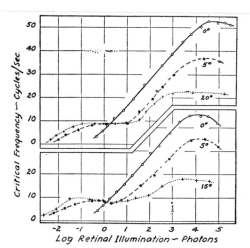

FIG. 73.28. Relation between critical frequency and log *I* for white light with a 2° field in four retinal locations; at the fovea, and at 5°, 15°, and 20° above the fovea. (After Hecht from Hecht and Verrijp.)

curve. With the image on extrafoveal regions the data form two intersecting straight lines, one at lower the other at higher intensities, the former presumably represents rod function, the latter peripheral cone function (fig. 73.28).

Lythgoe and Tansley observed that during dark adaptation the C.F.F. falls in both the fovea and the peripheral parts of the retina when the intensity of the test light was high (6.8 foot candles). At low intensities (0.020 foot candles) the C.F.F. also falls at the fovea, but rises in the peripheral retina. Now, as judged by other criteria, only cones are functioning at high intensities whether the fovea or the peripheral retina is being tested, at low intensities only rods. Also, it was found by Lythgoe and Tansley that when red light was used for testing (rods insensitive), and in a case of night blindness (defective rods) a fall in the value of the C.F.F. occurs during dark adaptation. The fall in the value with high illuminations of the test object is due presumably to the cones, and the rise with low illuminations, to the rods. At moderate illuminations of the test object a fall occurs during the first 5 minutes of dark adaptation (due to cones), (see p. 1142) followed by a rise (due to rods). The critical frequency due to the rods is highest with dark surrounds; that due to cones is increased by bright surrounds, the maximum being reached when the brightness of the latter and of the test object are equal.

A study of the retinal potentials (ch. 72) during intermittent stimulation shows that when a light flash falls upon the retina during the "off effect" of a preceding stimulus, the *d* wave is interrupted and a pronounced negative dip occurs. This is an exaggerated *a* deflection. The negative deflection is followed by a large positive swing which, if the second stimulus occurs soon after the first, is simply the return of the momentarily interrupted "off effect" of the first. If the interval between the two is greater, the upswing is higher, and is then due to the *b* deflection of the after coming stimulus. Thus, if the light flashes are so timed that each interrupts the "off effect" of its predecessor, a series of regular ripples appears in the electroretinogram which apparently are the cause of the flickering sensation. No negative dip occurs nor do the characteristic ripples appear if a flash falls upon the retina *before* the "off effect" of the preceding one—a continuous sensation should therefore result.

AFTER IMAGES. If the gaze is directed to a bright white light for a moment and the eyes then closed or turned towards a dark surface, an image of the light slowly floats into view, becomes more distinct for a time and then gradually fades. Similarly, if the eyes are stimulated by a colored light or a brightly colored object of any sort, and then darkened, an image of the same color appears. These are called *positive after images.* If, instead of closing the eyes or turning them to a dark surface after looking at a white light, the retinas are stimulated a second time and diffusely by white, e.g., by directing the eyes to a sheet of paper, one then sees a dark image against a white ground. This is called a *negative after image.* If the first stimulus was colored, then this after image is in the complementary color. Negative after images of colored objects are the cause of the phenomenon known as *successive contrast.*

On the basis of Young's theory of color vision, the phenomenon of negative after images is due to adaptation of one or other of the three types of mechanism by the first stimulus. A mechanism which has responded to a given stimulus will not for a time respond as strongly to one of the same type. White light stimulates all three mechanisms. The negative after image which appears upon applying a circumscribed and then a diffuse white stimulus to the retina is, therefore, a dark patch against a white background. When the object looked at is colored and the retina is then stimulated by directing the eyes to a white surface, the image is in the complementary color because those mechanisms which had not been previously stimulated respond more vigorously than the ones stimulated by the colored object. For example, if the object looked at is red, the red mechanism is less excited by a subsequent stimulus of white; those sensitive to green and to violet remain relatively normal and so give a sensation which is the complementary of red, namely, a bluish green.

Positive after images are apparently due to

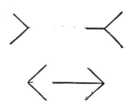

FIG. 73.29. Optical illusion. The distance from *A* to *B* appears to be greater than that from *B* to *C*; they are the same.

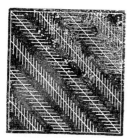

FIG. 73.30. Illusion of size. The vertical lines are the same length.

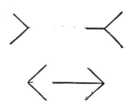

FIG. 73.31. Zollner's lines. The long diagonal lines appear to converge; actually, they are parallel.

chemicophysical changes in the receptors of the retina caused by and outlasting the stimulus—a form of visual persistence.

OPTICAL ILLUSION. The brain may be deceived by imitations of certain effects upon which our visual judgments of the size, shape and distance of objects are based. Visual errors of this nature are called optical illusions or optical deceptions. Some interesting examples are shown in figs. 73.29 to 73.31.

## REFERENCES

ADLER, F. H. Arch. Ophth., 1934, 11, 6.
ANDERSON, E. E. AND WEYMOUTH, F. W. Am. J. Physiol., 1923, 64, 561.
ARDEN, G. B. AND WEALE, R. A. J. Physiol., 1954, 125, 417.
BRINDLEY, G. S. J. Physiol., 1953, 122, 332; 1954, 124, 400.
CRAIK, K. J. W. J. Physiol., 1938, 92, 406; Proc. Roy. Soc. London, ser. B., 1940, 128, 232.
FLAMANT, F. AND STILES, W. S. J. Physiol., 1948, 107, 187.
HARTRIDGE, H. J. Physiol., 1922, 57, 52; 1946, 105, 5 P.
HECHT, S. AND VERRIJP, C. D. J. Gen. Physiol., 1933, 17, 251.
HUBEL, D. H. AND WIESEL, T. N. J. Physiol., 1959, 148, 574.
KÖNIG, A. S. B. Akad. Wiss. Berlin, 1894, p. 577.

LYTHGOE, R. J. Med. Res. Council Spec. Rep., 1926, No. 104; 1932, No. 173.
LYTHGOE, R. J. AND TANSLEY, K. Med. Res. Council Spec. Rep., 1929, No. 134.
STILES, W. S. Proc. Roy. Soc. London, ser. B, 1939, 127, 64.
THOMSON, L. C. AND WRIGHT, W. D. J. Physiol., 1947, 105, 316.
WEALE, R. A. J. Physiol., 1953, 121, 548.
WILCOX, W. W. AND PURDY, D. M. Brit. J. Psychol., 1933, 23, 233.
WILLMER, E. N. AND WRIGHT, W. D. Nature, 1945, 156, 119.
WRIGHT, W. D. J. Ophth. Soc. Am., 1952, 42, 509.

*Monographs and Reviews*

ABNEY, W. DE W. Researches in colour vision and the trichromatic theory. Longmans Green, London, 1913.
ADLER, F. H. Physiology of the eye. Kimpton, London; 1953.
BRINDLEY, G. S. Progress in biophysics. 1957, 8, 50.
BRINDLEY, G. S. Physiology of the retina and visual pathway. Arnold, London, 1959.
CAJAL, RAMON Y. Textura del sistema nervioso del hombre y de los vertebrados. Moya, Madrid, 1904.
CHAPANIS, A. Human factors in undersea warfare Nat. Res. Council. 1949.
DARTNALL, H. J. A. Visual pigments. Methuen, London, 1957.
DETWILER, S. R. Vertebrate photoreceptors. Macmillan, New York, 1943.
DUKE-ELDER, W. S. Text-book of ophthalmology. Kimpton, London, 1932.
GRANIT, R. Sensory mechanisms of the retina. Oxford University Press, London, 1947.
GRANIT, R. Reception and Sensory Perception, Yale University Press, New Haven, Conn., 1955.
HARTLINE, H. K. Neural mechanisms of vision. Harvey Lectures, 37, 39, 1941–1942.
HECHT, S. Physiol. Rev., 1937, 17, 239.
HELMHOLTZ, H. VON. Treatise on physiological optics, Ophth. Soc. Am., 1924.
HOUSTOUN, R. A. Vision and colour vision. Longmans, London, 1932.
JUDD, D. B. Docum. Ophth., 1949, 3, 251.
KLUVER, H. (editor), Visual mechanisms. Biological Symposia, Jaques Cattell, Philadelphia, 1942.
LE GRANDE, Y. Optique, Physiologique. Vols. 1, 2 and 3, Paris, 1956.
LeGRANDE, Y. Light, colour and vision. Chapman and Hall, Ltd., London, 1957.
MANN, I. C. The development of the human eye. Cambridge University Press, London, 1928.
MORTON, R. A. AND PITT, G. A. J. Fortschr. Chem. org. Naturstoffe, 1957, 14, 244.
PARSONS, J. H. An introduction to the theory of colour vision. Cambridge University Press, London, 1924.
PIRENNE, M. H. Vision and the eye. Pilot Press, London, 1948.
PIRIE, A. AND VAN HEYNINGEN, R. Biochemistry of the eye, Thomas; Blackwell; Ryerson; 1956.
POLYAK, S. L. The retina. University of Chicago Press, Chicago, 1941.

RAWDON-SMITH, A. F. Theories of sensation. Cambridge University Press, London, 1939.

ROCHON-DUVIGNEAUD, A. Les yeux et la vision des vertébrés. Masson & Cie, Paris, 1943.

SCHULTZE, M. Arch. mikr. Anat., 1866, **2**, 175.

SORSBY, A., BENJAMIN, B., DAVEY, J. B., SHERIDEN, M. AND TANNER, J. M. Emmetropia and its aberrations. Med. Res. Council Spec. Rep., Series 293, H. M. Stationery Office, London, 1957.

STILES, W. S. Docum. Ophth., 1949, **3**, 138.

WALD, G. The chemical evolution of vision. Harvey Lectures, **41**, 117, 1945–1946.

WALD, G. Docum. Ophth., 1949, **3**, 94.

WALLS, G. L. The vertebrate eye. Cranbrook, 1942.

WHITESIDE, T. C. D. Problems of vision in flight at high altitudes. Butterworth, London, 1957.

WILLMER, E. N. Retinal structure and colour vision. Cambridge University Press, London, 1946.

WILLMER, E. N. Docum. Ophth., 1955, **9**, 235.

WOLFF, E. Anatomy of the eye and orbit. Blakiston, Philadelphia, 1933.

WRIGHT, W. D. Researches on normal and defective colour vision. Kimpton, London, 1946.

# 74

# THE DIOPTRIC MECHANISMS OF THE EYE. CATARACT.
# OPTICAL DEFECTS. INTRA-OCULAR FLUIDS

### Principles of Reflection and Refraction.
### Definitions and Terminology

Light falling upon a surface undergoes *absorption* and *reflection*, and, if the material is transparent, the rays are transmitted through it, either with or without *reflection*.

The proportions of rays falling upon an opaque unpolished surface which undergo absorption and diffuse reflection, respectively, vary with the character of the surface. A large part of the rays striking an unpolished white surface, e.g., a sheet of paper, are reflected but, being thrown off at different angles to the perpendicular, they do not meet at a focus in front of, or, if continued backwards, behind the surface. The light reflected from such a surface is said to be *diffuse*.

The greater proportion of the light striking a polished surface (e.g., a mirror) is reflected, but *the incident and reflected rays are always in the same plane and the angles (angles of incidence and of reflection) which they make with the perpendicular are equal*. This statement is true for any polished surface whatever its shape (fig. 74.1).

Reflected rays from a plane mirror are divergent; if continued backwards they would meet at a point situated at the same distance behind the mirror as the object emitting the light lies in front of it. The eye placed in the path of the reflected rays projects them to this point, where a *full-sized erect image* is formed (fig. 74.2). Since the rays do not actually meet at this point but only appear to do so, the image is called *virtual*.

THE FORMATION OF IMAGES BY SPHERICAL MIRRORS. A spherical mirror is the segment of a sphere; its reflecting surface may be *concave* or *convex*; its *center of curvature* is the center of a sphere of which the reflecting surface forms a part. The middle point of the curved surface is called the *pole* of the mirror, and a line passing through the pole and the center of curvature is termed the *principal axis*. The radius of the mirror is the distance from the pole to the center of curvature. Since the latter may lie on the same side as the source of light (concave mirror) or on the opposite side (convex mirror) the radius may be *positive* or *negative*, respectively.

Rays of light coming from a distant object, i.e.,

from infinity, are *parallel* (1 and 2, fig. 74.3); if they fall upon a *concave mirror* they are reflected as converging rays and meet in front of the mirror at a point (F) on the principal axis (p-o). This point (F) is the *principal focus* and the distance from it to the reflecting surface is the *focal length* or *focal distance* of the mirror. It lies in the principal axis, midway between the center of curvature and the surface of the mirror. A *real inverted image* of the object and *smaller* than it, is formed in front of the mirror at the principal focus, that is, in space. The rays from a near object are divergent; the reflected rays are therefore less strongly convergent than when the incident rays are parallel. If the object is at the center of curvature (C) of the mirror then the rays are reflected back to this point. When the object is at *a* between the center of curvature of the mirror and the principal focus, the rays meet beyond the center of curvature at A; when the object is at A the reflected rays meet at *a*. These two points are therefore reciprocally related and are called *conjugate foci*. An object placed between the mirror and its principal focus emits rays which upon reflection are widely divergent and cannot be brought to a focus in front of the mirror. Projected backwards they meet at a point behind the mirror where a *virtual erect* and greatly *enlarged* image is formed.

Parallel rays striking a *convex mirror* are reflected as *divergent* rays which if continued backwards would meet behind the mirror at the principal focus. To the eye they therefore appear to come from this point. Here a *virtual erect image*, smaller than the object, is formed (fig. 74.4).

The position of an image formed by a concave mirror can be found from the construction in figure 74.5. The object AB is situated beyond the center of curvature C. The rays AP and BO parallel to the principal axis MN after reflection meet and cross at the principal focus F. The images of the points A and B, therefore, lie somewhere on the lines PQ and OL. Now, if lines AD and BH be drawn to pass through C, these lines, known as secondary axes, will cut lines PQ and OL at *a* and *b* respectively. Thus, a small inverted real image *ab* is formed. The image is called real because the rays actually pass through *a* and *b*. The construc-

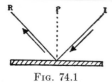

Fig. 74.1

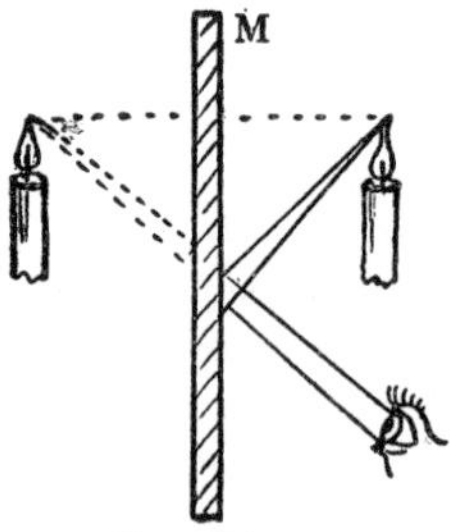

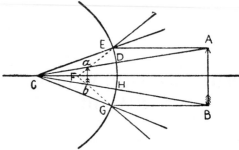

Fig. 74.6. Formation of a virtual erect image by a convex mirror.

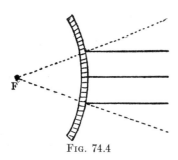

Fig. 74.2

tion of an erect virtual image by a convex mirror is shown in figure 74.6. The rays from the object AB diverge after reflection and appear to come from F (dotted lines); the image *ab* is formed at the intersection with the secondary axes AC and BC.

REFRACTION. Rays of light in passing obliquely from one transparent medium to another of a different optical density (e.g., from air to glass) are bent or refracted. If one medium is surrounded by the other (e.g., glass in air) the ray is refracted twice. In passing from the medium of lower to the one of higher optical density the rays are bent towards the perpendicular; in the transition from the denser to the rarer medium the bend is away from the perpendicular. With any two media the greater the obliquity of the incident rays the greater is the degree of refraction; rays perpendicular to the surface between the two media are not refracted. The ratio of the angle made by the incident ray (i.e., the ray falling upon the surface of the second medium) with the perpendicular (angle of incidence) to that made by the emergent ray (angle of refraction) is termed the *index of refraction*. The *refractive index* is the index of refraction when the incident rays enter a substance from a vacuum. In practice air is considered to be of the same optical density as a vacuum. The refractive index is expressed as the ratio of the sine of the angle of the incident ray (i) to sine of

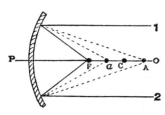

Fig. 74.3

Fig. 74.4

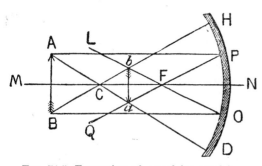

Fig. 74.5. Formation of a real inverted image by a concave mirror.

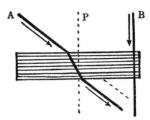

Fig. 74.7. The oblique ray (A) is refracted upon entering and leaving the block of glass. The emergent ray has the same direction as the entering ray but is not in the same line. P represents perpendicular. The ray B which strikes the glass surface perpendicularly is not refracted.

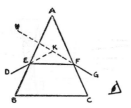

Fig. 74.8. ABC is a prism with the apex at A, the base BC, and the sides AB and AC. The angle of the prism is BAC. A ray of light DEFG is refracted at E and F as in figure [74.7]. The total amount of refraction, that is, the difference in direction between DE and FG, is represented by the angle DKH (the angle of deviation). If the eye is at G, the source of light, D, will appear to be at H. When the ray passing through the prism (EF) is parallel to the base (BC), the ray is said to traverse the prism symmetrically.

the angle of refraction (r), thus, refractive index = sine i/sine r. The refractive index is a measure of refractive power; it is 1.52 for crown glass and 1.66 for flint glass.

*Refraction by plane surfaces.* Oblique rays striking a medium with plane parallel surfaces, such as a sheet of glass, are refracted to an equal degree upon entering and emerging, but in opposite directions, i.e., towards and away from the perpendicular, respectively. The incident and emergent rays are therefore parallel though not quite in the same straight line (fig. 74.7). A *prism* has its sides inclined towards one another. Since a ray is refracted upon entering at one surface of the prism and again upon emerging at the other, and is bent so as to run more nearly perpendicular to the glass surface in the former instance and away from the perpendicular in the latter; it will be refracted each time towards the base of the prism (fig. 74.8).

*Lenses* are of two main types, *spherical* whose surfaces are the segments of spheres and *cylin-*

Fig. 74.9. Cross sections of lenses. A, planoconvex; B, biconvex; C, planoconcave; D, biconcave; E, convexoconcave; F, concavoconvex.

*drical.* There are six varieties of the former—*planoconvex, biconvex, planoconcave, biconcave, convexoconcave* and *concavoconvex* (see fig. 74.9). Many modern spectacle lenses are made in the convexoconcave or concavoconvex form in order to reduce distortion of the visual field when the wearer looks through a peripheral portion of the lens. Lenses of these two forms which also include a cylindrical element are described as *toric* lenses.

Convex lenses may be looked upon as a great number of truncated prisms with their bases directed towards the lens center. Concave lenses, on the other hand, are as a number of prisms arranged with their bases towards the periphery (fig. 74.10). It follows then that a symmetrical biconvex lens will bend rays to the same degree at equal distances from its center and bring them to a meeting point or focus, whereas concave lenses will cause divergence of the rays. In either instance the rays are bent towards the bases of the constituent prism.

*Refraction by convex lenses.* A line passing through the centers of curvature of the lens is termed the *principal axis of the lens.* Any other line intersecting the principal axis within the lens (i.e., a diagonal line) is called a *secondary axis.* The *radius* of curvature of the lens is the radius of a sphere of which the refracting surface forms a part. Rays passing through the principal axis are not refracted, for the incident and the emergent ray strike each surface perpendicularly, and the two surfaces at these points are parallel (see above). Moreover, rays in the secondary axes undergo only very slight refraction, and the incident and emergent rays, through not quite in a continuous line, are parallel, for again the surfaces which they pierce are parallel. The point where the principal axis is intersected by the secondary axes is termed the *optical center* or *nodal point* of the lens. In a biconvex lens with symmetrical surfaces the actual and the optical centers coincide, but in other biconvex lenses the nodal point may be situated nearer to one or other surface.

Light rays from a *distant object*, i.e., from infinity, are parallel (fig. 74.11). The point F where parallel rays meet after refraction is called the *principal focus.* The distance of this point from the lens is called the *focal length* or *focal distance of the lens.* The rays of a light placed at the prin-

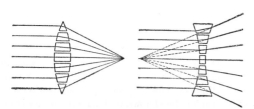

Fig. 74.10. See text.

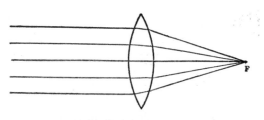

Fig. 74.11. See text.

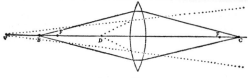

FIG. 74.12. See text.

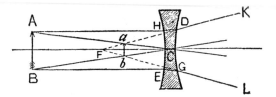

FIG. 74.15. Formation of a virtual erect image by a concave lens.

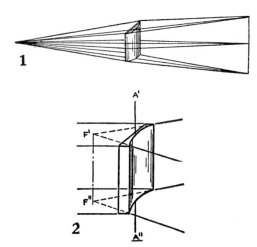

FIG. 74.16. 1, refraction by a convex cylinder. A point of light is brought to a focus as a line after refraction through a cylinder. 2, refraction of light by a concave cylinder. Rays of light striking the cylinder perpendicularly to the axis A'A" are diverged, and appear to be brought to a virtual focal line F'F". (After Duke-Elder.)

cipal focus traverse the same path but in the opposite direction, and emerge as parallel rays.

A *near object* emits divergent rays. If the source of light (fig. 74.12, B) is on the principal axis a little beyond the principal focus, an image is formed at a distance on the other side of the lens greater than its focal length (at C); when the object is placed in the second position (C) an image is formed at the first (B). These points, therefore, in respect to an object and its image, are interchangeable and are termed *conjugate foci*. If the object is situated at a distance exactly double the focal length of the lens the conjugate foci are at equal distances on the two sides of the lens. In all these instances a *real inverted image, smaller* than the object, is formed. If the source of light (D) lies between the lens and its principal focus, the rays, after passing through the lens, are widely divergent. To the eye placed in the path of the emergent rays they appear to come from a point (V) at a greater distance behind the lens than the actual. A *virtual, erect* and *enlarged image* is formed.

Light rays in passing through a *biconcave* lens are diverged (fig. 74.13), therefore a *true* image is not formed. The eye in the path of the rays takes no account of refraction, and the rays, in consequence, are projected backwards as straight lines which, meeting at a point on the other side of the

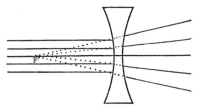

FIG. 74.13. See text.

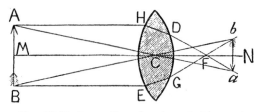

FIG. 74.14. Formation of an inverted image by a biconvex lens.

lens, from a *virtual erect image, smaller* than the object.

The formation of an image by a biconvex lens is shown in figure 74.14. AB is an object. The rays AH and BE lying parallel to the axis MN meet and cross at the principal focus F. The image of the point A will be at the intersection of the secondary axis AC with AHDF and that of B at the intersection of BC with BEGF. Thus, a small inverted image is formed at ab. The formation of an image by a concave lens is shown in figure 74.15. Rays AHDK and BEGL from points A and B of the object AB are diverged in passing through the lens and appear to come from the principal focus F, as shown by dotted lines. The image of A is formed at a and of B at b, where these lines are intersected by the secondary axes.

*Cylindrical lenses* (fig. 74.16) have one plane surface, the other may be *convex* (convex cylindrical lens) or *concave* (concave cylindrical lens). A convex cylindrical lens may be regarded as a section of a cylinder sliced down its long axis; its horizontal meridian is convex. Rays transmitted through it at right angles to its vertical axis are converged as they would be by a convex spherical lens. Light traversing its long axis is not refracted, the lens acting in this axis as a plate with parallel sides. A lens of this type may be looked upon as an infinite series of prisms arranged base to base in tiers. In the other type of cylindrical lens the horizontal meridian is concave; rays passing at right angles to the vertical axis are diverged.

*The diopter.* The converging or the diverging power of a lens depends upon the curvature of its surfaces (the greater the degree of curvature, the greater the refracting power) as well as upon the refractive index of the material of which it is composed. The focal length of a lens varies inversely with the refractive power and is therefore a convenient measurement for expressing the strength of a lens. The standard focal length is taken as 1 meter. The refracting power is expressed as the reciprocal of the focal length (given in meters), the unit being the *diopter* (D). Thus, the strength of a lens with a focal length of 1 meter is 1 diopter; of one with a focal length of 2 meters, ½ a diopter; of one having a focal length of ½ a meter, 2 diopters, and so on. The symbols + or − (+1 D, +2 D, −1 D, −2 D, etc.) are used respectively for a converging and a diverging lens. For example, if a concave lens has a refracting power of −1 D, a small virtual image of a distant object will be focussed 1 meter from the lens and on the same side as the object. A convex lens of a corresponding power (+1 D) will bring parallel rays to a true focus 1 meter behind the lens. The power of a cylindrical lens is expressed in a similar fashion.

THE REFRACTING MEDIA OF THE EYE. These are the cornea, the aqueous humor, the crystalline lens and the vitreous body. The refractive indices are given in the following table.

| | |
|---|---|
| Cornea | 1.37 |
| Aqueous humor | 1.33 |
| Crystalline lens (whole) | 1.42 |
| Vitreous body | 1.33 |

It will be noticed that the refractive indices of the cornea and of the aqueous humor and vitreous are approximately the same; for practical purposes they may be taken as identical and the eye then taken as having two refracting surfaces, (a) the anterior surface of the cornea in contact with

air, and (b) the lens surrounded by a common medium in so far as refraction is concerned. The greatest refraction occurs at the corneal surface (42 diopters); of less importance is refraction at the surfaces of the lens (19 diopters with accommodation relaxed and 36 diopters in full accommodation). The whole eye has a refracting power of between approximately 60 and 65 diopters. The value in the table above for the refractive index of the lens is calculated from the refractive power of of the lens as a whole, as though it were a homogenous structure, but such is not the case. On the contrary, the lens consists of an almost spherical *nucleus* with a high refractivity (1.41) surrounded by a zone called the *cortex* of lower optical density (1.38). The surrounding cortex is composed of a series of concave meniscus lens, as shown in figure 74.17. The peculiar structure of the lens accounts for the paradox that the mean value of the refractive indices of its parts (1.39) is less than the refracting power of the whole. Several important advantages are derived from this peculiar structure of the crystalline lens; it diminishes spherical aberration (p. 1393), tends to prevent the scattering of light within the eye and enhances the power of the lens to alter its converging power during accommodation (p. 1386).

THE CONSTANTS OF THE EYE. Knowing the curvatures of the refractive surfaces of the eye and the distances between them as well as the refractive indices of the media, the path taken by the rays of light can be determined and the image constructed. The values of the *constants of the eye* are given in the following table.

| | mm. |
|---|---|
| Position of anterior surface of cornea | 0 |
| Position of posterior surface of cornea | 0.6 |
| Position of anterior surface of lens | 3.6 |
| Position of posterior surface of lens | 7.2 |
| Position of retina | 24.1 |
| Radius of anterior surface of cornea | 7.7 |
| Radius of posterior surface of cornea | 6.8 |
| Radius of anterior surface of lens (distant vision) | 12.0 |
| Radius of posterior surface of lens | 6.0 |

The refractive indices of the media have been given above.

Construction of the image from the foregoing data is a very laborious proceeding. To start with, the image formed by the first refracting surface is constructed; this image now serves as the object

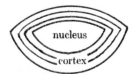

Fig. 74.17. Showing structure of the crystalline lens (diagrammatic).

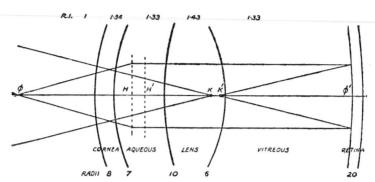

FIG. 74.18. The cardinal points of the eye. $\phi$, The anterior focus, 15.7 mm. in front of the cornea. $\phi'$, The posterior principal focus, 24.13 mm. behind the cornea—that is, upon the retina. H, H', the principal points, in the anterior chamber. KK', the nodal points, in the posterior part of the lens. (After Duke-Elder.)

for the next refracting surface, the second image in turn is the object of the third surface and so on. The matter is very much simplified, however, by constructing the *diagrammatic* or *schematic* eye by the application of the theorem of Gauss. This states that every optical system composed of spherical surfaces with their centers on the principal axis has three pairs of cardinal points. These are, two *principal points* (H and H', fig. 74.18), an *anterior* and a *posterior focal point* ($\varphi$ and $\varphi'$) and two *nodal points* (K and K').

The *first and second principal points* lie close together in the anterior chamber 2 mm. behind the cornea. Planes passing through the principal points and perpendicular to the axis are termed the *first* and *second principal planes*; an object in the first principal plane forms an erect *full-sized image* in the second and vice versa. The first and second principal points correspond, therefore, to the conjugate foci of a single lens.

The anterior focal point ($\varphi$) is situated 15.7 mm. in front of the cornea. Rays from this point in the axis would, after passing through the system, emerge as parallel rays. Parallel rays entering the system are focussed at $\varphi'$ which is situated on the retina. $\varphi$ and $\varphi'$ therefore correspond to the principal foci of a single lens.

The nodal points (K and K') also lie close together on the axis and near the posterior surface of the lens. They correspond to the optical center of a single lens. Rays passing through the nodal points are not refracted. A ray entering the system and passing through K appears to come from K' and emerges along a line parallel to that along which it entered. The following table for the schematic eye gives the distances of the six cardinal points from the anterior surface of the cornea.

|  | mm. |
|---|---|
| Anterior surface of cornea | 0 |
| First principal point, H | 1.7 |
| Second principal point, H' | 2.0 |
| First nodal point, K | 7.0 |
| Second nodal point, K' | 7.3 |
| Posterior focal point, $\varphi'$ | 24.1 |
| Anterior focal point, $\varphi$ | 15.7 |

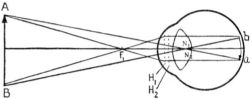

FIG. 74.19. Illustrating the inversion of the retinal image (schematic eye); $F_1$, first focal point; $H_1$ and $H_2$, first and second principal points; $N_1$ and $N_2$, first and second nodal points; AB, object; ab, image.

The two nodal points lie so close together that no significant error is entailed if they are taken as one; the same may be said for the principal points. Thus the compound optical system of the eye can be simplified to the so-called *reduced schematic eye* of Listing. This has a single ideally refracting surface situated in the anterior chamber 1.35 mm. behind the cornea and with a radius of 5.7 mm. The nodal point or optical center of the reduced eye lies 7.08 mm., the principal point 2.3 mm. and the posterior focal point 24.13 mm. behind the anterior corneal surface. The anterior focal point is 15.7 mm. in front of the cornea. The distance of the nodal point from the retina, i.e., the focal length of the eye, is $(24.13 - 7.08 =)$ 17.05 mm. The refracting power is therefore $(1000/17.05 =)$ 58.65 diopters.

By means of an X-ray beam, which is not refracted, projected into the eye Goldman and Hagen have measured the length of the globe in the living human subject. The value obtained (23.4 mm.) agrees closely with that of the schematic eye. The value for the total refractive power of the normal human eye, as determined by these observers, is also in close agreement, namely, 59.22 diopters.

THE FORMATION OF THE IMAGE ON THE RETINA. Knowing the foregoing measurements, the paths taken by the light rays can be drawn and a construction of the image upon the retina readily carried out. The formation of the retinal image is illustrated in figure 74.19. The large arrow A–B represents an object emitting divergent rays which are converged and brought to a focus to form the image represented by the small arrow a–b. The retinal image, it will be observed, is smaller than the object and inverted. For the sake of simplicity only a few rays are shown, two from a point at either end of the object and one from its center, but of course the surface of an object consists of an infinite number of points, each of which emits divergent rays. One of each pair of rays in the figure (solid line) passes unrefracted through a secondary axis (i.e., through the nodal point N), the ray from the upper part of the object to the lower part of the retina and vice versa. The other ray of each pair undergoes refraction and meets the corresponding unrefracted ray. Similarly, rays from a point on one side of the object will fall upon the retina as a point of light in the opposite part of the image. Thus, it is seen how the image on the retina becomes inverted. Of course we see objects in their true position. Reinversion is a cerebral function developed, probably, through the association of visual sensations with those of touch. If inverting spectacles are placed before the eyes, so as to produce an erect image of the environment on the retina, the visual world appears upside down for some time. But after a period of confusion lasting several weeks the visual environment appears the correct way up. On removing the spectacles only a short period of confusion results.

The idea that the retinal image is inverted was at first difficult to believe. Kepler (1604) inferred from his optical studies that this must be so, but it was Scheiner (1625) who furnished the proof by observing the back of an excised eye from which the sclerotic and choroid coats had been removed. The inverted image of an object was clearly visible upon the translucent retina. The inversion of the retinal image may also be demonstrated during life in persons of blonde complexion because their choroid contains little pigment. The subject is examined in a darkened room, the eye being turned towards a lighted candle placed well to the temporal side. An inverted image of the flame may be seen showing through the inner side of the wall of the globe.

The size of the retinal image is dependent upon the angle $a$ N $b$, (fig. 74.19) this—the angle subtended at the nodal point of the eye by an object in the visual field—is called the *visual angle*. The size of the image can be calculated if one knows the distance of the nodal point of the eye from the object and from the retina, and the size of the object. Thus in the figure A B is the object and

$a b$ its image. The triangle A N B and $a$ N $b$ being symmetrical, then

$$a b : A B = b \, N : B \, N$$
$$a b = A \, B \times b N / B N$$
$$b \, N = 17.05 \text{ mm.}$$
$$i = 17.05 \times O / d$$

$i$ is the size of the image, O the size of the object and $d$ its distance from the nodal point of the eye (17.05 = distance of retina from nodal point, see p. 1380). An object which subtends one minute of angle at the eye forms an image on the retina of size approximately 4.5 microns. The full moon subtends about $\frac{1}{2}°$, and its image on the retina would therefore be about 0.135 mm. diameter.

THE OPHTHALMOSCOPIC EXAMINATION OF THE EYE. Under ordinary circumstances we cannot see within the eye of another person, because only a limited quantity of light enters his eye through the relatively small pupillary aperture. It is like trying to look through a small window into a darkened room. Furthermore, of the light which enters the eye, a large part is absorbed by the pigment layer of the retina. Even when a light is brought close to the eye under observation, one is unable to see the retina, because the pencil of parallel rays which emerge do not enter the examiner's pupil unless his eye is directly in its path, and when he attempts to bring his eye into the proper position either his head comes between the light and the subject's eye or the light (if between himself and the subject) dazzles his sight.

These difficulties are overcome by means of the ophthalmoscope. This instrument consists of a small mirror with a central perforation through which the observer views the subject's eye. Light furnished by an electric lamp placed above the head of the patient is reflected from the mirror and the pencil of rays emerging from the subject's eye passes through the aperture of the mirror to the examiner's eye.

The invention of the ophthalmoscope is commonly attributed to Helmholtz (1851) but a crude device based upon the same principle was used by Babbage two years previously. The modern oph-

FIG. 74.20. Showing the two extreme pencils of parallel rays arising from the edges of the illuminated area of the fundus in an emmetropic eye. S, subject; O, observer. Vertical dotted line indicates the position in which the extreme ray pencils will enter the observer's eye. (After Duke-Elder.)

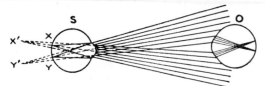

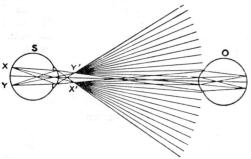

Fig. 74.21. Emergent rays from hypermetropic eye. A virtual erect image is formed at x′y′. (After Duke-Elder.)

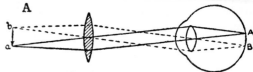

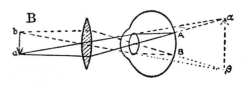

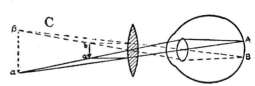

Fig. 74.22. Emergent rays from myopic eye which cross at x′y′ and then diverge; a real inverted image is formed at x′y′. (After Duke-Elder.)

Fig. 74.23. Path of the light from the eye in the indirect method of ophthalmoscopy in emmetropia, hypermetropia and myopia. (After Duke-Elder, *Text Book of Ophthalmology.*)

thalmoscope consists of a small electric tungsten lamp associated switch and battery; an optical system forms a beam of light which may be reflected from a small mirror into the patient's eye. The mirror has a small central aperture to permit the examiner to look through the mirror down the beam of light. Most ophthalmoscopes also have a chain of small lenses ranging from +20 D to −20 D between the aperture and the examiner's eye position, each of which may be brought into position to correct refractive errors both in the patient and in the examiner. The examiner seats himself 1 meter from the subject, adjusts the collimating optical system so that a divergent beam of light enters the subject's eye and looks through the sight hole in the mirror. If the observed eye is emmetropic (i.e., of normal refraction) a uniform red glow—the *red reflex of the fundus*—caused by reflection from the retina is seen lighting up the pupil. No detail, e.g., optic disc or retinal vessels, is visible. This is because the rays emerge from the subject's eye as diverging pencils of *parallel* rays. In order for an image of the subject's fundus to be formed upon the examiner's retina, rays from many pencils must enter his eye simultaneously. At a distance of 1 meter this is impossible, but can be effected if the observer brings his eye quite close to the patient's eye (see fig. 74.20). When the subject's eye is hypermetropic the rays composing the emergent pencils are *divergent*; it is therefore possible at a distance of 1 meter for many pencils to enter the observer's eye. The rays appear to meet behind the subject's eyes where a

*virtual erect* image is formed (fig. 74.21). When the observer moves his head the image moves in the *same* direction. In myopia, the emergent rays *converge*; they meet and cross in front of the eye. Again, diverging rays from several bundles enter the observer's eye and form a *real inverted* image in front of the subject's eye (fig. 74.22); it moves in a direction *opposite* to that of the examiner's head.

After this preliminary examination one or other of two methods of ophthalmoscopy—the indirect or the direct—may be employed. In the *indirect method* a separate biconvex lens with a focal length of 7.5 cm. (about 13 D) is held in front of the eye of the examinee. The observer seats himself 1 meter away and holds the lens in the path of the beam from the mirror and a short distance in front of the eye under observation. The subject turns his eye a little inwards in order to bring the optic disc into view, being directed, for example, to look at the observer's left ear if his left eye is being examined. The rays from the ophthalmoscope are converged upon the hand lens which converges them to the eye. They are more sharply converged by the refracting media and come to a focus in the vitreous. The retina is diffusely illuminated. By moving the hand lens toward or from the patient's eye his retina is brought into focus and the optic disc (Plate III) is clearly seen. The rays reflected from innumerable points of the patient's retina and after refraction emerge from his eye to form an image, the position of which differs according to the refractive state of the eye. The rays emerging from the emmetropic (normal) eye are parallel (fig. 74.23). They are converged

PLATE III

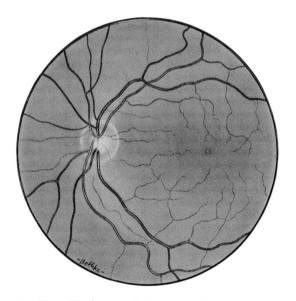

Normal Human Fundus. (From May's *Manual of Diseases of the Eye*, by permission of the author.)

by the hand lens and form a real, magnified and inverted image in the air between the hand lens and the examiner. This is focussed on the examiner's retina. In *hypermetropia* the rays issuing from the patient's eye are divergent, and appear to come from a magnified erect image behind the eye. The hand lens converts this into a small, inverted image in front of its principal focus (fig. 74.23). In *myopia* the emergent rays converge and form a large inverted real image; this is converted by the lens into a smaller image between it and its principal focus.

In the *direct method* a field of smaller area but of higher magnification is seen. The examiner brings the instrument as close as possible to the subject's eye, no hand lens being interposed. He views the subject's fundus with his own right eye, and the subject's left fundus with his left eye. In this position rays from both emergent pencils enter the eye of the observer, and, therefore, except when the observed eye is highly myopic, the details of the fundus can be seen. The image is always erect. The light, after coming to a focus on the retina, emerges from the emmetropic eye as parallel rays which are brought to a focus upon the observer's retina. If, however, the subject's eye is hypermetropic (as described above) the emergent rays will be divergent and can only be focussed by the examiner if he accommodates his eye or interposes a convex lens; if the observed eye is myopic the reflected rays are convergent; the examiner must then use a concave lens in order to focus the image upon his own retina. By the use of a concave or a convex lens which will just bring the image of the fundus into clear focus, and the refractive power of the lens required being known, the refractive error of the patient can be measured.

RETINOSCOPY; SKIASCOPY OR THE SHADOW TEST. This is a reliable objective method for determining the refraction of the eye. It is of special value in children and others for whom the reading of test type is impracticable, and for the detection of malingerers. The method depends upon the fact discovered by Bowman (1859) that the direction of the rays emerging from the eye varies with its state of refraction. Cuignet (1873) elaborated upon this discovery and brought the method into general use in the study of refractive errors. A retinoscope consists of a plane or concave mirror with a central aperture through which the examiner can look and inspect the pupil of the subject. A light source is placed several feet away and the mirror is used to reflect a beam of light into the pupil of the subject. Electric self-luminous versions of the retinoscope are also available. When the rays are reflected from a plane mirror they form a virtual image behind the reflecting surface. Tilting the mirror to one or the other side causes this image to move in the opposite direction. If a

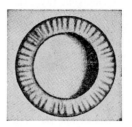

FIG. 74.24. Retinoscopy shadow. (After Duke-Elder.)

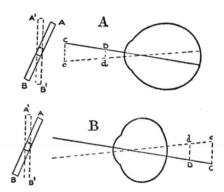

FIG. 74.25. Illustrating the movements of the shadow in retinoscopy. A, in *myopia*. When the mirror is in the position AB, the image is at D in the highly myopic eye, and at C in the less myopic eye. When the mirror is in the position A'B', the respective images are in the positions *d* and *c*. Since D*d* is less than C*c*, the lower the degree of myopia, the larger the excursion and the quicker the movement of the shadow. B, in *hypermetropia*. When the mirror is in the position AB, the image is at D, in the highly hypermetropic eye and at C in the less hypermetropic eye. When the mirror is in the position A'B' the respective images are at *d* and *c*. (After Duke-Elder, *The Practice of Refraction*.)

concave mirror were used the image, being formed in front of the mirror, would move in the same direction as the tilt of the mirror. Consequently, when a reflected light is thrown into the eye by means of a plane mirror, owing to a double reversal of the movement taking place (i.e., a movement of the mirror image which now serves as the luminous object in one direction and of the retinal image in the other), a change in the inclination of the mirror causes the illuminated area upon the retina to move in the *same* direction as the tilt. This movement of the illuminated area on the *retina* in relation to the tilt of the mirror is the same whatever the refractive state of the eye. But the rays from the illuminated area on the retina are directed back through the eye and after undergoing refraction emerge through the pupil; the direction of the movement of the illuminated area as it appears to an observer depends upon the direction of the emergent rays, that is, upon the state of refraction of the eye. The eye is examined with the retinoscope at a distance of 1 meter, in a dark room, a mydriatic, e.g., atropine or homatropine is usually employed.

If the subject is *hypermetropic* or *myopic* a pink glow fills his pupil except for a dark semilunar shadow on one side (see fig. 74.24). In the *emmetropic* eye light reflected from the illuminated area on the retina issues from ths pupil as diverging pencils of *parallel* rays (p. 1377). The rays meet and cross at the *far point* (punctum remotum), which for the normal eye is at infinity, that is, behind the observer. In a certain position of the mirror one or other of the pencils of rays (see fig. 74.25) enters the observer's eye. The subject's eye appears filled with a pink glare bounded on one side by a very faint shadow; when the mirror is tilted so that the interval between the pencils is in line with the observer's pupil, the subject's pupil is dark. Thus, in emmetropia the subject's pupil is either nearly uniformly bright or entirely dark. A bright area and a pronounced shadow are not seen together. In *myopia* the rays leaving the eye are convergent (fig. 74.22). If the myopia is *greater* than 1 D they meet and cross at the far point which lies somewhere between the subject and the observer. Therefore, when the mirror is tilted, up or down, or to one or other side, the shadow moves *against* it, i.e., in the opposite direction. If the myopia is *less* than 1 D the far point is behind the observer and, as in emmetropia, only a faint shadow is seen; it moves *with* the mirror. If the myopia is 1 D the far point is at the surface of the observer's eye and the subject's pupil appears, according to the tilt of the mirror, either completely dark or completely bright, that is, without any shadow. In *hypermetropia* the emergent rays are divergent and the far point is virtual; the rays appear to come from a point behind the mirror and therefore do not meet between the subject and observer. The shadow moves *with* the mirror.

In applying these facts to the correction of refractive errors, the movement of the shadow is noted and convex or concave glasses, according to whether the eye is hypermetropic or myopic, respectively, are placed in front of the subject's eye, until the pupil, as in a myopia of 1 D, appears uniformly bright or dark. This state when the shadow disappears is called the *point of reversal.* If the refractive error is even slightly overcorrected a shadow appears which moves in a direction opposite to that of the original movement. Now, when the point of reversal is reached, the far point of the subject's eye is at the surface of the observer's eye, i.e., 1 meter away. The subject therefore, as mentioned above, has still a myopia of 1 diopter. This must be taken into account in calculating the refractive power of the correcting

lenses required. If the eye is hypermetropic and, say +4 D brings it to the point of reversal, then a +3 D lens will be sufficient for correction. If the eye is myopic −1 D must be added to the refraction which was required to bring the eye to the point of reversal.

*Papilledema (choked disc, optic neuritis) and optic atrophy.* In conditions accompanied by high intracranial pressure, e.g., brain tumor, hydrocephalus and uremia, the optic disc loses its natural translucency and becomes reddened and swollen. The central vein is engorged and tortuous and the venules and capillaries dilated. Small hemorrhages may be seen. The swelling of the disc is due to the transudation of fluid from the engorged vessels and its collection in the anterior layers of the lamina cribrosa and between the nerve fibers. The physiological cup becomes gradually filled up, and may eventually be elevated above the general level of the surrounding retina. The circumference of the disc appears blurred or "woolly." The disc is enlarged and its lateral spread causes the retina to be thrown into folds or ridges. In the older terminology these changes were referred to as choked disc, optic neuritis or papillitis. The condition is now called *papilledema.* The separation and stretching of the nerve fibers, their compression where they penetrate the lamina cribrosa and the overgrowth of glial tissue set up by the presence of the edema fluid leads to nerve atrophy—*secondary optic atrophy.* The disc in this condition is a grayish or dead white, due to the obliteration of capillary vessels by the overgrowth of glial tissue. The optic cup is deepened as a result of the degenerated nerve fibers. The outline of the pale disc is clearly defined against the surrounding retina. The retinal veins are engorged but the arteries are narrower than normal.

It is now widely accepted that mechanical factors, e.g., changes in intracranial or intraocular pressure, are mainly concerned in the production of papilledema. The optic nerve, it will be recalled, is invested by prolongations of the cerebral meninges—the *pia, arachnoid* and *dura.* The spaces between these three layers of the nerve sheath— the *subarachnoid* and *subdural spaces*—are continous, as was first shown by Schwalbe (1870) with the corresponding spaces within the cranium. The dura and arachnoid of the nerve sheath, however, are in close opposition, there being only a potential subdural space in this situation. But the intracranial subarachnoid space is in free communication with the corresponding space of the nerve sheath and the intracranial pressure is transmitted through the cerebrospinal fluid to the intravaginal space right up to the lamina cribrosa. The central vein of the retina with its companion artery makes an almost right angled bend as it leaves the optic nerve and, crossing the intravaginal space, pierces the arachnoid and dura a short distance behind

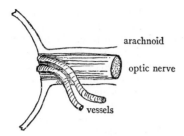

arachnoid

optic nerve

vessels

Fig. 74.26. Description in text.

the eyeball (fig. 74.26). Any marked rise in intracranial pressure distends the sheath, for the dura in this situation differs from that within the cranium in being unsupported by bone (Macdonald). The elevated pressure thus transmitted to the sheath tends to compress the vein in its course across the intravaginal space and to impede the venous return, as well as to block the lymph channels situated in the adventitia of the central vessels. Little or no interference is offered to the blood flow in the artery owing to its more resistant wall and to the higher arterial blood pressure. The venous pressure rises and the intraocular part of the vein and its branches become engorged since they are beyond the influence of the intracranial pressure.

Papilledema is therefore comparable with an edema which may occur in almost any situation as a result of obstruction of the venous and lymphatic channels while the arteries remain pervious. No evidence that papilledema is inflammatory in nature can be found upon histological examination (Holmes and Paton).

Atrophic changes in the disc occurring unpreceded by papilledema are referred to as *primary optic atrophy*. The main causes of primary optic atrophy are pressure upon the nerve within the cranium as by a tumor, certain nervous diseases (tabes, general paralysis of the insane and disseminated sclerosis) and toxic substances, e.g., wood alcohol, quinine, lead and salicylic compounds. Since the optic nerve fibers have their cell bodies in the retina (ganglion cell layer) the atrophy of the section between the point of pressure and the retina is in the nature of a retrograde degeneration (p. 1118). As already mentioned, the optic nerve fiber is devoid of a neurilemma; regeneration therefore never occurs. In tabes and general paralysis of the insane the atrophy is probably the result of a syphilitic meningitis which affects the nerve secondarily. The toxic substances mentioned exert their action apparently directly upon the ganglion cells of the retina.

BIOMICROSCOPY—THE SLIT LAMP. By means of this instrument an intense narrow beam of light is thrown obliquely into the eye and a small section of the cornea, anterior chamber, iris, lens or an-

terior part of the vitreous observed stereoscopically through a binocular microscope. The beam passes through an adjustable slit which when narrowed to minimum width concentrates the beam of light upon an area as small as 0.05 mm. in diameter. The illuminated section is in the form of a prism, or more correctly of a parallelepiped. The tissues within this section may be magnified some 25 diameters. Under this method of examination ocular structures which ordinarily appear homogeneous show a definite pattern, and any abnormality is readily recognized by one familiar with the appearance in health. For example, the anterior and posterior epithelial layers of the cornea are seen as bright lines bounding the less luminous substantia propria, and any pathological condition, e.g., erosions, small opacities, keratitis, etc., are easily detected. The laminated structure of the lens is clearly revealed. The central nucleus and the cortical layers are marked by luminous boundaries; the lens sutures appear as darker lines.

ENTOPTIC PHENOMENA. Visual sensations may arise from images of objects situated within the eye itself. The most familiar of these are the *muscae volitantes* (L. *flying flies*) which are seen as faint specks projected some distance in front of the eye. They are due to shadows cast upon the retina by small semi-opaque particles in the vitreous body, such as epithelial cells, small coagula or embryonic rudiments. Particles lying close to the retina are most likely to give rise to these sensations. Lying behind the axis of rotation of the globe such particles cast shadows which move downwards over the retina when the eye is turned upwards but, since the direction of any movement on the retina is reversed in consciousness, they appear to move upwards. This upward movement is followed by a slower downward movement. When any attempt is made to fix one's sight upon the specks they dart away, from which fact their name was derived. These *muscae volitantes* are usually noticed while viewing a bright uniform field, such as the clear blue sky, for then the pupil is small and sharper shadows are cast on the retina. Some of the reports on the sighting of "flying saucers" could be accounted for in this way.

Ordinarily the retinal vessels which, it will be recalled, lie outside the fovea and superficial to the retinal layers, are not perceived. Helmholtz thought that the sensitivity of the retina underlying the vessels was greater than elsewhere, so that the light reaching the retina through them, though reduced in intensity, caused as great an effect as light falling in unshielded regions. When light is thrown into the eye at such an angle (e.g.,

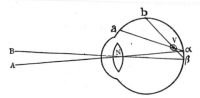

FIG. 74.27. Description in text.

obliquely through the sclera) that the shadows of the vessels fall upon a retinal region unaccustomed to receive them, they become visible. If, while his eye is being illuminated in this way in a dark room, the subject looks towards a wall, and the light falling on the sclera is given a slow circular movement, he sees a highly magnified image projected against the uniform surface. The vessels appear as an intricate branching pattern against a bright ground and are known, after their discoverer, as *Purkinje figures*. A method which anyone can employ himself to make the extrafoveal capillaries visible is to look at a uniformly bright surface through a pin-hole in a card held close to the eye while he oscillates the opening quickly (about once per second) from side to side and thereby shifts the shadows from point to point in the retina.

Mueller (1855) made use of Purkinje's observation (1811) to prove that the light sensitive elements are the rods and cones. Moving the source of light causes the images to change their positions on the screen. If we measure the distance of this shift (fig. 74.27, A–B) and the distance between the two positions of the light (a–b) then, knowing the distance of the nodal point of the schematic eye (N) from the retina and from the screen, the position of the shadow ($\alpha$–$\beta$) relative to the vessels (v), i.e., the distance $\alpha$ v, can be calculated. This was found to be from 0.17 to 0.36 mm., which is by actual measurement the approximate distance of the vessels in front of the rod and cone layer.

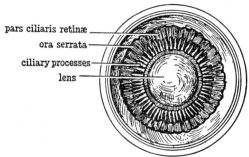

pars ciliaris retinæ
ora serrata
ciliary processes
lens

FIG. 74.28. Showing interior of anterior half of the eyeball.

The corpuscles moving in the retinal capillaries can be observed if the eye is directed to a uniformly illuminated surface. The best way to perform this experiment is to look at the sky through a dense blue-violet glass plate. The blood cells then appear projected upon the plate. It is actually possible to calculate the speed of the corpuscles from the distance between their positions at the beginning and end of a given time interval. Vierodt (1873) was the first to make such an estimation. Knowing the distance of the nodal point of the eye from the retina and from the glass screen, the magnification of the travelled distance can be determined.

Other entoptic phenomena which should be briefly mentioned are the colored halos seen around bright lights, especially in dark surroundings. The halos consist of a series of concentric rings of rainbow colors—from blue to red from without in. Actually they are diffraction spectra, due to the structures of the eye acting as diffraction gratings. There are two kinds of halo—*lenticular* and *corneal*. The first is attributed to the radial fibers of the lens and is the larger. The corneal type is believed to be due to the epithelial and endothelial cell layers of the cornea.

### The Accommodation of the Eye

#### ANATOMICAL SKETCH

Before giving an account of the physiological mechanism of accommodation, the structures concerned, e.g., the ciliary body and the crystalline *lens* will be briefly described.

THE CILIARY BODY. When the interior of the anterior half of the eyeball is exposed by a transection through its equator, a transparent disc—the *crystalline lens*—is seen occupying the center of the bowl-shaped structure (fig. 74.28). On the wall of the globe some distance behind the circumference of the lens lies the dendate border of the retina proper known as the *ora serrata* (p. 1316). The ciliary body is a circular zone of tissue extending forwards from the ora serrata to a short distance from the circumference of the lens. It is covered on its inner aspect by the pigment layer of the retina, which we have seen (ch. 72) is continued forwards (as the *pars ciliaris retinae*) from the point of termination of the neural layers. The ciliary body consists of three parts, the orbiculus ciliaris, the ciliary processes and the ciliary muscle. The *orbiculus ciliaris* immediately adjoins the choroid, of which it may be considered the direct continuation. It is a band about 4 mm. broad encircling the eyeball and presents on its inner aspect a number of radially arranged ridges. The *ciliary processes* appear as some seventy triangular elevations on the inner aspect of the ciliary body; they project towards the axis of the eye and form a series of radial fringes (*corona ciliaris*) which

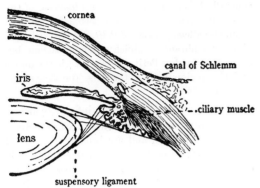

FIG. 74.29. Showing structures in the region of the angle of the iris.

FIG. 74.30. Showing arrangement of circular fibers of the ciliary muscle. (After Fincham.)

completely encircle the equator of the lens, but are separated from it by a very short interval. The great bulk of the ciliary body is composed of the ciliary processes and the ciliary muscle. The fibers of the *ciliary muscle* are arranged in two sets, an outer *meridional* and an inner *circular*. The meridional fibers arise from the scleral spur (p. 1400); they run backward to be attached to the ciliary processes and to the orbiculus, and through the latter to the choroid. The circular fibers are fewer; in meridional sections of the globe they appear as a small triangular bundle of cross-sectioned fibers lying behind the angle of the iris (fig. 74.29). As a matter of fact, these fibers are not uniformly circular in direction but take different courses and, interlacing with one another, form a reticulated ring-shaped band (fig. 74.30). Taken as a whole this part of the ciliary muscle constitutes a sphincter (*sphincter muscle of Mueller*) situated in front and to the outer side of the ciliary processes. The fibers composing the margin of the central opening are mainly circular and are attached to a band of elastic tissue situated at the angle of the iris; the outer circumference of the sphincter is connected to elastic fibers which are continuous with similar fibers of the choroid. The muscle is thus anchored by two elastic attachments.

THE CRYSTALLINE LENS is a transparent, biconvex, circular structure about 11 mm. in diameter and between 3.6 and 3.9 mm. thick at the center. It is situated with the center of its anterior surface coinciding with the center of the pupil; the pupil-

lary margin lies in contact with this surface. The center of the anterior surface is termed the *anterior pole* of the lens, the center of its posterior surface, the *posterior pole*. An imaginary line joining the poles is called the *principal axis*. The two surfaces meet at the circumference in a rounded edge termed the *equator*. The posterior surface in the young adult is decidedly more convex than the anterior (see table, p. 1380); this difference diminishes somewhat with age. The lens is enclosed in a structureless, highly elastic capsule. The latter is not of uniform thickness, being thinner over the posterior than over the anterior surface, and the part covering the central region of each surface is thinner than the corresponding peripheral parts. The values in ascending order of thicknesses are, center of posterior surface (av. 2.2$\mu$), peripheral part of posterior surface (av. 13.7$\mu$), center of anterior surface (av. 15.7$\mu$), peripheral part of anterior surface (av. 18.2$\mu$) (see fig. 74.31). A single layer of columnar epithelial cells covers the anterior surface of the lens immediately beneath the homogeneous capsule; the latter is formed as a secretion of these cells. The substance of the lens consists of a series of ribbon-like fibers which arise from the region of the equator and are actually greatly elongated epithelial cells (fig. 74.32). By careful examination of the lens, from the more central part of the anterior surface to the region of the equator the gradual transition of the columnar cells into the attenuated cells of the lens substance can be traced. The fibers proceed from the equator towards the lens center and, abutting against fibers coming from other segments of the periphery, fuse along well-defined lines—the *lens sutures*. These are seen in the adult lens as a series of faint irregular striae radiating from the center to form what is known

FIG. 74.31. Showing the regional variations in thickness of the lens capsule. (After Fincham.)

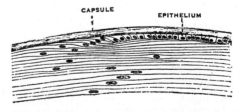

FIG. 74.32. Meridional section of the lens. (From Wolff after Poirier and Becker.)

as the *lens star*. On section, the lens shows a series of concentric laminae with a nucleus of extreme convexity and high refractive index, and a less refractive cortex. The optical advantages of this construction have been pointed out (p. 1379). The nucleus is also of much firmer consistency than the cortex which is relatively soft and pliable.

### The Mechanism of Accommodation

The interval between the ciliary processes and the equator of the lens is occupied by a circular membranous band; this is the anterior part of the *zonula ciliaris (zonula of Zinn)*. The precise origin of the fibers of the zonula is disputed, but they appear to arise as a system of transparent fibers from the anterior part of the hyaloid membrane 1.5 mm. or so in front of the ora serrata. Passing forwards they form a series of bundles which occupy grooves between the ciliary processes, and then bridge the gap, as just mentioned, between the ciliary processes and the lens. Near the lens circumference the zonula splits into an anterior and a posterior lamina; the former is the thicker of the two and blends with the lens capsule a little in front of the equator, and constitutes what is

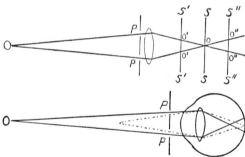

Fig. 74.33. Scheiner's experiment. Upper cut, O, position of needle; PP, pinholes in card; SS, screen with image of needle focussed at o. When the screen is moved forward or backward (S'S' or S"S" the two pencils of light are intercepted before they have reached a focus in the first instance, and after they have met and crossed in the second. Two images are formed at o' and o' or at o" and o". In the case of the eye (lower cut), any difference in its focus must be due to changes in the lens, since the retina is stationary. When the needle is viewed with one eye through the peep holes, and brought into focus one image is seen, but two blurred images appear if the eye is focussed upon a nearer or a more distant object. If when the eye looks at an object near than the needle, and the needle is moved a little nearer to the eye, the two images approach one another; when the needle is moved farther away they become more separated. When the eye is accommodated for far vision, changes in the distance of the needle cause converse movements of the images, becoming farther apart as the needle approaches the eye, and coming closer together as it is moved farther away. The continuous lines represent rays from the needle, the interrupted lines rays from a nearer point in focus.

generally known as the *suspensory ligament* of the lens. The space between the two layers of the zonula is called the *canal of Petit*. Slits in the layers of the membrane establish communications between the canal of Petit and the anterior chamber and the region behind the lens (postlenticular space, p. 1399).

Light rays from an object at infinity, which is taken as any point more than 20 feet (6 meters) distant, are parallel and are brought to a focus (principal focus) on the retina of the emmetropic eye. Rays from a near object are divergent, but they too are brought to a sharp focus. This adjustment of the dioptrics of the eye whereby it is able to focus the image of both far and near objects is called *accommodation*. That the refracting power of the eye does actually undergo a change when it is turned from a far to a near object or vice versa was shown by Scheiner (1619) by a simple experiment. A card with two pin-holes separated by a distance less than the diameter of the pupil is held before one eye. The eye is focussed upon a needle held in front of the card and perpendicular to a line joining the two holes. The needle appears single; but it appears double if the eye is focussed upon an object placed either beyond it or between it and the eye. The explanation will be evident from fig. 74.33.

There are at least three possible means by which accommodation of the eye could be brought about. The retina might be moved towards or away from the lens, i.e., the eye might be elongated or shortened so that divergent rays in the one instance or parallel rays in the other would be accurately focussed. This mechanism is actually made use of in the mollusc pecten. That it is not the method followed by the human eye was proved by Young (1801). A second possibility is that the distance between the retina and the lens is altered by a movement of the lens; this is the method used in photography, the distance between the film and the lens can be nicely adjusted for the focus of near objects. In the bony fishes accommodation is effected in such a manner.[1]

---

[1] These fish are myopic when the eye is at rest, i.e., the eye is adjusted for near vision; accommodation for far vision is an active process consisting of contraction of a structure called the campanula which moves the lens backward. In some birds the central part of the anterior surface of the lens moves forwards into the pupillary aperture and as a result of pressure against the rigid margin of the iris becomes highly convex. In other avian species the cornea consists of two lamellae, the posterior being drawn backwards during accommodation for far vision. In others again (owls and hawks) the curvature of the cornea is increased during near vision.

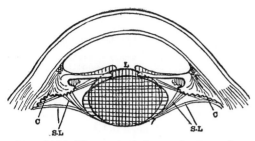

Fig. 74.34. Illustrating the mechanism of accommodation of the eye for near vision. The horizontally shaded lens and the unshaded iris show the position of the parts when at rest; the vertically shaded lens and iris show the position during accommodation for a near point. C. ciliary muscle; S.L., suspensory ligament. (Redrawn from Landolt.)

Variations in the convexity of the crystalline lens and consequently of its converging power is the third possibility (fig. 74.34). This is the method first suggested by Young for the human eye; the conception was later elaborated by Helmholtz. That such is the mechanism adopted by mammals in general is now almost universally accepted. A change in the convexity of the anterior surface of the lens during accommodation is a well-established fact and one which can be demonstrated by the following experiments. A lighted candle is held to the outer side and a little in front of the eye of a subject in a darkened room. Three images (Purkinje-Sanson images, fig. 74.35) within the subject's pupil will be seen by an observer, one bright and erect reflected from the cornea, another larger, erect and dimmer from the anterior surface (epithelial layer) of the lens which like the cornea, acts as a convex mirror. The third image is inverted, bright and smaller than the other two; it is reflected from the posterior (concave) surface of the lens. The subject is directed to gaze into the distance while the positions of the images are

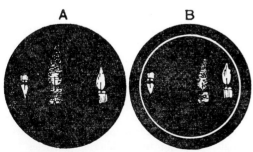

Fig. 74.35. Purkinje-Sanson images. A, during far vision; B, during accommodation for near vision. (Redrawn and modified from Williams.)

noted; he then looks at a near object when a change in the size and position of the reflection from the anterior surface of the lens will be observed. It becomes smaller and moves towards the corneal image which, of course, remains stationary, as does also the inverted image from the posterior surface of the lens. The change in size and position of the large erect image must mean that the anterior surface of the lens has become more convex. Now, if one knows the radius of curvature of the cornea, which can be measured by means of an instrument known as an ophthalmometer, then the radius of curvature of the surfaces of the lens and the changes in their curvature during accommodation can be calculated from careful comparative measurements of the sizes of the images from the cornea and lens. The average values for the radius of the anterior surface of the lens in five subjects examined by Fincham were 12.2 mm. for the "resting eye" and 6.8 mm. during accommodation for near vision. The change in curvature of the posterior lens surface was slight (about 0.5 mm.). The average increase in thickness of the central part of the lens was 0.47 mm., while the equatorial diameter diminished by 0.5 mm. The center of the anterior surface moved forward by from 0.3 to 0.4 mm. In general terms the change in shape of the lens during accommodation for near vision can be summed up as follows. The central part of the anterior surface becomes more convex, the posterior surface shows little change. The peripheral region of the anterior surface actually becomes somewhat flatter, this surface taken as a whole therefore assumes a hyperbolic form.

The manner in which the change in shape of the anterior surface of the lens is brought about was explained by Helmholtz as follows. When the eye is accommodated for distant vision the suspensory ligament which, as we have seen, is attached to the lens capsule, is drawn taut as a result of the pull of the elastic structures, e.g., the ciliary body and choroid. The peripherally directed traction exerted upon the lens capsule through the suspensory ligament results in flattening of the curvature of the anterior surface of the lens. Focussing the image of a near object is accomplished by contraction of the ciliary muscle which, by drawing the choroid forward, permits the ciliary processes to move forward and inward, thus reducing the diameter of the ring (corona ciliaris) which they form. The suspensory ligament and lens capsule are thus relaxed, and the lens, by virtue of its inherent elasticity, assumes a more convex form (figs. 74.34 and 74.36). The excised lens, i.e., one

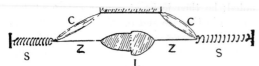

F<small>IG.</small> 74.36. Diagram to illustrate the mechanism of accommodation. C, ciliary muscle, relaxed (left), contracted (right); S, spring representing the elastic choroid; L, lens, left section, for far vision; right for near vision; Z, zonula.

TABLE 74.1

| Pupil Diameter in mm. | Depth of Focus (D) | Depth of Field, when Focused on: | | |
|---|---|---|---|---|
| | | Infinity | Hyperfocal distance | 25 cm |
| 1 | ±0.85 | α to 1.18 m. | α to 0.59 m. | 31.8 to 20.6 cm. |
| 2 | ±0.44 | α to 2.27 m. | α to 1.13 m. | 28.1 to 22.5 cm. |
| 3 | ±0.30 | α to 3.33 m. | α to 1.67 m. | 27.0 to 23.3 cm. |
| 4 | ±0.24 | α to 4.17 m. | α to 2.08 m. | 26.6 to 23.6 cm. |
| 5 | ±0.20 | α to 5.00 m. | α to 2.50 m. | 26.3 to 23.8 cm. |
| 6 | ±0.18 | α to 5.56 m. | α to 2.28 m. | 26.2 to 23.9 cm. |
| 7 | ±0.16 | α to 6.25 m. | α to 3.12 m. | 26.0 to 24.0 cm. |
| 8 | ±0.15 | α to 6.67 m. | α to 3.33 m. | 26.0 to 24.1 cm. |

Depth of field of the eye based on the detection of ±0.3 D with a 3 mm. diameter pupil and corrected for the retinal direction effect.

released from the restraint of surrounding structures, is therefore at its maximum convexity. Helmholtz's conception is supported in its main tenets by modern work. The movement inward of the ciliary processes during accommodation for near vision has been observed in the living human eye; and in an eye from which the lens substance had been adsorbed as a result of injury, tightening and slackening of the empty capsule was seen during the corresponding phases of accommodation. Yet the curvature assumed by the anterior surface of the lens is, as mentioned above, *hyperbolic*, whereas one would expect it to assume a spheroid form were the lens substance itself elastic and the change in shape due simply to its recoil when released from restraint.

The details of the mechanism with respect to this point have been elucidated by the work of Fincham. According to this observer, the change in shape of the lens during accommodation is explained by the high degree of elasticity possessed by the lens capsule and by the regional variations in its thickness (p. 1387), together with the pliable nature of the cortical part of the lens as compared with the nucleus. When the lens is accommodated for distant vision, its substance is confined under tension within the capsule and, as a consequence, distends the latter to the greatest degree where it is weakest, (i.e., thinnest) namely, on the posterior surface. The convexity of this surface is therefore near its maximum when the eye is adjusted for distant objects and little further change can occur during accommodation for near vision. Upon contraction of the ciliary muscle and the consequent slackening of the suspensory ligament the recoil of the elastic capsule moulds the plastic cortex; the peripheral part of the anterior surface is thus pressed back by the relatively thick capsule but the thinner central part of the latter permits the lens substance, chiefly the highly convex nucleus, to bulge forwards. That is, the anterior surface of the lens becomes somewhat "conoid" (Fincham).

T<small>HE</small> <small>VISUAL AXES AND PUPILLARY DIAMETER</small> <small>DURING ACCOMMODATION.</small> The complete act of accommodation for a near object comprises, besides an increase in the convexity of the anterior surface of the lens, *convergence of the eyes* and *constriction of the pupil*. The constriction of the pupil which occurs during accommodation serves three purposes. The narrowed aperture of the iris (a) reduces lateral chromatic and spherical aberration, thus increasing visual acuity, (b) diminishes the quantity of light entering the eye and (c) increases the *depth of focus*.

The depth of focus of any lens system is defined as the greatest distance through which an object may be moved and still be sharply focussed. When a clear image is formed by a lens, each point in the object is, as a result of diffraction, a series of small concentric circles of light, rather than a geometrical point. When the distance from the lens is increased the image is formed in front of its previous position (that is, in front of the surface, such as a photographic film or retina); if the distance is reduced, the image is formed behind. In either case the rings of light upon the surface become larger. If they are of such a size as to still remain confined, each to a particle making up the grain of the surface, film or retina, the image is sharp and appears in true focus; if they are large enough to spread to neighboring particles the image of the object is blurred. In the case of the fovea the "grain" is determined by the cones. The

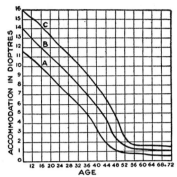

FIG. 74.37. The amplitude of accommoation at different ages. A. The lowest physiological valued. B. Average values. C. Maximum values. (After Duane.)

depth of focus of the eye is, therefore, given as the greatest distance through which a point can be moved while its image remains restricted to a single cone. The depth of focus of the eye varies with the diameter of the pupil. The values given in table 74.1 are based on measurements of the sensitivity of the eye to out-of-focus blur and are corrected for the retinal direction effect of Stiles and Crawford. If, for example, the observer has a pupil diameter of 3 mm. a change in the refractive power of the eye of $\pm 0.3$ diopter will just be detected, but with a 6 mm. pupil a change of $\pm 0.18$ D will be detected. These powers may be translated into distances. Thus, if the observer has a 3 mm. pupil and his eye is focussed on infinity, all objects from infinity down to 3.3 m. will be seen sharply. This near point—the hyperfocal distance—is the reciprocal of half the depth of focus when expressed in diopters. If the eye is focussed on the hyperfocal distance then all objects from infinity to 1.67 m. will be in focus. Similarly, it may be calculated that if the eye is in focus for a point 25 cm. away, objects within the range 27 to 23.3 cm. will be perceived sharply. The depth of focus decreases as the distance from the eye is reduced. This tendency is, therefore, counteracted by the constriction of the pupil which occurs as part of the mechanism of accommodation of the eye for near vision.

*The range and amplitude of accommodation.* The farthest point from the eye at which an object can be seen clearly is called the *far point* or *punctum remotum.* The corresponding point nearest the eye is termed the *near point* or *punctum proximum.* In the emmetropic eye the far point is at infinity, i.e., at a distance of over 20 feet (6 meters) and the near point at from 7 cm. to 40 cm., depending upon age (fig. 74.37). The difference between the far and the near point distances is termed the

*range of accommodation.* The difference between the refracting power of the eye when accommodation is completely relaxed for the far point and fully displaced for the near point is called the *amplitude of accommodation.* The far point is conjugate to a point on the retina, i.e., parallel rays entering the eye come to a focus on the retina and rays from the latter upon emerging from the eye are parallel and would meet at infinity. Similarly, in the accommodated eye the near point is conjugate with a point on the retina. The focal length of the eye in each state of accommodation therefore corresponds, respectively, to the far and near point distances. It will be recalled that the refractive power is expressed as the reciprocal of the focal distance, the unit being 1 meter and called a diopter. The reciprocal of the far point distance is termed the *static refraction* (designated R) of the eye, and that of the near point distance, the *dynamic refraction* (P). The difference between the two (P − R) gives in diopters the amplitude of accommodation. In the emmetropic eye, since the far point is at infinity, the static refraction is taken as zero. When the near point is at 10 cm. the dynamic refraction is $\dfrac{100 \ (1 \ \text{meter})}{10} = 10$ D. The amplitude of accommodation in such an emmetropic eye is therefore 10 D.

The amplitude of accommodation diminishes progressively from childhood to about sixty years of age being 16 D at twelve years, 6.5 D at the age of thirty and only about 1 D at sixty. In other words, with advancing years the near point gradually recedes from the eye and at sixty years of age an object must be 1 meter distant in order to be clearly focussed upon the retina (see *presbyopia*). This phenomenon is due mainly to physical changes in the properties of the lens and its capsule (reduced plasticity of the one or diminished elasticity of the other); there may also be a concomitant weakness of the ciliary muscle.

THE METABOLISM AND COMPOSITION OF THE LENS. The lens, devoid of a blood supply, must obtain all the necessary nutrients for growth and metabolism from the surrounding aqueous and vitreous humors. The aqueous humor is believed to be the main source of supply. The vitreous, aqueous and lens all contain glucose and this appears to supply the main source of energy, both by aerobic and by anaerobic metabolism. The oxygen tension of the aqueous humor of the rabbit is about 40 to 50 mm. Hg compared with about 72 mm. Hg in arterial blood, but the oxygen has to diffuse over a considerable distance to reach the inner layers of the lens. The rate of metabolism of the lens may be readily determined for it may be removed from the body and maintained in a tissue culture medium containing glucose. In one such experiment Merriam and Kinsey (1950) found that a rabbit lens used about 3.4 mg. of glucose per 24 hours, and that it produced about 2.0 mg. of lactic acid. Rabbit lenses use about 10 to 20 $\mu$l. of $O_2$ per hour and have an R.Q. near to 1. It appears that glucose metabolism in the lens is mainly anaerobic. This anaerobic breakdown of glucose to lactic acid appears to be similar to that found in other tissues, that is, the sequence of reactions in the Embden-Meyerhof scheme. Cytochrome oxidase and flavoproteins have been found in the epithelium of the lens which suggests that this tissue may be responsible for some at least of the small oxygen consumption. The high concentration of glutathione in the lens and of ascorbic acid in the lens and aqueous humor has led to the speculation whether a hydrogen acceptor other than oxygen might be playing a role as both these substances may be reversibly reduced and oxidized, but there is no evidence of their action in lens metabolism. The metabolic function of ascorbic acid remains obscure. Glutathione may be required in the synthesis of the lens proteins and it may be significant that the highest concentration of glutathione is found in the cortex where the new lens fibers are formed.

Four types of protein have been identified in the lens substance, (a) a *euglobin* or *"albuminoid"* (17 per cent) which is water-soluble, and two water-soluble proteins—*pseudoglobulins*, (b) $\alpha$-*crystalline* (11 per cent) and (c) $\beta$-*crystalline* (6 per cent), together with (d) a small quantity of albumin (0.2 per cent). The albuminoid is present mainly in the nucleus, $\alpha$-crystalline chiefly in the superficial part of the cortex and $\beta$-crystalline in the deeper parts. The two crystallines are particularly rich in the sulfur-containing amino-acids cystine and cysteine. The lens proteins as first shown by Uhlenhuth are *organ specific* not species specific, thus differing in their immunological behavior from red cells (p. 63) and blood serum. For example, a solution of lens protein when injected into an animal of the same or of another species causes the production of an antibody—a *precipitin*. This antiserum has then the power to precipitate a solution of lens protein from wherever derived, i.e., from a species other than the one which supplied the antiserum, from the same species or even from the same animal.

The lens substance contains a high concentration of potassium—400 mg. per 100 grams of wet weight—as compared with about 3 mg. per cent in the aqueous and 20 mg. per cent in serum. The concentrations of calcium (5 mg. per cent), sodium chloride (300 mg. per cent) magnesium and silicates are relatively low. The total salt concentration is between 0.7 and 0.8 per cent. Cholesterol and phosphatides amount to about 200 mg. per cent in young lenses, but are from two to four times this value in older specimens. (Consult Pirie and van Heyningen.)

CHANGES IN THE LENS WITH AGE—CATARACT.

The loss of plasticity and elasticity of the lens with age as a result of a gradual sclerosis, and the effect such changes have on the mechanism of accommodation are referred to on page 1391. Some alterations in lenticular color may accompany the sclerosing process; amber tinting, or even a reddish or brownish discoloration of the lens with consequent filtering of the shorter rays, is of common occurrence.

*Cataract* is the name given to any partial or complete opacity of the lens. In the commonest variety no ocular or general disease which can be held responsible precedes the development of the opacity, and this, since it appears to be simply a manifestation of age, is termed *senile cataract*. The process leading to the opacity is degenerative in nature, not inflammatory, for the lens is, as just stated, avascular. The opacity commences usually in the deeper part of the cortex and does not, as a rule, involve the nucleus. The lens swells as a result of accumulation of fluid between the fibers, the anterior chamber becoming shallow. So long as the superficial layers of the cortex are clear the cataract is called *immature*. It is said to be *mature* when the opacity has extended to include the superficial layers. The water content of the lens has by this time returned to normal. The mature stage is followed by disintegration of the cortex which becomes softened into a pultaceous mass; this is the stage of hypermaturity; drying and shrinkage of the lens finally result.

The essential change in the cataractous lens is a progressive coagulation of the lens proteins. According to the most generally accepted explanation, such a process is due to the prolonged action of ultraviolet light, and, in some instances, to the thermal effect of infrared rays. The lens as already pointed out, by absorbing a large proportion of the rays below $\lambda$ 350 m$\mu$ and 400 m$\mu$, protects the retina from their injurious effects. Wave lengths below 295 m$\mu$ are absorbed by the cornea. The rays absorbed by the lens are not without their effect upon the lens substance itself; it is these which cause the physical change in the lens proteins. Two stages are recognized in the coagulation process: (1) *denaturation of the lens proteins*, consisting presumably of a molecular rearrangement, by light or heat which renders them susceptible to (2) *aggregation (agglutination) of the protein particles* into a flocculent mass—coagulation. This ultimate result occurs only in the presence of certain salts and is enhanced by some organic substances, e.g. dextrose and acetone. The theory that radiant energy is responsible for denaturation of the lens proteins is in accord with many observations. For example, the absorption by the lens of the shorter rays increases with age. The opacity commences in the lower quadrant of the lens which receives the most intense light. In tropical countries, e.g. India and Egypt, cataract is much commoner than in temperate latitudes; it is also less frequent in the latter than in Arctic zones, presumably as a result of the high content in acitinic rays of the light reflected from snow and ice. It is also stated that on this continent the incidence of cataract increases from temperate zones to the equator, and that it is also higher in those who work in the fields than in city dwellers. Burge's experiments and the more recent ones of Clarke show convincingly the effect of light upon the development of lenticular opacities. Burge found that whereas exposure of a solution of lens protein to ultraviolet light for 100 hrs. did not cause coagulation, this occurred if $CaCl_2$, $MgCl$, dextrose or acetone were added. Moreover the exposure of the eye of a living fish or frog to short light waves was without effect if the animal had previously been kept in tap water, but definite opacity of the lens followed a few hours exposure, if the fish or frog had been for some days in water containing 0.8 per cent calcium chloride, 0.1 per cent dextrose or 0.1 per cent sodium silicate. Clarke found that heat enhanced the action of the light rays upon solutions of lens proteins, and that opacity could not be produced in the absence of calcium.

The incidence of cataract is much higher in diabetics than in normal persons; it is usually of the ordinary or so-called senile type, but it occurs at an earlier age. The opacity is attributed to the action of dextrose and possibly of acetone bodies in rendering the lens proteins more readily coagulable by light. Duke-Elder believes that as a result of the high blood sugar, the osmotic relationships between the lens and the surrounding fluids are disturbed, and the nutrition of the lens thereby interfered with.

Though the factors outlined above appear to be the main ones concerned in the production of the common or senile type of cataract, opinions differ considerably as to the details of the mechanism involved, as well as in regard to the production of other types of lenticular opacity. It is suggested, for example, that the action of ultraviolet rays in inducing denaturation of the lens proteins is due to the reduction of the glutathione and $\beta$-crystalline content and the consequent depression of the autoxidative mechanism. Such an effect of ultraviolet radiation has been shown experimentally; it has also been established that the content of the lens in glutathione and in the thermostable protein residue diminishes with age. The power of the lens to fluoresce upon exposure to short wave radiations (p. 1330) and the disposal of the surplus energy by converting them into long waves, is considered by Burge to be an important factor in ameliorating the effect of light upon the lens; fluorescing bacteria for example are much less readily killed by ultraviolet light than are other types. It is of some considerable interest therefore

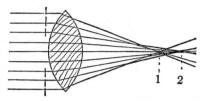

Fig. 74.38. Spherical aberration. Outer rays meet at 1, inner rays at 2.

that the power of the lens to fluoresce diminishes with age.

In glass blowers' cataract, infrared rays would appear to play an important auxiliary rôle. Early cataract has also developed in a few atomic physicists and in some of the Japanese atomic bomb victims. Much research has since been undertaken on the effect on lens metabolism of X-ray and fast neutron radiation. Young animals develop cataract more readily than older animals when irradiated in this way. A latent period of some weeks or months may elapse after the exposure before opacities in the lens appear.

An interesting type of cataract is that following parathyroidectomy; disordered calcium metabolism would appear to be in some way concerned in its production; the calcium content of the lens is increased, whereas that of the blood is reduced. There is no definite evidence, however, to connect ordinary senile cataract with parathyroid deficiency, but there seems little doubt that calcium is concerned in some obscure way with cataract development. A favorite method of producing cataract for experimental study is by the injection of naphthaline; opacities form only if the animal is on a low calcium diet. In rats, lenticular opacity is readily produced by a diet containing a high percentage of lactose or galactose; the former sugar increases the absorption of calcium, but whether this fact has any bearing upon the development of the cataract is difficult to say; it does not dovetail with other observations in respect to calcium and the development of cataract.

The composition of the cataractous lens shows marked differences from the normal. There is an increase in the insoluble albuminoid and a decrease of the soluble proteins and of glutathione; the oxygen uptake is much reduced. Of the inorganic constituents calcium shows a relatively enormous increase (up to 140 mg. per cent). The concentration of magnesium, sodium and silicates is also raised, whereas that of potassium is greatly reduced.

### OPTICAL DEFECTS

SPHERICAL ABERRATION. Rays traversing the peripheral parts of an ordinary convex lens are refracted more strongly and therefore come to a

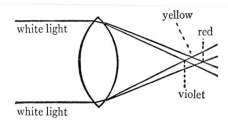

Fɪɢ. 74.39. Chromatic aberration.

focus nearer the lens than do those transmitted through more central regions. In other words, the outer and inner rays cross in front of the retina and a blurred image is formed (fig. 74.38). This is an inherent defect of convex spherical lenses and is called *spherical aberration.* Spherical aberration is corrected to a certain extent in the crystalline lens, the nucleus having a higher refractive power than the periphery (see p. 1379). The iris, since it covers the outer part of the lens and shuts off the peripheral rays, also serves to correct this defect.

Cʜʀᴏᴍᴀᴛɪᴄ ᴀʙᴇʀʀᴀᴛɪᴏɴ. The colors composing white light are refracted to different degrees according to their wave lengths. The violet rays are refracted most, the refractive power diminishing progressively from the violet to the red end of the spectrum (fig. 74.39). For this reason a series of fringes, colored from violet to red from within outwards, borders the image formed by a simple cheap lens. *Chromatic aberration,* as this defect is called, is corrected in camera and microscope lenses by cementing a biconvex lens of crown glass to a concave one of flint glass. Such a lens is called *achromatic.* The eye is only partially corrected for chromatic aberration. The yellow rays are focussed upon the retina, but the short blue rays being more acutely bent meet in front, while the longer less strongly refracted red rays come to a focus behind the retina. Other rays are bent similarly in accordance with their wavelengths. Furthermore, the fovea being on the temporal side of the optical axis, the blue rays fall upon the retina nearer to the point (*axial point*) where it is cut by the optical axis. This, of course, will obtain in both eyes, and lines projected outwards from the axial points will meet as shown in figure 74.39. The blue rays will therefore appear to come from a point farther away than the point emitting the red rays; the image formed on the retina by the shorter blue rays will also be smaller than that formed by the red rays. These effects of the unequal refraction of the different colors are called, respectively, *chromatic stereoscopy* and *chromatic difference of magnification.* In ordinary vision the

colors surrounding the images on the retina are not perceived.

*Diffraction and the scattering of light within the eyeball.* Light is diffracted by the pupillary margin and by the lens fibers and corneal epithelium; as a result of this and of spherical aberration the retinal image is not made up of points of light but of diffusion circles (blur circles), i.e., a bright central disc surrounded by light rings which diminish in intensity by almost imperceptible gradations towards the periphery. The relative size of the central bright area varies inversely with the diameter of the pupil and directly with the wave length of the light. The opposite effects of changes in the size of the pupil upon this defect and upon chromatic aberration have been pointed out.

None of the ocular media is perfectly homogeneous; owing to their colloidal nature a certain proportion of the light entering the eye is scattered (Tyndall phenomenon), that is, it is not focussed upon the retina but is deflected from the course which it would follow according to the laws of refraction if the contents of the globe were perfectly transparent. The colloidal particles have a size of the order of the wave length of light. The quantity of scattered light is directly proportional to the square of the size of the particles, and inversely proportional to the fourth power of the wave length (Rayleigh). Thus the greatest scattering within the eyeball occurs with violet and ultraviolet light and the least with red (see Le Grand).

Pʀᴇsʙʏᴏᴘɪᴀ (Gr. *presbos,* old; *ops,* the eye) is the term given to the gradual reduction in the amplitude of accommodation which goes hand in hand with advancing years.

Eᴍᴍᴇᴛʀᴏᴘɪᴀ ᴀɴᴅ ᴀᴍᴇᴛʀᴏᴘɪᴀ. The four optical defects just described may be regarded as physiological, the first three being inherent to some extent in optical systems in general; the fourth is a natural accompaniment of age. Two other defects of frequent occurrence are due to incongruity between the length of the eyeball and its refracting power and must be classed as definite abnormalities.

The refractive state of the normal eye, which has its far point (p. 1391) at infinity, i.e., at a distance greater than 6 meters (20 feet), is called *emmetropia.* Parallel rays entering the emmetropic eye are brought to a clear focus on the retina without any effort of accommodation. The static refraction of such an eye is therefore zero. If the far point is not at infinity the eye is *ametropic.* There are two forms of ametropia—myopia and hypermetropia (fig. 74.40).

In *myopia* (Gr. *myo,* I blink or half close the eye; *ops,* the eye) or *short sight,* the eyeball is too long relatively to its refracting power (fig. 74.40-B). Obviously, such an eye will bring parallel rays to a focus in front of the retina, i.e., in the vitreous. After meeting, the rays cross and form a blurred image or a diffusion circle upon the retina, just as a camera which is extended too far forms an indistinct image upon the film. In order to form a clear image on the retina of the myopic eye the rays must be, not parallel but divergent; such as are emitted by a near object. The far point is therefore at a finite distance, and in extreme instances may be only a few centimeters from the eye. Accommodation, of course, is relaxed for the far point as in the emmetropic eye for, obviously, increasing the converging power of the lens will only cause greater blurring of the image. The far and near points being close together, the range and the amplitude of accommodation (p. 1391) are reduced. Myopia is corrected by means of concave (diverging) lenses. If, for example, an object can be seen clearly no farther away than 1 meter, the myopia is—1 D, i.e., a concave lens of this power is required.

In *hypermetropia* (Gr. *hyper*, above; *metros*, measure; *ops*, the eye) or *long sight* (fig. 74.40C) the eye is too short for its refracting power. Therefore parallel rays after refraction fall upon the retina before they have come to a focus, and form an image blurred by diffusion circles. The rays as they emerge from the eye are divergent. The far point is *virtual*, i.e., it is behind the eye at the point where the rays would meet if continued backwards through the retina. The hypermetrope must accommodate when he views distant objects in order to focus the parallel rays upon the retina. The range of his accommodation (p. 1391) is the same as that of the emmetrope but the amplitude is greater. Suppose, for example, that the near point is 0.10 meter in front of the eye and the far point is 0.25 meter behind, i.e., negative ($-0.25$). Then the dynamic refraction is $100/10 = 10$ D, and the static refraction is $- 100/-25 = -4$ D; the amplitude of accommodation is therefore $10$ D $- (-4$ D$)$, or $10$ D $+ 4$ D $= 14$ D. Hypermetropia is corrected by means of a convex lens, the distance of the far point behind the eye giving the measure of the strength of lens required; if this is $-0.25$ meter then a $+4$ D lens would correct the defect (see p. 1384).

Although it is customary to account for myopia and hypermetropia in terms of variations in the axial length of the eye and to assume that the power of the cornea and lens is constant, recent studies suggest that this view is inadequate. If the

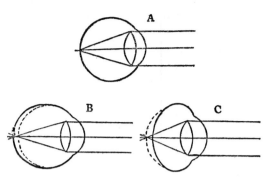

Fig. 74.40. A, emmetropia; B, myopia; C, hypermetropia.

optical constants of a large number of eyes are measured it is found that the power of the cornea varies from 39 to 47 D and that of the lens from 14 to 25 D. The axial length may range from 22 to 26 mm. Although hypermetropic eyes tend to have a shorter axial length than myopic eyes, it is only in the severe degrees of these defects (over $+$ or $-4$ D) that the axial length falls outside the normal statistical limits. The refractive errors in a population are so distributed that the three variables, cornea, lens and axial length cannot be distributed in a random fashion, for inspection of figure 74.41 indicates that there is an excess number of emmetropes in the population. A correlation mechanism must be postulated to maintain something like emmetropia during the period of growth of the eye from its newborn length of 16 mm. to that of 24 mm. in the adult state. Most of the growth in length occurs during the first few years of life although myopia often first declares itself at adolescence when the axial length has become stable. Nothing is known about the nature of the process which leads to such a high proportion of emmetropes in the population. Genetic factors are almost certainly involved for refractive errors can often be inherited.

ASTIGMATISM (Gr. *a*, privative; *stigma*, a point). In this condition, as its name implies, rays of light are not brought to sharp points upon the retina, but form short lines. The defect is present in all eyes to a certain degree; when moderate it is therefore physiological. Only when the fault seriously reduces visual acuity is it abnormal. It must be remembered that rays of light pass through all meridians of a lens; in converging to a focus they therefore form a cone of light, not simply a flat pennantlike beam. If all meridians of a lens have the same curvature, then rays in all planes will be refracted to the same degree and come to a focus together. If, on the other hand,

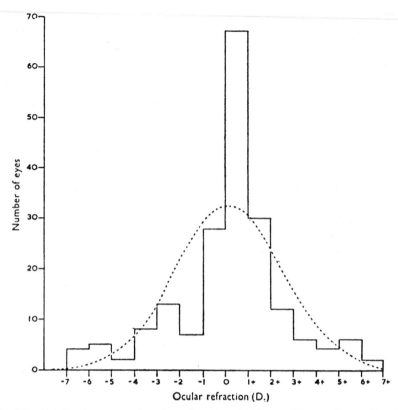

Fig. 74.41. The distribution curve of ocular refraction of 194 eyes. The continuous lines indicate the actual observations and the dotted line indicates the fitted normal curve. As the former is more peaked than the latter it may be concluded that whereas the individual optical components may vary over a wide range in an individual eye these components are usually so correlated that emmetropia results. (After Sorsby, Benjamin, Davey, Sheridan and Tanner.)

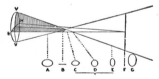

Fig. 74.42. Refraction by an astigmatic lens. VV, the vertical meridian of the refracting body, is more curved than HH, the horizontal meridian. A, B, C, D, E, F, G show different sections of the beam after refraction. At B the vertical rays are brought to a focus; at F the horizontal rays are brought to a focus. From B to F is the focal interval.

the curvatures differ, the rays transmitted through a meridian with the greater curvature will be refracted more strongly and brought to a focus in front of rays passing through other meridians. For example, should the vertical meridian be more curved than the horizontal, then when the rays passing through the vertical meridian are in focus those in the horizontal will form, not a point, but an ellipse, a circle or a line. Thus

there are two foci and the distance between two lines—the *focal interval*—is a measure of the degree of the astigmatism (see fig. 74.42). Such inequalities of curvature in the meridians of the cornea or, less commonly, of the crystalline lens, are the cause of what is known as *curvature astigmatism.* The greater curvature may be in either the vertical, horizontal or an oblique meridian. But in physiological astigmatism (which is due most probably to the pressure of the upper lid upon the eyeball during growth) the greater curvature is in the vertical meridian. In pathological types also this meridian has most commonly the greater curvature. When the refractive power though unequal in the various meridians is the same throughout any meridian, and the maximally and minimally curved meridians (*principal meridians*) are at right angles to one another, the astigmatism is called *regular.* In *irregular astigmatism* not only is the refractive power unequal in the different meridians, but it is not uniform throughout a meridian, and the principal meridians are not at right angles to one another. Astigmatism may result from inequalities in the refractive indices between different parts of the lens; this is termed *index astigmatism*. Slight inequalities of this nature in the refractive indices may also contribute to physiological astigmatism. An oblique or other malposition of the lens is sometimes a cause of astigmatism. When the subject of astigmatism looks at a clock face, the straight lines in the vertical numerals XII and VI may be clearly seen, while the horizontal lines in IX and III are blurred, or vice versa. Or, the diagonal numerals may be out of focus while the vertical and horizontal are sharply defined. A chart such as is shown in figure 74.43 is employed to detect the meridian or meridians in which the corneal curvature is abnormal.

Astigmatism is corrected by the use of spectacle lenses convex in the meridian corresponding to that of the cornea (or crystalline lens) having the lesser curvature. Thus if the curvature of the cornea is greater in the vertical meridian, the subject is fitted with a cylindrical lens, which, it will be recalled, refracts in a single plane, having its convexity in the horizontal meridian.

The young emmetrope becomes myopic by 1 to 2 D when viewing a scene in dim lighting, such as twilight. There is evidence that some of this "twilight myopia" is caused by the increased effects of spherical aberration resulting from the dilation of the pupil in dim lighting. However, some of the effect is also due to a small and variable amount of near accommodation of the lens system. Even in bright viewing conditions when the pupils are small and spherical aberration is minimal the emmetrope may become myopic to the extent of 0.25 to 1 D when viewing a scene devoid of visual detail, such as a clear blue sky. This "day myopia" is due to the lens system accommodating for near. It is not known why the accommodation mechanism does not remain focussed at infinity in the absence of a suitable visual stimulus. This condition may cause difficulty in high altitude aircraft when searching for approaching aircraft.

### Contact Lenses

The contact lens consists of a thin cuplike shell of glass moulded to fit the cornea and sclera and ground to the required curvature. It is applied directly to the eye and therefore moves with it. Contact lenses are employed for the correction of various types of refractive error, e.g., myopia and hypermetropia and those due to abnormalities in the form of the cornea (astigmatism or conical

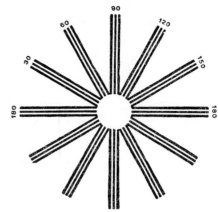

Fig. 74.43. Chart used in testing for astigmatism. One eye being closed the patient is asked to say which of the groups of lines are blackest and most distinct and which are lightest and indistinct.

Fig. 74.44. Contact lens.

cornea) or to absence of the lens (aphakia). Before being applied the concavity of the lens is filled with saline solution and when in position is separated from the cornea only by a thin film of the solution. The refractive indices of the cornea and the saline are approximately the same. The two therefore constitute a single refracting medium moulded as it were by the posterior surface of the glass shell into a normal form. Light rays are refracted at the anterior surface of the cornea in contact with the air and less strongly at the posterior surface, but undergo no further refraction until they reach the crystalline lens (fig. 74.44).

### The Intraocular Fluids

THE INTRAOCULAR PRESSURE. The pressure within the chambers of the eye of a living animal is from 15 to 20 mm. Hg and from 8 mm. to 10 mm. Hg in the excised but intact globe; it also falls to the latter level immediately after death or after arrest of the ocular circulation. The difference between these two sets of values, is due to the pressure of the blood in the vessels of the globe. This will be clear from figure 74.45. The vascular bed of the eyeball lies between the relatively resistant sclerotic on the outside and the incompressible intraocular contents on the other. It is evident that blood pumped into the vessels of the choroid will raise the intraocular pressure above

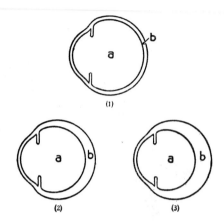

FIG. 74.45. Showing the distribution of volume-pressure in the eye with (1) a collapsed blood pressure, (2) in the normal state, and (3) with raised blood pressure and capillary dilatation. (After Duke-Elder, *The Nature of the Intraocular Fluids*.)

that of a bloodless eye. The intraocular pressure runs closely parallel with that of the blood in the choroidal capillaries. A rise or fall in general arterial pressure therefore may cause a corresponding change in intraocular pressure, though it will be much less in degree. The pulse beat causes a variation in intraocular pressure of from 1 to 2 mm. Hg, and the respiration one of from 3 to 5 mm. Hg. However, since it is the pressure in the capillary bed of the eye rather than that in the larger ocular vessels which is the determining factor and the former pressure can vary as a result of *local* changes in caliber of the minute vessels, the intraocular and arterial pressures do not necessarily change in the same direction. Thus arterial hypertension, in which the capillary pressure is not raised (p. 388), does not cause a rise in intraocular pressure; amyl nitrite, on the other hand, causes a *fall* in arterial pressure as a result of the peripheral vasodilation, accompanied by a *rise* in intraocular pressure (due to the dilation of the capillaries of the eye and the consequent increase in capillary pressure). The intraocular pressure therefore follows very closely the venous pressure; tying the vortex veins, for example, increases capillary pressure and causes a rise in intraocular pressure of from 50 to 60 mm. Hg. The pressure of 8 or 10 mm. Hg which, as mentioned above, exists within an eye immediately after its circulation has been arrested, may be looked upon as representing the balance struck between the production of intraocular fluid and its removal through the drainage channels.

Other factors which affect the intraocular tension are, pressure from without by the action of

the eyelids and of the extrinsic muscles of the eye. The effect exerted by the eye muscles in ordinary movements is negligible, but maximally strong convergence of the eyeballs may raise the pressure by from 4 to 10 mm. Hg. Movements of the lids have a greater influence, strong contraction of the orbicularis oculi causing a rise of 50 mm. Hg or more. Exposure of the eye to light causes a fall, and dark adaptation a rise in pressure which is attributed to constriction and dilation, respectively, of the ocular capillaries. Contraction of the ciliary muscle causes no change in the intraocular pressure, nor does the state of the pupil. A change in pressure does not occur therefore upon accommodation of the eye, provided that the associated convergent movement is prevented.

THE VITREOUS BODY. The vitreous body occupies the segment of the globe lying behind the lens and the ciliary processes. In front it presents a saucer-shaped depression—the *hyaloid fossa*—which lodges the posterior convexity of the lens. A narrow space (*postlenticular space*) filled with fluid separates the lens from the concave surface of the vitreous. The *hyaloid canal* (which lodged the hyaloid artery in the embryo) runs from the posterior pole of the lens to the center of the optic disc. The structureless *hyaloid membrane* surrounds the vitreous; anteriorly it is strengthened by radial fibers which have already been referred to as the *zonula ciliaris* (p. 1386). In this region it shows a series of grooves which lodge the ciliary processes. The vitreous body is a jellylike material, possessing no obvious structure; but it is claimed that by the use of special fixatives (e.g., a weak solution of chromic acid) a series of superimposed lamellae arranged concentrically around the hyaloid canal and composed of very thin flat cells can be demonstrated. The spaces between the lamellae contain fluid almost identical in composition with the aqueous humor. Though some maintain that the lamellae are fixation artefacts and that the vitreous body is a homogeneous gel, there seems little doubt that a framework does exist. If the vitreous body is examined with the phase contrast microscope a network of fibers of various sizes can be demonstrated and a clear cut hyaline membrane which encloses it. The human vitreous adheres firmly to the retina in the region of the macula and optic disc. Less firm adhesions also occur at the equator and this appears to lend support to the hypothesis that some retinal detachments are caused by traction of the vitreous fiber on the retina. Examination of the vitreous structure with the electron microscope has revealed three types of fibers: (1) fibers without cross striations of diameter 15 to 30 m$\mu$, this type being commonest; (2) fibers showing cross striations of period 61 m$\mu$ and diameter 15–30 m$\mu$, (3) fibers showing cross striations similar to collagen (64 m$\mu$) and diameter 50 to 80 m$\mu$.

THE AQUEOUS HUMOR is a clear watery fluid occupying the anterior and posterior chambers of the eye. It has a refractive index of 1.33; it is alkaline in reaction (pH 7.1 to 7.3) and has a specific gravity of from 1002 to 1004. The composition of the aqueous humor closely resembles that of an ultrafiltrate of plasma. The main difference between the composition of plasma and aqueous lines is the very low protein content of the latter (10 to 20 mg., 100 ml. in man). The aqueous contains a lower concentration of glucose and a higher concentration of lactic acid than does plasma. This may be due in part to the metabolism of glucose by the lens and cornea. The ascorbic acid concentration of the aqueous is some 10 to 50 times greater than that in the plasma, and it is thought to be passed into the fluid by the ciliary body. This high concentration may be connected with the metabolism of the avascular tissues such as the cornea, lens and vitreous body. The ascorbic acid content of the aqueous has been shown to fall dramatically in scorbutic guinea pigs but no ocular defects occur in prolonged scurvy in either guinea pigs or man.

### The Formation of the Intraocular Fluids

Owing to the importance of the subject to glaucoma, the formation of the intraocular fluids has been investigated most diligently, especially by Duke-Elder and his associates. But the precise mechanism involved has not yet been established. There have been three theories of the process proposed, namely, that it is one of (1) *ultrafiltration*, (2) *dialysis* or (3) *secretion*. None of these theories alone fits all the known facts. The principal process appears to be one of ultrafiltration, and involves those factors, capillary blood pressure and colloid osmotic pressures, which have been described elsewhere in connection with the interchange of water and substances in solution across capillary membranes (chs. 3 and 13). The high capillary pressure required for ultrafiltration into the interior of the eyeball has been shown to exist (owing to the relatively high hydrostatic pressure therein); the mean pressure in the capillaries derived from the retinal artery and the posterior ciliary arteries is 50 mm. Hg which is much higher than that in the capillaries of most other regions. Nevertheless, ultrafiltration is not a complete explanation of the formation of intraocular fluid, for when the concentrations of the constituents of plasma and of the aqueous humor are compared, it is evident that the latter is not simply an ultrafiltrate like the fluid in Bowman's capsule, for example. It is therefore thought that dialysis plays a part, though there are discrepancies here which

do not permit the formulation of a theory based upon simple dialysis alone. There is also some evidence that certain substances, e.g., sodium are secreted.

The surface of the ciliary body and the posterior aspect of the iris are believed to constitute the membrane interposed between the aqueous humor and the blood. That diffusion occurs across *both* these surfaces is indicated by the following observations. When the pupillary aperture is occluded either experimentally or as a result of disease, aqueous fluid accumulates behind the iris. On the other hand, fluid is formed after excision of the iris or when it is congenitally absent. In certain fish not possessing a ciliary body and in the congenital absence of the latter in man, normal aqueous humor is present; it has also been found in a cyst of the iris itself.

THE CIRCULATION OF THE INTRAOCULAR FLUIDS. THE DRAINAGE SYSTEM OF THE EYE. Intraocular fluid is probably reabsorbed to some extent from all parts of the interior of the globe. A small proportion of the dialyzed fluid passes from the posterior chamber through the zonule and down the hyaloid canal to the lymphatics of the optic nerve. However, less than 1 per cent is reabsorbed in this way, or indeed from any region of the eye lying posterior to the iris. The chief exits for the fluid are at the angle of the anterior chamber (*angle of the iris* or *filtration angle*) and from the anterior surface of the iris. It will perhaps be of advantage to the reader if the main structural features of this region are recalled.

On the deep aspect of the sclera at its junction with the cornea and in front of the angle of the anterior chamber lies an annular venous sinus—the *canal of Schlemm (sinus venosus sclerae)* (fig. 74.29). The sinus completely surrounds the corneal margin and in meridional sections of the eye appears as a small oval gap or cleft lined by endothelium. The inner or posterior wall of the canal is separated from the anterior chamber by a zone of trabecular tissue formed by the breaking up of the posterior elastic lamina of the cornea and termed the *pectinate ligament*; the intervals between the trabeculae are termed the *spaces of Fontana*. The trabecular tissue of the pectinate ligament is continued around the iridial angle, its fibers terminating in the tissue of the iris. Schlemm's canal is fed by an *afferent arteriole* derived from the ciliary arteries and drained by an *efferent venule* which empties into the episcleral venous plexus (Friedenwald). The spaces of Fontana communicate with the anterior chamber, but there is no *direct* communication between the former and the lumen of Schlemm's canal; the canal cannot be injected, for example, with a colloidal solution introduced into the anterior chamber.

The *scleral spur* is the term applied to a small triangular projection of the sclera on the posterior aspect of the sclerocorneal junction; it lies immediately behind the outer part of the posterior wall of Schlemm's canal and gives attachment to the meridional fibers of the ciliary muscle. Contraction of the muscle, by pulling upon the spur, is said to dilate the canal and thus favor the drainage of fluid from the anterior chamber.

Movement of the intraocular fluid from the posterior to the anterior chamber and from the latter to the filtration angle is brought about largely through intermittent variations in intraocular pressure occasioned by the several factors already discussed (e.g., pulsatile and respiratory variations in blood pressure and actions of the eyelids, etc.). Temperature differences between the superficial and deeper parts of the anterior chamber (*thermal factor*) cause convection currents to be set up which also play an important part in the movement of fluid. At the angle of the iris the fluid percolates into the spaces of Fontana whence it is absorbed across the posterior wall of the canal of Schlemm.

Friedenwald and Pierce have demonstrated a differential absorption between the water, crystalloids and protein constituents of the aqueous. From their experiments which involved the introduction of substances into the anterior chamber, these observers conclude that crystalloids and a small quantity of water are reabsorbed from the anterior surface of the iris, passing by diffusion through the walls of the capillaries. Colloids are removed by the phagocytic action of the surface layer of epithelial cells. A part of the protein is hydrolyzed by the action of enzymes present in the fluid and reabsorbed as amino-acids. Water is absorbed chiefly through the spaces of Fontana and the canal of Schlemm. The rate of passage of fluid through the wall of the canal is governed apparently by hydrostatic and osmotic forces. The pressure of blood in Schlemm's canal (or rather in the small veins leading from it) is stated to be equal to or about 1 mm. higher than that of the fluid in the anterior chamber, but after the absorption of crystalloids one would expect the osmotic pressure of the aqueous to be considerably lower than that of the serum; under such circumstances an uptake of fluid would occur, provided the blood flow through the canal did not fall below a certain level. Slowing of the circulation would tend (as a result of the dilution of serum colloid dilution by the reabsorbed fluid and consequent reduction in osmotic pressure) to reduce the rate of reabsorption, an increase in blood velocity to increase it. Such a relationship was actually observed by Friedenwald and Pierce. Increase in intraocular pressure would quite evidently increase reabsorption, the pressure would thus tend automatically to be restored to its original level.

According to some authorities (Maggiore, Duke-Elder) the canal of Schlemm contains blood only when the ocular venous pressure is inordinately high, being filled under usual circumstances with an aqueous fluid (with an osmotic pressure around that of the fluid in the anterior chamber). Since, as mentioned above, the pressure of blood in the small veins leading from it is higher than the normal intraocular pressure the canal could not serve as a pathway for the continued reabsorption of fluid; it is claimed that reabsorption can occur only if the intraocular pressure rises above the normal level. This conception attributes a safety-valve function to the canal, i.e., it is called into play presumably only in an emergency.

GLAUCOMA OR OCULAR HYPERTENSION. Persistent elevation of the intraocular pressure occurs as an accompaniment of several diseased states of the eye and may then be due to blockage of the drainage channels at the iridial angle or to the excessive production of fluid. The latter effect may result from mechanical irritation of the ciliary processes (e.g., by displacement of the lens) or obstruction of the venous channels with consequent rise in capillary pressure. Ocular hypertension associated with some such obvious disease of the eye is referred to as *secondary glaucoma*. When the intraocular pressure is persistently elevated above 35 mm. or so and no abnormality of the eye exists to account for the hypertension, it is termed *primary glaucoma*. At the outset it may be said that, though primary glaucoma has been the subject of much speculation, its cause remains obscure.

The excessively high intraocular tension causes compression of the vessels and in time serious disturbances in the nutrition of the eye result, namely, optic atrophy, excavation ("cupping") of the disc, blindness and ultimately disintegration of the optical mechanism. Owing to the readjustments which take place in the ocular circulation the hypertension may exist for some time before any of these effects make their appearance. The pressure as it gradually rises first compresses the venous channels but, as a result of the opening up of the arterioles and capillaries, a larger proportion of the arterial pressure is transmitted to the venous side; the compressing force is thus overcome and the circulation maintained. This stage in the progress of the condition is referred to as *compensated glaucoma*. A point will be reached, however, at which the pressure of the intraocular fluids approaches equality with that in the ophthalmic artery; then further compensation becomes impossible and the structural changes just mentioned supervene. The condition is then termed *inflammatory* or *decompensated glaucoma.*

The possible factors which have been suggested in explanation of the elevated pressure will be briefly considered. Mechanical obstruction at the filtration angle due to reduction in the depth of the anterior chamber and the consequent adhesion of the periphery of the iris to the cornea, is frequently present in decompensated cases, but this is secondary and not primarily related to the hypertension. It is not improbable that some abnormality in the nervous control of the vascular bed of the globe is fundamentally responsible. Friedenwald suggests that the reabsorption of water through the mechanism of Schlemm's canal (p. 1398) as a result of sclerosis and narrowing of the afferent vessels may be the essential factor concerned. Reduction in the caliber of these vessels would tend, by slowing the blood flow through the canal, to reduce the reabsorption rate. Spasm of the vessels feeding the sinus would have a similar effect. On the other hand, the reduced depth of the anterior chamber in decompensated glaucoma suggests that the increased pressure originates in the posterior chamber of the eye, and the theory has been advanced that swelling of the vitreous is responsible. From the gellike nature of the vitreous body one might expect its water content to vary with changes in its inorganic constituents or in pH. It has been found, however, that the chemical changes necessary to cause any significant increase in volume of the vitreous are far greater than any that could occur in the body. Finally, a vasodilator toxin of the histamine type has been suggested which supposedly, by causing dilation of the intraocular capillaries and an increase in the permeability of their walls, would lead to overproduction of intraocular fluid. The aqueous in decompensated glaucoma has a higher protein, and lower chloride content and osmotic pressure than normal; this fact lends some force to the theory of increased capillary permeability. The

abnormal permeability would also, by reducing the effective osmotic difference between the contents of the anterior chamber and the blood, tend to diminish reabsorption. Nevertheless, analysis of the aqueous humor in *compensated* cases shows no significant departure from the normal and therefore lends no support to the idea that a change in capillary permeability is the fundamental factor in the development of glaucoma.

There is no causative relationship between arterial and ocular hypertension.

## REFERENCES

BENHAM, G. H., DUKE-ELDER, W. S. AND HODGSON, T. H. J. Physiol., 1928, **92**, 355.

BURGE, W. E. Am. J. Physiol., 1915, **39**, 335.

CLARK, J. H. Am. J. Physiol., 1935, **113**, 538.

DUKE-ELDER, W. S. Lancet, 1926, **1**, 1188. Ibid., 1250, Brit. J. Ophth., 1940, **24**, 421.

FINCHAM, E. F. Proc. Optical Conv., Part I, 1926, p. 454.

FRIEDENWALD, J. S. Arch. Path., 1936, **16**, 65.

FRIEDENWALD, J. S. AND PIERCE, H. F. Arch. Ophth., 1937, **17**, 477.

FRIEDENWALD, J. S. AND STIEHLER, R. D. Arch. Ophth., 1935, **14**, 789.

GOLDMAN, H. AND HAGEN, R. Ophthalmologica (Basel), 1942, **104**, 15.

GOLDSCHMIDT, M. München. med. Wchnschr., 1914, **61**, 657.

HARTBRIDGE, H. AND HILL, A. V. Proc. Roy. Soc., London, ser. B, 1915, **89**, 58.

HOLMES, G. AND PATON, L. Brain, 1910, **33**, 389.

LUDVIGH, E. Nature, 1938, **141**, 1141.

*Monographs and Reviews*

ADAMS, D. R. Proc. Roy. Soc., London, ser. B., 1925, **98**, 244. Brit. J. Ophth., 1925, **9**, 281.

DUKE-ELDER, W. S. Brit. J. Ophth., 1927, Monograph Supp. III. The practice of refraction. Churchill, Lond., 1928.

HELMHOLTZ, H. VON. Treatise on physiological optics. Optic. Soc. Am. 1924.

LE GRAND, Y., Light, colour and vision. Chapman and Hall, London, 1957.

PIRIE, A. AND VAN HEYMINGEN, R., Biochemistry of the eye. Blackwell, Oxford, 1956.

SOUTHALL, J. P. C. Introduction to physiological optics. Oxford University Press, 1937.

# 75

# THE VISUAL FIELDS AND PATHWAY. MOVEMENTS OF THE OCULAR MUSCLE. STEREOSCOPIC VISION

THE VISUAL FIELDS. The visual field of one eye is the part of the external world which is seen by that eye at any given moment, i.e., when its gaze is fixed in one direction. It may be likened to a portion of a great hollow sphere—a bowl—upon the interior surface of which the images of the external world are projected. Traquair pictures the visual field as "an island of vision surrounded by a sea of blindness"; carrying the simile further, the surface contour of this imaginary island is described in terms of visual acuity, the highest point corresponding to the fovea, a deep (bottomless) pit to the blind spot and a gradual slope toward the peripheral retina. The visual field of each eye subtends an angle of about 160° in a horizontal and 145° in the vertical meridian. The visual field on each side is divided by a line passing vertically through the fixation point (p. 1417) into two unequal parts, an outer or *temporal* and an inner or *nasal*. The latter is smaller owing to the shadow of the nose, its diameter being about 60° whereas the diameter of the temporal part is around 100°. Similarly a line passing horizontally through the point of fixation divides the field into an upper and a lower part, the former being restricted by from 5° to 10° by the upper lid and orbital margin. Rays of light from the outer or temporal half of the visual field fall upon the nasal (inner) half of the retina, those from the inner or nasal half of the visual field fall upon the temporal half of the retina (fig. 75.7, p. 1408). Although an image is formed upon each retina the two are fused in consciousness into a single impression (see p. 1412). In most animals the visual fields of the two eyes overlap, that is, certain parts of the outside world are seen by both eyes at the same instant—*binocular vision*. In animals with eyes placed laterally in the head overlap of the visual fields must obviously be very small in extent, the visual fields being almost completely separate—*monocular vision*. The extent of overlap of the visual fields of the monkey and of man, whose eyes are placed in the front of the head, is large (120° horizontal diameter) and the monocular field of vision, that

is, the field which can be seen by one eye but not by the other, is relatively small (35°) (figs. 75.1 and 75.5). Rays of light entering the eyes from an object in the binocular field of vision fall upon the nasal half of one retina and upon the temporal half of the other. If, however, the object is well to the right or to the left of the line of vision, i.e., in the outer part of either temporal field, the rays then fall upon the nasal half of the peripheral retina of the nearer eye (right or left) but not upon the other retina which is shaded by the nose. So the monocular field of vision consists in man of a crescentic area (35°) at the outer limit of the temporal field of each eye.

When one looks directly at an object the eyes are turned so as to bring an image of the object upon the most sensitive area of each retina, i.e.; upon the nasal and temporal halves, respectively, of the foveae. The horizontal diameter of the entire visual field, that is, of the area of overlap of the two fields plus the monocular fields on each side is about 200°.

We shall see when the arrangement of the fibers conveying visual impulses is considered that fibers arising from the nasal halves of the retinas cross in the chiasma, whereas the temporal fibers remain uncrossed. Thus it is that the occipital cortex of one side receives impulses from the nasal half of the opposite retina and from the temporal half of the retina of the same side, that is, those retinal halves which receive impressions from the opposite halves of the visual fields (fig. 75.7, p. 1408). Loss of vision in one half of each eye is called hemianopia. When the blindness affects the right or the left halves of both retinas, i.e., the nasal half of the left retina (temporal half of visual field) and the temporal half of the right (nasal half of the visual field) or vice versa, the hemianopia is said to be *homonymous*—left or right respectively. If the blindness is in the *left* half of one retina and in the *right* half of the other, i.e., in either both temporal retinal halves (nasal halves of visual fields) or in both nasal retinal halves (temporal halves of visual fields) the hemi-

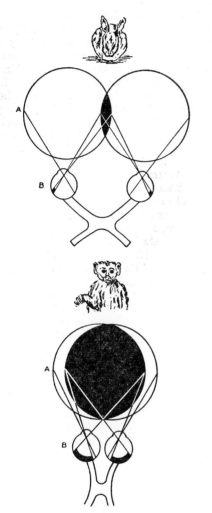

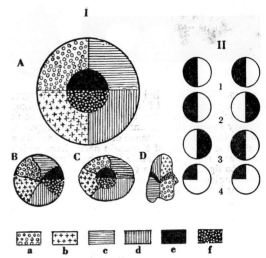

FIG. 75.2. *I*, distribution of visual fibers. *A*, right retina; *B*, optic nerve; *C*, optic chiasma; *D*, opposite lateral geniculate body; *a*, upper nasal quadrant of retina; *b*, lower nasal quadrant; *c*, upper temporal quadrant; *d*, lower temporal quadrant; *e*, upper macular fibers; *f*, lower macular fibers. (Redrawn and modified from Henschen and Brouwer and Zeeman). *II*, Diagram of types of hemianopia, *1*, homonymous; *2*, bitemporal; *3*, binasal; *4*, homonymous superior quadrantic.

FIG. 75.1. Showing monocular (white) and binocular (black) fields of vision. Upper rabbit; lower monkey (or man). (From Parsons, after Brouwer and Zeeman.)

anopia is *crossed* or *heteronymous* and is referred to as *binasal* or *bi-temporal*, respectively. It will be noted that the qualifying terms refer to the affected halves of the *visual fields* and not to the retinal halves. In other instances a quarter only of each visual field is affected, when the term *quadrantic hemianopia* is employed. It may be the upper or the lower quadrants of the nasal or of the temporal fields which are involved, or homonymous quadrants may be affected, i.e., a quadrant in the nasal field of one eye and in the temporal field of the other. The type of hemianopia is further specified by the use of the word "superior" or "inferior" (fig. 75.2). Thus, a superior nasal quadrantic hemianopia is one in which the eyes do not see objects in the upper nasal

quadrants of the visual fields (blindness of lower temporal retinal quadrants).

*Isopters.* The sensitivity of the retina from the periphery to the fovea can be explored by using a series of test objects of graduated sizes with the perimeter, and determining in different meridians the distance from the fixation point (p. 1417) at which each object is just perceptible. The points so determined are marked upon the perimeter chart and lines drawn through each set. Thus a series of boundary lines roughly concentric with the fovea are constructed which indicate the thresholds for the perception (minimum visible, p. 1364) of the different test objects, and therefore demarcate levels of retinal sensitivity. Each is called an *isopter of sensitivity*; they might be compared to the contour lines indicating elevations on a detailed geographical map.

THE BLIND SPOT. The entrance of the optic nerve since it is devoid of rods and cones is completely blind. An object whose image falls upon it is therefore invisible (see fig. 75.3). Not even a sensation of blackness results, for when the eye is fixated upon the cross, as described in the legend of the figure, and the book moved until the optic disc is occupied by the circle the latter simply disappears, no sensation whatever being experienced to indicate its existence. Ordinarily this "hole" in the visual field causes no inconvenience because, in any position of the eyes, should one

FIG. 75.3. The blind spot. Close the left eye, hold the figure about 6 inches in front of the right eye and look steadily at the cross. Move the book slowly toward the eye until the circle disappears. When this occurs the image of the circle has fallen upon the entrance of the optic nerve from which rods and cones are absent; it is therefore insensitive to light. Figure on the right shows the blind spot projected 6 inches in front of the right eye as mapped out by means of perimetry. (After Helmholtz.)

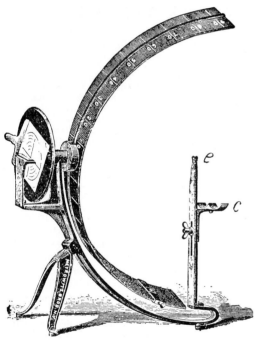

FIG. 75.4. Perimeter; *e*, position of the patient's eye; *c*, chin-rest; further description in the text.

image of an object fall upon the blind spot a sensitive part of the opposite retina receives the other image. Even when one eye is closed, or blind, we are not aware of the blind spot in the seeing eye unless it is specifically demonstrated. Patients, who have had portions of their peripheral retina destroyed some time previously by localized disease, are often unaware of the presence of the blind areas until they are demonstrated to exist by means of perimetry.

*Perimetry* is the term applied to the procedure of mapping out the visual fields. The instrument employed is called a *perimeter*. It comprises a metal band or arm, shaped in a large arc of a circle with its concavity directed towards the subject

(fig. 75.4). A holder sliding in the arc carries the test object which can be moved centrally or peripherally as required. The arm itself is pivoted at the center enabling it to be rotated to any angle. The subject's head is supported on a chin rest. One eye is covered; the eye under examination is placed at the center of the sphere of which the perimeter arm forms the arc, and made to fix a point straight ahead in the center of the arm. The latter is rotated by degrees through a full circle and at each new position the test object is moved centrally until it is just perceived by the subject. This point and corresponding points at the various positions of the arm are marked upon a perimeter chart and the contour of the visual field outlined through them. The chart (fig. 75.5) is ruled in circles (comparable to latitudes on a geographical map) to indicate degrees from the point of fixation, and in radiating lines ("longitudes" or meridians). The mapping of the blind spot and of the sensitivity of the retina in isopters has been referred to. The reader should consult texts on ophthalmology for a more detailed description of perimetry. A simple but rough method of perimetry (*confrontation method*) which will reveal a major limitation of the visual fields is the following. The observer stands facing the subject and about two feet in front of him. One eye of the patient is covered while the other, which he fixes upon the opposite eye of the examiner, is being tested. The examiner holds his finger midway between himself and the patient but outside the limit of his own visual field and then brings it slowly toward the midline. The observer compares the position at which he first sights his finger with that at which it is first seen by the patient. The procedure is

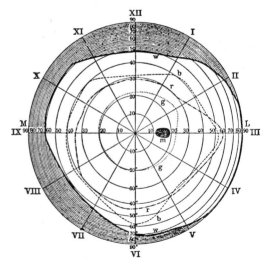

FIG. 75.5. Perimeter chart showing normal visual field of right eye. *M*, blind spot; *g, r, b* and *w* indicate boundaries of fields for green, red, blue and white, respectively. Meridians indicated by Roman numerals. (After Starling.)

repeated from various directions, above, below and from either side.

## The Visual Pathway

*The optic nerve.* The ganglion cells of the retina (ganglion cell layer) whose central processes constitute the optic nerve, are the secondary neurons of the visual pathway (ch. 72). The primary neurons are the bipolar cells of the inner nuclear layer, the peripheral processes of the latter connecting with the visual receptors—the rods and cones. Tertiary neurons complete the pathway from the lateral geniculate body to the visual cortex. The fibers of the ganglion cells as they enter into the formation of the optic nerve are arranged in groups corresponding, in their relative positions, to the quadrants of the peripheral retina from which they arise. That is, fibers from the upper and lower temporal quadrants of the retina are found in the upper lateral and lower lateral regions of the nerve, respectively (fig. 75.3). Those from the nasal quadrants are situated in the inner sections of the nerve, the fibers from the upper quadrant lying above those from the lower. In the distal part of the nerve the macular or foveal fibers are in a lateral position, being wedged between the upper and lower temporal bundles, but again, fibers from the upper half of the fovea lie above those from the lower half.[1]

*The optic chiasma.* The fibers from the temporal halves of the peripheral retina continue uncrossed into the corresponding optic tracts, while the fibers from the nasal halves cross in the chiasma to the optic tract of the opposite side.[2] In the chiasma the temporal fibers lie in its lateral angle. Those of upper retinal origin lie above those arising from the lower retinal quadrant. In the crossing of the nasal fibers, those from the upper quadrants lie upon the upper aspect, those from the inferior quadrants upon the under aspect of the chiasma; the macular fibers lie in between.

### *The Optic Tracts and Primary Optic Centers*

The visual pathway from the chiasma to the primary optic center consists of compact bundles

[1] There is some evidence that centrifugal fibers may be present in the optic nerve. Granit has recently succeeded in demonstrating centrifugal effects from the mesencephalic reticular activating system in the cat's retina. These centrifugal signals may adjust the peripheral sensitivity of the retina, although much more work will be required to establish their function. (See Granit.)

[2] The proportion of the fibers which cross in the chiasma varies in different mammalian forms. In the opossum, example $\frac{4}{5}$ cross to the opposite optic tract, whereas in the ferret $\frac{2}{3}$ cross; in the rabbit also the uncrossed fibers are few in number.

of fibers—the *optic tract*. In the optic tract, fibers from the upper quadrants of the peripheral retina tend to lie ventro-laterally, those from the lower quadrants ventro-medially. The foveal fibers lie dorso-laterally. The optic tract passes backwards and outwards between the tuber cinereum and the anterior perforated substance to the cerebral peduncle around which it turns as a flattened band to reach the *lateral (external) geniculate body*. In this, the *primary visual center*, the great majority of the optic fibers make connection. A smaller number are continued to the *superior colliculus* (superior corpus quadrigeminum) but none of these are of foveal origin.

The projection of the retina upon the external geniculate body has been studied by Brouwer and Zeeman in monkeys. These observers produced localized lesions in the retina and examined the geniculate body histologically after time had been allowed for degeneration of the optic fibers. It was found that the retinas were not projected diffusely throughout the primary optic center, but showed localization of their different regions to definite sections. Thus the upper parts of the peripheral retinas, both nasal and temporal, of the two eyes were projected to the medial parts of the geniculate body. The lower parts of the retinas were represented in the lateral part (fig. 75.3, E). Dorsal to these regions and wedged between them was an extensive area wherein the macular fibers terminated. Binocular and monocular types of vision have separate representations. In the monkey the area which receives fibers from only one eye is very small, occupying a small rim on the ventral aspect of the primary center. In the rabbit, on the other hand, the monocular projection occupies almost the entire geniculate body, binocular vision being represented by a narrow area on the medial aspect of the geniculate body.

The cells of the lateral geniculate body with which the visual fibers synapse are disposed in six well defined laminae which have been numbered 1 to 6 from the surface inwards by Le Gros Clark. One set of three (1, 4 and 6) receive crossed fibers, i.e., fibers from the nasal half of the opposite retina. The other set (2, 3 and 5) are cell stations for the uncrossed fibers, i.e., from the temporal half of the retina of the same side.

*The superior colliculi.* The superior colliculi are the chief centers for visual reflexes, and constitute as well the highest visual centers in submammalian forms. In the latter they are very prominent structures; in fishes and birds they are as large or larger than the cerebral hemispheres.

But in higher animals, they are much reduced in size, and in man, are relatively inconspicuous structures, their visual functions having been taken over by the cerebral cortex. The superior colliculi of mammals receive afferent impulses from (a) the retina through the *optic tracts*, (b) the *occipital cortex* (visual area) and (c) *the spinal cord* via the spinotectal tract. Their efferent connection are with the medulla and the spinal cord through the *tectobulbar* and *tectospinal tracts*.

The reflexes centered in the superior colliculi serve to correlate eye movements with the movements of the head, or with the trunk and limbs. The chief of these visual reflexes are, (a) turning the eyes in order to keep them fixed upon a stationary object when the head is turned in the opposite direction (compensatory reflexes), (b) movement of the head with the eyes so as to keep a moving object in view, and (c) movements of the limbs, neck or trunk as in avoiding a moving object or in fending off a blow threatening the eyes. Closure of the lids to protect the sight occurs simultaneously.

The *optic radiation (geniculocalcarine pathway)*. The visual fibers after leaving the external geniculate body pass through the posterior extremity of the internal capsule, and curving forward and outward into the temporal lobe sweep backward in relation to the outer aspect of the posterior horn of the lateral ventrical to reach the *area striata* (area 17) of the occipital cortex (pp. 1249 and 1408). The optic radiation also contains descending fibers which end in the superior colliculus and the external geniculate body.

*The visual cortex*. This comprises that part of the cortex referred to above as the area striata,[3] which forms the walls and lips of the calcarine fissure on the mesial aspect of the occipital lobe. The different retinal areas in their projections upon the cortex show definite localization. There is a point to point projection on to the striate area. The cortical cells, for example, are conceived as receiving individually impulses from single cones to form a pattern corresponding to that of retinal organization.[4] The homonymous halves of the peripheral retinas are represented in the anterior part of the visual area, the upper

[3] The histology of the striate area is described in ch. 67.

[4] Though the existence of poing to point projection of the retina upon the striate area has been definitely established, the cortical representation is not rigidly fixed and circumscribed by anatomical paths, but is capable of considerable functional adaptation and modification under changed conditions (See Hubel and Wiesel.)

quadrants in the upper wall and lip, the lower quadrants in the lower wall and lip. In other words, the nasal half of the right retina and the temporal half of the left are projected on to the left occipital cortex—the projection of the upper quadrant in each case lying above that of the lower quadrant. Similarly, the nasal half of the left retina and the temporal half of the right are projected onto the right striate area. The macular representation occupies the posterior part of the striate area reaching backwards to the occipital pole, but it also spreads forwards to overlap the projection area of the peripheral retina (fig. 75.6). As in the case of the peripheral retina, the upper and lower parts of the macula (fovea) are projected to the upper and lower halves, respectively, of this part of the striate area. The cortical projection of the macula is possibly bilateral, i.e., represented in its entirety in both hemispheres, since the retention of macular vision in both eyes after an extensive lesion of an occipital lobe is not infrequent. Indeed sparing of macular vision has been reported after apparently complete ablation of one occipital lobe. It has been supposed by those who believe that the macula is represented bilaterally that fibers pass from the lateral geniculate body of one side through the posterior part of the corpus callosum to join the optic radiation of the opposite hemisphere. In the monkey, however, excision of one occipital lobe is followed by retrograde degeneration of *all* cells of the corresponding lateral geniculate body, which would not be the case if some of its cells sent fibers to the opposite hemisphere. In so far as man is concerned the question is unsettled.

The subject of hemianopia may be quite unaware of his defect of vision. He compensates sometimes to a considerable extent for his half-blindness by turning his eyes more toward the blind side of the visual field, so as to bring the image on to the sound part of the retina. Compensation is also in part psychological; that portion of the image of a familiar object which falls upon the blind half of the retina is visualized mentally. Thus the image is completed subjectively. Normally, when an object is seen with one eye that part of the image which falls upon the blind spot is filled in mentally so that no gap is apparent.

*The Effects of Lesions at Different Levels of the Visual Pathway (see also p. 1405)*

(1) A destructive lesion of one optic nerve will result in total blindness of the corresponding eye

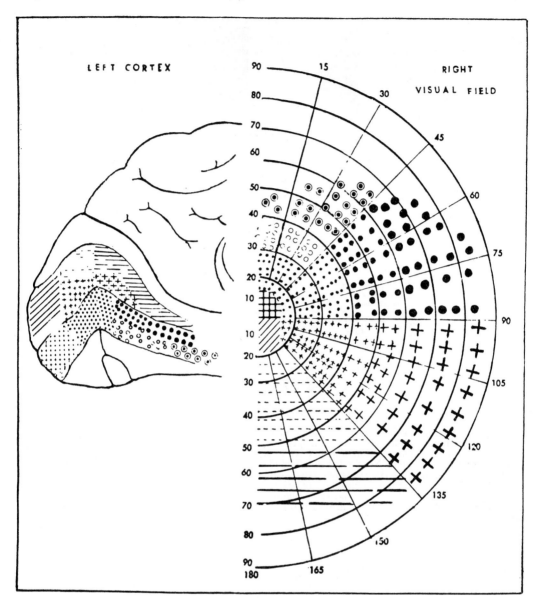

FIG. 75.6. Diagram showing the projection of the retina on the calcarine cortex. Right hand figure is temporal half of right visual field. (From Holmes, redrawn and slightly modified.)

(fig. 75.7). Increased intracranial pressure may cause atrophy of the optic nerves and a gradual concentric reduction of the visual fields of both eyes.

(2) A lesion involving the chiasma will result in visual defects whose nature will depend upon the fibers destroyed. (a) Pressure upon the uncrossed fibers in the outer angle of the chiasma, as by an aneurysmal dilatation of the internal carotid artery, may produce blindness in the temporal part of the retina of the same side. If

these fibers on both sides are affected, the sight in the temporal half of each retina (nasal half of the visual field) may be lost (*bi-nasal hemianopia*). According to Cushing a dilated third ventricle may, by pressing from above, force the angles of the chiasma against sclerosed internal carotid arteries and so produce a bi-nasal hemianopia. (b) Pituitary tumors, owing to their position, are likely to involve the nasal fibers at the point of their crossing and thus cause *bi-temporal hemi-anopia*. Since the nasal fibers from the lower ret-

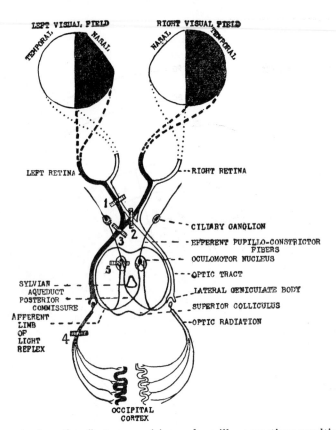

FIG. 75.7. Diagram to show the effects upon vision and pupillary reactions resulting from interruption of retinal impulses at various levels. *1*, Optic nerve; blindness of corresponding eye, direct reaction of this eye and consensual reaction of sound eye lost. Consensual reaction of blind eye and direct reaction of sound eye retained. Near reflex unaffected. *2*, Chiasma; bitemporal hemianopia. Wernicke's pupillary reaction. *3*, Optic tract; homonymous hemianopia (blindness in nasal half of right retina and temporal half of left). Wernicke's pupillary reaction. *4*, Optic radiation; homonymous hemianopia, light and near reflexes retained. *5*, At synapses in the oculomotor nucleus. Light reflex lost, near reflex retained (Argyll-Robertson pupil, see also p. 1412). The lesion is usually bilateral (as in tabes, disseminated sclerosis, etc.).

inal quadrants lie ventral to those from the upper, the lower are likely to be involved first in pituitary tumors; *superior temporal quadrantic hemianopia* will result. Lesions (e.g., tumors) pressing from above tend first to cause defects in the lower temporal quadrants of the visual fields. Dilation of the third ventricle or a tumor of the pituitary stalk may produce such an effect.

(3) Lesions of the optic tract, of the primary visual center or of the optic radiation will result in *homonymous hemianopia*. The right halves of the two eyes (left halves of the visual fields) being effected in right-sided lesions and the left halves in left-sided lesions. An abscess or tumor of the temporal lobe may, by involving the optic tract or optic radiation, cause a homonymous hemianopia. When the optic radiation is pressed upon by a temporal lobe lesion the hemianopia is very

often incomplete, i.e., quadrantic. The ventral fibers of the radiation are likely to be implicated by a tumor in the lower part of the lobe, and a superior quadrantic hemianopia result. Injury to the dorsal fibers tends to cause a defect confined at first to the lower homonymous quarters of the visual fields.

(4) *Lesions of the occipital cortex.* A lesion involving the area striata of one hemisphere or the optic radiation before their termination therein results in an homonymous hemianopia, right or left, depending upon the side of the brain affected. Quadrantic homonymous hemianopia will result when the lesion is restricted to the upper or lower part of the striate area. Owing to the large cortical area representing the macular region, or perhaps to the fact that the macula is bilaterally represented, extensive unilateral occipital lesions

or excision of a large part of this area often leave acute (central) vision intact, the blindness then involving only the peripheral half of each retina. In man, bilateral destruction of the visual cortex causes total blindness.

## The Pupil

*Pupillary reflexes.* Reflex changes in the size of the pupil occur under the following conditions: (a) Constriction of dilation occurs in response to changes in light intensity (*light reflex*). When light is thrown into the normal eye the pupil of that eye constricts promptly; this is the *direct pupillary reaction.* But the pupil of the opposite eye, though shaded, also narrows; this, the *indirect* or *consensual pupillary reaction,* is dependent upon fibers which cross to the pupillary-constrictor center of the opposite side. (b) Constriction occurs as a part of the mechanism of accommodation to near vision (*pupillary reaction of accommodation*). With it are associated convergence of the eyes and accommodation of the lens. These three reactions are appropriately grouped under the term *near reflex* or *accommodation reflex.* (c) Dilation follows stimulation of the skin of the neck (*ciliospinal reflex*). (d) Irritation of the eyelid or conjunctiva causes dilation followed by constriction of both pupils (oculo-sensory reflex). The afferent fibers of this reflex are contained in the ophthalmic division of the trigeminal nerve. (e) Closure of the eyelid, or an effort made to close the lid while it is forcibly held open causes slight pupillary constriction (lid or orbicularis reflex). (f) Pupillary dilation may occur during certain *emotional states* (e.g., fear), as a result of acute pain or a sudden sound. (e) Finally, stimulation of labyrinthine receptors causes changes in the diameter of the pupil (ch. 64). For example, rapid rotation of the body around its long axis causes dilation of the pupil and large rhythmical changes in its diameter (*hippus*). Even in a constant environment the pupil area is constantly fluctuating by about 10 per cent of its total area. These movements are called *physiological unrest.* These fluctuations are identical in amplitude and phase on both sides and, therefore, must originate central to the iris muscles.

## THE IRIS

The iris is the most anterior part of the vascular tunic of the eye. It is a thin contractile disc perforated a little to the nasal side of its center by the pupil. The pupillary margin rests upon the anterior surface of thelens. The space between the lens and the cornea is divided by the iris into a larger anterior and smaller *posterior chamber,* the two chambers communication through the pupil. The periphery (root) of the iris is attached to the anterior surface of the ciliary body and is continuous through the pectinate ligament (p. 1399) with the posterior elastic lamina of the cornea. The following five layers from before backwards compose the structure of the iris, (a) the anterior epithelium, (b) the anterior limiting membrane, (c) the stroma, (d) the posterior membrane and (e) the posterior epithelium. The *anterior epithelium* consists of a single layer of flat endothelial-like cells. Near the pupillary margin of the iris there are many small pits—the *crypts of Fuchs*—over which the epithelium is absent. The stroma is composed of loose connective tissue. It transmits the vessels and nerves and holds numerous branched cells which in dark eyes contain pigment granules. The iris contains two involuntary muscles—the sphincter pupillae and the dilator pupillae. The *sphincter pupillae* is embedded in the stroma and comprises a band of circular fibers about 1 mm. broad surrounding the pupil. When these fibers contract the pupil is constricted. The *dilator pupillae* constitutes the fourth layer of the iris, i.e., the posterior membrane, mentioned above. It consists of a thin layer of smooth muscle fibers which converge towards the pupillary margin where they blend with the fibers of the sphincter. At the root of the iris the dilator fibers pass into the ciliary body from which they take origin; when they contract they draw upon the pupillary margin and thus dilate the pupil. The *posterior epithelium* comprises two layers of deeply pigmented cubical cells; it is the continuation anteriorly of the pars ciliaris retinae (p. 1386). The arteries of the iris which are loosely coiled form two vascular circles, one near the pupillary margin—the *circulus arteriosus minor,* the other near the root of the iris— the *circulus arteriosus major.* The two circles are connected by vessels which, arising from the larger circle, converge towards the pupillary margin where they form the smaller circle.

Blue or gray eyes owe their appearance to the pigment in the posterior epithelial layer as seen through the unpigmented stroma and other layers of the iris. The pigment cells of the stroma are responsible for the color of dark eyes, the shade varying with the quantity of pigment present. In the white races nearly all newborn babies have light colored irides because pigment does not develop in the stroma until some weeks after birth. But Negro babies and others belonging to the dark races have brown eyes, the stroma pigment being well developed at birth.

*The functions of the iris.* The iris has three important functions; (a) it serves as an opaque screen, like the diaphragm or "stop" of a camera, to adjust the quantity of light reaching the retina under different intensities of illumination; (b) it prevents light from passing through the periphery of the lens and thus reduces spherical and lateral chromatic aberration. The image is thus more clearly defined by restricting the transmission of light through the central part of the lens; and (c) when the pupil constricts the depth of focus of the eye is increased (p. 1413).

The visual system operates over a very wide range of illumination ($10^{12}$ times). Over this range the pupil area only alters by a factor of 16 times and therefore, the pupil cannot maintain the retinal illumination at a constant level. The pupil light reflex probably adjusts the aperture of the eye so as to obtain the optimum visual acuity at each light level.

### Pupillo-constrictor Pathways

It is generally believed that the receptors of the light reflex are the same as those mediating visual sensations. Wagman and his associates have made the interesting observation that in dim light the curve of pupillary size at different wave-lengths agrees closely with the scotopic luminosity curve. The most effective wave-length in causing pupillary constriction of the dark adapted eye is, therefore, around 510 m$\mu$; in the light adapted eye, it is about 560 m$\mu$. Thus, the pupillary reaction shows a difference in sensitivity at high and low light intensities corresponding to the Purkinje shift.

The afferent fibers of the light reflex travel with the visual fibers and with the afferent fibers of the dilator response as far as the lateral geniculate bodies. Here they part company from the latter two sets of fibers. They do not enter the lateral geniculate body, but pass into the brachium of the superior colliculus. They then proceed to a group of cells in the pretectal region—*the pretectal nucleus*—where they make their first synaptic contacts. The impulses are finally conveyed by secondary neurons to the oculomotor nucleus on both sides of the brain, but mostly to that of the opposite side. The superior colliculus itself is not interposed in their path, for Ranson and Magoun did not observe pupillary constriction when this part was stimulated. The partial decussation of the afferent fibers, occurs, Ranson and Magoun believe, in the posterior commissure. An earlier crossing of some fibers occurs also in the optic chiasma. The fibers to the same side pass caudally and ventrally along the side of the central gray matter. Though under ordinary circumstances reduction in the tone of the pupillo-dilator center occurs reciprocally with activation of the pupillo-

constrictor center, the light reflex can be carried out through the latter alone. The reflex is therefore retained after section of the cervical sympathetic (which conveys the dilator fibers). Since the afferent fibers mediating the light reflex separate from the visual pathway at the level of the lateral geniculate body, lesions of the optic pathway beyond this point do not interfere with the light reflex.

The *efferent* fibers subserving the light reflex belong to the parasympathetic division of the autonomic nervous system. They originate in the oculomotor nucleus (probably the Edinger-Westphal nucleus) and are conveyed to the iris (sphincter pupillae) via the third nerve, ciliary ganglion and short ciliary nerves (fig. 75.8). The *near reflex* is dependent upon cortical centers. Impulses pass by association fibers from the occipital to the frontal cortex (frontal eye field) and thence via the internal capsule to the nucleus of the third nerve. Constriction of the pupil which accompanies accommodation of the lens is brought about through fibers which probably pass directly to the pretectal region from the occipital cortex adjacent to the visual area. The efferent path from the oculomotor nucleus is the same as that for the light reflex. The afferent pathway is via the visual fibers, i.e., lateral geniculate body and optic radiation, not through the superior colliculus. The reflex is bilateral, i.e., it occurs in both eyes when one is covered and the other directed to a near object.

### The Pupillo-dilator Pathway

The dilator muscle of the pupil receives sympathetic fibers which arise from the first and second thoracic segments of the spinal cord, and sometimes from the eighth cervical or the third thoracic. They issue by the white rami and pass via the cervical sympathetic to the superior cervical ganglion. From here postganglionic fibers are conveyed along the internal carotid artery into the cranial cavity. Entering the trunk of the nasociliary branch of the first division of the fifth nerve, they are transmitted to the iris in the long ciliary nerves. Some fibers also pass without interruption through the ciliary ganglion into the short ciliary nerves. These fibers supply in addition the smooth muscle of the orbit which lies in relation to the capsule of Tenon (fascia bulbi) and in the "check ligaments" of the ocular muscles. The smooth muscle forming the deep layer of the levator palpebrae superioris also receives innervation from the sympathetic.

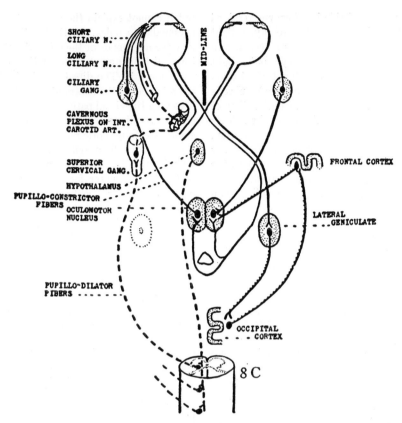

FIG. 75.8. Diagram to illustrate pupillary reflexes. Interrupted lines indicate the dilator reflex, plain lines the constrictor reflex and visual pathway to the level of the lateral geniculate body; hatched lines show path of near reflex from lateral geniculate body to the cortex and nucleus of the third nerve.

The *afferent* pathway of the pupillo-dilator reflex accompanies the pupillo-constrictor fibers as far as the lateral geniculate body. From here on their course has not been clearly defined, but they presumably descend through the tegmentum of the midbrain, and the reticular formation of the pons, medulla and spinal cord to reach the ciliospinal center.

A higher pupillo-dilator center is situated in the hypothalamus, which, in turn, is probably connected with the cortex of the frontal lobe. It sends fibers through the midbrain which, according to the researches of Beattie, pass ventrally by the posterior commissure to enter the superior colliculus.

The pupillo-dilator reflex involves reciprocal inhibition of pupillo-constrictor tone. This is the paramount factor in the dilator reflex, for after section of the sympathetic pupillary fibers, the pupil dilates in the dark, or in response to a painful stimulus or emotional excitement, in an almost normal fashion. Another factor in the dilation of

the pupil by sympathetic stimulation may be the constriction of the vessels of the iris.

When the sympathetic fibers are paralyzed the pupil is narrowed as a result of the unbalanced action of the constrictor fibers, and the dilation of the pupil which normally follows the application of a stimulus, such as a scratch or pinch, to the skin of the neck (ciliospinal reflex) fails to occur. The pupil, however, still reacts to light. Drooping of the upper lid (ptosis) will result from paralysis of the smooth muscle of the levator palpebrae superioris and there may be recession of the eyeball (enophthalmos) from paralysis of the unstriped muscle of the orbit.

An investigation of the pupillary reactions may give valuable information concerning the site of a lesion in the brain (see fig. 75.7, p. 1408). (a) A lesion destroying one optic nerve, since it interrupts the afferent pathway but leaves the efferent intact, abolishes the direct but not the indirect (consensual) reaction on the blind side. The direct reaction on the sound side is, of course, retained but the indirect is lost. That is to say, a light thrown into the sound eye causes a response in this eye as well as in the blind eye, but a light thrown into the blind eye is without effect upon either eye. The near (accommodation) reflex is not abolished. Blindness due to destruction of both optic nerves results in the loss of the reflexes for light as well as of those for accommodation. (b) Hemianopia due to a lesion of the chiasma, or of the optic tract, results in the loss of both the direct and indirect reactions to light thrown upon the blind half of either retina. Light falling upon the sound halves of the retinas causes the normal response. This is known as *Wernicke's hemianopic pupillary reaction*. However, owing to the difficulty of confining a beam of light to the blind half of the retina it is not an easy matter to demonstrate this reaction. (c) Loss of the light reflex (both direct and indirect reactions) with retention or even exaggeration of the accommodation-convergence reflex is known as the Argyll-Robertson pupil. The pupil is also, as a rule, smaller than normal (myosis) and does not dilate to a painful stimulus nor fully to atropinization; the vestibular reflex is frequently absent as well. The abnormal pupillary responses occur quite apart from any defect of vision. Though usually bilateral the Argyll-Robertson pupil is sometimes confined to one side. It is most commonly seen in syphilitic degeneration of the central nervous system (e.g., tabes), but occurs occasionally in other conditions as well. The site of the lesion responsible for the Argyll-Robertson pupil is not known precisely. Merritt and Moore give evidence for placing it in the region of the posterior commissure where presumably, the neighboring dilator pathway is also interrupted, but the pathway for the accommodation reflex from the cortex to the oculomotor nucleus would be spared. Scala and Spiegel believe from the results of their experiments that the disease involves the synapses between the afferent and efferent neurons of the light reflex, that is, in the oculomotor nucleus itself. But the oculomotor nerve supplies both pupils and a lesion here is difficult to reconcile with the unilateral loss of the light reflex which sometimes occurs. Langworthy and Ortego conclude, after a careful study, that the lesion is peripheral—due to changes in the iris itself involving sympathetic, parasympathetic and sensory nerves as well as the muscle cells of the sphincter. This theory can account for the irregularity of the pupil, and perhaps, if the sympathetic innervation were injured in greater degree than the parasympathetic, for the myosis;

but it cannot explain the preservation of the accommodation reflex. (d) Destruction of the oculomotor nucleus or of the efferent pathway abolishes all light and accommodation reactions on the same side. The direct and indirect reactions are retained on the contralateral side. (e) Lesions involving the visual pathway after the separation of the visual and pupillary fibers, e.g. lateral geniculate body, optic radiations or occipital cortex, leave the light reflex unaffected. (f) A bilateral lesion implicating the pathway from the cortex to the center for accommodation in the oculomotor nucleus will cause a loss of the near reflex and leave the light reflexes intact. This is the converse of the Argyll-Robertson pupil, and is sometimes seen in postdiphtheritic paralysis.

### The Effects of Drugs upon the Pupil and Ciliary Muscle

Dilation of the pupil is spoken of as *mydriasis*; constriction as *miosis*. Drugs which cause pupillary dilation are therefore called *mydriatics*; those which cause constriction, *miotics*. Paralysis of the ciliary muscles is known as *cycloplegia*; drugs which cause this effect are called *cycloplegics*. Mydriasis is caused by drugs which:

(a) Paralyze the peripheral constrictor (parasympathetic) mechanism, such as atropine, or homatropine. Atropine is also cycloplegic, homatropine much less so.

(b) Stimulate the dilator (sympathetic) mechanism, e.g., adrenaline, cocaine, hydroxy-amphetamine hydrobromide. These drugs have little effect upon accommodation.

Miosis is caused by drugs which:

(a) Stimulate the peripheral constrictor mechanism, e.g., pilocarpine, physostigmine, muscarine. Di-iso-fluorophosphate is a powerful anticholinesterase and produces miosis in small doses. These drugs also causes spasm of the ciliary muscles.

(b) Diminish the inhibition of the constrictor center, e.g., morphine. The action of this drug upon the pupil depends largely upon the intensity of the illumination. It appears, therefore, to exert its effect, mainly, by increasing the sensitivity of the light reflex.

(c) Stimulate the constrictor center, e.g., picrotoxin.

### Corresponding Retinal Points

When the gaze is directed to an object, an image is formed by each eye and impulses are conveyed to both sides of the brain, yet perfect fusion of the two images occurs in consciousness and only one image is seen. This characteristic of *binocular vision* is explained upon the theory of *corresponding retinal points*. The corresponding points in the retinas (foveas) which when stimulated simultaneously cause a single visual sensation, lie in the nasal half of one retina and the temporal half of the other. When the eyes are converged, the retinas are turned so that the images fall upon these corresponding parts. If, as a result of unequal action of the ocular muscles, this cannot be brought about, the separate images are not fused in consciousness and an object appears double. This abnormality of vision is known as *diplopia*.

*The horopter.* When the eyes are fixed upon a point in space, a number of other points can be located by calculation which are projected upon corresponding points of the two retinas (foveas). A line joining such points forms a circle called the *horopter* which passes through the fixation point and the nodal points of the eyes. The horopter will vary of course with the point of fixation of the eyes and does not exist unless the eyes act synergically (see fig. 75.9). Points in the visual field lying outside the horopter do not fall on the corresponding points in the two retinas (peripheral retinas) and, as a consequence, actually cause a double impression. But this *physiological diplopia* as it is called does not thrust itself upon consciousness; it is suppressed or ignored and therefore does not cause confusion. Yet one can easily demonstrate for oneself that it exists. For example, when the eyes are fixated upon a near object, such as a pencil tip held close to the face, a more distant object may, through a conscious effort, be observed in duplicate. For this reason, it is also sometimes referred to as *introspective diplopia*.

The double image is always projected to the plane of the object upon which the eyes are fixed, and the doubling of the image is either homonymous (uncrossed) or heteronymous (crossed) depending upon whether the object which produces the double image is beyond the point of fixation or between it and the eyes. That is to say, when the object (D in fig. 75.10) whose images fall on noncorresponding retinal points is closer to the eyes than the object upon which the eyes are fixed, the images, I and I, are projected across the lines of sight, the right hand image being formed by the left eye and the left hand image by the right eye. When the object is beyond the plane of fixation the projection of the images (I₁ and I₁) is homonymous, each being formed by the corresponding eye. The reader may demonstrate these facts for himself. When a pencil is held close to the eyes so as to form a double image while the eyes are focussed upon a more dis-

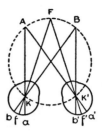

Fig. 76.9. The horopter (Müller). $F$ is the fixation point. The images of $A$, $F$, and $B$ fall upon the retinae at corresponding points as $aa'$, $ff'$, and $bb'$. The projection of all such corresponding points lies upon the circumference of the dotted circle. It is obvious that there is a different horopter for each position of $F$. (After Duke-Elder, *Text Book of Ophthalmology*.)

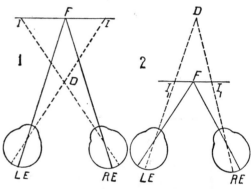

Fig. 75.10. Illustrating the projection of retinal images that fall upon noncorresponding retinal points, i.e., on different sides of the foveae—physiological diplopia. I, heteronymous diplopia (crossed); homonymous (uncrossed) diplopia; D, positions of object in relation to the fixation point. The images, I, I and I₁, I₁ are projected to the plane of the object F upon which the eyes are fixed; LE, left eye; RE, right eye.

tant object, closing the right eye causes the left hand image to disappear, whereas, if the eyes are focussed upon the pencil and the object giving rise to the double image is more distant, closure of the right eye abolishes the right hand image. Closure of the left eye, of course, produces converse effects.

## Depth Perception-Stereoscopic Vision (Gr. Stereos, Solid; Skopeo, I View)

Our visual judgment of solidity, that is, our recognition that the object has depth as well as height and width, is due largely to the fact that vision is normally binocular and corresponding points in the two retinas receive slightly dissimilar images of any given object. If the reader will look at some object in front of him, first closing one eye and then the other, he will find that the view

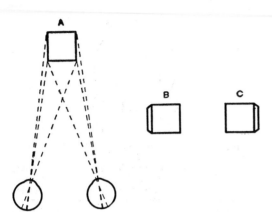

FIG. 75.11. Examples of aspect disparity. *A* is a view, seen from above, of lines of sight when the eyes look at a solid object. Notice that the right eye sees some of the right hand side of the object, while the left eye sees some of the left hand side.

*B* is a front view of a cube seen by the left eye with the right eye closed. *C* is a front view seen by the right eye with the left eye closed. When both eyes are open, we see a fusion of *B* and *C*. (After Graham.)

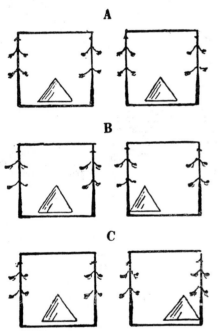

FIG. 75.12. Diagram of a tent and pine trees to show the impression of depth caused by the fusion of two dissimilar images. If the figures be gazed at steadily at a distance of about 5 inches from the eyes and a card held edgewise from the tip of the nose to the line of letters each horizontal pair of figures can, with a little practice be made to fuse. In *A* the aspect of the two scenes is practiaclly the same and the fused picture appears quite flat. In *B*, the tent in the right hand figure is placed more toward the midline and upon fusion appears to be in front of the pines. In *C*, the disparity of the right hand figure is farther from the midline; the tent is now projected to a point behind the pines.

seen by the right eye is slightly different from that seen by the left (fig. 75.11). The right eye is able to see more of the right side of the object, the left eye more of the left side. The two slightly disparate images are fused in the brain, yet the composite image has hidden within it something of each separate one; upon this the stereoscopic effect to a large extent depends. The fusion of the dissimilar images by the brain, and the impression of depth and solidity produced thereby, lies in the field of psychology.

In order for two dissimilar images to be fused in consciousness, it is not necessary that they fall upon retinal points which correspond exactly; unification of the images results though there is some degree of noncorrespondence. Actually, there is a greater impression of depth when the dissimilar images do not fall on retinal points which fail to correspond perfectly, provided that the discrepancy is not so great as to prevent fusion. In figure 75.12 a scene of a tent and pine trees is represented diagrammatically. When the two scenes are fused the tent is projected closer or farther from the eyes according to its position in the two pictures in lateral relation to the pines. When in one or in both pictures it is moved toward the mid-line it appears to advance in front of the pine trees; when moved laterally it seems to recede. The three dimensional effect is enhanced by increasing the noncorrespondence, as when the tent in one or both pictures is moved, to or away from the mid-line. But if moved too far the noncorrespondence is too great to permit fusion to occur, and the stereoscopic effect is lost.

The instrument known as a stereoscope produces an illusion of solidity by making use of the principle of simultaneous stimulation of the retinas by dissimilar images. A photograph taken with an ordinary camera appears flat because identical images are formed upon the retinas. A stereoscopic photograph, on the other hand, is taken by a camera provided with two lenses which are set, like the eyes, a short distance apart in the horizontal plane. Thus, an illusion of depth is produced. Two slightly dissimilar views are taken which, when looked at through the stereoscope, are projected by means of prisms, one to each eye, so as to fall on corresponding retinal points (fig. 75.13). Depth perception cannot, however, be explained entirely upon the basis of dissimilar retinal images, for though the discrimination of depth (or distance) is much more acute in binocular vision it is not abolished when one eye is closed. For example, when two objects are placed one in front of the other and viewed binocularly from a distance of about 6 meters the least distance between them which can be perceived by average normal eyes is around 20 mm. When one eye is covered the least perceptible difference is increased to 120 mm. The ability to detect a small difference in distance from the eyes of two objects, and so to appreciate depth and solidity, is called *stereoscopic acuity.* It is expressed as the least difference between the angles formed by the lines of sight to two objects when one is just perceived to be farther away than the other (fig. 75.14). The difference in angles is known as *stereoscopic parallax,* and may, in a person with very high visual acuity, be as little as 2 seconds of arc.

Other factors, listed below, do not depend upon binocular vision, but play an important part in depth perception through one eye alone (monocular vision).

(1) *The apparent size of various objects in our field of vision.* We know from experience the approximate dimensions of the objects which we see, but the image which an object casts upon the fovea diminishes as its distance increases (p. 1364). For example, a church steeple at a distance casts an image upon the retina no larger, perhaps smaller, then would a pencil held a few inches from the eyes. We know the relative sizes of the two objects, and therefore infer that the steeple must be far away and the pencil near.

(2) *Accommodation of the eye.* Since a near object requires a greater effort of accommodation than does a more distant one for its image to be focussed upon the retina, some cue may possibly be given as to the relative distance of two objects from the eyes. This factor however is of very minor importance, and may be negligible.

(3) *The apparent change in color of an object with distance.* The atmosphere is not perfectly transparent or equally so for all wave lengths. Tree-clad hills, which we know to be green, appear bluish in the distance; the colors of many other objects appear to fade with distance, their detail and outline being dimmed by haze. On rare occasions the atmosphere may be particularly clear and then distant hills, etc., will appear to be unnaturally near.

(4) *The blocking out of parts of a distant view by objects between it and the eyes* gives a sensation of depth, for the overlapping of parts of farther objects by nearer ones gives an indication of their relative from the eyes.

(5) *Linear perspective.* Straight lines running into the distance which are actually parallel (or objects along imaginary straight lines) are convergent in the retinal image. When we look down a railway track, for example, the rails appear to converge towards some point beyond the horizon.

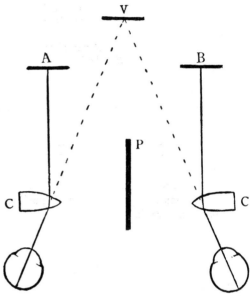

FIG. 75.13. Diagram to illustrate the principle of the stereoscope (Brewster's). *A* and *B* represent photographs of two scenes, slightly dissimilar because they were taken from different positions. *C,* curved prisms; *p,* partition to prevent one eye seeing the picture opposite the other eye; *LE,* left eye; *RE,* right eye. When the two pictures are viewed through the instrument, they are fused perfectly into one of apparently three dimensions, points in the background of which seem to be situated at V.

A similar stereoscopic effect is produced when two scenes are printed each in a different color, e.g., red and blue, and imperfectly superimposed so their outlines overlap. If they are viewed in the ordinary way, they appear as a flat jumbled picture, but if a red glass be held in front of one eye and a blue glass in front of the other, so as to sort out the separate scenes, one to each eye, a clear black and white view is seen in three dimensions. In the modern stereoscopic cinema it is usual to separate the two scenes by using polarized light beams set at right angles to each other, thus allowing color films to be shown stereoscopically.

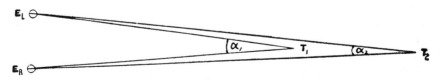

FIG. 75.14. Stereoscopic parallax in the viewing of two objects $T_1$ and $T_2$. It is expressed as the difference between the angles $\alpha_1$ and $\alpha_2$.

This arrangement of lines in the retinal image we have come to associate with distance. It depends upon the fact that points at a constant distance apart subtend a smaller angle at the eye the farther they are removed. The artist draws objects along imaginary lines which run towards a point in the background of his picture.

(6) *Parallax.* When one moves in any direction, near objects appear to move in the opposite direction, those in the background in the same direction as ourselves. This apparent movement of near objects in relation to ones farther away is called parallax.

(7) *The distribution of light and shade over the surface of an object and the shadow which it casts upon its surroundings is* also an important factor in the judgment of distance.

Normally, the images formed by the two eyes are very nearly equal in size, varying by less than one per cent. When they differ in size to a degree which prevents perfect fusion with a consequent impairment of binocular vision the condition is spoken of as *aniseikonia.* Little interference with binocular vision results unless the inequality of the images is more than 4 or 5 per cent.

## Ocular Movements

### The Innervation of the Ocular Muscles

The nerves supplying the extrinsic muscles of the eye are the third (oculomotor), fourth (trochlear) and the sixth (abducent). The oculomotor nerve supplies all the extrinsic muscles of the eyeball except the superior oblique and the external rectus. It also supplies the striated portion of the

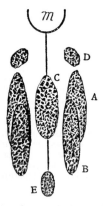

Fig. 75.15. A scheme of the various groups of cells which together constitute the nucleus of the oculomotor nerve. *A*, the dorsilateral nucleus; *B*, the ventrimedial nucleus; *C*, the central nucleus; *D*, the Edinger-Westphal nucleus; *E*, the caudal central nucleus; *m*, the third ventricle. (From Gray, *Anatomy of the Human Body*, after le Gros Clark, redrawn.)

levator palpebrae superioris and conveys parasympathetic fibers to the sphincter pupillae (p. 1410) and ciliary muscle. The deep smooth muscle component of the elevator of the lid is innervated by the sympathetic.

THE NUCLEUS OF THE THIRD NERVE is situated in the floor of the Sylvian (cerebral) aqueduct and subjacent to the superior colliculus. It is in close relation to the medial longitudinal fasciculus. It is composed of a group of five smaller nuclei (fig. 75.15).

(a) The *central nucleus* (Perlia's nucleus) fuses with its fellow of the opposite side to form a single gray mass in the mid-line. It is probably the center for convergence of the eyes (internal recti). (b) The *caudal central nucleus* lies in line with and behind the former. It also fuses with its fellow of the opposite side. Functionally it is considered a part of the central nucleus and is shown by Brouwer and others as actually continuous with the latter. (c) The *dorsi-lateral nucleus.* It and the next two nuclei are paired. The dorsilateral nucleusis probably the center for upward movements of the eyes (superior rectus and inferior oblique muscles). The *striped* muscle of the levator palpebrae superioris also, it is believed, receives its innervation from this nucleus. (d) The *ventrimedial nucleus*, lying medial, ventral and caudad to the preceding is thought to be concerned with downward movements (inferior rectus). (e) The *Edinger-Westphal* nucleus lies on each side dorsal and lateral to the central nucleus. It is believed to supply fibers to the sphincter pupillae and ciliary muscle.

The axons arising from these cell groups pass for the most part into the nerve of the same side. A few fibers supplying the internal and inferior recti and inferior oblique muscles decussate with those of the opposite side.

The fibers after issuing from the oculomotor nucleus form a well-defined tract (tract of the oculomotor nerve) which runs downwards and forwards through the tegmentum, traversing the red nucleus and medial portion of the substantia nigra. They emerge from the medial aspect of the cerebral peduncle.

THE NUCLEUS OF THE TROCHLEAR NERVE lies in the floor of the cerebral aqueduct adjacent to the posterior end of the ventri-medial nucleus of the oculomotor nerve, and on a level with the inferior colliculus. It supplies the superior oblique, and with the ventri-medial part of the oculomotor nucleus, forms a center for downward movements of the eye. The fibers arising from the trochlear nucleus differ from those of any other cranial nerve in that the great majority decussate with those of the opposite side. After leaving the nucleus the fibers curve dorsally around the central gray mass surrounding the aqueduct to reach the anterior medullary velum in which the decussation occurs. They emerge from the dorsal surface of the ante-

TABLE 75.1

| Muscle | | Movement | Innervation | Diplopia due to Ocular Paralysis Position of False Image in Relation to True when Right Eye Affected (Applicable to Left Eye if Right be Changed to Left and Vice Versa) |
|---|---|---|---|---|
| Rectus | Superior | *Elevation* (10), adduction (Inf. R, Int. R) intortion (SO) | Oculomotor | Above, to left of and tilted away from true image (crossed diplopia) |
| | Inferior | *Depression* (SO), adduction (Int. R, SO) extortion (SO) | Oculomotor | Below, to left and tilted towards true image (crossed diplopia) |
| | Internal | *Adduction* | Oculomotor | Level with, parallel to and on the left of true image (crossed diplopia) |
| | External | *Adduction* | Abducens | Level with, parallel to and on the right of true image |
| Oblique | Inferior | *Extortion* (IR), elevation (SR), abduction (Ext. R, SO) | Oculomotor | Above, to right of and tilted away from true image |
| | Superior | *Intortion* (SR), depression (Inf. R), abduction (Ext. R, SO) | Trochlear | Below, to right and tilted towards true image |
| Levator palp. sup. | | Elevator of eyelid antagonizes the action of the palpebral part of the orbicularis oculi | Oculomotor | |

rior medullary velum on one side of its frenulum and immediately behind the inferior colliculus.

THE ABDUCENT NUCLEUS furnishes fibers to the external rectus. It lies in the pons close to the median line and subjacent to the upper part of the floor of the fourth ventricle. Its fibers pass downwards and forwards through the pons to emerge without crossing at the latter's lower border. The fibers of the facial nerve loop around the abducent nucleus (ch. 65).

The nuclei of the three ocular nerves receive fibers from: (a) the pyramidal tract of the opposite side, (b) the medial longitudinal fasciculus through which the three nuclei are connected with one another, with the vestibular nucleus, with the spinal cord and probably with the facial nucleus. It has been suggested that fibers from the oculomotor nucleus may enter the latter nucleus and be then conveyed in the facial to the orbicularis oculi and the corrugator supercilii, (c) tectobulbar tract which relays to the three nuclei, impulses entering the superior colliculus from the optic tract and the visual cortex.

The eyes are said to be in a *position of rest* or in their *primary position* when their direction is maintained simply by the tone of the ocular muscles, that is, when the gaze is straight ahead and far away and not directed to any particular point in space. The visual axes are then parallel. When the eyes view some definite object they are turned by the contraction of the ocular muscles and converged so that the visual axes meet at the

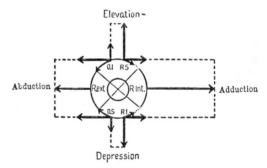

FIG. 75.16. Diagram of right eye from the front to illustrate the actions of the ocular muscles. O.I., inferior oblique; *RS*, superior rectus; *R ext*, external rectus; *R int*, internal rectus; *O.S.*, superior oblique; *RI*, inferior rectus. (From Fuchs after Marquez.)

observed object and an image of the object falls upon a corresponding point on each fovea (p. 1412). The closer the object to the eye the greater the degree of convergence (p. 1390). This movement of the eyes for the acute observation of an object is called *fixation*. The point where the visual axes meet is called the *fixation point* and the lines joining the latter to the fovea, i.e., the visual axes, are sometimes called the *fixation lines*. The widest limits of vision in all directions within which eyes can fixate is called the *field of fixation*. When surveyed by means of the perimeter it is found to be nearly circular with a diameter of about 100°. Its boundaries therefore lie well within the limits of the binocular visual field (p. 1402).

The eyeball is rotated in its socket (formed by the fascia bulbi) by the ocular muscles around one or other of three *primary axes* which intersect one another at right angles near the center of the globe. One axis is vertical, around it lateral movements (adduction and abduction) take place, i.e., in the horizontal plane. Another runs from before backwards and coincides with the visual axis; movements in the frontal plane (torsion or wheel movements) take place around it. The third is transverse, it is the axis of rotation for upward and downward movements, i.e., movements in the sagittal plane. Though the movements of the eyeball are essentially and for practical purposes rotary in character, a very slight translatory movement may take place as a result of movements of the lids and variations in the width of the palpebral fissure, closure and opening of the lids causing a displacement backward and outward, and forward and inward, respectively. A slight displacement at right angles to the rotary movement also takes place during contractions of the ocular muscles, the eyeball therefore executing what has been described by Berlin as a screw movement. Also for this reason the center of rotation of the eyeball is not an absolutely fixed point but varies slightly. For general purposes, however, it may be taken as the point of intersection of the primary axes. This point is on the visual axis about 13 mm. from the anterior surface of the cornea.

In table 75.1 the actions of the individual ocular muscles are given, but no normal movement is carried out by one of these muscles alone. Thus, when the eye is abducted, the external rectus and the two obliques act in unison to turn the eye outwards. The depressor and elevator components in the actions of the respective oblique muscles cancel one another. Similarly, adduction is effected by contraction of the internal rectus acting with the superior and inferior recti. Again, the depressor and elevating actions of the latter two muscles neutralize one another. In looking upwards the eye is elevated by the combined action of the superior rectus and the inferior oblique. In looking downwards the inferior rectus and the superior oblique act together, the subsidiary action of the inferior rectus in turning the eye inwards being offset by the opposite action of the superior oblique. This compound action of the ocular muscles makes for smooth and steady movement and rapid fixation of the eyeball. It will be seen from figure 75.16 that the obliques and the superior and inferior recti when contract-

ing individually produce a rotary or wheellike movement, outward (extortion) or inward (intortion). When acting in pairs the rotary actions being in opposite directions antagonize one another so that normally no such movement occurs.

The actions of the eye muscles follow the principle of reciprocal innervation. Thus, when the eye is turned outwards the external rectus and the two obliques contract while their antagonists (inferior, external and superior recti) are inhibited. The two eyes act in unison, both turning in the same direction—*conjugate deviation*—and reciprocal innervation is extended to include muscle groups in the two eyes, thus indicating their control from a single center. Thus, stimulation of the posterior part of the second frontal convolution causes conjugate deviation of the eyes to the opposite side. This involves contraction of the abductors and inhibition of the adductors of one eye and converse actions in the opposite eye (i.e. inhibition of the abductors accompanied by contraction of the adductors). Destruction of the cortical area results in the loss of the conjugate movement without paralysis of the individual muscles. The act of *convergence*, in which both eyes are adducted, is due to the conjoint contraction of the internal recti. The center for this movement is probably in the central nucleus of the oculomotor nerve. A higher center for the movement is also situated in the frontal cortex.

*The effects upon the eye movements of paralysis or weakness (paresis) of the ocular muscles.* (a) *Limitation of movement* of the eye in the direction of the normal action of the affected muscle. (b) *Paralytic strabismus or squint.* When an effort is made to turn the eyes in the direction of the paralyzed muscle, the affected eye remains stationary or makes a smaller movement than does the sound eye. That is, it deviates in relation to the latter in a direction opposite to that of the normal action of the paralyzed muscle. The visual axes, therefore, do not bear their normal relationship to one another. This is called the *primary deviation*. If a screen is placed in front of the sound eye while an attempt is made to fixate the affected eye upon an object situated towards the side of the paralyzed muscle, the sound eye deviates in the direction of action of the latter. This *secondary deviation*, as it is termed, is greater that the primary deviation of the paralyzed eye. The greater deviation of the sound eye is attributed to the unusual effort exerted in the attempt to fixate the paralyzed eye, an unnecessarily strong motor discharge being transmitted simultaneously to the muscle of the sound eye which normally acts conjointly (conjugate deviation) with the paralyzed muscle.

(c) *Diplopia; false projection of the visual field.* If, as a result of weakness or paralysis of the muscles of one eye, or of an imbalance from whatever cause between the actions of the ocular muscles of the two eyes, the images do not fall upon corresponding retinal points, *diplopia* or *double vision* results. The image seen by the sound eye is called the *true image*, that seen by the affected eye is called the *false image*. The false image lies to one side, above or below the true image, depending upon the ocular muscle which is paralyzed. In the case of the oblique muscles and the superior and inferior recti, the false image lies above or below the true image—a little to one or other side and tilted towards or away from it (see table 75.1, p. 1417). The false image is always displaced in the direction of the normal action of the paralyzed muscle. Thus, in paralysis of the right external rectus the right eye is not turned outwards when the subject attempts to look at an object towards his right side. The image of the object falls upon the temporal half of the left macula and is therefore projected into the nasal half of the visual field of that eye. But, in the affected eye the image falls upon the nasal half of the retina and is therefore projected into the temporal half of the right visual field. The image seen by the right eye (false image) therefore lies to the right of that seen by the left (true image). When the false image is on the same side of the true image as the affected eye the diplopia is said to be *simple* or *uncrossed;* if it lies on the opposite side of the true image the diplopia is said to be *crossed*.

If strabismus is congenital or of long standing, diplopia is not, as a rule, experienced. This is because though the images do not fall on anatomically symmetrical corresponding points in the two eyes, an area is developed in the peripheral retina of the squinting eye which assumes the function of a fovea. This pseudofovea or false macula, as it has been called, corresponds physiologically to the fovea of the sound eye. Fusion of the two images occurs and stereoscopic vision suffers little if at all. When squint of long standing is corrected surgically to bring the visual axes parallel, diplopia results since the true fovea of the corrected eye does not correspond functionally with fovea of the normal eye.

## REFERENCES

BEATTIE, J. J. Anat., 1932, **66**, 283.

BIELSCHOWSKY, A. Am. J. Ophth., 1938, **21**, 843.

BROUWER, B. AND ZEEMAN, W. P. C. Brain, 1926, **49**, 1.

CLARK, W. E. LE G. J. Anat., 1941, **75**, 225; Nature, 1947, **160**, 124.

CUSHING, H. Brain, 1921, 44, 341.

CUSHING, H. AND WALKER, G. B. Arch. Ophth. 1912, **41**, 559.

DUKE-ELDER, W. S. Textbook of Ophthalmology, 1949, Vol. 4.

GRAHAM, C. H. Proc. Fed. Am. Soc. Exper. Biol., 1943, **2**, 115.

HOLMES, G. Proc. Roy. Soc., London. ser. B., 1945, **132**, 348.

HUBEL, D. H. AND WIESEL, T. N. J. Physiol., 1959, **148**, 574.

RANSON, S. W. AND MAGOUN, H. W. Arch. Neurol. & Psychiat., 1933, **30**, 1193.

MERRITT, H. H. AND MOORE, M. Arch. Neurol. & Psychiat., 1933, **30**, 357.

SCALA, N. P. AND SPIEGEL, E. A. Arch. Ophth., 1936, **15**, 195.

WAGMAN, I. H. AND ASSOCIATES, Am. J. Physiol., 1942, **137**, 769. Proc. Soc. Exper. Biol. & Med., 1942, **49**, 466.

### *Monographs*

BRINDLEY, G. S. Physiology of the retina and visual pathway. Edward Arnold, London, 1960.

GRANIT, R. Receptors and Sensory Perception, Oxford University Press, London, 1955.

TRAQUAIR, H. M. An introduction to clinical perimetry. Kimpton, London, 1931.

# 76

# HEARING

## Anatomy of the Auditory System

The ear, like the other sense organs, is a *transducer*, a device for converting energy from one form into another. The specialized function of the ear is to change the mechanical energy of the airborne vibrations that constitute sound into a form of electrochemical energy capable of stimulating the fibers of the auditory nerve. How the ear accomplishes its task has been the subject of speculation and investigation ever since the time of the early Greek philosophers. Only in the past century, thanks to the development of microscopy and to the rise of the sciences of acoustics and electronics, has it become possible to find even a partial answer to the question "How do we hear?"

### ANATOMY OF THE EAR

The ear is divided into three parts: the external ear, consisting of the *pinna* and the *external meatus* or *canal*, ending blindly at the tympanic membrane; the *middle ear*, containing the three small auditory ossicles suspended in the air-filled tympanic cavity; and the fluid-filled *inner ear* or *labyrinth*, consisting of (1) the *cochlea*, which contains the *organ of Corti* with the endings of the cochlear division of the auditory nerve, (2) the *vestibule*, which contains the static organs the *utricle* and *saccule*, and (3) the three *semicircular canals* (fig. 76.1, *A* and *B*).

The *auricle* or *pinna* of the external ear consists of a thin, fibrocartilaginous plate, characteristically folded and ridged and covered with skin. In many animals it can readily be turned to locate the source of a sound or even folded down to exclude unwanted sound. In man the small extrinsic and intrinsic muscles of the auricle are usually functionless. A depression called the *concha* forms the orifice of the *external meatus* or *canal*, which extends inward in a slightly curving course of about 25 mm. to end at the *tympanic* or *drum membrane*. The wall of the outer third of the canal is formed by cartilage, that of the remainder by a tunnel in the temporal bone. The skin which lines the cartilaginous portion has

many *ceruminous glands* and laterally directed hairs, which discourage insects from entering the ear. The cerumen, however, can sometimes accumulate in such quantity as to block the canal and impede the passage of sound to the drum membrane.

The skin lining the osseous portion of the canal is thin, closely adherent to the periosteum, and extremely sensitive. It is continued as a delicate lamina, forming the outermost of the three layers, *cuticular*, *fibrous* and *mucous*, of which the tympanic membrane is composed.

The membrane lies obliquely across the end of the canal, sloping downward, forward and medially. It is attached to a bony ring or *annulus* formed by the wall of the canal, and to the handle or *manubrium* of the malleus, which draws the center or *umbo* of the membrane inward by about 2 mm., so that its shape is that of a flat cone. The diameter along the line of the manubrium is about 9 mm.; the diameter perpendicular to the manubrium is 8.5 mm. The total area of the membrane is approximately 69 sq. mm.

When the normal drum membrane is illuminated and viewed through an ear speculum or otoscope, it appears pearl grey, pinkish or yellowish in color. Several landmarks can be seen. The *lateral process of the malleus* projects as a white spot near the upper anterior border of the membrane. Above it, bounded by two faint ridges, the *anterior* and *posterior malleolar folds*, which extend forward and backward, is a small triangular area in which the membrane is thin and slack. This area is called *Shrapnell's membrane* or the *pars flaccida*. The greater part of the membrane is taut and glistening, and is called the *pars tensa*. For convenience in describing the location of lesions in the membrane, it is subdivided into four quadrants by the manubrium of the malleus and its imaginary projection downward and backward, and by an imaginary line through the umbo at right angles to the manubrium. A brightly reflecting triangular area in the antero-inferior quadrant is called the *cone of light*. In the postero-superior quadrant, the *long crus of the incus* can usually be seen through the drum,

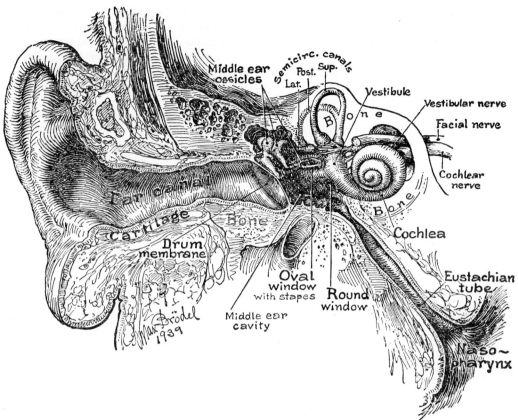

FIG. 76.1*A*. A dissection of the right ear. (From "Three Unpublished Drawings of the Anatomy of the Human Ear," by Max Brödel, W. B. Saunders Company, 1946.)

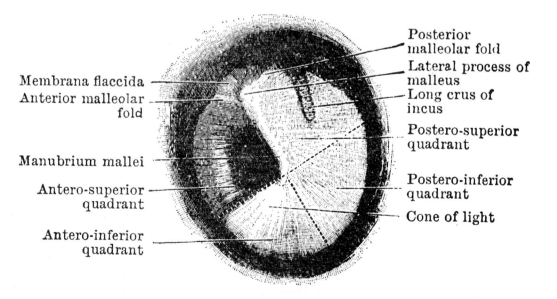

FIG. 76.1*B*. The left tympanic membrane, as viewed through the external meatus. (By permission from Cunningham's Textbook of Anatomy, 9th ed., 1951, Oxford University Press.)

just behind and parallel to the handle of the malleus.

The appearance of the membrane, its color, translucence, and degree of bulging or retraction, are of invaluable aid in diagnosing disease of the middle ear.

The *middle ear* or *tympanic cavity* is a narrow air-filled chamber in the mastoid portion of the temporal bone. It contains the chain of the miniature bones or *auditory ossicles*, which bear the fanciful descriptive names *malleus* (hammer), *incus* (anvil) and *stapes* (stirrup). The chain extends across the cavity from the drum membrane to the oval window of the cochlea on its inner wall.

The malleus, which more nearly resembles a club, has a handle (*manubrium*) attached to the drum membrane and a head (*capitellum*) which extends upward above the upper margin of the drum membrane into the *epitympanic recess*. It bears an articular facet for the body of the incus. The incus, shaped like a premolar tooth with spreading roots (*crura*), lies almost entirely in the epitympanum. It articulates with the head of the malleus by an articular surface on its body. The short crus is attached by a ligament in the *fossa incudis* of the epitympanum, whereas the long crus extends downward and medially parallel to the manubrium of the malleus. Its lower end is bent medially and bears a small knob of bone, the *lenticular process*, which articulates with the head of the stapes.

The stapes, which actually resembles a stirrup, is the smallest of the ossicles. It consists of a *head*, a *neck*, an *anterior* and a *posterior crus*, and a *footplate* which fits into the *oval* or *vestibular window* of the cochlea. According to Bast and Anson, the stapes varies considerably in size and weight from one individual to another. In their series the height varied from 2.50 to 3.78 mm., with an average of 3.26 mm.; the weight varied from 2.050 to 4.350 mg., with an average of 2.860 mg.

Five small ligaments connect the ossicles to the walls of the tympanic cavity. Three of them support the head and processes of the malleus and one supports the short crus of the incus. The fifth is the *annular ligament* of the stapes, which surrounds the footplate and connects its margin to the edge of the oval window. Two minute muscles also aid in controlling the movements of the ossicles. The larger, called the *tensor tympani*, issues from a canal parallel to the auditory tube. Its tendon bends laterally over a small

ridge of bone which serves as a pulley, and is inserted on the medial surface of the manubrium of the malleus. The smaller, called the *stapedius*, arises in a small, hollow, conical projection on the posterior wall of the tympanic cavity called the *pyramid*. Its tiny tendon is inserted on the posterior aspect of the neck of the stapes. When the tensor tympani, which is supplied by a branch from the mandibular division of the trigeminal nerve, contracts, it pulls the handle of the malleus inward and thus restricts the outward movement of the drum membrane. When the stapedius, supplied by a branch of the facial nerve, contracts, it pulls the neck of the stapes backward, thus tilting the anterior edge of the footplate outward and reducing its inward movement against the fluid in the cochlea. The function of the muscles and ligaments in modifying the movements of the ossicles will be considered in greater detail below.

The inner ear lies within the *periotic* or *bony labyrinth* in the petrous part of the temporal bone. It is divided into three main parts: the cochlea, the vestibule and the three semicircular canals. Suspended in the periotic labyrinth is an entirely closed system, the *otic* or *membranous labyrinth*, consisting of the *cochlear duct*, the *utricle* and *saccule*, the three *membranous canals* and the various ducts which interconnect them (fig. 76.2). The otic labyrinth is filled by the *otic fluid* or *endolymph*. The spaces of the periotic labyrinth contain a delicate, arachnoidlike tissue. Its interstices are filled with the *periotic fluid* or *perilymph*.

The cochlea, as its name implies, is coiled like a snail's shell. A section through its axis (fig. 76.3) reveals a central bony pillar, the *modiolus*, the base of which contains the internal auditory meatus with the auditory nerve. The periotic or osseous canal coils about the modiolus for approximately two and one-half turns, tapering in diameter from base to apex. A bony ledge, the *osseous spiral lamina*, projects into the canal, winding about the modiolus like the thread of a screw. It is widest in the basal coil, narrowing toward the apex.

The *basilar membrane* stretches from the tip of the osseous spiral lamina to a fibrous structure called the *spiral ligament* on the outer wall of the canal. A second partition, known as *Reissner's membrane*, extends from the upper surface of the osseous lamina obliquely to the upper margin of the spiral ligament. In cross section the membranes enclose a triangular area, the

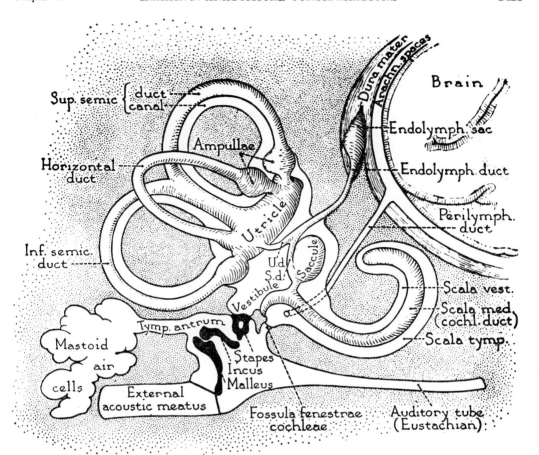

Fig. 76.2. General relationship of the membranous (otic) and periotic (osseous) labyrinths. Diagrammatic. U.d., utricular duct. S.d., saccular duct. (From Bast and Anson, *The Temporal Bone and the Ear*, 1949, Charles C Thomas.)

*scala media* or *cochlear duct*. In the conventional description, the *scala vestibuli* lies above it, and the *scala tympani* below it (fig. 76.4).

The scala media or cochlear duct, which is the otic or membranous cochlea, ends blindly, both at the apex of the cochlea and at the basal end. The slender *ductus reuniens* arises near the basal end and connects it with the saccule. The scala vestibuli and scala tympani are in communication at the apex of the cochlea through a narrow opening, the *helicotrema*. At the basal end, the scala vestibuli ends in the vestibule at the oval window, which is closed by the footplate of the stapes. The scala tympani ends at the round window, covered by the thin round window membrane.

The basilar membrane is a fibrous plate, its fibers continuous with those of the spiral ligament. On the tympanic (under) side it is covered by a layer of mesothelial cells. Its width tapers

from 0.50 mm. at the helicotrema to 0.04 mm. at the stapes. Von Békésy has found that when the basilar membrane is cut, the edges do not retract. Therefore, contrary to the opinion long held, it is not under tension.

*The cochlear fluids.* The *otic fluid* or *endolymph* fills the otic labyrinth, including the cochlear duct, the saccule, the utricle and the three semicircular canals. It is thought to be secreted by the stria vascularis and probably by secretory cells associated with the vestibular neuroepithelia as well. Where it is absorbed is not definitely known. The endolymphatic sac, lying between the two layers of dura on the intracranial surface of the petrous bone, has been considered a probable site. Since destruction of the sac does not cause distension (hydrops) of the otic labyrinth, the endolymph must have other sites of absorption, including perhaps the stria vascularis.

The *periotic fluid* or *perilymph* fills the periotic

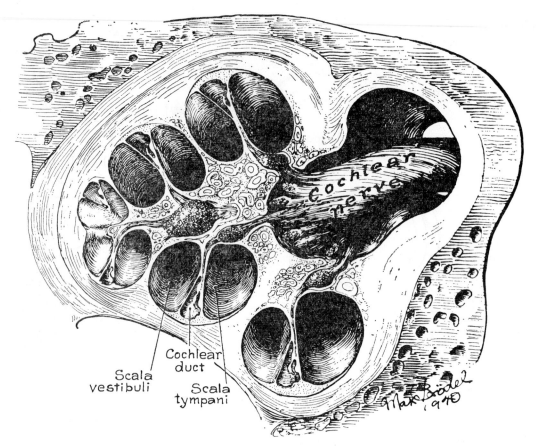

Fig. 76.3. The cochlea and the cochlear nerve. (A drawing by Max Brödel, from *1940 Year Book of the Eye, Ear, Nose and Throat*, edited by L. Bothman and S. J. Crowe, The Year Book Publishers, Inc.)

labyrinth, i.e., the scala vestibuli and scala tympani, the vestibule and the bony semicircular ducts. It is in direct communication with the cerebrospinal fluid in the arachnoid spaces surrounding the brain, by way of the perilymphatic duct. However, this may not represent its only source. Since radioactive sodium ($Na^{24}$) appears promptly in the perilymph after intravenous injection, it is clear that the perilymph must be an ultrafiltrate of the blood. It is thought to be resorbed into the capillaries of the spiral ligament.

The total volume of endolymph is small, and the difficulty of collecting an uncontaminated sample very great. Nevertheless it has been shown that the endolymph has an entirely different ionic composition from perilymph and cerebrospinal fluid, as demonstrated by the analyses of Smith, Lowry and Wu (table 76.1).

The inner ear obtains its blood supply by way of the internal auditory artery, which enters through the internal meatus with the auditory nerve. The cells of the organ of Corti however, receive no direct blood supply, but appear to be entirely dependent upon the stria vascularis for oxygen and nutrients.

The neuroepithelium of the cochlea, known as the *spiral organ of Corti*, rests upon the lip of the osseous spiral lamina and the basilar membrane. It is made up of an orderly arrangement of the actual sensory elements, the *hair cells*, and their various *supporting cells*, and is covered by a stiff cuticle, the *lamina reticularis*, which looks, from above, like a regularly patterned mosaic. A prominent feature is the triangular *tunnel of Corti*, formed by the inner and outer *pillar cells* or *rods of Corti*. The flat, expanded bars of the inner pillar cells rest on the lip of the osseous spiral lamina, those of the outer pillars on the basilar membrane. Their narrow bodies slope towards each other, so that their broader upper ends join to support the lamina reticularis. The pillars increase progressively in height from the basal coil to the apex.

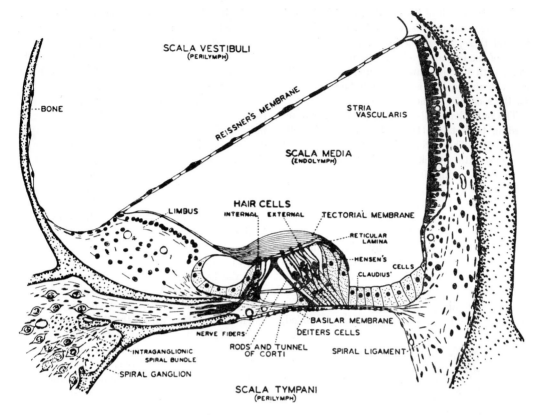

Fig. 76.4. Cross section of the cochlear partition in the guinea pig (lower part of second turn). (From Davis *et al.*, J. Acoust. Soc. Am. 1953, *25*, 1180.)

On the medial side of the tunnel, i.e., toward the modiolus, a single row of *inner hair cells* is arrayed, closely parallel to the inner pillars. They are surrounded by supporting elements, the *inner border cells* and *phalangeal cells*. On the lateral side of the tunnel are three or four parallel rows of *outer hair cells*. These are supported by the *cells of Deiters*, which actually rest on the basilar membrane and send stiff *phalangeal processes* upwards between the hair cells to form part of the lamina reticularis. The outer hair cells are surrounded by fluid spaces, the *space of Nuel*, lying between the first row and the pillar cells, and the outer tunnel, lying between the last row and the supporting *cells of Hensen*. Processes from these cells also contribute to the formation of the *lamina reticularis*. Beyond the Hensen cells is a series of cuboidal *cells of Claudius*. They are of simple structure, resembling the *inner sulcus cells* lying medial to the inner hair cells.

An eminence, the *limbus spiralis*, rests on the osseous spiral lamina medial to the inner sulcus. The thin *membrane of Reissner* is anchored at its inner margin. At its outer or vestibular lip the

TABLE 76.1

|  | Spinal Fluid | Perilymph | Endolymph |
|---|---|---|---|
| *m.eq./liter* | *m.eq./liter* | *m.eq./liter* | *m.eq./liter* |
| Potassium...... | 4.2 | 4.8 | 144.4 |
| Sodium......... | 152.0 | 150.3 | 15.8 |
| Chloride........ | 122.4 | 121.5 | 107.1 |
|  | *mg. %* | *mg. %* | *mg. %* |
| Protein......... | 21.0 | 50.0 | 15.0 |

Mammalian endolymph does not show the high viscosity that has often been attributed to it by analogy with that of the shark, which sets into a jelly after withdrawal.

*tectorial membrane* is attached. This membrane is composed of a gelatinous substance similar to that of the cupula of the semicircular canals and the otolithic membranes of the utricle and saccule. It arches over the inner sulcus and overlies the lamina reticularis. Whether the hairs of the hair cells actually penetrate the substance of the tectorial membrane has not been determined, but it is certain that they are in contact with it.

The lateral wall of the cochlear duct is formed by the *outer sulcus cells*, the *stria vascularis* and, beyond these, the *spiral ligament*, in which the fibers of the basilar membrane are anchored. The stria, with its pigmented granular cells and its rich vascular supply, is thought to be responsible for the secretion of the cochlear endolymph.

The outer hair cells number about 12,000 according to Retzius (1884), the inner hair cells only 3,500. The outer hair cells are cylindrical in shape, with a thickened cuticular layer at the upper end, bearing 60 to 70 sensory hairs (stereocilia) about 4 $\mu$ long, arranged in a regular pattern. The density of the cuticle is similar to that of the reticular lamina. The intracellular structures of the hair cells as revealed by electron microscopy are described by Engström and Wersäll. Figure 76.5 shows an outer hair cell in schematic form, and its relationship to the Deiters' cell supporting it.

The inner hair cells differ significantly in form from the outer hair cells. They are more rounded, and their hairs are fewer and somewhat coarser. The nucleus is smaller and more centrally located, and the intracellular structures differ in detail. These cytological differences are consistent with important differences in function as suggested by physiological studies.

*Innervation.* About the base of each hair cell (between it and the Deiters' cell) is a cluster of nerve endings. They are of two types: the smaller 0.5 to 1.0 $\mu$ in diameter, with a sparse granulation, and the larger as much as 5 $\mu$ long and 1 to 3 $\mu$ in diameter, with a dense granulation. The region of contact between a nerve ending and the hair cell membrane resembles a synapse. Characteristic membranous structures are seen in the "synaptic region" of the hair cell where it is in contact with the large nerve endings, but not with the small ones. It has been suggested that the two types of nerve endings may serve separate functions, the smaller afferent (presynaptic), the larger efferent (postsynaptic).

The nerve fibers within the fluid spaces of the organ of Corti are completely bare, with no myelin or neurilemma sheath. Those from the outer hair cells pass between the rods of Corti and cross the tunnel. On the inner side they join the fibers from the inner hair cells and enter a channel in the osseous spiral lamina. Their bipolar cells are located in the spiral ganglion of the modiolus. Central to the ganglion the fibers enter the internal meatus to form the auditory nerve trunk. The fibers from the apical region of the organ of Corti run a straight course, whereas the others are twisted about them like the strands of a rope.

The nerve supply of the organ of Corti provides for both a diffuse and a point-to-point type of innervation of the hair cells. Three main systems of fibers are recognized. *External spiral fibers* run for several millimeters in both directions along the basilar membrane. Each fiber has endings on many outer hair cells, and each hair cell receives endings from many fibers, so that there is much overlapping of innervation. *Radial fibers* supply mainly the inner hair cells, but some outer cells as well, in a more discrete fashion, with one or at most a few cells per fiber. At least half of the fine *internal spiral fibers* may be efferents. They give multiple innervation to the inner hair cells.

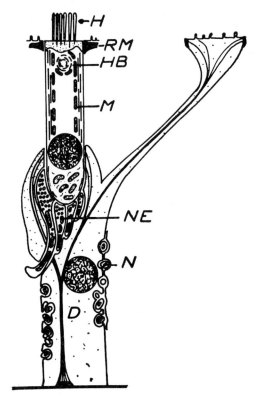

Fig. 76.5. Schematic drawing of an outer hair cell and a Deiters' cell in the organ of Corti. H, sensory hairs; RM, reticular membrane; HB, Hensen body; M, mitochondrion; NE, nerve endings; N, nerve fibers in cross section; D, Deiters' cell. (From Engström and Wersäll in International Review of Cytology VII, Academic Press, Inc., 1958.)

Major nuclear masses of the auditory pathway are located in the medulla, the midbrain and the thalamic region. The pathway terminates in the cortex of the temporal lobe. At each of these

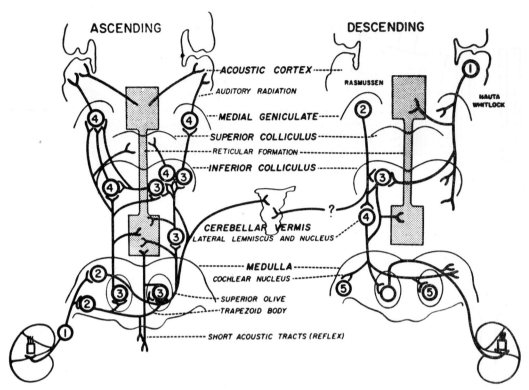

Fig. 76.6. The central ascending and descending auditory pathways. Numbers indicate orders of neurons. (From Galambos, Ann. Otol. Rhin. and Laryng. 1956, *65*, 1053.)

levels an orderly spatial arrangement of the neurons has been found, indicating that the organ of Corti is represented or "unrolled" again and again in the brain. The pathways are both crossed and uncrossed so that each cochlea is represented in both sides of the brain (fig. 76.6).

The fibers of first-order afferent neurons of the cochlear nerve enter the medulla and immediately divide, sending branches to the *dorsal* and *ventral cochlear nuclei*. Many second-order neurons pass medially from these to the *superior olives* of both sides, forming the *trapezoid body*, whereas others enter the *lateral lemniscus* directly, to terminate at the *nuclei of the lateral lemniscus*. The third-order neurons from the superior olive ascend in the lemniscus to the *inferior colliculus*, whereas those from the nuclei of the lemniscus proceed to the *medial geniculate*. From the geniculate, the auditory radiations pass in the internal capsule to the primary auditory area in the *superior transverse temporal gyrus*, or *gyrus of Heschl* (area 41 of Brodmann). In the carnivores this area is represented in the *middle ectosylvian gyrus*.

In addition to the direct pathway, there are numerous reflex connections with cranial motor nuclei. A cerebellar auditory center has been found in the *tuber vermis*, which receives fibers from the dorsal cochlear nucleus.

Since a cat with a complete transection at the midbrain level of the classical auditory pathways on both sides can easily be aroused from sleep by sounds, a second auditory route to the cortex has been postulated in the *reticular formation* of the midbrain, the only structure spared by the operation.

The existence of descending pathways from the cortex to the cochlea is strongly indicated (fig. 76.6). The best established of these is the *olivo cochlear tract of Rasmussen*, sending efferent fibers from the superior olive to the contralateral cochlea by way of the *bundle of Oort* in the eighth nerve and the internal spiral fibers, at least as far as the inner hair cells.

### The Nature of Sound

Sound may be characterized as a form of wave motion, a transmitted vibratory disturbance in the air or in some other elastic medium like water, wood, steel or bone. Although in this electronic era the sound waves used in the study of hearing usually come from a loudspeaker, an

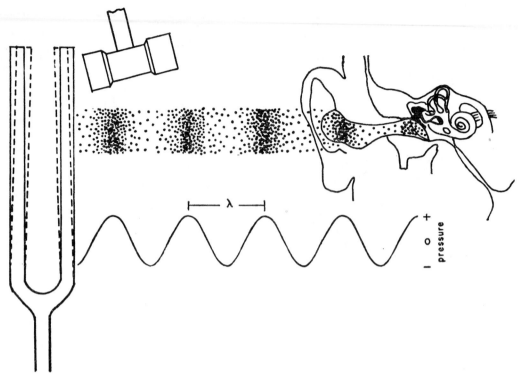

FIG. 76.7. Above, sound waves in air, with regions of compression and rarefaction, produced by a tuning fork. Below, the sinusoidal variation in pressure. $\lambda = 1$ wave length.

earphone or other type of electromechanical transducer, the nature of sound can best be understood by considering one of the simplest sound-producing instruments, the tuning fork. The motion of the fork, like that of all sounding bodies, is determined by three essential physical properties: *inertia*, *elasticity*, and *resistance*.

When the tuning fork is struck, the kinetic energy of the blow overcomes the *inertia* of the prong and displaces it to one side. The *elasticity*, or *stiffness*, tends to restore the prong to its original position, but the inertia keeps it moving beyond the position of rest until the elasticity brings it to a stop and causes it to swing back once more. At the end of its swing, the velocity of the fork is zero, and its energy is entirely in the potential form. As it passes through the equilibrium position, its velocity is maximal and its energy is entirely in the kinetic form. These alternating transformations continue until the energy is dissipated, partly in the form of heat due to internal and external frictional *resistance*, partly in the form of sound.

The rate at which the fork vibrates when struck is called its *natural frequency*. The greater its inertia or *mass* ($m$), the lower this frequency will be, whereas the greater the stiffness ($s$), the higher the frequency. If the resistance is assumed to be negligible, this relationship may be expressed by

$$f = \frac{1}{2\pi} \sqrt{\frac{s}{m}}$$

Although the natural frequency is actually reduced somewhat by the effect of resistance, it remains constant as the *amplitude* of vibration decreases continuously until the fork comes to rest.

As the fork vibrates, it transfers a part of its energy to the molecules of air surrounding the prongs and forces them to vibrate also. Movement of a prong in one direction momentarily pushes the air molecules in its path together, whereas movement in the opposite direction pulls them away from each other. Although these movements of the individual air molecules are exceedingly small, the alternate compressions and rarefactions of the air are transmitted in all directions as waves of air-borne sound.

Like a pendulum swinging through a small arc, the prongs of the tuning fork and the molecules of air execute a form of vibratory motion called *simple harmonic motion*. A body showing this type of motion is said to obey Hooke's law, since

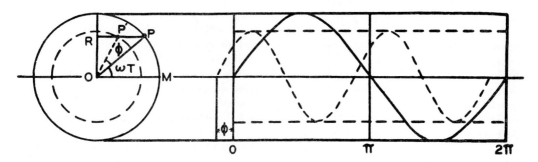

FIG. 76.8. Two sinusoidal waves generated by the projection of circular motions, differing in frequency, amplitude and phase. (Reprinted by permission from Stevens and Davis, *Hearing*, John Wiley and Sons, Inc., 1938.)

the force required to displace the body is proportional to the amount of the displacement. Simple harmonic motion is equivalent to the projection of the motion of a point which moves around a circle at a constant rate, as illustrated in figure 76.8. Here $R$ is the projection of the point $P$, which moves in a counterclockwise direction around the circle. As $P$ rotates at a constant angular velocity $\omega$ (in radians per second), $R$ moves up and down on the vertical axis, executing the same type of motion as the prong of the tuning fork. If we plot the position of $R$ as a function of the angular displacement of $P$, we have in effect spread out its motion in time. The resulting (solid) curve is called a sinusoid, since the distance $OR$ is proportional to the sine of the angle $POM$, which is measured by $\omega t$, the product of the angular velocity and the time elapsed since the point $P$ was at $M$. A writing point attached to a tuning fork vibrating against a revolving smoked drum makes a similar tracing. It may be represented by the equation

$$y = A \sin \omega t$$

where $y$ is the displacement $OR$, and $A$ is the length of the radius vector $OP$. The crest, where the angle $\omega t$ is $\pi/2$, represents the region of compression, and the trough, where $\omega t$ is $3\pi/2$, represents the region of rarefaction of a longitudinal sound-wave. At these points $y$ is at its maximum value $A$, called the *amplitude* of the wave.

In one revolution of $P$ the sinusoid completes one *cycle*. The number of cycles per second is called the *frequency*, $f$; its reciprocal, the duration of one cycle, is called the *period*, $T$. Since there are $2\pi$ radians in a circle, the relation of the angular velocity $\omega$ to the frequency $f$ is given by the equation

$$\omega = 2\pi f$$

A body may execute two forms of harmonic motion at the same time. This motion is represented in figure 76.8 by a second sinusoid of twice the frequency but smaller amplitude. It is also represented by the rotation of point $P'$ about the smaller circle at twice the angular velocity of $P$. At the instant illustrated, $P'$ leads in *phase* by the angle $\phi$. Adding the two curves would give a third curve showing the resultant motion of the body. The addition of other harmonic motions of various amplitudes and phases would give a resultant wave-form of greater and greater *complexity*.

A sound consisting of a single frequency is called a *pure tone*. A tone having 5 per cent of its energy at other frequencies than the lowest or the *fundamental* frequency is said to have "5 per cent distortion," or to be "95 per cent pure." Although the sounds used in measuring hearing often approximate pure tones, those of musical instruments are always more or less complex. They consist of a fundamental frequency or *first harmonic*, and a number of higher harmonics or *partials*, which are simple multiples of the fundamental frequency. The higher harmonics give to the tone of the instrument its characteristic *quality*.

In a sound wave, the individual molecules of air move to and fro in simple harmonic motion for very short distances. Their speed of movement is called the *particle-velocity*. It is zero at the troughs and crests of the waves, and reaches a maximum of a fraction of a millimeter per second as the particle passes its position of rest. The *velocity of propagation* of the sound wave is much greater, varying with the density and elasticity of the medium. In air at 0°C. it is 331 meters per second, increasing somewhat at higher temperatures. In water the velocity is over 1400 meters per second, and in a rigid solid such as ivory, which has physical properties resembling those of the petrous bone, it is 3000 meters per second. The *wave length* of sound, the distance travelled by sound in one period, is equal to the velocity of sound divided by its frequency. Thus a 1000-cycle tone in air has a wave length of about 0.33 meter, whereas a 100-cycle tone has a wave length of 3.3 meters. In water the wave lengths are about four times as great.

When sound in air encounters an obstacle in its path which is small relative to the wave length, the sound waves are *diffracted* around the obstacle. It is this process of a diffraction that enables us to hear around corners. Only if the obstacle is relatively large does it cast a significant "sound shadow." A part of the energy is *reflected*, and in suitable conditions gives rise to an *echo*. The multiple reflections of sound from the walls of a room are called *reverberations*. A third portion of the energy is absorbed and transmitted by the obstacle. The amount of energy transmitted depends upon the relationship of the *specific acoustic resistances* of the medium and the obstacle. These are $R_1 = \sqrt{\rho_1 S_1}$ and $R_2 = \sqrt{\rho_2 S_2}$, where $\rho_1$ and $\rho_2$ are the densities of the medium and the obstacle, and $S_1$ and $S_2$ are their respective elasticities. If $r$ is used to represent the ratio $R_2/R_1$, then the fraction of the energy transmitted is expressed by

$$T = \frac{4r}{(r+1)^2}$$

whereas the remainder $1 - T$ represents the energy reflected. If the specific acoustic resistances are similar, then $r$ approaches 1 and $T$ approaches 1. Most of the energy is transmitted, and very little is reflected. If, on the other hand, the properties of the medium and the obstacle are very different, then $r$ becomes large and $T$ becomes small, so that the obstacle becomes a sound mirror, and the greater part of the energy is reflected.

A body at rest can be forced to vibrate if it is coupled to another vibrating body, either directly or through the medium of the air. Thus the motion of a tuning fork can be transmitted to a table top by pressing the base of the fork firmly against the table. If a body is forced to vibrate at its natural frequency, the transmitted effect is greatly enhanced, and the body is said to *resonate*. Resonance may be illustrated by singing a brief note while pressing the loud pedal of a piano, so that the dampers are lifted and the

strings are allowed to vibrate freely. Those strings with the same natural frequencies as the voice resonate in response, and the note is still heard faintly after the singing has stopped.

Since the ear functions only in response to forced vibration, it is important to examine this phenomenon further. In the example of the tuning fork we have seen that when a body is caused to vibrate by applying a momentary force, it vibrates at its own natural frequency. Because of damping, the amplitude of the vibrations decreases exponentially, and they gradually die out. When a *periodic* force is suddenly applied to a body at rest, it gives a similar *transient* response at its natural frequency. The transient dies out more or less rapidly depending upon the degree of damping, but a *steady-state* response at the frequency of the driving force remains. Since we are not troubled by the persistence of transient responses in our own ears, it is clear that the damping of the ear must be very great.

The response of a vibrating body to an external force is limited by the mechanical impedance of the body. The amplitude of motion is directly proportional to the applied force, and inversely proportional to the mechanical impedance. The mechanical impedance is a complex function made up of three terms: the *mass reactance*, the *elastic reactance*, and the *frictional resistance*, all measured in mechanical ohms. The first two terms are dependent upon the frequency, but the third is not. In mathematical symbols, the expression for mass reactance is

$$X_m = 2\pi f \cdot m$$

where $2\pi f$ is the angular frequency and $m$ is the mass (in grams). The elastic reactance is

$$X_e = \frac{S}{2\pi f},$$

where $S$ represents the stiffness in dynes per centimeter. The complete expression for mechanical impedance, $Z$, is

$$Z = \sqrt{\left(2\pi f M - \frac{S}{2\pi f}\right)^2 + R_m^2}$$

where $R_m$ is the frictional resistance in ohms.

Mechanical impedance is directly analogous to electrical impedance in alternating current circuits, where inductance corresponds to mass, capacitance to the reciprocal of the stiffness (compliance) and the electrical to the frictional resistance. We shall see the importance of the impedance concept when we come to consider the transmission of sound across the middle ear to the cochlea.

### The Dimensions of Sound

#### WAVEFORM AND SPECTRUM

In order to investigate hearing, we must be able to measure and specify the sound stimuli that give rise to hearing. Sound waves in air consist in minute variations in pressure above and below the existing atmospheric pressure. If we plot these variations as a function of time for the simple case of a pure tone, we obtain a sinusoidal curve representing the *pressure waveform* for the tone (fig. 76.9). It has two dimensions, *amplitude* and *time*. Frequency is expressed by the number of cycles per second, in this instance 1000 c.p.s. The same information can be presented by plotting amplitude against frequency to show the *spectrum*, which for a pure tone consists of a single component. It is represented in the figure 76.9 by a vertical line, the height of which indicates the maximum amplitude or peak pressure of the tone.

Fourier (1822) discovered that any waveform, however complex, can be analyzed into a series of simple sinusoids. An example of frequency

analysis is given in figure 76.9. On the left, two frequencies of 12 and 15 c.p.s. are shown, and the complex wave produced by combining them. On the right, the spectrum of each indicates the amplitudes and frequencies of the respective components. Figure 76.10 (L-2) also shows the waveforms of several types of auditory stimuli, with the spectrum of each. The square wave (*B*) has a *line spectrum*, consisting of a fundamental of 1000 c.p.s. and a series of odd-numbered harmonics (3000, 5000, 7000 etc., c.p.s.), of decreasing amplitudes. The train of pulses (*C*) shows both odd and even harmonics, but the amplitudes are smaller. Furthermore, the phase is shifted by 90° because the pulses are not symmetrical about the baseline as the square waves are. The single pulse (*D*) consists of a uniform, continuous spectrum. The amplitude of each component is extremely small, and again the phase is shifted by 90°.

"White" noise (*E*) gets its name from the fact that, like white light, it consists of a random mixture of all frequencies. The spectrum is continuous, with uniform amplitude and random phase. White noise we have always with us, in the thermal agitation or Brownian movement of the air molecules, just below the threshold of hearing. The random movements of electrons in

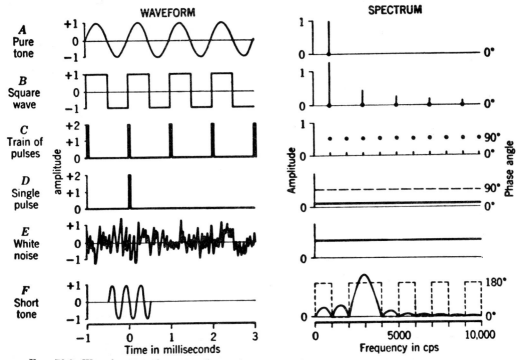

FIG. 76.9. Waveforms and spectra for various types of auditory stimulus. (Reprinted with permission from Licklider in *Handbook of Experimental Psychology*, edited by S. S. Stevens, John Wiley and Sons, Inc, 1951.)

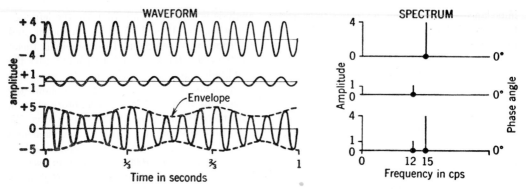

FIG. 76.10. Frequency analysis of a complex wave consisting of two components of different amplitude. (Reprinted with permission from Licklider in *Handbook of Experimental Psychology*, edited by S. S. Stevens, John Wiley and Sons, Inc., 1951.

conductors and vacuum tubes also produce white noise, which is audible as the characteristic background "s-h-h-h" from a phonograph or radio.

The spectrum for the short tone of 3000 c.p.s. (*F*) shows that when the tone is turned on and off other frequencies appear above and below 3000 c.p.s. This is always the case when a tone is changed in frequency, amplitude or phase. Only a tone of infinite duration is ideally pure.

The sounds of speech form a constantly changing pattern of complex tones, noise and transients. Although measurements of the average spectra show that frequencies below 1000 c.p.s. carry most of the energy, it is the transients of higher frequency that provide most of the perceptual clues to the listener.

### THE MEASUREMENT OF SOUND INTENSITY

The amplitudes of movement of the air particles in sound waves are exceedingly small, varying from about $10^{-9}$ cm. for sounds that are barely audible to $10^{-2}$ cm. for sounds sufficiently intense to injure the inner ear. Although the velocity of the air particles can be determined with great accuracy by noting the force that they exert on a light disk suspended in the path of the sound waves (Lord Rayleigh, 1882), the most convenient measure of sound intensity is the alternating pressure produced by the motion of the particles. This value is readily determined by measuring the electric current generated by a suitably calibrated condenser microphone placed in the sound field. (For measuring the sound pressure in a confined space such as the external canal, a narrow calibrated probe-tube is attached to the microphone.) Sound pressure can be expressed as the maximum or peak pressure ($P_{max}$) or as the root-mean-square (rms) pressure

which represents an average of all the pressures from moment to moment. For a sine wave, the rms pressure

$$P_{rms} = \frac{P_{max}}{\sqrt{2}} = 0.707\ P_{max}$$

For noise or speech the peak pressures may vary from one instant to the next over a wide range. The rms values are more stable and are therefore generally used for expressing sound pressures. The pressures of ordinary sounds amount to no more than a fraction of 1 dyne/cm.², in contrast to the atmospheric pressure of about $10^6$ dynes/cm.².

We use the term intensity loosely to mean sound pressure, particle velocity or amplitude of movement, sound energy or power. Strictly speaking it should apply only to power or energy. We must now examine some of the relationships among these various quantities. If we know the sound pressure $P$ and the specific acoustic resistance $R$ of the medium, then the particle velocity, u, measured in centimeters per second is

$$u = \frac{P}{R}$$

This is clearly analogous to the relationship of electric current to electromotive force and resistance, as expressed by Ohm's law:

$$I = \frac{E}{R}$$

For plane waves, the amplitude of particle movement, or displacement (in centimeters)

$$d = \frac{P}{2\pi f R}$$

where $f$ is the frequency.

The power $J$ is equal to the pressure times the velocity, or

$$J = P \cdot u = \frac{P^2}{R}.$$

$J$ is measured in ergs per second per cm.² or in microwatts per cm.², since 10 ergs per second $= 1$ microwatt. Similarly, the energy is proportional to the square of the sound pressure, just as electric energy and power are proportional to the square of the electromotive force.

### The Decibel Notation

In practice, measurements of sound intensity are not expressed as absolute magnitudes. Instead, a given intensity is compared with a standard value by expressing the ratio between the two. Because of the enormous range of intensities involved, it is convenient to express these ratios as logarithms. If one intensity is 10 times as great as another, their ratio is 10 and the logarithm (to the base 10) of the ratio is 1. The two intensities are said to differ by 1 *bel* (named for Dr. Alexander Graham Bell, inventor of the telephone). A more practical unit is one-tenth of a bel, the *decibel* (db). We may therefore express the number of decibels corresponding to a ratio between two intensities as

$$N_{\text{(db)}} = 10 \log_{10} \frac{J}{J_o}$$

where $J_o$ is a standard or reference intensity.

Since power is proportional to the square of the sound pressure, we can also write

$$N_{\text{(db)}} = 10 \log_{10} \frac{P^2}{P_o{}^2}$$

$$= 20 \log_{10} \frac{P}{P_o}.$$

Therefore, if one sound has a pressure 10 times as great as another, they are said to differ by 20 db. The ratio of the powers is 100, but the difference between them in decibels is still 20 db. The decibel notation is also used in comparing electric powers, voltages and currents.

Like all logarithmic scales, the decibel scale is particularly convenient because it is compressed. The intensity ratio between sounds that are dangerous to the organ of Corti and those that are just at the threshold of hearing is approximately one hundred million million or $10^{14}:1$, yet this vast range is expressed by only 140 db. Furthermore, if we multiply the power with an

amplifier or divide it with an attenuator, we add or subtract decibels. If a sound 60 db above the reference level is amplified by 20 db (corresponding to a 100-fold increase in its power) its new intensity is $60 + 20 = 80$ db. We must always remember, however, that the decibel scale has no absolute zero point. When we write *0 db*, we are simply expressing a power or pressure ratio of 1:1. Therefore the reference level must always be given if decibel readings are used to represent absolute values. Some investigators use a "zero level" of 1 dyne/cm.². The *standard reference level* adopted by the Acoustical Society of America is $10^{-16}$ watt per cm.². This corresponds to a 0-db pressure level of 0.000204 dyne/cm.². Sound level meters are usually calibrated to measure sound pressure levels in decibels above 0.0002 dyne/cm.². This value approximates the least intensity that can be heard by the average person. A decibel scale showing the approximate

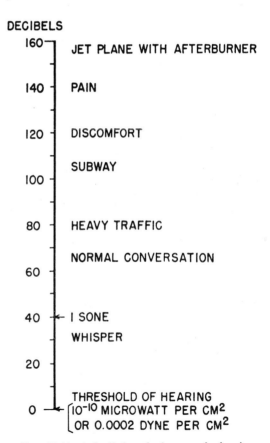

Fig. 76.11. A decibel scale for sound, showing approximate intensity levels produced by various sources. The *sone* is the unit of loudness; it is defined as the loudness of a 1,000-c.p.s. tone at 40-db intensity level. (From Stevens, Laryngoscope, **68**, 512, 1958.)

intensities of sounds from various sources is shown in figure 76.11.

## REFERENCES

ALTMANN, F. AND WALTNER, J. G. Ann. Otol. Rhin. & Laryng., 1950, **59,** 657.

ANSON, B. J. AND BAST, T. H. Quart. Bull. Northwestern Univ. M. School, 1958, **32,** 157.

ANSON, B. J. AND BAST, T. H. Quart. Bull. Northwestern Univ. M. School, 1958, **32,** 307.

GALAMBOS, R. Ann. Otol., Rhin. & Laryng., 1956, **65,** 1053.

LORENTE DE NÓ, R. Anatomy of the eighth nerve. The central projection of the nerve endings of the internal ear. Laryngoscope, 1933, **43,** 1.

RASMUSSEN, G. L. J. Comp. Neurol., 1953, **99, 61.**

SMITH, C. A., LOWRY, O. H. AND WU, M. L. Laryngoscope, 1954, **64,** 141.

STEVENS, S. S. Laryngoscope, 1958, **68,** 508.

*Monographs and Reviews*

BAST, T. H. AND ANSON, B. J. The temporal bone and the ear. Charles C Thomas, Springfield, Ill., 1949.

ENGSTRÖM, H. AND WERSÄLL, J. In International review of cytology, Vol. VII, edited by G. H. Bourne and J. F. Danielli, Academic Press Inc., New York, 1958.

LICKLIDER, J. C. R. In Handbook of experimental psychology, edited by S. S. Stevens, John Wiley and Sons, Inc., New York, 1951.

STEVENS, S. S., LORING, J. G. C. AND COHEN, D. Bibliography on hearing. Harvard University Press, Cambridge, Mass., 1955.

VAN BERGEIJK, W. A., PIERCE, J. R. AND DAVID, E. E., JR. Waves and the ear. Anchor Books, Doubleday and Company, Inc., Garden City, N. Y., 1960.

WEVER, E. G. AND LAWRENCE, M. Physiological acoustics. Princeton, N. J., 1954.

# 77

# HEARING:  MECHANICAL AND NEUROPHYSIOLOGICAL CONSIDERATIONS

## *Sensitivity and Dynamic Range of the Ear*

The range of frequencies to which the normal human ear is sensitive is usually said to extend from about 20 to 20,000 c.p.s., covering approximately ten octaves. The upper and lower limits are not sharply defined, but depend to some extent upon the intensity of sound available. For the common laboratory mammals, the upper limit seems to be at least an octave higher. Bats, however, emit and hear frequencies as high as 150,000 c.p.s. when flying in the dark, catching insects and avoiding obstacles in accordance with the patterns of echoes they receive. Porpoises use very high frequencies in a similar type of echo-location or "sonar" system to find their prey in the water.

The threshold of audibility for young adult human subjects with "normal" hearing, as determined at the Bell Telephone Laboratories by Sivian and White, is shown in the lowest curve of figure 77.1. This curve represents the *minimum audible field* pressures which the subjects could hear when placed in a sound field produced by a loudspeaker in an otherwise quiet, nonreverberant environment. The pressure measurements were made by replacing the subject with a condenser microphone in the exact position occupied by the subject's head.

The region of greatest sensitivity lies between 2000 and 3000 c.p.s. This is also the region of the broad resonance peak of the external canal. Here the threshold is 6 to 8 decibels (db) below 0.0002 dyne/cm², i.e., 0.0001 dyne/cm² or less.

Above 5000 c.p.s. the threshold curve rises at first slowly, then abruptly; below 2000 c.p.s. the rise is more gradual. At 15,000 c.p.s. and at 100 c.p.s. the threshold intensity is approximately 40 db higher than at 3000 c.p.s.

The values shown in this curve represent very sensitive ears having almost ideal hearing. According to an extensive survey by the U. S. Public Health Service, only 1 per cent of the population can hear sounds at or below the levels represented by the second curve, whereas half the population can hear the sounds represented by the fifth curve.

As the intensity of a sound is increased above the threshold value, the *loudness* or magnitude of the sensation increases. At about 120 db (*re* 0.0002 dyne/cm.²) the sound is not only heard but begins to be felt as a vague sensation of discomfort in the ear. This "threshold of feeling" is indicated as the uppermost curve in figure 77.1. Still higher levels cause a tickling or pricking sensation, and may produce definite pain if they exceed 140 db. These are the levels which readily cause temporary impairment of hearing. The area enclosed by the threshold and the "feeling" curves is sometimes called the *auditory area*. Any sound lying within this area produces an auditory sensation in a normal listener. How the ear encompasses this enormous dynamic range is one of the major questions of auditory research.

## *Transmission of Sound to the Cochlea*

THE EXTERNAL EAR. In many animals the shape and mobility of the external ear give it a directional and sound-gathering function which is of great assistance in localizing the source of a sound. In man the acoustical properties of the external ear are more or less unimportant, although the shape of the concha does serve to funnel sounds of relatively short wavelength (11 cm. or less, i.e., 3000 c.p.s. and higher) into the canal. Because the canal is a closed tube, it resonates at a wave-length corresponding to four times its own length. Wiener and Ross made probe-tube measurements and found a broad resonance peak in the external canal, centering about 3800 c.p.s., which has a wave-length of 9.2 cm., or four times the average length of the canal. The chief physiological importance of the canal seems to be protective. Not only do its length and shape help to shield the drum membrane from damage by blows or penetrating objects, but it also helps to maintain a favorable

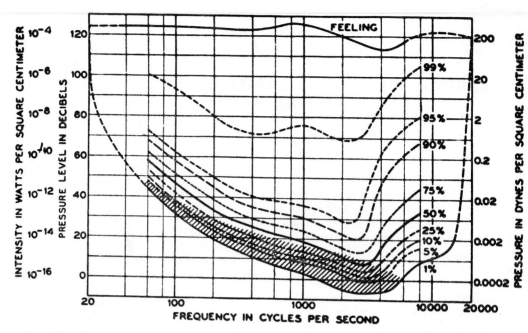

Fig. 77.1. Threshold contours for a typical group of listeners (U. S. Public Health Service Survey). Figures show percentage of group able to hear sounds below the given level. The 1 per cent curve represents ideal normal ears (Sivian and White). Shaded area represents masking by average room noise. (From Fletcher, *Speech and Hearing in Communication*, 2nd edition, 1953, D. Van Nostrand Company, Inc., Princeton, N. J.)

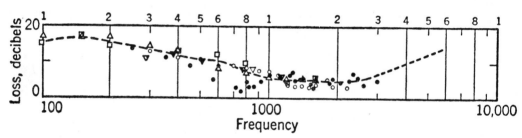

Fig. 77.2. The impedance of the ear expressed as transmission loss in decibels. Data of Tröger and other authors. (From Wever and Lawrence, *Physiological Acoustics*, 1954, Princeton University Press, Princeton, N. J.)

environmental temperature and humidity for the membrane.

THE MECHANICAL IMPEDANCE OF THE EAR. Part of the sound energy reaching the drum is reflected back, whereas the rest is absorbed by the drum, setting it in motion. How much energy is reflected and how much is absorbed are functions of the mechanical impedance of the ear. If the drum behaved like a rigid plug, offering an infinite impedance, all of the energy would be reflected. If, on the other hand, its impedance were precisely matched to that of the air in the external canal, all of the energy would be absorbed and none would be reflected. Impedance measurements by

Tröger (1930) and other investigators have shown that the characteristics of the ear vary with frequency. At the low frequencies the impedance is determined chiefly by the stiffness, and at the higher frequencies chiefly by the mass. At intermediate frequencies the frictional resistance alone is the determining factor. With the data of Tröger and others, the impedance of the ear can be expressed as transmission loss in decibels. The curve for transmission loss as a function of frequency shows that the impedance is greatest at the low frequencies (100 to 200 c.p.s.) and gradually declines to a broad minimum between 1000 and 2000 c.p.s. The data do not extend beyond 3000 c.p.s., but presumably the impedance increases again at higher frequencies, as the broken portion of the curve suggests.

THE TYMPANIC MEMBRANE. Békésy has made direct measurements of the amplitude of movements of the drum membrane as small as $10^{-5}$ mm. For this purpose he used a small capacitative proble, with its fixed plate 2 to 3 mm. in diameter and placed 0.5 mm. from the drum membrane, which itself formed the other plate. A high-frequency voltage of 100,000 c.p.s. was then applied across this condenser. When the drum vibrated, its movements varied the capacity and thus modulated the high frequency current. By measuring the modulated current he was able to calculate the displacement of the drum membrane.

Using this probe to measure the amplitude of motion of different portions of the drum membrane in response to a constant stimulus, Békésy found that, at all frequencies up to 2400 c.p.s., the whole central conical portion of the drum and the handle of the malleus move as a unit about an axis of rotation passing through the anterior and lateral processes. Figure 77.3 shows the contours of equal amplitude of movement for a tone of 2000 c.p.s. The amplitude is greatest near the inferior

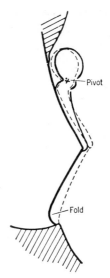

FIG. 77.3*B*. Vibration of the drum membrane as a rigid cone at low frequencies. (Békésy, 1941; reproduced by permission from Békésy and Rosenblith in *Handbook of Experimental Psychology*, Ed. by S. S. Stevens, John Wiley and Sons, Inc., New York, 1951.)

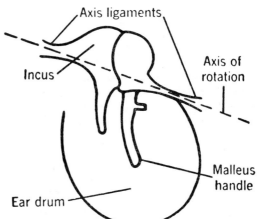

FIG. 77.4. The distribution of the mass of the ossicles about their axis of rotation. (Békésy, 1941; reproduced by permission from Békésy and Rosenblith in *Handbook of Experimental Psychology*, Ed. by S. S. Stevens, John Wiley and Sons, Inc., New York, 1951.)

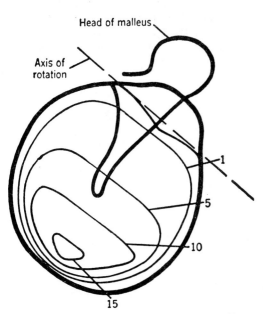

FIG. 77.3*A*. Vibration patterns of the human drum membrane for a 2000-c.p.s. tone. (Békésy, 1941; reproduced by permission from Békésy and Rosenblith in *Handbook of Experimental Psychology*, Ed. by S. S. Stevens, John Wiley and Sons, Inc., New York, 1951.)

edge of the membrane. Above 2400 c.p.s. the membrane no longer vibrates as a stiff cone but in segments, with the manubrium lagging behind the adjacent portions of the membrane.

THE TRANSFORMER ACTION OF THE MIDDLE EAR. Sound waves do not pass readily from one medium to another of different acoustical resistance, but are largely reflected at the boundary between the two media. Between air with an acoustical resistance of only 41.5 mechanical ohms per sq. cm. and sea water with a resistance of 161,000, the impedance mismatch is obviously very great. Only 0.1 per cent of the energy of sound would be transmitted, representing a loss of 30 db. A similar loss would occur in the transmission of sound from the air in the external canal to the fluids in the cochlea, if the middle ear mechanism did not act as a transformer to match the widely different impedances. This change from a slight pressure exerted over the large area of the drum to a greater pressure exerted over the smaller area of the stapes footplate is accomplished by the acoustical lever system formed by the drum and ossicles. The total area of the drum membrane is about 63 sq. mm. and its effective area is about 43 sq. mm., whereas the area of the footplate is only 3.2 sq. mm. This 13-fold reduction in area gives a corresponding increase in pressure at the oval window. Since an additional mechanical advantage of approximately 1.3 is available because the handle of the malleus is longer than the long process of the incus, the pressure exerted by the footplate is approximately 17 times as great as that at the drum membrane.

An additional virtue of the middle ear mechanism is that it provides for selective delivery of sound energy to one cochlear window rather than to both. If both windows were equally exposed to sound, little transfer of energy would occur because it would be opposed by the inertia and incompressibility of the cochlear fluids contained in the unyielding bony capsule. As it is, the fluids offer much less resistance because the round window is free to move outward as the stapes footplate moves inward, and *vice versa* (fig. 77.5).

MECHANICS OF THE OSSICLES. The mass of the malleus and incus is evenly distributed above and below their axis of rotation, as shown in figure 77.4. Since they are suspended by elastic ligaments and closely bound together, they move in and out as a unit. In response to moderate pressures the stapes follows them, so that the whole chain vibrates as a single mass. The footplate of the stapes rocks about its lower, posterior pole, moving like a bell-crank lever rather than a piston (fig. 77.5). When the intensity of a low-frequency tone rises above a critical value, this mode of vibration suddenly changes, and the footplate now rotates about its long axis. The amplitude of motion is decreased and less pressure is transmitted to the cochlea, thus reducing the risk of damage to the organ of Corti.

The intra-aural muscles provide another means of partial protection against intense sounds of low frequency. When the tensor tympani contracts, it pulls the handle of the malleus and the drum membrane inward. When the stapedius contracts, it pulls the footplate outward from the oval window. The effect of simultaneous contractions is to restrict the motion of the ossicular chain. Wiggers has shown in animal experiments

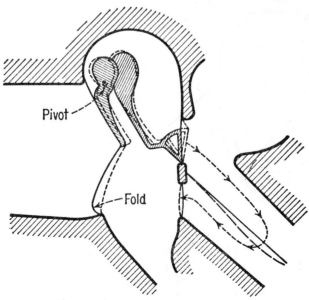

FIG. 77.5. Schematic diagram of movements of the tympanic membrane, the ossicles and the basilar membrane. (Reproduced by permission from H. Davis in *Hearing and Deafness*, Holt, Rinehart and Wilson, Inc., 1960.)

that the transmission of low frequencies to the cochlea is sharply reduced, whereas that for frequencies around 1300 c.p.s. is slightly increased, as if the stiffness of the middle ear mechanism had been increased by the contractions. Higher frequencies are unaffected. The muscles respond reflexly to sound, much as the eyelid and the sphincter of the iris respond reflexly to light. Just as in the eye, the reflex is consensual, so that a sound stimulus applied to one ear elicits muscle contractions in both ears. The protection offered against intense sounds is only partial at best. According to R. Wersäll, the reflex latency in the decorticate rabbit is 10 msec. for the stapedius and 17 msec. for the tensor tympani. Maximum tension is attained by the two muscles only after 63 and 132 msec., and in this time the ear can suffer severe injury from the initial waves of the noise of an explosion. The suggestion has been made that the intra-aural muscles may "tune" the ear by facilitating the transmission of the higher frequencies at the expense of the lower, but this possibility has received little support from experimental studies.

### The Cochlea

FREQUENCY ANALYSIS. Many attempts have been made to explain the role of the cochlea in the process of hearing, and particularly in the perception of pitch. Some investigators have held that the cochlea performs a frequency analysis of sound, whereas others have reserved that function to the brain. In formulating the *resonance theory* (1863), Helmholtz postulated a series of resonators in the cochlea, each tuned to a different frequency. He first suggested that the rods of Corti with their varying heights might serve as the resonators. Later he proposed the fibers of the basilar membrane, which he compared to the strings of a harp or pianoforte, postulating that the shorter fibers near the oval window respond to higher frequencies and the longer fibers near the apex to lower frequencies. In opposition to the resonance theory Rutherford (1880) put forward his *telephone theory*, ascribing to the cochlea the role of a telephone transmitter. He thought of it as transforming sounds into nerve impulses of the same frequency, which were then analyzed in the central nervous system.

The resonance theory continued to encounter the difficulty that no individual resonators could be identified. Gradually it evolved into the more widely accepted *place theory*, which holds that the entire cochlea is a tuned structure, with different portions of the basilar membrane and organ of Corti responding to sounds of different frequency. The corresponding nerve fibers then report to the brain which portions of the organ of Corti are being stimulated. The telephone theory on the other hand made it necessary to assume that the auditory nerve fibers have the unique property of responding at much higher rates than the theoretical maximum of 1000 impulses per second attributed to other nerve fibers of large diameter. At the same time it left entirely unexplored the question of how the brain might perform a frequency analysis. The implications and shortcomings of those two major theories and of variants put forward by other students of hearing have been reviewed by Wever (1949). He has shown that the two theories, so long thought to be irreconcilably opposed to each other, can be combined in his *resonance-volley theory*, which uses the telephone or volley principle to explain the response of the whole cochlea to low frequencies and the place or resonance principle to explain the cochlear analysis of higher frequencies. Both principles now have a solid basis of experimental fact derived from two types of investigation: (a) the study of the mechanics of the cochlear partition, and (b) the study of the electrical potentials of the organ of Corti.

MECHANICS OF THE COCHLEAR PARTITION. Békésy has shown, by painstaking evaluation of the physical properties of the various membranes and tissues that make up the cochlear partition, and by direct microscopic observation of their patterns of movement under stroboscopic illumination, that the place principle is correct. The cochlea is a tuned structure which performs a frequency analysis of sound. Part of the tuning is provided by the increasing width of the basilar membrane, from 0.04 mm. at the stapes to 0.5 mm. at the helicotrema, and part by the gradual increase in the mass of the organ of Corti in the same direction. The most important factor is the graded stiffness of the basilar membrane, which is greatest at the stapes and decreases steadily towards the apex. As a result, the stiffness, or "volume elasticity," of the cochlear partition as a whole is about 100 times as great at the stapes as it is at the apex.

The basilar membrane may be thought of as a gelatinous sheet covered by a thin, homogeneous layer of fibers, forming a continuous structure with the organ of Corti. Surprisingly enough, the membrane is not under tension, and therefore does not in any way resemble the strings of a piano as Helmholtz thought. Coupling between adjacent portions is both elastic and frictional,

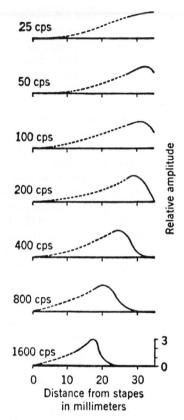

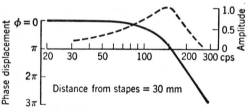

FIG. 77.6. Amplitude of displacement of the cochlear partition at various frequencies. (Békésy, J. Acoust. Soc. Am., **21**, 245, 1949.)

FIG. 77.7. The dashed curve represents the amplitude of displacement of a point 30 mm. from the stapes at different frequencies. The solid curve shows the phase lag behind the motion of the stapes. At frequencies over 150 c.p.s., the phase angle is greater than $\pi$, indicating that motion is due to travelling waves and not to a simple resonance. (Békésy, J. Acoust. Soc. Am., **21**, 245, 1949.)

and much of the frictional coupling is furnished by the endolymph and perilymph. As a result of the gradation in stiffness, the resonant frequency of the cochlear partition is highest at the stapes and decreases along its length, but because of the coupling the various portions cannot respond independently as separate tuned resonators.

Observing the movements of the cochlear partition under the microscope, von Békésy found that each part shows a maximum displacement for a certain frequency of sound. This maximum displacement moves towards the stapes as the frequency is raised (fig. 77.6), and towards the apex as the frequency is lowered. The amplitude of vibration at a given point plotted as a function of frequency resembles a resonance curve, but there is a vital difference. For a simple resonator like a pendulum, the phase angle changes from $\pi/2$ to $-\pi/2$ as the driving frequency is changed, and at the point of resonance the phase angle is zero. When the phase relations of the cochlear partition are measured, it is seen that the basilar membrane, the organ of Corti, the tectorial and Reissner's membranes all move together in phase. However, the phase lag between the movement of the stapes and that of a point on the basilar membrane near the helicotrema increases from 0 to 3 $\pi$ as the frequency is increased (figs. 77.7 and 77.8). Békésy has pointed out that this phase shift indicates the presence of travelling waves rather than a simple resonance.

The travelling waves are generated because the stiffest portion of the cochlear partition near the stapes in a sense drives the more flexible portions. Near the stapes the partition vibrates in response to all frequencies. As the waves move along the partition their amplitude gradually increases and reaches a maximum at the point where the natural frequency of the partition is the same as the driving frequency. Beyond this point the amplitude decreases rapidly as the velocity of travel diminishes and the wave-length grows shorter and shorter in the more flexible portions of the membrane. So great is the retardation that a single wave set up by a sudden, brief sound requires about 5 msec. to travel from the stapes to the helicotrema.

The travelling waves are demonstrable in the human cochlea only at frequencies above 150 c.p.s. At lower frequencies the basilar membrane moves more and more as a unit, so that below 50 c.p.s. the entire cochlear partition is moving in phase and the maximum amplitude occurs very close to the helicotrema.

On the basis of his measurements of the physical characteristics of the cochlear partition, von Békésy constructed models of the cochlea in which the travelling waves could readily be demonstrated. One of the most instructive of these models consisted of a plastic tube cast around a brass tube with a slit. When the tube was filled with fluid and the fluid set in motion by a vibrating piston at one end, travelling waves were set up with broad maxima that shifted with frequency over a two-octave range. When the

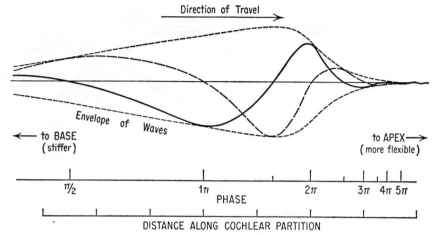

FIG. 77.8. The travelling wave pattern on the basilar membrane, showing the primary and secondary waves and the shortening of the wave length as the travelling wave pattern nears the apex. (Reproduced by permission from H. Davis in *Hearing and Deafness*, Holt, Rinehart and Wilson, Inc., 1960.)

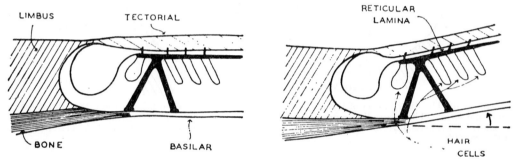

FIG. 77.9. *Left*, organ of Corti and tectorial membrane at rest. *Right*, bending of hairs by shearing action between reticular lamina and tectorial membrane. Based on von Békésy's description. (From Davis in *Physiological Triggers*, American Physiological Society, Inc., 1956.)

forearm was placed lengthwise along the vibrating membrane it provided a sensory surface representing the organ of Corti. As the frequency of vibration was changed the maximum could be felt to move along the arm. Although the maximum was quite broad and flat, the sensation of vibration was much more concentrated, so that any frequency shift could readily be recognized by a shift in the place of stimulation. Even with very brief tones lasting for only two cycles, the "pitch" discrimination was excellent. Some inhibitory process in the cutaneous innervation on either side of the maximum was presumably responsible for "sharpening" the pattern of stimulation. A similar mechanism is thought to act in the organ of Corti to aid in the discrimination of pitch.

### The Organ of Corti

THE FINE MOVEMENTS. Although the gross pattern of movement of the cochlear partition permits the cochlea to perform a frequency analysis,

it does not account for the actual transfer of energy to the hair cells. This stimulation occurs as the result of a double transformation, first of the up-and-down movement of the basilar membrane into a rocking motion of the rods of Corti and reticular lamina, and then into a shearing motion between the lamina and the tectorial membrane. The shearing motion causes a bending of the hairs, which are embedded at one end in the cuticular plates of the hair cells, firmly held by the reticular lamina, and extend at the other end into the tectorial membrane. Von Békésy has studied these fine movements under the microscope by stroboscopic illumination. He has observed that the direction of bending of the hairs varies from one side of the position of maximal amplitude of vibration to the other. On the side toward the stapes the hairs are bent radially, i.e., toward the Hensen cells. Further toward the apex, the hair cells move up and down only, whereas still further along, where the wave-length of the

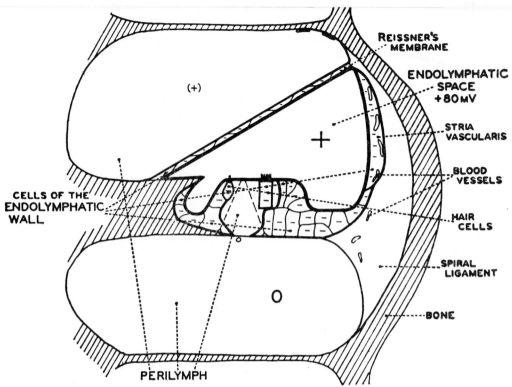

FIG. 77.10. The distribution of the DC endocochlear (positive) potential and the intracellular (negative) potentials. The heavy line represents the boundary of the endolymphatic space. The fluid in the tunnel of Corti may be perilymph or Engström's "cortilymph." (From Tasaki *et al.*, J. Acoust. Soc. Am., 1954, **26**, 765.)

travelling wave is shorter, the direction of bending is longitudinal. Although the bending of the hairs is the essential mechanical step in stimulating the hair cells, the significance of the different directions of bending is not yet understood.

THE ELECTRICAL RESPONSES. Attempting to observe the patterns of impulses in the auditory nerve in response to sound, Wever and Bray (1930) made the surprising discovery that the electrical potentials picked up from the nerve reproduced almost perfectly the frequencies and wave-forms of the sounds reaching the ear. Although this finding seemed at first to support Rutherford's telephone theory, it was soon demonstrated by Davis and Saul that two distinct types of potentials were involved: the cochlear microphonic potential (CM) and the action potentials of the auditory nerve fibers (AP). Although the AP response showed the typical threshold and refractory period, and differed in no way from the action potentials of other nerves, the CM response which preceded it in time had no all-or-none properties, but closely reproduced

the wave-form and polarity of the stimulus. More recent studies by von Békésy and by Davis and his collaborators have shown that five different types of electrical potentials can be recorded from the cochlea by means of fine electrodes inserted into the scalae. Two of these are DC resting potentials. The others are responses to sound stimuli.

*Intracellular potentials.* Like other cells, the cells of the organ of Corti and the auditory nerve fibers have a negative intracellular potential. As recorded with a microelectrode, these potentials range from −20 to −80 mv. referred to the perilymph.

*Endocochlear potential.* The endolymph in the cochlear duct shows a remarkable *positive* potential of 80 mv. referred to the perilymph in the vestibular and tympanic scalae. This high potential is a unique property of the cochlea, since the potential of the endolymph in the utricle is only +5 mv. It depends, not upon the ionic composition of the endolymph, but upon the metabolic activity of the stria vascularis. During asphyxia it decreases, and returns to its normal

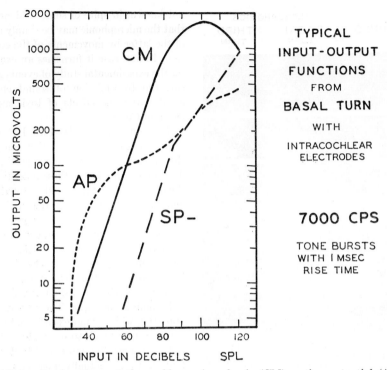

FIG. 77.11. Intensity functions of the cochlear microphonic (CM), action potential (AP) and negative summating potential (SP−), in response to brief tones of 7000 c.p.s., as recorded by intracochlear electrodes from the basal turn in the guinea pig. The voltage of CM is proportional to the sound pressure level up to 80 db SPL, then grows more slowly to a maximum of almost 1 mv. at about 105 db SPL. AP grows rapidly from threshold, then more slowly. The growth of SP− approximately parallels that of CM. (Unpublished, reproduced by special permission of Dr. Hallowell Davis.)

level only when oxygen is readmitted. Injection of azide or cyanide into the scala media abolishes the potential completely. The positive potential can be modified by movements of the basilar membrane. It is increased when the membrane is pushed "downward" towards scala tympani, by inward movement of the stapes, or by injecting fluid into the cochlear duct. Conversely, it is decreased by outward movement of the stapes, causing an "upward" movement of the basilar membrane. Movement of the tectorial membrane with respect to the organ of Corti causes similar changes in the endocochlear potential, suggesting a close relationship between the endocochlear and the cochlear microphonic potentials.

*Cochlear microphonic potential.* Unlike the DC intracellular and endocochlear potentials, the microphonic potential is an immediate response to acoustic stimulation. For many years it has been known to be associated with the hair cells, and at one time it was thought to be produced by compression and elongation of these cells in

much the same way as the piezo-electric potentials are produced in the crystal of a microphone. Recent studies have shown that the essential movement is the bending of the hairs as a result of vibration of the tectorial membrane. The response has no true threshold or refractory period, but closely reproduces the wave-form of the stimulus. Its amplitude is linearly proportional to the displacement of the cochlear partition, and therefore to the sound pressure of the stimulus from moment to moment. As the stimulus intensity is increased, the amplitude of the response grows proportionately (fig. 77.11). At higher levels the response becomes nonlinear, goes through a maximum, and eventually declines. Using intracochlear electrodes to record from individual turns of the guinea pig cochlea, Davis and his collaborators have shown that the basal turn responds to all frequencies, whereas the third turn responds only to frequencies below 3000 c.p.s. This is further evidence of the broad tuning of the basilar membrane (fig. 77.12).

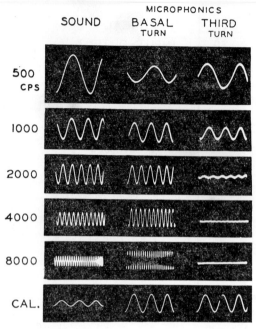

Fig. 77.12. Cochlear microphonic responses reproducing the sinusoidal wave-form of the stimulus, as recorded with intracochlear electrodes in scala vestibuli and scala tympani of the basal and third turns in the guinea pig. The basal turn responds to all frequencies, but the third turn only to frequencies below about 3000 c.p.s. (From Davis, Laryngoscope, **68**, 359, 1958.)

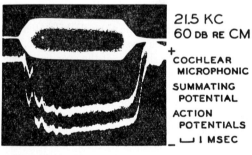

Fig. 77.13. Above: the stimulus, a brief tone of 21,500 c.p.s. Below: the response, including cochlear microphonic, summating and action potentials recorded from the round window in the guinea pig. CM is at the frequency of the stimulus; SP is the downward displacement of the baseline, and the action potentials are the peaks and valleys on the descending limb of SP. (From Pestalozza and Davis; Am. J. Physiol., **185**, 595, 1956.)

The microphonic potential is dependent upon an adequate oxygen supply. During anoxia it falls to a very low level, which may persist for some time after death. The precise relationship of the microphonic to the endocochlear potential is not known, in spite of some evidence suggesting that the microphonic may be simply a modulation of the latter by movements of the cochlear partition. In any case it furnishes an excellent means for the experimental study of events in the middle ear, the transmission of sound energy in the cochlea and the effects of toxic agents on the organ of Corti.

*Summating potentials.* Two DC potential responses to acoustic stimulation can be recorded, the positive and negative summating potentials. As seen in figure 77.13, these potentials reproduce the envelope of a brief burst of tonal stimulation, and are proportional to the root-mean-square value of the stimulus. They apparently represent a rectifier or detector action resulting from longitudinal movement of the tectorial membrane, accompanied by a persistent bending of the hairs in the same direction. The summating potentials appear at levels where the microphonic potential is becoming nonlinear. The positive summating potential, which is more sensitive to oxygen lack, is thought by Davis to originate in the outer air cells, whereas the more resistant negative potential, which actually increases in amplitude after mild injury to the organ of Corti, is attributed to the inner hair cells.

*Action potentials.* Although the action potentials can easily be recognized among the mixture of potentials recorded from the round window membrane, special electrode placements or cancellation procedures are required to record them uncontaminated by the microphonic potentials. They show the typical all-or-none behavior of axon-spike potentials of myelinated nerve fibers, having a definite threshold and a refractory period. The response to a click at a moderate intensity level consists of three successive volleys of "spike" potentials, called $N_1$, $N_2$ and $N_3$, representing synchronous, repetitive firing in many fibers. These action potentials are readily "masked" by noise, which stimulates the fibers in random fashion, so that the click finds many of them refractory and therefore unable to respond synchronously.

Synchronous volleys of action potentials occur in response to the sound waves of a steady tone of low or middle frequency. Above 1000 c.p.s. fibers may be responding in alternation or in rotation, since the refractory period of about 1 msec. prevents a given fiber from responding to each successive sound wave. At higher frequencies, synchronization of the action potentials decreases, to disappear completely above 4000 c.p.s.

The action potential lags behind the microphonic potential by 0.55 to 1.0 msec. This latency suggests a "synaptic delay" between the hair cells and the nerve endings, but it may also be ascribed to the conduction time of the nonmedullated fibers within the organ of Corti. Other properties of the action potentials also support the hypothesis that a synaptic type of transmission occurs at this point. Their sensitivity to oxygen lack greatly exceeds that of the microphonic response. Furthermore, they can be fatigued, and their recovery after masking is not as prompt as it should be if masking reflected only the refractory state of the nerve fibers. Whether a neurohumoral step occurs between the hair cell and the nerve fiber has not been ascertained. Davis's view is that the cochlear microphonic and negative summating potential excite the nonmedullated dendritic terminals directly.

The responses of single auditory nerve fibers have been studied by Tasaki by means of extremely fine pipette electrodes. Some fibers gave single and others repetitive responses; some had low, others high thresholds. Most of them responded to a wide range of frequencies below a sharp cut-off frequency, above which the fiber would not respond no matter how much the intensity was increased. As the frequency was increased, fibers would stop firing abruptly, and the higher the frequency, the smaller became the number of active fibers. These findings are in full accord with Békésy's description of the behavior of the travelling waves and their sharp decline just above the point of maximum amplitude of vibration of the partition.

The action potentials can be inhibited by stimulation of the olivocochlear tract of Rasmussen in the medulla, but the microphonic potentials are unaffected. The functional significance of this efferent inhibitory action is unknown, but it furnishes an example of the control of the responses of a sense organ by the central nervous system and presumably represents a sort of feed-back mechanism.

### The Central Auditory Pathway

RESPONSES OF MEDULLARY NEURONS. The responses of the second-order neurons of the cochlear nucleus as recorded with microelectrodes closely resemble those of the auditory nerve fibers. Galambos and Davis have observed that each unit responds to a limited range of frequencies, which is narrow at threshold but gradually broadens as the intensity of the stimulating tones is increased. As in the nerve, the high frequency cut-off is sharp (fig. 77.14). Many of the units show a "spontaneous" rhythmical discharge, which may be inhibited when a tone is sounded. Furthermore, when a unit is responding to a tone, presentation of a second tone may inhibit the discharge. The effect of this inhibition is to sharpen the cut-off at the low-frequency end. A tonal stimulus therefore increases the activity in some units and decreases or abolishes activity in others. Galambos suggests that each tonal frequency produces a characteristic pattern of "islands" of active and inactive neurons. In this way the broad tuning of the basilar membrane may be made more precise by a place principle operating at the medullary level, superimposed upon the repeated point-to-point projection of the organ of Corti which has been found in anatomical studies.

RESPONSES OF HIGHER AUDITORY CENTERS. The neurons of the inferior colliculus and medial geniculate body follow in general the patterns of activity seen in the cochlear nucleus. Discharge is increased by certain tones and suppressed by others, and the response areas of individual units are sharply defined. The point-to-point "tonotopic" projection of the cochlea is less firmly established at these levels, but the physiological evidence tends to support it.

The responses of the cortical auditory area have been most extensively studied in the cat. In this species and in the dog the area is located on the temporo-parietal surface of the hemisphere. It is bounded on three sides by the suprasylvian sulcus and extends ventrally almost to the rhinal fissure. On the basis of anatomical and electrophysiological data, as well as behavioral studies before and after cortical ablations, the six subdivisions shown in figure 77.15 have been delimited. AI receives the major projection of the medial geniculate body (pars principalis), and it is from this area that "onset responses" to clicks and pure tones are most easily recorded in anesthetized animals. According to Tunturi's experiments in the dog, using strychnine to sensitize 1-mm.[2] areas of the cortex, subdivision AI shows a tonotopic organization. Individual tones activate narrow bands of cortex 8 mm. long, with the lower frequencies represented more caudally and the higher frequencies more rostrally. A weak suprathreshold tone presented to the contra-

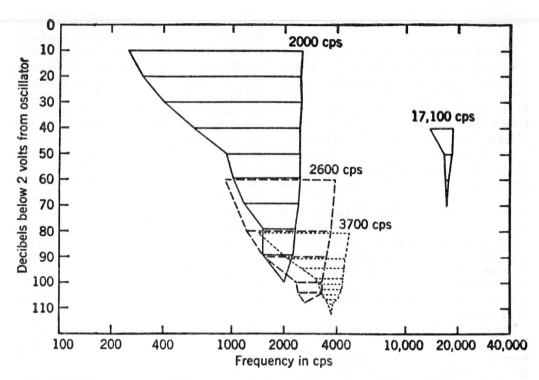

FIG. 77.14. Response areas of four neurons in the cochlear nucleus of the cat. Each neuron has a specific frequency at which a minimal acoustic energy is required to excite it. Each responds also to lower frequencies at higher intensity, but shows a sharp cut-off for higher frequencies, in accordance with the pattern of vibration of the basilar membrane described by Békésy. (From Galambos and Davis, J. Neurophysiol., **6**, 1943, 1939.)

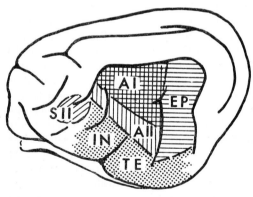

FIG. 77.15. The cortical auditory areas of the cat as described by various authors. AI and AII, first and second auditory areas; EP, posterior ecto-sylvian area; SII, second somatic area; IN, insular region; TE, temporal area. (Reproduced by permission from H. W. Ades in *Handbook of Physiology*, Section I: Neurophysiology, Vol. 1, American Physiological Society, Inc., 1959.)

lateral ear activates the entire band. The same tone presented to the ipsilateral ear activates only the dorsal portion of the band, but as the in-

tensity is increased more and more of the band is activated. Thus it would appear that pitch alone is represented in the contralateral cortex, but pitch and loudness are both represented in the ipsilateral cortex. A roughly similar tonotopic organization in the cat was revealed by the studies of Woolsey and Walzl, who stimulated nerve fibers at various points in the osseous spiral lamina of the cochlea and recorded the responses from the cortex. On the other hand, single unit studies with microelectrodes have revealed that relatively few cortical units respond selectively to tones, whereas more respond to noise and clicks only. Galambos has recently reported single units which appear to be sensitive to auditory stimuli only when a cat "pays attention" to the sound source.

The auditory cortex is not necessary, in the cat at least, for learning responses to tones or for discrimination between tones. It is required, however, for the recognition of simple auditory patterns, such as the difference between two different sequences of three tones each, the first *high-low-high*, and the second *low-high-low*. This type of discrimination depends upon the integrity of the insular (IN) and temporal (TE) areas (Diamond and Neff).

AUDITORY LOCALIZATION IN THE CORTEX. Both ears are represented about equally in the right and left auditory pathways, thanks to the trapezoid fiber crossing in the medulla, and to other intercommunications in the midbrain and corpus callosum. A sound applied to either ear alone evokes equal electrical responses in both cortices. On the other hand, when a sound is presented to both ears simultaneously, the responses of the two sides are equal only if the sound is in the median plane. As the source is moved to one side of the head, the response of the contralateral cortex becomes greater, and that of the ipsilateral cortex less (Rosenzweig). In spite of this important cortical correlate, auditory localization persists after bilateral destruction of the auditory areas.

Summarizing our still unsatisfactory knowledge of the auditory functions of the central nervous system, we may say that the rather broad frequency analysis performed by the cochlea is sharpened in the cochlear nucleus, where information concerning place of stimulation along the basilar membrane and frequency of stimulation is processed. Although a more or less point-to-point projection of the cochlea at various levels seems to be the rule, the frequency-sensitive units become proportionately fewer and more sharply tuned, whereas more and more units appear which have other functions.

Loudness has long been assumed to be correlated with the rate of discharge in individual fibers of the auditory nerve and with the total number of fibers discharging. At the same time, according to the volley principle, the rate of discharge signals the frequency for low tones. To resolve this apparent conflict, the suggestion has been made that loudness is not a simple function of the total number of impulses per second, and that the inner hair cells, with their higher thresholds, may make a significantly greater contribution to loudness than the more sensitive outer hair cells. How loudness is mediated in the central nervous system is still quite unknown. One of the few hints that we have comes from the studies of Bremer on the *encéphale isolé* in the unanesthetized cat. In this preparation a sustained activation of area AI occurs in response to tones. Raising the intensity of stimulation causes an increase

in the frequency of the rhythmical cortical discharge.

Thus far no auditory function has been found to have an exclusively cortical representation in animals except the discrimination of tonal patterns. This fact does not in any way call into question the importance of the auditory cortical areas. It does suggest that the experimental questions which we have been asking of the cortex may have been too simple.

## REFERENCES

BREMER, F. AND DOW, R. S. J. Neurophysiol., 1939, **2**, 308.

BREMER, F., BONNET, V. AND TERZUOLO, C. Arch. internat. de physiol., 1954, **62**, 390.

DAVIS, H. Laryngoscope, 1958, **68**, 359.

DERBYSHIRE, A. J. AND DAVIS, H. Am. J. Physiol., 1935, **113**, 476.

DIAMOND, I. T. AND NEFF, W. D. J. Neurophysiol., 1957, **20**, 300.

ERULKAR, S. D., ROSE, J. E. AND DAVIES, P. W. Bull. Johns Hopkins Hosp., 1956, **99**, 55.

GALAMBOS, R. AND DAVIS, H. J. Neurophysiol., 1943, **6**, 39.

GALAMBOS, R. AND DAVIS, H. J. Neurophysiol., 1944, **7**, 287.

NEFF, W. D., FISHER, J. F., DIAMOND, I. T. AND YELA, M. J. Neurophysiol., 1956, **19**, 500.

ROSENZWEIG, M. R. J. Comp. & Physiol. Psychol., 1954, **47**, 269.

RUTHERFORD, W. J. Anat. and Physiol., 1886, **21**, 166.

SAUL, L. J. AND DAVIS, H. Tr. Am. Otol. Soc., 1932, **22**, 137.

SIVIAN, L. J. AND WHITE, S. D. J. Acoust. Soc. Am., 1933, **4**, 288.

TASAKI, I. J. Neurophysiol., 1954, **17**, 97.

TASAKI, I., DAVIS, H. AND ELDREDGE, D. H. J. Acoust. Soc. Am., 1954, **26**, 765.

TRÖGER, J. Phys. Ztschr., 1930, **31**, 26.

TUNTURI, A. R. Am. J. Physiol., 1950, **160**, 395.

VON BÉKÉSY, G. Akus. Z., 1941, **6**, 1.

VON BÉKÉSY, G. J. Acoust. Soc. Am., 1947, **19**, 452.

VON BÉKÉSY, G. J. Acoust. Soc. Am., 1949, **21**, 245.

VON BÉKÉSY, G. J. Acoust. Soc. Am., 1952. **24**, 72.

VON BÉKÉSY, G. Acta oto-laryng., 1952, **42**, 197.

VON BÉKÉSY, G. Ann. Otol., Rhin. & Laryng., 1954, **63**, 448.

VON BÉKÉSY, G. Science, 1956, **123**, 779.

WALZI, E. M. AND WOOLSEY, C. N. Bull. Johns Hopkins Hosp., 1946, **79**, 309.

WEVER, E. G. AND BRAY, C. W. Science, 1930, **71**, 215.

WIENER, F. M. AND ROSS, D. A. J. Acoust. Soc. Am., 1946, **18**, 401.

WIGGERS, H. C. Am. J. Physiol., 1937, **120**, 771.

WOOLSEY, C. N. AND WALZL, E. M. Bull. Johns Hopkins Hosp., 1942, **71**, 315.

### Monographs and Reviews

ADES, H. W. In Handbook of physiology, Vol. I, Section 1. Edited by J. Field, H. W. Magoun and

V. E. Hall. American Physiological Society, Washington, D. C., 1959.

DAVIS, H. Physiological Reviews, 1957, **37**, 1.

DAVIS, H. In Handbook of physiology, Vol. I, Section 1. Edited by J. Field, H. W. Magoun and V. E. Hall. American Physiological Society, Washington, D. C., 1959.

DAVIS, H. AND SILVERMAN, S. R. (Editors). *Hearing and Deafness*. Revised ed., Holt, Rinehart and Wilson, Inc., 1960.

GALAMBOS, R. Physiological Reviews, 1954, **34**, 497.

GRIFFIN, D. R. Listening in the dark. Yale University Press, New Haven, 1958.

HELMHOLTZ, H. L. F. On the sensations of tone as a physiological basis for the theory of music.

Ed. 4 (1877), translated by A. J. Ellis, 1885. Reprinted, Dover Publications, Inc. New York, 1954.

STEVENS, S. S. AND DAVIS, H. Hearing: Its psychology and physiology. John Wiley and Sons, Inc. New York, 1938.

VON BÉKÉSY, G. Experiments in hearing. Translated and edited by E. G. Wever. McGraw-Hill Book Company, Inc., New York, 1960.

VON BÉKÉSY, G. AND ROSENBLITH, W. In Handbook of experimental psychology. Edited by S. S. Stevens. John Wiley and Sons, Inc., New York, 1951.

WERSÄLL, R. The tympanic muscles and their reflexes. Acta Otolaryngologica, Suppl. 139. Stockholm, 1958.

WEVER, E. G. Theory of hearing. John Wiley and Sons, Inc., New York, 1949.

# 78

# THE MEASUREMENT OF AUDITORY SENSATION:
## DEAFNESS

*Audiometry*

*Pure tones.* In the previous chapter the measurement of the absolute threshold of hearing was discussed, i.e., the smallest amount of acoustical energy that the ear can detect when pure tones of various frequencies are presented in quiet surroundings. An adaptation of this type of measurement is most commonly used in the clinic. The basic instrument, the *audiometer*, is an electro-acoustic device consisting of an oscillator, an amplifier, an attenuator for controlling intensity, and an earphone. Its frequency range usually extends from 125 to 8000 c.p.s., in discrete steps of an octave or less, whereas its intensity range covers approximately 100 decibels (db) in steps of 5 db. It must be remembered that the "zero-db" level of the audiometer is not the same as the standard reference level of 0.0002 dyne/cm.² Instead, it varies from frequency to frequency, representing the average normal threshold for each frequency, as determined in extensive hearing surveys conducted by the U. S. Public Health Service. The present American audiometer standard corresponds closely to the 50 per cent contour in figure 76.7. It is 10 db higher than the British and the proposed International Standard, which correspond closely to the thresholds of normal young adults as measured in ideal conditions in the laboratory.

A subject who is just able to detect all of the frequencies at 0 db is said to have normal hearing. If he can hear certain frequencies only when their intensity is increased by 30 db, he is said to have a *hearing loss* of 30 db at those frequencies. A graph showing the audiometric threshold plotted as a function of frequency is called an audiogram. The shape of the audiogram of a patient who is hard of hearing gives the otologist important evidence about the nature of the hearing impairment (figure 78.1).

OTHER FORMS OF AUDIOMETRY. Von Békésy has invented an audiometer which enables the patient to control the stimulus and at the same time to have his audiogram recorded automatically. So long as the patient hears the tone, he presses a button which causes it to diminish in intensity. When the tone disappears below his threshold, he releases the button and it grows again in intensity until he hears it and presses the button once more. At the same time, the frequency gradually increases. The recording pen therefore moves up and down on the intensity scale, writing the patient's reports of the disappearance and reappearance of the tone, and at the same time moves from left to right on the frequency scale. In this way a complete audiogram can be recorded in a few minutes. The size of the excursions of the pen also gives an indication of the rate of increase in loudness. As shown below, an abnormally rapid increase in loudness called *recruitment* is characteristic of certain forms of sensori-neural deafness.

*GSR and EEG audiometry.* Two other forms of audiometry are available for use with very young children or with patients who cannot understand or carry out the instructions for routine hearing tests. In one type of test, the patient is conditioned to expect a mild electric shock whenever he hears a tone. The shock evokes the galvanic skin response (GSR), a sudden transient change in the electrical resistance of the skin, and the tone, as the conditioned stimulus, comes to have the same effect. By recording the skin response and noting whether a change occurs when tones are sounded at various levels, the operator can determine the patient's threshold of hearing. In the EEG test, a change in the electroencephalographic pattern in response to sound, the so-called electroencephalic response (EER), which occurs in light sleep, is used as an indication that a given tone has been heard. Both of these tests require considerable skill in the interpretation of the records.

*Speech audiometry.* The frequencies of greatest importance for the understanding of speech are those in the middle of the audiometer range. If the hearing for 500, 1000 and 2000 c.p.s. is sig-

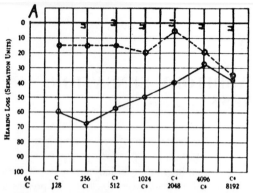

FIG. 78.1*A*. Audiogram showing conductive hearing loss in otosclerosis. The brackets represent bone-conduction thresholds, showing that cochlear function is normal. Broken line shows improvement of hearing after fenestration. (By permission from *The Inner Ear*, by H. G. Kobrak. Copyright 1959. The University of Chicago Press.)

words of two syllables equally stressed (spondees), such as *baseball* and *railroad*. Groups of six words are presented at successively lower intensity levels in steps of 4 db until the patient can no longer hear them. The intensity at which he can repeat half of the words correctly is taken as his threshold for speech, and the difference between this value and the average threshold for normal listeners represents his *hearing loss for speech*.

Additional information can be obtained by the use of the phonetically balanced (PB) lists of monosyllabic words. In these lists of 50 words each, the various speech sounds occur with approximately the same frequency as in normal conversational English. Each list is presented at a uniform intensity, and the percentage of words the patient is able to repeat correctly is his *articulation score*. His average articulation score for

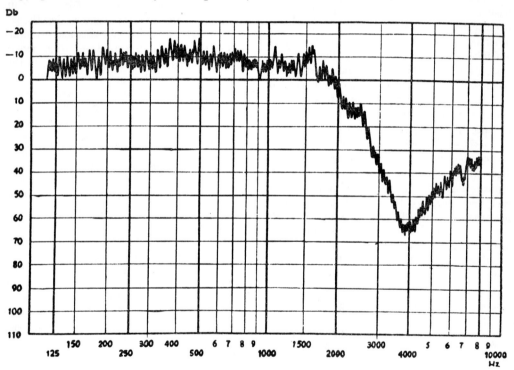

FIG. 78.2. Von Békésy audiogram, showing hearing impairment for high frequencies ("nerve-deafness") caused by dihydrostreptomycin. (By permission from L. J. Ranta, Acta Oto-laryng., Suppl. 136. Stockholm, 1958.)

nificantly impaired, the hearing for speech is also affected. The average hearing loss for these three frequencies usually gives a reasonably close estimate of the hearing loss for speech.

The hearing loss for speech can be measured directly using phonographic recordings of especially selected test words. These may be familiar

faint (55 db), normal (70 db) and loud (85 db) conversational speech is a useful measure of his ability to hear in everyday situations. Davis has given it the name *Social Adequacy Index* (SAI). For a person with normal hearing the SAI lies between 94 and 100. A score of 33 represents the lower limit for "socially adequate" hearing.

Patients with hearing impairment due to purely conductive lesions (see below) can usually attain an articulation score of 100 per cent if the speech is made sufficiently intense. Other patients with lesions in the end organ or nerve may not achieve a score of better than 60 per cent no matter at what intensity the speech is presented. The difference between this maximum articulation score and 100 per cent is called the *discrimination loss* (DL). From it and the hearing loss for speech the SAI can be estimated.

*Bone conduction audiometry.* Sound can be transmitted to the cochlea in two ways: by *air conduction*, through the external canal and across the middle ear, and by *bone conduction* as a result of vibrations of the skull. Bone conduction furnishes a means of testing the integrity of the cochlear mechanism in patients with damage to the middle ear. Bárány and von Békésy have shown that there are in fact two forms of bone conduction. When a vibrator is placed on the forehead, the skull can move as a rigid body, especially in response to frequencies below 800 c.p.s. The ossicles, however, are suspended in the middle ear cavity. They do not move with the skull because of their inertia. The cochlea and oval window therefore move with respect to the stapes, but the result is the same as if the footplate of the stapes itself were vibrating. Stimulation of the cochlea by this means is called *inertia bone conduction*. The second form, *compression bone conduction*, occurs at higher frequencies, where the skull no longer moves as a rigid body but vibrates in sections. The vibrations are transmitted directly to the cochlea. As its bony walls vibrate and set the fluids in motion the round window membrane moves more freely than the stapes in the oval window, and thus the basilar membrane is made to vibrate and stimulate the hair cells.

A calibrated bone conduction vibrator is usually furnished with the audiometer. The vibrator is applied to the mastoid process or to the forehead. Since the vibrations are transmitted to both inner ears, it is necessary to apply a masking noise to the ear not being tested in order to avoid confusion. The diagnostic use of bone conduction audiometry and the classical tuning fork tests are discussed later in this chapter.

DIFFERENTIAL THRESHOLDS. Discrimination, as in the understanding of speech, means the recognition of differences between sounds in terms of intensity, frequency, pattern, etc. Considerable interest has attached to the measurement of the *differential threshold*, also called the *difference limen* (DL) or *just noticeable difference* (JND) for the intensity and frequency of pure tones. Weber's law (1834) states that the increment of a stimulus that is just noticeable is a constant fraction of the intensity of the stimulus itself. In other words, for intensity, the fraction $\Delta I/I$ (or $\Delta I$ in db, which expresses the ratio) must be a constant if Weber's law holds. Actually the law does hold reasonably well over a considerable part of the intensity range, although the actual size of $\Delta I$ varies with frequency. For tones near threshold $\Delta I$ is relatively large, but it declines rapidly to reach a more or less constant value above a sensation level of 50 db. (Sensation level, SL, means *decibels above threshold*.) Thus for a 1000-c.p.s. tone at 5 db SL, $\Delta I$ is 3 db, whereas at 50 db SL, it is only 0.5 db. For white noise, $\Delta I$ is less than 0.5 db at 20 db SL, and remains almost constant at least up to 100 db SL.

For frequencies above 1000 c.p.s. at a sensation level of 40 db or more, the relative DL ($\Delta f/f$) remains almost constant at about 0.003 as the frequency is increased. At 1000 c.p.s. the normal listener can detect a change of 3 c.p.s., but at 5000 c.p.s. he would fail to notice a change of less than 15 c.p.s.

MASKING. In spite of the ability of the ear to analyze complex tones and separate out individual frequencies, weak sounds may be completely inaudible in the presence of sounds of greater intensity. This familiar phenomenon is called *masking*. White noise is particularly effective in masking other acoustic stimuli.

The degree of masking is measured as the number of decibels by which the intensity of the masked sound must be increased above the quiet threshold to become just audible in the presence of the masking noise. Fletcher has shown that when a tone is masked by noise, the frequencies effective in masking it are those lying in a relatively narrow band centered about the frequency of the masked tone. These frequencies make up the *critical band*. For a tone of 300 c.p.s., the critical band is about 50 c.p.s. wide, for 2000 c.p.s. it is 100 c.p.s. wide, and for 5000 c.p.s., it is 500 c.p.s. wide. Beyond these limits, further increase in the width of the band of frequencies does not increase the degree of masking.

The masking of tones by other pure tones has been extensively studied, but it is complicated by the fact that tones close together in frequency interfere with each other and cause fluctuations in loudness, or *beats*, which make the degree of masking difficult to judge. In general, low tones are much more effective in masking high tones than vice versa. This finding is in accord with the patterns of excitation of the basilar membrane described by Békésy, who noted that low tones affect the whole length of the membrane, whereas high tones affect only a limited region near the stapes.

Masking by noise is frequently used in clinical audiometry to "block" the better ear so that it will not respond to loud sounds or to bone-conducted sound used in testing the worse ear and thus give a false result.

LOUDNESS. Loudness is the psychological attribute of sound most closely associated with the physical property of intensity. Being a subjective quantity, loudness cannot be specified directly in terms of physical units, but must be expressed in terms of special psychophysical scales. One of these is the scale of *Loudness Level*, which is based upon judgments of equal loudness. If the experimenter takes a tone of 1000 c.p.s. at 40 db intensity level and asks the subject to adjust the intensity of other frequencies until each is equal in loudness to the 1000-c.p.s. tone, he obtains an equal-loudness contour. The loudness level of the 1000-c.p.s. tone is said to be 40 *phons*, and all

other frequencies on the contour have the same loudness level. We may therefore define the loudness level (in *phons*) of any tone as the intensity level (in db) of the 1000-c.p.s. tone which is equal to it in loudness. A set of equal-loudness contours is shown in figure 78.3. From the spacing of the curves it is evident that the loudness level of low-frequency tones grows much faster than that of medium and high-frequency tones.

A loudness scale can also be based on judgments of loudnesses that are multiples and fractions of a standard loudness. Stevens has set up such a scale, using as a unit the *sone*, which is defined as the loudness of a 1000-c.p.s. tone at 40 db intensity level. A tone that sounds twice as loud has a loudness of 2 sones, whereas one that sounds one-half as loud has a loudness of 0.5 sone. Stevens has shown that the relationship between loudness in sones ($S$) and sound pressure ($p$) is a simple power function: $S = kp^{0.6}$. When plotted in the form shown in fig. 78.4, this equation gives a straight line. The plot shows that for each increase of 10 db in sound pressure level, the loudness is approximately doubled.

An abnormally rapid increase in loudness can often be demonstrated in cases of unilateral hearing impairment due to injury or degeneration of

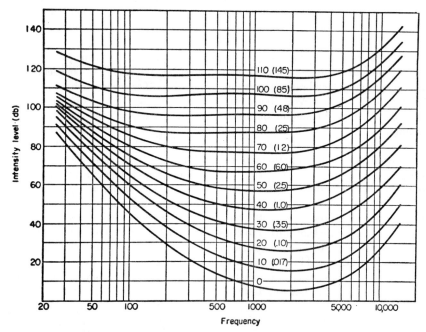

FIG. 78.3. Equal-loudness contours showing the relation between intensity level and frequency for tones at different loudness levels. All of the sounds represented by a given curve sound equally loud. The figures 0 to 110 represent *loudness level in phons*. The 0-phon contour is the normal free-field threshold curve. Figures in parentheses show the *loudness in sones*. (Reprinted with permission from Stevens and Davis, *Hearing*, 1938, John Wiley and Sons, Inc., New York.)

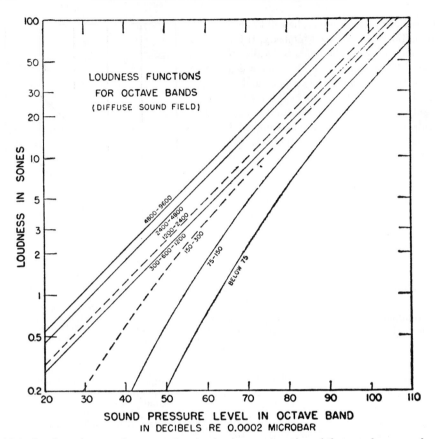

FIG. 78.4. Loudness in sones for octave bands of noise as a function of the sound pressure level of the bands. (By permission from S. S. Stevens, J. Acoust. Soc. Am., **28**, 807–832, 1956.)

the organ of Corti. If an alternate binaural loudness balance is carried out, it is seen that even though the threshold of the abnormal ear may be much higher than that of the normal, loudness increases so rapidly in the abnormal ear that at higher intensities both ears hear the same loudness when both are stimulated at the same intensity level. This phenomenon is called *recruitment of loudness*. It is of diagnostic importance in cases of perceptive deafness (fig. 78.5).

PITCH. Although we usually think of *pitch* as a function of frequency only, Stevens has shown that pitch can change with intensity. For frequencies below 1000 c.p.s., pitch decreases as intensity is increased, whereas for tones above 3000 c.p.s. pitch increases with intensity. For tones in the middle range, slight changes may occur in either direction, depending upon the intensity level.

Stevens and Volkmann have established a numerical scale of pitch by a fractionation method similar to that used for the scale of loudness. The unit of pitch is called the *mel*. A pitch of 1000 mels is assigned to a 1000-c.p.s. tone, a pitch of 500 mels to the tone which sounds one-half as high in pitch, and so on. Pitch intervals 50 mels wide sound to the ear to be equal in subjective extent. It may be noted that there is close agreement between the width in cycles of the 50-mel pitch intervals and the width of the critical bands which are effective in masking pure tones.

The same frequency does not necessarily produce the same sensation of pitch in both ears. In cases where a unilateral partial loss of hearing has occurred as a result of localized damage to the organ of Corti, a tone may sound higher in pitch in the abnormal than in the normal ear. This sensation of false pitch of which the patient is usually unaware, is called *diplacusis*. A small difference in tuning can sometimes be demonstrated even in "normal" ears.

LOCALIZATION. Judgment of the direction from which a sound is coming demands the use of both ears. The important cues are differences in time of arrival (or phase) in the case of frequencies below 1200 to 1400 c.p.s., and differences in intensity in the case of higher frequencies. When two tones differing only in intensity are led separately to each ear of an observer, he will localize the source on the side of greatest intensity. If the tones differ only in phase, he tends to localize it on the side of the leading phase. A sound which arrives simultaneously at the two ears and is equally loud in both is localized in the median plane. Slight head movements producing changes in these interaural differences are also important in localizing the source. With earphones, the source is judged to be in the center of the head if the sounds they produce at the two ears are synchronous and of equal intensity. If the sound in one earphone is made slightly more intense or is advanced slightly in phase, the source seems to move toward that side of the head.

DEAFNESS. Any abnormal condition or disease which interferes with the conduction of sound to the inner ear, with the setting up of nerve impulses in the cochlea, or with their transmission to the appropriate levels of the nervous system can cause an impairment of hearing. The otologist distinguishes between *conductive deafness*, caused by interference with the passage of sound waves through the external and middle ear, and *sensorineural (nerve) deafness*, caused by damage to the cochlear mechanism or to the auditory nerve. *Central deafness* involving the auditory pathways of the nervous system, is also recognized. *Conductive deafness* has many causes. One of the commonest of these is an accumulation of hard, dry wax in the external canal. Fortunately, it is a condition that can easily be corrected. The tympanic membrane itself may be altered by disease, resulting either in "hardening of the eardrum" with fibrous and calcareous deposits, or in a perforation. The effect of a perforation upon hearing depends upon its position and size, but it usually involves the low frequencies. Stiffening or interruption of the ossicular chain by destruction of an ossicle can occur in chronic otitis media. The hearing loss may amount to 30 db or more; when the drum membrane, malleus and incus are absent, it may be as great as 65 db.

*Otosclerosis* (or *otospongiosis*) is a localized disease of the bony capsule of the labyrinth and a common cause of conductive deafness. It involves destruction of bone in the neighborhood of the windows and replacement by new bone, which may be deposited around the stapes footplate in such a way as to interfere with its motion and ultimately to fix it in the oval window. The increasing stiffness causes a progressive loss of hearing for the low frequencies, usually beginning between puberty and the early thirties. Later the

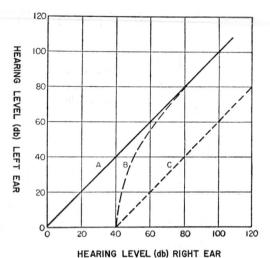

FIG. 78.5. Binaural loudness matching. Curve A represents two normal ears, in which the same hearing level in the right ear as in the left produces equal loudness. Curve B represents a right ear with a neural impairment showing recruitment, matched against a normal left ear. The right ear requires a 40-db greater hearing level at threshold, but the loudness increases more rapidly with intensity than in the normal ear, so that a tone at 80 db sounds equally loud to both ears. Curve C shows a right ear with a 40-db conductive impairment. The loudness increases at the same rate as in the normal left ear. (By permission from *The Measurement of Hearing*, by I. J. Hirsh. Copyright 1952. McGraw-Hill Book Company, Inc., New York.)

high frequencies may be affected by pathological changes in the cochlea itself.

In recent years, two surgical procedures have been perfected for the restoration of hearing in otosclerosis. One is Lempert's *fenestration* operation, in which a new window is made between the middle ear and the lateral semicircular canal. In this way the immobile ossicular chain is bypassed, and sound is once more permitted to reach the inner ear *via* the round window and the new "oval window." The second procedure is that of *stapes mobilization*, developed by Rosen. In this operation the ankylosed margins of the footplate are cut through with fine picks or chisels. The operation is performed under local anesthesia, and the restoration of hearing is sometimes dramatically sudden. A serious problem in the development of both operations has been the tendency of deafness to recur with closure of the fenestra or re-ankylosis of the footplate. An example of otosclerotic deafness and the improvement in hearing after fenestration is shown in figure 78.1.

*Tympanoplasty*, the surgical reconstruction of the sound-conducting system, is another example of middle ear surgery. It may be recommended in cases where the middle ear mechanism has been damaged by chronic otitis media. The operation must necessarily take various forms, depending upon the degree of injury found. In some cases a single ossicle between the drum and the oval window, resembling the avian *columella*, is substituted for the defective ossicular chain.

In all types of conductive deafness, the amplification provided by an electronic hearing aid may be of great assistance to the patient. The earphone is usually inserted in the external canal, but in some cases a bone conduction oscillator placed on the mastoid process may be preferable.

A temporary conductive deafness can occur when the drum membrane is strongly retracted (and its stiffness therefore increased) by a negative pressure in the middle ear. This condition is commonly experienced in aircraft during descents from altitude. When the external pressure exceeds that in the middle ear, the Eustachian tube, the only means by which the two pressures can be equalized, remains tightly closed, and the weak dilator muscle at its pharyngeal orifice, the *tensor veli palatini*, is unable to open it. The drum membrane does not rupture unless the pressure difference amounts to 100 to 500 mm. Hg. Usually the retraction persists for only a short time until the pressure difference is relieved by repeated swallowing, or by making a forced expiration with the nose and mouth closed (Valsalva's maneuver).

When the tube remains closed for any length of time, air trapped in the middle ear is gradually absorbed. If the partial pressure of oxygen in the cavity is reduced below the level of the hydrostatic pressure in the capillary bed, fluid leaves the capillaries and enters the middle ear, which may fill in minutes. Such an accumulation of fluid increases the friction of the system, and thus decreases the transmission of sound.

*Sensori-neural (nerve) deafness.* Deafness due to interference with the process of excitation in the cochlea or with the transmission of impulses by the auditory nerve may be caused in many ways. In its mildest, reversible form it appears as a *temporary threshold shift* after exposure to sound or noise of more than ordinary intensity. If the exposure is very intense or occurs day after day, as in a noisy industrial situation with sustained levels in the neighborhood of 100 db, it can result in the permanent impairment called *acoustic trauma*. Hearing for the upper frequencies is more affected than for the lower, and a "dip" in the audiogram at 4000 c.p.s. is a common finding.

The reason for the special vulnerability of this region of the basilar membrane is unknown.

In the temporary nerve deafness after exposure to a pure tone, the maximum loss is found about half an octave *above* the frequency of the exposure tone, but never below it. This result fits well with the known shape of the travelling wave. A loss of 40 to 60 db at one or more frequencies is usually accompanied by a ringing or sizzling *tinnitus* or subjective noise, presumably representing a sustained spontaneous discharge of injured hair cells. Recruitment of loudness is present, so that in spite of the elevation of threshold for certain frequencies, the loudness of sounds at higher intensity may be normal. Diplacusis, with an upward shift of pitch in the region of the hearing loss can usually be demonstrated (Davis *et al.*). In animals exposed to intense tones, degenerative changes are found in the hair cells of the organ of Corti. The outer hair cells are more susceptible to such injury than the inner, and the region of damage is usually localized in the basal half of the cochlea (Lurie *et al.*).

Nerve deafness can occur at any age. In childhood it can result from meningitis, or occasionally from certain virus infections such as mumps. A form of nerve deafness accompanied by violent attacks of vertigo is *Ménière's syndrome* which occurs most frequently in middle-aged persons. Hearing for the low frequencies is affected, and a roaring tinnitus is often present. The attacks are attributed to an increased hydrostatic pressure of the endolymph (hydrops), causing a bulging of the walls of the cochlear duct which has been demonstrated *post mortem*. The function of the auditory nerve may also be impaired by the pressure of a tumor in the cerebello-pontine angle. Finally, a gradual perceptive loss for the high frequencies occurs with advancing age and is called *presbycusis*.

A new hazard to hearing is found in the antibiotics of the streptomycin group, especially *dihydrostreptomycin, kanamycin* and *neomycin*, all of which can cause profound deafness by their ototoxic action. The hearing loss starts with the highest frequencies and may progress even after antibiotic therapy is discontinued. In experimental animals, the antibiotics have been shown to cause degeneration of the hair cells and disappearance of the organ of Corti. The electrical responses are diminished, especially the cochlear microphonic potential.

Bone conduction audiometry plays an important part in the diagnosis of nerve deafness. Because cochlear function is affected, the bone conduction audiogram shows the same pattern of loss as that for air conduction. In conductive deafness on the other hand, hearing by bone conduction may be perfectly normal, in contrast to the loss shown in the air conduction audiogram. The comparison can also be made in the classical *Rinné test* using the tuning fork. The vibrating fork is first placed on the mastoid process. When the patient reports that he can no longer hear its tone by bone conduction, it is removed from the bone and the vibrating prongs are held up to the open ear canal. The normal ear should then hear the fork by air conduction and continue to hear it for about 45 seconds. This "positive" Rinné test is also characteristic of partial nerve deafness. If the fork is heard longer by bone conduction, the test is negative, and a conductive deafness is present.

In the *Schwabach test*, the patient's bone conduction hearing is tested against the presumably normal hearing of the examiner. If there is a conductive lesion, the patient will be able to hear the fork longer than the examiner, because the presence of the lesion excludes masking noise. If a neural lesion is present, the patient will hear the fork for a shorter time than the examiner. The bone conduction test made with an audiometer is essentially similar to the Schwabach test.

The *occlusion* or *Bing test* consists in placing the fork on the vertex of the skull and determining the effect of gently occluding the canal on the thresholds for low frequencies. If the ear is normal or nerve deaf, sensation at low frequencies is increased because the bone conducted sound sets up vibrations in the air enclosed in the canal which are transmitted to the cochlea and reinforce the vibrations reaching it directly. If a conductive lesion is present, occlusion of the canal has no effect on the sensation.

The *Weber test* is valuable in the diagnosis of otosclerosis and highly reliable in spite of the difficult theoretical problem it has always raised. It consists simply in placing the vibrating fork on the patient's head and asking him to report in which ear he hears it. If one ear has a nerve lesion, the sound will be heard in the opposite, i.e., the *better ear*. If, however, one ear has a fixed stapes, the sound will be heard in the same, i.e., in the *worse ear*. Many hypotheses have been put forward attempting to explain this paradoxical result, but none has yet been generally accepted. One of the most attractive is that of Langenbeck, who has pointed out that only compression bone conduction can be effective in stimulating the cochlea of an ear with a fixed stapes and has shown how the localization of the sound may depend upon a difference in phase between the com-

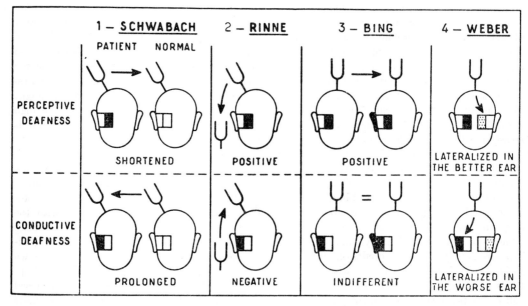

Fig. 78.6. The four classical bone conduction tests with tuning forks. Arrows indicate that the sound is heard for a longer period of time when the fork is moved from one position to the other. Black indicates location of lesion in middle ear or cochlea. (By permission from *The Inner Ear*, by H. G. Kobrak. Copyright 1959. The University of Chicago Press.)

pression bone conducted sound reaching that cochlea and the inertia bone conducted sound reaching the other cochlea.

## REFERENCES

FLETCHER, H. Auditory patterns. Rev. mod. phys., 1940, **12**, 47.

FLETCHER, G. AND MUNSON, W. A. Loudness, its definition, measurmeent and calculation. J. Acoust. Soc. Am., 1933, **5**, 82.

HALLPIKE, C. S. AND CAIRNS, H. Observations on the pathology of Ménière's syndrome. J. Laryng. & Otol., 1938, **53**, 625.

HAWKINS, J. E., JR. Antibiotics and the inner ear. Tr. Am. Acad. Ophth., 1959, **63**, 206.

HAWKINS, J. E., JR. AND LURIE, M. H. The ototoxicity of streptomycin. Ann. Otol., Rhin. and Laryng., 1952, **61**, 789.

HAWKINS, J. E., JR. AND STEVENS, S. S. The masking of pure tones and of speech by white noise. J. Acoust. Soc. Am., 1950, **22**, 6.

LEMPERT, J. Improvement of hearing in cases of otosclerosis. A new one-stage surgical technique. Arch. Otolaryng., 1938, **28**, 42.

LURIE, M. H., DAVIS, H. AND HAWKINS, J. E., JR. Acoustic trauma of the organ of Corti in the guinea pig. Laryngoscope, 1944, **54**, 375.

ROSEN, S. Simple method for restoring hearing in otosclerosis: mobilization of the stapes. Acta oto-laryng., 1954, **44**, 78.

SHOWER, E. G. AND BIDDULPH, R. Differential pitch sensitivity of the ear. J. Acoust. Soc. Am., 1931, **3**, 275.

STEVENS, S. S. Calculation of the loudness of complex noise. J. Acoust. Soc. Am., 1956, **28**, 807.

STEVENS, S. S. AND NEWMAN, E. B. The localization of actual sources of sound. Am. J. Psychol., 1936, **48**, 297.

STEVENS, S. S. AND VOLKMANN, J. The relation of pitch to frequency: a revised scale. Am. J. Psychol., 1940, **53**, 329.

VON BÉKÉSY, G. A new audiometer. Acta oto-laryngol., 1947, **35**, 411.

VON BÉKÉSY, G. Vibration of the head in a sound field and its role in hearing by bone conduction. J. Acoust. Soc. Am., 1948, **20**, 749.

*Monographs and Reviews*

BÁRÁNY, E. Acta. oto-laryng., Suppl. 26. Stockholm, 1938.

DAVIS, H., MORGAN, C. T., HAWKINS, J. E., JR., GALAMBOS, R. AND SMITH, F. W. Acta oto-laryng., Suppl. 88. Stockholm, 1950.

FLETCHER, H. Speech and hearing in communication. D. Van Nostrand Company, Inc. Princeton, N. J., 1953.

HIRSH, I. J. The measurement of hearing. McGraw Hill, New York, 1952.

KOBRAK, H. G. The middle ear. University of Chicago Press, Chicago, Ill., 1959.

RANTA, L. J. Acta oto-laryng., Suppl. 136. Stockholm, 1958.

RÜEDI, L. AND FURRER, W. Das akustische Trauma. Pract. oto-rhinolaryng. vol. **8**, 1. 1946.

# 79

# THE SENSES OF TASTE AND SMELL; COMMON CHEMICAL SENSE

## Taste, Gustation

Taste is a chemical sense, that is to say, the receptors (chemoreceptors) for this sense respond adequately to chemical stimuli. In order, therefore, for a substance to arouse a sensation of taste it must be dissolved—either taken in solution or dissolved in the saliva; a solid taken into a perfectly dry mouth is tasteless. For this reason the organs of taste or *taste buds* are present only upon a moist surface, being confined to the mouth region of all air-breathing vertebrates, but may be anywhere upon the body surface of aquatic forms.

THE ORGANS OF TASTE. The taste buds of man are mainly situated on the tongue but a few are also found in the mucous membrane covering the palate, fauces, epiglottis and the larynx in the region of the arytenoid cartilages. Taste buds are more widely distributed in children, and are especially plentiful over the anterior part of the tongue. In the adult they are much fewer at the tip of the tongue and are almost absent from the middle third. In most fishes the skin of the general body surface is plentifully supplied with taste receptors, and in the catfish and certain other species of fish they are contained in the filiform processes known as barbles projecting from the snout and angles of the mouth. In insects (flies, bees) taste receptors are located at the end of the proboscis antennae or upon the tarsal segments of the legs.

The mucosa of the human tongue is studded with large numbers of small elevations—the *lingual papillae*—caused by projections of the lamina propria and called secondary papillae. The papillae are of three main types, filiform, fungiform and vallate. The *filiform papillae* are very minute conical structures covering the anterior two-thirds or so of the dorsal surface of the tongue. They are arranged in rows running roughly parallel with the rows of vallate papillae. The *fungiform papillae* are considerably larger than the preceding type, round in shape and situated mainly at the tip and edges of the tongue. The *vallate papillae* are much larger and become especially prominent posteriorly where from 6 to 12 are arranged conspucuiously in the form of a V with its limbs open anteriorly. A vallate papilla consists of a central round elevation with perpendicular sides and surrounded by a sulcus; the taste buds are situated in the mucosa forming the walls of this circular trench. The filiform papillae rarely contains taste buds, but each fungiform papilla usually holds from 8 to 10 embedded in the epithelium covering its free surface.

A section of a taste bud is shown in figure 79.1. It measures about 70 $\mu$ long and 50 $\mu$ broad, and lies with its long axis perpendicular to the epithelial surface. It consists of groups of *supporting cells (peripheral supporting cells)* shaped somewhat like the sections of a musk melon and arranged side by side to enclose a small oval chamber which opens superficially through a circular gap—the *inner taste pore*—surrounded by the converging ends of the supporting cells. The inner taste pore usually leads into a short canal which opens in turn through the *outer taste pore* upon the surface of the tongue. The cavity of the taste bud is occupied by other supporting cells (*central supporting cells*) in the intervals between which the taste receptors (taste cells) are lodged. The taste cell is spindle-shaped and provided with a fine hairlike process which projects through the inner taste pore into the short canal mentioned above. The taste bud contains a variable number of these sensory cells, usually from 5 to 18. Nerve fibers after losing their medullary sheaths penetrate the bud and arborize upon the surface of the taste cells.

The total number of taste buds varies widely between different species from an estimated 800 in the bat to 35,000 in the ox; there are about 9,000 in man.

The chief nerves of taste are the *chorda tympani* branch of the facial nerve and the *glossopharyngeal nerve* (see fig. 79.2). The former nerve supplies the taste buds over the anterior two-thirds of the tongue, the latter is distributed to the posterior third. The *vagus nerve* innervates the taste buds present on the pharyngeal aspect of the tongue, on the soft palate, epiglottis and the region of the arytenoid cartilages. The *trigeminal nerve* mediates

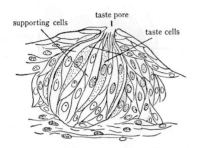

FIG. 79.1. Vertical section through a taste bud

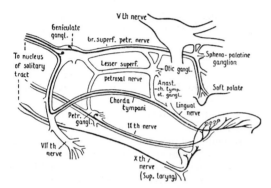

FIG. 79.2. Diagram of the course of the gustatory fibers. (Modified from Brodal, after Rowbotham.)

common chemical sense (p. 1469) and sensations of touch, temperature and pressure (common sensibility) from the entire buccal mucosa; it does not contain taste fibers. Cushing observed, for example, that removal of the Gasserian (trigeminal) ganglion did not cause any permanent loss of taste. Section of the nerves of taste in animals is followed by degeneration and gradual disappearance of the taste buds. Olmsted has shown in experiments upon the catfish that taste buds reappear upon regeneration of the nerve fibers. The latter evidently exert a formative influence, possibly through the medium of a chemical substance, upon the development of the taste organs.

The central connections of the nerves of taste are described in chapters 64 and 66 (see fig. 79.2).

### THE SENSATIONS OF TASTE

There are four *simple, primary* or *fundamental* tasts—*sweet, sour (acid), salty* and *bitter.* Two others are sometimes added, namely, *alkaline* and *metallic.*[1] The various other tastes which we ex-

[1] Opinions differ as to the nature of these two sensations, most investigators contending that the former is a compound sensation, resulting from the excitation of several types of end organs, including those for sweetness and for touch. Similarly, the metallic taste caused by the salts of heavy metals, copper, silver, mercury, etc., is believed to be a complex of sour and sweet. Some maintain indeed that it is due chiefly to the stim-

perience are (a) blends of two or more of the primary sensations or (b) combinations of the latter with sensations aroused by the stimulation of the nerves of common sensibility. For example, ginger is recognized not only by its taste (i.e., through impulses from the taste buds), but also by the burning sensation caused by the excitation of the ordinary sensory nerves of the mouth and also, we may add, by its odor. Many other substances, such as fats and oils and pungent condiments, are "felt" as well as tasted.

Many of the finer flavors are in reality sensations of smell, and olfaction enters very largely into many of the sensations which we generally class as tastes. For this reason when the nose is held or the nasal passages blocked, as during a common cold, the sense of taste is blunted. It may then be impossible if two bland foods are of the same consistency to distinguish between them; thus an apple and a pear, or a turnip and a potato, taste pretty much alike. On the other hand, certain substances which we think that we detect by smell are actually tasted. The sweetish smell of chloroform is an example; the vapor reaches the taste buds in the inspired air.

The four primary gustatory sensations are not aroused with equal intensity over all parts of the tongue. Apparently there is a functionally distinct type of receptor for each primary taste, and the distribution of each type is not uniform over the lingual mucosa. End organs sensitive to sweet and salty materials are most plentiful at the tip, those responsive to acid are distributed mainly along the margins, whereas those aroused by bitter substances are towards the base of the tongue and in the region of the epiglottis. These facts are recognized generally in practice, for one would no more think of sipping beer than he would of gulping a glass of wine, and a child prefers to lick rather than munch a stick of candy. The taste receptors adapt rather rapidly; for this reason food which we enjoy is moved over the surfaces of the tongue and mouth and brought into contact continually with fresh receptors. Some substances stimulate two types of taste bud. For example, *sodium salicylate, rhamnose* and *parabrom-benzoic-sulfinide,* a substance related to saccharine, give a sweet taste when applied to the tip of the tongue but when swallowed, and thus brought into contact with the vallate papillae, taste bitter. *Ortho-benzyl-benzoate,* on the other hand, gives a bitter followed by a sweet taste. *Magnesium* and *sodium*

ulation of olfactory receptors. Stimulation of the tongue by an electric current causes a metallic taste.

*sulfates* are salty-bitter, causing a salty taste at the tip of the tongue and a bitter taste at the base. When the papillae are explored individually with different sapid substances it is found that the filiform type are insensitive. Of the fungiform papillae, some respond to both sweet and salty compounds, others to acid and sweet and others again to bitter and acid. A few respond to all four types of stimulus. These results indicate the existence of functionally distinct types of taste receptors and that different types are present in the same fungiform papilla. Only taste buds responsive to bitter substances are present in the vallate papillae (fig. 79.3).

The sense of taste may be aroused by substances reaching the taste buds in the blood stream. Thus the intravenous injection of histamine causes a metallic taste, glucinum a sweet taste, and in jaundice a bitter taste may be experienced as a result of the high concentrations of biliary constituents in the blood.

*Theories of taste perception.* The results of experiments in which action potentials were recorded from single nerve fibers when sapid substances were applied to the tongue strongly support the conception of four specific types of taste receptor. Pfaffman identified three types of nerve fiber in the cat: (a) those which responded to acid, (b) those which responded to acid and salt, and (c) those which responded to acid and quinine. Although fibers responsive to sweetness were not found by this investigator, others using an improved method have obtained responses with sucrose. No difference was observed in the character of the impulses which might serve to distinguish the type of stimulus employed. Such a finding is in accord with what we know of other sense organs, namely, that the quality of sensation is determined by the central connections of the nerve fiber, i.e., upon the part of the brain where the impulses, set up in the receptor organ by an adequate stimulus, are delivered.

It is quite evident that stimulation of the different types of receptor in suitable proportions accompanied by the excitation of nongustatory nerves of the lingual and oral mucosa, as well as of the olfactory receptors, could account for the wide range of taste sensations that are experienced.

The mechanism through which the taste receptor is stimulated, and an impulse set up in the nerve fiber is unknown, but a theory has been proposed based upon the inhibition of enzyme systems in the taste cells by the sapid substance. Bourne, for example, found in various mammals

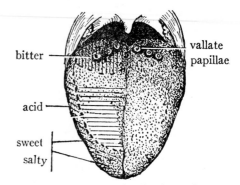

Fig. 79.3. Showing distribution of primary taste sensations on one side of the tongue.

a relatively high concentration of alkaline phosphatase in the epithelium overlying the taste buds, and El Baradi and Bourne have demonstrated that a 0.05 per cent concentration of vanillin strongly inhibits the action of this enzyme. Also a simple esterase is present in the taste buds in fairly high concentration; it is inhibited by quinine but not by salt or sugar.

Discrimination of differences in intensities of stimulation is relatively crude for taste and smell. In order for a change to be produced in either of these sensations the intensity of stimulation must alter by about 30 per cent, whereas the eye can detect a change in illumination of 1 per cent and the ear a change in sound intensity of 10 per cent.

TASTE SENSATIONS AND CHEMICAL CONSTITUTION. The *sweet* taste is associated predominantly with organic compounds, especially the *sugars* (e.g., sucrose, maltose, glucose, etc.) certain *polysaccharides*, *glycerol* and other *alcohols*, *aldehydes* and *ketones* of the aliphatic series, and *saccharine*, *dulcine* and *chloroform*. But certain inorganic substances, such as *lead acetate* (sugar of lead) and *alkalis* in high dilution, are also sweet to the taste.

Substances which arouse an acid or a salty taste are always electrolytes, but bitter or sweet substances may be either electrolytes or nonelectrolytes.

Several attempts have been made to relate the sweet taste to chemical constitution. Oertly and Myers, for example, from a study of a large number of sweet organic compounds have proposed the theory that every sweet molecule contains two particular types of radical or an atom upon which the sweet taste depends. One of these they call a *glucophore*, the other an *auxogluc*. A glucophore makes a given compound a potential tastestuff; if it is bound to an auxogluc a sweet compound is produced. Some six glucophores and nine auxoglucs have been identified; four of each are listed in the following table.

|                        | Glucophores                |     | Auxoglucs            |
|------------------------|----------------------------|-----|----------------------|
| (1)                    | —CO—CHOH—(H)               | (1) | H                    |
| (2)                    | $CO_2H \cdot CHNH_2$—       | (2) | $CH_3CH_2$           |
| (3)                    | $CH_2OH \cdot CHOH$—        | (3) | $CH_2OH$             |
| (4)                    | $CH_2ONO_2$—               | (4) | $CH_2OH$  CHOH       |

Thus the hexoses contain the glucophore (1) and the auxogluc (4), glycerol the glucophore (2) and the auxogluc (3), and amino-acetic acid the glucophore (2) and the auxogluc (1).

The *salty* taste is evoked primarily by inorganic compounds, notably the *chlorides* of *sodium, potassium, magnesium, ammonium* and *lithium,* by certain *sulfates, bromides* and *iodides* and by *sodium* and *potassium nitrates.* The saline taste of such compounds is attributed to the anions (Cl, Br, I, $SO_4$ and $NO_3$), a conclusion arrived at from a comparison of their tastes when in high dilution with that of an equally weak solution of sodium acetate. For example, a 0.04 molar solution of NaCl, of KCl or of LiCl has a slightly salty taste, whereas sodium acetate in equal or somewhat lower dilution is tasteless or at least is not salty. Similarly sodium bromide, iodide or nitrate loses its saline taste at a much higher dilution than does the acetate. Of the halogens the dilution at which the salty taste is just perceptible is highest for the chloride, next for the bromide and lowest for the iodide ion. The saline taste is not confined to inorganic compounds. Certain organic compounds, such as the *hydrochlorides of monomethylamine* and *diethylamine* also possess this property.

The *sour* taste is produced by acids or acid salts. It is generally agreed that the effective agent is the hydrogen ion. This statement would seem to be contradicted by the fact that solutions of certain organic acids, such as acetic, tartaric, citric, etc., are more acid to the taste than a solution of a mineral acid having a considerably greater hydrogen ion concentration. For example, the acid taste of a solution of acetic acid is about equal to one of HCl in a dilution one third as great. Yet as compared with the latter solution, the solution of HCl, since this acid is highly dissociated, is from four to five times as great. The greater effectiveness of acetic acid for a given H ion concentration is attributed to its greater power of penetrating the tissues, and therefore to its greater effectiveness in raising the hydrogen ion concentration within the taste buds. The *astringent taste* is attributed to acid in very high dilution, that is, to a greatly attenuated sensation of sourness.

The *bitter* taste, like sweetness, is associated chiefly with organic compounds, especially the *alkaloids* (*quinine, strychnine, morphine,* etc.) and certain *glucosides. Picric acid, dexiromannose* and *bile salts* are among the other bitter organic compounds. Of inorganic substances with a bitter taste are *magnesium, ammonium,* and *calcium salts.* The bitterness of these salts is due to the cation. A slight change in the chemical constitution of a substance often alters its taste from bitter to sweet. Saccharine, for example, is intensely sweet, but some of its derivatives are bitter; dulcin is some 500 times sweeter than cane sugar yet *phenylthiocarbamide,* in which one oxygen atom in the dulcin molecule is replaced by a sulfur atom, is bitter to most persons. Phenylthiocarbamide is peculiar in that to 3 persons out of 10 it is tasteless. The taste deficiency ("taste blindness") in respect to this substance is hereditary, being transmitted as a Mendelian recessive. Many organic compounds having a bitter taste contain $NO_2$ groups. If the molecule contains two such groups the compound is usually, atlthough not necessarily, bitter; if three are present it is invariably so.

INADEQUATE STIMULI. Of agents other than chemical which are capable of evoking a sensation of taste, by far the most effective is the electrical current. Electrical stimulation by means of the constant current, using a pair of electrodes placed upon the tongue causes, upon breaking the current, a metallic taste which persists for a little time. If one electrode is placed in contact with the surface of the tongue and the other upon some indifferent part of the body, a constant current during its passage causes an acid or alkaline taste, depending upon the direction of the current. If the lingual electrode is the anode an acid taste is experienced, whereas if the cathode is the stimulating electrode the taste is alkaline. Two factors, apparently, are concerned in the production of the acid or alkaline taste, namely, direct electrical stimulation of the taste cells and the production of H and OH ions at the anode and cathode, respectively, as a result of electrolysis of the buccal fluids. That a gustatory response can be produced by direct electrical stimulation is evident from the fact that it is more readily aroused by a rapidly alternating current, which has no appreciable electrolytic action, than by a direct current. Furthermore, when two persons are connected each to a pole of a battery and the circuit completed by bringing the tips of their tongues together, they experience different taste sensations, one acid the other alkaline. Now the two sets of taste buds must be exposed to the action of the same ions, the only condition of the experiment which is different in respect to the taste organs of the two persons is the direction of the current. The electrical taste evoked by a constant current is a rather complex sensation and cannot be described as purely acid or alkaline in quality. It frequently has a bitter metallic component which, as mentioned above, is usually the only taste caused by a single break shock. Very probably electrolytic products as well as the direct stimulating effect of the current are responsible for evoking the complex response. The gustatory sensation caused by a single shock is apparently due purely to direct electrical stimulation, since a current of such brief duration would not have any electrolytic action.

Thermal and mechanical types of stimulation may arouse faint sensations of taste but, as a rule, are ineffective.

*Thresholds of the primary taste sensations.* Minimum concentrations of the four main groups of sapid substances which will evoke the corresponding sensations are given in table 79.1.

AFTER TASTE AND TASTE CONTRASTS. The sense of taste exhibits phenomena analogous to positive after images and successive and simultaneous contrast, which have been described for vision (pp. 1341, 1372). It is a familiar experience that the tastes of certain substances (e.g., quinine) "cling" to the tongue. But it is unlikely that the persistent taste is a true after sensation comparable with an after image; it is most probably due simply to the continued action of the stimulating agent which, having entered the taste pore, is removed with difficulty by the saliva or even by rinsing the mouth with water. On the contrary, the metallic taste which outlasts a single break shock is in all likelihood an example of the persistence of sensation.

Several observations exemplifying *successive contrast* can be cited. A sweet taste is enhanced by a preceding salt or bitter taste and *vice versa.* In the same way sour and sweet tastes intensify one another. Even distilled water tastes sweet after rinsing the mouth with a weak solution of sulfuric acid, and lemon juice seems much more acid following a sweet stimulus. Other examples which should probably be placed under the heading of successive contrast are the sweet taste which is experienced upon smoking a cigar or cigarette after washing out the mouth with a weak solution of copper sulfate, and the bitter taste caused by smoking if the tongue or buccal mucosa has been treated with a solution of silver nitrate. *Simultaneous contrast* is also demonstrable. For example, if one border of the tongue is rubbed with salt the sensitivity of the opposite border to a sweet stimulus is increased. This contrast effect must, of course, be of cerebral origin. Salt and acid also show simultaneous contrast, but

## TABLE 79.1

| Sensation and substance | Concentraton |
|---|---|
| *Sweet* cane sugar........ | 1 part in 200 |
| dulcin................ | 1 part in 100,200 |
| α-antialdoxine | |
| perillaldehyde....... | 1 part in 600,000 |
| *Salty*, sodium chloride... | 1 part in 400 |
| *Acid*, hydrochloric...... | 1 part in 15,000 |
| *Bitter*, quinine........... | 1 part in 2,000,000 |
| strychnine............ | 1 part in 2,500,000 |

the phenomenon cannot be demonstrated for the bitter taste.

*The effects of drugs upon taste.* Certain drugs have a selective action upon the taste sensations, abolishing some while leaving others unaffected. For example, after the application of a decoction of the leaves of *Gymnema sylvestre* to the tongue, sweet and bitter substances cannot be tasted, but saline and acid tastes are retained, and are only slightly if at all depressed. *Stovaine* acts similarly to Gymnema but is less effective. *Cocaine* abolishes all taste as well as common sensibility, the several sensations disappearing in the following order; pain, bitter, sweet, saline, acid and touch.

### Smell, Olefaction

THE OLFACTORY EPITHELIUM. The mucous membrane lining the greater part of the nasal cavity has no true olfactory function. The olfactory receptors are confined to the nasal mucosa over a relatively small region—the *olfactory area.* This area comprises, on each side, the walls of a narrow niche (fig. 79.4) formed by the superior nasal concha, the upper part of the septum and the roof of the nose (cribriform plate of the ethmoid bone). The olfactory epithelium differs both in its gross appearance and histologically from the rest of the nasal mucosa. It is yellowish or brownish yellow in color; its total area, i.e., on both sides of the nose, is about 500 square millimeters.[2]

[2] The *vomeronasal organ* (organ of Jacobson) is a short tubular structure which, although well developed in certain lower vertebrates, is rudimentary in primates. It can be identified in a vestigial form in infants but, although it may persist throughout life, it is commonly absent in the adult. When present it is situated in the lower anterior part of the nasal septum and opens into the cavity of the nose by a minute pore a short distance within the external nares. In the dog and cat it receives both olfactory and trigeminal fibers and contains epithelium similar to that of the olfactory area. The function of the vomeronasal organ is not known with certainty but its general structure and innervation suggest very strongly that it is a subsidiary olfactory sense organ.

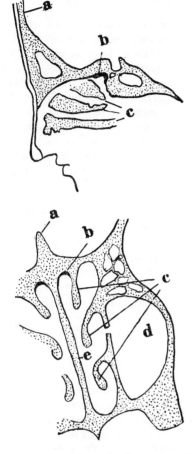

tory sense organs. Their two processes arise from opposite poles of the fusiform cell body, the dendrite from its superficial and the axon from its deep aspect. The dendrite is a long straight and relatively stout cylindrical process. It extends to the epithelial surface and projecting through one of the gaps between the supporting cells, expands slightly to form the *olfactory vesicle*. The latter contains from six to eight granules each of which gives rise to a hairlike protoplasmic process. The axon of the bipolar cell proceeds centrally from the deep aspect of the perikaryon and after traversing the lamina propria, joins with the central processes of neighboring cells to form some 20 nerve strands—the *fila olfactoria* or *olfactory nerves*. The latter ascend in grooves in the ethmoid bone and, entering the skull through perforations in the cribriform plate, end within the *olfactory lobe* (*bulb*) in a tuft of delicate filaments which synapse with dendrites of the *mitral cells* (fig. 79.5). The synapses form conspicuous spherical structures called the *olfactory glomeruli*. The axons of the mitral cells constitute the *olfactory tract*. Most of the fibers of the latter are continued into the *lateral olfactory stria* which conveys the impulses to the cortical center for smell (ch. 67). The olfactory nerves are nonmedullated, but possess a neurilemma. The lamina propria of the olfactory mucous membrane contains glands of the tubuloalveolar type—the *glands of Bowman*. They secrete a serous fluid which bathes the epithelial surface, thus providing a solvent for odorous materials.

Fig. 79.4. (*Upper*) sagittal section through skull to show position of olfactory area (*b*); (*a*) frontal bone; (*c*) nasal conchae. (*Lower*) coronal section through the nasal cavities; (*a*) crista gallae; (*b*) olfactory area; (*c*) nasal conchae; (*d*) maxillary sinus; (*e*) nasal septum.

The olfactory epithelium is composed of three types of cell (a) supporting cells, (b) basal cells and (c) bipolar nerve cells. The *supporting cells* are of a very high columnar type with large oval nuclei. Superficially, they form a continuous epithelial surface, except for small round gaps between them through which the olfactory vesicles with their tufts of hairs project (see below). Their cytoplasm contains granules of a golden brown pigment to which the color of the olfactory epithelium is due. Proximally, the supporting cell tapers into a long slender process which extends as far as the lamina propria (fig. 79.5). The *basal cells* are squat conical structures which extend for only a short distance above the lamina propria. They are believed to develop into supporting cells, thus serving as a reserve from which the latter when destroyed can be replaced.

The *bipolar nerve cells* are the essential olfac-

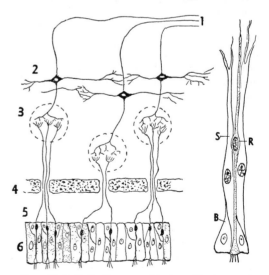

Fig. 79.5. *Left*, diagram showing olfactory epithelium and connections of olfactory nerve fibers. 1, olfactory tract; 2, mitral cells; 3, glomeruli; 4, cribriform plate; 5, olfactory nerves; 6, olfactory epithelium. *Right*, enlarged drawing of cells; B, basal cell; R, olfactory receptory cell; S, supporting cell.

The fluid is delivered by fine ducts which take a perpendicular course to the surface.

It will at once be recognized from the foregoing description that the end organs of smell differ from those of any other sense in that the cell body of the primary neuron is situated in the peripheral organ itself, and is stimulated directly without the intervention of a specialized receptor cell. No other sensory mechanism possesses both these features. Although the primary neuron of the visual pathway is situated in the retina, the stimulus is received by the rods and cones; pain sensations are subserved by bare nerve endings, the cell bodies of the pain fibers are located in the posterior root ganglia. It is also important to remember that here as nowhere else the nervous system is in direct contact with the external environment. The terminations of the dendrites of the olfactory cells, namely, the olfactory hairs, are covered only by a layer of fluid. Furthermore, the sheaths of the olfactory nerves are continuous with the subarachnoid space. Experimental work indicates that the olfactory nerves constitute one pathway through which the virus of anterior poliomyelitis may reach the central nervous system. Schultz and Gebhardt have shown, for example, that monkeys are protected against the intranasal injection of poliomyelitis virus by a previous section of the olfactory nerves. Intranasal sprays, consisting of solutions of zinc sulfate and other substances have been employed in monkeys with the purpose of blocking these channels. The encouragement derived from the success of these experiments in protecting animals from the disease has led to the trial of similar measures in poliomyelitis epidemics, but unfortunately they do not appear to have any value in reducing the number of cases. It is very difficult, especially in children, to bring the solution into contact with the olfactory epithelium, and this is probably the reason that reliance cannot be placed upon intranasal spraying as a preventive. The recent experiments of C. G. Smith are enlightening. The olfactory areas of rats were treated with a 1 per cent solution of zinc sulfate and examined histologically at periods of from 2 days to 2 months thereafter. In animals so treated, destructive changes amounting even to sloughing of the entire olfactory epithelium were found, and in all cases the bipolar cells showed widespread degeneration. Regeneration of non-sensory cells (supporting and basal) subsequently occurred, but, of course, the nerve cells were not restored. It would appear from these experiments that zinc sulfate solution, if it is to be effective in protecting against the virus of poliomyelitis, must entail permanent loss of the sense of smell.

## THE PHYSIOLOGY OF THE SENSE OF SMELL

OLFACTORY SENSATIONS. Smell is very closely allied to taste and has been aptly described as "taste at a distance." In many animals the sense of smell is almost incredibly acute, a relatively large part of the brain being given over to it. In the life of such macrosmatic animals the olfactory sense is of paramount importance, warning the animal of the approach of its enemies, guiding it in the quest for food and motivating the sex reflexes. Certain species of moth (e.g., great peacock and banded monk) are credited with a degree of olfactory acuity which seems almost mythical to microsmatic man, the female being able, it is claimed, to attract the male by the odor of its secretions from a distance of a mile or more. The olfactory organs of moths and most other insects are located in the antennae. Even man, in whom smell is a comparatively rudimentary sense, can detect certain substances (e.g., mercaptan and artificial musk) in a dilution of 1 part in several billion parts of air; smell is therefore much more acute than the sense of taste.

The adequate stimulus for the olfactory receptors, as for those of taste, is chemical.[3] An odorous material continuously emits particles of molecular size which reach the olfactory area through the air. Substances which pass readily into the gaseous state, such as turpentine, gasoline, the essential oils, etc., have strong odors, whereas non-volatile materials, e.g., the heavy metals, are nearly or quite inodorous. Arsenic, which ordinarily is odorless gives off a characteristic smell, however, when heated to a temperature at which it volatilizes, and Elsberg, Brewer and Levy found that the olfactory coefficients (p. 1467) of a number of odorous liquids vary directly with their boiling points. The niche at the roof of the nose which is lined by the olfactory epithelium, constitutes a blind pocket, from which the main air currents caused by the ordinary respiratory movements are excluded. Experiments upon the human cadaver have shown that the respired air does not come into direct contact with the olfactory area. A head was bisected in the median plane and the nasal septum replaced by glass. When smoke was forced back and forth through the nose by means of bellows, neither during the artificial inspiratory nor expiratory movement was the current ob-

---

[3] An electric current acts as an inadequate stimulus. When the nose is filled with normal saline and a constant current passed through the solution, an odor which is difficult to describe is experienced upon opening or closing the current.

served to enter the olfactory region. The air flow takes a curved course, the highest point being about the middle of the nose and below the superior concha. The stream reaches a lower level during expiration than in inspiration. In order to excite the olfactory cells the odorous particles must, therefore, be carried upward from the respiratory passages either by diffusion or by eddy currents. In the aforementioned experiment eddy currents were observed both during the inspiratory and expiratory movements. In the living subject it is probable that the ascending currents are more pronounced during inspiration; at this time air movements caused by convection are likely to occur, due to the mixing of the cooler ingoing stream with the warmer air within the nose. But, however produced, whether by convection or simply as a result of the mechanical mixing of the inspired air with that within the nasal passages, eddy currents constitute the main factor in the stimulation of the olfactory endings, and a sharp inspiration is the most effective means by which such currents are set up. When, for example, we wish to smell some particular scent more acutely we automatically make a sharp inspiration or "sniff."[4] Diffusion is a relatively slow process and is probably of minor importance in bringing the odorous material to the olfactory endings. Even though the nose is filled with odor laden air we cannot smell while the breath is held. It is during expiration that odorous materials liberated from the food as it is masticated and swallowed enter the nose through the posterior nares and ascend to the olfactory area.

It will be recalled that the olfactory hairs are immersed in a layer of fluid secreted by Bowman's glands. The odorous particles must therefore enter into solution before they can come into contact with and stimulate the sense organs. This fact emphasizes again the similarity between the senses of taste and smell. It is probable that odorous materials before they can act as stimuli must also be dissolved in the substance of the olfactory hairs themselves. These structures, since they are stained best by osmic acid, are believed to be composed largely of lipoid material. One would expect, therefore, that odorous substances must be soluble in oil as well as in water, and that those which are most freely soluble in both media would be the most potent in arousing an olfactory sensa-

tion. This supposition is borne out to some extent by experiment. Ethyl and methyl alcohols, for example, which are freely soluble in water but only slightly in oil, have weak odors as compared with butyl alcohol which dissolves very freely in oil and is also soluble in water. *Chlorobenzol, brombenzol, ether, citral* and many other substances with strong odors are soluble in both water and oil. It would appear that high solubility in oil is of more importance for olfactory stimulation than high water solubility; because, taking two substances, one with a high solubility in oil but sparingly soluble in water, and the other possessing solubilities of a converse kind, the former has the most powerful odor.

Although it is no longer questioned that the olfactory nerves subserve the sense of smell, some of the earlier investigators (e.g., Magendie) contended that olfaction was a function of the trigeminal nerve. The confusion arose from the fact that certain agents, e.g., *ammonia, nitric acid fumes, chlorine, pepper, menthol, peppermint* and many others, cause nasal sensations, usually described as pungent, acrid, irritating or cooling. These are not true olfactory sensations but are due to the stimulation of the trigeminal, which is the nerve mediating chemical sense and common sensibility in the respiratory part of the nasal mucosa. It is often very difficult, however, to dissociate these sensations from smell when the two types of ending are stimulated concurrently. A similar confusion arises, as already mentioned in the case of taste.

Strong reflex effects, e.g., sneezing, lachrymation, respiratory inhibition, vasomotor reactions, etc., result from irritation of the trigeminal endings, whereas reflexes initiated from the olfactory receptors are as a rule mild in character, and in man are concerned mainly with salivary and gastric secretion. In animals olfactory reflexes play their most important role in the reactions of sex and in self preservation—the search for food and protection from enemies. Olfaction is paramount among the senses in its power to awaken a train of associations in consciousness. Everyone is familiar with the strange reminiscent aura of long past events which is aroused by certain familiar scents.

THRESHOLD STIMULI. Among the most effective olfactory stimuli are *artificial musk, mercaptan, butyric acid, iodoform* and *oil of peppermint*. For example, methyl mercaptan (garlic odor) is perceptible to the average person in a concentration of 1/23,000,000,000 mg. per cu. cm. of air. Assum-

---

[4] The mechanism of the "sniff" appears to be a compressing together of the septum and the outer wall of the nose at the front of the respiratory passages so as to divert the inspired air to the olfactory area (Ogle).

ing that 50 cc. of air is required for arousing an olfactory sensation, this would mean that 1/460,000,000 mg. of the substance is an effective stimulus. The sense of smell is therefore many thousand times (about 25,000 times in the case of ethyl alcohol) more acute than the sense of taste. The minimum perceptible concentrations of various odorous substances are given in table 79.2.

SENSORY ADAPTATION. The olfactory receptors adapt fairly rapidly. It is a common experience that a disagreeable odor which when first smelled is almost overpowering soon becomes imperceptible. But although lost for one particular odor the sense of smell is retained for others; the phenomenon therefore is not due to fatigue of the olfactory mechanism (although it is often referred to as such), but is an example of sensory adaptation (p. 1147). The rate of adaptation varies for different odors. The receptors becomes insensitive to oil of orange or to oil of lemon after an exposure of from 2.5 to 11 minutes (average 3 minutes), whereas cumarin (0.2 per cent aqueous solution) cannot be smelled longer than from 1.75 to 2.3 minutes, and adaptation for the odor of benzoin is more rapid than for that of rubber. Olfactory adaptation commences to develop from the moment that the odor is first smelled, the threshold rising gradually until complete insensitivity to that particular odor is reached. Even a previous period of exposure to a given odor raises the minimum concentration at which it is perceived for a considerable length of time afterwards. Elsberg found, for example, that the olfactory coefficients (p. 1467) for peppermint, camphor and sassafras were increased to double their normal values if the subject had previously been smelling these substances; and the sensitivity of a person who had been for a time in the operating theater to the odor of ether was below normal several hours later.

CHEMICAL CONSTITUTION IN RELATION TO OLFACTORY STIMULATION. Generally speaking, the olfactory potency of chemical compounds belonging to an homologous series increases progressively from the lowest members of the series to a maximum and then undergoes a gradual reduction in the upper members. The odors of the monatomic alcohols, for example, increase in strength from methyl through ethyl, propyl and butyl to amyl; the relative potencies of methyl and amyl alcohols are as 1 to 10,000. Also, compounds which as a group resemble one another in their chemical and physical properties tend to have odors possessing certain common characteristics. For example, the elements sulfur, selenium and tellurium, which belong to the sixth group in Mendeljeff's periodic table, when combined with hydrogen, methyl or ethyl, etc., have

## TABLE 79.2

| Substance | Mg. per liter of Air |
|---|---|
| Ethyl ether.................. | 5.83 |
| Chloroform.................. | 3.30 |
| Pyridine..................... | 0.032 |
| Oil of peppermint............ | 0.024 |
| Iodoform.................... | 0.018 |
| Butyric acid................. | 0.009 |
| Propyl mercaptan............ | 0.006 |
| Artificial musk.............. | 0.00004 |

(From Allison and Katz.)

strong disagreeable smells. Similarly members of the seventh group, chlorine, bromine and iodine have kindred odors; the odors of chloroform and iodoform, compounds of the first and third elements respectively, are linked together by that of bromoform in which the fragrance of chloroform and the unpleasant odor of iodoform can be detected. Of chemically allied organic substances, ethyl, propyl and butyl acetates have an acetic odor, whereas amyl acetate has not; nevertheless the smell of the lowest of the series is linked with that of the highest through the two intermediate compounds.

Thus—

Ethyl acetate, acetic odor

Propyl acetate, acetic odor with slight pineapple flavor

Butyl acetate, slight acetic odor with pineapple flavor

Amyl acetate, no acetic odor, strong pineapple flavor

Though the foregoing are interesting examples of chemico-olfactory correlation, it is not possible to make anything more than broad generalizations in respect to chemical structure and smell, for compounds which closely resemble one another chemically may have quite different odors and others which show little resemblance in their chemical or physical properties (e.g., hydrocyanic acid and nitrobenzine, garlic and certain arsenical compounds, and artificial and natural musk) may smell very much alike. Many nitrile compounds have an odor resembling bitter almonds or hydrocyanic acid, whereas certain compounds of phosphorus and bismuth, as well as of arsenic, have a garlicky smell. An attempt has been made in the case of aromatic compounds to relate odor to a particular radical on the benzene ring. Hydroxyl, aldehyde, ketone, ester, nitro and nitril grouping—the so-called *osmophoric groups*—have been suggested as determing the character of the odor; it is believed, however, that the latter is dependent not so much upon which particular radical is present as upon the position which any one of them occupies in the benzene ring and the general architecture of the molecule.

A physical property common to many odors is their strong absorption of infrared rays. The significance of this fact, first remarked upon by Faraday, is unknown.

OLFACTOMETRY. The most widely known method of investigating the sense of smell is that of Zwaardemaker. His olfactometer consists of two glass tubes sliding one within the other, as shown in figure 79.6. The inner tube (a) is graduated in sections 0.7 cm. long. The inner surface of the outer tube carries a faintly odorous substance. The curved end (c) of the inner tube is introduced into a nostril, the opposite one being closed; the subject breathes quietly. The outer tube is gradually withdrawn, thus exposing a greater area of its inner surface to the air current and thereby increasing the concentration of the odorous particles in the inspired air. The highest figure visible on the inner graduated tube when the odor is just perceived indicates the subject's threshold for smell in units termed *olfacties*. This method gives at the best only approximate results, chiefly because the volume of inspired air drawn through the tubing varies considerably from subject to subject and in the same person at different times or even during a single period of observation. In the *blast method* of Elsberg and Levy this factor is controlled. Thirty cubic centimeters of an odorous liquid (e.g., benzene citral, oil of orange, oil of turpentine, butyric acid, etc.)

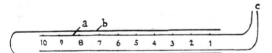

FIG. 79.6. Diagram of Zwaardemaker's olfactometer. See text.

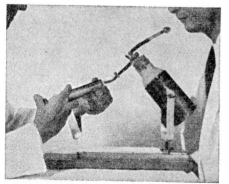

FIG. 79.7. Illustrating the blast method of olfactometry. (After Elsberg and Levy.)

are placed in the bottle shown in figure 79.7. The right hand tube is connected to a double nosepiece which fits into the nostrils. By means of a syringe connected to the other tube a measured volume of air is forced from the bottle in one blast at a constant pressure while the subject holds his breath. An equivalent volume of odor-laden air is thus forced into the nose. The volume of the injections is gradually increased in successive blasts until the odor is just perceived and can be named. The smallest volume necessary for identification is called the *minimum identifiable odor* (MIO) or the *olfactory coefficient*.

This method has been employed by Elsberg as an aid in the localization of tumors in the anterior part of the skull. In this situation a tumor (e.g., of the frontal lobe) is likely, through direct pressure, to involve the olfactory lobe or tract of one or of both sides; or the olfactory nerves may be torn in fractures through the cribiform plate. Unilateral involvement of the olfactory nerves, lobe or tract raises the MIO or completely abolishes the sense of smell on the affected side. A tumor involving both olfactory lobes or tracts will result in lowered acuity of smell or complete anosmia on both sides. Elsberg states that tests for olfactory "fatigue" give valuable localizing aid; the "fatigue" phenomenon is prolonged beyond the normal limits by tumors within the substance of the temporal lobe, but not by those situated extracerebrally (e.g., beneath the frontal lobe). In cases of a generalized increase of intracranial pressure due to other causes the MIO is often lowered.

CLASSIFICATION OF ODORS. The division of odors into categories has proved an extremely difficult problem. There are no basic qualities of olfaction comparable to sweet, salty, sour and bitter tastes. The number of different and distinct smells is legion, and no comprehensive classification upon the basis of chemical constitution or physical properties can be even attempted. The earliest classification of odors was made by the Swedish botanist Linnaeus (1750). The following one proposed by Zwaardemaker, which is little more than an elaboration of that proposed by Linnaeus, consists of nine categories. It has a purely subjective basis and is therefore of little scientific value.

1. *Ethereal odors;* e.g., of fruits, beeswax, ethers.
2. *Aromatic or resinous odors;* e.g., of camphor, bitter almonds, cloves, lavender.
3. *Fragrant or balsamic odors;* e.g., of flowers, extracted or artificial perfumes.

4. *Ambrosial odors;* e.g., of musk, ambergris.
5. *Garlic odors;* e.g., of garlic, onions and of sulfur and selenium compounds.
6. *Burning odors;* e.g., of burning feathers, tobacco, roasted coffee and meats.
7. *Goat odors;* e.g., caproic acid, sweat and ripe cheese.
8. *Repulsive odors;* e.g., of hyoscyamus and several of the family of the deadly nightshade, bedbug.
9. *Nauseating odors;* e.g., of excrement, decaying meat and vegetable matter.

ACTION POTENTIALS FROM THE OLFACTORY PATHWAYS. Gerard and Young have recorded the action currents from the olfactory bulb of the frog. A spontaneous rhythmical discharge occurs in in this part of the isolated brain at the rate of about 4 per second. The discharge is taken as representing true automatic activity of the nerve cells of the bulb itself, for the possibility that it was due to the irritation of traumatized structures seems to have been excluded.

In certain fishes (catfish, carp and tench) the olfactory bulb is connected with the forebrain by a nerve strand (the *olfactory stalk*) which measures about 2 cm. long and is composed of from 500 to 1000 medullated fibers. Adrian and Ludwig studied the action potentials in the olfactory stalk of the catfish during stimulation of the olfactory end organs. The latter are contained in a small sac which opens through a nipple upon the surface of the skin above the mouth. Potential changes of small amplitude pass up the stalk as long as the preparation survives, although nothing but distilled water has been introduced into the sac. This *resting discharge* is of very low frequency. When the sac was irrigated with fluid containing containing small fragments of some odorous material, e.g., putrefying earthworms, a burst of impulses occurred at high frequency after a latent period of from 0.5 to 5 seconds or longer. It was found that the irrigation was more powerfully stimulating if the fluid contained small fragments of the material than if it had been filtered.

THE QUESTION OF OLFACTORY DISCRIMINATION. The great multitude of distinguishable odors brings up a question for which no answer is forthcoming, namely, "What is the mechanism underlying olfactory differentiation?" "How do we detect the difference between two scents such as those of the violet and the rose?" Or, to make the question still more difficult, "How does a dog recognize the smell of his master among the smells of other persons?" Were there a limited number of basic odors, as there are of fundamental tastes, the problem would not be difficult. A theory of color vision can be conceived (ch. 62) based upon the existence of receptors responsive to different wave lengths, and which discharge impulses along specific nerve paths (pp. 1148, 1149). The resonance-volley theory explains the pitch-discriminating function of the ear (p. 1439), and four functionally distinct types of taste bud, each with its specific nerve fiber, for the perception of the fundamental sensations of taste. But it is not conceivably possible that every one of the immense number of different odors is subserved by a specific type of end organ with its own nerve fiber. Furthermore, new and distinct odors are being created in industry every day.

Theories of the mechanism through which an odorous substance sets up an impulse in an olfactory nerve fiber are of necessity almost wholly speculative. The following catalytic theory of olfaction has been proposed by Kistiakowsky similar to that already described for gustation. He postulates a series of catalytic reactions which may be represented as, $A \to A' \to A''$; $B \to B' \to B''$; $C \to C' \to C''$, etc. Each step is effected by a specific enzyme, and each compound formed $A'$, $B'$, $C'$, etc., stimulates an olfactory receptor and gives rise to a corresponding distinct "basic" odor. Presumably, the odoriferous substance itself inhibits one or more of the enzyme systems. This would lead to differences in the combination of the stimulating compounds, and even a slight change in their relative concentrations could arouse an olfactory sensation. The difficulty here is in defining a basic odor and having to assume an unreasonable number of functionally different receptor cells, for the nerve impulses themselves possess no differentiating characteristics which could serve the brain as cues. But if in addition, areas with different physical or chemical properties were distributed over the olfactory membrane which permitted a selective penetration or adsorption of the odorous substance to or upon the receptors, some sort of pattern of excitation might be established which could be interpreted by the cerebral cortex as a smell of a certain kind; or the different areas might possess specific affinities for certain chemical groups. A mechanism of this nature would not require an immense number of different types of receptor.

From what we know of other senses we can presume that the *intensity* of the olfactory sensation is related to the frequency of the impulses discharged to the olfactory center. This is borne out by the experiments of Adrian and Ludwig just described.

THE EFFECT OF ONE ODOR UPON THE PERCEPTION

OF ANOTHER. Strong odors tend to mask weaker ones. If two scents are of about equal strength a blend of the two is smelled or both are identified; but if one is considerably stronger than the other it alone, as a rule, is smelled. On the other hand, certain pairs of odors in appropriate relative concentrations are antagonistic, and when the two are sniffed together both are diminished. Iodoform, for example, is antagonized by balsam of Peru, musk by bitter almonds and ammonia by acetic acid. Other pairs of neutralizing odors are cedarwood and rubber, beeswax and balsam of Tolu, benzoin and rubber, and camphor and eau de Cologne. Although the neutralizing effect may in some cases be simply chemical or physical in nature, in others there seems to be a true physiological antagonism, for the phenomenon is observed when mixing is avoided by leading the two odors directly one to each nostril.

ANOMALIES OF OLFACTION. Loss of the sense of smell or *anosmia* is not infrequent as a temporary condition, e.g., as a result of inflammation of the nasal mucosa or of the local application of cocaine or adrenaline. Complete and permanent anosmia is rare in otherwise normal persons and is usually due to absence of the olfactory bulb or olfactory nerves, but bilateral or unilateral olfactory deficiencies are frequently associated with lesions in the region of the olfactory lobes. Albinos are said to be anosmic, which suggests that the pigment in the supporting cells of the olfactory epithelium, which possibly serves an essential function, is lacking. Inability to smell certain odors is not uncommon. Some persons, for example, cannot smell hydrocyanic acid; the odor of mignonette, benzoin, methyl alcohol or vanillin cannot be smelled by others. Even such a strong, disagreeable smell as that of a rotten egg or of feces may not be sensed. Partial anosmia for all scents may result from excessive smoking. *Hyperosmia* is not unusual in hysteria, in certain cerebral diseases, in raised intracranial pressure and during the initial stage of the action of cocaine. Olfactory hallucinations may occur in lesions of the temporal lobe (ch. 67). In cerebral tumors, especially of the frontal or temporal lobes, an odorous material introduced into one nostril may be referred to the other. This phenomenon, known as *olfactory alloesthesia*, is analogous to allocheiria mentioned on page 1140.

### Common Chemical Sense

The general body surface of fish and many other aquatic forms is sensitive to various types of chemical irritant, as are also the moist skins of amphibians. The elicitation of reflex responses from the foot of a pithed frog stimulated by a weak solution of sulfuric acid is a well known laboratory exercise. In man the common chemical sense is restricted to surfaces which are kept constantly moist, namely, the buccal and nasal mucous membranes, the conjunctivae and the mucosa of the anal canal. The common chemical sense of the first three is subserved by the trigeminal nerve, that of the anal canal by the pudendal nerve. It has already been pointed out that the sense organs subserving this sense in the mouth and nose are distinct from the gustatory and olfactory endings, and apparently they are not identical with those subserving pain, for dissociation of chemical and pain sensations can be effected by cocaine, the latter being abolished before the former. Thus, after the application of a 1 per cent solution of the anesthetic to the foot of the frog no response is given to pinching, pricking or scratching, whereas reactions to chemical agents can for a time be elicited.

### REFERENCES

ADRIAN, E. D. AND LUDWIG, C. J. Physiol., 1938, **94**, 441.

ALLISON, V. C. AND KATZ, S. H. J. Indust. Chem., 1919, **11**, 336.

EL BARADI, A. F. AND BOURNE, G. Science, 1951, **113**, 660.

BOURNE, G. Nature, 1948, **161**, 445.

CUSHING, H. Bull. Johns Hopkins Hosp., 1903, **14**, 71.

ELSBERG, C. A. AND LEVY, I. Bull. Neurol. Inst. New York, 1935, **4**, 5.

ELSBERG, C. A., BREWER, E. D. AND LEVY, I. Bull. Neurol. Inst. New York, 1935, **4**, 26.

GERARD, R. W. AND YOUNG, J. Z. Proc. Roy. Soc., London, ser. B, 1937, **122**, 343.

KISTIAKOWSKI, G. B. Science, 1950, **112**, 154.

OERTLY, E. AND MYERS, R. G. J. Am. Chem. Soc., 1919, **41**, 855.

OLMSTED, J. M. D. Am. J. Physiol., 1918, **46**, 443; J. Comp. Neurol., 1920, **31**, 465.

PFAFFMANN, C. J. Cell. & Comp. Physiol., 1941, **17**, 243.

READ, E. A. Am. J. Anat., 1908, **8**, 17.

SMITH, C. G. Canad. M. A. J., 1938, **39**, 138.

*Monographs and Reviews*

CROZIER, W. J. Murchison's handbook of general experimental psychology, p. 987. Clark University Press, 1934.

PARKER, G. H. Smell, taste and allied senses in the vertebrates. Monograph Experimental Biology, Lippincott, Philadelphia, 1922.

# INDEX

## A

ABDOMEN, nerve plexuses of, 1299

ABDOMINAL
cavity, lymphatic system of, 34
pain, referred, parietal origin of, Morley's theory on, 731
plexus, 1298
reflex, general discussion on, 1212

ABERRATION(S)
visual,
spherical, 1393, 1394
types of, 1393

ABSCESS, development of, 90

ABSORPTION BANDS, of hemoglobin and its derivatives, 57

ABSORPTION SPECTRA, of hemoglobin derivatives, 60

ACAPNIA, 509

ACCELERANSTUFFE, 1303

ACCELERATION
angular, 395
centripetal, 395
circulatory responses to, 394
horizontal linear, 395
negative,
definition of, 395
effects of, 395
positive,
definition of, 395
effects of, prevention of, 396
measurement of, 396
tolerances to, 397

ACCELERATOR REFLEXES, **1174**

ACCESSORY NERVE
spinal,
bulbar root of, 1202
central connections of, 1202
spinal root, 1202

ACCLIMATIZATION
to altitude, 510
changes associated with, 511

ACCOMMODATION OF THE EYE, **1386**
amplitude of, 1391
at different ages, 1391
anatomical structures involved in, 1386
convergence during, 1390
definition of, 1388
far point in, 1391
for near vision, 1389
means of accomplishing, 1388
mechanism of, 1388
illustration of, 1390
pupillary diameter during, 1390
pupillary reaction in, 1409

ACCOMMODATION OF THE EYE
—*cont.*
range of, 1391
visual axes during, 1390

ACCOUCHER'S HAND, 1049

ACETIC ACID, ionization of, 124

ACETOACETATE
production of, 858
utilization of, by liver tissue, 853

ACETOACETIC ACID
chemical formation of, 853
production of, 853

ACETYL-BETA-METHACHOLINE,
effects of, on cholinoceptive effectors, 1308

ACETYLATION,
coenzyme of,
general discussion on, 854
role of, in fatty acid metabolism, 854

ACETYLCHOLINE,
distribution of, in central nervous system, 1311
effects of,
on cardiac output, 307
on coronary circulation, 329
identification of, 1305
in brain, functional activity and, 1311
in cerebrospinal fluid, 1311
liberation of,
during discharge of adrenaline, 1306
from parasympathetic endings in iris, 1305
from sympathetic preganglionic fibers, 1306
role of,
as intermediary of parasympathetic effects to alimentary tract and bladder, 1305
as mediator of autonomic ganglia, 1303
as transmitter of effects to sweat glands, 1306
as transmitter of nerve impulses, 1310
experimental work on, 1305
in stimulation of the chorda tympani nerve to salivary glands, 1305
in synaptic transmission in central nervous system, 1311
synthesis of, by choline acetylase, 1303

ACETYLCHOLINESTERASE, 1303

ACETYL-COENZYME A, 854
formation and utilization of, by liver cells, 858
general discussion on, 926

ACHALASIA, 730

ACHLORHYDRIA, 615

ACHLORHYDRIA—*cont.*
due to adrenalectomy, 1034
incidence of, relation of age to, 616

ACHONDROPLASIA, general discussion on, 1068

ACHROMATIC INTERVAL, 1347

ACHYLIA GASTRICA, 616

ACID(S)
-base balance,
disturbance of, due to dehydration, 25
renal regulation of, 556
combined, definition of, 613
effects of,
on gastric emptying time, 699
on gastric secretion, 618
excretion of, regulation of, 557
fatty. *See* Fatty acids
free,
definition of, 613
determination of, 614
ionization of, 124
potential, sources of, in diet, 556
titratable, excretion of, 559
total, definition of, 613
un-ionization of, determination of amount of, 556
weak, excretion of, effects of pH on, 565

ACIDITY
gastric,
iso-secretory curves of, 614
normal curves of, 614

ACIDOSIS
definition of, 131
dyspnea due to, 505
in renal disturbance, 575
metabolic, 133
renal tubular, 575, 576
respiratory, 133

ACINOUS CELLS, of pancreatic tissue, 629

ACOUSTIC
analyzer, location of, 1269
resistance, specific, 1430
trauma, deafness due to, 1455

ACROCYANOSIS
general discussion on, 357

ACROMEGALY, 990
effects of, on carbohydrate metabolism, 829
general discussion on, 989
skull in, compared to that of normal person, 991

ACTH. *See* Corticotrophin

ADAPTATION
of receptors,
physiological importance of, 1148
to pressure, 1148
to stimulation, 1147

ADDISON'S
anemia. *See* Anemia, pernicious
disease,
  course of, 1043
  disturbances of renal function in, 577
  general discussion on, 1042
  skin pigmentation in, 1042
ADENASE, 800
ADENINE, 800
  chemical structure of, 799, 805
  conversion of, to uric acid, 801
ADENOHYPOPHYSIS, 957
  anatomical structure of, 957
  contact with neural lobes, 959
  functional activity of, effects of hypophysial blood supply on, 979
  hormones secreted by, 960
  nerve supply of, 959
  physiology of, **960**
  secretion of, control of, 978
ADENOMA, toxic, general discussion on, 1004
ADENOSINE TRIPHOSPHATE
  breakdown of, relationship of, to muscular contraction, 877
  chemical structure of, 876
  resynthesis of, in muscle, 877
ADENOSINES, 800
ADENYLIC ACID, 799
  chemical structure of, 802
  system, creatine phosphate and, 874
ADIADOCHOKINESIS
  general discussion on, 1287
  in cerebellar disorders, 1287
ADIPOKININ, 848
ADIPOSE TISSUE, metabolism of, **858**
ADRENAL CORTEX, 1022
  additional spheres of influence of, 1037
  ascorbic acid content of, factors effecting, 1038
  blood supply of, 1023
  diseases of, 1042
  effects of sex on, 1022
  endocrine activity of, role of hypothalamus in, 955
  function of, clinical tests of, 1045
  general discussion on, 1033
  hormone secretion by, 951
    regulation of, 1040
  nerve supply of, 1023
  role of,
    in carbohydrate metabolism, 828
     demonstration of, 829
    in renal hypertension, 387
  steroids of, listing of, 1038
  tumors of, 1043
    effects of, on sex characteristics, 1043
  zonation of, 1022
ADRENAL CORTICAL EXTRACT
  physiological actions of, 1035
  production of glucosuria by, 829

ADRENAL CORTICAL HORMONE
effects of,
  on lymphocytes, 91
  on lymphoid tissue, 91
ADRENAL GLAND(S), **1022**
  activity of, effects of corticotrophin on, 968
  anatomical structure of, 1022
  androgens isolated from, 1104
  atrophy of, following hypophysectomy, 967
  development of, 1022
  effects of age on size of, 1022
  medulla of. *See* Adrenal medulla
  role of, in carbohydrate metabolism, 828
  size of, effects of age on, 1022
  tumor of, virilism due to, 1044
ADRENAL HORMONES
  and reproduction, 1037
  role of, in salt and water metabolism, 1034
ADRENAL INSUFFICIENCY, disturbances of renal function in, 577
ADRENAL MEDULLA, **1023**
  activity of,
    effects of emotional excitement on, 1030
    nervous control of, 1030
  anatomical structure of, 1022
  essential to life?, 1031
  function of,
    emergency theory of, 1031
    tonus theory, 1032
  hormones secreted by, 952
  hyperplasia of, effects of, 1032
  pheochromocytoma of, effects of, 1032
  response of, to circulatory stress, 1030
  role of,
    in control of circulation, **257**
    in the body, 1031
  secretions of,
    rate of, 1030
    regulation of, 1030
  studies on, historical background of, 1023
ADRENAL STEROIDS. *See* Steroids, adrenal
ADRENALECTOMY
  bilateral, effects of, 1033
  effects of,
    in hypertension, 387
    on carbohydrate metabolism, causes of, 829
    on thirst, 25
ADRENALINE
  actions of, 1024
    effects of some substances on, 1028
  assay of, 1027
  chemical characteristics of, 1023
  chemical structure of, 1024
  chemical usage of, 1029
  discharge of, acetylcholine liberation during, 1306
  effects of,
    miscellaneous, 1027

ADRENALINE—*cont.*
effects of—*cont.*
  on blood concentration, 1034
  on blood flow, 1025
  on blood pressure, 1025
    of pregnant cat, 1028
  on carbohydrate metabolism, 1026
  on cardiac output, 307
  on circulation, 1034
  on coronary circulation, 329
  on general metabolism, 1027
  on heart, 1025
  on heat production, 1027
  on intestines of rabbit, 1026
  on melanophores of horned toad, 1027
  on metabolism, 1034
  on renal circulation, 374
  on respiration, 1025
  on skeletal muscle, 1026
  on smooth muscle, 1025
  vascular, 1024
  glycosuria produced by, 828
  inactivation of, 1024
  isolation of, 1023, 1306
  other names for, 1023
  role of, in carbohydrate metabolism, 828
  substances resembling, 1029
  synthesis of, 1023
ADRENERGIC
  blocking agents, 1028
  definition of, 1303
  fibers, distribution of, 1307
  mechanisms,
    formation of, 1306
    release of, 1306
    specific receptors for, 1307
  nerves,
    mediation of, 1306
    by levarterenol, 1307
ADRENIN. *See* Adrenaline
ADRENOCEPTIVE EFFECTORS, drugs acting at, 1309
ADRENOCHROME, formation of, 1306
ADRENOCORTICAL HORMONES, biochemistry of, 1037
ADRENOCORTICAL STEROIDS, role of, in sodium excretion, 554
ADRENOGENITAL SYNDROME, 1043
AEROEMBOLISM, in flyers, during rapid ascents, 513
AEROPHAGY, 691
AFFERENT LIMB, 1138
AFIBRINOGEMIA, 118
AFTER IMAGES,
  visual, 1372
    negative, 1372
    positive, 1372
AGGLUTINATION, nonspecific, causes of, 49
AGGLUTININ, definition of, 43 (footnote)
AGGLUTINOGENS,
  definition of, 43 (footnote)
  of erythrocytes, source of, 46

*Bold-face numbers indicate major discussion*

AGNOSIA,
  general discussion on, **1253**
  visual, following removal of
    temporal lobes, 1249
AGRANULOCYTES, 87
  classification of, 87
AGRANULOCYTOSIS, 96
AGRAPHIA, 1250, 1251, 1254
AIR
  fixed, 749
  hunger, in acidosis, 505
ALANINE
  chemical structure of, 774
  synthesis of, 778
ALBERS-SCHÖNBERG'S DISEASE.
    *See* Marble bone
ALBRIGHT'S SYNDROME, general
    discussion on, 1070
ALBUMIN(S)
  characteristics of, 771
  examples of, 771
  fraction,
    of blood serum, pathologi-
      cal variations in, 5
    of human serum, use of in
      transfusions, 50
  of blood, pathological varia-
    tions in, 5
  tagged, use of, in measure-
    ment of blood plasma
    volume, 18
ALBUMINOID(S), 1061
  characteristics of, 771
  examples of, 781
ALBUMINURIA. *See* Proteinuria
ALCOHOL
  action of, in fever, 897
  effects of, on gastric secre-
    tion, 618
ALDOSTERONE
  chemical structure of, 1039
  physiological actions of, 1036
    compared to those of des-
      oxycorticosterone, 1036
  secretion of, regulation of,
    1040
ALDOSTERONISM, primary, 1045
ALEXIA, 1251
ALIMENTARY CANAL
  movements of, **682**, 707
  effects of drugs on, 703
ALIMENTARY TRACT
  *See also* Viscera
  parasympathetic effects on,
    acetylcholine as inter-
      mediary of, 1305
  sensibility of,
    to chemicals, 733
    to cold, 733
    to heat, 733
    to touch, 733
    to various stimuli, **733**
  thermal sensibility of, 733
ALKALI(ES)
  antacid properties of, 617
  deficit,
    of blood,
      compensated, 133
      uncompensated, 133
  effects of, on gastric secre-
    tion, 617
  excess,
    of blood,
      compensated, 133
      uncompensated, 132

ALKALI(ES)—*cont.*
  excretion of, regulation of,
    557
  reserve, 556
    gain in, due to excretion of
      titratable acid, 559
    of blood, definition of, 130
    of body fluids, **130**
    role of excretion of am-
      monia in, 560
ALKALOSIS
  definition of, 131
  metabolic, 133
  role of, in production of
    tetany, 1052
  tetany associated with, 1050,
    1052
ALLANTOIC ACID, chemical
    structure of, 805
ALLANTOIN, 800
  chemical structure of, 805
  derivation of uric acid from,
    801
ALLERGIES, protein, 773
ALLOCHEIRIA, 1140
ALLOCORTEX, 1233
ALLOESTHESIA, olfactory, 1468
ALLOXAN DIABETES,
  causes of, 836
  general discussion on, 836
ALTITUDE
  acclimatization to, 510
    changes associated with,
      511
  arterial hypoxia at, 509
  effects of, 510
    on blood, 511
    on cardiac output, 512
    on chest development, 512
    on gases of gastrointes-
      tinal tract, 512
    on number of red blood
      cells, 12
    on respiration, **509**
ALUMINUM HYDROXIDE, effects
    of, on gastric secretion,
    618
ALVEOLAR AIR
  aqueous tension of, value of,
    451 (footnote)
  components of, 486
  general discussion on, 486
  samples of, methods of ob-
    taining, 486
ALVEOLAR-CAPILLARY DIFFU-
    SION, **486**
ALVEOLAR DUCTS, 468, 1094
ALVEOLAR SACS, 468
ALVEOLAR VENTS
  pulmonic, 476
    during respiration, 476
ALVEOLI, 1094
  isolated, absorption of air
    from, 520
  of parotid gland, 588
  of submaxillary gland, 588
  pulmonary, 468
AMACRINE CELLS, 1325
AMBOCEPTORS, 63
AMELOGNOSIA, 1226
AMENORRHEA, 1091
AMETROPIA, 1394
  *See also* Hypermetropia; My-
    opia
AMINO ACID(S), 769

AMINO ACID(S)—*cont.*
  *See also* Proteins
  absorption of, by small in-
    testine, 675
  aliphatic, 774
  anhydrides, 770
  aromatic, chemical structure
    of, 775
  carboxyl group of, activation
    of, 778
  chemical structure of, 769
    basic, 770
  classification of, 774
    according to their glyco-
      genic or ketogenic prop-
      erties, 776
  contained in some proteins,
    795
  deamination of, 774
    as test of liver function,
      653
  deficiencies of, effects of, 793
    utilization of protein in,
      795
  definition of, 769
  effects of, on nutritive value
    of proteins, 944
  fate of, after absorption, **774**
  heterocyclic, chemical struc-
    ture, of 775
  hydrolysis of, 770
  importance of,
    in growth, 793
    in maintenance of body,
      793
    in nutritional values of
      proteins, 793
  in transamination reactions,
    777
  in urine, 543
  intravenous injection of, ni-
    trogenous equilibrium
    maintained by, 773
  isoelectric points of, 775
  molecular weight of, 769
  of liver and soy beans, com-
    parison of, 793
  peptide linkage of, 770
  protein synthesis from, **778**
  rapid turnover of, causes of,
    779
  reabsorption of, 543
  requirements of,
    average minimal, 945
    for growth, opposed to
      those for maintenance,
      794
    for maintenance, opposed
      to those for growth, 794
    in adult man, 796
    investigations into, 795
    species differences in, 796
  synthesis of, **777**
  terminal, of peptide chains,
    770
  transamidation of, 777
  transamination of, 776
    in intestinal mucosa, 676
  transmethylation of, 777
AMINO-ACIDURIA, general dis-
    cussion on, 577
*p*-AMINOBENZOIC ACID, 929
  chemical structure of, 929
  chemistry of, 929
  general discussion on, 929

*Bold-face numbers indicate major discussion*

*Bold-face numbers indicate major discussion*

ANIONS—*cont.*
subject to tubular excretion, 555
ANISEIKONIA, 1416
ANISOCYTOSIS, 16
ANKLE
clonus of, 1164
jerk, 1163
ANNULO-SPIRAL NERVE END-INGS, 1153
ANNULUS, of ear, 1420
ANODAL CLOSING CORRECTION, 1122
ANODAL OPENING CONTRACTION, 1122
ANOMALOSCOPE, Nagel, 1357
ANOSMIA, 1469
ANOXEMIA, 508
oxygen therapy in, 527
ANOXIA. *See* Hypoxia
ANTIANEMIC FACTOR, 81
*See also* Vitamin B₁₂
chemical identification of, 81
gastric tissue and, 81
liver and, 81
liver extract and, 81
ANTIANEMIC PRINCIPLE
effect of, upon bone marrow, 83
production of, 82
extrinsic factor. *See* Vitamin B₁₂
ANTIBODIES
production of,
by blood serum proteins, 7
by spleen, 68
ANTICOAGULANTS, 114
anaphylactic shock, 115
avoidance of blood contact with foreign materials or wounded tissues, 114
azo dyes, 115
biological substances, 115
cold, 114
container with a smooth surface, 114
decalcification, 114
dicumarol, 115
heparin, 112, 115
hirudin, 115
neutral salts, 114
peptone solution, 115
snake venom, 115
sulphuric acid groups in, 113
ANTIDIURESIS, reabsorption of water in distal tubule in, 564
ANTIDIURETIC HORMONE
effects of, on urine concentration, 552
role of, in regulation of urine concentration, 548
ANTIDIURETIC PRINCIPLE, 982
ANTIGRAVITY MUSCLES, 1151, 1164
ANTIHEMOPHILIC GLOBULIN. *See* Antihemophilic factor
ANTIHORMONES, general discussion on, 979
ANTIMETABOLITES, 937
ANTIPERISTALSIS, in the esophagus, 691
ANTIPYRETIC DRUGS, action of, 897

ANTIRACHITIC PORTION OF SPECTRUM, 907
ANTIRENIN TITER, effects of renin on, in renal hypertensive dogs, 385
ANTITHROMBIN, 112
ANTITHYROID DRUGS, 1013
action of, 1013
clinical use of, 1014
ANTITRYPSINS, secretion of, 586
ANTIVITAMINS, 937
action of, first observation of, 937
examples of, 937
ANTRUM, coordination of, with sphincter and duodenum, 696
ANURIA
general discussion on, 573
in traumatic shock, 407
AORTA
arch of, innervation of, 260
arterial branches of, 155
blood volume in, 155
ascending, pressure in, tracing of, 285
blood pressure in, at subclavian artery junction, 285
blood vessels in, lumen of, 157
blood volume in, 155
central, arterial pressure pulses recorded from, 282
coarctation of, 443
arterial pressures in, intraradial and intrafemoral, 445
collateral circulation in, 444
effects of, on coronary circulation, 328
general discussion on, 443
heart sounds in, 443
hemodynamics of, 443
hypertension in, upper body, 444
treatment of, 444
distensibility of, active changes in, 156
pressure in,
drop between two points, 285
tracing of, 285
pressure-volume relationship in, general discussion on, 155
root of, pressure pulse at, 282
terminal, pressure in, tracing of, 285
thoracic, isolated segment of, pressure volume diagrams obtained from, 156
volume-pressure relationships of, influence of age on, 155
AORTIC ARCH, pressure in, tracing of, 285
AORTIC INSUFFICIENCY
murmur of, 425
valvular, pressure in left ventricle and femoral artery in, 425

AORTIC NERVE
fall in blood pressure after stimulation of, 259
role of, in control of circulation, 259
AORTIC STENOSIS. *See* Stenosis, aortic
AORTIC VALVE(S)
regurgitation by, 424
cardiac output in, 426
causes of, 424
heart sounds of, 424
hemodynamics of, 425
high pulse pressure in, 425
isometric period of left ventricle in, 425
treatment of, 426
stenosis of. *See* Stenosis, aortic
AORTICORENAL GANGLION, 1299
APF. *See* Vitamin B₁₂
APHASIA
auditory, 1251
Broca's, 1250
classification of, Head's, 1251
due to lesion of temporal lobe, 1248
general discussion on, 1249
motor, 1250
naming defects in, 1252
semantic defects in, 1252
severity of, tests for determination of, 1251
syntactical defects in, 1252
theories regarding, early, 1250
verbal defects in, 1252
visual, 1251
APNEUSES, 489
demonstration of, 489
effects of CO₂ tension of blood on, 489
APOCRINE CELLS, definition of, 585
APOCRINE SECRETION, 1099
APOFERRITIN, 73
APPETITE
and hunger, differentiation between, 734
definition of, 734
hunger contractions in, 694
increase of, in obesity, cause of, 867
inhibition of, by distention of stomach, 737
poor, use of insulin in, 827
to satiety, mechanisms taking part in, 738
APRAXIA, general discussion on, **1253**
APTYALISM, 597
AQUEOUS HUMOR
general discussion on, 1399
refractive properties of, 1379
ARACHIDONIC, dietary requirements of, 945
ARBOR VITAE, 1277
ARCHICEREBELLUM, 1276
ARCHIPALLIUM, 1233
ARCUATE FIBERS
dorsal external, 1279
ventral external, 1279
AREA STRIATA, 1234
AREAE GASTRICAE, 599

*Bold-face numbers indicate major discussion*

*Bold-face numbers indicate major discussion*

*Bold-face numbers indicate major discussion*

BLOOD—*cont.*
*carbon dioxide in—cont.*
deficit of,
compensated, 133
uncompensated, 132
excess of,
compensated, 133
uncompensated, 133
measurement of, 454
partial pressure of, 452
tension of,
effects of, on apneuses, 489
role in regulation of breathing, 488
transport of, role of hemoglobin in, 460
variations in, vascular effects of, 265
volume of, **453**
catecholamine levels of, changes in, during apnoeic oxygenation, 267
*cells,*
*See also* Corpuscles
band, 106
clumping of, effects of, on erythrocyte sedimentation rate, 66
constituents of, physiological, 3
development of, schools of thought on, 99
embryonic reticular, 101
entrance of, into blood stream, 105
littoral, 103
loss of, in hemorrhage, replacement of, 32
maturation of, 105
mesenchyme, undifferentiated, 101
number of, influence of spleen on, 68
origin of. *See* Hematopoesis *and specific types of cells*
osmotically active substances within, exchanges increasing, 130
primitive, 99
pyrrol, 101
reticular, definition of, 104
reticuloendothelial, 102
sinking of, in quiet blood, 64
stem, 99
structure of, influence of spleen on, 68
white. *See* Leukocytes
changes in,
causes of, intestinal obstruction, 713
in experimental pancreatic insufficiency, 634
in intestinal obstruction, 712
role of, in causing death in intestinal obstruction, 714
chemistry of,
changes in, in overdose of parathormone, 1053
in hyperparathyroidism, 1060

BLOOD—*cont.*
chloride, fall in, caused by vomiting, 713
cholesterol in, 8
circulation of,
role of, in regulation of body temperature, 886
time of, **225**
clot, formation of, general description of, **109**
*clotting of,* 109
*See also* Blood, coagulation of
effects of diet on, 946
effects of hemorrhage on, 31
role of blood serum proteins in, 7
role of fibrinogen by, 7
*coagulation of,* **109**
bleeding time, determination of, 116
clot retraction time, determination of, 116
conversion of fibrinogen to fibrin in, 112
conversion of prothrombin to thrombin in, 110
degree of, platelet count and, 109
diagram of, 111
effect of operation on, 121
factors involved in, 110
primary, 110
hastening, substances used in, 115
hemorrhagic diseases, 117
intravascular, 119
*See also* Thrombosis
mechanism of, **109**
defects in, tests used in investigating, **115**
prevention of, means used in, 114
*See also* Anticoagulants
rapidity of, platelet count and, 109
relation of blood fat to, 121
role of vitamin K in, 914
stages of, 110
thromboplastin formation in, 110
time, determining, methods of, 116
color index of,
in anemias, 79
obtaining, 79
composition of, **2**
changes in, sensation of thirst due to, 738
constituents of,
inorganic, 3
phosphorus, 4
organic, 4
physiological basis of, 3
plasma proteins, 4
coronary sinus, chemical composition of, as index to ventricular metabolism, 321
cross matching, 45
defibrinated, 112
distribution of, regional, 227
during output of carbon dioxide and uptake of

BLOOD—*cont.*
oxygen in the lung, processes occurring in, 464
effects of altitude on, 511
erythrocyte sedimentation rate of. *See* Erythrocyte sedimentation rate
estrogen content of, effects of menstrual cycle on, 1091
examinations of, used in evaluating renal function, 569
fat, **846**
milky appearance of, 846
relation of,
to atherosclerosis, 121
to clotting, 121
*flow of,*
*See also* Circulation
adrenaline and, 1025
aortic, phasic, 284
arterial,
amount of, 284
measurement of, **284**
artery to vein, 287
cerebral,
constancy of, under various physiological conditions, 345
factors determining, 344
coronary,
*See also* Circulation, coronary
determinants of, **322**
determination of, by nitrous oxide saturation curves, 216
effects of right atrial pressure on, 324
measurement of, 332
resistance of coronary bed to, 324
curves, pulmonary capillary, at rest and during exercise, 297
cutaneous,
in foot, 346
in hand, 346
to skin areas other than the extremities, control of, 349
distribution of, in exercise, 313
effects of, on skin color, 346
electromagnetic, uses of, 213
in arm, determination of, 220
in muscle, central nervous system control of, 351
in pulmonary circulation, resistance to, 164
in reactive hyperemia, calculation of, 355
in skin. *See* Circulation, cutaneous; Skin, blood flow in
in vessels, variable velocity of, schematic representation of, 161
interrelation between pressure, resistance and, 165
measurement of,
*See also* Flow meters

*Bold-face numbers indicate major discussion*

*Bold-face numbers indicate major discussion*

*Bold-face numbers indicate major discussion*

*Bold-face numbers indicate major discussion*

CAPILLARY(IES)—*cont.*
glomerular. *See* Glomerulus, capillaries of
increased permeability of, increased lymph flow due to, 38
loops, 345
permeability of, 158
poisons, increased lymph flow caused by, 38
pressure, increase in, as result of venous obstruction, 37
resistance test, 119
surface, increase in, increased lymph flow caused by, 38
walls of,
  anatomical structure of, 157
  exchange across, 158
  intercellular cement in, demonstration of, 157
CAPITELLUM, 1422
CARBAMINOYL - BETA - METHYL-CHOLINE, effects of, on cholinoceptive effectors, 1308
CARBAMINOYLCHOLINE, effects of, on cholinoceptive effectors, 1309
CARBAMYL-L-ASPARTATE, chemical structure of, 804
CARBAMYL PHOSPHATE, chemical structure of, 804
CARBHEMOGLOBIN
definition of, 463
determination of, 463
effect of carbon dioxide tension on amount of, 464
formation of, 58, 462
CARBOHYDRATE(S)
*See also* Glucose
adsorption of,
  by intestines, 674
  small and large, 674
Calories per gram of, 744
conversion of, to fat, 840
estimation of, **809**
  methods of, **809**
in diet, effect on amount of protein required to establish nitrogen equilibrium, 786
in food, determination of, 743
individual, energy content of, 744
linked with fatty substances, metabolism of, 809
metabolic constant of, 753
metabolism of, **808**
  abnormalities of, in adrenalectomized animals, causes of, 829
  factors effecting,
    acromegaly, 829
    adrenal glands, 828
    adrenaline, 1026
    anterior pituitary gland, 833
    brain lesions, 834
    endocrine glands, **828**
    fasting, mechanisms involved in, 835
    hypophysectomy, 830

CARBOHYDRATE(S)—*cont.*
metabolism of—*cont.*
  factors effecting—*cont.*
    noradrenaline, 1026
    pancreatectomy, 830
    pituitary gland substances, 831
    thyroid gland, 833
  in fevers, 896
  regulation of, nervous, 834
  relation of anterior pituitary gland to, 962
  relation to citric acid cycle, 875
  role of adrenal cortex in, 828
  role of pituitary in, 829
respiratory quotient of, 751
role of,
  as a fuel in exercise, 880
  as protein sparer, 786
specific dynamic action of, cause of, 788
stores of, effects of prolonged exercise on, 882
tolerance to, testing, 835
CARBON DIOXIDE
alveolar, reduction in, due to altitude, 511
arterial concentration of,
  effects of, on cerebral circulation, causes of, 344
  role of, in cerebral circulation, 344
carriage of, by blood, **459**
combination of, with hemoglobin, 58
deficit of, in blood, compensated, 133
disassociation curves, 516
  of blood and plasma from same blood, 462
  of reduced blood, 461
in blood,
  calculation of, **460**
  compensated, 133
  effects of, on oxygen dissociation curve, 456
  excess of, uncompensated, 133
  measurement of, 454
  partial pressures of, 452
  volume of, **453**
in inspired air,
  effect on amount of tidal air, 520
  effects of, on respiration, **496**
in the lungs, evolution of, 463
production of, by nerve, 1132
removal of, from blood, effects of, 462
role of, in regulation of breathing, 488
solubility of, in physiological fluids, at body temperature, 460
study of, historical survey on, 749
tension,
  effect of,
    on carbhemoglobin content of blood, 464
    on rate of hydrogen ion secretion, 562

CARBON DIOXIDE—*cont.*
transport of, in blood, role of hemoglobin in, 460
vasodilator effects of, 344
volumes of, in arterial and venous blood, 453
CARBON MONOXIDE
combination of, with hemoglobin, 58
poisoning, **523**
  general discussion on, 523
CARBONIC ACID
buffering of, 130
production of, 129
regeneration of, 558
CARBONIC ANHYDRASE
effects of, on hydrogen ion secretion, 563
in parietal cells of gastric gland, 602
in tissues, 463
role of, in regeneration of carbonic acid, 558
CARBONMONOXYHEMOGLOBIN, formation of, 58
CARDIA, **689**
anatomy of, 691
disorders of, 690
effects of esophageal and stomach pressure on, 690
innervation of, 690
tone of, effect of gastric mucosa on, 691
CARDIAC (*see also* Heart)
CARDIAC ASTHMA, 503
CARDIAC CYCLE
electrocardiogram versus onset of pressure events in, 245
information on, from jugular pulse records, 287
pressure and volume events of, **242**
pressure pulse asynchronisms in, 245
pressure pulse values in, 244
sequence of events in, 242
CARDIAC DEPRESSOR NERVE, role of, in control of circulation, 259
CARDIAC DYSPNEA, 502
CARDIAC GLYCOSIDES
action of,
  in heart failure, 199
  upon fibrillation and flutter, 199
effects of, on metabolism of myocardium, 200
CARDIAC OUTPUT, **305**
and cardiac work, comparison of, 305
basal, changes in, due to age, 400
changes in,
  normal, 306
  pathological, 306
decrease in,
  due to pathological causes, 306
  normal causes of, 306
definitions concerning, 305
distribution of, 314
factors effecting,
  altitude, 512
  catecholamines, 315

*Bold-face numbers indicate major discussion*

*Bold-face numbers indicate major discussion*

CEREBRAL CORTEX—*cont.*
functions of,
analyzing, **1265**
differentiation of, 1265
generalization of, 1265
synthesizing, **1265**
fusiform cell layer of, 1233
ganglionic layer of, 1233
granular layer of, 1234, 1278
internal, 1233
heterotypical, 1234
homotypical, 1234
inactivity of, as cause of
sleep, 1274
layers of, 1233
localization of function in,
**1234**, 1284
location of acoustic analyzer
in, 1269
location of visual analyzer in,
1269
minute structure of, **1233**
molecular layer of, 1233, 1277
motor and sensory representations in, 1235
figurines of, 1241
motor area of, stimulation of,
effects of, 1284
nerve cells in, 1233
occipital lobe,
lesions of, effects of, 1408
localization of function in,
1249
of precentral area, minute
structure of, 1234
orbitofrontal region of,
localization of function
in, 1240
parietal lobe, localization of
function in, 1243
plexiform layer of, 1233, 1277
portion of, removal of, effects
of, 1269
precentral, localization of
function in, 1235
precentral motor,
control over visceral and
vascular activities, 1239
differences in function of
various parts of, 1237
lesions of, effects of, 1236
removal of, effects of, 1236
prefrontal areas of,
connections of, 1241
cortical and subcortical,
1240
localization of functions in,
1240
removal of, effects of, 1241
Purkinje cell layer of 1278
pyramidal cell layer of, 1233
removal of, effects of, 1268
representation of tactile
sensibility in, 1244
role of, in control of vasoconstriction, 256
showing representation of
ipsilateral cochlea in,
1247
sigmoid gyrus, removal of,
effects of, 1236
somatic-receptive area in,
1284

CEREBRAL CORTEX—*cont.*
somesthetic area of, 1243
discriminative faculties of,
1245
speech areas in, 1250
study of, use of conditioned
reflexes in, 1268
synthesis of stimuli by, 1266
temporal lobes of,
extirpation of, effects of,
1249
lesions of, effects of, 1248
localization of functions
in, 1274
visual area of, 1406
structure of, 1234
CEREBRAL ISCHEMIA THEORY OF
SLEEP, 1271
CEREBRAL PEDUNCLES, excision
of, effects of, 1282
CEREBRAL VASCULAR RESIST-
ANCE
definition of, 343
effects of, in determination of
cerebral blood flow, 343
extravascular factors contributing to, 343
factors effecting,
arterial concentration of
carbon dioxide and oxy-
gen, 344
diameter of cerebral blood
vessels, 344
hypercapnia, 345
hypoxia, 345
CEREBRO - CERELLO - CEREBRAL
CIRCUIT, 1281
CEREBROSIDES
general discussion of, 843
occurring in body, 839
CEREBROSPINAL FIBER TRACTS,
1195
CEREBROSPINAL FLUID, **1290**
absorption of, **1291**
mechanism of, 1291
acetylcholine in, 1311
amount of, **1292**
anatomical considerations of,
**1290**
calcium of, 1056
circulation of, **1290**
composition of, **1291**
compared to that of blood
plasma, 1291
formation of,
mechanism of, **1291**
site of, **1290**
function of, **1292**
pressure of, **1292**
effects of fluid and salt
injections on, 1292
effects of position changes
on, 1292
CEROID, 912
CERVICAL GANGLION
inferior,
branches from, 1296
formation of, 1296
middle,
branches of, 1296
formation of, 1296

CERVICAL GANGLION—*cont.*
superior,
branches from, 1295
to internal carotid nerve,
1295
CERVICAL MUCUS, changes in, at
time of ovulation, 1080
CEUMINOUS GLANDS, of external
ear, 1420
CHALKY BONE. *See* Marble bone
CHARLES' LAW, 451
CHEMICAL SENSE, common, 1469
CHEMICO-OLFACTORY CORRE-
LATION, 1466
CHEMORECEPTORS, 1139
CHEMOREFLEX, coronary, 269
CHEMOTAXIS
definition of, 92
general discussion on, 92
CHEMOTROPISM, 1117
CHEST
development of, effects of
altitude on, 512
wall of, electrodes on, electrical potentials recorded
from, 180
CHEWING, innervation of, 684
CHEYNE-STOKES BREATHING,
500
after ventilation, basis for,
500
causes of, 500
examples of, 500
CHICKEN LEUKOSIS, 94
CHILLS, 895
heat reduction due to, 895
CHLORIDE
excretion of, role of kidney
in, 552
loss of, in vomitus, fall in
blood chloride due to, 713
reabsorption of, 552
shift, 130
transport, in the blood, 462
CHLOROCRUORIN, 55
CHLOROFORM, effects of, on
liver, 852
CHLOROLABE, 1333
curve, 1359
CHLOROTHIAZIDE, use of, in
treatment of essential
hypertension, 390
CHOLAGOGUE, definition of, 644
CHOLECYSTOGRAPHY, 659
CHOLECYSTOKININ, gall-bladder contractions caused
by, 659
CHOLELITHIASIS, **650**
CHOLERETIC, definition of, 644
CHOLESTEROL, 8, 843
absorption of, 843
by intestines, 678
bile acid ratio, changes in, as
cause of gallstones, 651
chemical nature of, 843
contained in normal tissues,
844
degradation of, 844
distribution of, 843
excretion of, 843
by gall-bladder mucosa,
656
in liver bile, origin and function of, 644

*Bold-face numbers indicate major discussion*

*Bold-face numbers indicate major discussion*

*Bold-face numbers indicate major discussion*

*Bold-face numbers indicate major discussion*

Color(s)—*cont.*
*vision—cont.*
mechanism of, 1360
detection of thresholds
of, 1360
estimation of sensitivity
of, 1360
foveal center and, 1357
physiological basis for,
1357
primitive form of, 1364
reduction of normal eye to
monochromatism, 1363
retinal function in, schemes
for, 1364
trichromatic character of,
1351
visual differentiation of,
1265
Colostrum
constituents of, 1099
role of, in initiation of
lactation, 1097
Comma tract, of Schultz, 1197
Compass test, for tactile
discrimination, 1140
Complement fixation, 63
Concave mirror, real inverted
image formed by, 1376
Concha, 1420
Condiments, effects of, on
gastric secretion, 618
Conditioned reflexes, **1261**
alimentary, 1261
artificial, definition of, 1263
biological significance of,
**1263**
concentration of, 1267
defense, 1262
definitions concerning, **1261**
delayed, 1264
inhibition of, 1264
disinhibition of, 1264
effects of drugs upon, **1270**
experiments upon, arrangements for, 1262
excitatory, **1261**
general discussion on, 1261
extinction of, 1263
for defecation, establishing,
720
induction in, 1268
negative, 1268
positive, 1268
inhibition of, **1263**
concentration of, 1267
conditioned, 1264
differential, 1264
external, 1263
internal, 1263
irradiation, 1267
natural, definition of, 1263
positive, **1262**
general discussion on, 1262
secondary, 1262
simultaneous, 1264
tertiary, 1262
trace, 1263
use of, in study of cortical
function, 1268
Cones
density of, on or near the
horizontal meridian, 1323
distance between, role of, in
visual acuity, 1366

Cones—*cont.*
distribution of, near center of
retina, 1355
general discussion on, 1321
illustration of, 1321
inner segments of, 1322
nuclei of, 1323
outer segments of, 1321
role of, in vision, 1324
synaptic connections of, 1320
Conjunctiva, 1314
Constipation, 720
causes of, 720
chronic, causes of, chief, 720
headache associated with,
1259
symptoms of,
origin of, 722
referrable to alimentary
tract, 772
Contact lenses, 1397
general discussion on, 1397
Contractility
definition of, 144
measurement of, in heart
muscle, 144
of cardiac muscle, measurement of 144
Contraction, tonic, energy
expenditure of, 1164
Contrast
demonstration of, 1341
simultaneous, 1341
Convection, and body heat
loss, 887
Convex cylinder, refraction
by, 1378
Convex lens. *See* Lens, convex
1378
Convex mirror, virtual erect
mirror formed by, 1376
Coombs, serum, anti-RH types
of antibodies developed
after administration of,
48
Copper
dietary allowances, recommended, 947
role of, in hemoglobin synthesis, **75**
Coproporphyrin, 54
chemical structure of, 58
formation of, 58
Cords, cortical, 1075
Cori cycle, 811, 1026
Cornea, 1316
distances of cardinal points
of eye to, 1380
epithelium of, 1316
layers of, 1316
refraction by, 1379
vertical section of, 1316
Corona ciliaris, 1386
Corona radiata, 1076
Coronary artery collat-
erals
prophylactic augmentation
of,
by natural stimuli, 335
physiological effects of, in
dog, 338
Coronary bed, resistance of,
to coronary flow, 324
Coronary chemoreflex, 269

Coronary circulation. *See*
Circulation, coronary
Coronary collateral cir-
culation, **333**. *See also*
Circulation, coronary
collateral
Coronary endarterectomy,
339
Coronary sinus
catheterization studies of,
325
oxygen saturation of during
ventricular asystole, 327
Corpora amylacea, 1107
Corpora lutea, production
and maintenace of, role
of estrogen in, 1084
Corpus albicans, 1076
Corpus cerebelli, 1276
Corpus fibrosum, 1077
Corpus hemorrhagicum, 1076
Corpus luteum, 1076
hormone secreted by, 1086
showing luteal tissue, 1076
Corpuscles
*See also* Blood cells
buffer systems of, 129
Golgi, 1146
Hassall's, 1110
Malpighian, 67
nitrogenous constituents of,
distribution in, 8
Corpuscles, Pacinian, 1142,
1146
size of, effects of, on erythrocyte sedimentation rate,
66
white blood. *See* Leukocytes
Cortex
adrenal. *See* Adrenal cortex
cerebral. *See* Cerebral cortex
factors effecting, emotional
feeling, 620
of thymus, 1110
renal,
dye-dilution curves in, 370
role of, in autoregulation of
renal blood flow, 371
Corti
organ of
action potentials of, 1444
synchronous volleys in,
1444
at rest, 1441
cochlear microphonic po-
tential, 1443
electrical responses in, 1442
endocochlear potentials in,
1442
fine movements of, 1441
intracellular potentials in,
1442
mechanical functions of,
1441
nerve fibers of, 1426
nerve supply of, 1426
summating potentials of,
1444
rods of, 1424
spiral organ of, 1424
tunnel of, 1424
Cortical hormone, natural,
1038
Corticobulbar fibers, 1204
of spinal cord, 1203

*Bold-face numbers indicate major discussion*

DIET—*cont.*
  effects of—*cont.*
    in blood clotting, 946
    on basal metabolic rate, 766
    on hemoglobin regeneration, 72
  fat in, indispensability of, 945
  fatty acids in, 945
  fatty liver caused by, mechanism involved in, 850
  hemoglobin production influenced by, 72
  in fevers, 896
  linoleic acid requirements in, 945
  lipotropic factors in, absence of, fatty livers resulting from, 851
  mineral constituents of, 946
  pancreatic enzyme secretion adaptation to, 637
  planning, requirements to be considered in, 942
  proportion of fats, carbohydrates, and proteins in, 948
  protein allowance in, general discussion on, 943
  protein-rich, effects of, on health, 943
  recommended, 947
    average minimal amino acid requirements, 945
    calories per day, 943
  reducing,
    delay in loss of weight while on, owing to retention of water, 867
    planning, 868
  requirements for, **942**
  role of, in atherosclerosis, 946
DIETARY HABITS, changes in, following removal of temporal lobes, 1249
DIETHYLSTILBESTROL, chemical structure of, 1083
DIFFERENCE, recognition of, localization of, 1245
DIGESTIBILITY, coefficient of, 791
DIGESTION
  *See various entries under the* Gastric *headings which apply*
  effects of, on arterial blood pressure, 274
  function of bile in, 646
  gastric. *See* Gastric digestion
  pancreatic enzymes in, importance of, 632
  serial photographs of stomach during, 695
  ultimate aim of, 671
DIGESTIVE GLANDS. *See* Glands, digestive; Glands, salivary; Secretions, salivary
DIGESTIVE PERISTALSIS, 694
  relation of hunger contractions to, 696

DIGITALIS
  action of,
    in fibrillation and flutter, 199
    in heart failure, 199
  effects of,
    on cardiac output, 307
    on electrocardiographic patterns, 189
DIHYDROETHYLSTILBESTROL, 1083
  chemical structure of, 1083
DIHYDROTACHYSTEROL, use of, as substitute for parathormone, 1061
DIHYDROXYESTRIN. *See* Estradiol
DIHYDROXYPHENYLALANINE. *See* Dopa
3:5-DI-IODO-4-(4'-METHOXY-PHENOXY)BENZALDEHYDE, chemical structure of, 1009
3:5-DI-IODOTHYRONINE, chemical structure of, 1009
DI-IODOTYROSINE, chemical structure of, 1010
DIKETOPIPERAZINES, 770
DINITROPHENOL, use of, in treatment of obesity, 868
DIODRAST, clearance of, use of, in measuring renal plasma flow, 546
DIOPTER, general discussion on, 1378
DIPEPTIDES, characteristics of, 772
DIPLACUSIS, 1453
DIPLOPIA, 1413
  causes of, 1418
  crossed, 1419
  introspective, 1413
  physiological, 1413
  position sense in, 1419
  simple, 1419
  uncrossed, 1419
DIPOLE, definition of, 170
DISACCHARIDASES, secretion of, by small intestines, 667
DISC, choked. *See* Papilledema
DISCOBULUS POSTURE, 1183
DISCUS PROLIGERUS, 1076
DISEQUILIBRIUM, caused by excision of cerebellum, 1282
DISK THROWING POSTURE, 1183
DISSOCIATION CONSTANT, 124
DISTANCE, judgement of, factors in, 1416
DIURESIS, osmotic, role of, in sodium excretion, 555
DIURETICS, use of, in treatment of essential hypertension, 390
DONATH PHENOMENON, 64
DONNAN THEORY, of membrane equilibrium, 128
DONOR, universal, danger of belief in concept of, 45
DOPA, chemical structure of, 1024
DOPAMINE, chemical structure of, 1024
DORSAL NUCLEUS, 1186
DORSAL ROOT VASODILATOR FIBERS, 350

DOUGLAS BAG, 761
  calorimetry, 761
DREAMS, production of, theory concerning, 1273
DREAMY STATES, due to lesions of temporal lobe, 1248
DRINKER RESPIRATOR, 530
DRUGS, effects of, upon conditioned reflexes, **1270**
DRUM MEMBRANE, 1420
  mechanical aspects of, 1436
  mode of vibration, 1437
  normal, appearance of, 1420
  vibration of,
    as a rigid cone, 1437
    patterns of, for 2000 c.p.s. tone, 1437
DUALISTIC SCHOOL of thought concerning development of blood cells, 99
DUCT(s)
  intercalary, definition of, 587
  interlobular, definition of, 587
DUCTILI EFFERENTES, 1100
DUCTUS ARTERIOSUS
  patent, 441, 523
    circulatory changes in, 442
    general discussion on, 441
    heart sound in, 441
    hemodynamic effects of, 441
    "machinery" murmur in, 441
    pulmonary hypertension in, 443
    sound of, 441
    treatment of, 443
DUCTUS DEFERENS, 1100
DUCTUS EPIDIDYMIS, 1100
DUOCRININ, 668
DUODENAL SECRETION, functions of, 668
DUODENAL ULCERS, 621
  *See also* Gastric ulcers; Peptic ulcers
  anacidity and, 622
  association of, with hyperacidity, 616
  effects of experimental pancreatic insufficiency on, 633
  gastric analysis findings in, 622
  hypersecretion in patients with, 622
  location of, 621
  pain in,
    cause of, 625
    duodenal muscle spasm as cause of, 625
    relief of, 625
    type of, 625
  symptoms of, 621
DUODENUM
  contractions of, relation between bile flow and, 658
  coordination of, with sphincter and antrum, 696
  of dog, myenteric reflex in, 710
  peristalsis of, effects of insulin on, 827
DUST CELLS, of lung, 103

*Bold-face numbers indicate major discussion*

*Bold-face numbers indicate major discussion*

EPHEDRINE—*cont.*
  chemical structure of, 1029
  effects of, on adreoceptive
    effectors, 1309
  general discussion on, 1029
EPICARDIAL LEADS, direct,
    taken over area of myo-
    cardial injury, 186
EPICRITIC SENSIBILITY, 1144
EPIDIDYMIS, caput of, 1100
EPILEPSY
  convulsions in, explanation
    for, 1255
  cryptogenic, 1255
  electroencephalograms in,
    1257
  focal, convulsions in, causes
    of, 1255
  general discussion on, **1254**
  grand mal, 1254
  idiopathic, 1255
    convulsions in, causes of,
      1255
  Jacksonian, 1254
  localized, 1254
  petit mal, 1254
  psychomotor, 1254
  stages of, 1254
EPIMYSIUM, 869
EPINEPHRINE. *See* Adrenaline
EPIPHYSIS, **1110**
  anatomical structure of, 1110
  functions of, 1111
  origin of, 1110
EPITHELIAL SURFACES, growth
    of, effects of iron on, 74
EPITHELIUM, secreting, of sali-
    vary glands, types of,
    587
EPITYMPANIC RECESS, 1422
EQUATOR, definition of, 1314
EQUILIBRATORY SENSE, locali-
    zation of, 1247
EQUILIBRIUM
  effects of prolonged wakeful-
    ness upon, 1271
  physiological mechanisms
    governing, **1162**, 1182
ERB'S SIGN, 1050
ERECTION, **1108**
  general discussion on, 1108
ERG, definition of, 742 (foot-
    note), 1329
ERGOSTEROL
  chemical structure of, 907
  irradiated, effects of, on
    serum calcium curve, of
    dog, 1061
ERGOTAMINE, adrenergic block-
    ing by, 1028
ERGOTOXINE, adrenergic block-
    ing by, 1028
ERIODICTIN, 937
ERYTHREMIA. *See* Polycy-
    themia vera
ERYTHROBLASTOSIS FETALIS, 47
  causes of, 47
  transfusions as factor in de-
    velopment of, 47
  treatment of, 47
ERYTHROBLASTS,
  basophilic, 105
  early, 105
  late, 105
  polychromatic, 105

ERYTHROBLASTS—*cont.*
  polychromatophil, 105
  primary, 99
ERYTHROCYTES, 10
  addition of hemoglobin to, 71
  agglutinogens of, source of,
    46
  alkalinity of, effects of alti-
    tude on, 512
  anatomical structure of, **10**
  buffers of, 129
  composition of, diagram of,
    11
  concentration of, local varia-
    tions in, 15
  counting, methods of, 15
  delivery of, into circulation,
    rhythm of, 105
  destruction of, 70
    anemias caused by, 77
    diseases with, hemosiderin
      in, 67
    in the body, methods of,
      70
  diameter of,
    distribution curves of, 11
    in pernicious anemia, 80
    in simple achlorhydric
      anemia, 80
    normal, 80
    in various clinical condi-
      tions, 80
  difference from leukocytes,
    87
  dimensions of, diagram of,
    11
  effect of altitude on, 12, 511
  effect of specific liver therapy
    upon, 83
  enzymes of, 10
  estimation of, 15
  exchange of inorganic phos-
    phate across membranes
    of, 62
  formation of, 70
    materials necessary for, 71
  fragility of,
    factors effecting, 62
    testing, 62
  hemoglobin held in, method
    of, 61
  inorganic constituents of, 3
  life span of, **70**
    measurement of, 70
    under pathological condi-
      tions, 71
  maturation of, 100, 105
    in liver, relationship to
      pteroylglutamic acid, 85
    necessary replacement for,
      105
  number of, **12**
    decreases in, causes of,
      physiological, 13
    effect of altitude on, 12
    in hemodilution, 15
    in hydremia, 15
    increases in,
      causes of, 13
        emotional states, 13
        heightened environ-
          mental temperature,
          13
        high altitude, 12, 13

ERYTHROCYTES—*cont.*
  number of—*cont.*
    increases in—*cont.*
      causes of—*cont.*
        muscular exercise, 13
        physiological, 12
        conditions occurring in,
          13
      in pathological states, 13
    variation in,
      daily, 12
      due to physiological
        causes, 12
      role of spleen in, 13
      with time of life, 12
  osmotic principles of, 61
  packed cell volume of, 15
  permeability properties of,
    62
  primary, 99
  production of, anoxia as fac-
    tor in, 71
  ratio of platelets to, in arte-
    rial blood, 108
  release of hemoglobin from,
    61
  resistance of,
    to disintegrating hypotonic
      solutions, 61
    to various hemolytic
      agents, 62
  reticulated, 13
  role of, in carbon dioxide
    transport, 461
  sedimentation rate of, **64**
    determination of, factors
      involved in, 66
    effect of protein fractions
      of plasma on, 65
    factors effecting, various,
      66
    in pregnancy, 65
    increases in,
      causes of, 65
        cell clumping, 66
        dextran, 66
        pathological states, 65
        physical changes, 66
          in blood, 66
        plasma specific grav-
          ity, 66
      nonspecificity of, 66
      normal, 65
      reduction of, causes of, 65
      test for, description of, 65
      value of, 66
  shape of, **10**
    in Cooley's anemia, 78
    variations in, **15**
  size of, **10**
    variations in, 15
  stress in, under normal cir-
    culatory activity, 70
  stroma of,
    constituents of, 10
    in formation of, 71
  structure of, **10**
    variation in, **15**
  thickness of, in various clini-
    cal conditions, 80
  total circulating,
    volume of,
      estimation of, 18
      method of, 18

*Bold-face numbers indicate major discussion*

ERYTHROCYTES—*cont.*
  volume of, in various clinical conditions, 80
ERYTHROLABE, 1333
  curve, 1359
ERYTHROMEMALGIA, general discussion on, 356
ERYTHROPHORES, 982
ERYTHROPOIESIS, 105
ESCULIN, 937
ESOPHAGEAL PLEXUS, 1298
ESOPHAGO-SALIVARY REFLEX, 597
ESOPHAGOSTOMY, use of, in study of gastric secretion, 605
ESOPHAGUS
  antiperistalsis in, 691
  motor nerves to, ending of, 689
  peristaltic wave over, pressure changes in, 686
  rate of progress of food through, 688
ESTRADIOL
  benzoate of, chemical structure of, 1082
  chemical structure of, 1082
  dipropionate, 1082
  general discussion on, 1082
  of placenta, 1092
ESTRIN, action of, in sensitizing an isolated uterus to pitocin, 1085
ESTRIOL
  chemical structure of, 1082
  general discussion on, 1082
  of placenta, 1092
ESTROGEN(S)
  and cancer, 1085
  assay of, 1085
  chemistry of, 1082
  distribution of, 1081
  effects of, 1084
    inhibition of lactation by, 1097
    on insulin content of pancreas, 826
    toward prolactin, 1097
  excretion of, 1083
  general discussion on, 1081
  inactivation of, by liver, 1083
  metabolism of, 1082
  origin of, 1081
  physiology of, 1084
  -progesterone interactions, on menstrual cycle, 1090
  role of,
    in mammary development, 1095
    in placenta, 1092
  standardization of, 1085
  synthetic, 1083
  terminology concerning, 1082
  withdrawal of, effects of, on menstrual cycle, 1090
ESTRONE
  chemical structure of, 1082
  general discussion on, 1082
  of placenta, 1092
ESTRUS
  cycle,
    diagram of, 1091
    in animals, 1078

ESTRUS—*cont.*
  cycle—*cont.*
    in rat, vaginal epithelium in, 1079
  definition of, 1078
  detection of, 1078
  in immature animals, due to estrogen, 1084
  suppression of, by progesterone, 1088
  uterus in, 1077
ETHINYL ESTRADIOL, 1082
EUNUCHOIDISM, 1107
  deferred type of, 1107
  description of, 1075
EUPNEA, 475
EVANS BLUE, use of, in estimating blood volume, 17
EXCITATION
  concentration of, 1268
  irradiation of, 1268
EXERCISE
  alcohol as fuel for, 882
  and reactive hyperemia, 353
  blood redistribution during, 459
  carbohydrate as fuel for, 882
  cardiac output and cardiac work during, regulation of, 307
  circulatory adjustments to, effects of aging on, 402
  dynamic action of fat and glucose in, utilization of waste heat of, 788
  dyspnea due to, effect of athletic training on, 504
  effects of,
    in tricuspid stenosis, 426
    on arterial blood pressure, 274
    on arteriovenous oxygen, 311
    on blood flow, mechanisms regulating, 294
    on blood volume, 29
    on body weight, 735
    on caloric intake, 735
    on coronary circulation, in dog, 333
    on metabolism, 504
    on protein metabolism, 882
    on pulmonary circulation, 297
    on regional distribution of blood flow, 313
    on renal circulation, 374
    on respiratory quotient, 880
    on size of heart, 311
    on splanchnic circulation, 367
    on venous blood pressure, 292
    on vital capacity, 504
  excess metabolism of, 880
  fuel of, 880
  heart rate during, regulation of, 307
  hemodynamic responses to, 313
  hemodynamic variables in, 312
  lactic acid production during, 879

EXERCISE—*cont.*
  mechanisms of hyperpnea in, **499**
  prolonged, effects of, on carbohydrate stores, 882
  protein as fuel for, 882
  regional distribution of oxygen in, 312
  simulated, effects of, on cardiovascular events, 312
  stimulus, 500
  strenuous, muscular fuel used in, 881
EXOPHTHALMOS
  in Graves' disease, pathogenesis of, 1003
  malignant, 1004
EXOSMOSIS, 26
EXPIRATION
  control of, **488**
  general discussion on, **475**
  movement of intercostal muscles during, 473
  position of diaphragm during, 475
EXPIRATORY CENTER
  in cat, 490
  localizing, method for, 492
EXPIRATORY RESERVE VOLUME, 481
EXTENSOR
  crossed, reflex of, **1157**
  muscles, reflexes acting upon, 1172
  reflex, crossed, 1166
  rigidity, in decerebrate cat, 1165
  tone, effects of labyrinthectomy on, 177
EXTEROCEPTORS, 1138
EXTEROFECTIVE SYSTEM, 1302
EXTRACELLULAR FLUID(S)
  acids in,
    disposal of, 557
    excretion of, as undissociated acid, 557
  buffer capacity of, restoration of, 556
EXTRAPYRAMIDAL SYSTEM, diseases of, clinical manifestations of, **1222**
EXTRASYSTOLES
  auricular, 195
    electrocardiography in, 196
  due to abnormal impulse formation, 194
  effects of,
    on arterial pulse, 195
    on electrocardiograms, 195
  experimental production of, 194
  interpolated, 195
  nodal, 195
  sinus, 195
  ventricular, 194
    arising in right ventricle, 193
    electrocardiography in, 195
EYE(S)
  accommodation of. *See* Accommodation of the eye
  anatomical features of, 1314
  aqueous humor, 1399

*Bold-face numbers indicate major discussion*

FAT(S)—*cont.*
metabolism of—*cont.*
in Niemann-Pick's disease, 859
in production of atherosclerosis, 860
in Tay-Sach's disease, 859
intermediary, 852
liver and, 848
neutral, transfer of, from epithelial cells, to central lacteals, 845
nutritive value of, differences in, 946
occurring in body, triglycerides, 839
of blood, **846**
of milk, 1100
oxidative degradation of, 855
respiratory quotient of, 752
role of,
as insulating mechanism, 840
as muscular fuel, 881
as protein sparer, 786
specific dynamic action of, cause of, 788
synthesis of, 856
enzymic, substrates involved in, 854
transportation of, 845, **847**
FATIGABILITY
easy, caused by section of peduncles, 1283
in cerebellar disorders, 1287
FATIGUE, receptor adaptation and, 1147
FATTY ACIDS
combined as liver phospholipids and glycerides, unsaturation of, compared with fatty acids found in other tissues, 849
deficiency, eczematous conditions due to, 946
in diet, 945
recovery of, 840
metabolism of,
energy required for, 857
relation to citric acid cycle, 875
role of coenzyme of acetylation in, 854
non-esterified,
effect of fasting on, 847
formation of, 847
removal of, from organs, 847
of milk, 1100
oxidation of, substances produced during, 852
oxidative degradation of, helical scheme representing, 855
resynthesis of, into triglycerides, 677
synthesis of, helical scheme of, 855
FATTY LIVER. *See* Liver, fatty
FATTY SUBSTANCES, occurring through the body, classification of, **839**
FECES
color of, 719

FECES—*cont.*
composition of, 719
effect of diet on, 719
fat content of, 719, 846
factors effecting, 719
odor of, 719
FEEDING REFLEXES, 736
classification of, 736
FEMALES, sexual life of, **1077**
FEMORAL ARTERY, contraction of, 157
FERRIHEMOGLOBIN, 57
amount of, effects of poisoning on, 57
FERRITIN, storage of iron in, 73
FERROHEMOGLOBIN, 57
FERRY-PORTER LAW, validity of, 1371
FETUS
calcium in, 1055
circulation in, 521
FEVER(S), **894**
antipyretic drugs used in, action of, 897
basal metabolism in, 895
beneficial effects of, 897
carbohydrate metabolism in, 896
chills in, 895
continued, 895
diet in, 896
fat metabolism in, 896
infectious, 895
limit of, favorable to survival, 894
nitrogen metabolism in, 896
protein metabolism in, 896
reducing drugs, action of, 897
relationship between body temperature and basal metabolism in, 895
rigors in, 895
salt metabolism in, 896
types of, 894
value of, 897
water metabolism in, 896
FIBER(S)
auricular, transmembrane potential of, 138
circular, arrangement of, in ciliary muscle, 1387
climbing, 1281
corticospinal, source of, 1236
moss, 1281
myocardial, transmembrane potential in, microelectrodes used for determining, 137
Purkinje. *See* Purkinje fibers
secretory, definition of, 586
sympathetic. *See* Sympathetic fibers
tropic, definition of, 586
ventricular, transmembrane potential of, 138
FIBRILLATION
atonic, 201
auricular, 198
action of cardiac glycosides on, 199
causes of, 198
production of, underlying causes of, 198
venous pulse in, 198

FIBRILLATION—*cont.*
ventricular, 200, 201
causes of, 201
effects of, upon circulation, 201
essential elements for production of, 201
factors leading to, investigation of, 201
general discussion on, 200
methods of stopping, 202
stages of, 201
FIBRILS, of cardiac muscle, 143
FIBRIN
change of, to fibrinogen, process of, 109
conversion of fibrinogen to, in blood coagulation, 112
formation of, 109
FIBRINOGEN
concentration of, pathological variations in, 5
conversion of, to fibrin, in blood coagulation, 112
formation of, from fibrin, process of, 109
functions of, 7
production of, by liver, 6
FIBRINOLYSIN. *See* Plasmin
FIBRINOLYSIS, 112
pathological conditions in which it occurs, 112
FIBROKINASE, 112
FICK METHOD
for determination of cardiac output, 214
using oxygen and carbon dioxide, 214
for determination of regional blood flow, 215
possibility of error in, 214
technique of, 214
use of foreign gases with, 215
FICK PRINCIPLE, 213
use of, to determine cardiac output, 214
FIGURES, visual differentiation of, 1265
FILIFORM PALPILLAE, 1458
FILLING PRESSURE GRADIENT, definition of, 414
FILTRATION FRACTION, 546
and renal blood flow, 546
FINGER
nail of, bed of, showing capillary loops and summits of skin papillae in, 345
vasoconstriction in, 269
FISH
composition of, 746
energy content of, 746
FISSURA POSREOLATERALIS, 1276
FISSURA PREPYRAMIDALIS, 1276
FISSURA PRIMA, of Elliot-Smith, 1276
FIXATION
field of, 1417
lines, 1417
point, 1417
visual, 1417
FLAGELLA, origin of rods from, 1322
FLAVONE GLUCOSIDES, 937

*Bold-face numbers indicate major discussion*

FLEISCHIG
  bundle of, 1197
  tract of, 1191
FLEXOR REFLEXES, general discussion on, **1156**
FLICKER
  critical fusion frequency, 1371
    value of, 1371
  visual effects of, 1371
FLOCCULONODULAR LOBE, 1276
  functions of, 1285
FLOW METER
  differential pressure, 209
  electromagnetic, 213
  for measurement of blood velocity, 224
  orifice, 209
  pendulum, 211
  Pitot tube, 209
  sonar, 213
FLOWER-SPRAY NERVE ENDINGS, 1153
FLUIDS
  body. *See* Body fluids
  interchange of, between tissues and the vessels, factors governing, **25**
FLUORINE, effects of, on tooth structure, 683
FLUTTER
  auricular, 197
    action of cardiac glycosides on, 199
    differentiation from paroxysmal tachycardia, 197
    effects of, on hemodynamic function of heart, 416
    impure, 197
    regularity of heart rhythm in, 197
    production of, underlying factors in, 198
    pure, 197
      with ventricular extrasystole, 197
FLUX, luminous, 1329
FOCI, conjugate, definition of, 1375
FOCUS, depth of, changes in, during accomodation, 1390
FOLIC ACID. *See* Pteroylglutamic acid
FOLINIC ACID. *See* Leucovorum
FOLLICLES
  atreitic, 1077
  Graafian, 1075
    development of, 1076
  primordial, 1075
FOLLICULAR EXTRACT, effects of injection of, into rabbits, 1084
FONTANA, spaces of, 1399
FOODS
  *See also general classes of foods, e.g.* Eggs; Fish; Vegetables; etc.
  ash components of, principal 741
  caloric values of, 743
  carbohydrate content of, determination of, 744

FOODS—*cont.*
  chemical analysis of, value of, in study of nutrition, 741
  chief functions of, 741
  common,
    ash content of edible portion of, 748
    character of proteins of, 796
    composition of, 745
    energy content of, 745
    typical vitamin content of, 936
  components of, data needed to calculate respiratory quotient and thermal equivalents of, 752
  composition of, **741**
    determination of, 743
    general outline of, **741**
  dynamic action of,
    specific, 787
    cause of, 788
  energy content of, **741, 742**
    by bomb calorimetry, 743
    historical survey of studies on, 749
    measurement of, 742
    oxycalorimeter for determination of, diagram of, 753
    uncertainties in, from composition, 743
  fat content of, determination of, 744
  function of, general outline of, **741**
  goitrogenic, 1012
  intake,
    and energy output, balance between, regulation of, 734
    gastrointestinal stimuli effecting, 736
    regulation of, **733**
      by metabolism of glucose, 738
      demonstration of, 734
      effect of gastrointestinal sensations on, 737
      effect of hypothalamus on, 735
      gastrointestinal mechanisms for, 736
      metabolic mechanisms for, 736
      neural mechanisms for, 735
      peripheral mechanisms in, 736
  main groups of, nutritional values of, 748
  metabolism of heat produced by, 763
  motor activity of colon stimulated by, 717
  nitrogen content of, conversion of, to protein, 745
  organic acids in, 744
  potential energy of, determination of, 750
  protein content of,
    determination of, 744

FOODS—*cont.*
  protein content of—*cont.*
    extra heat resulting from, 787
    protein values of, for maintenance and growth, 792
    representative sample of, difficulty in determining, 744
    role of,
      in lowering gastric acidity, 609
      in regulation of body heat, 891
    thermal equivalents of, determination of, 750
FOOT
  cutaneous blood flow in, 346
  immersion, 359
  reflex vasodilatation in, after body warming, 347
  trench, 359
FORAMEN OVALE, patent, 522
FOREARM, cutaneous blood flow in, control of, 348
FOREL, decussation of, 1196
N-FORMYLGLYCINAMIDE RIBOTIDE, chemical structure of, 803
FOVEA
  blue mechanism and, 1363
  central,
    and the nature of color mechanisms, 1357
  centralis, 1323
    color blindness and, 1359
    color discrimination by, 1358
    color properties of, description of, 1358
    main features of, 1325
    of normal person, receptors of, 1360
    receptors in,
      kinds of, 1358
      normal, 1360
    spectral sensitivity curve of, in different classes of color blindness, 1359
  passage of light through, 1319
  pigments in, analysis of, by use of bleaching with colored lights, 1333
  section through, 1320
FOWL
  composition of 746
  energy content of, 746
  vitamin content of, 936
FRAGILITAS OSSIUM, general discussion on, 1068
FREEMARTINS, 1074
FRENULA COLI, 715
FRIEDMAN PREGNANCY TEST, 1094
FRÖLICH'S SYNDROME, 994
  general discussion on, 993
FRONTAL LOBES. *See* Cerebral cortex, frontal lobes of
FRONTAL LOBE SYNDROME, 1242
FRONTOPONTINE-CEREBELLAR TRACT, fibers of, 1281
FROST BITE, general discussion on, 360

*Bold-face numbers indicate major discussion*

*Bold-face numbers indicate major discussion*

GASTRIC HYPERSECRETION, primary, causes of, 617

GASTRIC JUICE
*See also* Gastric secretion
acidity of, regulation of, 609
collection of, 604
composition of, 600
hydrochloric acid of, 600
origin of, 600
loss of, from body, effects of, 619
neutral chloride of, 600
origin of, 600
peptic activity of, determination of, 617
secretion of, **599**
continuous or interdigestive?, 605
curve of, 606

GASTRIC MUCOSA
blood supply of, interference with, role in production of gastric ulcer, 624
effect of, on cardiac tone, 691
mucus layer protecting, 624

GASTRIC MUSCLE
tonus of, 695
relationship to peristaltic movements, 695
use of, in propelling food from stomach, 698

GASTRIC RESECTION, subtotal, in peptic ulcer, to reduce gastric acidity, 626

GASTRIC SECRETION
*See also* Gastric juice
course of, normal, 610
during various phases of digestion, normal course of, 610
factors effecting,
alkalies, 617
emotional states, 619
hormones, 618
pyloric mucose, 608
sleep, 1270
various chemicals and drugs, 617
vitamins, 618
formed by gastrin stimulation, composition of, 607
histamine test for, 614
inhibition of, by fat, 608
loss of, from body, effects of, 619
phases of, 605, 610
cephalic, 605
chemical, 606
gastric, 606
dependence of, upon nervous system, 607
stimulus for, 607
initial reflex, 605
intestinal, 608
cause of, 608
erratic behavior of, causes of, 608
psychic effect upon, 606
regulation of, 604
study of,
methods for, 604
use of esophagostomy in, 605
use of stomach pouches in, 604

GASTRIC SECRETION—*cont.*
role of enterogastrone in, 609
urea-urease-ammonia mechanism in, 623

GASTRIC TETANY, 1050

GASTRIC TISSUE
and the antianemic factor, 81
use of, in treatment of anemia, response to, **83**

GASTRIC TUBES
passing of, technic of, 613
types of, 613
use of, in gastric analysis, 613

GASTRIC ULCER, 621
*See also* Duodenal ulcers; Peptic ulcers
acidity in patients with, 622
causes of,
bacterial infection, 624
emotional factors in, 625
tobacco smoking, 624
trauma, 624
experimental production of, 622
in hyperchlorhydria, 623
location of, 621
pathogenesis of, 621
production of, factors involved in, 624
symptoms of, 621

GASTRIN
discovery of, 606
function of, 606
release of, mechanism of, 607

GASTRITIS
chronic, anacidity associated with, 616

GASTROCOLIC REFLEX, 717
variation in susceptibility to, 717

GASTRODUODENAL PRESSURE CYCLE, 696
correlation of, with peristaltic rhythm, 697

GASTROILEAL REFLEX, 715, 717

GASTROINTESTINAL REFLEXES, 725
intestino-intestinal inhibitory reflex, 725
involving peripheral autonomic nerves, 725

GASTROINTESTINAL SENSATIONS, effect of, on regulation of food intake, 737

GASTROINTESTINAL SMOOTH MUSCLE, 723
hormonal regulation of, **723**
nervous regulation of, **723**
parasympathetic nerve supply of, 723
regulation of, 723
sympathetic nerve supply of, 723

GASTROINTESTINAL TRACT
*See also* Intestines
autonomic nerves of, effects of stimulating, 725
enteric plexuses, reflex arcs in, 723
extrinsic nerves of, 723
function of, 724
gases in, expansion of, due to rapid ascent, 512
innervation of, 723

GASTROINTESTINAL TRACT —*cont.*
myenteric plexus, 723
submucous plexus, 723

GAUCHER'S CELLS, 69

GAUCHER'S DISEASE
enlargement of spleen associated with, 69
fat metabolism in, 859

GAY-LUSSAC'S LAW, 451

GELATIN
animal, use of, in transfusions, 50
as a factor in growth, 793
utilization of, in nutrition, 797

GENERALISATA. *See* Rickets, renal

GENERATOR POTENTIALS, 1148

GENETICS, of various diseases, 1072

GENITAL RIDGE, 1075

GENITAL SYSTEM, development of, hormonal factors in, **1073**

GENITAL TRACT, adrenal steroids effecting, 1038

GENITONASAL RELATIONSHIPS, 1092

GERMINAL EPITHELIUM, 1075

GIANTISM, 990
general discussion on, 990

GLANDS
*See also name of specific gland*
digestive,
general description of, **585**
secretions of,
constituents of, 585
mechanisms of, **585**
salt, 586
water, 586
effects of autonomic nervous system on, 1303
heterocrine, definition of, 585
homocrine, definition of, 585
innervation of, 1303
monoptychial, definition of, 585
parotid,
alveoli of, 588
anatomy of, 587
innervation of, 589
polyptychial, definition of, 585
racemose, definition of, 587
salivary. *See* Salivary glands; Digestive glands
sublingual,
alveoli of, 588
anatomy of, 587
electrophysiology of, 590
innervation of, 588
submaxillary. *See* Submaxillary glands

GLANDULAR FEVER, leukocytosis in, 96

GLARE
blinding, 1370
classification of, 1369
dazzling, 1370
veiling, 1369

GLAUCOMA
causes of, 1401
compensated, 1400
decompensated, 1401
general discussion on, 1400

GLAUCOMA—*cont.*
  inflammatory, 1401
  primary, 1400
  secondary, 1400
GLIADIN(s),
  as a factor in growth, 793
  characteristics of, 771
  examples of, 771
GLOBIN
  synthesis of, 72
  utilization of, in hemoglobin
    synthesis, 71
GLOBULIN(s)
  characteristics of, 771
  examples of, 771
GLOBUS PALLIDUS, 1215
GLOMERULAR FILTRATION
  colloid osmotic pressure of
    plasma proteins in, 537
  correction of, 538
  glomerular membrane in, 536
  intracapsular     hydrostatic
    pressure in, 537
  measurement of, methods of,
    539
  rate of,
    in man, 538
    measurement of, 537
  relation to blood urea con-
    centration, 565
  relation to capacity of tu-
    bules to reabsorb bicar-
    bonate, 561
  role of capillary blood pres-
    sure in, 537
  role of, in sodium excretion,
    554
GLOMERULAR MEMBRANE
  area of, effect of, on glomeru-
    lar filtration, 536
  permeability of, effect of, on
    glomerular filtration, 536
GLOMERULAR SPACE. *See* Bow-
    man's capsule
GLOMERULI,    juxtamedullary,
    532
GLOMERULONEPHRITIS
  acute,
    general discussion on, 571
    of edema, 574
  chronic,   general   discussion
    on, 571
  discussion of, 571
  renin in blood of patient
    with, 384
GLOMERULOTUBULAR BALANCE,
    542
GLOMERULUS, 67
  anatomy of, 532
  capillaries of,
    difference from other capil-
      lary beds, 536
    permeability of, 536
    rate of filtration through
      walls of, 536
  diagrammatic representation
    of, 534
  filtration by, 535
    variables effecting, 536
  membrane of,
    passage of certain polysac-
      charides through, 536
    pore size in, 536
  reabsorption by, of glucose,
    540

GLOSSOPALATINE NERVE, defi-
    nition of, 1199 (footnote)
GLOSSOPHARYNGEAL NERVE
  carotid sinus nerve and, 1201
  central connections of, 1201
  parasympathetic   fibers   of,
    1300
  role of, in sense of taste, 1458
  sensory fibers of, course of,
    1201
GLUCAGON, 833
  effects of, on glucagon, 834
  general discussion on, 833
  metabolic changes due to, 834
GLUCOCORTICOIDS
  general discussion on, 1035
  increased liberation of, under
    stress, 1035
  physiological actions of, 1035
  secretion of,
    corticotrophin   in   control
      of, 968
    regulation of, 1040
GLUCOGENESIS
  in liver,
    interference with,
      clinical observations in,
        824
      in experimental animals,
        824
GLUCONEOGENESIS, 811
GLUCOPHORES, 1461
GLUCOSE
  absorption of, 810
    by intestines, demonstra-
      tion of, 674
  and acetate, relative oxida-
    tion rates of, 858
  and galactose, difference in
    chemical    configuration
    of, 809
  and $\beta$-hydroxybutyrate, rel-
    ative oxidation rates of,
    858
  chemical structure of, 808
  dynamic action of, utiliza-
    tion of waste heat in
    exercise, 788
  estimation of, 809
  filtered, calculation of, 540
  filtered load of, 540
  formation of,
    in the body, 810
    in the liver, **810**
    role of fructose in, 810
  general discussion on, 808
  importance of, in carbohy-
    drate metabolism, 808
  in combination with other
    substances, 808
  ingested, fate of, **810**
  injected, fate of, **810**
  load, 540
  metabolism of,
    common path of, 810
    regulation of food intake
      by, 738
  phosphorylation of, 674
  reabsorption of,
    by glomerulus, 540
    normal capacity for, 541
    titration of capacity of, 542
    transport mechanism in-
      volved in, 540

GLUCOSE—*cont.*
  relationship among filtration,
    reabsorption, and excre-
    tion of, 541
  tolerance
    curve, 834
    effects of transection of
      brain on, 834
  transport of,
    inhibition of, 541
    reactions involved in, 541
  utilization of, by heart, effect
    of removal of pancreas
    on, 814
  vulnerability of brain to lack
    of, 1134
$\alpha$-GLUCOSE, 808
$\beta$-GLUCOSE, 808
$\gamma$-GLUCOSE, 808
GLUCOSURIA, 813
  causes of, lesions in the hypo-
    thalamic region, 834
  dietary, 813
  due to pancreatic insuffi-
    ciency, 813
  experimental production of,
    813
  hormonal, 813
  loss of sugar in, 835
  production of, by adrenal ex-
    tracts, 829
  renal, 813
GLUTAMIC ACID
  chemical structure of, 774
  synthesis of, 778
GLUTEAL REFLEX, general dis-
    cussion on, 1212
GLUTELINS
  characteristics of, 771
  examples of, 771
GLYCERIDES, role of, in fat ab-
    sorption in the intes-
    tines, 677
GLYCINAMIDE RIBOTIDE, chemi-
    cal structure of, 802
GLYCINE
  behavior of,
    in acid, 771
    in alkali, 771
  chemical structure of, 774
  importance of, in synthesis
    of creatine, 782
  synthesis of, 777
GLYCINE  ANHYDRIDE,  forma-
    tion, of 770
GLYCOCOLL. *See* Glycine
GLYCOCYAMINE, importance of,
    in synthesis of creatine,
    783
GLYCOGEN
  and fat, in liver, 852
  breakdown of, **810**
    role of phosphorylase in,
      811
  description of, 808
  disease,
    cause of, 835
    general discussion on, 835
  effects of thyroxin on, 833
  estimation of, 809
  formation of, **810**
  of heart, effect of removal of
    insulin on, 819
  of liver, role of, in regulation
    of blood sugar, 811

GLYCOGEN—*cont.*
of muscle, effects of removal of pancreas on, 814
storage of,
during fasting, effect of hypophysectomy on, 832
effects of insulin on, mechanism of, 819
enlargement of spleen associated with, 69
muscle fiber, breakdown of, 872
GLYCOGENOLYSIS, 813
GLYCOLIPIDS. *See* Cerebrosides
GLYCOPROTEINS
characteristics of, 771
examples of, 771
GLYCOSURIA
causes of, uric acid, 836
renal, 576
GLYCYL-GLYCINE, formation of, 770
GLYOXYLIC ACID, chemical structure of, 805
GMELIN TEST, for bile in body fluids, 641
GOITER(S), **999**
adenomatous, general discussion on, 999
associated with hyperthyroidism, 999
associated with hypothyroidism, 999
classification of, 999
colloid, general discussion on, 999
sample of, 999
exophthalmic, 1002
emotional shock and, 1005
etiology of, 1004
facies in, 1002
general discussion on, 1002
signs and symptoms of, 1002
thyroid gland in, 1000
iodine in the prevention of, 1006
parenchymatous, general discussion on, 999
prevention of, use of Lugol's solution in, 1006
simple, 999
GOLGI
apparatus of, discussion on, 1116
corpuscles, 1146
ending, in a tendon, 1141
superficial reticulum of, 1116
types of nerve cells, 1116
GOLL, tract of, 1192
GONAD(S)
*See also* Ovaries; Testes
excision of,
effects of, **1074**
on sexual activity, 1109
general discussion on, 1072
transplantation of, effects of, 1075
GONADAL DYSGENESIS, 1074
GONADOTROPHINS, 971
actions of, 1093
assay of, 1093
bioassay of, 974
castration urinary, 973
discovery of, 972

GONADOTROPHINS—*cont.*
feed-back of, 976
function of, 1093
general discussion on, 1093
human chorionic, 972, 974
inactivation of, 974
menopause, 973
of placenta, 1093
origin of, 972
pregnant mare serum, 974, 1094
secretion of,
regulation of, 974
sexual differentiation of, 976
standardization of, 1093
GONADOTROPHS, 958
GOUT, **805**
acute inflammation in, causes of, 806
causes of, 806
general discussion on, 806
uric acid content of blood in, 806
GOWERS METHOD, for estimation of hemoglobin in blood, 56
GRAAFIAN FOLLICLES, 1075
development of, 1076
successive stages in, 1076
GRANULES, secretory, formation of, 586
GRANULOCYTES, 88
*See also* Leucocytes
classification of, 88
development of, 106
effect of folic acid on, in agranulocytosis, 97
maturation of, 100
GRANULOCYTOPENIA, 96
GRANULOPOIESIS, 106
in myeloid leukemia, 107
stages of, 106
GRASP
gentle, 1239
reflex, 1239
strong, 1239
GRASPING MOVEMENTS, localization of, in cerebral cortex, 1239
GRAVES' DISEASE. *See* Goiter, exophthalmic
GRAVITATIONAL STRESS, effects of,
on blood content of ear, 397
on blood pressure, 397
on circulation, **394**
on hydrostatic pressures in vascular system, 396
on pulse rate, 397
GRAVITY-FREE CONDITIONS, circulatory regulation in, 397
GRAVITY RECEPTOR(S), 1179
response of, 1184
stimulation of, 1184
GRAY COMMISSURE, of spinal cord, 1186
GRAY MATTER, 1277
of cortex, 1277
of spinal cord, 1186
GROWTH
effect of proteins on, 797

GROWTH—*cont.*
factors, and vitamins, early views on comparison of, 900
hormone. *See* Hormones, somatotrophic
lysine and, 793
role of anterior pituitary extracts in, demonstration of, 962
role of triglycerides in, 840
GUANASE, 800
GUANETHIDINE, use of, in treatment of essential hypertension, 391
GUANIDINE
as cause of intestinal intoxication, 722
effects of, on blood sugar, 836
GUANINE, 800
chemical structure of, 799, 805
conversion of, to uric acid, 801
GUANOSINE, 800
GUANYLIC ACID, 799
chemical structure of, 802
GULL'S DISEASE, general discussion on, 1001. (*See also* Myxedema)
GUM ACACIA
use of,
in tranfusions, 50
undesirable features of, 50
GUSTATION, general discussion on, **1458**
GYRUS, precentral, corticospinal tract from, destruction of, effects of, 1238

# H

H-SUBSTANCE, role of, in skin reactions to mechanical stimulation, 351
HAIR(S)
cells,
of cochlea, 1424
outer, drawing of, 1426
olfactory, 1464
touch receptors at base of, 1140
HALDANE
calorimeter, 760
gas analysis apparatus of, 762
Gowers method of estimation of hemoglobin in blood, 56
respiration apparatus of, 761
tube, and sampling bulb, 486
HALO
corneal, 1386
lenticular, 1386
HAMBERGER PHENOMENON, 462
HAND(S)
cutaneous blood flow in, 346
eye, and ear test, for recognition of aphasia, 1252
reflex vasodilatation in, after body warming, 347
thalamic, 1227
HAND'S DISEASE, general discussion of, 859

*Bold-face numbers indicate major discussion*

*Bold-face numbers indicate major discussion*

*Bold-face numbers indicate major discussion*

*Bold-face numbers indicate major discussion*

*Bold-face numbers indicate major discussion*

HEMOSIDERIN, 63
  in diseases with red cell destruction, 67
  storage of iron in, 73
HEMOSIDEROSIS, definition of, 75
HEMOSTATICS, 115
HENDERSON-HASSELBALCH EQUATION, 127, 556
HENLE
  loop of,
    anatomy of, 532
    diagram of, 533
    in regulation of water reabsorption by the kidney, 549
HENOCH'S PURPURA, 119
HENRY'S LAW, of solution of gases, 451
HENSEN, cells of, 1425
HEPARIN
  anticoagulant action of, 112
    control of, 113
    mechanism of, 113
  clinical use of, 113
  discovery of, 112
  production of, 113
  quantity of, in blood, determination of, 113
HEPARINEMIA, 113, 118
HEPATITIS, in blood donor, dangers of, in transfusions, 42
HEPATOCRONIN, 644
  role of, in regulation of bile flow, 645
HEPATOLENTICULAR DEGENERATION
  progressive, 1222
    clinical features of, 1222
HERING-BREUER REFLEXES, 493
  illustrating, 494
  mechanical problem in studying, 494
  physiological role of, 495
  proprioceptive nature of, 495
HERMAPHRODITISM, true, 1074
HESPERIDIN, 937
HETEROCRINE CELLS, definition of, 585
HETEROTRANSPLANT, definition of, 955
HEXESTROL, 1083
  chemical structure of, 1083
HICCUP, general discussion on, 477
HILUS, 1075
HIPPURIC ACID, synthesis of, as test of liver function, 653
HIPPUS, 1409
HIRUDIN, anticoagulant action of, 115
HISTAMINE
  adrenergic blocking by, 1028
  concentration of, in blood, following burns, 409
  effects of,
    on bronchial muscle, 519
    on cardiac output, 307
    on gastric secretion, 618
    when administered intestinally, 722
  headaches due to, 1258

HISTAMINE—cont.
  liberation of, as factor in production of anaphylaxis, 410
  test, for gastric secretion, 614
HISTIDINE
  chemical structure of, 775
  synthesis of, 778
HISTIOCYTES
  See also Reticuloendothelial cells; Reticuloendothelial system
  epitheloid and giant cells derived from, 103
  free, 102
  functions of, 103
  hematopoiesis of, 103
  role of,
    in chronic inflammation, 103
    in repair stage of an acute process, 103
  tissue, 102
HISTONES
  characteristics of, 771
  examples of, 771
HODGKIN'S DISEASE, leukocytic activity in, 96
HOFFMAN'S REFLEX, 1164
  elicitation of, 1152
  general discussion on, 1151
HOGBEN PREGNANCY TEST, 1094
HOLGER-NIELSON METHOD
  of artificial respiration, 528
  illustration of, 529
HOLOCRINE CELLS, definition of, 585
HOMEOSTASIS, 1302
HOMOTRANSPLANT, definition of, 955
HOOKWORM, eosinophilia in, 94
HOPPING REACTIONS, 1174
HORMONE(S)
  adrenal cortical, secretion of, regulation of, 1040
  adrenocorticotrophic, 967
  adrenotropic, hyperglycemia due to, 832
  and behavior, 954
  and their functions, 951
  androgens, 1103
  anti-, general discussion on, 979
  antidiabetic. See Insulin
  antidiuretic, 982
    action of, 985
    release of, reflex, due to physiological stimuli, 985
  blood levels of, at time of ovulation, 1080
  cellular action of, 954
  chemistry of, 951
  chromatophorotropic, 983
  clinical use of, in male sex disorders, 1108
  control of menstrual cycle by, 1089
  cortical, role of, in fat absorption in intestine, 678
  definition of, 950
  effects of,
    on action of insulin, 822
    on cholesterol metabolism, 844

HORMONE(S)—cont.
  effects of—cont.
    on coronary circulation, 329
    on gastric secretion, 618
  estrogenic, 1081
  excretion of, 954
  follicle-stimulating, 971, 972
    origin of, 972
    physiological properties of, 973
    production of, 972
    secretion of, regulation of, 975
  gonadotrophic, 971
  growth. See Hormones, somatotrophic
  in the blood, carriage and fate of, study of, 956
  interstitial-cell stimulating, 971
  involved in mammary development, 1095
  lactogenic, 976
  luteal, 1086
  luteinizing, 971
    origin of, 972
    physiological properties of, 973
    production of, 972
    secretion of, regulation of, 975
  luteotrophic, 972, 976
  nature of, 953
  neurohypophyseal, fate of, formation of, 988
  nomenclature regarding, 960 (footnote)
  ovarian, **1081**
  oxytocin, 987. See also Oxytocin
  oxytoxic, 984
    release of, cause of, 987
    role of, in seminal transport, 987
  posterior pituitary, assay of, 987
  pro-, general discussion on, 979
  progesterone, 1086
  prolactin, 1096
  relaxin, 1089
  role of,
    in development of genital system, **1073**
    in response of viscera to environmental stimuli, 625
  secreted by adenohypophysis, 960
  secreted by anterior pituitary gland, 951
  somatotrophic,
    bioassay of, 963
    diabetogenic properties of, 832
    effects of,
      on female daschund, 962
      on growth, demonstration of, 962
    general discussion on, 961
    insulin as a, 821
    loss of, effects of, 961
    preparation of, 961

*Bold-face numbers indicate major discussion*

*Bold-face numbers indicate major discussion*

*Bold-face numbers indicate major discussion*

*Bold-face numbers indicate major discussion*

*Bold-face numbers indicate major discussion*

LIVER—*cont.*
  *functions of—cont.*
    tests for—*cont.*
      rose bengal, 653
      serum alkaline phospha-
        tase level, 653
      Taka-Ara, 654
      thymol turbidity, 654
      urobilinogen excretion,
        652
      van den Berg reaction,
        652
  glycogen in, 852
    role of, in regulation of
      blood sugar, 811
  hydrocholeretic action if, 644
  inactivation of estrogens by,
    1083
  ketone formation in, 849, 853
  *Lactobacillus casei* factor. *See*
    Pteroylglutamic acid
  lipid content of, 849
  lymph of, composition of, 36
  necrosis of, protection
    against, 852
  phospholipid turnover in, as
    compared to that in
    other tissues, 849
  portal venous bed of, hemo-
    dynamic properties of,
    366
  portal venous pressure in,
    factors influencing, 367
  role of, in formation of glu-
    cose, **810**
  secretions of, composition of,
    640
  serum globulin production
    by, 6
  therapy,
    specific,
      effects of, 83
        upon erythrocytes, 83
        upon hemoglobin, 83
        upon plasma bilirubin,
          83
        upon reticulocytes, 83
  tissue, utilization of aceto-
    acetate by, 853
  urea production by, 781
  use of, in treatment of ane-
    mia, responses to, **83**
  vascular bed of, role of, in
    circulatory homeostasis,
    367
LOBULES, of testes, 1100
LOCOMOTOR ATAXIA
  clinical features of, 1208
  general discussion on, 1208
  signs and symptoms of, 1209
LOEB REACTION, 1086
LOOP, of Henle. *See* Henle, loop
  of
LOUDNESS, recruitment of, 1453
LOUDNESS LEVEL
  definition of, 1452
  scale of, 1452
LUGOL'S SOLUTION, use of, in
  the prevention of goiter,
  1006
LUMBAR SPLANCHNIC NERVES,
  1298
LUMEN
  definition of, 1329

LUMEN—*cont.*
  diameters, of various blood
    vessels, 154
LUMINOSITY, differentiation of,
  1265
LUMINOSITY CURVES, central
  foveal, 1358
LUNGS
  aeration of,
    in bronchopneumonia, 515
    in lobar pneumonia, 515
  air in, partial pressures of
    gases composing, 451
  at birth, expansion of, 468
  blood vessels in, reflexes in,
    268
  changes in, in pneumonia, 515
  dust cells of, 103
  epithelial surface of, 468
  evolution of carbon dioxide
    in, 463
  expanding,
    at birth, 468
    zones in, 471
  fibrosis of, 479
  functional residual capacity
    of, 481
    measurement of, 482
  gases in, exchange of, **451**
  intrapleural pressures, 470
  intrapulmonary pressure, 469
  lymphatic system of, 34
  pleural cavities, 469
  reflexes from, role of, in con-
    trol of circulation, **266**
  residual volume of, 481
    measurement of, 482
  root of, respiratory move-
    ment of, 472
  total lung capacity, 481
  vital capacity of, 481
    effects of disease on, 482
    effects of occupation on, 481
    general discussion on, 481
    variations in, 481
  volumes, **481**
    shown on spirographic
      tracing, 482
    terminology of, **481**
  x-ray photograph of, 515
LUTEAL HORMONE, 1086
LUTEAL TISSUE, 1076
LUTEMBACHER'S SYNDROME, 522
LUX, definition of, 1329
LYMPH, **34**
  *See also* Blood
  capillaries of, factors effect-
    ing, 34
  composition of, **35**
  *flow of*, **36**
    increase of,
      causes of, **37**
        capillary poisons, 38
        hypertonic solutions,
          38
        increase in capillary
          pressure, 37
        increase in capillary
          surface, 38
        increased functional
          activity, 39
        increased permeability
          of capillaries, 38
        isotonic saline injec-
          tions, 38

LYMPH—*cont.*
  *flow of—cont.*
    increase of—*cont.*
      causes of—*cont.*
        massage, 39
        muscular activity, 39
        oxygen want in tissues,
          38
        passive movement, 39
        peptone, 38
    rate of, 37
  formation of, **36**
  hepatic, composition of, 36
  nodes, as defense barriers,
    mechanism of, **35**
  peripheral,
    composition of, 36
    from the dog, chemical
      composition of, 36
  pressure of, **36**
  protein components of, 35
  thoracic duct, composition
    of, 35
LYMPHATIC OBSTRUCTION,
  edema due to, 41
LYMPHATIC SYSTEM
  functions of, **37**
  general description of, 34
  in areolar tissue, 34
  of abdominal cavity, 34
  of heart, 34
  of lungs, 34
  of skin, 34
  relationship of, to circulatory
    system, diagram of, 35
  structure of, **34**
LYMPHOBLASTS, 107
LYMPHOCYTES
  *See also* Leukocytes
  effect of adrenal cortical hor-
    mone on, 91
  fate of, **91**
  formation of, 107
  functions of, 90
  large, general discussion on,
    87
  manufacture of serum globu-
    lin by, 90
  production of,
    by spleen, 68
    in lymphoid tissue, 107
  small, general discussion on,
    87
LYMPHOCYTOSIS, 92
LYMPHOID TISSUE
  effect of adrenal cortical hor-
    mone upon, 91
  role of, in production of
    lymphocytes, 107
LYMPHOPENIA, 96
LYSINE
  chemical structure of, 774
  importance of, for growth,
    793

# M

MACROCYTES, 16
MACROPHAGE(s), 67, 101
  loaded with particles of India
    ink, 102
MACROPOLYCYTES, 88
MACULA LUTEA, 1322
MAGENSTRASSE, 698

MAGNESIUM
  deficiency of, effects of, tetany, 1051
  dietary requirements, 948
  silicate, effects of, on gastric secretion, 618
MAGNUS, and de Kleijn, static and stato-kinetic reflexes of, **1169**
MALLEUS, 1422
  lateral process of, 1420
MALNUTRITION, edema caused by, 40
MALONIC ACID, chemical structure of, 937 (footnote)
MALPHIGIAN CORPUSCLE. See Glomerulus
MAMMARY GLANDS
  development of,
    phases in, 1095
    role of anterior pituitary in, 1095
    role of hormones in, 1095
    role of ovaries in, 1095
    role of placenta in, 1096
    role of prolactin in, 1096
  of goat, myoepithelial cells in, 981
  structure of, **1094**
MAMMOGEN I, 1095
MAMMOGEN II, 1095
MAN, cat and dog test, for determination of aphasia, 1252
MANGANESE, role of, in hemoglobin synthesis, **75**
MANN-WILLIAMSON OPERATION, functional disturbances caused by, 633
MANOMETERS
  aneroid,
    description of, 236
    operation of, 236
  fluid-filled conduit, optical, 233
  frequency response characteristics of, 234
  mercury,
    description of, 236
    operation of, 236
  mounted in empty catheter tip, 234
MANUBRIUM
  of malleus, 1420, 1422
  sterni, respiratory movements of, 473
MARBLE BONE, 1068
MARCH HEMOGLOBINURIA, 64
MARCHIAFAVA, nocturnal hemoglobinuria of, 64
MARROW
  bone. See Bone marrow
  red, in anemia, 104 (footnote)
MASKING
  definition of, 1451
  measurement of, 1451
MASSA INTERMEDIA, 1224
MASSAGE, increase in lymph flow due to, 39
MASTER STEP-TEST, effects of aging on performance of, 402
MASTICATION, **682**
  bite, force of, 684
  general discussion on, 682

MASTICATION—*cont.*
  importance of, as a health measure, 682
  movements of lower jaw in, 684
MATING PERIOD, in females, 1077
MEALS, test, typical, 613
MEATS
  composition of, 746
  effects of, on gastric secretion, 618
  energy content of, 746
  in diet, amount necessary to establish nitrogen equilibrium, 786
  vitamin content of, 936
MEDIAL LEMNISCUS,
  diagram of, 1194
  fiber tracts in, 1193
MEDULLA
  adrenal. See Adrenal medulla
  dye-dilution curves in, 370
  oblongate,
    points yielding skeletal muscle vasodilatation secondary to inhibition of vasoconstrictor tone, 352
    points yielding sympathetic vasodilator discharges, 352
    sensory paths in, **1193**
  of thymus, 1110
  renal,
    relation of, to concentrating mechanism of kidney, 369
    role of, in experimental hypertension, 386
  role of, in control of vasoconstriction, 254
  vasomotor center of, 255
MEDULLARY LAMINA, internal, 1224
MEDULLARY NEURONS, responses of, 1445
MEDULLARY RESPIRATORY CENTERS, spontaneous activity of, 491
MEGAKARYOCYTES, origin of platelets from, 108
MEGALOBLASTS, 16, 105
MEGRIM, 1259
MEIOSIS, 1072
MEL, definition of, 1453
MELANIN, 1320
  production of, 983
MELANOBLASTS, 1094
MELANOPHORES
  effects of adrenaline on, 1027
  effects of pars intermedia on, 983
  effects of whole posterior pituitary extract on, 982
MEMBRANA GRANULOSA, 1076
MEMBRANE(S)
  basilar,
    movements of, 1438
    travelling wave pattern on, 1441
  capillary, interchange of fluid across, relation of osmotic to hydrostatic pressure in, 27

MEMBRANE(S)—*cont.*
  equilibrium, Donnan theory of, 128
  periodontal, 682
  potential, 128
  semipermeable,
    definition of, 26
    variations in, of passing ability, 26
  tectorial, at rest, 1441
  tympanic,
    movements of, 1438
    of ear, 1437
    vibration patterns of, 1437
MEMORY, disturbances of, due to lesions of temporal lobe, 1249
MENADIONE, 913
  chemical structure of, 913
MENARCHE, 1078
MÉNIÈRE'S SYNDROME, 1185
MENOPAUSE, 1080
  artificial, 1081
MENORRHAGIA, 1091
MENSTRUATION
  and estrogens, 1084
  *cycle of,*
    control of, by hormones, 1089
    destructive stage, 1090
    diagram of, 1091
    endocrine relationships of, 972
    estrogen-progesterone interactions on, 1090
    follicular phase, 1089
    in the human, 1078
    length of, 1079
    luteal phase, 1089
    "safe" period in, 1080
    stage of menstrual flow, 1090
    uterine changes in, 1089
  irregularities of, 1091
MERIDIAN, definition of, 1314
MERKEL'S DISKS, 1139
MEROCRINE CELLS, definition of, 585
MESENCHYME
  blood cells rising in, types of, 100
  cells, undifferentiated, 101
MESENTERIC CIRCUIT, vasomotor reactions in, importance of, in circulatory adjustments, 366
MESENTERIC GANGLION
  inferior, 1296, 1300
  superior, 1296, 1299
MESENTERY, nerves of, fibers in, 731 (footnote)
MESOPORPHYRIN, formation of, 58
METABOLIC BALANCE STUDIES, historical survey of, 750
METABOLIC RATES,
  basal, effects of age and sex on, 766
  total, effects of age and sex on, 766
METABOLIC TURNOVER, of average man, 514

*Bold-face numbers indicate major discussion*

*Bold-face numbers indicate major discussion*

*Bold-face numbers indicate major discussion*

MYASTHENIA GRAVIS
general discussion on, 1310
muscular weakness in, cause
of, 1311
treatment of, drugs used in,
1310
MYDRIASIS
definition of, 1412
drugs causing, 1412
MYELIN, 1117
sheath, 1117
MYELOBLASTS
development of granulocytes
from, 106
discussion on, 95
MYELOCYTES
A, 106
B, 106
C, 106
MYENTERIC PLEXUS
anatomy of, 723
effect of,
on intestinal polarity, 710
on myenteric reflex, 710
MYENTERIC REFLEX
abolishing, 710
definition of, 710
effect of myenteric plexus on,
710
in duodenum of dog, 710
MYOCARDIAL BUNDLES, ventricular, demonstration of,
240
MYOCARDIAL EFFICIENCY, 315
MYOCARDIAL INFARCTS
acute, electrocardiogram patterns of, 188
direct epicardial leads taken
over, 186
with cardiogenic shock, 336
use of vasopressor agents
in, 337
MYOCARDIAL MUSCLE MEM-
BRANE
polarization of, methods of
study of, 136
repolarization of, methods of
study of, 136
MYOCARDIUM
contractility of, measurement of, 144
depolarization of, 172
complexes from electrodes
in, 173
strip of, 170
effects of anoxia on, 321, 322
effects of sympathetic fibers
on, 147
electrical changes in, sequence
of, 174
hypertrophy of, biochemical
alterations in, 381
injury of,
electrocardiography in, 186
location of, by electro-
cardiography, 187
ischemia of, electrocardiography in, 186
metabolism of, effects of
cardiac glycosides on,
200
necrosis of, electrocardiography of, 186
overstressed,
natural response of, 335

MYOCARDIUM—cont.
overstressed—cont.
with shock, effects of drugs
in, 335
physical properties of, investigations of, prepara-
tions and methods for,
143
reactive hyperemia of, oxygen consumption during,
measurement of, 321
release of potassium from,
139
repolarization of, 172
use of oxygen by, determinants of, 326
MYOEPITHELIAL CELLS
definition of, 587
from mammary gland of
goat, 981
MYOFIBRILS, 869
filaments existing in, 870
MYOGLOBIN
discussion on, 56
function of, 56
MYOGRAM, of frog ventricle,
effect of excitation on,
146
MYONEURAL JUNCTION
drugs acting at, 1310
transmission of nerve im-
pulses at, 1309
MYOPIA, 1395
day, 1397
emergent rays from eye in,
1382
emmetropia becoming, in
certain light conditions,
1397
general discussion on, 1394
movements of retinoscopy
shadow in, 1383
ophthalmoscopy in, 1382
indirect, 1383
retinoscopy in, 1384
twilight, 1397
MYOSITIS OSSIFICANS, 1069
MYOTATIC REFLEXES, **1162**
MYOTATIC UNIT, of nerve fibers,
1163
MYOTOMES, 1188
general discussion on, 1001
MYXEDEMA
before and after treatment,
1001
effects of thyroxine in, 1016

# N

NAPHTHALINE, use of, in experimental production of
cataract, 1393
NARCOLEPSY, in hypothalamic
disorders, 1231
NARCOTICS, action of, theories
on, **1135**
NASOGENITAL RELATIONSHIPS,
1092
NASOLACRIMAL DUCT, 1315
NAUSEA, **733**
relief of, mechanisms in-
volved in, 733
vomiting and, 733

NECK
distribution of sympathetic
fibers to, 1298
muscles of, effects of rotation on, 1181
pain in, caused by irritation
of diaphragm, 729
reflexes of,
excluding, 1172
in the decerebrate preparation, 1166
reflex effect on red and
pale muscle, 1165
righting, acting upon body,
1170
vasoconstrictor fibers of, distribution of, 252
NECROSIN, 93
function of, 93
NEOANTERGEN, effects of, on
gastric secretion, 618
NEOCEREBELLUM, 1276
subdivisions of, 1276
NEOPALLIUM, 1234
NEOSTIGMINE, effects of, on
myoneural junction, 1310
NEPHROLITHIASIS, general discussion on, 1069
NEPHRON
anatomy of, 532
cortical, diagram of, 533
juxtamedullary, diagram of,
533
reabsorption of sodium in,
553
role of, in formation of ammonia, 560
NEPHROSCLEROSIS, arteriolar,
general discussion on,
571
NEPHROTIC SYNDROME, general
discussion on, 571
NERVE(S)
action current of, compound
nature of, recording, 1128
action potential of, relation
to propagated disturb-
ance, 1128
adrenergic, 723
after-potentials, 1128
"all or none" principle in,
1125
ammonia produced by, 1133
anelectrotonus of, 1122
annulo-spiral endings of, 1153
autonomic,
classification of, 723
of salivary glands, dis-
tribution of, 591
to submaxillary gland of
cat, functions of, 591
bipolar, 1116
carbon dioxide production
by, 1132
catelectrotonus of, 1122
cells,
body and dendrites of, end-
feet making contact
with, 1151
in cerebral cortex, 1233
nucleus of, 1116
types of, 1115, 1116
Golgi I, 1116
Golgi II, 1116

*Bold-face numbers indicate major discussion*

Nerve(s)—*cont.*
  chemical changes in, **1132**
    in absence of oxygen, 1132
    in presence of oxygen, 1133
  cholinergic, 723
  chorda tympani, course of, 588
  conduction currents through, oscillograph graphs of, 1129
  conduction in,
    Bernstein's theory of, 1130
    effects of constant current on, 1123
    membrane theory of, 1130
      illustration of, 1130
    velocity of, 1125
      general discussion of, 1125
      in different animals, 1125
      in growing animals, 1130
      in postganglionic sympathetic nerves, 1125
      relationship to diameter of nerve, 1129
  creatine in, 782
  current of action in, 1127
    definition of, 1128
    general discussion on, 1127
  current of injury in, 1127
  degenerating, stained with osmic acid, 1118
  degeneration of, 1117
    mechanism of, **1117**
    reactions of, 1121
      complete, 1122
      partial, 1122
      use as testing method, 1121
  demarcation current, 1127
  diameter of, relationship to conduction velocity in, 1129
  effects of current on, stimulating effects of making and breaking a constant current, 1123
  effects of lack of oxygen on, 1132
  effects of strong ascending current on, 1123
  effects of strong descending current on, 1123
  electrical changes in, 1127
  electrical stimulation of, limitations of, 592
  electrotonus of, 1122
  excitability of,
    alteration of, by constant current of different strengths, 1123
    recovery of, after perfusion of, with fluids of different pH, 1126
  excitation of, by electronic current, general discussion on, 1124
  facial. *See* Facial nerve
  fiber tracts of, in central nervous system, 1117
  *fibers,*
    afferent, 1117
    amyelinated, 1117
    auditory, responses of, 1445

Nerve(s)—*cont.*
  *fibers—cont.*
    conductivity by, 1119
    diameter of, relationship to properties of, 1129
    efferent, 1117
    excitability of, 1119
    excitatory state, local, 1119
    growth of, 1117
    nonmedullated, 1117
    of eye, responses of, to various stimuli, 1336
    of myotatic reflex units, 1163
    physiological properties of, 1119
    regeneration of, demonstration of, 1118
    response of, to a continued stimulus, 1148
    structure of, 1117
    visual, demonstration of, 1404
  flow of electronic currents through, 1123
  flower-spray endings of, 1153
  heat production in, 1131
    due to nervous impulses, diagrammatic representation of, 1132
    effect of frequency of stimulus on, 1131
    effect of strength of stimulus on, 1131
    general discussion on, 1131
    initial heat, 1131
    recovery heat, 1131
    types of, 1131
  *impulses,*
    afferent, course of, in spinal cord, 1192
    definition of, 1124
    general discussion of, 1124
    in eye of king crab, 1335
    in eyes of vertebrates, 1337
    in optic nerve, 1335
    mechanism of, 1124
    path of, through brain stem, **1193**
    sensory, pathway through spinal cord, 1193
    supraspinal paths of, destruction of, effects produced by, compared with those of spinal centers or peripheral nerves, **1205**
    transmission of,
      at myoneural junction, **1309**
      humoral, role of, in central nervous system, **1311**
      noncholinergic chemical, 1311
      role of acetylcholine in, 1310
  inorganic phosphate produced by, 1133
  metabolism of, 1131
  monophasic variation in, 1128
  motor, degeneration of, testing for, 1122
  multipolar, 1116

Nerve(s)—*cont.*
  narcotized, conduction of impulses through, set-up of experiment on, 1125
  negative variation, 1128
  neurotropism, 1117
  of heart,
    effects of,
      on conductivity, 142
      on rhythmicity, 142
  of pancreas, secretory, 635
  oxygen consumption by, 1132
  parasympathetic, 723
  physiological properties of, **1115**
  potassium of, 1133
  properties of,
    effects of electric current on, 1122
    relation to diameter of fibers, 1129
  refractory periods of, 1126
    absolute, 1126
    relative, 1126
  regeneration of, 1118
    effects of waiting time on speed of regeneration, 1119
    mechanism of, 1118
  resting, metabolism of, 1133
  retrograde degeneration of, 1118
  splanchnic, effect of, on stomach, 724
  stimulation of,
    *See also* Stimulus
    effects on heat production of nerve, 1131
  supply, parasympathetic, of salivary glands, 589
  sympathetic, 723
  time constant of accommodation of, 1124
    alteration of, 1124
  trigeminal. *See* Trigeminal nerve
  trunks, action potential of, measurement of, 1128
  unipolar, 1116
  vagus, effect of, on tone and peristaltic activity of stomach, 724
  Wallerian degeneration of, 1118
Nervous impulses
  chemical transmission of, **1303**
  transmission of, role of acetylcholine in, 1305
Nervous system
  and endocrine system, relationship between, 952
  autonomic. *See* Autonomic nervous system
  involuntary. *See* Autonomic nervous system
  vegetative. *See* Autonomic nervous system
Nervous tissue, structure of, **1115**
Nervus intermedius. *See* Facial nerve
Neural lobe, 957
Neural stalk, 957
  anatomical structure of, 957

*Bold-face numbers indicate major discussion*

*Bold-face numbers indicate major discussion*

*Bold-face numbers indicate major discussion*

*Bold-face numbers indicate major discussion*

*Bold-face numbers indicate major discussion*

PITUITARY GLAND—*cont.*
portal vessels of, functional significance of, 978
posterior,
anatomical structure of, 957
hormones secreted by, 951
role of, in renal hypertension, 387
unit, official, 980 (footnote)
removal of, effect on diabetes, 829
role of,
in carbohydrate metabolism, 829
in hypoglycemia, 830
in mammary development, 1095
in permanent diabetes, 830
in regulation of ovarian activity, 971
in regulation of supply of globulin to blood, 91
in regulation of water excretion by kidney, 548
saggital section through, showing large nerve tract, 960
substances in, effecting carbohydrate metabolism, 831
transplantation of, effects of, 978
PITUITARY INJECTION, posterior, official, 980 (footnote)
PITUITARY STALK, 957
anterior aspect of, photograph of, 960
section of, effects of, 978
PITUITRIN, 980
pK, discussion of derivation of, 127
PLACENTA
endocrine functions of, **1092**
role of, in mammary development, 1096
PLANTAR REFLEXES. *See* Reflexes, plantar
PLANTAR RESPONSE
extensor, in infants, 1211 (footnote)
normal, drawing of, 1211
PLASMA
*See also* Blood plasma
and liver, relationship of, in regard to phospholipids, 842
concentration of, relationship of a substance excreted by tubule, 544
constituents of, normal, excretion, filtration, and reabsorption of, 539
lipid components of, in fasting state, 844
phosphatase content of, changes in, in disease, 1067
proteins, colloid osmotic pressure of, role of, in glomerular filtration, 537
volume, effects of sleep upon, 1270
PLASMAPHERESIS, 7

PLATE, epiphyseal, 1063
PLATELET(s)
*See also* Thrombocytes
cofactor 2. *See* Plasma thromboplastin component
deposition of, thrombosis caused by, 120
influence of spleen on, 68
number of, relationship to rapidity and degree of clot, 109
origin of, from megakaryocytes, 108
ratio of erythrocytes to, in arterial blood, 108
PLETHORA, effects of, on relation between left ventricular diastolic volume and left ventricular systolic and end diastolic pressure, 147
PLETHYSMOGRAPH, cardiac, 221
PLETHYSMOGRAPHY, 220
electrical impedance, 223
mercury-rubber strain gage, 223
photocell, 223
use of, in determining regional blood volume, 226
PLEURAL CAVITIES, 469
PLEURAL SHOCK, 478
PLEXUS
abdominal, 1298
adrenal, 1299
aortic, 1299
cardiac, 1298
celiac, 1299
esophageal, 1298
gastric, 1299
hemorrhoidal, 1300
hepatic, 1299
inferior hypogastric, 1300
inferior mesenteric, 1300
intermesenteric, 1299
ovarian, 1299
pelvic, 1298, 1300
prostatic, 1300
pulmonary, 1298
renal, 1299
solar, 1299
spermatic, 1299
splenic, 1299
stroma, 1316
superior hypogastric, 1300
superior mesenteric, 1299
tympanic, 1301
uterine, 1300
vaginal, 1300
vesical, 1300
PLICAE CIRCULARES, 711
PNEUMONIA
hypoxia in, causes of, 515
lobar,
aeration of lungs during, 515
blood oxygen in, 515
lung changes in, 515
respiration in, **515**
shallow breathing in, 516
cause of, 516
PNEUMOTAXIC CENTER
importance of, in maintaining respiration after vagotomy, 493
in cat, 490

PNEUMOTHORAX
closed, 477
general discussion on, **477**
open, 477
role of, in respiration, 477
POIKILOCYTOSIS, 16
POISEUILLE'S LAW, 165
application of, to circulation, 166
POLYCHROMASIA, 16, 105
POLYCYTHEMIA, 526
*See also* Erythrocytes, number of, increases in
causes of, pathological states, 13
cerebral blood flow in, 344
enlargement of spleen associated with, 69
role of cobalt in, 75
splenomegalic. *See* Polycythemia vera
POLYCYTHEMIA VERA
causes of, 14
general discussion on, 14
pathogenesis of, latest views on, 14
production of, artificial, 14
signs of, 14
treatment of, 14
POLYESTRUS ANIMALS, 1078
POLYOSTOTIC FIBROUS DYSPLASIA. *See* Albright's syndrome
POLYPEPTIDES, characteristics of, 772
POLYPTYCHIAL GLANDS, definition of, 585
POLYURIA, 993
general discussion on, 573
PONS, sensory paths in, **1193**
PONTOCEREBELLAR RECEIVING AREA, subdivisions of, in the monkey, 1285
POPLITEAL NERVE, reflex responses of, tensions of, 1158
PORPHIN, chemical structure of, 52
PORPHYRIA
acute, 60
causes of, 60
congenital, 60
symptoms of, 60
types of, 60
PORPHYRIN(s)
animal, pigments derived from, **58**
chemical structure of, 52
formation of heme from, 54
general discussion on, 52
metallic, 54
types of, 53, 55
type I, chemical structure of, 53
type III, chemical structure of, 53
PORPHYRINURIA
cause of, 60
in anemias, 60
symptoms of, 60
PORPHYROPSIN, 1331
composition of, 1333
POSTCENTRAL GYRUS
effects of tactile stimulation of palm on, 1244

*Bold-face numbers indicate major discussion*

PULSE
  arterial, effects of heart block
    on, 192
  intermission of, 196
  intermittent, 196
  irregularity of, complete,
    198
  jugular, records of, informa-
    tion concerning cardiac
    cycle from, 287
  pattern,
    aortic, usefulness of, 283
    central, usefulness of, 283
    jugular venous, normal, 288
  pressure,
    See also Pressure pulse
    aortic, pattern of, deter-
      minants for, 282
    arterial, 275
      measurement of, 280
      recording of, 280
    measurement of, 232
  radial, changes in contour and
    amplitude of, under ab-
    normal cardiovascular
    conditions, 283
  rate,
    effects of sleep on, 1270
    increase of, in dehydration,
      25
    under gravitational stress,
      397
  subclavian, changes in con-
    tour and amplitude of,
    under abnormal cardio-
    vascular conditions, 283
  tracing, venous, in heart
    block, 193
  venous, in auricular fibrilla-
    tion, 198
  wave, velocity of, relation-
    ship to arterial blood
    pressure, 281
PULSUS ALTERNANS, **202**
  detection of, 202
PULSUS BIGEMINUS, 196
PUNCTA LACRIMALIA, 1315
PUNCTUM REMOTUM, 1391
PUPIL(S), **1409**
  diameter of, changes in, dur-
    ing accommodation of,
    1390
  effects of drugs upon, 1412
  size of, effect of, on resolving
    power of retina, 1369
PUPILLAE
  dilator, 1409
  muscles of,
    dilator, 1317
    sphincter, 1317
  sphincter, 1409
PUPILLARY REFLEXES
  consensual, 1409
  diagram illustrating, 1411
  direct, 1409
  due to emotional states, 1409
  effects of interruption of
    retinal impulses on, 1408
  effects of prolonged wakeful-
    ness on, 1271
  indirect, 1409
  investigation of, importance
    of, in establishing site of
    brain lesion, 1411
  light, 1409

PUPILLARY REFLEXES—*cont.*
  near, 1409
  of accommodation, 1409
  physiological unrest, 1409
  Wernicke's hemianopic, 1412
PUPILLO-CONSTRICTOR PATH-
  WAYS, 1410
PUPILLO - DILATOR PATHWAYS,
  1410
  afferent, 1411
PURINE
  metabolism of, **799**
    end products of, 800
  synthesis of,
    chemical reactions in, 803
    in the body, 802
PURKINJE CELL LAYER, of cortex, 1278
PURKINJE FIBER
  in a pacemaker area, spon-
    taneous activity in, 138
  transmembrane potentials of,
    137, 138
PURKINJE FIGURES, 1386
PURKINJE-SANSON IMAGES, 1389
PURPURA
  coagulation time in, 119
  fulminans, 119
  general discussion on, 118
  hemorrhagica, 119
  Henoch's, 119
  role of thrombocytopenia in,
    118
PUTAMEN, 1215
  connections from cerebral
    cortex to, 1216
PYELONEPHRITIS, general discussion on, 572
PYKNOSIS, 105
PYLORIC REFLEX, 699
PYLORIC SPHINCTER
  acid contol of, 699
  role of, in regulation of gas-
    tric emptying, 699
PYLOROSPASM, 703
PYLORUS
  anatomy of, 692
  obstruction of, effect of, on
    electrolytes in body
    fluid, 713
PYRAMID, of tympanic cavity,
  1422
PYREXIA. See Fever(s)
PYREXIN, 93
PYRIDOXALPHOSPHATE, 925
PYRIDOXAMINE, chemical structure of, 925
PYRIDOXINE, 924
  aldehyde of, 924
  amine of, 924
  chemical structure of, 925
  chemistry of, 925
  deficiency of, 925
  eluate factor of, 924
  filtrate factor of, 924
  growth-promoting aspects of,
    925
  isolation of, 925
  requirements of, daily, 926
  role of, in iron absorption, 74
  sources of, 926
  therapeutic use of, 926
  toxicity of, 926

PYRIMIDINE(S)
  fate of, 801
  metabolism of, end products
    of, 800
  synthesis of, chemical reac-
    tions involved in, 804
PYRIMIDINE BASES, metabolism
  of, **799**
PYRROL CELLS, 101
PYRROMETHENES, 53
  A and $B_1$, chemical structure
    of, 53

# Q

QUADRICEPS
  response of, to stretch, 1153
  stretch reflex of, in cat, 1163
QUADRIPLEGIA, due to complete
  transversion division of
  spinal cord, 1210
QUANTA, definition of, 1329
QUASI-EMOTIONAL STATE, 1229
QUICK'S METHOD, of determining prothrombin concen-
  tration, 116
QUINIDINE
  action of,
    in fibrillation, 200
    in fibrillation and flutter,
      199
    in heart failure, 199
  effects of,
    on electrocardiographic
      patterns, 189
    on the heart, 200
  overdosage of, effects of, 200

# R

RACEMOSE GLANDS, definition
  of, 587
RACHITIC ROSARY, 908
RADIANT ENERGY, general dis-
  cussion on, 1329
RADIATION
  cardiovascular effects of, **398**
  effects of,
    on arterial blood pressure,
      399
    on cardiac physiology and
      biochemistry, 399
    on skin, 398
    on vascular physiology, 398
    electrocardiographic obser-
      vations following, 399
    postmortem evidence of, 399
    total-body, cardiovascular
      effects of, 399
RADIATOR, full, definition of,
  1329
RAGE, sham, 1229
RAMI COMMUNICANTES, 1296
RAMIS COMMUNICANS, white,
  1296
RASMUSSEN, olivo-cochlear
  tract of, 1427
RATHKE'S POUCH, 957
RAUWOLFIA SERPENTINA
  BENTH, use of, in treat-
  ment of essential hyper-
  tension, 390
RAYLEIGH MATCH, 1357
RAYNAUD'S DISEASE
  cause of, 356

*Bold-face numbers indicate major discussion*

*Bold-face numbers indicate major discussion*

*Bold-face numbers indicate major discussion*

*Bold-face numbers indicate major discussion*

SALIVARY REFLEX—*cont.*
 adaptability of, 594
 conditioned, 594
 unconditioned, 593
SALT(S)
 depletion of, dehydration
  caused by, 24
 excretion of, in edema, 574
 injections of, effects of, on
  cerebrospinal fluid, 1292
 inorganic, absorption of, by
  intestines, 672
 metabolism of,
  in fevers, 896
  role of adrenal hormones
   in, 1034
 neutral, anticoagulant action of, 114
 secretion of, by digestive
  glands, 586
SALTY TASTE, chemical constituents of, 1461
SARCOPLASM, 869
SARCOSOMES, 869
SCALA MEDIA, 1423
SCHEINER'S EXPERIMENT, 1388
SCHILLING INDEX, 89
 stages of, 89
SCHLEMM, canal of, 1399
SCHONLEIN'S DISEASE, 119
SCHULTZ, comma tract of, 1197
SCHWABACH, test of, 1456
SCHWAMM, sheath of, 1117
SCLERA, 1316
SCLERAL SPUR, 1400
SCLEROCORNEAL JUNCTION, 1316
SCLEROPROTEINS
 characteristics of, 771
 examples of, 771
SCLEROSIS
 disseminated,
  clinical features of, 1209
  general discussion on, 1209
 multiple. *See* Sclerosis, dis-
  seminated
SCOLIOSIS, 908
SCOPOLAMINE, effects of, on cholinoceptive effectors,
  1309
SCOTOPIC CONDITIONS, 1327
SCOTOPIC DOMINATOR CURVE,
  1350
SCOTOPIC LUMINOSITY CURVE,
  comparison of absorp-
  tion curve of visual
  purple with, 1330
SCOTOPIC SENSITIVITY, absolute, 1327
SCOTOPIC VISIBILITY CURVE,
  1327
SCOTOPIC VISION, visibility
  curves for, 1346
SCRATCH REFLEX, general discussion on, **1158**
SCURVY
 role of, in discovery of vitamin A, 899
 vitamin C necessary to prevent, 935
SEA WATER, of today, difference
  from blood serum, 1
  (footnote)
SECRETION
 choleretic action of, 644
 clinical unit of, 635 (footnote)

SECRETION—*cont.*
 destruction of, by secretinase, 635
 discovery of, importance of,
  634
 effects of, 635
 hydrochloretic action of, 644
 release of, triggering action
  for, 635
 role of, in regulation of bile
  flow, 645
 test,
  for function of gall bladder,
   639
  for pancreatic function, 639
SECRETINASE, secretion destruction by, 635
SECRETIONS
 digestive,
  constituents of, 585
  formations of granules in,
   586
 gastric. *See* Gastric secretions
 pancreatic juice. *See* Pancreatic juice; Pancreas,
  secretion of
 saliva, 585. (*See also* Saliva)
SECRETORS, definition of, 46
SECRETORY FIBERS, definition
  of, 586
SELLA TURCICA, 957
SEMEN
 ejaculation of, 1108
 emission of, 1108
 general discussion on, 1101
  mechanisms of, **585**
  paralytic, 592
  reflex, 593
SEMICIRCULAR CANALS
 anatomy of, 1175
 disease of, reactions to, 1184
 effects of rotation on, 1179
 functions of, 1178
  experiments on, 1179
 maximal response of, 1178
 relation of, to plane of skull,
  1174
 stimulation of,
  by rotation, 1183
  caloric, effects of, 1183
  effects of, 1179
  galvanic, effects of, 1183
  mechanical, effects of, 1183
SEMILUNAR GANGLION, 1296
SEMINAL VESICLES
 epithelium of, effects of
  castration and testis hormone on, 1105
 general discussion on, 1101
SEMINIFEROUS TUBULES, convoluted, 1100
SEMISTARVATION
 *See also* Starvation
 effects of, 865
  beneficial, in certain diseases, 865
  on basal metabolic rate, 865
  on body weight, 865
  on internal fat, 865
  on physical stamina, 865
  on susceptibility to infection, 865
  psychological changes, 865
 metabolism in, **864**

SEMITENDINOSUS NERVE, af-
  ferent volleys in, facilitation of biceps reflex by,
  1156
SENSATION
 analysis of, 1139
 cutaneous, 1139
  dissociation of, 1143
  double, minimal points of
   separation necessary to
   recognize, 1141
 loss of, in tabes dorsalis, 1209
 paths and centers concerned
  in, diagram of, 1225
 vibration sense, 1145
 tactile, 1139
 visceral, **728**
SEPTAL DEFECTS
 *See* Atrial septal defects;
  Ventricular septal de-
  fects
 interventricular,
  circulatory effects of, 438
  with pulmonary hyper-
   tension, circulatory effects of, 439
SEPTUM, interauricular, defects of, 522
SERINE, chemical structure of,
  774
SEROTONIN
 effects of,
  on gastric secretion, 619
  on renal circulation, 375
 secretion of, by argentaffine
  cells, 666
SERTOLI, cells of, 1100, 1101
SERUM
 concentrations of different
  forms of sulfur in, 785
 human, use of, in trans-
  fusions, 49
SERUM ALKALINE PHOSPHATASE
  LEVEL, test of, for liver
  function, 653
SERUM CALCIUM
 curve, effects of irradiated
  ergosterol on, 1061
 effects of parathyroid extract
  on, 1053
 low, effects of, on low serum
  calcium, 189
SERUM CHOLESTEROL LEVELS,
  reduction of, 860
SEX
 characteristics,
  effects of tumors of adrenal
   cortex on, 1043
  secondary, 1072
 chromatin, 1072
 chromosomes, function of,
  1072
 cords,
  primary, 1075
  secondary, 1075
 disorders, in the male, hormonal treatment of, 1108
 effects of,
  on arterial blood pressure,
   274
  on calorie requirement in
   diet, **942**
 endocrine organs of, **1072**
 genetic, determination of,
  1072

*Bold-face numbers indicate major discussion*

*Bold-face numbers indicate major discussion*

STILBESTROL, effects of, on insulin content of pancreas, 826

STIMULUS
*See also under portion of anatomy being stimulated;* Reflex(es)
auditory, differentiation of, 1265
characters of, 1119
conditioned, definition of, 1261
cutaneous, differentiation of, 1266
definition of, 119
duration of, 1119
generalization of, 1265
gustatory, differentiation of, 1266
intensity of, 1119
olfactory, differentiation of, 1266
perception of, general discussion on, 1245
proprioceptive, differentiation of, 1266
strength of, 1119
subthreshold, 1119
synthesis of, 1266
unconditioned, definition of, 1261
visual, differentiation of, 1265

STOKES-ADAMS SYNDROME
causes of, 193
symptoms of, 193
treatment of, 193

STOMACH
anatomical terms referring to, 691
antiperistaltic waves in, during vomiting, 702
antrum of, definition of, 691
arrangement of food in, 698
body of, definition of, 691
carcinoma of, association of, with anacidity, 616
distention of, effects of, on appetite and hunger, 737
effect of splanchnic nerves on, 724
empty, periodic action of, 692
emptying of, 698
factors influencing, 698
regulation of, 699
enterogastric reflex in, 700
role of pyloric sphincter in, 699
summary of mechanics of, 700
with pyloric sphincter inoperative, 699
filling of, 698
fundus of, gland from, 600
hypermotility of, 703
hypomotility of, 703
innervation of, diagram of, 718
movements of, **691**
*See also* Hunger contractions
abnormal, 703
digestive peristalsis, 694
vomiting, 701
when empty, 692

STOMACH—*cont.*
mucosa of,
anatomy of, 599
potential difference across, 602
non-digestion of, by stomach wall, 623
parietal cells in, distribution of, 622
peristaltic movements of, relation of gastric muscle tonus to, 696
positions of, diagram showing, 692
pressure in, 696
measurement of, 696
pyloric portion of, 691
rate at which food leaves, factors determining, 698
receptive relaxation during, 688
shape of, variations in, 695
subdivisions of, diagram of, 692
systole and diastole of, 696
tone and peristaltic activity, effect of vagus nerves on, 724
tonus of, 695
discussion on, 695
effects of, on hunger contractions, 692
rhythm, after a meal, 693
tubes. *See* Gastric tubes
ulcers, location of, 621

STOVAINE, effects of, upon taste, 1462

STRABISMUS, paralytic, cause of, 1418

STRAWBERRY GALL-BLADDER, 656

STREPTOKINASE, 112

STREPTOMYCINS, deafness due to, 1455

STRESS
circulatory responses to, 328
effects of aging on, 402
effects of, on coronary circulation, 328, 329
role of, in etiology of peptic ulcer, 624

STRETCH REFLEXES, **1162**
effect of decerebration on, 1162
general discussion on, 1162
mechanism of, 1162
most important structures in, 1153
of clinical importance, 1164
of quadriceps, in cat, 1163
phasic and postural muscle contractions in, 1154
relation of, to knee and ankle jerks, 1163
types of muscle contractions normal in, 1163

STRIATUM, 1215

STROMA
of red cells. *See* Erythrocytes, stroma of
plexus, 1316

STROMATOLYSIS, 62

STROMUHR
Ludwig's, 207
mechanical, 207

STROPHANTHIN, effects of, on cardiac output, 307

SUBACIDITY, 615

SUBARACHNOID SPACES, 1384

SUBDURAL SPACES, 1384

SUBLINGUAL GLAND(S)
alveoli of, 588
electrophysiology of, 590
innervation of, 588

SUBMANDIBULAR GANGLION, 1300

SUBMAXILLARY GANGLION, 588, 1300

SUBMAXILLARY GLAND
alveoli of, 588
anatomy of, 587
electrophysiology of, 590
innervation of, 588
of cat, functions of autonomic nerves to, 591

SUBSTRATE, utilization of, by heart, 326

SUBSTANTIA GELITINOSA, of Rolando, 1186

SUBSTANTIA NIGRA, 1215

SUBSTANTIA PROPRIA, 1316

SUBTHALAMIC BODY, of Luys, 1215

SUCCINIC ACID, chemical structure of, 937 (footnote)

SUCCINYLCHOLINE, effects of, on myoneural junction, 1310

SUCCUS ENTERICUS, 666
*See also* Intestinal juice; Intestinal secretions
function of, 669
secretion of,
control of, 668
humoral regulation, 668
nervous regulation, 668
enzymes in, regulation of, 669
paralytic, 668

SUCROSE SPACE, 20

SUGAR
absorption of, **809**
in different parts of small intestine, 674
combustion of, effects of removal of pancreas on, 814
oxidation of, **810**
effects of insulin on, 820

SULCUS, of cerebellum, 1276

SULFANILAMIDE
chemical structure of, 929
effects of, on leukocytic activity, 93

SULFATE(S)
ethereal, distribution of, 784
reabsorption of, 543

SULFHEMOGLOBIN, 57
detection of, 57
effects of, 57
formation of, 57

SULFONYLUREAS, use of, as hypoglycemic agents, 837

SULFUR
concentration of different forms of, in whole blood and serum, 785
distribution of, in the body, 784
entrance of, into body, 784

*Bold-face numbers indicate major discussion*

*Bold-face numbers indicate major discussion*

*Bold-face numbers indicate major discussion*

TISSUE(S)—*cont.*
    various mammalian tissues, 1067
    fluids in, **34**
    lipids of, distribution of, 840
    normal, cholesterol content of, 844
    oxygen demand in, manner in which call is met, **458**
    oxygen unloading in, 458
    reactions of, effects of, on action of insulin, 822
    soft, calcification of, 1069
    transport and delivery of oxygen to, **455**
    water content of, maintenance of, role of body fluids in, 2
TITRATABLE ACID, 559
TITRATION CURVES, 542
    splay of, 542
TOBACCO
    effects of,
      in production of gastric ulcer, 624
      on gastric secretions and gastric acidity, 618
TOCOPHEROL. *See* Vitamin E
TONE, pure, 1429
TONGUE
    papillae of, 1458
    taste sensations on various parts of, 1459, 1460
TONOMETERS, series of, 455
TONSIL, of cerebellum, 1276
TONUS
    definition of, 695
    plastic, 1153
TOOTH
    enamel. *See* Enamel, tooth
    molar, section through, 683
TOPOGNOSIA, 1140
TORSION SPASM, 1224
TOUCH
    light,
      sensation of, 1139
        testing, 1140
    minimal pressures necessary for sensation of, 1140
    parietal lobe representation of sensations of, 1245
    receptors, stimulation of, essential factor in, 1139
    sensation of, localization of, 1140
    stereognosis, 1146
    two-point sensibility, 1140
TRACTUS INTERFASCICULARIS, 1197
TRANSAMIDATION, 777
TRANSAMINATION, 776
    amino acids able to take part in, 777
    chemical processes involved in, 777
    definition of, 776
TRANSFERRIN, 73
TRANSFUSION(S), **42**
    artificial solutions for, requirements of, 50
    *blood,*
      as factor in development of erythroblastosis fetalis, 47

TRANSFUSION(S)—*cont.*
    *blood—cont.*
      incompatibility of blood groups in, symptoms of, 45
      temperature rise following, 43
      usual rate, 42
      using whole blood, **42**
        advantages of, 42
        dangers of, 42
        donor with hepatitis, 42
        health of donor in, 42
        incompatibility in, 43
        quantity, 43
        rate of transfusion, 42
        safeguards to be taken in, 42
    dangers of, too rapid a transfusion rate, 42
    effects of, on coronary circulation, 328
    incompatibility in, effects of, 44
    universal donors and recipients, danger of following concepts of, 45
    using albumin fraction of human serum, 50
    using animal gelatin, 50
    using bovine plasma, 50
    using cadaver blood, 42 (footnote)
    using dextran, 50
    using gum acacia, 50
    using human plasma, **49**
    using human serum, **49**
      advantages of, 49
    using isinglass, 50
    using solutions of colloids, **50**
    using solutions of crystalloids, 51
TRANSMEMBRANE POTENTIAL
    in myocardial fiber, microelectrodes used for determination of, 137
    mechanism of, 139
    of atrium, 136
    of auricular fiber, 138
    of cardiac muscle, effect of inorganic ions on, 137
    of Purkinje fibers, 137, 138
    of specialized tissues of mammalian heart, 137
    of ventricle, 136
    of ventricular conducting system, 137
    of ventricular fiber, 138
TRANSMETHYLATION, 777
TREMOR
    cerebellar, production of, nervous mechanism in, 1283
    coarse,
      caused by section of peduncles, 1283
      in Parkinsonian syndrome, 1222
    general discussion on, 1287
    in cerebellar disorders, 1287
    intention, 1220, 1287
    static, 1287
TRENCH FOOT, 359

TREPHONES, production of, by blood serum proteins, 7
TRICHINOSIS, eosinophilia in, 94
TRICHROMATS, anomalous, 1356
TRICUSPID COMMISSUROTOMY, 427
TRICUSPID INSUFFICIENCY, 427
    cardiac output in, 428
    cause of, 427
    circulatory changes in, 428
    heart sounds in, 428
    pressure tracings of right artery and brachial artery in, 427
TRICUSPID VALVE, stenosis of. *See* Stenosis, tricuspid
TRIGEMINAL LEMNISCUS
    diagram of, 1194
    fiber tracts in, 1194
    formation of, 1198
TRIGEMINAL NERVE
    bulbospinal tract of, 1198
    central,
      connections of, **1197**
      diagram of, 1197
    mesencephalic nucleus of, 1198
    mesencephalic root of, 1198
    motor root of, 1198
    pathways of, lesions involving, effects of, 1198
    reflexes mediated through, 1198
    role of, in sense of taste, 1458
    roots of, 1197
    sensory root of, 1198
    spinal nucleus of, 1197
    upper sensory nucleus of, 1198
TRIGEMINAL NEURALGIA, 1199
TRIGLYCERIDES, 839
    chemical structure of, 839
    distribution of, 840
    effects of, on growth, 840
    physiology of, 840
    resynthesis of fatty acids into, 677
TRIGONE, 578
TRIGONUM VESICAE, 578
TRIHYDROXYESTRIN. *See* Estriol
3:5:3′-TRI-IODOTHYRONINE
    chemical structure of, 1011
    formation of, in the thyroid, 1011
    physiological properties of, 1009
TRIPEPTIDES, characteristics of, 772
TRITANOPES, 1356
TRITANOPIA, 1363
TROCHLEAR NERVE, nucleus of, 1416
TROLAND, definition of, 1329
TROPHIC FIBERS, definition of, 586
TROUSSEAU'S SIGN, 1050
TRUNK, distribution of sympathetic fibers to, 1297
TRYPSIN
    activation of trypsinogen by, 631
    chemical characteristics **of,** 631

*Bold-face numbers indicate major discussion*

*Bold-face numbers indicate major discussion*

*Bold-face numbers indicate major discussion*